SCOTT

# 2019

# STANDARD POSTAGE STAMP CATALOGUE

ONE HUNDRED AND SEVENTY-FIFTH EDITION IN SIX VOLUMES

## VOLUME 4A

J-L



Released July 2018
Includes New Stamp Listings through the May 2018 *Linn's Stamp News Monthly* Catalogue Update



AMOS MEDIA

911 Vandemark Road, Sidney, OH 45365-4129
Publishers of *Linn's Stamp News, Linn's Stamp News Monthly, Coin World* and *Coin World Monthly.*

# Table of Contents




See the following volumes for other country listings:
Volume 1A: United States, United Nations, Abu Dhabi-Australia; Volume 1B: Austria-B
Volume 2A: C-Cur; Volume 2B: Cyp-F
Volume 3A: G; Volume 3B: H-I
Volume 4B: M
Volume 5A: N-Phil; Volume 5B: Pit-Sam
Volume 6A: San-Tete; Volume 6B: Thai-Z


### Scott Catalogue Mission Statement

The Scott Catalogue Team exists to serve the recreational, educational and commercial hobby needs of stamp collectors and dealers.

We strive to set the industry standard for philatelic information and products by developing and providing goods that help collectors identify, value, organize and present their collections.

Quality customer service is, and will continue to be, our highest priority. We aspire toward achieving total customer satisfaction.




ISBN 978-0-89487-549-6

Library of Congress Card No. 2-3301

# Acknowledgments

Our appreciation and gratitude go to the following individuals who have assisted us in preparing information included in this year's Scott Catalogues. Some helpers prefer anonymity. These individuals have generously shared their stamp knowledge with others through the medium of the Scott Catalogue.

Those who follow provided information that is in addition to the hundreds of dealer price lists and advertisements and scores of auction catalogues and realizations that were used in producing the catalogue values. It is from those noted here that we have been able to obtain information on items not normally seen in published lists and advertisements. Support from these people goes beyond data leading to catalogue values, for they also are key to editorial changes.

A special acknowledgment to Liane and Sergio Sismondo of The Classic Collector for their assistance and knowledge sharing that have aided in the preparation of this year's Standard and Classic Specialized Catalogues.

Roland Austin
Jim Bardo (Bardo Stamps)
William Barclay (South Sudan Philatelic Society)
John Birkinbine II
Helmut Blaschczyk
Roger S. Brody
Tina & John Carlson (JET Stamps)
Henry Chlanda
Bob Coale
David & Julia Crawford
Tony L. Crumbley (Carolina Coin & Stamp, Inc.)
Chris de Haer
Christopher Dahle
Tony Davis
Ubaldo Del Toro
Leon Djerahian
Bob & Rita Dumaine (Sam Houston Duck Co.)
Sister Theresa Durand
Paul G. Eckman
George Epstein (Allkor Stamp Co.)
Robert A. Fisher
Jeffrey M. Forster
Richard Frajola
Robert S. Freeman
Ernest E. Fricks
Michael Fuchs
Bob Genisol (Sultan Stamp Center)
Stan Goldfarb
Allen Grant (Rushstamps (Retail) Ltd.)
Daniel E. Grau
Robin Harris
Bruce Hecht (Bruce L. Hecht Co.)
Peter Hoffman
John Hotchner
Armen Hovsepian (Armenstamp)
Doug Iams
Eric Jackson
John Jamieson (Saskatoon Stamp and Coin)
Peter Jeannopoulos
William A. Jones
Allan Katz (Ventura Stamp Co.)
Lewis Kaufman (The Philatelic Foundation)
Patricia Kaufmann (Confederate Stamp Alliance)
Jon Kawaguchi (Ryukyu Philatelic Specialist Society)
Roland Kretschmer
William V. Kriebel (Brazil Philatelic Association)
Frederick P. Lawrence
John R. Lewis (The William Henry Stamp Co.)
Ulf Lindahl
Ignacio Llach (Filatelia Llach S.L.)
Marilyn R. Mattke
William K. McDaniel
Mauricio Mejia
Gary Morris (Pacific Midwest Co.)
Peter Mosiondz, Jr.
Bruce M. Moyer (Moyer Stamps & Collectibles)
Richard H. Muller
Scott Murphy (Professional Stamp Experts)
Leonard Nadybal
Dr. Tiong Tak Ngo
Gerald Nylander
Nik & Lisa Oquist
Dr. Everett Parker
Don Peterson (International Philippine Philatelic Society)
Stanley M. Piller (Stanley M. Piller & Associates)
Virgil Pirvulescu
Todor Drumev Popov
Peter W. W. Powell
Bob Prager (Gary Posner, Inc.)
Siddique Mahmudur Rahman
Ghassan D. Riachi
Mehrdad Sadri (Persiphila)
Sabah Jawad Salih
Theodosios Sampson PhD
Alexander Schauss (Schauss Philatelics)
Michael Schreiber
Jeff Siddiqui
Sergio & Liane Sismondo (The Classic Collector)
Jay Smith
Kenneth Thompson
Peter Thy
Scott R. Trepel (Robert A. Siegel Auction Galleries, Inc.)
Dan Undersander (United Postal Stationery Society)
Herbert R. Volin
Philip T. Wall
Giana Wayman
Don White (Dunedin Stamp Centre)
Ralph Yorio
Val Zabijaka
Michal Zika

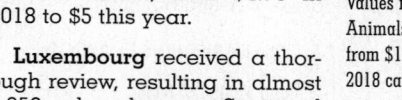

# What's new for 2019 Scott Standard Volume 4A?

Greetings, Fellow Scott Catalog User:

This year celebrates another milestone in the 150-year history of the Scott catalogs. The 2019 volumes are the 175th edition of the Scott *Standard Postage Stamp Catalogue*. Vol. 4A includes listings for countries of the world J-L. Listings for countries of the world beginning with the letter M can be found in Vol. 4B.

**Japan** received a line-by-line review through the stamps of 1950, resulting in more than 1,500 value changes. Most of the changes result in increases, some significant. The 1908 Empress Jingo set of two stamps (Scott 113-114) are among the stamps that reflect a strong market. The 5-yen green jumps from $850 unused to $900, and from $6 used to $11. The 10y dark violet moves from $1,200 unused to $1,500, and from $10 used to $15. Among the exceptions to the increases in value are a few of the early issues, including the first issue, Scott 1-6, which declines in value. The 1871 48-mon stamp (1) drops from $250 unused and used to $225 both ways. Scott 2-6 experience similar declines.

Value increases for Japan's 1908 Empress Jingo set of two stamps (Scott 113-114) reflect a continuing strong market for this Asian country.

Scattered value changes were made from 1951 onward, reflecting a strong market for Japanese stamps.

Many footnoted values for stamps of **Katanga** with inverted overprints rose substantially this year. Be sure to give them a careful review if you collect this country.

Collectors of **Kazakhstan** will be pleased to see that country's values on the rise. More than 920 changes were recorded, and the vast majority are increases of 10 percent or more. The more robust increases are seen among popular topicals such as fauna and Olympic sports. The 2005 Olympic Gold Medalists sheet of four (Scott 491) advances from $7.50 mint never-hinged and used in 2018 to $9 both ways in the 2019 catalog.

More than 4,300 value changes were made in **South Korea**. Increases predominate among the issues of Imperial Korea. The 1900 1 poon on 5p green stamp with red surcharge (Scott 15B) jumps significantly in value, from $3,500 unused to $6000, and from $750 used to $2,500. South Korea, beginning with United States military rule in 1946, is on the decline, with numerous decreases in values throughout. Among the exceptions is the iconic 1948 President Syngman Rhee stamp (90). This stamp moves from $375 in never-hinged condition to $450, from $200 unused to $260, and from $180 used to $200. Although many of the early souvenir sheets are on the decline, the 1957 Christmas and New Year imperforate souvenir sheets (265a-267a) increase from $625 each mint to $650.

Mostly decreases are found among the more than 875 value changes throughout the listings for the **Democratic People's Republic of Korea (North Korea)**.

The editors gave **Kyrgyzstan** a complete review, which resulted in more than 450 value changes. Overall, modest declines predominate, with some scattered increases. Among the Kyrgyz Express Post issues (found after the semipostal listings), increases are seen for the 2014 through early 2016 issues. The Wild Animals sheet of four (Scott 5) springs up, from $12 mint never-hinged and used in the 2018 catalog to $15 both ways this year.

A mixture of increases and decreases are spread throughout the listings in **Latvia**, resulting in more than 500 value changes. The editors did not see any significant movement in either direction. Fairly typical among recent issues is the 2012 Birds set of two (Scott 808-809), which moves up just 25¢ in mint and used condition, from $4.75 in 2018 to $5 this year.

Values for the Kyrgyz Express Post Wild Animals sheet of four (Scott 5) move upward, from $12 mint never-hinged and used in the 2018 catalog to $15 both ways this year.

**Luxembourg** received a thorough review, resulting in almost 1,650 value changes. Scattered increases can be found among the classic-era stamps. The 1921 15-centime Grand Duchess Charlotte sheet of five, perforated gauge 11 (Scott 125a), soars in value, from $150 unused to $400. The value for the sheet in used condition remains at $250. Values for stamps issued from 1945 into the 1990s show decreases.

***Editorial enhancements for Vol. 4A***

**Jamaica**: Scott 85a is newly assigned to the 3-shilling Monument to Sir Charles Metcalfe with the "C" of "CA" missing in error from the Multiple Crown and CA watermark.

**Japan**: New listings for booklet panes have been added to the classic issues. Values have been added to footnotes for numerous New Year sheets.

**Jordan**: Among the new images in this volume are images showing the differences between the bars on the normal 1½-millimeter spacing and the narrow ½mm spacing for Jordan's 1953 overprinted stamps (Scott 297-305). The bars were overprinted on Jordan's 1952 Relief Map stamps (270-278) issued to honor the unity of Jordan April 24, 1950. The values for the overprinted set remains unchanged at $21.75 mint and $11.95 used.

**Korea**: Two souvenir sheets for the Winter Universiade 1997 were added as Scott 1895a-1896a, with a value of $1.25 each mint and used.

**Kyrgyzstan**: More than 30 issues known to exist imperforate are described and valued for the first time in footnotes.

**Luxembourg**: A se-tenant pair of the 1952 Grand Duke William III stamps enters the 2019 catalog as Scott 279a, valued at $47.50 unused, $75 used, and $75 mint never-hinged.

The 35-santims stamp from Latvia's 2012 Birds set of two (Scott 808-809). The set moves up slightly in mint and used condition, from $4.75 in 2018 to $5 this year.

As with the stock market, a softening in the stamp market for some countries can be looked upon as an opportunity to buy stamps to fill spaces in your stamp albums.

As always, we encourage you to pay special attention to the Number Additions, Deletions & Changes found on page 860 in this volume. We also suggest reading the catalog introduction, which includes an abundance of useful information.

Set time aside each day to enjoy this wonderful hobby!

Donna Houseman

Donna Houseman/Catalogue Editor

# Addresses, Telephone Numbers, Web Sites, E-Mail Addresses of General & Specialized Philatelic Societies

Collectors can contact the following groups for information about the philately of the areas within the scope of these societies, or inquire about membership in these groups. Aside from the general societies, we limit this list to groups that specialize in particular fields of philately, particular areas covered by the Scott Standard Postage Stamp Catalogue, and topical groups. Many more specialized philatelic society exist than those listed below. These addresses are updated yearly, and they are, to the best of our knowledge, correct and current. Groups should inform the editors of address changes whenever they occur. The editors also want to hear from other such specialized groups not listed. Unless otherwise noted all website addresses begin with http://

**American Philatelic Society**
100 Match Factory Place
Bellefonte PA 16823-1367
Ph: (814) 933-3803
www.stamps.org
E-mail: apsinfo@stamps.org

**American Stamp Dealers Association, Inc.**
P.O. Box 692
Leesport PA 19553
Ph: (800) 369-8207
www.americanstampdealer.com
E-mail: asda@americanstampdealer.com

**National Stamp Dealers Association**
Richard Kostka, President
3643 Private Road 18
Pinckneyville IL 62274-3426
Ph: (800) 875-6633 or (618) 357-5497
www.nsdainc.org
E-mail: nsda@nsdainc.org

**International Society of Worldwide Stamp Collectors**
Joanne Berkowitz, MD
P.O. Box 19006
Sacramento CA 95819
www.iswsc.org
E-mail: executivedirector@iswsc.org

**Royal Philatelic Society**
41 Devonshire Place
London, W1G 6JY
UNITED KINGDOM
www.rpsl.org.uk
E-mail: secretary@rpsl.org.uk

**Royal Philatelic Society of Canada**
P.O. Box 69080
St. Clair Post Office
Toronto, ON, M4T 3A1
CANADA
Ph: (888) 285-4143
www.rpsc.org
E-mail: info@rpsc.org

**Young Stamp Collectors of America**
Janet Houser
100 Match Factory Place
Bellefonte PA 16823-1367
Ph: (814) 933-3820
www.stamps.org/ysca/intro.htm
E-mail: ysca@stamps.org

## Philatelic Research Resources

(The Scott editors encourage any additional research organizations to submit data for inclusion in this listing category)

**American Philatelic Research Library**
Scott Tiffney
100 Match Factory Place
Bellefonte PA 16823
Ph: (814) 933-3803
www.stamplibrary.org
E-mail: library@stamps.org

**Institute for Analytical Philately, Inc.**
P.O. Box 8035
Holland MI 49422-8035
Ph: (616) 399-9299
www.analyticalphilately.org
E-mail: info@analyticalphilately.org

**The Western Philatelic Library**
P.O. Box 2219
1500 Partridge Ave.
Sunnyvale CA 94087
Ph: (408) 733-0336
www.fwpf.org

## Groups focusing on fields or aspects found in worldwide philately (some might cover U.S. area only)

**American Air Mail Society**
Stephen Reinhard
P.O. Box 110
Mineola NY 11501
www.americanairmailsociety.org
E-mail: sreinhard1@optonline.net

**American First Day Cover Society**
Douglas Kelsey
P.O. Box 16277
Tucson AZ 85732-6277
Ph: (520) 321-0880
www.afdcs.org
E-mail: afdcs@afdcs.org

**American Revenue Association**
Eric Jackson
P.O. Box 728
Leesport PA 19533-0728
Ph: (610) 926-6200
www.revenuer.org
E-mail: eric@revenuer.com

**American Topical Association**
Vera Felts
P.O. Box 8
Carterville IL 62918-0008
Ph: (618) 985-5100
www.americantopicalassn.org
E-mail: americantopical@msn.com

**Christmas Seal & Charity Stamp Society**
John Denune
234 E. Broadway
Granville OH 43023
Ph: (740) 587-0276
www.seal-society.org
E-mail: john@christmasseals.net

**Errors, Freaks and Oddities Collectors Club**
Scott Shaulis
P.O. Box 549
Murrysville PA 15668-0549
Ph: (724) 733-4134
www.efocc.org
E-mail: Scott@shaulisstamps.com

**First Issues Collectors Club**
Kurt Streepy, Secretary
3128 E. Mattatha Drive
Bloomington IN 47401
www.firstissues.org
E-mail: secretary@firstissues.org

**International Society of Reply Coupon Collectors**
Peter Robin
P.O. Box 353
Bala Cynwyd PA 19004
E-mail: peterrobin@verizon.net

**The Joint Stamp Issues Society**
Richard Zimmermann
29A Rue Des Eviats
Lalaye F-67220
FRANCE
www.philarz.net
E-mail: richard.zimmermann@club-internet.fr

**National Duck Stamp Collectors Society**
Anthony J. Monico
P.O. Box 43
Harleysville PA 19438-0043
www.ndscs.org
E-mail: ndscs@ndscs.org

**No Value Identified Club**
Albert Sauvanet
Le Clos Royal B, Boulevard des Pas Enchantes
St. Sebastien-sur Loire, 44230
FRANCE
E-mail: alain.vailly@irin.univ nantes.fr

**The Perfins Club**
Ken Masters
111 NW 94th Street Apt. 102
Kansas City MO 64155-2993
Ph: (816) 835-5907
www.perfins.org
E-mail: kmasters@aol.com

**Postage Due Mail Study Group**
John Rawlins
13, Longacre
Chelmsford, CM1 3BJ
UNITED KINGDOM
E-mail: john.rawlins2@ukonline.co.uk

**Post Mark Collectors Club**
Bob Milligan
7014 Woodland Oaks
Magnolia TX 77354
Ph: (281) 259-2735
www.postmarks.org
E-mail: bob.milligan@gmail.net

**Postal History Society**
Gary Wayne Loew
P.O. Box 468101
Atlanta GA 31146-8101
www.postalhistorysociety.org
E-mail: garywloew@gmail.com

**Precancel Stamp Society**
Dick Kalmbach
2658 Iron Works Drive
Buford GA 30519
Ph: (610) 248-8844
www.precancels.com
E-mail: promo@precancels.com

**United Postal Stationery Society**
Stuart Leven
1659 Branham Lane Suite F-307
San Jose CA 95118-2291
www.upss.org
E-mail: poststat@gmail.com

**United States Possessions Philatelic Society**
Daniel F. Ring
P.O. Box 113
Woodstock IL 60098
www.uspps.net
E-mail: danielfring@hotmail.com

## Groups focusing on U.S. area philately as covered in the Standard Catalogue

**Canal Zone Study Group**
Tom Brougham
737 Neilson St.
Berkeley CA 94707
www.CanalZoneStudyGroup.com
E-mail: czsgsecretary@gmail.com

**Carriers and Locals Society**
Martin Richardson
P.O. Box 74
Grosse Ile MI 48138
www.pennypost.org
E-mail: martinr362@aol.com

**Confederate Stamp Alliance**
Patricia A. Kaufmann
10194 N. Old State Road
Lincoln DE 19960
Ph. (302) 422-2656
www.csalliance.org
E-mail: trishkauf@comcast.net

**Hawaiian Philatelic Society**
Gawwon Sugimura
P.O. Box 10115
Honolulu HI 96816-0115
E-mail: hiphilsoc@gmail.com

**Plate Number Coil Collectors Club**
Gene Trinks
16415 W. Desert Wren Court
Surprise AZ 85374
Ph: (623) 322-4619
www.pnc3.org
E-mail: gctrinks@cox.net

**Ryukyu Philatelic Specialist Society**
Laura Edmonds, Secy.
P.O. Box 240177
Charlotte NC 28224-0177
Ph: (336) 509-3739
www.ryukyustamps.org
E-mail: secretary@ryukyustamps.org

**United Nations Philatelists**
Blanton Clement, Jr.
P.O. Box 146
Morrisville PA 19067-0146
www.unpi.com
E-mail: bclemjunior@gmail.com

**United States Stamp Society**
Executive Secretary
Larry Ballantyne
P.O. Box 6634
Katy TX 77491-6634
www.usstamps.org

**U.S. Cancellation Club**
Roger Curran
20 University Avenue
Lewisburg PA 17837
E-mail: rcurran@dejazzd.com

**U.S. Philatelic Classics Society**
Rob Lund
2913 Fulton St.
Everett WA 98201-3733
www.uspcs.org
E-mail: membershipchairman@uspcs.org

### Groups focusing on philately of foreign countries or regions

**Aden & Somaliland Study Group**
Gary Brown
P.O. Box 106
Briar Hill, Victoria, 3088
AUSTRALIA
E-mail: garyjohn951@optushome.com.au

**American Society of Polar Philatelists (Antarctic areas)**
Alan Warren
P.O. Box 39
Exton PA 19341-0039
www.polarphilatelists.org

**Andorran Philatelic Study Circle**
D. Hope
17 Hawthorn Drive
Stalybridge, Cheshire, SK15 1UE
UNITED KINGDOM
www.andorranpsc.org.uk
E-mail: andorranpsc@btinternet.com

**Australian States Study Circle of The Royal Sydney Philatelic Club**
Ben Palmer
GPO 1751
Sydney, N.S.W., 2001
AUSTRALIA
www.philas.org.au/states

**Austria Philatelic Society**
Ralph Schneider
P.O. Box 23049
Belleville IL 62223
Ph: (618) 277-6152
www.austriaphilatelicsociety.com
E-mail: rschneiderstamps@att.net

**Bechuanalands and Botswana Society**
Neville Midwood
69 Porlock Lane
Furzton, Milton Keynes, MK4 1JY
UNITED KINGDOM
www.nevsoft.com
E-mail: bbsoc@nevsoft.com

**Bermuda Collectors Society**
John Pare
405 Perimeter Road
Mount Horeb WI 53572
www.bermudacollectorssociety.com
E-mail: pare16@mhtc.net

**Brazil Philatelic Association**
William V. Kriebel
1923 Manning St.
Philadelphia PA 19103-5728
www.brazilphilatelic.org
E-mail: info@brazilphilatelic.org

**British Caribbean Philatelic Study Group**
Duane Larson
2 Forest Blvd.
Park Forest IL 60466
www.bcpsg.com
E-mail: dlarson283@aol.com

**The King George VI Collectors Society (British Commonwealth)**
Brian Livingstone
21 York Mansions, Prince of Wales Drive
London, SW11 4DL
UNITED KINGDOM
www.kg6.info
E-mail: livingstone484@btinternet.com

**British North America Philatelic Society (Canada & Provinces)**
Andy Ellwood
10 Doris Avenue
Gloucester, ON, KIT 3W8
CANADA
www.bnaps.org
E-mail: secretary@bnaps.org

**British West Indies Study Circle**
John Seidl
4324 Granby Way
Marietta GA 30062
Ph: (404) 229-6863
www.bwisc.org
E-mail: john.seidl@gmail.com

**Burma Philatelic Study Circle**
Michael Whittaker
1, Ecton Leys, Hillside
Rugby, Warwickshire, CV22 5SL
UNITED KINGDOM
www.burmastamps.homecall.co.uk
E-mail: manningham8@mypostoffice.co.uk

**Cape and Natal Study Circle**
Dr. Guy Dillaway
P.O. Box 181
Weston MA 02493
www.nzsc.demon.co.uk

**Ceylon Study Circle**
R. W. P. Frost
42 Lonsdale Road, Cannington
Bridgwater, Somerset, TA5 2JS
UNITED KINGDOM
www.ceylonsc.org
E-mail: rodney.frost@tiscali.co.uk

**Channel Islands Specialists Society**
Richard Flemming
64, Falconers Green, Burbage
Hinckley, Leicestershire, LE10 2SX
UNITED KINGDOM
www.ciss1950.org.uk
E-mail: secretary@ciss1950.org.uk

**China Stamp Society**
H. James Maxwell
1050 West Blue Ridge Blvd.
Kansas City MO 64145-1216
www.chinastampsociety.org
E-mail: president@chinastampsociety.org

**Colombia/Panama Philatelic Study Group (COPAPHIL)**
Thomas P. Myers
P.O. Box 522
Gordonsville VA 22942
www.copaphil.org
E-mail: tpmphil@hotmail.com

**Association Filatelic de Costa Rica**
Giana Wayman (McCarty)
SJO 4935, P.O. Box 025723
Miami FL 33102-5723
E-mail: scotland@racsa.co.cr

**Society for Costa Rica Collectors**
Dr. Hector R. Mena
P.O. Box 14831
Baton Rouge LA 70808
www.socorico.org
E-mail: hrmena@aol.com

**International Cuban Philatelic Society**
Ernesto Cuesta
P.O. Box 34434
Bethesda MD 20827
www.cubafil.org
E-mail: ecuesta@philat.com

**Cuban Philatelic Society of America ®**
P.O. Box 141656
Coral Gables FL 33114-1656
www.cubapsa.com
E-mail: cpsa.usa@gmail.com

**Cyprus Study Circle**
Colin Dear
10 Marne Close, Wem
Shropshire, SY4 5YE
UNITED KINGDOM
www.cyprusstudycircle.org/index.htm
E-mail: colindear@talktalk.net

**Society for Czechoslovak Philately**
Tom Cossaboom
P.O. Box 4124
Prescott AZ 86302
Ph: (928) 771-9097
www.csphilately.org
E-mail: klfckl@aol.com

**Danish West Indies Study Unit of the Scandinavian Collectors Club**
Arnold Sorensen
7666 Edgedale Drive
Newburgh IN 47630
Ph: (812) 480-6532
www.scc-online.org
E-mail: valbydwi@hotmail.com

**East Africa Study Circle**
Michael Vesey-Fitzgerald
Gambles Cottage, 18 Clarence Road
Lyndhurst, SO43 7AL
UNITED KINGDOM
www.easc.org.uk
E-mail: secretary@easc.org.uk

**Egypt Study Circle**
Mike Murphy
109 Chadwick Road
London, SE15 4PY
UNITED KINGDOM
Trent Ruebush: North American Agent
E-mail: tkruebrush@gmail.com
www.egyptstudycircle.org.uk
E-mail: egyptstudycircle@hotmail.com

**Estonian Philatelic Society**
Juri Kirsimagi
29 Clifford Ave.
Pelham NY 10803
Ph: (914) 738-3713

**Ethiopian Philatelic Society**
Ulf Lindahl
21 Westview Place
Riverside CT 06878
Ph: (203) 722-0769
http://ethiopianphilatelicsociety.weebly.com
E-mail: ulindahl@optonline.net

**Falkland Islands Philatelic Study Group**
Carl J. Faulkner
615 Taconic Trail
Williamstown MA 01267-2745
Ph: (413) 458-4421
www.fipsg.org.uk
E-mail: cfaulkner@taconicwilliamstown.com

**Faroe Islands Study Circle**
Norman Hudson
40 Queen's Road, Vicar's Cross
Chester, CH3 5HB
UNITED KINGDOM
www.faroeislandssc.org
E-mail: jntropics@hotmail.com

**Former French Colonies Specialist Society**
COLFRA
BP 628
75367 Paris, Cedex 08
FRANCE
www.colfra.org
E-mail: secretaire@colfra.org

**France & Colonies Philatelic Society**
Edward Grabowski
111 Prospect St., 4C
Westfield NJ 07090
www.franceandcolps.org
E-mail: edjjg@alum.mit.edu

**Gibraltar Study Circle**
Susan Dare
22, Byways Park, Strode Road,
Clevedon, North Somerset, BS21 6UR
UNITED KINGDOM
www.gibraltarstudycircle.wordpress.com
E-mail: smldare@yahoo.co.uk

**Germany Philatelic Society**
P.O. Box 6547
Chesterfield MO 63006
www.germanyphilatelicusa.org

**Plebiscite-Memel-Saar Study Group of the German Philatelic Society**
Clayton Wallace
100 Lark Court
Alamo CA 94507
E-mail: claytonwallace@comcast.net

**Great Britain Collectors Club**
Steve McGill
10309 Brookhollow Circle
Highlands Ranch CO 80129
www.gbstamps.com/gbcc
E-mail: steve.mcgill@comcast.net

**International Society of Guatemala Collectors**
Jaime Marckwordt
449 St. Francis Blvd.
Daly City CA 94015-2136
www.guatemalastamps.com
E-mail:
membership@guatamalastamps.com

**Haiti Philatelic Society**
Ubaldo Del Toro
5709 Marble Archway
Alexandria VA 22315
www.haitiphilately.org
E-mail: u007ubi@aol.com

**Federacion Filatelica de la Republica de Honduras (Honduran Philatelic Federation, FFRH)**
Mauricio Mejia
Apartado postal 1465
Tegucigalpa
HONDURAS

**Hong Kong Stamp Society**
Ming W. Tsang
P.O. Box 206
Glenside PA 19038
www.hkss.org
E-mail: hkstamps@yahoo.com

**Society for Hungarian Philately**
Alan Bauer
P.O. Box 3024
Andover MA 01810
Ph: (978) 682-0242
www.hungarianphilately.org
E-mail: alan@hungarianstamps.com

**India Study Circle**
John Warren
P.O. Box 7326
Washington DC 20044
Ph: (202) 488-7443
www.indiastudycircle.org
E-mail: jw-kbw@earthlink.net

**Indian Ocean Study Circle**
E. S. Hutton
29 Patermoster Close
Waltham Abby, Essex, EN9 3JU
UNITED KINGDOM
www.indianoceanstudycircle.com
E-mail: secretary@
indianoceanstudycircle.com

**Society of Indo-China Philatelists**
Ron Bentley
2600 N. 24th St.
Arlington VA 22207
www.sicp-online.org
E-mail: ron.bentley@verizon.net

**Iran Philatelic Study Circle**
Mehdi Esmaili
P.O. Box 750096
Forest Hills NY 11375
www.iranphilatelic.org
E-mail: m.esmaili@earthlink.net

**Eire Philatelic Association (Ireland)**
David J. Brennan
P.O. Box 704
Bernardsville NJ 07924
www.eirephilatelicassoc.org
E-mail: brennan704@aol.com

**Society of Israel Philatelists**
Jacqueline Baca
100 Match Factory Place
Bellefonte PA 16823-1367
Ph: (814) 933-3803 ext. 212
www.israelstamps.com
E-mail: israelstamps@gmail.com

**Italy and Colonies Study Circle**
Richard Harlow
7 Duncombe House, 8 Manor Road
Teddington, TW11 8BE
UNITED KINGDOM
www.icsc.pwp.blueyonder.co.uk
E-mail: richardharlow@outlook.com

**International Society for Japanese Philately**
William Eisenhauer
P.O. Box 230462
Tigard OR 97281
www.isjp.org
E-mail: secretary@isjp.org

**Korea Stamp Society**
John Talmage
P.O. Box 6889
Oak Ridge TN 37831
www.koreastampsociety.org
E-mail: jtalmage@usit.net

**Latin American Philatelic Society**
Jules K. Beck
30½ St. #209
St. Louis Park MN 55426-3551

**Liberian Philatelic Society**
William Thomas Lockard
P.O. Box 106
Wellston OH 45692
Ph: (740) 384-2020
E-mail: tlockard@zoomnet.net

**Liechtenstudy USA (Liechtenstein)**
Paul Tremaine
410 SW Ninth St.
Dundee OR 97115
Ph: (503) 538-4500
www.liechtenstudy.org
E-mail: editor@liechtenstudy.org

**Lithuania Philatelic Society**
John Variakojis
8472 Carlisle Court
Burr Ridge IL 60527
Ph: (630) 974-6525
www.lithuanianphilately.com/lps
E-mail: variakojis@sbcglobal.net

**Luxembourg Collectors Club**
Gary B. Little
7319 Beau Road
Sechelt, BC, VON 3A8
CANADA
lcc.luxcentral.com
E-mail: gary@luxcentral.com

**Malaya Study Group**
David Tett
4 Amenbury Court
Harpenden Herts,
Wheathampstead Herts AL5 2BU
UNITED KINGDOM
www.m-s-g.org.uk
E-mail: davidtett@aol.com

**Malta Study Circle**
Rodger Evans
Ravensbourne, Hook Heath Road
Woking, Surrey, GU22 OLB
UNITED KINGDOM
www.maltastudycircle.org.uk
E-mail: carge@hotmail.co.uk

**Mexico-Elmhurst Philatelic Society International**
Eric Stovner
P.O. Box 10097
Santa Ana CA 92711-0097
www.mepsi.org
E-mail: treasurer@mepsi.org

**Asociacion Mexicana de Filatelia AMEXFIL**
Alejando Grossman
Jose Maria Rico, 129, Col. Del Valle
Mexico City DF, 03100
MEXICO
www.amexfil.mx
E-mail: amexfil@gmail.com

**Society for Moroccan and Tunisian Philately S.P.L.M.**
206, bld Pereire
Paris 75017
FRANCE
splm-philatelie.org
E-mail: splm206@aol.com

**Nepal & Tibet Philatelic Study Group**
Ken Goss
2643 Wagner Place
EL Dorado Hills CA 95762
Ph: (510) 207-5369
www.fuchs-online.com/ntpsc/
E-mail: kfgoss@comcast.net

**American Society for Netherlands Philately**
Hans Kremer
50 Rockport Court
Danville CA 94526
Ph: (925) 820-5841
www.asnp1975.com
E-mail: hkremer@usa.net

**New Zealand Society of Great Britain**
Michael Wilkinson
121 London Road
Sevenoaks, Kent, TN13 1BH
UNITED KINGDOM
www.nzsgb.org.uk
E-mail: mwilkin799@aol.com

**Nicaragua Study Group**
Erick Rodriguez
11817 SW 11th St.
Miami FL 33184-2501
clubs.yahoo.com/clubs/
nicaraguastudygroup
E-mail: nsgsec@yahoo.com

**Society of Australasian Specialists/Oceania**
David McNamee
P.O. Box 37
Alamo CA 94507
www.sasoceania.org
E-mail: treasurer@sasoceania.org

**Orange Free State Study Circle**
J. R. Stroud
24 Hooper Close
Burnham-on-sea, Somerset, TA8 1JQ
UNITED KINGDOM
orangefreestatephilately.org.uk
E-mail: richard@richardstroud.plus.com

**Pacific Islands Study Circle**
John Ray
24 Woodvale Ave.
London, SE25 4AE
UNITED KINGDOM
www.pisc.org.uk
E-mail: secretary@pisc.org.uk

**Pakistan Philatelic Study Circle**
Jeff Siddiqui
P.O. Box 7002
Lynnwood WA 98046
E-mail: jeffsiddiqui@msn.com

**Asociacion Filatelica de Panama (ASOFILPA)**
Edward D. Vianna
Apartado Postal 0819-03400
El Dorado, Panama
PANAMA
www.asociacionfilatelicadepanama.
blogspot.com
E-mail: asofilpa@gmail.com

**Papuan Philatelic Society**
Steven Zirinsky
P.O. Box 49, Ansonia Station
New York NY 10023
Ph: (718) 706-0616
www.communigate.co.uk/york/pps
E-mail: szirinsky@cs.com

**International Philippine Philatelic Society**
Donald J. Peterson
P.O. Box 122
Brunswick MD 21716
Ph: (301) 834-6419
www.theipps.info
E-mail: dpeterson4526@gmail.com

**Pitcairn Islands Study Group**
Dr. Everett L. Parker
117 Cedar Breeze South
Glenburn ME 04401-1734
Ph: (207) 573-1686
www.pisg.net
E-mail: eparker@hughes.net

**Polonus Philatelic Society (Poland)**
Daniel Lubelski
P.O. Box 2212
Benicia CA 94510
Ph: (419) 410-9115
www.polonus.org
E-mail: info@polonus.org

**International Society for Portuguese Philately**
Clyde Homen
1491 Bonnie View Road
Hollister CA 95023-5117
www.portugalstamps.com
E-mail: ispp1962@sbcglobal.net

**Rhodesian Study Circle**
William R. Wallace
P.O. Box 16381
San Francisco CA 94116
www.rhodesianstudycircle.org.uk
E-mail: bwall8rscr@earthlink.net

**Rossica Society of Russian Philately**
Alexander Kolchinsky
1506 Country Lake Drive
Champaign IL 6821-6428
www.rossica.org
E-mail: alexander.kolchinsky@rossica.org

**St. Helena, Ascension & Tristan Da Cunha Philatelic Society**
Dr. Everett L. Parker
117 Cedar Breeze South
Glenburn ME 04401-1734
Ph: (207) 573-1686
www.shatps.org
E-mail: eparker@hughes.net

**St. Pierre & Miquelon Philatelic Society**
James R. (Jim) Taylor
2335 Paliswood Road SW
Calgary, AB, T2V 3P6
CANADA
www.stamps.org/spm

**Asociacion Filatelica Salvadorena**
Joseph D. Hahn
301 Rolling Ridge Drive, Apt. 111
State College PA 16801-6149
www.elsalvadorphilately.org
E-mail: joehahn100@hotmail.com

**Fellowship of Samoa Specialists**
Donald Mee
23 Leo St.
Christchurch, 8051
NEW ZEALAND
www.samoaexpress.org
E-mail: donanm@xtra.co.nz

**Sarawak Specialists' Society**
Stephen Schumann
2417 Cabrillo Drive
Hayward CA 94545
Ph: (510) 785-4794
www.britborneostamps.org.uk
E-mail: stephen.schumann@att.net

**Scandinavian Collectors Club**
Steve Lund
P.O. Box 16213
St. Paul MN 55116
www.scc-online.org
E-mail: steve88h@aol.com

**Slovakia Stamp Society**
Jack Benchik
P.O. Box 555
Notre Dame IN 46556

**Philatelic Society for Greater Southern Africa**
Alan Hanks
34 Seaton Drive
Aurora, ON, L4G 2K1
CANADA
www.psgsa.thestampweb.com

**South Sudan Philatelic Society**
William Barclay
1370 Spring Hill Road
South Londonderry VT 05155
E-mail: barclayphilatelics@gmail.com

**Spanish Philatelic Society**
Robert H. Penn
1108 Walnut Drive
Danielsville PA 18038
Ph: (610) 844-8963
E-mail: roberthpenn43@gmail.com

**Sudan Study Group**
David Sher
5 Ellis Park Road
Toronto, ON, M6S2V1
CANADA
www.sudanstamps.org
e-mail: sh3603@hotmail.com

**American Helvetia Philatelic Society (Switzerland, Liechtenstein)**
Richard T. Hall
P.O. Box 15053
Asheville NC 28813-0053
www.swiss-stamps.org
E-mail: secretary2@swiss-stamps.org

**Tannu Tuva Collectors Society**
Ken R. Simon
P.O. Box 385
Lake Worth FL 33460-0385
Ph: (561) 588-5954
www.tuva.tk
E-mail: yurttuva@yahoo.com

**Society for Thai Philately**
H. R. Blakeney
P.O. Box 25644
Oklahoma City OK 73125
E-mail: HRBlakeney@aol.com

**Transvaal Study Circle**
Chris Board
36 Wakefield Gardens
London, SE19 2NR
UNITED KINGDOM
www.transvaalstamps.org.uk
E-mail: c.board@macace.net

**Ottoman and Near East Philatelic Society (Turkey and related areas)**
Bob Stuchell
193 Valley Stream Lane
Wayne PA 19087
www.oneps.org
E-mail: rstuchell@msn.com

**Ukrainian Philatelic & Numismatic Society**
Martin B. Tatuch
5117 8th Road N.
Arlington VA 22205-1201
www.upns.org
E-mail: treasurer@upns.org

**Vatican Philatelic Society**
Sal Quinonez
1 Aldersgate, Apt. 1002
Riverhead NY 11901-1830
Ph: (516) 727-6426
www.vaticanphilately.org

**British Virgin Islands Philatelic Society**
Giorgio Migliavacca
P.O. Box 7007
St. Thomas VI 00801-0007
www.islandsun.com/category/collectables/
E-mail: issun@candwbvi.net

**West Africa Study Circle**
Martin Bratzel
1233 Virginia Ave.
Windsor, ON, N8S 2Z1
CANADA
www.wasc.org.uk
E-mail: marty_bratzel@yahoo.ca

**Western Australia Study Group**
Brian Pope
P.O. Box 423
Claremont, Western Australia, 6910
AUSTRALIA
www.wastudygroup.com
E-mail: black5swan@yahoo.com.au

**Yugoslavia Study Group of the Croatian Philatelic Society**
Michael Lenard
1514 N. Third Ave.
Wausau WI 54401
Ph: (715) 675-2833
E-mail: mjlenard@aol.com

## Topical Groups

**Americana Unit**
Dennis Dengel
17 Peckham Road
Poughkeepsie NY 12603-2018
www.americanaunit.org
E-mail: ddengel@americanaunit.org

**Astronomy Study Unit**
John Budd
728 Sugar Camp Way
Brooksville FL 34604
Ph: (352) 345-4799
www.astronomystudyunit.net
E-mail: jwgbudd@gmail.com

**Bicycle Stamps Club**
Steve Andreasen
2000 Alaskan Way, Unit 157
Seattle WA 98121
E-mail: steven.w.andreasen@gmail.com

**Biology Unit**
Alan Hanks
34 Seaton Drive
Aurora, ON, L4G 2K1
CANADA
Ph: (905) 727-6993

**Bird Stamp Society**
S. A. H. (Tony) Statham
Ashlyns Lodge, Chesham Road,
Berkhamsted, Hertfordshire HP4 2ST
UNITED KINGDOM
www.bird-stamps.org/bss
E-mail: tony.statham@sky.com

**Captain Cook Society**
Jerry Yucht
8427 Leale Ave.
Stockton CA 95212
www.captaincooksociety.com
E-mail: US@captaincooksociety.com

**The CartoPhilatelic Society**
Marybeth Sulkowski
2885 Sanford Ave, SW, #32361
Grandville MI 49418-1342
www.mapsonstamps.org
E-mail: secretary@mapsonstamps.org

**Casey Jones Railroad Unit**
Jeff Lough
2612 Redbud Lane, Apt. C
Lawrence KS 66046
www.uqp.de/cjr/index.htm
E-mail: jeffydplaugh@gmail.com

**Cats on Stamps Study Unit**
Robert D. Jarvis
2731 Teton Lane
Fairfield CA 94533
www.catstamps.info
E-mail: bobmarci@aol.com

**Chemistry & Physics on Stamps Study Unit**
Dr. Roland Hirsch
20458 Water Point Lane
Germantown MD 20874
www.cpossu.org
E-mail: rfhirsch@cpossu.org

**Chess on Stamps Study Unit**
Ray C. Alexis
608 Emery St.
Longmont CO 80501
E-mail: chessstuff911459@aol.com

**Christmas Philatelic Club**
Jim Balog
P.O. Box 744
Geneva OH 44041
www.christmasphilatelicclub.org
E-mail: jpb4stamps@windstream.net

**Cricket Philatelic Society**
A. Melville-Brown, President
11 Weppons, Ravens Road
Shoreham-by-Sea
West Sussex, BN43 5AW
UNITED KINGDOM
www.cricketstamp.net
E-mail: mel.cricket.100@googlemail.com

**Dogs on Stamps Study Unit**
Morris Raskin
202A Newport Road
Monroe Township NJ 08831
Ph: (609) 655-7411
www.dossu.org
E-mail: mraskin@cellurian.com

**Earth's Physical Features Study Group**
Fred Klein
515 Magdalena Ave.
Los Altos CA 94024
epfsu.jeffhayward.com

**Ebony Society of Philatelic Events and Reflections, Inc. (African-American topicals)**
Manuel Gilyard
800 Riverside Drive, Suite 4H
New York NY 10032-7412
www.esperstamps.org
E-mail: gilyardmani@aol.com

**Europa Study Unit**
Tonny E. Van Loij
3002 S. Xanthia St.
Denver CO 80231-4237
Ph: (303) 752-0189
www.europastudyunit.org
E-mail: tvanloij@gmail.com

**Fine & Performing Arts**
Deborah L. Washington
6922 S. Jeffery Blvd., #7 - North
Chicago IL 60649
E-mail: brasslady@comcast.net

**Fire Service in Philately**
John Zaranek
81 Hillpine Road
Cheektowaga NY 14227-2259
Ph: (716) 668-3352
E-mail: jczaranek@roadrunner.com

**Gay & Lesbian History on Stamps Club**
Joe Petronie
P.O. Box 190842
Dallas TX 75219-0842
www.facebook.com/glhsc
E-mail: glhsc@aol.com

**Gems, Minerals & Jewelry Study Unit**
Mrs. Gilberte Proteau
138 Lafontaine
Beloeil QC J3G 2G7
CANADA
Ph: (978) 851-8283
E-mail: gilberte.ferland@sympatico.ca

**Graphics Philately Association**
Mark H. Winnegrad
P.O. Box 380
Bronx NY 10462-0380
www.graphics-stamps.org
E-mail: indybruce1@yahoo.com

**Journalists, Authors & Poets on Stamps**
Clete Delvaux
800 East River Drive
De Pere WI 54115
E-mail: cdelvaux@msn.com

**Lighthouse Stamp Society**
Dalene Thomas
1805 S Balsam St., #106
Lakewood CO 80232
Ph: (303) 986-6620
www.lighthousestampsociety.org
E-mail: dalene@lighthousestampsociety.org

**Lions International Stamp Club**
John Bargus
108-2777 Barry Road RR 2
Mill Bay, BC, V0R 2P2
CANADA
Ph: (250) 743-5782

**Mahatma Gandhi On Stamps Study Circle**
Pramod Shivagunde
Pratik Clinic, Akluj
Solapur, Maharashtra, 413101
INDIA
E-mail: drnanda@bom6.vsnl.net.in

**Masonic Study Unit**
Gene Fricks
25 Murray Way
Blackwood NJ 08012-4400
E-mail: genefricks@comcast.net

**Mathematical Study Unit**
Monty Strauss
4209 88th St.
Lubbock TX 79423-2941
www.mathstamps.org
E-mail: montystrauss@gmail.com

**Medical Subjects Unit**
Dr. Frederick C. Skvara
P.O. Box 6228
Bridgewater NJ 08807
E-mail: fcskvara@optonline.net

**Military Postal History Society**
Ed Dubin
1 S. Wacker Drive, Suite 3500
Chicago IL 60606
www.militaryPHS.org
E-mail: dubine@comcast.net

**Mourning Stamps and Covers Club**
James Camak, Jr.
3801 Acapulco Ct.
Irving TX 75062
www.mscc.ms
E-mail: jamescamak7@gmail.com

**Napoleonic Age Philatelists**
Ken Berry
4117 NW 146th St.
Oklahoma City OK 73134-1746
Ph: (405) 748-8646
www.nap-stamps.org
E-mail: krb4117@att.net

**Old World Archeological Study Unit**
Caroline Scannell
11 Dawn Drive
Smithtown NY 11787-1761
www.owasu.org
E-mail: editor@owasu.org

**Petroleum Philatelic Society International**
Feitze Papa
922 Meander Dr.
Walnut Creek CA 94598-4239
E-mail: oildad@astound.net

**Rotary on Stamps Unit**
Gerald L. Fitzsimmons
105 Calle Ricardo
Victoria TX 77904
rotaryonstamps.org
E-mail: glfitz@suddenlink.net

**Scouts on Stamps Society International**
Woodrow (Woody) Brooks
498 Baldwin Road
Akron OH 44312
Ph: (330) 612-1294
www.sossi.org
E-mail: rfrank@sossi.org

**Ships on Stamps Unit**
Les Smith
302 Conklin Ave.
Penticton, BC, V2A 2T4
CANADA
Ph: (250) 493-7486
www.shipsonstamps.org
E-mail: lessmith440@shaw.ca

**Space Unit**
David Blog
P.O. Box 174
Bergenfield NJ 07621
www.space-unit.com
E-mail: davidblognj@gmail.com

**Sports Philatelists International**
Mark Maestrone
2824 Curie Place
San Diego CA 92122-4110
www.sportstamps.org
Email: president@sportstamps.org

**Stamps on Stamps Collectors Club**
Alf Jordan
156 W. Elm St.
Yarmouth ME 04096
www.stampsonstamps.org
E-mail: ajordan1@maine.rr.com

**Windmill Study Unit**
Walter J. Hollien
607 N. Porter St.
Watkins Glenn NY 14891-1345
Ph: (607) 229-3541
www.windmillworld.com
E-mail: whollien@earthlink.net

**Wine On Stamps Study Unit**
David Wolfersberger
768 Chain Ridge Road
St. Louis MO 63122-3259
Ph: (314) 961-5032
www.wine-on-stamps.org
E-mail: dewolf2@swbell.net

**Women on Stamps Study Unit**
Hugh Gottfried
2232 26th St.
Santa Monica CA 90405-1902
E-mail: hgottfried@adelphia.net

# Expertizing Services

The following organizations will, for a fee, provide expert opinions about stamps submitted to them. Collectors should contact these organizations to find out about their fees and requirements before submiting philatelic material to them. The listing of these groups here is not intended as an endorsement by Amos Media Co.

## General Expertizing Services

**American Philatelic Expertizing Service (a service of the American Philatelic Society)**
100 Match Factory Place
Bellefonte PA 16823-1367
Ph: (814) 237-3803
Fax: (814) 237-6128
www.stamps.org
E-mail: twhorn@stamps.org
Areas of Expertise: Worldwide

**B. P. A. Expertising, Ltd.**
P.O. Box 1141
Guildford, Surrey, GU5 0WR
UNITED KINGDOM
www.bpaexpertising.com
E-mail: sec@bpaexpertising.org
Areas of Expertise: British Commonwealth, Great Britain, Classics of Europe, South America and the Far East

**Philatelic Foundation**
22 E. 35th St., 4th Floor
New York NY 10016
Ph: (212) 221-6555
Fax: (212) 221-6208
www.philatelicfoundation.org
E-mail: philatelicfoundation@verizon.net
Areas of Expertise: U.S. & Worldwide

**Philatelic Stamp Authentication and Grading, Inc.**
P.O. Box 41-0880
Melbourne FL 32941-0880
Customer Service: (305) 345-9864
www.psaginc.com
E-mail: info@psaginc.com
Areas of Expertise: U.S., Canal Zone, Hawaii, Philippines, Canada & Provinces

**Professional Stamp Experts**
P.O. Box 539309
Henderson NV 89053-9309
Ph: (702) 776-6522
www.gradingmatters.com
www.psestamp.com
E-mail: info@gradingmatters.com
Areas of Expertise: Stamps and covers of U.S., U.S. Possessions, British Commonwealth

**Royal Philatelic Society Expert Committee**
41 Devonshire Place
London, W1N 1PE
UNITED KINGDOM
www.rpsl.org.uk/experts.html
E-mail: experts@rpsl.org.uk
Areas of Expertise: Worldwide

## Expertizing Services Covering Specific Fields or Countries

**China Stamp Society Expertizing Service**
1050 W. Blue Ridge Blvd.
Kansas City MO 64145
Ph: (816) 942-6300
E-mail: hjmesq@aol.com
Areas of Expertise: China

**Confederate Stamp Alliance Authentication Service**
Gen. Frank Crown, Jr.
P.O. Box 278
Capshaw AL 35742-0396
Ph: (302) 422-2656
Fax: (302) 424-1990
www.csalliance.org
E-mail: csaas@knology.net
Areas of Expertise: Confederate stamps and postal history

**Errors, Freaks and Oddities Collectors Club Expertizing Service**
138 East Lakemont Drive
Kingsland GA 31548
Ph: (912) 729-1573
Areas of Expertise: U.S. errors, freaks and oddities

**Estonian Philatelic Society Expertizing Service**
39 Clafford Lane
Melville NY 11747
Ph: (516) 421-2078
E-mail: esto4@aol.com
Areas of Expertise: Estonia

**Hawaiian Philatelic Society Expertizing Service**
P.O. Box 10115
Honolulu HI 96816-0115
Areas of Expertise: Hawaii

**Hong Kong Stamp Society Expertizing Service**
P.O. Box 206
Glenside PA 19038
Fax: (215) 576-6850
Areas of Expertise: Hong Kong

**International Association of Philatelic Experts United States Associate members:**

Paul Buchsbayew
119 W. 57th St.
New York NY 10019
Ph: (212) 977-7734
Fax: (212) 977-8653
Areas of Expertise: Russia, Soviet Union

William T. Crowe
P.O. Box 2090
Danbury CT 06813-2090
E-mail: wtcrowe@aol.com
Areas of Expertise: United States

John Lievsay
(see American Philatelic Expertizing Service and Philatelic Foundation)
Areas of Expertise: France

Robert W. Lyman
P.O. Box 348
Irvington on Hudson NY 10533
Ph and Fax: (914) 591-6937
Areas of Expertise: British North America, New Zealand

Robert Odenweller
P.O. Box 401
Bernardsville NJ 07924-0401
Ph and Fax: (908) 766-5460
Areas of Expertise: New Zealand, Samoa to 1900

Sergio Sismondo
The Regency Tower, Suite 1109
770 James Street
Syracuse NY 13203
Ph: (315) 422-2331
Fax: (315) 422-2956
Areas of Expertise: British East Africa, Camerouns, Cape of Good Hope, Canada, British North America

**International Society for Japanese Philately Expertizing Committee**
132 North Pine Terrace
Staten Island NY 10312-4052
Ph: (718) 227-5229
Areas of Expertise: Japan and related areas, except WWII Japanese Occupation issues

**International Society for Portuguese Philately Expertizing Service**
P.O. Box 43146
Philadelphia PA 19129-3146
Ph and Fax: (215) 843-2106
E-mail: s.s.washburne@worldnet.att.net
Areas of Expertise: Portugal and Colonies

**Mexico-Elmhurst Philatelic Society International Expert Committee**
Expert Committee Administrator
Marc E. Gonzales
P.O. Box 29040
Denver CO 80229-0040
www.mepsi.org/expertization
Areas of Expertise: Mexico

**Ukrainian Philatelic & Numismatic Society Expertizing Service**
30552 Dell Lane
Warren MI 48092-1862
Areas of Expertise: Ukraine, Western Ukraine

**V. G. Greene Philatelic Research Foundation**
P.O. Box 204, Station Q
Toronto, ON, M4T 2M1
CANADA
Ph: (416) 921-2073
Fax: (416) 921-1282
www.greenefoundation.ca
E-mail: vggfoundation@on.aibn.com
Areas of Expertise: British North America

# Information on Catalogue Values, Grade and Condition

## Catalogue Value

The Scott Catalogue value is a retail value; that is, an amount you could expect to pay for a stamp in the grade of Very Fine with no faults. Any exceptions to the grade valued will be noted in the text. The general introduction on the following pages and the individual section introductions further explain the type of material that is valued. The value listed for any given stamp is a reference that reflects recent actual dealer selling prices for that item.

Dealer retail price lists, public auction results, published prices in advertising and individual solicitation of retail prices from dealers, collectors and specialty organizations have been used in establishing the values found in this catalogue. Amos Media Co. values stamps, but Amos Media is not a company engaged in the business of buying and selling stamps as a dealer.

Use this catalogue as a guide for buying and selling. The actual price you pay for a stamp may be higher or lower than the catalogue value because of many different factors, including the amount of personal service a dealer offers, or increased or decreased interest in the country or topic represented by a stamp or set. An item may occasionally be offered at a lower price as a "loss leader," or as part of a special sale. You also may obtain an item inexpensively at public auction because of little interest at that time or as part of a large lot.

Stamps that are of a lesser grade than Very Fine, or those with condition problems, generally trade at lower prices than those given in this catalogue. Stamps of exceptional quality in both grade and condition often command higher prices than those listed.

Values for pre-1900 unused issues are for stamps with approximately half or more of their original gum. Stamps with most or all of their original gum may be expected to sell for more, and stamps with less than half of their original gum may be expected to sell for somewhat less than the values listed. On rarer stamps, it may be expected that the original gum will be somewhat more disturbed than it will be on more common issues. Post-1900 unused issues are assumed to have full original gum. From breakpoints in most countries' listings, stamps are valued as never hinged, due to the wide availability of stamps in that condition. These notations are prominently placed in the listings and in the country information preceding the listings. Some countries also feature listings with dual values for hinged and never-hinged stamps.

## Grade

A stamp's grade and condition are crucial to its value. The accompanying illustrations show examples of Very Fine stamps from different time periods, along with examples of stamps in Fine to Very Fine and Extremely Fine grades as points of reference. When a stamp seller offers a stamp in any grade from fine to superb without further qualifying statements, that stamp should not only have the centering grade as defined, but it also should be free of faults or other condition problems.

**FINE** stamps (illustrations not shown) have designs that are quite off center, with the perforations on one or two sides very close to the design but not quite touching it. There is white space between the perforations and the design that is minimal but evident to the unaided eye. Imperforate stamps may have small margins, and earlier issues may show the design just touching one edge of the stamp design. Very early perforated issues normally will have the perforations slightly cutting into the design. Used stamps may have heavier than usual cancellations.

**FINE-VERY FINE** stamps will be somewhat off center on one side, or slightly off center on two sides. Imperforate stamps will have two margins of at least normal size, and the design will not touch any edge. For perforated stamps, the perfs are well clear of the design, but are still noticeably off center. *However, early issues of a country may be printed in such a way that the design naturally is very close to the edges. In these cases, the perforations may cut into the design very slightly.* Used stamps will not have a cancellation that detracts from the design.

**VERY FINE** stamps will be just slightly off center on one or two sides, but the design will be well clear of the edge. The stamp will present a nice, balanced appearance. Imperforate stamps will be well centered within normal-sized margins. *However, early issues of many countries may be printed in such a way that the perforations may touch the design on one or more sides. Where this is the case, a boxed note will be found defining the centering and margins of the stamps being valued.* Used stamps will have light or otherwise neat cancellations. This is the grade used to establish Scott Catalogue values.

**EXTREMELY FINE** stamps are close to being perfectly centered. Imperforate stamps will have even margins that are slightly larger than normal. Even the earliest perforated issues will have perforations clear of the design on all sides.

**Amos Media Co. recognizes that there is no formally enforced grading scheme for postage stamps, and that the final price you pay or obtain for a stamp will be determined by individual agreement at the time of transaction.**

## Condition

*Grade* addresses only centering and (for used stamps) cancellation. *Condition* refers to factors other than grade that affect a stamp's desirability.

Factors that can increase the value of a stamp include exceptionally wide margins, particularly fresh color, the presence of selvage, and plate or die varieties. Unusual cancels on used stamps (particularly those of the 19th century) can greatly enhance their value as well.

Factors other than faults that decrease the value of a stamp include loss of original gum, regumming, a hinge remnant or foreign object adhering to the gum, natural inclusions, straight edges, and markings or notations applied by collectors or dealers.

Faults include missing pieces, tears, pin or other holes, surface scuffs, thin spots, creases, toning, short or pulled perforations, clipped perforations, oxidation or other forms of color changelings, soiling, stains, and such man-made changes as reperforations or the chemical removal or lightening of a cancellation.

## Grading Illustrations

On the following two pages are illustrations of various stamps from countries appearing in this volume. These stamps are arranged by country, and they represent early or important issues that are often found in widely different grades in the marketplace. The editors believe the illustrations will prove useful in showing the margin size and centering that will be seen on the various issues.

In addition to the matters of margin size and centering, collectors are reminded that the very fine stamps valued in the Scott catalogues also will possess fresh color and intact perforations, and they will be free from defects.

Examples shown are computer-manipulated images made from single digitized master illustrations.

## Stamp Illustrations Used in the Catalogue

It is important to note that the stamp images used for identification purposes in this catlaogue may not be indicative of the grade of stamp being valued. Refer to the written discussion of grades on this page and to the grading illustrations on the following two pages for grading information.

Fine-Very Fine

SCOTT CATALOGUES VALUE STAMPS IN THIS GRADE

Very Fine

Extremely Fine

Fine-Very Fine

SCOTT CATALOGUES VALUE STAMPS IN THIS GRADE

Very Fine

Extremely Fine

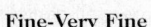

Fine-Very Fine

SCOTT CATALOGUES VALUE STAMPS IN THIS GRADE

Very Fine

Extremely Fine

Fine-Very Fine

SCOTT CATALOGUES VALUE STAMPS IN THIS GRADE

Very Fine

Extremely Fine

For purposes of helping to determine the gum condition and value of an unused stamp, Scott presents the following chart which details different gum conditions and indicates how the conditions correlate with the Scott values for unused stamps. Used together, the Illustrated Grading Chart on the previous pages and this Illustrated Gum Chart should allow catalogue users to better understand the grade and gum condition of stamps valued in the Scott catalogues.

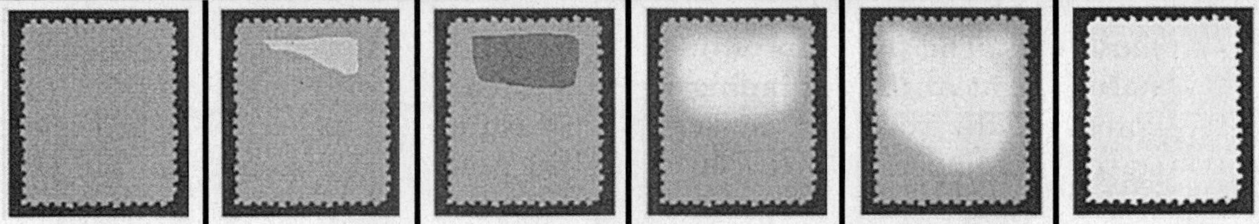

| Gum Categories: | MINT N.H. | ORIGINAL GUM (O.G.) | | | | NO GUM |
|---|---|---|---|---|---|---|
| | **Mint Never Hinged** *Free from any disturbance* | **Lightly Hinged** *Faint impression of a removed hinge over a small area* | **Hinge Mark or Remnant** *Prominent hinged spot with part or all of the hinge remaining* | **Large part o.g.** *Approximately half or more of the gum intact* | **Small part o.g.** *Approximately less than half of the gum intact* | **No gum** *Only if issued with gum* |
| Commonly Used Symbol: | ★★ | ★ | ★ | ★ | ★ | (★) |
| Pre-1900 Issues (Pre-1881 for U.S.) | *Very fine pre-1900 stamps in these categories trade at a premium over Scott value* | | | Scott Value for "Unused" | | Scott "No Gum" listings for selected unused classic stamps |
| From 1900 to breakpoints for listings of never-hinged stamps | Scott "Never Hinged" listings for selected unused stamps | Scott Value for "Unused" (Actual value will be affected by the degree of hinging of the full o.g.) | | | | |
| From breakpoints noted for many countries | Scott Value for "Unused" | | | | | |

**Never Hinged (NH; ★★):** A never-hinged stamp will have full original gum that will have no hinge mark or disturbance. The presence of an expertizer's mark does not disqualify a stamp from this designation.

**Original Gum (OG; ★):** Pre-1900 stamps should have approximately half or more of their original gum. On rarer stamps, it may be expected that the original gum will be somewhat more disturbed than it will be on more common issues. Post-1900 stamps should have full original gum. Original gum will show some disturbance caused by a previous hinge(s) which may be present or entirely removed. The actual value of a post-1900 stamp will be affected by the degree of hinging of the full original gum.

**Disturbed Original Gum:** Gum showing noticeable effects of humidity, climate or hinging over more than half of the gum. The significance of gum disturbance in valuing a stamp in any of the Original Gum categories depends on the degree of disturbance, the rarity and normal gum condition of the issue and other variables affecting quality.

**Regummed (RG; (★)):** A regummed stamp is a stamp without gum that has had some type of gum privately applied at a time after it was issued. This normally is done to deceive collectors and/or dealers into thinking that the stamp has original gum and therefore has a higher value. A regummed stamp is considered the same as a stamp with none of its original gum for purposes of grading.

# Catalogue Listing Policy

It is the intent of Amos Media Co. to list all postage stamps of the world in the *Scott Standard Postage Stamp Catalogue*. The only strict criteria for listing is that stamps be decreed legal for postage by the issuing country and that the issuing country actually have an operating postal system. Whether the primary intent of issuing a given stamp or set was for sale to postal patrons or to stamp collectors is not part of our listing criteria. Scott's role is to provide basic comprehensive postage stamp information. It is up to each stamp collector to choose which items to include in a collection.

It is Scott's objective to seek reasons why a stamp should be listed, rather than why it should not. Nevertheless, there are certain types of items that will not be listed. These include the following:

1. Unissued items that are not officially distributed or released by the issuing postal authority. If such items are officially issued at a later date by the country, they will be listed. Unissued items consist of those that have been printed and then held from sale for reasons such as change in government, errors found on stamps or something deemed objectionable about a stamp subject or design.

2. Stamps "issued" by non-existent postal entities or fantasy countries, such as Nagaland, Occusi-Ambeno, Staffa, Sedang, Torres Straits and others. Also, stamps "issued" in the names of legitimate, stamp-issuing countries that are not authorized by those countries.

3. Semi-official or unofficial items not required for postage. Examples include items issued by private agencies for their own express services. When such items are required for delivery, or are valid as prepayment of postage, they are listed.

4. Local stamps issued for local use only. Postage stamps issued by governments specifically for "domestic" use, such as Haiti Scott 219-228, or the United States non-denominated stamps, are not considered to be locals, since they are valid for postage throughout the country of origin.

5. Items not valid for postal use. For example, a few countries have issued souvenir sheets that are not valid for postage. This area also includes a number of worldwide charity labels (some denominated) that do not pay postage.

6. Egregiously exploitative issues such as stamps sold for far more than face value, stamps purposefully issued in artificially small quantities or only against advance orders, stamps awarded only to a selected audience such as a philatelic bureau's standing order customers, or stamps sold only in conjunction with other products. All of these kinds of items are usually controlled issues and/or are intended for speculation. These items normally will be included in a footnote.

7. Items distributed by the issuing government only to a limited group, club, philatelic exhibition or a single stamp dealer or other private company. These items normally will be included in a footnote.

8. Stamps not available to collectors. These generally are rare items, all of which are held by public institutions such as museums. The existence of such items often will be cited in footnotes.

The fact that a stamp has been used successfully as postage, even on international mail, is not in itself sufficient proof that it was legitimately issued. Numerous examples of so-called stamps from non-existent countries are known to have been used to post letters that have successfully passed through the international mail system.

There are certain items that are subject to interpretation. When a stamp falls outside our specifications, it may be listed along with a cautionary footnote.

A number of factors are considered in our approach to analyzing how a stamp is listed. The following list of factors is presented to share with you, the catalogue user, the complexity of the listing process.

**Additional printings** — "Additional printings" of a previously issued stamp may range from an item that is totally different to cases where it is impossible to differentiate from the original. At least a minor number (a small-letter suffix) is assigned if there is a distinct change in stamp shade, noticeably redrawn design, or a significantly different perforation measurement. A major number (numeral or numeral and capital-letter combination) is assigned if the editors feel the "additional printing" is sufficiently different from the original that it constitutes a different issue.

**Commemoratives** — Where practical, commemoratives with the same theme are placed in a set. For example, the U.S. Civil War Centennial set of 1961-65 and the Constitution Bicentennial series of 1989-90 appear as sets. Countries such as Japan and Korea issue such material on a regular basis, with an announced, or at least predictable, number of stamps known in advance. Occasionally, however, stamp sets that were released over a period of years have been separated. Appropriately placed footnotes will guide you to each set's continuation.

**Definitive sets** — Blocks of numbers generally have been reserved for definitive sets, based on previous experience with any given country. If a few more stamps were issued in a set than originally expected, they often have been inserted into the original set with a capital-letter suffix, such as U.S. Scott 1059A. If it appears that many more stamps than the originally allotted block will be released before the set is completed, a new block of numbers will be reserved, with the original one being closed off. In some cases, such as the U.S. Transportation and Great Americans series, several blocks of numbers exist. Appropriately placed footnotes will guide you to each set's continuation.

**New country** — Membership in the Universal Postal Union is not a consideration for listing status or order of placement within the catalogue. The index will tell you in what volume or page number the listings begin.

**"No release date" items** — The amount of information available for any given stamp issue varies greatly from country to country and even from time to time. Extremely comprehensive information about new stamps is available from some countries well before the stamps are released. By contrast some countries do not provide information about stamps or release dates. Most countries, however, fall between these extremes. A country may provide denominations or subjects of stamps from upcoming issues that are not issued as planned. Sometimes, philatelic agencies, those private firms hired to represent countries, add these later-issued items to sets well after the formal release date. This time period can range from weeks to years. If these items were officially released by the country, they will be added to the appropriate spot in the set. In many cases, the specific release date of a stamp or set of stamps may never be known.

**Overprints** — The color of an overprint is always noted if it is other than black. Where more than one color of ink has been used on overprints of a single set, the color used is noted. Early overprint and surcharge illustrations were altered to prevent their use by forgers.

**Personalized Stamps** — Since 1999, the special service of personalizing stamp vignettes, or labels attached to stamps, has been offered to customers by postal administrations of many countries. Sheets of these stamps are sold, singly or in quantity, only through special orders made by mail, in person, or through a sale on a computer website with the postal administrations or their agents for which an extra fee is charged, though some countries offer to collectors at face value personalized stamps having generic images in the vignettes or on the attached labels. It is impossible for any catalogue to know what images have been chosen by customers. Images can be 1) owned or created by the customer, 2) a generic image, or 3) an image pulled from a library of stock images on the stamp creation website. It is also impossible to know the quantity printed for any stamp having a particular image. So from a valuing standpoint, any image is equivalent to any other image for any personalized stamp having the same catalogue number. Illustrations of personalized stamps in the catalogue are not always those of stamps having generic images.

Personalized items are listed with some exceptions. These include:

1. Stamps or sheets that have attached labels that the customer cannot personalize, but which are nonetheless marketed as "personalized," and are sold for far more than the franking value.
2. Stamps or sheets that can be personalized by the customer, but where a portion of the print run must be ceded to the issuing country for sale to other customers.
3. Stamps or sheets that are created exclusively for a particular commercial client, or clients, including stamps that differ from any similar stamp that has been made available to the public.
4. Stamps or sheets that are deliberately conceived by the issuing authority that have been, or are likely to be, created with an excessive number of different face values, sizes, or other features that are changeable.
5. Stamps or sheets that are created by postal administrations using the same system of stamp personalization that has been put in place for use by the public that are printed in limited quantities and sold above face value.
6. Stamps or sheets that are created by licensees not directly affiliated or controlled by a postal administration.

Excluded items may or may not be footnoted.

**Se-tenants** — Connected stamps of differing features (se-tenants) will be listed in the format most commonly collected. This includes pairs, blocks or larger multiples. Se-tenant units are not always symmetrical. An example is Australia Scott 508, which is a block of seven stamps. If the stamps are primarily collected as a unit, the major number may be assigned to the multiple, with minors going to each component stamp. In cases where continuous-design or other unit se-tenants will receive significant postal use, each stamp is given a major Scott number listing. This includes issues from the United States, Canada, Germany and Great Britain, for example.

# Understanding the Listings

On the opposite page is an enlarged "typical" listing from this catalogue. Below are detailed explanations of each of the highlighted parts of the listing.

**1 Scott number** — Scott catalogue numbers are used to identify specific items when buying, selling or trading stamps. Each listed postage stamp from every country has a unique Scott catalogue number. Therefore, Germany Scott 99, for example, can only refer to a single stamp. Although the Scott catalogue usually lists stamps in chronological order by date of issue, there are exceptions. When a country has issued a set of stamps over a period of time, those stamps within the set are kept together without regard to date of issue. This follows the normal collecting approach of keeping stamps in their natural sets.

When a country issues a set of stamps over a period of time, a group of consecutive catalogue numbers is reserved for the stamps in that set, as issued. If that group of numbers proves to be too few, capital-letter suffixes, such as "A" or "B," may be added to existing numbers to create enough catalogue numbers to cover all items in the set. A capital-letter suffix indicates a major Scott catalogue number listing. Scott generally uses a suffix letter only once. Therefore, a catalogue number listing with a capital-letter suffix will seldom be found with the same letter (lower case) used as a minor-letter listing. If there is a Scott 16A in a set, for example, there will seldom be a Scott 16a. However, a minor-letter "a" listing may be added to a major number containing an "A" suffix (Scott 16Aa, for example).

Suffix letters are cumulative. A minor "b" variety of Scott 16A would be Scott 16Ab, not Scott 16b.

There are times when a reserved block of Scott catalogue numbers is too large for a set, leaving some numbers unused. Such gaps in the numbering sequence also occur when the catalogue editors move an item's listing elsewhere or have removed it entirely from the catalogue. Scott does not attempt to account for every possible number, but rather attempts to assure that each stamp is assigned its own number.

Scott numbers designating regular postage normally are only numerals. Scott numbers for other types of stamps, such as air post, semi-postal, postal tax, postage due, occupation and others have a prefix consisting of one or more capital letters or a combination of numerals and capital letters.

**2 Illustration number** — Illustration or design-type numbers are used to identify each catalogue illustration. For most sets, the lowest face-value stamp is shown. It then serves as an example of the basic design approach for other stamps not illustrated. Where more than one stamp use the same illustration number, but have differences in design, the design paragraph or the description line clearly indicates the design on each stamp not illustrated. Where there are both vertical and horizontal designs in a set, a single illustration may be used, with the exceptions noted in the design paragraph or description line.

When an illustration is followed by a lower-case letter in parentheses, such as "A2(b)," the trailing letter indicates which overprint or surcharge illustration applies.

Illustrations normally are 70 percent of the original size of the stamp. Oversized stamps, blocks and souvenir sheets are reduced even more. Overprints and surcharges are shown at 100 percent of their original size if shown alone, but are 70 percent of original size if shown on stamps. In some cases, the illustration will be placed above the set, between listings or omitted completely. Overprint and surcharge illustrations are not placed in this catalogue for purposes of expertizing stamps.

**3 Paper color** — The color of a stamp's paper is noted in italic type when the paper used is not white.

**4 Listing styles** — There are two principal types of catalogue listings: major and minor.

Major listings are in a larger type style than minor listings. The catalogue number is a numeral that can be found with or without a capital-letter suffix, and with or without a prefix.

Minor listings are in a smaller type style and have a small-letter suffix or (if the listing immediately follows that of the major number) may show only the letter. These listings identify a variety of the major item. Examples include perforation and shade differences, multiples (some souvenir sheets, booklet panes and se-tenant combinations), and singles of multiples.

Examples of major number listings include 16, 28A, B97, C13A, 10N5, and 10N6A. Examples of minor numbers are 16a and C13Ab.

**5 Basic information about a stamp or set** — Introducing each stamp issue is a small section (usually a line listing) of basic information about a stamp or set. This section normally includes the date of issue, method of printing, perforation, watermark and, sometimes, some additional information of note. *Printing method, perforation and watermark apply to the following sets until a change is noted.* Stamps created by overprinting or surcharging previous issues are assumed to have the same perforation, watermark, printing method and other production characteristics as the original. Dates of issue are as precise as Scott is able to confirm and often reflect the dates on first-day covers, rather than the actual date of release.

**6 Denomination** — This normally refers to the face value of the stamp; that is, the cost of the unused stamp at the post office at the time of issue. When a denomination is shown in parentheses, it does not appear on the stamp. This includes the non-denominated stamps of the United States, Brazil and Great Britain, for example.

**7 Color or other description** — This area provides information to solidify identification of a stamp. In many recent cases, a description of the stamp design appears in this space, rather than a listing of colors.

**8 Year of issue** — In stamp sets that have been released in a period that spans more than a year, the number shown in parentheses is the year that stamp first appeared. Stamps without a date appeared during the first year of the issue. Dates are not always given for minor varieties.

**9 Value unused and Value used** — The Scott catalogue values are based on stamps that are in a grade of Very Fine unless stated otherwise. Unused values refer to items that have not seen postal, revenue or any other duty for which they were intended. Pre-1900 unused stamps that were issued with gum must have at least most of their original gum. Later issues are assumed to have full original gum. From breakpoints specified in most countries' listings, stamps are valued as never hinged. Stamps issued without gum are noted. Modern issues with PVA or other synthetic adhesives may appear ungummed. Unused self-adhesive stamps are valued as appearing undisturbed on their original backing paper. Values for used self-adhesive stamps are for examples either on piece or off piece. For a more detailed explanation of these values, please see the "Catalogue Value," "Condition" and "Understanding Valuing Notations" sections elsewhere in this introduction.

In some cases, where used stamps are more valuable than unused stamps, the value is for an example with a contemporaneous cancel, rather than a modern cancel or a smudge or other unclear marking. For those stamps that were released for postal and fiscal purposes, the used value represents a postally used stamp. Stamps with revenue cancels generally sell for less.

Stamps separated from a complete se-tenant multiple usually will be worth less than a pro-rated portion of the se-tenant multiple, and stamps lacking the attached labels that are noted in the listings will be worth less than the values shown.

**10 Changes in basic set information** — Bold type is used to show any changes in the basic data given for a set of stamps. These basic data categories include perforation gauge measurement, paper type, printing method and watermark.

**11 Total value of a set** — The total value of sets of three or more stamps issued after 1900 are shown. The set line also notes the range of Scott numbers and total number of stamps included in the grouping. The actual value of a set consisting predominantly of stamps having the minimum value of 25 cents may be less than the total value shown. Similarly, the actual value or catalogue value of se-tenant pairs or of blocks consisting of stamps having the minimum value of 25 cents may be less than the catalogue values of the component parts.

A6

King George VI
A7

**1938-44** **Engr.** **Perf. 12½**

| | | | | | |
|---|---|---|---|---|---|
| **54** | A6 | ½p | green | .25 | *2.00* |
| **54A** | A6 | ½p | dk brown ('42) | .25 | *2.25* |
| **55** | A6 | 1p | dark brown | 2.50 | .35 |
| **55A** | A6 | 1p | green ('42) | .25 | 1.75 |
| **56** | A6 | 1½p | dark carmine | 5.00 | *6.00* |
| **56A** | A6 | 1½p | gray ('42) | .25 | *5.75* |
| *b.* | | | "A" of CA in watermark missing | 1,600. | |
| **57** | A6 | 2p | gray | 5.00 | 1.25 |
| *b.* | | | "A" of CA in watermark missing | | *1,300.* |
| **57A** | A6 | 2p | dark car ('42) | .25 | *2.00* |
| c. | | | "A" of CA in watermark missing | 1,600. | |
| **58** | A6 | 3p | blue | .60 | 1.00 |
| **59** | A6 | 4p | rose lilac | 1.75 | 2.00 |
| **60** | A6 | 6p | dark violet | 2.00 | 2.00 |
| **61** | A6 | 9p | olive bister | 2.00 | *5.25* |
| **62** | A6 | 1sh | orange & blk | 2.10 | *3.25* |

**Typo.**
**Perf. 14**
**Chalky Paper**

| | | | | | |
|---|---|---|---|---|---|
| **63** | A7 | 2sh | ultra & dl vio, *bl* | 7.00 | *17.50* |
| **64** | A7 | 2sh6p | red & blk, *bl* | 9.00 | *24.00* |
| **65** | A7 | 5sh | red & grn, *yel* | 35.00 | 30.00 |
| **a.** | | | 5sh dk red & dp grn, *yel* ('44) | 55.00 | *140.00* |
| **66** | A7 | 10sh | red & grn, *grn* | 35.00 | *70.00* |

**Wmk. 3**

| | | | | | |
|---|---|---|---|---|---|
| **67** | A7 | £1 | blk & vio, *red* | 30.00 | *52.50* |
| | | | *Nos. 54-67 (18)* | 138.20 | *228.85* |
| | | | Set, never hinged | 220.00 | |

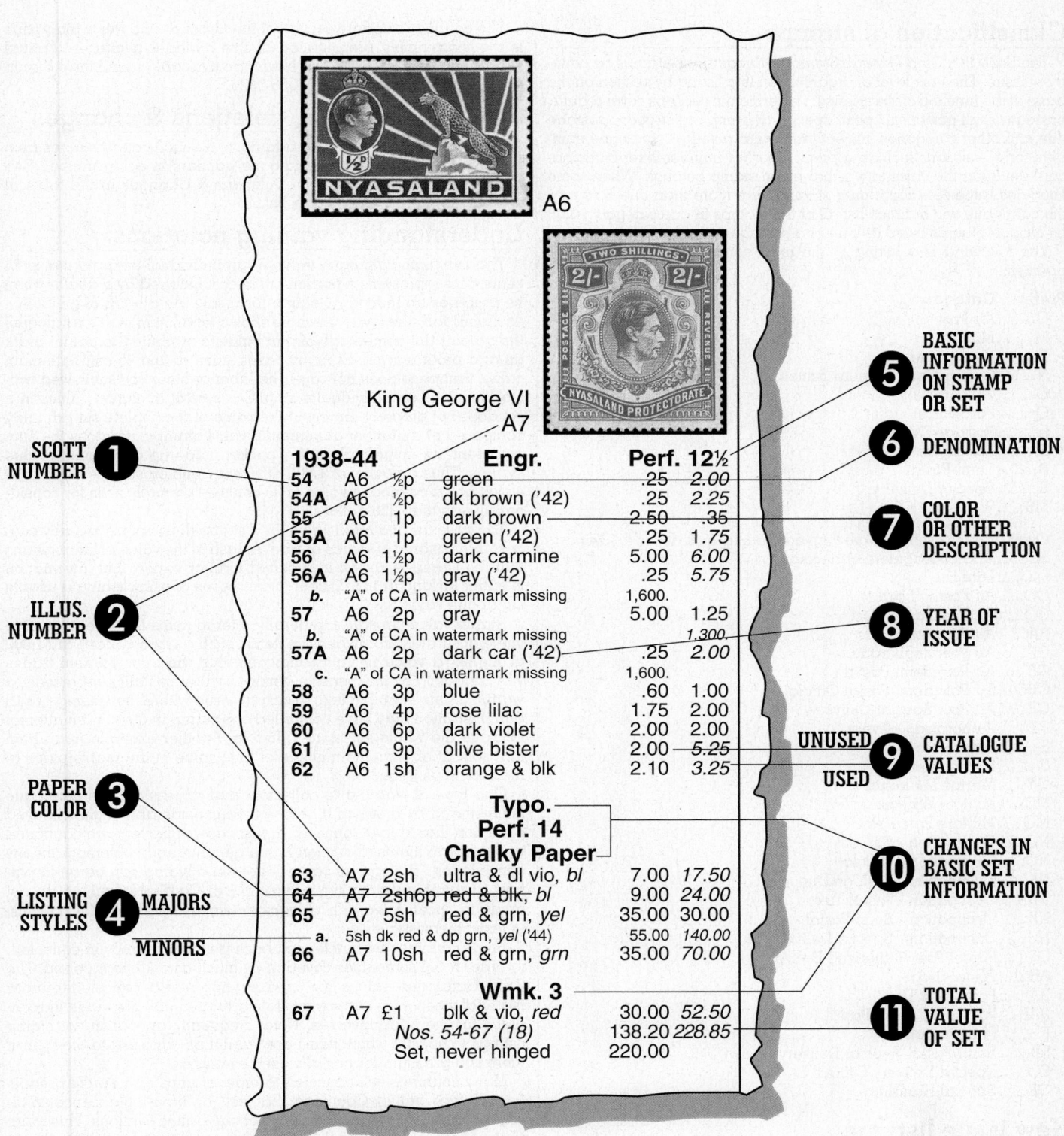

1 SCOTT NUMBER
2 ILLUS. NUMBER
3 PAPER COLOR
4 LISTING STYLES — MAJORS / MINORS
5 BASIC INFORMATION ON STAMP OR SET
6 DENOMINATION
7 COLOR OR OTHER DESCRIPTION
8 YEAR OF ISSUE
9 CATALOGUE VALUES — UNUSED / USED
10 CHANGES IN BASIC SET INFORMATION
11 TOTAL VALUE OF SET

# Special Notices

## Classification of stamps

The *Scott Standard Postage Stamp Catalogue* lists stamps by country of issue. The next level of organization is a listing by section on the basis of the function of the stamps. The principal sections cover regular postage, semi-postal, air post, special delivery, registration, postage due and other categories. Except for regular postage, catalogue numbers for all sections include a prefix letter (or number-letter combination) denoting the class to which a given stamp belongs. When some countries issue sets containing stamps from more than one category, the catalogue will at times list all of the stamps in one category (such as air post stamps listed as part of a postage set).

The following is a listing of the most commonly used catalogue prefixes.

**Prefix ....Category**
C.........Air Post
M........Military
P.........Newspaper
N.........Occupation - Regular Issues
O........Official
Q........Parcel Post
J..........Postage Due
RA......Postal Tax
B.........Semi-Postal
E.........Special Delivery
MR......War Tax

Other prefixes used by more than one country include the following:
H.........Acknowledgment of Receipt
I..........Late Fee
CO.....Air Post Official
CQ.....Air Post Parcel Post
RAC....Air Post Postal Tax
CF......Air Post Registration
CB......Air Post Semi-Postal
CBO...Air Post Semi-Postal Official
CE......Air Post Special Delivery
EY.......Authorized Delivery
S.........Franchise
G........Insured Letter
GY......Marine Insurance
MC.....Military Air Post
MQ.....Military Parcel Post
NC......Occupation - Air Post
NO......Occupation - Official
NJ........Occupation - Postage Due
NRA....Occupation - Postal Tax
NB......Occupation - Semi-Postal
NE......Occupation - Special Delivery
QY......Parcel Post Authorized Delivery
AR......Postal-fiscal
RAJ.....Postal Tax Due
RAB....Postal Tax Semi-Postal
F.........Registration
EB.......Semi-Postal Special Delivery
EO......Special Delivery Official
QE......Special Handling

## New issue listings

Updates to this catalogue appear each month in the *Linn's Stamp News* monthly magazine. Included in this update are additions to the listings of countries found in the *Scott Standard Postage Stamp Catalogue* and the *Specialized Catalogue of United States Stamps and Covers*, as well as corrections and updates to current editions of this catalogue.

From time to time there will be changes in the final listings of stamps from the *Linn's Stamp News* magazine to the next edition of the catalogue. This occurs as more information about certain stamps or sets becomes available.

The catalogue update section of the *Linn's Stamp News* magazine is the most timely presentation of this material available. Annual subscriptions to *Linn's Stamp News* are available from Linn's Stamp News, Box 926, Sidney, OH 45365-0926.

## Number additions, deletions & changes

A listing of catalogue number additions, deletions and changes from the previous edition of the catalogue appears in each volume. See Catalogue Number Additions, Deletions & Changes in the table of contents for the location of this list.

## Understanding valuing notations

The *minimum catalogue value* of an individual stamp or set is 25 cents. This represents a portion of the cost incurred by a dealer when he prepares an individual stamp for resale. As a point of philatelic-economic fact, the lower the value shown for an item in this catalogue, the greater the percentage of that value is attributed to dealer mark up and profit margin. In many cases, such as the 25-cent minimum value, that price does not cover the labor or other costs involved with stocking it as an individual stamp. The sum of minimum values in a set does not properly represent the value of a complete set primarily composed of a number of minimum-value stamps, nor does the sum represent the actual value of a packet made up of minimum-value stamps. Thus a packet of 1,000 different common stamps — each of which has a catalogue value of 25 cents — normally sells for considerably less than 250 dollars!

The *absence of a retail value* for a stamp does not necessarily suggest that a stamp is scarce or rare. A dash in the value column means that the stamp is known in a stated form or variety, but information is either lacking or insufficient for purposes of establishing a usable catalogue value.

Stamp values in *italics* generally refer to items that are difficult to value accurately. For expensive items, such as those priced at $1,000 or higher, a value in italics indicates that the affected item trades very seldom. For inexpensive items, a value in italics represents a warning. One example is a "blocked" issue where the issuing postal administration may have controlled one stamp in a set in an attempt to make the whole set more valuable. Another example is an item that sold at an extreme multiple of face value in the marketplace at the time of its issue.

One type of warning to collectors that appears in the catalogue is illustrated by a stamp that is valued considerably higher in used condition than it is as unused. In this case, collectors are cautioned to be certain the used version has a genuine and contemporaneous cancellation. The type of cancellation on a stamp can be an important factor in determining its sale price. Catalogue values do not apply to fiscal, telegraph or non-contemporaneous postal cancels, unless otherwise noted.

Some countries have released back issues of stamps in canceled-to-order form, sometimes covering as much as a 10-year period. The Scott Catalogue values for used stamps reflect canceled-to-order material when such stamps are found to predominate in the marketplace for the issue involved. Notes frequently appear in the stamp listings to specify which items are valued as canceled-to-order, or if there is a premium for postally used examples.

Many countries sell canceled-to-order stamps at a marked reduction of face value. Countries that sell or have sold canceled-to-order stamps at *full* face value include United Nations, Australia, Netherlands, France and Switzerland. It may be almost impossible to identify such stamps if the gum has been removed, because official government canceling devices are used. Postally used examples of these items on cover, however, are usually worth more than the canceled-to-order stamps with original gum.

## Abbreviations

Scott uses a consistent set of abbreviations throughout this catalogue to conserve space, while still providing necessary information.

**COLOR ABBREVIATIONS**

| | | |
|---|---|---|
| amb. amber | crim. crimson | ol ..... olive |
| anil.. aniline | cr ...... cream | olvn . olivine |
| ap.... apple | dk .... dark | org... orange |
| aqua aquamarine | dl ..... dull | pck .. peacock |
| az .... azure | dp.... deep | pnksh pinkish |
| bis ... bister | db.... drab | Prus. Prussian |
| bl ..... blue | emer emerald | pur... purple |
| bld... blood | gldn. golden | redsh reddish |
| blk ... black | gryshgrayish | res ... reseda |
| bril... brilliant | grn... green | ros ... rosine |
| brn... brown | grnsh greenish | ryl .... royal |
| brnsh brownish | hel ... heliotrope | sal ... salmon |
| brnz. bronze | hn .... henna | saph sapphire |
| brt.... bright | ind... indigo | scar . scarlet |
| brnt . burnt | int .... intense | sep .. sepia |
| car... carmine | lav ... lavender | sien . sienna |
| cer ... cerise | lem .. lemon | sil..... silver |
| chlky chalky | lil ..... lilac | sl...... slate |
| chamchamois | lt ...... light | stl .... steel |
| chnt . chestnut | mag. magenta | turq.. turquoise |
| choc chocolate | man. manila | ultra ultramarine |
| chr ... chrome | mar.. maroon | Ven .. Venetian |
| cit .... citron | mv ... mauve | ver ... vermilion |
| cl...... claret | multi multicolored | vio ... violet |
| cob .. cobalt | mlky milky | yel ... yellow |
| cop .. copper | myr .. myrtle | yelsh yellowish |

When no color is given for an overprint or surcharge, black is the color used. Abbreviations for colors used for overprints and surcharges include: "(B)" or "(Blk)," black; "(Bl)," blue; "(R)," red; and "(G)," green.

Additional abbreviations in this catalogue are shown below:

| | |
|---|---|
| Adm. | Administration |
| AFL | American Federation of Labor |
| Anniv. | Anniversary |
| APS | American Philatelic Society |
| Assoc. | Association |
| ASSR. | Autonomous Soviet Socialist Republic |
| b. | Born |
| BEP | Bureau of Engraving and Printing |
| Bicent. | Bicentennial |
| Bklt. | Booklet |
| Brit. | British |
| btwn. | Between |
| Bur. | Bureau |
| c. or ca. | Circa |
| Cat. | Catalogue |
| Cent. | Centennial, century, centenary |
| CIO | Congress of Industrial Organizations |
| Conf. | Conference |
| Cong. | Congress |
| Cpl. | Corporal |
| CTO | Canceled to order |
| d. | Died |
| Dbl. | Double |
| EDU | Earliest documented use |
| Engr. | Engraved |
| Exhib. | Exhibition |
| Expo. | Exposition |
| Fed. | Federation |
| GB | Great Britain |
| Gen. | General |
| GPO | General post office |
| Horiz. | Horizontal |
| Imperf. | Imperforate |
| Impt. | Imprint |
| Intl. | International |
| Invtd. | Inverted |
| L | Left |
| Lieut., lt. | Lieutenant |
| Litho. | Lithographed |
| LL | Lower left |
| LR | Lower right |
| mm | Millimeter |
| Ms. | Manuscript |
| Natl. | National |
| No. | Number |
| NY | New York |
| NYC | New York City |
| Ovpt. | Overprint |
| Ovptd. | Overprinted |
| P | Plate number |
| Perf. | Perforated, perforation |
| Phil. | Philatelic |
| Photo. | Photogravure |
| PO | Post office |
| Pr. | Pair |
| P.R. | Puerto Rico |
| Prec. | Precancel, precanceled |
| Pres. | President |
| PTT | Post, Telephone and Telegraph |
| R | Right |
| Rio | Rio de Janeiro |
| Sgt. | Sergeant |
| Soc. | Society |
| Souv. | Souvenir |
| SSR | Soviet Socialist Republic, see ASSR |
| St. | Saint, street |
| Surch. | Surcharge |
| Typo. | Typographed |
| UL | Upper left |
| Unwmkd. | Unwatermarked |
| UPU | Universal Postal Union |
| UR | Upper Right |
| US | United States |
| USPOD | United States Post Office Department |
| USSR | Union of Soviet Socialist Republics |
| Vert. | Vertical |
| VP | Vice president |
| Wmk. | Watermark |
| Wmkd. | Watermarked |
| WWI | World War I |
| WWII | World War II |

## Examination

Amos Media Co. will not comment upon the genuineness, grade or condition of stamps, because of the time and responsibility involved. Rather, there are several expertizing groups that undertake this work for both collectors and dealers. Neither will Amos Media Co. appraise or identify philatelic material. The company cannot take responsibility for unsolicited stamps or covers sent by individuals.

All letters, E-mails, etc. are read attentively, but they are not always answered due to time considerations.

## How to order from your dealer

When ordering stamps from a dealer, it is not necessary to write the full description of a stamp as listed in this catalogue. All you need is the name of the country, the Scott catalogue number and whether the desired item is unused or used. For example, "Japan Scott 422 unused" is sufficient to identify the unused stamp of Japan listed as "422 A206 5y brown."

# Basic Stamp Information

A stamp collector's knowledge of the combined elements that make a given stamp issue unique determines his or her ability to identify stamps. These elements include paper, watermark, method of separation, printing, design and gum. On the following pages each of these important areas is briefly described.

## Paper

Paper is an organic material composed of a compacted weave of cellulose fibers and generally formed into sheets. Paper used to print stamps may be manufactured in sheets, or it may have been part of a large roll (called a web) before being cut to size. The fibers most often used to create paper on which stamps are printed include bark, wood, straw and certain grasses. In many cases, linen or cotton rags have been added for greater strength and durability. Grinding, bleaching, cooking and rinsing these raw fibers reduces them to a slushy pulp, referred to by paper makers as "stuff." Sizing and, sometimes, coloring matter is added to the pulp to make different types of finished paper.

After the stuff is prepared, it is poured onto sieve-like frames that allow the water to run off, while retaining the matted pulp. As fibers fall onto the screen and are held by gravity, they form a natural weave that will later hold the paper together. If the screen has metal bits that are formed into letters or images attached, it leaves slightly thinned areas on the paper. These are called watermarks.

When the stuff is almost dry, it is passed under pressure through smooth or engraved rollers - dandy rolls - or placed between cloth in a press to be flattened and dried.

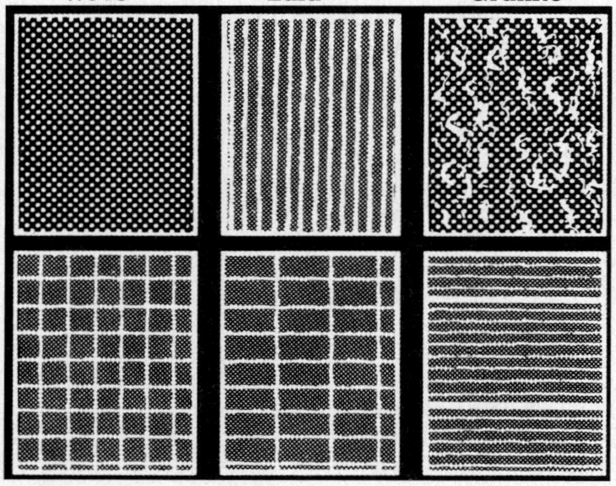


Stamp paper falls broadly into two types: wove and laid. The nature of the surface of the frame onto which the pulp is first deposited causes the differences in appearance between the two. If the surface is smooth and even, the paper will be of fairly uniform texture throughout. This is known as *wove paper*. Early papermaking machines poured the pulp onto a continuously circulating web of felt, but modern machines feed the pulp onto a cloth-like screen made of closely interwoven fine wires. This paper, when held to a light, will show little dots or points very close together. The proper name for this is "wire wove," but the type is still considered wove. Any U.S. or British stamp printed after 1880 will serve as an example of wire wove paper.

Closely spaced parallel wires, with cross wires at wider intervals, make up the frames used for what is known as *laid paper*. A greater thickness of the pulp will settle between the wires. The paper, when held to a light, will show alternate light and dark lines. The spacing and the thickness of the lines may vary, but on any one sheet of paper they are all alike. See Russia Scott 31-38 for examples of laid paper.

*Batonne*, from the French word meaning "a staff," is a term used if the lines in the paper are spaced quite far apart, like the printed ruling on a writing tablet. Batonne paper may be either wove or laid. If laid, fine laid lines can be seen between the batons.

*Quadrille* is the term used when the lines in the paper form little squares. *Oblong quadrille* is the term used when rectangles, rather than squares, are formed. Grid patterns vary from distinct to extremely faint. See Mexico-Guadalajara Scott 35-37 for examples of oblong quadrille paper.

Paper also is classified as thick or thin, hard or soft, and by color. Such colors may include yellowish, greenish, bluish and reddish.

Brief explanations of other types of paper used for printing stamps, as well as examples, follow.

**Colored** — Colored paper is created by the addition of dye in the paper-making process. Such colors may include shades of yellow, green, blue and red. *Surface-colored papers*, most commonly used for British colonial issues in 1913-14, are created when coloring is added only to the surface during the finishing process. Stamps printed on surface-colored paper have white or uncolored backs, while true colored papers are colored through. See Jamaica Scott 71-73.

**Pelure** — Pelure paper is a very thin, hard and often brittle paper that is sometimes bluish or grayish in appearance. See Serbia Scott 169-170.

**Native** — This is a term applied to handmade papers used to produce some of the early stamps of the Indian states. Stamps printed on native paper may be expected to display various natural inclusions that are normal and do not negatively affect value. Japanese paper, originally made of mulberry fibers and rice flour, is part of this group. See Japan Scott 1-18.

**Manila** — This type of paper is often used to make stamped envelopes and wrappers. It is a coarse-textured stock, usually smooth on one side and rough on the other. A variety of colors of manila paper exist, but the most common range is yellowish-brown.

**Silk** — Introduced by the British in 1847 as a safeguard against counterfeiting, silk paper contains bits of colored silk thread scattered throughout. The density of these fibers varies greatly and can include as few as one fiber per stamp or hundreds. U.S. revenue Scott R152 is a good example of an easy-to-identify silk paper stamp.

Silk-thread paper has uninterrupted threads of colored silk arranged so that one or more threads run through the stamp or postal stationery. See Great Britain Scott 5-6 and Switzerland Scott 14-19.

**Granite** — Filled with minute cloth or colored paper fibers of various colors and lengths, granite paper should not be confused with either type of silk paper. Austria Scott 172-175 and a number of Swiss stamps are examples of granite paper.

**Chalky** — A chalk-like substance coats the surface of chalky paper to discourage the cleaning and reuse of canceled stamps, as well as to provide a smoother, more acceptable printing surface. Because the designs of stamps printed on chalky paper are imprinted on what is often a water-soluble coating, any attempt to remove a cancellation will destroy the stamp. *Do not soak these stamps in any fluid.* To remove a stamp printed on chalky paper from an envelope, wet the paper from underneath the stamp until the gum dissolves enough to release the stamp from the paper. See St. Kitts-Nevis Scott 89-90 for examples of stamps printed on this type of chalky paper.

**India** — Another name for this paper, originally introduced from China about 1750, is "China Paper." It is a thin, opaque paper often used for plate and die proofs by many countries.

**Double** — In philately, the term double paper has two distinct meanings. The first is a two-ply paper, usually a combination of a thick and a thin sheet, joined during manufacture. This type was used experimentally as a means to discourage the reuse of stamps.

The design is printed on the thin paper. Any attempt to remove a cancellation would destroy the design. U.S. Scott 158 and other Banknote-era stamps exist on this form of double paper.

The second type of double paper occurs on a rotary press, when the end of one paper roll, or web, is affixed to the next roll to save time feeding the paper through the press. Stamp designs are printed over the joined paper and, if overlooked by inspectors, may get into post office stocks.

**Goldbeater's Skin** — This type of paper was used for the 1866 issue of Prussia, and was a tough, translucent paper. The design was printed in reverse on the back of the stamp, and the gum applied over the printing. It is impossible to remove stamps printed on this type of paper from the paper to which they are affixed without destroying the design.

**Ribbed** — Ribbed paper has an uneven, corrugated surface made by passing the paper through ridged rollers. This type exists on some copies of U.S. Scott 156-165.

Various other substances, or substrates, have been used for stamp manufacture, including wood, aluminum, copper, silver and gold foil, plastic, and silk and cotton fabrics.

## Watermarks

Watermarks are an integral part of some papers. They are formed in the process of paper manufacture. Watermarks consist of small designs, formed of wire or cut from metal and soldered to the surface of the mold or, sometimes, on the dandy roll. The designs may be in the form of crowns, stars, anchors, letters or other characters or symbols. These pieces of metal - known in the paper-making industry as "bits" - impress a design into the paper. The design sometimes may be seen by holding the stamp to the light. Some are more easily seen with a watermark detector. This important tool is a small black tray into which a stamp is placed face down and dampened with a fast-evaporating watermark detection fluid that brings up the watermark image in the form of dark lines against a lighter background. These dark lines are the thinner areas of the paper known as the watermark. Some watermarks are extremely difficult to locate, due to either a faint impression, watermark location or the color of the stamp. There also are electric watermark detectors that come with plastic filter disks of various colors. The disks neutralize the color of the stamp, permitting the watermark to be seen more easily.

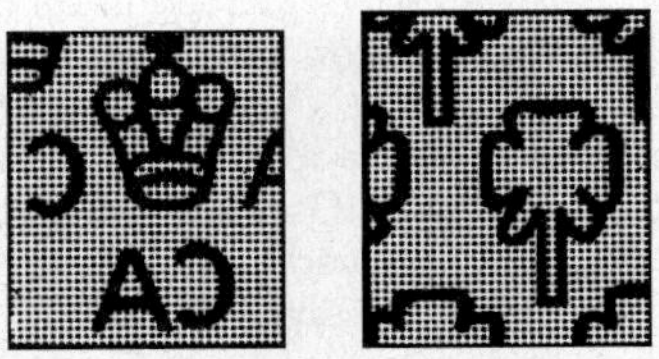

**Multiple watermarks of Crown Agents and Burma**

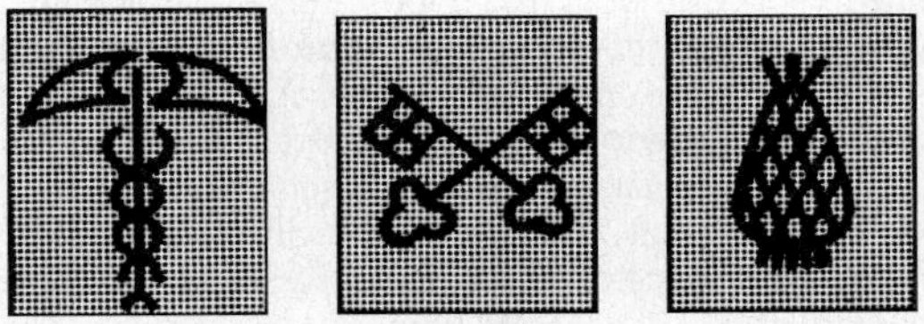

**Watermarks of Uruguay, Vatican City and Jamaica**

**WARNING: Some inks used in the photogravure process dissolve in watermark fluids (Please see the section on Soluble Printing Inks).** Also, see "chalky paper."

Watermarks may be found normal, reversed, inverted, reversed and inverted, sideways or diagonal, as seen from the back of the stamp. The relationship of watermark to stamp design depends on the position of the printing plates or how paper is fed through the press. On machine-made paper, watermarks normally are read from right to left. The design is repeated closely throughout the sheet in a "multiple-watermark design." In a "sheet watermark," the design appears only once on the sheet, but extends over many stamps. Individual stamps may carry only a small fraction or none of the watermark.

"Marginal watermarks" occur in the margins of sheets or panes of stamps. They occur on the outside border of paper (ostensibly outside the area where stamps are to be printed). A large row of letters may spell the name of the country or the manufacturer of the paper, or a border of lines may appear. Careless press feeding may cause parts of these letters and/or lines to show on stamps of the outer row of a pane.

## Soluble Printing Inks

**WARNING:** Most stamp colors are permanent; that is, they are not seriously affected by short-term exposure to light or water. Many colors, especially of modern inks, fade from excessive exposure to light. There are stamps printed with inks that dissolve easily in water or in fluids used to detect watermarks. Use of these inks was intentional to prevent the removal of cancellations. Water affects all aniline inks, those on so-called safety paper and some photogravure printings - all such inks are known as fugitive colors. *Removal from paper of such stamps requires care and alternatives to traditional soaking.*

## Separation

"Separation" is the general term used to describe methods used to separate stamps. The three standard forms currently in use are perforating, rouletting and die-cutting. These methods are done during the stamp production process, after printing. Sometimes these methods are done on-press or sometimes as a separate step. The earliest issues, such as the 1840 Penny Black of Great Britain (Scott 1), did not have any means provided for separation. It was expected the stamps would be cut apart with scissors or folded and torn. These are examples of imperforate stamps. Many stamps were first issued in imperforate formats and were later issued with perforations. Therefore, care must be observed in buying single imperforate stamps to be certain they were issued imperforate and are not perforated copies that have been altered by having the perforations trimmed away. Stamps issued imperforate usually are valued as singles. However, imperforate varieties of normally perforated stamps should be collected in pairs or larger pieces as indisputable evidence of their imperforate character.

### PERFORATION

The chief style of separation of stamps, and the one that is in almost universal use today, is perforating. By this process, paper between the stamps is cut away in a line of holes, usually round, leaving little bridges of paper between the stamps to hold them together. Some types of perforation, such as hyphen-hole perfs, can be confused with roulettes, but a close visual inspection reveals that paper has been removed. The little perforation bridges, which project from the stamp when it is torn from the pane, are called the teeth of the perforation.

As the size of the perforation is sometimes the only way to differentiate between two otherwise identical stamps, it is necessary to be able to accurately measure and describe them. This is done with a perforation gauge, usually a ruler-like device that has dots or graduated lines to show how many perforations may be counted in the space of two centimeters. Two centimeters is the space universally adopted in which to measure perforations.

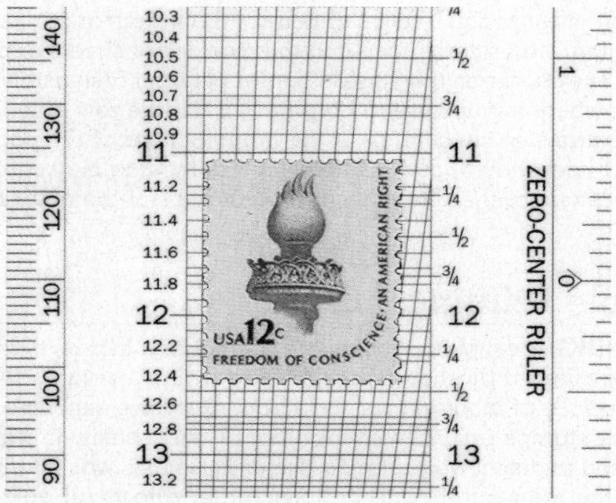

Perforation gauge

To measure a stamp, run it along the gauge until the dots on it fit exactly into the perforations of the stamp. If you are using a graduated-line perforation gauge, simply slide the stamp along the surface until the lines on the gauge perfectly project from the center of the bridges or holes. The number to the side of the line of dots or lines that fit the stamp's perforation is the measurement. For example, an "11" means that 11 perforations fit between two centimeters. The description of the stamp therefore is "perf. 11." If the gauge of the perforations on the top and bottom of a stamp differs from that on the sides, the result is what is known as *compound perforations*. In measuring compound perforations, the gauge at top and bottom is always given first, then the sides. Thus, a stamp that measures 11 at top and bottom and 10½ at the sides is "perf. 11 x 10½." See U.S. Scott 632-642 for examples of compound perforations.

Stamps also are known with perforations different on three or all four sides. Descriptions of such items are clockwise, beginning with the top of the stamp.

A perforation with small holes and teeth close together is a "fine perforation." One with large holes and teeth far apart is a "coarse perforation." Holes that are jagged, rather than clean-cut, are "rough perforations." *Blind perforations* are the slight impressions left by the perforating pins if they fail to puncture the paper. Multiples of stamps showing blind perforations may command a slight premium over normally perforated stamps.

The term *syncopated perfs* describes intentional irregularities in the perforations. The earliest form was used by the Netherlands from 1925-33, where holes were omitted to create distinctive patterns. Beginning in 1992, Great Britain has used an oval perforation to help prevent counterfeiting. Several other countries have started using the oval perfs or other syncopated perf patterns.

A new type of perforation, still primarily used for postal stationery, is known as microperfs. Microperfs are tiny perforations (in some cases hundreds of holes per two centimeters) that allows items to be intentionally separated very easily, while not accidentally breaking apart as easily as standard perforations. These are not currently measured or differentiated by size, as are standard perforations.

perce en arc

perce en lignes

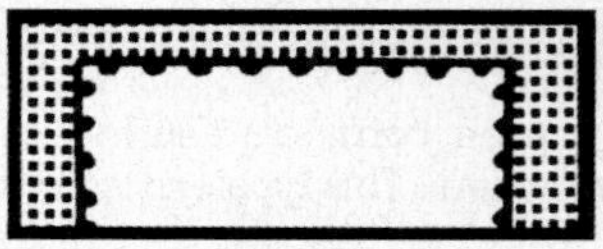
perce en points

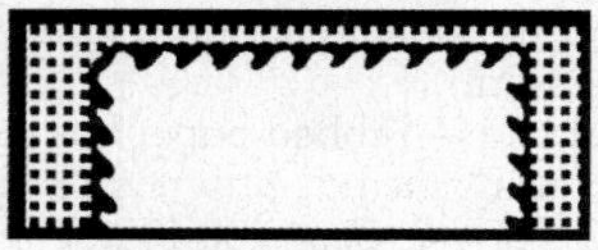
oblique roulette

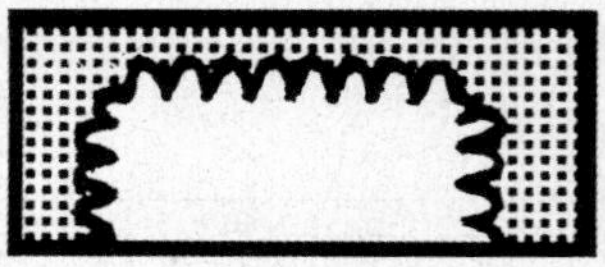
perce en scie

perce serpentin

### ROULETTING

In rouletting, the stamp paper is cut partly or wholly through, with no paper removed. In perforating, some paper is removed. Rouletting derives its name from the French roulette, a spur-like wheel. As the wheel is rolled over the paper, each point makes a small cut. The number of cuts made in a two-centimeter space determines the gauge of the roulette, just as the number of perforations in two centimeters determines the gauge of the perforation.

The shape and arrangement of the teeth on the wheels varies. Various roulette types generally carry French names:

*Perce en lignes* - rouletted in lines. The paper receives short, straight cuts in lines. This is the most common type of rouletting. See Mexico Scott 500.

*Perce en points* - pin-rouletted or pin-perfed. This differs from a small perforation because no paper is removed, although round, equidistant holes are pricked through the paper. See Mexico Scott 242-256.

*Perce en arc* and *perce en scie* - pierced in an arc or saw-toothed designs, forming half circles or small triangles. See Hanover (German States) Scott 25-29.

*Perce en serpentin* - serpentine roulettes. The cuts form a serpentine or wavy line. See Brunswick (German States) Scott 13-18.

Once again, no paper is removed by these processes, leaving the stamps easily separated, but closely attached.

### DIE-CUTTING

The third major form of stamp separation is die-cutting. This is a method where a die in the pattern of separation is created that later cuts the stamp paper in a stroke motion. Although some standard stamps bear die-cut perforations, this process is primarily used for self-adhesive postage stamps. Die-cutting can appear in straight lines, such as U.S. Scott 2522, shapes, such as U.S. Scott 1551, or imitating the appearance of perforations, such as New Zealand Scott 935A and 935B.

## Printing Processes

### ENGRAVING (Intaglio, Line-engraving, Etching)

**Master die** — The initial operation in the process of line engraving is making the master die. The die is a small, flat block of softened steel upon which the stamp design is recess engraved in reverse.

**Master die**

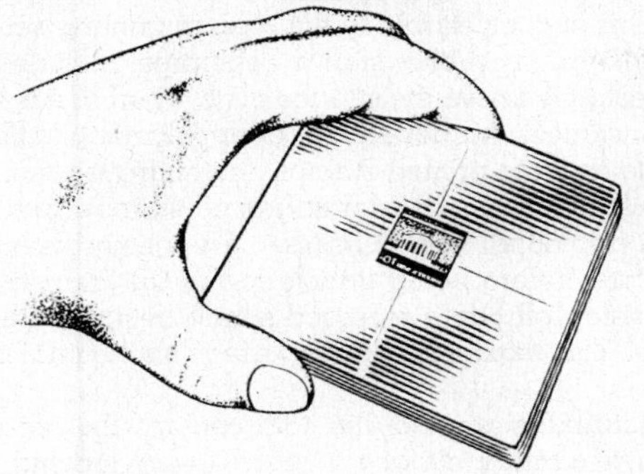

Photographic reduction of the original art is made to the appropriate size. It then serves as a tracing guide for the initial outline of the design. The engraver lightly traces the design on the steel with his graver, then slowly works the design until it is completed. At various points during the engraving process, the engraver hand-inks the die and makes an impression to check his progress. These are known as progressive die proofs. After completion of the engraving, the die is hardened to withstand the stress and pressures of later transfer operations.

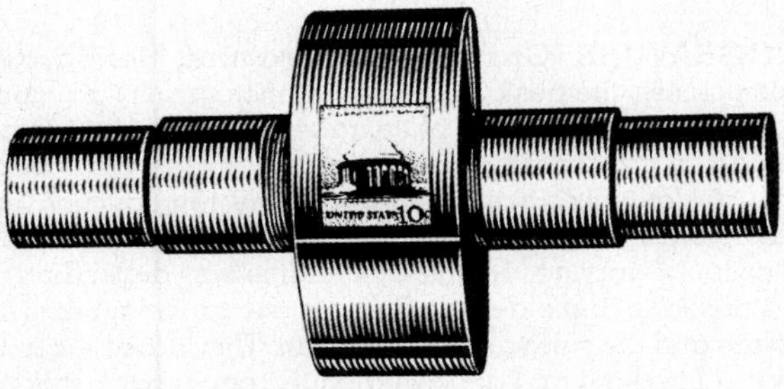

**Transfer roll**

**Transfer roll** — Next is production of the transfer roll that, as the name implies, is the medium used to transfer the subject from the master die to the printing plate. A blank roll of soft steel, mounted on a mandrel, is placed under the bearers of the transfer press to allow it to roll freely on its axis. The hardened die is placed on the bed of the press and the face of the transfer roll is applied to the die, under pressure. The bed or the roll is then rocked back and forth under increasing pressure, until the soft steel of the roll is forced into every engraved line of the die. The resulting impression on the roll is known as a "relief" or a "relief transfer." The engraved image is now positive in appearance and stands out from the steel. After the required number of reliefs are "rocked in," the soft steel transfer roll is hardened.

Different flaws may occur during the relief process. A defective relief may occur during the rocking in process because of a minute piece of foreign material lodging on the die, or some other cause. Imperfections in the steel of the transfer roll may result in a breaking away of parts of the design. This is known as a relief break, which will show up on finished stamps as small, unprinted areas. If a damaged relief remains in use, it will transfer a repeating defect to the plate. Deliberate alterations of reliefs sometimes occur. "Altered reliefs" designate these changed conditions.

**Plate** — The final step in pre-printing production is the making of the printing plate. A flat piece of soft steel replaces the die on the bed of the transfer press. One of the reliefs on the transfer roll is positioned over this soft steel. Position, or layout, dots determine the correct position on the plate. The dots have been lightly marked on the plate in advance. After the correct position of the relief is determined, the design is rocked in by following the same method used in making the transfer roll. The difference is that this time the image is being transferred from the transfer roll, rather than to it. Once the design is entered on the plate, it appears in reverse and is recessed. There are as many transfers entered on the plate as there are subjects printed on the sheet of stamps. It is during this process that double and shifted transfers occur, as well as re-entries. These are the result of improperly entered images that have not been properly burnished out prior to rocking in a new image.

Modern siderography processes, such as those used by the U.S. Bureau of Engraving and Printing, involve an automated form of rocking designs in on preformed cylindrical printing sleeves. The same process also allows for easier removal and re-entry of worn images right on the sleeve.

**Transferring the design to the plate**

Following the entering of the required transfers on the plate, the position dots, layout dots and lines, scratches and other markings generally are burnished out. Added at this time by the siderographer are any required *guide lines, plate numbers* or other *marginal markings.* The plate is then hand-inked and a proof impression is taken. This is known as a plate proof. If the impression is approved, the plate is machined for fitting onto the press, is hardened and sent to the plate vault ready for use.

On press, the plate is inked and the surface is automatically wiped clean, leaving ink only in the recessed lines. Paper is then forced under pressure into the engraved recessed lines, thereby receiving the ink. Thus, the ink lines on engraved stamps are slightly raised, and slight depressions (debossing) occur on the back of the stamp. Prior to the advent of modern high-speed presses and more advanced ink formulations, paper had to be dampened before receiving the ink. This sometimes led to uneven shrinkage by the time the stamps were perforated, resulting in improperly perforated stamps, or misperfs. Newer presses use drier paper, thus both *wet* and *dry printings* exist on some stamps.

**Rotary Press** — Until 1914, only flat plates were used to print engraved stamps. Rotary press printing was introduced in 1914, and slowly spread. Some countries still use flat-plate printing.

After approval of the plate proof, older *rotary press plates* require additional machining. They are curved to fit the press cylinder. "Gripper slots" are cut into the back of each plate to receive the "grippers," which hold the plate securely on the press. The plate is then hardened. Stamps printed from these bent rotary press plates are longer or wider than the same stamps printed from flat-plate presses. The stretching of the plate during the curving process is what causes this distortion.

**Re-entry** — To execute a re-entry on a flat plate, the transfer roll is re-applied to the plate, often at some time after its first use on the press. Worn-out designs can be resharpened by carefully burnishing out the original image and re-entering it from the transfer roll. If the original impression has not been sufficiently removed and the transfer roll is not precisely in line with the remaining impression, the resulting double transfer will make the re-entry obvious. If the registration is true, a re-entry may be difficult or impossible to distinguish. Sometimes a stamp printed from a successful re-entry is identified by having a much sharper and clearer impression than its neighbors. With the advent of rotary presses, post-press re-entries were not possible. After a plate was curved for the rotary press, it was impossible to make a re-entry. This is because the plate had already been bent once (with the design distorted).

However, with the introduction of the previously mentioned modern-style siderography machines, entries are made to the preformed cylindrical printing sleeve. Such sleeves are dechromed and softened. This allows individual images to be burnished out and re-entered on the curved sleeve. The sleeve is then rechromed, resulting in longer press life.

**Double Transfer** — This is a description of the condition of a transfer on a plate that shows evidence of a duplication of all, or a portion of the design. It usually is the result of the changing of the registration between the transfer roll and the plate during the rocking in of the original entry. Double transfers also occur when only a portion of the design has been rocked in and improper positioning is noted. If the worker elected not to burnish out the partial or completed design, a strong double transfer will occur for part or all of the design.

It sometimes is necessary to remove the original transfer from a plate and repeat the process a second time. If the finished re-worked image shows traces of the original impression, attributable to incomplete burnishing, the result is a partial double transfer.

With the modern automatic machines mentioned previously, double transfers are all but impossible to create. Those partially doubled images on stamps printed from such sleeves are more than likely re-entries, rather than true double transfers.

**Re-engraved** — Alterations to a stamp design are sometimes necessary after some stamps have been printed. In some cases, either the original die or the actual printing plate may have its "temper" drawn (softened), and the design will be re-cut. The resulting impressions from such a re-engraved die or plate may differ slightly from the original issue, and are known as "re-engraved." If the alteration was made to the master die, all future printings will be consistently different from the original. If alterations were made to the printing plate, each altered stamp on the plate will be slightly different from each other, allowing specialists to reconstruct a complete printing plate.

**Dropped Transfers** — If an impression from the transfer roll has not been properly placed, a dropped transfer may occur. The final stamp image will appear obviously out of line with its neighbors.

**Short Transfer** — Sometimes a transfer roll is not rocked its entire length when entering a transfer onto a plate. As a result, the finished transfer on the plate fails to show the complete design, and the finished stamp will have an incomplete design printed. This is known as a "short transfer." U.S. Scott No. 8 is a good example of a short transfer.

## TYPOGRAPHY (Letterpress, Surface Printing, Flexography, Dry Offset, High Etch)

Although the word "Typography" is obsolete as a term describing a printing method, it was the accepted term throughout the first century of postage stamps. Therefore, appropriate Scott listings in this catalogue refer to typographed stamps. The current term for this form of printing, however, is "letterpress."

As it relates to the production of postage stamps, letterpress printing is the reverse of engraving. Rather than having recessed areas trap the ink and deposit it on paper, only the raised areas of the design are inked. This is comparable to the type of printing seen by inking and using an ordinary rubber stamp. Letterpress includes all printing where the design is above the surface area, whether it is wood, metal or, in some instances, hardened rubber or polymer plastic.

For most letterpress-printed stamps, the engraved master is made in much the same manner as for engraved stamps. In this instance, however, an additional step is needed. The design is transferred to another surface before being transferred to the transfer roll. In this way, the transfer roll has a recessed stamp design, rather than one done in relief. This makes the printing areas on the final plate raised, or relief areas.

For less-detailed stamps of the 19th century, the area on the die not used as a printing surface was cut away, leaving the surface area raised. The original die was then reproduced by stereotyping or electrotyping. The resulting electrotypes were assembled in the required number and format of the desired sheet of stamps. The plate used in printing the stamps was an electroplate of these assembled electrotypes.

Once the final letterpress plates are created, ink is applied to the raised surface and the pressure of the press transfers the ink impression to the paper. In contrast to engraving, the fine lines of letterpress are impressed on the surface of the stamp, leaving a debossed surface. When viewed from the back (as on a typewritten page), the corresponding line work on the stamp will be raised slightly (embossed) above the surface.

## PHOTOGRAVURE (Gravure, Rotogravure, Heliogravure)

In this process, the basic principles of photography are applied to a chemically sensitized metal plate, rather than photographic paper. The design is transferred photographically to the plate through a halftone, or dot-matrix screen, breaking the reproduction into tiny dots. The plate is treated chemically and the dots form depressions, called cells, of varying depths and diameters, depending on the degrees of shade in the design. Then, like engraving, ink is applied to the plate and the surface is wiped clean. This leaves ink in the tiny cells that is lifted out and deposited on the paper when it is pressed against the plate.

Gravure is most often used for multicolored stamps, generally using the three primary colors (red, yellow and blue) and black. By varying the dot matrix pattern and density of these colors, virtually any color can be reproduced. A typical full-color gravure stamp will be created from four printing cylinders (one for each color). The original multicolored image will have been photographically separated into its component colors.

Modern gravure printing may use computer-generated dot-matrix screens, and modern plates may be of various types including metal-coated plastic. The catalogue designation of Photogravure (or "Photo") covers any of these older and more modern gravure methods of printing.

For examples of the first photogravure stamps printed (1914), see Bavaria Scott 94-114.

## LITHOGRAPHY (Offset Lithography, Stone Lithography, Dilitho, Planography, Collotype)

The principle that oil and water do not mix is the basis for lithography. The stamp design is drawn by hand or transferred from engraving to the surface of a lithographic stone or metal plate in a greasy (oily) substance. This oily substance holds the ink, which will later be transferred to the paper. The stone (or plate) is wet with an acid fluid, causing it to repel the printing ink in all areas not covered by the greasy substance.

Transfer paper is used to transfer the design from the original stone or plate. A series of duplicate transfers are grouped and, in turn, transferred to the final printing plate.

**Photolithography** — The application of photographic processes to lithography. This process allows greater flexibility of design, related to use of halftone screens combined with line work. Unlike photogravure or engraving, this process can allow large, solid areas to be printed.

**Offset** — A refinement of the lithographic process. A rubber-covered blanket cylinder takes the impression from the inked lithographic plate. From the "blanket" the impression is *offset* or transferred to the paper. Greater flexibility and speed are the principal reasons offset printing has largely displaced lithography. The term "lithography" covers both processes, and results are almost identical.

### EMBOSSED (Relief) Printing

Embossing, not considered one of the four main printing types, is a method in which the design first is sunk into the metal of the die. Printing is done against a yielding platen, such as leather or linoleum. The platen is forced into the depression of the die, thus forming the design on the paper in relief. This process is often used for metallic inks.

Embossing may be done without color (see Sardinia Scott 4-6); with color printed around the embossed area (see Great Britain Scott 5 and most U.S. envelopes); and with color in exact registration with the embossed subject (see Canada Scott 656-657).

### HOLOGRAMS

For objects to appear as holograms on stamps, a model exactly the same size as it is to appear on the hologram must be created. Rather than using photographic film to capture the image, holography records an image on a photoresist material. In processing, chemicals eat away at certain exposed areas, leaving a pattern of constructive and destructive interference. When the photoresist is developed, the result is a pattern of uneven ridges that acts as a mold. This mold is then coated with metal, and the resulting form is used to press copies in much the same way phonograph records are produced.

A typical reflective hologram used for stamps consists of a reproduction of the uneven patterns on a plastic film that is applied to a reflective background, usually a silver or gold foil. Light is reflected off the background through the film, making the pattern present on the film visible. Because of the uneven pattern of the film, the viewer will perceive the objects in their proper three-dimensional relationships with appropriate brightness.

The first hologram on a stamp was produced by Austria in 1988 (Scott 1441).

### FOIL APPLICATION

A modern technique of applying color to stamps involves the application of metallic foil to the stamp paper. A pattern of foil is applied to the stamp paper by use of a stamping die. The foil usually is flat, but it may be textured. Canada Scott 1735 has three different foil applications in pearl, bronze and gold. The gold foil was textured using a chemical-etch copper embossing die. The printing of this stamp also involved two-color offset lithography plus embossing.

### THERMOGRAPHY

In the 1990s stamps began to be enhanced with thermographic printing. In this process, a powdered polymer is applied over a sheet that has just been printed. The powder adheres to ink that lacks drying or hardening agents and does not adhere to areas where the ink has these agents. The excess powder is removed and the sheet is briefly heated to melt the powder. The melted powder solidifies after cooling, producing a raised, shiny effect on the stamps. See Scott New Caledonia C239-C240.

### COMBINATION PRINTINGS

Sometimes two or even three printing methods are combined in producing stamps. In these cases, such as Austria Scott 933 or Canada 1735 (described in the preceding paragraph), the multiple-printing technique can be determined by studying the individual characteristics of each printing type. A few stamps, such as Singapore Scott 684-684A, combine as many as three of the four major printing types (lithography, engraving and typography). When this is done it often indicates the incorporation of security devices against counterfeiting.

### INK COLORS

Inks or colored papers used in stamp printing often are of mineral origin, although there are numerous examples of organic-based pigments. As a general rule, organic-based pigments are far more subject to varieties and change than those of mineral-based origin.

The appearance of any given color on a stamp may be affected by many aspects, including printing variations, light, color of paper, aging and chemical alterations.

Numerous printing variations may be observed. Heavier pressure or inking will cause a more intense color, while slight interruptions in the ink feed or lighter impressions will cause a lighter appearance. Stamps printed in the same color by water-based and solvent-based inks can differ significantly in appearance. This affects several stamps in the U.S. Prominent Americans series. Hand-mixed ink formulas (primarily from the 19th century) produced under different conditions (humidity and temperature) account for notable color variations in early printings of the same stamp (see U.S. Scott 248-250, 279B, for example). Different sources of pigment can also result in significant differences in color.

Light exposure and aging are closely related in the way they affect stamp color. Both eventually break down the ink and fade colors, so that a carefully kept stamp may differ significantly in color from an identical copy that has been exposed to light. If stamps are exposed to light either intentionally or accidentally, their colors can be faded or completely changed in some cases.

Papers of different quality and consistency used for the same stamp printing may affect color appearance. Most pelure papers, for example, show a richer color when compared with wove or laid papers. See Russia Scott 181a, for an example of this effect.

The very nature of the printing processes can cause a variety of differences in shades or hues of the same stamp. Some of these shades are scarcer than others, and are of particular interest to the advanced collector.

## Luminescence

All forms of tagged stamps fall under the general category of luminescence. Within this broad category is fluorescence, dealing with forms of tagging visible under longwave ultraviolet light, and phosphorescence, which deals with tagging visible only under shortwave light. Phosphorescence leaves an afterglow and fluorescence does not. These treated stamps show up in a range of different colors when exposed to UV light. The differing wavelengths of the light activates the tagging material, making it glow in various colors that usually serve different mail processing purposes.

Intentional tagging is a post-World War II phenomenon, brought about by the increased literacy rate and rapidly growing mail volume. It was one of several answers to the problem of the need for more automated mail processes. Early tagged stamps served the purpose of triggering machines to separate different types of mail. A natural outgrowth was to also use the signal to trigger machines that faced all envelopes the same way and canceled them.

Tagged stamps come in many different forms. Some tagged stamps have luminescent shapes or images imprinted on them as a form of security device. Others have blocks (United States), stripes, frames (South Africa and Canada), overall coatings (United States), bars (Great Britain and Canada) and many other types. Some types of tagging are even mixed in with the pigmented printing ink (Australia Scott 366, Netherlands Scott 478 and U.S. Scott 1359 and 2443).

The means of applying taggant to stamps differs as much as the intended purposes for the stamps. The most common form of tagging is a coating applied to the surface of the printed stamp. Since the taggant ink is frequently invisible except under UV light, it does not interfere with the appearance of the stamp. Another common application is the use of phosphored papers. In this case the paper itself either has a coating of taggant applied before the stamp is printed, has taggant applied during the papermaking process (incorporating it into the fibers), or has the taggant mixed into the coating of the paper. The latter method, among others, is currently in use in the United States.

Many countries now use tagging in various forms to either expedite mail handling or to serve as a printing security device against counterfeiting. Following the introduction of tagged stamps for public use in 1959 by Great Britain, other countries have steadily joined the parade. Among those are Germany (1961); Canada and Denmark (1962); United States, Australia, France and Switzerland (1963); Belgium and Japan (1966); Sweden and Norway (1967); Italy (1968); and Russia (1969). Since then, many other countries have begun using forms of tagging, including Brazil, China, Czechoslovakia, Hong Kong, Guatemala, Indonesia, Israel, Lithuania, Luxembourg, Netherlands, Penrhyn Islands, Portugal, St. Vincent, Singapore, South Africa, Spain and Sweden to name a few.

In some cases, including United States, Canada, Great Britain and Switzerland, stamps were released both with and without tagging. Many of these were released during each country's experimental period. Tagged and untagged versions are listed for the aforementioned countries and are noted in some other countries' listings. For at least a few stamps, the experimentally tagged version is worth far more than its untagged counterpart, such as the 1963 experimental tagged version of France Scott 1024.

In some cases, luminescent varieties of stamps were inadvertently created. Several Russian stamps, for example, sport highly fluorescent ink that was not intended as a form of tagging. Older stamps, such as early U.S. postage dues, can be positively identified by the use of UV light, since the organic ink used has become slightly fluorescent over time. Other stamps, such as Austria Scott 70a-82a (varnish bars) and Obock Scott 46-64 (printed quadrille lines), have become fluorescent over time.

Various fluorescent substances have been added to paper to make it appear brighter. These optical brightners, as they are known, greatly affect the appearance of the stamp under UV light. The brightest of these is known as Hi-Brite paper. These paper varieties are beyond the scope of the Scott Catalogue.

Shortwave UV light also is used extensively in expertizing, since each form of paper has its own fluorescent characteristics that are impossible to perfectly match. It is therefore a simple matter to detect filled thins, added perforation teeth and other alterations that involve the addition of paper. UV light also is used to examine stamps that have had cancels chemically removed and for other purposes as well.

## Gum

The Illustrated Gum Chart in the first part of this introduction shows and defines various types of gum condition. Because gum condition has an important impact on the value of unused stamps, we recommend studying this chart and the accompanying text carefully.

The gum on the back of a stamp may be shiny, dull, smooth, rough, dark, white, colored or tinted. Most stamp gumming adhesives use gum arabic or dextrine as a base. Certain polymers such as polyvinyl alcohol (PVA) have been used extensively since World War II.

The *Scott Standard Postage Stamp Catalogue* does not list items by types of gum. The *Scott Specialized Catalogue of United States Stamps and Covers* does differentiate among some types of gum for certain issues.

Reprints of stamps may have gum differing from the original issues. In addition, some countries have used different gum formulas for different seasons. These adhesives have different properties that may become more apparent over time.

Many stamps have been issued without gum, and the catalogue will note this fact. See, for example, United States Scott 40-47. Sometimes, gum may have been removed to preserve the stamp. Germany Scott B68, for example, has a highly acidic gum that eventually destroys the stamps. This item is valued in the catalogue with gum removed.

## Reprints and Reissues

These are impressions of stamps (usually obsolete) made from the original plates or stones. If they are valid for postage and reproduce obsolete issues (such as U.S. Scott 102-111), the stamps are *reissues.* If they are from current issues, they are designated as *second, third,* etc., *printing*. If designated for a particular purpose, they are called *special printings.*

When special printings are not valid for postage, but are made from original dies and plates by authorized persons, they are *official reprints. Private reprints* are made from the original plates and dies by private hands. An example of a private reprint is that of the 1871-1932 reprints made from the original die of the 1845 New Haven, Conn., postmaster's provisional. *Official reproductions* or imitations are made from new dies and plates by government authorization. Scott will list those reissues that are valid for postage if they differ significantly from the original printing.

The U.S. government made special printings of its first postage stamps in 1875. Produced were official imitations of the first two stamps (listed as Scott 3-4), reprints of the demonetized pre-1861 issues (Scott 40-47) and reissues of the 1861 stamps, the 1869 stamps and the then-current 1875 denominations. Even though the official imitations and the reprints were not valid for postage, Scott lists all of these U.S. special printings.

Most reprints or reissues differ slightly from the original stamp in some characteristic, such as gum, paper, perforation, color or watermark. Sometimes the details are followed so meticulously that only a student of that specific stamp is able to distinguish the reprint or reissue from the original.

## Remainders and Canceled to Order

Some countries sell their stock of old stamps when a new issue replaces them. To avoid postal use, the *remainders* usually are canceled with a punch hole, a heavy line or bar, or a more-or-less regular-looking cancellation. The most famous merchant of remainders was Nicholas F. Seebeck. In the 1880s and 1890s, he arranged printing contracts between the Hamilton Bank Note Co., of which he was a director, and several Central and South American countries. The contracts provided that the plates and all remainders of the yearly issues became the property of Hamilton. Seebeck saw to it that ample stock remained. The "Seebecks," both remainders and reprints, were standard packet fillers for decades.

Some countries also issue stamps *canceled-to-order (CTO),* either in sheets with original gum or stuck onto pieces of paper or envelopes and canceled. Such CTO items generally are worth less than postally used stamps. In cases where the CTO material is far more prevalent in the marketplace than postally used examples, the catalogue value relates to the CTO examples, with postally used examples noted as premium items. Most CTOs can be detected by the presence of gum. However, as the CTO practice goes back at least to 1885, the gum inevitably has been soaked off some stamps so they could pass as postally used. The normally applied postmarks usually differ slightly from standard postmarks, and specialists are able to tell the difference. When applied individually to envelopes by philatelically minded persons, CTO material is known as *favor canceled* and generally sells at large discounts.

## Cinderellas and Facsimiles

*Cinderella* is a catch-all term used by stamp collectors to describe phantoms, fantasies, bogus items, municipal issues, exhibition seals, local revenues, transportation stamps, labels, poster stamps and many other types of items. Some cinderella collectors include in their collections local postage issues, telegraph stamps, essays and proofs, forgeries and counterfeits.

A *fantasy* is an adhesive created for a nonexistent stamp-issuing authority. Fantasy items range from imaginary countries (Occusi-Ambeno, Kingdom of Sedang, Principality of Trinidad or Torres Straits), to non-existent locals (Winans City Post), or nonexistent transportation lines (McRobish & Co.'s Acapulco-San Francisco Line).

On the other hand, if the entity exists and could have issued stamps (but did not) or was known to have issued other stamps, the items are considered *bogus* stamps. These would include the Mormon postage stamps of Utah, S. Allan Taylor's Guatemala and Paraguay inventions, the propaganda issues for the South Moluccas and the adhesives of the Page & Keyes local post of Boston.

*Phantoms* is another term for both fantasy and bogus issues.

*Facsimiles* are copies or imitations made to represent original stamps, but which do not pretend to be originals. A catalogue illustration is such a facsimile. Illustrations from the Moens catalogue of the last century were occasionally colored and passed off as stamps. Since the beginning of stamp collecting, facsimiles have been made for collectors as space fillers or for reference. They often carry the word "facsimile," "falsch" (German), "sanko" or "mozo" (Japanese), or "faux" (French) overprinted on the face or stamped on the back. Unfortunately, over the years a number of these items have had fake cancels applied over the facsimile notation and have been passed off as genuine.

## Forgeries and Counterfeits

Forgeries and counterfeits have been with philately virtually from the beginning of stamp production. Over time, the terminology for the two has been used interchangeably. Although both forgeries and counterfeits are reproductions of stamps, the purposes behind their creation differ considerably.

Among specialists there is an increasing movement to more specifically define such items. Although there is no universally accepted terminology, we feel the following definitions most closely mirror the items and their purposes as they are currently defined.

*Forgeries* (also often referred to as *Counterfeits*) are reproductions of genuine stamps that have been created to defraud collectors. Such spurious items first appeared on the market around 1860, and most old-time collections contain one or more. Many are crude and easily spotted, but some can deceive experts.

An important supplier of these early philatelic forgeries was the Hamburg printer Gebruder Spiro. Many others with reputations in this craft included S. Allan Taylor, George Hussey, James Chute, George Forune, Benjamin & Sarpy, Julius Goldner, E. Oneglia and L.H. Mercier. Among the noted 20th-century forgers were Francois Fournier, Jean Sperati and the prolific Raoul DeThuin.

Forgeries may be complete replications, or they may be genuine stamps altered to resemble a scarcer (and more valuable) type. Most forgeries, particularly those of rare stamps, are worth only a small fraction of the value of a genuine example, but a few types, created by some of the most notable forgers, such as Sperati, can be worth as much or more than the genuine. Fraudulently produced copies are known of most classic rarities and many medium-priced stamps.

In addition to rare stamps, large numbers of common 19th- and early 20th-century stamps were forged to supply stamps to the early packet trade. Many can still be easily found. Few new philatelic forgeries have appeared in recent decades. Successful imitation of well-engraved work is virtually impossible. It has proven far easier to produce a fake by altering a genuine stamp than to duplicate a stamp completely.

*Counterfeit* (also often referred to as *Postal Counterfeit* or *Postal Forgery*) is the term generally applied to reproductions of stamps that have been created to defraud the government of revenue. Such items usually are created at the time a stamp is current and, in some cases, are hard to detect. Because most counterfeits are seized when the perpetrator is captured, postal counterfeits, particularly used on cover, are usually worth much more than a genuine example to specialists. The first postal counterfeit was of Spain's 4-cuarto carmine of 1854 (the real one is Scott 25). Apparently, the counterfeiters were not satisfied with their first version, which is now very scarce, and they soon created an engraved counterfeit, which is common. Postal counterfeits quickly followed in Austria, Naples, Sardinia and the Roman States. They have since been created in many other countries as well, including the United States.

An infamous counterfeit to defraud the government is the 1-shilling Great Britain "Stock Exchange" forgery of 1872, used on telegraph forms at the exchange that year. The stamp escaped detection until a stamp dealer noticed it in 1898.

## Fakes

*Fakes* are genuine stamps altered in some way to make them more desirable. One student of this part of stamp collecting has estimated that by the 1950s more than 30,000 varieties of fakes were known. That number has grown greatly since then. The widespread existence of fakes makes it important for stamp collectors to study their philatelic holdings and use relevant literature. Likewise, collectors should buy from reputable dealers who guarantee their stamps and make full and prompt refunds should a purchased item be declared faked or altered by some mutually agreed-upon authority. Because fakes always have some genuine characteristics, it is not always possible to obtain unanimous agreement among experts regarding specific items. These students may change their opinions as philatelic knowledge increases. More than 80 percent of all fakes on the philatelic market today are regummed, reperforated (or perforated for the first time), or bear forged overprints, surcharges or cancellations.

Stamps can be chemically treated to alter or eliminate colors. For example, a pale rose stamp can be re-colored to resemble a blue shade of high market value. In other cases, treated stamps can be made to resemble missing color varieties. Designs may be changed by painting, or a stroke or a dot added or bleached out to turn an ordinary variety into a seemingly scarcer stamp. Part of a stamp can be bleached and reprinted in a different version, achieving an inverted center or frame. Margins can be added or repairs done so deceptively that the stamps move from the "repaired" into the "fake" category.

Fakers have not left the backs of the stamps untouched either. They may create false watermarks, add fake grills or press out genuine grills. A thin India paper proof may be glued onto a thicker backing to create the appearance an issued stamp, or a proof printed on cardboard may be shaved down and perforated to resemble a stamp. Silk threads are impressed into paper and stamps have been split so that a rare paper variety is added to an otherwise inexpensive stamp. The most common treatment to the back of a stamp, however, is regumming.

Some in the business of faking stamps have openly advertised fool-proof application of "original gum" to stamps that lack it, although most publications now ban such ads from their pages. It is believed that very few early stamps have survived without being hinged. The large number of never-hinged examples of such earlier material offered for sale thus suggests the widespread extent of regumming activity. Regumming also may be used to hide repairs or thin spots. Dipping the stamp into watermark fluid, or examining it under longwave ultraviolet light often will reveal these flaws.

Fakers also tamper with separations. Ingenious ways to add margins are known. Perforated wide-margin stamps may be falsely represented as imperforate when trimmed. Reperforating is commonly done to create scarce coil or perforation varieties, and to eliminate the naturally occurring straight-edge stamps found in sheet margin positions of many earlier issues. Custom has made straight-edged stamps less desirable. Fakers have obliged by perforating straight-edged stamps so that many are now uncommon, if not rare.

Another fertile field for the faker is that of overprints, surcharges and cancellations. The forging of rare surcharges or overprints began in the 1880s or 1890s. These forgeries are sometimes difficult to detect, but experts have identified almost all. Occasionally, overprints or cancellations are removed to create non-overprinted stamps or seemingly unused items. This is most commonly done by removing a manuscript cancel to make a stamp resemble an unused example. "SPECIMEN" overprints may be removed by scraping and repainting to create non-overprinted varieties. Fakers use inexpensive revenues or pen-canceled stamps to generate unused stamps for further faking by adding other markings. The quartz lamp or UV lamp and a high-powered magnifying glass help to easily detect removed cancellations.

The bigger problem, however, is the addition of overprints, surcharges or cancellations - many with such precision that they are very difficult to ascertain. Plating of the stamps or the overprint can be an important method of detection.

Fake postmarks may range from many spurious fancy cancellations to a host of markings applied to transatlantic covers, to adding normally appearing postmarks to definitives of some countries with stamps that are valued far higher used than unused. With the increased popularity of cover collecting, and the widespread interest in postal history, a fertile new field for fakers has come about. Some have tried to create entire covers. Others specialize in adding stamps, tied by fake cancellations, to genuine stampless covers, or replacing less expensive or damaged stamps with more valuable ones. Detailed study of postal rates in effect at the time a cover in question was mailed, including the analysis of each handstamp used during the period, ink analysis and similar techniques, usually will unmask the fraud.

## Restoration and Repairs

Scott bases its catalogue values on stamps that are free of defects and otherwise meet the standards set forth earlier in this introduction. Most stamp collectors desire to have the finest copy of an item possible. Even within given grading categories there are variances. This leads to a controversial practice that is not defined in any universal manner: stamp *restoration.*

There are broad differences of opinion about what is permissible when it comes to restoration. Carefully applying a soft eraser to a stamp or cover to remove light soiling is one form of restoration, as is washing a stamp in mild soap and water to clean it. These are fairly accepted forms of restoration. More severe forms of restoration include pressing out creases or removing stains caused by tape. To what degree each of these is acceptable is dependent upon the individual situation. Further along the spectrum is the freshening of a stamp's color by removing oxide build-up or the effects of wax paper left next to stamps shipped to the tropics.

At some point in this spectrum the concept of *repair* replaces that of restoration. Repairs include filling thin spots, mending tears by reweaving or adding a missing perforation tooth. Regumming stamps may have been acceptable as a restoration or repair technique many decades ago, but today it is considered a form of fakery.

Restored stamps may or may not sell at a discount, and it is possible that the value of individual restored items may be enhanced over that of their pre-restoration state. Specific situations dictate the resultant value of such an item. Repaired stamps sell at substantial discounts from the value of sound stamps.

# Terminology

**Booklets** — Many countries have issued stamps in small booklets for the convenience of users. This idea continues to become increasingly popular in many countries. Booklets have been issued in many sizes and forms, often with advertising on the covers, the panes of stamps or on the interleaving.

The panes used in booklets may be printed from special plates or made from regular sheets. All panes from booklets issued by the United States and many from those of other countries contain stamps that are straight edged on the sides, but perforated between. Others are distinguished by orientation of watermark or other identifying features. Any stamp-like unit in the pane, either printed or blank, that is not a postage stamp, is considered to be a *label* in the catalogue listings.

Scott lists and values booklet panes. Modern complete booklets also are listed and valued. Individual booklet panes are listed only when they are not fashioned from existing sheet stamps and, therefore, are identifiable from their sheet stamp counterparts.

Panes usually do not have a used value assigned to them because there is little market activity for used booklet panes, even though many exist used and there is some demand for them.

**Cancellations** — The marks or obliterations put on stamps by postal authorities to show that they have performed service and to prevent their reuse are known as cancellations. If the marking is made with a pen, it is considered a "pen cancel." When the location of the post office appears in the marking, it is a "town cancellation." A "postmark" is technically any postal marking, but in practice the term generally is applied to a town cancellation with a date. When calling attention to a cause or celebration, the marking is known as a "slogan cancellation." Many other types and styles of cancellations exist, such as duplex, numerals, targets, fancy and others. See also "precancels," below.

**Coil Stamps** — These are stamps that are issued in rolls for use in dispensers, affixing and vending machines. Those coils of the United States, Canada, Sweden and some other countries are perforated horizontally or vertically only, with the outer edges imperforate. Coil stamps of some countries, such as Great Britain and Germany, are perforated on all four sides and may in some cases be distinguished from their sheet stamp counterparts by watermarks, counting numbers on the reverse or other means.

**Covers** — Entire envelopes, with or without adhesive postage stamps, that have passed through the mail and bear postal or other markings of philatelic interest are known as covers. Before the introduction of envelopes in about 1840, people folded letters and wrote the address on the outside. Some people covered their letters with an extra sheet of paper on the outside for the address, producing the term "cover." Used airletter sheets, stamped envelopes and other items of postal stationery also are considered covers.

**Errors** — Stamps that have some major, consistent, unintentional deviation from the normal are considered errors. Errors include, but are not limited to, missing or wrong colors, wrong paper, wrong watermarks, inverted centers or frames on multicolor printing, inverted or missing surcharges or overprints, double impressions, missing perforations, unintentionally omitted tagging and others. Factually wrong or misspelled information, if it appears on all examples of a stamp, are not considered errors in the true sense of the word. They are errors of design. Inconsistent or randomly appearing items, such as misperfs or color shifts, are classified as freaks.

**Color-Omitted Errors** — This term refers to stamps where a missing color is caused by the complete failure of the printing plate to deliver ink to the stamp paper or any other paper. Generally, this is caused by the printing plate not being engaged on the press or the ink station running dry of ink during printing.

**Color-Missing Errors** — This term refers to stamps where a color or colors were printed somewhere but do not appear on the finished stamp. There are four different classes of color-missing errors, and the catalog indicates with a two-letter code appended to each such listing what caused the color to be missing. These codes are used only for the United States' color-missing error listings.

**FO** = A *foldover* of the stamp sheet during printing may block ink from appearing on a stamp. Instead, the color will appear on the back of the foldover (where it might fall on the back of the selvage or perhaps on the back of the stamp or another stamp). FO also will be used in the case of foldunders, where the paper may fold underneath the other stamp paper and the color will print on the platen.

**EP** = A piece of *extraneous paper* falling across the plate or stamp paper will receive the printed ink. When the extraneous paper is removed, an unprinted portion of stamp paper remains and shows partially or totally missing colors.

**CM** = A misregistration of the printing plates during printing will result in a *color misregistration*, and such a misregistraion may result in a color not appearing on the finished stamp.

**PS** = *A perforation shift* after printing may remove a color from the finished stamp. Normally, this will occur on a row of stamps at the edge of the stamp pane.

**Measurements** – When measurements are given in the Scott catalogues for stamp size, grill size or any other reason, the first measurement given is always for the top and bottom dimension, while the second measurement will be for the sides (just as perforation gauges are measured). Thus, a stamp size of 15mm x 21mm will indicate a vertically oriented stamp 15mm wide at top and bottom, and 21mm tall at the sides. The same principle holds for measuring or counting items such as U.S. grills. A grill count of 22x18 points (B grill) indicates that there are 22 grill points across by 18 grill points down.

**Overprints and Surcharges** — Overprinting involves applying wording or design elements over an already existing stamp. Overprints can be used to alter the place of use (such as "Canal Zone" on U.S. stamps), to adapt them for a special purpose ("Porto" on Denmark's 1913-20 regular issues for use as postage due stamps, Scott J1-J7) or to commemorate a special occasion (United States Scott 647-648).

A *surcharge* is a form of overprint that changes or restates the face value of a stamp or piece of postal stationery.

Surcharges and overprints may be handstamped, typeset or, occasionally, lithographed or engraved. A few hand-written overprints and surcharges are known.

**Personalized Stamps** — In 1999, Australia issued stamps with se-tenant labels that could be personalized with pictures of the customer's choice. Other countries quickly followed suit, with some offering to print the selected picture on the stamp itself within a frame that was used exclusively for personalized issues. As the picture used on these stamps or labels vary, listings for such stamps are for any picture within the common frame (or any picture on a se-tenant label), be it a "generic" image or one produced especially for a customer, almost invariably at a premium price.

**Precancels** — Stamps that are canceled before they are placed in the mail are known as precancels. Precanceling usually is done to expedite the handling of large mailings and generally allow the affected mail pieces to skip certain phases of mail handling.

In the United States, precancellations generally identified the point of origin; that is, the city and state. This information appeared across the face of the stamp, usually centered between parallel lines. More recently, bureau precancels retained the parallel lines, but the city and state designations were dropped. Recent coils have a service inscription that is present on the original printing plate. These show the mail service paid for by the stamp. Since these stamps are not intended to receive further cancellations when used as intended, they are considered precancels. Such items often do not have parallel lines as part of the precancellation.

In France, the abbreviation *Affranchts* in a semicircle together with the word *Postes* is the general form of precancel in use. Belgian precancellations usually appear in a box in which the name of the city appears. Netherlands precancels have the name of the city enclosed between concentric circles, sometimes called a "lifesaver." Precancellations of other countries usually follow these patterns, but may be any arrangement of bars, boxes and city names.

Precancels are listed in the Scott catalogues only if the precancel changes the denomination (Belgium Scott 477-478); if the precanceled stamp is different from the non-precanceled version (such as untagged U.S. precancels); or if the stamp exists only precanceled (France Scott 1096-1099, U.S. Scott 2265).

**Proofs and Essays** — Proofs are impressions taken from an approved die, plate or stone in which the design and color are the same as the stamp issued to the public. Trial color proofs are impressions taken from approved dies, plates or stones in colors that vary from the final version. An essay is the impression of a design that differs in some way from the issued stamp. "Progressive die proofs" generally are considered to be essays.

**Provisionals** — These are stamps that are issued on short notice and intended for temporary use pending the arrival of regular issues. They usually are issued to meet such contingencies as changes in government or currency, shortage of necessary postage values or military occupation.

During the 1840s, postmasters in certain American cities issued stamps that were valid only at specific post offices. In 1861, postmasters of the Confederate States also issued stamps with limited validity. Both of these examples are known as "postmaster's provisionals."

**Se-tenant** — This term refers to an unsevered pair, strip or block of stamps that differ in design, denomination or overprint.

Unless the se-tenant item has a continuous design (see U.S. Scott 1451a, 1694a) the stamps do not have to be in the same order as shown in the catalogue (see U.S. Scott 2158a).

**Specimens** — The Universal Postal Union required member nations to send samples of all stamps they released into service to the International Bureau in Switzerland. Member nations of the UPU received these specimens as samples of what stamps were valid for postage. Many are overprinted, handstamped or initial-perforated "Specimen," "Canceled" or "Muestra." Some are marked with bars across the denominations (China-Taiwan), punched holes (Czechoslovakia) or back inscriptions (Mongolia).

Stamps distributed to government officials or for publicity purposes, and stamps submitted by private security printers for official approval, also may receive such defacements.

The previously described defacement markings prevent postal use, and all such items generally are known as "specimens."

**Tete Beche** — This term describes a pair of stamps in which one is upside down in relation to the other. Some of these are the result of intentional sheet arrangements, such as Morocco Scott B10-B11. Others occurred when one or more electrotypes accidentally were placed upside down on the plate, such as Colombia Scott 57a. Separation of the tete-beche stamps, of course, destroys the tete beche variety.

# Pronunciation Symbols

ə .... banana, collide, abut

ˈə, ˌə .... humdrum, abut

ᵊ .... immediately preceding \l\, \n\, \m\, \ŋ\, as in battle, mitten, eaten, and sometimes open \ˈō-pᵊm\, lock and key \-ᵊŋ-\; immediately following \l\, \m\, \r\, as often in French table, prisme, titre

ər .... further, merger, bird

ˈər-, ˈə-r .... as in two different pronunciations of hurry \ˈhər-ē, ˈhə-rē\

a .... mat, map, mad, gag, snap, patch

ā .... day, fade, date, aorta, drape, cape

ä .... bother, cot, and, with most American speakers, father, cart

ȧ .... father as pronounced by speakers who do not rhyme it with *bother*; French patte

au̇ .... now, loud, out

b .... baby, rib

ch .... chin, nature \ˈnā-chər\

d .... did, adder

e .... bet, bed, peck

ˈē, ˌē .... beat, nosebleed, evenly, easy

ē .... easy, mealy

f .... fifty, cuff

g .... go, big, gift

h .... hat, ahead

hw .... whale as pronounced by those who do not have the same pronunciation for both *whale* and *wail*

i .... tip, banish, active

ī .... site, side, buy, tripe

j .... job, gem, edge, join, judge

k .... kin, cook, ache

k̲ .... German ich, Buch; one pronunciation of loch

l .... lily, pool

m .... murmur, dim, nymph

n .... no, own

ⁿ .... indicates that a preceding vowel or diphthong is pronounced with the nasal passages open, as in French *un bon vin blanc* \œⁿ-bōⁿ-vaⁿ-bläⁿ\

ŋ .... sing \ˈsiŋ\, singer \ˈsiŋ-ər\, finger \ˈfiŋ-gər\, ink \ˈiŋk\

ō .... bone, know, beau

ȯ .... saw, all, gnaw, caught

œ .... French boeuf, German Hölle

œ̄ .... French feu, German Höhle

ȯi .... coin, destroy

p .... pepper, lip

r .... red, car, rarity

s .... source, less

sh .... as in shy, mission, machine, special (actually, this is a single sound, not two); with a hyphen between, two sounds as in *grasshopper* \ˈgras-ˌhä-pər\

t .... tie, attack, late, later, latter

th .... as in thin, ether (actually, this is a single sound, not two); with a hyphen between, two sounds as in *knighthood* \ˈnīt-ˌhu̇d\

t͟h .... then, either, this (actually, this is a single sound, not two)

ü .... rule, youth, union \ˈyün-yən\, few \ˈfyü\

u̇ .... pull, wood, book, curable \ˈkyu̇r-ə-bəl\, fury \ˈfyu̇r-ē\

ᵫ .... German füllen, hübsch

ᵫ̄ .... French rue, German fühlen

v .... vivid, give

w .... we, away

y .... yard, young, cue \ˈkyü\, mute \ˈmyüt\, union \ˈyün-yən\

ʸ .... indicates that during the articulation of the sound represented by the preceding character the front of the tongue has substantially the position it has for the articulation of the first sound of *yard,* as in French *digne* \dēnʸ\

z .... zone, raise

zh .... as in vision, azure \ˈa-zhər\ (actually, this is a single sound, not two); with a hyphen between, two sounds as in *hogshead* \ˈhȯgz-ˌhed, ˈhägz-\

\ .... slant line used in pairs to mark the beginning and end of a transcription: \ˈpen\

ˈ .... mark preceding a syllable with primary (strongest) stress: \ˈpen-mən-ˌship\

ˌ .... mark preceding a syllable with secondary (medium) stress: \ˈpen-mən-ˌship\

\- .... mark of syllable division

( ) .... indicate that what is symbolized between is present in some utterances but not in others: *factory* \ˈfak-t(ə-)rē\

÷ .... indicates that many regard as unacceptable the pronunciation variant immediately following: *cupola* \ˈkyü-pə-lə, ÷-ˌlō\

# Currency Conversion

| Country | Dollar | Pound | S Franc | Yen | HK $ | Euro | Cdn $ | Aus $ |
|---|---|---|---|---|---|---|---|---|
| Australia | 1.2914 | 1.7779 | 1.3628 | 0.0121 | 0.1650 | 1.5728 | 1.0058 | — |
| Canada | 1.2840 | 1.7677 | 1.3550 | 0.0120 | 0.1640 | 1.5638 | — | 0.9943 |
| European Union | 0.8211 | 1.1304 | 0.8665 | 0.0077 | 0.1049 | — | 0.6395 | 0.6358 |
| Hong Kong | 7.8270 | 10.775 | 8.2598 | 0.0732 | — | 9.5323 | 6.0958 | 6.0609 |
| Japan | 106.92 | 147.20 | 112.83 | — | 13.660 | 130.22 | 83.271 | 82.794 |
| Switzerland | 0.9476 | 1.3046 | — | 0.0089 | 0.1211 | 1.1541 | 0.7380 | 0.7338 |
| United Kingdom | 0.7264 | — | 0.7665 | 0.0068 | 0.0928 | 0.8846 | 0.5657 | 0.5625 |
| United States | — | 1.3767 | 1.0553 | 0.0094 | 0.1278 | 1.2179 | 0.7788 | 0.7744 |

| Country | Currency | U.S. $ Equiv. |
|---|---|---|
| Jamaica | dollar | .0079 |
| Japan | yen | .0094 |
| Jordan | dinar | 1.4104 |
| Kazakhstan | tenge | .0032 |
| Kenya | shilling | .0099 |
| Kiribati | Australian dollar | .7744 |
| Korea (South) | won | .0009 |
| Korea (North) | won | .0011 |
| Kosovo | euro | 1.2179 |
| Kuwait | dinar | 3.3201 |
| Kyrgyzstan | som | .0147 |
| Laos | kip | .0001 |
| Latvia | euro | 1.2179 |
| Lebanon | pound | .0007 |
| Lesotho | maloti | .0838 |
| Liberia | dollar | .0077 |
| Libya | dinar | .7474 |
| Liechtenstein | Swiss franc | 1.0553 |
| Lithuania | euro | 1.2179 |
| Luxembourg | euro | 1.2179 |

*Source:* ***xe.com*** *Mar. 1, 2018. Figures reflect values as of Mar. 1, 2018.*

## COMMON DESIGN TYPES

Pictured in this section are issues where one illustration has been used for a number of countries in the Catalogue. Not included in this section are overprinted stamps or those issues which are illustrated in each country. Because the location of Never Hinged breakpoints varies from country to country, some of the values in the listings below will be for unused stamps that were previously hinged.

### EUROPA

### Europa, 1956

The design symbolizing the cooperation among the six countries comprising the Coal and Steel Community is illustrated in each country.

| | |
|---|---|
| *Belgium* | *496-497* |
| *France* | *805-806* |
| *Germany* | *748-749* |
| *Italy* | *715-716* |
| *Luxembourg* | *318-320* |
| *Netherlands* | *368-369* |

| | | |
|---|---|---|
| *Nos. 496-497 (2)* | 9.00 | .70 |
| *Nos. 805-806 (2)* | 5.25 | 1.00 |
| *Nos. 748-749 (2)* | 7.30 | 1.20 |
| *Nos. 715-716 (2)* | 9.25 | 1.25 |
| *Nos. 318-320 (3)* | 65.50 | 42.00 |
| *Nos. 368-369 (2)* | 25.75 | 1.50 |
| *Set total (13) Stamps* | 122.05 | 47.65 |

### Europa, 1958

"E" and Dove — CD1

European Postal Union at the service of European integration.

**1958, Sept. 13**

| | |
|---|---|
| Belgium | 527-528 |
| France | 889-890 |
| Germany | 790-791 |
| Italy | 750-751 |
| Luxembourg | 341-343 |
| Netherlands | 375-376 |
| Saar | 317-318 |

| | | |
|---|---|---|
| *Nos. 527-528 (2)* | 4.25 | .60 |
| *Nos. 889-890 (2)* | 1.65 | .55 |
| *Nos. 790-791 (2)* | 3.65 | .65 |
| *Nos. 750-751 (2)* | 1.05 | .60 |
| *Nos. 341-343 (3)* | 1.35 | .90 |
| *Nos. 375-376 (2)* | 1.25 | .75 |
| *Nos. 317-318 (2)* | 1.05 | 2.30 |
| *Set total (15) Stamps* | 14.25 | 6.35 |

### Europa, 1959

6-Link Enless Chain — CD2

**1959, Sept. 19**

| | |
|---|---|
| Belgium | 536-537 |
| France | 929-930 |
| Germany | 805-806 |
| Italy | 791-792 |
| Luxembourg | 354-355 |
| Netherlands | 379-380 |

| | | |
|---|---|---|
| *Nos. 536-537 (2)* | 1.55 | .60 |
| *Nos. 929-930 (2)* | 1.40 | .80 |
| *Nos. 805-806 (2)* | 1.55 | .65 |
| *Nos. 791-792 (2)* | .80 | .50 |
| *Nos. 354-355 (2)* | 2.65 | 1.00 |
| *Nos. 379-380 (2)* | 2.10 | 1.85 |
| *Set total (12) Stamps* | 10.05 | 5.40 |

### Europa, 1960

19-Spoke Wheel CD3

First anniverary of the establishment of C.E.P.T. (Conference Europeenne des Administrations des Postes et des Telecommunications.) The spokes symbolize the 19 founding members of the Conference.

**1960, Sept.**

| | |
|---|---|
| Belgium | 553-554 |
| Denmark | 379 |
| Finland | 376-377 |
| France | 970-971 |
| Germany | 818-820 |
| Great Britain | 377-378 |
| Greece | 688 |
| Iceland | 327-328 |
| Ireland | 175-176 |
| Italy | 809-810 |
| Luxembourg | 374-375 |
| Netherlands | 385-386 |
| Norway | 387 |
| Portugal | 866-867 |
| Spain | 941-942 |
| Sweden | 562-563 |
| Switzerland | 400-401 |
| Turkey | 1493-1494 |

| | | |
|---|---|---|
| *Nos. 553-554 (2)* | 1.25 | .55 |
| *No. 379 (1)* | .55 | .50 |
| *Nos. 376-377 (2)* | 1.70 | 1.80 |
| *Nos. 970-971 (2)* | .50 | .50 |
| *Nos. 818-820 (3)* | 2.25 | 1.50 |
| *Nos. 377-378 (2)* | 8.00 | 5.00 |
| *No. 688 (1)* | 5.00 | 2.00 |
| *Nos. 327-328 (2)* | 1.30 | 1.85 |
| *Nos. 175-176 (2)* | 47.50 | 27.50 |
| *Nos. 809-810 (2)* | .50 | .50 |
| *Nos. 374-375 (2)* | 1.00 | .80 |
| *Nos. 385-386 (2)* | 2.00 | 2.00 |
| *No. 387 (1)* | 1.25 | 1.25 |
| *Nos. 866-867 (2)* | 2.25 | 1.25 |
| *Nos. 941-942 (2)* | 1.50 | .75 |
| *Nos. 562-563 (2)* | 1.05 | .55 |
| *Nos. 400-401 (2)* | 1.25 | .65 |
| *Nos. 1493-1494 (2)* | 2.10 | 1.35 |
| *Set total (34) Stamps* | 80.95 | 50.30 |

### Europa, 1961

19 Doves Flying as One — CD4

The 19 doves represent the 19 members of the Conference of European Postal and Telecommunications Administrations C.E.P.T.

**1961-62**

| | |
|---|---|
| Belgium | 572-573 |
| Cyprus | 201-203 |
| France | 1005-1006 |
| Germany | 844-845 |
| Great Britain | 382-384 |
| Greece | 718-719 |
| Iceland | 340-341 |
| Italy | 845-846 |
| Luxembourg | 382-383 |
| Netherlands | 387-388 |
| Spain | 1010-1011 |
| Switzerland | 410-411 |
| Turkey | 1518-1520 |

| | | |
|---|---|---|
| *Nos. 572-573 (2)* | .75 | .50 |
| *Nos. 201-203 (3)* | *2.10* | *1.20* |
| *Nos. 1005-1006 (2)* | .50 | .50 |
| *Nos. 844-845 (2)* | .60 | .75 |
| *Nos. 382-384 (3)* | .75 | .75 |
| *Nos. 718-719 (2)* | .80 | .50 |
| *Nos. 340-341 (2)* | 1.10 | 1.60 |
| *Nos. 845-846 (2)* | .50 | .50 |
| *Nos. 382-383 (2)* | .55 | .55 |
| *Nos. 387-388 (2)* | .50 | .50 |
| *Nos. 1010-1011 (2)* | .70 | .55 |
| *Nos. 410-411 (2)* | 1.25 | .60 |
| *Nos. 1518-1520 (3)* | 2.45 | 1.30 |
| *Set total (29) Stamps* | 12.55 | 9.80 |

### Europa, 1962

Young Tree with 19 Leaves CD5

The 19 leaves represent the 19 original members of C.E.P.T.

**1962-63**

| | |
|---|---|
| Belgium | 582-583 |
| Cyprus | 219-221 |
| France | 1045-1046 |
| Germany | 852-853 |
| Greece | 739-740 |
| Iceland | 348-349 |
| Ireland | 184-185 |
| Italy | 860-861 |
| Luxembourg | 386-387 |
| Netherlands | 394-395 |
| Norway | 414-415 |
| Switzerland | 416-417 |
| Turkey | 1553-1555 |

| | | |
|---|---|---|
| *Nos. 582-583 (2)* | .65 | .65 |
| *Nos. 219-221 (3)* | *76.25* | *6.75* |
| *Nos. 1045-1046 (2)* | .60 | .50 |
| *Nos. 852-853 (2)* | .70 | .80 |
| *Nos. 739-740 (2)* | 2.25 | 1.15 |
| *Nos. 348-349 (2)* | .85 | .85 |
| *Nos. 184-185 (2)* | 2.00 | .50 |
| *Nos. 860-861 (2)* | 1.00 | .55 |
| *Nos. 386-387 (2)* | .75 | .55 |
| *Nos. 394-395 (2)* | 1.35 | .90 |
| *Nos. 414-415 (2)* | 2.25 | 2.25 |
| *Nos. 416-417 (2)* | 1.65 | 1.00 |
| *Nos. 1553-1555 (3)* | *3.00* | 1.55 |
| *Set total (28) Stamps* | 93.30 | 18.00 |

### Europa, 1963

Stylized Links, Symbolizing Unity — CD6

**1963, Sept.**

| | |
|---|---|
| Belgium | 598-599 |
| Cyprus | 229-231 |
| Finland | 419 |
| France | 1074-1075 |
| Germany | 867-868 |
| Greece | 768-769 |
| Iceland | 357-358 |
| Ireland | 188-189 |
| Italy | 880-881 |
| Luxembourg | 403-404 |
| Netherlands | 416-417 |
| Norway | 441-442 |
| Switzerland | 429 |
| Turkey | 1602-1603 |

| | | |
|---|---|---|
| *Nos. 598-599 (2)* | 1.60 | .55 |
| *Nos. 229-231 (3)* | *64.00* | *9.40* |
| *No. 419 (1)* | 1.25 | .55 |
| *Nos. 1074-1075 (2)* | .60 | .50 |
| *Nos. 867-868 (2)* | .50 | .55 |
| *Nos. 768-769 (2)* | 5.25 | 1.90 |
| *Nos. 357-358 (2)* | 1.20 | 1.20 |
| *Nos. 188-189 (2)* | 4.75 | 3.25 |
| *Nos. 880-881 (2)* | .50 | .50 |
| *Nos. 403-404 (2)* | .75 | .55 |
| *Nos. 416-417 (2)* | 1.30 | 1.00 |
| *Nos. 441-442 (2)* | 4.75 | 3.00 |
| *No. 429 (1)* | .90 | .60 |
| *Nos. 1602-1603 (2)* | 1.40 | .60 |
| *Set total (27) Stamps* | 88.75 | 24.15 |

### Europa, 1964

Symbolic Daisy — CD7

5th anniversary of the establishment of C.E.P.T. The 22 petals of the flower symbolize the 22 members of the Conference.

**1964, Sept.**

| | |
|---|---|
| Austria | 738 |
| Belgium | 614-615 |
| Cyprus | 244-246 |
| France | 1109-1110 |
| Germany | 897-898 |
| Greece | 801-802 |
| Iceland | 367-368 |
| Ireland | 196-197 |
| Italy | 894-895 |
| Luxembourg | 411-412 |
| Monaco | 590-591 |
| Netherlands | 428-429 |
| Norway | 458 |
| Portugal | 931-933 |
| Spain | 1262-1263 |
| Switzerland | 438-439 |
| Turkey | 1628-1629 |

| | | |
|---|---|---|
| *No. 738 (1)* | 1.20 | .80 |
| *Nos. 614-615 (2)* | 1.40 | .60 |
| *Nos. 244-246 (3)* | *32.25* | *5.10* |
| *Nos. 1109-1110 (2)* | .50 | .50 |
| *Nos. 897-898 (2)* | .50 | .50 |
| *Nos. 801-802 (2)* | 5.00 | 1.90 |
| *Nos. 367-368 (2)* | 1.40 | 1.15 |
| *Nos. 196-197 (2)* | 17.00 | 4.25 |
| *Nos. 894-895 (2)* | .50 | .50 |
| *Nos. 411-412 (2)* | .75 | .55 |
| *Nos. 590-591 (2)* | 2.50 | .70 |
| *Nos. 428-429 (2)* | .75 | .60 |
| *No. 458 (1)* | 4.50 | 4.50 |
| *Nos. 931-933 (3)* | *10.00* | *2.00* |
| *Nos. 1262-1263 (2)* | 1.30 | .80 |
| *Nos. 438-439 (2)* | 1.60 | .50 |
| *Nos. 1628-1629 (2)* | 2.65 | 1.35 |
| *Set total (34) Stamps* | 83.80 | 26.30 |

### Europa, 1965

Leaves and "Fruit" CD8

**1965**

| | |
|---|---|
| Belgium | 636-637 |
| Cyprus | 262-264 |
| Finland | 437 |
| France | 1131-1132 |
| Germany | 934-935 |
| Greece | 833-834 |
| Iceland | 375-376 |
| Ireland | 204-205 |
| Italy | 915-916 |
| Luxembourg | 432-433 |
| Monaco | 616-617 |
| Netherlands | 438-439 |
| Norway | 475-476 |
| Portugal | 958-960 |
| Switzerland | 469 |
| Turkey | 1665-1666 |

| | | |
|---|---|---|
| *Nos. 636-637 (2)* | .50 | .50 |
| *Nos. 262-264 (3)* | *25.35* | *6.00* |
| *No. 437 (1)* | 1.25 | .55 |
| *Nos. 1131-1132 (2)* | .70 | .55 |
| *Nos. 934-935 (2)* | .50 | .50 |
| *Nos. 833-834 (2)* | 2.25 | 1.15 |
| *Nos. 375-376 (2)* | 2.50 | 1.75 |
| *Nos. 204-205 (2)* | 16.00 | 3.35 |
| *Nos. 915-916 (2)* | .50 | .50 |
| *Nos. 432-433 (2)* | .75 | .55 |
| *Nos. 616-617 (2)* | 3.25 | 1.65 |
| *Nos. 438-439 (2)* | .55 | .50 |
| *Nos. 475-476 (2)* | 4.00 | 3.10 |
| *Nos. 958-960 (3)* | *10.00* | *2.75* |
| *No. 469 (1)* | 1.15 | .25 |
| *Nos. 1665-1666 (2)* | 3.50 | 2.10 |
| *Set total (32) Stamps* | 72.75 | 25.75 |

### Europa, 1966

Symbolic Sailboat — CD9

**1966, Sept.**

| | |
|---|---|
| Andorra, French | 172 |
| Belgium | 675-676 |
| Cyprus | 275-277 |
| France | 1163-1164 |
| Germany | 963-964 |

Greece 862-863
Iceland 384-385
Ireland 216-217
Italy 942-943
Liechtenstein 415
Luxembourg 440-441
Monaco 639-640
Netherlands 441-442
Norway 496-497
Portugal 980-982
Switzerland 477-478
Turkey 1718-1719

| | | |
|---|---|---|
| *No. 172 (1)* | 3.00 | 3.00 |
| *Nos. 675-676 (2)* | .80 | .50 |
| *Nos. 275-277 (3)* | *4.75* | *2.75* |
| *Nos. 1163-1164 (2)* | .55 | .50 |
| *Nos. 963-964 (2)* | .50 | .55 |
| *Nos. 862-863 (2)* | 2.25 | 1.05 |
| *Nos. 384-385 (2)* | 4.50 | 3.50 |
| *Nos. 216-217 (2)* | 6.75 | 2.00 |
| *Nos. 942-943 (2)* | .50 | .50 |
| *No. 415 (1)* | .40 | .35 |
| *Nos. 440-441 (2)* | .70 | .55 |
| *Nos. 639-640 (2)* | 2.00 | .65 |
| *Nos. 441-442 (2)* | .85 | .50 |
| *Nos. 496-497 (2)* | 5.00 | 3.00 |
| *Nos. 980-982 (3)* | *9.75* | 2.25 |
| *Nos. 477-478 (2)* | 1.60 | .60 |
| *Nos. 1718-1719 (2)* | 3.35 | 1.75 |
| *Set total (34) Stamps* | 47.25 | 24.00 |

**Europa, 1967**

Cogwheels
CD10

**1967**

Andorra, French 174-175
Belgium 688-689
Cyprus 297-299
France 1178-1179
Germany 969-970
Greece 891-892
Iceland 389-390
Ireland 232-233
Italy 951-952
Liechtenstein 420
Luxembourg 449-450
Monaco 669-670
Netherlands 444-447
Norway 504-505
Portugal 994-996
Spain 1465-1466
Switzerland 482
Turkey B120-B121

| | | |
|---|---|---|
| *Nos. 174-175 (2)* | 10.75 | 6.25 |
| *Nos. 688-689 (2)* | 1.05 | .55 |
| *Nos. 297-299 (3)* | *4.25* | *2.50* |
| *Nos. 1178-1179 (2)* | .55 | .50 |
| *Nos. 969-970 (2)* | .55 | .55 |
| *Nos. 891-892 (2)* | 3.75 | 1.00 |
| *Nos. 389-390 (2)* | 3.00 | 2.00 |
| *Nos. 232-233 (2)* | 5.90 | 2.30 |
| *Nos. 951-952 (2)* | .60 | .50 |
| *No. 420 (1)* | .45 | .40 |
| *Nos. 449-450 (2)* | 1.00 | .70 |
| *Nos. 669-670 (2)* | 2.75 | .70 |
| *Nos. 444-447 (4)* | 2.70 | 2.05 |
| *Nos. 504-505 (2)* | 3.25 | 2.75 |
| *Nos. 994-996 (3)* | *9.50* | 1.85 |
| *Nos. 1465-1466 (2)* | .50 | .50 |
| *No. 482 (1)* | .70 | .25 |
| *Nos. B120-B121 (2)* | 3.50 | 2.75 |
| *Set total (38) Stamps* | 54.75 | 28.10 |

**Europa, 1968**

Golden Key with C.E.P.T. Emblem
CD11

**1968**

Andorra, French 182-183
Belgium 705-706
Cyprus 314-316
France 1209-1210
Germany 983-984
Greece 916-917
Iceland 395-396
Ireland 242-243
Italy 979-980
Liechtenstein 442
Luxembourg 466-467
Monaco 689-691
Netherlands 452-453
Portugal 1019-1021
San Marino 687
Spain 1526
Switzerland 488
Turkey 1775-1776

| | | |
|---|---|---|
| *Nos. 182-183 (2)* | 16.50 | 10.00 |
| *Nos. 705-706 (2)* | 1.25 | .50 |
| *Nos. 314-316 (3)* | *2.90* | *2.50* |
| *Nos. 1209-1210 (2)* | .85 | .55 |
| *Nos. 983-984 (2)* | .50 | .55 |
| *Nos. 916-917 (2)* | 3.75 | 1.65 |
| *Nos. 395-396 (2)* | 3.00 | 2.20 |
| *Nos. 242-243 (2)* | 3.30 | 2.25 |
| *Nos. 979-980 (2)* | .50 | .50 |
| *No. 442 (1)* | .45 | .40 |
| *Nos. 466-467 (2)* | .80 | .70 |
| *Nos. 689-691 (3)* | *5.40* | .95 |
| *Nos. 452-453 (2)* | 1.05 | .70 |
| *Nos. 1019-1021 (3)* | *9.75* | 2.10 |
| *No. 687 (1)* | .55 | .35 |
| *No. 1526 (1)* | .25 | .25 |
| *No. 488 (1)* | .45 | .25 |
| *Nos. 1775-1776 (2)* | 5.00 | 2.00 |
| *Set total (35) Stamps* | 56.25 | 28.40 |

**Europa, 1969**

"EUROPA" and "CEPT"
CD12

Tenth anniversary of C.E.P.T.

**1969**

Andorra, French 188-189
Austria 837
Belgium 718-719
Cyprus 326-328
Denmark 458
Finland 483
France 1245-1246
Germany 996-997
Great Britain 585
Greece 947-948
Iceland 406-407
Ireland 270-271
Italy 1000-1001
Liechtenstein 453
Luxembourg 475-476
Monaco 722-724
Netherlands 475-476
Norway 533-534
Portugal 1038-1040
San Marino 701-702
Spain 1567
Sweden 814-816
Switzerland 500-501
Turkey 1799-1800
Vatican 470-472
Yugoslavia 1003-1004

| | | |
|---|---|---|
| *Nos. 188-189 (2)* | 18.50 | 12.00 |
| *No. 837 (1)* | .65 | .30 |
| *Nos. 718-719 (2)* | .75 | .50 |
| *Nos. 326-328 (3)* | *3.00* | *2.25* |
| *No. 458 (1)* | .75 | .75 |
| *No. 483 (1)* | 3.50 | .75 |
| *Nos. 1245-1246 (2)* | .55 | .50 |
| *Nos. 996-997 (2)* | .80 | .50 |
| *No. 585 (1)* | .25 | .25 |
| *Nos. 947-948 (2)* | 5.00 | 1.50 |
| *Nos. 406-407 (2)* | 4.20 | 2.40 |
| *Nos. 270-271 (2)* | 3.50 | 2.00 |
| *Nos. 1000-1001 (2)* | .50 | .50 |
| *No. 453 (1)* | .45 | .45 |
| *Nos. 475-476 (2)* | .95 | .50 |
| *Nos. 722-724 (3)* | *10.50* | 2.00 |
| *Nos. 475-476 (2)* | 1.35 | 1.00 |
| *Nos. 533-534 (2)* | 3.75 | 2.35 |
| *Nos. 1038-1040 (3)* | 17.75 | 2.40 |
| *Nos. 701-702 (2)* | .90 | .90 |
| *No. 1567 (1)* | .25 | .25 |
| *Nos. 814-816 (3)* | 4.00 | 2.85 |
| *Nos. 500-501 (2)* | 1.85 | .60 |
| *Nos. 1799-1800 (2)* | 3.85 | 2.25 |
| *Nos. 470-472 (3)* | .75 | .75 |
| *Nos. 1003-1004 (2)* | 4.00 | 4.00 |
| *Set total (51) Stamps* | 92.30 | 44.50 |

**Europa, 1970**

Interwoven Threads
CD13

**1970**

Andorra, French 196-197
Belgium 741-742
Cyprus 340-342
France 1271-1272
Germany 1018-1019
Greece 985, 987
Iceland 420-421
Ireland 279-281
Italy 1013-1014
Liechtenstein 470
Luxembourg 489-490
Monaco 768-770
Netherlands 483-484
Portugal 1060-1062
San Marino 729-730
Spain 1607
Switzerland 515-516
Turkey 1848-1849
Yugoslavia 1024-1025

| | | |
|---|---|---|
| *Nos. 196-197 (2)* | 20.00 | 8.50 |
| *Nos. 741-742 (2)* | 1.10 | .55 |
| *Nos. 340-342 (3)* | *2.70* | *2.75* |
| *Nos. 1271-1272 (2)* | .65 | .50 |
| *Nos. 1018-1019 (2)* | .60 | .50 |
| *Nos. 985,987 (2)* | 7.75 | 2.00 |
| *Nos. 420-421 (2)* | 6.00 | 4.00 |
| *Nos. 279-281 (3)* | 7.50 | 2.50 |
| *Nos. 1013-1014 (2)* | .50 | .50 |
| *No. 470 (1)* | .45 | .45 |
| *Nos. 489-490 (2)* | .80 | .55 |
| *Nos. 768-770 (3)* | *6.35* | 2.10 |
| *Nos. 483-484 (2)* | 1.30 | 1.15 |
| *Nos. 1060-1062 (3)* | *9.75* | 2.35 |
| *Nos. 729-730 (2)* | .90 | .55 |
| *No. 1607 (1)* | .25 | .25 |
| *Nos. 515-516 (2)* | 1.85 | .60 |
| *Nos. 1848-1849 (2)* | 5.00 | 2.25 |
| *Nos. 1024-1025 (2)* | .80 | .80 |
| *Set total (40) Stamps* | 74.25 | 32.85 |

**Europa, 1971**

"Fraternity, Cooperation, Common Effort"
CD14

**1971**

Andorra, French 205-206
Belgium 803-804
Cyprus 365-367
Finland 504
France 1304
Germany 1064-1065
Greece 1029-1030
Iceland 429-430
Ireland 305-306
Italy 1038-1039
Liechtenstein 485
Luxembourg 500-501
Malta 425-427
Monaco 797-799
Netherlands 488-489
Portugal 1094-1096
San Marino 749-750
Spain 1675-1676
Switzerland 531-532
Turkey 1876-1877
Yugoslavia 1052-1053

| | | |
|---|---|---|
| *Nos. 205-206 (2)* | 20.00 | 7.75 |
| *Nos. 803-804 (2)* | 1.30 | .55 |
| *Nos. 365-367 (3)* | *2.60* | *3.25* |
| *No. 504 (1)* | 5.00 | .75 |
| *No. 1304 (1)* | .45 | .40 |
| *Nos. 1064-1065 (2)* | .60 | .50 |
| *Nos. 1029-1030 (2)* | 4.00 | 1.80 |
| *Nos. 429-430 (2)* | 5.00 | 3.75 |
| *Nos. 305-306 (2)* | 4.50 | 1.50 |
| *Nos. 1038-1039 (2)* | .65 | .50 |
| *No. 485 (1)* | .45 | .45 |
| *Nos. 500-501 (2)* | 1.00 | .65 |
| *Nos. 425-427 (3)* | *.80* | *.80* |
| *Nos. 797-799 (3)* | *15.00* | 2.80 |
| *Nos. 488-489 (2)* | 1.20 | .95 |
| *Nos. 1094-1096 (3)* | *9.75* | 1.75 |
| *Nos. 749-750 (2)* | .65 | .55 |
| *Nos. 1675-1676 (2)* | .75 | .55 |
| *Nos. 531-532 (2)* | 1.85 | .65 |
| *Nos. 1876-1877 (2)* | 5.60 | 2.50 |
| *Nos. 1052-1053 (2)* | .50 | .50 |
| *Set total (43) Stamps* | 81.65 | 32.90 |

**Europa, 1972**

Sparkles, Symbolic of Communications
CD15

**1972**

Andorra, French 210-211
Andorra, Spanish 62
Belgium 825-826
Cyprus 380-382
Finland 512-513
France 1341
Germany 1089-1090
Greece 1049-1050
Iceland 439-440
Ireland 316-317
Italy 1065-1066
Liechtenstein 504
Luxembourg 512-513
Malta 450-453
Monaco 831-832
Netherlands 494-495
Portugal 1141-1143
San Marino 771-772
Spain 1718
Switzerland 544-545
Turkey 1907-1908
Yugoslavia 1100-1101

| | | |
|---|---|---|
| *Nos. 210-211 (2)* | 21.00 | 7.00 |
| *No. 62 (1)* | 45.00 | 45.00 |
| *Nos. 825-826 (2)* | .95 | .55 |
| *Nos. 380-382 (3)* | *5.95* | *4.25* |
| *Nos. 512-513 (2)* | 7.00 | 1.40 |
| *No. 1341 (1)* | .50 | .35 |
| *Nos. 1089-1090 (2)* | 1.30 | .50 |
| *Nos. 1049-1050 (2)* | 2.00 | 1.55 |
| *Nos. 439-440 (2)* | 2.90 | 2.65 |
| *Nos. 316-317 (2)* | 13.00 | 4.50 |
| *Nos. 1065-1066 (2)* | .55 | .50 |
| *No. 504 (1)* | .45 | .45 |
| *Nos. 512-513 (2)* | .95 | .65 |
| *Nos. 450-453 (4)* | 1.05 | 1.40 |
| *Nos. 831-832 (2)* | 5.00 | 1.40 |
| *Nos. 494-495 (2)* | 1.20 | .90 |
| *Nos. 1141-1143 (3)* | *9.75* | 1.50 |
| *Nos. 771-772 (2)* | .70 | .50 |
| *No. 1718 (1)* | .50 | .40 |
| *Nos. 544-545 (2)* | 1.65 | .60 |
| *Nos. 1907-1908 (2)* | 7.50 | 3.00 |
| *Nos. 1100-1101 (2)* | 1.20 | 1.20 |
| *Set total (44) Stamps* | 130.10 | 80.25 |

**Europa, 1973**

Post Horn and Arrows
CD16

**1973**

Andorra, French 219-220
Andorra, Spanish 76
Belgium 839-840
Cyprus 396-398
Finland 526
France 1367
Germany 1114-1115
Greece 1090-1092
Iceland 447-448
Ireland 329-330
Italy 1108-1109
Liechtenstein 528-529
Luxembourg 523-524
Malta 469-471
Monaco 866-867
Netherlands 504-505
Norway 604-605
Portugal 1170-1172
San Marino 802-803
Spain 1753
Switzerland 580-581
Turkey 1935-1936
Yugoslavia 1138-1139

| | | |
|---|---|---|
| *Nos. 219-220 (2)* | 20.00 | 11.00 |
| *No. 76 (1)* | .65 | .55 |
| *Nos. 839-840 (2)* | 1.00 | .65 |
| *Nos. 396-398 (3)* | *4.25* | *3.85* |
| *No. 526 (1)* | 1.25 | .55 |
| *No. 1367 (1)* | 1.25 | .75 |
| *Nos. 1114-1115 (2)* | .90 | .50 |
| *Nos. 1090-1092 (3)* | 2.10 | 1.40 |
| *Nos. 447-448 (2)* | 6.65 | 3.35 |

| | | |
|---|---|---|
| *Nos. 329-330 (2)* | 5.25 | 2.00 |
| *Nos. 1108-1109 (2)* | .50 | .50 |
| *Nos. 528-529 (2)* | .60 | .60 |
| *Nos. 523-524 (2)* | .90 | .75 |
| *Nos. 469-471 (3)* | .90 | 1.20 |
| *Nos. 866-867 (2)* | 15.00 | 2.40 |
| *Nos. 504-505 (2)* | 1.20 | .95 |
| *Nos. 604-605 (2)* | 6.25 | 2.40 |
| *Nos. 1170-1172 (3)* | *13.00* | 2.15 |
| *Nos. 802-803 (2)* | *1.00* | .60 |
| *No. 1753 (1)* | .35 | .25 |
| *Nos. 580-581 (2)* | 1.55 | .60 |
| *Nos. 1935-1936 (2)* | 10.00 | 4.50 |
| *Nos. 1138-1139 (2)* | 1.15 | 1.10 |
| *Set total (46) Stamps* | 95.70 | 42.60 |

**Europa, 2000**

CD17

**2000**

| | |
|---|---|
| Albania | 2621-2622 |
| Andorra, French | 522 |
| Andorra, Spanish | 262 |
| Armenia | 610-611 |
| Austria | 1814 |
| Azerbaijan | 698-699 |
| Belarus | 350 |
| Belgium | 1818 |
| Bosnia & Herzegovina (Moslem) | 358 |
| Bosnia & Herzegovina (Serb) | 111-112 |
| Croatia | 428-429 |
| Cyprus | 959 |
| Czech Republic | 3120 |
| Denmark | 1189 |
| Estonia | 394 |
| Faroe Islands | 376 |
| Finland | 1129 |
| Aland Islands | 166 |
| France | 2771 |
| Georgia | 228-229 |
| Germany | 2086-2087 |
| Gibraltar | 837-840 |
| Great Britain (Jersey) | 935-936 |
| Great Britain (Isle of Man) | 883 |
| Greece | 1959 |
| Greenland | 363 |
| Hungary | 3699-3700 |
| Iceland | 910 |
| Ireland | 1230-1231 |
| Italy | 2349 |
| Latvia | 504 |
| Liechtenstein | 1178 |
| Lithuania | 668 |
| Luxembourg | 1035 |
| Macedonia | 187 |
| Malta | 1011-1012 |
| Moldova | 355 |
| Monaco | 2161-2162 |
| Poland | 3519 |
| Portugal | 2358 |
| Portugal (Azores) | 455 |
| Portugal (Madeira) | 208 |
| Romania | 4370 |
| Russia | 6589 |
| San Marino | 1480 |
| Slovakia | 355 |
| Slovenia | 424 |
| Spain | 3036 |
| Sweden | 2394 |
| Switzerland | 1074 |
| Turkey | 2762 |
| Turkish Rep. of Northern Cyprus | 500 |
| Ukraine | 379 |
| Vatican City | 1152 |

| | | |
|---|---|---|
| *Nos. 2621-2622 (2)* | 11.00 | 11.00 |
| *No. 522 (1)* | 2.00 | 1.00 |
| *No. 262 (1)* | 1.60 | .70 |
| *Nos. 610-611 (2)* | 4.75 | 4.75 |
| *No. 1814 (1)* | 1.40 | 1.40 |
| *Nos. 698-699 (2)* | 6.00 | 6.00 |
| *No. 350 (1)* | 1.75 | 1.75 |
| *No. 1818 (1)* | 1.40 | .60 |
| *No. 358 (1)* | 4.75 | 4.75 |
| *Nos. 111-112 (2)* | 110.00 | 110.00 |
| *Nos. 428-429 (2)* | 6.25 | 6.25 |
| *No. 959 (1)* | 2.10 | 1.40 |
| *No. 3120 (1)* | 1.20 | .40 |
| *No. 1189 (1)* | 3.50 | 2.25 |
| *No. 394 (1)* | 1.25 | 1.25 |
| *No. 376 (1)* | 2.40 | 2.40 |
| *No. 1129 (1)* | 2.00 | .60 |
| *No. 166 (1)* | 2.00 | 1.10 |
| *No. 2771 (1)* | 1.25 | .40 |
| *Nos. 2086-2087 (2)* | 4.15 | 1.90 |
| *Nos. 837-840 (4)* | 5.50 | 5.30 |
| *Nos. 935-936 (2)* | 2.40 | 2.40 |
| *No. 883 (1)* | 1.75 | 1.75 |
| *No. 363 (1)* | 1.90 | 1.90 |
| *Nos. 3699-3700 (2)* | 6.50 | 2.50 |
| *No. 910 (1)* | 1.60 | 1.60 |
| *Nos. 1230-1231 (2)* | 4.35 | 4.35 |
| *No. 2349 (1)* | 1.50 | .40 |
| *No. 504 (1)* | 5.00 | 2.40 |
| *No. 1178 (1)* | 2.25 | 1.75 |
| *No. 668 (1)* | 1.50 | 1.50 |
| *No. 1035 (1)* | 1.40 | .85 |
| *No. 187 (1)* | 3.00 | 3.00 |
| *Nos. 1011-1012 (2)* | 4.35 | 4.35 |
| *No. 355 (1)* | 3.50 | 3.50 |
| *Nos. 2161-2162 (2)* | 2.80 | 1.40 |
| *No. 3519 (1)* | 1.10 | .50 |
| *No. 2358 (1)* | 1.25 | .65 |
| *No. 455 (1)* | 1.25 | .50 |
| *No. 208 (1)* | 1.25 | .50 |
| *No. 4370 (1)* | 2.50 | 1.25 |
| *No. 6589 (1)* | 2.00 | .85 |
| *No. 1480 (1)* | 1.00 | 1.00 |
| *No. 355 (1)* | 1.25 | .55 |
| *No. 424 (1)* | 3.25 | 1.60 |
| *No. 3036 (1)* | .75 | .40 |
| *No. 2394 (1)* | 3.00 | 2.25 |
| *No. 1074 (1)* | 2.10 | .75 |
| *No. 2762 (1)* | 2.00 | 2.00 |
| *No. 500 (1)* | 2.50 | 2.50 |
| *No. 379 (1)* | 4.50 | 3.00 |
| *No. 1152 (1)* | 1.25 | 1.25 |
| *Set total (66) Stamps* | 251.00 | 218.40 |

The Gibraltar stamps are similar to the stamp illustrated, but none have the design shown above. All other sets listed above include at least one stamp with the design shown, but some include stamps with entirely different designs. Bulgaria Nos. 4131-4132, Guernsey Nos. 802-803 and Yugoslavia Nos. 2485-2486 are Europa stamps with completely different designs.

## PORTUGAL & COLONIES

**Vasco da Gama**

Fleet Departing CD20

Fleet Arriving at Calicut — CD21

Embarking at Rastello CD22

Muse of History CD23

San Gabriel, da Gama and Camoens CD24

Archangel Gabriel, the Patron Saint CD25

Flagship San Gabriel — CD26

Vasco da Gama — CD27

Fourth centenary of Vasco da Gama's discovery of the route to India.

**1898**

| | |
|---|---|
| Azores | 93-100 |
| Macao | 67-74 |
| Madeira | 37-44 |
| Portugal | 147-154 |
| Port. Africa | 1-8 |
| Port. Congo | 75-98 |
| Port. India | 189-196 |
| St. Thomas & Prince Islands | 170-193 |
| Timor | 45-52 |

| | | |
|---|---|---|
| *Nos. 93-100 (8)* | 122.00 | 76.25 |
| *Nos. 67-74 (8)* | 136.00 | 96.75 |
| *Nos. 37-44 (8)* | 44.55 | 34.00 |
| *Nos. 147-154 (8)* | 169.30 | 43.45 |
| *Nos. 1-8 (8)* | 24.75 | 21.70 |
| *Nos. 75-98 (24)* | 50.50 | 34.45 |
| *Nos. 189-196 (8)* | 20.25 | 12.95 |
| *Nos. 170-193 (24)* | 38.75 | 34.30 |
| *Nos. 45-52 (8)* | 19.50 | 8.75 |
| *Set total (104) Stamps* | 625.60 | 362.60 |

**Pombal**
**POSTAL TAX**
**POSTAL TAX DUES**

Marquis de Pombal — CD28

Planning Reconstruction of Lisbon, 1755 — CD29

Pombal Monument, Lisbon — CD30

Sebastiao Jose de Carvalho e Mello, Marquis de Pombal (1699-1782), statesman, rebuilt Lisbon after earthquake of 1755. Tax was for the erection of Pombal monument. Obligatory on all mail on certain days throughout the year. Postal Tax Dues are inscribed "Multa."

**1925**

| | |
|---|---|
| Angola | RA1-RA3, RAJ1-RAJ3 |
| Azores | RA9-RA11, RAJ2-RAJ4 |
| Cape Verde | RA1-RA3, RAJ1-RAJ3 |
| Macao | RA1-RA3, RAJ1-RAJ3 |
| Madeira | RA1-RA3, RAJ1-RAJ3 |
| Mozambique | RA1-RA3, RAJ1-RAJ3 |
| Nyassa | RA1-RA3, RAJ1-RAJ3 |
| Portugal | RA11-RA13, RAJ2-RAJ4 |
| Port. Guinea | RA1-RA3, RAJ1-RAJ3 |
| Port. India | RA1-RA3, RAJ1-RAJ3 |
| St. Thomas & Prince Islands | RA1-RA3, RAJ1-RAJ3 |
| Timor | RA1-RA3, RAJ1-RAJ3 |

| | | |
|---|---|---|
| *Nos. RA1-RA3,RAJ1-RAJ3 (6)* | 6.60 | 6.60 |
| *Nos. RA9-RA11,RAJ2-RAJ4 (6)* | 6.60 | 9.30 |
| *Nos. RA1-RA3,RAJ1-RAJ3 (6)* | 6.00 | 5.40 |
| *Nos. RA1-RA3,RAJ1-RAJ3 (6)* | 18.50 | 10.50 |
| *Nos. RA1-RA3,RAJ1-RAJ3 (6)* | 4.35 | 12.45 |
| *Nos. RA1-RA3,RAJ1-RAJ3 (6)* | 2.40 | 2.55 |
| *Nos. RA1-RA3,RAJ1-RAJ3 (6)* | 52.50 | 38.25 |
| *Nos. RA11-RA13,RAJ2-RAJ4 (6)* | 5.80 | 5.20 |
| *Nos. RA1-RA3,RAJ1-RAJ3 (6)* | 3.30 | 2.70 |
| *Nos. RA1-RA3,RAJ1-RAJ3 (6)* | 3.45 | 3.45 |
| *Nos. RA1-RA3,RAJ1-RAJ3 (6)* | 3.60 | 3.60 |
| *Nos. RA1-RA3,RAJ1-RAJ3 (6)* | 2.10 | 3.90 |
| *Set total (72) Stamps* | 115.20 | 103.90 |

Vasco da Gama CD34

Mousinho de Albuquerque CD35

Dam CD36

Prince Henry the Navigator CD37

Affonso de Albuquerque CD38

Plane over Globe CD39

**1938-39**

| | |
|---|---|
| Angola | 274-291, C1-C9 |
| Cape Verde | 234-251, C1-C9 |
| Macao | 289-305, C7-C15 |
| Mozambique | 270-287, C1-C9 |
| Port. Guinea | 233-250. C1-C9 |
| Port. India | 439-453, C1-C8 |
| St. Thomas & Prince Islands | 302-319, 323-340, C1-C18 |
| Timor | 223-239, C1-C9 |

| | | |
|---|---|---|
| *Nos. 274-291,C1-C9 (27)* | 132.90 | 22.85 |
| *Nos. 234-251,C1-C9 (27)* | 100.00 | 31.20 |
| *Nos. 289-305,C7-C15 (26)* | 701.70 | 135.60 |
| *Nos. 270-287,C1-C9 (27)* | 63.45 | 11.20 |
| *Nos. 233-250,C1-C9 (27)* | 88.05 | 30.70 |
| *Nos. 439-453,C1-C8 (23)* | 74.75 | 25.50 |
| *Nos. 302-319,323-340,C1-C18 (54)* | 319.25 | 190.35 |
| *Nos. 223-239,C1-C9 (26)* | 149.25 | 73.15 |
| *Set total (237) Stamps* | 1,629. | 520.55 |

**Lady of Fatima**

Our Lady of the Rosary, Fatima, Portugal — CD40

**1948-49**

| | |
|---|---|
| Angola | 315-318 |
| Cape Verde | 266 |
| Macao | 336 |
| Mozambique | 325-328 |
| Port. Guinea | 271 |
| Port. India | 480 |
| St. Thomas & Prince Islands | 351 |
| Timor | 254 |

| | | |
|---|---|---|
| *Nos. 315-318 (4)* | 68.00 | 17.25 |
| *No. 266 (1)* | 8.50 | 4.50 |
| *No. 336 (1)* | 40.00 | 12.00 |
| *Nos. 325-328 (4)* | 73.25 | 16.85 |
| *No. 271 (1)* | 3.25 | 3.00 |
| *No. 480 (1)* | 2.50 | 2.25 |
| *No. 351 (1)* | 7.25 | 6.50 |
| *No. 254 (1)* | 2.75 | 2.75 |
| *Set total (14) Stamps* | 205.50 | 65.10 |

A souvenir sheet of 9 stamps was issued in 1951 to mark the extension of the 1950 Holy Year. The sheet contains: Angola No. 316, Cape Verde No. 266, Macao No. 336, Mozambique No. 325, Portuguese Guinea No. 271, Portuguese India Nos. 480, 485, St. Thomas & Prince Islands No. 351, Timor No. 254. The sheet also contains a portrait of Pope Pius XII and is inscribed "Encerramento do

Ano Santo, Fatima 1951." It was sold for 11 escudos.

### Holy Year

Church Bells and Dove CD41

Angel Holding Candelabra CD42

Holy Year, 1950.

**1950-51**

Angola ....331-332
Cape Verde ....268-269
Macao ....339-340
Mozambique ....330-331
Port. Guinea ....273-274
Port. India ....490-491, 496-503
St. Thomas & Prince Islands ....353-354
Timor ....258-259

| | | |
|---|---|---|
| *Nos. 331-332 (2)* | 7.60 | 1.35 |
| *Nos. 268-269 (2)* | 4.75 | 2.20 |
| *Nos. 339-340 (2)* | 55.00 | 12.50 |
| *Nos. 330-331 (2)* | 3.00 | 1.10 |
| *Nos. 273-274 (2)* | 3.50 | 2.60 |
| *Nos. 490-491,496-503 (10)* | 12.80 | 5.40 |
| *Nos. 353-354 (2)* | 7.50 | 4.40 |
| *Nos. 258-259 (2)* | 3.75 | 3.25 |
| *Set total (24) Stamps* | 97.90 | 32.80 |

A souvenir sheet of 8 stamps was issued in 1951 to mark the extension of the Holy Year. The sheet contains: Angola No. 331, Cape Verde No. 269, Macao No. 340, Mozambique No. 331, Portuguese Guinea No. 275, Portuguese India No. 490, St. Thomas & Prince Islands No. 354, Timor No. 258, some with colors changed. The sheet contains doves and is inscribed 'Encerramento do Ano Santo, Fatima 1951.' It was sold for 17 escudos.

### Holy Year Conclusion

Our Lady of Fatima — CD43

Conclusion of Holy Year. Sheets contain alternate vertical rows of stamps and labels bearing quotation from Pope Pius XII, different for each colony.

**1951**

Angola ....357
Cape Verde ....270
Macao ....352
Mozambique ....356
Port. Guinea ....275
Port. India ....506
St. Thomas & Prince Islands ....355
Timor ....270

| | | |
|---|---|---|
| *No. 357 (1)* | 5.25 | 1.50 |
| *No. 270 (1)* | 1.50 | 1.25 |
| *No. 352 (1)* | 37.50 | 10.00 |
| *No. 356 (1)* | 2.25 | 1.00 |
| *No. 275 (1)* | 1.00 | .65 |
| *No. 506 (1)* | 1.60 | 1.00 |
| *No. 355 (1)* | 2.50 | 2.00 |
| *No. 270 (1)* | 2.00 | 1.75 |
| *Set total (8) Stamps* | 53.60 | 19.15 |

### Medical Congress

CD44

First National Congress of Tropical Medicine, Lisbon, 1952. Each stamp has a different design.

**1952**

Angola ....358
Cape Verde ....287
Macao ....364
Mozambique ....359
Port. Guinea ....276
Port. India ....516
St. Thomas & Prince Islands ....356
Timor ....271

| | | |
|---|---|---|
| *No. 358 (1)* | 1.50 | .50 |
| *No. 287 (1)* | .70 | .50 |
| *No. 364 (1)* | 9.75 | 4.25 |
| *No. 359 (1)* | 1.25 | .55 |
| *No. 276 (1)* | .45 | .35 |
| *No. 516 (1)* | 4.75 | 2.00 |
| *No. 356 (1)* | .30 | .30 |
| *No. 271 (1)* | 1.00 | 1.00 |
| *Set total (8) Stamps* | 19.70 | 9.45 |

### Postage Due Stamps

CD45

**1952**

Angola ....J37-J42
Cape Verde ....J31-J36
Macao ....J53-J58
Mozambique ....J51-J56
Port. Guinea ....J40-J45
Port. India ....J47-J52
St. Thomas & Prince Islands ....J52-J57
Timor ....J31-J36

| | | |
|---|---|---|
| *Nos. J37-J42 (6)* | 4.05 | 3.15 |
| *Nos. J31-J36 (6)* | 2.80 | 2.30 |
| *Nos. J53-J58 (6)* | 17.45 | 6.85 |
| *Nos. J51-J56 (6)* | 1.80 | 1.55 |
| *Nos. J40-J45 (6)* | 2.55 | 2.55 |
| *Nos. J47-J52 (6)* | 6.10 | 6.10 |
| *Nos. J52-J57 (6)* | 4.15 | 4.15 |
| *Nos. J31-J36 (6)* | 6.20 | 3.50 |
| *Set total (48) Stamps* | 45.10 | 30.15 |

### Sao Paulo

Father Manuel da Nobrega and View of Sao Paulo — CD46

Founding of Sao Paulo, Brazil, 400th anniv.

**1954**

Angola ....385
Cape Verde ....297
Macao ....382
Mozambique ....395
Port. Guinea ....291
Port. India ....530
St. Thomas & Prince Islands ....369
Timor ....279

| | | |
|---|---|---|
| *No. 385 (1)* | .80 | .50 |
| *No. 297 (1)* | .70 | .60 |
| *No. 382 (1)* | 14.00 | 3.00 |
| *No. 395 (1)* | .40 | .30 |
| *No. 291 (1)* | .35 | .25 |
| *No. 530 (1)* | .80 | .40 |
| *No. 369 (1)* | .80 | .60 |
| *No. 279 (1)* | .85 | .70 |
| *Set total (8) Stamps* | 18.70 | 6.35 |

### Tropical Medicine Congress

CD47

Sixth International Congress for Tropical Medicine and Malaria, Lisbon, Sept. 1958. Each stamp shows a different plant.

**1958**

Angola ....409
Cape Verde ....303
Macao ....392
Mozambique ....404
Port. Guinea ....295
Port. India ....569
St. Thomas & Prince Islands ....371
Timor ....289

| | | |
|---|---|---|
| *No. 409 (1)* | 3.50 | 1.10 |
| *No. 303 (1)* | 5.50 | 2.10 |
| *No. 392 (1)* | 8.00 | 3.00 |
| *No. 404 (1)* | 2.50 | .85 |
| *No. 295 (1)* | 2.75 | 1.10 |
| *No. 569 (1)* | 1.75 | .75 |
| *No. 371 (1)* | 2.75 | 2.25 |
| *No. 289 (1)* | 3.00 | 2.75 |
| *Set total (8) Stamps* | 29.75 | 13.90 |

### Sports

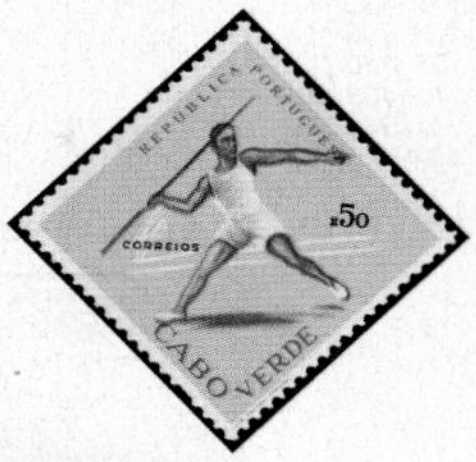


CD48

Each stamp shows a different sport.

**1962**

Angola ....433-438
Cape Verde ....320-325
Macao ....394-399
Mozambique ....424-429
Port. Guinea ....299-304
St. Thomas & Prince Islands ....374-379
Timor ....313-318

| | | |
|---|---|---|
| *Nos. 433-438 (6)* | 5.50 | 3.20 |
| *Nos. 320-325 (6)* | 15.25 | 5.20 |
| *Nos. 394-399 (6)* | 74.00 | 14.60 |
| *Nos. 424-429 (6)* | 5.70 | 2.45 |
| *Nos. 299-304 (6)* | 4.95 | 2.15 |
| *Nos. 374-379 (6)* | 6.75 | 3.20 |
| *Nos. 313-318 (6)* | 6.40 | 3.70 |
| *Set total (42) Stamps* | 118.55 | 34.50 |

### Anti-Malaria

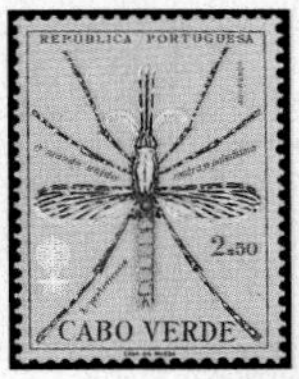


Anopheles Funestus and Malaria Eradication Symbol — CD49

World Health Organization drive to eradicate malaria.

**1962**

Angola ....439
Cape Verde ....326
Macao ....400
Mozambique ....430
Port. Guinea ....305
St. Thomas & Prince Islands ....380
Timor ....319

| | | |
|---|---|---|
| *No. 439 (1)* | 1.75 | .90 |
| *No. 326 (1)* | 1.40 | .90 |
| *No. 400 (1)* | 6.50 | 2.00 |
| *No. 430 (1)* | 1.40 | .40 |
| *No. 305 (1)* | 1.25 | .45 |
| *No. 380 (1)* | 2.00 | 1.50 |
| *No. 319 (1)* | .75 | .60 |
| *Set total (7) Stamps* | 15.05 | 6.75 |

### Airline Anniversary

Map of Africa, Super Constellation and Jet Liner — CD50

Tenth anniversary of Transportes Aereos Portugueses (TAP).

**1963**

Angola ....490
Cape Verde ....327
Mozambique ....434
Port. Guinea ....318
St. Thomas & Prince Islands ....381

| | | |
|---|---|---|
| *No. 490 (1)* | 1.00 | .35 |
| *No. 327 (1)* | 1.10 | .70 |
| *No. 434 (1)* | .40 | .25 |
| *No. 318 (1)* | .65 | .35 |
| *No. 381 (1)* | .70 | .60 |
| *Set total (5) Stamps* | 3.85 | 2.25 |

### National Overseas Bank

Antonio Teixeira de Sousa — CD51

Centenary of the National Overseas Bank of Portugal.

**1964, May 16**

Angola ....509
Cape Verde ....328
Port. Guinea ....319
St. Thomas & Prince Islands ....382
Timor ....320

| | | |
|---|---|---|
| *No. 509 (1)* | .90 | .30 |
| *No. 328 (1)* | 1.10 | .75 |
| *No. 319 (1)* | .65 | .40 |
| *No. 382 (1)* | .70 | .50 |
| *No. 320 (1)* | .75 | .60 |
| *Set total (5) Stamps* | 4.10 | 2.55 |

### ITU

ITU Emblem and the Archangel Gabriel — CD52

International Communications Union, Cent.

**1965, May 17**

Angola ....511
Cape Verde ....329
Macao ....402
Mozambique ....464
Port. Guinea ....320
St. Thomas & Prince Islands ....383
Timor ....321

| | | |
|---|---|---|
| *No. 511 (1)* | 1.25 | .65 |
| *No. 329 (1)* | 2.10 | 1.40 |
| *No. 402 (1)* | 5.00 | 2.00 |
| *No. 464 (1)* | .45 | .25 |
| *No. 320 (1)* | 1.90 | .75 |
| *No. 383 (1)* | 1.50 | 1.00 |
| *No. 321 (1)* | 1.50 | .90 |
| *Set total (7) Stamps* | 13.70 | 6.95 |

### National Revolution

CD53

40th anniv. of the National Revolution. Different buildings on each stamp.

**1966, May 28**

Angola ....525
Cape Verde ....338
Macao ....403
Mozambique ....465
Port. Guinea ....329
St. Thomas & Prince Islands ....392
Timor ....322

| | | |
|---|---|---|
| *No. 525 (1)* | .50 | .25 |
| *No. 338 (1)* | .60 | .45 |
| *No. 403 (1)* | 5.00 | 2.00 |
| *No. 465 (1)* | .50 | .30 |
| *No. 329 (1)* | .55 | .35 |
| *No. 392 (1)* | .75 | .50 |
| *No. 322 (1)* | 1.50 | .90 |
| *Set total (7) Stamps* | 9.40 | 4.75 |

### Navy Club

CD54

Centenary of Portugal's Navy Club. Each stamp has a different design.

**1967, Jan. 31**

| | |
|---|---|
| Angola | 527-528 |
| Cape Verde | 339-340 |
| Macao | 412-413 |
| Mozambique | 478-479 |
| Port. Guinea | 330-331 |
| St. Thomas & Prince Islands | 393-394 |
| Timor | 323-324 |

| | | |
|---|---|---|
| *Nos. 527-528 (2)* | 1.75 | .75 |
| *Nos. 339-340 (2)* | 2.00 | 1.40 |
| *Nos. 412-413 (2)* | 9.50 | 3.75 |
| *Nos. 478-479 (2)* | 1.40 | .65 |
| *Nos. 330-331 (2)* | 1.20 | .90 |
| *Nos. 393-394 (2)* | 3.20 | 1.25 |
| *Nos. 323-324 (2)* | 4.00 | 2.00 |
| *Set total (14) Stamps* | 23.05 | 10.70 |

### Admiral Coutinho

CD55

Centenary of the birth of Admiral Carlos Viegas Gago Coutinho (1869-1959), explorer and aviation pioneer. Each stamp has a different design.

**1969, Feb. 17**

| | |
|---|---|
| Angola | 547 |
| Cape Verde | 355 |
| Macao | 417 |
| Mozambique | 484 |
| Port. Guinea | 335 |
| St. Thomas & Prince Islands | 397 |
| Timor | 335 |

| | | |
|---|---|---|
| *No. 547 (1)* | .85 | .35 |
| *No. 355 (1)* | .35 | .25 |
| *No. 417 (1)* | 3.75 | 1.50 |
| *No. 484 (1)* | .25 | .25 |
| *No. 335 (1)* | .35 | .25 |
| *No. 397 (1)* | .50 | .35 |
| *No. 335 (1)* | 1.10 | .85 |
| *Set total (7) Stamps* | 7.15 | 3.80 |

### Administration Reform

Luiz Augusto Rebello da Silva — CD56

Centenary of the administration reforms of the overseas territories.

**1969, Sept. 25**

| | |
|---|---|
| Angola | 549 |
| Cape Verde | 357 |
| Macao | 419 |
| Mozambique | 491 |
| Port. Guinea | 337 |
| St. Thomas & Prince Islands | 399 |
| Timor | 338 |

| | | |
|---|---|---|
| *No. 549 (1)* | .35 | .25 |
| *No. 357 (1)* | .35 | .25 |
| *No. 419 (1)* | 5.00 | 1.00 |
| *No. 491 (1)* | .25 | .25 |
| *No. 337 (1)* | .25 | .25 |
| *No. 399 (1)* | .45 | .45 |
| *No. 338 (1)* | .40 | .25 |
| *Set total (7) Stamps* | 7.05 | 2.70 |

### Marshal Carmona

CD57

Birth centenary of Marshal Antonio Oscar Carmona de Fragoso (1869-1951), President of Portugal. Each stamp has a different design.

**1970, Nov. 15**

| | |
|---|---|
| Angola | 563 |
| Cape Verde | 359 |
| Macao | 422 |
| Mozambique | 493 |
| Port. Guinea | 340 |
| St. Thomas & Prince Islands | 403 |
| Timor | 341 |

| | | |
|---|---|---|
| *No. 563 (1)* | .45 | .25 |
| *No. 359 (1)* | .55 | .35 |
| *No. 422 (1)* | 2.25 | 1.25 |
| *No. 493 (1)* | .40 | .25 |
| *No. 340 (1)* | .35 | .25 |
| *No. 403 (1)* | .75 | .45 |
| *No. 341 (1)* | .25 | .25 |
| *Set total (7) Stamps* | 5.00 | 3.05 |

### Olympic Games

CD59

20th Olympic Games, Munich, Aug. 26-Sept. 11. Each stamp shows a different sport.

**1972, June 20**

| | |
|---|---|
| Angola | 569 |
| Cape Verde | 361 |
| Macao | 426 |
| Mozambique | 504 |
| Port. Guinea | 342 |
| St. Thomas & Prince Islands | 408 |
| Timor | 343 |

| | | |
|---|---|---|
| *No. 569 (1)* | .65 | .25 |
| *No. 361 (1)* | .65 | .30 |
| *No. 426 (1)* | 3.25 | 1.00 |
| *No. 504 (1)* | .30 | .25 |
| *No. 342 (1)* | .45 | .25 |
| *No. 408 (1)* | .35 | .25 |
| *No. 343 (1)* | .50 | .50 |
| *Set total (7) Stamps* | 6.15 | 2.80 |

### Lisbon-Rio de Janeiro Flight

CD60

50th anniversary of the Lisbon to Rio de Janeiro flight by Arturo de Sacadura and Coutinho, March 30-June 5, 1922. Each stamp shows a different stage of the flight.

**1972, Sept. 20**

| | |
|---|---|
| Angola | 570 |
| Cape Verde | 362 |
| Macao | 427 |
| Mozambique | 505 |
| Port. Guinea | 343 |
| St. Thomas & Prince Islands | 409 |
| Timor | 344 |

| | | |
|---|---|---|
| *No. 570 (1)* | .35 | .25 |
| *No. 362 (1)* | 1.50 | .30 |
| *No. 427 (1)* | 22.50 | 7.50 |
| *No. 505 (1)* | .25 | .25 |
| *No. 343 (1)* | .25 | .25 |
| *No. 409 (1)* | .35 | .25 |
| *No. 344 (1)* | .25 | .40 |
| *Set total (7) Stamps* | 25.45 | 9.20 |

### WMO Centenary

WMO Emblem — CD61

Centenary of international meterological cooperation.

**1973, Dec. 15**

| | |
|---|---|
| Angola | 571 |
| Cape Verde | 363 |
| Macao | 429 |
| Mozambique | 509 |
| Port. Guinea | 344 |
| St. Thomas & Prince Islands | 410 |
| Timor | 345 |

| | | |
|---|---|---|
| *No. 571 (1)* | .45 | .25 |
| *No. 363 (1)* | .65 | .30 |
| *No. 429 (1)* | 6.25 | 1.75 |
| *No. 509 (1)* | .30 | .25 |
| *No. 344 (1)* | .45 | .35 |
| *No. 410 (1)* | .60 | .50 |
| *No. 345 (1)* | 1.75 | 2.00 |
| *Set total (7) Stamps* | 10.45 | 5.40 |

### FRENCH COMMUNITY

**Upper Volta can be found under Burkina Faso in Vol. 1**

**Madagascar can be found under Malagasy in Vol. 3**

### Colonial Exposition

People of French Empire CD70

Women's Heads CD71

France Showing Way to Civilization CD72

"Colonial Commerce" CD73

International Colonial Exposition, Paris.

**1931**

| | |
|---|---|
| Cameroun | 213-216 |
| Chad | 60-63 |
| Dahomey | 97-100 |
| Fr. Guiana | 152-155 |
| Fr. Guinea | 116-119 |
| Fr. India | 100-103 |
| Fr. Polynesia | 76-79 |
| Fr. Sudan | 102-105 |
| Gabon | 120-123 |
| Guadeloupe | 138-141 |
| Indo-China | 140-142 |
| Ivory Coast | 92-95 |
| Madagascar | 169-172 |
| Martinique | 129-132 |
| Mauritania | 65-68 |
| Middle Congo | 61-64 |
| New Caledonia | 176-179 |
| Niger | 73-76 |
| Reunion | 122-125 |
| St. Pierre & Miquelon | 132-135 |
| Senegal | 138-141 |
| Somali Coast | 135-138 |
| Togo | 254-257 |
| Ubangi-Shari | 82-85 |
| Upper Volta | 66-69 |
| Wallis & Futuna Isls. | 85-88 |

| | | |
|---|---|---|
| *Nos. 213-216 (4)* | 23.00 | 18.25 |
| *Nos. 60-63 (4)* | 22.00 | 22.00 |
| *Nos. 97-100 (4)* | 26.00 | 26.00 |
| *Nos. 152-155 (4)* | 22.00 | 22.00 |
| *Nos. 116-119 (4)* | 19.75 | 19.75 |
| *Nos. 100-103 (4)* | 18.00 | *18.00* |
| *Nos. 76-79 (4)* | 30.00 | 30.00 |
| *Nos. 102-105 (4)* | 19.00 | 19.00 |
| *Nos. 120-123 (4)* | 17.50 | 17.50 |
| *Nos. 138-141 (4)* | 19.00 | 19.00 |
| *Nos. 140-142 (3)* | 12.00 | 11.50 |
| *Nos. 92-95 (4)* | 22.50 | 22.50 |
| *Nos. 169-172 (4)* | 7.90 | 5.00 |
| *Nos. 129-132 (4)* | 21.00 | 21.00 |
| *Nos. 65-68 (4)* | 22.00 | 22.00 |
| *Nos. 61-64 (4)* | 20.00 | 18.50 |
| *Nos. 176-179 (4)* | 24.00 | 24.00 |
| *Nos. 73-76 (4)* | 21.50 | 21.50 |
| *Nos. 122-125 (4)* | 22.00 | 22.00 |
| *Nos. 132-135 (4)* | 24.00 | 24.00 |
| *Nos. 138-141 (4)* | 20.00 | 20.00 |
| *Nos. 135-138 (4)* | 22.00 | 22.00 |
| *Nos. 254-257 (4)* | 22.00 | 22.00 |
| *Nos. 82-85 (4)* | 21.00 | 21.00 |
| *Nos. 66-69 (4)* | 19.00 | 19.00 |
| *Nos. 85-88 (4)* | 35.00 | 35.00 |
| *Set total (103) Stamps* | 552.15 | 542.50 |

### Paris International Exposition
### Colonial Arts Exposition

"Colonial Resources" CD74 CD77

Overseas Commerce CD75

Exposition Building and Women CD76

"France and the Empire" CD78

Cultural Treasures of the Colonies CD79

Souvenir sheets contain one imperf. stamp.

**1937**

| | |
|---|---|
| Cameroun | 217-222A |
| Dahomey | 101-107 |
| Fr. Equatorial Africa | 27-32, 73 |
| Fr. Guiana | 162-168 |
| Fr. Guinea | 120-126 |
| Fr. India | 104-110 |
| Fr. Polynesia | 117-123 |
| Fr. Sudan | 106-112 |
| Guadeloupe | 148-154 |
| Indo-China | 193-199 |
| Inini | 41 |
| Ivory Coast | 152-158 |
| Kwangchowan | 132 |
| Madagascar | 191-197 |
| Martinique | 179-185 |
| Mauritania | 69-75 |
| New Caledonia | 208-214 |
| Niger | 77-83 |
| Reunion | 167-173 |
| St. Pierre & Miquelon | 165-171 |
| Senegal | 172-178 |
| Somali Coast | 139-145 |
| Togo | 258-264 |
| Wallis & Futuna Isls. | 89 |

| | | |
|---|---|---|
| *Nos. 217-222A (7)* | 18.80 | 20.30 |
| *Nos. 101-107 (7)* | 23.60 | 27.60 |
| *Nos. 27-32, 73 (7)* | 28.10 | 32.10 |
| *Nos. 162-168 (7)* | 22.50 | 24.50 |
| *Nos. 120-126 (7)* | 24.00 | 28.00 |
| *Nos. 104-110 (7)* | 21.15 | 36.50 |
| *Nos. 117-123 (7)* | 58.50 | 75.00 |
| *Nos. 106-112 (7)* | 23.60 | 27.60 |
| *Nos. 148-154 (7)* | 19.55 | 21.05 |
| *Nos. 193-199 (7)* | 17.70 | 19.70 |
| *No. 41 (1)* | 21.00 | 27.50 |
| *Nos. 152-158 (7)* | 22.20 | 26.20 |
| *No. 132 (1)* | 9.25 | 11.00 |
| *Nos. 191-197 (7)* | 19.25 | 21.75 |
| *Nos. 179-185 (7)* | 19.95 | 21.70 |
| *Nos. 69-75 (7)* | 20.50 | 24.50 |
| *Nos. 208-214 (7)* | 39.00 | 50.50 |
| *Nos. 73-83 (11)* | 42.70 | 46.70 |
| *Nos. 167-173 (7)* | 21.70 | 23.20 |
| *Nos. 165-171 (7)* | 49.60 | 64.00 |
| *Nos. 172-178 (7)* | 21.00 | 23.80 |
| *Nos. 139-145 (7)* | 25.60 | 32.60 |
| *Nos. 258-264 (7)* | 20.40 | 20.40 |
| *No. 89 (1)* | 28.50 | 37.50 |
| *Set total (154) Stamps* | 618.15 | 743.70 |

## Curie

Pierre and Marie Curie CD80

40th anniversary of the discovery of radium. The surtax was for the benefit of the Intl. Union for the Control of Cancer.

**1938**

| | |
|---|---|
| Cameroun | B1 |
| Cuba | B1-B2 |
| Dahomey | B2 |
| France | B76 |
| Fr. Equatorial Africa | B1 |
| Fr. Guiana | B3 |
| Fr. Guinea | B2 |
| Fr. India | B6 |
| Fr. Polynesia | B5 |
| Fr. Sudan | B1 |
| Guadeloupe | B3 |
| Indo-China | B14 |
| Ivory Coast | B2 |
| Madagascar | B2 |
| Martinique | B2 |
| Mauritania | B3 |
| New Caledonia | B4 |
| Niger | B1 |
| Reunion | B4 |
| St. Pierre & Miquelon | B3 |
| Senegal | B3 |
| Somali Coast | B2 |
| Togo | B1 |

| | | |
|---|---|---|
| *No. B1 (1)* | 10.00 | 10.00 |
| *Nos. B1-B2 (2)* | 12.00 | 3.35 |
| *No. B2 (1)* | 9.50 | 9.50 |
| *No. B76 (1)* | 21.00 | 12.50 |
| *No. B1 (1)* | 24.00 | 24.00 |
| *No. B3 (1)* | 13.50 | 13.50 |
| *No. B2 (1)* | 8.75 | 8.75 |
| *No. B6 (1)* | 10.00 | 10.00 |
| *No. B5 (1)* | 20.00 | 20.00 |
| *No. B1 (1)* | 12.50 | 12.50 |
| *No. B3 (1)* | 11.00 | 10.50 |
| *No. B14 (1)* | 12.00 | 12.00 |
| *No. B2 (1)* | 11.00 | 7.50 |
| *No. B2 (1)* | 11.00 | 11.00 |
| *No. B2 (1)* | 13.00 | 13.00 |
| *No. B3 (1)* | 7.75 | 7.75 |
| *No. B4 (1)* | 16.50 | 17.50 |
| *No. B1 (1)* | 15.00 | 15.00 |
| *No. B4 (1)* | 14.00 | 14.00 |
| *No. B3 (1)* | 21.00 | 22.50 |
| *No. B3 (1)* | 10.50 | 10.50 |
| *No. B2 (1)* | 7.75 | 7.75 |
| *No. B1 (1)* | 20.00 | 20.00 |
| *Set total (24) Stamps* | 311.75 | 293.10 |

## Caillie

Rene Caillie and Map of Northwestern Africa — CD81

Death centenary of Rene Caillie (1799-1838), French explorer. All three denominations exist with colony name omitted.

**1939**

| | |
|---|---|
| Dahomey | 108-110 |
| Fr. Guinea | 161-163 |
| Fr. Sudan | 113-115 |
| Ivory Coast | 160-162 |
| Mauritania | 109-111 |
| Niger | 84-86 |
| Senegal | 188-190 |
| Togo | 265-267 |

| | | |
|---|---|---|
| *Nos. 108-110 (3)* | 1.20 | 3.60 |
| *Nos. 161-163 (3)* | 1.20 | 3.20 |
| *Nos. 113-115 (3)* | 1.20 | 3.20 |
| *Nos. 160-162 (3)* | 1.05 | 2.55 |
| *Nos. 109-111 (3)* | 1.05 | 3.80 |
| *Nos. 84-86 (3)* | 1.05 | 2.35 |
| *Nos. 188-190 (3)* | 1.05 | 2.90 |
| *Nos. 265-267 (3)* | 1.05 | 3.30 |
| *Set total (24) Stamps* | 8.85 | 24.90 |

## New York World's Fair

Natives and New York Skyline CD82

**1939**

| | |
|---|---|
| Cameroun | 223-224 |
| Dahomey | 111-112 |
| Fr. Equatorial Africa | 78-79 |
| Fr. Guiana | 169-170 |
| Fr. Guinea | 164-165 |
| Fr. India | 111-112 |
| Fr. Polynesia | 124-125 |
| Fr. Sudan | 116-117 |
| Guadeloupe | 155-156 |
| Indo-China | 203-204 |
| Inini | 42-43 |
| Ivory Coast | 163-164 |
| Kwangchowan | 133-134 |
| Madagascar | 209-210 |
| Martinique | 186-187 |
| Mauritania | 112-113 |
| New Caledonia | 215-216 |
| Niger | 87-88 |
| Reunion | 174-175 |
| St. Pierre & Miquelon | 205-206 |
| Senegal | 191-192 |
| Somali Coast | 179-180 |
| Togo | 268-269 |
| Wallis & Futuna Isls. | 90-91 |

| | | |
|---|---|---|
| *Nos. 223-224 (2)* | 2.80 | 2.40 |
| *Nos. 111-112 (2)* | 1.60 | 3.20 |
| *Nos. 78-79 (2)* | 1.60 | 3.20 |
| *Nos. 169-170 (2)* | 2.60 | 2.60 |
| *Nos. 164-165 (2)* | 1.60 | 3.20 |
| *Nos. 111-112 (2)* | 3.00 | *8.00* |
| *Nos. 124-125 (2)* | 4.80 | 4.80 |
| *Nos. 116-117 (2)* | 1.60 | 3.20 |
| *Nos. 155-156 (2)* | 2.50 | 2.50 |
| *Nos. 203-204 (2)* | 2.05 | 2.05 |
| *Nos. 42-43 (2)* | 7.50 | 9.00 |
| *Nos. 163-164 (2)* | 1.50 | 3.00 |
| *Nos. 133-134 (2)* | 2.50 | 2.50 |
| *Nos. 209-210 (2)* | 1.50 | 2.50 |
| *Nos. 186-187 (2)* | 2.35 | 2.35 |
| *Nos. 112-113 (2)* | 1.40 | 2.80 |
| *Nos. 215-216 (2)* | 3.35 | 3.35 |
| *Nos. 87-88 (2)* | 1.40 | 2.80 |
| *Nos. 174-175 (2)* | 2.80 | 2.80 |
| *Nos. 205-206 (2)* | 4.80 | 6.00 |
| *Nos. 191-192 (2)* | 1.40 | 2.80 |
| *Nos. 179-180 (2)* | 1.40 | 2.80 |
| *Nos. 268-269 (2)* | 1.40 | 2.80 |
| *Nos. 90-91 (2)* | 6.00 | 6.00 |
| *Set total (48) Stamps* | 63.45 | 86.65 |

## French Revolution

Storming of the Bastille CD83

French Revolution, 150th anniv. The surtax was for the defense of the colonies.

**1939**

| | |
|---|---|
| Cameroun | B2-B6 |
| Dahomey | B3-B7 |
| Fr. Equatorial Africa | B4-B8, CB1 |
| Fr. Guiana | B4-B8, CB1 |
| Fr. Guinea | B3-B7 |
| Fr. India | B7-B11 |
| Fr. Polynesia | B6-B10, CB1 |
| Fr. Sudan | B2-B6 |
| Guadeloupe | B4-B8 |
| Indo-China | B15-B19, CB1 |
| Inini | B1-B5 |
| Ivory Coast | B3-B7 |
| Kwangchowan | B1-B5 |
| Madagascar | B3-B7, CB1 |
| Martinique | B3-B7 |
| Mauritania | B4-B8 |
| New Caledonia | B5-B9, CB1 |
| Niger | B2-B6 |
| Reunion | B5-B9, CB1 |
| St. Pierre & Miquelon | B4-B8 |
| Senegal | B4-B8, CB1 |
| Somali Coast | B3-B7 |
| Togo | B2-B6 |
| Wallis & Futuna Isls. | B1-B5 |

| | | |
|---|---|---|
| *Nos. B2-B6 (5)* | 60.00 | 60.00 |
| *Nos. B3-B7 (5)* | 47.50 | 47.50 |
| *Nos. B4-B8,CB1 (6)* | 120.00 | 120.00 |
| *Nos. B4-B8,CB1 (6)* | 79.50 | 79.50 |
| *Nos. B3-B7 (5)* | 47.50 | 47.50 |
| *Nos. B7-B11 (5)* | 28.75 | *32.50* |
| *Nos. B6-B10,CB1 (6)* | 122.50 | 122.50 |
| *Nos. B2-B6 (5)* | 50.00 | 50.00 |
| *Nos. B4-B8 (5)* | 50.00 | 50.00 |
| *Nos. B15-B19,CB1 (6)* | 85.00 | 85.00 |
| *Nos. B1-B5 (5)* | 80.00 | 100.00 |
| *Nos. B3-B7 (5)* | 43.75 | 43.75 |
| *Nos. B1-B5 (5)* | 46.25 | 46.25 |
| *Nos. B3-B7,CB1 (6)* | 65.50 | 65.50 |
| *Nos. B3-B7 (5)* | 52.50 | 52.50 |
| *Nos. B4-B8 (5)* | 42.50 | 42.50 |
| *Nos. B5-B9,CB1 (6)* | 101.50 | 101.50 |
| *Nos. B2-B6 (5)* | 60.00 | 60.00 |
| *Nos. B5-B9,CB1 (6)* | 87.50 | 87.50 |
| *Nos. B4-B8 (5)* | 67.50 | 72.50 |
| *Nos. B4-B8,CB1 (6)* | 56.50 | 56.50 |
| *Nos. B3-B7 (5)* | 45.00 | 45.00 |
| *Nos. B2-B6 (5)* | 42.50 | 42.50 |
| *Nos. B1-B5 (5)* | 95.00 | 95.00 |
| *Set total (128) Stamps* | 1,577. | 1,606. |

Plane over Coastal Area CD85

All five denominations exist with colony name omitted.

**1940**

| | |
|---|---|
| Dahomey | C1-C5 |
| Fr. Guinea | C1-C5 |
| Fr. Sudan | C1-C5 |
| Ivory Coast | C1-C5 |
| Mauritania | C1-C5 |
| Niger | C1-C5 |
| Senegal | C12-C16 |
| Togo | C1-C5 |

| | | |
|---|---|---|
| *Nos. C1-C5 (5)* | 4.00 | 4.00 |
| *Nos. C1-C5 (5)* | 4.00 | 4.00 |
| *Nos. C1-C5 (5)* | 4.00 | 4.00 |
| *Nos. C1-C5 (5)* | 3.80 | 3.80 |
| *Nos. C1-C5 (5)* | 3.50 | 3.50 |
| *Nos. C1-C5 (5)* | 3.50 | 3.50 |
| *Nos. C12-C16 (5)* | 3.50 | 3.50 |
| *Nos. C1-C5 (5)* | 3.15 | 3.15 |
| *Set total (40) Stamps* | 29.45 | 29.45 |

## Defense of the Empire

Colonial Infantryman — CD86

**1941**

| | |
|---|---|
| Cameroun | B13B |
| Dahomey | B13 |
| Fr. Equatorial Africa | B8B |
| Fr. Guiana | B10 |
| Fr. Guinea | B13 |
| Fr. India | B13 |
| Fr. Polynesia | B12 |
| Fr. Sudan | B12 |
| Guadeloupe | B10 |
| Indo-China | B19B |
| Inini | B7 |
| Ivory Coast | B13 |
| Kwangchowan | B7 |
| Madagascar | B9 |
| Martinique | B9 |
| Mauritania | B14 |
| New Caledonia | B11 |
| Niger | B12 |
| Reunion | B11 |
| St. Pierre & Miquelon | B8B |
| Senegal | B14 |
| Somali Coast | B9 |
| Togo | B10B |
| Wallis & Futuna Isls. | B7 |

| | |
|---|---|
| *No. B13B (1)* | 1.60 |
| *No. B13 (1)* | 1.20 |
| *No. B8B (1)* | 3.50 |
| *No. B10 (1)* | 1.40 |
| *No. B13 (1)* | 1.40 |
| *No. B13 (1)* | 1.25 |
| *No. B12 (1)* | 3.50 |
| *No. B12 (1)* | 1.40 |
| *No. B10 (1)* | 1.00 |
| *No. B19B (1)* | 1.60 |
| *No. B7 (1)* | 1.75 |
| *No. B13 (1)* | 1.25 |
| *No. B7 (1)* | .85 |
| *No. B9 (1)* | 1.50 |
| *No. B9 (1)* | 1.40 |
| *No. B14 (1)* | .95 |
| *No. B12 (1)* | 1.40 |
| *No. B11 (1)* | 1.60 |
| *No. B8B (1)* | 4.50 |
| *No. B14 (1)* | 1.25 |
| *No. B9 (1)* | 1.60 |
| *No. B10B (1)* | 1.10 |
| *No. B7 (1)* | 2.40 |
| *Set total (23) Stamps* | 39.40 |

Each of the CD86 stamps listed above is part of a set of three stamps. The designs of the other two stamps in the set vary from country to country. Only the values of the Common Design stamps are listed here.

## Colonial Education Fund

CD86a

**1942**

| | |
|---|---|
| Cameroun | CB3 |
| Dahomey | CB4 |
| Fr. Equatorial Africa | CB5 |
| Fr. Guiana | CB4 |
| Fr. Guinea | CB4 |
| Fr. India | CB3 |
| Fr. Polynesia | CB4 |
| Fr. Sudan | CB4 |
| Guadeloupe | CB3 |
| Indo-China | CB5 |
| Inini | CB3 |
| Ivory Coast | CB4 |
| Kwangchowan | CB4 |
| Malagasy | CB5 |
| Martinique | CB3 |
| Mauritania | CB4 |
| New Caledonia | CB4 |
| Niger | CB4 |
| Reunion | CB4 |
| St. Pierre & Miquelon | CB3 |
| Senegal | CB5 |
| Somali Coast | CB3 |
| Togo | CB3 |
| Wallis & Futuna | CB3 |

| | | |
|---|---|---|
| *No. CB3 (1)* | 1.10 | |
| *No. CB4 (1)* | .80 | 5.50 |
| *No. CB5 (1)* | .80 | |
| *No. CB4 (1)* | 1.10 | |
| *No. CB4 (1)* | .40 | 5.50 |
| *No. CB3 (1)* | .90 | |
| *No. CB4 (1)* | 2.00 | |
| *No. CB4 (1)* | .40 | 5.50 |
| *No. CB3 (1)* | 1.10 | |
| *No. CB5 (1)* | 1.10 | |
| *No. CB3 (1)* | 1.25 | |
| *No. CB4 (1)* | 1.00 | 5.50 |
| *No. CB4 (1)* | 1.00 | |
| *No. CB5 (1)* | .65 | |
| *No. CB3 (1)* | 1.00 | |
| *No. CB4 (1)* | .80 | |
| *No. CB4 (1)* | 2.25 | |
| *No. CB4 (1)* | .35 | |
| *No. CB4 (1)* | .90 | |
| *No. CB3 (1)* | 7.00 | |
| *No. CB5 (1)* | .80 | 6.50 |
| *No. CB3 (1)* | .70 | |
| *No. CB3 (1)* | .35 | |
| *No. CB3 (1)* | 2.25 | |
| *Set total (24) Stamps* | 30.00 | 28.50 |

Cross of Lorraine & Four-motor Plane CD87

**1941-5**

| | |
|---|---|
| Cameroun | C1-C7 |
| Fr. Equatorial Africa | C17-C23 |
| Fr. Guiana | C9-C10 |
| Fr. India | C1-C6 |
| Fr. Polynesia | C3-C9 |
| Fr. West Africa | C1-C3 |
| Guadeloupe | C1-C2 |
| Madagascar | C37-C43 |

| | |
|---|---|
| Martinique | C1-C2 |
| New Caledonia | C7-C13 |
| Reunion | C18-C24 |
| St. Pierre & Miquelon | C1-C7 |
| Somali Coast | C1-C7 |

| | | |
|---|---|---|
| *Nos. C1-C7 (7)* | 6.30 | 6.30 |
| *Nos. C17-C23 (7)* | 10.40 | 6.35 |
| *Nos. C9-C10 (2)* | 3.80 | 3.10 |
| *Nos. C1-C6 (6)* | 9.30 | *15.00* |
| *Nos. C3-C9 (7)* | 13.75 | 10.00 |
| *Nos. C1-C3 (3)* | 9.50 | 3.90 |
| *Nos. C1-C2 (2)* | 3.75 | 2.50 |
| *Nos. C37-C43 (7)* | 5.60 | 3.80 |
| *Nos. C1-C2 (2)* | 3.00 | 1.60 |
| *Nos. C7-C13 (7)* | 8.85 | 7.30 |
| *Nos. C18-C24 (7)* | 7.05 | 5.00 |
| *Nos. C1-C7 (7)* | 11.60 | 9.40 |
| *Nos. C1-C7 (7)* | 13.95 | 11.10 |
| *Set total (71) Stamps* | 106.85 | 85.35 |

Somali Coast stamps are inscribed "Djibouti".

Transport Plane CD88

Caravan and Plane CD89

**1942**

| | |
|---|---|
| Dahomey | C6-C13 |
| Fr. Guinea | C6-C13 |
| Fr. Sudan | C6-C13 |
| Ivory Coast | C6-C13 |
| Mauritania | C6-C13 |
| Niger | C6-C13 |
| Senegal | C17-C25 |
| Togo | C6-C13 |

| | |
|---|---|
| *Nos. C6-C13 (8)* | 7.15 |
| *Nos. C6-C13 (8)* | 5.75 |
| *Nos. C6-C13 (8)* | 8.00 |
| *Nos. C6-C13 (8)* | 11.15 |
| *Nos. C6-C13 (8)* | 9.75 |
| *Nos. C6-C13 (8)* | 6.90 |
| *Nos. C17-C25 (9)* | 9.45 |
| *Nos. C6-C13 (8)* | 6.75 |
| *Set total (65) Stamps* | 64.90 |

### Red Cross

Marianne CD90

The surtax was for the French Red Cross and national relief.

**1944**

| | |
|---|---|
| Cameroun | B28 |
| Fr. Equatorial Africa | B38 |
| Fr. Guiana | B12 |
| Fr. India | B14 |
| Fr. Polynesia | B13 |
| Fr. West Africa | B1 |
| Guadeloupe | B12 |
| Madagascar | B15 |
| Martinique | B11 |
| New Caledonia | B13 |
| Reunion | B15 |
| St. Pierre & Miquelon | B13 |
| Somali Coast | B13 |
| Wallis & Futuna Isls. | B9 |

| | | |
|---|---|---|
| *No. B28 (1)* | 2.00 | 1.60 |
| *No. B38 (1)* | 1.60 | 1.20 |
| *No. B12 (1)* | 1.75 | 1.25 |
| *No. B14 (1)* | 1.50 | 1.25 |
| *No. B13 (1)* | 2.00 | 1.60 |
| *No. B1 (1)* | 6.50 | 4.75 |
| *No. B12 (1)* | 1.40 | 1.00 |
| *No. B15 (1)* | .90 | .90 |
| *No. B11 (1)* | 1.20 | 1.20 |
| *No. B13 (1)* | 1.50 | 1.50 |
| *No. B15 (1)* | 1.60 | 1.10 |
| *No. B13 (1)* | 2.40 | 2.40 |
| *No. B13 (1)* | 1.75 | 2.00 |
| *No. B9 (1)* | 4.50 | 3.25 |
| *Set total (14) Stamps* | 30.60 | 25.00 |

### Eboue

CD91

Felix Eboue, first French colonial administrator to proclaim resistance to Germany after French surrender in World War II.

**1945**

| | |
|---|---|
| Cameroun | 296-297 |
| Fr. Equatorial Africa | 156-157 |
| Fr. Guiana | 171-172 |
| Fr. India | 210-211 |
| Fr. Polynesia | 150-151 |
| Fr. West Africa | 15-16 |
| Guadeloupe | 187-188 |
| Madagascar | 259-260 |
| Martinique | 196-197 |
| New Caledonia | 274-275 |
| Reunion | 238-239 |
| St. Pierre & Miquelon | 322-323 |
| Somali Coast | 238-239 |

| | | |
|---|---|---|
| *Nos. 296-297 (2)* | 2.40 | 1.95 |
| *Nos. 156-157 (2)* | 2.55 | 2.00 |
| *Nos. 171-172 (2)* | 2.45 | 2.00 |
| *Nos. 210-211 (2)* | 2.20 | 1.95 |
| *Nos. 150-151 (2)* | 3.60 | 2.85 |
| *Nos. 15-16 (2)* | 2.40 | 2.40 |
| *Nos. 187-188 (2)* | 2.05 | 1.60 |
| *Nos. 259-260 (2)* | 2.00 | 1.45 |
| *Nos. 196-197 (2)* | 2.05 | 1.55 |
| *Nos. 274-275 (2)* | 3.40 | 3.00 |
| *Nos. 238-239 (2)* | 2.40 | 2.00 |
| *Nos. 322-323 (2)* | 4.40 | 3.45 |
| *Nos. 238-239 (2)* | 2.45 | 2.10 |
| *Set total (26) Stamps* | 34.35 | 28.30 |

### Victory

Victory — CD92

European victory of the Allied Nations in World War II.

**1946, May 8**

| | |
|---|---|
| Cameroun | C8 |
| Fr. Equatorial Africa | C24 |
| Fr. Guiana | C11 |
| Fr. India | C7 |
| Fr. Polynesia | C10 |
| Fr. West Africa | C4 |
| Guadeloupe | C3 |
| Indo-China | C19 |
| Madagascar | C44 |
| Martinique | C3 |
| New Caledonia | C14 |
| Reunion | C25 |
| St. Pierre & Miquelon | C8 |
| Somali Coast | C8 |
| Wallis & Futuna Isls. | C1 |

| | | |
|---|---|---|
| *No. C8 (1)* | 1.60 | 1.20 |
| *No. C24 (1)* | 1.60 | 1.25 |
| *No. C11 (1)* | 1.75 | 1.25 |
| *No. C7 (1)* | 1.00 | 4.00 |
| *No. C10 (1)* | 2.75 | 2.00 |
| *No. C4 (1)* | 1.60 | 1.20 |
| *No. C3 (1)* | 1.25 | 1.00 |
| *No. C19 (1)* | 1.00 | .55 |
| *No. C44 (1)* | 1.00 | .35 |
| *No. C3 (1)* | 1.30 | 1.00 |
| *No. C14 (1)* | 1.50 | 1.25 |
| *No. C25 (1)* | 1.10 | .90 |
| *No. C8 (1)* | 2.10 | 2.10 |
| *No. C8 (1)* | 1.75 | 1.40 |
| *No. C1 (1)* | 2.50 | 1.90 |
| *Set total (15) Stamps* | 23.80 | 21.35 |

### Chad to Rhine

Leclerc's Departure from Chad — CD93

Battle at Cufra Oasis — CD94

Tanks in Action, Mareth — CD95

Normandy Invasion — CD96

Entering Paris — CD97

Liberation of Strasbourg — CD98

"Chad to the Rhine" march, 1942-44, by Gen. Jacques Leclerc's column, later French 2nd Armored Division.

**1946, June 6**

| | |
|---|---|
| Cameroun | C9-C14 |
| Fr. Equatorial Africa | C25-C30 |
| Fr. Guiana | C12-C17 |
| Fr. India | C8-C13 |
| Fr. Polynesia | C11-C16 |
| Fr. West Africa | C5-C10 |
| Guadeloupe | C4-C9 |
| Indo-China | C20-C25 |
| Madagascar | C45-C50 |
| Martinique | C4-C9 |
| New Caledonia | C15-C20 |
| Reunion | C26-C31 |
| St. Pierre & Miquelon | C9-C14 |
| Somali Coast | C9-C14 |
| Wallis & Futuna Isls. | C2-C7 |

| | | |
|---|---|---|
| *Nos. C9-C14 (6)* | 12.05 | 9.70 |
| *Nos. C25-C30 (6)* | 14.70 | 10.80 |
| *Nos. C12-C17 (6)* | 12.65 | 10.35 |
| *Nos. C8-C13 (6)* | 12.80 | *15.00* |
| *Nos. C11-C16 (6)* | 17.55 | 13.40 |
| *Nos. C5-C10 (6)* | 16.05 | 11.95 |
| *Nos. C4-C9 (6)* | 12.00 | 9.60 |
| *Nos. C20-C25 (6)* | 6.40 | 6.40 |
| *Nos. C45-C50 (6)* | 10.30 | 8.40 |
| *Nos. C4-C9 (6)* | 8.85 | 7.30 |
| *Nos. C15-C20 (6)* | 13.40 | 11.90 |
| *Nos. C26-C31 (6)* | 10.25 | 6.55 |
| *Nos. C9-C14 (6)* | 17.30 | 14.35 |
| *Nos. C9-C14 (6)* | 18.10 | 12.65 |
| *Nos. C2-C7 (6)* | 13.75 | 10.45 |
| *Set total (90) Stamps* | 196.15 | 158.80 |

### UPU

French Colonials, Globe and Plane — CD99

Universal Postal Union, 75th anniv.

**1949, July 4**

| | |
|---|---|
| Cameroun | C29 |
| Fr. Equatorial Africa | C34 |
| Fr. India | C17 |
| Fr. Polynesia | C20 |
| Fr. West Africa | C15 |
| Indo-China | C26 |
| Madagascar | C55 |
| New Caledonia | C24 |
| St. Pierre & Miquelon | C18 |
| Somali Coast | C18 |
| Togo | C18 |
| Wallis & Futuna Isls. | C10 |

| | | |
|---|---|---|
| *No. C29 (1)* | 8.00 | 4.75 |
| *No. C34 (1)* | 16.00 | 12.00 |
| *No. C17 (1)* | 11.50 | 8.75 |
| *No. C20 (1)* | 20.00 | 15.00 |
| *No. C15 (1)* | 12.00 | 8.75 |
| *No. C26 (1)* | 4.75 | 4.00 |
| *No. C55 (1)* | 4.00 | 2.75 |
| *No. C24 (1)* | 7.50 | 5.00 |
| *No. C18 (1)* | 20.00 | 12.00 |
| *No. C18 (1)* | 14.00 | 10.50 |
| *No. C18 (1)* | 8.50 | 7.00 |
| *No. C10 (1)* | 12.50 | 8.25 |
| *Set total (12) Stamps* | 138.75 | 98.75 |

### Tropical Medicine

Doctor Treating Infant CD100

The surtax was for charitable work.

**1950**

| | |
|---|---|
| Cameroun | B29 |
| Fr. Equatorial Africa | B39 |
| Fr. India | B15 |
| Fr. Polynesia | B14 |
| Fr. West Africa | B3 |
| Madagascar | B17 |
| New Caledonia | B14 |
| St. Pierre & Miquelon | B14 |
| Somali Coast | B14 |
| Togo | B11 |

| | | |
|---|---|---|
| *No. B29 (1)* | 7.25 | 5.50 |
| *No. B39 (1)* | 7.25 | 5.50 |
| *No. B15 (1)* | 6.00 | 4.00 |
| *No. B14 (1)* | 10.50 | 8.00 |
| *No. B3 (1)* | 9.50 | 7.25 |
| *No. B17 (1)* | 5.50 | 5.50 |
| *No. B14 (1)* | 6.75 | 5.25 |
| *No. B14 (1)* | 14.00 | 13.00 |
| *No. B14 (1)* | 7.75 | 6.25 |
| *No. B11 (1)* | 5.00 | 3.50 |
| *Set total (10) Stamps* | 79.50 | 63.75 |

### Military Medal

Medal, Early Marine and Colonial Soldier — CD101

Centenary of the creation of the French Military Medal.

**1952**

| | |
|---|---|
| Cameroun | 322 |
| Comoro Isls. | 39 |
| Fr. Equatorial Africa | 186 |

Fr. India ....................................233
Fr. Polynesia.................................179
Fr. West Africa ...............................57
Madagascar...................................286
New Caledonia...............................295
St. Pierre & Miquelon.....................345
Somali Coast.................................267
Togo..........................................327
Wallis & Futuna Isls. ......................149

| | | |
|---|---|---|
| *No. 322 (1)* | 7.25 | 3.25 |
| *No. 39 (1)* | 50.00 | 40.00 |
| *No. 186 (1)* | 8.00 | 5.50 |
| *No. 233 (1)* | 5.50 | 7.00 |
| *No. 179 (1)* | 13.50 | 10.00 |
| *No. 57 (1)* | 8.75 | 6.50 |
| *No. 286 (1)* | 3.75 | 2.50 |
| *No. 295 (1)* | 6.50 | 6.00 |
| *No. 345 (1)* | 12.00 | 12.00 |
| *No. 267 (1)* | 9.00 | 8.00 |
| *No. 327 (1)* | 5.50 | 4.75 |
| *No. 149 (1)* | 9.50 | 7.00 |
| *Set total (12) Stamps* | 139.25 | 112.50 |

### Liberation

Allied Landing, Victory Sign and Cross of Lorraine — CD102

Liberation of France, 10th anniv.

**1954, June 6**

Cameroun.....................................C32
Comoro Isls. ..................................C4
Fr. Equatorial Africa ......................C38
Fr. India ....................................C18
Fr. Polynesia.................................C22
Fr. West Africa .............................C17
Madagascar..................................C57
New Caledonia...............................C25
St. Pierre & Miquelon.....................C19
Somali Coast.................................C19
Togo..........................................C19
Wallis & Futuna Isls. .....................C11

| | | |
|---|---|---|
| *No. C32 (1)* | 7.25 | 4.75 |
| *No. C4 (1)* | 35.00 | 20.00 |
| *No. C38 (1)* | 12.00 | 8.00 |
| *No. C18 (1)* | 11.00 | 8.00 |
| *No. C22 (1)* | 10.00 | 8.00 |
| *No. C17 (1)* | 12.00 | 5.50 |
| *No. C57 (1)* | 3.25 | 2.00 |
| *No. C25 (1)* | 7.50 | 5.00 |
| *No. C19 (1)* | 20.00 | 12.00 |
| *No. C19 (1)* | 10.50 | 8.50 |
| *No. C19 (1)* | 7.00 | 5.50 |
| *No. C11 (1)* | 12.50 | 8.25 |
| *Set total (12) Stamps* | 148.00 | 95.50 |

### FIDES

Plowmen CD103

Efforts of FIDES, the Economic and Social Development Fund for Overseas Possessions (Fonds d' Investissement pour le Developpement Economique et Social). Each stamp has a different design.

**1956**

Cameroun...............................326-329
Comoro Isls. ..................................43
Fr. Equatorial Africa ................189-192
Fr. Polynesia.................................181
Fr. West Africa ............................65-72
Madagascar............................292-295
New Caledonia...............................303
St. Pierre & Miquelon.....................350
Somali Coast..........................268-269
Togo..........................................331

| | | |
|---|---|---|
| *Nos. 326-329 (4)* | 6.90 | 3.20 |
| *No. 43 (1)* | 2.25 | 1.60 |
| *Nos. 189-192 (4)* | 3.20 | 1.65 |
| *No. 181 (1)* | 4.00 | 2.00 |
| *Nos. 65-72 (8)* | 16.00 | 6.35 |
| *Nos. 292-295 (4)* | 2.25 | 1.20 |
| *No. 303 (1)* | 1.90 | 1.10 |
| *No. 350 (1)* | 5.50 | 3.50 |
| *Nos. 268-269 (2)* | 5.35 | 3.15 |
| *No. 331 (1)* | 4.25 | 2.10 |
| *Set total (27) Stamps* | 51.60 | 25.85 |

### Flower

CD104

Each stamp shows a different flower.

**1958-9**

Cameroun.....................................333
Comoro Isls. ..................................45
Fr. Equatorial Africa ................200-201
Fr. Polynesia.................................192
Fr. So. & Antarctic Terr. ...................11
Fr. West Africa ............................79-83
Madagascar............................301-302
New Caledonia........................304-305
St. Pierre & Miquelon.....................357
Somali Coast.................................270
Togo.....................................348-349
Wallis & Futuna Isls. ......................152

| | | |
|---|---|---|
| *No. 333 (1)* | 1.60 | .80 |
| *No. 45 (1)* | 5.50 | 4.50 |
| *Nos. 200-201 (2)* | 3.60 | 1.60 |
| *No. 192 (1)* | 6.50 | 4.00 |
| *No. 11 (1)* | 8.75 | 7.50 |
| *Nos. 79-83 (5)* | 10.45 | 5.60 |
| *Nos. 301-302 (2)* | 1.60 | .60 |
| *Nos. 304-305 (2)* | 8.00 | 3.00 |
| *No. 357 (1)* | 4.25 | 2.10 |
| *No. 270 (1)* | 4.25 | 1.40 |
| *Nos. 348-349 (2)* | 1.10 | .50 |
| *No. 152 (1)* | 4.50 | 2.50 |
| *Set total (20) Stamps* | 60.10 | 34.10 |

### Human Rights

Sun, Dove and U.N. Emblem CD105

10th anniversary of the signing of the Universal Declaration of Human Rights.

**1958**

Comoro Isls. ..................................44
Fr. Equatorial Africa ......................202
Fr. Polynesia.................................191
Fr. West Africa ...............................85
Madagascar...................................300
New Caledonia...............................306
St. Pierre & Miquelon.....................356
Somali Coast.................................274
Wallis & Futuna Isls. ......................153

| | | |
|---|---|---|
| *No. 44 (1)* | 11.00 | 11.00 |
| *No. 202 (1)* | 2.40 | 1.25 |
| *No. 191 (1)* | 13.00 | 8.75 |
| *No. 85 (1)* | 2.40 | 2.00 |
| *No. 300 (1)* | .80 | .40 |
| *No. 306 (1)* | 2.00 | 1.50 |
| *No. 356 (1)* | 3.50 | 2.50 |
| *No. 274 (1)* | 3.50 | 2.10 |
| *No. 153 (1)* | 5.75 | 4.00 |
| *Set total (9) Stamps* | 44.35 | 33.50 |

### C.C.T.A.

CD106

Commission for Technical Cooperation in Africa south of the Sahara, 10th anniv.

**1960**

Cameroun.....................................339
Cent. Africa ....................................3
Chad............................................66
Congo, P.R. ...................................90
Dahomey ....................................138
Gabon.........................................150
Ivory Coast ..................................180
Madagascar...................................317
Mali...............................................9
Mauritania....................................117
Niger...........................................104
Upper Volta.....................................89

| | | |
|---|---|---|
| *No. 339 (1)* | 1.60 | .75 |
| *No. 3 (1)* | 1.90 | .65 |
| *No. 66 (1)* | 1.90 | .50 |
| *No. 90 (1)* | 1.00 | 1.00 |
| *No. 138 (1)* | .50 | .25 |
| *No. 150 (1)* | 1.40 | 1.10 |
| *No. 180 (1)* | 1.10 | .50 |
| *No. 317 (1)* | .60 | .30 |
| *No. 9 (1)* | 1.20 | .50 |
| *No. 117 (1)* | .75 | .40 |
| *No. 104 (1)* | .85 | .45 |
| *No. 89 (1)* | .65 | .40 |
| *Set total (12) Stamps* | 13.45 | 6.80 |

### Air Afrique, 1961

Modern and Ancient Africa, Map and Planes — CD107

Founding of Air Afrique (African Airlines).

**1961-62**

Cameroun.....................................C37
Cent. Africa ...................................C5
Chad............................................C7
Congo, P.R. ...................................C5
Dahomey ....................................C17
Gabon..........................................C5
Ivory Coast ..................................C18
Mauritania....................................C17
Niger...........................................C22
Senegal ......................................C31
Upper Volta.....................................C4

| | | |
|---|---|---|
| *No. C37 (1)* | 1.00 | .50 |
| *No. C5 (1)* | 1.00 | .55 |
| *No. C7 (1)* | 1.00 | .25 |
| *No. C5 (1)* | 1.75 | .90 |
| *No. C17 (1)* | .80 | .40 |
| *No. C5 (1)* | 11.00 | 6.00 |
| *No. C18 (1)* | 2.00 | 1.25 |
| *No. C17 (1)* | 2.50 | 1.25 |
| *No. C22 (1)* | 1.75 | .90 |
| *No. C31 (1)* | .80 | .30 |
| *No. C4 (1)* | 3.50 | 1.75 |
| *Set total (11) Stamps* | 27.10 | 14.05 |

### Anti-Malaria

CD108

World Health Organization drive to eradicate malaria.

**1962, Apr. 7**

Cameroun.....................................B36
Cent. Africa ...................................B1
Chad............................................B1
Comoro Isls. ...................................B1
Congo, P.R. ...................................B3
Dahomey ....................................B15
Gabon..........................................B4
Ivory Coast ..................................B15
Madagascar...................................B19
Mali..............................................B1
Mauritania....................................B16
Niger...........................................B14
Senegal ......................................B16
Somali Coast.................................B15
Upper Volta.....................................B1

| | | |
|---|---|---|
| *No. B36 (1)* | 1.00 | .45 |
| *No. B1 (1)* | 1.40 | 1.40 |
| *No. B1 (1)* | 1.25 | .50 |
| *No. B1 (1)* | 4.00 | 4.00 |
| *No. B3 (1)* | 1.40 | 1.00 |
| *No. B15 (1)* | .75 | .75 |
| *No. B4 (1)* | 1.00 | 1.00 |
| *No. B15 (1)* | 1.25 | 1.25 |
| *No. B19 (1)* | .75 | .50 |
| *No. B1 (1)* | 1.25 | .60 |
| *No. B16 (1)* | .80 | .80 |
| *No. B14 (1)* | .60 | .60 |
| *No. B16 (1)* | 1.10 | .65 |
| *No. B15 (1)* | 7.00 | 7.00 |
| *No. B1 (1)* | .75 | .70 |
| *Set total (15) Stamps* | 24.30 | 21.20 |

### Abidjan Games

CD109

Abidjan Games, Ivory Coast, Dec. 24-31, 1961. Each stamp shows a different sport.

**1962**

Cent. Africa ...........................19-20, C6
Chad.....................................83-84, C8
Congo, P.R. .........................103-104, C7
Gabon..................................163-164, C6
Niger.......................................109-111
Upper Volta...............................103-105

| | | |
|---|---|---|
| *Nos. 19-20,C6 (3)* | 3.90 | 2.60 |
| *Nos. 83-84,C8 (3)* | 6.30 | 1.55 |
| *Nos. 103-104,C7 (3)* | 3.85 | 1.80 |
| *Nos. 163-164,C6 (3)* | 5.00 | 3.00 |
| *Nos. 109-111 (3)* | 2.60 | 1.10 |
| *Nos. 103-105 (3)* | 2.80 | 1.75 |
| *Set total (18) Stamps* | 24.45 | 11.80 |

### African and Malagasy Union

Flag of Union CD110

First anniversary of the Union.

**1962, Sept. 8**

Cameroun.....................................373
Cent. Africa ...................................21
Chad............................................85
Congo, P.R. ..................................105
Dahomey ....................................155
Gabon.........................................165
Ivory Coast ..................................198
Madagascar...................................332
Mauritania....................................170
Niger...........................................112
Senegal ......................................211
Upper Volta....................................106

| | | |
|---|---|---|
| *No. 373 (1)* | 2.00 | .75 |
| *No. 21 (1)* | 1.25 | .60 |
| *No. 85 (1)* | 1.25 | .25 |
| *No. 105 (1)* | 1.50 | .50 |
| *No. 155 (1)* | 1.25 | .90 |
| *No. 165 (1)* | 1.60 | 1.25 |
| *No. 198 (1)* | 2.10 | .75 |
| *No. 332 (1)* | .80 | .80 |
| *No. 170 (1)* | .75 | .50 |
| *No. 112 (1)* | .80 | .40 |
| *No. 211 (1)* | .80 | .50 |
| *No. 106 (1)* | 1.10 | .75 |
| *Set total (12) Stamps* | 15.20 | 7.95 |

### Telstar

Telstar and Globe Showing Andover and Pleumeur-Bodou — CD111

First television connection of the United States and Europe through the Telstar satellite, July 11-12, 1962.

**1962-63**

Andorra, French ............................154
Comoro Isls. ..................................C7
Fr. Polynesia.................................C29
Fr. So. & Antarctic Terr. ...................C5
New Caledonia...............................C33
St. Pierre & Miquelon.....................C26
Somali Coast.................................C31
Wallis & Futuna Isls. .....................C17

| | | |
|---|---|---|
| *No. 154 (1)* | 2.00 | 1.60 |
| *No. C7 (1)* | 5.00 | 3.00 |
| *No. C29 (1)* | 11.50 | 8.00 |

| | | |
|---|---|---|
| *No. C5 (1)* | 29.00 | 21.00 |
| *No. C33 (1)* | 25.00 | 18.50 |
| *No. C26 (1)* | 6.00 | 4.50 |
| *No. C31 (1)* | 1.00 | 1.00 |
| *No. C17 (1)* | 3.50 | 3.50 |
| *Set total (8) Stamps* | 83.00 | 61.10 |

### Freedom From Hunger

World Map and Wheat Emblem CD112

U.N. Food and Agriculture Organization's "Freedom from Hunger" campaign.

**1963, Mar. 21**

| | |
|---|---|
| Cameroun | B37-B38 |
| Cent. Africa | B2 |
| Chad | B2 |
| Congo, P.R. | B4 |
| Dahomey | B16 |
| Gabon | B5 |
| Ivory Coast | B16 |
| Madagascar | B21 |
| Mauritania | B17 |
| Niger | B15 |
| Senegal | B17 |
| Upper Volta | B2 |

| | | |
|---|---|---|
| *Nos. B37-B38 (2)* | 2.25 | .75 |
| *No. B2 (1)* | 1.25 | 1.25 |
| *No. B2 (1)* | 2.00 | .50 |
| *No. B4 (1)* | 1.40 | 1.00 |
| *No. B16 (1)* | .80 | .80 |
| *No. B5 (1)* | 1.00 | 1.00 |
| *No. B16 (1)* | 1.50 | 1.50 |
| *No. B21 (1)* | .60 | .45 |
| *No. B17 (1)* | .80 | .80 |
| *No. B15 (1)* | .60 | .60 |
| *No. B17 (1)* | .80 | .50 |
| *No. B2 (1)* | .75 | .70 |
| *Set total (13) Stamps* | 13.75 | 9.85 |

### Red Cross Centenary

CD113

Centenary of the International Red Cross.

**1963, Sept. 2**

| | |
|---|---|
| Comoro Isls. | 55 |
| Fr. Polynesia | 205 |
| New Caledonia | 328 |
| St. Pierre & Miquelon | 367 |
| Somali Coast | 297 |
| Wallis & Futuna Isls. | 165 |

| | | |
|---|---|---|
| *No. 55 (1)* | 9.50 | 7.00 |
| *No. 205 (1)* | 15.00 | 12.00 |
| *No. 328 (1)* | 8.00 | 6.75 |
| *No. 367 (1)* | 12.00 | 5.50 |
| *No. 297 (1)* | 6.25 | 6.25 |
| *No. 165 (1)* | 4.00 | 3.50 |
| *Set total (6) Stamps* | 54.75 | 41.00 |

### African Postal Union, 1963

UAMPT Emblem, Radio Masts, Plane and Mail CD114

Establishment of the African and Malagasy Posts and Telecommunications Union.

**1963, Sept. 8**

| | |
|---|---|
| Cameroun | C47 |
| Cent. Africa | C10 |
| Chad | C9 |
| Congo, P.R. | C13 |
| Dahomey | C19 |
| Gabon | C13 |
| Ivory Coast | C25 |
| Madagascar | C75 |
| Mauritania | C22 |
| Niger | C27 |
| Rwanda | 36 |
| Senegal | C32 |
| Upper Volta | C9 |

| | | |
|---|---|---|
| *No. C47 (1)* | 2.25 | 1.00 |
| *No. C10 (1)* | 1.90 | .85 |
| *No. C9 (1)* | 2.40 | .60 |
| *No. C13 (1)* | 1.40 | .75 |
| *No. C19 (1)* | .75 | .25 |
| *No. C13 (1)* | 1.90 | .80 |
| *No. C25 (1)* | 2.50 | 1.50 |
| *No. C75 (1)* | 1.25 | .80 |
| *No. C22 (1)* | 1.50 | .60 |
| *No. C27 (1)* | 1.25 | .60 |
| *No. 36 (1)* | 1.00 | .75 |
| *No. C32 (1)* | 1.75 | .50 |
| *No. C9 (1)* | 1.50 | .75 |
| *Set total (13) Stamps* | 21.35 | 9.75 |

### Air Afrique, 1963

Symbols of Flight — CD115

First anniversary of Air Afrique and inauguration of DC-8 service.

**1963, Nov. 19**

| | |
|---|---|
| Cameroun | C48 |
| Chad | C10 |
| Congo, P.R. | C14 |
| Gabon | C18 |
| Ivory Coast | C26 |
| Mauritania | C26 |
| Niger | C35 |
| Senegal | C33 |

| | | |
|---|---|---|
| *No. C48 (1)* | 1.25 | .40 |
| *No. C10 (1)* | 2.40 | .60 |
| *No. C14 (1)* | 1.60 | .60 |
| *No. C18 (1)* | 1.40 | .65 |
| *No. C26 (1)* | 1.00 | .50 |
| *No. C26 (1)* | .70 | .25 |
| *No. C35 (1)* | .90 | .50 |
| *No. C33 (1)* | 2.00 | .65 |
| *Set total (8) Stamps* | 11.25 | 4.15 |

### Europafrica

Europe and Africa Linked — CD116

Signing of an economic agreement between the European Economic Community and the African and Malagasy Union, Yaounde, Cameroun, July 20, 1963.

**1963-64**

| | |
|---|---|
| Cameroun | 402 |
| Cent. Africa | C12 |
| Chad | C11 |
| Congo, P.R. | C16 |
| Gabon | C19 |
| Ivory Coast | 217 |
| Niger | C43 |
| Upper Volta | C11 |

| | | |
|---|---|---|
| *No. 402 (1)* | 2.25 | .60 |
| *No. C12 (1)* | 2.50 | 1.75 |
| *No. C11 (1)* | 2.00 | .50 |
| *No. C16 (1)* | 1.60 | 1.00 |
| *No. C19 (1)* | 1.40 | .75 |
| *No. 217 (1)* | 1.10 | .35 |
| *No. C43 (1)* | .85 | .50 |
| *No. C11 (1)* | 1.50 | .80 |
| *Set total (8) Stamps* | 13.20 | 6.25 |

### Human Rights

Scales of Justice and Globe CD117

15th anniversary of the Universal Declaration of Human Rights.

**1963, Dec. 10**

| | |
|---|---|
| Comoro Isls. | 56 |
| Fr. Polynesia | 206 |
| New Caledonia | 329 |
| St. Pierre & Miquelon | 368 |
| Somali Coast | 300 |
| Wallis & Futuna Isls. | 166 |

| | | |
|---|---|---|
| *No. 56 (1)* | 9.50 | 7.50 |
| *No. 205 (1)* | 15.00 | 12.00 |
| *No. 329 (1)* | 7.00 | 6.00 |
| *No. 368 (1)* | 7.00 | 3.50 |
| *No. 300 (1)* | 8.50 | 8.50 |
| *No. 166 (1)* | 8.00 | 7.50 |
| *Set total (6) Stamps* | 55.00 | 45.00 |

### PHILATEC

Stamp Album, Champs Elysees Palace and Horses of Marly CD118

Intl. Philatelic and Postal Techniques Exhibition, Paris, June 5-21, 1964.

**1963-64**

| | |
|---|---|
| Comoro Isls. | 60 |
| France | 1078 |
| Fr. Polynesia | 207 |
| New Caledonia | 341 |
| St. Pierre & Miquelon | 369 |
| Somali Coast | 301 |
| Wallis & Futuna Isls. | 167 |

| | | |
|---|---|---|
| *No. 60 (1)* | 4.50 | 4.00 |
| *No. 1078 (1)* | .25 | .25 |
| *No. 206 (1)* | 15.00 | 10.00 |
| *No. 341 (1)* | 6.50 | 6.50 |
| *No. 369 (1)* | 11.00 | 8.00 |
| *No. 301 (1)* | 7.75 | 7.75 |
| *No. 167 (1)* | 3.50 | 3.50 |
| *Set total (7) Stamps* | 48.50 | 40.00 |

### Cooperation

CD119

Cooperation between France and the French-speaking countries of Africa and Madagascar.

**1964**

| | |
|---|---|
| Cameroun | 409-410 |
| Cent. Africa | 39 |
| Chad | 103 |
| Congo, P.R. | 121 |
| Dahomey | 193 |
| France | 1111 |
| Gabon | 175 |
| Ivory Coast | 221 |
| Madagascar | 360 |
| Mauritania | 181 |
| Niger | 143 |
| Senegal | 236 |
| Togo | 495 |

| | | |
|---|---|---|
| *Nos. 409-410 (2)* | 2.50 | .50 |
| *No. 39 (1)* | 1.00 | .55 |
| *No. 103 (1)* | 1.00 | .25 |
| *No. 121 (1)* | .80 | .35 |
| *No. 193 (1)* | .80 | .35 |
| *No. 1111 (1)* | .25 | .25 |
| *No. 175 (1)* | .90 | .60 |
| *No. 221 (1)* | 1.10 | .35 |
| *No. 360 (1)* | .60 | .25 |
| *No. 181 (1)* | .60 | .35 |
| *No. 143 (1)* | .80 | .40 |
| *No. 236 (1)* | 1.60 | .85 |
| *No. 495 (1)* | .70 | .25 |
| *Set total (14) Stamps* | 12.65 | 5.30 |

### ITU

Telegraph, Syncom Satellite and ITU Emblem CD120

Intl. Telecommunication Union, Cent.

**1965, May 17**

| | |
|---|---|
| Comoro Isls. | C14 |
| Fr. Polynesia | C33 |
| Fr. So. & Antarctic Terr. | C8 |
| New Caledonia | C40 |
| New Hebrides | 124-125 |
| St. Pierre & Miquelon | C29 |
| Somali Coast | C36 |
| Wallis & Futuna Isls. | C20 |

| | | |
|---|---|---|
| *No. C14 (1)* | 20.00 | 10.00 |
| *No. C33 (1)* | 80.00 | 52.50 |
| *No. C8 (1)* | 200.00 | 160.00 |
| *No. C40 (1)* | 10.00 | 8.00 |
| *Nos. 124-125 (2)* | 40.50 | 34.00 |
| *No. C29 (1)* | 20.00 | 10.00 |
| *No. C36 (1)* | 15.00 | 9.00 |
| *No. C20 (1)* | 21.00 | 15.00 |
| *Set total (9) Stamps* | 406.50 | 298.50 |

### French Satellite A-1

Diamant Rocket and Launching Installation — CD121

Launching of France's first satellite, Nov. 26, 1965.

**1965-66**

| | |
|---|---|
| Comoro Isls. | C16a |
| France | 1138a |
| Reunion | 359a |
| Fr. Polynesia | C41a |
| Fr. So. & Antarctic Terr. | C10a |
| New Caledonia | C45a |
| St. Pierre & Miquelon | C31a |
| Somali Coast | C40a |
| Wallis & Futuna Isls. | C23a |

| | | |
|---|---|---|
| *No. C16a (1)* | 11.00 | 11.00 |
| *No. 1138a (1)* | .65 | .65 |
| *No. 359a (1)* | 3.50 | 3.00 |
| *No. C41a (1)* | 14.00 | 14.00 |
| *No. C10a (1)* | 29.00 | 24.00 |
| *No. C45a (1)* | 7.00 | 7.00 |
| *No. C31a (1)* | 12.50 | 12.50 |
| *No. C40a (1)* | 7.00 | 7.00 |
| *No. C23a (1)* | 9.25 | 9.25 |
| *Set total (9) Stamps* | 93.90 | 88.40 |

### French Satellite D-1

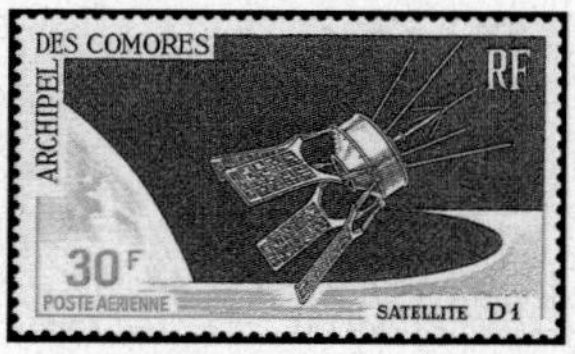


D-1 Satellite in Orbit — CD122

Launching of the D-1 satellite at Hammaguir, Algeria, Feb. 17, 1966.

**1966**

| | |
|---|---|
| Comoro Isls. | C17 |
| France | 1148 |

Fr. Polynesia ........ C42
Fr. So. & Antarctic Terr. ........ C11
New Caledonia ........ C46
St. Pierre & Miquelon ........ C32
Somali Coast ........ C49
Wallis & Futuna Isls. ........ C24

| | | |
|---|---|---|
| *No. C17 (1)* | 4.00 | 4.00 |
| *No. 1148 (1)* | .25 | .25 |
| *No. C42 (1)* | 7.00 | 4.75 |
| *No. C11 (1)* | 57.50 | 40.00 |
| *No. C46 (1)* | 2.25 | 2.00 |
| *No. C32 (1)* | 8.00 | 6.00 |
| *No. C49 (1)* | 4.25 | 2.75 |
| *No. C24 (1)* | 3.50 | 3.50 |
| *Set total (8) Stamps* | 86.75 | 63.25 |

### Air Afrique, 1966

Planes and Air Afrique Emblem — CD123

Introduction of DC-8F planes by Air Afrique.

**1966**

Cameroun ........ C79
Cent. Africa ........ C35
Chad ........ C26
Congo, P.R. ........ C42
Dahomey ........ C42
Gabon ........ C47
Ivory Coast ........ C32
Mauritania ........ C57
Niger ........ C63
Senegal ........ C47
Togo ........ C54
Upper Volta ........ C31

| | | |
|---|---|---|
| *No. C79 (1)* | .80 | .25 |
| *No. C35 (1)* | 1.00 | .40 |
| *No. C26 (1)* | 1.00 | .25 |
| *No. C42 (1)* | 1.00 | .25 |
| *No. C42 (1)* | .75 | .25 |
| *No. C47 (1)* | .90 | .35 |
| *No. C32 (1)* | 1.00 | .60 |
| *No. C57 (1)* | .80 | .30 |
| *No. C63 (1)* | .65 | .35 |
| *No. C47 (1)* | .80 | .30 |
| *No. C54 (1)* | .80 | .25 |
| *No. C31 (1)* | .75 | .50 |
| *Set total (12) Stamps* | 10.25 | 4.05 |

### African Postal Union, 1967

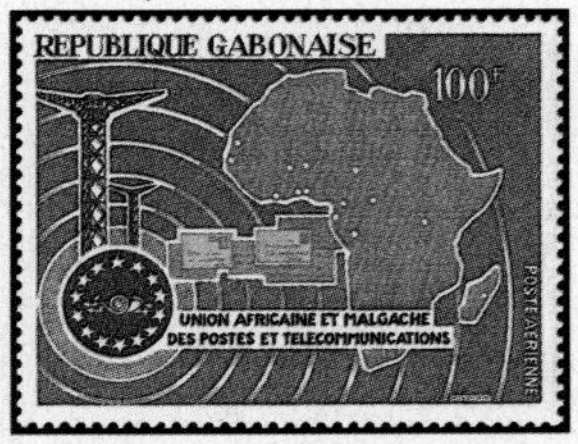


Telecommunications Symbols and Map of Africa — CD124

Fifth anniversary of the establishment of the African and Malagasy Union of Posts and Telecommunications, UAMPT.

**1967**

Cameroun ........ C90
Cent. Africa ........ C46
Chad ........ C37
Congo, P.R. ........ C57
Dahomey ........ C61
Gabon ........ C58
Ivory Coast ........ C34
Madagascar ........ C85
Mauritania ........ C65
Niger ........ C75
Rwanda ........ C1-C3
Senegal ........ C60
Togo ........ C81
Upper Volta ........ C50

| | | |
|---|---|---|
| *No. C90 (1)* | 2.40 | .65 |
| *No. C46 (1)* | 2.25 | .85 |
| *No. C37 (1)* | 2.00 | .60 |
| *No. C57 (1)* | 1.60 | .60 |
| *No. C61 (1)* | 1.75 | .95 |
| *No. C58 (1)* | 2.25 | .95 |
| *No. C34 (1)* | 3.50 | 1.50 |
| *No. C85 (1)* | 1.25 | .60 |
| *No. C65 (1)* | 1.25 | .60 |
| *No. C75 (1)* | 1.40 | .60 |
| *Nos. C1-C3 (3)* | 2.30 | 1.25 |
| *No. C60 (1)* | 1.75 | .50 |
| *No. C81 (1)* | 1.90 | .30 |
| *No. C50 (1)* | 1.80 | .70 |
| *Set total (16) Stamps* | 27.40 | 10.65 |

### Monetary Union

Gold Token of the Ashantis, 17-18th Centuries — CD125

West African Monetary Union, 5th anniv.

**1967, Nov. 4**

Dahomey ........ 244
Ivory Coast ........ 259
Mauritania ........ 238
Niger ........ 204
Senegal ........ 294
Togo ........ 623
Upper Volta ........ 181

| | | |
|---|---|---|
| *No. 244 (1)* | .65 | .65 |
| *No. 259 (1)* | .85 | .40 |
| *No. 238 (1)* | .45 | .25 |
| *No. 204 (1)* | .45 | .25 |
| *No. 294 (1)* | .60 | .25 |
| *No. 623 (1)* | .60 | .25 |
| *No. 181 (1)* | .65 | .35 |
| *Set total (7) Stamps* | 4.25 | 2.40 |

### WHO Anniversary

Sun, Flowers and WHO Emblem CD126

World Health Organization, 20th anniv.

**1968, May 4**

Afars & Issas ........ 317
Comoro Isls. ........ 73
Fr. Polynesia ........ 241-242
Fr. So. & Antarctic Terr. ........ 31
New Caledonia ........ 367
St. Pierre & Miquelon ........ 377
Wallis & Futuna Isls. ........ 169

| | | |
|---|---|---|
| *No. 317 (1)* | 3.00 | 3.00 |
| *No. 73 (1)* | 2.75 | 2.00 |
| *Nos. 241-242 (2)* | 22.00 | 12.75 |
| *No. 31 (1)* | 62.50 | 47.50 |
| *No. 367 (1)* | 4.00 | 2.25 |
| *No. 377 (1)* | 10.00 | 8.00 |
| *No. 169 (1)* | 6.50 | 4.50 |
| *Set total (8) Stamps* | 110.75 | 80.00 |

### Human Rights Year

Human Rights Flame — CD127

**1968, Aug. 10**

Afars & Issas ........ 322-323
Comoro Isls. ........ 76
Fr. Polynesia ........ 243-244
Fr. So. & Antarctic Terr. ........ 32
New Caledonia ........ 369
St. Pierre & Miquelon ........ 382
Wallis & Futuna Isls. ........ 170

| | | |
|---|---|---|
| *Nos. 322-323 (2)* | 6.75 | 4.00 |
| *No. 76 (1)* | 3.50 | 3.50 |
| *Nos. 243-244 (2)* | 24.00 | 14.00 |
| *No. 32 (1)* | 55.00 | 47.50 |
| *No. 369 (1)* | 2.75 | 1.50 |
| *No. 382 (1)* | 8.00 | 5.50 |
| *No. 170 (1)* | 3.75 | 3.75 |
| *Set total (9) Stamps* | 103.75 | 79.75 |

### 2nd PHILEXAFRIQUE

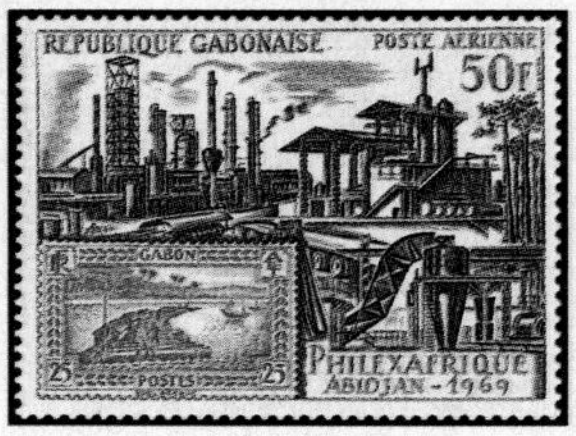


CD128

Opening of PHILEXAFRIQUE, Abidjan, Feb. 14. Each stamp shows a local scene and stamp.

**1969, Feb. 14**

Cameroun ........ C118
Cent. Africa ........ C65
Chad ........ C48
Congo, P.R. ........ C77
Dahomey ........ C94
Gabon ........ C82
Ivory Coast ........ C38-C40
Madagascar ........ C92
Mali ........ C65
Mauritania ........ C80
Niger ........ C104
Senegal ........ C68
Togo ........ C104
Upper Volta ........ C62

| | | |
|---|---|---|
| *No. C118 (1)* | 3.25 | 1.25 |
| *No. C65 (1)* | 1.90 | 1.90 |
| *No. C48 (1)* | 2.40 | 1.00 |
| *No. C77 (1)* | 2.00 | 1.75 |
| *No. C94 (1)* | 2.25 | 2.25 |
| *No. C82 (1)* | 2.25 | 2.25 |
| *Nos. C38-C40 (3)* | 14.50 | 14.50 |
| *No. C92 (1)* | 1.75 | .85 |
| *No. C65 (1)* | 1.75 | 1.00 |
| *No. C80 (1)* | 1.90 | .75 |
| *No. C104 (1)* | 2.75 | 1.90 |
| *No. C68 (1)* | 2.00 | 1.40 |
| *No. C104 (1)* | 2.25 | .45 |
| *No. C62 (1)* | 4.00 | 3.25 |
| *Set total (16) Stamps* | 44.95 | 34.50 |

### Concorde

Concorde in Flight CD129

First flight of the prototype Concorde supersonic plane at Toulouse, Mar. 1, 1969.

**1969**

Afars & Issas ........ C56
Comoro Isls. ........ C29
France ........ C42
Fr. Polynesia ........ C50
Fr. So. & Antarctic Terr. ........ C18
New Caledonia ........ C63
St. Pierre & Miquelon ........ C40
Wallis & Futuna Isls. ........ C30

| | | |
|---|---|---|
| *No. C56 (1)* | 26.00 | 16.00 |
| *No. C29 (1)* | 24.00 | 16.00 |
| *No. C42 (1)* | .75 | .35 |
| *No. C50 (1)* | 55.00 | 35.00 |
| *No. C18 (1)* | 55.00 | 37.50 |
| *No. C63 (1)* | 27.50 | 20.00 |
| *No. C40 (1)* | 30.00 | 11.00 |
| *No. C30 (1)* | 15.00 | 10.00 |
| *Set total (8) Stamps* | 233.25 | 145.85 |

### Development Bank

Bank Emblem — CD130

African Development Bank, fifth anniv.

**1969**

Cameroun ........ 499
Chad ........ 217
Congo, P.R. ........ 181-182
Ivory Coast ........ 281
Mali ........ 127-128
Mauritania ........ 267
Niger ........ 220
Senegal ........ 317-318
Upper Volta ........ 201

| | | |
|---|---|---|
| *No. 499 (1)* | .80 | .25 |
| *No. 217 (1)* | .70 | .25 |
| *Nos. 181-182 (2)* | .80 | .50 |
| *No. 281 (1)* | .70 | .40 |
| *Nos. 127-128 (2)* | 1.00 | .50 |
| *No. 267 (1)* | .60 | .25 |
| *No. 220 (1)* | .60 | .30 |
| *Nos. 317-318 (2)* | 1.55 | .50 |
| *No. 201 (1)* | .65 | .30 |
| *Set total (12) Stamps* | 7.40 | 3.25 |

### ILO

ILO Headquarters, Geneva, and Emblem — CD131

Intl. Labor Organization, 50th anniv.

**1969-70**

Afars & Issas ........ 337
Comoro Isls. ........ 83
Fr. Polynesia ........ 251-252
Fr. So. & Antarctic Terr. ........ 35
New Caledonia ........ 379
St. Pierre & Miquelon ........ 396
Wallis & Futuna Isls. ........ 172

| | | |
|---|---|---|
| *No. 337 (1)* | 2.75 | 2.00 |
| *No. 83 (1)* | 1.25 | .75 |
| *Nos. 251-252 (2)* | 24.00 | 12.50 |
| *No. 35 (1)* | 15.00 | 10.00 |
| *No. 379 (1)* | 2.25 | 1.10 |
| *No. 396 (1)* | 8.50 | 5.50 |
| *No. 172 (1)* | 3.00 | 2.90 |
| *Set total (8) Stamps* | 56.75 | 34.75 |

### ASECNA

Map of Africa, Plane and Airport CD132

10th anniversary of the Agency for the Security of Aerial Navigation in Africa and Madagascar (ASECNA, Agence pour la Securite de la Navigation Aerienne en Afrique et a Madagascar).

**1969-70**

Cameroun ........ 500
Cent. Africa ........ 119
Chad ........ 222
Congo, P.R. ........ 197
Dahomey ........ 269
Gabon ........ 260
Ivory Coast ........ 287
Mali ........ 130
Niger ........ 221
Senegal ........ 321
Upper Volta ........ 204

| | | |
|---|---|---|
| *No. 500 (1)* | 2.00 | .60 |
| *No. 119 (1)* | 2.25 | .80 |
| *No. 222 (1)* | 1.00 | .25 |
| *No. 197 (1)* | 2.00 | .40 |
| *No. 269 (1)* | .90 | .55 |
| *No. 260 (1)* | 1.75 | .75 |
| *No. 287 (1)* | .90 | .40 |
| *No. 130 (1)* | .90 | .40 |
| *No. 221 (1)* | 1.25 | .70 |
| *No. 321 (1)* | 1.60 | .50 |
| *No. 204 (1)* | 1.75 | 1.00 |
| *Set total (11) Stamps* | 16.30 | 6.35 |

### U.P.U. Headquarters

CD133

New Universal Postal Union headquarters, Bern, Switzerland.

### 1970

Afars & Issas ........ 342
Algeria ........ 443
Cameroun ........ 503-504
Cent. Africa ........ 125
Chad ........ 225
Comoro Isls. ........ 84
Congo, P.R. ........ 216
Fr. Polynesia ........ 261-262
Fr. So. & Antarctic Terr. ........ 36
Gabon ........ 258
Ivory Coast ........ 295
Madagascar ........ 444
Mali ........ 134-135
Mauritania ........ 283
New Caledonia ........ 382
Niger ........ 231-232
St. Pierre & Miquelon ........ 397-398
Senegal ........ 328-329
Tunisia ........ 535
Wallis & Futuna Isls. ........ 173

| | | |
|---|---|---|
| *No. 342 (1)* | 2.50 | 1.40 |
| *No. 443 (1)* | 1.10 | .40 |
| *Nos. 503-504 (2)* | 2.60 | .55 |
| *No. 125 (1)* | 1.90 | .70 |
| *No. 225 (1)* | 1.00 | .25 |
| *No. 84 (1)* | 5.50 | 2.00 |
| *No. 216 (1)* | .80 | .25 |
| *Nos. 261-262 (2)* | 20.00 | 10.00 |
| *No. 36 (1)* | 40.00 | 27.50 |
| *No. 258 (1)* | .90 | .55 |
| *No. 295 (1)* | 1.10 | .50 |
| *No. 444 (1)* | .55 | .25 |
| *Nos. 134-135 (2)* | 1.05 | .50 |
| *No. 283 (1)* | .60 | .30 |
| *No. 382 (1)* | 3.00 | 1.50 |
| *Nos. 231-232 (2)* | 1.20 | .60 |
| *Nos. 397-398 (2)* | 28.00 | 17.00 |
| *Nos. 328-329 (2)* | 1.55 | .55 |
| *No. 535 (1)* | .60 | .25 |
| *No. 173 (1)* | 4.00 | 4.00 |
| *Set total (26) Stamps* | 117.95 | 69.05 |

#### De Gaulle

CD134

First anniversary of the death of Charles de Gaulle, (1890-1970), President of France.

### 1971-72

Afars & Issas ........ 356-357
Comoro Isls. ........ 104-105
France ........ 1325a
Fr. Polynesia ........ 270-271
Fr. So. & Antarctic Terr. ........ 52-53
New Caledonia ........ 393-394
Reunion ........ 380a
St. Pierre & Miquelon ........ 417-418
Wallis & Futuna Isls. ........ 177-178

| | | |
|---|---|---|
| *Nos. 356-357 (2)* | 12.50 | 7.50 |
| *Nos. 104-105 (2)* | 9.00 | 5.75 |
| *No. 1325a (1)* | 3.00 | 2.50 |
| *Nos. 270-271 (2)* | 51.50 | 29.50 |
| *Nos. 52-53 (2)* | 40.00 | 29.50 |
| *Nos. 393-394 (2)* | 23.00 | 11.75 |
| *No. 380a (1)* | 9.25 | 8.00 |
| *Nos. 417-418 (2)* | 40.00 | 30.00 |
| *Nos. 177-178 (2)* | 24.00 | 16.25 |
| *Set total (16) Stamps* | 212.25 | 140.75 |

#### African Postal Union, 1971

UAMPT Building, Brazzaville, Congo — CD135

10th anniversary of the establishment of the African and Malagasy Posts and Telecommunications Union, UAMPT. Each stamp has a different native design.

### 1971, Nov. 13

Cameroun ........ C177
Cent. Africa ........ C89
Chad ........ C94
Congo, P.R. ........ C136
Dahomey ........ C146
Gabon ........ C120
Ivory Coast ........ C47
Mauritania ........ C113
Niger ........ C164
Rwanda ........ C8
Senegal ........ C105
Togo ........ C166
Upper Volta ........ C97

| | | |
|---|---|---|
| *No. C177 (1)* | 2.00 | .50 |
| *No. C89 (1)* | 2.25 | .85 |
| *No. C94 (1)* | 1.50 | .50 |
| *No. C136 (1)* | 1.60 | .75 |
| *No. C146 (1)* | 1.75 | .80 |
| *No. C120 (1)* | 1.75 | .70 |
| *No. C47 (1)* | 2.00 | 1.00 |
| *No. C113 (1)* | 1.20 | .65 |
| *No. C164 (1)* | 1.25 | .60 |
| *No. C8 (1)* | 2.75 | 2.50 |
| *No. C105 (1)* | 1.60 | .50 |
| *No. C166 (1)* | 1.25 | .40 |
| *No. C97 (1)* | 1.50 | .70 |
| *Set total (13) Stamps* | 22.40 | 10.45 |

#### West African Monetary Union

African Couple, City, Village and Commemorative Coin — CD136

West African Monetary Union, 10th anniv.

### 1972, Nov. 2

Dahomey ........ 300
Ivory Coast ........ 331
Mauritania ........ 299
Niger ........ 258
Senegal ........ 374
Togo ........ 825
Upper Volta ........ 280

| | | |
|---|---|---|
| *No. 300 (1)* | .65 | .25 |
| *No. 331 (1)* | 1.00 | .50 |
| *No. 299 (1)* | .75 | .25 |
| *No. 258 (1)* | .55 | .30 |
| *No. 374 (1)* | .50 | .30 |
| *No. 825 (1)* | .60 | .25 |
| *No. 280 (1)* | .60 | .25 |
| *Set total (7) Stamps* | 4.65 | 2.10 |

#### African Postal Union, 1973

Telecommunications Symbols and Map of Africa — CD137

11th anniversary of the African and Malagasy Posts and Telecommunications Union (UAMPT).

### 1973, Sept. 12

Cameroun ........ 574
Cent. Africa ........ 194
Chad ........ 294
Congo, P.R. ........ 289
Dahomey ........ 311
Gabon ........ 320
Ivory Coast ........ 361
Madagascar ........ 500
Mauritania ........ 304
Niger ........ 287
Rwanda ........ 540
Senegal ........ 393
Togo ........ 849
Upper Volta ........ 297

| | | |
|---|---|---|
| *No. 574 (1)* | 1.75 | .40 |
| *No. 194 (1)* | 1.25 | .75 |
| *No. 294 (1)* | 1.75 | .40 |
| *No. 289 (1)* | 1.60 | .50 |
| *No. 311 (1)* | 1.25 | .55 |
| *No. 320 (1)* | 1.40 | .75 |
| *No. 361 (1)* | 2.50 | 1.00 |
| *No. 500 (1)* | 1.10 | .35 |
| *No. 304 (1)* | 1.10 | .40 |
| *No. 287 (1)* | .90 | .60 |
| *No. 540 (1)* | 4.00 | 2.00 |
| *No. 393 (1)* | 1.60 | .50 |
| *No. 849 (1)* | 1.00 | .35 |
| *No. 297 (1)* | 1.25 | .70 |
| *Set total (14) Stamps* | 22.45 | 9.25 |

#### Philexafrique II — Essen

CD138

CD139

Designs: Indigenous fauna, local and German stamps. Types CD138-CD139 printed horizontally and vertically se-tenant in sheets of 10 (2x5). Label between horizontal pairs alternately commemorates Philexafrique II, Libreville, Gabon, June 1978, and 2nd International Stamp Fair, Essen, Germany, Nov. 1-5.

### 1978-1979

Benin ........ C286a
Central Africa ........ C201a
Chad ........ C239a
Congo Republic ........ C246a
Djibouti ........ C122a
Gabon ........ C216a
Ivory Coast ........ C65a
Mali ........ C357a
Mauritania ........ C186a
Niger ........ C292a
Rwanda ........ C13a
Senegal ........ C147a
Togo ........ C364a

| | | |
|---|---|---|
| *No. C286a (1)* | 9.00 | 8.50 |
| *No. C201a (1)* | 7.50 | 7.50 |
| *No. C239a (1)* | 8.00 | 4.00 |
| *No. C246a (1)* | 7.00 | 7.00 |
| *No. C122a (1)* | 8.50 | 8.50 |
| *No. C216a (1)* | 6.50 | 4.00 |
| *No. C65a (1)* | 9.00 | 9.00 |
| *No. C357a (1)* | 5.00 | 3.00 |
| *No. C186a (1)* | 4.50 | 4.00 |
| *No. C292a (1)* | 6.00 | 5.00 |
| *No. C13a (1)* | 4.00 | 4.00 |
| *No. C147a (1)* | 10.00 | 4.00 |
| *No. C364a (1)* | 3.00 | 1.50 |
| *Set total (13) Stamps* | 88.00 | 70.00 |

---

## BRITISH COMMONWEALTH OF NATIONS

The listings follow established trade practices when these issues are offered as units by dealers. The Peace issue, for example, includes only one stamp from the Indian state of Hyderabad. The U.P.U. issue includes the Egypt set. Pairs are included for those varieties issued with bilingual designs se-tenant.

#### Silver Jubilee

Windsor Castle and King George V CD301

Reign of King George V, 25th anniv.

### 1935

Antigua ........ 77-80
Ascension ........ 33-36
Bahamas ........ 92-95
Barbados ........ 186-189
Basutoland ........ 11-14
Bechuanaland Protectorate ........ 117-120
Bermuda ........ 100-103
British Guiana ........ 223-226
British Honduras ........ 108-111
Cayman Islands ........ 81-84
Ceylon ........ 260-263
Cyprus ........ 136-139
Dominica ........ 90-93
Falkland Islands ........ 77-80
Fiji ........ 110-113
Gambia ........ 125-128
Gibraltar ........ 100-103
Gilbert & Ellice Islands ........ 33-36
Gold Coast ........ 108-111
Grenada ........ 124-127
Hong Kong ........ 147-150
Jamaica ........ 109-112
Kenya, Uganda, Tanzania ........ 42-45
Leeward Islands ........ 96-99
Malta ........ 184-187
Mauritius ........ 204-207
Montserrat ........ 85-88
Newfoundland ........ 226-229
Nigeria ........ 34-37
Northern Rhodesia ........ 18-21
Nyasaland Protectorate ........ 47-50
St. Helena ........ 111-114
St. Kitts-Nevis ........ 72-75
St. Lucia ........ 91-94
St. Vincent ........ 134-137
Seychelles ........ 118-121
Sierra Leone ........ 166-169
Solomon Islands ........ 60-63
Somaliland Protectorate ........ 77-80
Straits Settlements ........ 213-216
Swaziland ........ 20-23
Trinidad & Tobago ........ 43-46
Turks & Caicos Islands ........ 71-74
Virgin Islands ........ 69-72

The following have different designs but are included in the omnibus set:

Great Britain ........ 226-229
Offices in Morocco (Sp. Curr.) ........ 67-70
Offices in Morocco (Br. Curr.) ........ 226-229
Offices in Morocco (Fr. Curr.) ........ 422-425
Offices in Morocco (Tangier) ........ 508-510
Australia ........ 152-154
Canada ........ 211-216
Cook Islands ........ 98-100
India ........ 142-148
Nauru ........ 31-34
New Guinea ........ 46-47
New Zealand ........ 199-201
Niue ........ 67-69
Papua ........ 114-117
Samoa ........ 163-165
South Africa ........ 68-71
Southern Rhodesia ........ 33-36
South-West Africa ........ 121-124

| | | |
|---|---|---|
| *Nos. 77-80 (4)* | 20.25 | *23.25* |
| *Nos. 33-36 (4)* | 58.50 | *127.50* |
| *Nos. 92-95 (4)* | 25.00 | *46.00* |
| *Nos. 186-189 (4)* | 30.00 | 46.80 |
| *Nos. 11-14 (4)* | 11.60 | *21.25* |
| *Nos. 117-120 (4)* | 15.75 | *36.00* |
| *Nos. 100-103 (4)* | 16.80 | *58.50* |
| *Nos. 223-226 (4)* | 18.35 | 35.50 |
| *Nos. 108-111 (4)* | 15.25 | *16.35* |
| *Nos. 81-84 (4)* | 21.60 | *24.50* |
| *Nos. 260-263 (4)* | 10.40 | 21.60 |
| *Nos. 136-139 (4)* | 39.75 | *34.40* |
| *Nos. 90-93 (4)* | 18.85 | 19.85 |
| *Nos. 77-80 (4)* | 55.00 | 14.75 |
| *Nos. 110-113 (4)* | 15.25 | 27.90 |
| *Nos. 125-128 (4)* | 12.20 | *25.25* |
| *Nos. 100-103 (4)* | 28.75 | 42.75 |
| *Nos. 33-36 (4)* | 36.80 | *67.00* |
| *Nos. 108-111 (4)* | 25.75 | *78.10* |
| *Nos. 124-127 (4)* | 16.70 | *40.60* |
| *Nos. 147-150 (4)* | 59.00 | 18.75 |
| *Nos. 109-112 (4)* | 17.00 | 39.00 |
| *Nos. 42-45 (4)* | 8.75 | *11.00* |
| *Nos. 96-99 (4)* | 35.75 | 49.60 |
| *Nos. 184-187 (4)* | 22.00 | 33.70 |
| *Nos. 204-207 (4)* | 47.60 | 58.25 |
| *Nos. 85-88 (4)* | 10.25 | *30.25* |
| *Nos. 226-229 (4)* | 17.50 | 12.05 |
| *Nos. 34-37 (4)* | 17.50 | *70.00* |
| *Nos. 18-21 (4)* | 16.75 | 16.25 |
| *Nos. 47-50 (4)* | 39.75 | *80.25* |
| *Nos. 111-114 (4)* | 31.15 | *33.25* |
| *Nos. 72-75 (4)* | 10.80 | *18.65* |
| *Nos. 91-94 (4)* | 16.00 | *20.80* |
| *Nos. 134-137 (4)* | 9.45 | *21.25* |
| *Nos. 118-121 (4)* | 17.50 | *32.50* |
| *Nos. 166-169 (4)* | 24.25 | *56.00* |
| *Nos. 60-63 (4)* | 27.25 | 38.00 |
| *Nos. 77-80 (4)* | 17.00 | *48.25* |
| *Nos. 213-216 (4)* | 15.00 | *25.10* |
| *Nos. 20-23 (4)* | 6.80 | 18.25 |
| *Nos. 43-46 (4)* | 14.05 | 27.75 |
| *Nos. 71-74 (4)* | 8.40 | 14.50 |
| *Nos. 69-72 (4)* | 25.00 | 55.25 |
| *Nos. 226-229 (4)* | 5.15 | *4.40* |

| | | |
|---|---|---|
| *Nos. 67-70 (4)* | 14.35 | *26.10* |
| *Nos. 226-229 (4)* | 8.20 | *28.90* |
| *Nos. 422-425 (4)* | 3.90 | 2.00 |
| *Nos. 508-510 (3)* | 18.80 | *23.85* |
| *Nos. 152-154 (3)* | 45.75 | 60.35 |
| *Nos. 211-216 (6)* | 24.85 | 13.35 |
| *Nos. 98-100 (3)* | 9.65 | *12.00* |
| *Nos. 142-148 (7)* | 28.85 | 14.00 |
| *Nos. 31-34 (4)* | 9.90 | *9.90* |
| *Nos. 46-47 (2)* | 4.35 | 1.70 |
| *Nos. 199-201 (3)* | 21.75 | *31.75* |
| *Nos. 67-69 (3)* | 11.80 | *26.50* |
| *Nos. 114-117 (4)* | 9.20 | *17.00* |
| *Nos. 163-165 (3)* | 4.40 | 5.50 |
| *Nos. 68-71 (4)* | 57.00 | *155.00* |
| *Nos. 33-36 (4)* | 27.75 | *45.25* |
| *Nos. 121-124 (4)* | 13.00 | *36.10* |
| *Set total (245) Stamps* | 1,326. | 2,150. |

### Coronation

Queen Elizabeth and King George VI
CD302

**1937**

Aden .......... 13-15
Antigua .......... 81-83
Ascension .......... 37-39
Bahamas .......... 97-99
Barbados .......... 190-192
Basutoland .......... 15-17
Bechuanaland Protectorate .......... 121-123
Bermuda .......... 115-117
British Guiana .......... 227-229
British Honduras .......... 112-114
Cayman Islands .......... 97-99
Ceylon .......... 275-277
Cyprus .......... 140-142
Dominica .......... 94-96
Falkland Islands .......... 81-83
Fiji .......... 114-116
Gambia .......... 129-131
Gibraltar .......... 104-106
Gilbert & Ellice Islands .......... 37-39
Gold Coast .......... 112-114
Grenada .......... 128-130
Hong Kong .......... 151-153
Jamaica .......... 113-115
Kenya, Uganda, Tanzania .......... 60-62
Leeward Islands .......... 100-102
Malta .......... 188-190
Mauritius .......... 208-210
Montserrat .......... 89-91
Newfoundland .......... 230-232
Nigeria .......... 50-52
Northern Rhodesia .......... 22-24
Nyasaland Protectorate .......... 51-53
St. Helena .......... 115-117
St. Kitts-Nevis .......... 76-78
St. Lucia .......... 107-109
St. Vincent .......... 138-140
Seychelles .......... 122-124
Sierra Leone .......... 170-172
Solomon Islands .......... 64-66
Somaliland Protectorate .......... 81-83
Straits Settlements .......... 235-237
Swaziland .......... 24-26
Trinidad & Tobago .......... 47-49
Turks & Caicos Islands .......... 75-77
Virgin Islands .......... 73-75

The following have different designs but are included in the omnibus set:

Great Britain .......... 234
Offices in Morocco (Sp. Curr.) .......... 82
Offices in Morocco (Fr. Curr.) .......... 439
Offices in Morocco (Tangier) .......... 514
Canada .......... 237
Cook Islands .......... 109-111
Nauru .......... 35-38
Newfoundland .......... 233-243
New Guinea .......... 48-51
New Zealand .......... 223-225
Niue .......... 70-72
Papua .......... 118-121
South Africa .......... 74-78
Southern Rhodesia .......... 38-41
South-West Africa .......... 125-132

| | | |
|---|---|---|
| *Nos. 13-15 (3)* | 2.70 | *5.65* |
| *Nos. 81-83 (3)* | 1.85 | *8.00* |
| *Nos. 37-39 (3)* | 2.75 | *2.75* |
| *Nos. 97-99 (3)* | 1.05 | *3.05* |
| *Nos. 190-192 (3)* | 1.10 | 1.95 |
| *Nos. 15-17 (3)* | 1.15 | *3.00* |
| *Nos. 121-123 (3)* | .95 | 3.35 |
| *Nos. 115-117 (3)* | 1.25 | 5.00 |
| *Nos. 227-229 (3)* | 1.45 | 3.05 |
| *Nos. 112-114 (3)* | 1.20 | 2.40 |
| *Nos. 97-99 (3)* | 1.10 | 2.70 |
| *Nos. 275-277 (3)* | 8.25 | 10.35 |
| *Nos. 140-142 (3)* | 3.75 | 6.50 |
| *Nos. 94-96 (3)* | .85 | 2.40 |
| *Nos. 81-83 (3)* | 2.90 | *2.30* |
| *Nos. 114-116 (3)* | 1.50 | *5.75* |
| *Nos. 129-131 (3)* | .95 | 3.95 |
| *Nos. 104-106 (3)* | 2.25 | 6.45 |
| *Nos. 37-39 (3)* | .85 | *2.15* |
| *Nos. 112-114 (3)* | 3.10 | *10.00* |
| *Nos. 128-130 (3)* | 1.00 | .85 |
| *Nos. 151-153 (3)* | 23.00 | 12.50 |
| *Nos. 113-115 (3)* | 1.25 | 1.25 |
| *Nos. 60-62 (3)* | 1.00 | 2.35 |
| *Nos. 100-102 (3)* | 1.55 | 4.00 |
| *Nos. 188-190 (3)* | 1.25 | 1.60 |
| *Nos. 208-210 (3)* | 2.05 | 3.75 |
| *Nos. 89-91 (3)* | 1.00 | 3.35 |
| *Nos. 230-232 (3)* | 7.00 | 2.80 |
| *Nos. 50-52 (3)* | 3.25 | 8.50 |
| *Nos. 22-24 (3)* | .95 | 2.25 |
| *Nos. 51-53 (3)* | 1.05 | 1.30 |
| *Nos. 115-117 (3)* | 1.45 | 2.05 |
| *Nos. 76-78 (3)* | .95 | 2.15 |
| *Nos. 107-109 (3)* | 1.05 | 2.05 |
| *Nos. 138-140 (3)* | .80 | *4.75* |
| *Nos. 122-124 (3)* | 1.20 | *1.90* |
| *Nos. 170-172 (3)* | 1.95 | 5.65 |
| *Nos. 64-66 (3)* | .90 | 2.00 |
| *Nos. 81-83 (3)* | 1.10 | *3.40* |
| *Nos. 235-237 (3)* | 3.25 | 1.60 |
| *Nos. 24-26 (3)* | 1.05 | 1.75 |
| *Nos. 47-49 (3)* | 1.00 | 1.00 |
| *Nos. 75-77 (3)* | 1.30 | 1.15 |
| *Nos. 73-75 (3)* | 2.20 | 6.90 |

| | | |
|---|---|---|
| *No. 234 (1)* | .25 | .25 |
| *No. 82 (1)* | .80 | .80 |
| *No. 439 (1)* | .35 | .25 |
| *No. 514 (1)* | .55 | .55 |
| *No. 237 (1)* | .35 | .25 |
| *Nos. 109-111 (3)* | .85 | .80 |
| *Nos. 35-38 (4)* | 1.10 | *5.50* |
| *Nos. 233-243 (11)* | 41.90 | 30.40 |
| *Nos. 48-51 (4)* | 1.40 | *7.90* |
| *Nos. 223-225 (3)* | 1.40 | *2.75* |
| *Nos. 70-72 (3)* | .80 | *2.05* |
| *Nos. 118-121 (4)* | 1.60 | *5.25* |
| *Nos. 74-78 (5)* | 9.25 | 10.80 |
| *Nos. 38-41 (4)* | 3.55 | 15.50 |
| *Nos. 125-132 (8)* | 5.00 | 8.40 |
| *Set total (189) Stamps* | 172.65 | 263.05 |

### Peace

King George VI and Parliament Buildings, London
CD303

Return to peace at the close of World War II.

**1945-46**

Aden .......... 28-29
Antigua .......... 96-97
Ascension .......... 50-51
Bahamas .......... 130-131
Barbados .......... 207-208
Bermuda .......... 131-132
British Guiana .......... 242-243
British Honduras .......... 127-128
Cayman Islands .......... 112-113
Ceylon .......... 293-294
Cyprus .......... 156-157
Dominica .......... 112-113
Falkland Islands .......... 97-98
Falkland Islands Dep. .......... 1L9-1L10
Fiji .......... 137-138
Gambia .......... 144-145
Gibraltar .......... 119-120
Gilbert & Ellice Islands .......... 52-53
Gold Coast .......... 128-129
Grenada .......... 143-144
Jamaica .......... 136-137
Kenya, Uganda, Tanzania .......... 90-91
Leeward Islands .......... 116-117
Malta .......... 206-207
Mauritius .......... 223-224
Montserrat .......... 104-105
Nigeria .......... 71-72
Northern Rhodesia .......... 46-47
Nyasaland Protectorate .......... 82-83
Pitcairn Islands .......... 9-10
St. Helena .......... 128-129
St. Kitts-Nevis .......... 91-92
St. Lucia .......... 127-128
St. Vincent .......... 152-153
Seychelles .......... 149-150
Sierra Leone .......... 186-187
Solomon Islands .......... 80-81
Somaliland Protectorate .......... 108-109
Trinidad & Tobago .......... 62-63
Turks & Caicos Islands .......... 90-91
Virgin Islands .......... 88-89

The following have different designs but are included in the omnibus set:

Great Britain .......... 264-265
Offices in Morocco (Tangier) .......... 523-524
Aden
  Kathiri State of Seiyun .......... 12-13
  Qu'aiti State of Shihr and Mukalla .......... 12-13
Australia .......... 200-202
Basutoland .......... 29-31
Bechuanaland Protectorate .......... 137-139
Burma .......... 66-69
Cook Islands .......... 127-130
Hong Kong .......... 174-175
India .......... 195-198
  Hyderabad .......... 51-53
New Zealand .......... 247-257
Niue .......... 90-93
Pakistan-Bahawalpur .......... O16
Samoa .......... 191-194
South Africa .......... 100-102
Southern Rhodesia .......... 67-70
South-West Africa .......... 153-155
Swaziland .......... 38-40
Zanzibar .......... 222-223

| | | |
|---|---|---|
| *Nos. 28-29 (2)* | .95 | 2.50 |
| *Nos. 96-97 (2)* | .50 | *.80* |
| *Nos. 50-51 (2)* | .80 | *2.00* |
| *Nos. 130-131 (2)* | .50 | 1.40 |
| *Nos. 207-208 (2)* | .50 | 1.10 |
| *Nos. 131-132 (2)* | .55 | .55 |
| *Nos. 242-243 (2)* | 1.05 | *1.40* |
| *Nos. 127-128 (2)* | .50 | .50 |
| *Nos. 112-113 (2)* | .80 | .80 |
| *Nos. 293-294 (2)* | .60 | *2.10* |
| *Nos. 156-157 (2)* | .90 | .70 |
| *Nos. 112-113 (2)* | .50 | .50 |
| *Nos. 97-98 (2)* | .90 | 1.35 |
| *Nos. 1L9-1L10 (2)* | 1.30 | 1.00 |
| *Nos. 137-138 (2)* | .50 | *1.75* |
| *Nos. 144-145 (2)* | .50 | .95 |
| *Nos. 119-120 (2)* | .75 | *1.00* |
| *Nos. 52-53 (2)* | .50 | *1.10* |
| *Nos. 128-129 (2)* | 1.85 | *3.75* |
| *Nos. 143-144 (2)* | .50 | *.95* |
| *Nos. 136-137 (2)* | .80 | *12.50* |
| *Nos. 90-91 (2)* | .65 | .65 |
| *Nos. 116-117 (2)* | .50 | 1.50 |
| *Nos. 206-207 (2)* | .65 | 2.00 |
| *Nos. 223-224 (2)* | .50 | 1.05 |
| *Nos. 104-105 (2)* | .50 | .50 |
| *Nos. 71-72 (2)* | .70 | *2.75* |
| *Nos. 46-47 (2)* | 1.25 | *2.00* |
| *Nos. 82-83 (2)* | .50 | .50 |
| *Nos. 9-10 (2)* | 1.40 | 1.40 |
| *Nos. 128-129 (2)* | .65 | .70 |
| *Nos. 91-92 (2)* | .50 | .50 |
| *Nos. 127-128 (2)* | .50 | .60 |
| *Nos. 152-153 (2)* | .50 | .50 |
| *Nos. 149-150 (2)* | .55 | .50 |
| *Nos. 186-187 (2)* | .50 | .50 |
| *Nos. 80-81 (2)* | .50 | 1.50 |
| *Nos. 108-109 (2)* | .70 | .50 |
| *Nos. 62-63 (2)* | .50 | .50 |
| *Nos. 90-91 (2)* | .50 | .50 |
| *Nos. 88-89 (2)* | .50 | .50 |

| | | |
|---|---|---|
| *Nos. 264-265 (2)* | .50 | .50 |
| *Nos. 523-524 (2)* | 1.50 | 3.00 |
| *Nos. 12-13 (2)* | .50 | .90 |
| *Nos. 12-13 (2)* | .50 | *1.25* |
| *Nos. 200-202 (3)* | 1.60 | *3.00* |
| *Nos. 29-31 (3)* | 2.10 | 2.60 |
| *Nos. 137-139 (3)* | 2.05 | *4.75* |
| *Nos. 66-69 (4)* | 1.60 | 1.30 |
| *Nos. 127-130 (4)* | 2.00 | 1.85 |
| *Nos. 174-175 (2)* | 6.75 | 3.15 |
| *Nos. 195-198 (4)* | 5.60 | 5.50 |
| *Nos. 51-53 (3)* | 1.50 | 1.70 |
| *Nos. 247-257 (11)* | 3.95 | 3.90 |
| *Nos. 90-93 (4)* | 1.70 | *2.20* |
| *No. O16 (1)* | 5.50 | *7.00* |
| *Nos. 191-194 (4)* | 2.05 | 1.00 |
| *Nos. 100-102 (3)* | 1.20 | 4.00 |
| *Nos. 67-70 (4)* | 1.40 | 1.75 |
| *Nos. 153-155 (3)* | 1.85 | 3.25 |
| *Nos. 38-40 (3)* | 2.40 | *5.50* |
| *Nos. 222-223 (2)* | .65 | 1.00 |
| *Set total (151) Stamps* | 75.20 | 116.95 |

### Silver Wedding

King George VI and Queen Elizabeth
CD304 CD305

**1948-49**

Aden .......... 30-31
  Kathiri State of Seiyun .......... 14-15
  Qu'aiti State of Shihr and Mukalla .......... 14-15
Antigua .......... 98-99
Ascension .......... 52-53
Bahamas .......... 148-149
Barbados .......... 210-211
Basutoland .......... 39-40
Bechuanaland Protectorate .......... 147-148
Bermuda .......... 133-134
British Guiana .......... 244-245
British Honduras .......... 129-130
Cayman Islands .......... 116-117
Cyprus .......... 158-159
Dominica .......... 114-115
Falkland Islands .......... 99-100
Falkland Islands Dep. .......... 1L11-1L12
Fiji .......... 139-140
Gambia .......... 146-147
Gibraltar .......... 121-122
Gilbert & Ellice Islands .......... 54-55
Gold Coast .......... 142-143
Grenada .......... 145-146
Hong Kong .......... 178-179
Jamaica .......... 138-139
Kenya, Uganda, Tanzania .......... 92-93
Leeward Islands .......... 118-119
Malaya
  Johore .......... 128-129
  Kedah .......... 55-56
  Kelantan .......... 44-45
  Malacca .......... 1-2
  Negri Sembilan .......... 36-37
  Pahang .......... 44-45
  Penang .......... 1-2
  Perak .......... 99-100
  Perlis .......... 1-2
  Selangor .......... 74-75
  Trengganu .......... 47-48
Malta .......... 223-224
Mauritius .......... 229-230
Montserrat .......... 106-107
Nigeria .......... 73-74
North Borneo .......... 238-239
Northern Rhodesia .......... 48-49
Nyasaland Protectorate .......... 85-86
Pitcairn Islands .......... 11-12
St. Helena .......... 130-131
St. Kitts-Nevis .......... 93-94
St. Lucia .......... 129-130
St. Vincent .......... 154-155
Sarawak .......... 174-175
Seychelles .......... 151-152
Sierra Leone .......... 188-189
Singapore .......... 21-22
Solomon Islands .......... 82-83
Somaliland Protectorate .......... 110-111
Swaziland .......... 48-49
Trinidad & Tobago .......... 64-65
Turks & Caicos Islands .......... 92-93
Virgin Islands .......... 90-91
Zanzibar .......... 224-225

The following have different designs but are included in the omnibus set:

Great Britain .......... 267-268
  Offices in Morocco (Sp. Curr.) .......... 93-94
  Offices in Morocco (Tangier) .......... 525-526
Bahrain .......... 62-63
Kuwait .......... 82-83
Oman .......... 25-26
South Africa .......... 106
South-West Africa .......... 159

| | | |
|---|---|---|
| *Nos. 30-31 (2)* | 40.40 | 47.25 |
| *Nos. 14-15 (2)* | 17.85 | *16.00* |
| *Nos. 14-15 (2)* | 18.55 | *12.50* |
| *Nos. 98-99 (2)* | 13.55 | *15.75* |
| *Nos. 52-53 (2)* | 55.55 | 50.45 |
| *Nos. 148-149 (2)* | 45.25 | 40.30 |
| *Nos. 210-211 (2)* | 18.35 | 13.05 |
| *Nos. 39-40 (2)* | 52.80 | *55.25* |
| *Nos. 147-148 (2)* | 42.85 | *47.75* |
| *Nos. 133-134 (2)* | 47.75 | *55.25* |
| *Nos. 244-245 (2)* | 24.25 | *28.45* |
| *Nos. 129-130 (2)* | 25.25 | *53.20* |
| *Nos. 116-117 (2)* | 25.25 | *33.50* |
| *Nos. 158-159 (2)* | 58.50 | *78.05* |
| *Nos. 114-115 (2)* | 25.25 | *32.75* |
| *Nos. 99-100 (2)* | 112.10 | 76.10 |
| *Nos. 1L11-1L12 (2)* | 4.25 | 6.00 |
| *Nos. 139-140 (2)* | 17.00 | 11.50 |
| *Nos. 146-147 (2)* | 21.25 | 21.25 |
| *Nos. 121-122 (2)* | 61.00 | *78.00* |
| *Nos. 54-55 (2)* | 14.25 | *26.25* |
| *Nos. 142-143 (2)* | 35.25 | 48.20 |
| *Nos. 145-146 (2)* | 21.75 | 21.75 |
| *Nos. 178-179 (2)* | 283.50 | 96.50 |
| *Nos. 138-139 (2)* | 27.85 | *60.25* |
| *Nos. 92-93 (2)* | 50.25 | *67.75* |
| *Nos. 118-119 (2)* | 7.00 | 8.25 |
| *Nos. 128-129 (2)* | 29.25 | *53.25* |
| *Nos. 55-56 (2)* | 35.25 | *50.25* |
| *Nos. 44-45 (2)* | 35.75 | *62.75* |
| *Nos. 1-2 (2)* | 35.40 | *49.75* |
| *Nos. 36-37 (2)* | 28.10 | *38.20* |
| *Nos. 44-45 (2)* | 28.00 | *38.05* |
| *Nos. 1-2 (2)* | 40.50 | 37.80 |

| | | |
|---|---|---|
| Nos. 99-100 (2) | 27.80 | 37.75 |
| Nos. 1-2 (2) | 33.50 | 58.00 |
| Nos. 74-75 (2) | 30.25 | 25.30 |
| Nos. 47-48 (2) | 35.25 | 62.75 |
| Nos. 223-224 (2) | 40.55 | 45.25 |
| Nos. 229-230 (2) | 17.75 | 45.25 |
| Nos. 106-107 (2) | 9.25 | 18.25 |
| Nos. 73-74 (2) | 17.85 | 22.80 |
| Nos. 238-239 (2) | 35.30 | 45.75 |
| Nos. 48-49 (2) | 92.80 | 90.25 |
| Nos. 85-86 (2) | 18.25 | 30.25 |
| Nos. 11-12 (2) | 44.75 | 48.50 |
| Nos. 130-131 (2) | 32.80 | 42.80 |
| Nos. 93-94 (2) | 11.25 | 10.50 |
| Nos. 129-130 (2) | 22.25 | 45.25 |
| Nos. 154-155 (2) | 27.75 | 30.25 |
| Nos. 174-175 (2) | 50.40 | 52.90 |
| Nos. 151-152 (2) | 16.25 | 45.75 |
| Nos. 188-189 (2) | 24.75 | 26.25 |
| Nos. 21-22 (2) | 116.00 | 45.40 |
| Nos. 82-83 (2) | 13.40 | 13.40 |
| Nos. 110-111 (2) | 8.40 | 8.75 |
| Nos. 48-49 (2) | 40.30 | 47.75 |
| Nos. 64-65 (2) | 32.75 | 38.25 |
| Nos. 92-93 (2) | 11.25 | 16.25 |
| Nos. 90-91 (2) | 16.25 | 22.25 |
| Nos. 224-225 (2) | 29.60 | 38.00 |
| Nos. 267-268 (2) | 30.40 | 25.25 |
| Nos. 93-94 (2) | 20.10 | 25.35 |
| Nos. 525-526 (2) | 23.10 | 29.25 |
| Nos. 62-63 (2) | 38.50 | 57.75 |
| Nos. 82-83 (2) | 45.50 | 45.50 |
| Nos. 25-26 (2) | 46.00 | 47.50 |
| No. 106 (1) | .90 | 1.25 |
| No. 159 (1) | 1.10 | .35 |
| Set total (136) Stamps | 2,461. | 2,677. |

### U.P.U.

Mercury and Symbols of Communications — CD306

Plane, Ship and Hemispheres — CD307

Mercury Scattering Letters over Globe CD308

U.P.U. Monument, Bern CD309

Universal Postal Union, 75th anniversary.

**1949**

Aden ....................32-35
Kathiri State of Seiyun ....................16-19
Qu'aiti State of Shihr and Mukalla ....................16-19
Antigua ....................100-103
Ascension ....................57-60
Bahamas ....................150-153
Barbados ....................212-215
Basutoland ....................41-44
Bechuanaland Protectorate ....................149-152
Bermuda ....................138-141
British Guiana ....................246-249
British Honduras ....................137-140
Brunei ....................79-82
Cayman Islands ....................118-121
Cyprus ....................160-163
Dominica ....................116-119
Falkland Islands ....................103-106
Falkland Islands Dep. ....................1L14-1L17
Fiji ....................141-144
Gambia ....................148-151
Gibraltar ....................123-126
Gilbert & Ellice Islands ....................56-59
Gold Coast ....................144-147
Grenada ....................147-150
Hong Kong ....................180-183
Jamaica ....................142-145
Kenya, Uganda, Tanzania ....................94-97
Leeward Islands ....................126-129
Malaya
Johore ....................151-154
Kedah ....................57-60
Kelantan ....................46-49
Malacca ....................18-21
Negri Sembilan ....................59-62
Pahang ....................46-49
Penang ....................23-26
Perak ....................101-104
Perlis ....................3-6
Selangor ....................76-79
Trengganu ....................49-52
Malta ....................225-228
Mauritius ....................231-234
Montserrat ....................108-111
New Hebrides, British ....................62-65
New Hebrides, French ....................79-82
Nigeria ....................75-78
North Borneo ....................240-243
Northern Rhodesia ....................50-53
Nyasaland Protectorate ....................87-90
Pitcairn Islands ....................13-16
St. Helena ....................132-135
St. Kitts-Nevis ....................95-98
St. Lucia ....................131-134
St. Vincent ....................170-173
Sarawak ....................176-179
Seychelles ....................153-156
Sierra Leone ....................190-193
Singapore ....................23-26
Solomon Islands ....................84-87
Somaliland Protectorate ....................112-115
Southern Rhodesia ....................71-72
Swaziland ....................50-53
Tonga ....................87-90
Trinidad & Tobago ....................66-69
Turks & Caicos Islands ....................101-104
Virgin Islands ....................92-95
Zanzibar ....................226-229

The following have different designs but are included in the omnibus set:

Great Britain ....................276-279
Offices in Morocco (Tangier) ....................546-549
Australia ....................223
Bahrain ....................68-71
Burma ....................116-121
Ceylon ....................304-306
Egypt ....................281-283
India ....................223-226
Kuwait ....................89-92
Oman ....................31-34
Pakistan-Bahawalpur 26-29, O25-O28
South Africa ....................109-111
South-West Africa ....................160-162

| | | |
|---|---|---|
| Nos. 32-35 (4) | 5.85 | 8.45 |
| Nos. 16-19 (4) | 2.75 | 5.50 |
| Nos. 16-19 (4) | 2.60 | 4.20 |
| Nos. 100-103 (4) | 3.60 | 7.70 |
| Nos. 57-60 (4) | 11.10 | 9.00 |
| Nos. 150-153 (4) | 5.35 | 9.30 |
| Nos. 212-215 (4) | 4.40 | 14.15 |
| Nos. 41-44 (4) | 4.75 | 10.00 |
| Nos. 149-152 (4) | 3.35 | 7.25 |
| Nos. 138-141 (4) | 4.75 | 6.15 |
| Nos. 246-249 (4) | 2.75 | 4.20 |
| Nos. 137-140 (4) | 3.30 | 6.35 |
| Nos. 79-82 (4) | 9.50 | 8.45 |
| Nos. 118-121 (4) | 3.60 | 7.25 |
| Nos. 160-163 (4) | 4.60 | 10.70 |
| Nos. 116-119 (4) | 2.30 | 5.65 |
| Nos. 103-106 (4) | 14.00 | 17.10 |
| Nos. 1L14-1L17 (4) | 14.60 | 14.50 |
| Nos. 141-144 (4) | 3.35 | 14.75 |
| Nos. 148-151 (4) | 3.10 | 7.10 |
| Nos. 123-126 (4) | 5.90 | 8.75 |
| Nos. 56-59 (4) | 4.30 | 13.00 |
| Nos. 144-147 (4) | 2.55 | 10.35 |
| Nos. 147-150 (4) | 2.15 | 3.55 |
| Nos. 180-183 (4) | 57.25 | 18.25 |
| Nos. 142-145 (4) | 2.25 | 2.45 |
| Nos. 94-97 (4) | 2.90 | 3.40 |
| Nos. 126-129 (4) | 3.05 | 9.60 |
| Nos. 151-154 (4) | 4.70 | 8.90 |
| Nos. 57-60 (4) | 4.80 | 12.00 |
| Nos. 46-49 (4) | 4.25 | 12.65 |
| Nos. 18-21 (4) | 4.25 | 17.30 |
| Nos. 59-62 (4) | 3.50 | 10.75 |
| Nos. 46-49 (4) | 3.00 | 7.25 |
| Nos. 23-26 (4) | 5.10 | 11.75 |
| Nos. 101-104 (4) | 3.65 | 10.75 |
| Nos. 3-6 (4) | 3.95 | 14.25 |
| Nos. 76-79 (4) | 4.90 | 12.30 |
| Nos. 49-52 (4) | 4.95 | 9.75 |
| Nos. 225-228 (4) | 4.50 | 4.85 |
| Nos. 231-234 (4) | 4.35 | 6.70 |
| Nos. 108-111 (4) | 3.40 | 3.85 |
| Nos. 62-65 (4) | 1.60 | 4.25 |
| Nos. 79-82 (4) | 24.25 | 24.25 |
| Nos. 75-78 (4) | 2.80 | 9.25 |
| Nos. 240-243 (4) | 7.15 | 6.50 |
| Nos. 50-53 (4) | 5.00 | 6.50 |
| Nos. 87-90 (4) | 4.05 | 4.05 |
| Nos. 13-16 (4) | 18.50 | 16.50 |
| Nos. 132-135 (4) | 4.85 | 7.10 |
| Nos. 95-98 (4) | 3.35 | 5.55 |
| Nos. 131-134 (4) | 2.55 | 3.85 |
| Nos. 170-173 (4) | 2.20 | 5.05 |
| Nos. 176-179 (4) | 8.15 | 10.85 |
| Nos. 153-156 (4) | 3.25 | 4.10 |
| Nos. 190-193 (4) | 3.00 | 5.10 |
| Nos. 23-26 (4) | 18.00 | 13.20 |
| Nos. 84-87 (4) | 4.05 | 4.90 |
| Nos. 112-115 (4) | 3.95 | 8.70 |
| Nos. 71-72 (2) | 1.95 | 2.25 |
| Nos. 50-53 (4) | 2.80 | 4.65 |
| Nos. 87-90 (4) | 3.00 | 5.25 |
| Nos. 66-69 (4) | 3.15 | 3.15 |
| Nos. 101-104 (4) | 2.70 | 4.10 |
| Nos. 92-95 (4) | 2.60 | 5.90 |
| Nos. 226-229 (4) | 5.45 | 13.50 |
| Nos. 276-279 (4) | 1.35 | 1.00 |
| Nos. 546-549 (4) | 3.20 | 10.15 |
| No. 223 (1) | .60 | .55 |
| Nos. 68-71 (4) | 4.75 | 16.50 |
| Nos. 116-121 (6) | 7.30 | 5.35 |
| Nos. 304-306 (3) | 3.35 | 4.25 |
| Nos. 281-283 (3) | 5.75 | 2.70 |
| Nos. 223-226 (4) | 27.25 | 10.50 |
| Nos. 89-92 (4) | 6.10 | 10.25 |
| Nos. 31-34 (4) | 5.55 | 15.75 |
| Nos. 26-29,O25-O28 (8) | 2.00 | 42.00 |
| Nos. 109-111 (3) | 2.20 | 3.00 |
| Nos. 160-162 (3) | 3.00 | 5.50 |
| Set total (313) Stamps | 460.00 | 696.15 |

### University

Arms of University College CD310

Alice, Princess of Athlone CD311

1948 opening of University College of the West Indies at Jamaica.

**1951**

Antigua ....................104-105
Barbados ....................228-229
British Guiana ....................250-251
British Honduras ....................141-142
Dominica ....................120-121
Grenada ....................164-165
Jamaica ....................146-147
Leeward Islands ....................130-131
Montserrat ....................112-113
St. Kitts-Nevis ....................105-106
St. Lucia ....................149-150
St. Vincent ....................174-175
Trinidad & Tobago ....................70-71
Virgin Islands ....................96-97

| | | |
|---|---|---|
| Nos. 104-105 (2) | 1.35 | 3.75 |
| Nos. 228-229 (2) | 1.85 | 1.55 |
| Nos. 250-251 (2) | 1.10 | 1.25 |
| Nos. 141-142 (2) | 1.40 | 2.20 |
| Nos. 120-121 (2) | 1.40 | 1.75 |
| Nos. 164-165 (2) | 1.20 | 1.60 |
| Nos. 146-147 (2) | .90 | .70 |
| Nos. 130-131 (2) | 1.35 | 4.00 |
| Nos. 112-113 (2) | .85 | 1.50 |
| Nos. 105-106 (2) | .90 | 2.25 |
| Nos. 149-150 (2) | 1.40 | 1.50 |
| Nos. 174-175 (2) | 1.00 | 2.15 |
| Nos. 70-71 (2) | .75 | .75 |
| Nos. 96-97 (2) | 1.50 | 3.75 |
| Set total (28) Stamps | 16.95 | 28.70 |

### Coronation

Queen Elizabeth II — CD312

**1953**

Aden ....................47
Kathiri State of Seiyun ....................28
Qu'aiti State of Shihr and Mukalla ....................28
Antigua ....................106
Ascension ....................61
Bahamas ....................157
Barbados ....................234
Basutoland ....................45
Bechuanaland Protectorate ....................153
Bermuda ....................142
British Guiana ....................252
British Honduras ....................143
Cayman Islands ....................150
Cyprus ....................167
Dominica ....................141
Falkland Islands ....................121
Falkland Islands Dependencies ....................1L18
Fiji ....................145
Gambia ....................152
Gibraltar ....................131
Gilbert & Ellice Islands ....................60
Gold Coast ....................160
Grenada ....................170
Hong Kong ....................184
Jamaica ....................153
Kenya, Uganda, Tanzania ....................101
Leeward Islands ....................132
Malaya
Johore ....................155
Kedah ....................82
Kelantan ....................71
Malacca ....................27
Negri Sembilan ....................63
Pahang ....................71
Penang ....................27
Perak ....................126
Perlis ....................28
Selangor ....................101
Trengganu ....................74
Malta ....................241
Mauritius ....................250
Montserrat ....................127
New Hebrides, British ....................77
Nigeria ....................79
North Borneo ....................260
Northern Rhodesia ....................60
Nyasaland Protectorate ....................96
Pitcairn Islands ....................19
St. Helena ....................139
St. Kitts-Nevis ....................119
St. Lucia ....................156
St. Vincent ....................185
Sarawak ....................196
Seychelles ....................172
Sierra Leone ....................194
Singapore ....................27
Solomon Islands ....................88
Somaliland Protectorate ....................127
Swaziland ....................54
Trinidad & Tobago ....................84
Tristan da Cunha ....................13
Turks & Caicos Islands ....................118
Virgin Islands ....................114

The following have different designs but are included in the omnibus set:

Great Britain ....................313-316
Offices in Morocco (Tangier) ....................579-582
Australia ....................259-261
Bahrain ....................92-95
Canada ....................330
Ceylon ....................317
Cook Islands ....................145-146
Kuwait ....................113-116
New Zealand ....................280-284
Niue ....................104-105
Oman ....................52-55
Samoa ....................214-215
South Africa ....................192
Southern Rhodesia ....................80
South-West Africa ....................244-248
Tokelau Islands ....................4

| | | |
|---|---|---|
| No. 47 (1) | 1.25 | 1.25 |
| No. 28 (1) | .75 | 1.50 |
| No. 28 (1) | 1.10 | .60 |
| No. 106 (1) | .40 | .75 |
| No. 61 (1) | 1.25 | 2.75 |
| No. 157 (1) | 1.40 | .75 |
| No. 234 (1) | 1.00 | .25 |
| No. 45 (1) | .50 | .60 |
| No. 153 (1) | .75 | .35 |
| No. 142 (1) | .85 | .50 |
| No. 252 (1) | .45 | .25 |
| No. 143 (1) | .60 | .40 |
| No. 150 (1) | .40 | 1.75 |
| No. 167 (1) | 1.60 | .75 |
| No. 141 (1) | .40 | .40 |
| No. 121 (1) | .90 | 1.50 |
| No. 1L18 (1) | 1.80 | 1.40 |
| No. 145 (1) | 1.00 | .60 |
| No. 152 (1) | .50 | .50 |
| No. 131 (1) | .50 | .50 |
| No. 60 (1) | .65 | 2.25 |
| No. 160 (1) | 1.00 | .25 |

| | | |
|---|---|---|
| No. 170 (1) | .30 | .25 |
| No. 184 (1) | 6.00 | .35 |
| No. 153 (1) | .70 | .25 |
| No. 101 (1) | .40 | .25 |
| No. 132 (1) | 1.00 | 2.25 |
| No. 155 (1) | 1.40 | .30 |
| No. 82 (1) | 2.25 | .60 |
| No. 71 (1) | 1.60 | 1.60 |
| No. 27 (1) | 1.10 | 1.50 |
| No. 63 (1) | 1.40 | .65 |
| No. 71 (1) | 2.25 | .25 |
| No. 27 (1) | 1.75 | .30 |
| No. 126 (1) | 1.60 | .25 |
| No. 28 (1) | 1.75 | 4.00 |
| No. 101 (1) | 1.75 | .25 |
| No. 74 (1) | 1.50 | 1.00 |
| No. 241 (1) | .50 | .25 |
| No. 250 (1) | 1.00 | .25 |
| No. 127 (1) | .65 | .50 |
| No. 77 (1) | .75 | .60 |
| No. 79 (1) | .45 | .25 |
| No. 260 (1) | 2.00 | 1.00 |
| No. 60 (1) | .70 | .25 |
| No. 96 (1) | .75 | .75 |
| No. 19 (1) | 2.25 | 2.25 |
| No. 139 (1) | 1.25 | 1.25 |
| No. 119 (1) | .35 | .25 |
| No. 156 (1) | .70 | .35 |
| No. 185 (1) | .50 | .30 |
| No. 196 (1) | 2.00 | 1.75 |
| No. 172 (1) | .80 | .80 |
| No. 194 (1) | .40 | .40 |
| No. 27 (1) | 2.50 | .40 |
| No. 88 (1) | 1.00 | 1.00 |
| No. 127 (1) | .40 | .25 |
| No. 54 (1) | .30 | .25 |
| No. 84 (1) | .25 | .25 |
| No. 13 (1) | 1.00 | 1.75 |
| No. 118 (1) | .40 | 1.10 |
| No. 114 (1) | .40 | 1.00 |
| Nos. 313-316 (4) | 16.35 | 5.95 |
| Nos. 579-582 (4) | 7.40 | 5.20 |
| Nos. 259-261 (3) | 4.60 | 3.25 |
| Nos. 92-95 (4) | 15.25 | 12.75 |
| No. 330 (1) | .25 | .25 |
| No. 317 (1) | 1.50 | .25 |
| Nos. 145-146 (2) | 2.65 | 2.65 |
| Nos. 113-116 (4) | 16.00 | 8.50 |
| Nos. 280-284 (5) | 5.65 | 6.85 |
| Nos. 104-105 (2) | 1.60 | 1.60 |
| Nos. 52-55 (4) | 15.25 | 6.50 |
| Nos. 214-215 (2) | 2.10 | 1.00 |
| No. 192 (1) | .30 | .25 |
| No. 80 (1) | 7.25 | 7.25 |
| Nos. 244-248 (5) | 3.00 | 2.35 |
| No. 4 (1) | 2.75 | 2.75 |
| Set total (106) Stamps | 169.00 | 118.45 |

Separate designs for each country for the visit of Queen Elizabeth II and the Duke of Edinburgh.

### Royal Visit 1953

**1953**

Aden ..........62
Australia ..........267-269
Bermuda ..........163
Ceylon ..........318
Fiji ..........146
Gibraltar ..........146
Jamaica ..........154
Kenya, Uganda, Tanzania ..........102
Malta ..........242
New Zealand ..........286-287

| | | |
|---|---|---|
| No. 62 (1) | .65 | 1.25 |
| Nos. 267-269 (3) | 2.35 | 1.90 |
| No. 163 (1) | .50 | .25 |
| No. 318 (1) | 1.25 | .25 |
| No. 146 (1) | .65 | .35 |
| No. 146 (1) | .50 | .30 |
| No. 154 (1) | .50 | .25 |
| No. 102 (1) | .50 | .25 |
| No. 242 (1) | .35 | .25 |
| Nos. 286-287 (2) | .50 | .50 |
| Set total (13) Stamps | 7.75 | 5.55 |

### West Indies Federation

Map of the Caribbean CD313

Federation of the West Indies, April 22, 1958.

**1958**

Antigua ..........122-124
Barbados ..........248-250
Dominica ..........161-163
Grenada ..........184-186
Jamaica ..........175-177
Montserrat ..........143-145
St. Kitts-Nevis ..........136-138
St. Lucia ..........170-172
St. Vincent ..........198-200
Trinidad & Tobago ..........86-88

| | | |
|---|---|---|
| Nos. 122-124 (3) | 5.80 | 3.80 |
| Nos. 248-250 (3) | 1.60 | 2.90 |
| Nos. 161-163 (3) | 1.95 | 1.85 |
| Nos. 184-186 (3) | 1.50 | 1.20 |
| Nos. 175-177 (3) | 2.65 | 3.45 |
| Nos. 143-145 (3) | 2.35 | 1.35 |
| Nos. 136-138 (3) | 3.00 | 3.10 |
| Nos. 170-172 (3) | 2.05 | 2.80 |
| Nos. 198-200 (3) | 1.50 | 1.75 |
| Nos. 86-88 (3) | .75 | .90 |
| Set total (30) Stamps | 23.15 | 23.10 |

### Freedom from Hunger

Protein Food CD314

U.N. Food and Agricultural Organization's "Freedom from Hunger" campaign.

**1963**

Aden ..........65
Antigua ..........133
Ascension ..........89
Bahamas ..........180
Basutoland ..........83
Bechuanaland Protectorate ..........194
Bermuda ..........192
British Guiana ..........271
British Honduras ..........179
Brunei ..........100
Cayman Islands ..........168
Dominica ..........181
Falkland Islands ..........146
Fiji ..........198
Gambia ..........172
Gibraltar ..........161
Gilbert & Ellice Islands ..........76
Grenada ..........190
Hong Kong ..........218
Malta ..........291
Mauritius ..........270
Montserrat ..........150
New Hebrides, British ..........93
North Borneo ..........296
Pitcairn Islands ..........35
St. Helena ..........173
St. Lucia ..........179
St. Vincent ..........201
Sarawak ..........212
Seychelles ..........213
Solomon Islands ..........109
Swaziland ..........108
Tonga ..........127
Tristan da Cunha ..........68
Turks & Caicos Islands ..........138
Virgin Islands ..........140
Zanzibar ..........280

| | | |
|---|---|---|
| No. 65 (1) | 1.50 | 1.75 |
| No. 133 (1) | .35 | .35 |
| No. 89 (1) | 1.00 | .50 |
| No. 180 (1) | .65 | .65 |
| No. 83 (1) | .50 | .25 |
| No. 194 (1) | .50 | .50 |
| No. 192 (1) | 1.00 | .50 |
| No. 271 (1) | .45 | .25 |
| No. 179 (1) | .60 | .25 |
| No. 100 (1) | 3.25 | 2.25 |
| No. 168 (1) | .55 | .30 |
| No. 181 (1) | .30 | .30 |
| No. 146 (1) | 10.50 | 2.50 |
| No. 198 (1) | 3.50 | 2.25 |
| No. 172 (1) | .50 | .25 |
| No. 161 (1) | 4.00 | 2.25 |
| No. 76 (1) | 1.40 | .40 |
| No. 190 (1) | .30 | .25 |
| No. 218 (1) | 47.50 | 7.50 |
| No. 291 (1) | 2.00 | 2.00 |
| No. 270 (1) | .50 | .50 |
| No. 150 (1) | .55 | .45 |
| No. 93 (1) | .60 | .25 |
| No. 296 (1) | 1.90 | .75 |
| No. 35 (1) | 10.00 | 4.50 |
| No. 173 (1) | 2.25 | 1.10 |
| No. 179 (1) | .40 | .40 |
| No. 201 (1) | .90 | .50 |
| No. 212 (1) | 1.60 | 1.75 |
| No. 213 (1) | .85 | .35 |
| No. 109 (1) | 3.00 | .85 |
| No. 108 (1) | .50 | .50 |
| No. 127 (1) | .60 | .35 |
| No. 68 (1) | .75 | .35 |
| No. 138 (1) | .50 | .25 |
| No. 140 (1) | .50 | .50 |
| No. 280 (1) | 1.50 | .80 |
| Set total (37) Stamps | 107.25 | 39.40 |

### Red Cross Centenary

Red Cross and Elizabeth II CD315

**1963**

Antigua ..........134-135
Ascension ..........90-91
Bahamas ..........183-184
Basutoland ..........84-85
Bechuanaland Protectorate ..........195-196
Bermuda ..........193-194
British Guiana ..........272-273
British Honduras ..........180-181
Cayman Islands ..........169-170
Dominica ..........182-183
Falkland Islands ..........147-148
Fiji ..........203-204
Gambia ..........173-174
Gibraltar ..........162-163
Gilbert & Ellice Islands ..........77-78
Grenada ..........191-192
Hong Kong ..........219-220
Jamaica ..........203-204
Malta ..........292-293
Mauritius ..........271-272
Montserrat ..........151-152
New Hebrides, British ..........94-95
Pitcairn Islands ..........36-37
St. Helena ..........174-175
St. Kitts-Nevis ..........143-144
St. Lucia ..........180-181
St. Vincent ..........202-203
Seychelles ..........214-215
Solomon Islands ..........110-111
South Arabia ..........1-2
Swaziland ..........109-110
Tonga ..........134-135
Tristan da Cunha ..........69-70
Turks & Caicos Islands ..........139-140
Virgin Islands ..........141-142

| | | |
|---|---|---|
| Nos. 134-135 (2) | 1.00 | 2.00 |
| Nos. 90-91 (2) | 6.75 | 3.35 |
| Nos. 183-184 (2) | 2.30 | 2.80 |
| Nos. 84-85 (2) | 1.20 | .90 |
| Nos. 195-196 (2) | .95 | .85 |
| Nos. 193-194 (2) | 3.00 | 2.80 |
| Nos. 272-273 (2) | 1.05 | .80 |
| Nos. 180-181 (2) | 1.00 | 2.50 |
| Nos. 169-170 (2) | 1.10 | 3.00 |
| Nos. 182-183 (2) | .70 | 1.05 |
| Nos. 147-148 (2) | 18.00 | 5.50 |
| Nos. 203-204 (2) | 3.25 | 2.80 |
| Nos. 173-174 (2) | .75 | 1.00 |
| Nos. 162-163 (2) | 6.25 | 5.40 |
| Nos. 77-78 (2) | 2.00 | 3.50 |
| Nos. 191-192 (2) | .80 | .50 |
| Nos. 219-220 (2) | 35.00 | 7.35 |
| Nos. 203-204 (2) | .75 | 1.65 |
| Nos. 292-293 (2) | 2.50 | 4.75 |
| Nos. 271-272 (2) | .90 | .90 |
| Nos. 151-152 (2) | 1.00 | .80 |
| Nos. 94-95 (2) | 1.00 | .50 |
| Nos. 36-37 (2) | 6.50 | 5.50 |
| Nos. 174-175 (2) | 1.70 | 2.30 |
| Nos. 143-144 (2) | .90 | .90 |
| Nos. 180-181 (2) | 1.25 | 1.25 |
| Nos. 202-203 (2) | .90 | .90 |
| Nos. 214-215 (2) | 1.10 | .90 |
| Nos. 110-111 (2) | 1.25 | 1.15 |
| Nos. 1-2 (2) | 1.25 | 1.25 |
| Nos. 109-110 (2) | 1.10 | 1.10 |
| Nos. 134-135 (2) | 1.00 | 1.25 |
| Nos. 69-70 (2) | 1.15 | .80 |
| Nos. 139-140 (2) | .85 | .75 |
| Nos. 141-142 (2) | .80 | 1.25 |
| Set total (70) Stamps | 111.00 | 74.00 |

### Shakespeare

Shakespeare Memorial Theatre, Stratford-on-Avon — CD316

400th anniversary of the birth of William Shakespeare.

**1964**

Antigua ..........151
Bahamas ..........201
Bechuanaland Protectorate ..........197
Cayman Islands ..........171
Dominica ..........184
Falkland Islands ..........149
Gambia ..........192
Gibraltar ..........164
Montserrat ..........153
St. Lucia ..........196
Turks & Caicos Islands ..........141
Virgin Islands ..........143

| | | |
|---|---|---|
| No. 151 (1) | .35 | .25 |
| No. 201 (1) | .60 | .35 |
| No. 197 (1) | .35 | .35 |
| No. 171 (1) | .35 | .30 |
| No. 184 (1) | .35 | .35 |
| No. 149 (1) | 1.60 | .50 |
| No. 192 (1) | .35 | .25 |
| No. 164 (1) | .65 | .55 |
| No. 153 (1) | .35 | .25 |
| No. 196 (1) | .45 | .25 |
| No. 141 (1) | .40 | .25 |
| No. 143 (1) | .45 | .45 |
| Set total (12) Stamps | 6.25 | 4.10 |

### ITU

ITU Emblem CD317

Intl. Telecommunication Union, cent.

**1965**

Antigua ..........153-154
Ascension ..........92-93
Bahamas ..........219-220
Barbados ..........265-266
Basutoland ..........101-102
Bechuanaland Protectorate ..........202-203
Bermuda ..........196-197
British Guiana ..........293-294
British Honduras ..........187-188
Brunei ..........116-117
Cayman Islands ..........172-173
Dominica ..........185-186
Falkland Islands ..........154-155
Fiji ..........211-212
Gibraltar ..........167-168
Gilbert & Ellice Islands ..........87-88
Grenada ..........205-206
Hong Kong ..........221-222
Mauritius ..........291-292
Montserrat ..........157-158
New Hebrides, British ..........108-109
Pitcairn Islands ..........52-53
St. Helena ..........180-181
St. Kitts-Nevis ..........163-164
St. Lucia ..........197-198
St. Vincent ..........224-225
Seychelles ..........218-219
Solomon Islands ..........126-127
Swaziland ..........115-116
Tristan da Cunha ..........85-86
Turks & Caicos Islands ..........142-143
Virgin Islands ..........159-160

| | | |
|---|---|---|
| Nos. 153-154 (2) | 1.45 | 1.35 |
| Nos. 92-93 (2) | 1.90 | 1.30 |
| Nos. 219-220 (2) | 1.35 | 1.50 |
| Nos. 265-266 (2) | 1.50 | 1.25 |
| Nos. 101-102 (2) | .85 | .65 |
| Nos. 202-203 (2) | 1.10 | .75 |
| Nos. 196-197 (2) | 2.15 | 2.25 |
| Nos. 293-294 (2) | .60 | .55 |
| Nos. 187-188 (2) | .75 | .75 |
| Nos. 116-117 (2) | 1.75 | 1.75 |
| Nos. 172-173 (2) | 1.00 | .85 |
| Nos. 185-186 (2) | .55 | .55 |
| Nos. 154-155 (2) | 6.75 | 3.15 |
| Nos. 211-212 (2) | 2.00 | 1.05 |
| Nos. 167-168 (2) | 9.00 | 5.95 |
| Nos. 87-88 (2) | .85 | .60 |
| Nos. 205-206 (2) | .50 | .50 |
| Nos. 221-222 (2) | 24.50 | 3.80 |
| Nos. 291-292 (2) | 1.20 | .65 |
| Nos. 157-158 (2) | 1.25 | 1.15 |
| Nos. 108-109 (2) | .65 | .50 |
| Nos. 52-53 (2) | 6.25 | 4.30 |
| Nos. 180-181 (2) | .80 | .60 |
| Nos. 163-164 (2) | .60 | .60 |
| Nos. 197-198 (2) | 1.25 | 1.25 |
| Nos. 224-225 (2) | .80 | .90 |
| Nos. 218-219 (2) | .90 | .60 |
| Nos. 126-127 (2) | .70 | .55 |
| Nos. 115-116 (2) | .75 | .75 |
| Nos. 85-86 (2) | 1.00 | .65 |
| Nos. 142-143 (2) | .75 | .50 |
| Nos. 159-160 (2) | .85 | .85 |
| Set total (64) Stamps | 76.30 | 42.40 |

### Intl. Cooperation Year

ICY Emblem CD318

**1965**

| | |
|---|---|
| Antigua | 155-156 |
| Ascension | 94-95 |
| Bahamas | 222-223 |
| Basutoland | 103-104 |
| Bechuanaland Protectorate | 204-205 |
| Bermuda | 199-200 |
| British Guiana | 295-296 |
| British Honduras | 189-190 |
| Brunei | 118-119 |
| Cayman Islands | 174-175 |
| Dominica | 187-188 |
| Falkland Islands | 156-157 |
| Fiji | 213-214 |
| Gibraltar | 169-170 |
| Gilbert & Ellice Islands | 104-105 |
| Grenada | 207-208 |
| Hong Kong | 223-224 |
| Mauritius | 293-294 |
| Montserrat | 176-177 |
| New Hebrides, British | 110-111 |
| New Hebrides, French | 126-127 |
| Pitcairn Islands | 54-55 |
| St. Helena | 182-183 |
| St. Kitts-Nevis | 165-166 |
| St. Lucia | 199-200 |
| Seychelles | 220-221 |
| Solomon Islands | 143-144 |
| South Arabia | 17-18 |
| Swaziland | 117-118 |
| Tristan da Cunha | 87-88 |
| Turks & Caicos Islands | 144-145 |
| Virgin Islands | 161-162 |

| | | |
|---|---|---|
| *Nos. 155-156 (2)* | .55 | .50 |
| *Nos. 94-95 (2)* | 1.30 | 1.40 |
| *Nos. 222-223 (2)* | .65 | 1.90 |
| *Nos. 103-104 (2)* | .75 | .85 |
| *Nos. 204-205 (2)* | .85 | 1.00 |
| *Nos. 199-200 (2)* | 2.05 | 1.25 |
| *Nos. 295-296 (2)* | .65 | .60 |
| *Nos. 189-190 (2)* | .60 | .55 |
| *Nos. 118-119 (2)* | .85 | .85 |
| *Nos. 174-175 (2)* | 1.00 | .75 |
| *Nos. 187-188 (2)* | .55 | .55 |
| *Nos. 156-157 (2)* | 6.00 | 1.65 |
| *Nos. 213-214 (2)* | 1.95 | 1.25 |
| *Nos. 169-170 (2)* | 1.25 | *2.75* |
| *Nos. 104-105 (2)* | .85 | .60 |
| *Nos. 207-208 (2)* | .50 | .50 |
| *Nos. 223-224 (2)* | 22.00 | 3.10 |
| *Nos. 293-294 (2)* | .70 | .70 |
| *Nos. 176-177 (2)* | .80 | .65 |
| *Nos. 110-111 (2)* | .50 | .50 |
| *Nos. 126-127 (2)* | 12.00 | 12.00 |
| *Nos. 54-55 (2)* | 6.35 | 4.50 |
| *Nos. 182-183 (2)* | .95 | .50 |
| *Nos. 165-166 (2)* | .80 | .60 |
| *Nos. 199-200 (2)* | .55 | .55 |
| *Nos. 220-221 (2)* | .90 | .65 |
| *Nos. 143-144 (2)* | .70 | .60 |
| *Nos. 17-18 (2)* | 1.20 | .50 |
| *Nos. 117-118 (2)* | .75 | .75 |
| *Nos. 87-88 (2)* | 1.05 | .65 |
| *Nos. 144-145 (2)* | .65 | .50 |
| *Nos. 161-162 (2)* | .65 | .50 |
| *Set total (64) Stamps* | 70.90 | 44.20 |

### Churchill Memorial

Winston Churchill and St. Paul's, London, During Air Attack CD319

**1966**

| | |
|---|---|
| Antigua | 157-160 |
| Ascension | 96-99 |
| Bahamas | 224-227 |
| Barbados | 281-284 |
| Basutoland | 105-108 |
| Bechuanaland Protectorate | 206-209 |
| Bermuda | 201-204 |
| British Antarctic Territory | 16-19 |
| British Honduras | 191-194 |
| Brunei | 120-123 |
| Cayman Islands | 176-179 |
| Dominica | 189-192 |
| Falkland Islands | 158-161 |
| Fiji | 215-218 |
| Gibraltar | 171-174 |
| Gilbert & Ellice Islands | 106-109 |
| Grenada | 209-212 |
| Hong Kong | 225-228 |
| Mauritius | 295-298 |
| Montserrat | 178-181 |
| New Hebrides, British | 112-115 |
| New Hebrides, French | 128-131 |
| Pitcairn Islands | 56-59 |
| St. Helena | 184-187 |
| St. Kitts-Nevis | 167-170 |
| St. Lucia | 201-204 |
| St. Vincent | 241-244 |
| Seychelles | 222-225 |
| Solomon Islands | 145-148 |
| South Arabia | 19-22 |
| Swaziland | 119-122 |
| Tristan da Cunha | 89-92 |
| Turks & Caicos Islands | 146-149 |
| Virgin Islands | 163-166 |

| | | |
|---|---|---|
| *Nos. 157-160 (4)* | 3.05 | 3.05 |
| *Nos. 96-99 (4)* | 10.00 | 6.40 |
| *Nos. 224-227 (4)* | 2.30 | *3.20* |
| *Nos. 281-284 (4)* | 3.00 | 4.45 |
| *Nos. 105-108 (4)* | 2.80 | 3.25 |
| *Nos. 206-209 (4)* | 2.50 | 2.50 |
| *Nos. 201-204 (4)* | 4.00 | *4.75* |
| *Nos. 16-19 (4)* | 37.85 | 18.00 |
| *Nos. 191-194 (4)* | 2.45 | 1.30 |
| *Nos. 120-123 (4)* | 7.65 | 6.55 |
| *Nos. 176-179 (4)* | 3.10 | 3.65 |
| *Nos. 189-192 (4)* | 1.15 | 1.15 |
| *Nos. 158-161 (4)* | 12.75 | 9.55 |
| *Nos. 215-218 (4)* | 4.40 | 3.00 |
| *Nos. 171-174 (4)* | 3.05 | 5.30 |
| *Nos. 106-109 (4)* | 1.50 | 1.30 |
| *Nos. 209-212 (4)* | 1.10 | 1.10 |
| *Nos. 225-228 (4)* | 52.50 | 11.40 |
| *Nos. 295-298 (4)* | 4.05 | 4.05 |
| *Nos. 178-181 (4)* | 1.60 | 1.55 |
| *Nos. 112-115 (4)* | 2.30 | 1.00 |
| *Nos. 128-131 (4)* | 10.25 | 10.25 |
| *Nos. 56-59 (4)* | 11.00 | 6.75 |
| *Nos. 184-187 (4)* | 1.85 | 1.95 |
| *Nos. 167-170 (4)* | 1.50 | 1.70 |
| *Nos. 201-204 (4)* | 1.50 | 1.50 |
| *Nos. 241-244 (4)* | 1.50 | 1.75 |
| *Nos. 222-225 (4)* | 3.20 | 3.60 |
| *Nos. 145-148 (4)* | 1.50 | 1.60 |
| *Nos. 19-22 (4)* | 2.95 | 2.20 |
| *Nos. 119-122 (4)* | 1.70 | 2.55 |
| *Nos. 89-92 (4)* | 5.95 | 2.70 |
| *Nos. 146-149 (4)* | 1.60 | 1.75 |
| *Nos. 163-166 (4)* | 1.90 | 1.90 |
| *Set total (136) Stamps* | 209.50 | 136.70 |

### Royal Visit, 1966

Queen Elizabeth II and Prince Philip CD320

Caribbean visit, Feb. 4 - Mar. 6, 1966.

**1966**

| | |
|---|---|
| Antigua | 161-162 |
| Bahamas | 228-229 |
| Barbados | 285-286 |
| British Guiana | 299-300 |
| Cayman Islands | 180-181 |
| Dominica | 193-194 |
| Grenada | 213-214 |
| Montserrat | 182-183 |
| St. Kitts-Nevis | 171-172 |
| St. Lucia | 205-206 |
| St. Vincent | 245-246 |
| Turks & Caicos Islands | 150-151 |
| Virgin Islands | 167-168 |

| | | |
|---|---|---|
| *Nos. 161-162 (2)* | 3.50 | 2.60 |
| *Nos. 228-229 (2)* | 3.05 | 3.05 |
| *Nos. 285-286 (2)* | 3.00 | 2.00 |
| *Nos. 299-300 (2)* | 3.35 | 1.60 |
| *Nos. 180-181 (2)* | 3.45 | 1.80 |
| *Nos. 193-194 (2)* | 3.00 | .60 |
| *Nos. 213-214 (2)* | .80 | .50 |
| *Nos. 182-183 (2)* | 1.70 | 1.00 |
| *Nos. 171-172 (2)* | .90 | .75 |
| *Nos. 205-206 (2)* | 1.50 | 1.35 |
| *Nos. 245-246 (2)* | 2.75 | 1.35 |
| *Nos. 150-151 (2)* | 1.20 | .55 |
| *Nos. 167-168 (2)* | 1.75 | 1.75 |
| *Set total (26) Stamps* | 29.95 | 18.90 |

### World Cup Soccer

Soccer Player and Jules Rimet Cup CD321

World Cup Soccer Championship, Wembley, England, July 11-30.

**1966**

| | |
|---|---|
| Antigua | 163-164 |
| Ascension | 100-101 |
| Bahamas | 245-246 |
| Bermuda | 205-206 |
| Brunei | 124-125 |
| Cayman Islands | 182-183 |
| Dominica | 195-196 |
| Fiji | 219-220 |
| Gibraltar | 175-176 |
| Gilbert & Ellice Islands | 125-126 |
| Grenada | 230-231 |
| New Hebrides, British | 116-117 |
| New Hebrides, French | 132-133 |
| Pitcairn Islands | 60-61 |
| St. Helena | 188-189 |
| St. Kitts-Nevis | 173-174 |
| St. Lucia | 207-208 |
| Seychelles | 226-227 |
| Solomon Islands | 167-168 |
| South Arabia | 23-24 |
| Tristan da Cunha | 93-94 |

| | | |
|---|---|---|
| *Nos. 163-164 (2)* | .80 | .85 |
| *Nos. 100-101 (2)* | 2.50 | 2.00 |
| *Nos. 245-246 (2)* | .65 | .65 |
| *Nos. 205-206 (2)* | 1.75 | 1.75 |
| *Nos. 124-125 (2)* | 1.30 | 1.25 |
| *Nos. 182-183 (2)* | .75 | .65 |
| *Nos. 195-196 (2)* | 1.20 | .75 |
| *Nos. 219-220 (2)* | 1.70 | .60 |
| *Nos. 175-176 (2)* | 1.85 | 1.75 |
| *Nos. 125-126 (2)* | .70 | .60 |
| *Nos. 230-231 (2)* | .65 | *.95* |
| *Nos. 116-117 (2)* | 1.00 | 1.00 |
| *Nos. 132-133 (2)* | 7.00 | 7.00 |
| *Nos. 60-61 (2)* | 5.50 | 5.00 |
| *Nos. 188-189 (2)* | 1.25 | .60 |
| *Nos. 173-174 (2)* | .85 | .80 |
| *Nos. 207-208 (2)* | 1.15 | .90 |
| *Nos. 226-227 (2)* | .85 | .85 |
| *Nos. 167-168 (2)* | 1.10 | 1.10 |
| *Nos. 23-24 (2)* | 1.90 | .55 |
| *Nos. 93-94 (2)* | 1.25 | .80 |
| *Set total (42) Stamps* | 35.70 | 30.40 |

### WHO Headquarters

World Health Organization Headquarters, Geneva — CD322

**1966**

| | |
|---|---|
| Antigua | 165-166 |
| Ascension | 102-103 |
| Bahamas | 247-248 |
| Brunei | 126-127 |
| Cayman Islands | 184-185 |
| Dominica | 197-198 |
| Fiji | 224-225 |
| Gibraltar | 180-181 |
| Gilbert & Ellice Islands | 127-128 |
| Grenada | 232-233 |
| Hong Kong | 229-230 |
| Montserrat | 184-185 |
| New Hebrides, British | 118-119 |
| New Hebrides, French | 134-135 |
| Pitcairn Islands | 62-63 |
| St. Helena | 190-191 |
| St. Kitts-Nevis | 177-178 |
| St. Lucia | 209-210 |
| St. Vincent | 247-248 |
| Seychelles | 228-229 |
| Solomon Islands | 169-170 |
| South Arabia | 25-26 |
| Tristan da Cunha | 99-100 |

| | | |
|---|---|---|
| *Nos. 165-166 (2)* | 1.15 | .55 |
| *Nos. 102-103 (2)* | 6.60 | 3.35 |
| *Nos. 247-248 (2)* | .80 | .80 |
| *Nos. 126-127 (2)* | 1.35 | 1.35 |
| *Nos. 184-185 (2)* | 2.25 | 1.20 |
| *Nos. 197-198 (2)* | .75 | .75 |
| *Nos. 224-225 (2)* | 4.70 | 3.30 |
| *Nos. 180-181 (2)* | 6.50 | 4.50 |
| *Nos. 127-128 (2)* | .80 | .70 |
| *Nos. 232-233 (2)* | .80 | .50 |
| *Nos. 229-230 (2)* | 11.25 | 2.30 |
| *Nos. 184-185 (2)* | 1.00 | 1.00 |
| *Nos. 118-119 (2)* | .75 | .50 |
| *Nos. 134-135 (2)* | 8.75 | 8.75 |
| *Nos. 62-63 (2)* | 7.25 | 6.50 |
| *Nos. 190-191 (2)* | 3.50 | 1.50 |
| *Nos. 177-178 (2)* | .60 | .60 |
| *Nos. 209-210 (2)* | .80 | .80 |
| *Nos. 247-248 (2)* | 1.15 | 1.05 |
| *Nos. 228-229 (2)* | 1.25 | .75 |
| *Nos. 169-170 (2)* | .95 | .80 |
| *Nos. 25-26 (2)* | 2.10 | .70 |
| *Nos. 99-100 (2)* | 1.90 | 1.25 |
| *Set total (46) Stamps* | 66.95 | 43.50 |

### UNESCO Anniversary

"Education" — CD323

"Science" (Wheat ears & flask enclosing globe). "Culture" (lyre & columns). 20th anniversary of the UNESCO.

**1966-67**

| | |
|---|---|
| Antigua | 183-185 |
| Ascension | 108-110 |
| Bahamas | 249-251 |
| Barbados | 287-289 |
| Bermuda | 207-209 |
| Brunei | 128-130 |
| Cayman Islands | 186-188 |
| Dominica | 199-201 |
| Gibraltar | 183-185 |
| Gilbert & Ellice Islands | 129-131 |
| Grenada | 234-236 |
| Hong Kong | 231-233 |
| Mauritius | 299-301 |
| Montserrat | 186-188 |
| New Hebrides, British | 120-122 |
| New Hebrides, French | 136-138 |
| Pitcairn Islands | 64-66 |
| St. Helena | 192-194 |
| St. Kitts-Nevis | 179-181 |
| St. Lucia | 211-213 |
| St. Vincent | 249-251 |
| Seychelles | 230-232 |
| Solomon Islands | 171-173 |
| South Arabia | 27-29 |
| Swaziland | 123-125 |
| Tristan da Cunha | 101-103 |
| Turks & Caicos Islands | 155-157 |
| Virgin Islands | 176-178 |

| | | |
|---|---|---|
| *Nos. 183-185 (3)* | 1.90 | *2.50* |
| *Nos. 108-110 (3)* | 11.00 | 5.80 |
| *Nos. 249-251 (3)* | 2.35 | 2.35 |
| *Nos. 287-289 (3)* | 2.50 | 2.15 |
| *Nos. 207-209 (3)* | 3.80 | *3.90* |
| *Nos. 128-130 (3)* | 4.65 | 5.40 |
| *Nos. 186-188 (3)* | 2.50 | 1.50 |
| *Nos. 199-201 (3)* | 1.60 | .75 |
| *Nos. 183-185 (3)* | 6.50 | 3.25 |
| *Nos. 129-131 (3)* | 2.50 | *2.45* |
| *Nos. 234-236 (3)* | 1.10 | 1.20 |
| *Nos. 231-233 (3)* | 69.50 | 17.50 |
| *Nos. 299-301 (3)* | 2.10 | 1.50 |
| *Nos. 186-188 (3)* | 2.40 | 2.40 |
| *Nos. 120-122 (3)* | 1.90 | 1.90 |
| *Nos. 136-138 (3)* | 7.75 | 7.75 |
| *Nos. 64-66 (3)* | 7.10 | 4.75 |
| *Nos. 192-194 (3)* | 5.25 | 3.65 |
| *Nos. 179-181 (3)* | .90 | .90 |
| *Nos. 211-213 (3)* | 1.15 | 1.15 |
| *Nos. 249-251 (3)* | 2.30 | 1.35 |
| *Nos. 230-232 (3)* | 2.40 | 2.40 |
| *Nos. 171-173 (3)* | 2.00 | 1.50 |
| *Nos. 27-29 (3)* | 5.50 | 5.50 |
| *Nos. 123-125 (3)* | 1.45 | 1.45 |
| *Nos. 101-103 (3)* | 2.00 | 1.40 |
| *Nos. 155-157 (3)* | 1.05 | .90 |
| *Nos. 176-178 (3)* | 1.40 | 1.30 |
| *Set total (84) Stamps* | 156.55 | 88.55 |

### Silver Wedding, 1972

Queen Elizabeth II and Prince Philip — CD324

Designs: borders differ for each country.

**1972**

| | |
|---|---|
| Anguilla | 161-162 |
| Antigua | 295-296 |
| Ascension | 164-165 |
| Bahamas | 344-345 |
| Bermuda | 296-297 |
| British Antarctic Territory | 43-44 |
| British Honduras | 306-307 |
| British Indian Ocean Territory | 48-49 |

Brunei ....................186-187
Cayman Islands ....................304-305
Dominica ....................352-353
Falkland Islands ....................223-224
Fiji ....................328-329
Gibraltar ....................292-293
Gilbert & Ellice Islands ....................206-207
Grenada ....................466-467
Hong Kong ....................271-272
Montserrat ....................286-287
New Hebrides, British ....................169-170
New Hebrides, French ....................188-189
Pitcairn Islands ....................127-128
St. Helena ....................271-272
St. Kitts-Nevis ....................257-258
St. Lucia ....................328-329
St.Vincent ....................344-345
Seychelles ....................309-310
Solomon Islands ....................248-249
South Georgia ....................35-36
Tristan da Cunha ....................178-179
Turks & Caicos Islands ....................257-258
Virgin Islands ....................241-242

| | | |
|---|---|---|
| *Nos. 161-162 (2)* | 1.30 | *1.50* |
| *Nos. 295-296 (2)* | .50 | .50 |
| *Nos. 164-165 (2)* | .70 | .70 |
| *Nos. 344-345 (2)* | .60 | .60 |
| *Nos. 296-297 (2)* | .50 | *.65* |
| *Nos. 43-44 (2)* | 7.75 | 6.10 |
| *Nos. 306-307 (2)* | .80 | .80 |
| *Nos. 48-49 (2)* | 2.00 | 1.00 |
| *Nos. 186-187 (2)* | .70 | .70 |
| *Nos. 304-305 (2)* | .75 | .75 |
| *Nos. 352-353 (2)* | .65 | .65 |
| *Nos. 223-224 (2)* | 1.00 | 1.15 |
| *Nos. 328-329 (2)* | .70 | .70 |
| *Nos. 292-293 (2)* | .50 | .50 |
| *Nos. 206-207 (2)* | .50 | .50 |
| *Nos. 466-467 (2)* | .70 | .70 |
| *Nos. 271-272 (2)* | 1.70 | 1.50 |
| *Nos. 286-287 (2)* | .55 | .55 |
| *Nos. 169-170 (2)* | .50 | .50 |
| *Nos. 188-189 (2)* | 1.05 | 1.05 |
| *Nos. 127-128 (2)* | .90 | .85 |
| *Nos. 271-272 (2)* | .70 | 1.20 |
| *Nos. 257-258 (2)* | .65 | .50 |
| *Nos. 328-329 (2)* | .75 | .75 |
| *Nos. 344-345 (2)* | .55 | .55 |
| *Nos. 309-310 (2)* | .95 | .95 |
| *Nos. 248-249 (2)* | .50 | .50 |
| *Nos. 35-36 (2)* | 1.40 | 1.40 |
| *Nos. 178-179 (2)* | .70 | .70 |
| *Nos. 257-258 (2)* | .50 | .50 |
| *Nos. 241-242 (2)* | .50 | .50 |
| *Set total (62) Stamps* | 31.55 | 29.50 |

### Princess Anne's Wedding

Princess Anne and Mark Phillips — CD325

Wedding of Princess Anne and Mark Phillips, Nov. 14, 1973.

**1973**

Anguilla ....................179-180
Ascension ....................177-178
Belize ....................325-326
Bermuda ....................302-303
British Antarctic Territory ....................60-61
Cayman Islands ....................320-321
Falkland Islands ....................225-226
Gibraltar ....................305-306
Gilbert & Ellice Islands ....................216-217
Hong Kong ....................289-290
Montserrat ....................300-301
Pitcairn Islands ....................135-136
St. Helena ....................277-278
St. Kitts-Nevis ....................274-275
St. Lucia ....................349-350
St. Vincent ....................358-359
St. Vincent Grenadines ....................1-2
Seychelles ....................311-312
Solomon Islands ....................259-260
South Georgia ....................37-38
Tristan da Cunha ....................189-190
Turks & Caicos Islands ....................286-287
Virgin Islands ....................260-261

| | | |
|---|---|---|
| *Nos. 179-180 (2)* | .55 | .55 |
| *Nos. 177-178 (2)* | .60 | .60 |
| *Nos. 325-326 (2)* | .50 | .50 |
| *Nos. 302-303 (2)* | .50 | .50 |
| *Nos. 60-61 (2)* | 1.10 | 1.10 |
| *Nos. 320-321 (2)* | .50 | .50 |
| *Nos. 225-226 (2)* | .70 | .60 |
| *Nos. 305-306 (2)* | .55 | .55 |
| *Nos. 216-217 (2)* | .50 | .50 |
| *Nos. 289-290 (2)* | 2.65 | 2.00 |
| *Nos. 300-301 (2)* | .65 | .65 |
| *Nos. 135-136 (2)* | .70 | .60 |
| *Nos. 277-278 (2)* | .50 | .50 |
| *Nos. 274-275 (2)* | .50 | .50 |
| *Nos. 349-350 (2)* | .50 | .50 |
| *Nos. 358-359 (2)* | .50 | .50 |
| *Nos. 1-2 (2)* | .50 | .50 |
| *Nos. 311-312 (2)* | .70 | .70 |
| *Nos. 259-260 (2)* | .70 | .70 |
| *Nos. 37-38 (2)* | .75 | .75 |
| *Nos. 189-190 (2)* | .50 | .50 |
| *Nos. 286-287 (2)* | .50 | .50 |
| *Nos. 260-261 (2)* | .50 | .50 |
| *Set total (46) Stamps* | 15.65 | 14.80 |

### Elizabeth II Coronation Anniv.

CD326

CD327

CD328

Designs: Royal and local beasts in heraldic form and simulated stonework. Portrait of Elizabeth II by Peter Grugeon. 25th anniversary of coronation of Queen Elizabeth II.

**1978**

Ascension ....................229
Barbados ....................474
Belize ....................397
British Antarctic Territory ....................71
Cayman Islands ....................404
Christmas Island ....................87
Falkland Islands ....................275
Fiji ....................384
Gambia ....................380
Gilbert Islands ....................312
Mauritius ....................464
New Hebrides, British ....................258
New Hebrides, French ....................278
St. Helena ....................317
St. Kitts-Nevis ....................354
Samoa ....................472
Solomon Islands ....................368
South Georgia ....................51
Swaziland ....................302
Tristan da Cunha ....................238
Virgin Islands ....................337

| | | |
|---|---|---|
| *No. 229 (1)* | 2.00 | 2.00 |
| *No. 474 (1)* | 1.35 | 1.35 |
| *No. 397 (1)* | 1.40 | 1.75 |
| *No. 71 (1)* | 6.00 | 6.00 |
| *No. 404 (1)* | 2.00 | 2.00 |
| *No. 87 (1)* | 3.50 | *4.00* |
| *No. 275 (1)* | 4.00 | 5.50 |
| *No. 384 (1)* | 1.75 | 1.75 |
| *No. 380 (1)* | 1.50 | 1.50 |
| *No. 312 (1)* | 1.25 | 1.25 |
| *No. 464 (1)* | 2.75 | 2.75 |
| *No. 258 (1)* | 1.75 | 1.75 |
| *No. 278 (1)* | 3.50 | 3.50 |
| *No. 317 (1)* | 1.75 | 1.75 |
| *No. 354 (1)* | 1.00 | 1.00 |
| *No. 472 (1)* | 2.00 | 2.00 |
| *No. 368 (1)* | 2.50 | 2.50 |
| *No. 51 (1)* | 3.00 | 3.00 |
| *No. 302 (1)* | 1.75 | 1.75 |
| *No. 238 (1)* | 1.50 | 1.50 |
| *No. 337 (1)* | 1.80 | 1.80 |
| *Set total (21) Stamps* | 48.05 | 50.40 |

### Queen Mother Elizabeth's 80th Birthday

CD330

Designs: Photographs of Queen Mother Elizabeth. Falkland Islands issued in sheets of 50; others in sheets of 9.

**1980**

Ascension ....................261
Bermuda ....................401
Cayman Islands ....................443
Falkland Islands ....................305
Gambia ....................412
Gibraltar ....................393
Hong Kong ....................364
Pitcairn Islands ....................193
St. Helena ....................341
Samoa ....................532
Solomon Islands ....................426
Tristan da Cunha ....................277

| | | |
|---|---|---|
| *No. 261 (1)* | .40 | .40 |
| *No. 401 (1)* | .45 | .75 |
| *No. 443 (1)* | .40 | .40 |
| *No. 305 (1)* | .40 | .40 |
| *No. 412 (1)* | .40 | .50 |
| *No. 393 (1)* | .35 | .35 |
| *No. 364 (1)* | 1.10 | 1.25 |
| *No. 193 (1)* | .60 | .60 |
| *No. 341 (1)* | .50 | .50 |
| *No. 532 (1)* | .55 | .55 |
| *No. 426 (1)* | .50 | .50 |
| *No. 277 (1)* | .45 | .45 |
| *Set total (12) Stamps* | 6.10 | 6.65 |

### Royal Wedding, 1981

Prince Charles and Lady Diana — CD331

CD331a

Wedding of Charles, Prince of Wales, and Lady Diana Spencer, St. Paul's Cathedral, London, July 29, 1981.

**1981**

Antigua ....................623-627
Ascension ....................294-296
Barbados ....................547-549
Barbuda ....................497-501
Bermuda ....................412-414
Brunei ....................268-270
Cayman Islands ....................471-473
Dominica ....................701-705
Falkland Islands ....................324-326
Falkland Islands Dep. ....................1L59-1L61
Fiji ....................442-444
Gambia ....................426-428
Ghana ....................759-764
Grenada ....................1051-1055
Grenada Grenadines ....................440-443
Hong Kong ....................373-375
Jamaica ....................500-503
Lesotho ....................335-337
Maldive Islands ....................906-909
Mauritius ....................520-522
Norfolk Island ....................280-282
Pitcairn Islands ....................206-208
St. Helena ....................353-355
St. Lucia ....................543-549
Samoa ....................558-560
Sierra Leone ....................509-518
Solomon Islands ....................450-452
Swaziland ....................382-384
Tristan da Cunha ....................294-296
Turks & Caicos Islands ....................486-489
Caicos Island ....................8-11
Uganda ....................314-317
Vanuatu ....................308-310
Virgin Islands ....................406-408

| | | |
|---|---|---|
| *Nos. 623-627 (5)* | 6.55 | 2.55 |
| *Nos. 294-296 (3)* | 1.00 | 1.00 |
| *Nos. 547-549 (3)* | .90 | .90 |
| *Nos. 497-501 (5)* | 10.95 | 10.95 |
| *Nos. 412-414 (3)* | 2.00 | 2.00 |
| *Nos. 268-270 (3)* | 2.15 | *4.50* |
| *Nos. 471-473 (3)* | 1.20 | 1.30 |
| *Nos. 701-705 (5)* | 8.35 | 2.35 |
| *Nos. 324-326 (3)* | 1.65 | 1.70 |
| *Nos. 1L59-1L61 (3)* | 1.45 | 1.45 |
| *Nos. 442-444 (3)* | 1.35 | 1.35 |
| *Nos. 426-428 (3)* | .80 | .80 |
| *Nos. 759-764 (9)* | 6.20 | 6.20 |
| *Nos. 1051-1055 (5)* | 9.85 | 1.85 |
| *Nos. 440-443 (4)* | 2.35 | 2.35 |
| *Nos. 373-375 (3)* | 3.05 | 2.85 |
| *Nos. 500-503 (4)* | 1.45 | 1.35 |
| *Nos. 335-337 (3)* | .90 | .90 |
| *Nos. 906-909 (4)* | 1.55 | 1.55 |
| *Nos. 520-522 (3)* | 2.75 | 2.75 |
| *Nos. 280-282 (3)* | 1.35 | 1.35 |
| *Nos. 206-208 (3)* | 1.10 | 1.10 |
| *Nos. 353-355 (3)* | .85 | .85 |
| *Nos. 543-549 (5)* | 8.50 | 8.50 |
| *Nos. 558-560 (3)* | .85 | .85 |
| *Nos. 509-518 (10)* | 15.50 | 15.50 |
| *Nos. 450-452 (3)* | 1.25 | 1.25 |
| *Nos. 382-384 (3)* | 1.30 | 1.25 |
| *Nos. 294-296 (3)* | .90 | .90 |
| *Nos. 486-489 (4)* | 2.20 | 2.20 |
| *Nos. 8-11 (4)* | 5.00 | 5.00 |
| *Nos. 314-317 (4)* | 3.30 | 3.00 |
| *Nos. 308-310 (3)* | 1.15 | 1.15 |
| *Nos. 406-408 (3)* | 1.10 | 1.10 |
| *Set total (131) Stamps* | 110.80 | 94.65 |

### Princess Diana

CD332

CD333

Designs: Photographs and portrait of Princess Diana, wedding or honeymoon photographs, royal residences, arms of issuing country. Portrait photograph by Clive Friend. Souvenir sheet margins show family tree, various people related to the princess. 21st birthday of Princess Diana of Wales, July 1.

**1982**

Antigua ....................663-666
Ascension ....................313-316
Bahamas ....................510-513
Barbados ....................585-588
Barbuda ....................544-547
British Antarctic Territory ....................92-95
Cayman Islands ....................486-489
Dominica ....................773-776
Falkland Islands ....................348-351
Falkland Islands Dep. ....................1L72-1L75
Fiji ....................470-473
Gambia ....................447-450
Grenada ....................1101A-1105
Grenada Grenadines ....................485-491
Lesotho ....................372-375
Maldive Islands ....................952-955
Mauritius ....................548-551
Pitcairn Islands ....................213-216
St. Helena ....................372-375
St. Lucia ....................591-594
Sierra Leone ....................531-534
Solomon Islands ....................471-474
Swaziland ....................406-409
Tristan da Cunha ....................310-313
Turks and Caicos Islands ....................531-534
Virgin Islands ....................430-433

| | | |
|---|---|---|
| *Nos. 663-666 (4)* | 8.25 | 7.35 |
| *Nos. 313-316 (4)* | 3.50 | 3.50 |
| *Nos. 510-513 (4)* | 6.00 | 3.85 |
| *Nos. 585-588 (4)* | 3.40 | 3.25 |
| *Nos. 544-547 (4)* | 9.75 | 7.70 |
| *Nos. 92-95 (4)* | 5.30 | 3.45 |
| *Nos. 486-489 (4)* | *4.75* | *2.70* |
| *Nos. 773-776 (4)* | 7.05 | 7.05 |
| *Nos. 348-351 (4)* | 2.95 | 2.95 |
| *Nos. 1L72-1L75 (4)* | 2.50 | 2.60 |
| *Nos. 470-473 (4)* | 3.25 | 2.95 |
| *Nos. 447-450 (4)* | 2.85 | 2.85 |
| *Nos. 1101A-1105 (7)* | 16.05 | 15.55 |

| | | |
|---|---|---|
| Nos. 485-491 (7) | 17.65 | 17.65 |
| Nos. 372-375 (4) | 4.00 | 4.00 |
| Nos. 952-955 (4) | 5.50 | 3.90 |
| Nos. 548-551 (4) | 5.50 | 5.50 |
| Nos. 213-216 (4) | 2.15 | 2.15 |
| Nos. 372-375 (4) | 2.95 | 2.95 |
| Nos. 591-594 (4) | 9.90 | 9.90 |
| Nos. 531-534 (4) | 7.20 | 7.20 |
| Nos. 471-474 (4) | 2.90 | 2.90 |
| Nos. 406-409 (4) | 3.85 | 2.25 |
| Nos. 310-313 (4) | 3.65 | 1.45 |
| Nos. 486-489 (4) | 2.20 | 2.20 |
| Nos. 430-433 (4) | 3.00 | 3.00 |
| Set total (110) Stamps | 146.05 | 130.80 |

**250th anniv. of first edition of Lloyd's List (shipping news publication) & of Lloyd's marine insurance.**

CD335

Designs: First page of early edition of the list; historical ships, modern transportation or harbor scenes.

**1984**

| | |
|---|---|
| Ascension | 351-354 |
| Bahamas | 555-558 |
| Barbados | 627-630 |
| Cayes of Belize | 10-13 |
| Cayman Islands | 522-526 |
| Falkland Islands | 404-407 |
| Fiji | 509-512 |
| Gambia | 519-522 |
| Mauritius | 587-590 |
| Nauru | 280-283 |
| St. Helena | 412-415 |
| Samoa | 624-627 |
| Seychelles | 538-541 |
| Solomon Islands | 521-524 |
| Vanuatu | 368-371 |
| Virgin Islands | 466-469 |

| | | |
|---|---|---|
| Nos. 351-354 (4) | 2.90 | 2.55 |
| Nos. 555-558 (4) | 4.15 | 2.95 |
| Nos. 627-630 (4) | 6.10 | 5.15 |
| Nos. 10-13 (4) | 2.65 | 2.65 |
| Nos. 522-526 (5) | 9.30 | 8.45 |
| Nos. 404-407 (4) | 3.50 | 3.65 |
| Nos. 509-512 (4) | 5.30 | 4.90 |
| Nos. 519-522 (4) | 4.20 | 4.30 |
| Nos. 587-590 (4) | 8.95 | 8.95 |
| Nos. 280-283 (4) | 2.40 | 2.35 |
| Nos. 412-415 (4) | 2.40 | 2.40 |
| Nos. 624-627 (4) | 2.75 | 2.55 |
| Nos. 538-541 (4) | 5.25 | 5.25 |
| Nos. 521-524 (4) | 4.65 | 3.95 |
| Nos. 368-371 (4) | 2.40 | 2.40 |
| Nos. 466-469 (4) | 4.25 | 4.25 |
| Set total (65) Stamps | 71.15 | 66.70 |

**Queen Mother 85th Birthday**

CD336

Designs: Photographs tracing the life of the Queen Mother, Elizabeth. The high value in each set pictures the same photograph taken of the Queen Mother holding the infant Prince Henry.

**1985**

| | |
|---|---|
| Ascension | 372-376 |
| Bahamas | 580-584 |
| Barbados | 660-664 |
| Bermuda | 469-473 |
| Falkland Islands | 420-424 |
| Falkland Islands Dep. | 1L92-1L96 |
| Fiji | 531-535 |
| Hong Kong | 447-450 |
| Jamaica | 599-603 |
| Mauritius | 604-608 |
| Norfolk Island | 364-368 |
| Pitcairn Islands | 253-257 |
| St. Helena | 428-432 |
| Samoa | 649-653 |
| Seychelles | 567-571 |
| Zil Elwannyen Sesel | 101-105 |
| Solomon Islands | 543-547 |
| Swaziland | 476-480 |
| Tristan da Cunha | 372-376 |
| Vanuatu | 392-396 |

| | | |
|---|---|---|
| Nos. 372-376 (5) | 4.65 | 4.65 |
| Nos. 580-584 (5) | 7.70 | 6.45 |
| Nos. 660-664 (5) | 8.00 | 6.70 |
| Nos. 469-473 (5) | 9.40 | 9.40 |
| Nos. 420-424 (5) | 7.35 | 6.65 |
| Nos. 1L92-1L96 (5) | 8.00 | 8.00 |
| Nos. 531-535 (5) | 6.15 | 6.15 |
| Nos. 447-450 (4) | 9.50 | 8.50 |
| Nos. 599-603 (5) | 6.15 | 7.00 |
| Nos. 604-608 (5) | 11.80 | 11.80 |
| Nos. 364-368 (5) | 5.05 | 5.05 |
| Nos. 253-257 (5) | 5.25 | 5.95 |
| Nos. 428-432 (5) | 5.25 | 5.25 |
| Nos. 649-653 (5) | 8.65 | 7.80 |
| Nos. 567-571 (5) | 8.70 | 8.70 |
| Nos. 101-105 (5) | 7.15 | 7.15 |
| Nos. 543-547 (5) | 3.95 | 3.95 |
| Nos. 476-480 (5) | 8.00 | 7.50 |
| Nos. 372-376 (5) | 5.40 | 5.40 |
| Nos. 392-396 (5) | 5.25 | 5.25 |
| Set total (99) Stamps | 141.35 | 137.30 |

**Queen Elizabeth II, 60th Birthday**

CD337

**1986, April 21**

| | |
|---|---|
| Ascension | 389-393 |
| Bahamas | 592-596 |
| Barbados | 675-679 |
| Bermuda | 499-503 |
| Cayman Islands | 555-559 |
| Falkland Islands | 441-445 |
| Fiji | 544-548 |
| Hong Kong | 465-469 |
| Jamaica | 620-624 |
| Kiribati | 470-474 |
| Mauritius | 629-633 |
| Papua New Guinea | 640-644 |
| Pitcairn Islands | 270-274 |
| St. Helena | 451-455 |
| Samoa | 670-674 |
| Seychelles | 592-596 |
| Zil Elwannyen Sesel | 114-118 |
| Solomon Islands | 562-566 |
| South Georgia | 101-105 |
| Swaziland | 490-494 |
| Tristan da Cunha | 388-392 |
| Vanuatu | 414-418 |
| Zambia | 343-347 |

| | | |
|---|---|---|
| Nos. 389-393 (5) | 2.80 | 3.30 |
| Nos. 592-596 (5) | 2.75 | 3.70 |
| Nos. 675-679 (5) | 3.35 | 3.20 |
| Nos. 499-503 (5) | 4.65 | 5.15 |
| Nos. 555-559 (5) | 4.55 | 5.60 |
| Nos. 441-445 (5) | 3.95 | 4.95 |
| Nos. 544-548 (5) | 3.00 | 3.00 |
| Nos. 465-469 (5) | 8.75 | 6.75 |
| Nos. 620-624 (5) | 2.75 | 2.70 |
| Nos. 470-474 (5) | 2.10 | 2.10 |
| Nos. 629-633 (5) | 3.70 | 3.70 |
| Nos. 640-644 (5) | 4.50 | 4.50 |
| Nos. 270-274 (5) | 2.70 | 2.70 |
| Nos. 451-455 (5) | 3.05 | 3.05 |
| Nos. 670-674 (5) | 2.90 | 2.90 |
| Nos. 592-596 (5) | 2.70 | 2.70 |
| Nos. 114-118 (5) | 2.25 | 2.25 |
| Nos. 562-566 (5) | 2.90 | 2.90 |
| Nos. 101-105 (5) | 3.30 | 3.65 |
| Nos. 490-494 (5) | 2.30 | 2.30 |
| Nos. 388-392 (5) | 3.00 | 3.00 |
| Nos. 414-418 (5) | 3.10 | 3.10 |
| Nos. 343-347 (5) | 1.75 | 1.75 |
| Set total (115) Stamps | 76.80 | 78.95 |

**Royal Wedding**

Marriage of Prince Andrew and Sarah Ferguson CD338

**1986, July 23**

| | |
|---|---|
| Ascension | 399-400 |
| Bahamas | 602-603 |
| Barbados | 687-688 |
| Cayman Islands | 560-561 |
| Jamaica | 629-630 |
| Pitcairn Islands | 275-276 |
| St. Helena | 460-461 |
| St. Kitts | 181-182 |
| Seychelles | 602-603 |
| Zil Elwannyen Sesel | 119-120 |
| Solomon Islands | 567-568 |
| Tristan da Cunha | 397-398 |
| Zambia | 348-349 |

| | | |
|---|---|---|
| Nos. 399-400 (2) | 1.60 | 1.60 |
| Nos. 602-603 (2) | 2.75 | 2.75 |
| Nos. 687-688 (2) | 2.25 | 1.25 |
| Nos. 560-561 (2) | 1.70 | 2.35 |
| Nos. 629-630 (2) | 1.35 | 1.35 |
| Nos. 275-276 (2) | 2.40 | 2.40 |
| Nos. 460-461 (2) | 1.05 | 1.05 |
| Nos. 181-182 (2) | 1.50 | 2.25 |
| Nos. 602-603 (2) | 2.50 | 2.50 |
| Nos. 119-120 (2) | 2.30 | 2.30 |
| Nos. 567-568 (2) | 1.00 | 1.00 |
| Nos. 397-398 (2) | 1.40 | 1.40 |
| Nos. 348-349 (2) | 1.10 | 1.30 |
| Set total (26) Stamps | 22.90 | 23.50 |

**Queen Elizabeth II, 60th Birthday**

Queen Elizabeth II & Prince Philip, 1947 Wedding Portrait — CD339

Designs: Photographs tracing the life of Queen Elizabeth II.

**1986**

| | |
|---|---|
| Anguilla | 674-677 |
| Antigua | 925-928 |
| Barbuda | 783-786 |
| Dominica | 950-953 |
| Gambia | 611-614 |
| Grenada | 1371-1374 |
| Grenada Grenadines | 749-752 |
| Lesotho | 531-534 |
| Maldive Islands | 1172-1175 |
| Sierra Leone | 760-763 |
| Uganda | 495-498 |

| | | |
|---|---|---|
| Nos. 674-677 (4) | 8.00 | 8.00 |
| Nos. 925-928 (4) | 5.50 | 6.20 |
| Nos. 783-786 (4) | 23.15 | 23.15 |
| Nos. 950-953 (4) | 7.25 | 7.25 |
| Nos. 611-614 (4) | 8.25 | 7.90 |
| Nos. 1371-1374 (4) | 6.80 | 6.80 |
| Nos. 749-752 (4) | 6.75 | 6.75 |
| Nos. 531-534 (4) | 5.25 | 5.25 |
| Nos. 1172-1175 (4) | 6.25 | 6.25 |
| Nos. 760-763 (4) | 6.30 | 6.30 |
| Nos. 495-498 (4) | 8.50 | 8.50 |
| Set total (44) Stamps | 92.00 | 92.35 |

**Royal Wedding, 1986**

CD340

Designs: Photographs of Prince Andrew and Sarah Ferguson during courtship, engagement and marriage.

**1986**

| | |
|---|---|
| Antigua | 939-942 |
| Barbuda | 809-812 |
| Dominica | 970-973 |
| Gambia | 635-638 |
| Grenada | 1385-1388 |
| Grenada Grenadines | 758-761 |
| Lesotho | 545-548 |
| Maldive Islands | 1181-1184 |
| Sierra Leone | 769-772 |
| Uganda | 510-513 |

| | | |
|---|---|---|
| Nos. 939-942 (4) | 7.00 | 8.75 |
| Nos. 809-812 (4) | 14.55 | 14.55 |
| Nos. 970-973 (4) | 7.25 | 7.25 |
| Nos. 635-638 (4) | 8.55 | 8.55 |
| Nos. 1385-1388 (4) | 8.30 | 8.30 |
| Nos. 758-761 (4) | 9.00 | 9.00 |
| Nos. 545-548 (4) | 7.45 | 7.45 |
| Nos. 1181-1184 (4) | 8.45 | 8.45 |
| Nos. 769-772 (4) | 5.35 | 5.35 |
| Nos. 510-513 (4) | 9.25 | 10.00 |
| Set total (40) Stamps | 85.15 | 87.65 |

**Lloyds of London, 300th Anniv.**

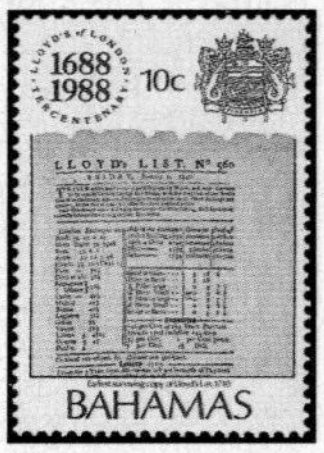


CD341

Designs: 17th century aspects of Lloyds, representations of each country's individual connections with Lloyds and publicized disasters insured by the organization.

**1986**

| | |
|---|---|
| Ascension | 454-457 |
| Bahamas | 655-658 |
| Barbados | 731-734 |
| Bermuda | 541-544 |
| Falkland Islands | 481-484 |
| Liberia | 1101-1104 |
| Malawi | 534-537 |
| Nevis | 571-574 |
| St. Helena | 501-504 |
| St. Lucia | 923-926 |
| Seychelles | 649-652 |
| Zil Elwannyen Sesel | 146-149 |
| Solomon Islands | 627-630 |
| South Georgia | 131-134 |
| Trinidad & Tobago | 484-487 |
| Tristan da Cunha | 439-442 |
| Vanuatu | 485-488 |

| | | |
|---|---|---|
| Nos. 454-457 (4) | 5.00 | 5.00 |
| Nos. 655-658 (4) | 8.90 | 4.95 |
| Nos. 731-734 (4) | 12.50 | 8.35 |
| Nos. 541-544 (4) | 8.00 | 6.60 |
| Nos. 481-484 (4) | 5.45 | 3.85 |
| Nos. 1101-1104 (4) | 4.25 | 4.25 |
| Nos. 534-537 (4) | 11.00 | 7.85 |
| Nos. 571-574 (4) | 8.35 | 8.35 |
| Nos. 501-504 (4) | 8.70 | 7.15 |
| Nos. 923-926 (4) | 9.40 | 9.40 |
| Nos. 649-652 (4) | 13.10 | 13.10 |
| Nos. 146-149 (4) | 11.25 | 11.25 |
| Nos. 627-630 (4) | 7.00 | 4.45 |
| Nos. 131-134 (4) | 6.30 | 3.70 |
| Nos. 484-487 (4) | 10.25 | 6.35 |
| Nos. 439-442 (4) | 7.60 | 7.60 |
| Nos. 485-488 (4) | 5.90 | 5.90 |
| Set total (68) Stamps | 142.95 | 118.10 |

**Moon Landing, 20th Anniv.**

CD342

Designs: Equipment, crew photographs, spacecraft, official emblems and report profiles created for the Apollo Missions. Two stamps in each set are square in format rather than like the stamp shown; see individual country listings for more information.

**1989**

| | |
|---|---|
| Ascension | 468-472 |
| Bahamas | 674-678 |
| Belize | 916-920 |
| Kiribati | 517-521 |
| Liberia | 1125-1129 |
| Nevis | 586-590 |
| St. Kitts | 248-252 |
| Samoa | 760-764 |
| Seychelles | 676-680 |
| Zil Elwannyen Sesel | 154-158 |
| Solomon Islands | 643-647 |
| Vanuatu | 507-511 |

| | | |
|---|---|---|
| Nos. 468-472 (5) | 9.40 | 8.60 |
| Nos. 674-678 (5) | 23.00 | 19.70 |
| Nos. 916-920 (5) | 22.85 | 18.10 |
| Nos. 517-521 (5) | 12.50 | 12.50 |
| Nos. 1125-1129 (5) | 8.50 | 8.50 |
| Nos. 586-590 (5) | 7.50 | 7.50 |

| | | |
|---|---|---|
| *Nos. 248-252 (5)* | 8.00 | 8.25 |
| *Nos. 760-764 (5)* | 9.60 | 9.05 |
| *Nos. 676-680 (5)* | 16.05 | 16.05 |
| *Nos. 154-158 (5)* | 26.85 | 26.85 |
| *Nos. 643-647 (5)* | 9.00 | 6.75 |
| *Nos. 507-511 (5)* | 9.90 | 9.90 |
| *Set total (60) Stamps* | 163.15 | 151.75 |

### Queen Mother, 90th Birthday

CD343

CD344

Designs: Portraits of Queen Elizabeth, the Queen Mother. See individual country listings for more information.

**1990**

Ascension ... 491-492
Bahamas ... 698-699
Barbados ... 782-783
British Antarctic Territory ... 170-171
British Indian Ocean Territory ... 106-107
Cayman Islands ... 622-623
Falkland Islands ... 524-525
Kenya ... 527-528
Kiribati ... 555-556
Liberia ... 1145-1146
Pitcairn Islands ... 336-337
St. Helena ... 532-533
St. Lucia ... 969-970
Seychelles ... 710-711
Zil Elwannyen Sesel ... 171-172
Solomon Islands ... 671-672
South Georgia ... 143-144
Swaziland ... 565-566
Tristan da Cunha ... 480-481

| | | |
|---|---|---|
| *Nos. 491-492 (2)* | 4.75 | 4.75 |
| *Nos. 698-699 (2)* | 5.25 | 5.25 |
| *Nos. 782-783 (2)* | 4.00 | 3.70 |
| *Nos. 170-171 (2)* | 6.75 | 6.75 |
| *Nos. 106-107 (2)* | 18.00 | 18.50 |
| *Nos. 622-623 (2)* | 4.00 | *5.50* |
| *Nos. 524-525 (2)* | 4.75 | 4.75 |
| *Nos. 527-528 (2)* | 7.00 | 7.00 |
| *Nos. 555-556 (2)* | 4.75 | 4.75 |
| *Nos. 1145-1146 (2)* | 3.25 | 3.25 |
| *Nos. 336-337 (2)* | 4.25 | 4.25 |
| *Nos. 532-533 (2)* | 5.25 | 5.25 |
| *Nos. 969-970 (2)* | 5.25 | 5.25 |
| *Nos. 710-711 (2)* | 6.60 | 6.60 |
| *Nos. 171-172 (2)* | 8.25 | 8.25 |
| *Nos. 671-672 (2)* | 5.00 | *5.30* |
| *Nos. 143-144 (2)* | 5.50 | 6.50 |
| *Nos. 565-566 (2)* | 4.35 | 4.35 |
| *Nos. 480-481 (2)* | 5.60 | 5.60 |
| *Set total (38) Stamps* | 112.55 | 115.55 |

### Queen Elizabeth II, 65th Birthday, and Prince Philip, 70th Birthday

CD345

CD346

Designs: Portraits of Queen Elizabeth II and Prince Philip differ for each country. Printed in sheets of 10 + 5 labels (3 different) between. Stamps alternate, producing 5 different triptychs.

**1991**

Ascension ... 506a
Bahamas ... 731a
Belize ... 970a
Bermuda ... 618a
Kiribati ... 572a
Mauritius ... 734a
Pitcairn Islands ... 349a
St. Helena ... 555a
St. Kitts ... 319a
Samoa ... 791a
Seychelles ... 724a
Zil Elwannyen Sesel ... 178a
Solomon Islands ... 689a
South Georgia ... 150a
Swaziland ... 587a
Vanuatu ... 541a

| | | |
|---|---|---|
| *No. 506a (1)* | 3.50 | 3.75 |
| *No. 731a (1)* | 4.00 | 4.00 |
| *No. 970a (1)* | 3.75 | 3.75 |
| *No. 618a (1)* | 3.50 | *4.00* |
| *No. 572a (1)* | 4.00 | 4.00 |
| *No. 734a (1)* | 3.75 | 3.75 |
| *No. 349a (1)* | 3.25 | 3.25 |
| *No. 555a (1)* | 2.75 | 2.75 |
| *No. 319a (1)* | 3.00 | 3.00 |
| *No. 791a (1)* | 4.25 | 4.25 |
| *No. 724a (1)* | 5.00 | 5.00 |
| *No. 178a (1)* | 6.50 | 6.50 |
| *No. 689a (1)* | 3.75 | 3.75 |
| *No. 150a (1)* | 4.75 | 7.00 |
| *No. 587a (1)* | 4.25 | 4.25 |
| *No. 541a (1)* | 2.50 | 2.50 |
| *Set total (16) Stamps* | 62.50 | 65.50 |

### Royal Family Birthday, Anniversary

CD347

Queen Elizabeth II, 65th birthday, Charles and Diana, 10th wedding anniversary: Various photographs of Queen Elizabeth II, Prince Philip, Prince Charles, Princess Diana and their sons William and Henry.

**1991**

Antigua ... 1446-1455
Barbuda ... 1229-1238
Dominica ... 1328-1337
Gambia ... 1080-1089
Grenada ... 2006-2015
Grenada Grenadines ... 1331-1340
Guyana ... 2440-2451
Lesotho ... 871-875
Maldive Islands ... 1533-1542
Nevis ... 666-675
St. Vincent ... 1485-1494
St. Vincent Grenadines ... 769-778
Sierra Leone ... 1387-1396
Turks & Caicos Islands ... 913-922
Uganda ... 918-927

| | | |
|---|---|---|
| *Nos. 1446-1455 (10)* | 21.70 | 20.05 |
| *Nos. 1229-1238 (10)* | 125.00 | 119.50 |
| *Nos. 1328-1337 (10)* | 30.20 | 30.20 |
| *Nos. 1080-1089 (10)* | 24.65 | 24.40 |
| *Nos. 2006-2015 (10)* | 25.45 | 22.10 |
| *Nos. 1331-1340 (10)* | 23.85 | 23.35 |
| *Nos. 2440-2451 (12)* | 21.40 | 21.15 |
| *Nos. 871-875 (5)* | 13.55 | 13.55 |
| *Nos. 1533-1542 (10)* | 28.10 | 28.10 |
| *Nos. 666-675 (10)* | 25.65 | 25.65 |
| *Nos. 1485-1494 (10)* | 26.75 | 25.90 |
| *Nos. 769-778 (10)* | 25.40 | 25.40 |
| *Nos. 1387-1396 (10)* | 26.55 | 26.55 |
| *Nos. 913-922 (10)* | 27.50 | 25.30 |
| *Nos. 918-927 (10)* | 26.60 | 26.60 |
| *Set total (147) Stamps* | 472.35 | 457.80 |

### Queen Elizabeth II's Accession to the Throne, 40th Anniv.

CD348

Various photographs of Queen Elizabeth II with local Scenes.

**1992**

Antigua ... 1513-1518
Barbuda ... 1306-1311
Dominica ... 1414-1419
Gambia ... 1172-1177
Grenada ... 2047-2052
Grenada Grenadines ... 1368-1373
Lesotho ... 881-885
Maldive Islands ... 1637-1642
Nevis ... 702-707
St. Vincent ... 1582-1587
St. Vincent Grenadines ... 829-834
Sierra Leone ... 1482-1487
Turks and Caicos Islands ... 978-987
Uganda ... 990-995
Virgin Islands ... 742-746

| | | |
|---|---|---|
| *Nos. 1513-1518 (6)* | 15.00 | *15.10* |
| *Nos. 1306-1311 (6)* | 125.25 | 83.65 |
| *Nos. 1414-1419 (6)* | 12.50 | 12.50 |
| *Nos. 1172-1177 (6)* | 16.60 | 16.35 |
| *Nos. 2047-2052 (6)* | 15.95 | 15.95 |
| *Nos. 1368-1373 (6)* | 17.00 | 15.35 |
| *Nos. 881-885 (5)* | 11.90 | 11.90 |
| *Nos. 1637-1642 (6)* | 17.55 | 17.55 |
| *Nos. 702-707 (6)* | 13.80 | 13.80 |
| *Nos. 1582-1587 (6)* | 14.40 | 14.40 |
| *Nos. 829-834 (6)* | 19.65 | 19.65 |
| *Nos. 1482-1487 (6)* | 22.50 | 22.50 |
| *Nos. 913-922 (10)* | 27.50 | 25.30 |
| *Nos. 990-995 (6)* | 19.50 | 19.50 |
| *Nos. 742-746 (5)* | 15.50 | 15.50 |
| *Set total (92) Stamps* | 364.60 | 319.00 |

CD349

**1992**

Ascension ... 531-535
Bahamas ... 744-748
Bermuda ... 623-627
British Indian Ocean Territory ... 119-123
Cayman Islands ... 648-652
Falkland Islands ... 549-553
Gibraltar ... 605-609
Hong Kong ... 619-623
Kenya ... 563-567
Kiribati ... 582-586
Pitcairn Islands ... 362-366
St. Helena ... 570-574
St. Kitts ... 332-336
Samoa ... 805-809
Seychelles ... 734-738
Zil Elwannyen Sesel ... 183-187
Solomon Islands ... 708-712
South Georgia ... 157-161
Tristan da Cunha ... 508-512
Vanuatu ... 555-559
Zambia ... 561-565

| | | |
|---|---|---|
| *Nos. 531-535 (5)* | 6.10 | 6.10 |
| *Nos. 744-748 (5)* | 6.90 | 4.70 |
| *Nos. 623-627 (5)* | 7.40 | *7.55* |
| *Nos. 119-123 (5)* | 22.75 | 19.25 |
| *Nos. 648-652 (5)* | 7.60 | 6.60 |
| *Nos. 549-553 (5)* | 5.95 | 5.90 |
| *Nos. 605-609 (5)* | 5.15 | *5.50* |
| *Nos. 619-623 (5)* | 5.10 | 5.25 |
| *Nos. 563-567 (5)* | 9.10 | 9.10 |
| *Nos. 582-586 (5)* | 3.85 | 3.85 |
| *Nos. 362-366 (5)* | 5.35 | 5.35 |
| *Nos. 570-574 (5)* | 5.70 | 5.70 |
| *Nos. 332-336 (5)* | 6.60 | 5.50 |
| *Nos. 805-809 (5)* | 8.10 | 6.15 |
| *Nos. 734-738 (5)* | 10.80 | 10.80 |
| *Nos. 183-187 (5)* | 9.40 | 9.40 |
| *Nos. 708-712 (5)* | 5.00 | 5.30 |
| *Nos. 157-161 (5)* | 5.60 | 5.90 |
| *Nos. 508-512 (5)* | 8.75 | 8.30 |
| *Nos. 555-559 (5)* | 3.65 | 3.65 |
| *Nos. 561-565 (5)* | 5.60 | 5.65 |
| *Set total (105) Stamps* | 154.45 | 145.45 |

### Royal Air Force, 75th Anniversary

CD350

**1993**

Ascension ... 557-561
Bahamas ... 771-775
Barbados ... 842-846
Belize ... 1003-1008
Bermuda ... 648-651
British Indian Ocean Territory ... 136-140
Falkland Is. ... 573-577
Fiji ... 687-691
Montserrat ... 830-834
St. Kitts ... 351-355

| | | |
|---|---|---|
| *Nos. 557-561 (5)* | 15.60 | 14.60 |
| *Nos. 771-775 (5)* | 24.65 | 21.45 |
| *Nos. 842-846 (5)* | 13.65 | 12.35 |
| *Nos. 1003-1008 (6)* | 16.55 | 16.50 |
| *Nos. 648-651 (4)* | 9.65 | *10.45* |
| *Nos. 136-140 (5)* | 16.10 | 16.10 |
| *Nos. 573-577 (5)* | 10.85 | 10.85 |
| *Nos. 687-691 (5)* | 17.75 | 17.40 |
| *Nos. 830-834 (5)* | 14.35 | 14.35 |
| *Nos. 351-355 (5)* | 22.80 | 23.55 |
| *Set total (50) Stamps* | 161.95 | 157.60 |

### Royal Air Force, 80th Anniv.

Design CD350 Re-inscribed

**1998**

Ascension ... 697-701
Bahamas ... 907-911
British Indian Ocean Terr ... 198-202
Cayman Islands ... 754-758
Fiji ... 814-818
Gibraltar ... 755-759
Samoa ... 957-961
Turks & Caicos Islands ... 1258-1265
Tuvalu ... 763-767
Virgin Islands ... 879-883

| | | |
|---|---|---|
| *Nos. 697-701 (5)* | 16.10 | 16.10 |
| *Nos. 907-911 (5)* | 13.60 | 12.65 |
| *Nos. 136-140 (5)* | 16.10 | 16.10 |
| *Nos. 754-758 (5)* | 15.25 | 15.25 |
| *Nos. 814-818 (5)* | 14.00 | 12.75 |
| *Nos. 755-759 (5)* | 9.70 | 9.70 |
| *Nos. 957-961 (5)* | 16.70 | 15.90 |
| *Nos. 1258-1265 (2)* | 27.50 | 27.50 |
| *Nos. 763-767 (5)* | 9.75 | 9.75 |
| *Nos. 879-883 (5)* | 15.00 | 15.00 |
| *Set total (47) Stamps* | 153.70 | 150.70 |

### End of World War II, 50th Anniv.

CD351

CD352

**1995**

Ascension ... 613-617
Bahamas ... 824-828
Barbados ... 891-895
Belize ... 1047-1050
British Indian Ocean Territory ... 163-167
Cayman Islands ... 704-708
Falkland Islands ... 634-638
Fiji ... 720-724
Kiribati ... 662-668
Liberia ... 1175-1179
Mauritius ... 803-805
St. Helena ... 646-654
St. Kitts ... 389-393
St. Lucia ... 1018-1022
Samoa ... 890-894
Solomon Islands ... 799-803
South Georgia ... 198-200
Tristan da Cunha ... 562-566

| | | |
|---|---|---|
| *Nos. 613-617 (5)* | 21.50 | 21.50 |

| | | |
|---|---|---|
| Nos. 824-828 (5) | 22.00 | 18.70 |
| Nos. 891-895 (5) | 14.20 | 11.90 |
| Nos. 1047-1050 (4) | 6.05 | 5.90 |
| Nos. 163-167 (5) | 16.25 | 16.25 |
| Nos. 704-708 (5) | 17.65 | 13.95 |
| Nos. 634-638 (5) | 18.65 | 17.15 |
| Nos. 720-724 (5) | 17.50 | 14.50 |
| Nos. 662-668 (7) | 16.30 | 16.30 |
| Nos. 1175-1179 (5) | 15.25 | 11.15 |
| Nos. 803-805 (3) | 7.50 | 7.50 |
| Nos. 646-654 (9) | 26.10 | 26.10 |
| Nos. 389-393 (5) | 16.40 | 16.40 |
| Nos. 1018-1022 (5) | 14.25 | 11.15 |
| Nos. 890-894 (5) | 14.25 | 13.50 |
| Nos. 799-803 (5) | 14.75 | 14.75 |
| Nos. 198-200 (3) | 14.50 | 15.50 |
| Nos. 562-566 (5) | 20.10 | 20.10 |
| Set total (91) Stamps | 293.20 | 272.30 |

### UN, 50th Anniv.

CD353

**1995**

| | |
|---|---|
| Bahamas | 839-842 |
| Barbados | 901-904 |
| Belize | 1055-1058 |
| Jamaica | 847-851 |
| Liberia | 1187-1190 |
| Mauritius | 813-816 |
| Pitcairn Islands | 436-439 |
| St. Kitts | 398-401 |
| St. Lucia | 1023-1026 |
| Samoa | 900-903 |
| Tristan da Cunha | 568-571 |
| Virgin Islands | 807-810 |

| | | |
|---|---|---|
| Nos. 839-842 (4) | 7.15 | 6.40 |
| Nos. 901-904 (4) | 7.00 | 5.75 |
| Nos. 1055-1058 (4) | 4.70 | 4.70 |
| Nos. 847-851 (5) | 5.40 | 5.45 |
| Nos. 1187-1190 (4) | 9.65 | 9.65 |
| Nos. 813-816 (4) | 3.90 | 3.90 |
| Nos. 436-439 (4) | 8.15 | 8.15 |
| Nos. 398-401 (4) | 6.15 | 7.15 |
| Nos. 1023-1026 (4) | 7.50 | 7.25 |
| Nos. 900-903 (4) | 9.35 | 8.20 |
| Nos. 568-571 (4) | 13.50 | 13.50 |
| Nos. 807-810 (4) | 7.45 | 7.45 |
| Set total (49) Stamps | 89.90 | 87.55 |

### Queen Elizabeth, 70th Birthday

CD354

**1996**

| | |
|---|---|
| Ascension | 632-635 |
| British Antarctic Territory | 240-243 |
| British Indian Ocean Territory | 176-180 |
| Falkland Islands | 653-657 |
| Pitcairn Islands | 446-449 |
| St. Helena | 672-676 |
| Samoa | 912-916 |
| Tokelau | 223-227 |
| Tristan da Cunha | 576-579 |
| Virgin Islands | 824-828 |

| | | |
|---|---|---|
| Nos. 632-635 (4) | 5.30 | 5.30 |
| Nos. 240-243 (4) | 10.50 | 8.90 |
| Nos. 176-180 (5) | 11.50 | 11.50 |
| Nos. 653-657 (5) | 13.55 | 11.20 |
| Nos. 446-449 (4) | 8.60 | 8.60 |
| Nos. 672-676 (5) | 12.70 | 12.70 |
| Nos. 912-916 (5) | 11.50 | 11.50 |
| Nos. 223-227 (5) | 10.50 | 10.50 |
| Nos. 576-579 (4) | 8.35 | 8.35 |
| Nos. 824-828 (5) | 11.30 | 11.30 |
| Set total (46) Stamps | 103.80 | 99.85 |

### Diana, Princess of Wales (1961-97)

CD355

**1998**

| | |
|---|---|
| Ascension | 696 |
| Bahamas | 901A-902 |
| Barbados | 950 |
| Belize | 1091 |
| Bermuda | 753 |
| Botswana | 659-663 |
| British Antarctic Territory | 258 |
| British Indian Ocean Terr. | 197 |
| Cayman Islands | 752A-753 |
| Falkland Islands | 694 |
| Fiji | 819-820 |
| Gibraltar | 754 |
| Kiribati | 719A-720 |
| Namibia | 909 |
| Niue | 706 |
| Norfolk Island | 644-645 |
| Papua New Guinea | 937 |
| Pitcairn Islands | 487 |
| St. Helena | 711 |
| St. Kitts | 437A-438 |
| Samoa | 955A-956 |
| Seycelles | 802 |
| Solomon Islands | 866-867 |
| South Georgia | 220 |
| Tokelau | 252B-253 |
| Tonga | 980 |
| Niuafo'ou | 201 |
| Tristan da Cunha | 618 |
| Tuvalu | 762 |
| Vanuatu | 718A-719 |
| Virgin Islands | 878 |

| | | |
|---|---|---|
| No. 696 (1) | 5.25 | 5.25 |
| Nos. 901A-902 (2) | 5.30 | 5.30 |
| No. 950 (1) | 5.00 | 5.00 |
| No. 1091 (1) | 5.00 | 5.00 |
| No. 753 (1) | 5.00 | 5.00 |
| Nos. 659-663 (5) | 8.25 | 8.80 |
| No. 258 (1) | 6.25 | 6.25 |
| No. 197 (1) | 5.50 | 5.50 |
| Nos. 752A-753 (3) | 7.40 | 7.40 |
| No. 694 (1) | 5.00 | 5.00 |
| Nos. 819-820 (2) | 5.25 | 5.25 |
| No. 754 (1) | 4.75 | 4.75 |
| Nos. 719A-720 (2) | 4.85 | 4.85 |
| No. 909 (1) | 1.75 | 1.75 |
| No. 706 (1) | 5.50 | 5.50 |
| Nos. 644-645 (2) | 5.25 | 5.25 |
| No. 937 (1) | 6.50 | 6.50 |
| No. 487 (1) | 4.75 | 4.75 |
| No. 711 (1) | 4.25 | 4.25 |
| Nos. 437A-438 (2) | 5.15 | 5.15 |
| Nos. 955A-956 (2) | 7.00 | 7.00 |
| No. 802 (1) | 6.25 | 6.25 |
| Nos. 866-867 (2) | 5.40 | 5.40 |
| No. 220 (1) | 4.50 | 5.00 |
| Nos. 252B-253 (2) | 5.50 | 5.50 |
| No. 980 (1) | 5.75 | 5.75 |
| No. 201 (1) | 6.50 | 6.50 |
| No. 618 (1) | 5.00 | 5.00 |
| No. 762 (1) | 4.00 | 4.00 |
| Nos. 718A-719 (2) | 8.00 | 8.00 |
| No. 878 (1) | 4.50 | 4.50 |
| Set total (46) Stamps | 168.35 | 169.40 |

### Wedding of Prince Edward and Sophie Rhys-Jones

CD356

**1999**

| | |
|---|---|
| Ascension | 729-730 |
| Cayman Islands | 775-776 |
| Falkland Islands | 729-730 |
| Pitcairn Islands | 505-506 |
| St. Helena | 733-734 |
| Samoa | 971-972 |
| Tristan da Cunha | 636-637 |
| Virgin Islands | 908-909 |

| | | |
|---|---|---|
| Nos. 729-730 (2) | 4.50 | 4.50 |
| Nos. 775-776 (2) | 4.95 | 4.95 |
| Nos. 729-730 (2) | 14.00 | 14.00 |
| Nos. 505-506 (2) | 7.00 | 7.00 |
| Nos. 733-734 (2) | 5.00 | 5.00 |
| Nos. 971-972 (2) | 5.00 | 5.00 |
| Nos. 636-637 (2) | 7.50 | 7.50 |
| Nos. 908-909 (2) | 7.50 | 7.50 |
| Set total (16) Stamps | 55.45 | 55.45 |

### 1st Manned Moon Landing, 30th Anniv.

CD357

**1999**

| | |
|---|---|
| Ascension | 731-735 |
| Bahamas | 942-946 |
| Barbados | 967-971 |
| Bermuda | 778 |
| Cayman Islands | 777-781 |
| Fiji | 853-857 |
| Jamaica | 889-893 |
| Kirbati | 746-750 |
| Nauru | 465-469 |
| St. Kitts | 460-464 |
| Samoa | 973-977 |
| Solomon Islands | 875-879 |
| Tuvalu | 800-804 |
| Virgin Islands | 910-914 |

| | | |
|---|---|---|
| Nos. 731-735 (5) | 12.80 | 12.80 |
| Nos. 942-946 (5) | 14.10 | 14.10 |
| Nos. 967-971 (5) | 8.65 | 7.75 |
| No. 778 (1) | 9.00 | 9.00 |
| Nos. 777-781 (5) | 9.25 | 9.25 |
| Nos. 853-857 (5) | 9.25 | 8.45 |
| Nos. 889-893 (5) | 8.30 | 7.18 |
| Nos. 746-750 (5) | 8.85 | 8.85 |
| Nos. 465-469 (5) | 9.25 | 8.00 |
| Nos. 460-464 (5) | 11.35 | 11.65 |
| Nos. 973-977 (5) | 13.45 | 13.30 |
| Nos. 875-879 (5) | 7.50 | 7.50 |
| Nos. 800-804 (5) | 7.45 | 7.45 |
| Nos. 910-914 (5) | 11.75 | 11.75 |
| Set total (66) Stamps | 140.95 | 137.03 |

### Queen Mother's Century

CD358

**1999**

| | |
|---|---|
| Ascension | 736-740 |
| Bahamas | 951-955 |
| Cayman Islands | 782-786 |
| Falkland Islands | 734-738 |
| Fiji | 858-862 |
| Norfolk Island | 688-692 |
| St. Helena | 740-744 |
| Samoa | 978-982 |
| Solomon Islands | 880-884 |
| South Georgia | 231-235 |
| Tristan da Cunha | 638-642 |
| Tuvalu | 805-809 |

| | | |
|---|---|---|
| Nos. 736-740 (5) | 15.50 | 15.50 |
| Nos. 951-955 (5) | 13.75 | 12.65 |
| Nos. 782-786 (5) | 8.35 | 8.35 |
| Nos. 734-738 (5) | 30.00 | 28.25 |
| Nos. 858-862 (5) | 12.80 | 13.25 |
| Nos. 688-692 (5) | 10.30 | 10.30 |
| Nos. 740-744 (5) | 16.15 | 16.15 |
| Nos. 978-982 (5) | 12.50 | 12.10 |
| Nos. 880-884 (5) | 7.50 | 7.00 |
| Nos. 231-235 (5) | 29.75 | 30.00 |
| Nos. 638-642 (5) | 18.00 | 18.00 |
| Nos. 805-809 (5) | 8.65 | 8.65 |
| Set total (60) Stamps | 183.25 | 180.20 |

### Prince William, 18th Birthday

CD359

**2000**

| | |
|---|---|
| Ascension | 755-759 |
| Cayman Islands | 797-801 |
| Falkland Islands | 762-766 |
| Fiji | 889-893 |
| South Georgia | 257-261 |
| Tristan da Cunha | 664-668 |
| Virgin Islands | 925-929 |

| | | |
|---|---|---|
| Nos. 755-759 (5) | 15.50 | 15.50 |
| Nos. 797-801 (5) | 11.15 | 10.90 |
| Nos. 762-766 (5) | 24.60 | 22.50 |
| Nos. 889-893 (5) | 12.90 | 12.90 |
| Nos. 257-261 (5) | 29.00 | 28.75 |
| Nos. 664-668 (5) | 21.50 | 21.50 |
| Nos. 925-929 (5) | 14.50 | 14.50 |
| Set total (35) Stamps | 129.15 | 126.55 |

### Reign of Queen Elizabeth II, 50th Anniv.

CD360

**2002**

| | |
|---|---|
| Ascension | 790-794 |
| Bahamas | 1033-1037 |
| Barbados | 1019-1023 |
| Belize | 1152-1156 |
| Bermuda | 822-826 |
| British Antarctic Territory | 307-311 |
| British Indian Ocean Territory | 239-243 |
| Cayman Islands | 844-848 |
| Falkland Islands | 804-808 |
| Gibraltar | 896-900 |
| Jamaica | 952-956 |
| Nauru | 491-495 |
| Norfolk Island | 758-762 |
| Papua New Guinea | 1019-1023 |
| Pitcairn Islands | 552 |
| St. Helena | 788-792 |
| St. Lucia | 1146-1150 |
| Solomon Islands | 931-935 |
| South Georgia | 274-278 |
| Swaziland | 706-710 |
| Tokelau | 302-306 |
| Tonga | 1059 |
| Niuafo'ou | 239 |
| Tristan da Cunha | 706-710 |
| Virgin Islands | 967-971 |

| | | |
|---|---|---|
| Nos. 790-794 (5) | 14.10 | 14.10 |
| Nos. 1033-1037 (5) | 15.25 | 15.25 |
| Nos. 1019-1023 (5) | 13.15 | 13.15 |
| Nos. 1152-1156 (5) | 12.65 | 12.25 |
| Nos. 822-826 (5) | 18.00 | 18.00 |
| Nos. 307-311 (5) | 25.00 | 25.00 |
| Nos. 239-243 (5) | 19.40 | 19.40 |
| Nos. 844-848 (5) | 13.25 | 13.25 |
| Nos. 804-808 (5) | 23.00 | 22.00 |
| Nos. 896-900 (5) | 6.65 | 6.65 |
| Nos. 952-956 (5) | 16.65 | 16.65 |
| Nos. 491-495 (5) | 17.75 | 17.75 |
| Nos. 758-762 (5) | 19.50 | 19.50 |
| Nos. 1019-1023 (5) | 14.50 | 14.50 |
| No. 552 (1) | 9.25 | 9.25 |
| Nos. 788-792 (5) | 19.75 | 19.75 |
| Nos. 1146-1150 (5) | 12.25 | 12.25 |
| Nos. 931-935 (5) | 12.40 | 12.40 |
| Nos. 274-278 (5) | 28.00 | 28.50 |
| Nos. 706-710 (5) | 12.75 | 12.75 |
| Nos. 302-306 (5) | 14.50 | 14.50 |
| No. 1059 (1) | 8.50 | 8.50 |
| No. 239 (1) | 8.75 | 8.75 |
| Nos. 706-710 (5) | 18.50 | 18.50 |
| Nos. 967-971 (5) | 16.50 | 16.50 |
| Set total (113) Stamps | 390.00 | 389.10 |

### Queen Mother Elizabeth (1900-2002)

CD361

**2002**

Ascension................................799-801
Bahamas.............................1044-1046
Bermuda..................................834-836
British Antarctic Territory..........312-314
British Indian Ocean Territory........245-247
Cayman Islands.......................857-861
Falkland Islands......................812-816
Nauru.......................................499-501
Pitcairn Islands.......................561-565
St. Helena...............................808-812
St. Lucia..............................1155-1159
Seychelles.....................................830
Solomon Islands.......................945-947
South Georgia..........................281-285
Tokelau...................................312-314
Tristan da Cunha.....................715-717
Virgin Islands...........................979-983

| | | |
|---|---|---|
| *Nos. 799-801 (3)* | 8.85 | 8.85 |
| *Nos. 1044-1046 (3)* | 9.10 | 9.10 |
| *Nos. 834-836 (3)* | 12.25 | 12.25 |
| *Nos. 312-314 (3)* | 19.25 | 19.25 |
| *Nos. 245-247 (3)* | 17.35 | 17.35 |
| *Nos. 857-861 (5)* | 15.00 | 15.00 |
| *Nos. 812-816 (5)* | 28.50 | 28.50 |
| *Nos. 499-501 (3)* | 14.00 | 14.00 |
| *Nos. 561-565 (5)* | 15.25 | 15.25 |
| *Nos. 808-812 (5)* | 12.00 | 12.00 |
| *Nos. 1155-1159 (5)* | 13.00 | 13.00 |
| *No. 830 (1)* | 6.50 | 6.50 |
| *Nos. 945-947 (3)* | 9.25 | 9.25 |
| *Nos. 281-285 (5)* | 19.50 | 19.50 |
| *Nos. 312-314 (3)* | 11.85 | 11.85 |
| *Nos. 715-717 (3)* | 16.25 | 16.25 |
| *Nos. 979-983 (5)* | 23.50 | 23.50 |
| *Set total (63) Stamps* | 251.40 | 251.40 |

### Head of Queen Elizabeth II

CD362

**2003**

Ascension.......................................822
Bermuda.........................................865
British Antarctic Territory.................322
British Indian Ocean Territory..........261
Cayman Islands...............................878
Falkland Islands..............................828
St. Helena.......................................820
South Georgia.................................294
Tristan da Cunha.............................731
Virgin Islands................................1003

| | | |
|---|---|---|
| *No. 822 (1)* | 12.50 | 12.50 |
| *No. 865 (1)* | 50.00 | 50.00 |
| *No. 322 (1)* | 10.00 | 10.00 |
| *No. 261 (1)* | 11.00 | 11.00 |
| *No. 878 (1)* | 14.00 | 14.00 |
| *No. 828 (1)* | 9.00 | 9.00 |
| *No. 820 (1)* | 9.00 | 9.00 |
| *No. 294 (1)* | 8.50 | 8.50 |
| *No. 731 (1)* | 10.00 | 10.00 |
| *No. 1003 (1)* | 10.00 | 10.00 |
| *Set total (10) Stamps* | 144.00 | 144.00 |

### Coronation of Queen Elizabeth II, 50th Anniv.

CD363

**2003**

Ascension................................823-825
Bahamas..............................1073-1075
Bermuda..................................866-868
British Antarctic Territory..........323-325
British Indian Ocean Territory........262-264
Cayman Islands.......................879-881
Jamaica...................................970-972
Kiribati....................................825-827
Pitcairn Islands.......................577-581
St. Helena...............................821-823
St. Lucia..............................1171-1173
Tokelau...................................320-322
Tristan da Cunha.....................732-734
Virgin Islands.......................1004-1006

| | | |
|---|---|---|
| *Nos. 823-825 (3)* | 12.50 | 12.50 |
| *Nos. 1073-1075 (3)* | 13.00 | 13.00 |
| *Nos. 866-868 (2)* | 14.25 | 14.25 |
| *Nos. 323-325 (3)* | 26.00 | 26.00 |
| *Nos. 262-264 (3)* | 28.00 | 28.00 |
| *Nos. 879-881 (3)* | 19.25 | 19.25 |
| *Nos. 970-972 (3)* | 10.00 | 10.00 |
| *Nos. 825-827 (3)* | 13.50 | 13.50 |
| *Nos. 577-581 (5)* | 14.40 | 14.40 |
| *Nos. 821-823 (3)* | 7.25 | 7.25 |
| *Nos. 1171-1173 (3)* | 8.75 | 8.75 |
| *Nos. 320-322 (3)* | 17.25 | 17.25 |
| *Nos. 732-734 (3)* | 16.75 | 16.75 |
| *Nos. 1004-1006 (3)* | 25.00 | 25.00 |
| *Set total (43) Stamps* | 225.90 | 225.90 |

### Prince William, 21st Birthday

CD364

**2003**

Ascension.......................................826
British Indian Ocean Territory..........265
Cayman Islands.......................882-884
Falkland Islands..............................829
South Georgia.................................295
Tokelau...........................................323
Tristan da Cunha.............................735
Virgin Islands.......................1007-1009

| | | |
|---|---|---|
| *No. 826 (1)* | 7.25 | 7.25 |
| *No. 265 (1)* | 8.00 | 8.00 |
| *Nos. 882-884 (3)* | 6.95 | 6.95 |
| *No. 829 (1)* | 13.50 | 13.50 |
| *No. 295 (1)* | 8.50 | 8.50 |
| *No. 323 (1)* | 7.25 | 7.25 |
| *No. 735 (1)* | 6.00 | 6.00 |
| *Nos. 1007-1009 (3)* | 10.00 | 10.00 |
| *Set total (12) Stamps* | 67.45 | 67.45 |

# British Commonwealth of Nations

## Dominions, Colonies, Territories, Offices and Independent Members

Comprising stamps of the British Commonwealth and associated nations.

A strict observance of technicalities would bar some or all of the stamps listed under Burma, Ireland, Kuwait, Nepal, New Republic, Orange Free State, Samoa, South Africa, South-West Africa, Stellaland, Sudan, Swaziland, the two Transvaal Republics and others but these are included for the convenience of collectors.

## 1. Great Britain

Great Britain: Including England, Scotland, Wales and Northern Ireland.

## 2. The Dominions, Present and Past

### AUSTRALIA

The Commonwealth of Australia was proclaimed on January 1, 1901. It consists of six former colonies as follows:

New South Wales
Queensland
South Australia
Victoria
Tasmania
Western Australia

The following islands and territories are, or have been, administered by Australia: Australian Antarctic Territory, Christmas Island, Cocos (Keeling) Islands, Nauru, New Guinea, Norfolk Island, Papua.

### CANADA

The Dominion of Canada was created by the British North America Act in 1867. The following provinces were former sepa- rate colonies and issued postage stamps:

British Columbia and Vancouver Island
New Brunswick
Newfoundland
Nova Scotia
Prince Edward Island

### FIJI

The colony of Fiji became an independent nation with dominion status on Oct. 10, 1970.

### GHANA

This state came into existence Mar. 6, 1957, with dominion status. It consists of the former colony of the Gold Coast and the Trusteeship Territory of Togoland. Ghana became a republic July 1, 1960.

### INDIA

The Republic of India was inaugurated on January 26, 1950. It succeeded the Dominion of India which was proclaimed August 15, 1947, when the former Empire of India was divided into Pakistan and the Union of India. The Republic is composed of about 40 predominantly Hindu states of three classes: governor's provinces, chief commissioner's provinces and princely states. India also has various territories, such as the Andaman and Nicobar Islands.

The old Empire of India was a federation of British India and the native states. The more important princely states were autonomous. Of the more than 700 Indian states, these 43 are familiar names to philatelists because of their postage stamps.

### CONVENTION STATES

Chamba
Faridkot
Gwalior
Jhind
Nabha
Patiala

### FEUDATORY STATES

Alwar
Bahawalpur
Bamra
Barwani
Bhopal
Bhor
Bijawar
Bundi
Bussahir
Charkhari
Cochin
Dhar
Dungarpur
Duttia
Faridkot (1879-85)
Hyderabad
Idar
Indore
Jaipur
Jammu
Jammu and Kashmir
Jasdan
Jhalawar
Jhind (1875-76)
Kashmir
Kishangarh
Kotah
Las Bela
Morvi
Nandgaon
Nowanuggur
Orchha
Poonch
Rajasthan
Rajpeepla
Sirmur
Soruth
Tonk
Travancore
Wadhwan

### NEW ZEALAND

Became a dominion on September 26, 1907. The following islands and territories are, or have been, administered by New Zealand:

Aitutaki
Cook Islands (Rarotonga)
Niue
Penrhyn
Ross Dependency
Samoa (Western Samoa)
Tokelau Islands

### PAKISTAN

The Republic of Pakistan was proclaimed March 23, 1956. It succeeded the Dominion which was proclaimed August 15, 1947. It is made up of all or part of several Moslem provinces and various districts of the former Empire of India, including Bahawalpur and Las Bela. Pakistan withdrew from the Commonwealth in 1972.

### SOUTH AFRICA

Under the terms of the South African Act (1909) the self-governing colonies of Cape of Good Hope, Natal, Orange River Colony and Transvaal united on May 31, 1910, to form the Union of South Africa. It became an independent republic May 3, 1961.

Under the terms of the Treaty of Versailles, South-West Africa, formerly German South-West Africa, was mandated to the Union of South Africa.

### SRI LANKA (CEYLON)

The Dominion of Ceylon was proclaimed February 4, 1948. The island had been a Crown Colony from 1802 until then. On May 22, 1972, Ceylon became the Republic of Sri Lanka.

## 3. Colonies, Past and Present; Controlled Territory and Independent Members of the Commonwealth

Aden
Aitutaki
Anguilla
Antigua
Ascension
Bahamas
Bahrain
Bangladesh
Barbados
Barbuda
Basutoland
Batum
Bechuanaland
Bechuanaland Prot.
Belize
Bermuda
Botswana
British Antarctic Territory
British Central Africa
British Columbia and Vancouver Island
British East Africa
British Guiana

British Honduras
British Indian Ocean Territory
British New Guinea
British Solomon Islands
British Somaliland
Brunei
Burma
Bushire
Cameroons
Cape of Good Hope
Cayman Islands
Christmas Island
Cocos (Keeling) Islands
Cook Islands
Crete,
  British Administration
Cyprus
Dominica
East Africa & Uganda
  Protectorates
Egypt
Falkland Islands
Fiji
Gambia
German East Africa
Gibraltar
Gilbert Islands
Gilbert & Ellice Islands
Gold Coast
Grenada
Griqualand West
Guernsey
Guyana
Heligoland
Hong Kong
Indian Native States
  (see India)
Ionian Islands
Jamaica
Jersey
Kenya
Kenya, Uganda & Tanzania
Kuwait
Labuan
Lagos
Leeward Islands
Lesotho
Madagascar
Malawi
Malaya
  Federated Malay States
  Johore
  Kedah
  Kelantan
  Malacca
  Negri Sembilan
  Pahang
  Penang
  Perak
  Perlis
  Selangor
  Singapore
  Sungei Ujong
  Trengganu
Malaysia
Maldive Islands
Malta
Man, Isle of
Mauritius
Mesopotamia
Montserrat
Muscat
Namibia
Natal
Nauru
Nevis
New Britain
New Brunswick
Newfoundland
New Guinea
New Hebrides
New Republic
New South Wales
Niger Coast Protectorate
Nigeria
Niue
Norfolk Island
North Borneo
Northern Nigeria
Northern Rhodesia
North West Pacific Islands
Nova Scotia
Nyasaland Protectorate
Oman
Orange River Colony
Palestine
Papua New Guinea
Penrhyn Island
Pitcairn Islands
Prince Edward Island
Queensland
Rhodesia
Rhodesia & Nyasaland
Ross Dependency
Sabah
St. Christopher
St. Helena
St. Kitts
St. Kitts-Nevis-Anguilla
St. Lucia
St. Vincent
Samoa
Sarawak
Seychelles
Sierra Leone
Solomon Islands
Somaliland Protectorate
South Arabia
South Australia
South Georgia
Southern Nigeria
Southern Rhodesia
South-West Africa
Stellaland
Straits Settlements
Sudan
Swaziland
Tanganyika
Tanzania
Tasmania
Tobago
Togo
Tokelau Islands
Tonga
Transvaal
Trinidad
Trinidad and Tobago
Tristan da Cunha
Trucial States
Turks and Caicos
Turks Islands
Tuvalu
Uganda
United Arab Emirates
Victoria
Virgin Islands
Western Australia
Zambia
Zanzibar
Zululand

**POST OFFICES IN FOREIGN COUNTRIES**

Africa
  East Africa Forces
  Middle East Forces
Bangkok
China
Morocco
Turkish Empire

# Colonies, Former Colonies, Offices, Territories Controlled by Parent States

## Belgium

Belgian Congo
Ruanda-Urundi

## Denmark

Danish West Indies
Faroe Islands
Greenland
Iceland

## Finland

Aland Islands

## France

**COLONIES PAST AND PRESENT, CONTROLLED TERRITORIES**

Afars & Issas, Territory of
Alaouites
Alexandretta
Algeria
Alsace & Lorraine
Anjouan
Annam & Tonkin
Benin
Cambodia (Khmer)
Cameroun
Castellorizo
Chad
Cilicia
Cochin China
Comoro Islands
Dahomey
Diego Suarez
Djibouti (Somali Coast)
Fezzan
French Congo
French Equatorial Africa
French Guiana
French Guinea
French India
French Morocco
French Polynesia (Oceania)
French Southern & Antarctic Territories
French Sudan
French West Africa
Gabon
Germany
Ghadames
Grand Comoro
Guadeloupe
Indo-China
Inini
Ivory Coast
Laos
Latakia
Lebanon
Madagascar
Martinique
Mauritania
Mayotte
Memel
Middle Congo
Moheli
New Caledonia
New Hebrides
Niger Territory
Nossi-Be
Obock
Reunion
Rouad, Ile
Ste.-Marie de Madagascar
St. Pierre & Miquelon
Senegal
Senegambia & Niger
Somali Coast
Syria
Tahiti
Togo
Tunisia
Ubangi-Shari
Upper Senegal & Niger
Upper Volta
Viet Nam
Wallis & Futuna Islands

**POST OFFICES IN FOREIGN COUNTRIES**

China
Crete
Egypt
Turkish Empire
Zanzibar

## Germany

**EARLY STATES**

Baden
Bavaria
Bergedorf
Bremen
Brunswick
Hamburg
Hanover
Lubeck
Mecklenburg-Schwerin
Mecklenburg-Strelitz
Oldenburg
Prussia
Saxony
Schleswig-Holstein
Wurttemberg

**FORMER COLONIES**

Cameroun (Kamerun)
Caroline Islands
German East Africa
German New Guinea
German South-West Africa
Kiauchau
Mariana Islands
Marshall Islands
Samoa
Togo

## Italy

**EARLY STATES**

Modena
Parma
Romagna
Roman States
Sardinia
Tuscany
Two Sicilies
- Naples
- Neapolitan Provinces
- Sicily

**FORMER COLONIES, CONTROLLED TERRITORIES, OCCUPATION AREAS**

Aegean Islands
- Calimno (Calino)
- Caso
- Cos (Coo)
- Karki (Carchi)
- Leros (Lero)
- Lipso
- Nisiros (Nisiro)
- Patmos (Patmo)
- Piscopi
- Rodi (Rhodes)
- Scarpanto
- Simi
- Stampalia

Castellorizo
Corfu
Cyrenaica
Eritrea
Ethiopia (Abyssinia)
Fiume
Ionian Islands
- Cephalonia
- Ithaca
- Paxos

Italian East Africa
Libya
Oltre Giuba
Saseno
Somalia (Italian Somaliland)
Tripolitania

**POST OFFICES IN FOREIGN COUNTRIES**

"ESTERO"*
Austria
China
- Peking
- Tientsin

Crete
Tripoli
Turkish Empire
- Constantinople
- Durazzo
- Janina

Jerusalem
Salonika
Scutari
Smyrna
Valona

*Stamps overprinted "ESTERO" were used in various parts of the world.

## Netherlands

Aruba
Caribbean Netherlands
Curacao
Netherlands Antilles (Curacao)
Netherlands Indies
Netherlands New Guinea
St. Martin
Surinam (Dutch Guiana)

## Portugal

**COLONIES PAST AND PRESENT, CONTROLLED TERRITORIES**

Angola
Angra
Azores
Cape Verde
Funchal
Horta
Inhambane
Kionga
Lourenco Marques
Macao
Madeira
Mozambique
Mozambique Co.
Nyassa
Ponta Delgada
Portuguese Africa
Portuguese Congo
Portuguese Guinea
Portuguese India
Quelimane
St. Thomas & Prince Islands
Tete
Timor
Zambezia

## Russia

**ALLIED TERRITORIES AND REPUBLICS, OCCUPATION AREAS**

Armenia
Aunus (Olonets)
Azerbaijan
Batum
Estonia
Far Eastern Republic
Georgia
Karelia
Latvia
Lithuania
North Ingermanland
Ostland
Russian Turkestan
Siberia
South Russia
Tannu Tuva
Transcaucasian Fed. Republics
Ukraine
Wenden (Livonia)
Western Ukraine

## Spain

**COLONIES PAST AND PRESENT, CONTROLLED TERRITORIES**

Aguera, La
Cape Juby
Cuba
Elobey, Annobon & Corisco
Fernando Po
Ifni
Mariana Islands
Philippines
Puerto Rico
Rio de Oro
Rio Muni
Spanish Guinea
Spanish Morocco
Spanish Sahara
Spanish West Africa

**POST OFFICES IN FOREIGN COUNTRIES**

Morocco
Tangier
Tetuan

# Dies of British Colonial Stamps

**DIE A:**

**1.** The lines in the groundwork vary in thickness and are not uniformly straight.

**2.** The seventh and eighth lines from the top, in the groundwork, converge where they meet the head.

**3.** There is a small dash in the upper part of the second jewel in the band of the crown.

**4.** The vertical color line in front of the throat stops at the sixth line of shading on the neck.

**DIE B:**

**1.** The lines in the groundwork are all thin and straight.

**2.** All the lines of the background are parallel.

**3.** There is no dash in the upper part of the second jewel in the band of the crown.

**4.** The vertical color line in front of the throat stops at the eighth line of shading on the neck.

**DIE I:**

**1.** The base of the crown is well below the level of the inner white line around the vignette.

**2.** The labels inscribed "POSTAGE" and "REVENUE" are cut square at the top.

**3.** There is a white "bud" on the outer side of the main stem of the curved ornaments in each lower corner.

**4.** The second (thick) line below the country name has the ends next to the crown cut diagonally.

DIE Ia.
1 as die II.
2 and 3 as die I.

DIE Ib.
1 and 3 as die II.
2 as die I.

**DIE II:**

**1.** The base of the crown is aligned with the underside of the white line around the vignette.

**2.** The labels curve inward at the top inner corners.

**3.** The "bud" has been removed from the outer curve of the ornaments in each corner.

**4.** The second line below the country name has the ends next to the crown cut vertically.

**Wmk. 1**
**Crown and C C**

**Wmk. 2**
**Crown and C A**

**Wmk. 3**
**Multiple Crown and C A**

**Wmk. 4**
**Multiple Crown and Script C A**

**Wmk. 4a**

**Wmk. 46**

**Wmk. 314**
**St. Edward's Crown and C A Multiple**

**Wmk. 373**

**Wmk. 384**

**Wmk. 406**

# British Colonial and Crown Agents Watermarks

Watermarks 1 to 4, 314, 373, 384 and 406, common to many British territories, are illustrated here to avoid duplication.

The letters "CC" of Wmk. 1 identify the paper as having been made for the use of the Crown Colonies, while the letters "CA" of the others stand for "Crown Agents." Both Wmks. 1 and 2 were used on stamps printed by De La Rue & Co.

Wmk. 3 was adopted in 1904; Wmk. 4 in 1921; Wmk. 46 in 1879; Wmk. 314 in 1957; Wmk. 373 in 1974; Wmk. 384 in 1985; Wmk 406 in 2008.

In Wmk. 4a, a non-matching crown of the general St. Edwards type (bulging on both sides at top) was substituted for one of the Wmk. 4 crowns which fell off the dandy roll. The non-matching crown occurs in 1950-52 printings in a horizontal row of crowns on certain regular stamps of Johore and Seychelles, and on various postage due stamps of Barbados, Basutoland, British Guiana, Gold Coast, Grenada, Northern Rhodesia, St. Lucia, Swaziland and Trinidad and Tobago. A variation of Wmk. 4a, with the non-matching crown in a horizontal row of crown-CA-crown, occurs on regular stamps of Bahamas, St. Kitts-Nevis and Singapore.

Wmk. 314 was intentionally used sideways, starting in 1966. When a stamp was issued with Wmk. 314 both upright and sideways, the sideways varieties usually are listed also – with minor numbers. In many of the later issues, Wmk. 314 is slightly visible.

Wmk. 373 is usually only faintly visible.

## JAMAICA

jə-'mā-kə

LOCATION — Caribbean Sea, about 90 miles south of Cuba
GOVT. — Independent state in the British Commonwealth
AREA — 4,411 sq. mi.
POP. — 2,652,443 (1999 est.)
CAPITAL — Kingston

Jamaica became an independent state in the British Commonwealth in August 1962. As a colony, it administered two dependencies: Cayman Islands and Turks and Caicos Islands.

12 Pence = 1 Shilling
20 Shillings = 1 Pound
100 Cents = 1 Dollar (1969)

**Catalogue values for unused stamps in this country are for Never Hinged items, beginning with Scott 129 in the regular postage section and Scott B4 in the semi-postal section.**

### Watermarks

Wmk. 45 — Pineapple

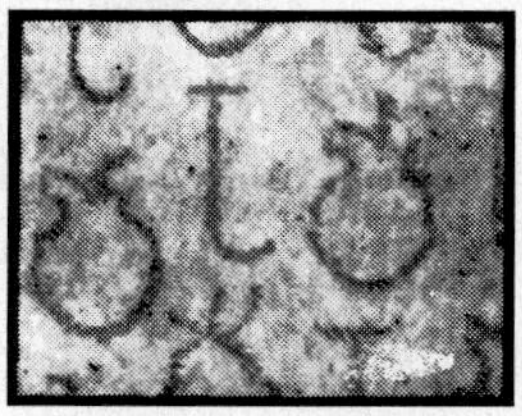

Wmk. 352 — J and Pineapple, Multiple

Values for unused stamps are for examples with original gum as defined in the catalogue introduction. Very fine examples of Nos. 1-12 will have perforations touching the design on at least one side due to the narrow spacing of the stamps on the plates. Stamps with perfs clear on all four sides are scarce and will command higher prices.

Queen Victoria
A1 A2

A3

A4

A5

A6

**1860-63 Typo. Wmk. 45 *Perf. 14***

| | | | | |
|---|---|---|---|---|
| 1 | A1 | 1p blue | 72.50 | 16.00 |
| *a.* | | Diagonal half used as ½p on cover | | 825.00 |
| *b.* | | 1p deep blue | 145.00 | 37.50 |
| *c.* | | 1p pale blue | 77.50 | 20.00 |
| *d.* | | 1p pale greenish blue | 115.00 | 24.00 |
| 2 | A2 | 2p rose | 225.00 | 60.00 |
| *a.* | | 2p deep rose | 220.00 | 60.00 |
| 3 | A3 | 3p green ('63) | 170.00 | 32.50 |
| 4 | A4 | 4p brown org | 275.00 | 62.50 |
| *a.* | | 4p orange | 250.00 | 25.00 |
| 5 | A5 | 6p lilac | 240.00 | 25.00 |
| *a.* | | 6p deep lilac | 1,050. | 60.00 |
| *b.* | | 6p gray lilac | 350.00 | 40.00 |
| 6 | A6 | 1sh brown | 230.00 | 35.00 |
| *a.* | | 1sh lilac brown | 650.00 | 30.00 |
| *b.* | | 1sh yellow brown | 575.00 | 32.50 |

All except No. 3 exist imperforate.

**1870-71 Wmk. 1**

| | | | | |
|---|---|---|---|---|
| 7 | A1 | 1p blue | 100.00 | .90 |
| 8 | A2 | 2p rose | 110.00 | .85 |
| *a.* | | 2p brownish rose | 120.00 | 1.10 |
| 9 | A3 | 3p green | 155.00 | 10.00 |
| 10 | A4 | 4p brown org ('72) | 350.00 | 13.50 |
| *a.* | | 4p red orange | 450.00 | 6.50 |
| 11 | A5 | 6p lilac ('71) | 100.00 | 6.00 |
| 12 | A6 | 1sh brown ('73) | 27.50 | 9.50 |
| | | *Nos. 7-12 (6)* | 842.50 | 40.75 |

The 1p and 4p exist imperf.
See Nos. 17-23, 28, 40, 43, 47-53.

A7

**1872, Oct. 29**

| | | | | |
|---|---|---|---|---|
| 13 | A7 | ½p claret | 22.00 | 4.00 |
| *a.* | | ½p deep claret | 29.00 | 6.00 |

Exists imperf. See No. 16.

A8 A9

**1875, Aug. 27 *Perf. 12½***

| | | | | |
|---|---|---|---|---|
| 14 | A8 | 2sh red brown | 50.00 | 37.50 |
| 15 | A9 | 5sh violet | 125.00 | *175.00* |

Exist imperf.
See Nos. 29-30, 44, 54.

**1883-90 Wmk. 2 *Perf. 14***

| | | | | |
|---|---|---|---|---|
| 16 | A7 | ½p blue green ('85) | 11.00 | 1.75 |
| *a.* | | ½p gray green | 3.75 | .25 |
| 17 | A1 | 1p blue ('84) | 350.00 | 8.25 |
| 18 | A1 | 1p carmine ('85) | 72.50 | 1.10 |
| *a.* | | 1p rose | 87.50 | 2.50 |
| 19 | A2 | 2p rose ('84) | 240.00 | 5.75 |
| 20 | A2 | 2p slate ('85) | 115.00 | .70 |
| *a.* | | 2p gray | 160.00 | 9.00 |
| 21 | A3 | 3p ol green ('86) | 2.75 | 2.25 |
| 22 | A4 | 4p red brown | 2.25 | .40 |
| *a.* | | 4p orange brown | 475.00 | 25.00 |
| 23 | A5 | 6p orange yel ('90) | 6.00 | 5.00 |
| *a.* | | 6p yellow | 40.00 | 8.75 |
| | | *Nos. 16-23 (8)* | 799.50 | 25.20 |

Nos. 18 and 20 exist imperf. Perf. 12 stamps are considered to be proofs.
For surcharge, see No. 27.

A10

**1889-91**

| | | | | |
|---|---|---|---|---|
| 24 | A10 | 1p lilac & red vio | 14.00 | .25 |
| 25 | A10 | 2p deep green | 25.00 | 9.00 |
| *a.* | | 2p green | 40.00 | 7.50 |
| 26 | A10 | 2½p lilac & ultra ('91) | 9.50 | .75 |
| | | *Nos. 24-26 (3)* | 48.50 | *10.00* |

No. 22 Surcharged in Black

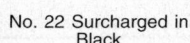

**1890, June**

| | | | | |
|---|---|---|---|---|
| 27 | A4 | 2½p on 4p red brn | 40.00 | 17.50 |
| *b.* | | Double surcharge | 350.00 | 250.00 |
| *d.* | | "PFNNY" | 100.00 | 70.00 |
| *f.* | | As "d," double surcharge | — | |

Three settings of surcharge.

**1897**

| | | | | |
|---|---|---|---|---|
| 28 | A6 | 1sh brown | 10.00 | 6.50 |
| 29 | A8 | 2sh red brown | 35.00 | 35.00 |
| 30 | A9 | 5sh violet | 70.00 | *100.00* |
| | | *Nos. 28-30 (3)* | 115.00 | *141.50* |

The 2sh exists imperf.

Llandovery Falls — A12

**1900, May 1 Engr. Wmk. 1**

| | | | | |
|---|---|---|---|---|
| 31 | A12 | 1p red | 14.50 | .25 |

**1901, Sept. 25**

| | | | | |
|---|---|---|---|---|
| 32 | A12 | 1p red & black | 12.00 | .25 |
| *a.* | | Pair, imperf. horiz. | 25,000. | |
| *b.* | | Bluish paper | 120.00 | 110.00 |

Arms of Jamaica — A13

**1903-04 Typo. Wmk. 2**

| | | | | |
|---|---|---|---|---|
| 33 | A13 | ½p grn & blk | 2.60 | .40 |
| *b.* | | "SERv ET" for "SERVIET" | 45.00 | *50.00* |
| 34 | A13 | 1p car & blk ('04) | 4.75 | .25 |
| *b.* | | "SERv ET" for "SERVIET" | 35.00 | 40.00 |
| 35 | A13 | 2½p ultra & black | 9.50 | .45 |
| *a.* | | "SERv ET" for "SERVIET" | 72.50 | *85.00* |
| 36 | A13 | 5p yel & blk ('04) | 17.50 | *26.00* |
| *a.* | | "SERv ET" for "SERVIET" | 875.00 | *1,100.* |
| | | *Nos. 33-36 (4)* | 34.35 | *27.10* |

**1905-11 Chalky Paper Wmk. 3**

| | | | | |
|---|---|---|---|---|
| 37 | A13 | ½p grn & blk | 4.50 | .25 |
| *b.* | | "SERv ET" for "SERVIET" | 32.50 | *45.00* |
| 38 | A13 | 1p car & black | 20.00 | 2.00 |
| 39 | A13 | 2½p ultra & blk ('07) | 7.25 | *9.25* |
| 39A | A3 | 3p vio, *yel* ('10) | 2.25 | 1.60 |
| 40 | A4 | 4p blk, *yel* ('10) | 16.00 | *60.00* |
| 41 | A13 | 5p yel & blk ('07) | 67.50 | *82.50* |
| *a.* | | "SERv ET" for "SERVIET" | 1,425. | *1,600.* |
| 42 | A13 | 6p red vio & vio ('11) | 15.50 | *21.00* |
| 42A | A5 | 6p purple ('10) | 11.50 | *32.50* |
| 43 | A6 | 1sh blk, *grn* ('10) | 12.00 | *10.00* |
| *a.* | | "$" for "S" in "SHILLING" | 1,450. | *1,600.* |
| 44 | A8 | 2sh vio, *blue* ('10) | 14.00 | 7.50 |
| 45 | A13 | 5sh vio & black | 57.50 | 57.50 |
| | | *Nos. 37-45 (11)* | 228.00 | 284.10 |

**1905-11 Ordinary Paper**

| | | | | |
|---|---|---|---|---|
| 46a | A3 | 2½p deep ultra | 2.75 | 1.90 |
| 47 | A3 | 3p sage grn ('07) | 8.00 | 3.25 |
| *a.* | | 3p olive green ('05) | 12.00 | 4.75 |
| 48 | A3 | 3p pale pur, *yel* ('10) | 9.50 | 3.75 |
| 49 | A4 | 4p red brn ('08) | 77.50 | *82.50* |
| 50 | A4 | 4p red, *yel* ('11) | 1.75 | *7.50* |
| 51 | A5 | 6p dull vio ('09) | 35.00 | *62.50* |
| 52 | A5 | 6p org yel ('09) | 45.00 | *70.00* |
| *a.* | | 6p orange ('06) | 17.00 | 27.50 |
| 53 | A6 | 1sh brown ('06) | 27.50 | *52.50* |
| *a.* | | 1sh deep brown | 40.00 | *62.50* |
| 54 | A8 | 2sh red brn ('08) | 160.00 | *170.00* |
| | | *Nos. 46-54 (8)* | 364.25 | *452.00* |

A14 A15

**1906**

| | | | | |
|---|---|---|---|---|
| 58 | A14 | ½p green | 4.00 | .25 |
| *a.* | | Booklet pane of 6 | — | |
| 59 | A15 | 1p carmine | 1.60 | .25 |
| *a.* | | Booklet pane of 6 | — | |

For overprints see Nos. MR1, MR4, MR7, MR10.

Edward VII — A16

**1911, Feb. 3**

| | | | | |
|---|---|---|---|---|
| 60 | A16 | 2p gray | 10.00 | *15.00* |

George V — A17

**1912-20**

| | | | | |
|---|---|---|---|---|
| 61 | A17 | 1p scarlet ('16) | 9.75 | .80 |
| *a.* | | 1p carmine ('12) | 1.75 | .25 |
| *b.* | | Booklet pane of 6 | — | |
| 62 | A17 | 1½p brn org ('16) | 2.00 | .70 |
| *a.* | | 1½p yellow orange | 18.50 | 1.25 |
| 63 | A17 | 2p gray | 2.50 | *2.00* |
| 64 | A17 | 2½p dp br blue | .90 | *1.25* |
| *a.* | | 2½p ultra ('13) | 2.00 | .25 |

**Chalky Paper**

| | | | | |
|---|---|---|---|---|
| 65 | A17 | 3p violet, *yel* | .60 | .50 |
| 66 | A17 | 4p scar & blk, *yel* ('13) | .60 | *4.00* |
| 67 | A17 | 6p red vio & dl vio | 1.90 | 2.00 |
| 68 | A17 | 1sh black, *green* | 2.60 | 2.25 |
| *a.* | | 1sh blk, *bl grn, olive back* ('20) | 4.25 | *11.00* |
| 69 | A17 | 2sh ultra & vio, *blue* ('19) | 26.00 | *42.50* |
| 70 | A17 | 5sh scar & grn, *yel* ('19) | 82.50 | *105.00* |

**Surface-colored Paper**

| | | | | |
|---|---|---|---|---|
| 71 | A17 | 3p violet, *yel* ('13) | .60 | .45 |
| 72 | A17 | 4p scar & blk, *yel* ('14) | .85 | *4.25* |
| 73 | A17 | 1sh blk, *grn* ('15) | 6.00 | *5.00* |
| | | *Nos. 61-73 (13)* | 136.80 | *170.70* |

See Nos. 101-102. For overprints see Nos. MR2-MR3, MR5-MR6, MR8-MR9, MR11.

Exhibition Buildings of 1891 — A18

Arawak Woman Preparing Cassava — A19

World War I Contingent Embarking for Overseas Duty — A20

King's House, Spanish Town — A21

Return of Overseas Contingent, 1919 — A22

Columbus Landing in Jamaica — A23

Cathedral in Spanish Town — A24

Statue of Queen Victoria — A26

Memorial to Admiral Rodney — A27

Monument to Sir Charles Metcalfe — A28

Woodland Scene — A29

King George V — A30

**1919-21 Typo. Wmk. 3 *Perf. 14***

**Chalky Paper**

**75** A18 ½p ol grn & dk grn ('20) 1.10 1.10
**76** A19 1p org & car ('21) 2.00 2.00

**Engr.**

**Ordinary Paper**

**77** A20 1½p green .45 *1.10*
**78** A21 2p grn & bl ('21) 1.25 *4.50*
**79** A22 2½p blue blk & blue 2.25 2.00
*a.* 2½p blue & dark blue ('21) 15.00 3.50
*b.* "C" of "CA" missing from watermark *350.00 300.00*
*c.* "A" of "CA" missing from watermark *350.00*
**80** A23 3p blue & grn ('21) 6.50 *2.75*
**81** A24 4p grn & dk brn ('21) 2.75 *10.00*
**83** A26 1sh brt org & org ('20) 4.25 *5.75*
*a.* Frame inverted *40,000. 25,000.*
As "a," revenue cancel *2,500.*
*b.* "C" of "CA" missing from watermark *1,100.*
*c.* "A" of "CA" missing from watermark *1,200. 1,000.*
**84** A27 2sh brn & bl ('20) 12.50 *37.50*
*b.* "C" of "CA" missing from watermark *800.00*
*c.* "A" of "CA" missing from watermark
**85** A28 3sh org & vio ('20) 27.50 *135.00*
*a.* "C" of "CA" missing from watermark *1,200.*
**86** A29 5sh ocher & blue ('21) 55.00 *82.50*
**87** A30 10sh dk myr grn ('20) 85.00 *160.00*
*Nos. 75-87 (12)* 200.55 *444.20*

See note after No. 100. Watermark varieties exist and sell for much higher values.

A 6p stamp depicting the abolition of slavery was sent to the Colony but was not issued. "Specimen" examples exist with wmk. 3 or 4. Value $875 each.

Without "Specimen," values: wmk. 3, $60,000; wmk. 4, $40,000.

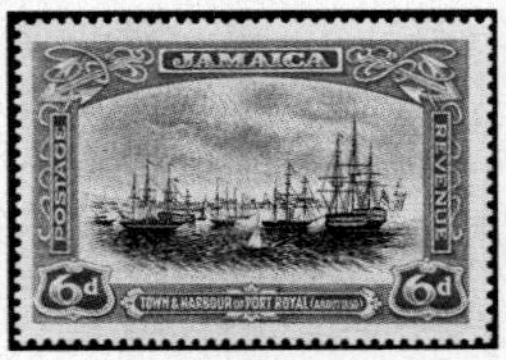

Port Royal in 1853 A31

**1921-23 Typo. Wmk. 4 *Perf. 14***

**Chalky Paper**

**88** A18 ½p ol grn & dk grn ('22) .60 .60
*a.* Booklet pane of 4 *150.00*
**89** A19 1p org & car ('22) 1.75 .25
*a.* Booklet pane of 6 *225.00*

**Engr.**

**Ordinary Paper**

**90** A20 1½p green 3.50 .55
**91** A21 2p grn & blue 8.50 .90
**92** A22 2½p bl & dk bl 6.50 2.00
**93** A23 3p bl & grn ('22) 6.50 .80
**94** A24 4p grn & dk brn 1.40 .40
**95** A31 6p bl & blk ('22) 16.00 2.25
**96** A26 1sh brn org & dl org 2.50 .90
**97** A27 2sh brn & bl ('22) 3.75 .75
**98** A28 3sh org & violet 20.00 11.00
**99** A29 5sh ocher & bl ('23) 35.00 29.00
*a.* 5sh orange & blue 82.50 *82.50*
**100** A30 10sh dk myr grn ('22) 60.00 80.00
*Nos. 88-100 (13)* 166.00 129.40
Set, never hinged 380.00

No. 89 differs from No. 76 in having the words "Postage and Revenue" at the bottom.

On No. 79 the horizontal bar of the flag at the left has a broad white line below the colored line. On No. 92 this has been corrected and the broad white line placed above the colored line.

Watermark is sideways on Nos. 76-77, 87, 89-90. Watermark varieties other than these and normal are scarce and sell for much higher values.

**Type of 1912-19 Issue**

**1921-27 Typo. Wmk. 4**

**101** A17 ½p green ('27) 4.00 .25
*a.* Booklet pane of 6
**102** A17 6p red vio & dl vio 18.50 5.00

No. 102 is on chalky paper.

A32

Type I

Type II

Type II — Cross shading beneath "Jamaica."

**1929-32 Engr. *Perf. 13½x14, 14***

**103** A32 1p red, type I 16.50 .25
*a.* 1p red, type II ('32) 16.50 .25
*b.* Booklet pane of 6, type II
**104** A32 1½p brown 10.00 .25
**105** A32 9p violet brown 10.00 1.25
*Nos. 103-105 (3)* 36.50 1.75
Set, never hinged 42.50

The frames on Nos. 103 to 105 differ.

Coco Palms at Columbus Cove — A33

Scene near Castleton, St. Andrew — A34

Priestman's River, Portland Parish — A35

**1932 *Perf. 12½***

**106** A33 2p grn & gray blk 40.00 4.50
*a.* Vertical pair, imperf. between *15,000.*
**107** A34 2½p ultra & sl bl 6.75 1.75
*a.* Vertical pair, imperf. between *25,000. 25,000.*
**108** A35 6p red vio & gray blk 37.50 6.00
*Nos. 106-108 (3)* 84.25 12.25
Set, never hinged 125.00

Common Design Types pictured following the introduction.

**Silver Jubilee Issue**

Common Design Type

**1935, May 6 *Perf. 11x12***

**109** CD301 1p car & blue .45 .25
*a.* Booklet pane of 6 *175.00*
**110** CD301 1½p black & ultra .55 *1.75*
**111** CD301 6p indigo & grn 10.00 *18.50*
**112** CD301 1sh brn vio & ind 6.00 *18.50*
*Nos. 109-112 (4)* 17.00 39.00
Set, never hinged 32.50

**Coronation Issue**

Common Design Type

**1937, May 12 *Perf. 13½x14***

**113** CD302 1p carmine .25 .25
**114** CD302 1½p gray black .40 .30
**115** CD302 2½p bright ultra .60 *.70*
*Nos. 113-115 (3)* 1.25 1.25
Set, never hinged 1.75

King George VI — A36

Coco Palms at Columbus Cove — A37

Scene near Castleton, St. Andrew — A38

Bananas A39

Citrus Grove A40

Priestman's River, Portland Parish — A41

Kingston Harbor A42

Sugar Industry A43

Bamboo Walk — A44

Woodland Scene — A45

King George VI — A46

**1938-51 *Perf. 13½x14***

**116** A36 ½p dk blue grn 1.25 .25
*a.* Booklet pane of 6 8.00
*b.* Wmkd. sideways — *9,000.*
**117** A36 1p carmine .85 .25
*a.* Booklet pane of 6 12.00
**118** A36 1½p brown .85 .25

***Perf. 12½, 13x13½, 13½x13, 12½x13***

**119** A37 2p grn & gray blk, perf. 12½ .85 .85
*a.* Perf. 13x13½ ('39) 1.90 .50
*b.* Perf. 12½x13 ('51) .85 .25
**120** A38 2½p ultra & sl bl 5.75 *2.75*
**121** A39 3p grn & lt ultra .75 *1.50*
**122** A40 4p grn & yel brn .60 .25
**123** A41 6p red vio & gray blk, perf. 13½x13 ('50) 2.00 .25
*a.* Perf. 12½ 5.75 .30
*b.* As "a," double impression of gray blk —
**124** A42 9p rose lake .60 .50
**125** A43 1sh dk brn & brt grn 10.00 .25
**126** A44 2sh brn & brt bl 21.00 1.00

***Perf. 13, 14***

**127** A45 5sh ocher & bl, perf. 13 ('50) 7.25 3.75
*a.* Bluish paper, perf. 13 ('49) 7.25 3.00
*b.* Perf. 14 12.00 3.25
**128** A46 10sh dk myr grn, perf. 14 6.75 *11.50*
*a.* Perf. 13 ('50) 11.00 *7.50*
*Nos. 116-128 (13)* 58.50 23.35
Set, never hinged 100.00

See Nos. 140, 148, 149, 152.

**Catalogue values for unused stamps in this section, from this point to the end of the section, are for Never Hinged items.**

Courthouse, Falmouth A47

Kings Charles II and George VI A48

House of Assembly, 1762-1869 A50

Institute of Jamaica — A49

Allegory of Labor and Learning — A51

Constitution and Flag of Jamaica A52

*Perf. 12½*

**1945, Aug. 20 Engr. Wmk. 4**

| | | | | |
|---|---|---|---|---|
| 129 | A47 | 1½p brown | .30 | .30 |
| a. | | Booklet pane of 4 | 37.50 | |
| b. | | Perf. 12½x13½ ('46) | 11.00 | 1.75 |
| 130 | A48 | 2p dp grn, perf. 12½x13½ | .30 | *.50* |
| a. | | Perf. 12½ | 14.00 | 1.10 |
| 131 | A49 | 3p bright ultra | .25 | *.50* |
| a. | | Perf. 13 ('46) | 3.00 | *2.50* |
| 132 | A50 | 4½p slate black | 1.10 | .35 |
| a. | | Perf. 13 ('46) | 4.50 | *4.75* |
| 133 | A51 | 2sh chocolate | 1.25 | .50 |
| 134 | A52 | 5sh deep blue | 3.00 | 1.10 |
| 135 | A49 | 10sh green | 2.75 | *2.00* |
| | | *Nos. 129-135 (7)* | 8.95 | *5.25* |

Granting of a new Constitution in 1944.

**Peace Issue**

Common Design Type

**1946, Oct. 14 Wmk. 4 *Perf. 13½***

| | | | | |
|---|---|---|---|---|
| 136 | CD303 | 1½p black brown | .30 | *4.50* |
| a. | | Perf. 13½x14 | 2.50 | .25 |

*Perf. 13½x14*

| | | | | |
|---|---|---|---|---|
| 137 | CD303 | 3p deep blue | .50 | 8.00 |
| a. | | Perf. 13½ | 6.50 | *2.75* |

**Silver Wedding Issue**

Common Design Types

**1948, Dec. 1 Photo. *Perf. 14x14½***

| | | | | |
|---|---|---|---|---|
| 138 | CD304 | 1½p red brown | .35 | .25 |

**Engr.; Name Typo.**

***Perf. 11½x11***

| | | | | |
|---|---|---|---|---|
| 139 | CD305 | £1 red | 27.50 | *60.00* |

**Type of 1938 and**

Tobacco Industry A53

**1949, Aug. 15 Engr. *Perf. 12½***

| | | | | |
|---|---|---|---|---|
| 140 | A39 | 3p ultra & slate blue | 3.25 | 1.00 |
| 141 | A53 | £1 purple & brown | 45.00 | 32.50 |

**UPU Issue**

Common Design Types

***Perf. 13½, 11x11½***

**1949, Oct. 10 Wmk. 4**

| | | | | |
|---|---|---|---|---|
| 142 | CD306 | 1½p red brown | .25 | .25 |
| 143 | CD307 | 2p dark green | 1.10 | 1.00 |
| 144 | CD308 | 3p indigo | .40 | *.50* |
| 145 | CD309 | 6p rose violet | .50 | *.70* |
| | | *Nos. 142-145 (4)* | 2.25 | 2.45 |

**University Issue**

Common Design Types

**1951, Feb. 16 *Perf. 14x14½***

| | | | | |
|---|---|---|---|---|
| 146 | CD310 | 2p brown & gray blk | .35 | .40 |
| 147 | CD311 | 6p rose lil & gray blk | .55 | .30 |

**George VI Type of 1938**

**1951, Oct. 25 *Perf. 13½x14***

| | | | | |
|---|---|---|---|---|
| 148 | A36 | ½p orange | 2.25 | .30 |
| a. | | Booklet pane of 6 | 16.00 | |
| 149 | A36 | 1p blue green | 3.00 | .25 |
| a. | | Booklet pane of 6 | 21.00 | |

Boy Scout Emblem with Map — A54

Map and Emblem A55

***Perf. 13½x13, 13x13½***

**1952, Mar. 5 Typo. Wmk. 4**

| | | | | |
|---|---|---|---|---|
| 150 | A54 | 2p blk, yel grn & blue | .30 | .25 |
| 151 | A55 | 6p blk, yel grn & dk red | .70 | .60 |

1st Caribbean Boy Scout Jamboree, 1952.

**Banana Type of 1938**

**1952, July 1 Engr. *Perf. 12½***

| | | | | |
|---|---|---|---|---|
| 152 | A39 | 3p rose red & green | 3.75 | .30 |

**Coronation Issue**

Common Design Type

**1953, June 2 *Perf. 13½x13***

| | | | | |
|---|---|---|---|---|
| 153 | CD312 | 2p dk green & black | .70 | .25 |

**Type of 1938 with Portrait of Queen Elizabeth II and Inscription: "ROYAL VISIT 1953"**

**1953, Nov. 25 *Perf. 13***

| | | | | |
|---|---|---|---|---|
| 154 | A37 | 2p green & gray black | .50 | .25 |

Visit of Queen Elizabeth II and the Duke of Edinburgh, 1953.

Warship off Port Royal A56

Designs: 2½p, Old Montego Bay. 3p, Old Kingston. 6p, Proclaiming abolition of slavery.

**1955, May 10 Engr. *Perf. 12x12½***

**Center in Black**

| | | | | |
|---|---|---|---|---|
| 155 | A56 | 2p olive green | .50 | .25 |
| 156 | A56 | 2½p light ultra | .25 | .30 |
| 157 | A56 | 3p deep plum | .25 | .30 |
| 158 | A56 | 6p rose red | .25 | .25 |
| | | *Nos. 155-158 (4)* | 1.25 | 1.10 |

300th anniv. of Jamaica's establishment as a British territory.

Palm Trees — A57

Blue Mountain Peak — A58

Arms of Jamaica — A59

Arms of Jamaica — A60

1p, Sugar cane. 2p, Pineapple. 2½p, Bananas. 3p, Mahoe flower. 4p, Breadfruit. 5p, Ackee fruit. 6p, Streamer (hummingbird). 1sh, Royal Botanic Gardens, Hope. 1sh6p, Rafting on the Rio Grande. 2sh, Fort Charles.

**1956 Wmk. 4 *Perf. 12½***

| | | | | |
|---|---|---|---|---|
| 159 | A57 | ½p org ver & blk | .25 | .25 |
| a. | | Booklet pane of 6 | .30 | |
| 160 | A57 | 1p emer & blk | .25 | .25 |
| a. | | Booklet pane of 6 | .50 | |
| 161 | A57 | 2p rose red & blk | .25 | .25 |
| a. | | Booklet pane of 6 | .85 | |
| 162 | A57 | 2½p lt ultra & black | 1.00 | .50 |
| a. | | Booklet pane of 6 | 6.00 | |
| 163 | A57 | 3p brn & grn | .25 | .25 |
| 164 | A57 | 4p dk blue & ol grn | .50 | .25 |
| 165 | A57 | 5p ol green & car | 1.00 | *2.00* |
| 166 | A57 | 6p car & blk | 3.25 | .25 |

***Perf. 13½***

| | | | | |
|---|---|---|---|---|
| 167 | A58 | 8p red org & brt ultra | 1.75 | .25 |
| 168 | A58 | 1sh blue & yel grn | 1.75 | .25 |
| 169 | A58 | 1sh6p dp cl & ultra | 1.00 | .25 |
| 170 | A58 | 2sh ol grn & ultra | 13.50 | 2.50 |

***Perf. 11½***

| | | | | |
|---|---|---|---|---|
| 171 | A59 | 3sh blue & black | 2.75 | *3.25* |
| 172 | A59 | 5sh carmine & blk | 4.00 | *6.00* |
| 173 | A60 | 10sh blue grn & blk | 27.50 | *14.00* |
| 174 | A60 | £1 purple & blk | 27.50 | *14.00* |
| | | *Nos. 159-174 (16)* | 86.50 | 44.50 |

For overprints see Nos. 185-196. For types overprinted see Nos. 208-216.

**West Indies Federation**

Common Design Type

***Perf. 11½x11***

**1958, Apr. 22 Engr. Wmk. 314**

| | | | | |
|---|---|---|---|---|
| 175 | CD313 | 2p green | .70 | .25 |
| 176 | CD313 | 5p blue | .95 | *2.75* |
| 177 | CD313 | 6p carmine rose | 1.00 | .45 |
| | | *Nos. 175-177 (3)* | 2.65 | 3.45 |

Britannia Plane over 1860 Packet Boat A61

1sh Stamps of 1860 and 1956 — A62

6p, Victorian post cart and mail truck.

**1960, Jan. 4 *Perf. 13x13½***

| | | | | |
|---|---|---|---|---|
| 178 | A61 | 2p lilac & blue | .50 | .25 |
| 179 | A61 | 6p ol grn & car rose | .50 | .45 |

***Perf. 13***

| | | | | |
|---|---|---|---|---|
| 180 | A62 | 1sh blue, yel grn & brn | .60 | .50 |
| | | *Nos. 178-180 (3)* | 1.60 | 1.20 |

Centenary of Jamaican postal service.

**Independent State**

Zouave Bugler and Map of Jamaica A63

1sh6p, Gordon House (Legislature) & hands of three races holding banner. 5sh, Map & symbols of agriculture & industry.

**1962, Aug. 8 Photo. *Perf. 13***

| | | | | |
|---|---|---|---|---|
| 181 | A63 | 2p multicolored | 1.40 | .25 |
| 182 | A63 | 4p multicolored | 1.00 | .25 |
| a. | | Yellow omitted | | |
| 183 | A63 | 1sh6p red, black & brn | 3.00 | .80 |
| 184 | A63 | 5sh multicolored | 4.25 | 5.50 |
| | | *Nos. 181-184 (4)* | 9.65 | 6.80 |

**Issue of 1956 Overprinted**

a

b

***Perf. 12½***

**1962, Aug. 8 Wmk. 4 Engr.**

| | | | | |
|---|---|---|---|---|
| 185 | A57(a) | ½p org ver & blk | .25 | *.80* |
| 186 | A57(a) | 1p emer & blk | .25 | .25 |
| 187 | A57(a) | 2½p lt ultra & blk | .25 | *.80* |
| 188 | A57(b) | 3p brn & grn | .25 | .25 |
| 189 | A57(b) | 5p ol grn & car | .25 | *.55* |
| 190 | A57(b) | 6p car & black | 2.25 | .25 |

***Perf. 13½***

| | | | | |
|---|---|---|---|---|
| 191 | A58(b) | 8p red org & brt ultra | .25 | .25 |
| 192 | A58(b) | 1sh bl & yel grn | .30 | .25 |
| 193 | A58(b) | 2sh ol green & ultra | 1.00 | *1.25* |

***Perf. 11½***

| | | | | |
|---|---|---|---|---|
| 194 | A59(a) | 3sh blue & blk | 1.00 | *1.50* |
| 195 | A60(a) | 10sh bl grn & blk | 3.75 | *3.50* |
| 196 | A60(a) | £1 pur & black | 4.00 | *4.25* |
| | | *Nos. 185-196 (12)* | 13.80 | *13.90* |

Nos. 181-196 issued to commemorate Jamaica's independence.

"Independence" measures 17½x1½mm on Nos. 185-187; 18x1mm on Nos. 194-196.

See Nos. 208-216.

Weight Lifting, Soccer, Boxing and Cycling A64

Designs: 6p, Various water sports. 8p, Running and jumping. 2sh, Arms and runner.

***Perf. 14½x14***

**1962, Aug. 11 Photo. Wmk. 314**

| | | | | |
|---|---|---|---|---|
| 197 | A64 | 1p car & dk brown | .25 | .25 |
| 198 | A64 | 6p blue & brown | .25 | .25 |
| 199 | A64 | 8p olive & dk brown | .25 | .25 |
| 200 | A64 | 2sh multicolored | .30 | *.70* |
| | | *Nos. 197-200 (4)* | 1.05 | 1.45 |

IX Central American and Caribbean Games, Kingston, Aug. 11-25.

A souvenir sheet containing one each of Nos. 197-200, imperf., was sold exclusively by National Sports, Ltd., at 5sh (face 3sh3p). The Jamaican Post Office sold the entire issue of this sheet to National Sports at face value, plus the printing cost. The stamps are postally valid. The sheet has marginal inscriptions and simulated perforations in ultramarine. Value $14.

**Freedom from Hunger Issue**

Man Planting Mango Tree and Produce A65

*Perf. 12½*

**1963, June 4 Unwmk. Litho.**

**201** A65 1p blue & multi .25 .25
**202** A65 8p rose & multi .80 .60

See note after CD314, Common Design section.

### Red Cross Centenary Issue

Common Design Type

**1963, Sept. 2 Wmk. 314** ***Perf. 13***

**203** CD315 2p black & red .25 .25
**204** CD315 1sh6p ultra & red .50 *1.40*

Carole Joan Crawford — A66

**Unwmk.**

**1964, Feb. 14 Photo.** ***Perf. 13***

**205** A66 3p multicolored .25 .25
**206** A66 1sh olive & multi .30 .25
**207** A66 1sh6p multicolored .40 .40
*a.* Souvenir sheet of 3 1.50 1.50
*Nos. 205-207 (3)* .95 .90

Carole Joan Crawford, Miss World, 1963.

No. 207a contains one each of Nos. 205-207 with simulated perforations. Issued May 25. Sold for 4sh.

### Types of 1956 Overprinted like 1962 Independence Issue

**Wmk. 314**

**1963-64 Engr.** ***Perf. 12½***

**208** A57(a) ½p org ver & blk .25 .25
**209** A57(a) 1p emer & blk ('64) .25 *1.25*
**210** A57(a) 2½p lt ultra & blk ('64) .25 *2.00*
**211** A57(b) 3p brn & grn .25 .25
**212** A57(b) 5p ol grn & car ('64) .40 *2.00*

*Perf. 13½*

**213** A58(b) 8p red org & brt ultra ('64) .30 *.75*
**214** A58(b) 1sh bl & yel grn .35 .75
**215** A58(b) 2sh ol grn & ultra ('64) .60 *6.00*

*Perf. 11½*

**216** A59(a) 3sh bl & blk ('64) 2.75 *4.50*
*Nos. 208-216 (9)* 5.40 17.75

Overprint is at bottom on Nos. 214-215, at top on Nos. 192-193.

Lignum Vitae, National Flower, and Map — A67

1½p, Ackee, national fruit, and map. 2p, Blue Mahoe, national tree, and map, vert. 2½p, Land shells (snails). 3p, Flag over map. 4p, Murex antillarum, sea shell. 6p, Papilio homerus. 8p, Streamer (hummingbird). 9p, Gypsum industry. 1sh, Stadium and statue of runner. 1sh6p, Palisadoes International Airport. 2sh, Bauxite mining. 3sh, Blue marlin and boat. 5sh, Port Royal exploration of sunken city, map, ship and artifacts. 10sh, Coat of arms, vert. £1, Flag and Queen Elizabeth II.

*Perf. 14½, 14x14½*

**1964, May 4 Photo. Wmk. 352**

**Size: 26x22mm, 22x26mm**

**217** A67 1p bis, vio bl & grn .25 .25
*a.* Booklet pane of 6 .40
**218** A67 1½p multicolored .25 .25
**219** A67 2p multicolored .25 .25
*a.* Booklet pane of 6 .90
**220** A67 2½p multicolored .90 .50
**221** A67 3p emer, yel & black .25 .25
*a.* Booklet pane of 6 3.00
**222** A67 4p violet & buff .50 .25
**223** A67 6p multicolored 1.90 .25
*a.* Ultramarine omitted 95.00
*b.* Denomination omitted *2,200.*
**224** A67 8p multicolored 2.00 1.25
*a.* Red omitted 200.00

*Perf. 14½x14, 13½x14½, 14x14½*

**Size: 32x26mm, 26x32mm**

**225** A67 9p blue & yel 1.25 .25
**226** A67 1sh yel brn & blk .25 .25
*a.* Yellow brown omitted 3,000. 3,000.
*b.* Black omitted 2,200.
*c.* Denomination (only) omitted 1,600.
**227** A67 1sh6p sl, buff & bl 3.00 .25
**228** A67 2sh bl, brn red & black 2.25 .25
**229** A67 3sh grn, saph & dk bl, perf. 14½x14 .35 *.60*
*a.* Perf. 14x14½ 1.00 1.00
**230** A67 5sh bl, blk & bis 1.00 1.00
**231** A67 10sh multicolored 1.25 1.10
*a.* Blue ("Jamaica" etc.) omitted 450.00
**232** A67 £1 multicolored 2.75 1.00
*Nos. 217-232 (16)* 18.40 7.95

See Nos. 306-318. For overprints & surcharges see Nos. 248-251, 279-291, 305.

Scout Hat, Globe, Neckerchief — A68

Scout Emblem, American Crocodile — A69

Design: 3p, Scout belt buckle.

*Perf. 14½x14, 14*

**1964, Aug. 27 Wmk. 352**

**233** A68 3p pink, black & red .25 .25
**234** A68 8p ultra, black & olive .25 *.25*
**235** A69 1sh ultra & gold .25 *.45*
*Nos. 233-235 (3)* .75 *.95*

6th Inter-American Scout Conference, Kingston, Aug. 25-29.

Gordon House, Kingston, and Commonwealth Parliamentary Association Emblem — A70

6p, Headquarters House, Kingston. 1sh6p, House of Assembly, Spanish Town.

**1964, Nov. 16 Photo.** ***Perf. 14½x14***

**236** A70 3p yel green & blk .25 .25
**237** A70 6p red & black .30 .25
**238** A70 1sh6p ultra & black .40 .25
*Nos. 236-238 (3)* .95 .75

10th Commonwealth Parliamentary Conf.

Eleanor Roosevelt — A71

**1964, Dec. 10 Wmk. 352**

**239** A71 1sh lt green, blk & red .25 .25

Eleanor Roosevelt (1884-1962) on the 16th anniv. of the Universal Declaration of Human Rights.

Map of Jamaica and Girl Guide Emblem — A72

Girl Guide Emblems — A73

*Perf. 14x14½, 14*

**1965, May 17 Photo. Wmk. 352**

**240** A72 3p lt blue, yel & yel grn .25 .25
**241** A73 1sh lt yel grn, blk & bis .25 .30

50th anniv. of the Girl Guides of Jamaica.

Salvation Army Cap — A74

1sh6p, Flag bearer, drummer, globe, vert.

*Perf. 14x14½, 14½x14*

**1965, Aug. 23 Photo. Wmk. 352**

**242** A74 3p dp blue, yel, mar & blk .25 .25
**243** A74 1sh6p emerald & multi .50 .40

Centenary of the Salvation Army.

Paul Bogle, William Gordon and Morant Bay Court House A75

**1965, Dec. 29 Unwmk.** ***Perf. 14x13***

**244** A75 3p vio blue, blk & brn .25 .25
**245** A75 1sh6p yel grn, blk & brn .25 .25
**246** A75 3sh pink & brown .30 *.80*
*Nos. 244-246 (3)* .80 1.30

Cent. of the Morant Bay rebellion against governor John Eyre.

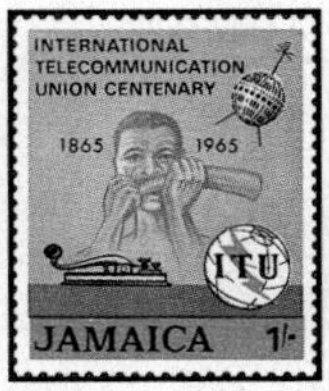


ITU Emblem, Telstar, Telegraph Key and Man Blowing Horn — A76

*Perf. 14x14½*

**1965, Dec. 29 Photo. Wmk. 352**

**247** A76 1sh gray, black & red .50 .25

Cent. of the ITU.

Nos. 221, 223, 226-227 Overprinted

*Perf. 14½, 14½x14*

**1966, Mar. 3 Photo. Wmk. 352**

**Size: 26x22mm**

**248** A67 3p emer, yel & black .30 .25
**249** A67 6p multicolored 2.00 .40

**Size: 32x26mm**

**250** A67 1sh yel brown & blk .65 .25
**251** A67 1sh6p slate, buff & blue 3.25 2.50
*Nos. 248-251 (4)* 6.20 3.40

See note after Antigua No. 162.

Winston Churchill A77

**1966, Apr. 18** ***Perf. 14, 14x14½***

**252** A77 6p olive green & gray .55 .35
**253** A77 1sh violet & sepia .80 .95

Sir Winston Leonard Spencer Churchill (1874-1965), statesman and WWII leader.

Runner, Flags of Jamaica, Great Britain and Games' Emblem A78

Designs: 6p, Bicyclists and waterfall. 1sh, Stadium. 3sh, Games' Emblem.

*Perf. 14½x14*

**1966, Aug. 4 Photo. Wmk. 352**

**254** A78 3p multicolored .25 .25
**255** A78 6p multicolored .35 .25
**256** A78 1sh multicolored .25 .25
**257** A78 3sh gold & dk vio blue .35 .40
*a.* Souvenir sheet of 4 5.00 5.00
*Nos. 254-257 (4)* 1.20 1.15

8th British Empire and Commonwealth Games, Aug. 4-13, 1966.

No. 257a contains 4 imperf. stamps with simulated perforations similar to Nos. 254-257. Issued Aug. 25, 1966.

Bolivar Statue, Kingston, Flags of Jamaica and Venezuela — A79

**1966, Dec. 5** ***Perf. 14x14½***

**258** A79 8p multicolored .35 .25

150th anniv. of the "Bolivar Letter," written by Simon Bolivar, while in exile in Jamaica.

Jamaican Pavilion — A80

**1967, Apr. 28** ***Perf. 14½x14***

**259** A80 6p multicolored .25 .25
**260** A80 1sh multicolored .25 .25

EXPO '67 Intl. Exhibition, Montreal, Apr. 28-Oct. 27.

Donald Burns Sangster — A81

*Perf. 13x13½*

**1967, Aug. 28 Unwmk.**

**261** A81 3p multicolored .25 .25
**262** A81 1sh6p multicolored .25 .25

Sir Donald Burns Sangster (1911-1967), Prime Minister.

Traffic Police and Post Office — A82

Designs: 1sh, Officers representing various branches of police force in front of Police Headquarters. 1sh6p, Constable, 1867, Old House of Assembly, and 1967 constable with New House of Assembly.

*Perf. 13½x14*

**1967, Nov. 28 Photo. Wmk. 352**

**Size: 42x25mm**

**263** A82 3p red brown & multi .40 .25

**Size: 56½x20½mm**

*Perf. 13½x14½*

**264** A82 1sh yellow & multi .40 .25

**Size: 42x25mm**

*Perf. 13½x14*

**265** A82 1sh6p gray & multi .70 *.75*
*Nos. 263-265 (3)* 1.50 1.25

Centenary of the Constabulary Force.

A Human Rights set of three (3p, 1sh, 3sh) was prepared and announced for release on Jan. 2, 1968. The Crown Agents distributed sample sets, but the stamps were not issued. On Dec. 3, Nos. 271-273 were issued instead. Designs of the unissued set show bowls of food, an abacus and praying hands. Value, $175.

Wicketkeeper, Emblem of West Indies Cricket Team — A82a

Designs: No. 266, Wicketkeeper and emblem of West Indies Cricket Team. No. 267, Batsman and emblem of Marylebone Cricket Club. No. 268, Bowler and emblem of West Indies Cricket Team.

**1968, Feb. 8 Photo.** *Perf. 14*

**266** A82a 6p multicolored .35 *.35*
**267** A82a 6p multicolored .35 *.35*
**268** A82a 6p multicolored .35 *.35*
*a.* Horiz. strip of 3, #266-268 1.75 *1.75*
*Nos. 266-268 (3)* 1.05 *1.05*

Visit of the Marylebone Cricket Club to the West Indies, Jan.-Feb. 1968. Miniature sheet of 3 of No 268a. Value, $5.75.

Sir Alexander and Lady Bustamante — A83

**1968, May 23** *Perf. 14½*

**269** A83 3p brt rose & black .25 .25
**270** A83 1sh olive green & black .25 .25

Labor Day, May 23, 1968.

Human Rights Flame and Map of Jamaica A84

Designs: 1sh, Hands shielding Human Rights flame, vert. 3sh, Man kneeling on Map of Jamaica, and Human Rights flame.

**1968, Dec. 3 Wmk. 352** *Perf. 14½*

**271** A84 3p multicolored .25 .25
*a.* Gold (flame) omitted 150.00
**272** A84 1sh multicolored .25 .25
**273** A84 3sh multicolored .40 *.80*
*a.* Gold (flame) omitted 175.00
*Nos. 271-273 (3)* .90 1.30

International Human Rights Year.

ILO Emblem A85

**Unwmk.**

**1969, May 23 Litho.** *Perf. 14*

**274** A85 6p black & orange yel .25 .25
**275** A85 3sh black & brt green .30 .30

50th anniv. of the ILO.

WHO Emblem, Children and Nurse — A86

Designs: 1sh, Malaria eradication, horiz. 3sh, Student nurses.

**1969, May 30 Photo.** *Perf. 14*

**276** A86 6p org, black & brown .25 .25
**277** A86 1sh blue grn, blk & brn .25 .25
**278** A86 3sh ultra, black & brn .25 *.80*
*Nos. 276-278 (3)* .75 1.30

WHO, 20th anniv.

Nos. 217-219, 221-223, 225-232 Surcharged

**1969, Sept. 8 Wmk. 352** *Perf. 14½*

**Size: 26x22mm, 22x26mm**

**279** A67 1c on 1p multi .25 .25
**280** A67 2c on 2p multi .25 .25
**281** A67 3c on 3p multi .25 .25
**282** A67 4c on 4p multi 1.00 .25
**283** A67 5c on 6p multi 1.00 .25
*a.* Blue (wing dots) omitted *100.00*

*Perf. 14½x14, 13½x14½, 14x14½*

**Size: 32x26mm, 26x32mm**

**284** A67 8c on 9p multi .25 .25
**285** A67 10c on 1sh multi .25 .25
**286** A67 15c on 1sh6p multi .40 *.50*
**287** A67 20c on 2sh multi 1.10 *.90*
**288** A67 30c on 3sh multi 2.00 *1.50*
**289** A67 50c on 5sh multi 1.00 *2.00*
**290** A67 $1 on 10sh multi 1.00 *4.00*
**291** A67 $2 on £1 multi 2.00 *5.00*
*Nos. 279-291 (13)* 10.75 15.65

Introduction of decimal currency.

The old denomination is obliterated by groups of small rectangles on the 1c and 3c, and with a square on the 2c, 4c and 8c; old denominations not obliterated on others.

Madonna and Child with St. John, by Raphael — A87

Christmas (Paintings): 2c, The Adoration of the Kings, by Vincenzo Foppa. 8c, The Adoration of the Kings, by Dosso Dossi.

**1969, Oct. 25 Litho.** *Perf. 13*

**292** A87 2c vermilion & multi .25 .35
**293** A87 5c multicolored .25 .35
**294** A87 8c orange & multi .25 .35
*Nos. 292-294 (3)* .75 1.05

First Jamaica Penny — A88

Design: 3c, First Jamaica halfpenny.

**1969, Oct. 27** *Perf. 12x12½*

**295** A88 3c brt pink, blk & silver .25 .25
**296** A88 15c emerald, blk & silver .25 .25

Centenary of the first Jamaican coinage.

George William Gordon — A89

Portraits: 3c, Sir Alexander Bustamante (1884-1977). 5c, Norman W. Manley (1893-1969). 10c, Marcus M. Garvey (1887-1940). 15c, Paul Bogle (1820-1865).

*Perf. 12x12½*

**1970, Mar. 11 Photo. Unwmk.**

**297** A89 1c lt violet & multi .25 .25
**298** A89 3c lt blue & multi .25 .25
**299** A89 5c lt gray & multi .25 .25
**300** A89 10c pale rose & multi .25 .25
**301** A89 15c pale green & multi .25 .25
*Nos. 297-301 (5)* 1.25 1.25

National heroes connected with Jamaica's independence.

Crucifixion, by Antonello da Messina — A90

Easter: 3c, Christ Appearing to St. Peter, by Annibale Carracci. 20c, Easter lily.

**1970, Mar. 23**

**302** A90 3c pink & multi .25 .25
**303** A90 10c gray green & multi .25 .25
**304** A90 20c gray & multi .25 *.55*
*Nos. 302-304 (3)* .75 1.05

No. 219 Surcharged

**1970, July 16 Wmk. 352** *Perf. 14½*

**305** A67 2c on 2p multicolored .30 .25

**Type of Regular Issue, 1964**

Values in Cents and Dollars

Designs: 1c, Lignum vitae and map. 2c, Blue mahoe and map, vert. 3c, Flag over map. 4c, Murex antillarum, sea shell. 5c, Papilio homerus. 8c, Gypsum industry. 10c, Stadium and statue of runner. 15c, Palisadoes International Airport. 20c, Bauxite mining. 30c, Blue marlin and boat. 50c, Port Royal exploration of sunken city, map, ship and artifacts. $1, Coat of arms, vert. $2, Flag and Queen Elizabeth II.

**1970 Wmk. 352 Photo.** *Perf. 14½*

**Size: 26x22mm, 22x26mm**

**306** A67 1c bister & multi .65 *1.00*
**307** A67 2c gray grn & multi .30 .25
**308** A67 3c emer, yel & black .50 *.80*
**309** A67 4c violet & buff 2.25 .30
**310** A67 5c green & multi 2.25 .50

*Perf. 14½x14, 13½x14½, 14x14½*

**Size: 32x26mm, 26x32mm**

**311** A67 8c blue & yellow 1.50 .25
**312** A67 10c yel brn & black .50 .25
**313** A67 15c multicolored 2.00 1.50
**314** A67 20c multicolored 1.00 *1.50*
**315** A67 30c multicolored 3.00 *4.50*
**316** A67 50c multicolored 1.25 *3.50*
**317** A67 $1 multicolored 1.00 *5.00*
**318** A67 $2 multicolored 1.50 *4.00*
*Nos. 306-318 (13)* 17.70 23.35

Issued: Nos. 306-312, 9/7; Nos. 313-318, 11/2.

Bright's Cable Gear on "Dacia" A91

Designs: 3c, Telegraph cable ship "Dacia." 50c, Double current Morse key, 1870, and map of Jamaica.

**1970, Oct. 12 Litho.** *Perf. 14½*

**319** A91 3c red orange & multi .25 .25
**320** A91 10c blue green & multi .25 .25
**321** A91 50c emerald & multi .75 .75
*Nos. 319-321 (3)* 1.25 1.25

Centenary of telegraph service.

Bananas, Citrus Fruit, Sugar Cane and Tobacco — A92

**1970, Nov. 2 Wmk. 352** *Perf. 14*

**322** A92 2c brown & multi .25 .30
**323** A92 10c black & multi .35 .25

Jamaica Agricultural Society, 75th anniv.

"The Projector," 1845 — A93

Locomotives: 15c, Engine 54, 1944. 50c, Engine 102, 1967.

**1970, Nov. 21 Litho. *Perf. 13½***

| | | | | |
|---|---|---|---|---|
| **324** | A93 | 3c green & multi | .25 | .25 |
| **325** | A93 | 15c org brown & multi | .80 | .80 |
| **326** | A93 | 50c multicolored | 2.00 | 2.00 |
| | | *Nos. 324-326 (3)* | 3.05 | 3.05 |

125th anniv. of the Jamaican railroad.

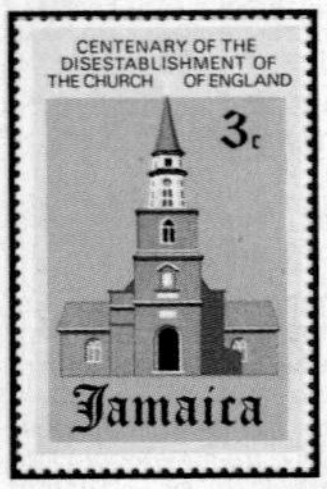

Kingston Cathedral — A94

30c, Arms of Jamaica Bishopric. 10c, 20c, like 3c.

**1971, Feb. 22 *Perf. 14½***

| | | | | |
|---|---|---|---|---|
| **327** | A94 | 3c lt green & multi | .25 | .25 |
| **328** | A94 | 10c dull orange & multi | .25 | .25 |
| **329** | A94 | 20c ultra & multi | .30 | .30 |
| **330** | A94 | 30c gray & multi | .30 | *.60* |
| | | *Nos. 327-330 (4)* | 1.10 | 1.40 |

Centenary of the disestablishment of the Church of England.

Henry Morgan, Ships in Port Royal Harbor A95

Designs: 15c, Mary Read, Anne Bonny and pamphlet on their trial. 30c, 18th century merchantman surrendering to pirate schooner.

**1971, May 10 Litho. Wmk. 352**

| | | | | |
|---|---|---|---|---|
| **331** | A95 | 3c red brown & multi | 1.00 | .25 |
| **332** | A95 | 15c gray & multi | 1.25 | .35 |
| **333** | A95 | 30c lilac & multi | 1.60 | 1.25 |
| | | *Nos. 331-333 (3)* | 3.85 | 1.85 |

Pirates and buccaneers.

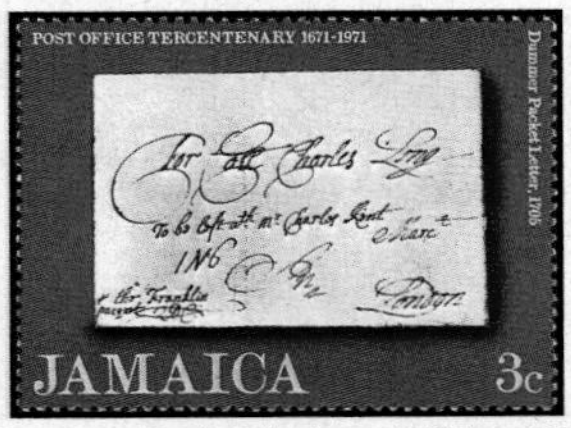

Dummer Packet Letter, 1705 — A96

Designs: 5c, Stampless cover, 1793. 8c, Post office, Kingston, 1820. 10c, Modern date cancellation on No. 312. 20c, Cover with stamps of Great Britain and Jamaica cancellations, 1859. 50c, Jamaica No. 83a, vert.

**1971, Oct. 30 *Perf. 13½***

| | | | | |
|---|---|---|---|---|
| **334** | A96 | 3c dk carmine & black | .25 | .25 |
| **335** | A96 | 5c lt ol grn & black | .25 | .25 |
| **336** | A96 | 8c purple & black | .25 | .25 |
| **337** | A96 | 10c slate, black & brn | .25 | .25 |
| **338** | A96 | 20c multicolored | .30 | .30 |
| **339** | A96 | 50c dk gray, blk & org | .50 | .60 |
| | | *Nos. 334-339 (6)* | 1.80 | 1.90 |

Tercentenary of Jamaica Post Office.

Earth Station and Satellite — A97

**1972, Feb. 17 *Perf. 14x13½***

| | | | | |
|---|---|---|---|---|
| **340** | A97 | 3c red & multi | .25 | .25 |
| **341** | A97 | 15c gray & multi | .30 | .25 |
| **342** | A97 | 50c multicolored | .65 | *1.00* |
| | | *Nos. 340-342 (3)* | 1.20 | 1.50 |

Jamaica's earth satellite station.

Bauxite Industry — A98

National Stadium A99

1c, Pimento, vert. 2c, Red ginger, vert. 4c, Kingston harbor. 5c, Oil refinery. 6c, Senate Building, Univ. of the West Indies. 9c, Devon House, Hope Road. 10c, Stewardess and Air Jamaica plane. 15c, Old Iron Bridge, vert. 20c, College of Arts, Science & Technology. 30c, Dunn's River Falls, vert. 50c, River raft. $1, Jamaica House. $2, Kings House. $5, Map and arms of Jamaica ('79).

***Perf. 14½x14, 14x14½***

**1972-79 Litho. Wmk. 352**

| | | | | |
|---|---|---|---|---|
| **343** | A98 | 1c multicolored | .25 | .25 |
| **344** | A98 | 2c multicolored | .25 | .25 |
| **345** | A98 | 3c shown | .25 | .25 |
| **346** | A98 | 4c multicolored | .25 | .25 |
| **347** | A98 | 5c multicolored | .25 | .25 |
| **348** | A98 | 6c multicolored | .25 | .25 |

***Perf. 13½***

| | | | | |
|---|---|---|---|---|
| **349** | A99 | 8c shown | .25 | .25 |
| **350** | A99 | 9c multicolored | .25 | .25 |
| **351** | A99 | 10c multicolored | .25 | .25 |
| **352** | A99 | 15c multicolored | 1.25 | .25 |
| **353** | A99 | 20c multicolored | .30 | .25 |
| **354** | A99 | 30c multicolored | .55 | .25 |
| **355** | A99 | 50c multicolored | 1.10 | .35 |
| **356** | A99 | $1 multicolored | .60 | *1.00* |
| **357** | A99 | $2 multicolored | .80 | *1.25* |

***Perf. 14½x14***

**Size: 37x26½mm**

| | | | | |
|---|---|---|---|---|
| **358** | A99 | $5 multicolored | 1.50 | *1.75* |
| | | *Nos. 343-358 (16)* | 8.35 | 7.35 |

For overprints see Nos. 360-362, 451.

Nos. 345, 351, 355 Overprinted

**1972, Aug. 8 *Perf. 14½x14, 13½***

| | | | | |
|---|---|---|---|---|
| **360** | A98 | 3c multicolored | .30 | .30 |
| **361** | A99 | 10c multicolored | .30 | .25 |
| **362** | A99 | 50c multicolored | .55 | *1.40* |
| | | *Nos. 360-362 (3)* | 1.15 | 1.95 |

Arms of Kingston — A100

Design: 5c, 30c, Arms of Kingston, vert.

**1972, Dec. 4 *Perf. 13½x14, 14x13½***

| | | | | |
|---|---|---|---|---|
| **363** | A100 | 5c pink & multi | .25 | .25 |
| **364** | A100 | 30c lemon & multi | .30 | .25 |
| **365** | A100 | 50c lt blue & multi | .50 | *1.50* |
| | | *Nos. 363-365 (3)* | 1.05 | 2.00 |

Centenary of Kingston as capital.

Mongoose and Map of Jamaica A101

40c, Mongoose & rat. 60c, Mongoose & chicken.

***Perf. 14x14½***

**1973, Apr. 9 Litho. Wmk. 352**

| | | | | |
|---|---|---|---|---|
| **366** | A101 | 8c yel green & blk | .25 | .25 |
| **367** | A101 | 40c blue & black | .35 | .35 |
| **368** | A101 | 60c salmon & black | .65 | *1.00* |
| *a.* | | Souvenir sheet of 3, #366-368 | 1.75 | 1.75 |
| | | *Nos. 366-368 (3)* | 1.25 | 1.60 |

Centenary of the introduction of the mongoose to Jamaica.

Euphorbia Punicea — A102

Flowers: 6c, Hylocereus triangularis. 9c, Columnea argentea. 15c, Portlandia grandiflora. 30c, Samyda pubescens. 50c, Cordia sebestena.

**1973, July 9 *Perf. 14***

| | | | | |
|---|---|---|---|---|
| **369** | A102 | 1c dp green & multi | .25 | .25 |
| **370** | A102 | 6c vio blue & multi | .25 | .25 |
| **371** | A102 | 9c orange & multi | .25 | .25 |
| **372** | A102 | 15c brown & multi | .25 | .25 |
| **373** | A102 | 30c olive & multi | .50 | .50 |
| **374** | A102 | 50c multicolored | .75 | *1.10* |
| | | *Nos. 369-374 (6)* | 2.25 | 2.60 |

Broughtonia Sanguinea — A103

Orchids: 10c, Arpophyllum jamaicense, vert. 20c, Oncidium pulchellum, vert. $1, Brassia maculata.

**1973, Oct. 8 *Perf. 14x13½, 13½x14***

| | | | | |
|---|---|---|---|---|
| **375** | A103 | 5c multicolored | .45 | .25 |
| **376** | A103 | 10c multicolored | .60 | .25 |
| **377** | A103 | 20c slate & multi | 1.25 | .30 |
| **378** | A103 | $1 ultra & multi | 3.00 | *3.25* |
| *a.* | | Souv. sheet of 4, #375-378, perf 12 | 5.00 | 5.00 |
| | | *Nos. 375-378 (4)* | 5.30 | 4.05 |

Mailboat "Mary" (1808-1815) — A104

Mailboats: 10c, "Queensbury" (1814-27). 15c, "Sheldrake" (1829-34). 50c, "Thames" (1842).

***Perf. 13½ (5c, 50c), 14½ (10c, 15c)***

**1974, Apr. 8 Wmk. 352**

| | | | | |
|---|---|---|---|---|
| **379** | A104 | 5c shown | .80 | .25 |
| *a.* | | Perf. 14½ | 1.75 | *2.50* |
| **380** | A104 | 10c multicolored | .80 | .25 |
| **381** | A104 | 15c multicolored | 1.10 | .50 |
| **382** | A104 | 50c multicolored | 2.00 | 2.00 |
| *a.* | | Souv. sheet of 4, #379-382, perf 13½ | 5.00 | 5.00 |
| | | *Nos. 379-382 (4)* | 4.70 | 3.00 |

Jamaican Dancers — A105

Designs: Dancers.

**1974, Aug. 1 Litho. *Perf. 13½***

| | | | | |
|---|---|---|---|---|
| **383** | A105 | 5c green & multi | .25 | .25 |
| **384** | A105 | 10c black & multi | .25 | .25 |
| **385** | A105 | 30c brown & multi | .30 | .30 |
| **386** | A105 | 50c lilac & multi | .45 | .45 |
| *a.* | | Souvenir sheet of 4, #383-386 | 2.00 | 2.00 |
| | | *Nos. 383-386 (4)* | 1.25 | 1.25 |

National Dance Theatre.

Globe, Letter, UPU Emblem A106

**1974, Oct. 9 *Perf. 14***

| | | | | |
|---|---|---|---|---|
| **387** | A106 | 5c plum & multi | .25 | .25 |
| **388** | A106 | 9c olive & multi | .25 | .25 |
| **389** | A106 | 50c multicolored | .30 | .30 |
| | | *Nos. 387-389 (3)* | .80 | .80 |

Centenary of Universal Postal Union.

Senate Building and Sir Hugh Wooding A107

10c, 50c, Chapel & Princess Alice. 30c, like 5c.

**1975, Jan. 13 Wmk. 352**

| | | | | |
|---|---|---|---|---|
| **390** | A107 | 5c yellow & multi | .25 | .25 |
| **391** | A107 | 10c salmon & multi | .25 | .25 |
| **392** | A107 | 30c dull orange & multi | .25 | .25 |
| **393** | A107 | 50c multicolored | .30 | .30 |
| | | *Nos. 390-393 (4)* | 1.05 | 1.05 |

University College of the West Indies, 25th anniversary.

Commonwealth Symbol — A108

Commonwealth Symbol and: 10c, Arms of Jamaica. 30c, Dove of peace. 50c, Jamaican flag.

**1975, Apr. 29 Litho. *Perf. 13½***

| | | | | |
|---|---|---|---|---|
| **394** | A108 | 5c buff & multi | .25 | .25 |
| **395** | A108 | 10c rose & multi | .25 | .25 |
| **396** | A108 | 30c violet blue & multi | .25 | .25 |
| **397** | A108 | 50c multicolored | .25 | .25 |
| | | *Nos. 394-397 (4)* | 1.00 | 1.00 |

Commonwealth Heads of Government Conference, Jamaica, Apr.-May.

Graphium Marcellinus A109

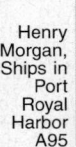

Butterflies: 20c, Papilio thoas melonius. 25c, Papilio thersites. 30c, Papilio homerus.

| 1975, Aug. 25 | Litho. | Perf. 14 | |
|---|---|---|---|
| **398** A109 10c lt green & multi | | 1.00 | .25 |
| **399** A109 20c lt green & multi | | 1.40 | .70 |
| **400** A109 25c lt green & multi | | 1.50 | *1.75* |
| **401** A109 30c lt green & multi | | 2.00 | *2.25* |
| *a.* Souvenir sheet of 4, #398-401 | | 8.00 | 8.00 |
| *Nos. 398-401 (4)* | | 5.90 | *4.95* |

See Nos. 423-426, 435-438.

Koo Koo, "Actor-boy" — A110

Christmas: 10c, Red "set-girls." 20c, French "set-girls." 50c, Jawbone or "House John Canoe." Festival dancers drawn by I. M. Belisario in Kingston, 1837.

| 1975, Nov. 3 | Litho. | Wmk. 352 | |
|---|---|---|---|
| **402** A110 8c multicolored | | .25 | .25 |
| **403** A110 10c olive & multi | | .25 | .25 |
| **404** A110 20c ultra & multi | | .40 | .40 |
| **405** A110 50c multicolored | | .80 | .80 |
| *a.* Souv. sheet of 4, #402-405, perf. 13½ | | 2.25 | 2.25 |
| *Nos. 402-405 (4)* | | 1.70 | 1.70 |

See Nos. 416-418.

Map of Jamaica, by Benedetto Bordone, 1528 — A111

Maps of Jamaica by: 20c, Tommaso Porcacchi, 1576. 30c, Theodor DeBry, 1594. 50c, Barent Langenes, 1598.

| 1976, Mar. 12 | | Perf. 13½x14 | |
|---|---|---|---|
| **406** A111 10c brown, buff & red | | .30 | .25 |
| **407** A111 20c bister & multi | | .45 | .25 |
| **408** A111 30c lt blue & multi | | .75 | .75 |
| **409** A111 50c multicolored | | 1.00 | *1.25* |
| *Nos. 406-409 (4)* | | 2.50 | 2.50 |

See Nos. 419-422.

Olympic Rings — A112

| 1976, June 14 | Litho. | Perf. 13½x14 | |
|---|---|---|---|
| **410** A112 10c black & multi | | .25 | .25 |
| **411** A112 20c blue & multi | | .30 | .25 |
| **412** A112 25c red & multi | | .30 | .25 |
| **413** A112 50c green & multi | | .45 | *1.00* |
| *Nos. 410-413 (4)* | | 1.30 | 1.75 |

21st Olympic Games, Montreal, Canada, July 17-Aug. 1.

Map of West Indies, Bats, Wicket and Ball A112a

Prudential Cup — A112b

| 1976, Aug. 9 | Unwmk. | Perf. 14 | |
|---|---|---|---|
| **414** A112a 10c lt blue & multi | | .35 | .30 |
| **415** A112b 25c lilac rose & blk | | .65 | *1.10* |

World Cricket Cup, won by West Indies Team, 1975.

### Christmas Type of 1975

Belisario Prints, 1837: 10c, Queen of the "set-girls." 20c, Band of Jawbone John Canoe. 50c, Koo Koo, "actor-boy."

| 1976, Nov. 8 | Wmk. 352 | Perf. 13½ | |
|---|---|---|---|
| **416** A110 10c brick red & multi | | .25 | .25 |
| **417** A110 20c bister & multi | | .25 | .25 |
| **418** A110 50c tan & multi | | .40 | .60 |
| *a.* Souv. sheet of 3, #416-418, perf. 14 | | 1.25 | 1.25 |
| *Nos. 416-418 (3)* | | .90 | 1.10 |

Christmas.

### Map Type of 1976

Maps of Jamaica by: 9c, Edmund Hickeringill, 1661. 10c, John Ogilby, 1671. 25c, House of Visscher, 1680. 40c, John Thornton, 1689.

| 1977, Feb. 28 | Litho. | Perf. 13 | |
|---|---|---|---|
| **419** A111 9c lt blue & multi | | .30 | *.40* |
| **420** A111 10c buff & multi | | .40 | .25 |
| **421** A111 25c multicolored | | .70 | .55 |
| **422** A111 40c multicolored | | .85 | *1.40* |
| *Nos. 419-422 (4)* | | 2.25 | 2.60 |

### Butterfly Type of 1975

10c, Eurema elathea. 20c, Dynamine egaea. 25c, Atlantea pantoni. 40c, Hypolimnas misippus.

| 1977, May 9 | Wmk. 352 | Perf. 13½ | |
|---|---|---|---|
| **423** A109 10c black & multi | | .40 | .25 |
| **424** A109 20c black & multi | | .80 | .50 |
| **425** A109 25c black & multi | | 1.25 | 1.25 |
| **426** A109 40c black & multi | | 2.25 | *3.50* |
| *a.* Souv. sheet of 4, #423-426, perf. 14½ | | 7.00 | 7.00 |
| *Nos. 423-426 (4)* | | 4.70 | 5.50 |

Scout Emblem, Doctor Bird, Outline of Jamaica — A113

| 1977, Aug. 5 | Litho. | Perf. 14 | |
|---|---|---|---|
| **427** A113 10c multicolored | | .65 | .25 |
| **428** A113 20c multicolored | | .90 | .25 |
| **429** A113 25c multicolored | | 1.00 | .35 |
| **430** A113 50c multicolored | | 1.50 | 1.50 |
| *Nos. 427-430 (4)* | | 4.05 | 2.35 |

6th Caribbean Jamboree, Hope Gardens, Kingston, Aug. 3-17.

Trumpeter A114

10c, 2 clarinetists and oboist. 20c, kettle drummer and oboist, vert. 25c, Cellist and trumpeter, vert.

| 1977, Dec. 19 | Litho. | Perf. 14 | |
|---|---|---|---|
| **431** A114 9c multicolored | | .25 | .25 |
| **432** A114 10c multicolored | | .25 | .25 |
| **433** A114 20c multicolored | | .40 | .30 |
| **434** A114 25c multicolored | | .50 | .60 |
| *a.* Souvenir sheet of 4, #431-434 | | 3.00 | 3.00 |
| *Nos. 431-434 (4)* | | 1.40 | 1.40 |

Jamaica Military Band, 50th anniversary.

### Butterfly Type of 1975

Butterflies: 10c, Callophrys crethona. 20c, Siproeta stelenes. 25c, Urbanus proteus. 50c, Anaea troglodyta.

| 1978, Apr. 17 | Litho. | Perf. 14½ | |
|---|---|---|---|
| **435** A109 10c black & multi | | .55 | .25 |
| **436** A109 20c black & multi | | 1.00 | .25 |
| **437** A109 25c black & multi | | 1.25 | .60 |
| **438** A109 50c black & multi | | 2.25 | *2.75* |
| *a.* Souvenir sheet of 4, #435-438 | | 5.75 | 5.75 |
| *Nos. 435-438 (4)* | | 5.05 | 3.85 |

Half Figure with Canopy — A115

Arawak Artifacts, found 1792: 20c, Standing figure. 50c, Birdman.

| 1978, July 10 | Litho. | Perf. 13½x13 | |
|---|---|---|---|
| **439** A115 10c multicolored | | .25 | .25 |
| **440** A115 20c multicolored | | .25 | .25 |
| **441** A115 50c multicolored | | .35 | .35 |
| *a.* Souv. sheet of 3, #439-441, perf. 14 | | 1.00 | 1.00 |
| *Nos. 439-441 (3)* | | .85 | .85 |

Norman Manley Statue — A116

Designs: 20c, Alexander Bustamante statue. 25c, Kingston coat of arms. 40c, Gordon House Chamber, House of Representatives.

| 1978, Sept. 25 | Litho. | Wmk. 352 | |
|---|---|---|---|
| **442** A116 10c multicolored | | .25 | .25 |
| **443** A116 20c multicolored | | .25 | .25 |
| **444** A116 25c multicolored | | .25 | .25 |
| **445** A116 40c multicolored | | .30 | *.35* |
| *Nos. 442-445 (4)* | | 1.05 | 1.10 |

24th Commonwealth Parliamentary Conf.

Salvation Army Band A117

Designs: 20c, Trumpeter. 25c, "S" and Cross entwined on pole of Army flag. 50c, William Booth and Salvation Army shield.

| 1978, Dec. 4 | | Perf. 14 | |
|---|---|---|---|
| **446** A117 10c multicolored | | .30 | .25 |
| **447** A117 20c multicolored | | .35 | .25 |
| **448** A117 25c multicolored | | .35 | .30 |
| **449** A117 50c multicolored | | .50 | *.75* |
| *Nos. 446-449 (4)* | | 1.50 | 1.55 |

Christmas; Salvation Army centenary.

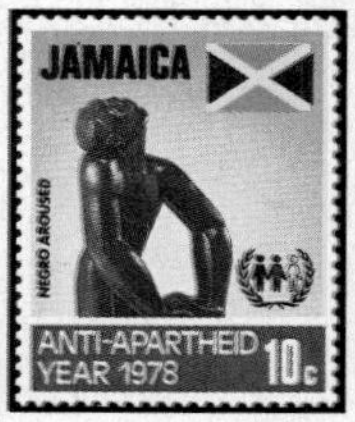


"Negro Aroused," by Edna Manley — A118

| 1978, Dec. 11 | | Perf. 13 | |
|---|---|---|---|
| **450** A118 10c multicolored | | .35 | .25 |

International Anti-Apartheid Year.

No. 351 Overprinted

| 1979, Apr. 2 | Litho. | Perf. 13½ | |
|---|---|---|---|
| **451** A99 10c multicolored | | .45 | .45 |

Arawak Grinding Stone, c. 400 B.C. — A119

Arawak Artifacts (all A.D.): 10c, Stone implements, c. 500, horiz. 20c, Cooking pot, c. 300, horiz. 25c, Serving boat, c. 300, horiz. 50c, Storage jar fragment, c. 300.

| 1979, Apr. 23 | | Perf. 14 | |
|---|---|---|---|
| **452** A119 5c multicolored | | .25 | .25 |
| **453** A119 10c multicolored | | .25 | .25 |
| **454** A119 20c multicolored | | .25 | .25 |
| **455** A119 25c multicolored | | .25 | .25 |
| **456** A119 50c multicolored | | .25 | .25 |
| *Nos. 452-456 (5)* | | 1.25 | 1.25 |

Jamaica No. 183, Hill Statue A120

Hill Statue and Stamps of Jamaica: 20c, No. 83a. 25c, No. 5. 50c, No. 271.

| 1979, Aug. 13 | Litho. | Perf. 14 | |
|---|---|---|---|
| **457** A120 10c multicolored | | .25 | .25 |
| **458** A120 20c multicolored | | .25 | .25 |
| *a.* Souvenir sheet of 1 | | .55 | .55 |
| **459** A120 25c multicolored | | .25 | .25 |
| **460** A120 50c multicolored | | .25 | *.50* |
| *Nos. 457-460 (4)* | | 1.00 | 1.25 |

Sir Rowland Hill (1795-1879), originator of penny postage.

Children, IYC Emblem A121

International Year of the Child: 20c, Doll, vert. 25c, "The Family." 25c, "House on the Hill." 25c, 50c are children's drawings.

| 1979, Oct. 1 | | | |
|---|---|---|---|
| **461** A121 10c multicolored | | .25 | .25 |
| **462** A121 20c multicolored | | .25 | .25 |
| **463** A121 25c multicolored | | .25 | .25 |
| **464** A121 50c multicolored | | .25 | .25 |
| *Nos. 461-464 (4)* | | 1.00 | 1.00 |

Tennis, Montego Bay — A122

Jamaican Tody — A123

Designs: 2c, Golfing, Tryall Hanover. 4c, Horseback riding, Negril Beach. 5c, Old Waterwheel, Tryall Hanover. 6c, Fern Gully, Ocho Rios. 7c, Dunn's River Falls, Ocho Rios. 10c, Doctorbird. 12c, Yellow-billed parrot. 15c,

Hummingbird. 35c, White-chinned thrush. 50c, Jamaican woodpecker. 65c, Rafting Martha Brae Trelawny. 75c, Blue marlin fishing, Port Antonio. $1, Scuba diving. Ocho Rios. $2, Sail boats, Montego Bay.

**Wmk. 352**

**1979-80 Litho.** ***Perf. 13½***

| | | | | |
|---|---|---|---|---|
| **465** A122 | 1c multicolored | .70 | *.90* |
| **466** A122 | 2c multicolored | 2.00 | *2.50* |
| **467** A122 | 4c multicolored | 1.00 | *2.00* |
| **468** A122 | 5c multicolored | 1.25 | .30 |
| **469** A122 | 6c multicolored | 1.25 | *2.25* |
| **470** A122 | 7c multicolored | .50 | .30 |
| **472** A123 | 8c multicolored | 1.00 | 1.00 |
| **473** A123 | 10c multicolored | 1.00 | .25 |
| **474** A123 | 12c multicolored | 1.00 | *1.50* |
| **475** A123 | 15c multicolored | 1.00 | .30 |
| **476** A123 | 35c multicolored | 1.50 | .35 |
| **477** A123 | 50c multicolored | 2.00 | .35 |
| **478** A122 | 65c multicolored | 2.00 | *2.50* |
| **479** A122 | 75c multicolored | 2.25 | 2.25 |
| **480** A122 | $1 multicolored | 2.25 | 2.25 |
| **481** A122 | $2 multicolored | 2.25 | 1.00 |
| | *Nos. 465-481 (16)* | 22.95 | 20.00 |

Issued: Nos. 465-470, 11/26/79; Nos. 472-481, 5/80.

For surcharges see Nos. 581-582, 665-666.

Institute of Jamaica Centenary — A124

15c, Institute building, 1980. 35c, "The Ascension" on microfilm reader, vert. 50c, Hawksbill and green turtles. 75c, Jamaican owl, vert.

**1980, Feb. 25 Litho.** ***Perf. 13½***

| | | | |
|---|---|---|---|
| **484** A124 | 5c shown | .25 | .25 |
| **485** A124 | 15c multicolored | .25 | .25 |
| **486** A124 | 35c multicolored | .25 | .25 |
| **487** A124 | 50c multicolored | .30 | .30 |
| **488** A124 | 75c multicolored | 1.50 | 1.50 |
| | *Nos. 484-488 (5)* | 2.55 | 2.55 |

Don Quarrie, 1976 Gold Medalist, 200-Meter Race, Moscow '80 Emblem A125

1952 4x400-meter Relay Team: a, Arthur Wint. b, Leslie Laing. c, Herbert McKenley. d, George Rhoden.

**1980, July 21 Litho.** ***Perf. 13***

| | | | |
|---|---|---|---|
| **489** A125 | 15c shown | .40 | .25 |
| **490** | Strip of 4 | 2.00 | 2.00 |
| ***a.-d.*** | A125 35c any single | .45 | .40 |

22nd Summer Olympic Games, Moscow, July 19-Aug. 3.

Parish Church, Kingston A126

20c, Coke Memorial. 25c, Church of the Redeemer. $5, Holy Trinity Cathedral.

**1980, Nov. 24 Litho.** ***Perf. 14***

| | | | |
|---|---|---|---|
| **491** A126 | 15c shown | .25 | .25 |
| **492** A126 | 20c multicolored | .25 | .25 |
| **493** A126 | 25c multicolored | .25 | .25 |
| **494** A126 | $5 multicolored | 1.00 | 1.00 |
| ***a.*** | Souvenir sheet of 4, #491-494 | 2.00 | 2.00 |
| | *Nos. 491-494 (4)* | 1.75 | 1.75 |

Christmas.

Tube Sponge A127

20c, Blood cup sponge, vert. 60c, Black coral, vert. 75c, Tire reef.

**1981, Feb. 27 Wmk. 352** ***Perf. 14***

| | | | |
|---|---|---|---|
| **495** A127 | 20c multicolored | .25 | .25 |
| **496** A127 | 45c shown | .35 | .35 |
| **497** A127 | 60c multicolored | .45 | .45 |
| **498** A127 | 75c multicolored | .55 | .55 |
| | *Nos. 495-498 (4)* | 1.60 | 1.60 |

See Nos. 523-527.

Indian Coney A128

Designs: b, Facing left. c, Eating. d, Family.

**1981, May 25 Wmk. 352** ***Perf. 14***

| | | | |
|---|---|---|---|
| **499** | Strip of 4 | 1.25 | 1.25 |
| ***a.-d.*** | A128 20c any single | .25 | .25 |

**Royal Wedding Issue**

Common Design Type

20c, White orchid. 45c, Royal coach. 60c, Couple. $5, St. James' Palace.

**1981, July 29 Litho.** ***Perf. 15***

| | | | |
|---|---|---|---|
| **500** CD331 | 20c multicolored | .25 | .25 |
| **501** CD331 | 45c multicolored | .25 | .25 |
| **502** CD331 | 60c multicolored | .25 | .25 |

***Perf. 13½***

| | | | |
|---|---|---|---|
| **503** CD331 | $5 multicolored | .70 | .60 |
| ***a.*** | Souvenir sheet of 1 | .90 | .90 |
| ***b.*** | Bklt. pane of 4, perf 14x14½ | 1.60 | |
| | *Nos. 500-503 (4)* | 1.45 | 1.35 |

Also issued in sheets of 5 + label, perf. 13½.

Intl. Year of the Disabled A129

20c, Blind weaver. 45c, Artist. 60c, Learning sign language. $1.50, Basketball players.

**1981, Sept. 14 Wmk. 352** ***Perf. 13½***

| | | | |
|---|---|---|---|
| **504** A129 | 20c multicolored | .25 | .25 |
| **505** A129 | 45c multicolored | .35 | .35 |
| **506** A129 | 60c multicolored | .45 | .45 |
| **507** A129 | $1.50 multicolored | 1.75 | 1.75 |
| | *Nos. 504-507 (4)* | 2.80 | 2.80 |

World Food Day — A130

***Perf. 13x13½, 13½x13***

**1981, Oct. 16 Litho. Wmk. 352**

| | | | |
|---|---|---|---|
| **508** A130 | 20c No. 218 | .40 | .25 |
| **509** A130 | 45c No. 76, vert. | .70 | .40 |
| **510** A130 | $2 No. 121 | 1.75 | 1.25 |
| **511** A130 | $4 No. 125 | 2.75 | 2.25 |
| | *Nos. 508-511 (4)* | 5.60 | 4.15 |

Bob Marley (1945-1981), Reggae Musician — A131

Portraits of Bob Marley and song titles.

**1981, Oct. 20 Wmk. 373** ***Perf. 14½***

| | | | |
|---|---|---|---|
| **512** A131 | 1c multicolored | .60 | *.90* |
| **513** A131 | 2c multicolored | .60 | *.90* |
| **514** A131 | 3c multicolored | .60 | *.90* |
| **515** A131 | 15c multicolored | 2.50 | .30 |
| **516** A131 | 20c multicolored | 2.50 | .30 |
| **517** A131 | 60c multicolored | 3.50 | 2.50 |
| **518** A131 | $3 multicolored | 5.25 | *9.50* |
| | *Nos. 512-518 (7)* | 15.55 | 15.30 |

**Souvenir Sheet**

| | | | |
|---|---|---|---|
| **519** A131 | $5.25 multicolored | 6.75 | 6.75 |

Christmas A132

10c, Webb Memorial Baptist Church. 45c, Church of God. $5, Bryce United Church.

**1981, Dec. 11 Wmk. 352** ***Perf. 14***

| | | | |
|---|---|---|---|
| **520** A132 | 10c multicolored | .30 | .25 |
| **521** A132 | 45c multicolored | .50 | .25 |
| **522** A132 | $5 multicolored | 1.40 | *2.00* |
| ***a.*** | Souvenir sheet of 3, #520-522, perf. 12½x12 | 3.50 | 3.50 |
| | *Nos. 520-522 (3)* | 2.20 | 2.50 |

See Nos. 547-549.

**Marine Life Type of 1981**

20c, Gorgonian coral, vert. 45c, Hard sponge. 60c, Sea cow. 75c, Plume worm. $3, Coral-banded shrimp.

**1982, Feb. 22 Litho.** ***Perf. 14***

| | | | |
|---|---|---|---|
| **523** A127 | 20c multicolored | .50 | .25 |
| **524** A127 | 45c multicolored | .70 | .25 |
| **525** A127 | 60c multicolored | .80 | .40 |
| **526** A127 | 75c multicolored | .90 | .50 |
| **527** A127 | $3 multicolored | 2.25 | 1.50 |
| | *Nos. 523-527 (5)* | 5.15 | 2.90 |

Scouting Year — A133

20c, 45c, 60c, Various scouts. $2, Baden-Powell.

**1982, July 12 Litho.** ***Perf. 13½***

| | | | |
|---|---|---|---|
| **528** A133 | 20c multicolored | .50 | .25 |
| **529** A133 | 45c multicolored | .75 | .30 |
| **530** A133 | 60c multicolored | 1.00 | .65 |
| **531** A133 | $2 multicolored | 1.90 | 1.90 |
| ***a.*** | Souvenir sheet of 4, #528-531 | 5.75 | 5.75 |
| | *Nos. 528-531 (4)* | 4.15 | 3.10 |

Princess Diana, 21st Birthday — A134

20c, Lignum vitae. 45c, Couple in coach. 60c, Wedding portrait. 75c, Saxifraga longifolia. $2, Diana. $3, Viola gracilis major. $5, Honeymoon.

**1982, Sept. 1** ***Perf. 14½***

| | | | |
|---|---|---|---|
| **532** A134 | 20c multicolored | .35 | .25 |
| **533** A134 | 45c multicolored | .55 | .35 |
| **534** A134 | 60c multicolored | .65 | .45 |
| ***a.*** | Booklet pane of 3, #532-534 | 1.75 | |
| **535** A134 | 75c multicolored | 1.00 | *1.25* |
| **536** A134 | $2 multicolored | 1.50 | 1.50 |
| **537** A134 | $3 multicolored | 1.75 | *2.50* |
| ***a.*** | Booklet pane of 3, #535-537 | 7.00 | |
| | *Nos. 532-537 (6)* | 5.80 | 6.30 |

**Souvenir Sheet**

| | | | |
|---|---|---|---|
| **538** A134 | $5 multicolored | 3.25 | 3.25 |

Nos. 535, 537 in sheets of 5.

Nos. 532-538 Overprinted

**1982, Sept. 13**

| | | | |
|---|---|---|---|
| **539** A134 | 20c multicolored | .30 | .25 |
| **540** A134 | 45c multicolored | .35 | .35 |
| **541** A134 | 60c multicolored | .45 | .45 |
| ***a.*** | Booklet pane of 3, #539-541 | 1.75 | |
| **542** A134 | 75c multicolored | .70 | *1.25* |
| **543** A134 | $2 multicolored | 1.00 | 1.00 |
| **544** A134 | $3 multicolored | 1.25 | *1.75* |
| ***a.*** | Booklet pane of 3, #542-544 | 6.00 | |
| | *Nos. 539-544 (6)* | 4.05 | 5.05 |

**Souvenir Sheet**

| | | | |
|---|---|---|---|
| **545** A134 | $5 multicolored | 2.75 | 2.75 |

Birth of Prince William of Wales, June 21.

Lizard Cuckoo Capturing Prey — A135

Designs: b, Searching for prey. c, Calling. d, Landing. e, Flying.

**1982, Oct. 25**

| | | | |
|---|---|---|---|
| **546** | Strip of 5 | 8.00 | 8.00 |
| ***a.-e.*** | A135 $1 any single | 1.25 | 1.25 |

**Christmas Type of 1981**

20c, United Pentecostal Church. 45c, Disciples of Christ Church. 75c, Open Bible Church.

***Perf. 13x13½***

**1982, Dec. 8 Wmk. 352**

| | | | |
|---|---|---|---|
| **547** A132 | 20c multicolored | .60 | .25 |
| **548** A132 | 45c multicolored | .75 | .25 |
| **549** A132 | 75c multicolored | 1.60 | *2.00* |
| | *Nos. 547-549 (3)* | 2.95 | 2.50 |

Visit of Queen Elizabeth II — A136

**1983, Feb. 14 Litho.** ***Perf. 14***

| | | | |
|---|---|---|---|
| **550** A136 | $2 Queen Elizabeth II | 3.00 | 3.25 |
| **551** A136 | $3 Arms | 4.00 | *5.75* |

A136a

**1983, Mar. 14 Litho. Wmk. 352**

| | | | |
|---|---|---|---|
| **552** A136a | 20c Dancers | .25 | .25 |
| **553** A136a | 45c Bauxite mining | .35 | .35 |
| **554** A136a | 75c Map | .50 | .50 |
| **555** A136a | $2 Arms, citizens | 1.00 | *1.25* |
| | *Nos. 552-555 (4)* | 2.10 | 2.35 |

Commonwealth Day.

25th Anniv. of Intl. Maritime Org. A137

15c, Cargo ship. 20c, Cruise liner. 45c, Container vessel. $1, Intl. Seabed Headquarters.

**1983, Mar. 17 Litho. *Perf. 14***

| | | | | |
|---|---|---|---|---|
| **556** | A137 | 15c multi | 1.00 | .30 |
| **557** | A137 | 20c multi | 1.50 | .35 |
| **558** | A137 | 45c multi | 2.00 | .75 |
| **559** | A137 | $1 multi | 3.00 | *4.00* |
| | | *Nos. 556-559 (4)* | 7.50 | 5.40 |

21st Anniv. of Independence A138

Prime Ministers Alexander Bustamante and Norman Washington Manley.

**1983, July 25 Litho. *Perf. 14***

| | | | | |
|---|---|---|---|---|
| **560** | A138 | 15c blue & multi | .25 | .25 |
| **561** | A138 | 20c lt green & multi | .25 | .25 |
| **562** | A138 | 45c yellow & multi | .30 | .30 |
| | | *Nos. 560-562 (3)* | .80 | .80 |

World Communications Year — A139

20c, Ship-to-shore radio. 45c, Postal services. 75c, Telephone communication. $1, TV satellite.

**1983, Oct. 18 Wmk. 352 *Perf. 14***

| | | | | |
|---|---|---|---|---|
| **563** | A139 | 20c multi | .60 | .25 |
| **564** | A139 | 45c multi | 1.25 | .35 |
| **565** | A139 | 75c multi | 1.50 | *2.00* |
| **566** | A139 | $1 multi | 1.75 | *2.50* |
| | | *Nos. 563-566 (4)* | 5.10 | 5.10 |

Christmas 1983 A140

Paintings: 15c, Racing at Caymanas, by Sidney McLaren. 20c, Seated Figures, by Karl Parboosingh. 75c, The Petitioner, by Henry Daley, vert. $2, Banana Plantation, by John Dunkley, vert.

**1983, Dec. 12 Litho. *Perf. 13½***

| | | | | |
|---|---|---|---|---|
| **567** | A140 | 15c multicolored | .25 | .25 |
| **568** | A140 | 20c multicolored | .25 | .25 |
| **569** | A140 | 75c multicolored | .40 | .55 |
| **570** | A140 | $2 multicolored | 1.25 | *2.00* |
| | | *Nos. 567-570 (4)* | 2.15 | 3.05 |

Alexander Bustamante (1884-1977), First Prime Minister — A141

**1984, Feb. 24 Litho. *Perf. 14***

| | | | |
|---|---|---|---|
| **571** | 20c Portrait | .85 | .85 |
| **572** | 20c Blenheim (birthplace) | .85 | .85 |
| *a.* | A141 Pair, #571-572 | 2.00 | *2.00* |

Sea Planes A142

25c, Gypsy Moth. 55c, Consolidated Commodore. $1.50, Sikorsky S-38. $3, Sikorsky S-40.

**1984, June 11 Litho. *Perf. 14***

| | | | | |
|---|---|---|---|---|
| **573** | A142 | 25c multi | 1.50 | .30 |
| **574** | A142 | 55c multi | 2.00 | .75 |
| **575** | A142 | $1.50 multi | 3.00 | 3.50 |
| **576** | A142 | $3 multi | 4.25 | 5.00 |
| | | *Nos. 573-576 (4)* | 10.75 | 9.55 |

1984 Summer Olympics A143

25c, Bicycling. 55c, Relay race. $1.50, Running. $3, Women's running.

**1984, July 11**

| | | | | |
|---|---|---|---|---|
| **577** | A143 | 25c multi | 1.75 | .50 |
| **578** | A143 | 55c multi | .75 | .30 |
| **579** | A143 | $1.50 multi | 1.60 | *3.25* |
| **580** | A143 | $3 multi | 2.25 | *3.50* |
| *a.* | | Souvenir sheet of 4, #577-580 | 6.25 | 6.25 |
| | | *Nos. 577-580 (4)* | 6.35 | 7.55 |

Nos. 469, 474 Surcharged

**1984, Aug. 7 Litho. *Perf. 13½***

| | | | | |
|---|---|---|---|---|
| **581** | A122 | 5c on 6c #469 | .40 | .40 |
| **582** | A123 | 10c on 12c #474 | 1.25 | .55 |

Early Steam Engines — A144

25c, Enterprise, 1845. 55c, Tank Locomotive, 1880. $1.50, Kitson-Meyer Tank, 1904. $3, Superheater, 1916.

**1984, Nov. 16 Litho. *Perf. 13½***

| | | | | |
|---|---|---|---|---|
| **583** | A144 | 25c multicolored | 1.40 | .30 |
| **584** | A144 | 55c multicolored | 2.00 | .60 |
| **585** | A144 | $1.50 multicolored | 3.00 | 3.00 |
| **586** | A144 | $3 multicolored | 3.75 | *5.00* |
| | | *Nos. 583-586 (4)* | 10.15 | 8.90 |

See Nos. 608-611.

Christmas — A145

Local sculptures: 20c, Accompong Madonna, by Namba Roy. 25c, Head, by Alvin Marriott. 55c, Moon, by Edna Manley. $1.50, All Women are Five Women, by Mallica Reynolds.

**1984, Dec. 6 Wmk. 352 *Perf. 14***

| | | | | |
|---|---|---|---|---|
| **587** | A145 | 20c multicolored | .30 | .25 |
| **588** | A145 | 25c multicolored | .35 | .25 |
| **589** | A145 | 55c multicolored | 1.00 | .50 |
| **590** | A145 | $1.50 multicolored | 1.90 | *2.25* |
| | | *Nos. 587-590 (4)* | 3.55 | 3.25 |

Jamaican Boas — A146

25c, Head of boa. 55c, Boa over water. 70c, Boa with young. $1, Boa on branch.

**1984, Oct. 22 Litho. *Perf. 14½***

| | | | | |
|---|---|---|---|---|
| **591** | A146 | 25c multi | *9.50* | *.60* |
| **592** | A146 | 55c multi | *10.00* | *1.25* |
| **593** | A146 | 70c multi | *11.50* | *4.25* |
| **594** | A146 | $1 multi | *14.50* | *4.75* |
| *a.* | | Souv. sheet of 4, #591-594 | *11.00* | *11.00* |
| | | *Nos. 591-594 (4)* | *45.50* | *10.85* |

Stamps in No. 594a do not have WWF emblem.

Brown Pelicans — A147

**1985, Apr. 15 Wmk. 352 *Perf. 13***

| | | | | |
|---|---|---|---|---|
| **595** | A147 | 20c multicolored | 1.00 | .25 |
| **596** | A147 | 55c multicolored | 1.50 | .40 |
| **597** | A147 | $2 multicolored | 2.25 | 2.75 |
| **598** | A147 | $5 multicolored | 3.00 | *4.75* |
| *a.* | | Souvenir sheet of 4, #595-598 | 8.00 | 8.00 |
| | | *Nos. 595-598 (4)* | 7.75 | 8.15 |

Birth bicentenary of artist and naturalist John J. Audubon (1785-1851).

### Queen Mother 85th Birthday
Common Design Type

25c, Holding photograph album, 1963. 55c, With Prince Charles, Windsor Castle, 1983. $1.50, At Belfast University. $3, Holding Prince Henry.

$5, With limousine.

**1985, June 7 Litho. *Perf. 14½x14***

| | | | | |
|---|---|---|---|---|
| **599** | CD336 | 25c multicolored | .30 | .25 |
| **600** | CD336 | 55c multicolored | .55 | .25 |
| **601** | CD336 | $1.50 multicolored | .80 | *1.25* |
| **602** | CD336 | $3 multicolored | 1.50 | *2.25* |
| | | *Nos. 599-602 (4)* | 3.15 | 4.00 |

**Souvenir Sheet**

| | | | | |
|---|---|---|---|---|
| **603** | CD336 | $5 multicolored | 3.00 | 3.00 |

Maps of Americas and Jamaica, IYY and Jamboree Emblems A148

**1985, July 30 Litho. *Perf. 14***

| | | | | |
|---|---|---|---|---|
| **604** | A148 | 25c multicolored | .85 | .25 |
| **605** | A148 | 55c multicolored | 1.10 | .30 |
| **606** | A148 | 70c multicolored | 1.60 | 1.25 |
| **607** | A148 | $4 multicolored | 3.25 | *5.00* |
| | | *Nos. 604-607 (4)* | 6.80 | 6.80 |

Intl. Youth Year and 5th Pan-American Scouting Jamboree.

### Locomotives Type of 1984

**1985, Sept. 30 Size: 39x25mm**

| | | | | |
|---|---|---|---|---|
| **608** | A144 | 25c Baldwin | 1.40 | .30 |
| **609** | A144 | 55c Rogers | 1.75 | .50 |
| **610** | A144 | $1.50 Projector | 2.75 | 2.75 |
| **611** | A144 | $4 Diesel | 3.50 | *5.00* |
| | | *Nos. 608-611 (4)* | 9.40 | 8.55 |

The Old Settlement, by Ralph Campbell — A149

Christmas (Paintings by local artists): 55c, The Vendor, by Albert Hiue, vert. 75c, Road Menders, by Gaston Tabois. $4, Woman, Must I Not Be About My Father's Business? by Carl Abrahams, vert.

**1985, Dec. 9**

| | | | | |
|---|---|---|---|---|
| **612** | A149 | 20c multicolored | .25 | .25 |
| **613** | A149 | 55c multicolored | .25 | .25 |
| **614** | A149 | 75c multicolored | .25 | .25 |
| **615** | A149 | $4 multicolored | 1.00 | 1.00 |
| | | *Nos. 612-615 (4)* | 1.75 | 1.75 |

Birds — A150

25c, Chestnut-bellied cuckoo. 55c, Jamaican becard. $1.50, White-eyed thrush. $5, Rufous-tailed flycatcher.

**1986, Feb. 10 Litho. *Perf. 14***

| | | | | |
|---|---|---|---|---|
| **616** | A150 | 25c multicolored | .55 | .25 |
| **617** | A150 | 55c multicolored | .75 | .30 |
| **618** | A150 | $1.50 multicolored | 1.00 | 1.00 |
| **619** | A150 | $5 multicolored | 1.75 | *3.50* |
| | | *Nos. 616-619 (4)* | 4.05 | 5.05 |

### Queen Elizabeth II 60th Birthday
Common Design Type

Designs: 20c, With Princess Margaret, 1939. 25c, Leaving Liverpool Street Station for Sandringham with Princes Charles and Andrew, 1962. 70c, Visiting the Montego Bay war memorial, Jamaica, 1983. $3, State visit to Luxembourg, 1976. $5, Visiting Crown Agents' offices, 1983.

**1986, Apr. 21 *Perf. 14½***

| | | | | |
|---|---|---|---|---|
| **620** | CD337 | 20c scar, blk & sil | .35 | .25 |
| **621** | CD337 | 25c ultra & multi | .35 | .25 |
| **622** | CD337 | 70c green & multi | .40 | .30 |
| **623** | CD337 | $3 violet & multi | .65 | .65 |
| **624** | CD337 | $5 rose vio & multi | 1.00 | *1.25* |
| | | *Nos. 620-624 (5)* | 2.75 | 2.70 |

A151

AMERIPEX '86: 25c, Bustamante Childrens Hospital. 55c, Vacation cities. $3, Norman Manley Law School. $5, Exports.

**1986, May 19**

| | | | | |
|---|---|---|---|---|
| **625** | A151 | 25c multicolored | .60 | .25 |
| **626** | A151 | 55c multicolored | 1.75 | .40 |
| **627** | A151 | $3 multicolored | 1.10 | *2.00* |
| **628** | A151 | $5 multicolored | 5.75 | 5.75 |
| *a.* | | Souvenir sheet of 4, #625-628 | 9.75 | 9.75 |
| | | *Nos. 625-628 (4)* | 9.20 | 8.40 |

### Royal Wedding Issue, 1986
Common Design Type

Designs: 20c, At the races. $5, Andrew addressing the press.

***Perf. 14½x14***

**1986, July 23 Wmk. 352**

| | | | | |
|---|---|---|---|---|
| **629** | CD338 | 20c multicolored | .25 | .25 |
| **630** | CD338 | $5 multicolored | 1.10 | 1.10 |

Boxing Champions A152

Champions: 45c, Richard "Shrimpy" Clarke, 1986 Commonwealth flyweight. 70c, Michael McCallum, 1984 WBA junior middleweight. $2, Trevor Berbick, 1986 WBC heavyweight. $4, Clarke, McCallum and Berbick.

**1986, Oct. 27 Litho. *Perf. 14***

**631** A152 45c multicolored .25 .25
**632** A152 70c multicolored .35 .30
**633** A152 $2 multicolored .75 *1.00*
**634** A152 $4 multicolored 1.60 *2.00*
*Nos. 631-634 (4)* 2.95 3.55

Flowers A153

20c, Heliconia wagneriana, vert. 25c, Heliconia psittacorum. 55c, Heliconia rostrata, vert. $5, Strelitzia reginae.

**1986, Dec. 1 *Perf. 14***

**635** A153 20c multicolored .25 .25
**636** A153 25c multicolored .25 .25
**637** A153 55c multicolored .25 .25
**638** A153 $5 multicolored 1.60 *3.00*
*Nos. 635-638 (4)* 2.35 3.75

Christmas. See Nos. 675-678, 706-709.

Shells — A154

**1987, Feb. 23 Litho. *Perf. 15***

**639** A154 35c Crown cone .55 .25
**640** A154 75c Measled cowrie .75 .55
**641** A154 $1 Trumpet triton .85 *.85*
**642** A154 $5 Rooster-tail conch 1.25 *2.50*
*Nos. 639-642 (4)* 3.40 4.15

Prime Ministers A155

Natl. Coat of Arms A156

Designs: 1c-9c, 55c, Norman Washington Manley. 10c-50c, 60c-90c, Sir Alexander Bustamante.

**1987-94 *Perf. 12½x13***

**No inscription below design unless noted**

**643** A155 1c dull red .25 *.85*
**644** A155 2c rose pink .25 *.85*
**645** A155 3c light olive .25 *.85*
**646** A155 4c dull green .25 *.85*
**647** A155 5c slate blue .45 *.75*
*a.* Inscribed "1988" .60 *.75*
**648** A155 6c ultramarine .30 *.75*
**649** A155 7c dull magenta .60 .75
**650** A155 8c red lilac .30 .25
**651** A155 9c brown olive .70 .25
**652** A155 10c deep rose 2.00 *.75*
*a.* Inscribed "1993" 1.25 .75
*b.* Inscribed "1994" 2.75 .75
**653** A155 20c bright org .40 .40
*a.* Inscribed "1988" .50 .25
*b.* Inscribed "1989" .50 .25
*c.* Inscribed "1992" .55 .25
*d.* Inscribed "1993" .55 .25
*e.* Inscribed "1994" .40 .40
**654** A155 30c emerald .50 .25
*a.* Inscribed "1994" 1.25 *1.75*
**655** A155 40c lt blue green 1.00 *1.25*
*a.* Inscribed "1991" 1.25 *.85*
*b.* Inscribed "1992" 1.00 *1.25*
*c.* Inscribed "1994" .85 *.85*
**656** A155 50c gray olive 1.00 .85
*a.* Inscribed "1991" 2.00 1.00
*b.* Inscribed "1992" .85 *1.00*
*c.* Inscribed "1993" .85 *.85*
*d.* Inscribed "1994" .85 *.85*
**656A** A155 55c ol brn, inscr. "1994" 1.50 1.50
**657** A155 60c light ultra .40 .35
**658** A155 70c pale violet .40 .30
**659** A155 80c violet .55 .45
**660** A155 90c light brown 1.25 *1.50*
*a.* Inscribed "1992" 2.75 1.00
*b.* Inscribed "1993" 1.25 *1.50*
**661** A156 $1 dull brn & buff .55 .40
*a.* Inscribed "1991" .65 .50
*b.* Inscribed "1992" .75 .50
*c.* Inscribed "1993" .75 .50
*d.* Inscribed "1997" .50 .40
**661A** A156 $1.10 dl brn & buff, inscr. "1994" 1.00 1.00
**662** A156 $2 orange .85 *.95*
*a.* Inscribed "1997" *1.50* 1.25
**663** A156 $5 gray ol & grnsh buff .95 *1.25*
*a.* Inscribed "1997" 1.50 1.50
**664** A156 $10 royal bl & pale bl *.90* *1.75*

***Perf. 13x13½***

**664A** A156 $25 vio & pale vio, inscr. "1991" 3.00 2.00
**664B** A156 $50 lil & pale lil, inscr. "1991" 5.75 3.25
*Nos. 643-664B (26)* 25.35 24.35

Issued: $25, $50 (dated "1991"), 10/9/91; 55c, $1.10 (dated "1994"), 10/10/94; others (undated), 5/18/87.

Reprints issued: No. 647a, 653a, 6/6/88; 653b, 1989; 645a, 656a, 2/12/91; 661a, 6/6/91; 661b, 1992; 653c, 655b, 656b, 660a, 5/92; 653d, 656c, 660b, 661c, 1993; 652a, 11/93; 654d, 655c, 656c, 1994; 652b, 654a, 10/10/94; 661d, 662a, 663a, 4/30/97.

Nos. 477-478 Surcharged

**1986, Nov. 3 *Perf. 13½***

**665** A123 5c on 50c multi 3.25 3.25
**666** A122 10c on 65c multi 1.75 1.75

A157

**Wmk. 352**

**1987, July 27 Litho. *Perf. 14***

**667** A157 55c Flag, sunset 1.60 .60
**668** A157 70c Flag, horiz. 1.60 *2.25*

Natl. Independence, 25th anniv.

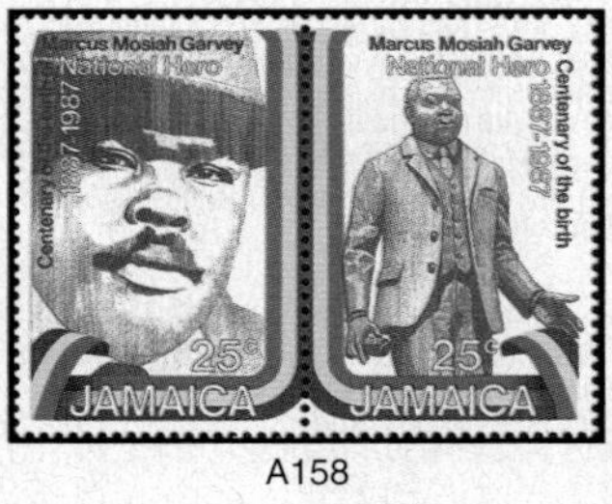


A158

**1987, Aug. 17**

**669** 25c Portrait 1.25 *1.25*
**670** 25c Statue 1.25 *1.25*
*a.* A158 Pair, #669-670 3.75 *3.75*

Marcus Mosiah Garvey (1887-1940), natl. hero. No. 670a has a continuous design.

Salvation Army in Jamaica, Cent. A159

Designs: 25c, School for the Blind. 55c, Col. Mary Booth, Bramwell-Booth Memorial Hall. $3, "War Chariot," 1929. $5, Arrival of col. Abram Davey on the S.S. Alene, 1887.

**1987, Oct. 8 *Perf. 13***

**671** A159 25c multicolored 1.50 .35
**672** A159 55c multicolored 1.50 .35
**673** A159 $3 multicolored 3.50 3.50
**674** A159 $5 multicolored 5.25 *7.50*
*a.* Souvenir sheet of 4, #671-674 17.50 17.50
*Nos. 671-674 (4)* 11.75 11.70

**Flower Type of 1986**

20c, Hibiscus hybrid. 25c, Hibiscus elatus. $4, Hibiscus cannabinus. $5, Hibiscus rosa sinensis.

**1987, Nov. 30 Litho. *Perf. 14½***

**675** A153 20c multicolored .25 .25
**676** A153 25c multicolored .25 .25
**677** A153 $4 multicolored 2.75 2.50
**678** A153 $5 multicolored 3.00 3.00
*Nos. 675-678 (4)* 6.25 6.00

Christmas. Nos. 675-678 vert.

Birds — A160

Designs: No. 679, Chestnut-bellied cuckoo, black-billed parrot, Jamaican euphonia. No. 680, Jamaican white-eyed vireo, rufous-throated solitaire, yellow-crowned elaenia. No. 681, Snowy plover, little blue heron, great white heron. No. 682, Common stilt, snowy egret, black-crowned night heron.

**1988, Jan. 22 Litho. *Perf. 14***

**679** 45c multicolored 1.50 1.50
**680** 45c multicolored 1.50 1.50
*a.* A160 Pair, #679-680 4.75 *4.75*
**681** $5 multicolored 4.00 *4.00*
**682** $5 multicolored 4.00 *4.00*
*a.* A160 Pair, #681-682 10.00 *11.50*
*Nos. 679-682 (4)* 11.00 11.00

Nos. 680a, 682a have continuous designs.

Marine Mammals A161

20c, Blue whales. 25c, Gervais's whales. 55c, Killer whales. $5, Common dolphins.

**1988, Apr. 14 Litho. *Perf. 14***

**683** A161 20c multicolored 1.50 .75
**684** A161 25c multicolored 2.00 .75
**685** A161 55c multicolored 3.50 .85
**686** A161 $5 multicolored 6.00 *7.00*
*Nos. 683-686 (4)* 13.00 9.35

Cricket A162

Bat, wicket posts, ball, 18th cent. belt buckle and batsmen: 25c, Jackie Hendriks. 55c, George Headley. $2, Michael Holding. $3, R.K. Nunes. $4, Allan Rae.

**1988, June 6 Litho. *Perf. 14***

**687** A162 25c multicolored 1.60 .45
**688** A162 55c multicolored 1.75 .45
**689** A162 $2 multicolored 3.00 3.00
**690** A162 $3 multicolored 3.25 3.25
**691** A162 $4 multicolored 4.50 4.50
*Nos. 687-691 (5)* 14.10 11.65

Intl. Red Cross and Red Crescent Organizations, 125th Annivs. — A163

Anniversary emblem, Jamaica Red Cross emblem and: 55c, Ambulances. $5, Jean-Henri Dunant, 1828-1910, treating the wounded after the Battle of Solferino, 1859.

**1988, Aug. 8 Litho. *Perf. 14½***

**692** A163 55c multicolored .75 .30
**693** A163 $5 multicolored 2.75 2.75

1988 Summer Olympics, Seoul A164

**1988, Aug. 24 Wmk. 352 *Perf. 14***

**694** A164 25c Boxing .45 .25
**695** A164 45c Cycling 2.00 .65
**696** A164 $4 Women's running 2.50 2.50
**697** A164 $5 Hurdling 2.75 2.75
*a.* Souvenir sheet of 4, #694-697 7.50 7.50
*Nos. 694-697 (4)* 7.70 6.15

No. 697a sold for $9.90. For surcharges see Nos. B4-B7.

Natl. Olympic Bobsled Team A165

No. 698, Team members. No. 699, Two-man bobsled. No. 700, Team members, diff. No. 701, Four-man bobsled.

**1988, Nov. 4 Litho. *Perf. 14***

**698** A165 25c multi .50 .50
**699** A165 25c multi .50 .50
*a.* Pair, #698-699 2.50 *3.00*
**700** A165 $5 multi 2.00 2.00
**701** A165 $5 multi 2.00 2.00
*a.* Pair, #700-701 6.00 *7.50*
*Nos. 698-701 (4)* 5.00 5.00

Nos. 699a, 701a have continuous designs.

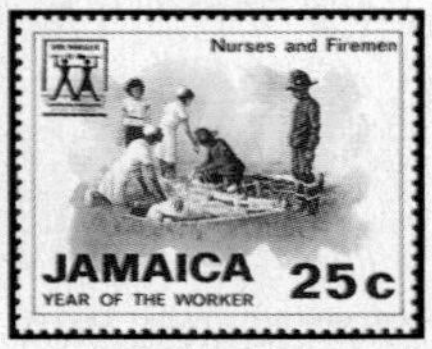


Labor Year — A166

25c, Medicine, fire fighting. 55c, Handicrafts. $3, Garment industry. $5, Fishing.

***Perf. 14½x14***

**1988, Nov. 24 Wmk. 352**

**702** A166 25c multicolored 1.25 .45
**703** A166 55c multicolored .55 .45
**704** A166 $3 multicolored 1.50 1.25
**705** A166 $5 multicolored 1.75 1.75
*Nos. 702-705 (4)* 5.05 3.90

**Flower Type of 1986**

25c, Euphorbia pulcherrima, vert. 55c, Spathodea campanulata. $3, Hylocereus triangularis, vert. $4, Broughtonia sanguinea.

**1988, Dec. 15**

| | | | |
|---|---|---|---|
| **706** A153 25c multicolored | .65 | .25 |
| **707** A153 55c multicolored | .80 | .25 |
| **708** A153 $3 multicolored | 1.75 | 1.75 |
| **709** A153 $4 multicolored | 2.25 | 2.25 |
| *Nos. 706-709 (4)* | 5.45 | 4.50 |

Christmas.

Methodist Church in Jamaica, Bicent. — A167

25c, Old York Castle School. 45c, Parade Chapel, Kingston, Rev. Thomas Coke. $5, Fr. Hugh Sherlock, St. John's Church.

**1989, Jan. 19** ***Perf. 13½***

| | | |
|---|---|---|
| **710** A167 25c multicolored | .30 | .25 |
| **711** A167 45c multicolored | .35 | .25 |
| **712** A167 $5 multicolored | 2.50 | 2.50 |
| *Nos. 710-712 (3)* | 3.15 | 3.00 |

Indigenous Moths — A168

25c, Syntomidopsis variegata. 55c, Himantoides undata-perkinsi. $3, Hypercompe nigriplaga. $5, Sthenognatha toddi.

**Wmk. 352**

**1989, Aug. 30 Litho. *Perf. 14***

| | | |
|---|---|---|
| **713** A168 25c multicolored | .75 | .25 |
| **714** A168 55c multicolored | 1.25 | .30 |
| **715** A168 $3 multicolored | 2.00 | 2.00 |
| **716** A168 $5 multicolored | 3.50 | 3.50 |
| *Nos. 713-716 (4)* | 7.50 | 6.05 |

See Nos. 725-728, 752-755. For surcharges & overprints see Nos. 729-732, 756-759.

A169

Discovery of America, 500th Anniv. (in 1992): 25c, Arawak spear fisherman. 70c, Smoking tobacco. $5, Ferdinand and Isabella inspecting caravels. $10, Columbus studying chart.

**1989, Dec. 22** ***Perf. 13½***

| | | |
|---|---|---|
| **717** A169 25c multicolored | .25 | .25 |
| **718** A169 70c multicolored | .50 | .30 |
| **719** A169 $5 multicolored | 2.00 | 2.00 |
| **720** A169 $10 multicolored | 5.75 | *5.75* |
| *a.* Souvenir sheet of 4, #717-720, perf. 12½ | 17.50 | 17.50 |
| *Nos. 717-720 (4)* | 8.50 | 8.30 |

No. 720a exists imperf. Value $25.

A171

**Wmk. 352**

**1990, June 28 Litho. *Perf. 14***

| | | |
|---|---|---|
| **721** A171 45c multicolored | 1.25 | .30 |
| **722** A171 55c multi, diff. | 1.25 | .30 |
| **723** A171 $5 multi, diff. | 5.50 | *7.00* |
| *Nos. 721-723 (3)* | 8.00 | 7.60 |

Girl Guides of Jamaica, 75th anniv.

**Indigenous Moths Type of 1989**

25c, Eunomia rubripunctata. 55c, Perigonia jamaicensis. $4, Uraga haemorrhoa. $5, Empyreuma pugione.

**Wmk. 352**

**1990, Sept. 12 Litho. *Perf. 14***

| | | |
|---|---|---|
| **725** A168 25c multicolored | 1.00 | .30 |
| **726** A168 55c multicolored | 1.60 | .30 |
| **727** A168 $4 multicolored | 2.75 | 3.00 |
| **728** A168 $5 multicolored | 3.00 | 3.00 |
| *Nos. 725-728 (4)* | 8.35 | 6.60 |

Nos. 725-728 Ovptd. in Black

**1990, Sept. 12**

| | | |
|---|---|---|
| **729** A168 25c No. 725 | .80 | .35 |
| **730** A168 55c No. 726 | 1.25 | .35 |
| **731** A168 $4 No. 727 | 2.75 | 2.75 |
| **732** A168 $5 No. 728 | 3.25 | 3.25 |
| *Nos. 729-732 (4)* | 8.05 | 6.70 |

Expo '90, International Garden and Greenery Exposition, Osaka, Japan.

Intl. Literacy Year A172

**Wmk. 352**

**1990, Oct. 10 Litho. *Perf. 14***

| | | |
|---|---|---|
| **733** A172 55c shown | .75 | .30 |
| **734** A172 $5 Mathematics class | 5.00 | *6.00* |

Christmas — A173

Children's art — 20c, To the market. 25c, Untitled (houses). 55c, Jack and Jill. 70c, Untitled (market). $1.50, Lonely (beach). $5, Market woman, vert.

***Perf. 13½x14***

**1990, Dec. 7 Litho. Wmk. 352**

| | | |
|---|---|---|
| **735** A173 20c multicolored | .50 | .25 |
| **736** A173 25c multicolored | .60 | .25 |
| **737** A173 55c multicolored | .70 | .25 |
| **738** A173 70c multicolored | 1.00 | .40 |
| **739** A173 $1.50 multicolored | 1.75 | 1.75 |
| **740** A173 $5 multicolored | 2.25 | *4.25* |
| *Nos. 735-740 (6)* | 6.80 | 7.15 |

See Nos. 760-763.

Discovery of America, 500th Anniv. (in 1992) A174

Maps of Columbus' voyages.

**1990, Dec. 19** ***Perf. 14***

| | | |
|---|---|---|
| **741** A174 25c First, 1492 | 1.00 | .40 |
| **742** A174 45c Second, 1493 | 1.25 | .40 |
| **743** A174 $5 Third, 1498 | 3.75 | 3.75 |
| **744** A174 $10 Fourth, 1502 | 6.50 | *8.00* |
| *Nos. 741-744 (4)* | 12.50 | 12.55 |

**Souvenir Sheet**

| | | |
|---|---|---|
| **745** Sheet of 4 | 13.00 | 13.00 |
| *a.* A174 25c Cuba, Jamaica | 1.00 | 1.00 |
| *b.* A174 45c Hispaniola, Puerto Rico | 1.10 | 1.10 |
| *c.* A174 $5 Central America | 3.00 | 3.00 |
| *d.* A174 $10 Venezuela | 5.00 | 5.00 |

Souvenir sheet also exists imperf. Value, $20.

See Nos. 764-767.

Natl. Meteorological Service — A175

**1991, May 20 Litho. Wmk. 352**

| | | |
|---|---|---|
| **746** A175 50c multicolored | .55 | .25 |
| **747** A175 $10 multicolored | 6.00 | 6.00 |

11th World Meteorological Congress.

Intl. Council of Nurses Council of Natl. Representatives, Jamaica — A176

50c, Mary Seacole. $1.10, Mary Seacole House. $8, Hospital at Scutari.

**Wmk. 352**

**1991, June 24 Litho. *Perf. 13½***

| | | |
|---|---|---|
| **748** A176 50c multicolored | 1.00 | .35 |
| **749** A176 $1.10 multicolored | 1.75 | 1.75 |

**Souvenir Sheet**

| | | |
|---|---|---|
| **750** A176 $8 multicolored | 4.00 | 4.00 |

Cyclura Collei (Jamaican Iguana) — A177

Designs: a, Head pointed to UR. b, Facing right. c, Climbing rock. d, Facing left. e, Head pointed to UL.

**Wmk. 352**

**1991, July 29 Litho. *Perf. 13***

| | | |
|---|---|---|
| **751** A177 $1.10 Strip of 5, #a.-e. | 4.50 | 4.50 |

Natural History Soc. of Jamaica, 50th anniv.

**Moths Type of 1989**

50c, Urania sloanus. $1.10, Phoenicoprocta jamaicensis. $1.40, Horama grotei. $8, Amplypterus gannascus.

**1991, Aug. 12** ***Perf. 14***

| | | |
|---|---|---|
| **752** A168 50c multicolored | 1.00 | .25 |
| **753** A168 $1.10 multicolored | 1.10 | .50 |
| **754** A168 $1.40 multicolored | 1.25 | 1.00 |
| **755** A168 $8 multicolored | 3.25 | 3.25 |
| *Nos. 752-755 (4)* | 6.60 | 5.00 |

Nos. 752-755 Overprinted

**1991, Sept. 23**

| | | |
|---|---|---|
| **756** A168 50c on No. 752 | 1.00 | .25 |
| **757** A168 $1.10 on No. 753 | 1.25 | .65 |
| **758** A168 $1.40 on No. 754 | 1.50 | 1.10 |
| **759** A168 $8 on No. 755 | 4.50 | *6.50* |
| *Nos. 756-759 (4)* | 8.25 | 8.50 |

**Children's Christmas Art Type**

Children's drawings.

**1991, Nov. 27** ***Perf. 14x15***

| | | |
|---|---|---|
| **760** A173 50c Doctor bird | .70 | .25 |
| **761** A173 $1.10 Road scene | 1.00 | .30 |
| **762** A173 $5 House, people | 3.00 | 3.00 |
| **763** A173 $10 Cows grazing | 6.00 | *8.00* |
| *Nos. 760-763 (4)* | 10.70 | 11.55 |

Christmas.

**Discovery of America Type of 1990**

Designs: 50c, Explorers did not land at Santa Gloria because of hostile Indians. $1.10, Fierce dog used to subdue the Indians. $1.40, Indians brought gifts of fruit. $25, Columbus describes Jamaica with crumpled paper.

**1991, Dec. 16** ***Perf. 13½x14***

| | | |
|---|---|---|
| **764** A174 50c multicolored | .65 | .25 |
| **765** A174 $1.10 multicolored | .85 | .30 |
| **766** A174 $1.40 multicolored | .95 | .30 |
| **767** A174 $25 multicolored | 6.25 | *8.00* |
| *a.* Souvenir sheet of 4, #764-767 | 9.00 | 9.00 |
| *Nos. 764-767 (4)* | 8.70 | 8.85 |

Souvenir sheet also exists imperf. Same value as perf.

First Provincial Grand Master of English Freemasonry in Jamaica, 250th Anniv. — A178

Masonic symbols: 50c, Square and compass. $1.10, Stained glass window. $1.40, Square and compass on Bible. $25, Seeing eye.

**1992, May 1** ***Perf. 13½***

| | | |
|---|---|---|
| **768** A178 50c multicolored | .85 | .30 |
| **769** A178 $1.10 multicolored | 1.00 | .40 |
| **770** A178 $1.40 multicolored | 1.25 | .45 |
| **771** A178 $25 multicolored | 10.00 | 10.00 |
| *a.* Souvenir sheet of 4, #768-771 | 18.00 | 18.00 |
| *Nos. 768-771 (4)* | 13.10 | 11.15 |

Destruction of Port Royal by Earthquake, 300th Anniv. — A179

Scenes of destruction: 50c, Ship in harbor. $1.10, Homes, church. $1.40, Homes toppling. $5, Port Royal from contemporary broadsheet. $25, Fissure in street.

**1992, June 7** ***Perf. 14x13½***

| | | |
|---|---|---|
| **772** A179 50c multicolored | .50 | .40 |
| **773** A179 $1.10 multicolored | .60 | .45 |
| **774** A179 $1.40 multicolored | .75 | .50 |
| **775** A179 $25 multicolored | 7.75 | *8.75* |
| *Nos. 772-775 (4)* | 9.60 | 10.10 |

**Souvenir Sheet**

***Perf. 13x12***

| | | |
|---|---|---|
| **776** A179 $5 multicolored | 5.75 | 5.75 |

No. 776 inscribed on reverse.

Independence, 30th Anniv. — A180

**1992, Aug. 6** ***Perf. 13½***

| | | |
|---|---|---|
| **777** A180 50c black & multi | .25 | .25 |
| **778** A180 $1.10 green & multi | .35 | .35 |
| **779** A180 $25 yellow & multi | 3.00 | 3.00 |
| *Nos. 777-779 (3)* | 3.60 | 3.60 |

Credit Union Movement in Jamaica, 50th Anniv. — A181

50c, Emblem. $1.40, Emblem, O'Hare Hall.

**1992, Aug. 24** ***Perf. 14x15***

**780** A181 50c multi 1.00 .50
**781** A181 $1.40 multi 2.00 1.75

Pottery — A182

Designs: 50c, "Rainbow" vase, by Cecil Baugh O.D. $1.10, "Yabba Pot," by Louisa Jones (MaLou) O.D. $1.40, "Sculptured Vase," by Gene Pearson. $25, "Lidded Form," by Norma Rodney Harrack.

**1993, Apr. 26** ***Perf. 13½***

**782** A182 50c multicolored .25 .25
**783** A182 $1.10 multicolored .35 .25
**784** A182 $1.40 multicolored .40 .25
**785** A182 $25 multicolored 3.75 3.75
*Nos. 782-785 (4)* 4.75 4.50

Girls' Brigade, Cent. A183

50c, Parade. $1.10, Brigade members.

**1993, Aug. 9** ***Perf. 14x13½***

**786** A183 50c multicolored 1.00 .50
**787** A183 $1.10 multicolored 1.25 1.25

Jamaica Combined Cadet Force, 50th Anniv. — A184

Designs: 50c, Tank, cadet, vert. $1.10, Airplane, female cadet. $1.40, Ships, female cadet, vert. $3, Cap badge, cadet.

**1993, Nov. 8** ***Perf. 14***

**788** A184 50c multicolored .35 .25
**789** A184 $1.10 multicolored .45 .40
**790** A184 $1.40 multicolored .55 .40
**791** A184 $3 multicolored 1.10 *1.25*
*Nos. 788-791 (4)* 2.45 2.30

Golf Courses A185

50c, $1.10, Constant Spring. $1.40, $2, Half Moon. $3, $10, Jamaica Jamaica. $25, Tryall, vert.

**1993-94 Litho. Wmk. 352** ***Perf. 14***

**792** A185 50c yellow & multi .40 .25
**793** A185 $1.10 blue & multi .45 .25
**794** A185 $1.40 brn org & multi .60 .25
**795** A185 $2 lilac & multi .90 .90
**796** A185 $3 dark blue & multi 1.00 1.00
**797** A185 $10 tan & multi 2.00 2.00
*Nos. 792-797 (6)* 5.35 4.65

**Souvenir Sheets**

**798** A185 $25 green & multi 5.50 5.50
**799** A185 $25 #798 inscribed with Hong Kong '94 emblem 5.50 5.50

Issued: Nos. 792-797, 12/21/93; No. 798, 12/16/93; No. 799, 2/18/94.

A186

**1994, Jan. 12** ***Perf. 14x15***

**800** A186 $25 Portrait 2.50 2.50
**801** A186 $50 Portrait, diff. 3.00 3.00
*a.* Pair, #800-801 8.25 *10.00*

Norman Washington Manley, birth cent.

A187

Royal Visit: $1.10, Jamaican, United Kingdom flags. $1.40, Royal yacht Britannia. $25, Queen Elizabeth II. $50, Prince Philip, Queen.

**1994, Mar. 1** ***Perf. 14***

**802** A187 $1.10 multicolored .75 .25
**803** A187 $1.40 multicolored 1.60 .40
**804** A187 $25 multicolored 3.25 3.25
**805** A187 $50 multicolored 5.25 *6.50*
*Nos. 802-805 (4)* 10.85 10.40

Air Jamaica, 25th Anniv. — A188

**Wmk. 352**

**1994, Apr. 26 Litho.** ***Perf. 14***

**806** A188 50c Douglas DC9 .30 .25
**807** A188 $1.10 Douglas DC8 .35 .25
**808** A188 $5 Boeing 727 .75 .75
**809** A188 $50 Airbus A300 3.75 3.75
*Nos. 806-809 (4)* 5.15 5.00

Giant Swallowtail A189

Various views of the butterfly.

***Perf. 14x13½***

**1994, Aug. 18 Litho. Wmk. 352**

**810** A189 50c multicolored .50 .30
**811** A189 $1.10 multicolored .50 .30
**812** A189 $10 multicolored 2.00 2.00
**813** A189 $25 multicolored 3.75 3.75
*Nos. 810-813 (4)* 6.75 6.35

**Souvenir Sheet**

**814** 189 $50 multicolored 9.50 9.50

A190

Tourism A191

Designs: 50c, Royal Botanical Gardens, by Sidney McClaren. $1.10, Blue Mountains, coffee beans, leaves. $5, Woman in hammock, waterfalls.

Tourist poster: No. 818a, Flowers, birds (c). b, Diver (d). c, Vegetation, coastline (a, d). d, Guide, tourists on raft.

**Wmk. 352**

**1994, Sept. 7 Litho.** ***Perf. 14***

**815** A190 50c multicolored .40 .25
**816** A190 $1.10 multicolored .65 .30
**817** A190 $5 multicolored 3.00 3.00
*Nos. 815-817 (3)* 4.05 3.55

**Souvenir Sheet**

**818** A191 $25 Sheet of 4, #a.-d. 6.50 6.50

Caribbean Tourism Conf. (No. 818).

Red Poll Cattle A192

**1994, Nov. 16** ***Perf. 14x13½***

**819** A192 50c Calf .25 .25
**820** A192 $1.10 Heifer .25 .25
**821** A192 $25 Cow 1.50 1.50
**822** A192 $50 Bull 3.75 3.75
*Nos. 819-822 (4)* 5.75 5.75

Christmas — A193

Paintings by Children: 50c, Clean-up crew. 90c, Hospital Room. $1.10, House. $50, Meadow.

**1994, Dec. 1** ***Perf. 14x14½***

**823** A193 50c multicolored .25 .25
**824** A193 90c multicolored .25 .25
**825** A193 $1.10 multicolored 1.00 .25
**826** A193 $50 multicolored 2.00 *3.75*
*Nos. 823-826 (4)* 3.50 4.50

Birds — A194

50c, Ring-tailed pigeon. 90c, Yellow-billed parrot. $1.10, Black-billed parrot. No. 830, Brown owl.

No. 831, Streamertail.

**Wmk. 384**

**1995, Apr. 24 Litho.** ***Perf. 14***

**827** A194 50c multicolored .70 .35
**828** A194 90c multicolored .80 .35
**829** A194 $1.10 multicolored .80 .35
**830** A194 $50 multicolored 5.50 *7.00*
*Nos. 827-830 (4)* 7.80 8.05

**Souvenir Sheet**

**831** A194 $50 multicolored 7.50 7.50
*a.* Ovptd. in sheet margin 6.00 6.00

No. 831 is a continuous design.

No. 831a ovptd. with Singapore '95 emblem. Issued: 9/1/95.

Caribbean Development Bank, 25th Anniv. — A195

Anniversary emblem and: 50c, $1, Jamaican flag, graph, vert. $1.10, Industries, agriculture. $50, Bank notes, coins.

**Wmk. 352**

**1995, May 11 Litho.** ***Perf. 13½***

**832** A195 50c green & multi .25 .25
**833** A195 $1 black & multi .25 .25
**834** A195 $1.10 multicolored .25 .25
**835** A195 $50 multicolored 3.50 *4.00*
*Nos. 832-835 (4)* 4.25 4.75

Bob Marley (1945-81), Reggae Musician — A196

Marley performing songs: 50c, Songs of Freedom, by Adrian Boot. $1.10, Fire, by Neville Garrick. $1.40, Time Will Tell, by Peter Murphy. $3, Natural Mystic, by Boot. $10, Live at Lyceum, by Boot.

$100, Legend, by Boot.

**Wmk. 352**

**1995, July 31 Litho.** ***Perf. 14***

**836** A196 50c multicolored .35 .25
**837** A196 $1.10 multicolored .55 .25
**838** A196 $1.40 multicolored .60 .35
**839** A196 $3 multicolored .90 .90
**840** A196 $10 multicolored 1.75 1.75
*Nos. 836-840 (5)* 4.15 3.50

**Souvenir Sheet**

**841** A196 $100 multicolored 7.50 7.50

Souvenir Sheet

Queen Mother, 95th Birthday — A197

**1995, Aug. 4** ***Perf. 14x13½***

**842** A197 $75 multicolored 5.25 5.25

Order of the Caribbean Community — A198

Designs: 50c, Michael Manley, former prime minister, Jamaica. $1.10, Sir Alister McIntyre, Vice Chancellor, UWI, Jamaica. $1.40, P. Telford Georges, former Chief Justice, Bahamas. $50, Dame Nita Barrow, Governor General, Barbados.

**1995, Aug. 23** *Perf. 14x14½*

| | | | | |
|---|---|---|---|---|
| **843** | A198 | 50c multicolored | .25 | .25 |
| **844** | A198 | $1.10 multicolored | .25 | .25 |
| **845** | A198 | $1.40 multicolored | .30 | .25 |
| **846** | A198 | $50 multicolored | 3.25 | *5.00* |
| | | *Nos. 843-846 (4)* | 4.05 | 5.75 |

**UN, 50th Anniv.**

Common Design Type

Designs: 50c, Signals Land Rover. $1.10, Antonov AN-32. $3, Bedford Articulated Tanker. $5, Fairchild DC-119 Flying Boxcar. $50, Observation vehicles.

**Wmk. 352**

**1995, Oct. 24** **Litho.** *Perf. 14*

| | | | | |
|---|---|---|---|---|
| **847** | CD353 | 50c multicolored | .30 | .25 |
| **848** | CD353 | $1.10 multicolored | .50 | .25 |
| **849** | CD353 | $3 multicolored | .70 | .70 |
| **850** | CD353 | $5 multicolored | .90 | *1.25* |
| | | *Nos. 847-850 (4)* | 2.40 | 2.45 |

**Souvenir Sheet**

| | | | | |
|---|---|---|---|---|
| **851** | CD353 | $50 multicolored | 3.00 | 3.00 |

No. 851 has continuous design.

Arrival of East Indians in Jamaica, 150th Anniv. A199

$2.50, Coming ashore. $10, Musicians, dancers.

**Wmk. 352**

**1996, May 22** **Litho.** *Perf. 14*

| | | | | |
|---|---|---|---|---|
| **852** | A199 | $2.50 multicolored | .25 | .25 |
| **853** | A199 | $10 multicolored | .75 | .75 |

UNICEF, 50th Anniv. — A200

**1996, Sept. 2** *Perf. 14½x14*

| | | | | |
|---|---|---|---|---|
| **854** | A200 | $2.50 multicolored | .60 | .60 |
| **855** | A200 | $8 multicolored | 1.10 | 1.10 |
| **856** | A200 | $10 multicolored | 1.50 | 1.50 |
| | | *Nos. 854-856 (3)* | 3.20 | 3.20 |

Jamaican Hutia (Indian Coney) A201

$2.50, Two in den. $10, One on ledge. $12.50, Mother, young. $25, One up close.

**1996, Sept. 23** *Perf. 13½x14*

| | | | | |
|---|---|---|---|---|
| **857** | A201 | $2.50 multicolored | .30 | .25 |
| **858** | A201 | $10 multicolored | .65 | .25 |
| **859** | A201 | $12.50 multicolored | .80 | .80 |
| **860** | A201 | $25 multicolored | 1.40 | *2.50* |
| | | *Nos. 857-860 (4)* | 3.15 | 3.80 |

World Wildlife Fund.

Kingston Parish Church of St. Thomas the Apostle, 300th Anniv. A202

$2, High altar. $8, Exterior view. $12.50, Carving, "The Angel," by Edna Manley, vert. $60, Exterior view at sunset.

**Unwmk.**

**1997, Feb. 7** **Litho.** *Perf. 14*

| | | | | |
|---|---|---|---|---|
| **861** | A202 | $2 multicolored | .40 | .25 |
| **862** | A202 | $8 multicolored | 1.00 | 1.00 |
| **863** | A202 | $12.50 multicolored | 1.50 | 1.50 |
| | | *Nos. 861-863 (3)* | 2.90 | 2.75 |

**Souvenir Sheet**

| | | | | |
|---|---|---|---|---|
| **864** | A202 | $60 multicolored | 3.50 | 3.50 |

No. 864 contains one 42x56mm stamp.

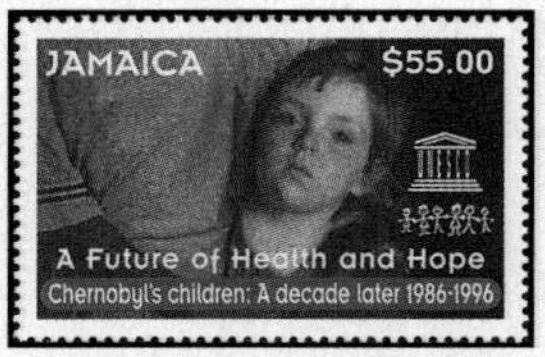


Chernobyl's Children — A203

*Perf. 13½x14*

**1997, Apr. 7** **Litho.** **Unwmk.**

| | | | | |
|---|---|---|---|---|
| **865** | A203 | $55 multicolored | 4.00 | 4.00 |

Caribbean Integration, 50th Anniv. — A203a

$2.50, Map of Caribbean. $8, $10, View of coastline.

**Wmk. 352**

**1997, June 30** **Litho.** *Perf. 14*

| | | | | |
|---|---|---|---|---|
| **865A** | A203a | $2.50 multi | *8.00* | *7.00* |
| **865B** | A203a | $8 multi | *9.00* | *3.25* |
| **865C** | A203a | $10 multi | *10.00* | *3.25* |
| | | *Nos. 865A-865C (3)* | *27.00* | *13.50* |

Orchids A204

$1, Coelia triptera. $2, Oncidium pulchellum. $2.50, Oncidium triquetrum. $3, Broughtonia negrilensis. $5, Enclycia frangrans.

**Wmk. 352**

**1997, Oct. 6** **Litho.** *Perf. 14*

| | | | | |
|---|---|---|---|---|
| **866** | A204 | $1 multi, vert. | .30 | .25 |
| **867** | A204 | $2 multi | .35 | .25 |
| **868** | A204 | $2.50 multi, vert. | .40 | .25 |
| **869** | A204 | $3 multi, vert. | .45 | .25 |
| **870** | A204 | $5 multi | .50 | .35 |
| | | *Nos. 866-870 (5)* | 2.00 | 1.35 |

See Nos. 873-877.

Diana, Princess of Wales (1961-97) — A205

**Unwmk.**

**1998, Feb. 24** **Litho.** *Perf. 14*

| | | | | |
|---|---|---|---|---|
| **871** | A205 | $20 Portrait | 1.25 | 1.25 |

**Souvenir Sheet**

| | | | | |
|---|---|---|---|---|
| **872** | A205 | $80 With Mother Teresa | 6.00 | 6.00 |

No. 871 was issued in sheets of 6. No. 872 contains one 42x56mm stamp.

**Orchid Type of 1997**

Designs: $4.50, Oncidium gauntlettii. $8, Broughtonia sanguinea. $12, Phaius tankervilleae, vert. $25, Cochleanthes flabelliformis. $50, Broughtonia sanguinea (3 varieties).

**Wmk. 352**

**1997, Dec. 1** **Litho.** *Perf. 14*

| | | | | |
|---|---|---|---|---|
| **873** | A204 | $4.50 multicolored | .60 | .60 |
| **874** | A204 | $8 multicolored | .85 | .85 |
| **875** | A204 | $12 multicolored | 1.00 | 1.00 |
| **876** | A204 | $25 multicolored | 2.00 | 2.00 |
| *a.* | | Inscribed "1999" | *2.00* | *2.00* |
| **877** | A204 | $50 multicolored | 2.00 | 2.00 |
| | | *Nos. 873-877 (5)* | 6.45 | 6.45 |

CARICOM, 25th Anniv. — A206

*Perf. 13½*

**1998, Sept. 17** **Litho.** **Unwmk.**

| | | | | |
|---|---|---|---|---|
| **878** | A206 | $30 multicolored | 3.00 | 3.00 |

University of the West Indies, Mona, 50th Anniv. A207

$8, Chapel. $10, Philip Sherlock Centre for the Creative Arts. $50, University arms.

**1998, July 31** **Wmk. 352**

| | | | | |
|---|---|---|---|---|
| **879** | A207 | $8 multi | .50 | .50 |
| **880** | A207 | $10 multi | .50 | .50 |
| **881** | A207 | $50 multi, vert. | 2.25 | 2.25 |
| | | *Nos. 879-881 (3)* | 3.25 | 3.25 |

1998 World Cup Soccer Championships, France, Jamaica's Debut in Tournament — A208

**Wmk. 373**

**1998, Sept. 28** **Litho.** *Perf. 13½*

| | | | | |
|---|---|---|---|---|
| **882** | A208 | $10 Player, vert. | .50 | .35 |
| **883** | A208 | $25 Team picture | 1.40 | 1.25 |
| **884** | A208 | $100 Team picture, diff. | 4.50 | *5.50* |
| | | *Nos. 882-884 (3)* | 6.40 | 7.10 |

Intl. Year of the Ocean A209

Designs: $10, Underwater scene. $30, Fishermen, Negril. $50, Long spiny black urchin. $100, Design elements from Nos. 885-887, vert.

**Wmk. 352**

**1998, Dec. 23** **Litho.** *Perf. 14*

| | | | | |
|---|---|---|---|---|
| **885** | A209 | $10 multicolored | 1.50 | .40 |
| **886** | A209 | $30 multicolored | 2.75 | 1.50 |
| **887** | A209 | $50 multicolored | 4.00 | 4.00 |

**Size: 28x42mm**

| | | | | |
|---|---|---|---|---|
| **888** | A209 | $100 multicolored | 7.50 | *10.00* |
| | | *Nos. 885-888 (4)* | 15.75 | 15.90 |

Christmas.

**1st Manned Moon Landing, 30th Anniv.**

Common Design Type

Designs: $7, Michael Collins. $10, Service module reverses to dock with lunar module. $25, Aldrin walks on lunar surface. $30, Command module back in earth orbit.

$100, Looking at earth from moon.

*Perf. 14x13¾*

**1999, July 20** **Litho.** **Wmk. 352**

| | | | | |
|---|---|---|---|---|
| **889** | CD357 | $7 multicolored | .50 | .50 |
| **890** | CD357 | $10 multicolored | .65 | .65 |
| **891** | CD357 | $25 multicolored | 1.25 | .125 |
| **892** | CD357 | $30 multicolored | 1.40 | 1.40 |
| | | *Nos. 889-892 (4)* | 3.80 | 2.68 |

**Souvenir Sheet**

*Perf. 14*

| | | | | |
|---|---|---|---|---|
| **893** | CD357 | $100 multicolored | 4.50 | 4.50 |

No. 893 contains one 40mm circular stamp.

Athletes A210

Designs: $5, Polo player Lesley Ann Masterton Fong-Yee. $10, Men's cricketers Collie Smith, Lawrence Rowe and Alfred Valentine. $20, Women's cricketer Vivalyn Latty-Scott, vert. $25, Soccer player Lindy Delapenha, vert. $30, Netball player Joy Grant-Charles, vert. $50, Boxers Percy Hayles, Gerald Gray and Bunny Grant.

$100, Delapenha and Grant-Charles.

*Perf. 13¼x13¾, 13¾x13¼*

**1999, Aug. 3** **Litho.** **Wmk. 352**

| | | | | |
|---|---|---|---|---|
| **894** | A210 | $5 multicolored | .75 | .45 |
| **895** | A210 | $10 multicolored | 1.00 | .55 |
| **896** | A210 | $20 multicolored | 1.25 | 1.25 |
| **897** | A210 | $25 multicolored | 1.50 | 1.50 |
| **898** | A210 | $30 multicolored | 1.60 | 1.60 |
| **899** | A210 | $50 multicolored | 1.75 | *2.50* |
| | | *Nos. 894-899 (6)* | 7.85 | 7.85 |

**Souvenir Sheet**

| | | | | |
|---|---|---|---|---|
| **900** | A210 | $100 multicolored | 6.50 | 6.50 |

No. 900 contains one 52x38mm stamp.

UPU, 125th Anniv. A211

Designs: $7, Mail ship "Spey." $10, Mail ship "Jamaica Planter." $25, Lockheed Constellation. $30, Airbus A-310.

**Wmk. 352**

**1999, Oct. 8** **Litho.** *Perf. 14*

| | | | | |
|---|---|---|---|---|
| **901** | A211 | $7 multicolored | 1.00 | .40 |
| **902** | A211 | $10 multicolored | 1.25 | .50 |
| **903** | A211 | $25 multicolored | 2.00 | 2.00 |
| **904** | A211 | $30 multicolored | 2.25 | *2.75* |
| | | *Nos. 901-904 (4)* | 6.50 | 5.65 |

Air Jamaica, 30th Anniv. — A212

**Wmk. 352**

**1999, Nov. 1** **Litho.** *Perf. 14*

| | | | | |
|---|---|---|---|---|
| **905** | A212 | $10 A-310 | .75 | .50 |
| **906** | A212 | $25 A-320 | 1.25 | 1.25 |
| **907** | A212 | $30 A-340 | 1.75 | *2.25* |
| | | *Nos. 905-907 (3)* | 3.75 | 4.00 |

Dogs — A213

**1999, Nov. 25** *Perf. 14¼*

| | | | | |
|---|---|---|---|---|
| **908** | A213 | $7 Shih tzu | 1.25 | .75 |
| **909** | A213 | $10 German shepherd | 1.75 | .75 |
| **910** | A213 | $30 Doberman pinscher | 3.00 | *3.25* |
| | | *Nos. 908-910 (3)* | 6.00 | 4.75 |

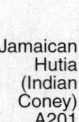

Parks A214

Designs: $7, Nelson Mandela Park. $10, St. William Grant Park. $25, Seaview Park. $30, Holruth Park.

**1999, Dec. 15** *Perf. 14*

| | | | |
|---|---|---|---|
| **911** A214 $7 multi | .40 | .35 |
| **912** A214 $10 multi | .50 | .40 |
| **913** A214 $25 multi | 1.10 | 1.00 |
| **914** A214 $30 multi | 1.40 | 1.40 |
| *Nos. 911-914 (4)* | 3.40 | 3.15 |

Edna Manley (1900-87), Sculptor A215

Designs: $10, The Prophet, 1935. $25, Horse of the Morning, 1943. $30, The Angel, 1970. $100, Portrait of Manley.

**2000, Mar. 1 Litho.** *Perf. 13¾*

| | | |
|---|---|---|
| **915** A215 $10 multi | .65 | .65 |
| **916** A215 $25 multi | 1.50 | 1.50 |
| **917** A215 $30 multi | 1.75 | 1.75 |
| **918** A215 $100 multi | 5.00 | 5.00 |
| *a.* Souvenir sheet, #915-918 | 9.00 | 9.00 |
| *Nos. 915-918 (4)* | 8.90 | 8.90 |

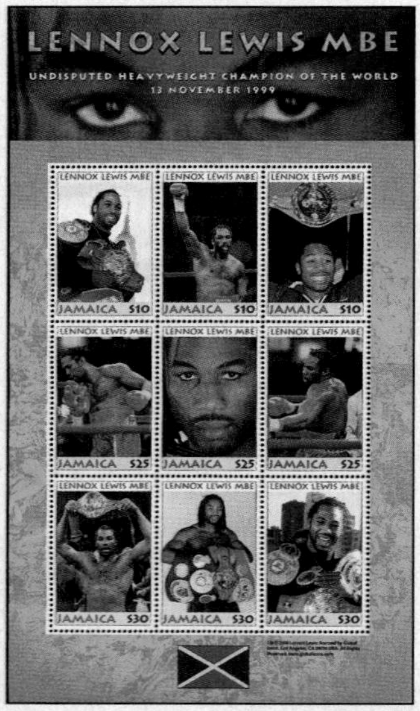


Lennox Lewis, Heavyweight Boxing Champion of the World — A216

a, $10, With belt & Empire State Building. b, $10, Holding up arm. c, $10, Holding up belt. d, $25, In ring with opponent. e, $25, Close-up. f, $25, In ring with referee. g, $30, Holding up belt, diff. h, $30, Holding 4 belts. i, $30, Holding belts in front of buildings.

**Wmk. 352**

**2000, Mar. 24 Litho.** *Perf. 14*

**919** A216 Sheet of 9, #a.-i. 9.00 9.00

Ferrari Automobiles — A217

**Unwmk.**

**2000, May 26 Litho.** *Perf. 14*

| | | |
|---|---|---|
| **920** A217 $10 1947 125S | .75 | .75 |
| **921** A217 $10 1950 375F1 | .75 | .75 |
| **922** A217 $10 1966 312F1 | .75 | .75 |
| **923** A217 $25 1965 Dino 166P | 1.50 | 1.50 |
| **924** A217 $25 1971 312P | 1.50 | 1.50 |
| **925** A217 $25 1990 F190 | 1.50 | 1.50 |
| *Nos. 920-925 (6)* | 6.75 | 6.75 |

Queen Mother, 100th Birthday — A218

Various photos.

**2000, Aug. 4** **Wmk. 352**

| | | |
|---|---|---|
| **926** A218 $10 multi | .60 | .60 |
| **927** A218 $25 multi | 1.00 | 1.00 |
| **928** A218 $30 multi | 1.50 | 1.50 |
| **929** A218 $50 multi | 3.25 | 3.25 |
| *Nos. 926-929 (4)* | 6.35 | 6.35 |

2000 Summer Olympics, Sydney — A219

Jamaican flag and various views of sculpture, "The Runner," by Alvin Marriott. Denominations, $10, $25, $30, vert., $50, vert.

**Wmk. 352**

**2000, Sept. 1 Litho.** *Perf. 14*

**930-933** A219 Set of 4 6.75 6.75

Trees — A220

Designs: $10, Bull thatch palm. $25, Blue mahoe. $30, Silk cotton. $50, Yellow pout. $100, Lignum vitae, horiz.

**2000, Oct. 6**

**934-937** A220 Set of 4 7.75 7.75

**Souvenir Sheet**

**938** A220 $100 multi 8.00 8.00

Christmas — A221

Designs: $10, Madonna and Child, by Osmond Watson, vert. $20, Boy in the Temple, by Carl Abrahams. $25, Ascension, by Abrahams, vert. $30, Jah Lives, by Watson.

**Wmk. 352**

**2000, Dec. 6 Litho.** *Perf. 13¾*

**939-942** A221 Set of 4 4.25 4.25

Commonwealth Day, 25th Anniv. — A222

**Wmk. 352**

**2001, Mar. 12 Litho.** *Perf. 12½*

**943** A222 $30 multi 2.00 2.00

Father Andrew Duffus Mowatt, Founder of Jamaica Burial Scheme Society A223

**Wmk. 352**

**2001, Oct. 12 Litho.** *Perf. 13¼*

**944** A223 $15 multi 1.50 1.50

Lithographs of Daguerrotypes by Adolphe Duperly (1801-64) — A224

Designs: $15, The Market, Falmouth. $40, Ferry Inn, Spanish Town Road. $45, Coke Chapel. $60, King Street, Kingston.

**2001, Nov. 14** *Perf. 13*

| | | |
|---|---|---|
| **945-948** A224 Set of 4 | 9.25 | 9.25 |
| *a.* Souvenir sheet, #945-948 | 8.75 | 8.75 |

Christmas — A225

Poinsettias with background colors of: $15, Light blue. $30, Pink. $40, Pale orange.

**2001, Dec. 10** *Perf. 13¼*

**949-951** A225 Set of 3 6.00 6.00

**Reign Of Queen Elizabeth II, 50th Anniv. Issue**

Common Design Type

Designs: Nos. 952, 956a, $15, Princess Elizabeth. Nos. 953, 953b, $40, Wearing striped dress. Nos. 954, 956c, $45, In 1953. Nos. 955, 956d, $60, In 1995. No. 956e, $30, 1955 portrait by Annigoni (38x50mm).

*Perf. 14¼x14½, 13¾ (#956e)*

**2002, Feb. 6 Litho. Wmk. 373**

**With Gold Frames**

| | | |
|---|---|---|
| **952** CD360 $15 multicolored | .65 | .65 |
| **953** CD360 $40 multicolored | 2.00 | 2.00 |
| **954** CD360 $45 multicolored | 2.25 | 2.25 |
| **955** CD360 $60 multicolored | 3.25 | 3.25 |
| *Nos. 952-955 (4)* | 8.15 | 8.15 |

**Souvenir Sheet**

**Without Gold Frames**

**956** CD360 Sheet of 5, #a-e 8.50 8.50

Visit of Queen Elizabeth II and Prince Philip, Feb. 18-20 A226

Designs: $15, Queen and Prince in 1983, flag of the Royal Standard. $45, Queen in 1983, Jamaican arms.

*Perf. 13¼x13¾*

**2002, Feb. 18 Litho. Wmk. 352**

**957-958** A226 Set of 2 5.75 5.75

Sir Philip Sherlock (1902-2000), Educator — A227

**2002, Mar. 11** *Perf. 13¾*

**959** A227 $40 multi 2.00 2.00

Pan-American Health Organization, Cent. — A228

**Wmk. 352**

**2002, Dec. 2 Litho.** *Perf. 13¾*

**960** A228 $40 multi 2.25 2.25

Christmas — A229

Art: $15, Masquerade, by Osmond Watson, vert. $40, John Canoe in Guanaboa Vale, by Gaston Tabois. $45, Mother and Child, sculpture, by Kapo, vert. $60, Hills of Papine, sculpture by Edna Manley.

**2002, Dec. 6**

**961-964** A229 Set of 4 6.75 6.75

Natl. Dance Theater Company, 40th Anniv. — A230

**2002, Dec. 27** *Perf. 14*

**965** A230 $15 multi 1.75 1.75

Independence, 40th Anniv. — A231

Flag and: $15, Natl. Dance Theater Company performers. $40, Sir Alexander Bustamante, Michael Manley. $60, Factory workers.

**2002, Dec. 27**
**966-968** A231 Set of 3 7.25 7.25

Kingston, Bicent. — A232

Historical views of Kingston and panel colors of: a, Brown. b, Olive green. c, Indigo.

**2002, Dec. 31** ***Perf. 13¾***
**969** A232 Horiz. strip of 3 3.75 3.75
*a.-c.* $15 Any single 1.00 1.00

**Coronation of Queen Elizabeth II, 50th Anniv.**

Common Design Type

Designs: Nos. 970, $15, 972b, $100, Queen in chair awaiting crown. Nos. 971, $45, 972a, $50, Queen and Prince Philip in carriage.

***Perf. 14¼x14½***

**2003, June 2 Litho. Wmk. 352**

**Vignettes Framed, Red Background**

**970** CD363 $15 multicolored 1.00 1.00
**971** CD363 $45 multicolored 3.00 3.00

**Souvenir Sheet**

**Vignettes Without Frame, Purple Panel**

**972** CD363 Sheet of 2, #a-b 6.00 6.00

Caribbean Community (CARICOM), 30th Anniv. — A233

**Wmk. 352**

**2003, July 4 Litho. *Perf. 14***
**973** A233 $40 multi 3.25 3.25

Bird Life International — A234

Designs: $15, Jamaican stripe-headed tanager, vert. $40, Crested quail dove. $45, Jamaican tody. $60, Blue Mountain vireo.

No. 978 — Jamaican blackbird: a, With beak open (35x30mm). b, Chicks in nest (35x30mm). c, In palm fronds, vert. (30x35mm). d, With beak open, vert. (30x35mm) e, With insect in beak (35x30mm).

**2003, Sept. 19** ***Perf. 14***
**974-977** A234 Set of 4 8.50 8.50

**Souvenir Sheet**

***Perf. 14¼x14½, 14½x14¼***

**978** A234 $30 Sheet of 5, #a-e 9.00 9.00

Maritime Heritage — A235

No. 979: a, Map, sailing ships. b, Sailing ships, ship with passengers. c, The Sugar Refiner and barges.

**2003, Sept. 25** ***Perf. 14x14¾***
**979** A235 Horiz. strip of 3 8.00 8.00
*a.-c.* $40 Any single 2.00 2.00

Christmas — A236

Flowers and: $15, Adoration of the Magi. $30, Christ child. $60, Holy Family.

**2003, Dec.** ***Perf. 13¼***
**980-982** A236 Set of 3 6.00 6.00

Haitian Revolution, Bicent. — A237

**Wmk. 352**

**2004, Jan. 30 Litho. *Perf. 13½***
**983** A237 $40 multi 2.75 2.75

Caribbean Bird Festival A238

No. 984: a, Yellow-billed amazon. b, Jamaican oriole. c, Orangequit. d, Yellow-shouldered grassquit. e, Jamaican woodpecker. f, Red-billed streamertail. g, Jamaican mango. h, White-eyed thrush. i, Jamaican lizard cuckoo. j, Arrow-headed warbler.

**Wmk. 352**

**2004, May 17 Litho. *Perf. 13¾***
**984** Block of 10 10.00 10.00
*a.-j.* A238 $10 Any single .80 .60

Miniature Sheet

World Environment Day — A239

No. 985: a, $10, Water lilies. b, $10, Hawksbill turtle. c, $10, Tube sponge. d, $10, Boater on Parattee Pond. e, $40, Vase sponge, star coral. f, $40, Sea fan, black and white crinoid. g, $40, Glassy sweepers. h, $40, Giant sea anemone.

**Unwmk.**

**2004, June 4 Litho. *Perf. 14***
**985** A239 Sheet of 8, #a-h 9.50 9.50

2004 Summer Olympics, Athens — A240

Jamaican athletes: $30, Women's hurdles. $60, Running. $70, Swimming. $90, Rifle shooting, women's badminton.

**Wmk. 352**

**2004, Aug. 10 Litho. *Perf. 14***
**986-989** A240 Set of 4 9.50 9.50

FIFA (Fédération Internationale de Football Association), Cent. — A241

FIFA emblem and various soccer players: $10, $30, $45, $50.

**Wmk. 352**

**2004, Oct. 13 Litho. *Perf. 14***
**990-993** A241 Set of 4 6.75 6.75

Jamaica Hotels Law, Cent. A242

Designs: No. 994, Ralph Lauren, Doctors Cave Beach, Montego Bay.

No. 995 — Ambassador John Pringle, Round Hill Hotel and: a, Pink panel. b, Lilac panel.

No. 996 — Tower Isle Hotel and: a, Abe Issa, yellow green panels. b, John Issa, green panels. c, Abe Issa, red panels. d, John Issa, yellow green panels. e, Abe Issa, green panels. f, John Issa, red panels.

**2004 Unwmk. *Perf. 13¼x13½***
**994** A242 $40 multi 6.00 6.00
**995** A242 $40 Pair, #a-b 8.00 8.00
**996** A242 $40 Sheet of 6, #a-f 10.00 10.00
*Nos. 994-996 (3)* 24.00 24.00

Issued: No. 994, 11/19; Nos. 995-996, 11/12. No. 994 printed in sheets of six; No. 995 printed in sheets containing three pairs. Value, set of three sheets $45.

Christmas — A243

White sorrel stalks: $10, $20, $50, $60. $50 and $60 are horiz.

**Wmk. 352**

**2004, Nov. 22 Litho. *Perf. 14¼***
**997-1000** A243 Set of 4 7.50 7.50

Founding of Moravian Church in Jamaica, 250th Anniv. A244

Designs: 90c, Mary Morris Knibb, Mizpah Moravian Church. $10, Rev. W. O'Meally, Mizpah Moravian Church. $50, Bishop S. U. Hastings, Redeemer Moravian Church.

**2004, Dec. 14**
**1001-1003** A244 Set of 3 4.00 4.00

Buildings — A245

Designs: 90c, Rose Hall Great House, St. James. $5, Holy Trinity Cathedral. $30, National Commercial Bank, New Kingston. $60, Court House, Falmouth.

**2005, Jan. 13 Wmk. 352 *Perf. 13¼***
**1004** A245 90c multi .25 .25
**1004A** A245 $5 multi .30 .25
**1005** A245 $30 multi 1.50 1.10
*a.* Dated 2006 at bottom 2.00 1.50
*b.* Dated 2008 at bottom 1.00 .75
**1006** A245 $60 multi 3.00 2.75
*a.* Dated 2008 at bottom 2.00 1.50
*Nos. 1004-1006 (4)* 5.05 4.35

**Self-Adhesive**

***Serpentine Die Cut 12¼x12½***

**Unwmk.**

**1008** A245 $5 multi .40 .25
**1008A** A245 $30 multi 1.50 1.50
*b.* Booklet pane of 10 15.00
Complete booklet, #1008Ab 15.00
*c.* Dated 2006 at right 2.00 2.00
**1009** A245 $60 multi 3.50 3.50

See Nos. 1038-1053.

Chinese in Jamaica, 150th Anniv. A246

Flags of People's Republic of China and Jamaica and: $30, Food and fruits from China and Jamaica. $60, Chinatown. $90, Chinese Benevolent Association Building.

**2005, Feb. 5 Wmk. 352 *Perf. 14¼***
**1010-1012** A246 Set of 3 9.00 9.00

European Philatelic Cooperation, 50th Anniv. (in 2006) — A247

Designs: $60, Green square. $70, Yellow diamond. $100 Blue square.

***Perf. 13½***

**2005, June 1 Litho. Unwmk.**
**1013-1015** A247 Set of 3 8.00 8.00
*1015a* Souvenir sheet, #1013-1015 8.00 8.00

Europa stamps, 50th anniv. (in 2006).

Battle of Trafalgar, Bicent. — A248

Designs: $20, Gun captain holding powder cartridge. $30, Admiral Horatio Nelson, vert. $50, British 12-pounder cannon. $60, HMS Africa, vert. $70, HMS Leviathan being attacked by the Intrepide, vert. $90, HMS Victory.

$200, HMS Africa at Port Royal, Jamaica.

**Wmk. 352, Unwmkd. ($90)**

**2005, June 23 Litho. *Perf. 13¼***
**1016-1021** A248 Set of 6 12.00 12.00

**Souvenir Sheet**

***Perf. 13½***

**1022** A248 $200 multi 10.00 10.00

No. 1021 has particles of wood from the HMS Victory embedded in areas covered by a thermographic process that produces a raised, shiny effect. No. 1022 contains one 44x44mm stamp.

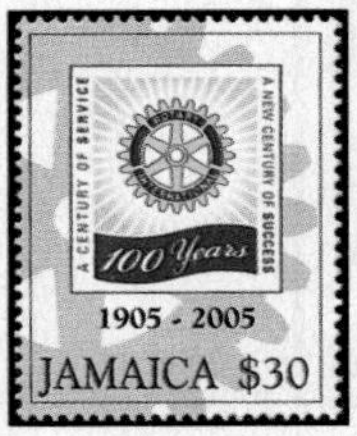

Rotary International, Cent. — A249

**2005, June 30 Wmk. 352 *Perf. 13¾***
**1023** A249 $30 multi 2.00 2.00

Pope John Paul II (1920-2005) A250

**Unwmk.**

**2005, Aug. 18 Litho. *Perf. 14***
**1024** A250 $30 multi 1.75 1.75

Battle of Trafalgar, Bicent. — A251

Designs: $50, HMS Victory. $90, Ships in battle, horiz. $100, Admiral Horatio Nelson.

***Perf. 13¼***

**2005, Oct. 18 Litho. Unwmk.**
**1025-1027** A251 Set of 3 12.50 12.50

Mary Seacole (1805-81), Nurse — A252

Seacole and: $30, Herbal remedies and medicines. $50, Seacole Hall, University of the West Indies. $60, Crimean War soldiers. $70, Medals.

**Wmk. 352**

**2005, Nov. 21 Litho. *Perf. 13½***
**1028-1031** A252 Set of 4 7.50 7.50

World AIDS Day — A253

**2005, Dec. 1 *Perf. 14¾x14***
**1032** A253 $30 multi 1.50 1.50

Christmas A254

Star of Bethlehem and poinsettia with various frame designs: $20, $30, $50, $80.

**2005, Dec. 1**
**1033-1036** A254 Set of 4 6.75 6.75

Jessie Ripoll (Sister Mary Peter Claver), Founder of Alpha Schools — A255

**2005, Dec. 12 *Perf. 13½***
**1037** A255 $30 multi 1.25 1.25

Alpha Schools, 125th anniv.

**Buildings Type of 2005**

Designs: $10, Court House, Morant Bay. $15, Spanish Town Square, St. Catherine. $20, Mico College. $25, Simms Building, Jamaica College. $50, Devon House, St. Andrew. $70, Ward Theater, Kingston. $90, Vale Royal, St. Andrew. $100, Falmouth Post Office.

***Perf. 14x13¼***

**2006, May 12 Litho. Wmk. 352**

**No date inscription below design**

| | | | | |
|---|---|---|---|---|
| **1038** | A245 $10 multi | | .70 | .40 |
| *a.* | Inscribed "2008" | | .35 | .35 |
| **1039** | A245 $15 multi | | .60 | .50 |
| **1040** | A245 $20 multi | | 1.25 | 1.00 |
| *a.* | Inscribed "2008" | | .70 | .65 |
| **1041** | A245 $25 multi | | .90 | .80 |
| **1042** | A245 $50 multi | | 2.75 | 1.75 |
| *a.* | Inscribed "2008" | | 1.75 | 1.00 |
| **1043** | A245 $70 multi | | 3.25 | 3.25 |
| *a.* | Inscribed "2008" | | 2.25 | 1.75 |
| **1044** | A245 $90 multi | | 4.50 | 4.50 |
| *a.* | Inscribed "2008" | | 2.75 | 2.25 |
| **1045** | A245 $100 multi | | 3.25 | 3.25 |
| | *Nos. 1038-1045 (8)* | | 17.20 | 15.45 |

**Self-Adhesive**

**Unwmk.**

***Serpentine Die Cut 13¼x14***

| | | | |
|---|---|---|---|
| **1046** | A245 $10 multi | .40 | .40 |
| **1047** | A245 $15 multi | .65 | .65 |
| **1048** | A245 $20 multi | .75 | .75 |
| **1049** | A245 $25 multi | .90 | .90 |
| **1050** | A245 $50 multi | 2.00 | 2.00 |
| **1051** | A245 $70 multi | 2.50 | 2.50 |
| **1052** | A245 $90 multi | 3.00 | 3.00 |
| **1053** | A245 $100 multi | 3.25 | 3.25 |
| | *Nos. 1046-1053 (8)* | 13.45 | 13.45 |

Worldwide Fund for Nature (WWF) A256

Black-billed Amazon parrot: $5, Chicks. $10, Head of adult bird. $30, Bird on branch. $50, Two birds.

***Perf. 13¼x13½***

**2006, Nov. 30 Litho. Wmk. 352**
**1054-1057** A256 Set of 4 *7.00* 7.00
*1057a* Sheet, 4 each #1054-1057 *28.00 28.00*

Christmas A257

Flowers: $20, Cup and saucer. $30, Lignum vitae. $50, Neocogniauxia monophylla, vert. $60, Ghost orchid, vert.

***Perf. 13¼x13¾, 13¾x13¼***

**2006, Nov. 30**
**1058-1061** A257 Set of 4 7.00 7.00

2007 ICC Cricket World Cup, West Indies — A258

Designs: No. 1062, $30, Courtney Walsh. No. 1063, $30, Collie Smith. $40, New Sabrina Park, horiz. $50, Like #1062. $60, Trelawney Multi-purpose Sports Complex, horiz.
$200, ICC Cricket World Cup.

**Wmk. 352**

**2007, Feb. 28 Litho. *Perf. 14***
**1062-1066** A258 Set of 5 11.00 11.00

**Souvenir Sheet**

**1067** A258 $200 multi 10.00 10.00

British Abolition of the Slave Trade, Bicent. — A259

**Wmk. 352**

**2007, June 7 Litho. *Perf. 14***
**1068** A259 $30 multi 1.50 1.50

Scouting, Cent. A260

Designs: $5, Boy scout, Jamaican flag, Scout salute. $10, Scouts, compass. $30, Scouts, lashed poles. $70, Scouts handling Jamaican flag, Scout making craft.
No. 1073, vert.: a, $50, Scouts on parade. b, $100, Lord Robert Baden-Powell blowing kudu horn.

**2007, July 9 *Perf. 13¾***
**1069-1072** A260 Set of 4 5.00 5.00

**Souvenir Sheet**

**1073** A260 Sheet of 2, #a-b 8.00 8.00

Christmas — A261

Flowers: $20, Tolumnia triquetra. $30, Broughtonia negrilensis, horiz. $50, Broughtonia sanguinea, horiz. $60, Spathelia sorbifolia.

**Wmk. 352**

**2007, Nov. 9 Litho. *Perf. 14***
**1074-1077** A261 Set of 4 7.00 7.00

2008 Summer Olympics, Beijing A262

Designs: $20, Fish, Asafa Powell. $60, Lanterns, Veronica Campbell-Brown.
No. 1079: a, Bamboo, Aleen Bailey, Veronica Campbell-Brown. b, Sherone Simpson, Tayna Lawrence, dragon.

**Wmk. 352**

**2008, Apr. 30 Litho. *Perf. 13¼***
**1078** A262 $20 multi 1.00 1.00
**1079** A262 $30 Horiz. pair, #a-b 3.00 3.00
**1080** A262 $60 multi 3.00 3.00
*Nos. 1078-1080 (3)* 7.00 7.00

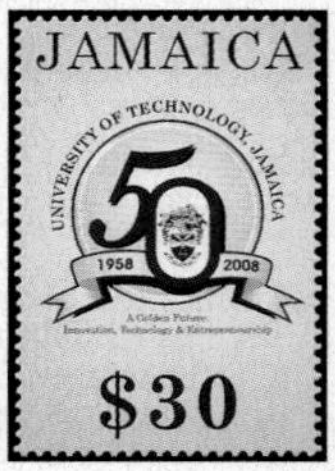


University of Technology, 50th Anniv. — A263

**2008, May 26 Litho. *Perf. 14***
**1081** A263 $30 multi 2.00 2.00
*a.* Souvenir sheet of 1 2.10 2.10

Associated Board of the Royal Schools of Music in Jamaica, Cent. — A264

Map of Jamaica and: $30, Piano keyboard. $70, Violin.

**Wmk. 352**

**2008, Oct. 30 Litho. *Perf. 14***
**1082-1083** A264 Set of 2 5.00 5.00

Christmas A265

Various ferns: $20, $30, $50, $60.

**Wmk. 352**

**2008, Nov. 21 Litho. *Perf. 13¾***
**1084-1087** A265 Set of 4 7.00 7.00

George Headley (1909-83), Cricket Player — A266

Designs: $10, Head of Headley. $30, Headley in front of wickets. $200, Statue of Headley.
$250, Statue of Headley, Sabina Park, Kingston.

**Wmk. 352**

**2009, Sept. 25 Litho. *Perf. 14***
**1088-1090** A266 Set of 3 *8.00* 8.00

**Souvenir Sheet**

***Perf. 14¼x14***

**1091** A266 $250 multi 8.50 8.50

No. 1091 contains one 43x57mm stamp.

Christmas — A267

Paintings by Juanita Isabel Ramos: $20, Guardian Angel. $30, Madonna and Child. $50, Madonna and Flowers, horiz.

**Wmk. 352**

**2009, Nov. 20 Litho. *Perf. 13½***

**1092-1094** A267 Set of 3 3.50 3.50

Christmas A268

Musical groups: $40, NDTC Singers. $60, Kingston College Chapel Choir. $120, The University Singers. $160, The Jamaican Folk Singers.

**Wmk. 352**

**2010, Dec. 13 Litho. *Perf. 13¾***

**1095-1098** A268 Set of 4 11.00 11.00

Souvenir Sheet

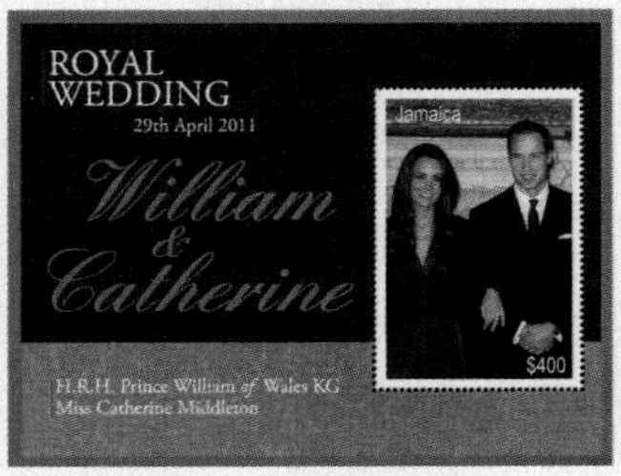


Wedding of Prince William and Catherine Middleton — A269

**2011, Apr. 29 *Perf. 14¾x14¼***

**1099** A269 $400 multi 11.00 11.00

Lighthouses — A270

Designs: $20, Negril Lighthouse. $50, Morant Point Lighthouse. $60, Lover's Leap Lighthouse, vert. $200, Galina Lighthouse, vert.

**2011, July 4 *Perf. 14***

| | | | | |
|---|---|---|---|---|
| **1100** | A270 | $20 multi | .50 | .50 |
| *a.* | | Dated "2012" | .50 | .50 |
| *b.* | | Dated "2013" | .40 | .40 |
| *c.* | | Dated "2015" | .35 | .35 |
| **1101** | A270 | $50 multi | 1.25 | 1.25 |
| *a.* | | Dated "2012" | 1.25 | 1.25 |
| *b.* | | Dated "2013" | 1.00 | 1.00 |
| *c.* | | Dated "2015" | .85 | .85 |
| **1102** | A270 | $60 multi | 1.40 | 1.40 |
| *a.* | | Dated "2012" | 1.40 | 1.40 |
| *b.* | | Dated "2013" | 1.25 | 1.25 |
| *c.* | | Dated "2015" | 1.00 | 1.00 |
| **1103** | A270 | $200 multi | 4.75 | 4.75 |
| *a.* | | Dated "2012" | 4.75 | 4.75 |
| *b.* | | Dated "2013" | 4.00 | 4.00 |
| *c.* | | Dated "2015" | 3.25 | 3.25 |
| | | *Nos. 1100-1103 (4)* | 7.90 | 7.90 |

Issued: Nos. 1100a, 1101a, 1102a, 1103a, 3/23/12. Nos. 1100b, 1101b, 1102b, 1103b, 6/13/13. Nos. 1100c, 1101c, 112c, 1103c, 3/14/16.

See Nos. 1122-1125.

Independence, 50th Anniv. — A271

Designs: $60, Fiftieth anniversary emblem. $120, Coat of arms, vert.

***Perf. 14x14¾, 14¾x14***

**2012, Aug. 31**

**1104-1105** A271 Set of 2 4.25 4.25

Medalists at 2008 Summer Olympics A272

Designs: No. 1106, $60, Usain Bolt, Men's 100-meter and 200-meter gold medalist (orange panel). No. 1107, $60, Melaine Walker, Women's 400-meter hurdles gold medalist (red panel). No. 1108, $60, Veronica Campbell-Brown, women's 200-meter gold medalist (blue panel). No. 1109, $60, Men's 4x100-meter relay team (Bolt, Michael Frater, Nesta Carter, Asafa Powell) (green panel). No. 1110, $60, Shelly-Ann Fraser, gold medalist, Sherone Simpson and Kerron Stewart, silver medalists in women's 100-meter (black panel).

**2013, May 3 *Perf. 13¼***

**1106-1110** A272 Set of 5 6.25 6.25

Christmas A273

Bells and: $20, Night-blooming cereus. $60, Coffee berries and flowers. $120, Century palm. $160, Cactus flower.

**Wmk. 352**

**2013, Dec. 6 Litho. *Perf. 13¼***

**1111-1114** A273 Set of 4 7.50 7.50

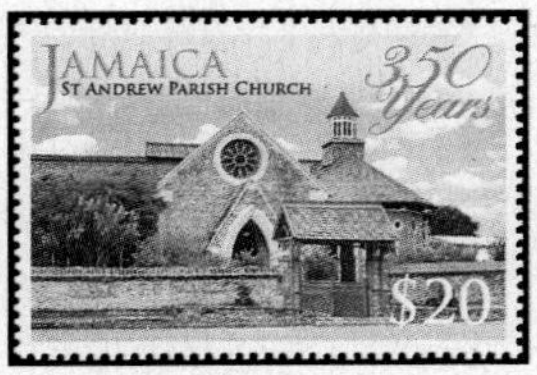


St. Andrew Parish Church, 350th Anniv. — A274

Various views of church's exterior: $20, $60, $120.

$200, Stained-glass windows, vert.

***Perf. 14¼x14¾***

**2014, Dec. 11 Litho.**

**1115-1117** A274 Set of 3 3.50 3.50

**Souvenir Sheet**

***Perf. 14¾x14¼***

**1118** A274 $200 multi 3.50 3.50

2016 Summer Olympics, Rio de Janeiro — A275

No. 1119: a, Shelly-Ann Fraser-Price with medal. b, Usain Bolt with medal.

$120, Fraser-Price and Bolt in track uniforms. $300, Fraser-Price and Bolt with medal ribbons around necks.

**Wmk. 352**

**2016, July 3 Litho. *Perf. 14***

| | | | | |
|---|---|---|---|---|
| **1119** | | Horiz. pair | 1.90 | 1.90 |
| *a.-b.* | A275 | $60 Either single | .95 | .95 |
| *c.* | | Souvenir sheet of 2, #1119a-1119b | 1.90 | 1.90 |
| **1120** | A275 | $120 multi | 1.90 | 1.90 |
| **1121** | A275 | $300 multi | 4.75 | 4.75 |
| | | *Nos. 1119-1121 (3)* | 8.55 | 8.55 |

**Lighthouses Type of 2011**

Designs: $40, Folly Lighthouse, vert. $140, Rosehall Lighthouse. $180, Plumb Point Lighthouse, vert. $300, Portland Point Lighthouse.

**2016 Litho. Wmk. 352 *Perf. 14***

| | | | | |
|---|---|---|---|---|
| **1122** | A270 | $40 multi | .65 | .65 |
| **1123** | A270 | $140 multi | 2.25 | 2.25 |
| **1124** | A270 | $180 multi | 2.75 | 2.75 |
| **1125** | A270 | $300 multi | 4.75 | 4.75 |
| | | *Nos. 1122-1125 (4)* | 10.40 | 10.40 |

Dated 2015.

Butterflies — A276

No. 1126: a, Giant swallowtail. b, Monarch.

***Perf. 13¼***

**2016, Oct. 28 Litho. Unwmk.**

**1126** A276 $60 Horiz. pair, #a-b 1.90 1.90

See Mexico Nos. 3029-3030.

## SEMI-POSTAL STAMPS

Native Girl — SP1

Native Boy — SP2

Native Boy and Girl — SP3

**1923, Nov. 1 Engr. *Perf. 12***

| | | | | |
|---|---|---|---|---|
| **B1** | SP1 | ½p green & black | 1.25 | *5.50* |
| **B2** | SP2 | 1p car & black | 3.50 | *11.50* |
| **B3** | SP3 | 2½p blue & black | 15.00 | *15.00* |
| | | *Nos. B1-B3 (3)* | 19.75 | *32.00* |

Each stamp was sold for ½p over face value. The surtax benefited the Child Saving League of Jamaica.

**Catalogue values for unused stamps in this section, from this point to the end of the section, are for Never Hinged items.**

**Nos. 694-697 Surcharged in Black**

**Wmk. 352**

**1988, Nov. 11 Litho. *Perf. 14***

| | | | | |
|---|---|---|---|---|
| **B4** | A164 | 25c +25c multi | .30 | .25 |
| **B5** | A164 | 45c +45c multi | .40 | .25 |
| **B6** | A164 | $4 +$4 multi | 2.25 | *3.00* |
| **B7** | A164 | $5 +$5 multi | 2.50 | *3.00* |
| | | *Nos. B4-B7 (4)* | 5.45 | 6.50 |

**Red Surcharge**

| | | | | |
|---|---|---|---|---|
| *B4a* | A164 | 25c + 25c | .30 | .25 |
| *B5a* | A164 | 45c + 45c | .40 | .25 |
| *B6a* | A164 | $4 + $4 | 2.25 | *3.00* |
| *B7a* | A164 | $5 + $5 | 2.50 | *3.00* |
| | | *Nos. B4a-B7a (4)* | 5.45 | 6.50 |

## WAR TAX STAMPS

Regular Issues of 1906-19 Overprinted

**1916 Wmk. 3 *Perf. 14***

| | | | | |
|---|---|---|---|---|
| **MR1** | A14 | ½p green | .25 | .40 |
| *a.* | | Without period | 17.50 | *27.50* |
| *b.* | | Double overprint | 140.00 | *160.00* |
| *c.* | | Inverted overprint | 130.00 | *150.00* |
| *d.* | | As "c," without period | 350.00 | |
| **MR2** | A17 | 3p violet, *yel* | 3.25 | *24.00* |
| *a.* | | Without period | 42.50 | *100.00* |

**Surface-colored Paper**

| | | | | |
|---|---|---|---|---|
| **MR3** | A17 | 3p violet, *yel* | 37.50 | *52.50* |
| | | *Nos. MR1-MR3 (3)* | 41.00 | *76.90* |

Regular Issues of 1906-18 Overprinted

| | | | | |
|---|---|---|---|---|
| **MR4** | A14 | ½p green | .25 | .30 |
| *a.* | | Without period | 22.50 | *57.50* |
| *b.* | | Pair, one without ovpt. | 6,500. | 5,250. |
| *c.* | | "R" inserted by hand | 1,800. | 1,500. |
| *d.* | | "WAR" only | 125.00 | |
| **MR5** | A17 | 1½p orange | .25 | .25 |
| *a.* | | Without period | 5.75 | *8.50* |
| *b.* | | "TAMP" | 210.00 | *240.00* |
| *c.* | | "S" inserted by hand | 450.00 | |
| *d.* | | "R" omitted | 3,600. | 3,100. |
| *e.* | | "R" inserted by hand | 1,550. | 1,250. |
| **MR6** | A17 | 3p violet, *yel* | 7.50 | 1.25 |
| *a.* | | Without period | 70.00 | *75.00* |
| *b.* | | "TAMP" | 1,000. | 1,000. |
| *c.* | | "S" inserted by hand | 225.00 | 225.00 |
| *d.* | | Inverted overprint | 350.00 | 190.00 |
| *e.* | | As "a," inverted | | |
| | | *Nos. MR4-MR6 (3)* | 8.00 | 1.80 |

Regular Issues of 1906-19 Overprinted

**1917, Mar.**

| | | | | |
|---|---|---|---|---|
| **MR7** | A14 | ½p green | 2.50 | .35 |
| *a.* | | Without period | 18.50 | *30.00* |
| *b.* | | Overprinted on back instead of face | 290.00 | |
| *c.* | | Inverted overprint | 27.50 | 57.50 |
| **MR8** | A17 | 1½p orange | .25 | .25 |
| *a.* | | Without period | 4.00 | *20.00* |
| *b.* | | Double overprint | 92.50 | *100.00* |
| *c.* | | Inverted overprint | 92.50 | 85.00 |
| *d.* | | As "a," inverted | *400.00* | |
| **MR9** | A17 | 3p violet, *yel* | 2.25 | *1.30* |
| *a.* | | Without period | 27.50 | *52.50* |
| *b.* | | Vertical overprint | 425.00 | 425.00 |
| *c.* | | Inverted overprint | 160.00 | 190.00 |
| *d.* | | As "a," inverted | *450.00* | |
| *e.* | | Pair, overprint omitted on one | 4,250. | |
| | | *Nos. MR7-MR9 (3)* | 5.00 | 1.90 |

There are many minor varieties of Nos. MR1-MR9.

Regular Issues of 1906-19 Overprinted in Red

**1919, Oct. 4**

| | | | | |
|---|---|---|---|---|
| **MR10** | A14 | ½p green | .25 | .25 |
| **MR11** | A17 | 3p violet, *yel* | 15.00 | 3.75 |
| *a.* | | 3p pale pur, *buff* | 6.25 | 1.50 |

## OFFICIAL STAMPS

No. 16 Overprinted in Black

Type I — Word 15 to 16mm long.
Type II — Word 17 to 17½mm long.

**1890** **Wmk. 2** ***Perf. 14***

| | | | | |
|---|---|---|---|---|
| **O1** | A7 | ½p green (II) | 18.50 | 2.50 |
| *a.* | | Type I | 47.50 | 30.00 |
| *b.* | | Inverted overprint (II) | 110.00 | *120.00* |
| *c.* | | Double overprint (II) | 110.00 | *120.00* |
| *d.* | | Dbl. ovpt., one invtd. (II) | 575.00 | 575.00 |
| *e.* | | Dbl. ovpt., one vert. (II) | 1,100. | |
| *f.* | | Double overprint (I) | 825.00 | |

Missing "O," "L" or one or both "I's" known.

No. 16 and Type of 1889 Overprinted

**1890-91**

| | | | | |
|---|---|---|---|---|
| **O2** | A7 | ½p green | 10.00 | 1.80 |
| **O3** | A10 | 1p carmine rose | 8.50 | 1.40 |
| **O4** | A10 | 2p slate | 32.50 | 1.40 |
| | | *Nos. O2-O4 (3)* | 51.00 | 4.60 |

# JAPAN

jə-'pan

LOCATION — North Pacific Ocean, east of China
GOVT. — Constitutional monarchy
AREA — 142,726 sq. mi.
POP. — 126,182,077 (1999 est.)
CAPITAL — Tokyo

1000 Mon = 10 Sen
100 Sen = 1 Yen (or En)
10 Rin = 1 Sen

**Catalogue values for unused stamps in this country are for Never Hinged items, beginning with Scott 375 in the regular postage section, Scott B8 in the semi-postal section, and Scott C9 in the airpost section.**

**Watermarks**

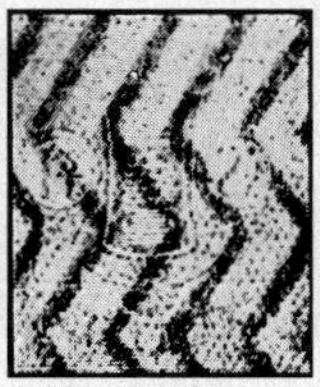
Wmk. 141 — Zigzag Lines

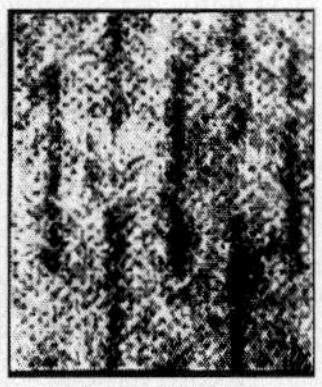
Wmk. 142 — Parallel Lines

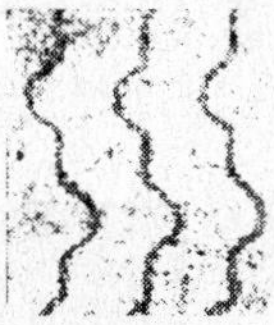
Wmk. 257 — Curved Wavy Lines

After 1945, Wmk. 257 exists also in a narrow spacing on a small number of issues.

Counterfeits of Nos. 1-71 are plentiful. Some are excellent and deceive many collectors.

Nos. 1-54A were printed from plates of 40 with individually engraved subjects. Each stamp in the sheet is slightly different.

Pair of Dragons Facing Characters of Value — A1

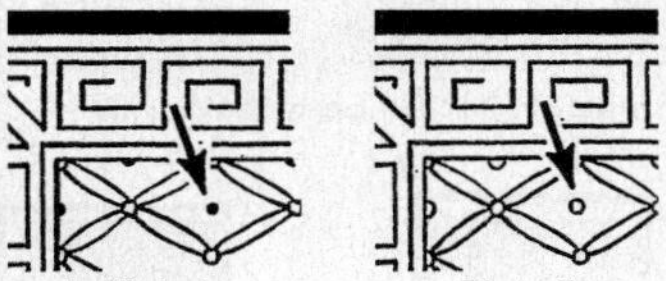
Plate I Plate II

48 mon:
Plate I — Solid dots in inner border.
Plate II — Tiny circles replace dots.

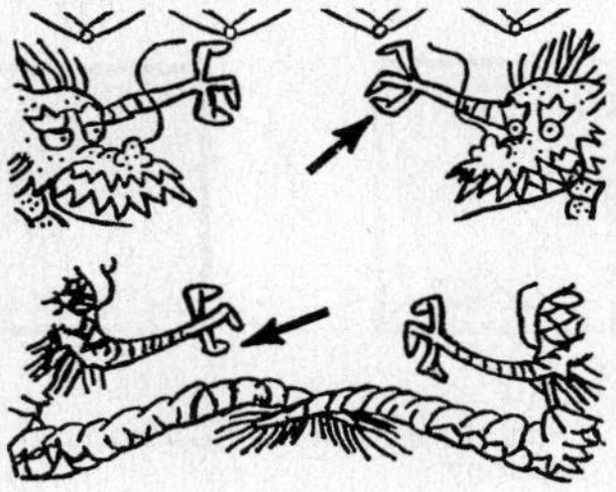
Plate I

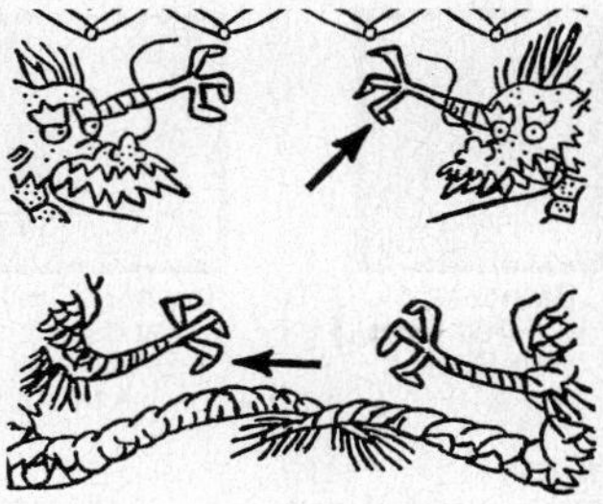
Plate II

100 mon:
Plate I — Lowest dragon claw at upper right and at lower left point upward.
Plate II — Same two claws point downward.

Plate I Plate II

200 mon:
Plate I — Dot in upper left corner.
Plate II — No dot. (Some Plate I copies show dot faintly; these can be mistaken for Plate II.)

Plate I Plate II

500 mon:
Plate I — Lower right corner of Greek-type border incomplete
Plate II — Short horizontal line completes corner border pattern.

**Unwmk.**

**1871, Apr. 20 Engr. *Imperf.***

**Native Laid Paper Without Gum**
**Denomination in Black**

| | | | | |
|---|---|---|---|---|
| **1** | A1 | 48m brown (I) | 225. | 225. |
| *a.* | | 48m red brown (I) | 375. | 375. |
| *b.* | | Wove paper (I) | 300. | 300. |
| *c.* | | 48m brown (II) | 325. | 325. |
| *d.* | | Wove paper (II) | 400. | 400. |
| **2** | A1 | 100m blue (I) | 225. | 225. |
| *a.* | | Wove paper (I) | 350. | 350. |
| *b.* | | Plate II | 550. | 550. |
| *c.* | | Wove paper (II) | 800. | 800. |
| **3** | A1 | 200m ver (I) | 350. | 325. |
| *a.* | | Wove paper (I) | 500. | 425. |
| *b.* | | Plate II | 2,500. | 2,000. |
| *c.* | | Wove paper (II) | | *4,000.* |
| **4** | A1 | 500m bl grn (I) | 575. | 550. |
| *a.* | | 500m greenish blue (I) | 650. | 625. |
| *b.* | | 500m green (I) | 2,000. | 1,400. |
| *c.* | | 500m yellow green (I) | 3,500. | 1,500. |
| *d.* | | Wove paper (I) | 725. | 625. |
| *e.* | | 500m blue green (II) | 750. | *4,000.* |
| *f.* | | 500m greenish blue (II) | 750. | *4,000.* |
| *g.* | | Wove paper (II) | 2,750. | *5,000.* |
| *h.* | | Denomination inverted (I) | | *175,000.* |

Perforations, Nos. 5-8

Perforations on Nos. 5-8 generally are rough and irregular due to the perforating equipment used and the quality of the paper. Values are for stamps with rough perfs that touch the frameline on one or more sides.

Dragons and Denomination — A1a

½ sen:
Plate I — Same as 48m Plate II. Measures not less than 19.8x19.8mm. Some subjects on this plate measure 20.3x20.2mm.
Plate II — Same as 48m Plate II. Measures not more than 19.7x19.3mm. Some subjects measure 19.3x18.7mm.

Plate I & II Plate III

1 sen:
Plate I — Same as 100m Plate I. Narrow space between frameline and Greek-type border.
Plate II — Same as 100m Plate II. Same narrow space between frameline and border.
Plate III — Space between frameline and border is much wider. Frameline thinner. Shading on dragon heads heavier than on Plates I and II.

**Native Laid Paper**
**With or Without Gum**

**1872 *Perf. 9-12 & compound***
**Denomination in Black**

| | | | | |
|---|---|---|---|---|
| **5** | A1a | ½s brown (II) | 110.00 | 100.00 |
| *a.* | | ½s red brown (II) | 125.00 | 110.00 |
| *b.* | | ½s gray brown (II) | 125.00 | 110.00 |
| *c.* | | Wove paper (II) | 725.00 | 675.00 |
| *d.* | | ½s brown (I) | 200.00 | 200.00 |
| *e.* | | ½s red brown (I) | 200.00 | 200.00 |
| *f.* | | ½s gray brown (I) | 200.00 | 200.00 |
| *g.* | | Wove paper (I) | 275.00 | 275.00 |
| **6** | A1a | 1s blue (II) | 375.00 | 325.00 |
| *a.* | | Wove paper (II) | 675.00 | 675.00 |
| *b.* | | Plate I | 1,400. | *3,000.* |
| *c.* | | Wove paper (I) | *7,000.* | |
| *d.* | | Plate III | *15,000.* | 2,500. |
| *e.* | | Wove paper (III) | | *7,500.* |
| **7** | A1a | 2s vermilion | 500.00 | 475.00 |
| *a.* | | Wove paper | 625.00 | 575.00 |
| **8** | A1a | 5s blue green | 800.00 | 725.00 |
| *a.* | | 5s yellow green | 850.00 | 800.00 |
| *b.* | | Wove paper | 900.00 | 900.00 |

In 1896 the government made imperforate imitations of Nos. 6-7 to include in a presentation book.

Beginning with No. 9, Japanese stamps intended for distribution outside the Postal Ministry were overprinted with three characters, as shown above, reading "Mihon" (specimen). These specimens were included in ministry announcements detailing forthcoming issues and were in presentation booklets given to government officials, foreign governments, etc.

Expect perforations on Nos. 9-71 to be rough and irregular.

Imperial Crest and Branches of Kiri Tree — A2

Dragons and Chrysanthemum Crest — A3

Imperial Chrysanthemum Crest — A4

Imperial Crest and Branches of Kiri Tree — A5

***Perf. 9 to 13 and Compound***

**1872-73**

**Native Wove or Laid Paper of Varying Thickness**

| | | | | |
|---|---|---|---|---|
| **9** | A2 | ½s brn, *hard wove* | 25.00 | 20.00 |
| *a.* | | Upper character in left label has 2 diagonal top strokes missing | 2,100. | 1,250. |
| *b.* | | Laid paper | 80.00 | — |
| *c.* | | As "a," laid paper | 2,200. | — |
| *d.* | | ½s gray brown, *soft porous native wove* | 80.00 | — |

Nos. 9, 9a are on stiff, brittle wove paper. Nos. 9b, 9c and 9d on a soft, fibrous paper. Nos. 9b, 9c and 9d probably were never put in use, though genuine used examples do exist.

| | | | | |
|---|---|---|---|---|
| **10** | A2 | 1s blue, *wove* | 50.00 | 26.00 |
| *a.* | | Laid paper | 52.50 | 29.00 |
| **11** | A2 | 2s ver, *wove* | 100.00 | 50.00 |
| **12** | A2 | 2s dull rose, *laid* | 75.00 | 35.00 |
| *a.* | | Wove paper | 100.00 | 50.00 |
| **13** | A2 | 2s yel, *laid* ('73) | 75.00 | 21.00 |
| *a.* | | Wove paper ('73) | 175.00 | 26.00 |
| **14** | A2 | 4s rose, *laid* ('73) | 67.50 | 26.00 |
| *a.* | | Wove paper ('73) | 210.00 | 32.00 |
| **15** | A3 | 10s blue grn, *wove* | 250.00 | 150.00 |
| **16** | A3 | 10s yel grn, *laid* | 400.00 | 275.00 |
| *a.* | | Wove paper ('73) | 1,150. | 500.00 |
| **17** | A4 | 20s lilac, *wove* | 600.00 | 350.00 |
| *a.* | | 20s violet, *wove* | 750.00 | 350.00 |
| *b.* | | 20s red violet, *laid* | | — |
| **18** | A5 | 30s gray, *wove* | 625.00 | 375.00 |

See Nos. 24-25, 30-31, 37-39, 51-52.

**1874 Foreign Wove Paper**

| | | | | |
|---|---|---|---|---|
| **24** | A2 | 4s rose | 650. | 300. |
| **25** | A5 | 30s gray | *30,000.* | *7,500.* |

A6

A7

A8

Design A6 differs from A2 by the addition of a syllabic character in a box covering crossed kiri branches above SEN. Stamps of design A6 differ for each value in border and spandrel designs.

In design A7, the syllabic character appears just below the buckle. In design A8, it appears in an oval frame at bottom center below SE of SEN. Design A3 and A4 have a syllabic character immediately below the central design, above the 'S' of 'SEN'.

**With Syllabic Characters**

| イ | ロ | ハ | ニ | ホ | ヘ | ト | チ |
|---|---|---|---|---|---|---|---|
| i | ro | ha | ni | ho | he | to | chi |
| 1 | 2 | 3 | 4 | 5 | 6 | 7 | 8 |

| リ | ヌ | ル | ヲ | ワ | カ | ヨ | タ |
|---|---|---|---|---|---|---|---|
| ri | nu | ru | wo | wa | ka | yo | ta |
| 9 | 10 | 11 | 12 | 13 | 14 | 15 | 16 |

| レ | ソ | ツ | 子 | ナ | ラ | ム |
|---|---|---|---|---|---|---|
| re | so | tsu | ne | na | ra | mu |
| 17 | 18 | 19 | 20 | 21 | 22 | 23 |

***Perf. 9½ to 12½ and Compound***

**1874 Native Laid or Wove Paper**

**28** A6 2s yel (Syll. 1) *27,000.* 400.00
 Syllabic 16 425.00
**29** A7 6s vio brn (Syll. 1) 1,700. 475.00
 Syllabic 2 1,900. 500.00
 Syllabic 3 20,000. 1,100.
 Syllabic 4 20,000. 600.00
 Syllabic 5 20,000. 600.00
 Syllabic 6 20,000. 700.00
 Syllabic 7 25,000. 550.00
 Syllabic 8 25,000. 550.00
 Syllabic 9 20,000. 700.00
 Syllabic 10 3,500.
 Syllabic 11 3,000.
 Syllabic 12 20,000. 1,900.
**30** A4 20s red vio (Syll. 3) *10,000.*
 Syllabic 1 150,000.
 Syllabic 2 *10,000.*
**31** A5 30s gray (Syll. 1) 3,000. 3,000.
 *a.* Very thin laid paper 3,000. 3,000.

No. 30, syll. 1, comes only with small, eliptical specimen dot (*Sumiten*, "secret mark").

***Perf. 11 to 12½ and Compound***

**1874 Foreign Wove Paper**

**32** A6 ½s brn (Syll. 1) 25.00 20.00
 Syllabic 2 40.00 40.00
**33** A6 1s blue (Syll. 4) 160.00 40.00
 Syllabic 1 150.00 35.00
 Syllabic 2 225.00 40.00
 Syllabic 3 200.00 40.00
 Syllabic 5 650.00 150.00
 Syllabic 6, 9 150.00 45.00
 Syllabic 7 350.00 50.00
 Syllabic 8 150.00 40.00
 Syllabic 10 225.00 70.00
 Syllabic 11 215.00 60.00
 Syllabic 12 250.00 65.00
**34** A6 2s yel (Syll. 2-4, 15, 17, 20) 175.00 30.00
 Syllabic 1 400.00 35.00
 Syllabic 5 450.00 30.00
 Syllabic 6 2,000. 50.00
 Syllabic 7 2,000. 30.00
 Syllabic 8 200.00 55.00
 Syllabic 9 200.00 35.00
 Syllabic 10 *2,750.* 50.00
 Syllabic 11 200.00 30.00
 Syllabic 12,22 *2,650.* 30.00
 Syllabic 13 *2,500.* 30.00
 Syllabic 14 *2,650.* 45.00
 Syllabic 16 *2,500.* 35.00
 Syllabic 18,19 200.00 30.00
 Syllabic 21 250.00 30.00
 Syllabic 23 265.00 30.00
**35** A6 4s rose (Syll. 1) 3,500. 475.00
**36** A7 6s vio brn (Syll. 16) 175.00 65.00
 Syllabic 10 650.00 650.00
 Syllabic 11 500.00
 Syllabic 13 14,000. *5,000.*
 Syllabic 14 300.00 275.00
 Syllabic 15 25,000. *3,000.*
 Syllabic 17 225.00 80.00
 Syllabic 18 325.00 110.00
**37** A3 10s yel grn (Syll. 2) 200.00 65.00
 Syllabic 1 525.00 80.00
 Syllabic 3 1,000. 300.00
**38** A4 20s violet (Syll. 5) 425.00 90.00
 Syllabic 4 450.00 95.00
**39** A5 30s gray (Syll. 1) 475.00 95.00

**1875 *Perf. 9 to 13 and Compound***

**40** A6 ½s gray (Syll. 2, 3) 25.00 20.00
 Syllabic 4 30.00 1,000.
**41** A6 1s brn (Syll. 15) 35.00 22.50
 Syllabic 5 375.00 50.00
 Syllabic 7 2,250. 275.00
 Syllabic 8 *32,500.* 275.00
 Syllabic 12 1,300. 225.00
 Syllabic 13 50.00 22.50
 Syllabic 14 50.00 22.50
 Syllabic 16-17 45.00 25.00
**42** A6 4s grn (Syll. 1) 130.00 29.00
 Syllabic 2 200.00 29.00
 Syllabic 3 130.00 29.00
**43** A7 6s org (Syll. 16,17) 90.00 27.50
 Syllabic 10 175.00 55.00
 Syllabic 11 150.00 50.00
 Syllabic 13 325.00 45.00
 Syllabic 14 160.00 32.50
 Syllabic 15 162,500.
**44** A8 6s org (Syll. 20) 110.00 27.50
 Syllabic 19 125.00 27.50
 Syllabic 21 100.00 27.50
 Syllabic 22 4,250. 1,750.

Dragons
A9

Wild Goose
A10

Wagtail — A11

Imperial Crest — A11a

Kiri Branches — A11b

Goshawk — A12

**45** A9 10s ultra (Syll. 4) 180.00 30.00
 Syllabic 5 *4,250.* 375.00
**46** A10 12s rose (Syll. 1) 375.00 160.00
 Syllabic 2 500.00 185.00
 Syllabic 3 *3,500.* 500.00
**47** A11 15s lilac (Syll. 1) 350.00 160.00
 Syllabic 2 400.00 175.00
 Syllabic 3 350.00 190.00
**48** A11a 20s rose (Syll. 8) 140.00 22.50
 Syllabic 9 —
**49** A11b 30s vio (Syll. 2-4) 175.00 70.00
**50** A12 45s lake (Syll. 1) 500.00 240.00
 Syllabic 2 1,250. 550.00
 Syllabic 3 1,200. 425.00

Issued: No. 46, syll. 2, 1882; No. 46, syll. 3, 1883; others, 1875.

The 1s brown on laid paper, type A6, formerly listed as No. 50A, is one of several stamps of the preceding issue which exist on a laid type paper. They are difficult to identify and mainly of interest to specialists.

**1875 Without Syllabic Characters**

**51** A2 1s brown *7,500.* 675.00
**52** A2 4s dark gray green 375.00 100.00

Branches of Kiri Tree Tied with Ribbon
A13

Imperial Crest and Kiri Branches
A14

**1875-76**

**53** A13 1s brown 75.00 18.00
**54** A13 2s yellow 110.00 18.00
**54A** A14 5s green ('76) 220.00 110.00
 *Nos. 53-54A (3)* 405.00 146.00

Postal Cancellations

Beta Cancel

Postal Cancel

Telegraph Cancellation

Nos. 58, 61-62, 64-65, 71-84 are found with telegraph or telephone office cancellations. These sell at considerably lower prices than postally used examples. Examples with beta cancels are valued the same as postally used examples.

A15

A16

Imperial Crest, Star and Kiri Branches
A17

Sun, Kikumon and Kiri Branches
A18

***Perf. 8 to 14 and Compound***

**1876-77 Typo.**

**55** A15 5r slate 25.00 15.00
**56** A16 1s black 50.00 4.75
 *a.* Horiz. pair, imperf. btwn.
**57** A16 2s brown ol 90.00 4.50
**58** A16 4s blue grn 50.00 4.00
 *a.* 4s green 50.00 4.00
**59** A17 5s brown 65.00 20.00
**60** A17 6s orange ('77) 200.00 85.00
**61** A17 8s vio brn ('77) 75.00 5.50
**62** A17 10s blue ('77) 55.00 2.50
**63** A17 12s rose ('77) 240.00 160.00
**64** A18 15s yel grn ('77) 150.00 2.50
**65** A18 20s dk blue ('77) 160.00 15.00
**66** A18 30s violet ('77) 250.00 110.00
 *a.* 30s red violet 275.00 110.00
**67** A18 45s carmine ('77) 700.00 600.00

**1879**

**68** A16 1s maroon 17.50 1.25
**69** A16 2s dk violet 70.00 2.50
**70** A16 3s orange 75.00 30.00
**71** A18 50s carmine 250.00 17.50
 *Nos. 68-71 (4)* 412.50 51.25

**1883**

**72** A16 1s green 11.00 1.25
**73** A16 2s car rose 16.00 .30
**74** A17 5s ultra 27.50 1.10
 *Nos. 72-74 (3)* 54.50 2.65

Imperial Crest and Kiri Branches
A19

Kikumon
A20

**1888-92**

**75** A15 5r gray blk ('89) 6.00 .85
**76** A16 3s lilac rose ('92) 22.50 .75
**77** A16 4s olive bis 17.50 .75
**78** A17 8s blue lilac 35.00 2.50
**79** A17 10s brown org 25.00 .75
**80** A18 15s purple 60.00 1.00
**81** A18 20s orange 75.00 3.00
 *a.* 20s yellow 75.00 3.00
**82** A19 25s blue green 110.00 3.25
**83** A18 50s brown 120.00 5.75
**84** A20 1y carmine 160.00 6.25
 *Nos. 75-84 (10)* 631.00 24.85

Stamps of types A16-A18 differ for each value, in backgrounds and ornaments.

Cranes and Imperial Crest — A21

***Perf. 11½ to 13 and Compound***

**1894, Mar. 9**

**85** A21 2s carmine 19.00 3.00
**86** A21 5s ultra 30.00 14.00

25th wedding anniv. of Emperor Meiji (Mutsuhito) and Empress Haru.

Gen. Yoshihisa
A22

Kitashirakawa
A23

Field Marshal Akihito Arisugawa
A24 A25

**1896, Aug. 1 Engr.**

**87** A22 2s rose 22.50 4.75
**88** A23 5s deep ultra 45.00 4.75
**89** A24 2s rose 22.50 4.75
**90** A25 5s deep ultra 45.00 4.75
 *Nos. 87-90 (4)* 135.00 19.00

Victory in Chinese-Japanese War (1894-95).

A26

A27

A28

A29

***Perf. 11½ to 14 and Compound***

**1899-1907 Typo.**

**91** A26 5r gray 14.00 2.25
**92** A26 ½s gray ('01) 7.50 .25
**93** A26 1s lt red brn 10.00 .30
**94** A26 1½s ultra ('00) 28.00 1.75

When it's time—whether quality Japan, China, Korea or any Asian country—come to us.
The Sizzling Asian Market Place is at your fingertips with our offices & public auctions in Hong Kong. How may we help you?
The Kelleher & Rogers firm in Hong Kong is under the direction of Laurence Gibson, Former director of John Bull Stamp Auctions, Hong Kong, and a respected authority on Asian philately. Mr. Gibson has handled numerous powerful Japan/China/Asia collections and major rarities over the past 25 years including the Varro Tyler estate and the outstanding collections of Lois Evans deViolini and Michael Ruggiero.
Kelleher & Rogers Ltd
Fine Asian Auctions
In Hong Kong: Telephone: 852.3153.5541 • Fax: 852.3153.5543
Email: stamps@kelleherasia.com
U.S. Offices: 22 Shelter Rock Lane • Unit 53 • Danbury, CT 06810 USA
203.297.6056 • Fax: 203.297.6059
Email: info@kelleherauctions.com
www.kelleherauctions.com

| | | | | |
|---|---|---|---|---|
| **95** | A26 | 1½s violet ('06) | 20.00 | .55 |
| *a.* | | Booklet pane of 6 | *500.00* | |
| **96** | A26 | 2s lt green | 20.00 | .30 |
| *a.* | | Booklet pane of 6 | *130.00* | |
| **97** | A26 | 3s violet brn | 20.00 | .35 |
| *a.* | | Double impression | | |
| **98** | A26 | 3s rose ('06) | 12.00 | .30 |
| *a.* | | Booklet pane of 6 | *500.00* | |
| **99** | A26 | 4s rose | 14.00 | 2.25 |
| *a.* | | 4s pink ('06) | 37.50 | 4.25 |
| *b.* | | As No. 99, booklet pane of 6 | *125.00* | |
| **100** | A26 | 5s orange yel | 27.50 | .40 |
| **101** | A27 | 6s maroon ('07) | 50.00 | 5.00 |
| *a.* | | Booklet pane of 6 | *500.00* | |
| **102** | A27 | 8s olive grn | 60.00 | 7.50 |
| **103** | A27 | 10s deep blue | 24.00 | .30 |
| *a.* | | Booklet pane of 6 | *200.00* | |
| **104** | A27 | 15s purple | 80.00 | 3.50 |
| **105** | A27 | 20s red orange | 47.50 | .30 |
| **106** | A28 | 25s blue green | 80.00 | 1.50 |
| **107** | A28 | 50s red brown | 90.00 | 2.25 |
| **108** | A29 | 1y carmine | 140.00 | 3.25 |
| | | *Nos. 91-108 (18)* | 744.50 | 32.30 |

For overprints see Nos. M1, Offices in China, 1-18, Offices in Korea, 1-14.

Boxes for Rice Cakes and Marriage Certificates — A30

***Perf. 11½ to 12½ and Compound***

**1900, May 10**

| | | | | |
|---|---|---|---|---|
| **109** | A30 | 3s carmine | 26.00 | 2.50 |

Wedding of the Crown Prince Yoshihito and Princess Sadako.

For overprints see Offices in China No. 19, Offices in Korea No. 15.

Symbols of Korea and Japan — A31

**1905, July 1**

| | | | | |
|---|---|---|---|---|
| **110** | A31 | 3s rose red | 85.00 | 22.50 |

Issued to commemorate the amalgamation of the postal services of Japan and Korea. Korean stamps were withdrawn from sale June 30, 1905, but remained valid until Aug. 31. No. 110 was used in the Korea and China Offices of Japan, as well as in Japan proper.

Field-piece and Japanese Flag — A32

**1906, Apr. 29**

| | | | | |
|---|---|---|---|---|
| **111** | A32 | 1½s blue | 27.50 | 6.50 |
| **112** | A32 | 3s carmine rose | 55.00 | 25.00 |

Triumphal military review following the Russo-Japanese War.

Empress Jingo — A33

**1908** **Engr.**

| | | | | |
|---|---|---|---|---|
| **113** | A33 | 5y green | 900.00 | 11.00 |
| **114** | A33 | 10y dark violet | 1,400. | 15.00 |

The frame of No. 114 differs slightly from the illustration.

See Nos. 146-147.

For overprints see Offices in China Nos. 20-21, 48-49.

A34

A35

A36

***Perf. 12, 12x13, 13x13½***

**1913** **Typo.** **Unwmk.**

| | | | | |
|---|---|---|---|---|
| **115** | A34 | ½s brown | 9.00 | 1.50 |
| **116** | A34 | 1s orange | 17.50 | 1.50 |
| **117** | A34 | 1½s lt blue | 25.00 | 2.50 |
| *a.* | | Booklet pane of 6 | *600.00* | |
| **118** | A34 | 2s green | 27.50 | 1.50 |
| *a.* | | Booklet pane of 6 | *1,200.* | |
| **119** | A34 | 3s rose | 35.00 | 1.50 |
| *a.* | | Booklet pane of 6 | *750.00* | |
| **120** | A35 | 4s red | 40.00 | 17.50 |
| *a.* | | Booklet pane of 6 | *350.00* | |
| **121** | A35 | 5s violet | 47.50 | 3.00 |
| **122** | A35 | 10s deep blue | 120.00 | 2.00 |
| *a.* | | Booklet pane of 6 | *750.00* | |
| **123** | A35 | 20s claret | 150.00 | 3.50 |
| **124** | A35 | 25s olive green | 140.00 | 6.00 |
| **125** | A36 | 1y yel grn & mar | 650.00 | 40.00 |
| | | *Nos. 115-125 (11)* | 1,262. | 80.50 |

**1914-25** **Wmk. 141** **Granite Paper**

**Size: 19x22½mm ("Old Die")**

| | | | | |
|---|---|---|---|---|
| **127** | A34 | ½s brown | 4.50 | .25 |
| **128** | A34 | 1s orange | 5.00 | .25 |
| **129** | A34 | 1½s blue | 5.50 | .25 |
| *a.* | | Booklet pane of 6 | *100.00* | |
| *d.* | | As "a," imperf. | | |
| **130** | A34 | 2s green | 7.50 | .30 |
| *a.* | | Booklet pane of 6 | *150.00* | |
| **131** | A34 | 3s rose | 4.00 | .30 |
| *a.* | | Booklet pane of 6 | *100.00* | |
| **132** | A35 | 4s red | 25.00 | 2.25 |
| *a.* | | Booklet pane of 6 | *160.00* | |
| **133** | A35 | 5s violet | 17.50 | .75 |
| **134** | A35 | 6s brown ('19) | 37.50 | 7.00 |
| **136** | A35 | 8s gray ('19) | 32.50 | 17.50 |
| **137** | A35 | 10s deep blue | 22.50 | .30 |
| *a.* | | Booklet pane of 6 | *200.00* | |
| **138** | A35 | 13s olive brn ('25) | 40.00 | 6.00 |
| **139** | A35 | 20s claret | 120.00 | 2.00 |
| **140** | A35 | 25s olive grn | 22.50 | 2.00 |
| **141** | A36 | 30s org brn ('19) | 30.00 | 1.50 |
| **143** | A36 | 50s dk brown ('19) | 50.00 | 2.25 |
| **145** | A36 | 1y yel grn & mar | 150.00 | 2.50 |
| *b.* | | Imperf., pair | | |
| **146** | A33 | 5y green | 400.00 | 6.00 |
| **147** | A33 | 10y violet | 600.00 | 11.00 |
| | | *Nos. 127-147 (18)* | 1,574. | 62.40 |

**"New Die" Size: 18½x22mm (Flat Plate) or 18½x22½mm (Rotary)**

**1924-33**

| | | | | |
|---|---|---|---|---|
| *127a* | A34 | ½s brown | 3.75 | 2.25 |
| *128a* | A34 | 1s orange | 3.75 | 2.25 |
| *129b* | A34 | 1½s blue | 4.25 | .30 |
| *c.* | | Bklt. pane of 6 ('30) | 40.00 | |
| *131b* | A34 | 3s rose | 3.50 | .30 |
| *c.* | | Bklt. pane of 6 ('28) | 40.00 | |
| *133a* | A35 | 5s violet | 35.00 | .30 |
| **135** | A35 | 7s red org ('30) | 18.00 | .40 |
| *138a* | A35 | 13s bister brn ('25) | 13.00 | .40 |
| *140a* | A35 | 25s olive green | 100.00 | 1.25 |
| **142** | A36 | 30s org & grn ('29) | 40.00 | .60 |
| **144** | A36 | 50s yel brn & dk bl ('29) | 17.50 | .90 |
| *145a* | A36 | 1y yel grn & mar | 140.00 | 1.10 |
| | | *Nos. 127a-145a (11)* | 378.75 | 10.05 |

See Nos. 212-213, 239-241, 243, 245, 249-252, 255. For overprints see Nos. C1-C2, M2-M5, Offices in China, 22-47.

Ceremonial Cap — A37

Imperial Throne — A38

Enthronement Hall, Kyoto — A39

***Perf. 12½***

**1915, Nov. 10** **Typo.** **Unwmk.**

| | | | | |
|---|---|---|---|---|
| **148** | A37 | 1½s red & blk | 4.00 | .80 |
| **149** | A38 | 3s orange & vio | 5.50 | 1.25 |

**Engr.**

***Perf. 12x12½***

| | | | | |
|---|---|---|---|---|
| **150** | A39 | 4s carmine rose | 22.50 | 14.00 |
| **151** | A39 | 10s ultra | 42.50 | 18.00 |
| | | *Nos. 148-151 (4)* | 74.50 | 34.05 |

Enthronement of Emperor Yoshihito.

Mandarin Duck — A40

Ceremonial Cap — A41

**1916, Nov. 3** **Typo.** ***Perf. 12½***

| | | | | |
|---|---|---|---|---|
| **152** | A40 | 1½s grn, red & yel | 4.25 | 1.75 |
| **153** | A40 | 3s red & yellow | 8.00 | 2.00 |
| **154** | A41 | 10s ultra & dk bl | 800.00 | 300.00 |

Nomination of the Prince Heir Apparent, later Emperor Hirohito.

A42

Dove and Olive Branch — A43

***Perf. 12, 12½, 13½x13***

**1919, July 1** **Engr.**

| | | | | |
|---|---|---|---|---|
| **155** | A42 | 1½s dark brown | 3.00 | 1.25 |
| **156** | A43 | 3s gray green | 3.25 | 2.00 |
| **157** | A42 | 4s rose | 9.00 | 6.50 |
| **158** | A43 | 10s dark blue | 25.00 | 17.50 |
| | | *Nos. 155-158 (4)* | 40.25 | 27.25 |

Restoration of peace after World War I.

Census Officer, A.D. 652 — A44

***Perf. 12½***

**1920, Sept. 25** **Typo.** **Unwmk.**

| | | | | |
|---|---|---|---|---|
| **159** | A44 | 1½s red violet | 7.50 | 5.50 |
| **160** | A44 | 3s vermilion | 9.00 | 6.00 |

Taking of the 1st modern census in Japan. Not available for foreign postage except to China.

Meiji Shrine, Tokyo — A45

**1920, Nov. 1** **Engr.**

| | | | | |
|---|---|---|---|---|
| **161** | A45 | 1½s dull violet | 3.75 | 1.75 |
| **162** | A45 | 3s rose | 3.75 | 1.75 |

Dedication of the Meiji Shrine. Not available for foreign postage except to China.

National and Postal Flags — A46

Ministry of Communications Building, Tokyo — A47

**Typographed (A46), Engraved (A47)**

**1921, Apr. 20** ***Perf. 12½, 13x13½***

| | | | | |
|---|---|---|---|---|
| **163** | A46 | 1½s gray grn & red | 3.25 | 1.75 |
| **164** | A47 | 3s violet brn | 4.00 | 2.25 |
| **165** | A46 | 4s rose & red | 47.50 | 37.50 |
| **166** | A47 | 10s dark blue | 275.00 | 185.00 |
| | | *Nos. 163-166 (4)* | 329.75 | 226.50 |

50th anniv. of the establishment of postal service and Japanese postage stamps.

Battleships "Katori" and "Kashima" — A48

**1921, Sept. 3** **Litho.** ***Perf. 12½***

| | | | | |
|---|---|---|---|---|
| **167** | A48 | 1½s violet | 3.25 | 1.75 |
| **168** | A48 | 3s olive green | 3.00 | 1.75 |
| **169** | A48 | 4s rose red | 35.00 | 20.00 |
| **170** | A48 | 10s deep blue | 47.50 | 27.50 |
| | | *Nos. 167-170 (4)* | 88.75 | 51.00 |

Return of Crown Prince Hirohito from his European visit.

Mount Fuji — A49

**Granite Paper**

**Size: 18½x22mm ("New Die")**

***Perf. 13x13½***

**1930-37** **Typo.** **Wmk. 141**

| | | | | |
|---|---|---|---|---|
| **171** | A49 | 4s green ('37) | 4.25 | .80 |
| **172** | A49 | 4s orange | 12.00 | .50 |
| **174** | A49 | 8s olive green | 19.00 | .45 |
| *175a* | A49 | 20s blue ('37) | 30.00 | 30.00 |
| **176** | A49 | 20s brown violet | 85.00 | .50 |
| | | *Nos. 171-176 (5)* | 150.25 | 32.25 |

**1922-29**

**Size: 19x22½mm ("Old Die")**

| | | | | |
|---|---|---|---|---|
| *171a* | A49 | 4s green | 12.00 | 3.00 |
| *172a* | A49 | 4s orange ('29) | 110.00 | 11.00 |
| **173** | A49 | 8s rose | 22.50 | 7.50 |
| *174a* | A49 | 8s olive green ('29) | 275.00 | 90.00 |
| **175** | A49 | 20s deep blue | 35.00 | 1.00 |
| *176a* | A49 | 20s brown vio ('29) | 110.00 | 2.25 |
| | | *Nos. 171a-176a (6)* | 564.50 | 114.75 |

See Nos. 242, 246, 248.

Mt. Niitaka, Taiwan — A50

***Perf. 12½***

**1923, Apr. 16** **Unwmk.** **Engr.**

| | | | | |
|---|---|---|---|---|
| **177** | A50 | 1½s orange | 12.50 | 9.50 |
| **178** | A50 | 3s dark violet | 17.50 | 8.50 |

1st visit of Crown Prince Hirohito to Taiwan. The stamps were sold only in Taiwan, but were valid throughout the empire.

Cherry Blossoms A51

Sun and Dragonflies A52

**Without Gum; Granite Paper**

**1923 Wmk. 142 Litho. *Imperf.***

| | | | | |
|---|---|---|---|---|
| **179** | A51 | ½s gray | 4.50 | 4.25 |
| **180** | A51 | 1½s lt blue | 6.75 | 2.00 |
| **181** | A51 | 2s red brown | 8.00 | 2.00 |
| **182** | A51 | 3s brt rose | 3.75 | 1.25 |
| **183** | A51 | 4s gray green | 40.00 | 32.50 |
| **184** | A51 | 5s dull violet | 17.50 | 2.00 |
| **185** | A51 | 8s red orange | 65.00 | 45.00 |
| **186** | A52 | 10s deep brown | 40.00 | 2.00 |
| **187** | A52 | 20s deep blue | 60.00 | 2.50 |
| | | *Nos. 179-187 (9)* | 245.50 | 93.50 |

Nos. 179-187 exist rouletted and with various perforations. These were made privately.

Empress Jingo — A53

**Granite Paper**

***Perf. 12, 13x13½***

**1924 Engr. Wmk. 141**

| | | | | |
|---|---|---|---|---|
| **188** | A53 | 5y gray green | 275.00 | 4.00 |
| **189** | A53 | 10y dull violet | 450.00 | 3.25 |

See Nos. 253-254.

Cranes — A54

Phoenix — A55

***Perf. 10½ to 13½ and Compound***

**1925, May 10 Litho. Unwmk.**

| | | | | |
|---|---|---|---|---|
| **190** | A54 | 1½s gray violet | 2.25 | 1.75 |
| **191** | A55 | 3s silver & brn org | 7.50 | 3.75 |
| *a.* | | Vert. pair, imperf. btwn. | 425.00 | |
| **192** | A54 | 8s light red | 30.00 | 19.00 |
| **193** | A55 | 20s sil & gray grn | 67.50 | 57.50 |
| | | *Nos. 190-193 (4)* | 107.25 | 82.00 |

25th wedding anniv. of the Emperor Yoshihito (Taisho) and Empress Sadako.

Mt. Fuji — A56

Yomei Gate, Nikko — A57

Nagoya Castle — A58

**Granite Paper**

***Perf. 13½x13***

**1926-37 Typo. Wmk. 141**

| | | | | |
|---|---|---|---|---|
| **194** | A56 | 2s green | 3.25 | .25 |
| **195** | A57 | 6s carmine | 15.00 | .60 |
| **196** | A58 | 10s dark blue | 15.00 | .25 |
| **197** | A58 | 10s carmine ('37) | 12.00 | *20.00* |
| | | *Nos. 194-197 (4)* | 45.25 | 21.10 |

See Nos. 244, 247. For surcharges see People's Republic of China No. 2L5-2L6.

Baron Hisoka Maeshima — A59

Map of World on Mollweide's Projection — A60

***Perf. 12½, 13x13½***

**1927, June 20 Unwmk.**

| | | | | |
|---|---|---|---|---|
| **198** | A59 | 1½s lilac | 3.75 | 2.00 |
| **199** | A59 | 3s olive green | 3.75 | 2.00 |
| **200** | A60 | 6s carmine rose | 62.50 | 55.00 |
| **201** | A60 | 10s blue | 80.00 | 55.00 |
| | | *Nos. 198-201 (4)* | 150.00 | 114.00 |

50th anniv. of Japan's joining the UPU. Baron Maeshima (1835-1919) organized Japan's modern postal system and was postmaster general.

Phoenix — A61

Enthronement Hall, Kyoto — A62

**Yellow Paper**

**1928, Nov. 10 Engr. *Perf. 12½***

| | | | | |
|---|---|---|---|---|
| **202** | A61 | 1½s deep green | 1.25 | .85 |
| **203** | A62 | 3s red violet | 1.25 | .95 |
| **204** | A61 | 6s carmine rose | 5.50 | 3.25 |
| **205** | A62 | 10s deep blue | 6.00 | 3.75 |
| | | *Nos. 202-205 (4)* | 14.00 | 8.80 |

Enthronement of Emperor Hirohito.

Great Shrines of Ise — A63

**1929, Oct. 2 *Perf. 12½***

| | | | | |
|---|---|---|---|---|
| **206** | A63 | 1½s gray violet | 2.25 | 1.50 |
| **207** | A63 | 3s carmine | 2.75 | 2.10 |

58th rebuilding of the Ise Shrines.

Map of Japanese Empire — A64

**1930, Sept. 25 Unwmk.**

| | | | | |
|---|---|---|---|---|
| **208** | A64 | 1½s deep violet | 3.50 | 1.75 |
| **209** | A64 | 3s deep red | 4.00 | 2.50 |

2nd census in the Japanese Empire.

Meiji Shrine — A65

**1930, Nov. 1 Litho.**

| | | | | |
|---|---|---|---|---|
| **210** | A65 | 1½s green | 2.75 | 2.25 |
| **211** | A65 | 3s brown org | 3.75 | 2.75 |

10th anniv. of dedication of Meiji Shrine.

**Coil Stamps**

**Wmk. Zigzag Lines (141)**

**1933 Typo. *Perf. 13 Horiz.***

| | | | | |
|---|---|---|---|---|
| **212** | A34 | 1½s light blue | 22.50 | 22.50 |
| **213** | A34 | 3s rose | 34.00 | 34.00 |

Japanese Red Cross Badge — A66

Red Cross Building, Tokyo — A67

***Perf. 12½***

**1934, Oct. 1 Engr. Unwmk.**

| | | | | |
|---|---|---|---|---|
| **214** | A66 | 1½s green & red | 2.25 | 1.90 |
| **215** | A67 | 3s dull vio & red | 2.50 | 2.50 |
| **216** | A66 | 6s dk car & red | 13.50 | 10.00 |
| **217** | A67 | 10s blue & red | 16.50 | 8.00 |
| | | *Nos. 214-217 (4)* | 34.75 | 22.40 |

15th International Red Cross Congress. Sheets of 20 with commemorative marginal inscription. One side of sheet is perf. 13.

White Tower of Liaoyang and Warship "Hiei" — A68

Akasaka Detached Palace, Tokyo — A69

**1935, Apr. 2**

| | | | | |
|---|---|---|---|---|
| **218** | A68 | 1½s olive green | 1.75 | 1.50 |
| **219** | A69 | 3s red brown | 3.25 | 1.75 |
| **220** | A68 | 6s carmine | 11.00 | 8.00 |
| **221** | A69 | 10s blue | 14.50 | 10.00 |
| | | *Nos. 218-221 (4)* | 30.50 | 21.25 |

Visit of Emperor Kang Teh of Manchukuo (Henry Pu-yi) to Tokyo, April 6, 1935. Four sheets of 20 each with commemorative marginal inscription. One side of sheet is perf. 13. Value, set of 4, $900.

Mt. Fuji — A70

**Granite Paper**

**1935 Typo. *Perf. 13x13½***

| | | | | |
|---|---|---|---|---|
| **222** | A70 | 1½s rose carmine | 11.50 | .75 |
| *a.* | | Miniature sheet of 20 | 700.00 | 500.00 |

Issued to pay postage on New Year's cards from Dec. 1-31, 1935. After Jan. 1, 1936, used for ordinary letter postage. No. 222 was issued in sheets of 100.

Mt. Fuji A71

Fuji from Lake Ashi A72

Fuji from Lake Kawaguchi — A73

Fuji from Mishima A74

**Granite Paper**

**1936, July 10 Photo. Wmk. 141**

| | | | | |
|---|---|---|---|---|
| **223** | A71 | 1½s red brown | 3.75 | 3.50 |
| **224** | A72 | 3s dark green | 4.75 | 4.25 |
| **225** | A73 | 6s carmine rose | 12.50 | 11.00 |
| **226** | A74 | 10s dark blue | 13.50 | 13.00 |
| | | *Nos. 223-226 (4)* | 34.50 | 31.75 |

Fuji-Hakone National Park.

Dove, Map of Manchuria and Kwantung — A75

Shinto Shrine, Port Arthur — A76

Headquarters of Kwantung Government A77

**Granite Paper**

**1936, Sept. 1 Litho. *Perf. 12½***

| | | | | |
|---|---|---|---|---|
| **227** | A75 | 1½s gray violet | 17.50 | 17.50 |
| **228** | A76 | 3s red brown | 21.00 | 20.00 |
| **229** | A77 | 10s dull green | 190.00 | 160.00 |
| | | *Nos. 227-229 (3)* | 228.50 | 197.50 |

30th anniv. of Japanese administration of Kwantung Leased Territory and the South Manchuria Railway Zone.

Imperial Diet Building A78

Grand Staircase A79

**1936, Nov. 7 Engr. *Perf. 13***

| | | | | |
|---|---|---|---|---|
| **230** | A78 | 1½s green | 2.25 | 2.00 |
| **231** | A79 | 3s brown vio | 2.75 | 2.25 |
| **232** | A79 | 6s carmine | 7.50 | 6.50 |
| **233** | A78 | 10s blue | 14.00 | 10.00 |
| | | *Nos. 230-233 (4)* | 26.50 | 20.75 |

Opening of the new Diet Building, Tokyo.

"Wedded Rocks," Futamigaura — A80

**1936, Dec. 10** **Photo.**

| | | | | |
|---|---|---|---|---|
| 234 | A80 | 1½s rose carmine | 4.00 | .40 |

Issued to pay postage on New Year's greeting cards.

### Types of 1913-26

***Perf. 13½x13, 13x13½***

**1937** **Typo.** **Wmk. 257**

| | | | | |
|---|---|---|---|---|
| 239 | A34 | ½s brown | 3.75 | 2.75 |
| 240 | A34 | 1s orange yel | 7.00 | 4.50 |
| 241 | A34 | 3s rose | 3.25 | .55 |
| 242 | A49 | 4s green | 8.00 | .40 |
| 243 | A35 | 5s violet | 11.00 | .40 |
| 244 | A57 | 6s crimson | 14.50 | 2.75 |
| 245 | A35 | 7s red org | 12.50 | .40 |
| 246 | A49 | 8s olive bister | 18.50 | 2.00 |
| 247 | A58 | 10s carmine | 12.50 | .40 |
| 248 | A49 | 20s blue | 20.00 | .60 |
| 249 | A35 | 25s olive grn | 80.00 | 3.75 |
| 250 | A36 | 30s org & grn | 50.00 | 1.00 |
| 251 | A36 | 50s brn org & dk bl | 250.00 | 2.75 |
| 252 | A36 | 1y yel grn & mar | 140.00 | 1.50 |
| | | *Nos. 239-252 (14)* | 631.00 | 23.75 |

**Engr.**

| | | | | |
|---|---|---|---|---|
| 253 | A53 | 5y gray green | 400.00 | 12.50 |
| 254 | A53 | 10y dull violet | 550.00 | 10.00 |

For overprint see People's Republic of China No. 2L6.

### Coil Stamps

**1938** **Typo.** ***Perf. 13 Horiz.***

| | | | | |
|---|---|---|---|---|
| 255 | A34 | 3s rose | 7.50 | 7.50 |

New Year's Decoration — A81

**1937, Dec. 15** **Photo.** ***Perf. 13***

| | | | | |
|---|---|---|---|---|
| 256 | A81 | 2s scarlet | 7.00 | .50 |

Issued to pay postage on New Year's cards, later for ordinary use.

Trading Ship A82

Harvesting A83

Gen. Maresuke Nogi — A84

Power Plant — A85

Admiral Heihachiro Togo A86

Mount Hodaka A87

Garambi Lighthouse, Taiwan — A88

Diamond Mountains, Korea — A89

Meiji Shrine, Tokyo — A90

Yomei Gate, Nikko — A91

Plane and Map of Japan — A92

Kasuga Shrine, Nara — A93

Mount Fuji and Cherry Blossoms A94

Horyu Temple, Nara A95

Miyajima Torii, Itsukushima Shrine — A96

Golden Pavilion, Kyoto — A97

Great Buddha, Kamakura A98

Kamatari Fujiwara A99

Plum Blossoms — A100

### Typographed or Engraved

**1937-45** **Wmk. 257** ***Perf. 13***

| | | | | |
|---|---|---|---|---|
| 257 | A82 | ½s purple | 1.25 | .75 |
| 258 | A83 | 1s fawn | 3.50 | .65 |
| 259 | A84 | 2s crimson | 1.00 | .25 |
| *a.* | | Booklet pane of 20 | 75.00 | |
| *b.* | | 2s pink, perf. 12 ('45) | 17.50 | 12.00 |
| *c.* | | 2s vermilion ('44) | 6.50 | 5.00 |
| 260 | A85 | 3s green ('39) | 1.00 | .30 |
| 261 | A86 | 4s dark green | 1.75 | .25 |
| *a.* | | Booklet pane of 20 | 22.50 | |
| 262 | A87 | 5s dark ultra ('39) | 2.25 | .25 |
| 263 | A88 | 6s orange ('39) | 4.75 | 2.00 |
| 264 | A89 | 7s deep green ('39) | 1.25 | .50 |
| 265 | A90 | 8s dk pur & pale vio ('39) | 1.50 | .65 |
| 266 | A91 | 10s lake ('38) | 7.00 | .35 |
| 267 | A92 | 12s indigo ('39) | 1.25 | 1.00 |
| 268 | A93 | 14s rose lake & pale rose ('38) | 1.40 | .50 |
| 269 | A94 | 20s ultra ('40) | 1.75 | .25 |
| 270 | A95 | 25s dk brn & pale brn ('38) | 1.25 | .35 |
| 271 | A96 | 30s pck blue ('39) | 3.25 | .30 |
| *a.* | | Imperf., pair | *900.00* | |
| 272 | A97 | 50s ol & pale ol ('39) | 1.75 | .30 |
| *a.* | | Pale olive (forest) omitted | *750.00* | *600.00* |
| 273 | A98 | 1y brn & pale brn ('39) | 6.50 | 1.00 |
| 274 | A99 | 5y dp gray grn ('39) | 35.00 | 3.25 |
| 275 | A100 | 10y dk brn vio ('39) | 32.50 | 2.00 |
| | | *Nos. 257-275 (19)* | 109.90 | 14.90 |

Nos. 257-261, 265, 268, 270, 272- 273 are typographed; the others are engraved.

### Coil Stamps

**1938-39** **Typo.** ***Perf. 13 Horiz.***

| | | | | |
|---|---|---|---|---|
| 276 | A82 | ½s purple ('39) | 7.00 | 7.00 |
| 277 | A84 | 2s crimson | 7.25 | 7.25 |
| 278 | A86 | 4s dark green | 7.75 | 7.75 |
| 279 | A93 | 14s rose lake & pale rose | 150.00 | 125.00 |
| | | *Nos. 276-279 (4)* | 172.00 | 147.00 |

See Nos. 329, 331, 333, 341, 351, 360 and 361. For surcharges see Nos. B4-B5, Burma 2N4-2N27, China-Taiwan, 8-9, People's Republic of China 2L3, 2L7, 2L9-2L10, 2L39, Korea 55-56. For overprints see Ryukyu Islands (Scott US Specialized catalogue) Nos. 2X1-2X2, 2X4-2X7, 2X10, 2X13-2X14, 2X17, 2X20, 2X23, 2X27, 2X29, 2X33-2X34, 3X2-3X7, 3X10-3X11, 3X14, 3X17, 3X19, 3X21, 3X23, 3X26-3X30, 5X1-5X3, 5X5-5X8, 5X10.

Mount Nantai — A101

Kegon Falls — A102

Sacred Bridge, Nikko A103

Mount Hiuchi A104

**Unwmk.**

**1938, Dec. 25** **Photo.** ***Perf. 13***

| | | | | |
|---|---|---|---|---|
| 280 | A101 | 2s brown orange | 1.00 | 1.00 |
| 281 | A102 | 4s olive green | 1.00 | 1.00 |
| 282 | A103 | 10s deep rose | 10.00 | 7.50 |
| 283 | A104 | 20s dark blue | 10.00 | 7.50 |
| *a.* | | Souvenir sheet of 4, #280-283 | 90.00 | 80.00 |
| | | Never hinged | 140.00 | |
| | | *Nos. 280-283 (4)* | 22.00 | 17.00 |
| | | Set, never hinged | 40.00 | |

Nikko National Park.
No. 283a sold for 50s.

---

Many souvenir sheets were sold in folders. Values are for sheets without folders.

---

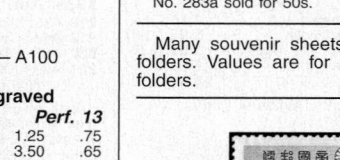

Mount Daisen A106

Yashima Plateau, Inland Sea A107

Abuto Kwannon Temple A108

Tomo Bay, Inland Sea A109

**1939, Apr. 20**

| | | | | |
|---|---|---|---|---|
| 285 | A106 | 2s lt brown | 1.00 | 1.00 |
| 286 | A107 | 4s yellow grn | 3.75 | 2.75 |
| 287 | A108 | 10s dull rose | 8.75 | 8.00 |
| 288 | A109 | 20s blue | 9.00 | 9.00 |
| *a.* | | Souvenir sheet of 4, #285-288 | 47.50 | 40.00 |
| | | Never hinged | 65.00 | |
| | | *Nos. 285-288 (4)* | 22.50 | 20.75 |
| | | Set, never hinged | 37.50 | |

Daisen and Inland Sea National Parks.
No. 288a sold for 50s.

View from Kuju Village, Kyushu A111

Mount Naka A112

Crater of Mount Naka A113

Volcanic Cones of Mt. Aso A114

**1939, Aug. 15**

| | | | | |
|---|---|---|---|---|
| 290 | A111 | 2s olive brown | 1.00 | 1.00 |
| 291 | A112 | 4s yellow green | 3.75 | 3.75 |
| 292 | A113 | 10s carmine | 20.00 | 17.50 |
| 293 | A114 | 20s sapphire | 25.00 | 22.50 |
| *a.* | | Souvenir sheet of 4, #290-293 | 145.00 | 145.00 |
| | | Never hinged | 210.00 | |
| | | *Nos. 290-293 (4)* | 49.75 | 44.75 |
| | | Set, never hinged | 95.00 | |

Aso National Park. No. 293a sold for 50s.

Globe — A116

Tsunetami Sano — A117

**1939, Nov. 15** ***Perf. 12½***

**Cross in Carmine**

| | | | | |
|---|---|---|---|---|
| 295 | A116 | 2s brown | 1.90 | 1.75 |
| 296 | A117 | 4s yellow green | 2.25 | 2.25 |
| 297 | A116 | 10s crimson | 9.00 | 8.50 |
| 298 | A117 | 20s sapphire | 9.00 | 8.50 |
| | | *Nos. 295-298 (4)* | 22.15 | 21.00 |
| | | Set, never hinged | 37.50 | |

Intl. Red Cross Society founding, 75th anniv.

Sacred Golden Kite — A118

Mount Takachiho — A119

Five Ayu Fish and Sake Jar — A120

Kashiwara Shrine — A121

**1940 Engr. *Perf. 12***

| | | | | |
|---|---|---|---|---|
| **299** | A118 | 2s brown orange | 1.00 | 1.00 |
| **300** | A119 | 4s dark green | .60 | .60 |
| **301** | A120 | 10s dark carmine | 4.50 | 4.50 |
| **302** | A121 | 20s dark ultra | 1.75 | 1.75 |
| | | *Nos. 299-302 (4)* | 7.85 | 7.85 |
| | | Set, never hinged | 12.50 | |

2,600th anniv. of the legendary date of the founding of Japan.

Mt. Hokuchin, Hokkaido A122

Mt. Asahi, Hokkaido A123

Sounkyo Gorge — A124

Tokachi Mountain Range A125

**1940, Apr. 20 Photo. *Perf. 13***

| | | | | |
|---|---|---|---|---|
| **303** | A122 | 2s brown | 1.00 | 1.00 |
| **304** | A123 | 4s yellow green | 3.00 | 3.00 |
| **305** | A124 | 10s carmine | 10.00 | 10.00 |
| **306** | A125 | 20s sapphire | 12.50 | 12.50 |
| *a.* | | Souvenir sheet of 4, #303-306 | 185.00 | 175.00 |
| | | Never hinged | 350.00 | |
| | | *Nos. 303-306 (4)* | 26.50 | 26.50 |
| | | Set, never hinged | 55.00 | |

Daisetsuzan National Park. No. 306a sold for 50s.

Mt. Karakuni, Kyushu A127

Mt. Takachiho A128

Torii of Kirishima Shrine A129

Lake of the Six Kwannon A130

**1940, Aug. 21**

| | | | | |
|---|---|---|---|---|
| **308** | A127 | 2s brown | 1.00 | 1.00 |
| **309** | A128 | 4s green | 1.25 | 1.25 |
| **310** | A129 | 10s carmine | 10.00 | 10.00 |
| **311** | A130 | 20s deep ultra | 13.00 | 13.00 |
| *a.* | | Souvenir sheet of 4, #308-311 | 240.00 | 225.00 |
| | | Never hinged | 360.00 | |
| | | *Nos. 308-311 (4)* | 25.25 | 25.25 |
| | | Set, never hinged | 55.00 | |

Kirishima National Park.
No. 311a sold for 50s.

Education Minister with Rescript on Education A132

Characters Signifying Loyalty and Filial Piety A133

**1940, Oct. 25 Engr. *Perf. 12½***

| | | | | |
|---|---|---|---|---|
| **313** | A132 | 2s purple | 1.00 | 1.00 |
| **314** | A133 | 4s green | 1.40 | 1.40 |
| | | Set, never hinged | 4.00 | |

50th anniv. of the imperial rescript on education, given by Emperor Meiji to clarify Japan's educational policy.

Mt. Daiton, Taiwan A134

Central Peak of Mt. Niitaka A135

Buddhist Temple on Mt. Kwannon A136

View from Mt. Niitaka A137

**1941, Mar. 10 Photo. *Perf. 13***

| | | | | |
|---|---|---|---|---|
| **315** | A134 | 2s brown | 1.25 | 1.25 |
| **316** | A135 | 4s brt green | 2.50 | 2.50 |
| **317** | A136 | 10s rose red | 7.00 | 7.00 |
| **318** | A137 | 20s brilliant ultra | 9.00 | 9.00 |
| *a.* | | Souv. sheet of 4, #315-318 | 125.00 | 125.00 |
| | | Never hinged | 175.00 | |
| | | *Nos. 315-318 (4)* | 19.75 | 19.75 |
| | | Set, never hinged | 47.50 | |

Daiton and Niitaka-Arisan National Parks.
No. 318a sold with No. 323a in same folder for 90s.

Seisui Precipice, East Taiwan Coast — A139

Taroko Gorge — A141

Mt. Tsugitaka A140

Upper River Takkiri District A142

**1941, Mar. 10**

| | | | | |
|---|---|---|---|---|
| **320** | A139 | 2s brown | 1.25 | 1.25 |
| **321** | A140 | 4s brt green | 2.50 | 2.50 |
| **322** | A141 | 10s rose red | 7.00 | 7.00 |
| **323** | A142 | 20s bril ultra | 9.00 | 9.00 |
| *a.* | | Souv. sheet of 4, #320-323 | 125.00 | 125.00 |
| | | Never hinged | 175.00 | |
| | | *Nos. 320-323 (4)* | 19.75 | 19.75 |
| | | Set, never hinged | 42.50 | |

Tsugitaka-Taroko National Park.
See note after No. 318.

War Factory Girl — A144

Building of Wooden Ship — A145

Hyuga Monument and Mt. Fuji A146

War Worker and Planes A147

Palms and Map of "Greater East Asia" A148

"Enemy Country Surrender" A149

Aviator Saluting and Japanese Flag A150

Torii of Yasukuni Shrine A151

Mt. Fuji and Cherry Blossoms A152

Torii of Miyajima A153

Garambi Lighthouse, Taiwan — A154

**Typographed; Engraved**

**1942-45 Wmk. 257 *Perf. 13***

| | | | | |
|---|---|---|---|---|
| **325** | A144 | 1s org brn ('43) | .50 | .40 |
| **328** | A145 | 2s green | .70 | .70 |
| **329** | A84 | 3s brown ('44) | 1.50 | .70 |
| **330** | A146 | 4s emerald | .45 | .30 |
| **331** | A86 | 5s brown lake | .50 | .40 |
| **332** | A147 | 6s lt ultra ('44) | .75 | .60 |
| *a.* | | Imperf., pair | | |
| **333** | A86 | 7s org ver ('44) | .50 | .40 |
| **334** | A148 | 10s crim & dl rose | 1.00 | .25 |
| *a.* | | Dull rose (map) omitted | 475.00 | 475.00 |
| **335** | A149 | 10s lt gray ('45) | 5.25 | 5.25 |
| **336** | A150 | 15s dull blue | 3.50 | 2.00 |
| **337** | A151 | 17s gray vio ('43) | 1.00 | .60 |
| **338** | A152 | 20s blue ('44) | 1.10 | .30 |
| **339** | A151 | 27s rose brn ('45) | 1.00 | 1.00 |
| **340** | A153 | 30s bluish grn ('44) | 3.25 | 2.00 |
| **341** | A88 | 40s dull violet | 2.00 | .30 |
| **342** | A154 | 40s dk violet ('44) | 2.75 | 2.50 |
| | | *Nos. 325,328-342 (16)* | 25.75 | 17.70 |

Nos. 325-335, 337-340 and 342 are typo. Nos. 336 and 341 are engr.

Nos. 329, 331, 333-334, 342 issued with and without gum. No. 335 issued only without gum. These are valued without gum.

Nos. 328, 342 exist with watermark sideways. No. 328 exists printed on gummed side.

Most stamps of the above series exist in numerous shades.

For overprints and surcharges see North Borneo Nos. N34, N37, N41-N42, People's Republic of China 2L4, 2L8, Korea 57-60, Ryukyu Islands (US Specialized) Nos. 2X3, 2X9, 2X12, 2X15-2X16, 2X18-2X19, 2X21-2X22, 2X24-2X26, 2X28, 3X1, 3X8-3X9, 3X12-3X13, 3X15-3X16, 3X18, 3X20, 3X25, 3X31, 4X1-4X2, 5X4.

Kenkoku Shrine, Hsinking — A155

Boys of Japan and Manchukuo A156

Orchid Crest of Manchukuo A157

**1942 Unwmk. Engr. *Perf. 12***

| | | | | |
|---|---|---|---|---|
| **343** | A155 | 2s brown | .85 | .85 |
| **344** | A156 | 5s olive | 1.00 | 1.00 |
| **345** | A155 | 10s red | 1.75 | 1.75 |
| **346** | A157 | 20s dark blue | 3.25 | *5.00* |
| | | *Nos. 343-346 (4)* | 6.85 | 8.60 |
| | | Set, never hinged | 11.50 | |

The 2s and 10s were issued Mar. 1 for the 10th anniv. of the creation of Manchukuo; 5s and 20s on Sept. 15 for the 10th anniv. of Japanese diplomatic recognition of Manchukuo.

C-59 Locomotive A158

**1942, Oct. 14** **Photo.**

**347** A158 5s Prus green 4.00 *6.00*
Never hinged 9.00

70th anniv. of Japan's 1st railway.

Yasukuni Shrine, Tokyo — A159

**1944, June 29** ***Perf. 13***

**348** A159 7s Prus green .85 .85
Never hinged 2.00

75th anniversary of Yasukuni Shrine.

Kwantung Shrine and Map of Kwantung Peninsula — A160

**1944, Oct. 1**

**349** A160 3s red brown 4.00 *10.00*
**350** A160 7s gray violet 4.50 *10.00*
Set, never hinged 14.00

Dedication of Kwantung Shrine, Port Arthur.

Sun and Cherry Blossoms A161

Sunrise at Sea and Plane A162

Coal Miners A163

Yasukuni Shrine A164

**Lithographed, Typographed**

**1945-47** **Wmk. 257** ***Imperf.***

**Without Gum**

| | | | | |
|---|---|---|---|---|
| **351** | A84 | 2s rose red | .90 | .90 |
| **352** | A161 | 3s rose carmine | .50 | .50 |
| **353** | A162 | 5s green | .60 | .40 |
| *a.* | | 5s blue | 11.00 | 7.50 |
| **354** | A149 | 10s lt gray | 11.50 | 11.50 |
| **354A** | A149 | 10s blue | 29.00 | |
| **355** | A152 | 10s red orange | .60 | .30 |
| **356** | A152 | 20s ultra ('46) | .65 | .35 |
| **357** | A153 | 30s brt blue ('46) | 2.50 | 1.25 |
| **358** | A163 | 50s dk brn ('46) | .75 | .30 |
| *a.* | | Souvenir sheet of 5 ('47) | 11.00 | *12.50* |
| **359** | A164 | 1y dp ol grn ('46) | 2.00 | 2.00 |
| **360** | A99 | 5y dp gray grn | 7.25 | 1.50 |
| **361** | A100 | 10y dk brown vio | 40.00 | 1.60 |
| | | *Nos. 351-361 (12)* | 96.25 | |
| | | *Nos. 351-354,355-361 (11)* | | 20.60 |

Nos. 351 and 354 are typographed. The other stamps in this set are printed by offset lithography.

No. 358a was issued with marginal inscriptions to commemorate the Sapporo (Hokkaido) Philatelic Exhibition, Nov., 1947.

Nos. 351 to 361 are on grayish paper, and Nos. 355 to 361 also exist on white paper.

Most stamps of the above series exist in numerous shades and with private perforation or roulette.

Beware of forgeries of Nos. 352, 353, 355-357 and 360 on unwatermarked paper.

See No. 404. For overprints see Ryukyu Islands (US Specialized) Nos. 2X8, 2X11, 2X30, 3X22, 4X3, 5X9.

Baron Hisoka Maeshima A165

Horyu Temple Pagoda A166

"Thunderstorm below Fuji," by Hokusai A167

"First Geese," Print by Hokusai A168

Kintai Bridge, Iwakuni A169

Kiyomizu Temple, Kyoto A170

Goldfish A171

Noh Mask A172

Plum Blossoms — A173

**Characters Read Right to Left**

**1946-47** **Wmk. 257** **Litho.** ***Imperf.***

**Without Gum**

| | | | | |
|---|---|---|---|---|
| **362** | A165 | 15s dark green | .70 | .70 |
| **363** | A166 | 30s dull lilac | 1.50 | .55 |
| **364** | A167 | 1y ultra | 3.00 | .35 |
| *a.* | | 1y deep ultramarine | 5.00 | .35 |
| *b.* | | 1y light blue | 2.75 | .35 |
| **365** | A168 | 1.30y olive bister | 4.00 | 1.25 |
| **366** | A169 | 1.50y dark gray | 4.50 | 1.00 |
| **367** | A170 | 2y vermilion ('47) | 3.75 | .40 |
| *a.* | | Souvenir sheet of 5 ('47) | 35.00 | *55.00* |
| **368** | A171 | 5y lilac rose | 9.50 | 1.25 |
| | | *Nos. 362-368 (7)* | 26.95 | 5.50 |

**Engr.**

| | | | | |
|---|---|---|---|---|
| **369** | A172 | 50y bister brn | 87.50 | 2.00 |
| **370** | A173 | 100y brn car ('47) | 87.50 | 2.00 |

***Perf. 13***

| | | | | |
|---|---|---|---|---|
| **371** | A172 | 50y bis brn, with gum ('47) | 87.50 | 1.25 |
| **372** | A173 | 100y brn car, with gum ('47) | 87.50 | 1.25 |

**Litho.**

***Perf. 13x13½, 12, 12x12½***

**373** A166 30s dull lilac 4.25 3.50

***Rouletted in Colored Lines***

**Typo.** **Unwmk.**

**With Gum**

**374** A166 30s deep lilac 2.50 *2.75*

Nos. 363, 368, 373 exist with and without gum, valued without gum, as are Nos. 371-372, 374.

No. 367a for the "Know Your Stamps" exhibition, Kyoto, Aug. 19-24, 1947. Size: 113x71mm

Nos. 362, 369 exist with watermark horizontal. Values, $27.50, $100, respectively.

Beware of Nos. 362-364, 364a, 364b, 365 and 367 on unwatermarked paper.

See Nos. 384-387, 512A. For overprints see Ryukyu Islands (US Specialized) Nos. 2X32, 3X24, 4X4.

**Catalogue values for unused stamps in this section, from this point to the end of the section, are for Never Hinged items.**

Medieval Postman's Bell A175

Baron Hisoka Maeshima A176

Design of First Japanese Stamp — A177

Communication Symbols — A178

***Perf. 12½, 13½x13***

**1946, Dec. 12** **Engr.** **Unwmk.**

| | | | | |
|---|---|---|---|---|
| **375** | A175 | 15s orange | 5.50 | 5.00 |
| **376** | A176 | 30s deep green | 7.00 | 6.00 |
| **377** | A177 | 50s carmine | 3.50 | 3.00 |
| **378** | A178 | 1y deep blue | 3.50 | 3.00 |
| *a.* | | Souvenir sheet of 4, #375-378, imperf. | 200.00 | 200.00 |
| | | Hinged | 125.00 | |
| | | *Nos. 375-378 (4)* | 19.50 | 17.00 |

Government postal service in Japan, 75th anniv.

No. 378a measures 180-183x125-127mm and is ungummed. There were 2 printings: I — The 4 colors were printed simultaneously. Arched top inscription and other inscriptions in high relief (no more than 2,000 sheets). II — Stamps were printed in one step, sheet inscriptions and 15s orange stamp in another. Lines of top inscription and inscriptions at lower left and lower right (flanking the 1y blue stamp) are much flatter (less raised) than the lines of the green, carmine and blue stamps, almost level with paper's surface (about 49,000 sheets). 1st printing value $800.

Mother and Child, Diet Building — A180

Bouquet of Japanese May Flowers — A181

**Wmk. 257**

**1947, May 3** **Litho.** ***Perf. 12½***

**Without Gum**

| | | | | |
|---|---|---|---|---|
| **380** | A180 | 50s rose brown | .75 | .50 |
| **381** | A181 | 1y brt ultra | 1.25 | 1.00 |
| *a.* | | Souv. sheet of 2, #380-381, imperf, without gum | 14.00 | 14.00 |
| *b.* | | As "a," 50s stamp omitted | 800.00 | |
| *c.* | | As "a," 1y stamp omitted | 800.00 | |

Inauguration of the constitution of May 3, 1947.

A182

**1947, Aug. 15** **Photo.** ***Perf. 12½***

**382** A182 1.20y brown 3.00 2.25
**383** A182 4y brt ultra 6.00 1.40

Reopening of foreign trade on a private basis.

The ornaments on No. 383 differ from those shown in the illustration.

**Types of 1946 Redrawn**
**Characters Read Left to Right**

**1947-48** **Wmk. 257** **Typo.** ***Perf. 13***

| | | | | |
|---|---|---|---|---|
| **384** | A166 | 30s deep lilac | 5.75 | 2.00 |
| **385** | A166 | 1.20y lt olive grn | 2.75 | .50 |
| *a.* | | Souvenir sheet of 15 | 225.00 | 225.00 |
| **386** | A170 | 2y vermilion ('48) | 12.50 | 1.50 |
| **387** | A168 | 4y lt ultra | 8.50 | .40 |
| | | *Nos. 384-387 (4)* | 29.50 | 4.40 |

No. 385a was issued with marginal inscriptions to commemorate the "Know Your Stamps" Exhibition, Tokyo, May, 1947.

On No. 386, the chrysanthemum crest has been eliminated and the top inscription centered.

Plum Blossoms — A183

**1947** **Typo.** ***Imperf.***

**Without Gum**

**388** A183 10y dk brown vio 50.00 1.75

This stamp is similar to type A100 but with new inscription "Nippon Yubin" (Japan Post), reading from left to right. The characters for the denomination are likewise transposed.

A184

A185

Baron Hisoka Maejima A186

Whaling A187

National Art, Imperial Treasure House, Nara — A188

**1947** **Typo.** ***Perf. 13x13½***

**389** A184 35s green 1.25 1.00

**Litho.**

| | | | | |
|---|---|---|---|---|
| **390** | A185 | 45s lilac rose | 1.60 | 1.40 |
| *a.* | | Imperf., pair | 1,500. | |
| *b.* | | Perf. 11x13½ | 12.00 | 10.00 |
| **391** | A186 | 1y dull brown | 6.50 | 1.00 |

**Typo.**

| | | | | |
|---|---|---|---|---|
| **392** | A187 | 5y blue | 11.50 | .30 |
| *a.* | | Imperf., pair | 650.00 | |
| *b.* | | Perf. 11x13½ | 32.50 | 4.75 |

**Engr.**

***Perf. 13½x13***

| | | | | |
|---|---|---|---|---|
| **393** | A188 | 10y lilac | 15.00 | .25 |
| *a.* | | Imperf., pair | | *3,000.* |
| | | *Nos. 389-393 (5)* | 35.85 | 3.95 |

No. 389 was produced on both rotary and flat press. Sheets of the rotary press printing have a border. Those of the flat press printing have none.

Lily of the Valley — A188a

**1947, Sept. 13 Unwmk. *Perf. 12½***
**394** A188a 2y dk Prus green 6.00 3.25

Relief of Ex-convicts Day, Sept. 13, 1947.

Souvenir Sheet

A189

**1947 Wmk. 257 Litho. *Imperf.***
**Without Gum**
**395** A189 Sheet of 5, ultra 4.75 4.75

Stamp Hobby Week, Nov. 1-7, 1947. Sheet size: 113½x71½mm, on white or grayish paper.
For overprint, see No. 408.

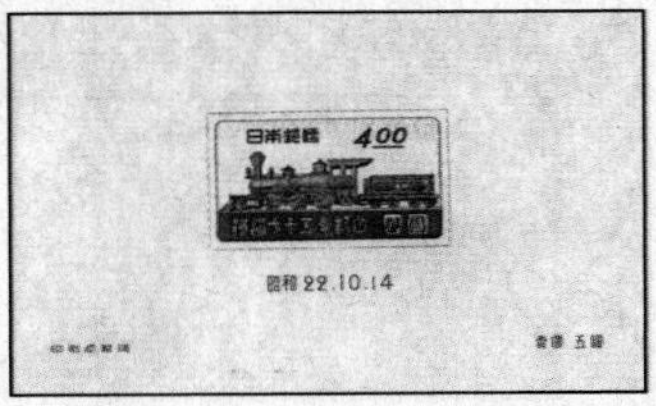
"Benkei," 1880 Locomotive — A190

**1947, Oct. 14 Unwmk. Engr.**
**Without Gum**
**396** A190 4y deep ultra 17.50 17.50

75th anniv. of railway service in Japan.

Hurdling — A191

Diving — A192

Discus Throwing A193

Volleyball A194

**1947, Oct. 25 Photo. *Perf. 12½***
**397** A191 1.20y red violet 8.50 7.50
**398** A192 1.20y red violet 8.50 7.50
**399** A193 1.20y red violet 8.50 7.50
**400** A194 1.20y red violet 8.50 7.50
*a.* Block of 4, #397-400 50.00 50.00

2nd Natl. Athletic Meet, held in Kanazawa, Oct. 30-Nov. 3.

Souvenir Sheets

A195

**1948 Wmk. 257 Litho. *Imperf.***
**Without Gum**
**401** A195 Sheet of 2, As #368, rose carmine 15.00 *15.00*

**Same, Inscribed with Three instead of Two Japanese Characters at Bottom Center**

**402** A195 Sheet of 2, #368 18.00 *17.50*

Philatelic exhibitions at Osaka (No. 401) and Nagoya (No. 402).
For Nos. 401-402 overprinted in green, see Nos. 407, 407b.

Stylized Tree — A196

***Perf. 12½***
**1948, Apr. 1 Unwmk. Photo.**
**403** A196 1.20y dp yellow grn 1.40 1.25

Forestation movement. Sheets of 30, marginal inscription.

**Coal Miners Type of 1946 and**

National Art Treasure, Nara — A197

***Perf. 13x13½***
**1948 Wmk. 257 Litho.**
**404** A163 50s dark brown 1.60 1.25

**Typo.**
***Perf. 13x13½***
**405** A197 10y rose violet 15.00 .30
*a.* Imperf., pair

See No. 515A.

School Children — A198

***Perf. 12½***
**1948, May 3 Unwmk. Photo.**
**406** A198 1.20y dark carmine 1.40 1.25

Reorganization of Japan's educational system. Sheets of 30, marginal inscription.

**No. 402 Overprinted at Top, Bottom and Sides with Japanese Characters and Flowers in Green**

**1948, Apr. 3 Souvenir Sheets**
**407** A195 Sheet of 2 70.00 40.00
*a.* Overprint inverted 150.00 150.00
*b.* Overprint on No. 401 125.00 125.00

Mishima Philatelic Exhibition, Apr. 3-9.

**No. 395 Overprinted at Top and Bottom With Japanese Characters in Plum**

**1948, Apr. 18**
**408** A189 Sheet of 5, ultra 25.00 25.00

Centenary of the death of Katsushika Hokusai, painter.

Sampans on Inland Sea, Near Suma — A199

**Engr. & Litho.**
**1948, Apr. 22 Unwmk. *Imperf.***
**Without Gum**
**409** A199 Sheet of 2, grn & rose car 16.00 11.00

Communications Exhib., Tokyo, Apr. 27-May 3, 1948. Sheet contains two 2y deep carmine stamps.
Sheet exists with green border omitted.

**1948, May 20 Without Gum**
**410** A199 Sheet of 2, ultra & rose car 20.00 18.00

Aomori Newspaper and Stamp Exhibition. Border design of apples and apple blossoms.

**Type A199 With Altered Border and Inscriptions**

**1948, May 23 Without Gum**
**411** A199 Sheet of 2, blue & rose car 20.00 18.00

Fukushima Stamp Exhibition. Border design of cherries and crossed lines.

Horse Race — A200

**1948, June 6 Photo. *Perf. 12½***
**412** A200 5y brown 3.50 1.75

25th anniv. of the enforcement of Japan's horse racing laws. Each sheet contains 30 stamps and 2 labels, with marginal inscription. Stamps with labels are worth more than values listed.

A201

A202

**Wmk. 257**
**1948, Sept. 10 Litho. *Perf. 13***
**413** A201 1.50y blue 4.00 .80
**414** A202 3.80y lt brown 11.50 5.25

**Souvenir Sheet**
**Without Gum**
***Imperf***
**415** Sheet of 4 35.00 35.00

Kumamoto Stamp Exhibition, Sept. 20. Souvenir sheet, issued Sept. 20, contains two each of 1.50y deep blue (A201) and 3.80y brown (A202).

Rectifying Tower — A203

***Perf. 12½***
**1948, Sept. 14 Photo. Unwmk.**
**416** A203 5y dark olive bister 4.50 2.75

Government alcohol monopoly.

Swimmer — A204

Runner — A205

Designs: No. 419, High jumper. No. 420, Baseball players. No. 421, Bicycle racers.

**1948**
**417** A204 5y blue 5.50 2.75
**418** A205 5y green 10.00 5.50
**419** A205 5y green 10.00 5.50
**420** A205 5y green 10.00 5.50
**421** A205 5y green 10.00 5.50
*a.* Block of 4, #418-421 60.00 60.00
*Nos. 417-421 (5)* 45.50 24.75

3rd Natl. Athletic Meet. Swimming matches held at Yawata, Sept. 16-19, field events, Fukuoka, Oct. 29-Nov. 3.
No. 417 was issued in sheets of 50 with labels. Stamps with labels are worth more than values listed.

"Beauty Looking Back," Print by Moronobu A206

**1948, Nov. 29 *Perf. 13***
**422** A206 5y brown 70.00 40.00
*a.* Sheet of 5 350.00 300.00
Sheet, hinged 250.00 —

Philatelic Week, Nov. 29-Dec. 5.
See Nos. 2418-2419.

**Souvenir Sheets**

**1948, Dec. 3 Without Gum *Imperf.***
**423** A206 5y brown, sheet of 1 55.00 40.00

Kanazawa and Takaoka stamp exhibitions.

Child Playing Hane-tsuki — A207

**1948, Dec. 13 Litho. *Perf. 13***
**424** A207 2y scarlet 6.00 5.00

Issued to pay postage on New Year's cards, later for ordinary use.

Farm Woman A208

Whaling A209

Miner
A210

Tea Picking
A211

Girl Printer
A212

Factory Girl with Cotton Bobbin
A213

Mt. Hodaka
A214

Planting
A215

Postman
A216

Blast Furnace
A217

Locomotive Assembly
A218

**Typographed, Engraved**

**1948-49 Wmk. 257** ***Perf. 13x13½***

**425** A208 2y green 3.50 .25
*a.* Overprinted with 4 characters in frame 1.40 1.00
*b.* As "a," overprint inverted *125.00*
**426** A209 3y lt grnsh bl ('49) 7.50 .30
**427** A210 5y olive bis 22.50 1.50
*a.* Booklet pane of 20 475.00 *15.00*
Hinged 175.00
**428** A211 5y blue grn ('49) 60.00 9.50
**429** A212 6y red org ('49) 12.50 .25
**430** A210 8y brn org ('49) 14.00 .25
*a.* Booklet pane of 20 *325.00* *10.00*
Hinged 175.00
**431** A213 15y blue 4.50 .25
**432** A214 16y ultra ('49) 15.00 7.00
**433** A215 20y dk grn ('49) 52.50 .25
**434** A216 30y violet bl ('49) 62.50 .25
**435** A217 100y car lake ('49) 600.00 4.50
**436** A218 500y dp blue ('49) 550.00 7.00
*Nos. 425-436 (12)* 1,405. 31.30
Set, hinged 550.00

No. 425a has a red control overprint of four characters ("Senkyo Jimu," or "Election Business") arranged vertically in a rectangular frame. Each candidate received 1,000 copies.

Nos. 432, 435-436 are engraved.

See Nos. 442, 511-512, 514-515, 518, 520, 521A-521B.

**Souvenir Sheets**

**Typo. and Litho.**

**1948, Oct. 16** ***Imperf.***

**437** A213 15y blue, sheet of 1 60.00 60.00

Nagano Stamp Exhibition, Oct. 16.

**1948, Nov. 2** ***Imperf.***

**438** A210 5y ol bis, sheet of 2 72.50 65.00

Shikoku Traveling Stamp Exhib., Nov. 1948.

Sampans on Inland Sea
A219

***Perf. 13x13½***

**1949 Wmk. 257 Engr.**

**439** A219 10y rose lake 30.00 20.00
**440** A219 10y car rose 22.50 17.50
**441** A219 10y orange ver 45.00 25.00
**442** A214 16y brt blue 11.00 6.25
*Nos. 439-442 (4)* 108.50 68.75
Set, hinged 60.00

Issued in sheets of 20 stamps with marginal inscription publicizing expositions at Takamatsu (No. 439), Okayama (No. 440) and Matsuyama (No. 441), Nagano Peace Exposition, Apr. 1-May 31, 1949 (No. 442).

Ice Skater — A221

Ski Jumper — A222

**1949 Unwmk. Photo.** ***Perf. 12***

**444** A221 5y violet 3.25 2.25
**445** A222 5y ultra 4.00 2.25

Winter events of the 4th Natl. Athletic Meet: skating at Suwa Jan. 27-30, skiing at Sapporo Mar. 3-6. Issued: No. 444, 1/27; No. 445, 3/3.

Steamer in Beppu Bay — A223

**1949, Mar. 10 Engr.** ***Perf. 13x13½***

**446** A223 2y carmine & ultra 1.50 1.25
**447** A223 5y green & ultra 5.75 1.75

Scene at Fair — A224

**1949, Mar. 15 Photo.** ***Imperf.***

**448** A224 5y brt rose 2.50 1.75
*a.* Perf. 13 4.00 2.50
*b.* Sheet of 20, imperf. 65.00 45.00

Issued to publicize the Japan Foreign Trade Fair, Yokohama, 1949.

No. 448a was printed in sheets of 50 (10x5); No. 448 in sheets of 20 (4x5) with marginal inscriptions (No. 448b).

Stylized Trees — A225

**1949, Apr. 1 Unwmk.** ***Perf. 12***

**449** A225 5y bright green 12.00 2.50

Issued to publicize the forestation movement.

Lion Rock
A226

Daiho-zan (Mt. Ohmine) — A227

Doro Gorge
A228

Bridge Pier Rocks
A229

**1949, Apr. 10 Photo.** ***Perf. 13***

**450** A226 2y brown 1.50 1.00
**451** A227 5y yellow grn 5.00 1.75
**452** A228 10y scarlet 22.00 14.00
**453** A229 16y blue 10.00 8.50
*a.* Souv. sheet of 4, #450-453, no gum 50.00 37.50
*b.* As "a," 10y stamp omitted
*Nos. 450-453 (4)* 38.50 25.25

Yoshino-Kumano National Park.

No. 453a sold for 40y.

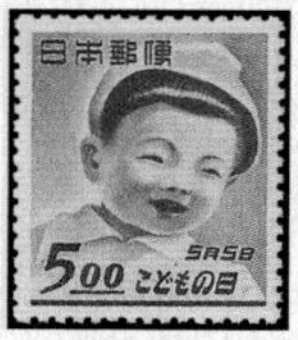
Boy — A230

**1949, May 5** ***Perf. 12***

**455** A230 5y rose brn & org 7.50 2.57
*a.* Orange omitted 275.00

Children's Day, May 5, 1949.

**Souvenir Sheets**

**1949, May 5** ***Imperf.***

**456** A230 5y rose brn & org, sheet of 10 450.00 300.00
Hinged 275.00

Children's Exhib., Inuyama, Apr. 1-May 31.

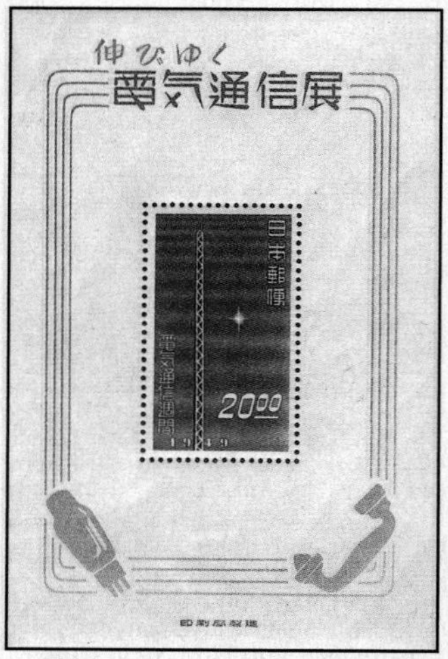

Radio Tower and Star — A231

**1949, May 11** ***Perf. 13***

**457** A231 20y dp blue 140.00 120.00
Hinged 75.00

Electrical Communication Week, May 11-18.

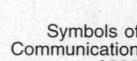

Symbols of Communication
A232

**Wmk. 257**

**1949, June 1 Engr.** ***Perf. 12***

**458** A232 8y brt ultra 4.50 2.25

Establishment of the Post Ministry and the Ministry of Electricity and Communication.

Central Meteorological Observatory, Tokyo — A233

**1949, June 1 Unwmk.** ***Perf. 12½***

**459** A233 8y deep green 4.50 2.25

75th anniv. of the establishment of the Central Meteorological Observatory.

Mt. Fuji in Autumn
A234

Lake Kawaguchi — A235

Mt. Fuji from Mt. Shichimen — A236

Shinobuno Village and Mt. Fuji — A237

**1949, July 15 Photo.** ***Perf. 13***

**460** A234 2y yellow brown 4.50 1.00
**461** A235 8y yellow green 5.00 1.75
**462** A236 14y carmine lake 2.50 .75
**463** A237 24y blue 9.00 1.00
*a.* Souv. sheet of 4, #460-463 47.50 47.50
*Nos. 460-463 (4)* 21.00 4.50

Fuji-Hakone National Park.

No. 463a sold for 55y.

Allegory of Peace
A238

Doves over Nagasaki — A239

*Perf. 13x13½, 13½x13*

**1949** **Photo.** **Unwmk.**

| | | | |
|---|---|---|---|
| **465** | A238 8y yellow brown | 11.003.00 | |
| **466** | A239 8y green | 6.50 | 3.00 |

Establishment of Hiroshima as the City of Eternal Peace and of Nagasaki as the International City of Culture. Issued: No. 465, 8/6; No. 466, 8/9.

Boy Scout — A240

**1949, Sept. 22** ***Perf. 13x13½***

| | | | |
|---|---|---|---|
| **467** | A240 8y brown | 9.00 | 3.00 |

Natl. Boy Scout Jamboree.

Pen Nib of Newspaper Stereotype Matrix — A241

**1949, Oct. 1** ***Perf. 13½x13***

| | | | |
|---|---|---|---|
| **468** | A241 8y deep blue | 7.00 | 3.00 |

Natl. Newspaper Week.

Racing Swimmer Poised for Dive — A242

Javelin Thrower — A243

**1949** ***Perf. 13½***

| | | | |
|---|---|---|---|
| **469** | A242 8y dull blue | 6.00 | 2.25 |

***Perf. 12***

| | | | |
|---|---|---|---|
| **470** | A243 8y shown | 8.00 | 3.00 |
| **471** | A243 8y Yacht Racing | 8.00 | 3.00 |
| **472** | A243 8y Relay Race | 8.00 | 3.00 |
| **473** | A243 8y Tennis | 8.00 | 3.00 |
| *a.* | Block of 4, #470-473 | 40.00 | *55.00* |
| | *Nos. 469-473 (5)* | 38.00 | 14.25 |

4th Natl. Athletic Meet. The swimming matches were held at Yokohama, Sept. 15-18 and the fall events at Tokyo, Oct. 30.

Issued: No. 469, 9/15; Nos. 470-473, 10/30.

Nos. 470-473 exist perf 12½. Values 50 percent above those of perf 12 copies.

No. 469 was issued in sheets with labels. Value, stamp with label, $22.50.

Map and Envelopes Forming "75" — A244

Symbols of UPU — A245

**1949, Oct. 10** **Engr.** ***Perf. 12, 13½***

| | | | |
|---|---|---|---|
| **474** | A244 2y dull green | 4.00 | 2.25 |
| **475** | A245 8y maroon | 5.00 | 2.25 |
| *a.* | Souv. sheet of 2, #474-475, imperf. | 7.00 | 7.00 |
| **476** | A244 14y carmine | 13.00 | 9.00 |
| **477** | A245 24y aqua | 19.00 | 11.00 |
| *a.* | Imperf., pair | | |
| | *Nos. 474-477 (4)* | 41.00 | 24.50 |

75th anniv. of the UPU.

No 475a was issued without gum.

Floating Zenith Telescope — A246

**1949, Oct. 30** **Photo.** ***Perf. 12***

| | | | |
|---|---|---|---|
| **478** | A246 8y dk blue grn | 5.50 | 2.25 |

50th anniv. of the Mizusawa Latitudinal Observatory.

"Moon and Geese," Print by Hiroshige — A247

**1949, Nov. 1** ***Perf. 13x13½***

| | | | |
|---|---|---|---|
| **479** | A247 8y purple | 150.00 | 55.00 |
| *a.* | Sheet of 5 | 800.00 | 450.00 |
| | Sheet, hinged | 240.00 | |

Postal Week, Nov. 1-7. See Nos. 2420-2421.

Dr. Hideyo Noguchi A248

Yukichi Fukuzawa A249

Soseki Natsume A250

Shoyo Tsubouchi A251

Danjuro Ichikawa — A252

Joseph Hardy Niijima — A253

Hogai Kano A254

Kanzo Uchimura A255

Ichiyo Higuchi — A256

Ogai Mori — A257

Shiki Masaoka — A258

Shunso Hishida — A259

Amane Nishi — A260

Kenjiro Ume — A261

Hisashi Kimura — A262

Inazo Nitobe — A263

Torahiko Terada — A264

Tenshin Okakura — A265

**1949-52** **Unwmk.** **Engr.** ***Perf. 12½***

| | | | |
|---|---|---|---|
| **480** | A248 8y green | 13.00 | 1.50 |
| *a.* | Imperf., pair | | |
| **481** | A249 8y deep olive ('50) | 6.50 | 1.50 |
| *a.* | Imperf., pair | | |
| **482** | A250 8y dk Prus grn ('50) | 6.50 | 1.50 |
| **483** | A251 8y Prus grn ('50) | 6.00 | 1.50 |
| *a.* | Imperf., pair | | |
| **484** | A252 8y dk violet ('50) | 15.00 | 5.00 |
| **485** | A253 8y vio brn ('50) | 6.00 | 1.50 |
| **486** | A254 8y dk green ('51) | 14.00 | 3.25 |
| **487** | A255 8y dp purple ('51) | 14.00 | 3.25 |
| **488** | A256 8y carmine ('51) | 22.50 | 3.50 |
| **489** | A257 8y vio brn ('51) | 34.00 | 3.50 |
| **490** | A258 8y choc ('51) | 23.00 | 3.50 |
| **491** | A259 8y dk blue ('51) | 17.50 | 3.50 |
| **492** | A260 10y dk green ('52) | 80.00 | 6.00 |
| **493** | A261 10y brn vio ('52) | 15.00 | 2.00 |
| **494** | A262 10y carmine ('52) | 6.00 | 2.00 |
| **495** | A263 10y dk grn ('52) | 8.00 | 2.00 |
| **496** | A264 10y choc ('52) | 7.00 | 2.00 |
| **497** | A265 10y dk blue ('52) | 8.00 | 2.00 |
| | *Nos. 480-497 (18)* | 302.00 | 49.00 |
| | Set, hinged | 100.00 | |

Tiger — A266

**1950, Feb. 1** **Photo.** ***Perf. 12***

| | | | |
|---|---|---|---|
| **498** | A266 2y dark red | 11.00 | 3.00 |

New Year, 1950. 6th prize (lottery), sheet of 5, value $190.

Microphones of 1925 and 1950 — A267

**1950, Mar. 21** ***Perf. 13***

| | | | |
|---|---|---|---|
| **499** | A267 8y ultra | 6.00 | 2.50 |

25th anniversary of broadcasting in Japan. Sheets of 20 with marginal inscription.

Dove and Olive Twig on Letter Box — A268

**1950, Apr. 20** ***Perf. 12***

| | | | |
|---|---|---|---|
| **500** | A268 8y dp yellow grn | 5.00 | 2.50 |

Day of Posts, Apr. 20.

Lake Akan and Mt. Akan A269

Lake Kutcharo, Hokkaido A270

Mt. Akan-Fuji A271

Lake Mashu A272

**1950, July 15** **Unwmk.** ***Perf. 13***

| | | | |
|---|---|---|---|
| **501** | A269 2y yellow brn | 2.50 | 1.25 |
| **502** | A270 8y dp yellow grn | 3.50 | 1.75 |
| **503** | A271 14y rose car | 16.00 | 7.00 |
| **504** | A272 24y brt blue | 18.00 | 7.75 |
| *a.* | Souv. sheet of 4, #501-504 | 55.00 | 40.00 |
| | *Nos. 501-504 (4)* | 40.00 | 17.75 |

Akan National Park.

No. 504a sold for 55y.

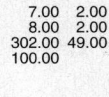

Gymnast on Rings — A273

Designs: No. 506, Pole vault. No. 507, Soccer. No. 508, Equestrian.

**1950, Oct. 28** *Perf. 13½x13*

| | | | |
|---|---|---|---|
| **505** | A273 8y rose brown | 40.00 | 17.50 |
| **506** | A273 8y rose brown | 40.00 | 17.50 |
| **507** | A273 8y rose brown | 40.00 | 17.50 |
| **508** | A273 8y rose brown | 40.00 | 17.50 |
| *a.* | Strip of 4, #505-508 | 175.00 | *140.00* |
| *b.* | Block of 4, #505-508 | 190.00 | *150.00* |
| | As "b," hinged | 85.00 | |

5th National Athletic Meet. Sheets of 20 stamps in which each horizontal row contains all four designs. Value, sheet $850.

**Types of 1947-49 and**

Ishiyama-dera Pagoda A274

Hisoka Maeshima A275

Long-tailed Cock of Tosa A276

Goddess Kannon A277

Himeji Castle A278

Nyoirin Kannon of Chuguji A280

Phoenix Hall, Byodoin Temple A279

***Perf. 13x13½, 13½x13 (14y)***

**1950-52 Typo. Unwmk.**

| | | | | |
|---|---|---|---|---|
| **509** | A274 | 80s carmine ('51) | 2.75 | 2.25 |
| *a.* | | Sheet of 1 | 11.00 | *13.00* |
| | | **Photo.** | | |
| **510** | A275 | 1y dk brn ('51) | 5.00 | 1.00 |
| *a.* | | Souvenir sheet of 4 | 22.50 | 17.50 |
| | | **Typo.** | | |
| **511** | A208 | 2y green ('51) | 2.50 | .25 |
| **512** | A209 | 3y lt grnsh bl ('51) | 67.50 | 2.25 |
| **512A** | A168 | 4y lt ultra ('52) | 45.00 | 4.00 |
| **513** | A276 | 5y dp grn & org brn ('51) | 7.50 | .25 |
| *a.* | | Orange brown omitted | 425.00 | |
| **514** | A212 | 6y red org ('51) | 9.00 | .75 |
| **515** | A210 | 8y dk org brn ('51) | 45.00 | 1.00 |
| **515A** | A197 | 10y rose vio ('51) | 77.50 | 6.50 |
| **516** | A277 | 10y red brn & lil ('51) | 27.50 | .25 |
| | | **Engr.** | | |
| **517** | A278 | 14y brn & car ('51) | 65.00 | 42.50 |
| *a.* | | Sheet of 1 | 80.00 | 75.00 |
| | | **Typo.** | | |
| **518** | A215 | 20y dk green ('51) | 70.00 | 2.50 |
| | | **Engr.** | | |
| **519** | A279 | 24y dp ultra | 52.50 | 22.50 |
| *a.* | | Sheet of 1 | 65.00 | 45.00 |
| | | **Typo.** | | |
| **520** | A216 | 30y vio bl ('52) | 225.00 | 3.00 |
| | | **Photo.** | | |
| **521** | A280 | 50y dk brn ('51) | 175.00 | 2.50 |
| | | Hinged | 85.00 | |
| *c.* | | Sheet of 1 | 375.00 | 375.00 |
| | | Hinged | 175.00 | |
| | | **Engr.** | | |
| **521A** | A217 | 100y car lake ('52) | 500.00 | 3.25 |
| **521B** | A218 | 500y dp blue ('52) | 450.00 | 3.75 |
| | | *Nos. 509-521B (17)* | 1,827. | 98.50 |

No. 510a for the 80th anniv. of Japan's postal service. On No. 512A, characters read from left to right.

Compare designs: A274 with A314c; A275 with A314a, A447, A563a; A277 with A332a; A278 with A373a; A279 with A385a; A280 with A314b and A565f.

Girl and Rabbit — A281

**1951, Jan. 1 Photo.** *Perf. 12*

**522** A281 2y rose pink 8.00 1.25

New Year Greetings 1951. 9th prize (lottery), sheet of 5, value $50.

See No. 2655a.

**Scenic Spots Issue**

Skiers on Mt. Zao
A282 A283

**1951, Feb. 15** *Perf. 13*

| | | | |
|---|---|---|---|
| **523** | A282 8y olive | 11.50 | 2.00 |
| **524** | A283 24y blue | 14.50 | 4.50 |

Tea Picking — A284

Mt. Fuji Seen from Nihon Plateau A285

Nihon-daira Plateau.

**1951, Apr. 2**

| | | | |
|---|---|---|---|
| **525** | A284 8y olive green | 12.00 | 2.75 |
| **526** | A285 24y bright blue | 75.00 | 20.00 |

Hot Springs, Hakone — A286

Lake Ashi, Hakone A287

**1951, May 25**

| | | | |
|---|---|---|---|
| **527** | A286 8y chestnut brown | 7.50 | 2.25 |
| **528** | A287 24y deep blue | 6.50 | 2.75 |

Senju Waterfall — A288

Ninai Waterfall A289

Akame 48 Waterfalls.

**1951, June 1**

| | | | |
|---|---|---|---|
| **529** | A288 8y deep green | 9.00 | 2.25 |
| **530** | A289 24y deep blue | 9.00 | 2.75 |

Pavilion, Wakanoura Bay — A290

Wakanoura Bay — A291

Wakanoura & Tomogashima.

**1951, June 25**

| | | | |
|---|---|---|---|
| **531** | A290 8y brown | 6.50 | 2.10 |
| **532** | A291 24y brt blue | 6.00 | 2.50 |

Uji River — A292

View from Uji Bridge A293

***Perf. 13x13½, 13½x13***

**1951, Aug. 1 Engr.**

| | | | |
|---|---|---|---|
| **533** | A292 8y brown | 6.50 | 2.10 |
| **534** | A293 24y deep blue | 6.00 | 2.50 |

Oura Catholic Church, Nagasaki — A294

Sofuku Temple A295

**1951, Sept. 15 Photo.** *Perf. 13½*

| | | | |
|---|---|---|---|
| **535** | A294 8y carmine rose | 8.50 | 2.10 |
| **536** | A295 24y dull blue | 7.00 | 2.50 |

Marunuma — A296

Sugenuma A297

**1951, Oct. 1**

| | | | |
|---|---|---|---|
| **537** | A296 8y rose violet | 10.00 | 2.10 |
| *a.* | Imperf., pair | | |
| **538** | A297 24y dull blue grn | 5.50 | 2.50 |

Kakuenpo (peak) — A298

Nagatoro Bridge A299

Shosenkyo Gorge.

**1951, Oct. 15**

| | | | |
|---|---|---|---|
| **539** | A298 8y brown red | 8.00 | 2.10 |
| **540** | A299 24y dp Prus grn | 8.50 | 2.50 |
| | *Nos. 523-540 (18)* | 217.50 | 62.25 |

Boy's Head and Seedling — A300

**1951, May 5** *Perf. 13½*

**541** A300 8y orange brown 22.50 2.25

Issued to publicize Children's Day, May 5, 1951.

Oirase River A301

Lake Towada A302

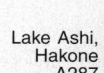

View from Kankodai A303

Mt. Hakkoda from Mt. Yokodake A304

**1951, July 20 Photo. *Perf. 13x13½***

**542** A301 2y brown 2.50 .95
**543** A302 8y green 10.00 1.40
**544** A303 14y dark red 11.50 4.75
**545** A304 24y blue 12.00 5.50
*a.* Souv. sheet of 4, #542-545 47.50 30.00
*Nos. 542-545 (4)* 36.00 12.60

Towada Natl. Park. No. 545a sold for 55y.

Chrysanthemum A305

National Flag A306

**1951, Sept. 9 *Perf. 13½***

**546** A305 2y orange brown 1.90 .95
**547** A306 8y slate blue & red 5.75 2.25
**548** A305 24y blue green 17.00 6.00
*Nos. 546-548 (3)* 24.65 9.20

Signing of the peace treaty of 1951.

Putting the Shot — A307

Hockey — A308

**1951, Oct. 27**

**549** A307 2y orange brown 3.50 1.75
**550** A308 2y gray blue 3.50 1.75
*a.* Pair, #549-550 10.00 8.00

6th Natl. Athletic Meet, Hiroshima, 10/27-31.

Okina Mask — A309

**1952, Jan. 16 Photo. *Perf. 13½x13***

**551** A309 5y crimson rose 14.00 1.25

New Year Greetings 1952

Sheets reproducing four of these stamps with Japanese inscriptions and floral ornament at left were awarded as sixth prize in the national lottery. Value $150.

Southern Cross from Ship — A310

Earth and Big Dipper — A311

**1952, Feb. 19**

**552** A310 5y purple 5.00 1.00
**553** A311 10y dark green 14.50 2.00

75th anniv. of Japan's admission to the UPU.

Red Cross and Lilies — A312

Red Cross Nurse — A313

**1952, May 1**

**554** A312 5y rose red & dk red 4.25 .95
**555** A313 10y dk green & red 10.00 2.00
*a.* Red cross omitted *500.00*
*b.* Imperf., pair *75.00*

75th anniv. of the formation of the Japanese Red Cross Society.

Goldfish — A314

A314a

A314b

A314c

**1952 *Perf. 13x13½***

**556** A314 35y red orange 10.00 .25
*a.* Imperf., pair

**Types of 1951**
**Redrawn; Zeros Omitted**
**Unwmk.**

**557** A314a 1y dark brown .55 .25
**558** A314b 50y dark brown 5.00 .30

**Typo.**

**559** A314c 4y dp cl & pale rose 1.75 .30
*a.* Background (pale rose) omitted

Ornamental frame and background added, denomination at upper left, Japanese characters at upper right.

Japanese Serow — A315

**Photo.**

**560** A315 8y brown .30 .25
*Nos. 556-560 (5)* 17.60 1.35

Mt. Yari — A316

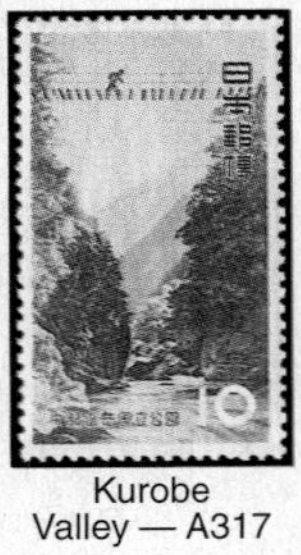
Kurobe Valley — A317

Mt. Shirouma A318

Mt. Norikura A319

**1952, July 5 *Perf. 13½x13, 13x13½***

**561** A316 5y brown 4.50 .50
**562** A317 10y blue green 22.50 1.75
**563** A318 14y bright red 5.75 3.00
**564** A319 24y bright blue 9.50 3.00
*a.* Souv. sheet of 4, #561-564, imperf. 100.00 60.00
*Nos. 561-564 (4)* 42.25 8.25

Japan Alps (Chubu-Sangaku) National Park. No. 564a sold for 60y.

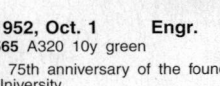

Yasuda Hall, Tokyo University — A320

**1952, Oct. 1 Engr. *Perf. 13***

**565** A320 10y green 16.00 2.00

75th anniversary of the founding of Tokyo University.

Yomei Gate, Nikko — A321

**1952, Oct. 15 Photo. *Perf. 13x13½***

**566** A321 45y blue 3.50 .25

Mountain Climber — A322

**1952, Oct. 18 Dated "1952"**

**567** A322 5y shown 6.00 1.50
**568** A322 5y Wrestlers 6.00 1.50
*a.* Pair, #567-568 17.50 9.00

7th Nat.l Athletic Meet, Fukushima, 10/18-22.

Mt. Azuma A323

Mt. Asahi A324

Mt. Bandai A325

Mt. Gatsun A326

**Unwmk.**

**1952, Oct. 18 Photo. *Perf. 13***

**569** A323 5y brown 3.75 .60
**570** A324 10y olive grn 11.50 1.50
**571** A325 14y rose red 4.50 2.25
**572** A326 24y blue 10.00 4.00
*a.* Souv. sheet of 4, #569-572, imperf. 80.00 60.00
*Nos. 569-572 (4)* 29.75 8.35

Bandai-Asahi National Park. No. 572a sold for 60y.

Kirin — A327

Flag of Crown Prince — A328

**Engr. and Photo.**

**1952, Nov. 10 *Perf. 13½***

**573** A327 5y red org & pur 1.90 .55
**574** A327 10y red org & dk grn 2.25 .80
**575** A328 24y deep blue 12.00 4.50
*a.* Souv. sheet of 3, #573-575, imperf. 70.00 *90.00*
*Nos. 573-575 (3)* 16.15 5.85

Issued to commemorate the nomination of Crown Prince Akihito as Heir Apparent.

No. 575a measures 130x129mm, and has a background design of phoenix and clouds in violet brown and blue. Sold for 50y.

Sambaso Doll — A329

***Perf. 13½x13***

**1953, Jan. 1 Photo. Unwmk.**

**576** A329 5y carmine 9.50 1.00

For postage on New Year's cards, later for ordinary use.

Sheets of 4 were awarded as 6th prize in the natl. lottery. Value $80.

First Electric Lamp in Japan — A330

**1953, Mar. 25**

**577** A330 10y brown 6.25 1.90

75th anniv. of electric lighting in Japan.

"Kintai Bridge," Print by Hiroshige — A331

Kintai Bridge as Rebuilt in 1953 — A332

**1953, May 3** ***Perf. 13***
578 A331 10y chestnut 6.50 2.10
579 A332 24y blue 6.00 3.00

**Kannon Type of 1951**
**Redrawn; Zeros Omitted**

A332a

**1953-54** **Typo.**
580 A332a 10y red brn & lil 4.00 .25
*a.* Booklet pane 10 + 2 labels (souvenir) ('54) 125.00 100.00
*b.* Bklt. pane 10 + 2 labels ('54) 67.50 60.00

No. 580a was issued in honor of Philatelic Week 1954. The inscriptions on the two labels are arranged in two columns of boldface characters.
On No. 580b, the left-hand label inscriptions are arranged in three columns of mixed heavy and thin characters.
See Nos. 611a-611b and 672.

Lake Shikotsu, Hokkaido
A333

Mt. Yotei
A334

**1953, July 25** **Photo.** ***Perf. 13***
581 A333 5y ultra 2.00 .55
582 A334 10y green 5.00 1.10
*a.* Souv. sheet of 2, #581-582, imperf., no gum 32.50 29.00

Shikotsu-Toya National Park.
No. 582a sold for 20 yen.

Akita Dog
A335

Cormorant Fishing
A336

**1953** **Unwmk.**
583 A335 2y gray .25 .25
**Engr.**
584 A336 100y dark red 35.00 .25
*a.* Imperf., pair *2,750.*

See No. 1622.

Futamigaura Beach — A337

Namikiri Coast
A338

**1953, Oct. 2** **Photo.**
585 A337 5y red 1.90 .55
586 A338 10y blue 3.75 1.10
*a.* Souv. sheet of 2, #585-586, imperf., no gum 20.00 17.50

Ise-Shima National Park.

Phoenix — A339

Design: 10y, Japanese crane in flight.

**1953, Oct. 12** **Engr.** ***Perf. 12½***
587 A339 5y brown carmine 2.75 1.10
**Photo.**
588 A339 10y dark blue 5.50 1.90

Nos. 587-588 were issued on the occasion of the return of Crown Prince Akihito from his visit to Europe and America. Issued in sheets of 20 with marginal inscription.

Rugby Match — A340

Judo — A341

**1953, Oct. 22** ***Perf. 13½***
589 A340 5y black 5.75 1.25
590 A341 5y blue green 5.75 1.25
*a.* Pair, #589-590 13.50 7.50

8th Natl. Athletic Meet, Matsuyama, Oct. 22-26.

Sky and Top of Observatory
A342

**1953, Oct. 29**
591 A342 10y dk gray blue 9.00 1.50

75th anniversary of the Tokyo Astronomical Observatory.

Mt. Unzen from Golf Course
A343

Mt. Unzen from Chijiwa Beach
A344

**1953, Nov. 20** ***Perf. 13***
592 A343 5y red 1.75 .55
593 A344 10y blue 4.50 1.10
*a.* Souv. sheet of 2, #592-593, imperf., no gum 20.00 17.50

Unzen National Park.

Toy Horse — A345

**1953, Dec. 25** ***Perf. 13½x13***
594 A345 5y rose 7.50 .80

New Year Greetings 1953
Issued to pay postage on New Year's cards, later for ordinary use. A sheet reproducing four of these stamps was awarded as sixth prize in the national lottery. Value, $47.50.

Racing Skaters — A346

**1954, Jan. 16**
595 A346 10y blue 4.50 1.40

World Speed Skating Matches for Men, Sapporo City, Jan. 16-17, 1954.

Golden Hall, Chusonji Temple — A347

**1954, Jan. 20**
596 A347 20y olive green 1.00 .25

Thread, Pearls, Gears, Buttons and Globe — A348

**1954, Apr. 10**
597 A348 10y dark red 3.25 1.00

International Trade Fair, Osaka, Apr. 10-23.

Little Cuckoo — A349

**1954, May 10** ***Perf. 13x13½***
598 A349 3y blue green .25 .25
*a.* Imperf., pair *500.00*

For stamp inscribed "NIPPON," see No. 1067.

Wrestlers
A350

**1954, May 22** **Engr.**
599 A350 10y deep green 2.75 1.00

World Free Style Wrestling Championship Matches, Tokyo, 1954.

Mt. Asama
A351

Mt. Tanikawa
A352

**1954, June 25** ***Perf. 13***
600 A351 5y dk gray brn 2.00 .55
601 A352 10y dk blue grn 3.50 1.10
*a.* Souvenir sheet of 2, #600-601, no gum 17.50 15.00

Jo-Shin-etsu National Park.

Table Tennis — A353

Archery — A354

**1954, Aug. 22** **Engr.** ***Perf. 12***
602 A353 5y dull brown 4.00 1.00
603 A354 5y gray green 4.00 1.00
*a.* Pair, #602-603 9.00 5.75

9th Natl. Athletic Meet, Sapporo, Aug. 22-26.

Morse Telegraph Instrument
A355

ITU Monument
A356

**1954, Oct. 13** ***Perf. 13x13½, 13½x13***
604 A355 5y dark purple brown 1.75 .55
605 A356 10y deep blue 4.75 1.10

75th anniv. of Japanese membership in the ITU.

Daruma Doll — A357

**1954, Dec. 20** **Photo.** ***Perf. 13½x13***
606 A357 5y black & red 5.25 .55

Sheets reproducing four of these stamps with Japanese inscriptions and ornaments were awarded as fifth prize in the national lottery. Value $37.50.

Mountain Stream, Tama Gorge — A358

Chichibu Mountains — A359

**1955, Mar. 1** **Engr.** ***Perf. 13***
607 A358 5y blue 1.50 .55
608 A359 10y red brown 1.90 .75
*a.* Souv. sheet of 2, #607-608, imperf., no gum 20.00 17.50

Chichibu-Tama National Park.

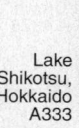

Bridge and Iris — A360

**1955, Mar. 15** *Perf. 13x13½*
**609** A360 500y brown purple 50.00 .60

Paper Carp as Flown on Boys' Day — A361

**Unwmk.**
**1955, May 16** **Photo.** *Perf. 13*
**610** A361 10y multicolored 4.25 1.10

15th congress of the International Chamber of Commerce, Tokyo, May 16-21, 1955.

Mandarin Ducks — A362

**1955-64**
**611** A362 5y lt bl & red brn .25 .25
*a.* Bklt. pane, 4 #611, 8 #580 ('59) *50.00*
*b.* Bklt. pane, 4 #611, 8 #725 ('63) *35.00* 17.00
*c.* Bklt. pane of 4 ('64) 4.25 2.75
*d.* Imperf., pair 1,400.

See Nos. 738, 881d, 914b.

Benten Cape — A363

Jodo Beach A364

**1955, Sept. 30**
**612** A363 5y deep green 1.40 .45
**613** A364 10y rose lake 1.90 .75
*a.* Souv. sheet of 2, #612-613, imperf., no gum 20.00 17.50

Rikuchu-Kaigan National Park.
No. 613a sold for 20y.

Gymnastics A365

Runners A366

**1955, Oct. 30** **Engr.**
**614** A365 5y brown lake 1.75 .75
**615** A366 5y bluish black 1.75 .75
*a.* Pair, #614-615 6.50 5.00

10th National Athletic Meet, Kanagawa Prefecture.
See Nos. 639-640, 657.

"A Girl Blowing Glass Toy," by Utamaro A367

**1955, Nov. 1** **Photo.**
**616** A367 10y multicolored 10.00 5.75

150th anniv. of the death of Utamaro, wood-cut artist, and to publicize Philatelic Week, Nov. 1955. Issued in sheets of 10.

Kokeshi Dolls — A368

**1955, Dec. 30** **Unwmk.** *Perf. 13*
**617** A368 5y olive grn & red 4.00 .80

New Year Greetings 1956
Sheets reproducing four of these stamps, were awarded as fifth prize in the New Year's lottery. Value, $35.

Table Tennis — A369

**1956, Apr. 2** *Perf. 13x13½*
**618** A369 10y red brown 1.25 .75

Intl. Table Tennis Championship, Tokyo, 4/2-11.

Judo — A370

**1956, May 2** *Perf. 13*
**619** A370 10y green & brn pur 1.50 .75

Issued to publicize the first World Judo Championship Meet, Tokyo, May 3, 1956.

Boy and Girl with Paper Carp A371

**1956, May 5**
**620** A371 5y lt blue & blk 1.10 .55

Establishment of World Children's Day, 5/5/56.

Water Plants, Lake Akan A372

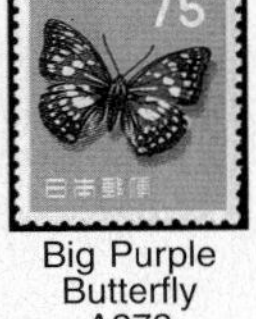

Big Purple Butterfly A373

**1956** **Unwmk.** *Perf. 13*
**621** A372 55y lt blue, grn & blk 12.50 .55
**622** A373 75y multicolored 7.00 .55

See Nos. 887A, 917.

**Castle Type of 1951**
**Redrawn; Zeros Omitted**

A373a

**1956** **Engr.** *Perf. 13½x13*
**623** A373a 14y gray olive 5.00 1.75

Osezaki Promontory — A374

Kujuku Island A375

**1956, Oct. 1** **Photo.**
**624** A374 5y red brown 1.00 .45

**Engr. & Photo.**
**625** A375 10y lt blue & indigo 1.25 .75
*a.* Souv. sheet of 2, #624-625, imperf., no gum 17.00 16.00

Saikai National Park.
No. 625a sold for 20y.

Palace Moat and Modern Tokyo A376

**1956, Oct. 1** **Engr.**
**626** A376 10y dull purple 1.90 .75

500th anniv. of the founding of Tokyo.

Sakuma Dam — A377

**1956, Oct. 15** **Unwmk.** *Perf. 13*
**627** A377 10y dark blue 1.90 .75

Completion of Sakuma Dam.

Long Jump A378

Basketball A379

**1956, Oct. 28** *Perf. 13½x13*
**628** A378 5y brown violet 1.00 .55
**629** A379 5y steel blue 1.00 .55
*a.* Pair, #628-629 3.00 2.50

11th Natl. Athletic Meet, Hyogo Prefecture.
See No. 658.

Kabuki Actor Ebizo Ichikawa by Sharaku A380

**1956, Nov. 1** **Photo.** *Perf. 13*
**630** A380 10y multicolored 8.50 5.50

Stamp Week. Sheets of 10.

Mount Manaslu A381

**1956, Nov. 3**
**631** A381 10y multicolored 3.00 1.60

Japanese expedition which climbed Mount Manaslu in the Himalayas on May 9 and 11, 1956.

Electric Locomotive and Hiroshige's "Yui Stage" — A382

**1956, Nov. 19** **Unwmk.** *Perf. 13*
**632** A382 10y dk ol bis, blk & grn 4.00 2.00

Electrification of Tokaido Line.

Cogwheel, Vacuum Tube and Ship — A383

**1956, Dec. 18** **Engr.**
**633** A383 10y ultra .90 .75

Japanese Machinery Floating Fair.

Toy Whale — A384

**1956, Dec. 20** **Photo.**
**634** A384 5y multicolored 2.00 .35
*a.* Imperf., pair

Sheets reproducing four of these stamps, with inscriptions and ornaments, were awarded as sixth prize in the national lottery. Value $13.50.

United Nations Emblem A385

**Photogravure and Engraved**
**1957, Mar. 8** **Unwmk.** *Perf. 13½x13*
**635** A385 10y lt blue & dk car .70 .55

Japan's admission to the UN, Dec. 18, 1956.

### Temple Type of 1950
### Redrawn; Zeros Omitted

A385a

**1957-59 Engr. *Perf. 13x13½***

| | | | | |
|---|---|---|---|---|
| **636** | A385a | 24y violet | 17.50 | 3.00 |
| **636A** | A385a | 30y rose lil ('59) | 45.00 | .90 |
| *b.* | | Imperf., pair | *6,000.* | 2,000. |

IGY Emblem, Penguin and "Soya" — A386

**1957, July 1 Photo. *Perf. 13***

**637** A386 10y blue, yel & blk 1.00 .50

International Geophysical Year.

Atomic Reactor — A387

**1957, Sept. 18 Engr. *Perf. 13***

**638** A387 10y dark purple .45 .25

Completion of Japan's atomic reactor at Tokai-Mura, Ibaraki Prefecture.

### Sports Type of 1955

No. 639, Girl on parallel bars. No. 640, Boxers.

**1957, Oct. 26 Unwmk. *Perf. 13***

| | | | | |
|---|---|---|---|---|
| **639** | A366 | 5y ultra | .35 | .25 |
| **640** | A366 | 5y dark red | .35 | .25 |
| *a.* | | Pair, #639-640 | 1.00 | .75 |

12th Natl. Athletic Meet, Shizuoka Prefecture.

"Girl Bouncing Ball," by Suzuki Harunobu A388

**1957, Nov. 1 Photo.**

**641** A388 10y multicolored 1.50 1.25

1957 Stamp Week. Issued in sheets of 10. See Nos. 646, 671, 728, 757.

Lake Okutama and Ogochi Dam — A389

**1957, Nov. 26 Engr. *Perf. 13½***

**642** A389 10y ultra .30 .25

Completion of Ogochi Dam, part of the Tokyo water supply system.

Modern and First Japanese Blast Furnaces A390

**1957, Dec. 1 Photo. Unwmk.**

**643** A390 10y orange & dk pur .25 .25

Centenary of Japan's iron industry.

Toy Dog (Inu-hariko) — A391

**1957, Dec. 20 *Perf. 13½x13***

**644** A391 5y multicolored .50 .40

New Year 1958. Sheets reproducing 4 No. 644, with inscriptions and ornaments, were awarded as 5th prize in the New Year lottery. Value $6.

Shimonoseki-Moji Tunnel — A392

**1958, Mar. 9 *Perf. 13x13½***

**645** A392 10y multicolored .25 .25

Completion of the Kan-Mon Underwater Highway connecting Honshu and Kyushu Islands.

### Stamp Week Type of 1957

Design: 10y, Woman with Umbrella, woodcut by Kiyonaga.

**1958, Apr. 20 Unwmk. *Perf. 13***

**646** A388 10y multicolored .65 .25

Stamp Week, 1958. Sheets of 10.

Statue of Ii Naosuke and Harbor A393

**Unwmk.**

**1958, May 10 Engr. *Perf. 13***

**647** A393 10y gray blue & car .25 .25

Cent. of the opening of the ports of Yokohama, Nagasaki and Hakodate to foreign powers.

National Stadium — A394

3rd Asian Games, Tokyo: 10y, Torch and emblem. 14y, Runner. 24y, Woman diver.

**1958, May 24 Photo.**

| | | | | |
|---|---|---|---|---|
| **648** | A394 | 5y bl grn, bis & pink | .25 | .25 |
| **649** | A394 | 10y multicolored | .25 | .30 |
| **650** | A394 | 14y multicolored | .30 | .25 |
| **651** | A394 | 24y multicolored | .35 | .30 |
| | | *Nos. 648-651 (4)* | 1.15 | 1.10 |

Kasato Maru, Map and Brazilian Flag A395

**1958, June 18**

**652** A395 10y multicolored .25 .25

50 years of Japanese emigration to Brazil.

Sado Island and Local Dancer A396

Mt. Yahiko and Echigo Plain — A397

**1958, Aug. 20 Unwmk. *Perf. 13***

| | | | | |
|---|---|---|---|---|
| **653** | A396 | 10y multicolored | .70 | .25 |
| **654** | A397 | 10y multicolored | .55 | .25 |

Sado-Yahiko Quasi-National Park.

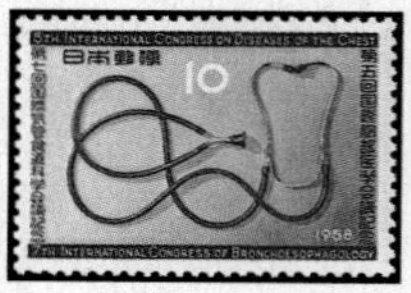


Stethoscope A398

**1958, Sept. 7 Photo. *Perf. 13***

**655** A398 10y Prussian green .25 .25

5th Intl. Cong. on Diseases of the Chest and the 7th Intl. Cong. of Bronchoesophagology.

"Kyoto" (Sanjo Bridge), Print by Hiroshige A399

**1958, Oct. 5**

**656** A399 24y multicolored 2.00 .70

Issued for International Letter Writing Week, Oct. 5-11. See No. 679.

### Sports Types of 1955-56

Designs: No. 657, Weight lifter. No. 658, Girl badminton player.

**1958, Oct. 19 Engr.**

| | | | | |
|---|---|---|---|---|
| **657** | A365 | 5y gray blue | .25 | .25 |
| **658** | A379 | 5y claret | .25 | .25 |
| *a.* | | Pair, #657-658 | 1.00 | *2.00* |

13th Natl. Athletic Meet, Toyama Prefecture.

Keio University and Yukichi Fukuzawa — A400

**1958, Nov. 8 Engr. *Perf. 13½***

**659** A400 10y magenta .35 .25

Centenary of Keio University.

Globe and Playing Children A401

**1958, Nov. 23 Photo. *Perf. 13***

**660** A401 10y deep green .25 .25

9th Intl. Conf. of Social Work and the 2nd Intl. Study Conf. on Child Welfare.

Flame: Symbol of Human Rights — A402

**1958, Dec. 10 Unwmk. *Perf. 13***

**661** A402 10y multicolored .25 .25

10th anniv. of the signing of the Universal Declaration of Human Rights.

Toy of Takamatsu (Tai-Ebisu) — A403

**1958, Dec. 20 *Perf. 13½***

**662** A403 5y multicolored .65 .40

New Year 1959. Sheets reproducing 4 No. 662, with inscriptions and ornaments, were awarded as prizes in the New Year lottery. Size: 103x89mm. Value $7.50.

Tractor and Map of Kojima Bay — A404

**1959, Feb. 1 *Perf. 12½***

**663** A404 10y claret & bister brn .25 .25

Completion of the embankment closing Kojima Bay for reclamation.

Karst Plateau A405

Akiyoshi Cave — A406

**1959, Mar. 16 Photo. *Perf. 13½***

| | | | | |
|---|---|---|---|---|
| **664** | A405 | 10y green, bl & ocher | .90 | .25 |
| **665** | A406 | 10y multicolored | 1.50 | .25 |

Akiyoshidai Quasi-National Park.

Map of Southeast Asia — A407

**1959, Mar. 27**
**666** A407 10y deep carmine .25 .25

Asian Cultural Cong., Tokyo, Mar. 27-31, marking the 2,500th anniv. of the death of Buddha.

Ceremonial Fan — A408

Prince Akihito and Princess Michiko — A409

**Photogravure; Portraits Engraved**

**1959, Apr. 10**
**667** A408 5y magenta & violet .25 .25
**668** A409 10y red brn & dull pur .50 .25
*a.* Souv. sheet of 2, #667-668, imperf. 6.00 6.00
**669** A408 20y org brn & brn .85 .25
**670** A409 30y yel grn & dk grn 2.50 .30
*Nos. 667-670 (4)* 4.10 1.05

Wedding of Crown Prince Akihito and Princess Michiko, Apr. 10, 1959.

**Type of 1957**

Women Reading Poetry, print by Eishi Fujiwara.

**1959, May 20 Photo. *Perf. 13***
**671** A388 10y multicolored 2.10 .90

Stamp Week. Issued in sheets of 10.

**Redrawn Kannon Type of 1953**
Coil Stamp
***Perf. 13 Horiz.***

**1959, Jan. 20 Typo. Unwmk.**
**672** A332a 10y red brn & lilac 18.00 *20.00*

Measuring Glass, Tape Measure and Scales — A410

**1959, June 5 Photo. *Perf. 13***
**673** A410 10y lt blue & blk .25 .25

Adoption of the metric system.

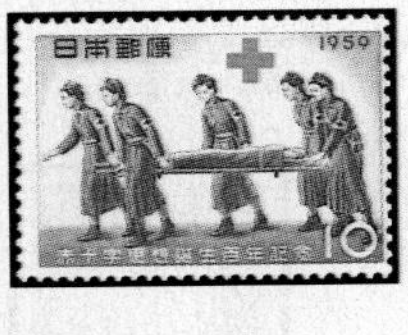
Nurses Carrying Stretcher A411

**1959, June 24**
**674** A411 10y olive grn & red .25 .25

Centenary of the Red Cross idea.

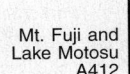

Mt. Fuji and Lake Motosu A412

**1959, July 21 Engr. *Perf. 13***
**675** A412 10y green, bl & sepia .50 .25

Establishment of Natural Park Day and 1st Natural Park Convention, Yumoto, Nikko, July 21, 1959.

Ao Cave Area of Yabakei A413

Hita, Mt. Hiko and Great Cormorant A414

**1959, Sept. 25 Photo. *Perf. 13***
**676** A413 10y multicolored .90 .25
**677** A414 10y multicolored .90 .25

Yaba-Hita-Hiko Quasi National Park.

Golden Dolphin, Nagoya Castle — A415

**1959, Oct. 1**
**678** A415 10y brt bl, gold & blk .60 .25

350th anniversary of Nagoya.

**Hiroshige Type of 1958**

Design: 30y, "Kuwana," the 7-ri Crossing Point, print by Hiroshige.

**1959, Oct. 4 Unwmk.**
**679** A399 30y multicolored 6.00 1.25

Intl. Letter Writing Week, Oct. 4-10.

Japanese Crane, IATA Emblem — A416

**1959, Oct. 12 Engr.**
**680** A416 10y brt grnsh blue .35 .25

15th General Meeting of the International Air Transport Association.

Shoin Yoshida and PTA Symbol — A417

**1959, Oct. 27 Photo. *Perf. 13***
**681** A417 10y brown .25 .25

Centenary of the death of Shoin Yoshida, educator, and in connection with the Parent-Teachers Association convention.

Throwing the Hammer — A418

Design: No. 683, Woman Fencer.

**1959, Oct. 25 Engr.**
**682** A418 5y gray blue .35 .25
**683** A418 5y olive bister .35 .25
*a.* Pair, #682-683 1.00 1.00

14th National Athletic Meet, Tokyo.

Globes A419

**1959, Nov. 2 Photo.**
**684** A419 10y brown red .25 .25

15th session of GATT (General Agreement on Tariffs & Trade), Tokyo, Oct. 12-Nov. 21.

Toy Mouse of Kanazawa — A420

**1959, Dec. 19 Unwmk. *Perf. 13½***
**685** A420 5y gold, red, grn & blk .80 .40

New Year 1960. Sheets reproducing 4 No. 685, with marginal inscription and ornaments, were awarded as prizes in natl. lottery. Value $7.50.

Yukio Ozaki and Clock Tower, Ozaki Memorial Hall — A421

**1960, Feb. 25 Photo. *Perf. 13½***
**686** A421 10y red brn & dk brn .25 .25

Completion of Ozaki Memorial Hall, erected in memory of Yukio Ozaki (1858-1954), statesman.

Nara Period Artwork, Shosoin Treasure House — A422

**1960, Mar. 10**
**687** A422 10y olive gray .40 .25

Transfer of the capital to Nara, 1250th anniv.

**Scenic Trio Issue**

Bay of Matsushima A423

Ama-no-hashidate (Heavenly Bridge) — A424

Miyajima from the Sea — A425

**1960 Engr.**
**688** A423 10y maroon & bl grn 1.25 .45
**689** A424 10y green & lt bl 1.60 .45
**690** A425 10y vio blk & bl grn 1.60 .45
*Nos. 688-690 (3)* 4.45 1.35

Issued: No. 688, 3/15; No. 689, 7/15; No. 690, 11/15.

Takeshima, off Gamagori A426

**1960, Mar. 20 Photo. *Perf. 13½***
**691** A426 10y multicolored .75 .25

Mikawa Bay Quasi-National Park.

Poetess Isé, 13th Century Painting — A427

**1960, Apr. 20 Unwmk. *Perf. 13***
**692** A427 10y multicolored 2.00 2.00

Stamp Week, 1960.

Kanrin Maru — A428

Design: 30y, Pres. Buchanan receiving first Japanese diplomatic mission.

**1960, May 17 Engr.**
**693** A428 10y bl grn & brn .40 .25
**694** A428 30y car & indigo 1.25 .40

Cent. of the Japan-US Treaty of Amity and Commerce. Nos. 694 and 693 form pages of an open book when placed next to each other. Souvenir sheet is No. 703.

Crested Ibis (Toki) — A429

**1960, May 24 Photo. *Perf. 13½***
**695** A429 10y gray, pink & red .55 .45

12th Intl. Congress for Bird Preservation.

Radio Waves Encircling Globe — A430

**1960, June 1 Engr.**
**696** A430 10y carmine rose .30 .25

25th anniv. of the Intl. Radio Program by the Japanese Broadcasting Corporation.

Flower Garden (Gensei Kaen) — A431

**1960, June 15** **Photo.**
**697** A431 10y multicolored 1.00 .40

Abashiri Quasi-National Park.

Cape Ashizuri A432

**1960, Aug. 1** **Unwmk.**
**698** A432 10y multicolored .65 .40

Ashizuri Quasi-National Park.

Rainbow Spanning Pacific, Cherry Blossoms and Pineapples A433

**1960, Aug. 20** ***Perf. 13½***
**699** A433 10y multicolored .60 .25

75th anniversary of Japanese contract emigration to Hawaii.

Henri Farman's Biplane and Jet — A434

**1960, Sept. 20** ***Perf. 13***
**700** A434 10y brn & chlky bl .35 .25

50th anniversary of Japanese aviation.

Seat Plan of Diet — A435

"Red Fuji" by Hokusai and Diet Building — A436

**1960, Sept. 27**
**701** A435 5y indigo & org .25 .25
**702** A436 10y blue & red brn .40 .25

49th Inter-Parliamentary Conference.

### Souvenir Sheet

**1960, Sept. 27** **Engr.**
**703** A428 Sheet of 2, #693-694 22.50 22.50

Visit of Prince Akihito and Princess Michiko to the US.

"Night Snow at Kambara," by Hiroshige A437

**1960, Oct. 9** **Photo.**
**704** A437 30y multicolored 12.00 4.00

Issued for International Letter Writing Week, Oct. 9-15. See Nos. 735, 769.

Japanese Fencing (Kendo) — A438

No. 706, Girl gymnast and vaulting horse.

**1960, Oct. 23** **Engr.** ***Perf. 13½***
**705** A438 5y dull blue .40 .30
**706** A438 5y rose violet .40 .30
*a.* Pair, #705-706 1.50 1.50

15th National Athletic Meet, Kumamoto.

Okayama Astrophysical Observatory A439

**1960, Oct. 19**
**707** A439 10y brt violet .50 .25

Opening of the Okayama Astrophysical Observatory.

Lt. Naoshi Shirase and Map of Antarctica A440

**1960, Nov. 29** **Photo.**
**708** A440 10y fawn & black .55 .25

50th anniv. of the 1st Japanese Antarctic expedition.

Little Red Calf of Aizu, Gold Calf of Iwate — A441

**1960, Dec. 20** **Unwmk.** ***Perf. 13½***
**709** A441 5y multicolored .80 .40

New Year 1961. Sheets reproducing 4 No. 709 were awarded as prizes in the New Year lottery. Size: 102x89mm. Value $8.50.

Diet Building at Night — A442

Opening of First Session — A443

**1960, Dec. 24** **Photo.; Engr. (10y)**
**710** A442 5y gray & dk bl .35 .25
**711** A443 10y carmine .45 .25

70th anniversary of the Japanese Diet.

Narcissus — A444

No. 713, Plum blossoms. No. 714, Camellia japonica. No. 715, Cherry blossoms. No. 716, Peony. No. 717, Iris. No. 718, Lily. No. 719, Morning glory. No. 720, Bellflower. No. 721, Gentian. No. 722, Chrysanthemum. No. 723, Camellia sasanqua.

**1961** **Photo.** ***Perf. 13½***
**712** A444 10y lilac, yel & grn 3.75 .80
**713** A444 10y brown, grn & yel 1.60 .80
**714** A444 10y lem, grn, pink & yel 1.40 .80
**715** A444 10y gray, brn, pink, yel & blk 1.40 .80
**716** A444 10y blk, grn, pink & yel 1.00 .80
**717** A444 10y gray, pur, grn & yel .65 .50
**718** A444 10y gray grn, yel & brn .50 .40
**719** A444 10y lt bl, grn & lil .50 .40
**720** A444 10y lt yel grn, vio & grn .50 .40
**721** A444 10y org, vio bl & grn .50 .40
**722** A444 10y blue, yel & grn .50 .40
**723** A444 10y sl, pink, yel & grn .50 .40
*Nos. 712-723 (12)* 12.80 6.90

Nojima Cape Lighthouse and Fisherwomen A445

**1961, Mar. 15**
**724** A445 10y multicolored .55 .25

South Boso Quasi-National Park.

Cherry Blossoms — A446

**Unwmk.**

**1961, Apr. 1** **Photo.** ***Perf. 13***
**725** A446 10y lilac rose & gray .30 .25
*a.* Lilac rose omitted 300.00
*b.* Imperf., pair 1,100.
*c.* Booklet pane of 4 5.50 2.25
*d.* Gray omitted 200.00

See No. 611b.

### Coil Stamp

**1961, Apr. 25** ***Perf. 13 Horiz.***
**726** A446 10y lil rose & gray 5.00 1.90

Hisoka Maeshima — A447

**1961, Apr. 20** ***Perf. 13***
**727** A447 10y olive & black 1.10 .25

90th anniv. of Japan's modern postal service from Tokyo to Osaka, inaugurated by Deputy Postmaster General Hisoka Maeshima.

### Type of 1957

"Dancing Girl" from a "Screen of Dancers."

**1961, Apr. 20** ***Perf. 13½***
**728** A388 10y multicolored 1.00 .60

Stamp Week, 1961. Sheets of 10 (5x2).

Lake Biwa — A448

**1961, Apr. 25**
**729** A448 10y blk, dk bl & yel grn .55 .25

Lake Biwa Quasi-National Park.

Rotary Emblem and People of Various Races — A449

**1961, May 29** **Engr.** ***Perf. 13***
**730** A449 10y gray & orange .25 .25

52nd convention of Rotary Intl., Tokyo, May 29-June 1, 1961.

Faucet, Wheat, Insulator & Cogwheel — A450

**1961, July 7** **Photo.** ***Perf. 13½***
**731** A450 10y violet & aqua .30 .25

Aichi irrigation system, Kiso river.

Sun, Earth and Meridian — A451

**1961, July 12**
**732** A451 10y yellow, red & blk .30 .25

75th anniv. of Japanese standard time.

Parasol Dance on Dunes of Tottori A452

**1961, Aug. 15**
**733** A452 10y multicolored .55 .25

San'in Kaigan Quasi-National Park.

Onuma Lake and Komagatake Volcano A453

**1961, Sept. 15**
**734** A453 10y grn, red brn & bl .60 .25

Onuma Quasi-National Park.

### Hiroshige Type of 1960

Design: 30y, "Hakone," print by Hiroshige from the 53 Stages of the Tokaido.

**1961, Oct. 8** ***Perf. 13***
**735** A437 30y multicolored 5.25 4.25

Intl. Letter Writing Week, Oct. 8-14.

Gymnast on Horizontal Bar — A454

Design: No. 737, Women rowing.

**1961, Oct. 8** **Engr.** ***Perf. 13½***
**736** A454 5y blue green .30 .25
**737** A454 5y ultra .30 .25
*a.* Pair, #736-737 1.00 1.00

16th National Athletic Meet, Akita. See Nos. 770-771, 816-817, 852-853.

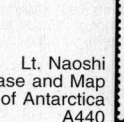

**Duck Type of 1955**
Coil Stamp

**1961, Oct. 2 Photo. *Perf. 13 Horiz.***
**738** A362 5y lt bl & red brn 2.50 2.00

National Diet Library and Book — A455

**1961, Nov. 1** ***Perf. 13½***
**739** A455 10y dp ultra & gold .25 .25

Opening of the new Natl. Diet Library, Tokyo.

Paper Mâché Tiger — A456

**1961, Dec. 15** ***Perf. 13½***
**740** A456 5y multicolored .80 .40

New Year 1962. Sheets reproducing 4 No. 740 were awarded as 5th prize in the New Year lottery. Size: 102x90, Value $9.

Mt. Fuji from Lake Ashi — A457

Minokake-Iwa at Irozaki A458

Mt. Fuji from Mitsu Pass — A459

Mt. Fuji from Cape of Ose — A460

**1962, Jan. 16 Unwmk. Photo.**
**741** A457 5y deep green .40 .25
**742** A458 5y dark blue .40 .25
**743** A459 10y red brown 1.10 .25
**744** A460 10y black 1.10 .30
*Nos. 741-744 (4)* 3.00 1.05

Fuji-Hakone-Izu National Park.

Omishima A461

**1962, Feb. 15** ***Perf. 13½***
**745** A461 10y ultra, red & yel .55 .25

Kitanagato-Kaigan Quasi-National Park.

Perotrochus Hirasei A462

Sacred Bamboo A463

Shari-den of Engakuji A464

Yomei Gate, Nikko A465

Noh Mask — A466

Copper Pheasant A466a

Wind God, Fujin, by Sotatsu A467

Japanese Crane A468

Mythical Winged Woman, Chusonji A469

**1962-65 Unwmk. *Perf. 13***
**746** A462 4y dk brn & red ('63) .25 .25
**747** A463 6y gray grn & car .25 .25
**748** A464 30y violet black 4.00 .25
**749** A465 40y rose red 4.50 .25
**750** A466 70y yel brn & blk ('65) 2.00 .25
**751** A466a 80y crim & brn ('65) 1.00 .25
**752** A467 90y brt blue grn 26.00 .35
**753** A468 100y pink & blk ('63) 8.00 .25
**754** A469 120y purple 8.00 .65
*Nos. 746-754 (9)* 54.00 2.75

See Nos. 888, 888A, 1076, 1079, 1257.

**Coil Stamp**
***Perf. 13 Horiz.***

**755** A464 30y dull violet ('63) 3.75 3.00

Hinamatsuri, Doll Festival — A470

**1962, Mar. 3** ***Perf. 13½***
**756** A470 10y brn, blk, bl & car 1.00 .50

The Doll Festival is celebrated Mar. 3 in honor of young girls.

**Type of 1957**

Design: Dancer from "Flower Viewing Party" by Naganobu Kano.

**1962, Apr. 20 Photo. *Perf. 13½***
**757** A388 10y multicolored 1.00 .75

Stamp Week, 1962. Sheets of 10.

Sakurajima Volcano and Kagoshima Bay — A471

**1962, Apr. 30**
**758** A471 10y multicolored .35 .25

Kinkowan Quasi-National Park.

Mount Kongo A472

**1962, May 15** ***Perf. 13½***
**759** A472 10y gray bl, dk grn & sal .35 .25

Kongo-Ikoma Quasi-National Park.

Suigo Park Scene and Iris — A473

**1962, June 1** ***Perf. 13½***
**760** A473 10y multicolored .35 .25

Suigo Quasi-National Park.

Train Emerging from Hokuriku Tunnel — A474

**1962, June 10 Photo.**
**761** A474 10y olive gray .85 .40

Opening of Hokuriku Tunnel between Tsuruga and Imajo, Fukui Prefecture.

Star Festival (Tanabata Matsuri) — A475

**1962, July 7 Unwmk. *Perf. 13½***
**762** A475 10y multicolored .30 .25

The Tanabata festival is celebrated on the evening of July 7.

Boy Scout Hat on Map of Southeast Asia — A476

**1962, Aug. 3**
**763** A476 10y red org, blk & bis .30 .25

Asian Boy Scout Jamboree, Mt. Fuji, Aug. 3-7.

Ozegahara Swampland and Mt. Shibutsu A477

Fumes on Mt. Chausu, Nasu — A478

Lake Chuzenji and Mt. Nantai A479

Senryu-kyo Narrows, Shiobara A480

**1962, Sept. 1**
**764** A477 5y greenish blue .35 .30
**765** A478 5y maroon .35 .30
**766** A479 10y purple .45 .30
**767** A480 10y olive .45 .30
*Nos. 764-767 (4)* 1.60 1.20

Nikko National Park.

Wakato Suspension Bridge — A481

***Perf. 13½x13***
**1962, Sept. 26 Engr. Unwmk.**
**768** A481 10y rose red .65 .25

Opening of Wakato Bridge over Dokai Bay in North Kyushu.

**Hiroshige Type of 1960**

Design: 40y, "Nihonbashi," print by Hiroshige from the 53 Stages of the Tokaido.

**1962, Oct. 7 Photo. *Perf. 13***
**769** A437 40y multicolored 4.50 3.75

Intl. Letter Writing Week, Oct. 7-13.

**Sports Type of 1961**

Design: No. 770, Woman softball pitcher. No. 771, Rifle shooting.

**1962, Oct. 21 Engr. *Perf. 13½***
**770** A454 5y bluish black .25 .25
**771** A454 5y brown violet .25 .25
*a.* Pair, #770-771 .85 .85

17th National Athletic Meeting, Okayama.

Shichi-go-san Festival — A482

**1962, Nov. 15 Photo. *Perf. 13½***
**772** A482 10y multicolored .30 .25

This festival for 7 and 3-year-old girls and 5-year-old boys is celebrated on Nov. 15.

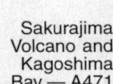

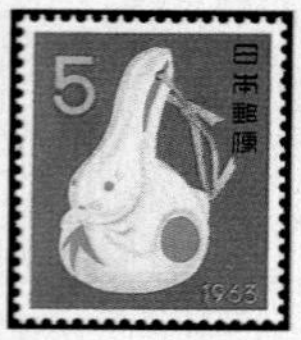

Rabbit Bell — A483

**1962, Dec. 15**

**773** A483 5y multicolored .45 .35

New Year 1963. Sheets reproducing 4 No. 773 were awarded as prizes in the New Year lottery. Value $8.75.

See No. 2655b.

Mt. Ishizuchi A484

**1963, Jan. 11 Unwmk. *Perf. 13½***

**774** A484 10y multicolored .35 .25

Ishizuchi Quasi-National Park.

Setsubun, Spring Festival, Bean Scattering Ceremony — A485

**1963, Feb. 3 Photo.**

**775** A485 10y multicolored .30 .25

Map of City, Birds, Ship and Factory — A486

**1963, Feb. 10**

**776** A486 10y chocolate .25 .25

Consolidation of the communities of Moji, Kokura, Wakamatsu, Yawata and Tobata into Kita-Kyushu City.

"Frost Flowers" on Mt. Fugen A487

Amakusa Island and Mt. Unzen A488

**1963, Feb. 15**

**777** A487 5y gray blue .25 .25
**778** A488 10y carmine rose .35 .25

Unzen-Amakusa National Park.

Green Pond, Midorigaike A489

Hakusan Range A490

***Perf. 13½***

**1963, Mar. 1 Unwmk. Photo.**

**779** A489 5y violet brown .25 .25
**780** A490 10y dark green .35 .25

Hakusan National Park.

Keya-no-Oto Rock — A491

**1963, Mar. 15**

**781** A491 10y multicolored .30 .25

Genkai Quasi-National Park.

Wheat Emblem and Globe — A492

**1963, Mar. 21**

**782** A492 10y dark green .25 .25

FAO "Freedom from Hunger" campaign.

"Girl Reading Letter," Yedo Screen A493

**1963, Apr. 20 *Perf. 13½***

**783** A493 10y multicolored .45 .45

Issued to publicize Stamp Week, 1963.

World Map and Centenary Emblem A494

**1963, May 8**

**784** A494 10y multicolored .25 .25

Centenary of the International Red Cross.

Globe and Leaf with Symbolic River System — A495

**1963, May 15 Photo.**

**785** A495 10y blue .25 .25

5th Congress of the Intl. Commission on Irrigation and Drainage.

Ito-dake, Asahi Range A496

Lake Hibara and Mt. Bandai A497

**1963, May 25 Unwmk. *Perf. 13½***

**786** A496 5y green .25 .25
**787** A497 10y red brown .35 .25

Bandai-Asahi National Park.

Lidth's Jay — A498

No. 789, Rock ptarmigan. No. 790, Eastern turtle dove. No. 791, Japanese white stork. No. 792, Bush warbler. No. 792A, Meadow bunting.

**1963-64 *Perf. 13½***

**Design and Inscription**

| | | | | | |
|---|---|---|---|---|---|
| **788** | A498 | 10y | lt green | .65 | .40 |
| **789** | A498 | 10y | blue | .30 | .25 |
| **790** | A498 | 10y | pale yellow | .30 | .25 |
| **791** | A498 | 10y | grnsh blue ('64) | .30 | .25 |
| **792** | A498 | 10y | green ('64) | .30 | .25 |
| **792A** | A498 | 10y | lt rose brn ('64) | .30 | .25 |
| | *Nos. 788-792A (6)* | | | 2.15 | 1.65 |

Intersection at Ritto, Shiga — A499

**1963, July 15 Unwmk. *Perf. 13½***

**793** A499 10y bl grn, blk & org .25 .25

Opening of the Nagoya-Kobe expressway, linking Nagoya with Kyoto, Osaka and Kobe.

Girl Scout and Flag — A500

**1963, Aug. 1 Photo.**

**794** A500 10y multicolored .30 .25

Asian Girl Scout and Girl Guides Camp, Togakushi Heights, Nagano, Aug. 1-7.

View of Nashu A501

Whirlpool at Naruto A502

**1963, Aug. 20**

**795** A501 5y olive bister .25 .25
**796** A502 10y dark green .35 .25

Inland Sea National Park.

Lake Shikaribetsu, Hokkaido A503

Mt. Kurodake from Sounkyo Valley — A504

**1963, Sept. 1 Unwmk. *Perf. 13½***

**797** A503 5y deep Prus blue .25 .25
**798** A504 10y rose violet .35 .25

Daisetsuzan National Park.

Parabolic Antenna for Space Communications A505

**1963, Sept. 9 Photo.**

**799** A505 10y multicolored .25 .25

14th General Assembly of the International Scientific Radio Union, Tokyo.

"Great Wave off Kanagawa," by Hokusai A506

**1963, Oct. 10 *Perf. 13***

**800** A506 40y gray, dk bl & yel 3.75 1.50

Issued for International Letter Writing Week, Oct. 6-12. Design from Hokusai's "36 Views of Fuji." Printed in sheets of 10 (5x2).

Diver, Pole Vaulter and Relay Runner — A507

**1963, Oct. 11 *Perf. 13½***

**801** A507 10y bl, ocher, blk & red .25 .25

Tokyo Intl. (Pre-Olympic) Sports Meet, Tokyo, Oct. 11-16.

Woman Gymnast — A508

No. 803, Japanese wrestling (sumo).

***Perf. 13½***

**1963, Oct. 27 Unwmk. Engr.**

**802** A508 5y slate green .25 .25
**803** A508 5y brown .25 .25
*a.* Pair, #802-803 .60 *.85*

18th National Athletic Meet, Yamaguchi.

Phoenix Tree and Hachijo Island — A509

**1963, Dec. 10 Photo.**

**804** A509 10y multicolored .30 .25

Izu Islands Quasi-National Park.

Toy Dragons of Tottori and Yamanashi — A510

**1963, Dec. 16**
**805** A510 5y gold, pink, aqua, ind & red .40 .30
*a.* Aqua omitted

New Year 1964. Sheets containing 4 No. 805 were awarded as 5th prize in the New Year lottery. Value $4.75.

Wakasa-Fuji from Takahama A511

**1964, Jan 25** ***Perf. 13½***
**806** A511 10y multicolored .30 .25

Wakasa Bay Quasi-National Park.

Agave and View from Horikiri Pass — A512

**1964, Feb. 20** **Unwmk.**
**807** A512 10y multicolored .30 .25

Nichinan-Kaigan Quasi-National Park.

Uji Bridge A513

View of Toba — A514

**1964, Mar. 15** **Photo.**
**808** A513 5y sepia .25 .25
**809** A514 10y red lilac .30 .25

Ise-Shima National Park.

Takayama Festival Float and Mt. Norikura — A515

No. 811, Yamaboko floats & Gion Shrine, Kyoto.

**1964** **Photo.** ***Perf. 13½***
**810** A515 10y lt green & multi .25 .25
**811** A515 10y grnsh blue & multi .25 .25

No. 810 issued for the annual Takayama spring and autumn festivals, Takayama City, Gifu Prefecture. No. 811 for the annual Gion festival of Kyoto, July 10-30.
Issue dates: No. 810, 4/15. No. 811, 7/15.

Yadorigi Scene from Genji Monogatari Scroll — A516

**1964, Apr. 20**
**814** A516 10y multicolored .25 .25

Stamp Week, 1964. Sheets of 10 (2x5).

Himeji Castle — A517

**1964, June 1** ***Perf. 13½***
**815** A517 10y dark brown .25 .25

Restoration of Himeji Castle.

**Sports Type of 1961**

**1964, June 6** ***Perf. 13½***
**816** A454 5y Handball .25 .25
**817** A454 5y Woman on beam .25 .25
*a.* Pair, #816-817 .65 .65

19th National Athletic Meeting, Niigata.

Cable Cross Section, Map of Pacific Ocean A518

**1964, June 19**
**818** A518 10y gray grn, dp mag & yel .25 .25

Opening of the transpacific cable.

Tokyo Expressway Crossing Nihonbashi — A519

**1964, Aug. 1** **Photo.**
**819** A519 10y green, silver & blk .25 .25

Opening of the Tokyo Expressway.

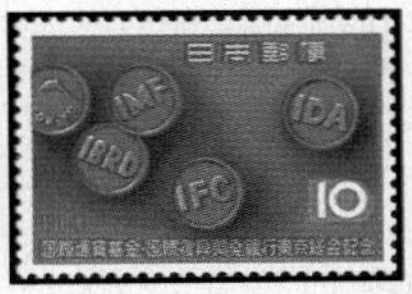
Coin-like Emblems A520

**1964, Sept. 7** **Unwmk.** ***Perf. 13½***
**820** A520 10y scarlet, gold & blk .25 .25

Annual general meeting of the Intl. Monetary Fund, Intl. Bank for Reconstruction and Development, Intl. Financial Corporation and the Intl. Development Assoc., Tokyo, Sept. 7-11.

Athletes, Olympic Flame and Rings — A521

National Stadium, Tokyo — A522

30y, Nippon Bodokan (fencing hall). 40y, Natl. Gymnasium. 50y, Komazawa Gymnasium.

**1964**
**821** A521 5y multicolored .25 .25
**822** A522 10y multicolored .25 .25
**823** A522 30y multicolored .35 .25
**824** A522 40y multicolored .45 .25
**825** A522 50y multicolored .50 .25
*a.* Souvenir sheet of 5, #821-825 3.75 4.25
*Nos. 821-825 (5)* 1.80 1.25

18th Olympic Games, Tokyo, Oct. 10-25.
Issue dates: 5y, Sept. 9. Others, Oct. 10.

Hand with Grain, Cow and Fruit — A523

**1964, Sept. 15** ***Perf. 13½***
**826** A523 10y violet brn & gold .25 .25

Draining of Hachirogata Lagoon, providing new farmland for the future.

Express Train — A524

**1964, Oct. 1**
**827** A524 10y blue & black .35 .25

Opening of the new Tokaido railroad line.

Mt. Fuji Seen from Tokaido, by Hokusai A525

**1964, Oct. 4** ***Perf. 13***
**828** A525 40y multicolored 1.00 .50

Issued for International Letter Writing Week, Oct. 4-10. Issued in sheets of 10 (5x2). See Nos. 850, 896, 932, 971, 1016.

"Straw Snake" Mascot — A526

**1964, Dec. 15** **Photo.** ***Perf. 13½***
**829** A526 5y crimson, blk & yel .30 .30

New Year 1965. Sheets containing 4 No. 829 were awarded as prizes in the New Year lottery (issued Jan. 20, 1965). Value $2.75.

Mt. Daisen A527

Paradise Cove, Oki Islands A528

**1965, Jan. 20** **Unwmk.** ***Perf. 13½***
**830** A527 5y dark blue .25 .25
**831** A528 10y brown orange .30 .25

Daisen-Oki National Park.

Niseko-Annupuri — A529

**1965, Feb. 15** **Photo.**
**832** A529 10y multicolored .30 .25

Niseko-Shakotan-Otarukaigan Quasi-Natl. Park.

Meteorological Radar Station on Mt. Fuji — A530

**1965, Mar. 10** **Photo.** ***Perf. 13½***
**833** A530 10y multicolored .25 .25

Completion of the Meteorological Radar Station on Kengamine Heights of Mt. Fuji.

Kiyotsu Gorge — A531

Lake Nojiri and Mt. Myoko A532

**1965, Mar. 15**
**834** A531 5y brown .25 .25
**835** A532 10y magenta .30 .25

Jo-Shin-etsu Kogen National Park.

Communications Museum, Tokyo — A533

**1965, Mar. 25** **Unwmk.** ***Perf. 13½***
**836** A533 10y green .25 .25

Philatelic Exhibition celebrating the completion of the Communications Museum.

"The Prelude" by Shoen Uemura A534

**1965, Apr. 20** **Photo.**
**837** A534 10y gray & multi .30 .25

Issued for Stamp Week, 1965.

Playing Children, Cows and Swan — A535

**1965, May 5** **Unwmk.** ***Perf. 13½***
**838** A535 10y pink & multi .25 .25

Opening of the National Garden for Children, Tokyo-Yokohama.

Stylized Tree and Sun — A536

**1965, May 9**

**839** A536 10y multicolored .25 .25

Issued to publicize the forestation movement and the forestation ceremony, Tottori Prefecture.

Globe, Old and New Communication Equipment — A537

**1965, May 17**

**840** A537 10y brt blue, yel & blk .25 .25

Cent. of the ITU.

Crater of Mt. Naka, Kyushu A538

Five Central Peaks of Aso and Mountain Road — A539

**1965, June 15 Photo.** ***Perf. 13½***

**841** A538 5y carmine rose .25 .25
**842** A539 10y deep green .30 .25

Aso National Park.

ICY Emblem and Doves A540

**1965, June 26** **Unwmk.**

**843** A540 40y multicolored .45 .25

Intl. Cooperation Year, 1965, and 20th anniv. of the UN.

Horse Chase, Soma A541

Chichibu Festival Scene A542

**1965 Photo.** ***Perf. 13x13½***

**844** A541 10y multicolored .25 .25
**845** A542 10y multicolored .25 .25

No. 844 issued to publicize the ancient Soma Nomaoi Festival, Fukushima Prefecture; No. 845, to publicize the festival dedicated to the Chichibu Myoken Shrine (built 1584).

Issue dates: No. 844, 7/16; No. 845, 12/3.

Meiji Maru, Black-tailed Gulls — A543

**1965, July 20** ***Perf. 13½***

**846** A543 10y grn, gray, blk & yel .25 .25

25th Maritime Day, July 20.

Drop of Blood, Girl's Face and Bloodmobile A544

**1965, Sept. 1** ***Perf. 13½***

**847** A544 10y yel, grn, blk & red .25 .25

Issued to publicize the national campaign for blood donations, Sept. 1-30.

Tokai Atomic Power Station and Structure of Alpha Uranium — A545

**1965, Sept. 21** **Photo.**

**848** A545 10y multicolored .25 .25

9th General Conf. of the Intl. Atomic Energy Agency, IAEA, Tokyo, Sept. 21-30.

People and Flag — A546

**1965, Oct. 1**

**849** A546 10y multicolored .25 .25

Tenth national census.

### Hokusai Type of 1964

Design: No. 850, "Waters at Misaka" by Hokusai (Mt. Fuji seen across Lake Kawaguchi).

**1965, Oct. 6 Unwmk.** ***Perf. 13***

**850** A525 40y multicolored .75 .40

Issued for International Letter Writing Week, Oct. 6-12. Issued in sheets of 10 (5x2).

Emblems and Diagram of Seats in National Diet — A547

**1965, Oct. 15** ***Perf. 13½***

**851** A547 10y multicolored .25 .25

75th anniv. of natl. suffrage, 40th anniv. of universal suffrage and 20th anniv. of women's suffrage.

### Sports Type of 1961

Designs: No. 852, Gymnast on vaulting horse. No. 853, Walking race.

**1965, Oct. 24 Engr.** ***Perf. 13½***

**852** A454 5y red brown .25 .25
**853** A454 5y yellow green .25 .25
*a.* Pair, #852-853 .55 .65

20th National Athletic Meeting, Gifu.

Profile and Infant A548

**1965, Oct. 30 Photo.** ***Perf. 13***

**854** A548 30y car lake, yel & lt bl .35 .25

8th Intl. Conf. of Otorhinolaryngology and the 11th Intl. Conf. of Pediatrics.

Mt. Iwo from Shari Coast, Hokkaido — A549

Rausu Lake and Mt. Rausu A550

**1965, Nov. 15** ***Perf. 13½***

**855** A549 5y Prus green .25 .25
**856** A550 10y bright blue .30 .25

Shiretoko National Park.

Aurora Australis, Map of Antarctica and "Fuji" — A551

**1965, Nov. 20**

**857** A551 10y bl, yel & dk bl .25 .25

Issued to publicize the Antarctic expedition, which left on the observation ship "Fuji," Nov. 20, 1965.

"Secret Horse" Straw Toy, Iwate Prefecture — A552

**1965, Dec. 10**

**858** A552 5y lt blue & multi .45 .30

Issued for New Year 1966. Sheets containing four of No. 858 were awarded as prizes in the New Year lottery (issued Jan. 20, 1966). Value $2.50.

Telephone Dial and 1890 Switchboard — A553

**1965, Dec. 16**

**859** A553 10y multicolored .25 .25

75th anniversary of telephone service in Japan.

Japanese Spiny Lobster A554

Carp — A555

Bream A555a

Skipjack Tuna A555b

Three Ayu — A555c

Eel A555d

Jack Mackeral A555e

Chum Salmon A555f

Yellowtail A555g

Tiger Puffer A555h

Squid A555i

Turbo Cornutus A555j

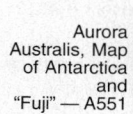

**1966-67 Photo. *Perf. 13***
**Multicolored; Background in Colors Indicated**

| | | | | | |
|---|---|---|---|---|---|
| **860** | A554 | 10y | green & ultra | .25 | .25 |
| **861** | A555 | 10y | blue green | .25 | .25 |
| **862** | A555a | 10y | dk blue | .25 | .25 |
| **863** | A555b | 10y | dk ultra | .25 | .25 |
| **864** | A555c | 10y | bis & dk grn | .25 | .25 |
| **865** | A555d | 15y | grnsh bl & yel | .30 | .25 |
| **866** | A555e | 15y | brt grn | .30 | .25 |
| **867** | A555f | 15y | brt grn & bl | .30 | .25 |
| **868** | A555g | 15y | lt bl grn ('67) | .30 | .25 |
| **869** | A555h | 15y | brt grn ('67) | .30 | .25 |
| **870** | A555i | 15y | ultra & grn ('67) | .30 | .25 |
| **871** | A555j | 15y | chlky bl ('67) | .55 | .25 |
| | | | *Nos. 860-871 (12)* | 3.60 | 3.00 |

**Famous Gardens Issue**

A556

A557

A558

10y, Kobuntei Pavilion and plum blossoms, Kairakuen Garden, Ibaraki. No. 873, Japanese cranes and Okayama Castle, Korakuen Garden, Okayama. No. 874, Kenrokuen Garden in the snow.

**1966-67 *Perf. 13½***

| | | | | | |
|---|---|---|---|---|---|
| **872** | A556 | 10y | gold, blk & grn | .25 | .25 |
| **873** | A557 | 15y | blue, blk & mag | .35 | .25 |
| **874** | A558 | 15y | silver, grn & dk brn | .35 | .25 |
| | | | *Nos. 872-874 (3)* | .95 | .75 |

Issued: 10y, 2/25; No. 873, 11/3; No. 874, 1/25/67.

Crater Lake, Zao — A559

**1966, Mar. 15**

**875** A559 10y multicolored .30 .25

Zao Quasi-National Park.

Muroto Cape — A560

Senba Cliffs, Anan Coast — A561

**1966, Mar. 22 *Perf. 13½***

| | | | | | |
|---|---|---|---|---|---|
| **876** | A560 | 10y | multicolored | .30 | .25 |
| **877** | A561 | 10y | multicolored | .30 | .25 |

Muroto-Anan Coast Quasi-National Park.

AIPPI Emblem A562

**1966, Apr. 11 *Perf. 13***

**878** A562 40y multicolored .75 .25

26th General Assembly of the Intl. Association for the Protection of Industrial Properties, Tokyo, Apr. 11-16.

"Butterflies" by Takeji Fujishima — A563

**Photogravure and Engraved**

**1966, Apr. 20 *Perf. 13½***

**879** A563 10y gray & multi .30 .25

Stamp Week, 1966. Sheets of 10 (2x5). See No. 907.

Hisoka Maeshima — A563a

Goldfish — A564

Chrysanthemums A565

Wisteria A565a

Hydrangea A565b

Golden Hall, Chusonji A565c

Yomei Gate, Nikko A565d

Nyoirin Kannon of Chuguji — A565f

Central Hall, Enryakuji Temple — A566

Ancient Clay Horse (Haniwa) — A567

A567a

A567b

A567c

Katsura Palace Garden — A568

A569

Bodhisattva Playing Flute (from Todaiji Lantern) — A570

Designs: 20y, Wisteria. 25y, Hydrangea. 35y, Luminescent squid. 45y, Lysichiton camtschatsense (white flowers). 500y, Deva King statue, South Gate, Todaiji.

**1966-69 Photo. *Perf. 13***

| | | | | | |
|---|---|---|---|---|---|
| **879A** | A563a | 1y | olive bis ('68) | .25 | .25 |
| **880** | A564 | 7y | ol & dp org | 1.50 | .25 |
| **881** | A565 | 15y | bl & yel (bl "15") | .95 | .25 |
| *b.* | | | Bklt. pane of 2 + label ('67) | 3.25 | |
| *c.* | | | Bklt. pane of 4 ('67) | 2.25 | |
| *d.* | | | Bklt. pane of 4 (2 #881 + 2 #611) ('67) | 6.00 | |
| *e.* | | | Imperf., pair | 400.00 | |
| **881A** | A565a | 20y | vio & multi ('67) | 2.25 | *2.50* |
| **882** | A565b | 25y | grn & lt ultra | .50 | .25 |
| **882A** | A565c | 30y | dp ultra & gold ('68) | .55 | .25 |
| **883** | A564 | 35y | blue, gray & blk | 1.25 | .25 |
| **883A** | A565d | 40y | bl grn & brn ('68) | .60 | .25 |
| **884** | A565 | 45y | blue & multi ('67) | .55 | .25 |
| **885** | A565f | 50y | dk car rose | 7.50 | .25 |
| | | | **Engr.** | | |
| **886** | A566 | 60y | slate green | 1.75 | .25 |
| | | | **Photo.** | | |
| **887** | A567 | 65y | orange brown | 9.00 | .25 |
| **887A** | A567a | 75y | rose, blk, yel & pur | 1.00 | .25 |
| **888** | A567b | 90y | gold & brn | 2.00 | .25 |
| **888A** | A567c | 100y | ver & blk ('68) | 1.90 | .25 |
| | | | **Engr.** | | |
| **889** | A568 | 110y | brown | 1.90 | .25 |
| **890** | A569 | 120y | red | 2.50 | .25 |
| **891** | A570 | 200y | Prus grn (22x33mm) | 4.00 | .25 |
| **891A** | A570 | 500y | dull pur ('69) | 9.50 | .25 |
| | | | *Nos. 879A-891A (19)* | 49.45 | 7.00 |

Nos. 880-881 were also issued with fluorescent frame on July 18, 1966.
Compare type A563a with type A2682.
See Nos. 913-916, 918, 926, 1072, 1079, 1081, 1244, 1256.

UNESCO Emblem — A571

**1966, July 2 Photo. *Perf. 13***

**892** A571 15y multicolored .30 .25

20th anniv. of UNESCO.

Map of Pacific Ocean — A572

**1966, Aug. 22 *Perf. 13***

**893** A572 15y bis brn, dl bl & rose .30 .25

11th Pacific Science Congress, Tokyo, Aug. 22-Sept. 10.

Amakusa Bridges, Kyushu — A573

**1966, Sept. 24 Photo. *Perf. 13***

**894** A573 15y multicolored .30 .25

Completion of five bridges linking Misumi Harbor, Kyushu, with Amakusa islands.

Emblem of Post Office Life Insurance and Family — A574

**1966, Oct. 1**

**895** A574 15y yellow grn & multi .30 .25

Post office life insurance service, 50th anniv.

**Hokusai Type of 1964**

50y, "Sekiya on the Sumida" (horseback riders and Mt. Fuji) from Hokusai's "36 Views of Fuji."

**1966, Oct. 6**

**896** A525 50y multicolored .95 .70

Intl. Letter Writing Week, Oct. 6-12. Printed in sheets of 10 (5x2).

Sharpshooter A575

Design: No. 898, Hop, skip and jump.

**1966, Oct. 23 Engr. *Perf. 13½***

| | | | | | |
|---|---|---|---|---|---|
| **897** | A575 | 7y | ultra | .25 | .25 |
| **898** | A575 | 7y | carmine rose | .25 | .25 |
| *a.* | | | Pair, #897-898 | .55 | .55 |

21st Natl. Athletic Meet, Oita, Oct. 23-28.

National Theater A576

Kabuki Scene — A577

Bunraku Puppet Show — A578

**1966, Nov. 1** ***Perf. 13, 13½***

**899** A576 15y multicolored .25 .25
**900** A577 25y multicolored .45 .30
**901** A578 50y multicolored .85 .45
*Nos. 899-901 (3)* 1.55 1.00

Inauguration of first National Theater in Japan. Nos. 900-901 issued in sheets of 10.

Rice Year Emblem — A579

**1966, Nov. 21** ***Perf. 13½***

**902** A579 15y red, blk & ocher .30 .25

FAO International Rice Year.

Ittobori Carved Sheep, Nara Prefecture — A580

**1966, Dec. 10 Photo.** ***Perf. 13½***

**903** A580 7y bl, gold, blk & pink .40 .30

New Year 1967. Sheets containing 4 No. 903 were awarded as prizes in the New Year lottery. Value $2.

International Communications Satellite, Lani Bird 2 — A581

**1967, Jan. 27** ***Perf. 13½***

**904** A581 15y dk Prus bl & sepia .30 .25

Inauguration in Japan of Intl. commercial communications service via satellite.

Around the World Air Route and Jet Plane — A582

**1967, Mar. 6 Photo.** ***Perf. 13½***

**905** A582 15y multicolored .30 .25

Issued to publicize the inauguration of Japan Air Lines Tokyo-London service via New York, which completes the around the world air route.

Library of Modern Japanese Literature A583

**1967, Apr. 11**

**906** A583 15y grnsh bl, lt & dk brn .30 .25

Opening of the Library of Modern Japanese Literature, Komaba Park, Meguro-ku, Tokyo.

### Painting Type of 1966

Design: 15y, Lakeside (seated woman), by Seiki (Kiyoteru) Kuroda.

**1967, Apr. 20**

**907** A563 15y multicolored .40 .25

Stamp Week, 1967. Sheets of 10 (2x5).

Kobe Harbor A584

**1967, May 8 Photo.** ***Perf. 13x13½***

**908** A584 50y multicolored .95 .25

5th Cong. of the Intl. Association of Ports and Harbors, Tokyo, May 8-13.

Welfare Commissioner's Emblem — A585

**1967, May 12** ***Perf. 13½***

**909** A585 15y dk brown & gold .30 .25

50th anniversary of the Welfare Commissioner System.

Traffic Light, Automobile and Children — A586

**1967, May 22** ***Perf. 13x13½***

**910** A586 15y emer, red, blk & yel .30 .25

Issued to publicize traffic safety.

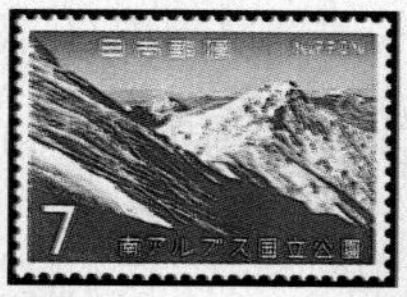

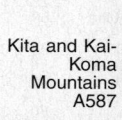

Kita and Kai-Koma Mountains A587

Akaishi and Hijiri Mountains A588

**1967, July 10**

**911** A587 7y Prus blue .25 .25
**912** A588 15y rose lilac .30 .25

South Japan Alps National Park.

### Types of 1966-69 Redrawn and

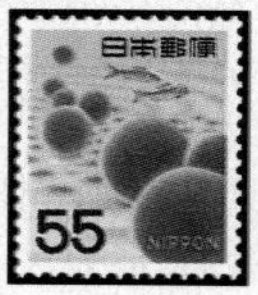

A588a

Original - No. 881A

Redrawn - No. 915

On No. 915 the wisteria leaves do not touch frame at left and top. On No. 881A they do.

**1967-69 Photo.** ***Perf. 13***

**913** A564 7y brt yel grn & dp org .25 .25
**914** A565 15y bl & yel (white "15") .30 .25
*a.* Pane of 10 (5x2) ('68) 2.75
*b.* Bklt. panes of 4 with gutter (6 #914 + 2 #611) ('68) 7.00
*c.* Imperf., pair 500.00
*d.* Blue shading omitted
*e.* Bklt. panes of 2 & 4 with gutter ('68) 45.00 45.00
**915** A565a 20y vio & multi ('69) 1.10 .25
**916** A565f 50y brt carmine .90 .25
**917** A588a 55y lt bl, grn & blk ('69) .85 .25
**918** A567 65y deep orange 1.10 .25
*Nos. 913-918 (6)* 4.50 1.50

Issued for use in facer-canceling machines. Issue dates: 7y, Aug. 1; 15y, 50y, July 1; 65y, July 20, 1967; 20y, Apr. 1, 1969; 55y, Sept. 1, 1969.

On No. 913 the background has been lightened and a frame line of shading added at top and right side.

No. 914a is imperf. on four sides.

The two panes of Nos. 914b and 914e are connected by a vertical creased gutter 21mm wide. The left pane of No. 914b consists of 2 No. 914 and 2 No. 611; the right pane, 4 of No. 914. The left pane of 2 of No. 914e includes a 4-line inscription.

### Coil Stamp

**1968, Jan. 9** ***Perf. 13 Horiz.***

**926** A565 15y bl & yel (white "15") .55 .30

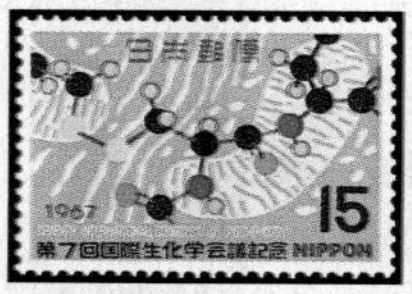

Mitochondria and Protein Model A589

**1967, Aug. 19 Photo.** ***Perf. 13***

**927** A589 15y gray & multi .30 .25

7th Intl. Biochemistry Cong., Tokyo, Aug. 19-25.

Gymnast on Horizontal Bar — A590

Universiade Emblem — A591

**1967, Aug. 26**

**928** A590 15y red & multi .30 .25
**929** A591 50y yellow & multi .95 .25

World University Games, Universiade 1967, Tokyo, Aug. 26-Sept. 4.

Paper Lantern, ITY Emblem — A592

"Sacred Mt. Fuji" by Taikan Yokoyama — A593

**1967, Oct. 2 Photo.** ***Perf. 13***

**930** A592 15y ultra & multi .25 .25
**931** A593 50y multicolored 1.25 1.00

International Tourist Year, 1967. No. 931 issued in sheets of 10.

### Hokusai Type of 1964

50y, "Kajikazawa, Koshu" (fisherman and waves) from Hokusai's "36 Views of Fuji."

**1967, Oct. 6**

**932** A525 50y multicolored 1.25 .55

Issued for International Letter Writing Week, Oct. 6-12. Sheets of 10 (5x2).

Athlete, Wild Primrose and Chichibu Mountains — A594

**1967, Oct. 22 Photo.** ***Perf. 13***

**933** A594 15y gold & multi .30 .25

22nd Natl. Athletic Meet, Saitama, 10/22-27.

Miroku Bosatsu, Koryuji Temple, Kyoto — A595

Kudara Kannon, Horyuji Temple, Nara — A596

Golden Hall and Pagoda, Horyuji Temple, Nara — A597

**1967, Nov. 1** **Photo.**

**934** A595 15y multicolored .30 .25

**Engr.**

**935** A596 15y pale grn, blk & red .30 .25

**Photo. & Engr.**

**936** A597 50y multicolored 1.25 .75
*Nos. 934-936 (3)* 1.85 1.25

National treasures of Asuka Period (6th-7th centuries). No. 936 issued in sheets of 10.

Highway and Congress Emblem A598

**1967, Nov. 5** **Photo.** ***Perf. 13***

**937** A598 50y multicolored .95 .25

13th World Road Cong., Tokyo, Nov. 5-11.

Mt. Kumotori A599

Lake Chichibu A600

**1967, Nov. 27**

**938** A599 7y olive .25 .25
**939** A600 15y red lilac .30 .25

Chichibu-Tama National Park

Climbing Monkey Toy (Noborizaru), Miyazaki Prefecture — A601

**1967, Dec. 11** **Photo.** ***Perf. 13***

**940** A601 7y multicolored .40 .30

New Year 1968. Sheets containing 4 No. 940 were awarded as prizes in the New Year lottery. Value $1.75.

Mt. Sobo — A602

Takachiho Gorge — A603

**1967, Dec. 20**

**941** A602 15y multicolored .30 .25
**942** A603 15y multicolored .30 .25

Sobo Katamuki Quasi-National Park.

Girl, Boy and Sakura Maru — A604

**1968, Jan. 19** **Photo.** ***Perf. 13***

**943** A604 15y ultra, ocher & blk .30 .25

Cent. of the Meiji Era, and 1st Japanese Youth Good Will Cruise in celebration of the centenary.

Ashura, Kofukuji Temple, Nara — A605

Gakko Bosatsu, Todaiji Temple, Nara — A606

Kichijo Ten, Yakushiji Temple, Nara — A607

**1968, Feb. 1** **Engr.** ***Perf. 13***

**944** A605 15y sepia & car .30 .25

**Engr. & Photo.**

**945** A606 15y dk brn, pale grn & org .30 .25

**Photo.**

**946** A607 50y multicolored .95 .95
*Nos. 944-946 (3)* 1.55 1.45

Issued to show National Treasures of the Nara Period (710-784).

Grazing Cows and Mt. Yatsugatake A608

Mt. Tateshina A609

**1968, Mar. 21** **Photo.** ***Perf. 13***

**947** A608 15y multicolored .30 .25
**948** A609 15y multicolored .30 .25

Yatsugatake-Chushin-Kogen Quasi-Natl. Park.

Young Dancer (Maiko) in Tenjuan Garden, by Bakusen Tsuchida A610

**1968, Apr. 20** **Photo.** ***Perf. 13***

**949** A610 15y multicolored .30 .25

Stamp Week, 1968. Sheets of 10 (5x2).

Rishiri Isl. Seen from Rebun Isl. — A611

**1968, May 10** **Photo.** ***Perf. 13***

**950** A611 15y multicolored .30 .25

Rishiri-Rebun Quasi-National Park.

Gold Lacquer and Mother-of-Pearl Box — A612

"The Origin of Shigisan" Painting from Chogo-sonshiji, Nara — A613

Bodhisattva Samantabhadra — A614

**1968, June 1** **Engr. & Photo.**

**951** A612 15y lt blue & multi .30 .25

**Photo.**

**952** A613 15y tan & multi .30 .25
**953** A614 50y sepia & multi 1.75 1.50
*Nos. 951-953 (3)* 2.35 2.00

Issued to show national treasures of the Heian Period (8-12th centuries).

Memorial Tower and Badge of Hokkaido — A615

**1968, June 14**

**954** A615 15y grn, vio bl, bis & red .30 .25

Centenary of development of Hokkaido.

Sunrise over Pacific and Fan Palms — A616

**1968, June 26** **Photo.** ***Perf. 13***

**955** A616 15y blk, org & red org .30 .25

Return of Bonin Islands to Japan by US.

Map of Japan Showing Postal Codes — A617

**Two types of inscription:**

Type I (enlarged)

あなたの住所にも郵便番号を

"Postal code also on your address"

Type II (enlarged)

あて名に郵便番号を

"Don't omit postal code on the address"

**1968, July 1**

**956** A617 7y yel grn & red (I) 2.00 .30
**957** A617 7y yel grn & red (II) 2.00 .30
*a.* Pair, #956-957 5.00 1.50
**958** A617 15y sky bl & car (I) .60 .30
*a.* Bklt. panes of 4 with gutter (4 #958 + 2 #959 + 2 #611) 65.00 65.00
**959** A617 15y sky bl & car (II) .60 .30
*d.* Pair, #958-959 1.75 1.25
*Nos. 956-959 (4)* 5.20 1.20

Introduction of the postal code system.

The double booklet pane, No. 958a, comes in two forms, the positions of the Postal Code types being transposed.

**Coil Stamps**

***Perf. 13 Horiz.***

**959A** A617 15y sky blue & car (I) 1.50 .85
**959B** A617 15y sky blue & car (II) 1.50 .85
*c.* Pair, #959A-959B 4.00 4.00

Kiso River — A618

Inuyama Castle A619

**1968, July 20** ***Perf. 13½***

**960** A618 15y multicolored .30 .25
**961** A619 15y multicolored .30 .25

Hida-Kisogawa Quasi-National Park.

Youth Hostel Emblem, Trees and Sun — A620

**1968, Aug. 6** **Photo.** ***Perf. 13***

**962** A620 15y citron & multi .30 .25

27th Intl. Youth Hostel Cong., Tokyo, 8/6-20.

Boys Forming Tournament Emblem A621

Pitcher and Tournament Flag — A622

**1968, Aug. 9**

**963** A621 15y yel grn, yel, blk & red .30 .25
**964** A622 15y red, yellow & blk .30 .25
*a.* Pair, #963-964 .65 .60

50th All-Japan High School Baseball Championship Tournament, Koshi-en Baseball Grounds, Aug. 9. Nos. 963-964 printed checkerwise.

Minamoto Yoritomo, Jingoji, Kyoto — A623

Heiji Monogatari Scroll Painting — A624

Red-threaded Armor, Kasuga Shrine, Nara — A625

**1968, Sept. 16 Photo. *Perf. 13***

| | | | |
|---|---|---|---|
| **965** A623 15y black & multi | .35 | .25 |
| **966** A624 15y tan & multi | .35 | .25 |

**Photo. & Engr.**

| | | |
|---|---|---|
| **967** A625 50y multicolored | 1.25 | 1.25 |
| *Nos. 965-967 (3)* | 1.95 | 1.75 |

National treasures of Kamakura period (1180-1192 to 1333).

Mt. Iwate, seen from Hachimantai A626

Lake Towada, seen from Mt. Ohanabe A627

**1968, Sept. 16 Photo.**

| | | |
|---|---|---|
| **968** A626 7y red brown | .25 | .25 |
| **969** A627 15y green | .30 | .25 |

Towada-Hachimantai National Park.

Gymnast, Tojimbo Cliff and Narcissus — A628

**1968, Oct. 1 Photo. *Perf. 13***

| | | |
|---|---|---|
| **970** A628 15y multicolored | .30 | .25 |

23rd National Athletic Meet, Fukui Prefecture, Oct. 1-6.

### Hokusai Type of 1964

Design: 50y, "Fujimihara in Owari Province" (cooper working on a barrel) from Hokusai's "36 Views of Fuji."

**1968, Oct. 7**

| | | |
|---|---|---|
| **971** A525 50y multicolored | 1.25 | .70 |

Issued for International Letter Writing Week, Oct. 7-13. Sheets of 10 (5x2).

Centenary Emblem, Sun and First Western Style Warship — A629

Imperial Carriage Arriving in Tokyo (1868), by Tomote Kobori A630

**1968, Oct. 23**

| | | |
|---|---|---|
| **972** A629 15y vio bl, red, gold & gray | .30 | .25 |
| **973** A630 15y multicolored | .30 | .25 |
| *a.* Imperf., pair | | |

Meiji Centenary Festival.

Old and New Lighthouses A631

**1968, Nov. 1 Photo. *Perf. 13***

| | | |
|---|---|---|
| **974** A631 15y multicolored | .30 | .25 |

Centenary of the first western style lighthouse in Japan.

Ryo'o Court Dance and State Hall, Imperial Palace — A632

**1968, Nov. 14**

| | | |
|---|---|---|
| **975** A632 15y multicolored | .30 | .25 |

Completion of the new Imperial Palace.

Mt. Takachiho A633

Mt. Motobu, Yaku Island A634

**1968, Nov. 20**

| | | |
|---|---|---|
| **976** A633 7y purple | .25 | .25 |
| **977** A634 15y orange | .30 | .25 |

Kirishima-Yaku National Park.

Carved Toy Cock of Yonezawa, Yamagata Prefecture — A635

**1968, Dec. 5 Photo. *Perf. 13***

| | | |
|---|---|---|
| **978** A635 7y lt blue & multi | .40 | .30 |

New Year 1969. Sheets containing 4 No. 978 were awarded as prizes in the New Year lottery. Value $1.75.

Human Rights Flame, Dancing Children and Globe — A636

**1968, Dec. 10**

| | | |
|---|---|---|
| **979** A636 50y orange & multi | .95 | .25 |

International Human Rights Year.

Striped Squirrel — A637

**1968, Dec. 14**

| | | |
|---|---|---|
| **980** A637 15y emerald & blk | .30 | .25 |

Issued to promote saving.

Kochomon Cave and Road — A638

**1969, Jan. 27 Photo.**

| | | |
|---|---|---|
| **981** A638 15y multicolored | .30 | .25 |

Echizen-Kaga-Kaigan Quasi-National Park.

Silver Pavilion, Jishoji Temple, Kyoto — A639

Pagoda, Anrakuji Temple, Nagano — A640

Winter Landscape by Sesshu A641

**1969, Feb. 10 Photo. *Perf. 13***

| | | |
|---|---|---|
| **982** A639 15y multicolored | .30 | .25 |

**Photo. & Engr.**

| | | |
|---|---|---|
| **983** A640 15y lt green & multi | .30 | .25 |

**Photo.**

| | | |
|---|---|---|
| **984** A641 50y tan, blk & ver | 1.10 | .75 |
| *Nos. 982-984 (3)* | 1.70 | 1.25 |

Issued to show national treasures of the Muromachi Period (1333-1572).

Mt. Chokai, seen from Tobishima Island — A642

**1969, Feb. 25 Photo.**

| | | |
|---|---|---|
| **985** A642 15y brt blue & multi | .30 | .25 |

Chokai Quasi-National Park.

Mt. Koya Seen from Jinnogamine A643

Mt. Gomadan and Rhododendron — A644

**1969, Mar. 25 Photo. *Perf. 13***

| | | |
|---|---|---|
| **986** A643 15y multicolored | .30 | .25 |
| **987** A644 15y multicolored | .30 | .25 |

Koya-Ryujin Quasi-National Park.

Hair (Kami), by Kokei Kobayashi A645

**1969, Apr. 20 Photo. *Perf. 13***

| | | |
|---|---|---|
| **988** A645 15y multicolored | .30 | .25 |

Issued for Philatelic Week.

Mother, Son Crossing Street — A646

**1969, May 10 Photo. *Perf. 13***

| | | |
|---|---|---|
| **989** A646 15y lt blue, red & grn | .30 | .25 |

National traffic safety campaign.

Tokyo-Nagoya Expressway and Sakawagawa Bridge A647

**1969, May 26**

| | | |
|---|---|---|
| **990** A647 15y multicolored | .30 | .25 |

Completion of Tokyo-Nagoya Expressway.

Nuclear Ship Mutsu and Atom Diagram A648

**1969, June 12**

| | | |
|---|---|---|
| **991** A648 15y gray, blk, pink & bl | .30 | .25 |

Issued to publicize the launching of the first Japanese nuclear ship, Mutsu.

Museum of Modern Art and Palette
A649

**1969, June 11 Photo. *Perf. 13½***
**992** A649 15y lt bl, brn, yel & blk .30 .25

Opening of the new National Museum of Modern Art, Tokyo.

Cable Ship KKD Maru and Map of Japan Sea — A650

**1969, June 25**
**993** A650 15y lt bl, blk & ocher .30 .25

Completion of the Japan sea cable between Naoetsu, Japan, and Nakhodka, Russia.

Postcards, Postal Code Symbol
A651

Mailbox, Postal Code Symbol
A652

**1969, July 1 Photo. *Perf. 13***
**997** A651 7y yellow grn & car .25 .25
**998** A652 15y sky blue & car .30 .25

1st anniv. of the postal code system and to promote its use.

Lions Emblem and Rose — A653

**1969, July 2**
**999** A653 15y bl, blk, rose & gold .30 .25

52nd Convention of Lions Intl., Tokyo, July 2-5.

Hotoke-ga-ura on Shimokita Peninsula, Northern Honshu
A654

**1969, July 15**
**1000** A654 15y multicolored .30 .25

Shimokita Hanto Quasi-National Park.

Himeji Castle, Hyogo Prefecture
A655

"Pine Forest" (Detail), by Tohaku Hasegawa
A656

"Cypresses," Attributed to Eitoku Kano — A657

**1969, July 21 Photo. & Engr.**
**1001** A655 15y lt blue & multi .30 .25

**Photo.**

**1002** A656 15y pale brown & blk .30 .25
**1003** A657 50y gold & multi 1.10 .60
*Nos. 1001-1003 (3)* 1.70 1.10

Issued to show national treasures of the Momoyama period (1573-1614). The 50y is in sheets of 10 (2x5); Nos. 1001-1002 in sheets of 20 (5x4).

Harano-fudo Waterfall — A658

Mt. Nagisan
A659

**1969, Aug. 20**
**1004** A658 15y multicolored .30 .25
**1005** A659 15y multicolored .30 .25

Hyobosen-Ushiroyama-Nagisan Quasi-Natl. Park.

Mt. O-akan, Hokkaido — A660

Mt. Iwo — A661

**1969, Aug. 25 Photo. *Perf. 13***
**1006** A660 7y bright blue .25 .25
**1007** A661 15y sepia .30 .25

Akan National Park.

Angling, by Taiga Ikeno — A662

The Red Plum, by Korin Ogata — A663

Pheasant-shaped Incense Burner — A664

No. 1010, The White Plum, by Korin Ogata.

**1969, Sept. 25 Photo. *Perf. 13x13½***
**1008** A662 15y multicolored .30 .25

***Perf. 13***

**1009** A663 15y gold & multi .30 .25
**1010** A663 15y gold & multi .30 .25
*a.* Pair, #1009-1010 .75 .75

**Photo. & Engr.**

**1011** A664 50y multicolored 1.00 .65
*Nos. 1008-1011 (4)* 1.90 1.40

Natl. treasures, Edo Period (1615-1867).

Birds Circling Globe and UPU Congress Emblem
A665

Woman Reading Letter, by Utamaro
A666

Designs (UPU Congress Emblem and): 50y, Two Women Reading a Letter, by Harunobu. 60y, Man Reading a Letter (Miyako Dennai), by Sharaku.

**1969, Oct. 1 Photo. *Perf. 13***
**1012** A665 15y red & multi .30 .25
**1013** A666 30y multicolored .55 .40
**1014** A666 50y multicolored .90 .50
**1015** A666 60y multicolored 1.00 .65
*Nos. 1012-1015 (4)* 2.75 1.80

16th UPU Congress, Tokyo, 10/1-11/16. 15y issued in sheets of 20, others in sheets of 10.

**Hokusai Type of 1964**

Design: 50y, "Passing through Koshu down to Mishima" from Hokusai's 36 Views of Fuji.

**1969, Oct. 7 Photo. *Perf. 13***
**1016** A525 50y multicolored 1.25 .65

Issued for International Letter Writing Week Oct. 7-13. Sheets of 10 (5x2).

Rugby Player, Camellia and Oura Catholic Church — A667

**1969, Oct. 26**
**1017** A667 15y lt ultra & multi .30 .25

24th Natl. Athletic Meet, Nagasaki, 10/26-31.

Cape Kitayama — A668

Goishi Coast — A669

**1969, Nov. 20 Photo. *Perf. 13***
**1018** A668 7y gray & dk blue .25 .25
**1019** A669 15y salmon & dk red .30 .25

Rikuchu Coast National Park.

Worker in Hard Hat — A670

**1969, Nov. 26**
**1020** A670 15y ultra, blk yel & brn .30 .25

50th anniv. of the ILO.

Dog Amulet, Hokkeji, Nara — A671

**1969, Dec. 10**
**1021** A671 7y orange & multi .40 .30

New Year 1970. Sheets containing 4 No. 1021 were awarded as prizes in the New Year lottery. Value $1.75.

Aso Bay and Tsutsu Women with Horse — A672

**1970, Feb. 25 Photo. *Perf. 13***
**1022** A672 15y multicolored .30 .25

Iki-Tsushima Quasi-National Park.

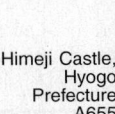

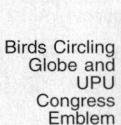

Fireworks over EXPO '70 — A673

Cherry Blossoms Around Globe — A674

Irises, by Korin Ogata (1658-1716) — A675

**1970, Mar. 14 Photo. *Perf. 13***

**1023** A673 7y red & multi .25 .25
**1024** A674 15y gold & multi .30 .25
**1025** A675 50y gold & multi .90 .45
*a.* Souv. sheet of 3, #1023-1025 1.75 1.75
*b.* Bklt. pane of 4 & 3 with gutter 3.00
*Nos. 1023-1025 (3)* 1.45 .95

EXPO '70 Intl. Exposition, Senri, Osaka, Mar. 15-Sept. 13.

No. 1025b contains a pane of 4 No. 1023 and a pane with Nos. 1023-1025. A 35mm gutter separates the panes.

Woman with Hand Drum, by Saburosuke Okada A676

**1970, Apr. 20 Photo. *Perf. 13***

**1026** A676 15y multicolored .45 .25

Issued for Stamp Week, Apr. 20-26.

Mt. Yoshino — A677

Nachi Waterfall A678

**1970, Apr. 30 Photo. *Perf. 13***

**1027** A677 7y gray & pink .25 .25
**1028** A678 15y pale blue & grn .30 .25

Yoshino-Kumano National Park.

Pole Lanterns at EXPO — A679

View of EXPO Within Globe — A680

Grass in Autumn Wind, by Hoitsu Sakai (1761-1828) — A681

**1970, June 15 Photo. *Perf. 13***

**1029** A679 7y red & multi .25 .25
**1030** A680 15y blue & multi .30 .25
**1031** A681 50y silver & multi 1.25 .25
*a.* Souv. sheet of 3, #1029-1031 2.00
*b.* Bklt. panes of 4 & 3 with gutter 3.25
*Nos. 1029-1031 (3)* 1.80 .75

EXPO '70, 2nd issue.

No. 1031b contains a pane of 4 No. 1029 and a pane with Nos. 1029-1031. A 35mm gutter separates the panes.

Buildings and Postal Code Symbol — A682

**1970, July 1 Photo. *Perf. 13***

**1032** A682 7y emerald & vio .35 .25
**1033** A682 15y brt blue & choc .40 .25

Postal code system.

"Maiden at Dojo Temple" A683

Scene from "Sukeroku" A684

"The Subscription List" (Kanjincho) — A685

**1970, July 10**

**1034** A683 15y multicolored .30 .25
**1035** A684 15y multicolored .30 .25
**1036** A685 50y multicolored .90 .30
*Nos. 1034-1036 (3)* 1.50 .80

Issued to publicize the Kabuki Theater.

Girl Scout — A686

**1970, July 26**

**1037** A686 15y multicolored .30 .25

50th anniversary of Japanese Girl Scouts.

Kinoura Coast and Festival Drum — A687

Tate Mountains Seen from Himi Coast — A688

**1970, Aug. 1**

**1038** A687 15y multicolored .30 .25
**1039** A688 15y multicolored .30 .25

Noto Hanto Quasi-National Park.

Sunflower and UN Emblem — A689

**1970, Aug. 17**

**1040** A689 15y lt blue & multi .30 .25

Issued to publicize the 4th United Nations Congress on the Prevention of Crime and the Treatment of Offenders, Kyoto, Aug. 17-26.

Mt. Myogi — A690

Mt. Arafune A691

**1970, Sept. 11 Photo. *Perf. 13***

**1041** A690 15y multicolored .30 .25
**1042** A691 15y multicolored .30 .25

Myogi-Arafune-Sakukogen Quasi-Natl. Park.

G.P.O., Tokyo, by Hiroshige III — A692

**1970, Oct. 6**

**1043** A692 50y multicolored .95 .30

Intl. Letter Writing Week, Oct. 6-12. Sheets of 10 (5x2). Design from wood block series, "Noted Places in Tokyo."

Equestrian, Mt. Iwate and Paulownia — A693

**1970, Oct. 10 Photo. *Perf. 13***

**1044** A693 15y silver & multi .30 .25

25th Natl. Athletic Meet, Morioka, 10/10-16.

Hodogaya Stage, by Hiroshige III — A694

**1970, Oct. 20**

**1045** A694 15y silver & multi .30 .25

Centenary of telegraph service in Japan.

Tree and UN Emblem A695

50y, UN emblem and Headquarters with flags.

**1970, Oct. 24**

**1046** A695 15y olive, ap grn & gold .30 .25
**1047** A695 50y multicolored .90 .25

25th anniversary of United Nations.

Vocational Training Competition Emblem — A696

**1970, Nov. 10 Photo. *Perf. 13***

**1048** A696 15y multicolored .30 .25

The 19th International Vocational Training Competition, Chiba City, Nov. 10-19.

Diet Building and Doves A697

**1970, Nov. 29**

**1049** A697 15y multicolored .30 .25

80th anniversary of Japanese Diet.

Wild Boar, Folk Art, Arai City, Niigata Prefecture — A698

**1970, Dec. 10**

**1050** A698 7y multicolored .30 .25

New Year 1971. Sheets containing 4 No. 1050 were awarded as prizes in the New Year lottery. Value $1.60.

Gen-jo-raku
A699

Ko-cho
A700

Tai-hei-raku — A701

**1971, Apr. 1** **Photo.** ***Perf. 13***
**1051** A699 15y multicolored .30 .25
**1052** A700 15y multicolored .30 .25
**1053** A701 50y multicolored .90 .25
*Nos. 1051-1053 (3)* 1.50 .75

Gagaku, classical Japanese court entertainment.

Woman Voter and Parliament — A702

**1971, Apr. 10** **Photo.** ***Perf. 13***
**1054** A702 15y orange & multi .30 .25

25th anniversary of woman suffrage.

Pines and Maple Leaves — A703

**1971, Apr. 18**
**1055** A703 7y emerald & violet .25 .25

National forestation campaign.

Woman of Tokyo, by Kiyokata Kaburagi — A704

**1971, Apr. 19**
**1056** A704 15y gray & multi .35 .25

Philatelic Week, Apr. 19-25.

Mailman
A705

Mailbox
A706

Railroad Post Office — A707

**1971, Apr. 20**
**1057** A705 15y blk & org brn .30 .25
**1058** A706 15y multicolored .30 .25
**1059** A707 15y multicolored .30 .25
*Nos. 1057-1059 (3)* .90 .75

Centenary of Japanese postage stamps.

Titmouse — A708

**1971, May 10** **Photo.** ***Perf. 13***
**1060** A708 15y emer, blk & bis .30 .25

25th Bird Week.

Penguins — A709

**1971, June 23** **Photo.** ***Perf. 13***
**1061** A709 15y dk blue, yel & grn .30 .25

Antarctic Treaty pledging peaceful uses of and scientific co-operation in Antarctica, 10th anniv.

Goto Wakamatsu Seto Region — A710

Kujukushima ("99 Islands"), Kyushu
A711

**1971, June 26** **Photo.** ***Perf. 13***
**1062** A710 7y dark green .25 .25
**1063** A711 15y deep brown .30 .25

Saikai National Park.

Arabic Numerals and Postal Code Symbol — A712

**1971, July 1**
**1064** A712 7y emerald & red .25 .25
**1065** A712 15y blue & carmine .30 .25

Promotion for postal code system.

**Types of 1962-67 and**

Little Cuckoo
A713

Mute Swan
A714

Sika Deer
A715

Beetle
A716

Pine — A717

Noh Mask
A717a

Pheasant
A717b

Golden Eagle — A717c

Bronze Phoenix, Uji — A718

Burial Statue of Warrior, Ota — A718a

Buddha, Sculpture, 685
A718b

Tentoki Sculpture, 11th Century
A718c

Bazara-Taisho, c. 710-794
A718d

Goddess Kissho
A718e

**Inscribed "NIPPON"**

**Photo., Engr. (No. 1087)**

**1971-75** ***Perf. 13***
**1067** A713 3y emerald .25 .25
*a.* Bklt. pane of 20 ('72) 3.00
**1068** A714 5y bright blue .25 .25
**1069** A715 10y yel grn & sep ('72) .25 .25
*a.* Bklt. pane of 6 (2 #1069, 4 #1071 with gutter btwn.) ('72) 3.00
**1070** A716 12y deep brown .25 .25
**1071** A717 20y grn & sep ('72) .25 .25
*a.* Pane of 10 (5x2) ('72) 4.00
**1072** A565b 25y emer & lt ultra ('72) .40 .25
**1074** A717a 70y dp org & blk 1.00 .25
**1075** A717b 80y crim & brn 1.25 .25
**1076** A467 90y org & dk brn 1.50 .25
**1077** A717c 90y org & brn ('73) 1.50 .25
**1079** A569 120y dk brn & lt grn ('72) 2.00 .25
**1080** A718 150y lt & dk grn 2.50 .25
**1081** A570 200y dp car (18x22mm; '72) 3.50 .25
**1082** A718a 200y red brn ('74) 3.50 .30
**1083** A718b 300y dk blue ('74) 5.50 .25
**1084** A718c 400y car rose ('74) 7.00 .25
**1085** A718d 500y green ('74) 9.00 .35
**1087** A718e 1000y multi ('75) 17.50 .75
*a.* Miniature sheet of 1 22.50 22.50
*Nos. 1067-1087 (18)* 57.40 5.15

No. 1071a is imperf. on four sides.
Compare type A718a with types A1207 and A2686. Compare types A713, A714 and A718d with types A2683, A2684 and A2687.
See Nos. 1249-1250, 1254.

**Coil Stamp**

***Perf. 13 Horiz.***
**1088** A717 20y green & sep ('72) .45 .30

Boy Scout Bugler — A719

**1971, Aug. 2**
**1090** A719 15y lt blue & multi .30 .25

13th World Boy Scout Jamboree, Asagiri Plain, Aug. 2-10.

Rose and Rings — A720

**1971, Oct. 1**
**1091** A720 15y ultra & multi .30 .25

50th anniv. of Japanese Conciliation System.

Tokyo Horsedrawn Streetcar, by Yoshimura
A721

**1971, Oct. 6**
**1092** A721 50y multicolored .95 .30

Intl. Letter Writing Week. Sheets of 10 (5x2).

Emperor's Flag, Chrysanthemums and Phoenix — A722

"Beyond the Sea," by Empress Nagako
A723

**1971, Oct. 14**
**1093** A722 15y gold, vio, red & bl .30 .25
**1094** A723 15y gold, vio, red & bl .30 .25
*a.* Souv. sheet of 2, #1093-1094, imperf. .85 .85
*b.* Pair, #1093-1094 .60 .25

European trip of Emperor Hirohito and Empress Nagako, Sept. 28-Oct. 15. No. 1094a has violet map of Asia, Africa and Europe in background.

Tennis, Cape Shiono-misaki, Plum Blossoms — A724

**1971, Oct. 24 Photo. *Perf. 13***

**1095** A724 15y orange & multi .30 .25

26th National Athletic Meet, Wakayama Prefecture, Oct. 24-29.

Child's Face and "100" — A725

**1971, Oct. 27**

**1096** A725 15y pink, car & blk .30 .25

Centenary of Japanese Family Registration System.

Tiger, by Gaho Hashimoto A726

Design: No. 1098, Dragon, from "Dragon and Tiger," by Gaho Hashimoto.

**1971, Nov. 1 Engr. *Perf. 13***

**1097** A726 15y olive & multi .30 .25
**1098** A726 15y olive & multi .30 .25
*a.* Pair, #1097-1098 .75 .65

Centenary of Government Printing Works. Nos. 1097-1098 printed checkerwise.

Mt. Yotei from Lake Toya — A727

Mt. Showa-Shinzan — A728

**1971, Dec. 6**

**1099** A727 7y slate grn & yel .25 .25
**1100** A728 15y pink & vio bl .30 .25

Shikotsu-Toya National Park.

Treasure Ship — A729

**1971-72**

**1101** A729 7y emerald, gold & org .35 .30
**1102** A729 10y lt blue, org & gold .35 .30

New Year 1972. Sheets containing 3 No. 1102 were awarded as prizes in the New Year lottery. Value $1.50.

Issued: 7y, 12/10; 10y, 1/11/72.

Downhill Skiing — A730

No. 1104, Bobsledding. 50y, Figure skating, pairs.

**1972, Feb. 3 Photo. *Perf. 13***

**Size: 24x34mm**

**1103** A730 20y ultra & multi .40 .25
**1104** A730 20y ultra & multi .40 .25

**Size: 49x34mm**

**1105** A730 50y ultra & multi .90 .25
*a.* Souv. sheet of 3, #1103-1105 1.60 1.60
*Nos. 1103-1105 (3)* 1.70 .75

11th Winter Olympic Games, Sapporo, Feb. 3-13. No. 1105a has continuous design extending into margin.

Bunraku, Ningyo Jyoruri Puppet Theater

A731 A732

A733

**1972, Mar. 1 Photo. *Perf. 13½***

**1106** A731 20y gray & multi .40 .25

***Perf. 12½x13***

**1107** A732 20y multicolored .40 .25

**Lithographed and Engraved**

***Perf. 13½x13***

**1108** A733 50y multicolored .90 .25
*Nos. 1106-1108 (3)* 1.70 .75

Japanese classical entertainment.

Express Train on New Sanyo Line — A734

**1972, Mar. 15 Photo. *Perf. 13***

**1109** A734 20y multicolored .40 .25

Centenary of first Japanese railroad.

Taishaku-kyo Valley — A735

Hiba Mountains Seen from Mt. Dogo — A736

**1972, Mar. 24**

**1110** A735 20y gray & multi .40 .25
**1111** A736 20y green & multi .40 .25

Hiba-Dogo-Taishaku Quasi-National Park.

Heart and UN Emblem A737

**1972, Apr. 15**

**1112** A737 20y gray, red & black .40 .25

"Your heart is your health," World Health Day.

"A Balloon Rising," by Gakuryo Nakamura A738

**1972, Apr. 20**

**1113** A738 20y violet bl & multi .40 .25

Philatelic Week, Apr. 20-26.

Shurei Gate, Okinawa — A739

**1972, May 15**

**1114** A739 20y ultra & multi .40 .25

Ratification of the Reversion Agreement with US under which the Ryukyu Islands were returned to Japan.

Camellia — A740

**1972, May 20**

**1115** A740 20y brt grn, vio bl & yel .40 .25

National forestation campaign and 23rd Arbor Day, May 21.

Mt. Kurikoma and Kijiyama Kokeshi Doll — A741

Naruko-kyo Gorge and Naruko Kokeshi Doll — A742

**1972, June 20 Photo. *Perf. 13***

**1116** A741 20y blue & multi .40 .25
**1117** A742 20y red & multi .40 .25

Kurikoma Quasi-National Park.

Envelope, Postal Code Symbol A743

Mailbox, Postal Code Symbol A744

**1972, July 1**

**1118** A743 10y blue, blk & gray .25 .25
**1119** A744 20y emerald & org .40 .25

Publicity for the postal code system.

Mt. Hodaka A745

Mt. Tate — A746

**1972, Aug. 10 Photo. *Perf. 13***

**1120** A745 10y rose & violet .25 .25
**1121** A746 20y blue & buff .40 .25

Chubu Sangaku National Park.

Ghost in "Tamura" A747

Lady Rokujo in "Lady Hollyhock" A748

"Hagoromo" (Feather Robe) — A749

**1972, Sept. 20 Engr.**

**1122** A747 20y multicolored .40 .25

**Photo.**

**1123** A748 20y multicolored .40 .25

***Perf. 13½x13***

**1124** A749 50y multicolored .90 .25
*Nos. 1122-1124 (3)* 1.70 .75

Noh, classical public entertainment.

School Children — A750

**1972, Oct. 5 Photo. *Perf. 13***

**1125** A750 20y lt ultra, vio bl & car .40 .25

Centenary of modern education system.

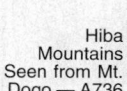

Eitai Bridge, Tokyo, by Hiroshige III — A751

**1972, Oct. 9**

**1126** A751 50y multicolored .90 .25

Intl. Letter Writing Week, Oct. 9-15.

Inauguration of Railway Service, by Hiroshige III — A752

Locomotive, Class C62 — A753

**1972, Oct. 14**

**1127** A752 20y multicolored .40 .25
**1128** A753 20y multicolored .40 .25

Centenary of Japanese railroad system.

Kendo (Fencing) and Sakurajima Volcano — A754

**1972, Oct. 22**

**1129** A754 10y yellow & multi .30 .25

27th National Athletic Meet, Kagoshima Prefecture, Oct. 22-27.

Boy Scout Shaking Hand of Cub Scout — A755

**1972, Nov. 4**

**1130** A755 20y yellow & multi .40 .25

50th anniversary of the Boy Scouts of Japan.

US Ship, Yokohama Harbor — A756

**1972, Nov. 28 Photo. *Perf. 13***

**1131** A756 20y multicolored .40 .25

Centenary of Japanese customs. Wood block by Hiroshige III (d. 1896).

"Clay Plate with Plum Blossoms" — A757

**1972, Dec. 11**

**1132** A757 10y blue & multi .30 .25

New Year 1973. Art work by Kenzan Ogata (1663-1743). Sheets containing 3 No. 1132 were awarded as prizes in the New Year lottery. Value $1.60.

Mt. Tsurugi A758

Oboke Valley — A759

**1973, Feb. 20 Photo. *Perf. 13***

**1133** A758 20y multicolored .30 .25
**1134** A759 20y multicolored .30 .25

Mt. Tsurugi Quasi-National Park.

Mt. Takao — A760

Minoo Falls — A761

**1973, Mar. 12 Photo. *Perf. 13***

**1135** A760 20y multicolored .30 .25
**1136** A761 20y multicolored .30 .25

Meiji Forests Quasi-National Park.

Phoenix Tree — A762

**1973, Apr. 7 Photo. *Perf. 13***

**1137** A762 20y brt grn, yel & dk bl .30 .25

National forestation campaign.

Sumiyoshi Shrine Visitor — A763

**1973, Apr. 20**

**1138** A763 20y multicolored .30 .25

Philatelic Week, Apr. 20-26. Design from painting by Ryusei Kishida (1891-1929) of his daughter, "A Portrait of Reiko Visiting Sumiyoshi Shrine."

Mt. Kamagatake A764

Mt. Haguro A765

**1973, May 25 Photo. *Perf. 13***

**1139** A764 20y multicolored .30 .25
**1140** A765 20y multicolored .30 .25

Suzuka Quasi-National Park.

Chichijima Beach A766

Coral Reef on Minami Island — A767

**1973, June 26**

**1141** A766 10y grnsh bl & Prus bl .30 .25
**1142** A767 20y lilac & dk pur .30 .25

Ogasawara National Park.
5th anniversary of the return of the Bonin (Ogasawara Islands) to Japan.

Tree, Postal Code Symbol A768

Mailman, Postal Code Symbol A769

**1973, July 1 Photo. *Perf. 13***

**1143** A768 10y brt green & gold .25 .25
**1144** A769 20y blue, purple & car .40 .25

Postal code system, 5th anniversary.

Sandan Gorge — A770

Mt. Shinnyu A771

**1973, Aug. 28 Photo. *Perf. 13***

**1145** A770 20y multicolored .40 .25
**1146** A771 20y multicolored .40 .25

Nishi-Chugoku-Sanchi Quasi-National Park.

Tenryu Valley — A772

Mt. Horaiji — A773

**1973, Sept. 18 Photo. *Perf. 13***

**1147** A772 20y lilac & multi .40 .25
**1148** A773 20y vio bl, lt bl & sil .40 .25

Tenryu-Okumikawa Quasi-National Park.

Cock, by Jakuchu Ito (1716-1800) A774

**1973, Oct. 6**

**1149** A774 50y gold & multi .90 .25

International Letter Writing Week, Oct. 7-13. Sheets of 10.

Woman Runner at Start — A775

**1973, Oct. 14**

**1150** A775 10y silver & multi .25 .25

28th National Athletic Meet, Chiba Prefecture, Oct. 14-19.

Kan Mon Bridge A776

**1973, Nov. 14 Engr. *Perf. 13***

**1151** A776 20y black, rose & yel .40 .25

Opening of Kan Mon Bridge connecting Honshu and Kyushu.

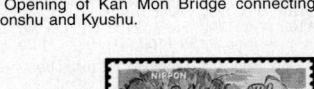

Old Man and Dog — A777

Designs: No. 1153, Old man and wife pounding rice mortar, which yields gold. No. 1154, Old man sitting in tree and landlord admiring tree.

**1973, Nov. 20 Photo.**

**1152** A777 20y multicolored .40 .25
**1153** A777 20y multicolored .40 .25
**1154** A777 20y multicolored .40 .25
*Nos. 1152-1154 (3)* 1.20 .75

Folk tale "Hanasaka-jijii" (The Old Man Who Made Trees Bloom).

Bronze Lantern, Muromachi Period — A778

**1973, Dec. 10**

**1155** A778 10y emerald, blk & org .30 .25

New Year 1974. Sheets containing 3 No. 1155 were awarded as prizes in the New Year lottery. Value $1.75.

Nijubashi, Tokyo A779

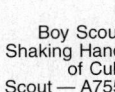

Imperial Palace, Tokyo A780

**1974, Jan. 26 Photo. *Perf. 13***

| | | | | |
|---|---|---|---|---|
| **1156** | A779 20y gold & multi | .40 | .25 |
| **1157** | A780 20y gold & multi | .40 | .25 |
| *a.* | Souv. sheet of 2, #1156-1157 | .90 | .40 |

50th anniversary of the wedding of Emperor Hirohito and Empress Nagako.

Young Wife A781

Crane Weaving A782

Cranes in Flight A783

**1974, Feb. 20 Photo. *Perf. 13***

| | | | |
|---|---|---|---|
| **1158** | A781 20y multicolored | .40 | .25 |
| **1159** | A782 20y multicolored | .40 | .25 |
| **1160** | A783 20y multicolored | .40 | .25 |
| | *Nos. 1158-1160 (3)* | 1.20 | .75 |

Folk tale "Tsuru-nyobo" (Crane becomes wife of peasant).

Marudu Falls — A784

Marine Scene — A785

**1974, Mar. 15**

| | | | |
|---|---|---|---|
| **1161** | A784 20y multicolored | .40 | .25 |
| **1162** | A785 20y multicolored | .40 | .25 |

Iriomote National Park.

"Finger," by Ito Shinsui A786

**1974, Apr. 20 Photo. *Perf. 13***

| | | | |
|---|---|---|---|
| **1163** | A786 20y multicolored | .40 | .25 |

Philatelic Week, Apr. 20-27.

Nambu Red Pine Sapling & Mt. Iwate — A787

**1974, May 18**

| | | | |
|---|---|---|---|
| **1164** | A787 20y multicolored | .30 | .25 |

National forestation campaign.

Supreme Court Building A788

**1974, May 23 Engr.**

| | | | |
|---|---|---|---|
| **1165** | A788 20y redsh brown | .30 | .25 |

Completion of Supreme Court Building, Tokyo.

Midget Using Bowl as Boat A789

Designs: No. 1167, Midget fighting demon. No. 1168, Princess and midget changed into prince with magic hammer.

**1974, June 10 Photo. *Perf. 13***

| | | | |
|---|---|---|---|
| **1166** | A789 20y yellow & multi | .40 | .25 |
| **1167** | A789 20y bister & multi | .40 | .25 |
| **1168** | A789 20y bister & multi | .40 | .25 |
| | *Nos. 1166-1168 (3)* | 1.20 | .75 |

Folk tale "Issun Hoschi" (The Story of the Mini-mini Boy).

"Police," by Kunimasa Baido — A790

**1974, June 17 *Perf. 13***

| | | | |
|---|---|---|---|
| **1169** | A790 20y multicolored | .30 | .25 |

Centenary of the Tokyo Metropolitan Police Department.

Japanese Otter A791

No. 1170, Mayailurus iriomotensis. No. 1172, Pentalagus furnessi. No. 1173, Pteropus pselaphon.

**Litho. and Engr.; Photo. and Engr. (Nos. 1172-1173)**

**1974**

| | | | |
|---|---|---|---|
| **1170** | A791 20y multicolored | .40 | .25 |
| **1171** | A791 20y multicolored | .40 | .25 |
| **1172** | A791 20y multicolored | .40 | .25 |
| **1173** | A791 20y multicolored | .40 | .25 |
| | *Nos. 1170-1173 (4)* | 1.60 | 1.00 |

Nature conservation.

Issue dates: No. 1170, 3/25; No. 1171, 6/25; No. 1172, 8/30; No. 1173, 11/15.

Transfusion Bottle, Globe, Doves — A794

**1974, July 1 Photo.**

| | | | |
|---|---|---|---|
| **1174** | A794 20y brt blue & multi | .40 | .25 |

Intl. Red Cross Blood Donations Year.

Discovery of Kaguya Hime in Shining Bamboo A795

Kaguya Hime as Grown-up Beauty A796

Kaguya Hime and Escorts Returning to Moon A797

**1974, July 29 Photo. *Perf. 13***

| | | | |
|---|---|---|---|
| **1175** | A795 20y multicolored | .40 | .25 |
| **1176** | A796 20y multicolored | .40 | .25 |
| **1177** | A797 20y multicolored | .40 | .25 |
| | *Nos. 1175-1177 (3)* | 1.20 | .75 |

Folk tale "Kaguya Hime" or "Tale of the Bamboo Cutter."

Rich and Poor Men with Wens A798

Poor Man Dancing With Spirits A798a

Design: No. 1180, Rich man with two wens, poor man without wen, spirits.

**1974, Sept. 9 Photo. *Perf. 13***

| | | | |
|---|---|---|---|
| **1178** | A798 20y multicolored | .40 | .25 |
| **1179** | A798a 20y multicolored | .40 | .25 |
| **1180** | A798 20y multicolored | .40 | .25 |
| | *Nos. 1178-1180 (3)* | 1.20 | .75 |

Folk tale "Kobutori Jiisan," or "The Old Man who had his Wen Taken by Spirits."

Goode's Projection and Diet — A799

"Aizen" by Ryushi Kawabata — A800

**1974, Oct. 1 Photo. *Perf. 13***

| | | | |
|---|---|---|---|
| **1181** | A799 20y multicolored | .30 | .25 |
| **1182** | A800 50y multicolored | .90 | .25 |

Interparliamentary Union, 61st Meeting, Tokyo, Nov. 2-11.

Pine and Hawk, by Sesson — A801

**1974, Oct. 7**

| | | | |
|---|---|---|---|
| **1183** | A801 50y sepia, blk & dk brn | .90 | .25 |

Intl. Letter Writing Week, Oct. 6-12.

UPU Emblem — A802

Tending Cow, Fan by Sotatsu Tawaraya — A803

**1974, Oct. 9**

| | | | |
|---|---|---|---|
| **1184** | A802 20y multicolored | .30 | .25 |
| **1185** | A803 50y multicolored | .90 | .25 |

Centenary of Universal Postal Union.

Soccer Players and Sailboat — A804

**1974, Oct. 20 Photo.**

| | | | |
|---|---|---|---|
| **1186** | A804 10y multicolored | .25 | .25 |

29th National Athletic Meet, Ibaraki Prefecture, Oct. 20-25.

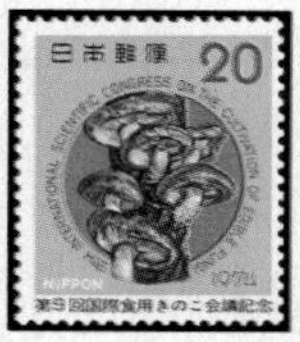

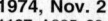

Various Mushrooms — A805

**1974, Nov. 2**

| | | | |
|---|---|---|---|
| **1187** | A805 20y multicolored | .40 | .25 |

9th International Congress on the Cultivation of Edible Fungi, Japan, Nov. 4-13.

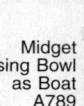

Steam Locomotive Class D51 — A806

Class C57 — A807

Designs: Steam locomotives.

**1974, Nov. 26 Photo.** *Perf. 13*

| | | | |
|---|---|---|---|
| **1188** | A806 20y shown | .45 | .25 |
| **1189** | A807 20y shown | .45 | .25 |
| *a.* | Pair, #1188-1189 | .95 | .60 |

**1975, Feb. 25**

| | | | |
|---|---|---|---|
| **1190** | A806 20y Class D52 | .45 | .25 |
| **1191** | A807 20y Class C58 | .45 | .25 |
| *a.* | Pair, #1190-1191 | .95 | .60 |

Class 8620 — A808

Class C11 — A809

**1975, Apr. 3**

| | | | |
|---|---|---|---|
| **1192** | A808 20y shown | .45 | .25 |
| **1193** | A809 20y shown | .45 | .25 |
| *a.* | Pair, #1192-1193 | .95 | .60 |

**1975, May 15**

| | | | |
|---|---|---|---|
| **1194** | A806 20y Class 9600 | .45 | .25 |
| **1195** | A807 20y Class C51 | .45 | .25 |
| *a.* | Pair, #1194-1195 | .95 | .60 |

**1975, June 10 Photo. & Engr.**

| | | | |
|---|---|---|---|
| **1196** | A806 20y Class 7100 | .45 | .25 |
| **1197** | A806 20y Class 150 | .45 | .25 |
| *a.* | Pair, #1196-1197 | .95 | .60 |
| | *Nos. 1188-1197 (10)* | 4.50 | 2.50 |

Japanese National Railways.

Ornamental Nail Cover, Katsura Palace — A810

**1974, Dec. 10**

| | | | |
|---|---|---|---|
| **1198** | A810 10y blue & multi | .30 | .25 |

New Year 1975. Sheets containing 3 No. 1198 were awarded as prizes in the New Year Lottery. Value $1.60.

Short-tailed Albatrosses A811

Bonin Island Honey-eater A812

Temminck's Robin A813

Ryukyu-Yamagame Tortoise — A814

Design: No. 1200, Japanese cranes.

**1975-76 Photo. & Engr.** *Perf. 13*

| | | | |
|---|---|---|---|
| **1199** | A811 20y multicolored | .40 | .25 |
| **1200** | A811 20y multicolored | .40 | .25 |
| **1201** | A812 20y multicolored | .40 | .25 |
| **1202** | A813 50y multicolored | .90 | .25 |
| **1203** | A814 50y multicolored | .90 | .25 |
| | *Nos. 1199-1203 (5)* | 3.00 | 1.25 |

Nature conservation.

Issued: No. 1199, 1/16; No. 1200, 2/13; No. 1201, 8/8; No. 1202; 2/27/76; No. 1203, 3/25/76.

Taro Urashima Releasing Turtle A815

Palace of the Sea God and Fish A816

Smoke from Casket Making Taro an Old Man A817

**1975, Jan. 28 Photo.** *Perf. 13*

| | | | |
|---|---|---|---|
| **1204** | A815 20y multicolored | .40 | .25 |
| **1205** | A816 20y multicolored | .40 | .25 |
| **1206** | A817 20y multicolored | .40 | .25 |
| | *Nos. 1204-1206 (3)* | 1.20 | .75 |

Folk tale "Legend of Taro Urashima."

Kan-mon-sho (Seeing and Hearing), by Shiko Munakata — A818

**1975, Mar. 20 Photo.** *Perf. 13*

| | | | |
|---|---|---|---|
| **1207** | A818 20y brown & multi | .40 | .25 |

Japan Broadcasting Corp., 50th anniv.

Old Man Feeding Mouse A819

Man Following Mouse Underground — A820

Mice Entertaining and Bringing Gifts A821

**1975, Apr. 15 Photo.** *Perf. 13*

| | | | |
|---|---|---|---|
| **1208** | A819 20y multicolored | .40 | .25 |
| **1209** | A820 20y multicolored | .40 | .25 |
| **1210** | A821 20y multicolored | .40 | .25 |
| | *Nos. 1208-1210 (3)* | 1.20 | .75 |

Folk tale "Paradise for the Mice."

Matsuura Screen (detail), 16th Century — A822

**1975, Apr. 21**

| | | | |
|---|---|---|---|
| **1211** | 20y denomination at lower left | .40 | .25 |
| **1212** | 20y denomination at lower right | .40 | .25 |
| *a.* | A822 Pair, #1211-1212 | .80 | .65 |

Philatelic Week, Apr. 21-27.

Oil Derricks, Congress Emblem — A824

**1975, May 10 Photo.** *Perf. 13*

| | | | |
|---|---|---|---|
| **1213** | A824 20y multicolored | .30 | .25 |

9th World Petroleum Cong., Tokyo, May 11-16.

Trees and River — A825

**1975, May 24**

| | | | |
|---|---|---|---|
| **1214** | A825 20y green & multi | .30 | .25 |

National forestation campaign.

IWY Emblem, Sun and Woman — A826

**1975, June 23**

| | | | |
|---|---|---|---|
| **1215** | A826 20y orange & multi | .30 | .25 |

International Women's Year 1975.

Okinawan Dancer, EXPO 75 Emblem A827

Birds in Flight (Bingata) A828

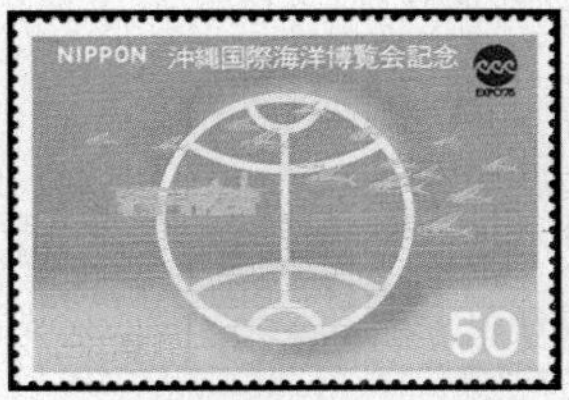

Aquapolis and Globe — A829

**1975, July 19 Photo.** *Perf. 13*

| | | | |
|---|---|---|---|
| **1216** | A827 20y ultra & multi | .30 | .25 |
| **1217** | A828 30y blue grn & multi | .50 | .25 |
| **1218** | A829 50y ultra & multi | .90 | .25 |
| *a.* | Souv. sheet of 3, #1216-1218 | 1.75 | 1.75 |
| | *Nos. 1216-1218 (3)* | 1.70 | .75 |

Oceanexpo 75, 1st Intl. Ocean Exposition, Okinawa, July 20, 1975-Jan. 18, 1976.

**Historic Ship Issue**

Kentoshi-sen 7th-9th Centuries — A830

Ships: No. 1220, Kenmin-sen, 7th-9th cent. No. 1221, Goshuin-sen, merchant ship, 16th-17th cent. No. 1222, Tenchi-maru, state barge, built 1630. No. 1223, Sengoku-bune (cargo ship) and fishing vessel. No. 1224, Shoheimaru, 1852, European-type sailing ship. No. 1225, Taisei-maru, four-mast bark training ship, 1903. No. 1226, Tenyomaru, first Japanese passenger liner, 1907. No. 1227, Asama-maru, passenger liner. No. 1228, Kinai-maru, transpacific freighter and Statue of Liberty. No. 1229, Container ship. No. 1230, Tanker.

**1975-76 Engr.** *Perf. 13*

| | | | |
|---|---|---|---|
| **1219** | A830 20y rose red | .40 | .25 |
| **1220** | A830 20y sepia | .40 | .25 |
| *a.* | Pair, #1219-1220 | .80 | .65 |
| **1221** | A830 20y lt olive | .40 | .25 |
| **1222** | A830 20y dark blue | .40 | .25 |
| *a.* | Pair, #1221-1222 | .80 | .65 |
| **1223** | A830 50y violet blue | .90 | .25 |
| **1224** | A830 50y lilac | .90 | .25 |
| *a.* | Pair, #1223-1224 | 1.90 | 1.00 |
| **1225** | A830 50y gray | .90 | .25 |
| **1226** | A830 50y dark brown | .90 | .25 |
| *a.* | Pair, #1225-1226 | 1.90 | 1.00 |
| **1227** | A830 50y olive green | .90 | .25 |
| **1228** | A830 50y olive brown | .90 | .25 |
| *a.* | Pair, #1227-1228 | 1.90 | 1.00 |
| **1229** | A830 50y ultra | .90 | .25 |
| **1230** | A830 50y violet blue | .90 | .25 |
| *a.* | Pair, #1229-1230 | 1.90 | 1.00 |
| | *Nos. 1219-1230 (12)* | 8.80 | 3.00 |

Printed checkerwise in sheets of 20.

Issued: Nos. 1219-1220, 8/30; Nos. 1221-1222, 9/25; Nos. 1223-1224, 3/11/76; Nos. 1225-1226, 4/12/76; Nos. 1227-1228, 6/1/76; Nos. 1229-1230, 8/18/76.

Apple and Apple Tree — A831

**1975, Sept. 17 Photo.** *Perf. 13*

| | | | |
|---|---|---|---|
| **1231** | A831 20y gray, black & red | .35 | .25 |

Centenary of apple cultivation in Japan.

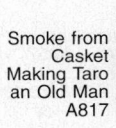

Peacock, by Korin Ogata — A832

**1975, Oct. 6** **Photo.** ***Perf. 13***

**1232** A832 50y gold & multi .90 .25

Intl. Letter Writing Week, Oct. 6-12.

American Flag and Cherry Blossoms A833

Japanese Flag and Dogwood A834

**1975, Oct. 14**

**1233** A833 20y ultra & multi .35 .25

**1234** A834 20y green & multi .35 .25

*a.* Souv. sheet of 2, #1233-1234 1.00 .75

Visit of Emperor Hirohito and Empress Nagako to the United States, Oct. 1-14.

Savings Box and Coins — A835

**1975, Oct. 24**

**1235** A835 20y multicolored .30 .25

Japan's Postal Savings System, centenary.

Weight Lifter — A836

**1975, Oct. 25**

**1236** A836 10y multicolored .25 .25

30th National Athletic Meet, Mie Prefecture, Oct. 26-31.

Papier-mache Dragon, Fukushima Prefecture — A837

**1975, Dec. 13** **Photo.** ***Perf. 13***

**1237** A837 10y multicolored .30 .25

New Year 1976. Sheets containing 3 No. 1237 were awarded as prizes in the New Year Lottery. Value $1.75.

**Types of 1963-74 and**

Japanese Narcissus A841

Noh Mask, Old Man A843

Guardian Dog, Katori Shrine A845

Sho-Kannon, Yakushiji Temple A846

**Inscribed "NIPPON"**

Designs: 50y, Nyoirin Kannon, Chuguji Temple. 150y, Bronze phoenix, Uji. 200y, Clay burial figure of warrior, Ota.

**1976-79** **Photo.** ***Perf. 13***

**1244** A565f 50y emerald .90 .25

*a.* Bklt. panes of 2 & 4 with gutter 6.00

**1245** A841 60y multicolored 1.10 .25

**1248** A843 140y lil rose & lil 2.50 .25

**1249** A718 150y red org & brn 2.75 .25

**1250** A718a 200y red orange 3.75 .25

**1251** A845 250y blue 4.50 .25

**1253** A846 350y dk violet brn 6.25 .25

*Nos. 1244-1253 (7)* 21.75 1.75

**Coil Stamps**

***Perf. 13 Horiz.***

**1254** A715 10y yel grn & sep ('79) .25 .25

**1256** A565f 50y emerald 1.25 .25

**1257** A567c 100y ver & blk ('79) 1.90 .30

*Nos. 1254-1257 (3)* 3.40 .80

See No. 1631.

Hikone Folding Screen (detail), 17th Century — A850

**1976, Apr. 20** **Photo.** ***Perf. 13***

**1258** 50y denomination at lower right .90 .25

**1259** 50y denomination at upper right .90 .25

*a.* A850 Pair, #1258-1259 1.90 1.25

Philatelic Week, Apr. 20-26.

Plum Blossoms, Cedars, Mt. Tsukuba — A852

**1976, May 22**

**1260** A852 50y multicolored .90 .25

National forestation campaign.

Green Tree Frog — A853

Bitterlings A854

Sticklebacks A855

**1976** **Photo. & Engr.** ***Perf. 13***

**1261** A853 50y multicolored .90 .25

**1262** A854 50y multicolored .90 .25

**1263** A855 50y multicolored .90 .25

*Nos. 1261-1263 (3)* 2.70 .75

Nature conservation.

Issued: No. 1261, 7/20; No. 1262, 8/26; No. 1263, 9/16.

Crows, by Yosa Buson — A856

**1976, Oct. 6** **Photo.** ***Perf. 13***

**1264** A856 100y gray, blk & buff 1.75 .25

Intl. Letter Writing Week, Oct. 6-12.

Gymnasts and Stadium — A857

**1976, Oct. 23** **Photo.** ***Perf. 13***

**1265** A857 20y multicolored .30 .25

31st National Athletic Meet, Saga Prefecture, Oct. 24-29.

Cable, Cable Ship, Map of East China Sea — A858

**1976, Oct. 25**

**1266** A858 50y blue, blk & silver .90 .25

Opening of Sino-Japanese cable between Shanghai and Reihoku-cho, Kumamoto Prefecture.

Classical Court Dance A859

Imperial Coach A860

**1976, Nov. 10** **Photo.** ***Perf. 13***

**1267** A859 50y multicolored .90 .25

**1268** A860 50y multicolored .90 .25

*a.* Souv. sheet of 2, #1267-1268 1.90 1.90

Emperor Hirohito's accession to the throne, 50th anniversary.

Kindergarten Class — A861

**1976, Nov. 16**

**1269** A861 50y multicolored .90 .25

Centenary of first kindergarten in Japan.

Healthy Family A862

**1976, Nov. 24**

**1270** A862 50y multicolored .90 .25

Natl. Health Insurance, 50th anniv.

Bamboo Toy Snake — A863

**1976, Dec. 1** **Photo.** ***Perf. 13***

**1271** A863 20y multicolored .40 .30

New Year 1977. Sheets containing 2 No. 1271 were awarded as prizes in the New Year lottery. Value $1.75.

**National Treasures**

East Pagoda, Yakushiji Temple, c. 730 — A864

Deva King in Armor Holding Spear, Nara Period A865

**1976, Dec. 9** **Photo.** ***Perf. 13***

**1272** A864 50y multicolored .90 .25

**Engr.**

**1273** A865 100y green & multi 1.75 .30

Golden Pavilion, Toshodai-ji Temple, 8th Century — A866

Praying Women, from Heike Nokyo Sutra, 12th Century A867

**Photogravure and Engraved**

**1977, Jan. 20** *Perf. 13*

**1274** A866 50y multicolored .90 .25

**Photo.**

**1275** A867 100y multicolored 1.75 .30

Comic Picture Scroll, Attributed to Toba Sojo Kakuyu (1053-1140) — A868

Saint on Cloud, 11th Century Wood Carving, Byodoin Temple A869

**1977, Mar. 25 Photo.** *Perf. 13*

**1276** A868 50y multicolored .90 .25

**Engr.**

**1277** A869 100y multicolored 1.75 .30

Noblemen on Way to Court, from Picture Scroll, Heian Period — A870

Statue of Seitaka-doji, Messenger, Kamakura Period A871

**1977, June 27 Photo.** *Perf. 13*

**1278** A870 50y multicolored .90 .25

**Engr.**

**1279** A871 100y multicolored 1.75 .30

The Recluse Han Shan, 14th Century Painting — A872

Tower, Matsumoto Castle, 16th Century — A873

**1977, Aug. 25 Photo.** *Perf. 13*

**1280** A872 50y multicolored .90 .25

**Photogravure and Engraved**

**1281** A873 100y black & multi 1.75 .30

Pine and Flowers, Chishakuin Temple, Kyoto, 1591 — A874

Main Hall, Kiyomizu Temple, 1633 — A875

**1977, Nov. 16 Photo.** *Perf. 13*

**1282** A874 50y multicolored .90 .25

**Engr.**

**1283** A875 100y multicolored 1.75 .30

Scene from Tale of Genji, by Sotatsu Tawaraya — A876

Inkstone Case, by Koetsu Honami — A877

**1978, Jan. 26 Photo.** *Perf. 13*

**1284** A876 50y multicolored .90 .25

**Photogravure and Engraved**

**1285** A877 100y black & multi 1.75 .30

Family Enjoying Cool Evening, by Morikage Kusumi — A878

Yomeimon, Toshogu Shrine, 1636 — A879

**1978, Mar. 3 Photo.** *Perf. 13*

**1286** A878 50y gray & multi .90 .25

**Photogravure and Engraved**

**1287** A879 100y multicolored 1.75 .30

Horseshoe Crabs A884

Graphium Doson Albidum — A885

Firefly A886

Cicada — A887

Dragonfly — A888

**1977 Photo.** *Perf. 13*

**1292** A884 50y multicolored .95 .25

**Photogravure and Engraved**

**1293** A885 50y multicolored .95 .25
**1294** A886 50y multicolored .95 .25
**1295** A887 50y multicolored .95 .25

**Photo.**

**1296** A888 50y multicolored .95 .25
*Nos. 1292-1296 (5)* 4.75 1.25

Issued: No. 1292, 2/18; No. 1293, 5/18; No. 1294, 7/22; No. 1295, 8/15; No. 1296, 9/14.

Figure Skating — A889

Figure Skating Pair — A890

**1977, Mar. 1**

**1297** A889 50y silver & multi .90 .25
**1298** A890 50y silver & multi .90 .25

World Figure Skating Championships, National Yoyogi Stadium, March 1-6.

Sun Shining on Forest — A891

**1977, Apr. 16 Photo.** *Perf. 13*

**1299** A891 50y green & multi .90 .25

National forestation campaign.

Weavers and Dyers (Detail from Folding Screen) — A892

**1977, Apr. 20**

**1300** 50y denomination at lower left .90 .25
**1301** 50y denomination at upper left .90 .25
*a.* A892 Pair, #1300-1301 1.90 .90

Philatelic Week, Apr. 20-26.

Nurses A894

**1977, May 30 Photo.** *Perf. 13*

**1302** A894 50y multicolored .90 .25

16th Quadrennial Congress of the Intl. Council of Nurses, Tokyo, May 30-June 3.

Fast Breeder Reactor, Central Part — A895

**1977, June 6**

**1303** A895 50y multicolored .90 .25

Experimental fast breeder reactor "Joyo," which began operating Apr. 24, 1977.

Workers and Safety Emblems A896

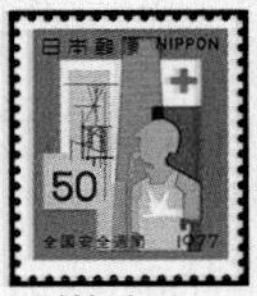

Work on High-rise Buildings A897

Cargo Unloading A898

Machinery Work A899

**1977, July 1**

**1304** A896 50y multicolored .90 .25
**1305** A897 50y multicolored .90 .25
**1306** A898 50y multicolored .90 .25
**1307** A899 50y multicolored .90 .25
*a.* Block or strip of 4, #1304-1307 4.00 1.00

National Safety Week, July 1-July 7.

Carrier Pigeons, Mail Box, UPU Emblem A900

UPU Emblem, Postal Service Flag of Meiji Era, world Map A900a

**1977, June 20 Photo. *Perf. 13***

**1308** A900 50y multicolored .90 .25
**1309** A900a 100y multicolored 1.75 .30
*a.* Souv. sheet of 2, #1308-1309 2.75 2.00

Cent. of Japan's admission to the UPU.

Surgeon in Operating Room — A901

**1977, Sept. 3 Photo. *Perf. 13***

**1310** A901 50y multicolored .90 .25

27th Cong. of the Intl. Surgeon's Society on the 75th anniv. of its founding, Kyoto, 9/3-8.

Child Using Telephone, Map of New Cable Route — A902

**1977, Aug. 26**

**1311** A902 50y multicolored .90 .25

Inauguration of underwater telephone cable linking Okinawa, Luzon and Hong Kong.

Early Speaker, Waves and Telegraph Key — A903

**1977, Sept. 24 Photo. *Perf. 13***

**1312** A903 50y multicolored .90 .25

50th anniversary of amateur radio in Japan.

Bicyclist, Mt. Iwaki and Iwaki River — A904

**1977, Oct. 1**

**1313** A904 20y multicolored .35 .25

32nd National Athletic Meet, Aomori Prefecture, Oct. 2-7.

Flowers and Ducks, Attributed to Hasegawa Tohaku — A905

**1977, Oct. 6**

**1314** A905 100y multicolored 1.75 .30

Intl. Letter Writing Week, Oct. 6-12.

Dinosaur, Stars, Museum A906

**1977, Nov. 2 Photo. *Perf. 13***

**1315** A906 50y multicolored .90 .25

Centenary of National Science Museum.

Decorated Horse, Fushimi Toy — A907

**1977, Dec. 1 Photo. *Perf. 13***

**1316** A907 20y multicolored .40 .30

New Year 1978. Sheets containing 2 No. 1316 were awarded as prizes in the New Year lottery. Value $1.75.

Tokyo Subway, 1927 A908

**1977, Dec. 6**

**1317** 50y shown .90 .25
**1318** 50y Subway, 1977 .90 .25
*a.* A908 Pair, #1317-1318 2.00 .90

Tokyo Subway, 50th anniversary.

Primrose — A909

Pinguicula Ramosa — A910

Dicentra — A911

**1978 Photo. & Engr. *Perf. 13***

**1319** A909 50y multicolored .90 .25
**1320** A910 50y multicolored .90 .25
**1321** A911 50y multicolored .90 .25
*Nos. 1319-1321 (3)* 2.70 .75

Nature protection.

Issued: No. 1319, 4/12; No. 1320, 6/8; No. 1321, 7/25.

Kanbun Bijinzu Folding Screen, Edo Period — A912

**1978, Apr. 20 Photo. *Perf. 13***

**1322** 50y inscribed at left .90 .25
**1323** 50y inscribed at right .90 .25
*a.* A912 Pair, #1322-1323 1.90 .90

Philatelic Week, Apr. 16-22.

Rotary Emblem, Mt. Fuji — A914

**1978, May 13 Photo. *Perf. 13***

**1324** A914 50y multicolored .90 .25

69th Rotary International Convention, Tokyo, May 14-18.

Congress Emblem, by Taro Okamoto — A915

**1978, May 15**

**1325** A915 50y multicolored .90 .25

23rd International Ophthalmological Congress, Kyoto, May 14-20.

Narita International Airport, Tokyo — A916

**1978, May 20**

**1326** A916 50y multicolored .90 .25

Opening of Tokyo International Airport.

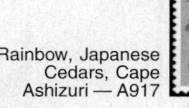

Rainbow, Japanese Cedars, Cape Ashizuri — A917

**1978, May 20**

**1327** A917 50y multicolored .90 .25

National forestation campaign.

Lion, by Sotatsu Tawaraya, Lions Emblem — A918

**1978, June 21 Photo. *Perf. 13***

**1328** A918 50y multicolored .90 .25

61st Lions Intl. Convention, Tokyo, 6/21-24.

**Sumo Print Issues**

Grand Champion Hidenoyama with Sword Bearer and Herald, by Kunisada I (Toyokuni III) — A919

Ekoin Drum Tower, Ryogoku, by Hiroshige — A921

**Photogravure and Engraved**

**1978, July 1 *Perf. 13***

**1329** 50y multicolored .90 .25
**1330** 50y multicolored .90 .25
*a.* A919 Pair, #1329-1330 1.90 .90

**Photo.**

**1331** A921 50y multicolored .95 .25
*Nos. 1329-1331 (3)* 2.75 .75

Champions Tanikaze and Onogawa in Ring-entry Ceremony, 1782, by Shunsho — A922

Jimmaku, Raiden and Referee Shonosuke, 1791 Bout, by Shun'ei — A924

**Photogravure and Engraved**

**1978, Sept. 9** ***Perf. 13***

**1332** 50y multicolored .90 .25
**1333** 50y multicolored .90 .25
*a.* A922 Pair, #1332-1333 1.90 .90
**1334** A924 50y multicolored .90 .25
*Nos. 1332-1334 (3)* 2.70 .75

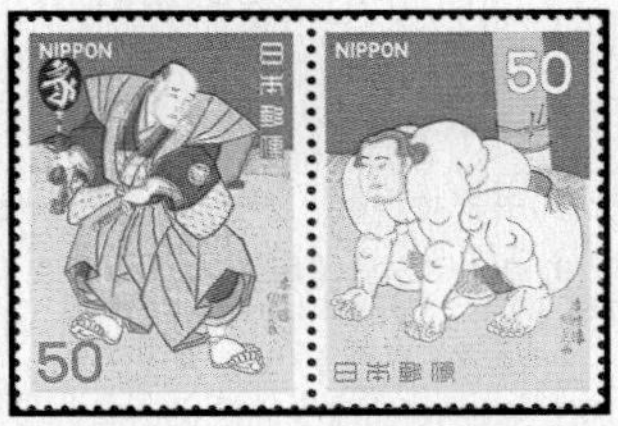

Referee Shonosuke and Champion Onomatsu, by Kunisada I — A925

Children's Sumo Play, by Utamaro — A927

**1978, Nov. 11** ***Perf. 13***

**1335** 50y multicolored .90 .25
**1336** 50y multicolored .90 .25
*a.* A925 Pair, #1335-1336 1.90 .90
**1337** A927 50y multicolored .90 .25
*Nos. 1335-1337 (3)* 2.70 .75

Wrestlers on Ryogoku Bridge, by Kunisada I — A928

Bow-receiving Ceremony at Tournament, by Kunisada II — A930

**1979, Jan. 13** ***Perf. 13***

**1338** 50y multicolored .90 .25
**1339** 50y multicolored .90 .25
*a.* A928 Pair, #1338-1339 1.90 .90
**1340** A930 50y multicolored .90 .25
*Nos. 1338-1340 (3)* 2.70 .75

Takekuma and Iwamigata (Hidenoyama) Wrestling, by Kuniyoshi — A931

Daidozan (Great Child Mountain) in Ring-entry Ceremony, by Sharaku — A933

**1979, Mar. 10** ***Perf. 13***

**1341** 50y multicolored .90 .25
**1342** 50y multicolored .90 .25
*a.* A931 Pair, #1341-1342 1.90 .90
**1343** A933 50y multicolored .90 .25
*Nos. 1341-1343 (3)* 2.70 .75

Radio Gymnastics Emblem — A934

**1978, Aug. 1** **Photo.** ***Perf. 13***

**1344** A934 50y multicolored .90 .25

Radio gymnastics program exercises, 50th anniversary.

Chamber of Commerce and Industry A935

**1978, Aug. 28** **Photo.** ***Perf. 13***

**1345** A935 50y multicolored .90 .25

Tokyo Chamber of Commerce, centenary.

Symbolic Sculptures, Tokyo Stock Exchange — A936

**1978, Sept. 14** **Engr.** ***Perf. 13***

**1346** A936 50y lilac, grn & brn .90 .25

Centenary of the Tokyo and Osaka Stock Exchanges.

Flowering Plum with Pheasant, from Screen, Tenkyuin Temple — A937

**1978, Oct. 6** **Photo.** ***Perf. 13***

**1347** A937 100y multicolored 1.75 .30

Intl. Letter Writing Week, Oct. 6-12.

Softball and Mt. Yarigatake — A938

**1978, Oct. 14**

**1348** A938 20y multicolored .35 .25

33rd National Athletic Meet, Nagano Prefecture, Oct. 15-20.

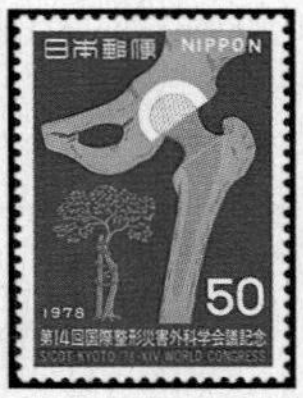

Artificial Hip, Orthopedists' Emblem — A939

**1978, Oct. 16**

**1349** A939 50y multicolored .90 .25

14th World Cong. of Intl. Soc. of Orthopedic Surgeons (50th anniv.), Kyoto, Oct. 15-20.

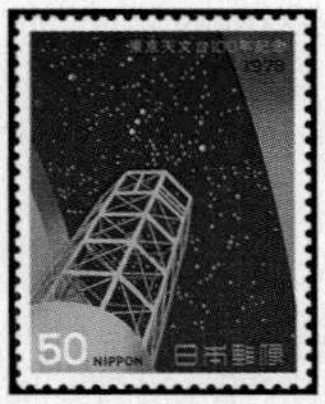

Telescope and Stars — A940

**1978, Dec. 1** **Photo.**

**1350** A940 50y multicolored .90 .25

Tokyo Astronomical Observatory, cent.

Sheep Bell, Nakayama Toy — A941

**1978, Dec. 4**

**1351** A941 20y multicolored .40 .30

New Year 1979. Sheets containing 2 No. 1351 were awarded as prizes in the New Year Lottery. Value $1.75.

Family, Human Rights Emblem — A942

**1978, Dec. 4**

**1352** A942 50y multicolored .90 .25

Human Rights Week, Dec. 4-10.

Hands Shielding Children — A943

**1979, Feb. 16** **Photo.** ***Perf. 13***

**1353** A943 50y multicolored .90 .25

Education of the handicapped, centenary.

Telephone Dials — A944

**1979, Mar. 14** **Photo.** ***Perf. 13***

**1354** A944 50y multicolored .90 .25

Nation-wide telephone automatization completion.

Sketch of Man, by Leonardo da Vinci — A945

**Photogravure and Engraved**

**1979, Apr. 7** ***Perf. 13***

**1355** A945 50y multicolored .90 .25

Centenary of promulgation of State Medical Act, initiating modern medicine.

Standing Beauties, Middle Edo Period — A946

**1979, Apr. 20** **Photo.**

**1356** 50y multicolored .90 .25
**1357** 50y multicolored .90 .25
*a.* A946 Pair, #1356-1357 1.90 .90

Philatelic Week, Apr. 16-22.

Mt. Horaiji and Maple — A948

**1979, May 26** **Photo.** ***Perf. 13***

**1358** A948 50y multicolored .90 .25

National forestation campaign.

**Modern Japanese Art Issue**

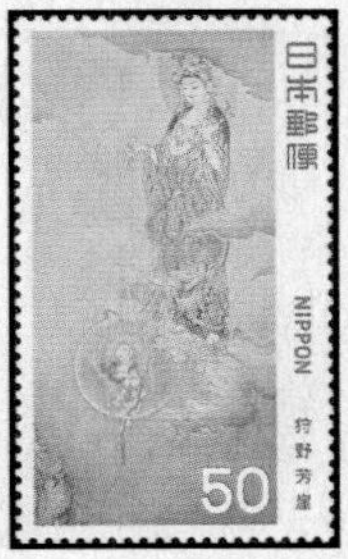

Merciful Mother Goddess, by Kano Hogai — A949

Sea God's Princess, by Aoki Shigeru — A950

**1979, May 30** **Photo.** ***Perf. 13***

**1359** A949 50y multicolored .90 .25
**1360** A950 50y multicolored .90 .25

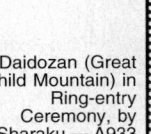

Fire Dance, by Gyoshu Hayami — A951

Leaning Figure, by Tetsugoro Yorozu — A952

**1979, June 25 Photo. *Perf. 13***

**1361** A951 50y red & multi .90 .25

**Photogravure and Engraved**

**1362** A952 50y red & multi .90 .25

The Black Cat, by Shunso Hishida — A953

Kinyo, by Sotaro Yasui — A954

**1979, Sept. 21 Photo. *Perf. 13***

**1363** A953 50y multicolored .90 .25

**1364** A954 50y multicolored .90 .25

Nude, by Kagaku Murakami A955

Harvest, by Asai Chu — A956

**Photogravure and Engraved**

**1979, Nov. 22 *Perf. 13***

**1365** A955 50y multicolored .90 .25

**1366** A956 50y multicolored .90 .25

Salmon, by Yuichi Takahashi A956a

Hall of the Supreme Buddha, by Kokei Kabayashi A956b

**Photogravure and Engraved**

**1980, Feb. 22 *Perf. 13½***

**1367** A956a 50y multicolored .90 .25

**Photo.**

**1368** A956b 50y multicolored .90 .25

Quarantine Officers, Ships, Plane, Microscope A957

**1979, July 14 Photo.**

**1369** A957 50y multicolored .90 .25

Centenary of Japanese Quarantine system.

Girl Mailing Letter — A958

Hakata Doll with Letter-paper Roll — A959

**1979, July 23**

**1370** A958 20y multicolored .30 .25

**1371** A959 50y multicolored .90 .25

Letter Writing Day.

Pitcher, Baseball with Black Lion Emblem — A960

**1979, July 27**

**1372** A960 50y multicolored .90 .25

50th National Inter-city Amateur Baseball Tournament, Tokyo, August.

Girl Floating in Space A961

Design: No. 1374, Boy floating in space.

**1979, Aug. 1**

**1373** A961 50y magenta & multi .90 .25

**1374** A961 50y blue & multi .90 .25

*a.* Souv. sheet of 2, #1373-1374 1.90 1.90

International Year of the Child.

**Japanese Song Issue**

Moon over Castle, by Rentaro Taki A962

Evening Glow, by Shin Kusakawa A963

**1979, Aug. 24 Photo. & Engr.**

**1375** A962 50y multicolored .90 .25

**1376** A963 50y multicolored .90 .25

Maple Leaves, by Teiichi Okano A964

The Birthplace, by Teiichi Okano — A965

**1979, Nov. 26**

**1377** A964 50y multicolored .90 .25

**1378** A965 50y multicolored .90 .25

Winter Landscape A966

Mt. Fuji — A967

**1980, Jan. 28 *Perf. 13***

**1379** A966 50y multicolored .90 .25

**1380** A967 50y multicolored .90 .25

Spring Brook A968

Cherry Blossoms A969

**1980, Mar. 21**

**1381** A968 50y multicolored .90 .25

**1382** A969 50y multicolored .90 .25

*Nos. 1375-1382 (8)* 7.20 2.00

Great Owl, by Okyo Maruyama — A970

**1979, Oct. 8 Photo. *Perf. 13***

**1383** A970 100y multicolored 1.75 .30

Intl. Letter Writing Week, Oct. 8-14.

Runner — A971

**1979, Oct. 13**

**1384** A971 20y multicolored .35 .25

34th National Athletic Meet, Miyazaki, Oct. 4-19.

"ITU," Globe — A972

**1979, Oct. 13 Litho. *Perf. 13½***

**1385** A972 50y multicolored .90 .25

Admission to ITU, cent.

Woman and Fetus — A973

**1979, Nov. 12 Photo.**

**1386** A973 50y multicolored .90 .25

9th World Congress of Gynecology and Obstetrics, Tokyo, Oct. 25-31.

Happy Monkeys, Osaka Toy — A974

**1979, Dec. 1 Photo. *Perf. 13x13½***

**1387** A974 20y multicolored .40 .30

New Year 1980. Sheets of 2 No. 1387 were New Year Lottery prizes. Value $1.75.

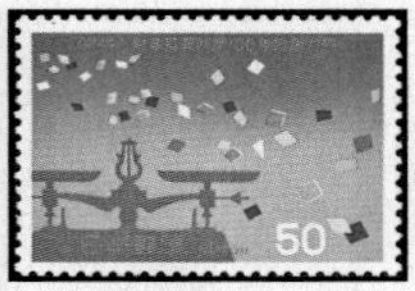

Government Auditing Centenary A975

**1980, Mar. 5 Photo. *Perf. 13½***
**1388** A975 50y multicolored .90 .25

Scenes of Outdoor Play in Spring, by Sukenobu Nishikawa — A976

**1980, Apr. 21 Photo. *Perf. 13½***
**1389** 50y multicolored .90 .25
**1390** 50y multicolored .90 .25
*a.* A976 Pair, #1389-1390 1.90 .90

Philatelic Week, Apr. 21-27. Sheets of 10.

**Japanese Song Issue**

The Sea — A978

The Night of the Hazy Moon — A979

Memories of Summer — A981

The Sun Flag — A980

**1980 Photo. & Engr. *Perf. 13***
**1391** A978 50y multicolored .90 .25
**1392** A979 50y multicolored .90 .25
**1393** A980 50y multicolored .90 .25
**1394** A981 50y multicolored .90 .25
*Nos. 1391-1394 (4)* 3.60 1.00

Issued: Nos. 1391-1392, 4/28; Nos. 1393-1394, 6/16.

The Red Dragonfly A982

Song by the Sea — A983

**1980, Sept. 18 *Perf. 13***
**1395** A982 50y multicolored .90 .25
**1396** A983 50y multicolored .90 .25

Lullaby A984

Coconut, by Toraji Ohnaka — A985

**1981, Feb. 9 *Perf. 13***
**1397** A984 60y multicolored 1.00 .25
**1398** A985 60y multicolored 1.00 .25

Spring Has Come, by Tatsuyuki Takano — A986

Cherry Blossoms, by Hagoromo Takeshima A987

**1981, Mar. 10 *Perf. 13***
**1399** A986 60y multicolored 1.00 .25
**1400** A987 60y multicolored 1.00 .25

**Modern Japanese Art Issue**

Dancers, by Seiki Kuroda — A988

Mother and Child, by Shoen Uemura A989

**1980, May 12 Photo. *Perf. 13½***
**1401** A988 50y multicolored .90 .25
**1402** A989 50y multicolored .90 .25

The Black Fan, by Takeji Fujishima — A990

Dear Me . . . It's a Shower, by Seiho Takeuchi A991

**1980, July 7 Photo. *Perf. 13½***
**1403** A990 50y multicolored .90 .25
**1404** A991 50y multicolored .90 .25

Woman, by Morie Ogiwara — A992

Kurofuneya, by Yumeji Takehisa — A993

**1980, Oct. 27 Photo. *Perf. 13½***
**1405** A992 50y multicolored .90 .25
**1406** A993 50y multicolored .90 .25

Nippon Maru, Institute Emblem — A994

**1980, May 17**
**1407** A994 50y multicolored .90 .25

Institute for Nautical Training, training ships Nippon Maru and Kaio Maru, 50th anniversary.

Mt. Gozaisho-dake, Cedars, Flowers — A995

**1980, May 24 *Perf. 13x13½***
**1408** A995 50y multicolored .90 .25

National forestation campaign.

Yayosu Fire Brigade Review, by Hiroshige III — A996

**1980, May 31**
**1409** A996 50y multicolored .90 .25

Fire fighting centenary.

A997

A997a

Letter Writing Day: 20y, Teddy Bear holding letter. 50y, Folded and tied letter of good wishes, horiz.

**1980, July 23 *Perf. 13x13½, 13½x13***
**1410** A997 20y multicolored .40 .25
**1411** A997a 50y multicolored .90 .25

Lühdorfla Japonica A998

**1980, Aug. 2 *Perf. 13½***
**1412** A998 50y multicolored .90 .25

16th Intl. Cong. of Entomology, Kyoto, Aug. 3-9.

Three-dimensional World Map — A999

**1980, Aug. 25 Photo.**
**1413** A999 50y multicolored .90 .25

24th Intl. Geographic Cong. and 10th Intl. Cartographic Conf., Tokyo, August.

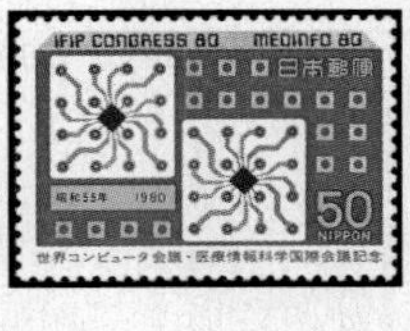


Integrated Circuit A1000

**1980, Sept. 29**
**1414** A1000 50y multicolored .90 .25

Intl. Federation for Information Processing Cong. '80, Tokyo, Oct. 6-9 and World Conf. on Medical Informatics '80, Tokyo, 9/29-10/4.

Camellia — A1001

40y, Rape flower, cabbage butterflies. 50y, Cherry blossoms.

**1980, Oct. 1**

| | | | | |
|---|---|---|---|---|
| **1415** A1001 30y shown | .50 | .25 |
| **1416** A1001 40y multicolored | .75 | .25 |
| **1417** A1001 50y multicolored | .90 | .25 |
| *Nos. 1415-1417 (3)* | 2.15 | .75 |

See No. 1437.

Cranes, by Motooki Watanabe
A1002

**1980, Oct. 6** *Perf. 13*

**1418** A1002 100y multicolored 1.75 .30

24th Intl. Letter Writing Week, Oct. 6-12.

Archery, Mt. Nantai — A1003

**1980, Oct. 11**

**1419** A1003 20y multicolored .35 .25

35th Natonal Athletic Meet, Tochigi, Oct.

Globe, Jaycee Emblem — A1004

**1980, Nov. 8** *Perf. 13*

**1420** A1004 50y multicolored .90 .25

35th Jaycee (Intl. Junior Chamber of Commerce) World Congress, Osaka, Nov. 9-15.

Diet Building and Doves — A1005

**1980, Nov. 29** *Perf. 13½*

**1421** A1005 50y multicolored .90 .25

90th anniversary of Japanese Diet.

**Type of 1980 and**

Amur Adonis
A1006

White Trumpet Lily
A1007

Hanging Bell, Byodoin Temple
A1008

Bronze Buddhist Ornament, 7th Century
A1009

Writing Box Cover
A1010

Mirror with Figures
A1011

Heart-shaped Figurine
A1012

Silver Crane
A1013

Maitreya, Horyuji Temple
A1014

Ichiji Kinrin, Chusonji Temple
A1015

Komokuten, Todaiji Temple
A1016

Lady Maya
A1017

Enamel Jar, by Ninsei Nonomura
A1018

Miroku Bosatsu, Koryuji Temple
A1019

**1980-82** **Photo.** *Perf. 13x13½*

| | | |
|---|---|---|
| **1422** A1006 10y multicolored | .25 | .25 |
| **1423** A1007 20y multicolored | .30 | .25 |
| **1424** A1008 60y multicolored | 1.00 | .25 |
| *a.* Bklt. pane (#1424, 4 #1424 with gutter btwn.) ('81) | 5.50 | |
| **1425** A1009 70y multicolored | 1.50 | .30 |
| **1426** A1010 70y multicolored | 1.25 | .25 |
| **1427** A1011 80y multicolored | 1.60 | .25 |
| **1428** A1012 90y multicolored | 1.75 | .25 |
| **1429** A1013 100y multicolored | 1.90 | .25 |
| **1430** A1014 170y multicolored | 3.00 | .25 |
| **1431** A1015 260y multicolored | 4.50 | .30 |
| **1432** A1016 310y multicolored | 5.50 | .30 |
| **1433** A1017 410y multicolored | 8.50 | .60 |
| **1434** A1018 410y multicolored | 7.50 | .40 |
| **1435** A1019 600y multicolored | 10.00 | .60 |
| *Nos. 1422-1435 (14)* | 48.55 | 4.50 |

**Coil Stamps**

***Perf. 13 Horiz.***

| | | |
|---|---|---|
| **1436** A1006 10y multi ('82) | .25 | .25 |
| **1437** A1001 40y as #1416 | .90 | .30 |
| **1438** A1008 60y multi ('82) | 1.00 | .30 |
| **1439** A1013 100y multi ('82) | 1.75 | .35 |
| *Nos. 1436-1439 (4)* | 3.90 | 1.20 |

Compare type A1013 with type A2685. See Nos. 1627-1628.

Clay Chicken, Folk Toy — A1026

**1980, Dec. 1** *Perf. 13 Horiz.*

**1442** A1026 20y multicolored .40 .30

New Year 1981.

Sheets of two were New Year Lottery Prizes. Value $1.75.

**Modern Japanese Art Issue**

Snow-Covered Power Station, by Shikanosuke Oka — A1027

NuKada-no-Ohkimi and Nara in Spring, by Yukihiko Yasuda — A1028

**1981, Feb. 26** *Perf. 13½*

**1443** A1027 60y multicolored 1.00 .25

**Photo.**

**1444** A1028 60y multicolored 1.00 .25

Artist's Family, by Narashige Koide — A1029

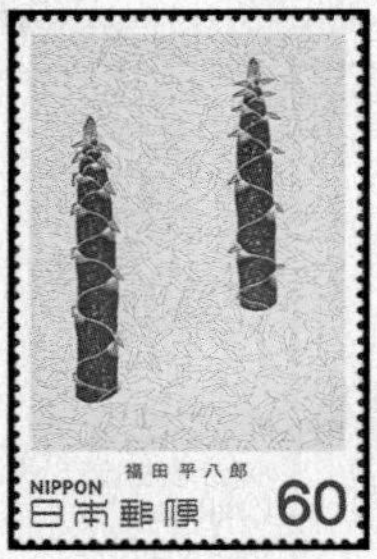

Bamboo Shoots, by Heihachiro Fukuda
A1030

**Photo. & Engr., Photo.**

**1981, June 18** *Perf. 13½*

| | | |
|---|---|---|
| **1445** A1029 60y multicolored | 1.00 | .25 |
| **1446** A1030 60y multicolored | 1.00 | .25 |

Portrait of Ichiyo, by Kiyokata Kaburagi (1878-1972)
A1031

Portrait of Reiko, by Ryusei Kishida (1891-1929)
A1032

**Photo., Photo. and Engr.**

**1981, Nov. 27** **Engr.** *Perf. 13½*

| | | |
|---|---|---|
| **1447** A1031 60y multicolored | 1.00 | .25 |
| **1448** A1032 60y multicolored | 1.00 | .25 |

Yoritomo in a Cave, by Seison Maeda — A1033

Advertisement of a Terrace, by Yuzo Saeki — A1034

**1982, Feb. 25** **Photo.** *Perf. 13½*

| | | |
|---|---|---|
| **1449** A1033 60y multicolored | 1.00 | .25 |
| **1450** A1034 60y multicolored | 1.00 | .25 |

Emblem, Port Island
A1035

**1981, Mar. 20** *Perf. 13*

**1451** A1035 60y multicolored 1.00 .25

Portopia '81, Kobe Port Island Exhibition, Mar. 20-Sept. 15.

Agriculture, Forestry and Fishery Promotion Centenary
A1036

**1981, Apr. 7**

**1452** A1036 60y multicolored 1.00 .25

Moonflower, by Harunobu Suzuki — A1037

**1981, Apr. 20 Photo. *Perf. 13½***
**1453** 60y multicolored 1.00 .25
**1454** 60y multicolored 1.00 .25
*a.* A1037 Pair, #1453-1454 2.25 .90

Philatelic Week, Apr. 21-27.

Cherry Blossoms — A1039

**1981, May 23 Photo. *Perf. 13x13½***
**1455** A1039 60y multicolored 1.00 .25

Cargo Ship and Crane A1040

**1981, May 25 *Perf. 13***
**1456** A1040 60y multicolored 1.00 .25

International Port and Harbor Association, 12th Convention, Nagoya, May 23-30.

Land Erosion Control Cent. — A1041

**1981, June 27 *Perf. 13½***
**1457** A1041 60y multicolored 1.00 .25

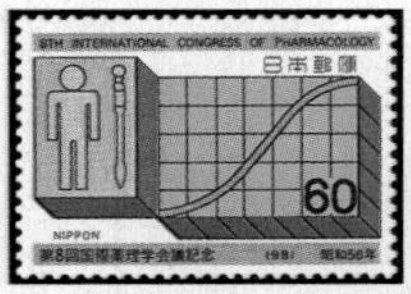
Stylized Man and Spinal Cord Dose Response Curve A1042

**1981, July 18 Photo. *Perf. 13***
**1458** A1042 60y multicolored 1.00 .25

8th Intl. Pharmacology Cong., Tokyo, July 19-24.

Girl Writing Letter — A1043

**1981, July 23**
**1459** A1043 40y shown .75 .25
**1460** A1043 60y Boy, stamp 1.00 .25

Letter Writing Day (23rd of each month).

Japanese Crested Ibis — A1044

**1981, July 27 Litho.**
**1461** A1044 60y multicolored 1.00 .25

Plug, faucet A1044a

Plugs A1045

**1981, Aug. 1 Photo.**
**1462** A1044a 40y multicolored .75 .25
**1463** A1045 60y multicolored 1.00 .25

Energy conservation.

**Western Architecture Issue**

Oura Cathedral — A1046

Hyokei Hall, Tokyo A1047

**Photogravure and Engraved**
**1981, Aug. 22**
**1464** A1046 60y multicolored 1.00 .25
**1465** A1047 60y multicolored 1.00 .25

Old Kaichi School, Nagano A1048

Doshisha University Chapel, Kyoto A1049

**1981, Nov. 9 *Perf. 13***
**1466** A1048 60y multicolored 1.00 .25
**1467** A1049 60y multicolored 1.00 .25

St. John's Church, Meiji-mura A1050

Military Exercise Hall (Former Sapporo Agricultural School), Sapporo A1051

**1982, Jan. 29 *Perf. 13***
**1468** A1050 60y multicolored 1.00 .25
**1469** A1051 60y multicolored 1.00 .25

Former Kyoto Branch of Bank of Japan A1052

Main Building, Former Saiseikan Hospital — A1053

**1982, Mar. 10 *Perf. 13***
**1470** A1052 60y multicolored 1.00 .25
**1471** A1053 60y multicolored 1.00 .25

Oyama Shrine Gate, Kanazawa A1054

Former Iwasaki Family Residence, Tokyo A1055

**1982, June 12 *Perf. 13***
**1472** A1054 60y multicolored 1.00 .25
**1473** A1055 60y multicolored 1.00 .25

Hokkaido Prefectural Govt. Building, Sapporo A1056

Former Residence of Tsugumichi Saigo A1057

**1982, Sept. 10 *Perf. 13***
**1474** A1056 60y multicolored 1.00 .25
**1475** A1057 60y multicolored 1.00 .25

Old Mutsuzawa School — A1058

Sakuranomiya Public Hall — A1059

**1983, Feb. 15**
**1476** A1058 60y multicolored 1.00 .25
**1477** A1059 60y multicolored 1.00 .25

Globe on Brain A1060

**1981, Sept. 12 Photo.**
**1478** A1060 60y multicolored 1.00 .25

Intl. medical conferences, Kyoto: 12th Neurology, Sept. 20-25; 10th Brainwaves and Clinical Neurophysiology, Sept. 13-17; 1981 Intl. Epilepsy Conference, Sept. 17-21.

Congress Emblem — A1061

**1981, Sept. 16**
**1479** A1061 60y multicolored 1.00 .25

24th World PTTI (Post, Telegraph and Telephone Intl. Labor Federation) Cong., Tokyo, Sept. 16-22.

Plum Trees and Fowl, by Sanraku Kano — A1062

**1981, Oct. 6 Photo.**
**1480** A1062 130y multicolored 2.10 .30

25th Intl. Letter Writing Week, Oct. 6-12.

A1063

**1981, Oct. 9 Photo. & Engr.**
**1481** A1063 60y No. 1 1.00 .25
**1482** A1063 60y No. 2 1.00 .25
**1483** A1063 60y No. 3 1.00 .25
**1484** A1063 60y No. 4 1.00 .25
*a.* Strip or block of 4, #1481-1484 4.50 4.50

Philatokyo '81 Intl. Stamp Exhibition,Tokyo, Oct. 9-18.

A1064

**1981, Oct. 13** **Photo.**

| | | | | |
|---|---|---|---|---|
| **1485** | A1064 | 40y multicolored | .75 | .25 |

36th Natl. Athletic Meet, Oct. 13-18.

A1065

**1981, Dec. 1** **Photo.** ***Perf. 13x13½***

| | | | | |
|---|---|---|---|---|
| **1486** | A1065 | 40y multicolored | .80 | .30 |

New Year of 1982 (Year of the Dog). Sheets of 2 were lottery prizes. Value $1.75.

A1066

Ueno Zoo Centenary: a, Gorilla, flamingo. b, Penguins, lion. c, Panda, elephants. d, Zebras, giraffe.

**1982, Mar. 20** **Photo.**

| | | | | |
|---|---|---|---|---|
| **1487** | A1066 | Strip of 4 | 4.50 | 1.75 |
| ***a.-d.*** | | 60y any single | 1.00 | .30 |

Views of the Snow on Matsuchiyama, by Kiyonaga Torii — A1067

**1982, Apr. 20** **Photo.** ***Perf. 13½***

| | | | | |
|---|---|---|---|---|
| **1488** | | 60y multicolored | 1.00 | .30 |
| **1489** | | 60y multicolored | 1.00 | .30 |
| ***a.*** | A1067 | Pair, #1488-1489 | 2.25 | .90 |

Philatelic Week.

Shisa (Lion-shaped Guard Dog) — A1069

**1982, May 15** **Photo.**

| | | | | |
|---|---|---|---|---|
| **1490** | A1069 | 60y multicolored | 1.10 | .30 |

10th anniv. of Reversion Agreement returning Ryukyu Islands.

Natl. Forestation Campaign — A1070

**1982, May 22** ***Perf. 13x13½***

| | | | | |
|---|---|---|---|---|
| **1491** | A1070 | 60y multicolored | 1.00 | .25 |

16th Intl. Dermatology Conference Tokyo, May 23-28 — A1071

**1982, May 24** ***Perf. 13***

| | | | | |
|---|---|---|---|---|
| **1492** | A1071 | 60y Noh mask | 1.00 | .25 |

Tohoku-Shinkansen Railroad Line Opening — A1072

**1982, June 23**

| | | | | |
|---|---|---|---|---|
| **1493** | | 60y Diesel locomotive | 1.00 | .30 |
| **1494** | | 60y Steam model 1290 | 1.00 | .30 |
| ***a.*** | A1072 | Pair, #1493-1494 | 2.25 | .90 |

Letter Writing Day — A1073

**1982, July 23** ***Perf. 13x13½, 13½x13***

| | | | | |
|---|---|---|---|---|
| **1495** | A1073 | 40y Sea gull, letter | .75 | .25 |
| **1496** | A1073 | 60y Fairy, letter, horiz. | 1.00 | .30 |

**Modern Japanese Art Issue**

Kimono Patterned with Irises, by Saburosuke Okada (1869-1939) A1074

Bodhisattva Kuan-yin on Potalaka Island, by Tessai Tomioka (1837-1924) A1075

**1982, Aug. 5** **Photo.** ***Perf. 13½***

| | | | | |
|---|---|---|---|---|
| **1497** | A1074 | 60y multicolored | 1.00 | .30 |
| **1498** | A1075 | 60y multicolored | 1.00 | .30 |

The Sarasvati, by Shiko Munakata (1903-1975) A1076

Saltim-banque, by Seiji Togo (1897-1978) A1077

**1982, Nov. 24**

| | | | | |
|---|---|---|---|---|
| **1499** | A1076 | 60y multicolored | 1.00 | .30 |
| **1500** | A1077 | 60y multicolored | 1.00 | .30 |

Snowstorm, by Shinsui Ito — A1078

Spiraeas and Callas with Persian Pot, by Zenzaburo Kojima A1079

**1983, Jan. 24** **Photo.**

| | | | | |
|---|---|---|---|---|
| **1501** | A1078 | 60y multicolored | 1.00 | .30 |
| **1502** | A1079 | 60y multicolored | 1.00 | .30 |

Innocence, by Taikan Yokoyama (1868-1958) A1080

Roen, by Koun Takamura (1852-1934) A1081

**Photo., Photo. and Engr.**

**1983, Mar. 10** ***Perf. 13½***

| | | | | |
|---|---|---|---|---|
| **1503** | A1080 | 60y multicolored | 1.00 | .30 |
| **1504** | A1081 | 60y multicolored | 1.00 | .30 |

A1082

A1083

A1084

**1982, Aug. 23** ***Perf. 13x13½***

| | | | | |
|---|---|---|---|---|
| **1505** | A1082 | 60y Wreath | 1.00 | .35 |
| **1506** | A1083 | 60y Crane | 1.00 | .35 |
| **1507** | A1084 | 70y Tortoise | 1.25 | .35 |
| | | *Nos. 1505-1507 (3)* | 3.25 | 1.05 |

For use on greeting (Nos. 1506-1507) and condolence (No. 1505) cards.

See Nos. 1555-1556, 1836-1839, 2227-2230 and footnotes after Nos. 1708, 1765.

400th Anniv. of Boys' Delegation to Europe, Tensho Era — A1085

60y, 16th cent. ship, map.

**1982, Sept. 20** **Photo.** ***Perf. 13***

| | | | | |
|---|---|---|---|---|
| **1508** | A1085 | 60y multicolored | 1.00 | .25 |

10th Anniv. of Japanese-Chinese Relations Normalization — A1086

Design: Hall of Prayer for Good Harvests, Temple of Heaven, Peking, by Ryuzaburo Umehara.

**1982, Sept. 29**

| | | | | |
|---|---|---|---|---|
| **1509** | A1086 | 60y multicolored | 1.10 | .30 |

Table Tennis — A1087

**1982, Oct. 2**

| | | | | |
|---|---|---|---|---|
| **1510** | A1087 | 40y multicolored | .75 | .25 |

37th Natl. Athletic Meet, Matsue, Oct. 3-8.

"Amusement," Doll by Goyo Hirata — A1088

**1982, Oct. 6**
**1511** A1088 130y multicolored 2.10 .45

Intl. Letter Writing Week, Oct. 6-12.

Central Bank System Centenary A1089

Design: The Bank of Japan near Eitaibashi in Snow, by Yasuji Inoue.

**Photogravure and Engraved**
**1982, Oct. 12** ***Perf. 13½***
**1512** A1089 60y multicolored 1.00 .25

Opening of Joetsu Shinkansen Railroad Line — A1090

**1982, Nov. 15**
**1513** 60y Locomotive, 1982 1.00 .30
**1514** 60y Locomotive, 1931 1.00 .30
*a.* A1090 Pair, #1513-1514 2.25 .90

New Year 1983 — A1092

40y, Kintaro on Wild Boar.

**1982, Dec. 1** ***Perf. 13x13½***
**1515** A1092 40y multicolored .80 .30

Sheets of 2 were lottery prizes. Value, $1.50.

Natl. Museum of History and Folklore Opening A1093

**1983, Mar. 16 Photo.** ***Perf. 13½x13***
**1516** A1093 60y multicolored 1.00 .25

Women Working in the Kitchen, by Utamaro Kitagawa (1753-1806) — A1094

**1983, Apr. 20 Photo.** ***Perf. 13***
**1517** 60y multicolored 1.00 .30
**1518** 60y multicolored 1.00 .30
*a.* A1094 Pair, #1517-1518 2.25 .90

Philatelic Week.

Natl. Forestation Campaign — A1096

Hakusan Mountains, black lily, forest.

**1983, May 21** ***Perf. 13***
**1519** A1096 60y multicolored 1.00 .25

50th Nippon Derby — A1097

**1983, May 28**
**1520** A1097 60y Colt, racing horse 1.00 .25

Islands Cleanup Campaign — A1098

**1983, June 13 Photo.** ***Perf. 13½***
**1521** A1098 60y multicolored 1.00 .25

**Western Architecture Series**

Hohei Hall Sapporo A1099

Old Glover House, Nagasaki A1100

**Photogravure and Engraved**
**1983, June 23** ***Perf. 13***
**1522** A1099 60y multicolored 1.00 .30
**1523** A1100 60y multicolored 1.00 .30

Gojyuku Bank, Hirosaki A1101

Gakushuin Elementary School, Tokyo A1102

**1983, Aug. 15**
**1524** A1101 60y multicolored 1.00 .30
**1525** A1102 60y multicolored 1.00 .30

Bank of Japan, Tokyo A1103

Old Hunter House, Kobe A1104

**1984, Feb. 16**
**1526** A1103 60y multicolored 1.00 .30
**1527** A1104 60y multicolored 1.00 .30
*Nos. 1522-1527 (6)* 6.00 1.80

Official Gazette Centenary A1107

Design: First issue, Drawing of the Government Bulletin Board at Nihonbashi, by Hiroshige Ando III.

**1983, July 2** **Photo.**
**1530** A1107 60y multicolored 1.00 .25

Letter Writing Day — A1108

40y, Boy writing letter. 60y, Fairy bringing letter, horiz.

**1983, July 23** ***Perf. 13x13½, 13½x13***
**1531** A1108 40y multicolored .75 .25
**1532** A1108 60y multicolored 1.00 .30

Opening of Natl. Noh Theater, Tokyo A1109

60y, Masked actor, theater.

**1983, Sept. 14 Photo.** ***Perf. 13***
**1533** A1109 60y multicolored 1.00 .25

**Endangered Birds Issue**

Rallus Okinawae A1110

Ketupa Blakistoni A1111

**Photo. and Engr., Photo.**
**1983, Sept. 22** ***Perf. 13***
**1534** A1110 60y multicolored 1.00 .30
**1535** A1111 60y multicolored 1.00 .30

No. 1536, Sapheopipo noguchii. No. 1537, Branta canadensis leucopareia.

**Photo., Photo. & Engr.**
**1983, Nov. 25**
**1536** A1110 60y multicolored 1.00 .30
**1537** A1111 60y multicolored 1.00 .30

No. 1538, Megalurus pryeri pryeri. No. 1539, Spilornis cheela perplexus.

**Photo., Photo. and Engr.**
**1984, Jan. 26**
**1538** A1111 60y multicolored 1.00 .30
**1539** A1110 60y multicolored 1.00 .30

No. 1540, Columba janthina nitens. No. 1541, Tringa guttifer.

**1984, Mar. 15** **Photo.**
**1540** A1110 60y multicolored 1.00 .30
**1541** A1111 60y multicolored 1.00 .30

No. 1542, Falco peregrinus frutti. No. 1543, Dendrocopus leucutus austoni.

**1984, June 22**
**1542** A1110 60y multicolored 1.00 .30

**Photo. and Engr.**
**1543** A1111 60y multicolored 1.00 .30
*Nos. 1534-1543 (10)* 10.00 3.00

**Souvenir Sheet**

**1984, Dec. 10** **Photo. & Engr.**
**1544** Sheet of 3 3.50 3.50
*a.* A1111 60y Prus grn, engr., #1535 1.00 .30
*b.* A1110 60y vio brn, engr., #1539 1.00 .30
*c.* A1110 60y ol blk, engr., #1542 1.00 .30

Intl. Letter Writing Week — A1124

Chikyu Doll by Juzo Kagoshima (1898-1982).

**1983, Oct. 6 Photo.** ***Perf. 13***
**1548** A1124 130y multicolored 2.10 .40

38th Natl. Athletic Meet — A1125

**1983, Oct. 15** ***Perf. 13***
**1549** A1125 40y Naginata event .75 .25

A1126

World Communications Year — A1127

**1983, Oct. 17 Photo.** ***Perf. 13***
**1550** A1126 60y multicolored 1.00 .25
**1551** A1127 60y multicolored 1.00 .25

Showa Memorial National Park Opening A1128

**1983, Oct. 26 Photo.** ***Perf. 13***
**1552** A1128 60y multicolored 1.00 .30

A1129

**1983, Nov. 14** **Photo.**
**1553** A1129 60y multicolored 1.00 .25

71st World Dentistry Congress.

A1130

**1983, Nov. 14** **Photo.** ***Perf. 13***
**1554** A1130 60y multicolored 1.00 .30

Shirase, Antarctic observation ship, maiden voyage.

**Type of 1982**

**1983, Nov. 22** **Photo.** ***Perf. 12½***
**1555** A1082 40y Wreath .75 .25
**1556** A1083 40y Crane .75 .25

For use on condolence and greeting cards.

New Year 1984 — A1131

40y, Rat riding hammer.

**1983, Dec. 1** **Photo.** ***Perf. 13x13½***
**1557** A1131 40y multicolored .80 .30

Sheets of 2 were lottery prizes. Value, $1.90.

Emblem — A1132

**1983, Dec. 5** **Photo.** ***Perf. 13½***
**1558** A1132 60y multicolored 1.00 .25

Universal Declaration of Human Rights, 35th anniv.

20th Grand Confectionery Fair, Tokyo, Feb. 24-Mar. 12 — A1133

60y, Confection, tea whisk.

**1984, Feb. 24** **Photo.**
**1559** A1133 60y multicolored 1.00 .25

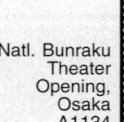

Natl. Bunraku Theater Opening, Osaka A1134

60y, Bunraku puppet.

**1984, Apr. 6** **Photo.** ***Perf. 13***
**1560** A1134 60y multicolored 1.00 .25

A1135

Philatelic Week (Sharaku Prints): No. 1561, Hanshiro Iwai IV (facing right) Playing Shigenoi. No. 1562, Oniji Otani (facing left) Playing Edobe.

**Photogravure and Engraved**

**1984, Apr. 20** ***Perf. 13½***
**1561** 60y multicolored 1.00 .30
**1562** 60y multicolored 1.00 .30
*a.* A1135 Pair, #1561-1562 2.25 .90

Natl. Forestation Campaign A1137

60y, Cedar Forest, Sakurajima.

**1984, May 19** **Photo.**
**1563** A1137 60y multicolored 1.00 .25

Weather Forecasting Centenary A1138

60y, Himawari satellite, map.

**1984, June 1** ***Perf. 13x13½***
**1564** A1138 60y multicolored 1.00 .30

UNESCO Emblem, Doves — A1139

**1984, July 16** **Photo.**
**1565** A1139 60y multicolored 1.00 .25

UNESCO Clubs and Associations World Congress, July 16-24.

Letter Writing Day — A1140

40y, Birds in tree. 60y, Bird holding letter, horiz.

**1984, July 23** ***Perf. 13x13½, 13½x13***
**1566** A1140 40y multicolored .75 .25
**1567** A1140 60y multicolored 1.00 .30

Disaster Relief A1141

40y, Fire, wind. 60y, Mother, child, vert.

***Perf. 13x12½, 12½x13***

**1984, Aug. 23** **Photo.**
**1568** A1141 40y multicolored .75 .25
**1569** A1141 60y multicolored 1.00 .30

**Alpine Plant Series**

Leontopodium Fauriei — A1142

Lagotis Glauca A1143

**Photogravure and Engraved**

***Perf. 12½x13, 13x12½***

**1984, Aug. 27**
**1570** A1142 60y multicolored 1.00 .30
**1571** A1143 60y multicolored 1.00 .30

Trollius Riederianus A1144

Primula Cuneifolia A1145

**1984, Sept. 21** ***Perf. 13***
**1572** A1144 60y multicolored 1.00 .30
**1573** A1145 60y multicolored 1.00 .30

Rhododendron Aureum — A1146

Oxytropis Nigrescens Var. Japonica A1147

**1985, Jan. 25** ***Perf. 13***
**1574** A1146 60y multicolored 1.00 .30
**1575** A1147 60y multicolored 1.00 .30

Draba Japonica — A1148

Dryas Octopetala A1149

**1985, Feb. 28**
**1576** A1148 60y multicolored 1.00 .30
**1577** A1149 60y multicolored 1.00 .30

Callianthemum Insigne Var. Miyabeanum A1150

Gentiana Nipponica A1151

**1985, July 31** ***Perf. 13***
**1578** A1150 60y multicolored 1.00 .30
**1579** A1151 60y multicolored 1.00 .30

Campanula Chamissonis A1152

Viola Crassa A1153

**1985, Sept. 27**
**1580** A1152 60y multicolored 1.00 .30
**1581** A1153 60y multicolored 1.00 .30

Diapensia Lapponica A1154

Pedicularis Apodochila A1155

**1986, Feb. 13** ***Perf. 13***
**1582** A1154 60y multicolored 1.00 .30
**1583** A1155 60y multicolored 1.00 .30

Basho's Street, Sendai — A1156

**1984, Sept. 1** **Photo.** ***Perf. 13***
**1584** A1156 60y multicolored 1.00 .25

Intl. Microbiological Association's 6th Intl. Congress of Virology, Sendai, Sept. 1-7.

Electronic Mail — A1157

**1984, Oct. 1** **Photo.**
**1585** A1157 500y multicolored 9.50 4.50

28th Intl. Letter Writing Week, Oct. 6-12 — A1158

**1984, Oct. 6**

**1586** A1158 130y Wooden doll 2.10 .50

17th Intl. Internal Medicine Congress, Kyoto, Oct. 7-12 A1159

**1984, Oct. 8**

**1587** A1159 60y Ginkakuji Temple 1.00 .25

39th Natl. Athletic Meet, Nara City, Oct. 12-17 — A1160

**1984, Oct. 12**

**1588** A1160 40y Field hockey .75 .25

**Traditional Crafts Series**

Kutaniyaki Plates — A1161

Nishijinori Weavings — A1163

**1984, Nov. 2 Photo. *Perf. 12½x13***

**1589** 60y Birds 1.00 .30
**1590** 60y Flowers 1.00 .30
*a.* A1161 Pair, #1589-1590 2.25 .90
**1591** 60y Flowers 1.00 .30
**1592** 60y Leaves 1.00 .30
*a.* A1163 Pair, #1591-1592 2.25 .90

Edokimekomi Dolls — A1165

Ryukyubingata Cloth — A1167

**1985, Feb. 15 Photo. *Perf. 13***

**1593** 60y Adult figures 1.00 .30
**1594** 60y Child and pet 1.00 .30
*a.* A1165 Pair, #1593-1594 2.25 .90
**1595** 60y Bird and branch 1.00 .30
**1596** 60y Birds 1.00 .30
*a.* A1167 Pair, #1595-1596 2.25 .90

Ichii-ittobori Carved Birds — A1169

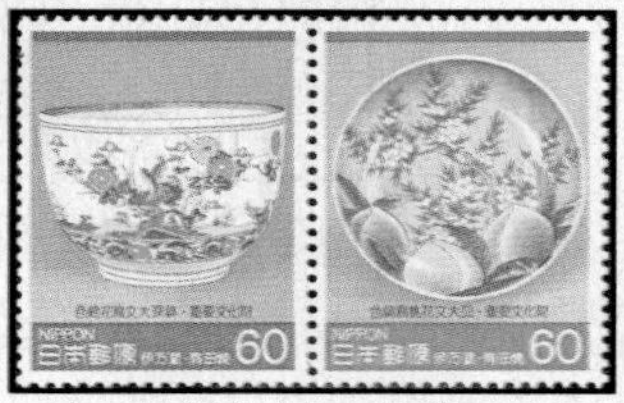

Imariyaki & Aritayaki Ceramic Ware — A1171

**1985, May 23 Photo. *Perf. 13***

**1597** 60y Bird 1.00 .30
**1598** 60y Birds 1.00 .30
*a.* A1169 Pair, #1597-1598 2.25 .90
**1599** 60y Bowl 1.00 .30
**1600** 60y Plate 1.00 .30
*a.* A1171 Pair, #1599-1600 2.25 .90

Kamakurabori Wood Carvings — A1173

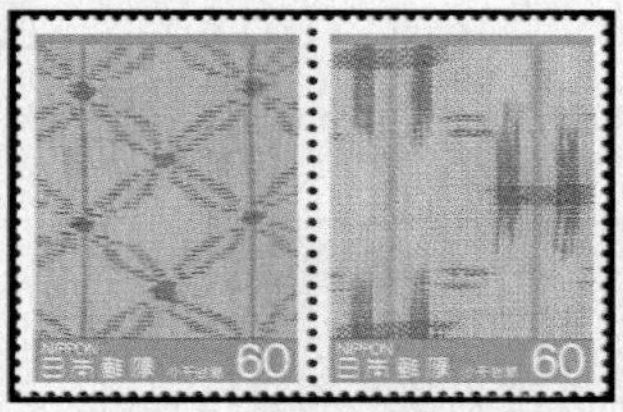

Ojiyachijimi Weavings — A1175

**1985, June 24 Photo. & Engr.**

**1601** 60y Bird and flower panel 1.00 .30
**1602** 60y Round flower panel 1.00 .30
*a.* A1173 Pair, #1601-1602 2.25 .90

**Litho.**

**1603** 60y Hemp star pattern 1.00 .30
**1604** 60y Hemp linear pattern 1.00 .30
*a.* A1175 Pair, #1603-1604 2.25 .90

Hakata Ningyo Clay Figures — A1177

Nanbu Tekki Iron Ware — A1179

**1985, Aug. 8 Photo.**

**1605** 60y Man 1.00 .30
**1606** 60y Woman and child 1.00 .30
*a.* A1177 Pair, #1605-1606 2.25 .90

**Photogravure and Engraved**

**1607** 60y Silver kettle 1.00 .30
**1608** 60y Black kettle 1.00 .30
*a.* A1179 Pair, #1607-1608 2.25 .90

Wajimanuri Lacquerware — A1181

Izumo-ishidoro Sandstone Sculptures — A1183

**Photo., Photo. & Engr. (#1611-1612)**
**1985, Nov. 15**

**1609** 60y Bowl on table 1.00 .30
**1610** 60y Bowl 1.00 .30
*a.* A1181 Pair, #1609-1610 2.25 .90
**1611** 60y Columnar lantern 1.00 .30
**1612** 60y Lantern on four legs 1.00 .30
*a.* A1183 Pair, #1611-1612 2.25 .90

Kyo-sensu Silk Fans — A1185

Tobeyaki Porcelain — A1187

**1986, Mar. 13 Photo. *Perf. 13***

**1613** 60y Flower bouquets 1.00 .30
**1614** 60y Sun and trees 1.00 .30
*a.* A1185 Pair, #1613-1614 2.25 .90
**1615** 60y Jug 1.00 .30
**1616** 60y Jar 1.00 .30
*a.* A1187 Pair, #1615-1616 2.25 .90
*Nos. 1613-1616 (4)* 4.00 1.20

Japanese Professional Baseball, 50th Anniv. — A1189

**1984, Nov. 15 *Perf. 13½***

**1617** 60y Pitcher 1.00 .30
**1618** 60y Batter 1.00 .30
*a.* A1189 Pair, #1617-1618 2.25 .90
**1619** A1189 60y Matsutaro Shoriki 1.00 .30
*Nos. 1617-1619 (3)* 3.00 .90

Industrial Education Centenary A1190

**1984, Nov. 20 *Perf. 13x12½***

**1620** A1190 60y Workers, symbols 1.00 .25

New Year 1985 — A1191

40y, Sakushu Cattle Folk Toy.

**1984, Dec. 1 Photo. *Perf. 13½x13***

**1621** A1191 40y .80 .30

Sheets of 2 were lottery prizes. Value, $1.90.

A1200 Akita — A1201 Ivory Shell

A1202 Hiougi-gai (Bivalve) — A1203 Rinbo Shell

A1204 — A1205

A1206 — A1207

A1208 A1209

### Photo., Engr. (300y)

**1984-89** *Perf. 13x13½*

| | | | | |
|---|---|---|---|---|
| **1622** | A1200 | 2y turq blue ('89) | .25 | .25 |
| **1623** | A1201 | 40y multi ('88) | .90 | .25 |
| **1624** | A1202 | 41y multi ('89) | .80 | .25 |
| **1624B** | A1202 | 41y Imperf., self-adhesive | .80 | .25 |
| **1625** | A1203 | 60y multi ('88) | 1.10 | .25 |
| *a.* | | Bklt. pane, 5 each #1623, 1625 | 9.25 | |
| **1626** | A1204 | 62y multi ('89) | 1.10 | .25 |
| *a.* | | Bklt. pane, 2 #1624, 4 #1626 | 6.00 | |
| **1626B** | A1204 | 62y Imperf., self-adhesive | 1.10 | .25 |
| *c.* | | Bklt. pane, 2 #1624B, 4 #1626B ('89) | 6.00 | |
| **1627** | A1205 | 72y dark vio, blk & org yel ('89) | 1.25 | .25 |
| **1628** | A1206 | 175y multi ('89) | 2.75 | .25 |
| **1629** | A1207 | 210y multi ('89) | 3.25 | .30 |
| **1630** | A1208 | 300y dk red brown | 5.00 | .35 |
| **1631** | A1209 | 360y dull pink & brn ('89) | 6.00 | .35 |
| | | *Nos. 1622-1631 (12)* | 24.30 | 3.25 |

### Coil Stamps

*Perf. 13 Horiz.*

| | | | | |
|---|---|---|---|---|
| **1636** | A1202 | 41y multi ('89) | .80 | .25 |
| **1637** | A1204 | 62y multi ('89) | 1.10 | .25 |

No. 1622 inscribed "Nippon," unlike No. 583.

No. 1626Bc is adhered to the booklet cover, made of peelable paper, folded in half and rouletted down the center fold.

Issued: 40y, 60y, 4/1; 300y, 4/3; 2y, 72y, 4/1; 42y, Nos. 1626, 1626a, 41y, No. 1637, 3/24; 175y, 210y, 360y, 6/1; No.1626d, 7/3.

A1210

EXPO '85 — A1211

**1985, Mar. 16** **Photo.** *Perf. 13*

| | | | | |
|---|---|---|---|---|
| **1640** | A1210 | 40y multicolored | .75 | .25 |
| **1641** | A1211 | 60y multicolored | 1.00 | .30 |
| *a.* | | Souv. sheet of 2, #1640-1641 | 2.25 | 2.00 |

University of the Air — A1212

60y, University broadcast tower.

**1985, Apr. 1** **Photo.** *Perf. 13½*

**1642** A1212 60y multicolored 1.00 .30

Inauguration of adult education through broadcasting.

Nippon Telegraph & Telephone Co. — A1213

**1985, Apr. 1**

**1643** A1213 60y Satellite receiver 1.00 .25

Inauguration of Japan's new telecommunications system.

World Import Fair, Nagoya A1214

60y, 16th century map of Japan.

**1985, Apr. 5** **Photo.** *Perf. 13*

**1644** A1214 60y multicolored 1.00 .25

Industrial Proprietary System Cent. — A1215

Design: Portrait of Korekiyo Takashashi, system promulgator, inscriptions in English.

**1985, Apr. 18** **Photo.** *Perf. 13½*

**1645** A1215 60y multicolored 1.00 .25

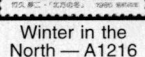

Winter in the North — A1216 To the Morning Light — A1217

Paintings by Yumeji Takehisa (1884-1934).

**1985, Apr. 20** *Perf. 13*

| | | | | |
|---|---|---|---|---|
| **1646** | A1216 | 60y multicolored | 1.00 | .30 |
| **1647** | A1217 | 60y multicolored | 1.00 | .30 |
| *a.* | | Pair, #1646-1647 | 2.25 | .90 |

Philatelic Week. Printed in sheets of 10.

Natl. Land Forestation Project — A1218

Intl. Year of the Forest: Autumn bellflower, camphor tree, cattle and Mt. Aso.

**1985, May 10** *Perf. 13½*

**1648** A1218 60y multicolored 1.00 .25

Radio Japan, 50th Anniv. — A1219

Painting: Cherry Blossoms at Night, by Taikan Yokoyama.

**1985, June 1** **Photo.** *Perf. 13*

| | | | | |
|---|---|---|---|---|
| **1649** | | 60y multi (Left) | 1.00 | .30 |
| **1650** | | 60y multi (Right) | 1.00 | .30 |
| *a.* | A1219 | Pair, #1649-1650 | 2.25 | .90 |

Hisoka Maejima, 1st Postmaster General — A1220

60y, Portrait, former P.O. building.

**1985, June 5** **Photo.** *Perf. 13*

**1651** A1220 60y multicolored 1.00 .30

Oonaruto Bridge Opening A1221

**1985, June 7** *Perf. 13½*

**1652** A1221 60y multicolored 1.00 .25

Intl. Youth Year A1222

60y, Emblem, silhouette.

**1985, July 20** **Photo.** *Perf. 13*

**1653** A1222 60y multicolored 1.00 .25

Owl Carrying Letter — A1223

60y, Girl, cat, bird, letter.

*Perf. 13½x13, 13x13½*

**1985, July 23** **Photo.**

| | | | | |
|---|---|---|---|---|
| **1654** | A1223 | 40y shown | .75 | .25 |
| **1655** | A1223 | 60y multicolored | 1.00 | .30 |

Letter Writing Day (23rd of each month).

Electronic Mail — A1224

**1985, Aug. 1** **Photo.** *Perf. 13x13½*

**1656** A1224 500y multicolored 9.50 2.75

Meson Theory, 50th Anniv. A1225

60y, Portrait, nuclear particles.

**1985, Aug. 15** **Photo.** *Perf. 13*

**1657** A1225 60y multicolored 1.00 .25

Dr. Hideki Yukawa was presented the Nobel Prize for Physics for the Meson Theory in 1949, which is the foundation for high-energy physics.

A1226

60y, Gymnast, horse.

**1985, Aug. 24** **Photo.** *Perf. 13½*

**1658** A1226 60y multicolored 1.00 .25

Universiade 1985, Kobe.

A1227

40y, Emblem, competitor.

**1985, Sept. 13** **Photo.**

**1659** A1227 40y multicolored .75 .25

28th Intl. Vocational Training Competition, Oct. 21-27.

Normalization of Diplomatic Relations Between Japan and the Republic of Korea, 20th Anniv. — A1228

**1985, Sept. 18**

**1660** A1228 60y Rose of Sharon 1.00 .30

Kan-Etsu Tunnel Opening A1229

60y, Mountains, diagram, cross sections.

**1985, Oct. 2** *Perf. 13*

**1661** A1229 60y multicolored 1.00 .25

Seisen Doll by Goyo Hirata (1903-1981) A1230

**1985, Oct. 7**

**1662** A1230 130y multicolored 2.10 .50

Intl. Letter Writing Week, Oct. 6-12.

30th Intl. Apicultural Congress, Oct. 10-16, Nagoya A1231

60y, Honeybee, strawberry plants.

**1985, Oct. 9**

**1663** A1231 60y multicolored 1.00 .25

Japanese Overseas Cooperation Volunteers, 20th Anniv. A1232

**1985, Oct. 9** **Litho.**
**1664** A1232 60y Planting crop 1.00 .30

40th Natl. Athletic Meet, Oct. 20-25, Tottori City Sports Arena — A1233

40y, Handball player, Mt. Daisen.

**1985, Oct. 19** **Photo.**
**1665** A1233 40y multicolored .75 .25

New Year 1986 — A1234

40y, Shinno papier-mache tiger.

**1985, Dec. 2** **Photo.** ***Perf. 13x13½***
**1666** A1234 40y multicolored .80 .30

Sheets of 2 were lottery prizes. Value, $1.90.

Natl. Ministerial System of Government, Cent. A1235

60y, Official seal, Cabinet emblem.

**1985, Dec. 20** **Litho.** ***Perf. 13½***
**1667** A1235 60y multicolored 1.00 .25

Building Institute, Cent. — A1236

**1986, Apr. 9** **Photo.** ***Perf. 13***
**1668** A1236 60y multicolored 1.00 .25

Philately Week — A1237

Southern Hateroma (details), by Keigetsu Kikuchi.

**1986, Apr. 15**

| | | | |
|---|---|---|---|
| **1669** | 60y Woman standing | 1.00 | .30 |
| **1670** | 60y Seated woman | 1.00 | .30 |
| *a.* | A1237 Pair, #1669-1670 | 2.25 | .90 |

Kyoto Imperial Palace, Phoenix A1238

No. 1672, Imperial chrysanthemum crest & partridges.

**1986, Apr. 28**

| | | | |
|---|---|---|---|
| **1671** | A1238 60y multicolored | 1.00 | .30 |
| **1672** | A1238 60y multicolored | 1.00 | .30 |
| *a.* | Souv. sheet of 2, #1671-1672 | 2.40 | 2.40 |

Reign of Emperor Hirohito, 60th anniv.

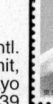

6th Intl. Summit, Tokyo A1239

**1986, May 2**
**1673** A1239 60y Mt. Fuji 1.00 .30

Shrike on Reed, Emperor Nintoku's Mausoleum A1240

**1986, May 9** ***Perf. 13½***
**1674** A1240 60y multicolored 1.00 .30

Natl. Land Afforestation Campaign.

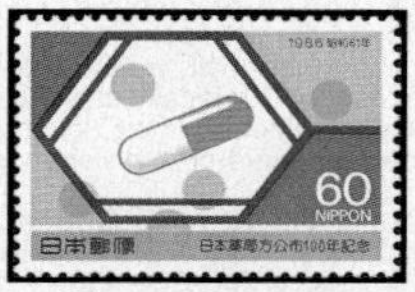

Japanese Pharmaceutical Regulatory Syst., Cent. — A1241

**1986, June 25** **Photo.** ***Perf. 13½***
**1675** A1241 60y multicolored 1.00 .30

Japanese Standard Time, Cent. — A1242

**1986, July 11** **Litho.** ***Perf. 13***
**1676** A1242 60y Meridian, clock 1.00 .30

Letter Writing Day — A1243

**1986, July 23** **Photo.** ***Perf. 13x13½***

| | | | |
|---|---|---|---|
| **1677** | A1243 40y Bird | .75 | .25 |
| **1678** | A1243 60y Girl, rabbit, birds | 1.00 | .30 |
| *a.* | Bklt. pane, 5 each #1677-1678 | 9.25 | |

Sheets of 2 were lottery prizes. Value, *$60.*

Merchant Marine Education, 110th Anniv. A1244

Training ship Nihonmaru & navigation training institute founders Makoto Kondo, Yataro Iwasaki.

**1986, July 26** ***Perf. 13***
**1679** A1244 60y multicolored 1.00 .30

CTO's exist for Nos. 1680-1681, 1684-1685, 1688-1689, 1694-1695, 1696-1697. They read "Japan" between two arcs in a corner.

### Insects

A1245

No. 1680, Parnassius eversmanni. No. 1681, Poecilocoris lewisi. No. 1682, Rasalia batesi. No. 1683, Epiophlebia superstes.

**Photogravure and Engraved**

**1986, July 30** ***Perf. 13***

| | | | |
|---|---|---|---|
| **1680** | 60y multicolored | 1.00 | .35 |
| **1681** | 60y multicolored | 1.00 | .35 |
| *a.* | A1245 Pair, #1680-1681 | 2.25 | 1.00 |
| **1682** | 60y multicolored | 1.00 | .35 |
| **1683** | 60y multicolored | 1.00 | .35 |
| *a.* | A1245 Pair, #1682-1683 | 2.25 | 1.00 |

No. 1684, Dorcus hopei. No. 1685, Thermozephyrus ataxus. No. 1686, Sympetrum pedemontanum. No. 1687, Damaster blaptoides.

**1986, Sept. 26**

| | | | |
|---|---|---|---|
| **1684** | 60y multicolored | 1.00 | .35 |
| **1685** | 60y multicolored | 1.00 | .35 |
| *a.* | A1245 Pair, #1684-1685 | 2.25 | 1.00 |
| **1686** | 60y multicolored | 1.00 | .35 |
| **1687** | 60y multicolored | 1.00 | .35 |
| *a.* | A1245 Pair, #1686-1687 | 2.25 | 1.00 |

No. 1688, Elcysma westwoodii. No. 1689, Rhyothemis variegata. No. 1690, Tibicen japonicus. No. 1691, Chrysochroa holstii.

**1986, Nov. 21**

| | | | |
|---|---|---|---|
| **1688** | 60y multicolored | 1.00 | .35 |
| **1689** | 60y multicolored | 1.00 | .35 |
| *a.* | A1245 Pair, #1688-1689 | 2.25 | 1.00 |
| **1690** | 60y multicolored | 1.00 | .35 |
| **1691** | 60y multicolored | 1.00 | .35 |
| *a.* | A1245 Pair, #1690-1691 | 2.25 | 1.00 |

No. 1692, Parantica sita. No. 1693, Cheirotonus jambar. No. 1694, Lucanus maculifemoratus. No. 1695, Anotogaster sieboldii.

**1987, Jan. 23**

| | | | |
|---|---|---|---|
| **1692** | 60y multicolored | 1.00 | .35 |
| **1693** | 60y multicolored | 1.00 | .35 |
| *a.* | A1245 Pair, #1692-1693 | 2.25 | 1.00 |
| **1694** | 60y multicolored | 1.00 | .35 |
| **1695** | 60y multicolored | 1.00 | .35 |
| *a.* | A1245 Pair, #1694-1695 | 2.25 | 1.00 |

No. 1696, Ascaraphus ramburi. No. 1697, Polyphylla laticollis. No. 1698, Kallima inachus. No. 1699, Calopteryx cornelia.

**1987, Mar. 12**

| | | | |
|---|---|---|---|
| **1696** | 60y multicolored | 1.00 | .35 |
| **1697** | 60y multicolored | 1.00 | .35 |
| *a.* | A1245 Pair, #1696-1697 | 2.25 | 1.00 |
| **1698** | 60y multicolored | 1.00 | .35 |
| **1699** | 60y multicolored | 1.00 | .35 |
| *f.* | A1245 Pair, #1698-1699 | 2.25 | 1.00 |
| | *Nos. 1680-1699 (20)* | 20.00 | 7.00 |

**Miniature Sheet**

| | | | |
|---|---|---|---|
| **1699A** | Sheet of 4 (#1680, 1692, 1699b-1699c) | 3.75 | 3.75 |
| *b.* | 40y Anthocaris cardamines | .75 | .35 |
| *c.* | 40y Sasakia charonda | .75 | .35 |
| *d.* | Bklt. pane, 5 #1680, 5 #1699b | 9.25 | |
| *e.* | Bklt. pane, 5 #1692, 5 #1699c | 9.25 | |
| *g.* | A1245 Pair, #1699b, 1680 | 1.90 | |
| *h.* | A1245 Pair, #1699c, 1692 | 1.90 | |

Booklet panes are perf. 13x13½ on 2 or 3 sides.

Folkways in Twelve Months (Detail), by Shunsho Katsukawa A1265

**1986, Aug. 23** **Photo.** ***Perf. 13***
**1700** A1265 60y multicolored 1.00 .30

52nd conference of the Intl. Federation of Library Associations, Tokyo, Aug. 24-29.

Electron Microscope A1266

**1986, Aug. 30**
**1701** A1266 60y multicolored 1.00 .30

11th Int. Congress of Electron Microscopy, Kyoto, Aug. 31-Sept. 7.

23rd Intl. Conference on Social Welfare, Tokyo, Aug. 31-Sept. 5 — A1267

**1986, Aug. 30** **Litho.**
**1702** A1267 60y multicolored 1.00 .25

Ohmorimiyage Doll, by Juzoh Kagoshima A1268

**1986, Oct. 6** **Photo.**
**1703** A1268 130y multicolored 2.10 .60

Intl. Letter Writing Week.

41st Natl. Athletic Meet, Oct. 12-17, Kofu — A1269

**1986, Oct. 9**
**1704** A1269 40y multicolored .75 .25

5th World Ikebana Convention A1270

Painting: Flower in Autumn and a Girl in Rakuhoku.

**1986, Oct. 17** **Photo.** ***Perf. 13½x13***
**1705** A1270 60y multicolored 1.00 .30

A1271

Intl. Peace Year A1272

**Lithographed, Photogravure (#1707)**
**1986, Nov. 28**

| | | | | | |
|---|---|---|---|---|---|
| 1706 | A1271 | 40y | multicolored | .75 | .25 |
| 1707 | A1272 | 60y | multicolored | 1.00 | .30 |

New Year 1987 (Year of the Hare) — A1273

Design: A Couple of Rabbits Making Rice Cake, Nagoya clay figurine.

**1986, Dec. 1 Photo. *Perf. 13x13½***

| | | | | | |
|---|---|---|---|---|---|
| 1708 | A1273 | 40y | multicolored | .90 | .30 |

Sheets of two containing Nos. 1506 and 1708 were lottery prizes. Value, $2.10.
See No. 2655c.

Real Estate Registry System, Cent. A1274

**1987, Jan. 30 Photo. *Perf. 13½***

| | | | | | |
|---|---|---|---|---|---|
| 1709 | A1274 | 60y | multicolored | 1.00 | .25 |

## Basho Series, Part I

A1275

A1277

A1279

A1281

A1283

A1285

A1287

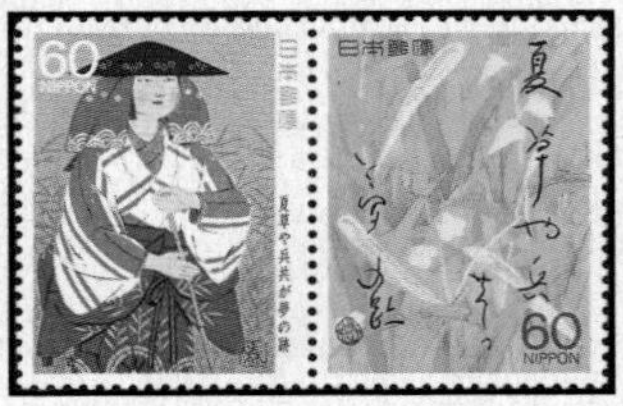

A1289

A1291

A1293

No. 1710, Basho. No. 1711, Basho's haiku. No. 1712, Kegon Falls. No. 1713, Haiku. No. 1714, Cuckoo. No. 1715, Horse and haiku. No. 1716, Willow Tree. No. 1717, Rice Paddy and haiku. No. 1718, Chestnut Tree in Bloom. No. 1719, Chestnut Leaves and haiku. No. 1720, Planting Rice Paddy. No. 1721, Fern Leaves and haiku. No. 1722, Sweetflags. No. 1723, Sweetflags and haiku. No. 1724, Prosperous Man, 17th Cent. No. 1725, Summer Grass and haiku. No. 1726, Safflowers in Bloom. No. 1727, Haiku. No. 1728, Yamadera (Temple). No. 1729, Forest and haiku.

**1987-89 Photo. *Perf. 13x13½***

| | | | | |
|---|---|---|---|---|
| 1710 | 60y multicolored | | 1.00 | .35 |
| 1711 | 60y multicolored | | 1.00 | .35 |
| | *a.* Sheet of 2, #1710-1711, imperf. ('89) | | 2.50 | 2.50 |
| | *b.* A1275 Pair, #1710-1711 | | 2.25 | 1.00 |
| 1712 | 60y multicolored | | 1.00 | .35 |
| 1713 | 60y multicolored | | 1.00 | .35 |
| | *a.* Sheet of 2, #1712-1713, imperf. ('89) | | 2.50 | 2.50 |
| | *b.* A1277 Pair, #1712-1713 | | 2.25 | 1.00 |
| 1714 | 60y multicolored | | 1.00 | .35 |
| 1715 | 60y multicolored | | 1.00 | .35 |
| | *a.* Sheet of 2, #1714-1715, imperf. ('89) | | 2.50 | 2.50 |
| | *b.* A1279 Pair, #1714-1715 | | 2.25 | 1.00 |
| 1716 | 60y multicolored | | 1.00 | .35 |
| 1717 | 60y multicolored | | 1.00 | .35 |
| | *a.* Sheet of 2, #1716-1717, imperf. ('89) | | 2.50 | 2.50 |
| | *b.* A1281 Pair, #1716-1717 | | 2.25 | 1.00 |
| 1718 | 60y multicolored | | 1.00 | .35 |
| 1719 | 60y multicolored | | 1.00 | .35 |
| | *a.* Sheet of 2, #1718-1719, imperf. ('89) | | 2.50 | 2.50 |
| | *b.* A1283 Pair, #1718-1719 | | 2.25 | 1.00 |
| 1720 | 60y multicolored | | 1.00 | .35 |
| 1721 | 60y multicolored | | 1.00 | .35 |
| | *a.* Sheet of 2, #1720-1721, imperf. ('89) | | 2.50 | 2.50 |
| | *b.* A1285 Pair, #1720-1721 | | 2.25 | 1.00 |
| 1722 | 60y multi ('88) | | 1.00 | .35 |
| 1723 | 60y multi ('88) | | 1.00 | .35 |
| | *a.* Sheet of 2, #1722-1723, imperf. ('89) | | 2.50 | 2.50 |
| | *b.* A1287 Pair, #1722-1723 | | 2.25 | 1.00 |
| 1724 | 60y multi ('88) | | 1.00 | .35 |
| 1725 | 60y multi ('88) | | 1.00 | .35 |
| | *a.* Sheet of 2, #1724-1725, imperf. ('89) | | 2.50 | 2.50 |
| | *b.* A1289 Pair, #1724-1725 | | 2.25 | 1.00 |
| 1726 | 60y multi ('88) | | 1.00 | .35 |
| 1727 | 60y multi ('88) | | 1.00 | .35 |
| | *a.* Sheet of 2, #1726-1727, imperf. ('89) | | 2.50 | 2.50 |
| | *b.* A1291 Pair, #1726-1727 | | 2.25 | 1.00 |
| 1728 | 60y multi ('88) | | 1.00 | .35 |
| 1729 | 60y multi ('88) | | 1.00 | .35 |
| | *a.* Sheet of 2, #1728-1729, imperf. ('89) | | 2.50 | 2.50 |
| | *b.* A1293 Pair, #1728-1729 | | 2.25 | 1.00 |
| | *Nos. 1710-1729 (20)* | | 20.00 | 7.00 |

Issued to commemorate the 300th anniversary of a trip from Edo (now Tokyo) to northern Japan by the famous haiku poet Matsuo Munefusa "Basho" (1644-1694). His prose account of the journey, *Oku no hosomichi* (*Narrow Road to a Far Province*), contains numerous 17-syllable poems (*haiku*), which are shown on the stamps.

In each setenant pair, a complete *haiku* by Basho is inscribed vertically at right on the left stamp and in the center of the right stamp. The same poem appears on both stamps in each pair.

Issued: Nos. 1710-1713, 2/26; Nos. 1714-1717, 6/23; Nos. 1718-1721, 8/25; Nos. 1722-1725, 1/3; Nos. 1726-1729, 3/26.

See Nos. 1775-1794.

12th World Orchid Congress, Tokyo
A1295 A1296

**1987, Mar. 19 Photo. *Perf. 13***

| | | | | | |
|---|---|---|---|---|---|
| 1730 | A1295 | 60y | multicolored | 1.00 | .30 |
| 1731 | A1296 | 60y | multicolored | 1.00 | .30 |

Railway Post Office Termination, Oct. 1, 1986 A1297

**1987, Mar. 26 Litho. *Perf. 13½***

| | | | |
|---|---|---|---|
| 1732 | 60y Mail car | 1.00 | .30 |
| 1733 | 60y Loading mail on car | 1.00 | .30 |
| | *a.* A1297 Pair, #1732-1733 | 2.25 | 1.00 |

Privatization of Japan Railways A1298

No. 1734, Locomotive No. 137, c. 1900. No. 1735, Linear induction train, 1987.

**1987, Apr. 1 Photo. *Perf. 13½***

| | | | | | |
|---|---|---|---|---|---|
| 1734 | A1298 | 60y | multicolored | 1.00 | .35 |
| 1735 | A1298 | 60y | multicolored | 1.00 | .35 |

Natl. Marine Biology Research, Cent. A1299

**1987, Apr. 2 *Perf. 13***

| | | | | | |
|---|---|---|---|---|---|
| 1736 | A1299 | 60y | Sea slugs | 1.00 | .25 |

Paintings by Hashiguchi Goyo (1880-1921) — A1300

**1987, Apr. 14**

| | | | |
|---|---|---|---|
| 1737 | 60y denomination at upper right | 1.00 | .30 |
| 1738 | 60y denomination at lower left | 1.00 | .30 |
| | *a.* A1300 Pair, #1737-1738 | 2.25 | 1.00 |

Philately Week.

Map of Asia and Oceania A1302

**1987, Apr. 27 Photo. *Perf. 13½***

| | | | | | |
|---|---|---|---|---|---|
| 1739 | A1302 | 60y | multicolored | 1.00 | .25 |

20th annual meeting of the Asian Development Bank.

Nat'l. Land Afforestation Campaign A1303

60y, Magpie, seashore.

**1987, May 23**

| | | | | | |
|---|---|---|---|---|---|
| 1740 | A1303 | 60y | multicolored | 1.00 | .25 |

## National Treasures Series

A1304

A1305

Designs: No. 1741, Yatsuhashi gold ink-stone box, by Kohrin Ogata. No. 1742, Donjon of Hikone Castle, c. 1573-1592.

**1987, May 26 Photo. *Perf. 13***
**1741** A1304 60y multicolored 1.00 .35

**Photo. & Engr.**
***Perf. 13½***
**1742** A1305 110y multicolored 1.90 .50

Golden Turtle Sharito — A1306

Imuyama Castle Donjon, 1469 — A1307

**1987, July 17 Photo. *Perf. 13***
**1743** A1306 60y multicolored 1.00 .35

**Photo. & Engr.**
***Perf. 13½***
**1744** A1307 110y multicolored 1.90 .50

Kongo Sanmai in Tahotoh Temple, Kamakura Era — A1308

Wood Ekoh-Dohji Statue in the Likeness of Kongobuji Fudodo, Kamakura Era, by Unkei — A1309

**1988, Feb. 12 Photo. *Perf. 13***
**1745** A1308 60y multicolored 1.00 .35

**Photo. & Engr.**
***Perf. 13½***
**1746** A1309 110y multicolored 1.90 .50

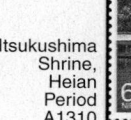

Itsukushima Shrine, Heian Period A1310

Kozakura-gawa, Braided Armor Worn by Minamoto-no-Yoshimitsu, Heian Period War Lord, Kai Province — A1311

**1988, June 23 Photo. *Perf. 13***
**1747** A1310 60y multicolored 1.00 .35

**Photo. & Engr.**
***Perf. 13½***
**1748** A1311 100y multicolored 1.75 .50

Statue of *Nakatsu-hime-no-mikoto,* a Hachiman Goddess, Heian Period, Yakushiji Temple — A1312

Murou-ji Temple Pagoda, 9th Cent. — A1313

**1988, Sept. 26 Photo. *Perf. 13***
**1749** A1312 60y multicolored 1.00 .35

**Photo. & Engr.**
***Perf. 13½***
**1750** A1313 100y multicolored 1.75 .50
*Nos. 1741-1750 (10)* 14.20 4.25

Letter Writing Day — A1314

40y, Flowers, envelope. 60y, Elephant.

**1987, July 23 Photo. *Perf. 13x13½***
**1751** A1314 40y multicolored .75 .30
**1752** A1314 60y multicolored 1.00 .35
***a.*** Bklt. pane, 5 ea #1751-1752 9.00

Sheets of 2, Nos. 1751-1752, were lottery prizes. Value, *$4.25.*

Kiso Three Rivers Flood Control, Cent. A1315

60y, Kiso, Nagara and Ibi Rivers.

**1987, Aug. 7 Photo. *Perf. 13½***
**1753** A1315 60y multicolored 1.00 .25

Japan — Thailand Diplomatic Relations, Cent. A1316

Design: Temple of the Emerald Buddha and cherry blossoms.

**1987, Sept. 26 *Perf. 13***
**1754** A1316 60y multicolored 1.00 .30

Intl. Letter Writing Week — A1317

Dolls by Goyo Hirata: 130y, Gensho Kanto, by Royojo Hori (1898-1984). 150y, Utage-no-Hana (Fair Woman at the Party).

**1987, Oct. 6 Photo. *Perf. 13***
**1755** A1317 130y multicolored 2.10 .75
**1756** A1317 150y multicolored 2.50 .85

13th World Congress of Certified Public Accountants, Tokyo, Oct. 11-15 — A1318

Design: Three Beauties (adaptation), by Toyokuni Utagawa (1769-1825).

**1987, Oct. 9 *Perf. 13***
**1757** A1318 60y multicolored 1.00 .35

Modern Waterworks, Cent. — A1319

Design: Lion's head public fountain, 1887, Waterworks Museum, Yokohama.

**1987, Oct. 16 Engr.**
**1758** A1319 60y multicolored 1.00 .25

Shurei Gate, Okinawa, Basketball Players — A1320

**1987, Oct. 24 Photo.**
**1759** A1320 40y multicolored .75 .25

42nd Natl. Athletic Meet, Okinawa.

6th World Cong. on Smoking & Health, Nov. 9-12, Tokyo — A1321

**1987, Nov. 9**
**1760** A1321 60y multicolored 1.00 .25

World Telecommunications Conf., Nov. 15-18, Tokyo — A1322

Design: Microwave dish antenna at Kashima Station Radio Research Laboratory.

**1987, Nov. 13 *Perf. 13½***
**1761** A1322 60y multicolored 1.00 .25

World Conference on Large Historic Cities, Nov. 18-21, Kyoto A1323

Design: Nijo Castle guardhouse roof and Ninomaru Hall, 17th cent.

**1987, Nov. 18 *Perf. 13***
**1762** A1323 60y multicolored 1.00 .30

Intl. Year of Shelter for the Homeless A1324

Prize-winning illustrations by: 40y, Takahiro Nahahama. 60y, Yoko Sasaki.

**1987, Nov. 25**
**1763** A1324 40y multicolored .75 .25
**1764** A1324 60y multicolored 1.00 .30

New Year 1988 (Year of the Dragon) — A1325

Design: Kurashiki papier-mache dragon, 1869, by Tajuro Omizu.

**1987, Dec. 1 *Perf. 13x13½***
**1765** A1325 40y multicolored .90 .30

Sheets of 2, Nos. 1506, 1765, were lottery prizes. Value, $2.40.

Seikan Tunnel Opening A1326

60y, ED 79 locomotive, map.

**1988, Mar. 11 Photo. *Perf. 13¼***
**1766** A1326 60y multicolored 1.00 .35
***a.*** Booklet pane of 10 12.00

### Opening of Seto-Oohashi Bridge

Kagawa Side
A1327 A1328

Okayama Side
A1329 A1330

**1988, Apr. 8 Engr.** ***Perf. 13½***

| | | | |
|---|---|---|---|
| **1767** | A1327 60y multicolored | 1.00 | .35 |
| **1768** | A1328 60y multicolored | 1.00 | .35 |
| **1769** | A1329 60y multicolored | 1.00 | .35 |
| **1770** | A1330 60y multicolored | 1.00 | .35 |
| *a.* | Strip of 4, #1767-1770 | 4.50 | 4.50 |

Nos. 1767-1768 and 1769-1770 have continuous designs.

Philately Week — A1331

Prints by Kotondo Torii (1900-76): No. 1771, Long Undergarment. No. 1772, Kimono Sash.

**1988, Apr. 19 Photo.** ***Perf. 13***

| | | | |
|---|---|---|---|
| **1771** | 60y denomination at lower right | 1.00 | .35 |
| **1772** | 60y denomination at upper left | 1.00 | .35 |
| *a.* | A1331 Pair, #1771-1772 | 2.50 | 1.50 |

Souv. sheet of 2 exists. Value $6.

Silk Road Exposition, Apr. 24-Oct. 23, Nara — A1333

Design: Plectrum guard playing the biwa, detail of Raden-Shitan-no-Gogen-Biwa, a five-panel work of gold lacquer nacre on sandalwood preserved at Shosoin.

**1988, Apr. 23 Photo. & Engr.**

| | | | |
|---|---|---|---|
| **1773** | A1333 60y multicolored | 1.00 | .30 |

Natl. Afforestation Campaign
A1334

Design: Yahsima, site of the Genji-Heike war, and cuckoo on olive tree branch.

**1988, May 20 Photo.** ***Perf. 13½***

| | | | |
|---|---|---|---|
| **1774** | A1334 60y multicolored | 1.00 | .25 |

### Basho Series, Part II

A1335

A1337

No. 1775, Mogami River. No. 1776, Haiku and flower. No. 1777, Mt. Gassan. No. 1778, Haiku and mountain.

**1988, May 30 Photo.** ***Perf. 13x13½***

| | | | |
|---|---|---|---|
| **1775** | 60y multicolored | 1.00 | .35 |
| **1776** | 60y multicolored | 1.00 | .35 |
| *a.* | Souv. sheet of 2, #1775-1776, imperf. ('89) | 2.50 | 2.50 |
| *b.* | A1335 Pair, #1775-1776 | 2.25 | 1.00 |
| **1777** | 60y multicolored | 1.00 | .35 |
| **1778** | 60y multicolored | 1.00 | .35 |
| *a.* | Souv. sheet of 2, #1777-1778, imperf. ('89) | 2.50 | 2.50 |
| *b.* | A1337 Pair, #1777-1778 | 2.25 | 1.00 |

A1339

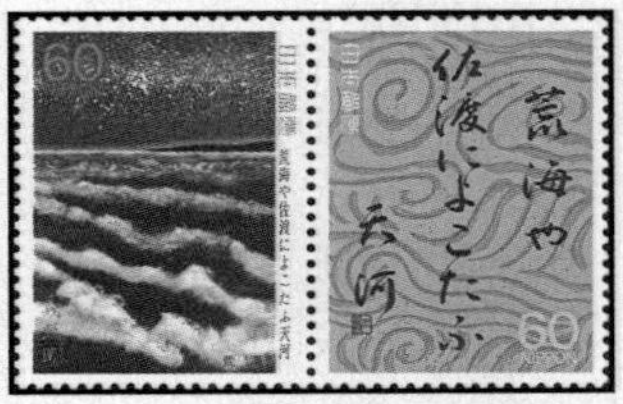

A1341

No. 1779, Mimosa in bloom. No. 1780, Verse, birds, Kisagata Inlet. No. 1781, Ocean waves. No. 1782, Verse and current.

**1988, Aug. 23**

| | | | |
|---|---|---|---|
| **1779** | 60y multicolored | 1.00 | .35 |
| **1780** | 60y multicolored | 1.00 | .35 |
| *a.* | Souv. sheet of 2, #1779-1780, imperf ('89) | 2.50 | 2.50 |
| *b.* | A1339 Pair, #1779-1780 | 2.25 | 1.00 |
| **1781** | 60y multicolored | 1.00 | .35 |
| **1782** | 60y multicolored | 1.00 | .35 |
| *a.* | Souv. sheet of 2, #1781-1782, imperf. ('89) | 2.50 | 2.50 |
| *b.* | A1341 Pair, #1781-1782 | 2.25 | 1.00 |

A1343

A1345

No. 1783, Rice. No. 1784, Birds in flight, haiku. No. 1785, Sun glow. No. 1786, Rice, haiku.

**1988, Nov. 11**

| | | | |
|---|---|---|---|
| **1783** | 60y multicolored | 1.00 | .35 |
| **1784** | 60y multicolored | 1.00 | .35 |
| *a.* | Souv. sheet of 2, #1783-1784, imperf. ('89) | 2.50 | 2.50 |
| *b.* | A1343 Pair, #1783-1784 | 2.25 | 1.00 |
| **1785** | 60y multicolored | 1.00 | .35 |
| **1786** | 60y multicolored | 1.00 | .35 |
| *a.* | Souv. sheet of 2, #1785-1786, imperf. ('89) | 2.50 | 2.50 |
| *b.* | A1345 Pair, #1785-1786 | 2.25 | 1.00 |

A1347

A1349

No. 1787, Nata-dera Temple. No. 1788, Haiku, white grass. No. 1789, Trees. No. 1790, Haiku, moonlit forest.

**1989, Feb. 13**

| | | | |
|---|---|---|---|
| **1787** | 60y multicolored | 1.00 | .35 |
| **1788** | 60y multicolored | 1.00 | .35 |
| *a.* | Souv. sheet of 2, #1787-1788, imperf. | 2.50 | 2.50 |
| *b.* | A1347 Pair, #1787-1788 | 2.25 | 1.00 |
| **1789** | 60y multicolored | 1.00 | .35 |
| **1790** | 60y multicolored | 1.00 | .35 |
| *a.* | Souv. sheet of 2, #1789-1790, imperf. | 2.50 | 2.50 |
| *b.* | A1349 Pair, #1789-1790 | 2.25 | 1.00 |

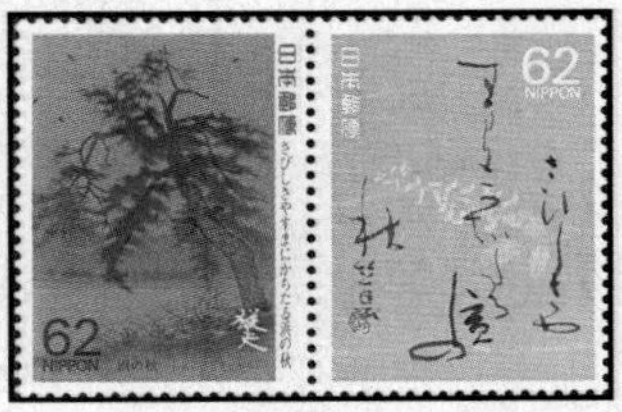

A1351

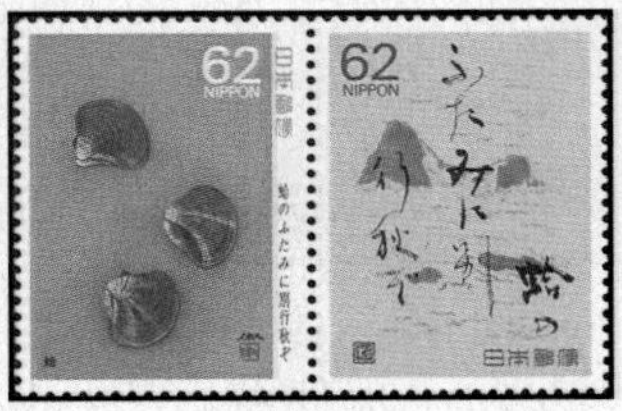

A1353

No. 1791, Autumn on the beach. No. 1792, Haiku. No. 1793, Clams. No. 1794, Haiku.

**1989, May 12**

| | | | |
|---|---|---|---|
| **1791** | 62y multicolored | 1.00 | .35 |
| **1792** | 62y multicolored | 1.00 | .35 |
| *a.* | Souv. sheet of 2, #1791-1792, imperf. | 2.50 | 2.50 |
| *b.* | A1351 Pair, #1791-1792 | 2.25 | 1.00 |
| **1793** | 62y multicolored | 1.00 | .35 |
| **1794** | 62y multicolored | 1.00 | .35 |
| *a.* | Souv. sheet of 2, #1793-1794, imperf. | 2.50 | 2.50 |
| *b.* | A1353 Pair, #1793-1794 | 2.25 | 1.00 |

Haiku from *Oku-no-hosomichi, "Narrow Road to a Far Province,"* 1694, a travel description written by Matsuo Munefusa (1644-94), a haiku poet best known by his pen-name Basho.

In each setenant pair, a complete *haiku* by Basho is inscribed vertically at right on the left stamp and in the center of the right stamp. The same poem appears on both stamps in each pair.

Issued: Nos. 1776a-1794a, Aug. 1, 1989.

Intl. Conference on Volcanoes, Kagoshima
A1355

**1988, July 19 Photo.** ***Perf. 14***

| | | | |
|---|---|---|---|
| **1795** | A1355 60y multicolored | 1.00 | .30 |

A1356

A1357

A1358

Letter Writing Day, 10th Anniv. — A1359

Designs and contest-winning children's drawings: No. 1796, Cat and letter. No. 1797, *Crab and Letter,* by Katsuyuki Yamada. No. 1798, Fairy and letter. No. 1799, *Girl and Letter,* by Takashi Ukai.

**Photo., Litho. (Nos. 1797, 1799)**

**1988, July 23** ***Perf. 13x13½***

| | | | |
|---|---|---|---|
| **1796** | A1356 40y multicolored | .75 | .30 |
| **1796A** | A1356 40y Imperf., self-adhesive | .75 | .30 |
| **1797** | A1357 40y multicolored | .75 | .30 |
| **1798** | A1358 60y multicolored | 1.00 | .30 |
| *a.* | Bklt. pane, 5 each #1796, 1798 | 9.25 | |
| **1798B** | A1358 60y Imperf., self-adhesive | 1.00 | .30 |
| *c.* | Bklt. pane, 3 each #1796A, 1798B | 7.50 | |
| **1799** | A1359 60y multicolored | 1.00 | .30 |
| | *Nos. 1796-1799 (6)* | 5.25 | 1.80 |

No. 1798c is adhered to the booklet cover, made of peelable paper, folded in half and rouletted down the center fold, with No. 1796a at left and No. 1798b at right of the roulette.

Sheets of 2 containing Nos. 1796, 1798 were lottery prizes. Value, $5.

15th World Puppetry Festival, July 27-Aug. 11 — A1360

Puppets: No. 1800, *Ohana,* string puppet from the film *Spring and Fall in the Meiji Era,* by Kinosuke Takeda (1923-1979), Japan. No. 1801, Girl, stick puppet from the Natl. Radost Puppet Theater, Brno, Czechoslovakia. No. 1802, Woman, shadow puppet from China. No. 1803, Knight, a marionette from Sicily.

**1988, July 27 Photo. *Perf. 13***

**1800** 60y multicolored 1.00 .35
**1801** 60y multicolored 1.00 .35
**1802** 60y multicolored 1.00 .35
**1803** 60y multicolored 1.00 .35
*a.* A1360 Block or strip of 4, #1800-1803 4.50 1.75

Japan-China Treaty, 10th Anniv. — A1364

**1988, Aug. 12 Photo.**

**1804** 60y Peony 1.00 .35
**1805** 60y Panda 1.00 .35
*a.* A1364 Pair, #1804-1805 2.25 1.00

18th World Poultry Congress, Nagoya, Sept. 4-9 — A1366

**1988, Sept. 3 *Perf. 13½***

**1806** A1366 60y multicolored 1.00 .30

Rehabilitation Intl. 16th World Congress, Tokyo, Sept. 5-9 — A1367

**Photo. & Embossed**

**1988, Sept. 5 *Perf. 13***

**1807** A1367 60y multicolored 1.00 .25

Intl. Letter-Writing Week — A1368

Prints: 80y, *Kumesaburo Iwai as Chiyo,* by Kunimasa Utagawa (1773-1810), late Edo Period. 120y, *Komazo Ichikawa III as Ganryu Sasaki,* by Toyokuni Utagawa (1769-1825).

**1988, Oct. 6 Photo.**

**1808** A1368 80y multicolored 1.40 .50
**1809** A1368 120y multicolored 2.00 .50

43rd Natl. Athletic Meet, Kyoto — A1369

Design: Gymnast on parallel bars and "Kinkakuji," Temple of the Golden Pavilion.

**1988, Oct. 14**

**1810** A1369 40y multicolored .75 .25

Japan-Mexico Trade Agreement, Cent. — A1370

**1988, Nov. 30 Photo.**

**1811** A1370 60y multicolored 1.00 .30

New Year 1989 (Year of the Snake) — A1371

Clay bell snake by Masanobu Ogawa.

**1988, Dec. 1**

**1812** A1371 40y multicolored .90 .35

Sheets of two containing Nos. 1506, 1812 were lottery prizes. Value, $2.50.

UN Declaration of Human Rights, 40th Anniv. — A1372

**1988, Dec. 5 Litho. *Perf. 13½***

**1813** A1372 60y multicolored 1.00 .25

**National Treasures Series**

Votive Silver Lidded Bowl Used in Todai-ji Temple Ground-Breaking Ceremony, 8th Cent. — A1373

Bronze Yakushi-nyorai Buddha, Asuka Period, 7th Cent. — A1374

**Photo., Photo & Engr. (100y)**

**1989, Jan. 20 *Perf. 13, 13½ (100y)***

**1814** A1373 60y multicolored 1.00 .35
**1815** A1374 100y multicolored 1.75 .50

Kondo-Sukashibori-Kurakanagu, Bronze Saddle from Ohjin Imperial Mausoleum — A1375

Tamamushi-no-Zushi, Buddhist Altar in Lacquered Cypress from the Asuka Era — A1376

**1989, June 30**

**1816** A1375 62y multicolored 1.10 .35
**1817** A1376 100y multicolored 1.75 .50

Kin-in, a Gokan Era Gold Seal Given to the King of Na by Emperor Kobutei — A1377

Shinninshaba-gazokyo, a 5th Cent. European Bronze Mirror Back — A1378

**1989, Aug. 15**

**1818** A1377 62y multicolored 1.10 .35
**1819** A1378 100y multicolored 1.75 .50
*Nos. 1814-1819 (6)* 8.45 2.55

Asian-Pacific Expo, Fukuoka, Mar. 17-Sept. 3 — A1383

**1989 Photo. *Perf. 13***

**1822** A1383 60y multicolored 1.00 .30
**1823** A1383 62y multicolored 1.50 .50

Issue dates: 60y, Mar. 16; 62y, Apr. 18.

Yokohama Exposition (Space and Children), Yokohama City, Mar. 25 to Oct. 1 — A1384

Design: Detail of *Russian Lady Sight-seeing at the Port,* by Yoshitora, and entrance to the Yokohama City Art Museum.

**1989, Mar. 24 Litho.**

**1824** A1384 60y multicolored 1.00 .30
**1825** A1384 62y multicolored 1.50 .50

World Bonsai Convention, Omiya, Apr. 6-9 — A1385

**1989, Apr. 6 Photo. *Perf. 13***

**1826** A1385 62y multicolored 1.10 .35

*Awa-odori,* by Tsunetomi Kitano (b. 1880) — A1386

**1989, Apr. 18 *Perf. 13***

**1827** 62y multicolored 1.10 .35
**1828** 62y multicolored 1.10 .35
*a.* A1386 Pair, #1827-1828 2.25 1.00

Philately Week. Sheets of 2 containing Nos. 1827-1828 were lottery prizes. Value, $5.

Holland Festival 1989 — A1388

**1989, Apr. 19 *Perf. 13½***

**1829** A1388 62y Ship 1.10 .30

Fiber-optic Cable, the 3rd Transpacific Line Relay Linking Japan and the US — A1389

62y, Station tower, map.

**1989, May 10 *Perf. 13½x13***

**1830** A1389 62y Station tower, map 1.10 .30

Natl. Afforestation Campaign — A1390

62y, Bayberry, lime, Mt. Tsurugi.

**1989, May 19 *Perf. 13½***

**1831** A1390 62y multicolored 1.10 .30

World Design Exposition, Nagoya, July 15-Nov. 26

A1391 A1392

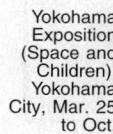

**1989, July 14**

1832 A1391 41y multicolored .80 .35
1833 A1392 62y multicolored 1.10 .35

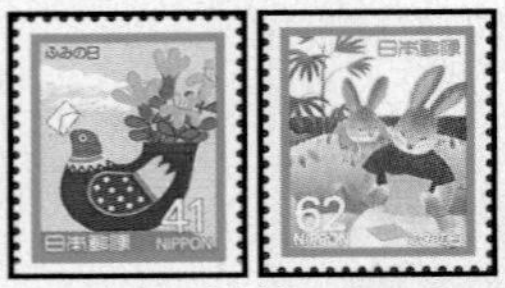

Letter Writing Day
A1393 A1394

**1989, July 21** ***Perf. 13x13½***

1834 A1393 41y multicolored .80 .30
1835 A1394 62y multicolored 1.10 .30
*a.* Bklt. pane, 5 each #1834-1835 9.50

Sheets of 2 containing Nos. 1834-1835 were lottery prizes. Value, $3.

### Congratulations and Condolences Types of 1982

**1989, Aug. 10 Photo.** ***Perf. 13x13½***

1836 A1082 41y Wreath .80 .25
1837 A1083 41y Crane .80 .30
1838 A1083 62y Crane 1.10 .30
1839 A1084 72y Tortoise 1.30 .35
*Nos. 1836-1839 (4)* 4.00 1.20

6th Interflora World Congress, Tokyo, Aug. 27-30 — A1395

**1989, Aug. 25 Photo.** ***Perf. 13½***

1840 A1395 62y multicolored 1.10 .35

### Prefecture Issues

Nos. 1841-1990 have been changed to Nos. Z1-Z150. The listings can be found in the section immediately following the postage section and preceding the semi-postal listings.

Far East and South Pacific Games for the Disabled (FESPIC), Kobe, Sept. 15-20
A1546

**1989, Sept. 14 Photo.** ***Perf. 13½***

1991 A1546 62y multicolored 1.10 .30

*Okuni Kabuki* Screen
A1547 A1548

**1989, Sept. 18** ***Perf. 13***

1992 A1547 62y multicolored 1.10 .35
1993 A1548 70y multicolored 1.25 .40

EUROPALIA '89, Japan.

A1549

A1550

Scenes from the Yadorigi and Takekawa Chapters of the Tales of the Genji picture scroll, attributed to Fujiwara-no-Takeyoshi, late Heian Period (897-1185).

**1989, Oct. 6 Photo.** ***Perf. 13½***

1994 A1549 80y multicolored 1.40 .45
1995 A1550 120y multicolored 2.00 .55

Intl. Letter Writing Day.

Intl. Conference on Irrigation and Drainage — A1551

**1989, Oct. 13**

1996 A1551 62y Rice 1.10 .30

100th Tenno Sho Horse Race — A1552

62y, Jockey riding Shinzan.

**1989, Oct. 27** ***Perf. 13***

1997 A1552 62y multicolored 1.10 .30

9th Hot Air Balloon World Championships, Saga — A1553

**1989, Nov. 17 Photo.** ***Perf. 13x13½***

1998 A1553 62y multicolored 1.10 .35

Copyright Control System, 50th Anniv. A1554

**1989, Nov. 17** ***Perf. 13***

1999 A1554 62y Conductor 1.10 .30

New Year 1990 (Year of the Horse)
A1555 A1556

41y, *Yawata-Uma* festival horse. 62y, *Kazari-Uma*, Meiji Period.

**1989, Dec. 1** ***Perf. 13x13½, 13½***

2000 A1555 41y multicolored .85 .30
2001 A1556 62y multicolored 1.10 .35

No. 2001 was sold through Jan. 10, 1990, serving as a lottery ticket.

Sheets of two containing Nos. 1838, 2000 were lottery prizes. Value, $2.50.

### Electric Locomotives

10,000 A1557

**Photo. & Engr., Photo.**

**1990** ***Perf. 13***

2002 A1557 62y shown 1.10 .35
2003 A1557 62y EF58 1.10 .35
2004 A1557 62y ED40 1.10 .35
2005 A1557 62y EH10 1.10 .35
2006 A1557 62y EF53 1.10 .35
2007 A1557 62y ED70 1.10 .35
2008 A1557 62y EF55 1.10 .35
2009 A1557 62y ED61 1.10 .35
2010 A1557 62y EF57 1.10 .35
2011 A1557 62y EF30 1.10 .35
*Nos. 2002-2011 (10)* 11.00 3.50

Issued two stamps at a time, the first photo. & engr., the second photo.

Issued: Nos. 2002-2003, 1/31; Nos. 2004-2005, 2/28; Nos. 2006-2007, 4/23; Nos. 2008-2009, 5/23; Nos. 2010-2011, 7/18.

Intl. Garden and Greenery Exposition, Osaka A1558

**1990, Mar. 30 Photo.** ***Perf. 13***

2021 A1558 62y multicolored 1.10 .30

See No. B45.

Philately Week — A1559

Painting: *Women Gazing at the Stars,* by Chou Ohta.

**1990, Apr. 20 Photo.** ***Perf. 13***

2022 A1559 62y multicolored 1.10 .30
*a.* Souvenir sheet of 1 1.25 1.25

A1560

62y, Azalea, Mt. Unzen.

**1990, May 18 Photo.** ***Perf. 13½***

2023 A1560 62y multicolored 1.10 .30

Natl. Land Afforestation Campaign.

Flower, Butterfly A1561

Abstract Art — A1561a

**1990, June 1 Photo.** ***Perf. 13***

2024 A1561 62y multicolored 1.10 .35
2025 A1561a 70y multicolored 1.25 .35

Japan-Turkey Relations, Cent. — A1562

**1990, June 13**

2026 A1562 62y multicolored 1.10 .30

### Horses Series

Horses at Stable from Umaya-zu Byobu — A1563

Foals A1564

Lacquered Saddle, 16th Cent. A1565

Lacquered Stirrups, 16th Cent. A1566

Horse by S. Nishiyama A1567

Kettei A1568

"Kamo-Kurabeuma-Monyo-Kosode" A1569

***Perf. 13x13½, 13***

**1990** **Litho. & Engr.**

**Color of Horse**

2027 62y red brown 1.10 .35
2028 62y gray 1.10 .35
2029 62y beige 1.10 .35
2030 62y tan 1.10 .35

2031 62y mottled 1.10 .35
*a.* A1563 Strip of 5, #2027-2031 6.75 2.75

**Photo.**

2032 A1564 62y shown 1.10 .35

**Photo. & Engr.**

2033 A1565 62y shown 1.10 .35
2034 A1566 62y shown 1.10 .35
*a.* Pair, #2033-2034 2.75 1.00

**Photo.**

2035 A1567 62y multicolored 1.10 .35
2036 A1568 62y multicolored 1.10 .35
2037 A1569 62y multicolored 1.10 .35

Postal Carriages — A1569a

Inkstone Case "Sano-no-Watashi" — A1570

"Bushu-Senju-zu" by Hokusai — A1571

"Shudan" by Kogetsu Saigo A1571a

**Photo. & Engr., Photo. (#2040, 2042)**
**1991** ***Perf. 12½x13***

2038 62y one horse 1.10 .35
2039 62y two horses 1.10 .35
*a.* A1569a Pair, #2038-2039 2.75 1.00

***Perf. 13½x13***

2040 A1570 62y multicolored 1.10 .35
2041 A1571 62y multicolored 1.10 .35
2042 A1571a 62y multicolored 1.10 .35
*Nos. 2027-2042 (16)* 17.60 5.60

Issued: Nos. 2027-2032, 6/20; Nos. 2033-2035, 7/31; Nos. 2036-2037, 9/27; Nos. 2038-2040, 1/31. Nos. 2041-2042, 2/28.

38th Intl. Youth Hostel Fed. Conference A1573

**1990, June 25** **Litho.** ***Perf. 13***

2057 A1573 62y multicolored 1.10 .30

Letter Writing Day
A1574 A1575

**1990, July 23** **Photo.** ***Perf. 13½***

2058 A1574 41y multicolored .80 .35
2059 A1575 62y multicolored 1.10 .40
*a.* Souv. sheet of 1 1.25 1.25
*b.* Bklt. pane, 5 ea #2058-2059 9.50

See No. 2117.

21st Intl. Congress of Mathematicians — A1576

**1990, Aug. 17** **Photo.** ***Perf. 13***

2060 A1576 62y multicolored 1.10 .30

World Cycling Championships A1577

**1990, Aug. 20** **Litho.** ***Perf. 13½***

2061 A1577 62y multicolored 1.10 .30

Ogai Mori, Educator A1578

**1990, Aug. 27** **Photo.**

2062 A1578 62y multicolored 1.10 .30

Intl. Assoc. for Germanic Studies (IVG), 8th Congress.

Character "Ji" in Shape of Rosetta Stone — A1579

**1990, Sept. 7** ***Perf. 13***

2063 A1579 62y multicolored 1.10 .30

Intl. Literacy Year.

Decade for Natural Disaster Reduction A1580

**1990, Sept. 27** **Photo.**

2064 A1580 62y multicolored 1.10 .30

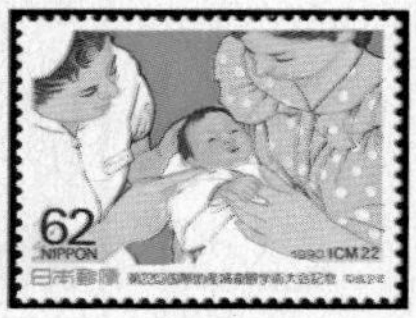

Intl. Confederation of Midwives, 22nd Congress A1581

**1990, Oct. 5** **Photo.**

2065 A1581 62y multicolored 1.10 .30

A1582

"Choju-Jinbutsu-Giga" — A1583

**Photo. & Engr.**
**1990, Oct. 5** ***Perf. 13½***

2066 A1582 80y multicolored 1.40 .45
2067 A1583 120y multicolored 2.00 .55

Intl. Letter Writing Week.

"Fumizukai-zu" by Harunobu Suiendo A1584

**1990, Oct. 16** **Photo.**

2068 A1584 100y multicolored 1.75 .55
*a.* Souv. sheet of 1 1.75 1.75

No. 2068a exists with surcharge which paid admission to PHILANIPPON '91. These were not sold by the post office.

Court System, Cent. — A1585

**1990, Nov. 1** **Photo.** ***Perf. 13x13½***

2069 A1585 62y "Justice" 1.10 .35

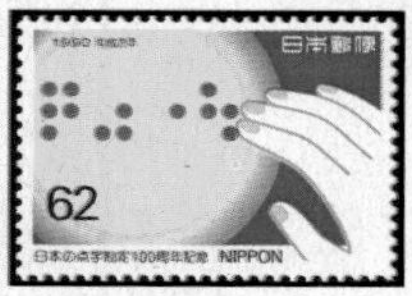

Japanese Braille, Cent. A1586

**Photo & Embossed**
**1990, Nov. 1** ***Perf. 13½***

2070 A1586 62y multicolored 1.10 .30

Enthronement of Akihito — A1587

No. 2071, Chinese phoenix depicted on Emperor's chair. No. 2072, Diamond pattern for costume worn at banquet ceremony.

**1990, Nov. 9** **Photo.** ***Perf. 13***

2071 A1587 62y multicolored 1.10 .35
2072 A1587 62y multicolored 1.10 .35
*a.* Souv. sheet of 2, #2071-2072 2.50 2.50

Japanese Diet, Cent. — A1588

**1990, Nov. 29** **Litho.**

2073 A1588 62y multicolored 1.10 .35

New Year 1991 (Year of the Sheep)
A1589 A1590

**1990, Dec. 3** **Photo.** ***Perf. 13x13½***

2074 A1589 41y multicolored .75 .30

**Photo. & Engr.**
***Perf. 13½***

2075 A1590 41y multicolored .90 .35
2076 A1590 62y multi, diff. 1.25 .40
*Nos. 2074-2076 (3)* 2.90 1.05

Sheets of 2 No. 2074 were lottery prizes. Value, $1.50.

Dr. Yoshio Nishina, Physicist — A1591

**1990, Dec. 6** **Photo.** ***Perf. 13***

2077 A1591 62y multicolored 1.10 .30

Use of radio isotopes in Japan, 50th anniv.

Telephone Service, Cent. — A1592

**1990, Dec. 14**

2078 A1592 62y multicolored 1.10 .30

A1593

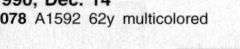

41y, Figure skating. 62y, Speed skating, horiz.

**1991, Mar. 1** **Photo.** ***Perf. 13½***

2079 A1593 41y multi .80 .30

***Perf. 13½x13***

2080 A1593 62y multi 1.10 .30

1991 Winter Universiade.

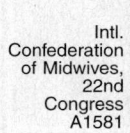

A1594

| 1991, Apr. 1 | Photo. | *Perf. 13* | |
|---|---|---|---|
| **2081** A1594 62y multicolored | | 1.10 | .30 |

Postal Life Insurance System.

Philately Week
A1595 A1596

No. 2082, Beauty Looking Back by Moronobu. No. 2083, Opening Dance by Shuho Yamakawa.

| **1991, Apr. 19** | | |
|---|---|---|
| **2082** A1595 62y multicolored | 1.10 | .35 |
| **2083** A1596 62y multicolored | 1.10 | .35 |
| *a.* Souv. sheet of 2, #2082-2083 | 2.40 | 2.40 |
| *b.* Pair, #2082-2083 | 2.40 | 2.40 |

Postal Service, 120th anniv.

Pairs of Nos. 2082-2083 with label between are available from sheets of 20.

A1597

| 1991, Apr. 19 | *Perf. 13½* | |
|---|---|---|
| **2084** A1597 62y multicolored | 1.10 | .30 |

Ceramic World Shigaraki '91.

A1598

| 1991, May 24 | Photo. | *Perf. 13½* | |
|---|---|---|---|
| **2085** A1598 41y multicolored | | .80 | .30 |

Natl. Land Afforestation Campaign.

Standard Datum of Leveling, Cent. — A1599

| 1991, May 30 | Photo. | *Perf. 13* | |
|---|---|---|---|
| **2086** A1599m 62y mutlicolored | | 1.10 | .35 |

### Int'l Stamp Design Contest Winning Entries

Flowers — A1600

Couple in Ethnic Dress A1601

World Peace — A1601a

Butterfly — A1601b

| 1991, May 31 | Photo. | *Perf. 13* | |
|---|---|---|---|
| **2087** A1600 41y multi | | .80 | .30 |
| **2088** A1601 62y multi | | 1.10 | .30 |
| **2089** A1601a 70y multi | | 1.25 | .40 |
| **2090** A1601b 100y multi | | 1.75 | .50 |
| *Nos. 2087-2090 (4)* | | 4.90 | 1.50 |

Int'l. Stamp Design Contest winning entries.

### Kabuki Series

Kagamijishi A1602

Yaegakihime A1603

Koshiro Matsumoto VII A1604

Danjuro Ichikawa XI A1605

Baigyoku Nakamura III A1606

Ganjiro Nakamura II A1607

Kichiemon Nakamura I — A1608

Nizaemon Kataoka XIII — A1609

Enjaku Jitsukawa II A1610

Hakuo Matsumoto I A1611

Fuji-Musume A1612

Kotobuki-Soganotaimen — A1613

*Perf. 13 (62y), 13½ (100y)*

| **1991-92** | **Photo.** | | |
|---|---|---|---|
| **2091** A1602 62y dp bl grn & gold | | 1.10 | .35 |
| **2092** A1603 100y multicolored | | 1.75 | .55 |
| **2093** A1604 62y multicolored | | 1.10 | .35 |
| **2094** A1605 100y multicolored | | 1.75 | .55 |
| **2095** A1606 62y multicolored | | 1.10 | .35 |
| **2096** A1607 100y multicolored | | 1.75 | .55 |
| **2097** A1608 62y multicolored | | 1.10 | .35 |
| **2098** A1609 100y multicolored | | 1.75 | .55 |
| **2099** A1610 62y multicolored | | 1.10 | .35 |
| **2100** A1611 100y multicolored | | 1.75 | .55 |
| **2101** A1612 62y multicolored | | 1.10 | .35 |
| **2102** A1613 100y multicolored | | 1.75 | .55 |
| *Nos. 2091-2102 (12)* | | 17.10 | 5.40 |

Issued: Nos. 2091-2092, 6/28; Nos. 2093-2094, 9/27; Nos. 2095-2096, 11/20; Nos. 2097-2098, 2/20/92; Nos. 2099-2100, 4/10/92; Nos. 2101-2102, 6/30/92.

### Waterbird Series

Gallinago Hardwickii (Latham's Snipe) A1614

No. 2104, Sula leucogaster. No. 2105, Larus crassirostris. No. 2106, Podiceps ruficollis. No. 2107, Lunda cirrhata. No. 2108, Grus monacha. No. 2109, Cygnus cygnus. No. 2110, Rostratula benghalensis. No. 2111, Calonectris leucomelas. No. 2112, Halcyon coromanda. No. 2113, Alcedo atthis. No. 2114, Bubulcus ibis.

| **1991-93** | **Photo.** | ***Perf. 13½*** | |
|---|---|---|---|
| **2103** A1614 62y multicolored | | 1.10 | .35 |
| **2104** A1614 62y multicolored | | 1.10 | .35 |
| **2105** A1614 62y multicolored | | 1.10 | .35 |
| **2106** A1614 62y multicolored | | 1.10 | .35 |
| **2107** A1614 62y multicolored | | 1.10 | .35 |
| **2108** A1614 62y multicolored | | 1.10 | .35 |
| **2109** A1614 62y multicolored | | 1.10 | .35 |
| **2110** A1614 62y multicolored | | 1.10 | .35 |
| **2111** A1614 62y multicolored | | 1.10 | .35 |
| **2112** A1614 62y multicolored | | 1.10 | .35 |
| **2113** A1614 62y multicolored | | 1.10 | .35 |
| **2114** A1614 62y multicolored | | 1.10 | .35 |
| *Nos. 2103-2114 (12)* | | 13.20 | 4.20 |

Nos. 2103-2104 printed in blocks of 12 with gutter between in sheet of 24.

Issued: Nos. 2103-2104, 6/28; Nos. 2105-2106, 9/27; Nos. 2107-2108, 1/30/92; Nos. 2109-2110, 3/25/92; Nos. 2111-2112, 8/31/92; Nos. 2113-2114, 1/29/93.

See Nos. 2192-2195.

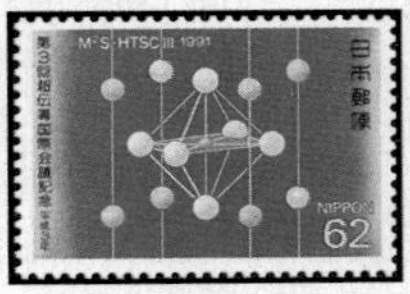


Intl. Conf. on Superconductivity — A1620

| **1991, July 19** | **Litho.** | ***Perf. 13½*** | |
|---|---|---|---|
| **2115** A1620 62y multicolored | | 1.10 | .30 |

**Type of Letter Writing Day of 1990 and**

A1621

**1991, July 23 Photo.** ***Perf. 13x13½***

**2116** A1621 41y multicolored .80 .35
**2117** A1575 62y multicolored 1.10 .35
*a.* Souvenir sheet of 1 1.25 1.25
*b.* Bklt. pane, 5 each #2116-2117 9.50

Nos. 2117, 2117a have light blue frameline and inscription and violet denomination.

3rd IAAF World Track & Field Championships, Tokyo — A1622

**1991, Aug. 23** ***Perf. 13***

**2118** A1622 41y High jump .80 .30
**2119** A1622 62y Shot put 1.10 .30

Intl. Symposium on Environmental Change and Geographical Information Systems — A1623

**1991, Aug. 23**

**2120** A1623 62y multicolored 1.10 .30

Intl. Letter Writing Week A1624

Bandainagon-emaki picture scroll probably by Mitsunaga Tokiwa: 80y, Crowd of people. 120y, People, house.

**Photo. & Engr.**

**1991, Oct. 7** ***Perf. 13½***

**2121** A1624 80y multicolored 1.40 .45
**2122** A1624 120y multicolored 2.00 .55

A1625

62y, Breezy Fine Weather by Hokusai.

**1991, Oct. 8 Photo.** ***Perf. 13***

**2123** A1625 62y multicolored 1.10 .35

Summit Conf. on Earthquake and Natural Disasters Countermeasures.

A1626

**1991, Oct. 31 Litho.** ***Perf. 13***

**2124** A1626 62y multicolored 1.10 .35

Japanese Green Tea, 800th anniv.

A1627

Koshaku-Musume by Kunisada Utagawa.

**Photo. & Engr.**

**1991, Nov. 15** ***Perf. 13***

**2125** A1627 62y multicolored 1.10 .35
*a.* Sheet of 2 3.00 3.00

World Stamp Exhibition, Nippon '91.

A1628

**1991, Nov. 20** **Photo.**

**2126** A1628 62y multicolored 1.10 .30

Administrative Counselors System, 30th anniv.

A1629

A1630

New Year 1992 (Year of the Monkey)

A1631 A1632

**1991, Dec. 2 Photo.** ***Perf. 13½***

**2127** A1629 41y multicolored .75 .30
**2128** A1630 62y multicolored 1.10 .40
**2129** A1631 41y +3y, multi .90 .40
**2130** A1632 62y +3y, multi 1.25 .40
*Nos. 2127-2130 (4)* 4.00 1.50

Sheets of 2 No. 2127 were lottery prizes. Value, $2.10.

8th Conference on Intl. Trade in Endangered Species (CITES) A1633

**1992, Mar. 2 Photo.** ***Perf. 13***

**2131** A1633 62y multicolored 1.10 .30

Philately Week — A1634

Flowers on the Chair, by Hoshun Yamaguchi.

**1992, Apr. 20**

**2132** A1634 62y multicolored 1.10 .30

A1635

**1992, May 15**

**2133** A1635 62y multicolored 1.10 .35

Return of Ryukyu Islands to Japan, 20th anniv.

Intl. Space Year — A1636

No. 2134, Satellite at left. No. 2135, Space station upper right.

**1992, July 7 Photo.** ***Perf. 13***

**2134** 62y multicolored 1.10 .35
**2135** 62y multicolored 1.10 .35
*a.* A1636 Pair, #2134-2135 2.25 1.25

Letter Writing Day

A1638 A1639

**1992, July 23** ***Perf. 13x13½***

**2136** A1638 41y multicolored .80 .35

***Perf. 13½***

**2137** A1639 62y multicolored 1.10 .35
*a.* Souvenir sheet of 1 1.25 1.25
*b.* Bklt. pane, 5 each #2136-2137 9.50

29th Intl. Geological Congress, Kyoto A1640

**1992, Aug. 24 Photo.** ***Perf. 13½x13***

**2138** A1640 62y multicolored 1.10 .30

47th Natl. Athletic Meet, Yamagata Prefecture — A1641

**1992, Sept. 4** ***Perf. 13½***

**2139** A1641 41y multicolored .80 .30

Normalization of Japanese-Chinese Relations, 20th Anniv. — A1642

**Photo. & Engr.**

**1992, Sept. 29** ***Perf. 13***

**2140** 62y jug 1.10 .35
**2141** 62y long-neck jar 1.10 .35
*a.* A1642 Pair, #2140-2141 2.25 1.00

Intl. Letter Writing Week — A1644

Heiji picture scroll: 80y, Nobles, servants in carriages by Taikenmon gate. 120y, Fujiwara-no Nobuyori seated before samurai.

**Photo. & Engr.**

**1992, Oct. 6** ***Perf. 13½***

**2142** A1644 80y multicolored 1.40 .45
**2143** A1644 120y multicolored 2.00 .55

Cat and Birds A1644a

Design: 70y, Santa Claus, snow scene, vert.

***Perf. 13½x13, 13x13½***

**1992, Oct. 9** **Photo.**

**2144** A1644a 62y multicolored 1.10 .30
**2145** A1644a 70y multicolored 1.25 .30

Winners of Third Postage Stamp Design contest.

30th Congress of Intl. Cooperative Alliance, Tokyo — A1644b

**1992, Oct. 27** ***Perf. 13x13½***

**2146** A1644b 62y multicolored 1.10 .30

A1645

Cultural Pioneers: No. 2147, Takakazu Seki (1642?-1708), mathematician. No. 2148, Akiko Yosano (1878-1942), poet.

**Photo. & Engr.**

**1992, Nov. 4** *Perf. 13*

| | | | | | |
|---|---|---|---|---|---|
| **2147** | A1645 | 62y | multicolored | 1.10 | .30 |
| **2148** | A1645 | 62y | multicolored | 1.10 | .30 |

See Nos. 2217-2219, 2434-2435, 2642, 2717-2718.

A1646

**1992, Nov. 9 Photo.** *Perf. 13x13½*

| | | | | | |
|---|---|---|---|---|---|
| **2149** | A1646 | 62y | multicolored | 1.10 | .30 |

Certified Public Tax Accountant System, 50th anniv.

A1647

A1648

New Year 1993 (Year of the Rooster)

A1649 A1650

**1992, Nov. 16** *Perf. 13x13½*

| | | | | | |
|---|---|---|---|---|---|
| **2150** | A1647 | 41y | multicolored | .75 | .30 |
| **2151** | A1648 | 62y | multicolored | 1.10 | .40 |
| *a.* | | | Souvenir sheet of 2, #2150-2151 | 2.40 | 2.40 |

*Perf. 13½*

| | | | | | |
|---|---|---|---|---|---|
| **2152** | A1649 | 41y | +3y multi | .90 | .40 |
| **2153** | A1650 | 62y | +3y multi | 1.25 | .40 |
| | | | *Nos. 2150-2153 (4)* | 4.00 | 1.50 |

Surtax on Nos. 2152-2153 for lottery. No. 2151a also was a lottery prize.

Flora and Fauna — A1651

9y, Dragonfly. 15y, Swallowtail. 18y, Ladybug. 41y, Mandarin duck. No. 2158, 50y, Japanese white-eye. No. 2159, 62y, Rufous turtle dove. 72y, Varied tit. 80y, Pied kingfisher. 90y, Spotbill duck. 130y, Bullfinch. 190y, Fringed orchid. 270y, Wild pink. 350y, Adder's tongue lily. 420y, Japanese iris. 430y, Violet.

**1992-94 Photo.** *Perf. 13x13½*

| | | | | | |
|---|---|---|---|---|---|
| **2154** | A1651 | 9y | multi | .25 | .25 |
| **2155** | A1651 | 15y | multi | .30 | .25 |
| **2156** | A1651 | 18y | multi | .35 | .25 |
| **2157** | A1651 | 41y | multi | .80 | .35 |
| **2158** | A1651 | 50y | multi | .90 | .30 |
| **2159** | A1651 | 62y | multi | 1.10 | .25 |
| *a.* | | | Bklt. pane, 5 ea #2157, 2159 | 9.50 | |
| *b.* | | | Booklet pane of 10 | 11.00 | |
| **2160** | A1651 | 72y | multi | 1.30 | .40 |
| **2161** | A1651 | 80y | multi | 1.40 | .25 |
| *a.* | | | Miniature sheet, 5 #2158, 10 #2161 + 3 labels | *45.00* | |
| **2162** | A1651 | 90y | multi | 1.60 | .50 |
| **2163** | A1651 | 130y | multi | 2.10 | .65 |
| **2164** | A1651 | 190y | multi | 3.50 | .75 |
| **2165** | A1651 | 270y | multi | 4.75 | 1.00 |
| **2166** | A1651 | 350y | multi | 6.25 | 1.10 |
| **2167** | A1651 | 420y | multi | 6.75 | 1.25 |
| **2167A** | A1651 | 430y | multi | 7.00 | 1.50 |
| | | | *Nos. 2154-2167A (15)* | 38.35 | 9.05 |

**Coil Stamps**

*Perf. 13 Horiz.*

| | | | | | |
|---|---|---|---|---|---|
| **2168** | A1651 | 50y | like #2158 | .90 | .40 |
| **2169** | A1651 | 80y | like #2161 | 1.40 | .55 |

**Booklet Stamps**

**Self-Adhesive**

*Die Cut*

| | | | | | |
|---|---|---|---|---|---|
| **2170** | A1651 | 41y | like #2157 | .80 | .35 |
| **2171** | A1651 | 50y | like #2158 | .95 | .45 |
| **2172** | A1651 | 62y | like #2159 | 1.10 | .50 |
| *a.* | | | Bklt. pane, 2 #2170, 4 #2172 | 6.00 | |
| **2173** | A1651 | 80y | like #2161 | 1.50 | .70 |
| *a.* | | | Bklt. pane, 4 #2171, 4 #2173 | 10.00 | |

Issued: 41y, 62y, 72y, 11/30/92; 9y, 18y, Nos. 2158, 2161, 90y, 1/13/94; 270y, 350y, 420y, 1/24/94; 15y, 130y, 190y, 430y, 4/25/94.

Nos. 2172a, 2173a are adhered to the booklet cover, made of peelable paper, folded in half and rouletted down the center fold.

See Nos. 2475-2483, 2486-2488. Compare No. 2166 with No. 3446.

World Alpine Skiing Championships, Morioka-Shizukuishi — A1657

**1993, Feb. 3 Photo.** *Perf. 13*

| | | | | | |
|---|---|---|---|---|---|
| **2174** | A1657 | 41y | shown | .80 | .40 |
| **2175** | A1657 | 62y | Skier, diff. | 1.10 | .55 |

**Seasonal Flowers Series**

Poppy A1658

Cherry Blossoms A1659

Lily — A1660

Thistle — A1661

Chinese Bellflowers A1662

Chrysanthemums A1663

Plum Blossom A1664

Winter Camellia A1665

*Perf. 13½ (41y, 50y), 13 (62y, 80y)*

**1993-94 Photo.**

| | | | | | |
|---|---|---|---|---|---|
| **2176** | A1658 | 41y | multicolored | .80 | .35 |

*Perf. 13*

| | | | | | |
|---|---|---|---|---|---|
| **2177** | A1659 | 62y | multicolored | 1.10 | .35 |
| **2178** | A1660 | 41y | multicolored | .80 | .35 |

*Perf. 13*

| | | | | | |
|---|---|---|---|---|---|
| **2179** | A1661 | 62y | multicolored | 1.10 | .35 |
| **2180** | A1662 | 41y | multicolored | .80 | .35 |
| **2181** | A1663 | 62y | multicolored | 1.10 | .35 |
| **2182** | A1664 | 50y | multicolored | .90 | .35 |
| **2183** | A1665 | 80y | multicolored | 1.40 | .55 |
| | | | *Nos. 2176-2183 (8)* | 8.00 | 3.00 |

Issued: Nos. 2176-2177, 3/12; Nos. 2178-2179, 6/18; Nos. 2180-2181, 9/16; Nos. 2182-2183, 1/28/94.

**Waterbird Type**

**1993 Photo.** *Perf. 13½*

| | | | | | |
|---|---|---|---|---|---|
| **2192** | A1614 | 62y | Grus vipio | 1.10 | .35 |
| **2193** | A1614 | 62y | Ansner albifrons | 1.10 | .35 |
| **2194** | A1614 | 62y | Anas formosa | 1.10 | .35 |
| **2195** | A1614 | 62y | Haliaeetus albicilla | 1.10 | .35 |
| | | | *Nos. 2192-2195 (4)* | 4.40 | 1.40 |

Issued: Nos. 2192-2193, 3/31; Nos. 2194-2195, 5/25.

Philately Week — A1674

Painting: In the Studio, by Nampu Katayama.

**1993, Apr. 20 Photo.** *Perf. 13*

| | | | | | |
|---|---|---|---|---|---|
| **2196** | A1674 | 62y | multicolored | 1.10 | .30 |

Natl. Land Afforestation Campaign — A1675

**1993, Apr. 23** *Perf. 13½*

| | | | | | |
|---|---|---|---|---|---|
| **2197** | A1675 | 41y | multicolored | .80 | .30 |

Mandarin Duck in the Nest — A1676

Gardenia in the Nest — A1677

Design: 70y, Mandarin Duck and Gardenia emblems, horiz.

**1993, June 8 Photo.** *Perf. 13*

| | | | | | |
|---|---|---|---|---|---|
| **2198** | A1676 | 62y | multicolored | 1.10 | .35 |
| **2199** | A1677 | 62y | multicolored | 1.10 | .35 |
| *a.* | | | Pair, #2198-2199 | 2.25 | 1.25 |
| **2200** | A1676 | 70y | multicolored | 1.25 | .40 |
| | | | *Nos. 2198-2200 (3)* | 3.45 | 1.10 |

Royal Wedding of Crown Prince Naruhito and Masako Owada.

5th Meeting of Signatories to Ramsar, Iran Convention on Wetlands and Waterfowl Habitats A1678

No. 2201, Crane with young. No. 2202, Crane's head.

**1993, June 10 Photo.** *Perf. 13½*

| | | | | | |
|---|---|---|---|---|---|
| **2201** | A1678 | 62y | multicolored | 1.10 | .35 |
| **2202** | A1678 | 62y | multicolored | 1.10 | .35 |
| *a.* | | | Pair, #2201-2202 | 2.50 | 2.00 |

Commercial Registration System, Cent. — A1679

**1993, July 1 Photo.** *Perf. 13x13½*

| | | | | | |
|---|---|---|---|---|---|
| **2203** | A1679 | 62y | multicolored | 1.10 | .30 |

Letter Writing Day

A1680 A1681

**1993, July 23** *Perf. 13x13½*

| | | | | | |
|---|---|---|---|---|---|
| **2204** | A1680 | 41y | multicolored | .80 | .35 |

*Perf. 13½x13*

| | | | | | |
|---|---|---|---|---|---|
| **2205** | A1681 | 62y | multicolored | 1.10 | .35 |
| *a.* | | | Souvenir sheet of 1 | 1.25 | 1.25 |
| *b.* | | | Booklet pane, 5 each #2204-2205 | 10.00 | |

15th Intl. Botanical Congress, Tokyo A1682

Designs: No. 2206, Glaucidium palmatum. No. 2207, Sciadopitys verticillata.

**1993, Aug. 23 Photo.** *Perf. 13½x13*

| | | | | | |
|---|---|---|---|---|---|
| **2206** | | 62y | multicolored | 1.10 | .35 |
| **2207** | | 62y | multicolored | 1.10 | .35 |
| *a.* | A1682 | | Pair, #2206-2207 | 2.50 | 1.25 |

World Federation for Mental Health Congress, Chiba City — A1683

**1993, Aug. 23** *Perf. 13½x13*

| | | | | | |
|---|---|---|---|---|---|
| **2208** | A1683 | 62y | multicolored | 1.10 | .30 |

A1684

**1993, Sept. 3 Photo.** *Perf. 13½*

| | | | | | |
|---|---|---|---|---|---|
| **2209** | | 41y | Swimming | .80 | .30 |
| **2210** | | 41y | Karate | .80 | .30 |
| *a.* | A1684 | | Pair, #2209-2210 | 1.75 | 1.00 |

48th natl. athletic meet, Kagawa Prefecture.

A1685

Japanese-Portuguese Relations, 450th Anniv.: No. 2211, Arrival of Portuguese, folding screen, c. 1560-1630. No. 2212, Mother-of-Pearl Host Box, Jesuit symbols and grape motif.

**1993, Sept. 22 Photo. *Perf. 13***

**2211** 62y multicolored 1.10 .35
**2212** 62y multicolored 1.10 .35
*a.* A1685 Pair, #2211-2212 2.50 1.25

Intl. Letter Writing Week A1686

Portraits from Picture Scrolls of the Thirty-Six Immortal Poets: 80y, Ki no Tsurayuki. 120y, Kodai no Kimi.

**1993, Oct. 6 *Perf. 13½***

**2213** A1686 80y multicolored 1.40 .40
**2214** A1686 120y multicolored 2.00 .50

10th World Veterans' Track and Field Championships, Miyazaki Prefecture A1687

**1993, Oct. 7 *Perf. 14***

**2215** A1687 62y multicolored 1.10 .30

Souvenir Sheet

Wedding of Crown Prince Naruhito and Princess Masako — A1688

**1993, Oct. 13 Photo. *Perf. 13½***

**2216** A1688 62y multicolored 1.25 1.25

### Cultural Pioneers Type of 1992

No. 2217, Kazan Watanabe (1793-1841), artist. No. 2218, Umetaro Suzuki (1874-1943), chemist. No. 2219, Toson Shimazaki (1872-1943), poet.

**1993, Nov. 4 Photo. *Perf. 13***

**2217** A1645 62y multicolored 1.10 .30

**Photo. & Engr.**

**2218** A1645 62y multicolored 1.10 .30
**2219** A1645 62y multicolored 1.10 .30
*Nos. 2217-2219 (3)* 3.30 .90

Agricultural Research Center, Cent. — A1689

**1993, Nov. 17 *Perf. 13½***

**2220** A1689 62y multicolored 1.10 .30

A1690

A1691

New Year 1994 (Year of the Dog)
A1692 A1693

**1993, Nov. 17 *Perf. 13x13½***

**2221** A1690 41y multicolored .75 .30
**2222** A1691 62y multicolored 1.10 .40

***Perf. 13½***

**2223** A1692 41y +3y multi .90 .40
**2224** A1693 62y +3y multi 1.25 .40
*Nos. 2221-2224 (4)* 4.00 1.50

Sheets of 2, Nos. 2221-2222, were lottery prizes. Value, $2.40.

Declaration of Human Rights, 45th Anniv. — A1694

Designs: 62y, Man with bird perched on head. 70y, Globe, dove, person breaking chains, peace symbol.

**1993, Dec. 10 Photo. *Perf. 13***

**2225** A1694 62y multicolored 1.10 .30
**2226** A1694 70y multicolored 1.25 .40

### Congratulations and Condolences Types of 1982

**1994, Mar. 10 Photo. *Perf. 13x13½***

**2227** A1082 50y Wreath .90 .35
**2228** A1083 50y Crane .90 .35
**2229** A1083 80y Crane 1.40 .40
**2230** A1084 90y Tortoise 1.60 .40
*Nos. 2227-2230 (4)* 4.80 1.50

For use on condolence and greeting cards.

1994 World Figure Skating Championships, Tokyo — A1695

No. 2231, Ice dancing. No. 2232, Women's singles. No. 2233, Men's singles, vert. No. 2234, Pairs, vert.

**1994, Mar. 17 Photo. *Perf. 13***

**2231** A1695 50y multicolored .90 .35
**2232** A1695 50y multicolored .90 .35
*a.* Pair, #2231-2232 2.25 1.25
**2233** A1695 80y multicolored 1.40 .40
**2234** A1695 80y multicolored 1.40 .40
*a.* Pair, #2233-2234 3.00 1.50
*Nos. 2231-2234 (4)* 4.60 1.50

Philately Week — A1696

**1994, Apr. 20 Photo. *Perf. 13***

**2235** A1696 80y Irises 1.40 .40

Intl. Year of the Family — A1697

Designs: No. 2236, "Love" spelled by people. No. 2237, Faces in flowers. No. 2238, Sun shining on people, homes. No. 2239, Family flying inside bird.

**1994, May 13 Photo. *Perf. 13***

**2236** A1697 50y multicolored .90 .30
**2237** A1697 50y multicolored .90 .30
**2238** A1697 80y multicolored 1.40 .35
*a.* Pair, #2236, 2238 2.50 1.25
**2239** A1697 80y multicolored 1.40 .35
*a.* Pair, #2237, 2239 2.50 1.25
*Nos. 2236-2239 (4)* 4.60 1.30

Natl. Land Afforestation Campaign A1698

**1994, May 20**

**2240** A1698 50y multicolored .90 .35

Intl. Conference on Natural Disaster Reduction A1699

**1994, May 23**

**2241** A1699 80y multicolored 1.40 .35

No. 2241 printed in sheets of 16 with 4 labels.

A1700

**1994, May 24**

**2242** A1700 80y multicolored 1.40 .35

Prototype Fast Breeder Reactor, Monju.

Environment Day — A1701

**1994, June 3 Photo. *Perf. 13***

**2243** A1701 80y multicolored 1.40 .40

Letter Writing Day
A1702 A1703

**1994, July 22**

**2244** A1702 50y multicolored .90 .35
**2245** A1703 80y multicolored 1.40 .40
*a.* Souvenir sheet of 1 1.60 1.60
*b.* Bklt. pane, 5 each #2244-2245 12.50

### Prefecture Issues

Nos. 2246-2400B have been changed to #Z151-Z307. The listings can be found in a new section immediately following the postage section and preceding the semi-postal listings.

10th Intl. Conference on AIDS, Yokohama — A1859

**1994, Aug. 5 Photo. *Perf. 13***

**2401** A1859 80y multicolored 1.40 .35

### Postal History Series

A1860

First Japanese stamps (Baron Hisoka Maeshima and): No. 2402, #1. No. 2403, #2. No. 2404, #3. No. 2405, #4.

CTO's exist for Nos. 2402-2405. They read "Japan" between two arcs in a corner.

**Photo. & Engr.**

**1994, Aug. 10 *Perf. 13***

**2402** A1860 80y brown & black 1.40 .40
**2403** A1860 80y blue & black 1.40 .40
**2404** A1860 80y ver & black 1.40 .40
**2405** A1860 80y olive grn & blk 1.40 .40
*a.* Strip of 4, #2402-2405 6.00 6.00

A1861

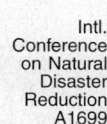

Early Japanese stamps (Edoardo Chiossone and): No. 2406, #55. No. 2407, Type A16. No. 2408, #63. No. 2409, #65.

**1994, Nov. 18** *Perf. 13½*
**2406** A1861 80y buff, slate & blk 1.40 .40
**2407** A1861 80y gray & dk brown 1.40 .40
**2408** A1861 80y gray lilac & rose 1.40 .40
**2409** A1861 80y lt blue & dk blue 1.40 .40
*a.* Strip of 4, #2406-2409 6.00 6.00

A1862

Designs: No. 2410, #85, transporting mail by ricksha. No. 2411, #86, transporting mail by horse-drawn carriage.

**1995, Jan. 25**
**2410** A1862 80y multicolored 1.40 .40
**2411** A1862 80y multicolored 1.40 .40
*Nos. 2402-2411 (10)* 14.00 4.00

A1863

Designs: No. 2412, #C3, First Osaka-Tokyo airmail flight. No. 2413, #C6, Workers loading freight onto airplane.

**Photo. & Engr.**

**1995, May 25** *Perf. 13½*
**2412** A1863 110y multicolored 2.00 .50
**2413** A1863 110y multicolored 2.00 .50

Nos. 2412-2413 printed in blocks of 10 with gutter between in sheets of 20.

A1864

No. 2414, Light mail van, #436. No. 2415, Cherub commemorative mail box, #428. No. 2416, Mail box, #435. No. 2417, Van, #433.

**Photo. & Engr.**

**1995, Sept. 19** *Perf. 13½*
**2414** A1864 80y multicolored 1.40 .40
**2415** A1864 80y multicolored 1.40 .40
**2416** A1864 80y multicolored 1.40 .40
**2417** A1864 80y multicolored 1.40 .40
*a.* Block of 4, #2414-2417 6.00 6.00

**Postal History Series**
**Types of 1948-49 With "NIPPON" Inscribed at Bottom**
**Size: 22x47mm**
**Photo. & Engr.**

**1996, June 3** *Perf. 13½*
**2418** A206 80y like #422, brown 1.40 .40
**2419** A206 80y like #422, multi 1.40 .40
**2420** A247 80y like #479, purple 1.40 .40
**2421** A247 80y like #479, multi 1.40 .40
*a.* Strip of 4, #2418-2421 6.00 6.00

Opening of Kansai Intl. Airport — A1877

Designs: No. 2422, Airport, part of plane's vertical stabilizer. No. 2423, Aft section of airplane. No. 2424, Airport, jet.

**1994, Sept. 2** **Photo.** *Perf. 13*
**2422** A1877 80y multicolored 1.40 .35
**2423** A1877 80y multicolored 1.40 .35
*a.* Vert. pair, #2422-2423 3.00 3.00
*b.* Vert. strip of 3, #2422-2424 4.50 4.50
**2424** A1877 80y multicolored 1.40 .35
*Nos. 2422-2424 (3)* 4.20 1.05

A1878

**1994, Sept. 19**
**2425** A1878 80y multicolored 1.40 .35

ITU Plenipotentiary Conference, Kyoto.

12th Asian Games, Hiroshima A1879

No. 2426, Kick volleyball. No. 2427, Steeplechase. No. 2428, Synchronized swimming

**1994, Sept. 30**
**2426** A1879 50y multicolored .90 .30
**2427** A1879 80y multicolored 1.40 .35
**2428** A1879 80y multicolored 1.40 .35
*a.* Pair, #2427-2428 3.00 1.75
*Nos. 2426-2428 (3)* 3.70 1.00

Intl. Letter Writing Week A1880

Screen paintings of popular indoor games, Momoyama, Edo periods: 90y, Sugoroku. 110y, Japanese chess. 130y, Go.

**1994, Oct. 6** **Photo.** *Perf. 13x13½*
**2429** A1880 90y multicolored 1.60 .45
**2430** A1880 110y multicolored 1.90 .55
**2431** A1880 130y multicolored 2.10 .55
*Nos. 2429-2431 (3)* 5.60 1.55

49th Natl. Athletic Meet, Aichi Prefecture — A1881

**1994, Oct. 28** *Perf. 13½*
**2432** A1881 50y multicolored .90 .30

A1882

**1994, Nov. 4** **Photo.** *Perf. 13*
**2433** A1882 80y multicolored 1.40 .35

Intl. Diabetes Federation, 15th Congress, Kobe.

**Cultural Pioneers Type of 1992**

Cultural pioneers: No. 2434, Michio Miyagi (1894-1956), Musician. No. 2435, Gyoshu Hayami (1894-1935), artist.

**1994, Nov. 4** **Photo. & Engr.**
**2434** A1645 80y multicolored 1.40 .35
**2435** A1645 80y multicolored 1.40 .35

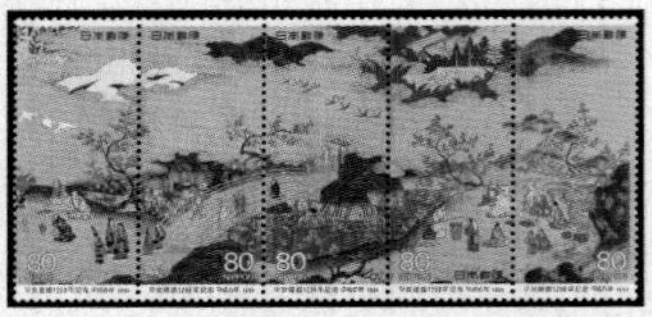
A1884

Heiankyo (Kyoto), 1200th Anniv. — A1885

Kanpuzu, by Hideyori Kano, Momoyama period depicts autumn scene on Kiyotakigawa River: No. 2436, People seated, white birds. No. 2437, Bridge, people. No. 2438, Bridge, birds flying. No. 2439, People, Jingoji Temple, Atago-Jinja Shrine. No. 2440, People seated, tree.

No. 2441, Painting of Dry Garden (Sekitei), Ryoanji Temple, by Eizo Kato. No. 2442, Painting of artificial pond, Shugakuin Rikyu, by Kanji Kawai, horiz.

**1994, Nov. 8** **Photo.** *Perf. 13x13½*
**2436** 80y multicolored 1.40 .40
**2437** 80y multicolored 1.40 .40
**2438** 80y multicolored 1.40 .40
**2439** 80y multicolored 1.40 .40
**2440** 80y multicolored 1.40 .40
*a.* A1884 Strip of 5, #2436-2440 8.50 8.50
**2441** A1885 80y multicolored 1.40 .40

*Perf. 13½x13*
**2442** A1885 80y multicolored 1.40 .40
*Nos. 2436-2442 (7)* 9.80 2.80

A1886

A1887

New Year 1995 (Year of the Boar)
A1888 A1889

**1994, Nov. 15** *Perf. 13x13½*
**2443** A1886 50y multicolored .95 .30
**2444** A1887 80y multicolored 1.40 .40

*Perf. 13½*
**2445** A1888 50y +3y multi .95 .40
**2446** A1889 80y +3y multi 1.50 .40
*Nos. 2443-2446 (4)* 4.80 1.50

Sheets of two containing Nos. 2443-2444 were lottery prizes. Value $2.75.

**World Heritage Series**

Himeji Castle
A1890 A1891

**1994, Dec. 14** **Photo.** *Perf. 13*
**2447** A1890 80y multicolored 1.40 .40
**2448** A1891 80y multicolored 1.40 .40

A1892

Horyuji Temple A1893

Designs: 80y, Goddess Kannon from inner temple wall. 110y, Temple exterior.

**1995, Feb. 22**
**2449** A1892 80y multicolored 1.40 .40
**2450** A1893 110y multicolored 1.90 .55

Cryptomeria Japonica A1894
Cervus Nippon Yakushimae A1895

**1995, July 28**
**2451** A1894 80y multicolored 1.40 .40
**2452** A1895 80y multicolored 1.40 .40

Virgin Beech Forest A1896
Black Woodpecker A1897

**1995, Nov. 21**
**2453** A1896 80y multicolored 1.40 .40
**2454** A1897 80y multicolored 1.40 .40
*Nos. 2447-2454 (8)* 11.70 3.35

Japan-Brazil Friendship, Cent. A1898

Designs: No. 2455, Natl. emblems, flowers. No. 2456, Soccer players.

**1995, Mar. 3 Photo. *Perf. 13½***

| | | | | | |
|---|---|---|---|---|---|
| **2455** | A1898 | 80y | multicolored | 1.40 | .35 |
| **2456** | A1898 | 80y | multicolored | 1.40 | .35 |

A1899

Fujiwara-Kyo Palace, 1300th Anniv. — A1900

Designs: 50y, Unebiyama, Nijozan Mountains, roofing tile from palace. 80y, Portrait of a Woman, in Asuka and Hakuho era style, by Okada, 1925.

**1995, Mar. 28**

| | | | | | |
|---|---|---|---|---|---|
| **2457** | A1899 | 50y | multicolored | .90 | .35 |
| **2458** | A1900 | 80y | multicolored | 1.40 | .40 |

Modern Anatomical Education A1901

**1995, Mar. 31 *Perf. 13***

| | | | | | |
|---|---|---|---|---|---|
| **2459** | A1901 | 80y | multicolored | 1.40 | .35 |

1995 Census — A1902

**1995, Apr. 12 Photo. *Perf. 13***

| | | | | | |
|---|---|---|---|---|---|
| **2460** | A1902 | 80y | multicolored | 1.40 | .40 |

A1903

**1995, Apr. 20**

| | | | | | |
|---|---|---|---|---|---|
| **2461** | A1903 | 80y | multicolored | 1.40 | .40 |

Japanese Overseas Cooperation Volunteers, 30th anniv.

A1904

A1905

A1906

A1907

A1908

**1995, Apr. 25 *Perf. 13x13½***

| | | | | | |
|---|---|---|---|---|---|
| **2462** | A1904 | 50y | multicolored | .90 | .30 |
| **2463** | A1905 | 50y | multicolored | .90 | .30 |
| **2464** | A1906 | 80y | multicolored | 1.40 | .35 |
| **2465** | A1907 | 80y | multicolored | 1.40 | .35 |
| **2466** | A1908 | 90y | multicolored | 1.75 | .55 |
| | | | *Nos. 2462-2466 (5)* | 6.35 | 1.85 |

For use on condolence and greeting cards.

A1909

**1995, May 19 Photo. *Perf. 13½x13***

| | | | | | |
|---|---|---|---|---|---|
| **2467** | A1909 | 50y | multicolored | .90 | .30 |

Natl. land afforestation campaign.

A1910

Greetings: No. 2468, Rainbow, hearts. No. 2469, Girl holding heart-shaped balloon. No. 2470, Flower holding pencil, sign. No. 2471, Star, sun, moon as flowers, fauna. No. 2472, Person, dog with flowers, butterfly in hair.

**Self-Adhesive**

**1995, June 1 *Die Cut Perf. 13½***

| | | | | | |
|---|---|---|---|---|---|
| **2468** | A1910 | 80y | multicolored | 1.40 | .40 |
| **2469** | A1910 | 80y | multicolored | 1.40 | .40 |
| **2470** | A1910 | 80y | multicolored | 1.40 | .40 |
| **2471** | A1910 | 80y | multicolored | 1.40 | .40 |
| **2472** | A1910 | 80y | multicolored | 1.40 | .40 |
| *a.* | | | Miniature sheet, #2468-2472 + 5 labels | 8.00 | 8.00 |

Letter Writing Day
A1911 A1912

**1995, July 21 Photo. *Perf. 13½***

| | | | | | |
|---|---|---|---|---|---|
| **2473** | A1911 | 50y | multicolored | .90 | .30 |
| **2474** | A1912 | 80y | multicolored | 1.40 | .35 |
| *a.* | | | Souvenir sheet of 1 | 1.60 | 1.60 |
| *b.* | | | Bklt. pane, 5 ea #2473-2474 | 12.50 | |
| | | | Complete booklet, #2474b | 12.50 | |

**Flora & Fauna Type of 1992 and**

Shikikacho-zu A1926

Matsutaka-Zu A1926a

10y, Scarab, dandelions. 20y, Honey bee, flower. 30y, Hairstreak, flowers. 70y, Great tit. 110y, Plover. 120y, Shrike. 140y, Japanese grosbeak. 160y, Jay. 390y, Dayflower.

**1995-98 Photo. *Perf. 13½***

| | | | | | |
|---|---|---|---|---|---|
| **2475** | A1651 | 10y | multi | .25 | .25 |
| **2476** | A1651 | 20y | multi | .30 | .25 |
| **2477** | A1651 | 30y | multi | .50 | .35 |
| **2478** | A1651 | 70y | multi | 1.25 | .40 |
| **2479** | A1651 | 110y | multi | 1.90 | .50 |
| **2480** | A1651 | 120y | multi | 2.00 | .50 |
| **2481** | A1651 | 140y | multi | 2.25 | .50 |
| **2482** | A1651 | 160y | multi | 2.75 | .60 |

***Perf. 13x13½***

| | | | | | |
|---|---|---|---|---|---|
| **2483** | A1651 | 390y | multi | 7.50 | 1.25 |

***Perf. 13½***

| | | | | | |
|---|---|---|---|---|---|
| **2484** | A1926 | 700y | multi | 13.00 | 3.50 |

**Photo. & Engr.**

| | | | | | |
|---|---|---|---|---|---|
| **2485** | A1926a | 1000y | multi | 17.50 | 3.75 |
| *a.* | | | Imperf. (3799b) | 30.00 | 30.00 |

**Self-Adhesive**

***Die Cut Perf. 13x13½***

| | | | | | |
|---|---|---|---|---|---|
| **2486** | A1651 | 50y | Like #2158 | .75 | .40 |
| **2487** | A1651 | 80y | Like #2161 | 1.10 | .35 |

**Coil Stamp**

***Perf. 13 Horiz.***

| | | | | | |
|---|---|---|---|---|---|
| **2488** | A1651 | 10y | like #2475 | .25 | .25 |
| | | | *Nos. 2475-2488 (14)* | 51.30 | 12.85 |

Issued: 700y, 7/4/95; 390y, 1000y, 3/28/96; 70y, 110y, 7/22/97; No. 2475, 20y, 30y, 11/28/97; 120y, 140y, 2/16/98 160y, 2/23/98; No. 2488, 9/11/98. Nos. 2486-2487, 3/25/02. No. 2485a, 2/2/15.

Nos. 2486 and 2487 were issued in panes of 10.

End of World War II, 50th Anniv.
A1937 A1938

Design: No. 2491, Children holding hands behind stained glass window, peace dove, earth from space.

**1995, Aug. 1 Photo. *Perf. 13***

| | | | | | |
|---|---|---|---|---|---|
| **2489** | A1937 | 50y | multicolored | .90 | .30 |
| **2490** | A1938 | 80y | multicolored | 1.40 | .35 |
| **2491** | A1938 | 80y | multicolored | 1.40 | .35 |
| | | | *Nos. 2489-2491 (3)* | 3.70 | 1.00 |

18th Universiade, Fukuoka — A1939

**1995, Aug. 23**

| | | | | | |
|---|---|---|---|---|---|
| **2492** | A1939 | 80y | multicolored | 1.40 | .35 |

A1940

50y, Radio controlled plane, transmitter. 80y, Radio controlled helicopter, competitor, assistant.

**1995, Aug. 25**

| | | | | | |
|---|---|---|---|---|---|
| **2493** | A1940 | 50y | multicolored | .90 | .30 |
| **2494** | A1940 | 80y | multicolored | 1.40 | .35 |

1995 Aeromodel World Championships, Okayama Prefecture.

World Veterinary Congress, Yokohama A1941

80y, Dog, cow & horse.

**1995, Sept. 1 Photo. *Perf. 13***

| | | | | | |
|---|---|---|---|---|---|
| **2495** | A1941 | 80y | multicolored | 1.40 | .35 |

World Sports Championships A1942

No. 2496, 1995 World Judo Championships, Chiba Prefecture. No. 2497, 1995 World Gymnastics Championships, Sabae, Fukui Prefecture.

**1995, Sept. 28**

| | | | | | |
|---|---|---|---|---|---|
| **2496** | A1942 | 80y | multicolored | 1.40 | .35 |
| **2497** | A1942 | 80y | multicolored | 1.40 | .35 |

Letter Writing Week A1943

Screen paintings: 90y, Shell-matching game. 110y, Battledore and shuttlecock. 130y, Playing cards.

**1995, Oct. 6 *Perf. 13½***

| | | | | | |
|---|---|---|---|---|---|
| **2498** | A1943 | 90y | multicolored | 1.60 | .45 |
| **2499** | A1943 | 110y | multicolored | 1.90 | .55 |
| **2500** | A1943 | 130y | multicolored | 2.40 | .55 |
| | | | *Nos. 2498-2500 (3)* | 5.90 | 1.55 |

A1944

**1995, Oct. 13 *Perf. 13x13½***

| | | | | | |
|---|---|---|---|---|---|
| **2501** | A1944 | 50y | multicolored | .90 | .30 |

50th Natl. athletic meet, Fukushima prefecture.

UN, UNESCO, 50th Anniv. — A1945

No. 2502, UN, hearts. No. 2503, UNESCO, children.

**1995, Oct. 24** *Perf. 13*

**2502** A1945 80y multi 1.40 .35
**2503** A1945 80y multi 1.40 .35

### Cultural Pioneers Type of 1992

No. 2504, Tadataka Ino (1745-1818), cartographer. No. 2505, Kitaro Nishida (1870-1945), philosopher.

**Photo. & Engr.**

**1995, Nov. 6** *Perf. 13*

**2504** A1645 80y multicolored 1.40 .40
**2505** A1645 80y multicolored 1.40 .40

A1947

A1948

New Year 1996 (Year of the Rat)
A1949 A1950

**1995, Oct. 15** **Photo.** *Perf. 13x13½*

**2506** A1947 50y multicolored .95 .30
**2507** A1948 80y multicolored 1.40 .40

*Perf. 13½*

**2508** A1949 50y +3y multi .95 .40
**2509** A1950 80y +3y multi 1.50 .40
*Nos. 2506-2509 (4)* 4.80 1.50

Sheets of two containing Nos. 2506-2507 were lottery prizes. Value $2.75.

Japanese-Korean Diplomatic Relations, 30th Anniv. — A1951

**1995, Dec. 18** *Perf. 13*

**2510** A1951 80y multicolored 1.40 .35

Nos. 2511-2512 are unassigned.

A1952

**1996, Feb. 16** **Photo.** *Perf. 13*

**2513** A1952 80y multicolored 1.40 .35

Philipp Franz von Siebold (1796-1866), naturalist.

A1953

**1996, Mar. 1**

**2514** A1953 80y multicolored 1.40 .35

Labor Relations Commissions, 50th anniv.

Senior Citizens — A1954

**1996, Mar. 21** *Perf. 13½*

**2515** A1954 80y multicolored 1.40 .35

No. 2515 issued in sheets of 5.

50th Postwar Memorial Year
A1955 A1956

No. 2516, Crowd, Emperor's limosine approaching Diet. No. 2517, Prime Minister Yoshida signing Peace Treaty, San Francisco, 9/8/51. No. 2518, Women performing traditional Okinawan dance.

**1996, Apr. 1** **Photo.** *Perf. 13*

**2516** A1955 80y multicolored 1.40 .40
**2517** A1955 80y multicolored 1.40 .40
*a.* Pair, Nos. 2516-2517 3.00 2.25
**2518** A1956 80y multicolored 1.40 .40
*Nos. 2516-2518 (3)* 4.20 1.20

Promulgation of the the Constitution, 11/7/46 (No. 2517a). Return of Okinawa, 5/15/72 (No. 2518).

Woman Suffrage, 50th Anniv. — A1957

**1996, Apr. 10** *Perf. 13½*

**2519** A1957 80y multicolored 1.40 .35

Philately Week — A1958

**1996, Apr. 19** *Perf. 13*

**2520** A1958 80y multicolored 1.40 .40

UNICEF, 50th Anniv. — A1959

**1996, May 1** **Photo.** *Perf. 13*

**2521** A1959 80y multicolored 1.40 .35

Child Welfare Week, 50th Anniv. — A1960

**1996, May 1**

**2522** A1960 80y multicolored 1.40 .35

Bird Week, 50th Anniv. — A1961

**1996, May 10**

**2523** 80y Birds 1.40 .40
**2524** 80y Field Glasses 1.40 .40
*a.* A1961 Pair, #2523-2524 3.00 1.75

Natl. Afforestation Campaign — A1963

**1996, May 17**

**2525** A1963 50y multicolored .90 .30

50th Postwar Memorial Year
A1964 A1965

**1996, June 24** **Photo.** *Perf. 13*

**2526** A1964 80y multicolored 1.40 .40
**2527** A1965 80y multicolored 1.40 .40

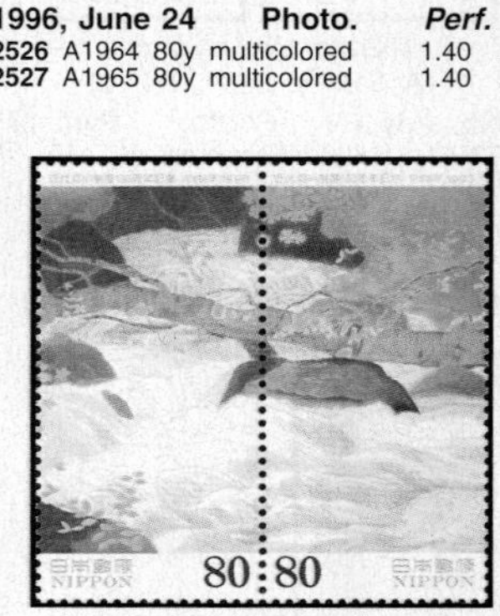
River Administration System, Cent. — A1966

**1996, July 5** **Photo.** *Perf. 13½*

**2528** 80y denomination lower right 1.40 .40
**2529** 80y denomination lower left 1.40 .40
*a.* A1966 Pair, #2528-2529 3.00 1.75

A1968

Marine Day's Establishment
A1969

**1996, July 19**

**2530** A1968 50y multicolored .90 .35
**2531** A1969 80y multicolored 1.40 .40

Letter Writing Day
A1970 A1971

**1996, July 23**

**2532** A1970 50y multicolored .90 .35
**2533** A1971 80y multicolored 1.40 .40
*a.* Souvenir sheet of 1 1.50 1.50
*b.* Bklt. pane, 5 ea #2532-2533 12.00
Complete booklet 12.50

### Cultural Pioneers Type of 1992

No. 2534, Kenji Miyazaw (1896-1933). No. 2535, Hokiichi Hanawa (1746-1821).

**Photo. & Engr.**

**1996, Aug. 27** *Perf. 13*

**2534** A1645 80y multicolored 1.40 .35
**2535** A1645 80y multicolored 1.40 .35

A1974 A1975

Designs: No. 2536, Advances of women in society, diffusion of home electrical products. No. 2537, Modern highway, railway systems.

**1996, Aug. 27** **Photo.** *Perf. 13*

**2536** A1974 80y multicolored 1.40 .40
**2537** A1975 80y multicolored 1.40 .40

51st Natl. Athletic Meet — A1976

**1996, Sept. 6** **Photo.** *Perf. 13½*

**2538** A1976 50y Archery .90 .30

Community Chest, 50th Anniv. — A1977

**1996, Sept. 30**
**2539** A1977 80y multicolored 1.40 .35

Intl. Music Day — A1978

**1996, Oct. 1** ***Perf. 13***
**2540** A1978 80y multicolored 1.40 .35

A1979

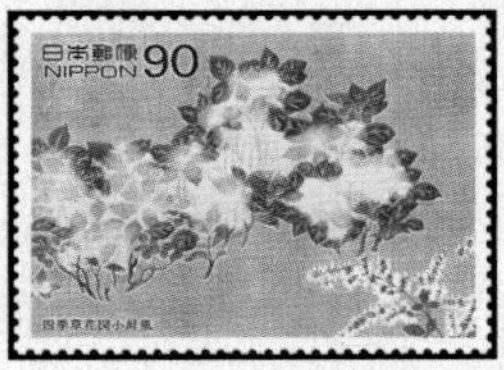

A1980

A1980a

Intl. Letter Writing Week — A1980b

Paintings: No. 2541, Water wheel, Mt. Fuji. No. 2543, Mt. Fuji in Clear Weather (Red Fuji), by Hokusai. No. 2545, Mt. Fuji, lake.

**1996, Oct. 7** ***Perf. 13½***
**2541** A1979 90y multicolored 1.60 .50
**2542** A1980 90y multicolored 1.60 .50
*a.* Pair, #2541-2542 3.50 1.75
**2543** A1979 110y multicolored 1.90 .55
**2544** A1980a 110y multicolored 1.90 .55
*a.* Pair, #2543-2544 4.25 2.00
**2545** A1979 130y multicolored 2.25 .60
**2546** A1980b 130y multicolored 2.25 .60
*a.* Pair, #2545-2546 5.00 2.25
*Nos. 2541-2546 (6)* 11.50 3.30

18th World Congress of Savings Banks — A1981

**1996, Oct. 23** ***Perf. 13***
**2547** A1981 80y multicolored 1.40 .35

50th Postwar Memorial Year
A1982 A1983

No. 2548, Earth from space. No. 2549, Cellular telephone, fiber optic cable, satellite in orbit.

**1996, Nov. 8** **Photo.** ***Perf. 13***
**2548** A1982 80y multicolored 1.40 .40
**2549** A1983 80y multicolored 1.40 .40

A1984 A1985

New Year 1997 (Year of the Ox)
A1986 A1987

**1996, Nov. 15** **Photo.** ***Perf. 13x13½***
**2550** A1984 50y multicolored .95 .30
**2551** A1985 80y multicolored 1.40 .40

***Perf. 13½***
**2552** A1986 50y +3y multi .95 .40
**2553** A1987 80y +3y multi 1.50 .40
*Nos. 2550-2553 (4)* 4.80 1.50

Sheets of 2 containing Nos. 2550-2551 were lottery prizes. Value $2.75.

Yujiro Ishihara, Actor — A1988

Hibari Misora, Entertainer — A1990

Osamu Tezuka, Cartoonist — A1992

**1997, Jan. 28** **Photo.** ***Perf. 13***
**2554** 80y multicolored 1.40 .40
**2555** 80y multicolored 1.40 .40
*a.* A1988 Pair, #2554-2555 3.00 1.75
**2556** 80y multicolored 1.40 .40
**2557** 80y multicolored 1.40 .40
*a.* A1990 Pair, #2556-2557 3.00 1.75
**2558** 80y multicolored 1.75 .45
**2559** 80y multicolored 1.75 .45
*a.* A1992 Pair, #2558-2559 4.00 2.25
*Nos. 2554-2559 (6)* 9.10 2.50

Sparrow, Rice Plant, Camellia
A1994

Sparrow, Maple, Camellia
A1995

***Perf. 14 Horiz. Syncopated Type A***

**1997, Apr. 10** **Photo.**
**2560** A1994 50y multi 1.25 .50
**2560A** A1994 80y multi 1.75 .50
**2560B** A1994 90y multi 2.00 .60
**2560C** A1994 120y multi 2.75 .65
**2560D** A1994 130y multi *25.00 11.50*
**2561** A1995 270y multi 5.50 2.00
*Nos. 2560-2561 (6)* 38.25 15.75

Denominations of Nos. 2560-2561 were printed by machine at point of sale, and were limited to the denominations listed.

Daigo, by Okumura Dogyu (1889-1990)
A1996

**1997, Apr. 18** **Litho.** ***Perf. 13½***
**2562** A1996 80y multicolored 1.40 .35

Philately Week.

Supreme Court, 50th Anniv. — A1997

**1997, May 2** **Photo.** ***Perf. 13***
**2563** A1997 80y Main court room 1.40 .35

Doraemon — A1998

Designs: No. 2564, Shown. No. 2565, With envelope. No. 2566, Standing on hand. No. 2567, With propeller. No. 2568, In love.

**Booklet Stamps**

***Serpentine Die Cut 13½***

**1997, May 2** **Self-Adhesive**
**2564** A1998 80y multicolored 1.40 .40
**2565** A1998 80y multicolored 1.40 .40
**2566** A1998 80y multicolored 1.40 .40
**2567** A1998 80y multicolored 1.40 .40
**2568** A1998 80y multicolored 1.40 .40
*a.* Pane of 5, #2564-2568 7.50 *7.50*

Japanese Migration to Mexico, Cent. — A1999

**1997, May 12** ***Perf. 13***
**2569** A1999 80y multicolored 1.40 .35

See Mexico No. 2035.

Natl. Afforestation Campaign — A2000

50y, Miyagi bush clover.

**1997, May 16** ***Perf. 13½***
**2570** A2000 50y multicolored .90 .30

Natl. Diet — A2001

**1997, May 20** ***Perf. 13***
**2571** A2001 80y multicolored 1.40 .35

Natl. House of Councilors, 50th anniv.

**Letter Writing Day**

A2002 A2003

A2004 A2005

**1997, July 23** **Photo.** ***Perf. 13***
**2572** A2002 50y multicolored .90 .30
**2573** A2003 70y multicolored 1.25 .35
**2574** A2004 80y multicolored 1.40 .35
*a.* Souvenir sheet of 1 1.60 1.60
*b.* Bklt. pane, 5 ea #2572, 2574 13.00
Complete booklet, #2574b 13.00
**2575** A2005 90y multicolored 1.60 .45
*Nos. 2572-2575 (4)* 5.15 1.45

A2006

**1997, Aug. 11** **Photo.** ***Perf. 13***
**2576** A2006 50y multicolored .90 .30

Part-time and correspondence education at upper secondary schools, 50th anniv.

Labor Standards Law, 50th Anniv. — A2007

**1997, Sept. 1**
**2577** A2007 80y multicolored 1.40 .35

Friendship Between Japan and Chile, Cent. — A2008

**1997, Sept. 1** *Perf. 13½*
**2578** A2008 80y multicolored 1.40 .35

See Chile No. 1217.

52nd Natl. Sports Festival — A2009

**1997, Sept. 12**
**2579** A2009 50y multicolored .90 .30

A2010

A2010a

A2010b

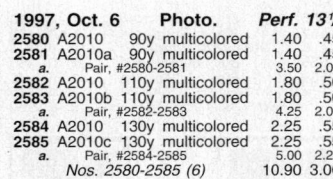

Intl. Letter Writing Week — A2010c

Paintings of Tokaido's 53 Stations by Hiroshige: No. 2580, Hodogaya (bridge over waterway). No. 2582, Kameyama snow-covered mountain slope).
No. 2584, Sumida Riverbank Snowscape (woman in traditional attire beside river), by Hiroshige
From Scrolls of Flowers and Birds of the Four Seasons by Hoitsu Sakai: No. 2581, Bird on tree. No. 2583, Leaves and berries. No. 2585, Bird on tree branch of blossoms.

**1997, Oct. 6** **Photo.** *Perf. 13½*
**2580** A2010 90y multicolored 1.40 .45
**2581** A2010a 90y multicolored 1.40 .45
*a.* Pair, #2580-2581 3.50 2.00
**2582** A2010 110y multicolored 1.80 .50
**2583** A2010b 110y multicolored 1.80 .50
*a.* Pair, #2582-2583 4.25 2.00
**2584** A2010 130y multicolored 2.25 .55
**2585** A2010c 130y multicolored 2.25 .55
*a.* Pair, #2584-2585 5.00 2.25
*Nos. 2580-2585 (6)* 10.90 3.00

Grand Opening of the Natl. Theater of Tokyo — A2011

**1997, Oct. 9** *Perf. 13*
**2586** A2011 80y multicolored 1.40 .35

Favorite Songs
A2012 A2013

50y Departure on a Fine Day, by Tanimura Shinji. 80y, Desert Under the Moon, by Kato Masao & Sakasi Suguru.

**1997, Oct. 24**
**2587** A2012 50y multicolored .90 .30
**2588** A2013 80y multicolored 1.40 .40

**Cultural Pioneers Type of 1992**

No. 2589, Rohan Kouda (1867-1947), writer. No. 2590, Ando Hiroshige (1797-1858), artist.

**1997, Nov. 4**
**2589** A1645 80y multicolored 1.40 .35
**2590** A1645 80y multicolored 1.40 .35

A2016

A2017

New Year 1997 (Year of the Tiger)
A2018 A2019

**1997, Nov. 14** *Perf. 13x13½*
**2591** A2016 50y multicolored .95 .30
**2592** A2017 80y multicolored 1.40 .40

*Perf. 13½*
**2593** A2018 50y +3y multi .95 .40
**2594** A2019 80y +3y multi 1.50 .40

Sheets of two containing Nos. 2591-2592 were lottery prizes. Value $2.50.

Return of Okinawa to Japan, 25th Anniv. — A2020

**1997, Nov. 21** *Perf. 13*
**2595** A2020 80y multicolored 1.40 .35

Shibuya Family's House A2021

Tomizawa Family's House A2022

**Photo. & Engr.**

**1997, Nov. 28** *Perf. 13½*
**2596** A2021 80y multicolored 1.40 .45
**2597** A2022 80y multicolored 1.40 .45

A2023

Woodprints: No. 2598, Mother Sea. No. 2599, Mother Earth.

**1997, Dec. 1** **Photo.** *Perf. 13*
**2598** A2023 80y multicolored 1.40 .35
**2599** A2023 80y multicolored 1.40 .35
*a.* Pair, #2598-2599 3.00 2.00

3rd Conference of the Parties to the UN Framework Convention on Climate Change, Kyoto.

A2024

**1997, Dec. 2**
**2600** A2024 80y multicolored 1.40 .35

Agricultural Insurance System, 50th anniv.

**Favorite Songs**

Sunayama
A2025

Jingle Bells
A2026

**1997, Dec. 8**
**2601** A2025 50y multicolored .90 .30
**2602** A2026 80y multicolored 1.40 .35

Shabondama
A2027

Kitaguni no Haru
A2028

**1998, Jan. 26** **Photo.** *Perf. 13*
**2603** A2027 50y multicolored .90 .30
**2604** A2028 80y multicolored 1.40 .35

1998 Winter Olympic & Paralympic Games, Nagano
A2029 A2030

Paralympic logo and: No. 2605, Glaucidium palmatum. No. 2606, Ice hockey.
Olympic rings and: No. 2607: a, Gentiana nipponica. b, Caltha palustris. c, Fritillaria camtschatcensis. d, Paeonia japonica. e, Erythronium japonicum. f, Snowboarding. g, Curling. h, Speed skating. i, Cross-country skiing. j, Downhill skiing.

**1998, Feb. 5**
**2605** A2029 50y multicolored .90 .30
**2606** A2030 80y multicolored 1.40 .35
*a.* Pair, #2605-2606 2.50 1.00
**2607** Sheet of 10 12.50 12.50
*a.-e.* A2029 50y Any single .90 .30
*f.-j.* A2030 80y Any single 1.40 .35

**Historic Houses**

A2031

A2032

**Photo. & Engr.**

**1998, Feb. 23** *Perf. 13½*
**2608** A2031 80y multicolored 1.40 .45
**2609** A2032 80y multicolored 1.40 .45

Japanese Fire Service, 50th Anniv. — A2033

**1998, Mar. 6** **Photo.** *Perf. 13*
**2610** 80y multicolored 1.40 .40
**2611** 80y multicolored 1.40 .40
*a.* A2033 Pair, #2610-2611 3.00 1.25

Favorite Songs
A2035 A2036

50y, Medaka-no-Gakko. 80y, Aoi Sanmyaku.

**1998 Photo. *Perf. 13***
**2612** A2035 50y multicolored .90 .30
**2613** A2036 80y multicolored 1.40 .35

Issued: 50y, 3/23; 80y, 3/16.

Greetings Stamps — A2037

Designs: a, Puppy. b, Kitten. c, Parakeets. d, Pansies. e, Bunny.

**1998, Mar. 13 Photo. *Die Cut***
**Self-Adhesive**
**2614** Sheet of 5 7.50
***a.-e.*** A2037 80y any single 1.40 .75

Philately Week — A2038

"Poppies," by Kokei Kobayashi (1883-1957).

**1998, Apr. 17 *Perf. 13½***
**2615** A2038 80y multicolored 1.40 .35

1998 Year of France in Japan A2039

"Liberty Leading the People," by Delacroix.

**1998, Apr. 28 *Perf. 13½***
**2616** A2039 110y multicolored 1.90 .55

Natl. Afforestation Campaign — A2040

50y, Trout, Renge azalea.

**1998, May 8**
**2617** A2040 50y multicolored .90 .30

**Favorite Songs**

A2041 A2042

Designs: 50y, "Wild Roses," by Franz Schubert. 80y, "Hill Abloom with Tangerine Flowers," by Minoru Uminuma and Shogo Kato.

**1998, May 25 *Perf. 13***
**2618** A2041 50y multicolored .90 .30
**2619** A2042 80y multicolored 1.40 .35

**Historic Houses**

Kowata Residence A2043

Kamihaga Residence A2044

**Photo. & Engr.**
**1998, June 22 *Perf. 13½***
**2620** A2043 80y multicolored 1.40 .45
**2621** A2044 80y multicolored 1.40 .45

**Favorite Songs**

A2045 A2046

50y, Kono Michi, "This Road." 80y, Ware Wa Umino Ko, "I'm a Boy of the Sea."

**1998, July 6 Photo. *Perf. 13***
**2622** A2045 50y multicolored .90 .30
**2623** A2046 80y multicolored 1.40 .35

Letter Writing Day — A2047

Stylized drawings of children: No. 2624, Child writing letter. No. 2625, Child wearing glasses, letter on table. No. 2626, Child with ink pen, flowers overhead. No. 2627, Child with ink pen, dove overhead. No. 2628, Children holding letters, envelopes.

**1998, July 23 *Perf. 13***
**2624** A2047 50y multi .90 .30
**2625** A2047 50y multi .90 .30
*a.* Pair, #2624-2625 1.90 1.10
**2626** A2047 80y multi 1.40 .35
**2627** A2047 80y multi 1.40 .35
**2628** A2047 80y multi, horiz. 1.40 .35
*a.* Souvenir sheet of 1 1.60 1.60
*b.* Sheet, 4 each #2626-2627, 2 #2628 17.50 17.50
*c.* Bklt. pane, 2 ea #2624-2628 14.00 14.00
Complete booklet, #2628c 15.00

See Nos. 2682-2686, 2738-2742, 2779-2783, 2824-2828. See Nos. 2733h-2733j for self-adhesive stamps.

**Historic Houses**

Kamio Residence A2048

Nakamura Residence A2049

**Photo. & Engr.**
**1998, Aug. 24 *Perf. 13½***
**2629** A2048 80y multicolored 1.40 .45
**2630** A2049 80y multicolored 1.40 .45

53rd Natl. Sports Festival, Kanagawa — A2050

**1998, Sept. 11 Photo. *Perf. 13½***
**2631** A2050 50y multicolored .90 .30

A2051

A2051a

A2051b

Intl. Letter Writing Week, Greetings — A2051c

Details or complete paintings by Jakuchu Ito: No. 2632, "Birds & Autumn Maple." No. 2633, "Parakeet in Oak Tree." No. 2634, "Mandarin Ducks in the Snow." No. 2635, "Golden Pheasant & Bamboo in Snow." No. 2636, "Leafy Peonies & Butterflies." No. 2637, "Parakeet in Rose Bush."

**1998, Oct. 6 Photo. *Perf. 13½***
**2632** A2051 90y multicolored 1.60 .45
**2633** A2051a 90y multicolored 1.60 .45
*a.* Pair, #2632-2633 3.50 1.75
**2634** A2051 110y multicolored 1.90 .55
**2635** A2051b 110y multicolored 1.90 .55
*a.* Pair, #2634-2635 4.25 1.75
**2636** A2051 130y multicolored 2.10 .65
**2637** A2051c 130y multicolored 2.10 .65
*a.* Pair, #2636-2637 5.00 1.75
*Nos. 2632-2637 (6)* 11.20 3.30

Nos. 2632, 2634, 2636 are from "Plants and Animals" and are inscribed for Intl. Letter Writing Week. Nos. 2633, 2635, 2637 are from "Painted Woodcuts of Flowers and Birds."

1998 World Volleyball Championships for Men and Women, Japan — A2052

**1998, Nov. 2 *Perf. 13***
**2638** A2052 80y Serve 1.40 .35
**2639** A2052 80y Receive 1.40 .35
**2640** A2052 80y Set & spike 1.40 .35
**2641** A2052 80y Block 1.40 .35
*a.* Strip of 4, #2638-2641 6.00 6.00

**Cultural Pioneer Type of 1992 and**

Yoshie Fujiwara(1898-1976) — A2053

No. 2642, Bakin Takizawa (1767-1848).

**Photo. & Engr.**
**1998, Nov. 4 *Perf. 13***
**2642** A1645 80y multicolored 1.40 .35
**2643** A2053 80y multicolored 1.40 .35

See Nos. 2719, 2747-2748, 2839-2840.

A2054 A2055

New Year 1999 (Year of the Rabbit)
A2056 A2057

**1998, Nov. 13 Photo. *Perf. 13x13½***
**2644** A2054 50y multicolored .95 .30
**2645** A2055 80y multicolored 1.40 .40

***Perf. 13½x13***
**2646** A2056 50y +3y multi .95 .40
**2647** A2057 80y +3y multi 1.50 .40
*Nos. 2644-2647 (4)* 4.80 1.50

Sheets of two containing Nos. 2644-2645 were lottery prizes. Value $2.75.
See No. 2655.

### Favorite Songs

A2058

A2059

50y, The Apple Song. 80y, Toys Cha-Cha-Cha at Night.

**1998, Nov. 24** *Perf. 13x13½*
**2648** A2058 50y multicolored .90 .30
**2649** A2059 80y multicolored 1.40 .35

Japan-Argentina Friendship Treaty, Cent. — A2060

**1998, Dec. 2** **Photo.** *Perf. 13*
**2650** A2060 80y multicolored 1.40 .35

A2061

A2062

Universal Declaration of Human Rights, 50th Anniv.
A2063 A2064

**1998, Dec. 10**
**2651** A2061 50y multicolored .90 .35
**2652** A2062 70y multicolored 1.25 .40
**2653** A2063 80y multicolored 1.40 .35
**2654** A2064 90y multicolored 1.60 .45
*Nos. 2651-2654 (4)* 5.15 1.55

### Greetings Types of 1951, 1962, 1986 and 1998

**1998, Dec. 15** **Photo.** *Perf. 13x13½*
**2655** 50y Sheet of 8, 2 each #a.-c., 2644 7.75 7.75
*a.* A281 rose pink, like #522 .90 .40
*b.* A483 multi, like #773 .90 .40
*c.* A1273 multi, like #1708 .90 .40

### Favorite Songs

A2065

A2066

50y, Flowing Like a River. 80y, Song of the Four Seasons.

**1999, Jan. 26** **Photo.** *Perf. 13*
**2656** A2065 50y multicolored .90 .30
**2657** A2066 80y multicolored 1.40 .35

### Traditional Houses

Iwase Family House, Gokayama District A2067

Gassho-Zukuri Houses, Shirakawa-mura District — A2068

Gassho-Zukuri House — A2069

**Photo. & Engr.**
**1999, Feb. 16** *Perf. 13½*
**2658** A2067 80y multicolored 1.40 .45
**2659** A2068 80y multicolored 1.40 .45
**2660** A2069 80y multicolored 1.40 .45
*a.* Pair, #2659-2660 3.50 3.50
*Nos. 2658-2660 (3)* 4.20 1.35

### Rakugo (Comic Storytellers) Stamps

Kokontei Shinshou V — A2070

Katsura Bunraku VIII — A2071

Sanyutei Enshou VI — A2072

Yanagiya Kosan V — A2073

Katsura Beichou III — A2074

**1999, Mar. 12** **Photo.** *Perf. 13*
**2661** A2070 80y multicolored 1.40 .55
**2662** A2071 80y multicolored 1.40 .55
**2663** A2072 80y multicolored 1.40 .55
**2664** A2073 80y multicolored 1.40 .55
**2665** A2074 80y multicolored 1.40 .55
*a.* Sheet, 2 each #2661-2665 15.00 15.00

### Favorite Songs

Sukiyaki Song A2075

Soushunfu A2076

**1999, Mar. 16**
**2666** A2075 50y multicolored .90 .30
**2667** A2076 80y multicolored 1.40 .35

Greetings Stamps — A2077

a, Kitten, daisies. b, Checks, flowers, roses. c, Tartan, puppy. d, Flowers, brown rabbit. e, Gray and white rabbit, moon and stars.

**1999, Mar. 23** *Die Cut*
**Self-Adhesive**
**2668** Sheet of 5 7.50
*a.-e.* A2077 80y Any single 1.40 .75

25th General Assembly of Japan Medical Congress A2078

**1999, Apr. 2** *Perf. 13*
**2669** A2078 80y multicolored 1.40 .35

Philately Week — A2079

Rabbits Playing in the Field in Spring, by Doumoto Inshou (1891-1975): No. 2670, Three rabbits. No. 2671, Two rabbits.

**1999, Apr. 20** *Perf. 13½*
**2670** 80y Three rabbits 1.40 .40
**2671** 80y Two rabbits 1.40 .40
*a.* A2079 Pair, #2670-2671 3.00 1.50

No. 2671a is a continuous design. No. 2671a also exists as a strip of two with central label. Value, $6.50.

A2080

**1999, May 18** **Photo.** *Perf. 13*
**2672** A2080 80y multicolored 1.40 .35

Japanese migration to Peru, cent.

Natl. Afforestation Campaign — A2081

**1999, May 28** *Perf. 13¼*
**2673** A2081 50y multicolored .90 .30

A2082

Painting: Ruins of Tholos, by Masayuki Murai.

**1999, June 1** **Photo.** *Perf. 13*
**2674** A2082 80y multicolored 1.40 .35

Japanese-Greek Treaty of Commerce & Navigation, cent.

A2083

**1999, June 3**
**2675** A2083 80y multicolored 1.40 .35

Japanese emigration to Bolivia, cent.

Land Improvement System, 50th Anniv. — A2084

**1999, June 4**
**2676** A2084 80y multicolored 1.40 .35

Family Court, 50th Anniv. — A2085

**1999, June 16**
**2677** A2085 80y multicolored 1.40 .35

Patent Attorney System in Japan, Cent. — A2086

**1999, July 1** **Photo.** *Perf. 13*
**2678** A2086 80y multicolored 1.40 .35

A2087

**1999, July 1**

| | | | | |
|---|---|---|---|---|
| **2679** | A2087 | 80y multicolored | 1.40 | .35 |

Japanese Community-Based Treatment of Offenders System, 50th anniv.

A2088

Enforcement of Civil and Commercial Codes, Cent.: Masaakira Tomii (1858-1935), Kenjiro Ume (1860-1910) and Nobushige Hozumi (1856-1926), drafters of Civil and Commerical Codes.

**1999, July 19**

| | | | | |
|---|---|---|---|---|
| **2680** | A2088 | 80y multicolored | 1.40 | .35 |

Copyright System in Japan, Cent. — A2089

**1999, July 22**

| | | | | |
|---|---|---|---|---|
| **2681** | A2089 | 80y multicolored | 1.40 | .35 |

### Letter Writing Day Type of 1998

Stylized drawings of children and toys: No. 2682, Boy and clown, letter. No. 2683, Teddy bear seated on pencil. No. 2684, Girl, ink pen. No. 2685, Clown with yellow hat, jumping up out of envelope.

No. 2686: a, Giraffes. b, Kite, bird, horiz. c, Boy holding kite string. d, Girl with pencil and paper. e, Bunny and bear. f, Boy blowing trumpet. g, Girl playing cello. h, Girl in red. i, Girl in yellow holding envelope. j, Three ducks.

| **1999, July 23** | | **Photo.** | ***Perf. 13*** | |
|---|---|---|---|---|
| **2682** | A2047 | 50y multicolored | .90 | .30 |
| **2683** | A2047 | 50y multicolored | .90 | .30 |
| **2684** | A2047 | 50y multicolored | .90 | .30 |
| **2685** | A2047 | 50y multicolored | .90 | .30 |
| *a.* | | Strip of 4, #2682-2685 | 4.00 | 3.50 |
| **2686** | | Sheet of 10 | 16.00 | 16.00 |
| *a.-j.* | | A2047 80y any single | 1.40 | .35 |
| *k.* | | Booklet pane, #2682-2685, 2 each #2686c, 2686g, 2686i | 14.00 | |
| | | Complete booklet, #2686k | 14.50 | |
| *l.* | | Sheet of 2, #2682, 2686g | 2.75 | 2.75 |

Nos. 2686a is 53x27mm. Nos. 2686d, 2686h, 2686j are 30mm in diameter. No. 2686f is 38x39mm. Sheet numbers are in center of rectangles at top of sheets.

The 20th Century — A2090

1900-10 (Sheet 1) — No. 2687: a, 50y, 1905-06 Serialized novel "Wagahai wa Neko de aru," by Soseki Natsume (stamp 7). b, 50y, 1906 Novel "Bochan," by Natsume (stamp 8). c, 80y, 1901 Collection of poems "Midare-gami," by Akiko Yosano (stamp 1). d, 80y, Opening of Denkikan movie theater in Asakusa, 1903 (stamp 2). e, 80y, Electrification of streetcars, 1903 (stamp 3). f, 80y, Otojirou Kawakami & Sadayakko, actors (stamp 4). g, 80y, Westernization of fashion (stamp 9). h, 80y, Completion of Ryogoku Kokugikan sumo arena, 1909 (stamp 10). i, 80y, Russo-Japanese War soldiers on horseback (stamp 5). j, 80y, Russo-Japanese War soldiers in tent (stamp 6).

A2090a

1910-13 (Sheet 2) — No. 2688: a, 50y, 1st Japanese-produced airship, tail of 1st Japanese airplane (stamp 3). b, 50y, Front of 1st Japanese airplane (stamp 4). c, 80y, Elementary school song book published by Education ministry, 1910 (stamp 1). d, 80y, Antarctic expedition led by Nobu Shirase, 1910 (stamp 2). e, 80y, Dr. Hideyo Noguchi (stamp 5). f, 80y, Extinction of Japanese wolves (stamp 6). g, 80y, Runner Shizo Kanaguri at 1st participation in Olympic Games, 1912 (stamp 7). h, Takarazuka Musical Review founded, 1913 (stamp 8). i, 80y, "Song of Kachusha," by Sumako Matsui & Hogetsu Shimamura (stamp 9). j, 80y, 1st sale of caramels, 1913 (stamp 10).

A2090b

1914-20 (Sheet 3) — No. 2689: a, 50y, Painting of couple in boat by Yumeji Takehisa (stamp 9). b, 50y, Takehisa, painting of flowers (stamp 10). c, 80y, 1914 Opening of Tokyo train station (blimp in sky) (stamp 1). d, 80y, Tokyo train station main entrance (stamp 2). e, 80y, Japanese WWI seamen (stamp 3). f, 80y, Western-style women's hair styles (stamp 4). g, 80y, 1915 Poetry book "Rashomon," by Ryunosuke Akutagawa (stamp 5). h, 80y, 1916 Start of postal life insurance (goddess in clouds) (stamp 6). i, 80y, Sakuzo Yoshino, political scientist & democracy advocate, & tree (stamp 7). j, 80y, 1918 Rice riots (painting, photo of crowds) (stamp 8).

A2090c

1920-25 (Sheet 4) — No. 2690: a, 50y, Silent film star Matsunosuke Onoe (denomination at UR) (stamp 8). b, 50y, Silent film star Tsumasaburo Bandoh (denomination at UL) (stamp 9). c, 80y, 1st Hakone Relay Marathon, 1920 (stamp 1). d, 80y, Popularity of "Gondola Song" recording, spread of phonographs (stamp 2). e, 80y, Ruins from 1923 Kanto earthquake (stamp 3). f, "Nonki na Tosan" comic strip (man with dog) (stamp 4). g, 80y, "Adventures of Sho-chan" comic strip (man with vulture). h, 80y, Japanese crane nears extinction (stamp 6). i, 80y, 1924 Opening of Koshien Stadium (stamp 7). j, 80y, Man, woman in Western-style clothing (stamp 10).

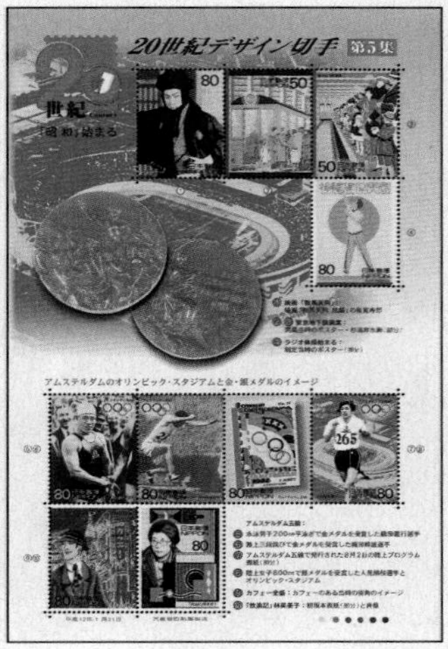


A2090d

1927-28 (Sheet 5) — No. 2691: a, 50y, 1927 Opening of Tokyo subway (close-up of car) (stamp 2). b, 50y, Subway car approaching station (stamp 3). c, 80y, Movie "Kurama Tengu" (Samurai) (stamp 1). d, 80y, Radio broadcast of "National Health Gymnastics" exercise program (stamp 4). e, 80y, Yoshiyuki Tsuruta, 1928 Olympic swimming champion (stamp 5). f, 80y, Mikio Oda, 1928 Olympic triple jump champion (stamp 6). g, 80y, Olympic Games program (stamp 7). h, 80y, Runner Kinue Hitomi, 1st female Japanese Olympic medalist (stamp 8). i, 80y, Man in Western clothing, cafe (stamp 9). j, 1928 Publishing of "Horoki," by Fumiko Hayashi (stamp 10).

A2090e

1929-32 (Sheet 6) — No. 2692: a, 50y, Mass production of Japanese automobiles (green 1932 Datsun Model 10) (stamp 4). b, 50y, Black 1936 Toyota Model AA (stamp 5). c, 80y, Volcano, Mt. Asama (stamp 1). d, 80y, Takiji Kobayashi, writer of "Kani-kosen," crane, smokestacks (stamp 2). e, 80y, Man with shirt with open collar, woman with handbag (stamp 3). f, 80y, "Norakuro" comic strip (cat, brick wall) (stamp 6). g, 80y, 1932 Nippon Derby winner Wakataka & jockey (stamp 7). h, 80y, Nippon Derby winner Kabutoyama (stamp 8). i, 80y, Song "Longing for Your Shadow" (woman with closed eyes) (stamp 9). j, 80y, 1932, 1936 Political assassinations (soldiers, truck, building) (stamp 10).

A2090f

1932-36 (Sheet 7) — No. 2693: a, 50y, Front of D51 steam locomotive (stamp 8). b, 50y, Rear of D51 (stamp 9). c, 80y, Fumihiko Otsuki, lexicographer (Otsuki, geometric design) (stamp 1). d, 80y, Song "Tokyo Ondo" (woman, buildings) (stamp 2). e, 80y, Keinichi Enomoto, comic actor, with feather (stamp 3). f, 80y, Formation of Japanese Baseball League (catcher, umpire) (stamp 4). g, 80y, Batter (stamp 5). h, 80y, Hachiko, dog that waited for dead owner, statue of Hachiko (stamp 6). i, 80y, Eiji Yoshikawa, author of "Miyamoto Musashi." (stamp 7). j, Extinct species Okinawan pigeon (stamp 10).

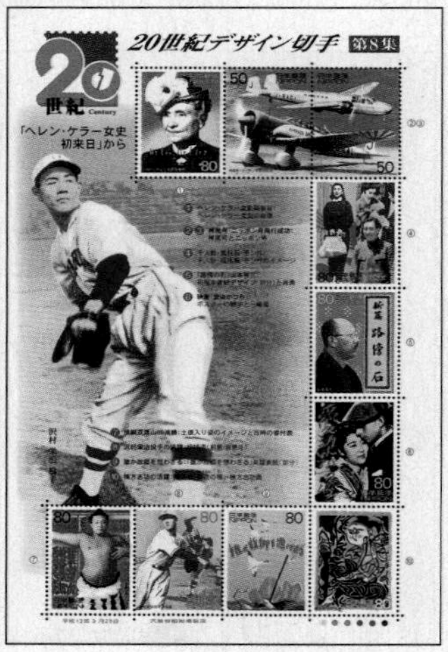


A2090g

1937-40 (Sheet 8) — No. 2694: a, 50y, Nose of Kamikaze plane, tail of Nippon cargo plane (stamp 2). b, 50y, Nose of Nippon cargo plain, tail of Kamikaze plane (stamp 3). c, 80y, Helen Keller's 1st trip to Japan (stamp 1). d, 80y, Women with senninbari cloths, monpe work pants, man with kokumin-fuku uniform (stamp 4). e, 80y, Yuzo Yamamoto, author of "Robo No Ishi" (stamp 5). f, 80y, Woman & man embracing in movie, "Aizenkatsura" (stamp 6). g, 80y, Sumo wrestler Yokozuna Futabayama, winner of 69 consecutive matches (stamp 7). h, 80y, Baseball pitcher Eiji Sawamura (stamp 8). i, 80y, Song, "Dareka Kokyo" (ducks in flight) (stamp 9). j, 80y, Woodblock art of Shiko Munakata (stamp 10).

A2090h

1940-45 (Sheet 9) — No. 2695: a, 50y, "Ohgon Bat," cartoon by Ichiro Suzuki (character without hat) (stamp 9). b, 50y, "Ohgon Bat" character wearing hat (stamp 10). c, 80y, Chiune Sugihara, vice-consul in Lithuania who saved Jews from Holocaust (stamp 1). d, 80y, Start of Kokumin Gakko school system (children exercising) (stamp 2). e, 80y, Airplane in attack on Pearl Harbor (stamp 3). f, 80y, Kotaro Takamura, poet, winner of 1st Imperial Art Academy prize, & Japanese characters (stamp 4). g, 80y, Eruption of Mt. Showashinzan (stamp 5). h, 80y, Atomic Bomb Memorial Dome (stamp 6). i, 80y, Statue at Nagasaki Atomic Bomb Museum (stamp 7). j, Signing of World War II surrender documents on USS Missouri (stamp 8).

A2090i

1945-52 (Sheet 10) — No. 2696: a, 50y, "Captain Atom" cartoon by Osamu Tezuka (stamp 7). b, 50y, "Astro Boy," cartoon by Tezuka (stamp 8). c, 80y, Song, "Ringo No Uta" (Apple Song) (stamp 1). d, 80y, "Sazae San," cartoon by Machiko Hasegawa (stamp 2). e, 80y, Promulgation of Japanese Constitution (woman, child, buildings) (stamp 3). f, 80y, Swimming records by Hironoshin Furuhashi (stamp 4). g, 80y, Dr. Hideki Yukawa, Nobel laureate for Physics (stamp 5). h, 80y, New Year's Eve radio program "Kohaku Uta Gassen" on NHK (stamp 6). i, 80y, Radio soap opera "Kimino Na Wa" (woman and man) (stamp 9). j, 80y, Novel "Nijyu-Yon No Hitomi," by Sakae Tsuboi (stamp 10).

A2090j

1953-58 (Sheet 11) — No. 2697: a, 50y, Tokyo Tower (olive green panel) (stamp 9). b, 50y, Tokyo Tower from ground (stamp 10). c, 80y, Popularity of radio and television (stamp 1). d, 80y, Director Akira Kurosawa, camera, two Samurai from "Shinchinin No Samurai." (stamp 2). e, 80y, Five Samurai from "Shinchinin No Samurai." (stamp 3). f, 80y, Sumo wrestler Rikidozan and championship belt (stamp 4). g, 80y, Rikidozan in action (stamp 5). h, 80y, Movie "Godzilla" (stamp 6). i, 80y, Taiyozoku fashions (man, woman at seaside) (stamp 7), j, 80y, Portrait of Shotokutaishi from 10,000-yen bank note (stamp 8, 31x42mm oval stamp).

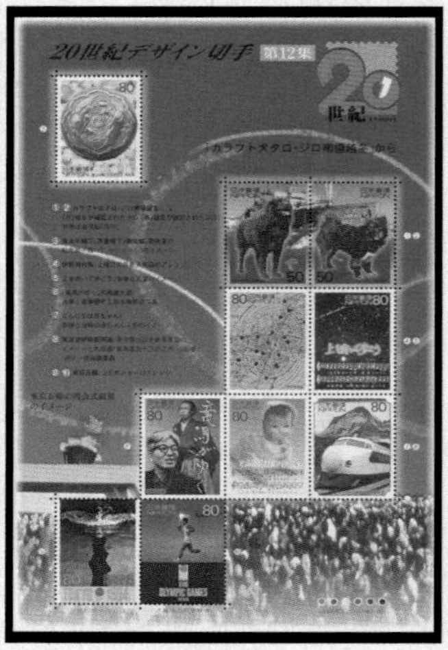


A2090k

1959-64 (Sheet 12) — No. 2698: a, 50y, Dog Taro, survivor of abandonment in Antarctica, ship's stern (stamp 1). b, 50y, Dog Giro, survivor of abandonment in Antarctic, ship's bow (stamp 2). c, 80y, Commemorative cake box from Wedding of Crown Prince Akihito (stamp 3). d, 80y, Weather map of Isewan Typhoon (stamp 4). e, 80y, "Sukiyaki Song," by Rokusuke Ei (stamp 5). f, 80y, Novelist Ryotaro Shiba and cover from "Ryomaga Yuku," depicting Ryoma Sakamoto (stamp 6). g, 80y, Baby doll, and song "Konnichiwa Akachan," by Ei (stamp 7). h, 80y, Inauguration of Bullet Train (stamp 8). i, 80y, Poster depicting swimmer from Tokyo Olympics (stamp 9). j, 80y, Poster depicting torchbearer from Tokyo Olympics (stamp 10).

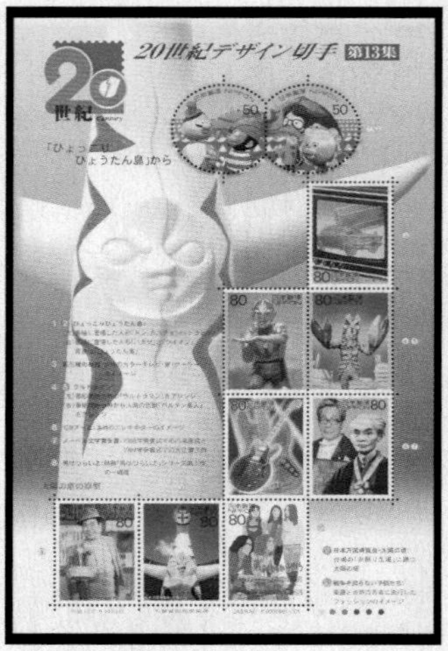


A2090l

1964-71 (Sheet 13) — No. 2699: a, 50y, TV show puppets Don Gabacho and Torahige (stamp 1, 31x30mm semi-oval stamp with straight side at right). b, 50y, TV show puppets Hakase and Lion (stamp 2, 31x30mm semi-oval stamp with straight side at left). c, 80y, Color television, automobile and air conditioner (stamp 3). d, 80y, TV character, Ultraman (stamp 4). e, 80y, Baltan Seijin, character from Ultraman TV series (stamp 5). f, 80y, Electric guitars (stamp 6). g, 80y, Yasunari Kawabata and Kenzaburo Oe, Nobel laureates for Literature (stamp 7). h, 80y, Scene from movie "Otokowa Tsuraiyo" (man holding basket) (stamp 8). i, 80y, Tower from Expo '70, Osaka (stamp 9). j, 80y, Youth fashions and song "Senso O Shiranai Kodomotachi" (stamp 10).

A2090m

1972-74 (Sheet 14) — No. 2700: a, 50y, Baseball player Sadaharu Oh (leg in air) (stamp 7). b, 50y, Baseball player Shigeo Nagashima (Tokyo uniform) (stamp 8). c, 80y, Two men from Takamatsu Zuka wall paintings, Asuka (stamp 1). d, 80y, Four women from Takamatsu Zuka wall paintings (stamp 2). e, 80y, Pandas Kankan and Ranran, gift from China (stamp 3). f, Shureimon, Return of Okinawa to Japanese control (stamp 4). g, 80y, Oscar, from cartoon "Roses of Versailles," by Riyoko Ikeda (stamp 5). h, 80y, Conductor Seiji Ozawa (stamp 6). i, 80y, Erimo Cape, and song "Erimo Misaki" (stamp 9). j, 80y, Space battleship Yamato from cartoon "Uchu Senkan Yamato," by Reiji Matsumoto (stamp 10).

A2090n

1975-83 (Sheet 15) — No. 2701: a, 50y, Gundam and Zaku, from TV cartoon series "Kidosenshi Gundam" (blue background) (stamp 7). b, 50y, Amuro and Gundam, from "Kidonsenshi Gundam" (orange background) (stamp 8). c, 80y, Guitar, and song "Jidai" (stamp 1). d, 80y, Fish character Taiyaki Kun, from children's song "Oyoge! Taiyaki Kun" (stamp 2). e, 80y, Musical notes and microphones (popularity of karaoke) (stamp 3). f, 80y, Flower, and song "Cosmos" (stamp 4). g, 80y, UFO, and song "UFO" (stamp 5). h, 80y, Students from TV series, "San Nen B Gumi Kinpachi Sensei" (stamp 6). i, 80y, Musical notes and electronic synthesizer (stamp 9). j, 80y, Oshin, from TV series "Oshin" (stamp 10).

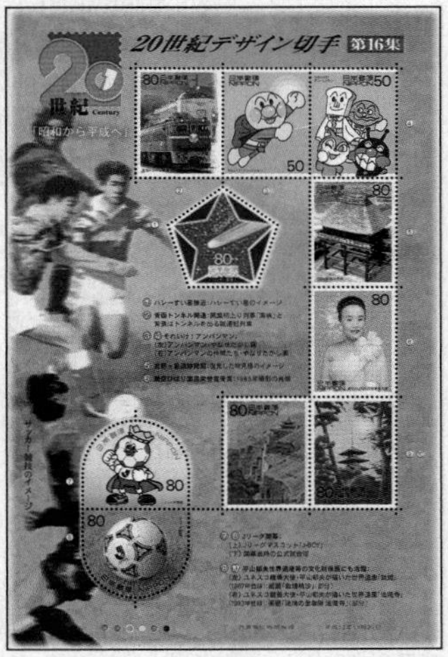

A2090o

1986-93 (Sheet 16) — No. 2702: a, 50y, Character from cartoon show "Soreike! Anpanman" (stamp 3). b, 50y, Four characters from "Soreike! Anpanman" (stamp 4). c, 80y, Return of Halley's Comet (stamp 1, pentagonal). d, 80y, Opening of Seikan Railroad Tunnel (stamp 2). e, 80y, Watchtower excavated at Yoshinogari Iseki ruins (stamp 5). f, 80y, Singer Hibari Misora, National Medal of Honor recipient (stamp 6). g, 80y, Mascot of J-League Soccer Games (stamp 7, 34x28mm semi-oval stamp with straight side at bottom). h, 80y, Soccer ball (stamp 8, 34x28mm stamp with straight side at top). i, 80y, Selection of Dunjuang as World Heritage Site (Cliffside, stamp 9). j, 80y, Selection of Horyuji Temple as World Heritage Site (Temple and sun, stamp 10).

A2090p

1993-98 (Sheet 17) — No. 2703: a, 50y, Nagano Winter Olympics emblem (stamp 7). b, 50y, Four owl mascots of Nagano Winter Olympics (stamp 8). c, 80y, Wedding of Crown Prince Naruhito and Masako Owada (stamp 1). d, 80y, Phoenix and damage from Hanshin-Awaji earthquake (stamp 2). e, 80y, Cellular phone and computer (stamp 3). f, 80y, Launch of Japanese astronaut aboard Space Shuttle Endeavor (stamp 4). g, 80y, Astronaut Mamoru Mohri in space (stamp 5). h, 80y, Details from Kyoto Climate Change Conf. stamps, #2598-2599 (stamp 6). i, 80y, Poster for Nagano Winter Olympics (stamp 9). j, Soccer player at 1998 World Cup Championships (stamp 10, 42x31mm elliptical stamp).

Illustrations reduced.

**1999-2000 Photo. *Perf. 13x13¼***

**Sheets of 10**

| | | | | |
|---|---|---|---|---|
| **2687** | A2090 | #a.-j. | 17.50 | 17.50 |
| *a.-b.* | | 50y any single | .90 | .50 |
| *c.-j.* | | 80y any single | 1.40 | .50 |
| **2688** | A2090a | #a.-j. | 17.50 | 17.50 |
| *a.-b.* | | 50y any single | .90 | .50 |
| *c.-j.* | | 80y any single | 1.40 | .50 |
| **2689** | A2090b | #a.-j. | 17.50 | 17.50 |
| *a.-b.* | | 50y any single | .90 | .50 |
| *c.-j.* | | 80y any single | 1.40 | .50 |
| **2690** | A2090c | #a.-j. | 17.50 | 17.50 |
| *a.-b.* | | 50y any single | .90 | .50 |
| *c.-j.* | | 80y any single | 1.40 | .50 |
| **2691** | A2090d | #a.-j. | 17.50 | 17.50 |
| *a.-b.* | | 50y any single | .90 | .50 |
| *c.-j.* | | 80y any single | 1.40 | .50 |
| **2692** | A2090e | #a.-j. | 17.50 | 17.50 |
| *a.-b.* | | 50y any single | .90 | .50 |
| *c.-j.* | | 80y any single | 1.40 | .50 |
| **2693** | A2090f | #a.-j. | 17.50 | 17.50 |
| *a.-b.* | | 50y any single | .90 | .50 |
| *c.-j.* | | 80y any single | 1.40 | .50 |
| **2694** | A2090g | #a.-j. | 17.50 | 17.50 |
| *a.-b.* | | 50y Any single | .90 | .50 |
| *c.-j.* | | 80y Any single | 1.40 | .50 |
| **2695** | A2090h | #a-j | 17.50 | 17.50 |
| *a.-b.* | | 50y Any single | .90 | .50 |
| *c.-j.* | | 80y Any single | 1.40 | .50 |
| **2696** | A2090i | #a-j | 17.50 | 17.50 |
| *a.-b.* | | 50y Any single | .90 | .50 |
| *c.-j.* | | 80y Any single | 1.40 | .50 |
| **2697** | A2090j | #a-j | 17.50 | 17.50 |
| *a.-b.* | | 50y Any single | .90 | .50 |
| *c.-j.* | | 80y Any single | 1.40 | .50 |
| **2698** | A2090k | #a-j | 17.50 | 17.50 |
| *a.-b.* | | 50y Any single | .90 | .50 |
| *c.-j.* | | 80y Any single | 1.40 | .50 |
| **2699** | A2090l | #a-j | 17.50 | 17.50 |
| *a.-b.* | | 50y Any single | .90 | .50 |
| *c.-j.* | | 80y Any single | 1.40 | .50 |
| **2700** | A2090m | #a-j | 17.50 | 17.50 |
| *a.-b.* | | 50y Any single | .90 | .50 |
| *c.-j.* | | 80y Any single | 1.40 | .50 |
| **2701** | A2090n | #a-j | 17.50 | 17.50 |
| *a.-b.* | | 50y Any single | .90 | .50 |
| *c.-j.* | | 80y Any single | 1.40 | .50 |
| **2702** | A2090o | #a-j | 17.50 | 17.50 |
| *a.-b.* | | 50y Any single | .90 | .50 |
| *c.-j.* | | 80y Any single | 1.40 | .50 |
| **2703** | A2090p | #a-j | 17.50 | 17.50 |
| *a.-b.* | | 50y Any single | .90 | .50 |
| *c.-j.* | | 80y Any single | 1.40 | .50 |

Sheet numbers are in UR corner of sheets or in center of rectangles at top of sheet. Stamp numbers are in sheet margin.

Issued: No. 2687, 8/23; No. 2688, 9/22; No. 2689, 10/22; No. 2690, 12/22; No. 2691, 1/21/00; No. 2692, 2/9/00; No. 2693, 2/23/00; No. 2694, 3/23/00; No. 2695, 4/21/00; No. 2696, 5/23/00; No. 2697, 6/23/00; No. 2698, 7/21/00; No. 2699, 8/23/00; No. 2700, 9/22/00; No. 2701, 10/23/00; No. 2702, 11/22; No. 2703, 12/22.

Hearts and Doves A2092

Celebration A2093

Red-crowned Crane — A2094

**1999, Aug. 16 Photo. *Perf. 13¼***

| | | | | |
|---|---|---|---|---|
| **2704** | A2092 | 50y multi | .90 | .30 |
| **2705** | A2093 | 80y multi | 1.40 | .35 |
| **2706** | A2094 | 90y multi | 1.60 | .40 |
| | | *Nos. 2704-2706 (3)* | 3.90 | 1.05 |

54th Natl. Sports Festival — A2095

**1999, Sept. 10**

| | | | | |
|---|---|---|---|---|
| **2707** | A2095 | 50y multi | .90 | .30 |

A2096

**1999, Oct. 1 *Perf. 12¾x13***

| | | | | |
|---|---|---|---|---|
| **2708** | A2096 | 80y multi | 1.40 | .35 |

Intl. Year of Older Persons.

A2097

A2098

A2099

Intl. Letter Writing Week A2100

Hokusai Paintings: No. 2709, Sea Route in Kazusa Area. No. 2710, Roses & a Sparrow. No. 2711, Rain Beneath the Mountaintop. No. 2712, Chrysanthemums & a Horsefly. No. 2713, Under the Fukagawa Bridge. No. 2714, Peonies & a Butterfly.

**1999, Oct. 6 *Perf. 13¼***

| | | | | |
|---|---|---|---|---|
| **2709** | A2097 | 90y multi | 1.50 | .45 |
| **2710** | A2098 | 90y multi | 1.50 | .45 |
| *a.* | | Pair, #2709-2710 | 3.50 | 1.75 |
| **2711** | A2097 | 110y multi | 2.00 | .55 |
| **2712** | A2099 | 110y multi | 2.00 | .55 |
| *a.* | | Pair, #2711-2712 | 4.25 | 1.75 |
| **2713** | A2097 | 130y multi | 2.10 | .60 |
| **2714** | A2100 | 130y multi | 2.10 | .60 |
| *a.* | | Pair, #2713-2714 | 5.00 | 1.75 |
| | | *Nos. 2709-2714 (6)* | 11.20 | 3.20 |

Central and Pacific Baseball Leagues, 50th Anniv. — A2101

Mascots wearing uniforms of: a, Yokohama Bay Stars. b, Chunichi Dragons. c, Seibu Lions. d, Nippon Ham Fighters. e, Yomiuri Giants. f, Yakult Swallows g, Orix Blue Wave. h, Fukuoka Daiei Hawks. i, Hiroshima Toyo Carp. j, Hanshin Tigers. k, Kintetsu Buffaloes. l, Chiba Lotte Marines.

**1999, Oct. 22 *Die Cut***

**Self-Adhesive**

| | | | | |
|---|---|---|---|---|
| **2715** | A2101 | Sheet of 12 | 18.00 | |
| *a.-l.* | | 80y any single | 1.40 | .35 |

Natl. Science Council, 50th Anniv. — A2102

**1999, Oct. 28 *Perf. 13x13¼***

| | | | | |
|---|---|---|---|---|
| **2716** | A2102 | 80y multi | 1.40 | .35 |

**Cultural Pioneers Types of 1992-98**

No. 2717, Hokusai (1760-1849), painter. No. 2718: Yasunari Kawabata (1899-1972), writer. No. 2719, Shoen Uemura (1875-1949), painter.

**1999, Nov. 4 Photo. *Perf. 12¾x13***

| | | | | |
|---|---|---|---|---|
| **2717** | A1645 | 80y multi | 1.40 | .35 |

**Photo. & Engr.**

***Perf. 13***

| | | | | |
|---|---|---|---|---|
| **2718** | A1645 | 80y multi | 1.40 | .35 |
| **2719** | A2053 | 80y multi | 1.40 | .35 |
| | | *Nos. 2717-2719 (3)* | 4.20 | 1.05 |

Reign of Emperor Akihito, 10th Anniv. A2103

Designs: No. 2720, Paulownia and bamboo crest. No. 2721, Phoenix crest.

**1999, Nov. 12 Photo. *Perf. 12¼***

| | | | | |
|---|---|---|---|---|
| **2720** | A2103 | 80y red & multi | 1.40 | .35 |
| **2721** | A2103 | 80y yel & multi | 1.40 | .35 |
| *a.* | | Souvenir sheet, #2720-2721 | 3.00 | 3.00 |

A2104

A2105

New Year 2000 (Year of the Dragon)

A2106 A2107

**1999, Nov. 15** ***Perf. 13x13¼***

| | | | | |
|---|---|---|---|---|
| **2722** | A2104 | 50y multi | .95 | .30 |
| **2723** | A2105 | 80y multi | 1.40 | .40 |

***Perf. 13¼***

| | | | | |
|---|---|---|---|---|
| **2724** | A2106 | 50y +3y multi | .95 | .40 |
| **2725** | A2107 | 80y +3y multi | 1.50 | .40 |

Sheets of 2 containing Nos. 2722-2723 were lottery prizes. Value $2.75.

Children's Book Day — A2108

a, Flower with child reading, bird in flight. b, Flower with child reading, bird perched. c, Child, left half of new Intl. Library of Children's Literature. d, Child, right half of library. e, Butterfly with child's head. f, Two children, library.

***Perf. 12¾x13¼***

**2000, Mar. 31** **Photo.**

| | | | | |
|---|---|---|---|---|
| **2726** | A2108 Sheet of 10, #e-f, 2 each #a-d | | 17.50 | 17.50 |
| *a.-f.* | 80y any single | | 1.40 | .35 |

Seishu Hanaoka (1760-1835), Physician, and Flower — A2109

**2000, Apr. 11** ***Perf. 12¾x13***

| | | | | |
|---|---|---|---|---|
| **2727** | A2109 | 80y multi | 1.40 | .35 |

Japan Surgical Society, 100th congress.

Japan-Netherlands Relations, 400th Anniv. — A2110

**2000, Apr. 19** ***Perf. 13***

| | | | | |
|---|---|---|---|---|
| **2728** | | 80y multi | 1.40 | .35 |
| **2729** | | 80y multi | 1.40 | .35 |
| *a.* | A2110 | Pair, #2728-2729 | 3.00 | 1.50 |

Dragon and Tiger by Gaho Hashimoto — A2112

**2000, Apr. 20** ***Perf. 13¼***

| | | | | |
|---|---|---|---|---|
| **2730** | | 80y multi | 1.40 | .40 |
| **2731** | | 80y multi | 1.40 | .40 |
| *a.* | A2112 | Pair, #2730-2731 | 3.25 | 2.50 |

Philately week.

Natl. Land Afforestation Campaign — A2114

**2000, Apr. 21** ***Perf. 13¼***

| | | | | |
|---|---|---|---|---|
| **2732** | A2114 | 50y multi | .90 | .40 |

Phila Nippon 2001, Tokyo — A2115

Designs: a, Wild goose (dull green frame background). b, Wagtail (dull violet frame background). c, Goshawk (dull rose frame background). d, A Girl Blowing Glass Toy, by Utamaro. e, Kabuki Actor Ebizo Ichikawa, by Sharaku. f, Flowers. g, Dog and cat. h, Children with pen and envelope (blue background). i, Child with clown. j, Children with pen and envelope (red background).

**2000, May 19** **Photo.** ***Die Cut***

**Self-Adhesive**

| | | | | |
|---|---|---|---|---|
| **2733** | A2115 | Sheet of 10, #a-j | 17.50 | |
| *a.-j.* | | 80y any single | 1.40 | .55 |

Kyushu-Okinawa Summit — A2116

**2000, June 21** **Photo.** ***Perf. 12¾x13***

| | | | | |
|---|---|---|---|---|
| **2734** | | 80y multi | 1.40 | .35 |
| **2735** | | 80y multi | 1.40 | .35 |
| *a.* | A2116 | Pair, #2734-2735 | 3.00 | 1.50 |

A2117

**2000, June 30**

| | | | | |
|---|---|---|---|---|
| **2736** | | 80y Three flowers | 1.40 | .35 |
| **2737** | | 80y Two flowers | 1.40 | .35 |
| *a.* | A2117 | Pair, #2736-2737 | 3.00 | 1.50 |

Crime Prevention Campaign, 50th anniv.

### Letter Writing Day Type of 1998

Designs: No. 2738, Girl with bows in hair, pen. No. 2739, Birds, house, letter. No. 2740, Clown with red hat, open envelope. No. 2741, Boy reading letter, puppy.

No. 2742: a, Child, dog, in basket. b, Apple tree, flower (circular stamp). c, Parrots holding envelope (elliptical stamp). d, Bicycle, rabbit, flower (oval stamp). e, Boy, girl, dove. f, Girl, letter, snail, porcupine (oval stamp). g, Child playing harp. h, Child playing recorder. i, Child playing bass (semicircular stamp). j, Girl with blue hat, pen, birds holding envelope.

**2000, July 21** ***Perf. 12¾x13¼***

| | | | | |
|---|---|---|---|---|
| **2738** | A2047 | 50y multi | .90 | .35 |
| **2739** | A2047 | 50y multi | .90 | .35 |
| **2740** | A2047 | 50y multi | .90 | .35 |
| **2741** | A2047 | 50y multi | .90 | .35 |
| *a.* | | Strip of 4, #2738-2741 | 4.00 | 4.00 |
| **2742** | | Sheet of 10 | 17.50 | 17.50 |
| *a.-j.* | | A2047 80y Any single | 1.40 | .40 |
| *k.* | | Booklet pane, #2738-2741, 2742g, 2742h, 2 #2742e, 2742j | 14.50 | |
| | | Booklet, #2742k | 14.50 | |
| *l.* | | Souvenir sheet, #2739, 2742e | 2.50 | 2.50 |

No. 2742b is 30mm in diameter, No. 2742c is 23x34mm, Nos. 2742d, 2742f are 28x40mm, and No. 2742i is 24x40mm.

Women's Private Higher Education, Cent. — A2118

**2000, Sept. 22** **Photo.** ***Perf. 13***

| | | | | |
|---|---|---|---|---|
| **2743** | A2118 | 80y multi | 1.40 | .35 |

Intl. Letter Writing Week A2119

Artwork by Hiroshige: 90y, Okabe. 110y, Maisaka. 130y, Okazaki.

**2000, Oct. 6** ***Perf. 13¼***

| | | | | |
|---|---|---|---|---|
| **2744** | A2119 | 90y multi | 1.60 | .50 |
| **2745** | A2119 | 110y multi | 2.00 | .60 |
| **2746** | A2119 | 130y multi | 2.25 | .65 |
| | | *Nos. 2744-2746 (3)* | 5.85 | 1.75 |

See Nos. 2791-2793, 2835-2837, 2865-2867, 2904-2906, 2938-2940, 2999-3001, 3064-3066.

### Cultural Pioneers Type of 1998 and

Ukichiro Nakaya (1900-62), Snow Crystal Researcher A2120

Designs: No. 2747, Hantaro Nagaoka (1865-1950), physicist. No. 2748, Teijo Nakamura (1900-88), poet.

**Photo. & Engr.**

**2000, Nov. 6** ***Perf. 13***

| | | | | |
|---|---|---|---|---|
| **2747** | A2053 | 80y multi | 1.40 | .35 |
| **2748** | A2053 | 80y multi | 1.40 | .35 |
| **2749** | A2120 | 80y multi | 1.40 | .35 |
| | | *Nos. 2747-2749 (3)* | 4.20 | 1.05 |

See No. 2841.

A2121 A2122

New Year 2001 (Year of the Snake)

A2123 A2124

**2000, Nov. 15** **Photo.** ***Perf. 13x13¼***

| | | | | |
|---|---|---|---|---|
| **2750** | A2121 | 50y multi | .95 | .30 |
| **2751** | A2122 | 80y multi | 1.40 | .40 |

***Perf. 13¼x13½***

| | | | | |
|---|---|---|---|---|
| **2752** | A2123 | 50y +3y multi | .95 | .40 |
| **2753** | A2124 | 80y +3y multi | 1.50 | .40 |
| | | *Nos. 2750-2753 (4)* | 4.80 | 1.50 |

Sheets of 2, Nos. 2750-2751, were lottery prizes. Value, $2.75.

Diet, 110th Anniv. — A2125

**2000, Nov. 29** ***Perf. 13***

| | | | | |
|---|---|---|---|---|
| **2754** | A2125 | 80y multi | 1.40 | .35 |

Internet Expo 2001 — A2126

**2001, Jan. 5** ***Perf. 13x13¼***

| | | | | |
|---|---|---|---|---|
| **2755** | | 80y Denom. at L | 1.40 | .35 |
| **2756** | | 80y Denom. at R | 1.40 | .35 |
| *a.* | A2126 | Pair, #2755-2756 | 3.00 | 1.50 |

Intl. Volunteers Year — A2127

**2001, Jan. 17** ***Perf. 13½x13¼***

| | | | | |
|---|---|---|---|---|
| **2757** | A2127 | 80y multi | 1.40 | .35 |

Administrative Scriveners System, 50th Anniv. — A2128

**2001, Feb. 22 Photo. *Perf. 13¼***

| | | | |
|---|---|---|---|
| **2758** A2128 80y multi | 1.40 | .35 |

**World Heritage Sites**

Sheet 1 — A2129

Sheet 2 — A2130

Sheet 3 — A2131

Sheet 4 — A2132

Sheet 5 — A2133

Sheet 6 — A2134

No. 2759 — Nikko: a, Bridge (stamp 1). b, Shrine with pillars in foreground (stamp 2). c, Temple gate (stamp 3). d, Dragon (stamp 4). e, Peacock (stamp 5). f, Cat (stamp 6). g, Statue of blue green figure (stamp 7). h, Statue of red figure (stamp 8). i, Shrine (stamp 9). j, Shrine and walkways (stamp 10).

No. 2760 — Itsukushima: a, Marodo Jinjya and pillar in water (stamp 1). b, Marodo Jinjya (stamp 2). c, Honsha (shrine entrance with steps, stamp 3). d, Koma-inu (lion statue, stamp 4). e, Marodo Jinjya and Gojyuno-tou (stamp 5). f, Bugakumen (sculpture with blue water background, stamp 6). g, Kazari-uma (horse statue, stamp 7). h, Noubutai (building with brown eaves, stamp 8). i, Tahoutou (building with cherry blossoms, stamp 9). j, Oomoto Jinjya (building with red fence, stamp 10).

No. 2761 — Kyoto: a, Hosodono Hall, Maidono Hall and Tsuchinoya Hall, Kamowakeikazuchi Shrine (buildings with cones in foreground, stamp 1). b, Romon Gate, Kamowakeikazuchi Shrine (building with stream, stamp 2). c, East Main Hall, Kamomioya Shrine (building with guardian dog statue on landing, stamp 3). d, Guardian dog statue, Kamomioya Shrine (stamp 4). e, South Great Gate and 5-Story Pagoda (deep blue sky, stamp 5). f, Fukuu Joju Nyorai Statue, Toji Temple (gold statue, stamp 6). g, Nyoirin Kannon, Toji Temple (painting, stamp 7). h, Daiitoku Myoo Statue, Toji Temple (stone statue, stamp 8). i, West Gate, 3-Story Pagoda, Kiyomizudera Temple (red gate and temple, stamp 9). j, Main Hall, Kiyomizudera Temple (building with cherry bloosoms, stamp 10).

No. 2762 — Kyoto: a, Konpon Chudo Hall, Enryakuji Temple (roof, stamp 1). b, Eternal Flame, Enryakuji Temple (stamp 2). c, Ninaido Hall, Enryakuji Temple (building with large trees in foreground, stamp 3). d, Sanbo-in Temple Garden, Daigoji Temple (building, one end of small bridge, stamp 4). e, Sanbo-in Temple Garden (end of bridge, trees, stamp 5). f, 5-Story Pagoda, Daigoji Temple (white sky, stamp 6). g, Goten, Ninnaji Temple (buildings with walkways, stamp 7). h, 5-Story Pagoda (cherry trees in foreground, stamp 8). i, Phoenix Hall, Byodoin Temple (black sky, stamp 9). j, Wooden carving of Bodhisattvas Floating on Clouds, Byodoin Temple (stamp 10).

No. 2763 — Kyoto: a, Ujikami Shrine (low fence around shrine with denomination at UL, stamp 1). b, Kaeru Mata, Ujikami Shrine (thin, crossing diagonal strips, stamp 2). c, Front approach to Kozanji Temple (walkway of square panels, stamp 3). d, Sekisuiin, Kozanji Temple (yellow tree blossoms in front of temple, stamp 4). e, Kasumijima Garden, Saihoji Temple (moss-covered bridge, stamp 5) f, Kojokan Garden, Saihoji Temple (Stone stairs and rocks, stamp 6). g, View of garden and pond from under roof, Tenryuji Temple (denomination at left, stamp 7). h, View of garden and pond from under roof, Tenryuji Temple (denomination at right, stamp 8). i, Rokuonji Temple in autumn (Building on lake, green leaves on trees, stamp 9). j, Rokuonji Temple in winter (snow covered roofs and trees, stamp 10).

No. 2764 — Kyoto: a, Snow-covered Silver Pavilion, Jishoji Temple (stamp 1). b, Silver Pavilion without snow (stamp 2). c, Moss-covered rock, Hojo Garden, Ryoanji Temple (stamp 3). d, Rock and snow, Hojo Garden (stamp 4). e, Karamon, Honganji Temple (gate with curved roof, stamp 5). f, Hiunkaku, Honganji Temple (building near pond, stamp 6). g, Shoin, Honganji Temple (wall with landscape, stamp 7). h, Ninomaur Palace, Nijo Castle (roof with chrysanthemum crest at peak, stamp 8). i, Detail from "Hawks on Pine," Nijo Castle (hawk looking left, stamp 9). j, Detail from "Hawks on Pine," Nijo Castle (hawk looking down, stamp 10).

**2001 Photo. *Perf. 13x13¼***

| | | | | |
|---|---|---|---|---|
| **2759** | A2129 | Sheet of 10 | 18.00 | 18.00 |
| ***a.-j.*** | | 80y Any single | 1.40 | .55 |
| **2760** | A2130 | Sheet of 10 | 18.00 | 18.00 |
| ***a.-j.*** | | 80y Any single | 1.40 | .55 |
| **2761** | A2131 | Sheet of 10 | 18.00 | 18.00 |
| ***a.-j.*** | | 80y Any single | 1.40 | .55 |
| **2762** | A2132 | Sheet of 10 | 18.00 | 18.00 |
| ***a.-j.*** | | 80y Any single | 1.40 | .55 |
| **2763** | A2133 | Sheet of 10 | 18.00 | 18.00 |
| ***a.-j.*** | | 80y Any single | 1.40 | .55 |
| **2764** | A2134 | Sheet of 10 | 18.00 | 18.00 |
| ***a.-j.*** | | 80y Any single | 1.40 | .55 |

Issued: No. 2759, 2/23; No. 2760, 3/23; No. 2761, 6/22; No. 2762, 8/23. No. 2763, 12/21. No. 2764, 2/22/02.

Sheet numbers are in center of colored rectangles at top of sheet. Stamp numbers are in sheet margins.

Exhibit of Italian Art at Museum of Western Art, Tokyo — A2135

Designs: 80y, Show emblem. No. 2766, Angel, from The Annunciation, by Botticelli. No. 2767, Virgin Mary, from The Annunciation.

**2001, Mar. 19 Photo. *Perf. 13***

| | | |
|---|---|---|
| **2765** A2135 80y multi | 1.40 | .35 |

**Size: 33x44mm**

***Perf. 13¼***

| | | |
|---|---|---|
| **2766** A2135 110y multi | 1.90 | .55 |
| **2767** A2135 110y multi | 1.90 | .55 |
| ***a.*** Pair, #2766-2767 | 5.00 | 3.00 |
| *Nos. 2765-2767 (3)* | 5.20 | 1.45 |

Japanese Dermatological Association, 100th Annual Meeting — A2136

**2001, Apr. 6 *Perf. 13¼***

**Color of Triangle Behind "0" in Denomination**

| | | |
|---|---|---|
| **2768** A2136 80y pink | 1.40 | .35 |
| **2769** A2136 80y orange | 1.40 | .35 |
| **2770** A2136 80y yellow | 1.40 | .35 |
| **2771** A2136 80y green | 1.40 | .35 |
| **2772** A2136 80y blue | 1.40 | .35 |
| ***a.*** Vert. strip of 5, #2768-2772 | 7.50 | 5.00 |

Depositing Mail, by Senseki Nakamura A2137

**2001, Apr. 20 *Perf. 13x13¼***

| | | |
|---|---|---|
| **2773** A2137 80y multi | 1.40 | .35 |

Philately Week, Cent. of red cylindrical mailboxes.

Membership in UNESCO, 50th Anniv. — A2138

**2001, July 2** *Perf. 13¼*

2774 A2138 80y multi 1.40 .35

9th FINA World Swimming Championships, Fukuoka A2139

Designs: No. 2775, Swimming race. No. 2776, Synchronized swimming. No. 2777, Diving. No. 2778, Water polo.

**2001, July 16** *Perf. 13x13¼*

2775 A2139 80y multi 1.40 .35
2776 A2139 80y multi 1.40 .35
2777 A2139 80y multi 1.40 .35
2778 A2139 80y multi 1.40 .35
*a.* Horiz. strip of 4, #2775-2778 6.00 6.00

### Letter Writing Day Type of 1998

Designs: No. 2779, Three rabbits, tulip background. No. 2780, Girl with pencil, pencil background. No. 2781, Boy with envelope, bird background. No. 2782, Girl, flower background.

No. 2783: a, Girl with rabbit, bird, flower (oval stamp). b, Bird in tree (circular stamp). c, Boy with pen behind back. d, Girl with envelope and dog. e, Girl on bicycle, flowers (semi-circular stamp). f, Flowers, bird with envelope, insect (circular stamp). g, Bird flying, bird on roof. h, Chicken, chicks, pig (oval stamp). i, Rabbit, flowers (elliptical stamp). j, Boy with hat, rabbit (oval stamp).

**2001, July 23** *Perf. 13x13¼*

2779 A2047 50y multi .90 .30
2780 A2047 50y multi .90 .30
2781 A2047 50y multi .90 .30
2782 A2047 50y multi .90 .30
*a.* Horiz. strip of 4, #2779-2782 4.00 4.00
2783 Sheet of 10 15.00 15.00
*a.-j.* A2047 80y Any single 1.40 .35
*k.* Booklet pane, #2779-2782, 2 each #2783c, 2783d, 2783g 13.50
Booklet, #2783k 14.00
*l.* Souvenir sheet, #2780, 2783g 2.50 2.50

Phila Nippon '01 (Nos. 2783, 2783l). Nos. 2783a and 2783e are 35x29mm; Nos. 2783b and 2783f are 29mm in diameter; No. 2783h is 40x28mm; No. 2783i is 35x23mm; No. 2783j is 34x28mm.

On No. 2783e, the bicycle appears in the selvage below the stamp.

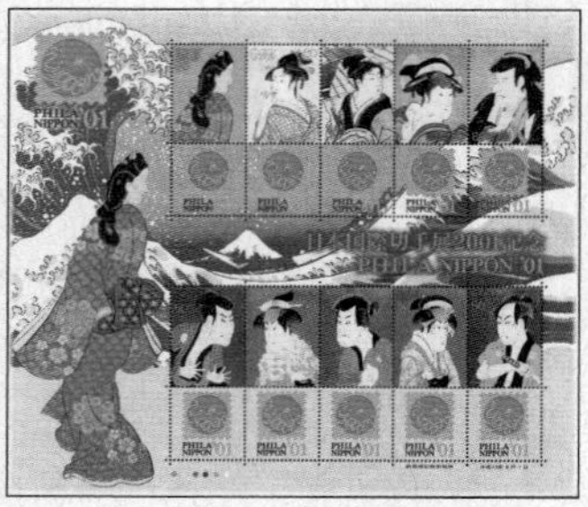

Phila Nippon '01 — A2140

Art: a, Oniji Otani as Edobei (striped kimono), by Sharaku. b, Hanshiro Iwai as Shigenoi (flowered kimono, facing left), by Sharaku. c, Hangoro Sakata as Mizuemon Fujikawa (brown kimono), by Sharaku. d, Kikunojo Segawa as Oshizu, Bunzo Tanabe's Wife (kimono with stars), by Sharaku. e, Omezo Ichikawa as Ippei Yakko (with sword), by Sharaku. f, Beauty Looking Back (flowered kimono), by Moronobu Hishikawa. g, A Girl Whistling a Vidro (checkered kimono), by Utamaro. h, Nishiki Fuzoku Higashino Returning From a Bathhouse in the Rain (with umbrella), by Kiyonaga Torii. i, Kumesaburo Iwai as Chiyo (blue background), by Kunimasa Utagawa. j, Komazo Ichikawa as Ganryu Sasaki (with sword), by Toyokuni Utagawa.

**2001, Aug. 1** *Perf. 13*

2784 A2140 Sheet of 10+10 labels 12.50 12.50
*a.-e.* 50y Any single .90 .50
*f.-j.* 80y Any single 1.40 .50

Labels could be personalized by customers at Phila Nippon stamp exhibition.

2001 World Games, Akita — A2141

Designs: No. 2785, Fishing, Frisbee throwing. No. 2786, Aerobics, billiards. No. 2787, Life saving, water skiing. No. 2788, Body building, tug-of-war.

**2001, Aug. 16** *Perf. 13*

2785 A2141 50y multi .90 .30
2786 A2141 50y multi .90 .30
*a.* Pair, #2785-2786 1.90 1.00
2787 A2141 80y multi 1.40 .35
2788 A2141 80y multi 1.40 .35
*a.* Pair, #2787-2788 3.00 1.50
*Nos. 2785-2788 (4)* 4.60 1.30

Phila Nippon '01 — A2142

Designs: a, Hanshiro Iwai as Shigenoi (figure with stick in hair), by Sharaku. b, Oniji Otani as Edobei (figure with fingers splayed), by Sharaku. c, Mandarin duck in water. d, White-eye on branch. e, Children with letters. f, Kumesaburo Iwai as Chiyo (lilac background), by Kunimasa Utagawa. g, Komazo Ichikawa as Ganryu Sasaki (brown background), by Toyokuni Utagawa. h, Turtledove (blue background). i, Greater pied kingfisher (green background). j, Japan #1.

**2001, Aug. 1** **Photo.** *Die Cut*

**Self-Adhesive**

2789 A2142 Sheet of 10 14.00
*a.-e.* 50y Any single .90 .30
*f.-j.* 80y Any single 1.40 .35

San Francisco Peace Treaty, 50th Anniv. — A2143

**2001, Sept. 7** *Perf. 13*

2790 A2143 80y multi 1.40 .35

### Intl. Letter Writing Week Type of 2000

Hiroshige paintings from 53 Stations of the Tokaido: 90y, Hara. 110y, Oiso. 130y, Sakanoshita.

**2001, Oct. 5** *Perf. 13¼*

2791 A2119 90y multi 1.40 .50
2792 A2119 110y multi 1.90 .55
2793 A2119 130y multi 2.10 .60
*Nos. 2791-2793 (3)* 5.40 1.65

Town Safety Campaign — A2144

Designs: No. 2794, Boy, duck chicks, owl, frogs, insects. No. 2795, Girl, dogs, cats, birds, insects.

**2001, Oct. 11** *Perf. 13x13¼*

2794 80y multi 1.40 .35
2795 80y multi 1.40 .35
*a.* A2144 Horiz. pair, #2794-2795 3.00 1.50

1st National Games for the Disabled — A2145

Designs: No. 2796, Disc throwing. No. 2797, Wheelchair race.

**2001, Oct. 26** *Perf. 12¾x13*

2796 80y multi 1.40 .35
2797 80y multi 1.40 .35
*a.* A2145 Horiz. pair, #2796-2797 3.00 1.50

Norinaga Motoori (1730-1801), Physician, Scholar — A2146

Gidayu Takemoto (1651-1714), Joruri Chanter — A2147

**Photo. & Engr.**

**2001, Nov. 5** *Perf. 12¾x13*

2798 A2146 80y multi 1.40 .35
2799 A2147 80y multi 1.40 .35

Commercial Broadcasting, 50th Anniv. — A2148

**2001, Nov. 15** **Photo.**

2800 A2148 80y multi 1.40 .35

A2149

A2150

New Year 2002 (Year of the Horse)

A2151 A2152

**2001, Nov. 15** *Perf. 13x13¼*

2801 A2149 50y multi .95 .30
2802 A2150 80y multi 1.40 .40

*Perf. 13¼x13½*

2803 A2151 50y +3y multi .95 .40
2804 A2152 80y +3y multi 1.50 .40
*Nos. 2801-2804 (4)* 4.80 1.50

Sheets of two containing Nos. 2801-2802 were lottery prizes. Value, $3.

Legal Aid System, 50th Anniv. — A2153

**2002, Jan. 24** *Perf. 12¾x13*

2805 A2153 80y multi 1.40 .35

Japan — Mongolia Diplomatic Relations, 30th Anniv. — A2154

**2002, Feb. 15**

2806 A2154 80y multi 1.40 .35

Lions Clubs in Japan, 50th Anniv. — A2155

**2002, Mar. 1** **Photo.** *Perf. 13x13¼*

2807 A2155 80y multi 1.40 .35

2002 World Figure Skating Championships, Nagano — A2156

**2002, Mar. 8**

2808 80y Men's Singles 1.40 .90
2809 80y Pairs 1.40 .90
*a.* A2156 Horiz. pair, #2808-2809 3.00 1.90

Diplomatic Relations Anniversaries A2157

Designs: No. 2810, Taj Mahal, India. No. 2811, Sculpture of "Priest King," Mohenjo Daro excavations, Pakistan. No. 2812, Sigiriya goddess, Lion's Rock, Sri Lanka. No. 2813, Carving from Buddhist Vihara, Paharpur, Bangladesh.

**2002, Apr. 12**

**2810** A2157 80y multi 1.40 .40
**2811** A2157 80y multi 1.40 .40
**2812** A2157 80y multi 1.40 .40
**2813** A2157 80y multi 1.40 .40
*Nos. 2810-2813 (4)* 5.60 1.60

Japanese diplomatic relations with India, 50th anniv. (No. 2810); Pakistan, 50th anniv. (No. 2811). Sri Lanka, 50th anniv. (No. 2812), and Bangladesh, 30th anniv. (No. 2813).

Philately Week — A2158

Folding screen panels depicting horse racing scenes: No. 2814, Denomination at bottom. No. 2815, Denomination at top.

**2002, Apr. 19** ***Perf. 13¼***

**2814** 80y multi 1.40 .40
**2815** 80y multi 1.40 .40
*a.* A2158 Horiz. pair, #2814-2815 3.00 1.75

Fulbright Exchange Program, 50th Anniv. — A2159

**2002, May 8** ***Perf. 12¾x13***

**2816** A2159 80y multi 1.40 .35

Return of Okinawa, 30th Anniv. — A2160

**2002, May 15** ***Perf. 13x13¼***

**2817** A2160 80y multi 1.40 .35

2002 World Cup Soccer Championships, Japan and Korea — A2161

**2002, May 24**

**2818** 80y Soccer field 1.40 .35
**2819** 80y World Cup 1.40 .35
*a.* A2161 Horiz. pair, #2818-2819 3.00 1.75

Nos. 2818-2819 were issued in sheets of 10 stamps, containing five of each. Thirteen different sheet margins exist.

### World Heritage Sites

Sheet 7 — A2162

No. 2820 — Todaiji and Koufukuji Temples, Nara: a, Great Buddha Hall, Todaiji Temple (stamp 1). b, Underside of roof of Nandaimon Gate, Todaiji Temple (stamp 2). c, Engraving on lotus petal, Todaiji Temple (stamp 3). d, Head of Koumokuten, Todaiji Temple (stamp 4). e, Hokkedo Hall and steps, Todaiji Temple (stamp 5). f, Five-story pagoda, Koufukuji Temple (stamp 6). g, Hokuendo Hall (with roof ornament), Koufukuji Temple (stamp 7). h, Ashura (statue with four arms), Koufukuji Temple (stamp 8). i, Head of Buddha, Koufukuji Temple (stamp 9). j, Ogre under dragon lantern, Koufukuji Temple (stamp 10).

**2002** **Photo.** ***Perf. 13x13¼***

**2820** A2162 Sheet of 10 16.00 16.00
*a.-j.* 80y Any single 1.40 .55

Issued: No. 2820, 6/21.

Numbers have been reserved for additional sheets. Sheet numbers are in center of colored rectangle at top of sheet. Stamp numbers are in sheet margins.

### World Heritage Series

Sheet 8 — A2163

Sheet 9 — A2164

Sheet 10 — A2165

No. 2821 — Nara: a, Covered passageway, Kasuga Taisha Shrine (stamp 1). b, Chumon, Kasuga Taisha Shrine (stamp 2). c, Deer in Kasuga-yama Primeval Forest (stamp 3). d, Gokurakubo Zenshitsu and Gokurakubo Hondo, Gango-ji Temple (stamp 4). e, Gokurakubo Five-story Pagoda, Gango-ji Temple (stamp 5). f, East and West Pagodas, Yakushi-ji Temple (stamp 6). g, Yakushi Nyorai (seated Buddha), Yakushi-ji Temple (stamp 7). h, Golden Hall, Toshodai-ji Temple (stamp 8). i, Senju Kannon Ryu-zo (standing image with hands together of Thousand-handed Goddess of Mercy), Toshodai-ji Temple (stamp 9). j, Suzakumon Gate, Heijo Imperial Palace (stamp 10).

No. 2822 — Villages of Shirakawa-go and Gokayama: a, House with large tree at left, Ogimachi (stamp 1). b, Two houses, trees in fall colors Ogimachi (stamp 2). c, House with flowers, Ogimachi (stamp 3). d, Myozen-ji Temple and house, Ogimachi (stamp 4). e, Two houses covered in snow at night, Ogimachi (stamp 5). f, Neighborhood of houses, Ainokura (stamp 6). g, Sonen-ji Temple with stone wall, Ainokura (stamp 7). h, Two houses, Ainokura (stamp 8). i, House with shrub in front, Suganuma (stamp 9). j, House covered in snow, Suganuma (stamp 10).

No. 2823 — Gusuku Sites of the Ryukyu Kingdom: a, Stone lion at royal mausoleum (stamp 1). b, Three steps and stone gate to Sonohyan'utaki Sanctuary (stamp 2). c, Cherry blossoms and ruins of Nakijinjou Castle (stamp 3). d, Steps and stone gate at ruins of Zakimijou Castle (stamp 4). e, Ruins of Katsurenjou Castle walls (stamp 5). f, Ruins of Nakagusukujou Castle citadel (walls with gate, stamp 6). g Kankaimon, main gate of Shurijou Castle (stamp 7). h, Main hall of Shurijou Castle (red building, stamp 8). i, Shikina'en, royal garden (stamp 9). j, Seifautaki Sanctuary (niche in rocks, stamp 10).

**2002** **Photo.** ***Perf. 13x13¼***

**2821** A2163 Sheet of 10 16.00 16.00
*a.-j.* 80y Any single 1.40 .55
**2822** A2164 Sheet of 10 16.00 16.00
*a.-j.* 80y Any single 1.40 .55
**2823** A2165 Sheet of 10 16.00 16.00
*a.-j.* 80y Any single 1.40 .55

Issued: No. 2821, 7/23; No. 2822, 9/20; No. 2823, 12/20. Sheet numbers are in center of colored rectangle at top of sheet. Stamp numbers are in sheet margins.

### Letter Writing Day Type of 1998

Designs: No. 2824, Girl with bows in hair holding envelope. No. 2825, Monkey in tree holding envelope. No. 2826, House and flowers. No. 2827, Boy with arms raised, fence.

No. 2828: a, Cow and bird (triangular stamp). b, Boy and sheep (elliptical stamp). c, Caterpillar and ladybug under magnifying glass (round stamp). d, Girl with bows in hair, flowers (oval stamp). e, Boy with soccer ball. f, Girl with tennis racquet and ball. g, Man on bicycle. h, Girl with flower in vase (round stamp). i, Truck and automobile. j, Woman holding gift and coat, boy holding envelope

***Perf. 13x13¼, 13 (#2828a)***

**2002, July 23** **Photo.**

**2824** A2047 50y multi .90 .40
**2825** A2047 50y multi .90 .40
**2826** A2047 50y multi .90 .40
**2827** A2047 50y multi .90 .40
*a.* Strip of 4, #2824-2827 4.00 2.75
**2828** Sheet of 10 16.00 16.00
*a.-j.* A2047 80y Any single 1.40 .45
*k.* Booklet pane, #2824-2827, 3 each #2828g, 2828j 16.00 —
Booklet, #2828k 16.00
*l.* Souvenir sheet, #2825, 2828j 2.50 2.50

No. 2828a is 34x28mm; No. 2828b is 29x26mm; No. 2828c is 29mm in diameter; No. 2828d is 28x40mm; Nos. 2828e and 2828f are 22x36mm; No. 2828h is 28mm in diameter; No. 2828i is 25x25mm.

12th World Congress of Psychiatry, Yokohama — A2166

**2002, Aug. 1** **Photo.** ***Perf. 12¾x13***

**2829** A2166 80y multi 1.40 .35

World Wheelchair Basketball Championships, Kitakyushu A2167

**2002, Aug. 9**

**2830** A2167 80y multi 1.40 .35

Civil Aviation, 50th Anniv. — A2168

**2002, Sept. 6**

**2831** A2168 80y multi 1.40 .35

Normalization of Diplomatic Relations Between Japan and People's Republic of China, 30th Anniv. — A2169

Designs: No. 2832, Purple wisteria flowers. No. 2833, Goldfish and cherry blossoms.

**2002, Sept. 13** *Perf. 13x13¼*

**2832** 80y multi 1.40 .55
**2833** 80y multi 1.40 .55
*a.* A2169 Horiz. pair, #2832-2833 3.00 2.50

Intl. Fleet Review, Tokyo Bay — A2170

**2002, Oct. 1**

**2834** A2170 80y multi 1.40 .40

### Letter Writing Week Type of 2000

Hiroshige paintings from 53 Stations of the Tokaido Highway: 90y, Yui. 110y, Shono. 130y, Tozuka.

**2002, Oct. 7** *Perf. 13¼*

**2835** A2119 90y multi 1.40 .50
**2836** A2119 110y multi 1.90 .55
**2837** A2119 130y multi 2.10 .60
*Nos. 2835-2837 (3)* 5.40 1.65

Asian and Pacific Decade of Disabled Persons — A2171

**2002, Oct. 10** *Perf. 12¾x13*

**2838** A2171 80y multi 1.40 .40

### Cultural Pioneers Types of 1998-2000

Designs: No. 2839, Shiki Masaoka (1867-1902), poet. No. 2840, Ookawabata Yusuzumi-zu, by Kiyonaga Torii (1752-1815), artist. No. 2841, Aikitu Tanakadate (1856-1952), physicist.

**Photo. & Engr., Photo. (#2840)**

**2002, Nov. 5** *Perf. 13*

**2839** A2053 80y multi 1.40 .40
**2840** A2053 80y multi 1.40 .40
**2841** A2120 80y multi 1.40 .40
*Nos. 2839-2841 (3)* 4.20 1.20

A2172

A2173

New Year 2003 (Year of the Ram)

A2174 A2175

**2002, Nov. 15 Photo.** *Perf. 13x13¼*

**2842** A2172 50y multi .95 .30
**2843** A2173 80y multi 1.40 .40

*Perf. 13½x13¼*

**2844** A2174 50y +3y multi .95 .40
**2845** A2175 80y +3y multi 1.50 .40
*Nos. 2842-2845 (4)* 4.80 1.50

Sheets of two containing Nos. 2842-2843 were lottery prizes. Value, $3.

Kabuki, 400th Anniv. — A2176

Designs: No. 2846, Shibaraku and Tsuchigumo. No. 2847, Okuni Kabuki-zu, detail from painted screen.

**2003, Jan. 15 Photo.** *Perf. 13x13¼*

**2846** 80y multi 1.40 .50
**2847** 80y multi 1.40 .50
*a.* A2176 Horiz. pair, #2846-2847 3.50 2.00

Japanese Television, 50th Anniv.

A2177 A2178

**2003, Jan. 31**

**2848** A2177 80y multi 1.40 .40
**2849** A2178 80y multi 1.40 .40

A2179

Greetings — A2180

No. 2850: a, Roses. b, Reindeer. c, Cat and butterfly. d, Rabbits in automobile. e, White flowers.

No. 2851: a, Heart and flower. b, Dog with noisemaker. c, Bird and snowman. d, Bird and strawberries. e, Cranes and turtle.

**2003, Feb. 10** *Die Cut Perf. 13½*

**Self-Adhesive**

**2850** A2179 Pane of 5 + 5 labels 10.00 10.00
*a.-e.* 80y Any single 1.40 .75
**2851** A2180 Pane of 5 + 5 labels 10.00 10.00
*a.-e.* 80y Any single 1.40 .75

See Nos. 2855A-2855J.

### World Heritage Series

Sheet 11 — A2181

No. 2852 — Hiroshima buildings and stamps on theme of "Peace": a, Atomic Bomb Dome (stamp 1). b, Hiroshima Prefectural Commercial Exhibit Hall (stamp 2). c, Dove over Atomic Bomb Dome, yellow denomination (stamp 3). d, Child's drawing of person with flower (stamp 4). e, Dove over Atomic Bomb Dome, blue denomination (stamp 5). f, Dove over Atomic Bomb Dome, red denomination (stamp 6). g, Doves, stylized person holding child (stamp 7). h, People on hill (stamp 8). i, Bird (stamp 9). j, Rabbit, butterflies and flowers (stamp 10).

**2003, Mar. 20 Photo.** *Perf. 13x13¼*

**2852** A2181 Sheet of 10 16.00 16.00
*a.-j.* 80y Any single 1.40 .55

Sheet numbers are in center of colored rectangle at top of sheet. Stamp numbers are in sheet margin.

Inauguration of Japan Post — A2182

No. 2853 — Flowers: a, Adonis (yellow flowers). b, Primrose (pink flowers). c, Violets and Japanese quince (violet and red flowers). d, Field horsetail (flowerless). e, Japanese wisteria (white hanging flowers). f, Weeping cherry tree (pink buds and flowers) and swallow. g, Hydrangea (lilac flowers). h, Japanese magnolia (white and pink flowers). i, Candock (yellow flower) and moorhen. j, Peony (pink flower and bud) and butterfly.

**2003, Apr. 1** *Die Cut Perf. 13¼*

**Self-Adhesive**

**2853** A2182 Sheet of 10 16.00 16.00
*a.-j.* 80y Any single 1.40 .55

Japan Post Mascots — A2183

Designs: a, Aichan (squirrel with pink bow). b, Male Kanchan (with heart on shorts). c, Posuton (with hands extended). d, Yuchan (squirrel with cap). e, Female Kanchan (with flower). f, Posuton (with letter). g, Posuton (with letter). h, Aichan (with pink bow), diff. i, Female Kanchan (with flower), diff. j, Posuton (with hands extended), diff. k, Yuchan (with cap), diff. l, Male Kanchan (waving).

**2003, Apr. 1** *Die Cut Perf. 13¼*

**Self-Adhesive**

**2854** A2183 Sheet of 12 16.00 16.00
*a.-f.* 50y Any single .85 .40
*g.-l.* 80y Any single 1.25 .55

Ram and Tree Batik Screen Design — A2184

**2003, Apr. 18** *Perf. 13¼*

**2855** A2184 80y multi 1.40 .40

Philately Week.

### Greetings Type of 2003

**2003 Photo.** *Perf. 13*

**2855A** A2180 80y Like No. 2851a + label —
**2855B** A2179 80y Like No. 2850d + label —
**2855D** A2179 80y Like No. 2850e + label —
**2855E** A2180 80y Like No. 2851b + label —
**2855F** A2180 80y Like No. 2851c + label —
**2855H** A2180 80y Like No. 2851e + label —
**2855I** A2179 80y Like No. 2850b + label —
**2855J** A2179 80y Like No. 2850c + label —

Issued: Nos. 2855A, 2855B, 2855D, 4/19; Nos. 2855E, 2855F, 2855H, 2855I, 2855j, 6/11. Below each stamp was a label that could be personalized. Two additional stamps were issued in this set. The editors would like to examine any examples.

### Edo Shogunate, 400th Anniv.

Screen Depicting Edo — A2185

Wall Decoration, Edo Castle — A2186

Armor of Ieyasu Tokugawa A2187

Detail from Writing Box A2188

Noh Mask and Costume — A2189

Sheet 2 — A2190

A2191

No. 2857 — Sheet 2: a, Nihonbashi, from 53 Stations of the Tokaido Road, by Hiroshige (stamp 1). b, Fireman's coat (stamp 2). c, Screen depicting Kabuki theater (stamp 3). d, Hina-matsuri fesitval doll of empress (no number). e, Hina-matsuri festival doll of emperor (stamp 4). f, Danjurou Ichikawa playing role of Goro Takenuki (stamp 5).

No. 2858 — Sheet 3: a, Stern of USS Powhatan (stamp 1). b, Bow of USS Powhatan (no number). c, Screen art depicting return of Commodore Perry's fleet to Japan (stamp 2). d, Ceramic platter for export to Europe (stamp 3). e, Portrait of a European Woman, probably by Gennai Hiraga (stamp 4). f, Perpetual clock (stamp 5).

**2003** *Perf. 13x13¼*

| | | | | |
|---|---|---|---|---|
| **2856** | | Vert. strip of 5 | 7.00 | 7.00 |
| *a.* | A2185 80y multi | | 1.40 | .55 |
| *b.* | A2186 80y multi | | 1.40 | .55 |
| *c.* | A2187 80y multi | | 1.40 | .55 |
| *d.* | A2188 80y multi | | 1.40 | .55 |
| *e.* | A2189 80y multi | | 1.40 | .55 |
| | Sheet, 2 #2856 (Sheet 1) | | 16.50 | 16.50 |
| **2857** | A2190 | Sheet of 10, #2857d-2857e, 2 each #2857a-2857c, 2857f | 16.50 | 16.50 |
| *a.-f.* | 80y Any single | | 1.40 | .55 |
| **2858** | A2191 | Sheet of 10, #2858a-2858b, 2 each #2858c-2858f | 16.50 | 16.50 |
| *a.-f.* | 80y Any single | | 1.40 | .55 |

Issued: No. 2856, 5/23; No. 2857, 6/12; No. 2858, 7/1. Sheet numbers are in center of arrows at top of sheet. Stamp numbers are in sheet margins.

ASEAN — Japan Exchange Year — A2192

No. 2859: a, Omar Ali Saifuddien Mosque, Brunei (stamp 1). b, Angkor Wat, Cambodia (stamp 2). c, Borobudur Temple, Indonesia (stamp 3). d, That Luang, Laos (stamp 4). e, Sultan Abdul Samad Building, Malaysia (stamp 5). f, Shwedagon Pagoda, Myanmar (stamp 6). g, Rice terraces, Philippines (stamp 7). h, Merlion Statue, Singapore (stamp 8). i, Wat Phra Kaeo, Thailand (stamp 9). j, Van Mieu, Viet Nam (stamp 10).

**2003, June 16 Photo.** *Perf. 13x13¼*

| | | | | |
|---|---|---|---|---|
| **2859** | A2192 | Sheet of 10 | 16.50 | 16.50 |
| *a.-j.* | 80y Any single | | 1.40 | .55 |

Letter Writing Day — A2193

Designs: No. 2860, Bear with guitar, bird. No. 2861, Monkey with letter. No. 2862, Crocodile with accordion, bird. No. 2863, Cat with camera, letter.

No. 2864: a, Hippopotamus with umbrella, flowers, birds (oval stamp). b, Parakeet with letter. c, Owl (round stamp). d, Bear with letter, bird (oval stamp). e, Elephant with flowers. f, Giraffe with letter (oval stamp). g, Rabbit with letter, flowers (semi-circular stamp). h, Lion with letter, lantern. i, Goat with letter. j, Gorilla with koala, bird and owl.

**2003, July 23 Photo.** *Perf. 13x13¼*

| | | | |
|---|---|---|---|
| **2860** | A2193 50y multi | .85 | .35 |
| **2861** | A2193 50y multi | .85 | .35 |
| **2862** | A2193 50y multi | .85 | .35 |
| **2863** | A2193 50y multi | .85 | .35 |
| *a.* | Horiz. strip of 4, #2860-2863 | 3.50 | 2.25 |
| **2864** | Sheet of 10 | 16.50 | 16.50 |
| *a.-j.* | A2193 80y Any single | 1.40 | .55 |
| *k.* | Booklet pane of 10, #2860-2863, 2 each #2864b, 2864h, 2864i | 14.00 | — |
| | Complete booklet, #2864k | 14.00 | |
| *l.* | Souvenir sheet, #2860, #2864b | 2.50 | 2.50 |

Nos. 2864a, 2864d and 2864f are 28x40mm; No. 2864c is 30mm in diameter; No. 2864g is 40x24mm.

### Intl. Letter Writing Week Type of 2000

Hiroshige paintings from 53 Stations of the Tokaido Highway: 90y, Kawasaki. 110y, Miya. 130y, Otsu.

**2003, Oct. 6** *Perf. 13¼*

| | | | |
|---|---|---|---|
| **2865** | A2119 90y multi | 1.60 | .45 |
| **2866** | A2119 110y multi | 1.90 | .55 |
| **2867** | A2119 130y multi | 2.10 | .65 |
| | *Nos. 2865-2867 (3)* | 5.60 | 1.65 |

Cultural Pioneers — A2194

Designs: No. 2868, Mokichi Saito (1882-1953), poet. No. 2869, Shibasaburo Kitasato (1853-1931), bacteriologist.

**Photo. & Engr.**

**2003, Nov. 4** *Perf. 13*

| | | | |
|---|---|---|---|
| **2868** | A2194 80y multi | 1.40 | .40 |
| **2869** | A2194 80y multi | 1.40 | .40 |

See Nos. 2907-2909.

Reversion of the Amami Islands to Japanese Control, 50th Anniv. — A2195

**2003, Nov. 7** **Photo.**

| | | | |
|---|---|---|---|
| **2870** | A2195 80y multi | 1.40 | .40 |

A2196

A2197

New Year 2004 (Year of the Monkey)

A2198 A2199

**2003, Nov. 14** *Perf. 13x13¼*

| | | | |
|---|---|---|---|
| **2871** | A2196 50y multi | .95 | .30 |
| **2872** | A2197 80y multi | 1.40 | .40 |

**Photo. & Litho.**

*Perf. 13½x13¼*

| | | | |
|---|---|---|---|
| **2873** | A2198 50y +3y multi | .95 | .40 |
| **2874** | A2199 80y +3y multi | 1.50 | .40 |
| | *Nos. 2871-2874 (4)* | 4.80 | 1.50 |

Sheets of two containing Nos. 2871-2872 were lottery prizes. Value, $3.

Happy Face — A2199a

Sky — A2199b

*Serpentine Die Cut 9¼x9*

**2003, Dec. 1** **Photo.**

**Self-Adhesive**

| | | | |
|---|---|---|---|
| **2874A** | A2199a 80y multi + label | 1.90 | 1.25 |

*Serpentine Die Cut 6½x5½*

**Stamp + Label**

**Color of Japanese Inscription**

| | | | |
|---|---|---|---|
| **2874B** | A2199b 80y blue | 1.90 | 1.25 |
| **2874C** | A2199b 80y red orange | 1.90 | 1.25 |
| **2874D** | A2199a 80y white | — | — |
| | *Nos. 2874A-2874C (3)* | 5.70 | 3.75 |

Stamps and labels are separated by a line of rouletting on Nos. 2874B-2874D. Labels could be personalized. No. 2874A was printed in sheets of 4 stamps and 4 labels that sold for 500y, and sheets of 10 stamps and 10 labels that sold for 1000y. Nos. 2874B-2874C were printed in sheets containing five of each stamp and 10 labels that sold for 1000y. No. 287D was printed in sheets of 10 and 10 labels and sold for 1000y.

Bubbles — A2199c

Bubbles — A2199d

Rose — A2199e

*Serpentine Die Cut 6*

**2004, Jan. 23** **Photo.**

**Self-Adhesive**

| | | | |
|---|---|---|---|
| **2874E** | A2199c 50y multi + label | 1.25 | 1.25 |
| **2874F** | A2199d 50y multi + label | 1.25 | 1.25 |
| **2874G** | A2199e 90y multi + label | 2.00 | 1.50 |
| | *Nos. 2874E-2874G (3)* | 4.50 | 4.00 |

Stamps and labels are separated by a line of rouletting. Labels could be personalized. Nos. 2874E-2874F were printed in sheets containing ten of each stamp and 20 labels that sold for 1200y. No. 2874G was printed in a sheet of 20 stamps and 20 labels that sold for 2000y.

### Science, Technology and Animation

Astro Boy — A2200

Bowman Doll — A2201

Hantaro Nagaoka A2202

H-II Rocket A2203

Morph 3 — A2204

Astro Boy — A2205

Astro Boy — A2206

Astro Boy — A2207

Super Jetter — A2208

Japanese Clock — A2209

Otomo — A2210

KAZ — A2211

Stratospheric Platform Airship — A2212

Super Jetter — A2213

Super Jetter — A2214

Super Jetter — A2215

**2003-2004** **Photo.** ***Perf. 13x13¼***

| | | | |
|---|---|---|---|
| **2875** | Vert. strip of 5 | 8.00 | 8.00 |
| *a.* | A2200 80y multi | 1.40 | .55 |
| *b.* | A2201 80y multi | 1.40 | .55 |
| *c.* | A2202 80y multi | 1.40 | .55 |
| *d.* | A2203 80y multi | 1.40 | .55 |
| *e.* | A2204 80y multi | 1.40 | .55 |
| | Sheet, 2 #2875 | 17.50 | 17.50 |
| **2876** | Sheet, #2875b-2875e, 2 each #2876a-2876c | 17.50 | 17.50 |
| *a.* | A2205 80y multi | 1.40 | .55 |
| *b.* | A2206 80y multi | 1.40 | .55 |
| *c.* | A2207 80y multi | 1.40 | .55 |
| **2877** | Vert. strip of 5 | 8.00 | 8.00 |
| *a.* | A2208 80y multi | 1.40 | .55 |
| *b.* | A2209 80y multi | 1.40 | .55 |
| *c.* | A2210 80y multi | 1.40 | .55 |
| *d.* | A2211 80y multi | 1.40 | .55 |
| *e.* | A2212 80y multi | 1.40 | .55 |
| | Sheet, 2 #2875 | 17.50 | 17.50 |
| **2878** | Sheet, #2877b-2877e, 2 each #2878a-2878c | 17.50 | 17.50 |
| *a.* | A2213 80y multi | 1.40 | .55 |
| *b.* | A2214 80y multi | 1.40 | .55 |
| *c.* | A2215 80y multi | 1.40 | .55 |

Issued: Nos. 2875-2876, 12/16/03; Nos. 2877-2878, 1/23/04.

### Science, Technology and Animation

Marvelous Melmo and Baby — A2216

Seishu Hanaoka (1760-1835), Surgeon — A2217

Wooden Microscope A2218

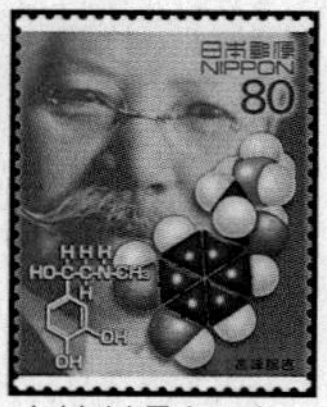

Jokichi Takamine (1854-1922), Chemist A2219

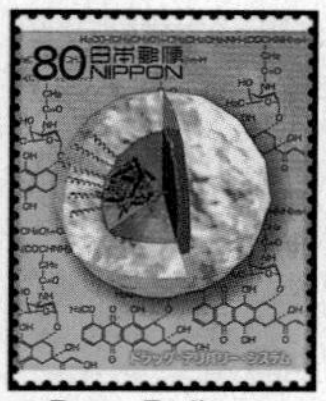

Drug Delivery System — A2220

Marvelous Melmo with Mother — A2221

Marvelous Melmo with Man — A2222

Marvelous Melmo and Others in Bottle — A2223

Science Ninja Team Gatchaman A2224

Proposed Perpetual Motion Machine of Michitaka Kume A2225

OHSUMI Satellite — A2226

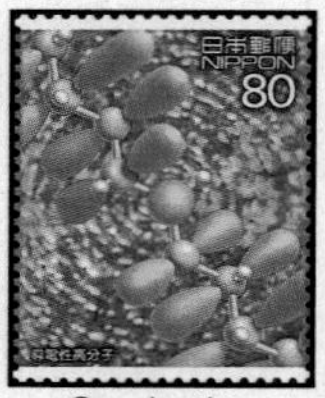

Conducting Polymer — A2227

Tissue and Organ Reproduction A2228

Science Ninja Team Gatchaman A2229

Science Ninja Team Gatchaman A2230

Science Ninja Team Gatchaman A2231

**2004** **Photo.** ***Perf. 13x13¼***

| | | | |
|---|---|---|---|
| **2879** | Vert. strip of 5 | 8.00 | 8.00 |
| *a.* | A2216 80y multi | 1.40 | .55 |
| *b.* | A2217 80y multi | 1.40 | .55 |
| *c.* | A2218 80y multi | 1.40 | .55 |
| *d.* | A2219 80y multi | 1.40 | .55 |
| *e.* | A2220 80y multi | 1.40 | .55 |
| | Sheet, 2 #2879 | 17.50 | 17.50 |
| **2880** | Sheet, #2879b-2879e, 2 each #2880a-2880c | 17.50 | 17.50 |
| *a.* | A2221 80y multi | 1.40 | .55 |
| *b.* | A2222 80y multi | 1.40 | .55 |
| *c.* | A2223 80y multi | 1.40 | .55 |
| **2881** | Vert. strip of 5 | 8.00 | 8.00 |
| *a.* | A2224 80y multi | 1.40 | .55 |
| *b.* | A2225 80y multi | 1.40 | .55 |
| *c.* | A2226 80y multi | 1.40 | .55 |
| *d.* | A2227 80y multi | 1.40 | .55 |
| *e.* | A2228 80y multi | 1.40 | .55 |
| | Sheet, 2 #2881 | 17.50 | 17.50 |
| **2882** | Sheet, #2881b-2881e, 2 each #2882a-2882c | 17.50 | 17.50 |
| *a.* | A2229 80y multi | 1.40 | .55 |
| *b.* | A2230 80y multi | 1.40 | .55 |
| *c.* | A2231 80y multi | 1.40 | .55 |

Issued: Nos. 2879-2880, 2/23/04. Nos. 2881-2882, 3/23/04.

A2232

Hello Kitty — A2233

No. 2883: a, Red, white and blue flowers under chin. b, Red flower under chin, beige background. c, No flower under chin. d, Blue and red flowers under chin. e, Red flower under chin. f, Two blue flowers under chin. g, White flowers with green leaves under chin. h, Two pink flowers under chin. i, One blue flower under chin. j, Pink, yellow and green flower under chin.

No. 2884 — Head of Kitty with: a, Cherries. b, Bow. c, Strawberries. d, Blue flower. e, Spray of flowers.

***Die Cut Perf. 13¼***

**2004, Feb. 6 Litho.**

**Self-Adhesive**

**2883** A2232 Sheet of 10 9.50
*a.-j.* 50y Any single .90 .55
**2884** A2233 Sheet of 5 8.00
*a.-e.* 80y Any single 1.40 .55

Uchu-no Sakura Gohiki-no Saru-zu, by Sosen Mori — A2234

***Perf. 12½x12¾ Syncopated***

**2004, Apr. 20 Photo.**

**2885** A2234 80y multi 1.40 .45

Philatelic Week.

Japanese Racing Association, 50th Anniv. — A2235

Designs: No. 2886, Ten Point and Tosho Boy, 22nd Armia Memorial Stakes. No. 2887, Narita Brian, 61st Tolyo Yushun.

**2004, May 28** ***Perf. 13x13¼***

**2886** 80y green & multi 1.40 .45
**2887** 80y blue & multi 1.40 .45
*a.* A2235 Horiz. pair, #2886-2887 3.00 2.25

Police Law, 50th Anniv. — A2236

**2004, June 21** ***Perf. 13***

**2888** 80y Police car 1.40 .45
**2889** 80y Police motorcycle 1.40 .45
*a.* A2236 Horiz. pair, #2888-2889 3.00 2.25

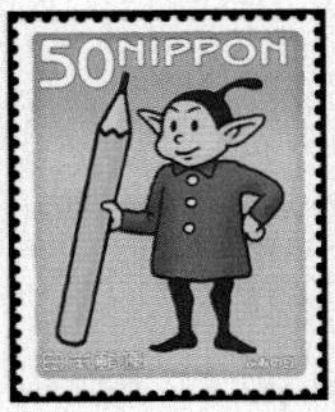


Letter Writing Day — A2237

Designs: No. 2890, Donkichi with pencil. No. 2891, Hime (woman with letter). No. 2892, Shouchan (man with ski cap). No. 2893, Owl with letter.

No. 2894: a, Dove with letter, rainbow. b, Squirrel with wings, rainbow. c, Stork (round stamp). d, Hime with wings (oval stamp). e, Donkichi with wings, letter. f, Kuriko (elf in pink) with wings. g, Megami (woman in white) (oval stamp). h, Shouchan with wings. i, Squirrel with flowers, letter. j, Rabbit (round stamp).

**2004, July 23 Photo.** ***Perf. 13x13¼***

**2890** A2237 50y multi .90 .35
**2891** A2237 50y multi .90 .35
**2892** A2237 50y multi .90 .35
**2893** A2237 50y multi .90 .35
*a.* Horiz. strip of 4, #2890-2893 4.00 2.75
**2894** Sheet of 10 16.50 16.50
*a.-j.* A2237 80y Any single 1.40 .55
*k.* Booklet pane of 10, #2890-2893, 2 each #2894b, 2894e, 2894f 14.00 —
Complete booklet, #2894k 14.00
*l.* Souvenir sheet, #2890, #2894f 2.50 2.50

Nos. 2894c, 2894j are 30mm in diameter; No. 2894d is 28x37mm; No. 2894g is 28x40mm; No. 2894i is 28x29mm.

2004 Summer Olympics, Athens — A2238

Olympic rings and: No. 2895, Olympic Flame, Olympia. No. 2896, 2004 Athens Olympics emblem.

**2004, Aug. 6** ***Perf. 13***

**2895** 80y multi 1.40 .45
**2896** 80y multi 1.40 .45
*a.* A2238 Horiz. pair, #2895-2896 3.00 2.25

**Science, Technology and Animation**

Mazinger-Z A2239

Steam Locomotive A2240

New KS Steel A2241

Shinkai 6500 Research Submarine A2242

Fuel Cell A2243

Mazinger-Z A2244

Mazinger-Z A2245

Mazinger-Z A2246

**2004, Aug. 23 Photo.** ***Perf. 13x13¼***

**2897** Vert. strip of 5 8.00 8.00
*a.* A2239 80y multi 1.40 .55
*b.* A2240 80y multi 1.40 .55
*c.* A2241 80y multi 1.40 .55
*d.* A2242 80y multi 1.40 .55
*e.* A2243 80y multi 1.40 .55
Sheet, 2 #2897 17.50 17.50
**2898** Sheet, #2897b-2897e, 2 each #2898a-2898c 17.50 17.50
*a.* A2244 80y multi 1.40 .55
*b.* A2245 80y multi 1.40 .55
*c.* A2246 80y multi 1.40 .55

**Science, Technology and Animation**

Doraemon A2247

Gennai Hiraga A2248

Mechanical Netsuke A2249

Television A2250

Optical Fiber A2251

Doraemon A2252

Doraemon A2253

Doraemon A2254

**2004, Nov. 22 Photo.** ***Perf. 13x13¼***

**2899** Vert. strip of 5 8.00 8.00
*a.* A2247 80y multi 1.40 .55
*b.* A2248 80y multi 1.40 .55
*c.* A2249 80y multi 1.40 .55
*d.* A2250 80y multi 1.40 .55
*e.* A2251 80y multi 1.40 .55
Sheet, 2, #2899 17.50 17.50
**2900** Sheet, #2899b-2899e, 2 each #2900a-2900c 17.50 17.50
*a.* A2252 80y multi 1.40 .55
*b.* A2253 80y multi 1.40 .55
*c.* A2254 80y multi 1.40 .55

Japan — United States Relationships, 150th Anniv. — A2255

Designs: No. 2901, Mt. Fuji, by Frederick Harris. No. 2902, Cafe, by Yasuo Kuniyoshi.

**2004, Sept. 22** ***Perf. 13***

**2901** 80y multi 1.40 .50
**2902** 80y multi 1.40 .50
*a.* A2255 Horiz. pair, #2901-2902 3.00 2.25

World Medical Association General Assembly, Tokyo — A2256

**2004, Oct. 6** ***Perf. 12¾x13***

**2903** A2256 80y multi 1.40 .40

**International Letter Writing Week Type of 2000**

Hiroshige paintings from 53 Stations of the Tokaido Highway: 90y, Hiratsuka. 110y, Yokkaichi. 130y, Tsuchiyama.

**2004, Oct. 8** ***Perf. 13¼***

**2904** A2119 90y multi 1.60 .45
**2905** A2119 110y multi 1.90 .55
**2906** A2119 130y multi 2.10 .65
*Nos. 2904-2906 (3)* 5.60 1.65

**Cultural Pioneers Type of 2003**

Designs: No. 2907, Lafcadio Hearn (1850-1904), writer. No. 2908, Isamu Noguchi (1904-88), sculptor. No. 2909, Masao Koga (1904-78), composer.

**Litho. & Engr.**

**2004, Nov. 4** ***Perf. 12¾x13***

**2907** A2194 80y multi 1.40 .40
**2908** A2194 80y multi 1.40 .40
**2909** A2194 80y multi 1.40 .40
*Nos. 2907-2909 (3)* 4.20 1.20

A2257

A2258

New Year 2005 (Year of the Cock)
A2259 A2260

**2004, Nov. 15 Photo.** ***Perf. 13x13¼***

| | | | | |
|---|---|---|---|---|
| **2910** | A2257 | 50y multi | .95 | .30 |
| **2911** | A2258 | 80y multi | 1.40 | .40 |

**Photo. & Typo.**
***Perf. 13½x13¼***

| | | | | |
|---|---|---|---|---|
| **2912** | A2259 | 50y +3y multi | 1.00 | .40 |
| **2913** | A2260 | 80y +3y multi | 1.50 | .40 |
| | | *Nos. 2910-2913 (4)* | 4.85 | 1.50 |

Sheets of two containing Nos. 2910-2911 were lottery prizes. Value, $3.

Miniature Sheet

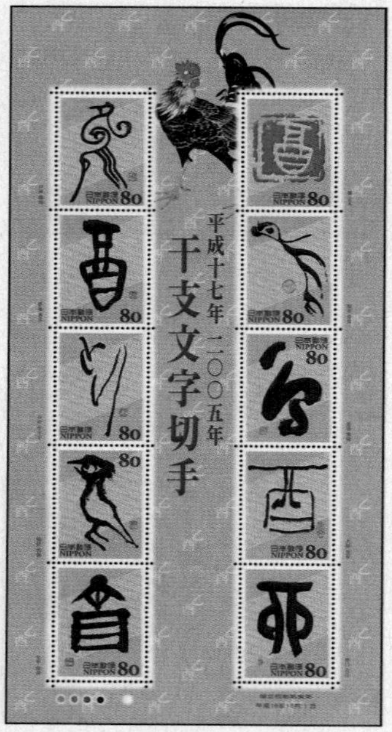


Eto Calligraphy — A2261

Word "tori" in: a, Tensho style. b, Kinbun style (red). c, Kinbun style (black). d, Pictographic tensho style. e, Kana style. f, Sousho style. g, Kobun style (denomination at UR). h, Reisho style. i, Koukotsumoji style. j, Kobun style (denomination at LR).

**Photo. & Embossed**

**2004, Dec. 1** ***Perf. 13***

| | | | | |
|---|---|---|---|---|
| **2914** | A2261 | Sheet of 10 | 17.50 | 17.50 |
| *a.-j.* | | 80y Any single | 1.40 | .55 |

"Japan Post" — A2261a

A2261b

A2261c

Rose — A2261d

A2261e

A2261f

***Die Cut Perf. 12½***

**2004, Dec. 15 Photo.**

**Stamp + Label**

**Denomination Color**

| | | | | | |
|---|---|---|---|---|---|
| **2914K** | A2261a | 80y rose | 2.00 | 1.25 |
| **2914L** | A2261a | 80y blue | 2.00 | 1.25 |
| **2914M** | A2261b | 80y lilac | 2.00 | 2.00 |
| **2914N** | A2261c | 80y green | 2.00 | 2.00 |
| **2914O** | A2261d | 80y rose | 2.00 | 2.00 |
| **2914P** | A2261e | 80y gray | 2.00 | 2.00 |
| **2914Q** | A2261f | 80y rose | 2.00 | 2.00 |
| | *Nos. 2914K-2914Q (7)* | | 14.00 | 12.50 |

Stamps and labels are separated by a line of rouletting. Labels could be personalized. Nos. 2914K-2914L were printed in sheets containing five of each stamp and 10 labels that sold for 1000y. Nos. 2914M-2914Q were printed in sheets of two of each stamp and 10 labels that sold for 1000y.

World Conference on Disaster Reduction
A2262

**2005, Jan. 11 Photo.** ***Perf. 13***

| | | | | |
|---|---|---|---|---|
| **2915** | A2262 | 80y multi | 1.40 | .40 |

Opening of Chubu Natl. Airport — A2263

**2005, Feb. 1**

| | | | | |
|---|---|---|---|---|
| **2916** | A2263 | 80y multi | 1.40 | .40 |

**Science, Technology and Animation**

Time Bokan — A2264

Circular Loom — A2265

Bullet Train — A2266

Micromachines A2267

International Space Station — A2268

Time Bokan — A2269

Time Bokan — A2270

Time Bokan — A2271

**2005, Mar. 23 Photo.** ***Perf. 13x13¼***

| | | | |
|---|---|---|---|
| **2917** | Vert. strip of 5 | 8.00 | 8.00 |
| *a.* | A2264 80y multi | 1.40 | .55 |
| *b.* | A2265 80y multi | 1.40 | .55 |
| *c.* | A2266 80y multi | 1.40 | .55 |
| *d.* | A2267 80y multi | 1.40 | .55 |
| *e.* | A2268 80y multi | 1.40 | .55 |
| | Sheet, 2 #2917 | 17.50 | 17.50 |
| **2918** | Sheet, #2917b-2917e, 2 each #2918a-2918c | 17.50 | 17.50 |
| *a.* | A2269 80y multi | 1.40 | .55 |
| *b.* | A2270 80y multi | 1.40 | .55 |
| *c.* | A2271 80y multi | 1.40 | .55 |

**Pokémon**

Gonbe — A2272

Rayquaza A2273

Mew — A2274

Rizadon — A2275

Pikachu — A2276

**2005, June 23 Litho. *Perf. 13x13¼***

| | | | |
|---|---|---|---|
| **2919** | Vert. strip of 5 | 6.50 | 6.50 |
| *a.* | A2272 50y multi | .90 | .55 |
| *b.* | A2273 50y multi | .90 | .55 |
| *c.* | A2274 80y multi | 1.40 | .55 |
| *d.* | A2275 80y multi | 1.40 | .55 |
| *e.* | A2276 80y multi | 1.40 | .55 |
| | Sheet, 2 #2919 | 14.00 | 14.00 |

**Self-Adhesive Booklet Stamps**

| | | | |
|---|---|---|---|
| **2919F** | A2272 50y multi | 1.25 | 1.00 |
| *i.* | Booklet pane of 2 | 3.00 | 3.00 |
| **2919G** | A2276 80y multi | 1.75 | 1.25 |
| **2919H** | A2274 80y multi | 1.75 | 1.25 |
| *j.* | Booklet pane, #2919G-2919H | 4.75 | 4.75 |
| | Complete booklet, #2919Fi, 2919Hj + 8 postal cards | 19.00 | |

Complete booklet sold for 1000y.

**Mobile Suit Gundam**

Freedom Gundam and Kira Yamato — A2277

Justice Gundam and Athrun Zala — A2278

Gundam W — A2279

Hiiro — A2280

Kamille Bidan — A2281

Z Gundam A2282

Zaku — A2283

Char Aznable — A2284

Amuro Ray — A2285

Gundam A2286

**2005, Aug. 1**

| | | | |
|---|---|---|---|
| **2920** | Sheet of 10 | 17.50 | 17.50 |
| *a.* | A2277 50y multi | .90 | .55 |
| *b.* | A2278 50y multi | .90 | .55 |
| *c.* | A2279 50y multi | .90 | .55 |
| *d.* | A2280 50y multi | .90 | .55 |
| *e.* | A2281 80y multi | 1.40 | .55 |
| *f.* | A2282 80y multi | 1.40 | .55 |
| *g.* | A2283 80y multi | 1.40 | .55 |
| *h.* | A2284 80y multi | 1.40 | .55 |
| *i.* | A2285 80y multi | 1.40 | .55 |
| *j.* | A2286 80y multi | 1.40 | .55 |

Expo 2005, Aichi — A2287

Designs: No. 2921, Earth and mammoth skull and tusks. No. 2922, Earth and mammoth.

**2005, Mar. 25 Photo. *Perf. 13x13¼***

| | | | |
|---|---|---|---|
| **2921** | 80y multi | 1.40 | .45 |
| **2922** | 80y multi | 1.40 | .45 |
| *a.* | A2287 Horiz. pair, #2921-2922 | 3.00 | 2.25 |

Daikei-shiyu-zu, by Jakuchu Itou — A2288

***Perf. 12½x12¾ Syncopated***

**2005, Apr. 20**

| | | | |
|---|---|---|---|
| **2923** | A2288 80y multi | 1.40 | .45 |

Philately Week.

Rotary International, Cent. — A2289

**2005, Apr. 28 Litho. *Perf. 12¾x13***

| | | | |
|---|---|---|---|
| **2924** | A2289 80y multi | 1.40 | .40 |

Hodakadake A2290

Hakusan-ichige A2291

Yarigatake A2292

Miyama-odamaki A2293

**2005, May 2 *Perf. 13¼***

| | | | |
|---|---|---|---|
| **2925** | A2290 50y multi | .90 | .40 |
| **2926** | A2291 50y multi | .90 | .40 |
| **2927** | A2292 50y multi | .90 | .40 |
| **2928** | A2293 50y multi | .90 | .40 |
| *a.* | Horiz. strip of 4, #2925-2928 | 5.00 | 5.00 |

Japanese Alpine Club, cent.

Letter Writing Day — A2294

Designs: No. 2929, Owl on branch with envelope. No. 2930, Kuriko with letter. No. 2931, Squirrel with acorn. No. 2932, Rabbit and flowers.

No. 2933: a, Pigeon with pink letter. b, Donkichi in tree (round stamp). c, Castle and rainbow (oval stamp). d, Shochan with blue ski cap. e, Rabbit with pink letter (round stamp). f, Kuriko with flute on horse. g, Hime with bows in hair. h, Squirrel. i, Fox with letter (round stamp). j, Violets (oval stamp).

**2005, July 22 Photo. *Perf. 13x13¼***

| | | | |
|---|---|---|---|
| **2929** | A2294 50y multi | .90 | .35 |
| **2930** | A2294 50y multi | .90 | .35 |
| **2931** | A2294 50y multi | .90 | .35 |
| **2932** | A2294 50y multi | .90 | .35 |
| *a.* | Horiz. strip of 4, #2929-2932 | 5.00 | 2.75 |
| **2933** | Sheet of 10 | 16.50 | 16.50 |
| *a.-j.* | A2294 80y Any single | 1.40 | .55 |
| *k.* | Booklet pane of 10, #2929-2932, 2 each #2933d, 2933f, 2933g | 14.00 | — |
| | Complete booklet, #2933k | 14.00 | |
| *l.* | Souvenir sheet, #2932, #2933d | 2.50 | 2.50 |

Nos. 2933a, 2933h are 28x29mm, Nos. 2933b, 2933e, 2933i are 30mm in diameter; No. 2933c, 2933j are 28x40mm.

Poetry Collections — A2295

Poets: No. 2934, Ono no Komachi. No. 2935, Fujiwara no Teika.

**2005, Sept. 1 Litho. *Perf. 12¾x13***

| | | | |
|---|---|---|---|
| **2934** | 80y multi | 1.40 | .45 |
| **2935** | 80y multi | 1.40 | .45 |
| *a.* | A2295 Horiz. pair, #2934-2935 | 3.00 | 2.25 |

Kokin Wakashu, 1100th anniv. (No. 2934), Shinkokin Wakashu, 800th anniv. (No. 2935).

Intl Astronautics Congress, Fukuoka — A2296

Designs: No. 2936, Himawari-6 satellite. No. 2937, H-IIA rocket launch.

**2005, Oct. 3**

| | | | |
|---|---|---|---|
| **2936** | 80y multi | 1.40 | .55 |
| **2937** | 80y multi | 1.40 | .55 |
| *a.* | A2296 Horiz. pair, #2934-2935 | 3.00 | 2.25 |

**Intl. Letter Writing Week Type of 2000**

Hiroshige paintings from 53 Stations of the Tokaido Highway: 90y, Mariko. 110y, Minakuchi. 130y, Shinagawa.

**2005, Oct. 7 Photo. *Perf. 13¼***

| | | | |
|---|---|---|---|
| **2938** | A2119 90y multi | 1.40 | .45 |
| **2939** | A2119 110y multi | 1.60 | .55 |
| **2940** | A2119 130y multi | 2.10 | .65 |
| | *Nos. 2938-2940 (3)* | 5.10 | 1.65 |

Souvenir Sheets

A2297

Greetings Stamps — A2298

No. 2941: a, Cyclamen. b, Elf and flower. c, Bear and bird. d, Owl, gorilla playing banjo. e, Snowman.

No. 2942: a, Santa Claus. b, Poinsettias and candle. c, Angel with gift. d, Hamster and strawberries. e, Owl, cat playing drums.

**Litho. With Foil Application**

***Serpentine Die Cut 13¼***

**2005, Oct. 21** **Self-Adhesive**

**2941** A2297 Sheet of 5 5.50
*a.-e.* 50y Any single .90 .90

***Serpentine Die Cut 13¼x13½***

**2942** A2298 Sheet of 5 8.50
*a.-e.* 80y Any single 1.40 .90

A2299

A2300

New Year 2006 (Year of the Dog)
A2301 A2302

**2005, Nov. 15** **Photo.** ***Perf. 13x13¼***

**2943** A2299 50y multi .95 .30
**2944** A2300 80y multi 1.40 .40

**Photo. & Typo.**

***Perf. 13¼***

**2945** A2301 50y +3y multi 1.00 .40
**2946** A2302 80y +3y multi 1.50 .40
*Nos. 2943-2946 (4)* 4.85 1.50

Sheets of two containing Nos. 2943-2944 were lottery prizes. Value, $3.

Miniature Sheet

Germany — Japan Exchange Year — A2303

No. 2947: a, Ludwig van Beethoven. b, Benz automobile. c, Meissen porcelain figurine of Japanese man playing drum. d, Meissen porcelain figurine of female musician. e, Meissen porcelain figurine of woman on circus horse. f, Meissen porcelain figurine of a harlequin.

**2005, Dec. 1** **Photo.** ***Perf. 13***

**2947** A2303 Sheet of 10, #a-b, 2 each #c-f 17.50 17.50
*a.-f.* 80y Any single 1.40 .55

Miniature Sheet

Eto Calligraphy — A2304

Word "inu" in: a, Tensho style (connected lines). b, Kinbun style (on brown red panel). c, Pictograph (denomination at UL). d, Phonetic letters (2 lines unconnected, denomination at LR). e, Tensho style (2 red chops). f, Tensho style (blue half-circle). g, Symbolic characters (red). h, Semi-cursive style (red chop at L, denomination at LL). i, Semi-cursive style (oval chop in red at L). j, Koukotsumoji style (denomination at L, red chop at R).

**Photo. & Embossed**

**2005, Dec. 1** ***Perf. 13x13¼***

**2948** A2304 Sheet of 10 17.50 17.50
*a.-j.* 80y Any single 1.40 .55

**Animation**

Galaxy Express 999 — A2305

No. 2949: a, Tetsuro and Galaxy Express 999 in flight. b, Matael and passenger cars. c, Claire holding book. d, The Conductor. e, Freija and Matael. f, Tetsuro and Moriki Yutaka. g, Emeraldas and Count Mecha. h, Herlock. i, Matael and galaxy. j, Galaxy Express 999.

**2006, Feb. 1** **Litho.** ***Perf. 13x13¼***

**2949** A2305 Sheet of 10 17.50 17.50
*a.-j.* 80y Any single 1.40 .55

Detective Conan — A2306

No. 2950: a, Conan in green jacket. b, Conan wearing glasses, with woman in light blue jacket. c, With Shinichi, scratching chins. d, Ran holding letter. e, Dr. Agasa, Ayumi, front of car. f, Mitsuhiko, Genta, rear of car. g, Haibara Ai. h, Conan with backpack. i, Mysterious Thief Kid. j, Shinichi and Conan, city in background.

**2006, Apr. 3** **Litho.** ***Perf. 13x13¼***

**2950** A2306 Sheet of 10 17.50 17.50
*a.-j.* 80y Any single 1.40 .55

International Exchanges and Friendships A2307

Designs: No. 2951, Rabbit and flowers. No. 2952, Children kissing. No. 2953, Bears and caught fish. No. 2954, Children's drawing of two animals. No. 2955, Chick, cat, dog, rabbit, squirrel and rocket.

**2006, Mar. 1** **Photo.** ***Perf. 13***

**2951** A2307 80y multi 1.40 .55
**2952** A2307 80y multi 1.40 .55
**2953** A2307 80y multi 1.40 .55
**2954** A2307 80y multi 1.40 .55
**2955** A2307 80y multi 1.40 .55
*a.* Vert. strip of 5, #2951-2955 8.50 5.00
Sheet, 2 each #2951-2955 17.50 17.50

Morning Glories and Puppies, Door Painting by Okyu Maruyama — A2308

Designs: No. 2956, Morning glories. No. 2957, Puppies.

***Perf. 13½x13 Syncopated***

**2006, Apr. 20** **Photo.**

**2956** 80y multi 1.40 .55
**2957** 80y multi 1.40 .55
*a.* A2308 Horiz. pair, #2956-2957 5.00 3.00

Philately Week.

Miniature Sheet

Australia-Japan Year of Exchange — A2309

No. 2958: a, Australian flag, Ayers Rock. b, Kangaroo and Ayers Rock. c, Sydney Opera House. d, Australian flag and Sydney Opera House. e, Fish of Great Barrier Reef. f, Heart Reef. g, Golden wattle flowers. h, Bottlebrush flowers. i, Koalas. j, Kookaburra.

**2006, May 23** **Photo.** ***Perf. 13***

**2958** A2309 Sheet of 10 17.50 17.50
*a.-j.* 80y Any single 1.40 .55

Miniature Sheet

Sacred Sites and Pilgrimage Routes of the Kii Mountains World Heritage Site — A2310

No. 2959: a, Kumano Hongu-Taisha Shrine Building 3 (brown roof, part of stairs seen at bottom). b, Kumano Hongu-Taisha Shrine Building 4 (brown roof, full set of stairs at LR). c, Great Waterfall of Nachi. d, Overhead view of Kumano Nachi-Taisha Shrine (denomination at LL). e, Nachi Fire Festival. f, Seigantoji Temple (dark blue roof). g, Kongobuji Temple (blue green roof). h, Wooden Kongara-Doji-Ryuzo (statue, denomination at UL). i, Kinpusenji Temple (gray roof). j, Wooden Zao-Gongen-Ryuzo (statue, denomination at LL).

**2006, June 23** *Perf. 13x13¼*

| | | | | |
|---|---|---|---|---|
| **2959** | A2310 | Sheet of 10 | 17.50 | 17.50 |
| *a.-j.* | | 80y Any single | 1.40 | .55 |

Miniature Sheets

A2311

Greetings Stamps — A2312

No. 2960: a, Fairy and flower. b, Church bell. c, Flower bouquet and ribbons. d, Dolphin. e, Hibiscus and hummingbird.

No. 2961: a, Pink cattleya orchid. b, Fairy, flowers and trees. c, Flower and oranges. d, Parrot and flowers. e, Fairy with pail and orange flowers.

**Litho. With Foil Application**

***Serpentine Die Cut 13¼***

**2006, June 30** **Self-Adhesive**

| | | | | |
|---|---|---|---|---|
| **2960** | A2311 | Sheet of 5 | 6.00 | |
| *a.-e.* | | 50y Any single | .90 | .80 |

***Serpentine Die Cut 13½***

| | | | | |
|---|---|---|---|---|
| **2961** | A2312 | Sheet of 5 | 9.00 | |
| *a.-e.* | | 80y Any single | 1.40 | 1.00 |

No. 2960 sold for 300y; No. 2961 for 500y.

Taifu Iseno, Poet — A2313

Sadaijin Gotokudaijino, Poet — A2314

Mitsune Ooshikochino, Poet — A2315

Akahito Yamabeno, Poet — A2316

Naishi Suono, Poet — A2317

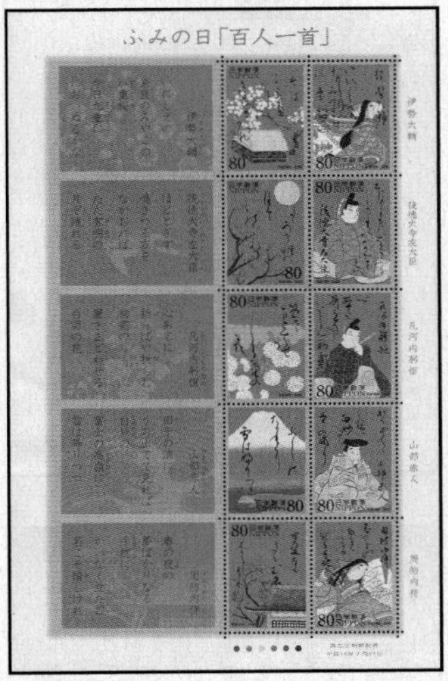


Poets and Poetry — A2318

No. 2963: a, Double Cherry Blossoms, by Yasuko Koyama. b, Iseno and poetry. c, Pale Morning Moon, by Keiso Mitsuoka. d, Gotokudaijino and poetry. e, White Chrysanthemum, by Shiko Miyazaki. f, Ooshikochino and poetry. g, Mt. Fuji, by Eiko Matsumoto. h, Yamabeno and poetry. i, Spring Night, by Soshu Miyake. j, Suono and poetry.

**2006, July 21** **Photo.** ***Perf. 13¼***

| | | | | |
|---|---|---|---|---|
| **2962** | | Vert. strip of 5 | 6.00 | 4.00 |
| *a.* | A2313 50y multi | | .90 | .45 |
| *b.* | A2314 50y multi | | .90 | .45 |
| *c.* | A2315 50y multi | | .90 | .45 |
| *d.* | A2316 50y multi | | .90 | .45 |
| *e.* | A2317 50y multi | | .90 | .45 |
| | Sheet, 2 #2962 | | 13.00 | 13.00 |

***Perf. 13***

| | | | | |
|---|---|---|---|---|
| **2963** | A2318 | Sheet of 10 | 16.00 | 16.00 |
| *a.-j.* | | 80y Any single | 1.60 | 1.00 |

Letter Writing Day.

Horizontal Lines and Colored Circles — A2318a

***Die Cut Perf. 13¼***

**2006, Sept. 1** **Litho.**

**Self-Adhesive**

| | | | | |
|---|---|---|---|---|
| **2963K** | A2318a | 80y multi | 2.50 | 2.50 |

Printed in sheets of 10 that sold for 1000y. The image portion could be personalized. The image shown is a generic image.

Blue Flowers — A2318b

Pink Flowers — A2318c

***Die Cut Perf. 13¼***

**2006, Sept. 1** **Litho.**

**Self-Adhesive**

| | | | | |
|---|---|---|---|---|
| **2963L** | A2318b | 80y multi | 2.50 | 2.50 |
| **2963M** | A2318c | 80y multi | 2.50 | 2.50 |

Nos. 2963L-2963M were printed in sheets of 10, containing five of each stamp, that sold for 1000y. The image portions could be personalized. The images shown are generic images.

Accession to the United Nations, 50th Anniv. — A2319

Paintings by Toshiro Sawanuki: 90y, Glorious World To Come. 110y, Eternity.

**2006, Sept. 29** **Litho.** ***Perf. 13¾x14***

| | | | | |
|---|---|---|---|---|
| **2964** | A2319 | 90y multi | 1.50 | .60 |
| **2965** | A2319 | 110y multi | 1.90 | .90 |

Miniature Sheet

Greetings — A2320

No. 2966: a, Mokara Lion's Gold orchid. b, Renanthera Singaporean orchid. c, Vanda Miss Joaquim orchid. d, Vanda Mimi Palmer orchid. e, Hollyhocks and Egret, by Hoitsu Sakai, horiz. f, Irises and Moorhens, by Sakai, horiz.

**Litho. With Foil Application**

**2006, Oct. 3** ***Die Cut Perf. 13½x13¾***

**Self-Adhesive**

| | | | | |
|---|---|---|---|---|
| **2966** | A2320 | Sheet of 6 | 10.00 | *10.00* |
| *a.-b.* | | 50y Either single | .90 | .90 |
| *c.-d.* | | 80y Either single | 1.40 | .90 |
| *e.* | | 90y multi | 1.50 | .90 |
| *f.* | | 110y multi | 1.90 | .90 |

Roulettes separate adjacent 50y and 80y stamps. No. 2966 sold for 500y. See Singapore Nos. 1225-1231.

Miniature Sheets

A2321

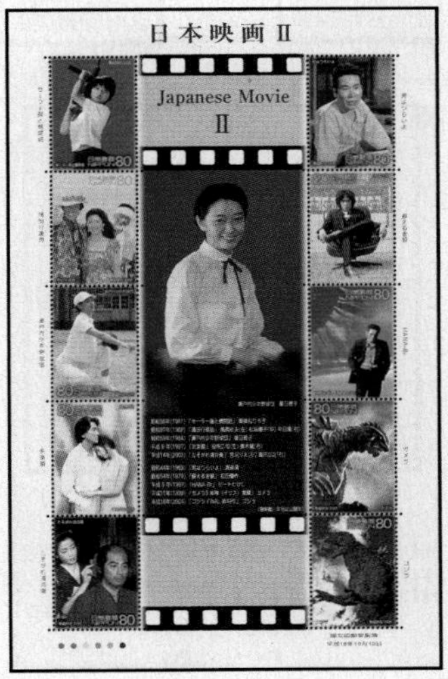


Scenes From Japanese Movies — A2322

No. 2967: a, Tange Sazen (scarred samurai, green). b, Carmen Kokyo-Ni-Kaeru (women waving, lilac). c, Ugetsu Monogatari (man and woman, maroon). d, Tokyo Monogatari (man and woman, brown). e, Shichinin-No-Samurai (helmeted samurai, deep green). f, Hawaii-No-Yoru (man and woman, olive green). g, Nemuri Kyoshiro (samurai, blue green). h, Guitar-Wo-Motta-Wataridori (man with guitar, blue). i, Miyamoto Musashi (swordsman, blue gray). j, Cupola-No-Aru-Machi (girl, brown).

No. 2968: a, Sailor-Fuku-To-Kikanju (woman with gun). b, Otoko-Ha-Tsuraiyo (man in light blue kimono). c, Kamata Koshin Kyoku (Three people). d, Yomigaeru Kinro (man in chair). e, Setouchi-Shonen-Yakyu-Dan (woman with baseball glove). f, HANA-BI (man standing). g, Shitsurakuen (Woman hugging man). h, Gamera (monster, denomination at UL). i, Tasogare Seibei (woman grooming man). j, Godzilla (monster, denomination at UR).

**2006, Oct. 10** **Photo.** ***Perf. 13***

| | | | | |
|---|---|---|---|---|
| **2967** | A2321 | Sheet of 10 | 17.50 | 17.50 |
| *a.-j.* | | 80y Any single | 1.40 | .55 |
| **2968** | A2322 | Sheet of 10 | 17.50 | 17.50 |
| *a.-j.* | | 80y Any single | 1.40 | .55 |

Ikebana International Ninth World Convention — A2323

**2006, Oct. 23 Litho. *Perf. 13x13¼***

**Background Colors**

| | | | | |
|---|---|---|---|---|
| **2969** | | 80y grn & lt grn | 1.40 | .55 |
| **2970** | | 80y red & yel | 1.40 | .55 |
| | *a.* | A2323 Horiz. pair, #2969-2970 | 3.00 | 2.00 |

A2324

A2325

New Year 2007 (Year of the Pig)

A2326 A2327

**2006, Nov. 1 Photo. *Perf. 13x13¼***

| | | | | |
|---|---|---|---|---|
| **2971** | A2324 | 50y multi | .95 | .30 |
| **2972** | A2325 | 80y multi | 1.40 | .40 |

**Photo. & Typo.**

***Perf. 13¼***

| | | | | |
|---|---|---|---|---|
| **2973** | A2326 | 50y +3y multi | 1.00 | .40 |
| **2974** | A2327 | 80y +3y multi | 1.60 | .40 |
| | | *Nos. 2971-2974 (4)* | 4.95 | 1.50 |

Sheets of two containing Nos. 2971-2972 were lottery prizes. Value, $3.

New Year Greetings — A2327a

**Inscribed "'07 New Year"**

**Stamp + Label**

**Panel Color**

**2006, Nov. 1 Photo. *Perf. 13¼***

| | | | | |
|---|---|---|---|---|
| **2974A** | A2327a | 50y blue | 1.25 | .75 |
| **2974B** | A2327a | 50y red violet | 1.25 | .75 |
| *c.* | | Pair, #2974A-2974B + 2 labels | 3.50 | 3.50 |

Labels could be personalized.

See Nos. 3010P-3010Q, 3074-3075.

Miniature Sheets

A2328

Greetings Stamps — A2329

No. 2975: a, Squirrel in mug. b, Bell with flowers. c, Clown with flower. d, Skating polar bear. e, Bear in Santa Claus suit, guitar, birds.

No. 2976: a, Cat in Santa Claus suit ringing bell. b, Fairy and cyclamen. c, Snowman with gift. d, Reindeer and star. e, Floral wreath.

**Litho. with Foil Application**

***Die Cut Perf. 13½x13¼***

**2006, Nov. 24 Self-Adhesive**

| | | | | |
|---|---|---|---|---|
| **2975** | A2328 | Sheet of 5 | 6.00 | |
| *a.-e.* | | 50y Any single | .90 | .90 |

***Die Cut Perf. 13***

| | | | | |
|---|---|---|---|---|
| **2976** | A2329 | Sheet of 5 | 9.00 | |
| *a.-e.* | | 80y Any single | 1.40 | .90 |

No. 2975 sold for 300y; No. 2976 for 500y.

Miniature Sheet

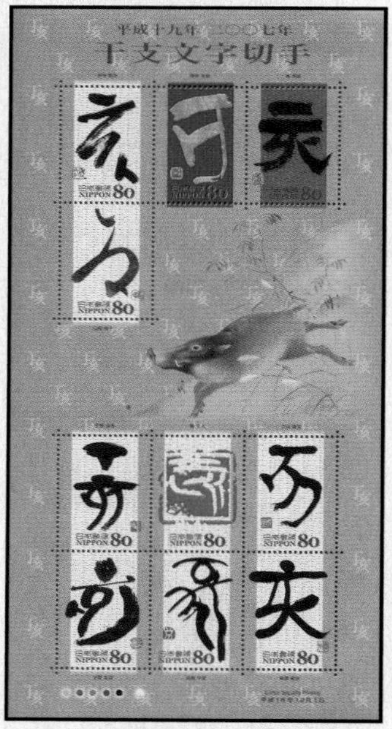


Eto Calligraphy — A2330

No. 2977: a, Semicursive style (white background, red chop at lower left). b, Kinbun style (blue background). c, Reisho style (red background). d, Japanese cursive syllabary (white background, red chop at lower right, character with small arc at top). e, Kinbun style (white background, red chop at lower right, character with funnel-shaped line at top). f, Kinbun style (red character). g, Kinbun style (white background, red chop at lower left, character with flat line at top. h, Kinbun style (white background. red chop at lower right, character with large blotch at top). i, Tensho style (white background, red chop at lower left, character with long curved arc and circle at top) j, Reisho style (white background, red chop at lower right, character with dot and straight line at top).

**Litho. & Embossed**

**2006, Dec. 1 *Perf. 13x13¼***

| | | | | |
|---|---|---|---|---|
| **2977** | A2330 | Sheet of 10 | 17.50 | 17.50 |
| *a.-j.* | | 80y Any single | 1.40 | .55 |

Miniature Sheet

A2331

Japanese Antarctic Research Expeditions, 50th Anniv. — A2332

No. 2978: a, Observation ship Fuji. b, Spotter plane. c, Adult emperor penguin and chick. d, Adult emperor penguins and five chicks. e, Observation ship Soya and Adelie penguins. f, Adult Adelie penguins and chick. g, Dog, Jiro, in snow, dog team. h, Dog, Taro, standing, dog sled. i, Scientist, observation ship Shirase. j, Snowmobile with cabin.

No. 2979: a, Snowmobile with cabin (26x28mm). b, Spotter plane (28mm diameter). c, Soya and dog sled (34x26mm). d, Weddell seal (28x23mm ellipse). e, Head of emperor penguin (26x37mm oval). f, Two Adelie penguins (26x28mm). g, Dog, Taro, standing with mouth open (28mm diameter). h, Emperor penguin chicks (28mm diameter). i, Adult emperor penguin and chick (26x28mm). j, Dog, Jiro, in snow (26x37mm oval).

**2007, Jan. 23 Litho. *Perf. 13***

| | | | | |
|---|---|---|---|---|
| **2978** | A2331 | Sheet of 10 | 16.50 | 16.50 |
| *a.-j.* | | 80y Any single | 1.40 | .40 |

**Self-Adhesive**

***Die Cut Perf. 13¾x13½***

| | | | | |
|---|---|---|---|---|
| **2979** | A2332 | Sheet of 10 | 20.00 | |
| *a.-j.* | | 80y Any single | 1.40 | .55 |

**Animation**

Miniature Sheet

Neon Genesis Evangelion — A2333

No. 2980: a, Evangelion Unit 01. b, Shinji Ikari. c, Rei Ayanami. d, Evangelion Unit 00. e, Soryu Asuka Langley. f, Evangelion Unit 02. g, Rei Ayanami and Soryu Asuka Langley. h, Misato Katsuragi. i, Kawora Nagisa. j, Sachiel, the third angel.

**2007, Feb. 23 *Perf. 13x13¼***

| | | | | |
|---|---|---|---|---|
| **2980** | A2333 | Sheet of 10 | 16.50 | 16.50 |
| *a.-j.* | | 80y Any single | 1.40 | .55 |

**Animation**

Miniature Sheet

Future Boy Conan — A2334

No. 2981: a, Conan (with name). b, Lana (with name). c, Lana (without name). d, Conan (without name). e, Monsley and airplane. f, Lepka. g, Jimsy and Umaso. h, Dyce on running robot. i, Dr. Lao and hovering craft. j, Grandpa.

**2007, June 22 Litho. *Perf. 13x13¼***

| | | | | |
|---|---|---|---|---|
| **2981** | A2334 | Sheet of 10 | 16.50 | 16.50 |
| *a.-j.* | | 80y Any single | 1.40 | .55 |

**World Heritage Sites**
Miniature Sheet

Sacred Sites and Pilgrimage Routes of the Kii Mountains World Heritage Site — A2335

No. 2982: a, Yoshino Mikumari Shrine, cherry blossoms at left. b, Pictoral and rope decoration at Yoshino Mikumari shrine. c, Omine-Okugake-Michi trail. d, Kumano Hayatama-Taisha Shrine (black-roofed building with red trim). e, Kumano Hayatama-Taisha Shrine, diff. f, Wooden icon of Kumano-Fusumino-Okami-Zazo. g, Cherry trees in bloom at Kumano Sankei-Michi Nakahechi. h, Stone sculpture of Emperor Kazan riding ox and horse. i, Kongo-Sanmaiin Temple. j, Steps to Kong-Sanmaiin Temple.

**2007, Mar. 23 Photo.** ***Perf. 13x13¼***

| | | | | |
|---|---|---|---|---|
| **2982** | A2335 | Sheet of 10 | 16.50 | 16.50 |
| *a.-j.* | | 80y Any single | 1.40 | .55 |

**World Heritage Sites**
Miniature Sheet

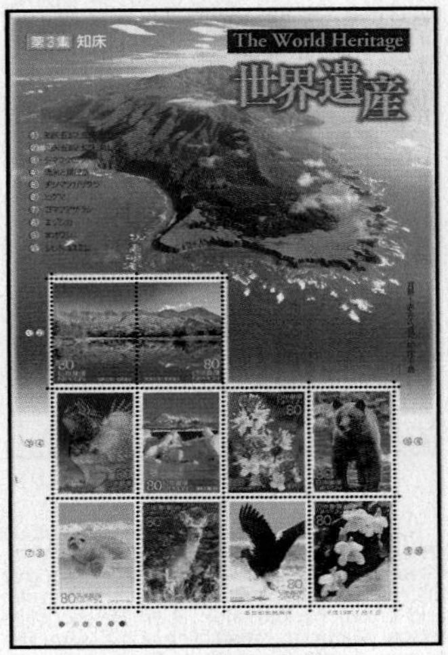


Shiretoko World Heritage Site — A2336

No. 2983: a, Lake and mountain, cloudless sky. b, Lake and mountain, cloud in sky. c, Blakiston's fish owl. d, Sea ice, Mt. Rausu. e, Cherry blossoms. f, Brown bear. g, Harbor seal. h, Ezo deer. i, Sea eagle. j, Shiretoko violets (white and yellow flowers).

**2007, July 6 Photo.** ***Perf. 13x13¼***

| | | | | |
|---|---|---|---|---|
| **2983** | A2336 | Sheet of 10 | 16.50 | 16.50 |
| *a.-j.* | | 80y Any single | 1.40 | .55 |

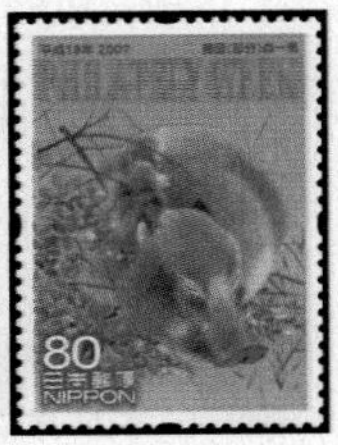

Sleeping Boar, by Ippo Mori — A2337

Boar Loping Across Fields, by Mori — A2338

Sparrow, by Mori — A2339

Cherry Blossoms, by Mori — A2340

Bird Flock, by Mori — A2341

Great Tits Sitting In a Japanese Bush Clover, by Mori — A2342

***Perf. 13¼x13 Syncopated***

**2007, Apr. 20 Photo.**

| | | | | |
|---|---|---|---|---|
| **2984** | A2337 | 80y multi | 1.40 | .55 |
| **2985** | A2338 | 80y multi | 1.40 | .55 |
| *a.* | | Horiz. pair, #2984-2985 | 3.00 | 2.00 |
| | | Sheet, 5 #2985a | 16.00 | 16.00 |
| **2986** | A2339 | 80y multi | 1.40 | .55 |
| **2987** | A2340 | 80y multi | 1.40 | .55 |
| **2988** | A2341 | 80y multi | 1.40 | .55 |
| **2989** | A2342 | 80y multi | 1.40 | .55 |
| *a.* | | Vert. strip of 4, #2986-2989 | 7.50 | 4.00 |
| | | Sheet, 2 each #2985-2989 | 16.00 | 16.00 |
| | | *Nos. 2984-2989 (6)* | 8.40 | 3.30 |

Miniature Sheet

Japan - India Friendship Year — A2343

No. 2990: a, Taj Mahal. b, Taj Mahal and camels. c, Bengal tiger. d, Peacock. e, Buddhist monastery, Sanchi, India. f, Statue of goddess, Sanchi. g, Painting of Indian woman facing left. h, Calico print of Indian facing right. i, Indian folk dancer. j, Character from Kathakali, Indian dance drama.

**2007, May 23** ***Perf. 13***

| | | | | |
|---|---|---|---|---|
| **2990** | A2343 | Sheet of 10 | 17.50 | 17.50 |
| *a.-j.* | | 80y Any single | 1.40 | .55 |

Tsurayuki Kino, Poet — A2344

Empress Jito, Poet — A2345

Dayu Sarumaru, Poet — A2346

Kanemasa Minamotono, Poet — A2347

Sanuki Nijoinno, Poet — A2348

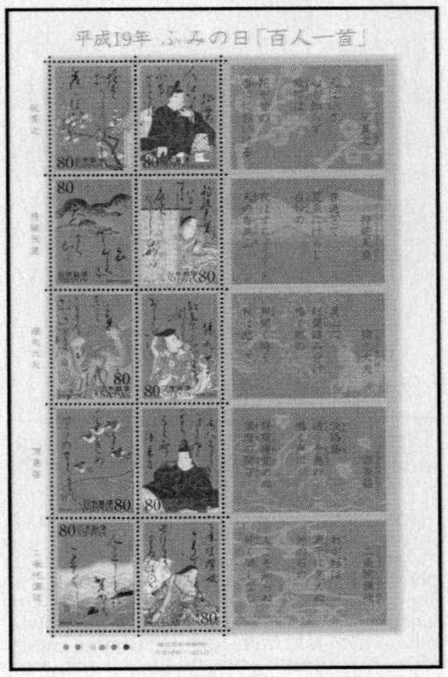

Poetry — A2349

No. 2996 — Poetry in Japanese calligraphy and: a, Plum blossoms. b, Tsurayuki Kino. c, Mount Kagu. d, Empress Jito. e, Deer. f, Dayu Sarumaru. g, Plovers. h, Kanemasa Minamotono. i, Stone in sea. j, Sanuki Nijoinno.

**2007, July 23 Photo.** ***Perf. 13½***

| | | | | |
|---|---|---|---|---|
| **2991** | A2344 | 50y multi | .90 | .45 |
| **2992** | A2345 | 50y multi | .90 | .45 |
| **2993** | A2346 | 50y multi | .90 | .45 |
| **2994** | A2347 | 50y multi | .90 | .45 |
| **2995** | A2348 | 50y multi | .90 | .45 |
| *a.* | | Vert. strip of 5, #2991-2995 | 5.75 | 4.00 |

***Perf. 13***

| | | | | |
|---|---|---|---|---|
| **2996** | A2349 | Sheet of 10 | 17.50 | 17.50 |
| *a.-j.* | | 80y Any single | 1.40 | .55 |

Letter Writing Day.

Miniature Sheet

11th World Track and Field Championships, Osaka — A2350

No. 2997: a, Dai Tamesue (athlete 545), hurdler. b, Kumiko Ikeda (athlete 426), sprinter. c, Yuzo Kanemaru (athlete 300), runner. d, Shingo Suetsugu (athlete 526), runner. e, Kayoko Fukushi (athlete 422), runner. f, Masato Naito running over hurdle. g, Naoyuki Daigo high jumping. h, Kenji Narisako (athlete 531), hurdler. i, Daichi Sawano pole vaulting. j, Koji Murofushi (athlete 774), hammer throw.

**2007, Aug. 23 Litho.** ***Perf. 13x13¼***

| | | | | |
|---|---|---|---|---|
| **2997** | A2350 | Sheet of 10 | 17.50 | 17.50 |
| *a.-j.* | | 80y Any single | 1.40 | .55 |

Miniature Sheet

Diplomatic Relations Between Japan and Thailand, 120th Anniv. — A2351

No. 2998: a, Maple leaves, bamboo. b, Cherry blossoms. c, Ratchaphruek (yellow flower) blossom. d, Rhynchostylis gigantea (purple and white orchids). e, Mother-of-pearl elephant. f, Mother-of-pearl flower. g, Thai dancer. h, Statue, Wat Phra Keo. i, Elephant with head at left, from Toshogu Shrine, Japan, horiz. j, Elephant with head at right, from Toshogu Shrine, horiz.

***Die Cut Perf. and Serpentine Die Cut***

**2007, Sept. 26 — Litho.**

**Self-Adhesive**

| | | | | |
|---|---|---|---|---|
| **2998** | A2351 | Sheet of 10 | 16.50 | 16.50 |
| *a.-j.* | | 80y Any single | 1.40 | .55 |

Vertical stamps are die cut perf. 13 at top and bottom, serpentine die cut 10¼ on side adjacent to another stamp, and die cut perf. 12½ on remaining side. Horizontal stamps are die cut perf. 13 at top and bottom, serpentine die cut 10¼ on side adjacent to another stamp, and die cut perf. 12¾ on remaining side.

See Thailand No. 2316.

**International Letter Writing Week Type of 2000**

Hiroshige paintings from 53 Stations of the Tokaido Highway: 90y, Hodogaya. 110y, Arai. 130y, Kusatsu.

**2007, Sept. 28 — Litho. — *Perf. 14***

| | | | | |
|---|---|---|---|---|
| **2999** | A2119 | 90y multi | 1.50 | .45 |
| **3000** | A2119 | 110y multi | 1.90 | .55 |
| **3001** | A2119 | 130y multi | 2.10 | .65 |
| | | *Nos. 2999-3001 (3)* | 5.50 | 1.65 |

Mandarin Duck A2352

Eastern Turtle Dove A2353

**2007, Oct. 1 — Photo. — *Perf. 13x13½***

| | | | | |
|---|---|---|---|---|
| **3002** | A2352 | 50y multi | .85 | .50 |
| **3003** | A2353 | 80y multi | 1.40 | .55 |

See No. 3281.

Miniature Sheets

A2354

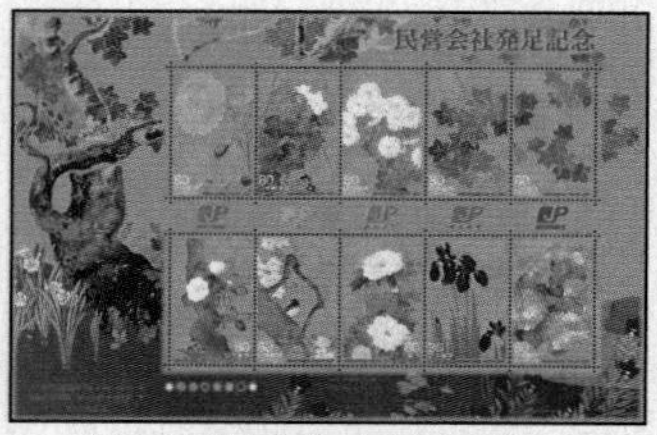

Establishment of Japan Post Corporation — A2355

No. 3004: a, Baron Hisoka Maejima (red panels). b, Japan #2 (red panels). c, Post office counter (orange panels). d, Postal workers loading mail coach (dark red panels). e, Postal saving counter (green panels). f, People at post office counters (blue panels).

No. 3005 — Paintings of flowers: a, Sunflower, by Hoitsu Sakai. b, Confederate Roses, by Sakai. c, Chrysanthemums, by Sakai. d, Maple Leaves, by Kiitsu Suzuki (showing branch). e, Maple Leaves, by Suzuki (no branch). f, Camellia, by Sakai. g, Cherry Tree, by Sakai (bird in tree). h, Tree Peony, by Sakai. i, Iris, by Sakai, j, Hydrangeas, by Sakai.

**2007, Oct. 1 — Photo. — *Perf. 13¼***

| | | | | |
|---|---|---|---|---|
| **3004** | A2354 | Sheet of 10, #a-b, 2 each #c-f | 16.50 | 16.50 |
| *a.-f.* | | 80y Any single | 1.40 | .55 |
| **3005** | A2355 | Sheet of 10 | 16.50 | 16.50 |
| *a.-j.* | | 80y Any single | 1.40 | .55 |

Miniature Sheet

Intl. Skills Festival For All — A2356

No. 3006: a, Computer operator and robot. b, Computer operator. c, Plasterer and Geisha. d, Plasterer and pillar. e, Pastry chef and cake. f, Pastry chef and bowls. g, Flower arranger and flowers. h, Flower arranger holding scissors. i, Sheet metal worker and automobile. j, Sheet metal worker hammering metal.

**2007, Oct. 23 — Litho. — *Perf. 13***

| | | | | |
|---|---|---|---|---|
| **3006** | A2356 | Sheet of 10 | 17.50 | 17.50 |
| *a.-j.* | | 80y Any single | 1.40 | .55 |

A2357

A2358

New Year 2008 (Year of the Rat)
A2359 A2360

**2007, Nov. 1 — Photo. — *Perf. 13x13½***

| | | | | |
|---|---|---|---|---|
| **3007** | A2357 | 50y multi | .95 | .30 |
| **3008** | A2358 | 80y multi | 1.40 | .40 |

**Photo. & Typo.**

***Perf. 13¼***

| | | | | |
|---|---|---|---|---|
| **3009** | A2359 | 50y +3y multi | 1.00 | .40 |
| **3010** | A2360 | 80y +3y multi | 1.60 | .40 |
| | | *Nos. 3007-3010 (4)* | 4.95 | 1.50 |

Sheets of two containing stamps similar to Nos. 3009-3010 were lottery prizes. Value, $4.

Diamonds — A2360a

Diamonds — A2360b

***Die Cut Perf. 13¼***

**2007, Nov. 1 — Litho.**

**Self-Adhesive**

**Green Diamonds**

**Color of Country Name**

| | | | | | |
|---|---|---|---|---|---|
| **3010A** | A2360a | 50y | blue | 4.00 | 4.00 |
| **3010B** | A2360a | 50y | green | 4.00 | 4.00 |
| **3010C** | A2360a | 50y | red | 4.00 | 4.00 |
| **3010D** | A2360a | 50y | purple | 4.00 | 4.00 |
| **3010E** | A2360a | 50y | black | 4.00 | 4.00 |

**Blue Diamonds**

| | | | | | |
|---|---|---|---|---|---|
| **3010F** | A2360a | 80y | blue | 3.50 | 3.50 |
| **3010G** | A2360a | 80y | green | 3.50 | 3.50 |
| **3010H** | A2360a | 80y | red | 3.50 | 3.50 |
| **3010I** | A2360a | 80y | purple | 3.50 | 3.50 |
| **3010J** | A2360a | 80y | black | 3.50 | 3.50 |

**Blue Diamonds**

**Color of Country Name**

| | | | | |
|---|---|---|---|---|
| **3010L** | A2360b | 80y | black | — |
| **3010M** | A2360b | 80y | brt grn | — |
| **3010N** | A2360b | 80y | orange | — |

Nos. 3010A-3010E were printed in sheets of 10, containing two of each stamp, that sold for 900y. Nos. 3010F-3010J were printed in sheets of 10, containing two of each stamp, that sold for 1200y. The image portion could be personalized. The image shown is a generic image.

The image portions of Nos. 3010L-3010N could be personalized. Three additional stamps were issued in this set. The editors would like to examine any examples.

**New Year Greetings Type of 2006 Inscribed "'08 New Year" Stamp + Label Panel Color**

**2007, Nov. 1 — Photo. — *Perf. 13¼***

| | | | | |
|---|---|---|---|---|
| **3010P** | A2327a | 50y red violet | 1.50 | 1.00 |
| **3010Q** | A2327a | 50y orange | 1.50 | 1.00 |
| *r.* | | Pair, #3010P-3010Q + 2 labels | 4.00 | 4.00 |

Labels could be personalized.

Miniature Sheets

A2361

Greetings Stamps — A2362

No. 3011: a, White buildings. b, Fairies on flying swans. c, Santa Claus. d, Flowers and snow-covered trees. e, Cat and candy cane.

No. 3012: a, Santa Claus and reindeer. b, Fairy and flowers. c, Snowman with green cap. d, Strawberries. e, Snowman and flying reindeer.

**2007, Nov. 26 — Litho. — *Die Cut Perf.***

**Self-Adhesive**

| | | | | |
|---|---|---|---|---|
| **3011** | A2361 | Sheet of 5 | 5.00 | |
| *a.-e.* | | 50y Any single | .90 | .80 |

***Die Cut Perf. 13***

| | | | | |
|---|---|---|---|---|
| **3012** | A2362 | Sheet of 5 | 7.50 | |
| *a.-e.* | | 80y Any single | 1.40 | .80 |

Miniature Sheet

Edo Calligraphy — A2363

No. 3013 — Charcters for "rat": a, In Kinbun style (red character). b, Black character with three long vertical lines at top, with red chop at LR. c, In Tensho style (gold character on red and brown background). d, In Reisho style (black character resembling a "3" with line through it, with red chop at LR). e, In Shoden style (gold character on blue and pink background). f, In Kana style (black characters resembling "12" with a check mark, with red chop at LR). g, In Reisho style (black characters, with red chop at LL). h, In Sosho style (black character with pink lines, with red chop at LL). i, Black character resembling stick figure with raised arms, with red chop at LR. j, In Kinbun style (black character with five short vertical lines at top, red chop at LL).

**Litho. & Embossed**

**2007, Dec. 3 — *Perf. 13***

| | | | | |
|---|---|---|---|---|
| **3013** | A2363 | Sheet of 10 | 17.50 | 17.50 |
| *a.-j.* | | 80y Any single | 1.40 | .55 |

Mt. Fuji A2364

Mt. Fuji
A2365

Mt. Fuji
A2366

Mt. Fuji
A2367

Mt. Fuji
A2368

Bamboo — A2369

Someiyoshino Blossoms — A2370

Hydrangea Blossoms — A2371

Maple
Leaves
A2372

Narcissuses — A2373

**2008, Jan. 23 Litho. *Perf. 13¾x14***

| | | | |
|---|---|---|---|
| **3014** | Sheet of 10 | 17.50 | 17.50 |
| *a.* | A2364 80y multi | 1.40 | .55 |
| *b.* | A2365 80y multi | 1.40 | .55 |
| *c.* | A2366 80y multi | 1.40 | .55 |
| *d.* | A2367 80y multi | 1.40 | .55 |
| *e.* | A2368 80y multi | 1.40 | .55 |
| *f.* | A2369 80y multi | 1.40 | .55 |
| *g.* | A2370 80y multi | 1.40 | .55 |
| *h.* | A2371 80y multi | 1.40 | .55 |
| *i.* | A2372 80y multi | 1.40 | .55 |
| *j.* | A2373 80y multi | 1.40 | .55 |

Yokoso! Japan Weeks.

Souvenir Sheet

New Year 2008 (Year of the Rat) — A2374

No. 3015: a, Two rats. b, One rat.

**2008, Jan. 28 Photo. *Perf. 13***

| | | | |
|---|---|---|---|
| **3015** | A2374 Sheet of 2 | 2.50 | 2.50 |
| *a.* | 50y multi | .90 | .45 |
| *b.* | 80y multi | 1.40 | .55 |

Miniature Sheet

Animated Folktales — A2375

No. 3016: a, Man on horse, cherry trees, pagoda. b, Man in cherry tree. c, Moon Princess in bamboo stump, woodsman with ax. d, Moon Princess, flying horse and wagon, archers. e, Four statues in snow. f, Two statues in snow, man with basket. g, Boy in ship. h, Demons. i, Woman carrying roll of cloth. j, Man, woman, crane.

**2008, Feb. 22 Litho. *Perf. 13***

| | | | |
|---|---|---|---|
| **3016** | A2375 Sheet of 10 | 17.50 | 17.50 |
| *a.-j.* | 80y Any single | 1.40 | .55 |

Folktales "The Old Man Who Made Cherry Trees Blossom" (No. 3016a-3016b), "The Moon Princess" (Nos. 3016c-3016d), "Six Little Statues" (Nos. 3016e-3016f), "The Peach Boy" (NOs. 3016g-3016h), "The Grateful Crane" (Nos. 3016i-3016j).

Miniature Sheet

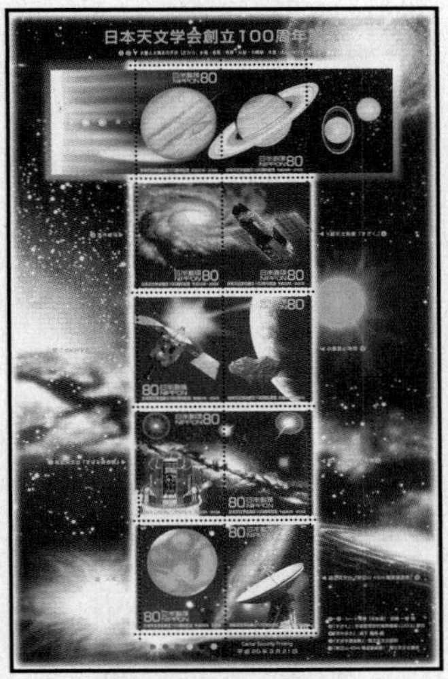

Astronomical Society of Japan, Cent. — A2376

No. 3017: a, Jupiter. b, Saturn. c, Spiral galaxy. d, Suzaku X-ray satellite. e, Hayabusa probe. f, Asteroids and Earth. g, Subaru Telescope. h, Stars. i, Mars. j, Nobeyama Radio Telescope.

**2008, Mar. 21**

| | | | |
|---|---|---|---|
| **3017** | A2376 Sheet of 10 | 17.50 | 17.50 |
| *a.-j.* | 80y Any single | 1.40 | .55 |

Miniature Sheet

Diplomatic Relations Between Japan and Indonesia, 50th Anniv. — A2377

No. 3018: a, Kelimutu Volcano, Indonesia. b, Mt. Fuji, Japan, and cherry blossoms. c, Borobudur, Indonesia. d, Toji Temple, Kyoto. e, Rafflesia arnoldii. f, Cherry blossoms. g, Angklung (Indonesian musical instrument). h, Gaku biwa (Japanese musical instrument). i, Red arowana fish, horiz. j, Three koi, horiz.

**2008, June 23 Photo. *Perf. 13***

| | | | |
|---|---|---|---|
| **3018** | A2377 Sheet of 10 | 15.00 | 15.00 |
| *a.-j.* | 80y Any single | 1.40 | .55 |

See Indonesia Nos. 2135-2139.

Small Bird in Cherry Blossom, by Seitei Watanabe
A2378

Butterfly in Peony Branch, by Watanabe
A2379

Egrets in the Rain Beneath Willow Trees, by Watanabe
A2380

Grapes, by Watanabe
A2381

Sea Birds on a Rocky Crag, by Watanabe
A2382

***Perf. 13½x13 Syncopated***

**2008, Apr. 18 Photo.**

| | | | |
|---|---|---|---|
| **3019** | A2378 80y multi | 1.40 | .55 |
| **3020** | A2379 80y multi | 1.40 | .55 |
| **3021** | A2380 80y multi | 1.40 | .55 |
| **3022** | A2381 80y multi | 1.40 | .55 |
| **3023** | A2382 80y multi | 1.40 | .55 |
| *a.* | Vert. strip of 5, #3019-3023 | 8.75 | 8.75 |
| | Sheet, 2 #3023a | 17.50 | 17.50 |

Philately Week.

See note after No. Z827 in the Prefecture Stamp listings.

Miniature Sheet

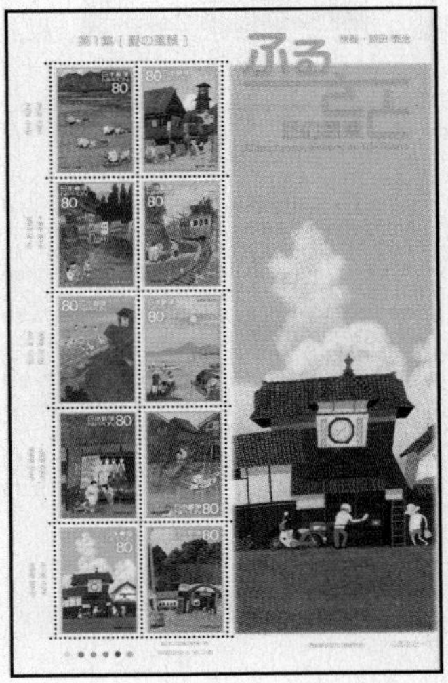


Home Towns — A2383

No. 3024 — Paintings by Taiji Harada of views of towns: a, Water Shield (Yamamoto District, Akita prefecture). b, Bell of Time (Kawago, Saitama prefecture). c, Enjoying the Evening Cool (Gujo, Gifu prefecture). d, The Little Electric Train (Choshi, Chiba prefecture).

e, Sea of the Heart (Shozu District, Kagawa prefecture). f, Lake in the Evening Sun (Gamo District, Shiga prefecture). g, Tanabata Dolls (Matsumoto, Nagano prefecture). h, Town of Outdoor Warehouses (Ise, Mie prefecture). i, The Farm Clock (Aki, Kochi prefecture). j, Late Summer Heat in the Street (Hakusan, Ishikawa prefecture).

**2008, May 2 Photo. *Perf. 13***

| | | | | |
|---|---|---|---|---|
| **3024** | A2383 | Sheet of 10 | 16.00 | 16.00 |
| *a.-j.* | | 80y Any single | 1.40 | .55 |

Hideyo Noguchi Africa Prize — A2384

**2008, May 23 Litho. *Perf. 13***

| | | | | |
|---|---|---|---|---|
| **3025** | | 80y Noguchi | 1.40 | .55 |
| **3026** | | 80y Map of Africa | 1.40 | .55 |
| *a.* | A2384 | Horiz. pair, #3025-3026 | 3.25 | 2.50 |

Miniature Sheet

National Afforestation Campaign — A2385

No. 3027 — Scenes from Akita prefecture: a, Aleutian avens and Mt. Moriyoshi, denomination at UL. b, Aleutian avens and Mt. Moriyoshi, denomination at UR. c, Fringed galax flowers, denomination at LL. d, Fringed galax flowers, denomination at LR. e, Autumn leaves, denomination at LL. f, Autumn leaves, denomination at UR. g, Beech forest in autumn, denomination in UL. h, Beech forest in autumn, denomination in UR. i, Weigela. j, Waterfall.

**2008, June 13 Photo. *Perf. 13***

| | | | | |
|---|---|---|---|---|
| **3027** | A2385 | Sheet of 10 | 9.50 | 9.50 |
| *a.-j.* | | 50y Any single | .90 | .55 |

Miniature Sheet

Year of Exchange Between Japan and Brazil — A2386

No. 3028: a, Roasted coffee beans, seal of Brazilian vice-consulate in Kobe. b, Coffee cherries, ship. c, Christ the Redeemer Statue, Rio de Janeiro. d, Sugarloaf Mountain, Rio de Janeiro. e, Iguaçu Falls, denomination at UL. f, Iguaçu Falls, denomination at UR. g, Houses, denomination at LL. h, Houses, denomination at LR. i, Butterflies. j, Toucan.

**2008, June 18 Litho. *Perf. 13***

| | | | | |
|---|---|---|---|---|
| **3028** | A2386 | Sheet of 10 | 16.00 | 16.00 |
| *a.-j.* | | 80y Any single | 1.40 | .55 |

See Brazil No. 3051.

Miniature Sheet

Publication of *Anne of Green Gables,* by Lucy Maud Montgomery, Cent. — A2387

No. 3029: a, Anne holding buttercups. b, Green Gables House. c, Matthew Cuthbert, wearing hat, vert. d, Marilla Cuthbert, wearing hat, vert. e, Anne, Diana Barry holding hands, vert. f, Diana, vert. g, Anne in black dress, vert. h, Anne and Gilbert Blythe, vert. i, Matthew Cuthbert, without hat, vert. j, Anne, Marilla Cuthbert, vert.

***Perf. 13¼x13 (#3029a-3029b), 13x13¼***

**2008, June 20**

| | | | | |
|---|---|---|---|---|
| **3029** | A2387 | Sheet of 10 | 16.00 | 16.00 |
| *a.-j.* | | 80y Any single | 1.40 | .55 |

See Canada Nos. 2276-2278.

Lily — A2388

Rugosa Rose — A2389

Rhododendron A2390

Safflower A2391

Gentian — A2392

Lily — A2393

Rugosa Rose A2394

Rhododendron A2395

Safflower A2396

Gentian A2397

**2008, July 1 Photo. *Perf. 13¼***

| | | | | |
|---|---|---|---|---|
| **3030** | A2388 | 50y multi | .90 | .50 |
| **3031** | A2389 | 50y multi | .90 | .50 |
| **3032** | A2390 | 50y multi | .90 | .50 |
| **3033** | A2391 | 50y multi | .90 | .50 |
| **3034** | A2392 | 50y multi | .90 | .50 |
| *a.* | | Vert. strip of 5, #3030-3034 | 5.50 | 5.00 |
| **3035** | A2393 | 80y multi | 1.40 | .60 |
| **3036** | A2394 | 80y multi | 1.40 | .60 |
| **3037** | A2395 | 80y multi | 1.40 | .60 |
| **3038** | A2396 | 80y multi | 1.40 | .60 |
| **3039** | A2397 | 80y multi | 1.40 | .60 |
| *a.* | | Vert. strip of 5, #3035-3039 | 8.75 | 8.00 |
| | | *Nos. 3030-3039 (10)* | 11.50 | 5.50 |

Flowers of Kanagawa, Hokkaido, Fukushima, Yamagata and Nagano prefectures.

Miniature Sheet

Hokkaido Local Autonomy Law, 60th Anniv. — A2398

No. 3040: a, Lake Toya, cranes (32x39mm). b, Goryokaku Fortress (28x33mm). c, Hills around Biei (28x33mm). d, Sea angel (28x33mm). e, Otaru Canal (28x33mm).

**2008, July 1 *Perf. 13¼ (#3040a), 13***

| | | | | |
|---|---|---|---|---|
| **3040** | A2398 | Sheet of 5 | 7.50 | 7.50 |
| *a.-e.* | | 80y Any single | 1.40 | .55 |

Miniature Sheet

G8 Summit, Toyako — A2399

No. 3041: a, Mt. Yotei (stamp 1). b, Showa Shinzan (stamp 2). c, Mt. Yotei and Lake Toya (stamp 3). d, Mt. Yotei and Fukidashi Park (stamp 4). e, Mt. Eniwa and Lake Shikotsu (stamp 5). f, Pink Japanese wood poppies (stamp 6). g, Squirrel (stamp 7). h, Beardtongue flowers (stamp 8). i, Mountain ash leaves and berries (stamp 9). j, Northern fox (stamp 10).

**2008, July 7 Litho. *Perf. 13¾x14***

| | | | | |
|---|---|---|---|---|
| **3041** | A2399 | Sheet of 10 | 15.00 | 15.00 |
| *a.-j.* | | 80y Any single | 1.50 | 1.10 |

Lady Shikibu Murasaki, Poet — A2400

Sanekata Fujiwara, Poet — A2401

Lady Shonagon Sei, Poet — A2402

Kinto Dainagon, Poet — A2403

Lady Shikibu Izumi, Poet — A2404

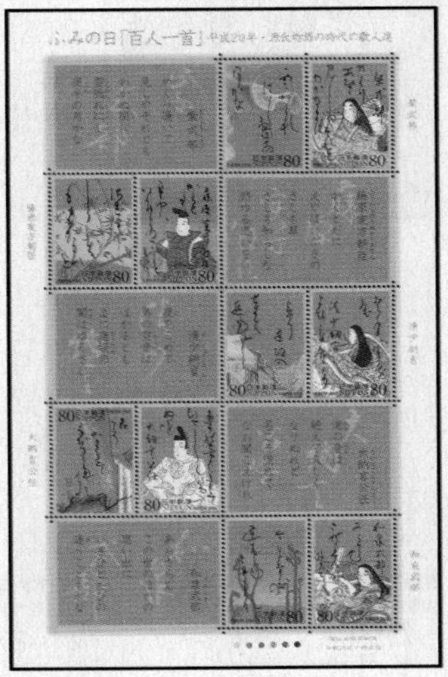

Poetry — A2405

No. 3047 — Poetry in Japanese calligraphy and: a, Moon behind cloud. b, Lady Shikibu Murasaki. c, Mugwort. d, Sanekata Fujiwara. e, Waterfall. f, Lady Shonagon Sei. g, Barrier. h, Kinto Dainagon. i, Bare branches. j, Lady Shikibu Izumi.

**2008, July 23 Photo. *Perf. 13¼***

| | | | | | |
|---|---|---|---|---|---|
| **3042** | A2400 | 50y multi | | .90 | .45 |
| **3043** | A2401 | 50y multi | | .90 | .45 |
| **3044** | A2402 | 50y multi | | .90 | .45 |
| **3045** | A2403 | 50y multi | | .90 | .45 |
| **3046** | A2404 | 50y multi | | .90 | .45 |
| *a.* | Vert. strip of 5, #3042-3046 | | | 5.50 | 3.75 |

***Perf. 12¾x13***

| | | | | |
|---|---|---|---|---|
| **3047** | A2405 | Sheet of 10 | 17.50 | 17.50 |
| *a.-j.* | 80y Any single | | 1.40 | .55 |

Letter Writing Day.

Miniature Sheets

A2406

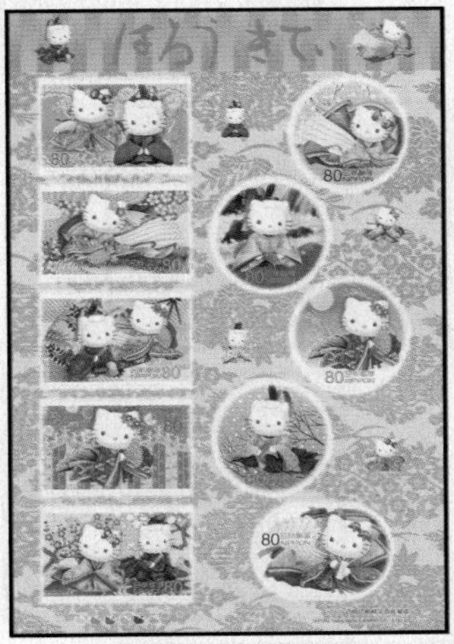

Hello Kitty — A2407

No. 3048 — Hello Kitty characters with: a, Gold denomination at UR. b, Green denomination at UR. c, Yellow denomination at UL, Kitty with pink flowers on head. d, Yellow denomination at UR, Kitty wearing green patterned kimono. e, Green denomination at UL, Kitty wearing black kimono. f, Green denomination at UL, Kitty with pink and blue flowers on head. g, Green denomination at UL, Kitty with bow and flowers on head. h, Yellow denomination at UL, Kitty wearing dark green kimono. i, Green denomination at UL, Kitty wearing brown kimono. j, Green denomination at UL, Kitty with purple and green flowers on head.

No. 3049 — Hello Kitty characters with: a, Green denomination at LL (41x27mm). b, Gold denomination at LR, one Kitty with two pink flowers on head (41x27mm). c, Gold denomination at LR, Kitty at right with purple and green flowers on head (41x27mm). d, Green denomination at UR (41x27mm). e, Gold denomination at LR, Kitty at left with bow and flower on head (41x27mm). f, Blue denomination (34mm diameter). g, Gold denomination, Kitty wearing gray kimono (34mm diameter). h, Gold denomination, Kitty holding fan (34mm diameter). i, Gold denomination, Kitty with snowflakes in background (34mm diameter). j, Blue denomination (40x28mm oval stamp).

***Die Cut Perf. and Serpentine Die Cut (see note)***

**2008, July 23 Litho.**

**Self-Adhesive**

| | | | | |
|---|---|---|---|---|
| **3048** | A2406 | Sheet of 10 | 9.50 | |
| *a.-j.* | 50y Any single | | .90 | .45 |

***Die Cut Perf. 13x13¼ (#3049a-3049e), Die Cut Perf.***

| | | | | |
|---|---|---|---|---|
| **3049** | A2407 | Sheet of 10 | 15.00 | 15.00 |
| *a.-j.* | 80y Any single | | 1.50 | 1.10 |

Stamps on No. 3048 are arranged in five rows of se-tenant pairs. Each pair is die cut perf. 13¾ at top and bottom, die cut perf. 13½ on the outer sides, and serpentine die cut 11¼ between the stamps in the pair.

Love That Meets the Night, by Utamaro A2408

Yatsumi Bridge, by Hiroshige A2409

Mannen Bridge, Fukagawa, by Hiroshige A2410

Koshiro Matsumoto IV as Gorobe Sakanaya of San'ya, by Sharaku A2411

Hanazuma From Hyogoya, by Utamaro A2412

Ayase River at Kanegafuchi, by Hiroshige A2413

Tsukiji Hongan-ji Temple, Teppozu, by Hiroshige A2414

Hikosaburo Bando III as Sanai Sagisaka, by Sharaku A2415

Roko of Tatsumi, by Utamaro A2416

Kameido Plum Gardens, by Hiroshige A2417

**2008, Aug. 1 Litho. *Perf. 13¼***

| | | | |
|---|---|---|---|
| **3050** | Sheet of 10 | 17.50 | 17.50 |
| *a.* | A2408 80y multi | 1.40 | .55 |
| *b.* | A2409 80y multi | 1.40 | .55 |
| *c.* | A2410 80y multi | 1.40 | .55 |
| *d.* | A2411 80y multi | 1.40 | .55 |
| *e.* | A2412 80y multi | 1.40 | .55 |
| *f.* | A2413 80y multi | 1.40 | .55 |
| *g.* | A2414 80y multi | 1.40 | .55 |
| *h.* | A2415 80y multi | 1.40 | .55 |
| *i.* | A2416 80y multi | 1.40 | .55 |
| *j.* | A2417 80y multi | 1.40 | .55 |

Life in Edo (Tokyo).

Miniature Sheet

Hometown Festivals — A2418

No. 3051: a, Streamers for Sendai Tanabata Festival, Miyagi prefecture (light green background, denomination at UR). b, Streamers for Sendai Tanabata Festival (light green background, denomination at UL). c, Portable shrine for Kanda Festival, Tokyo prefecture (yellow background, denomination in red at LL). d, Portable shrine for Kanda Festival (yellow background, denomination in blue at UR). e, Dancers from Awa Dance Festival, Tokushima prefecture (pink background, denomination at LR). f, Dancers from Awa Dance Festival (pink background, denomination at UR). g, Participants and lanterns for Hakata Gion Yamakasa Festival, Fukuoka prefecture (light blue background, denomination at UL). h, Participants and float for Hakata Gion Yamakasa Festival (light blue background, denomination at UR). i, Drummers for Eisa Festival, Okinawa prefecture (yellow background, denomination in red at LR). j, Drummers for Eisa Festival (yellow background, denomination in blue at UR).

**2008, Aug. 1 Photo. *Perf. 13½x13¼***

| | | | | |
|---|---|---|---|---|
| **3051** | A2418 | Sheet of 10 | 9.50 | 9.50 |
| *a.-j.* | 50y Any single | | .90 | .45 |

Miniature Sheet

Treaty of Peace and Friendship Between Japan and People's Republic of China, 30th Anniv. — A2419

No. 3052: a, Temple of Heaven, Beijing. b, Huangshan Mountains, China. c, Mogao Cave Shrines, China. d, Temple of the Flourishing Law, Ikaruga, Japan. e, Female mandarin duck. f, Male mandarin duck. g, Panel from painting by Wang Chuanfeng depicting three stylized fish and red Japanese apricot flower. h, Panel from painting by Wang Chuanfeng depicting two stylized fish and water lily. i, Panel from painting by Wang Chuanfeng depicting one stylized fish and autumn leaves. j, Panel from painting by Wang Chuanfeng depicting two staylized fish and white and red narcissi. Nos. 3052a-3052d, 3052g-3052j are 28x49mm; Nos. 3052e-3052f, 32x49mm.

**2008, Aug. 12 Photo. *Perf. 13***

| | | | | |
|---|---|---|---|---|
| **3052** | A2419 | Sheet of 10 | 15.00 | 15.00 |
| *a.-j.* | | 80y Any single | 1.40 | .55 |

**Animation**

Miniature Sheet

Patlabor — A2420

No. 3053: a, Ingfram Model 1 robot. b, Noa Izumimn, with "2" on sleeve patch. c, Isao Ota, with crossed arms. d, Ingram Model 2 robot. e, Shinobu Nagumo, with long hair. f, Ingram Model 3 robot. g, Robot, diff. h, Asumo Shinohara, with hand on head. i, Ingram Model 1 robot and eight characters. j, Ingram Model 2 robot and three characters.

**2008, Aug. 22 Litho. *Perf. 13x13¼***

| | | | | |
|---|---|---|---|---|
| **3053** | A2420 | Sheet of 10 | 15.00 | 15.00 |
| *a.-j.* | | 80y Any single | 1.40 | .55 |

Miniature Sheet

Home Towns — A2421

No. 3054 — Paintings by Taiji Harada of views of towns: a, Idyllic Village (Farmhouses, Tonami, Toyama prefecture). b, Blessing (Wedding at Yamate Catholic Church, Yokohama, Kanagawa prefecture). c, Approaching Winter (Lake Nojiri, Kamiminochi District, Nagano prefecture). d, Konjac Field (Farmers planting, Numata, Gunma prefecture). e, Vespers (Family in garden near houses, Nara, Nara prefecture). f, Cosmos (Flowers, boats and boathouses, Mikatakaminaka District, Fukui prefecture). g, Voices of Excited Children (Farmhouse and hill, Haga District, Tochigi prefecture). h, Autumn Colors Everywhere (Farmhouse and train car, Namegata, Ibaraki prefecture). i, Small Market (Family at roadside market, Asakura District, Fukuoka prefecture). j, Lullaby Village (Village and bridge, Kuma District, Kumamoto prefecture).

**2008, Sept. 1 Photo. *Perf. 13***

| | | | | |
|---|---|---|---|---|
| **3054** | A2421 | Sheet of 10 | 15.00 | 15.00 |
| *a.-j.* | | 80y Any single | 1.40 | .55 |

Miniature Sheet

Kyoto Travel Scenes — A2422

No. 3055: a, Otagi Nebutsu Temple and stone sculptures (stamp 1). b, Toriimoto (stamp 2). c, Adashino Nenbutsu Temple (stamp 3). d, Gio Temple (stamp 4). e, Buddha sculptures, Nison Temple (stamp 5). f, Hut of Fallen Persimmons, persimmons on tree (stamp 6). g, Jojakko Temple (stamp 7). h, Sagano Scenic Railway bridge and trains (stamp 8). i, Rowboats on Hozu River (stamp 9). j, Togetsu Bridge (stamp 10).

**2008, Sept. 1 Litho. *Perf. 13x13¼***

| | | | | |
|---|---|---|---|---|
| **3055** | A2422 | Sheet of 10 | 15.00 | 15.00 |
| *a.-j.* | | 80y Any single | 1.40 | .55 |

Personalized Stamp — A2423

***Die Cut Perf. 12¾ Syncopated***

**2008, Aug. 7 Litho.**

**Self-Adhesive**

**Color of Denomination**

| | | | | |
|---|---|---|---|---|
| **3056** | A2423 80y blue | | 2.00 | 2.00 |
| **3057** | A2423 80y red | | 2.00 | 2.00 |
| **3058** | A2423 80y orange | | 2.00 | 2.00 |
| **3059** | A2423 80y green | | 2.00 | 2.00 |
| **3060** | A2423 80y black | | 2.00 | 2.00 |
| | *Nos. 3056-3060 (5)* | | 10.00 | 10.00 |

Nos. 3056-3060 were printed in sheets of 10 containing 2 of each stamp that sold for 1200y. The image portion could be personalized. The image shown is a generic image.

A2424

A2425

A2426

A2427

A2428

A2429

A2430

A2431

A2432

The Tale of Genji, by Shikibu Murasaki — A2433

**2008, Sept. 22 Photo. *Perf. 13¼***

| | | | |
|---|---|---|---|
| **3061** | Sheet of 10 | 16.00 | 16.00 |
| *a.* | A2424 80y multi | 1.40 | .55 |
| *b.* | A2425 80y multi | 1.40 | .55 |
| *c.* | A2426 80y multi | 1.40 | .55 |
| *d.* | A2427 80y multi | 1.40 | .55 |
| *e.* | A2428 80y multi | 1.40 | .55 |
| *f.* | A2429 80y multi | 1.40 | .55 |
| *g.* | A2430 80y multi | 1.40 | .55 |
| *h.* | A2431 80y multi | 1.40 | .55 |
| *i.* | A2432 80y multi | 1.40 | .55 |
| *j.* | A2433 80y multi | 1.40 | .55 |

Kyushu Oil Dome, Oita Sports Park — A2435

Fencing — A2436

Hurdler — A2437

Kayaker — A2438

**2008, Sept. 26** ***Perf. 13x13¼***

**3062** Sheet of 10, 2 each #3062a, 3062b, 3062d, 4 #3062c 9.50 9.50
*a.* A2435 50y multi .90 .50
*b.* A2436 50y multi .90 .50
*c.* A2437 50y multi .90 .50
*d.* A2438 50y multi .90 .50

Miniature Sheet

Travel Scenes — A2439

No. 3063: a, Sanjunoto Pagoda (stamp 1). b, Kiyomizudera Temple (stamp 2). c, Detail from painted sliding partition showing flowers from Chishaku Temple, denomination at LL (stamp 3). d, Like "c," denomination at LR (stamp 4). e, Kodai Temple (stamp 5). f, Temple garden (stamp 6). g, Sannei Hill (stamp 7). h, Yasaka Pagoda (stamp 8). i, Apprentice geisha (stamp 9). j, Kamo River and waterfront (stamp 10).

**2008, Oct. 1** **Litho.** ***Perf. 13x13¼***

**3063** A2439 Sheet of 10 16.00 16.00
*a.-j.* 80y Any single 1.40 .55

**International Letter Writing Week Type of 2000**

Hiroshige paintings from 53 Stations of the Tokaido Highway: 90y, Kanagawa. 110y, Mishima. 130y, Ishibe.

**2008, Oct. 9** **Photo.** ***Perf. 13¼x13½***

**3064** A2119 90y multi 1.60 .45
**3065** A2119 110y multi 1.90 .55
**3066** A2119 130y multi 2.10 .65
*Nos. 3064-3066 (3)* 5.60 1.65

**World Heritage Sites**
Miniature Sheet

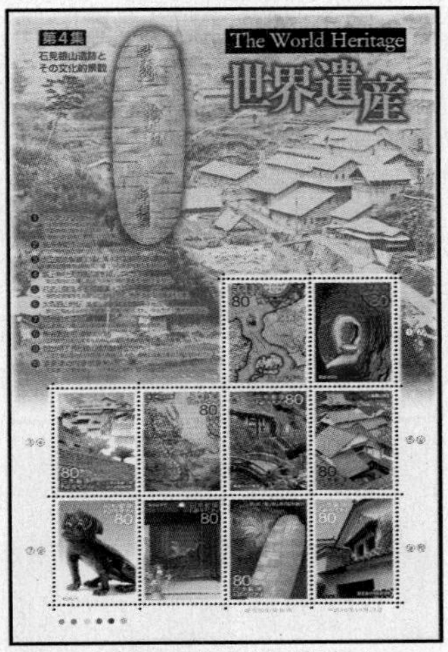


Iwami Silver Mine World Heritage Site — A2440

No. 3067: a, Map of Tartary by Abraham Ortelius (stamp 1). b, Ryugenji mine shaft (stamp 2). c, Smelting plant and ruins of Shimizudani smelting works (stamp 3). d, Painting of dragon, ceiling of Kigami Shinto shrine (stamp 4). e, Rakanji Temple (stamp 5). f, Omori silver mine district (stamp 6). g, Silver guardian dog (stamp 7). h, Interior of Kumagai family residence (stamp 8). i, Silver coin for official use and picture scroll (stamp 9). j, Naito Mansion, Yunotsu (stamp 10).

**2008, Oct. 23** ***Perf. 13x13¼***

**3067** A2440 Sheet of 10 16.00 16.00
*a.-j.* 80y Any single 1.40 .55

Miniature Sheet

Kyoto Prefecture Local Autonomy Law, 60th Anniv. — A2441

No. 3068: a, Scene from The Tale of Genji, by Shikibu Murasaki (33x39mm). b, Cherry blossoms, Kyoto Prefectural Botanical Garden (28x33mm). c, Thatched-roof house, Nantan (28x33mm). d, Kaijusen Pagoda, Wazuka tea plantation (28x33mm). e, Amanohashidate Sandbar (28x33mm).

***Perf. 13¼ (#3068a), 13x13¼***

**2008, Oct. 27** **Photo.**

**3068** A2441 Sheet of 5 8.00 8.00
*a.-e.* 80y Any single 1.40 .55

Miniature Sheet

Home Towns — A2442

No. 3069 — Paintings by Taiji Harada of views of towns: a, Stove Train (train, Kitatsugaru District, Aomori prefecture). b, New Year (buildings with snow-covered roofs, man shoveling snow, Nishimurayama District, Yamagata prefecture). c, Seaside Station (train station and telephone pole, Abashiri, Hokkaido prefecture). d, Incense Waterwheel (mill with waterwheel, Tsuyama, Okayama prefecture). e, Harness Straps (horse dragging log, Kurayoshi, Tottori prefecture). f, Life in the Snow Country (postman delivering mail to people at snow-covered house, Waga District, Iwate prefecture). g, Good Friends (people on town street in snowfall, Aizu Wakamatsu, Fukushima prefecture). h, Community of Stone Walls (people walking by stone wall, Minamiuwa District, Ehime prefecture). i, Village on Steep Slope (houses on mountainside, Miyoshi, Toskushima prefecture). j, Sedge-woven Hat (woman standing outside of building in snowstorm, Nakauonuma District, Niigata prefecture).

**2008, Nov. 4** ***Perf. 13***

**3069** A2442 Sheet of 10 16.00 16.00
*a.-j.* 80y Any single 1.40 .55

A2443 A2444

New Year 2009 (Year of the Ox)
A2445 A2446

**2008, Nov. 4** **Photo.** ***Perf. 13x13¼***

**3070** A2443 50y multi .95 .30
**3071** A2444 80y multi 1.40 .40

***Perf. 13¼***

**3072** A2445 50y +3y multi 1.00 .40
**3073** A2446 80y +3y multi 1.60 .40
*Nos. 3070-3073 (4)* 4.95 1.50

Sheets of two containing Nos. 3070-3071 were lottery prizes. Value, $4.

**New Year Greetings Type of 2006 Inscribed "'09 New Year" Stamp + Label Panel Color**

**2008, Nov. 4** **Photo.** ***Perf. 13¼***

**3074** A2327a 50y blue green 1.75 1.25
**3075** A2327a 50y red 1.75 1.25
*a.* Pair, #3074-3075 + 2 labels 4.50 4.50

Labels could be personalized.

Miniature Sheet

Keio University, 150th Anniv. — A2447

No. 3076: a, Yukichi Fukuzawa (1835-1901), founder (stamp 1). b, University emblem (stamp 2). c, Old Library, denomination at LL (stamp 3). d, Old Library, denomination at LR (stamp 4). e, Keio and Waseda University rugby players (stamp 5). f, Keio and Waseda University baseball players (stamp 6). g, Stained-glass window depicting horse's head (stamp 7). h, Stained-glass window depicting goddess with upraised arm (stamp 8). i, Stained-glass window depicting feudal warrior (stamp 9). j, Stained-glass window with Latin inscription "Calamus Gladio Fortior" (stamp 10).

**2008, Nov. 7** ***Perf. 13***

**3076** A2447 Sheet of 10 16.00 16.00
*a.-j.* 80y Any single 1.40 .55

Miniature Sheet

Edo Calligraphy — A2448

No. 3077 — Characters for "ox": a, Depiction of ox head (Kinbun style) with red chop at LL. b, Blue character on lilac background, in Kokotsubun style. c, Character with three horizontal lines and two vertical lines, in standard script, with red chop at LR. d, Red character in Kinbun style. e, Character with two horizontal lines and one vertical line, in standard script, with red chop at left center. f, Character in Tensho style with red chop at right center. g, Character with arc and crossed lines in Tensho style, with red chop at LR. h, Character with two crossing curves in Kokotsubun style, with red chop in center. i, Character with two components in Reisho style, with red chop at left. j, Character with dot above sinuous line in Hiragana style, with red chop at LR.

**Litho. & Embossed**

**2008, Nov. 21** ***Perf. 13x13¼***

**3077** A2448 Sheet of 10 17.50 17.50
*a.-j.* 80y Any single 1.40 .55

A2449

A2450

A2451

A2452

A2453

Iron and Steel Industry, 150th Anniv. — A2454

**2008, Dec. 1** **Photo.** ***Perf. 12¾x13***

**3078** Sheet of 10, #3078a, 3078b, 2 each #3078c-3078f 17.50 17.50
*a.* A2449 80y multi 1.40 .55
*b.* A2450 80y multi 1.40 .55
*c.* A2451 80y multi 1.40 .55
*d.* A2452 80y multi 1.40 .55
*e.* A2453 80y multi 1.40 .55
*f.* A2454 80y multi 1.40 .55

Daffodils
A2455

Plum Blossoms
A2456

Fuki
A2457

Plum Blossoms
A2458

Weeping Cherry Blossoms
A2459

Daffodils
A2460

Plum Blossoms
A2461

Fuki
A2462

Plum Blossoms
A2463

Weeping Cherry Blossoms
A2464

**2008, Dec. 1** **Photo.** ***Perf. 13¼***

**3079** A2455 50y multi .90 .45
**3080** A2456 50y multi .90 .45
**3081** A2457 50y multi .90 .45
**3082** A2458 50y multi .90 .45
**3083** A2459 50y multi .90 .45
*a.* Vert. strip of 5, #3079-3083 5.50 4.25
**3084** A2460 80y multi 1.40 .55
**3085** A2461 80y multi 1.40 .55
**3086** A2462 80y multi 1.40 .55
**3087** A2463 80y multi 1.40 .55
**3088** A2464 80y multi 1.40 .55
*a.* Vert. strip of 5, #3084-3088 8.75 7.00
*Nos. 3079-3088 (10)* 11.50 5.00

Flowers of Fukui, Wakayama, Akita, Fukuoka and Kyoto prefectures.

Miniature Sheets

A2465

Greetings Stamps — A2466

No. 3089: a, Santa Claus holding star (26x30mm). b, Stylized man, woman as bell (26x30mm). c, Kittens (26x30mm). d, Teddy bears and gift box (26x30mm). e, Chick, flowers (29mm diameter).

No. 3090: a, Kittens (34x28mm oval). b, Elf with bag of toys (25x34mm). c, Bluebirds in bouquet of roses (25x34mm). d, Santa Claus with horn (25x34mm). e, Fruit and flowers (25x34mm).

***Die Cut Perf. 13¼***

**2008, Dec. 8** **Litho.**

**3089** A2465 Sheet of 5 5.50 5.50
*a.-e.* 50y Any single .90 .45

***Die Cut Perf. 13***

**3090** A2466 Sheet of 5 8.75 8.75
*a.-e.* 80y Any single 1.40 .55

Miniature Sheet

Shimane Prefecture Local Autonomy Law, 60th Anniv. — A2467

No. 3091: a, Tree peony, silver coin for official use (33x39mm). b, Kuniga Coast (28x33mm). c, Matsue Castle (28x33mm). d, Tsuwano (28x33mm). e, Bronze bell (28x33mm).

***Perf. 13¼ (#3091a), 13x13¼***

**2008, Dec. 8** **Photo.**

**3091** A2467 Sheet of 5 8.75 8.75
*a.-e.* 80y Any single 1.40 .55

Miniature Sheet

Travel Scenes — A2468

No. 3092: a, Dragon from Shuri Castle Main Hall (stamp 1). b, Shuri Castle Main Hall (stamp 2). c, Ryukyuan dancer with arm raised at left (stamp 3). d, Ryukuan dancer with arm raised at right (stamp 4). e, Shurei Gate (stamp 5). f, Zuisen Gate and Rokoku Gate, Shuri Castle (stamp 6). g, Shikina Garden (stamp 7). h, Stone pavement, Kinjo (stamp 8). i, Guardian lion, International Street, Naha (stamp 9). j, Yui Monorail, Naha (stamp 10).

**2009, Jan. 23** **Litho.** ***Perf. 13x13¼***

**3092** A2468 Sheet of 10 18.00 18.00
*a.-j.* 80y Any single 1.40 .60

Miniature Sheet

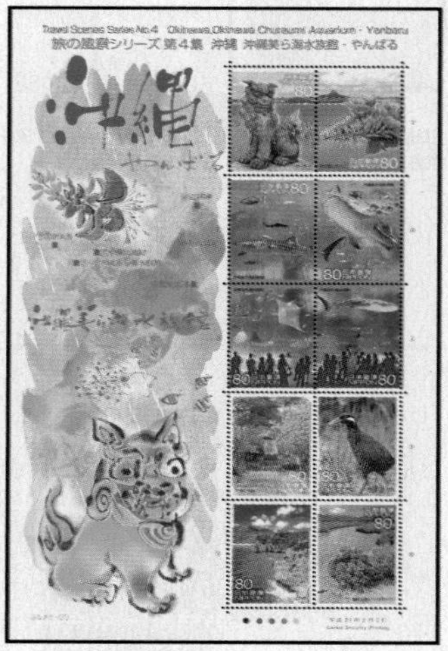
Travel Scenes — A2469

No. 3093: a, Guardian Lion (stamp 1). b, Indian coral tree, Iejima (stamp 2). c, Fish in Okinawa Churaumi Aquarium, denomination at UR (stamp 3). d, As "c," denomination at LL (stamp 4). e, People watching fish in Okinawa Churaumi Aquarium, denomination at LL (stamp 5). f, As "e," denomination at LR (stamp 6). g, Nakijin Castle ruins (stamp 7). h, Okinawa rail (stamp 8). i, Cape Hedo, Okinawa (stamp 9). j, Mangroves, Gesashi Inlet (stamp 10).

**2009, Feb. 2**

**3093** A2469 Sheet of 10 16.00 16.00
*a.-j.* 80y Any single 1.40 .60

Yoshino Cherry Blossoms
A2470

Azaleas
A2471

Tulips
A2472

Rhododendron
A2473

Nara Cherry Blossoms
A2474

Yoshino Cherry Blossoms
A2475

Azaleas
A2476

Tulips
A2477

Rhododendrons
A2478

Nara Cherry Blossoms
A2479

**2009, Feb. 2 Photo. *Perf. 13¼***

| | | | | | |
|---|---|---|---|---|---|
| **3094** | A2470 | 50y multi | | .90 | .50 |
| **3095** | A2471 | 50y multi | | .90 | .50 |
| **3096** | A2472 | 50y multi | | .90 | .50 |
| **3097** | A2473 | 50y multi | | .90 | .50 |
| **3098** | A2474 | 50y multi | | .90 | .50 |
| *a.* | | Vert. strip of 5, #3094-3098 | | 5.00 | 3.75 |
| **3099** | A2475 | 80y multi | | 1.40 | .60 |
| **3100** | A2476 | 80y multi | | 1.40 | .60 |
| **3101** | A2477 | 80y multi | | 1.40 | .60 |
| **3102** | A2478 | 80y multi | | 1.40 | .60 |
| **3103** | A2479 | 80y multi | | 1.40 | .60 |
| *a.* | | Vert. strip of 5, #3099-3103 | | 8.00 | 6.25 |
| | | *Nos. 3094-3103 (10)* | | 11.50 | 5.50 |

Flowers of Tokyo, Tochigi, Niigata, Shiga and Nara prefectures.

**Animation**
Miniature Sheet

GeGeGe no Kitaro — A2480

No. 3104: a, Kitaro and Otoko Nezumi. b, Daddy Eyeball in bowl. c, Kitaro kicking. d, Kitaro in fire. e, Villain with elongated head, villain with blades for arms. f, Villains with red face, villain with snake. g, Kitaro and mermaid. h, Musume Neko. i, Otoko Nezumi, Musume Neko, Babaa Sunakake and Nurikabe. j, Kitaro, Daddy Eyeball, Jijii Konaki, Momen Ittan.

**2009, Feb. 23 Litho. *Perf. 13x13¼***

| | | | | |
|---|---|---|---|---|
| **3104** | A2480 | Sheet of 10 | 16.00 | 16.00 |
| *a.-j.* | | 80y Any single | 1.40 | .60 |

Miniature Sheet

Travel Scenes — A2481

No. 3105: a, Todai Temple (stamp 1). b, Buddha, Todai Temple (stamp 2). c, Asura, Kofuku Temple (stamp 3). d, Nara National Museum (stamp 4). e, Kasuga Taisha Shrine (stamp 5). f, Roof of Kasuga Taisha Shrine and overhanging roof (stamp 6). g, Japanese deer, Wakakusa Hill (stamp 7). h, Inanuishi family residence (stamp 8). i, Gazebo, Nara Park (stamp 9). j, Bridge to gazebo, Nara Park (stamp 10).

**2009, Mar. 2**

| | | | | |
|---|---|---|---|---|
| **3105** | A2481 | Sheet of 10 | 16.00 | 16.00 |
| *a.-j.* | | 80y Any single | 1.40 | .60 |

Miniature Sheet

Home Towns — A2482

No. 3106 — Paintings by Taiji Harada of views of towns: a, Cultivating (farmer in field, Nishitama District, Tokyo prefecture). b, Children Planting Rice (children in rice paddy, Katta District, Miyagi prefecture). c, I'm Home (child running up hill to farmhouse, Yamagata District, Hiroshima prefecture). d, Northern Springtime (farmer and wheelbarrow in field of yellow flowers, Iwanai District, Hokkaido prefecture). e, Chinese Milk Vetch Field (people near farmhouse, Kyoto, Kyoto prefecture). f, Water Mortar (farmer near water mortar, Hita, Oita prefecture). g, Short Rest (woman resting on bench in front of building, Numazu, Shizuoka prefecture). h, Red Train (street scene with train in background, Izumo, Shimane prefecture). i, Oven-shaped Thatch Roofs (woman, children with toy car in front of farm house, Kishima District, Saga prefecture). j, Little Post Office (people outside of post office, Hosu District, Ishikawa prefecture).

**2009, Mar. 2 Photo. *Perf. 13***

| | | | | |
|---|---|---|---|---|
| **3106** | A2482 | Sheet of 10 | 16.00 | 16.00 |
| *a.-j.* | | 80y Any single | 1.40 | .60 |

Miniature Sheets

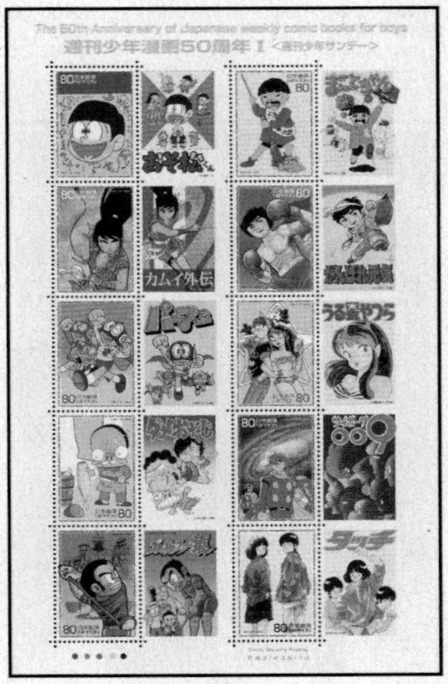

A2483

Weekly Comic Books For Boys, 50th Anniv — A2484

No. 3107: a, Osomatsu-kun (boy's face, green panel at top). b, Makoto Chan (boy with broom). c, Kamui Gaiden (swordsman with black hair). d, Gambare Genki (boxer, dark blue background). e, Paman (three characters with masks and capes). f, Urusei Yatsura (boy in cap, girl in bikini). g, Dame Oyaji (man holding radish and knife). h, Saibogu 009 (characters with galaxy in background). i, Purogorufa Saru (golfer). j, Tacchi (boy and girl looking over their shoulders).

No. 3108: a, Eitoman (android with "8" on chest). b, Taiga Masuku (caped man with tiger mask). c, Kyojin no Hoshi (Yomiuri Giants pitcher). d, Karate Baka Ichidai (karate master with green hair). e, GeGeGe no Kitaro (Kitaro, Daddy Eyeball and Otoko Nezumi). f, Ai to Makoto (girl with orange hair, boy with green hair). g, Tensai Bakabon (woman with yellow hair bow, screaming man). h, Tsurikichi Sanpei (boy holding fish). i, Ashita no Jo (boxer, pale blue background). j, Tonda Kappuru (boy, girl with green dress and orange bow).

**2009, Mar. 17 Litho. *Perf. 13***

| | | | | |
|---|---|---|---|---|
| **3107** | A2483 | Sheet of 10 | 16.00 | 16.00 |
| *a.-j.* | | 80y Any single | 1.40 | .60 |
| **3108** | A2484 | Sheet of 10 | 16.00 | 16.00 |
| *a.-j.* | | 80y Any single | 1.40 | .60 |

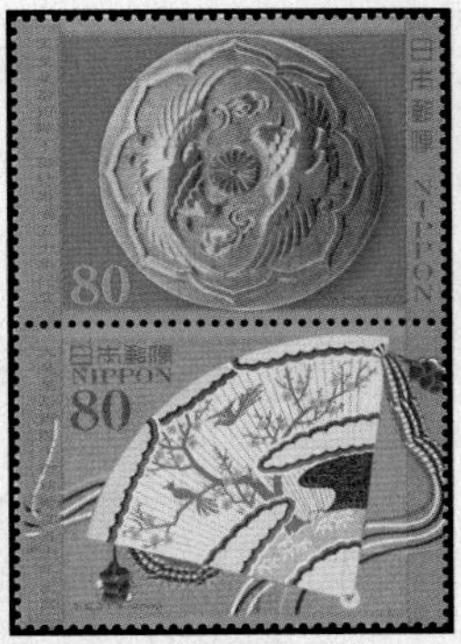

Wedding of Emperor Akihito and Empress Michiko, 50th Anniv. — A2485

Designs: No. 3109, Confectionery box. No. 3110, Fan.

**2009, Apr. 10 Photo. *Perf. 13¼***

| | | | | |
|---|---|---|---|---|
| **3109** | 80y multi | | 1.40 | .60 |
| **3110** | 80y multi | | 1.40 | .60 |
| *a.* | A2485 Pair, #3109-3110 | | 3.20 | 2.50 |
| *b.* | Souvenir sheet, #3109-3110 | | 3.25 | 3.25 |

**Animation**
Miniature Sheet

Detective Conan — A2486

No. 3111: a, Ai Haibara and Conan and brick wall. b, Mitsuhiko Tsuburaya, Ayumi Yoshida, and Genta Kojima and brick wall. c, Heiji Hattori and cherry blossoms. d, Kazuha Toyama and cherry blossoms. e, Conan and night sky. f, Gin and night sky. g, Conan and fence. h, Ran Mori and fence. i, Kiddo Kaito holding Christmas gift. j, Conan, Moon and hang-glider.

**2009, Apr. 17 Litho. *Perf. 13x13¼***

| | | | | |
|---|---|---|---|---|
| **3111** | A2486 | Sheet of 10 | 17.50 | 17.50 |
| *a.-j.* | | 80y Any single | 1.40 | .60 |

Peonies, by Yu Fei'an
A2487

Peonies, by Ren Bonian
A2488

Peonies, by Keika Kanashima
A2489

Peonies, by Keika Kanashima
A2490

Peonies, by Keika Kanashima
A2491

Peonies, by Keika Kanashima
A2492

**2009, Apr. 20 Photo. *Perf. 13¼***

| | | | | |
|---|---|---|---|---|
| **3112** | | Sheet of 10, #3112c-3112f, 3 each, #3112a-3112b | 17.50 | 17.50 |
| *a.* | A2487 | 80y multi | 1.40 | .60 |
| *b.* | A2488 | 80y multi | 1.40 | .60 |
| *c.* | A2489 | 80y multi | 1.40 | .60 |
| *d.* | A2490 | 80y multi | 1.40 | .60 |
| *e.* | A2491 | 80y multi | 1.40 | .60 |
| *f.* | A2492 | 80y multi | 1.40 | .60 |

Philately Week.

Red Cross, 150th Anniv. — A2493

Designs: No. 3113, Henri Dunant (1828-1910), founder of Red Cross. No. 3114, Japanese Red Cross Day poster, 1933.

**2009, May 8 Litho. *Perf. 13***

| | | | | |
|---|---|---|---|---|
| **3113** | | 80y multi | 1.40 | .60 |
| **3114** | | 80y multi | 1.40 | .60 |
| *a.* | A2493 | Pair, #3113-3114 | 3.50 | 2.50 |

Miniature Sheet

Nagano Prefecture Local Autonomy Law, 60th Anniv. — A2494

No. 3115: a, Kappa Bridge, Azusa River, Mt. Hodaka (33x39mm). b, Nanohana Park and Chikuma River, Iiyama City (28x33mm). c, Anraku Temple (28x33mm). d, Matsumoto Castle (28x33mm). e, Manji Buddha statue (28x33mm).

***Perf. 13¼ (#3115a), 13x13¼***

**2009, May 14 Photo.**

| | | | | |
|---|---|---|---|---|
| **3115** | A2494 | Sheet of 5 | 8.75 | 8.75 |
| *a.-e.* | | 80y Any single | 1.40 | .60 |

Inauguration of Lay Judge System — A2495

Designs: No. 3116, Lay Judge System emblem. No. 3117, Birds on scale.

**2009, May 21 Litho. *Perf. 13x13¼***

| | | | | |
|---|---|---|---|---|
| **3116** | | 80y multi | 1.40 | .60 |
| **3117** | | 80y multi | 1.40 | .60 |
| *a.* | A2495 | Pair, #3116-3117 | 3.50 | 2.50 |

Miniature Sheets

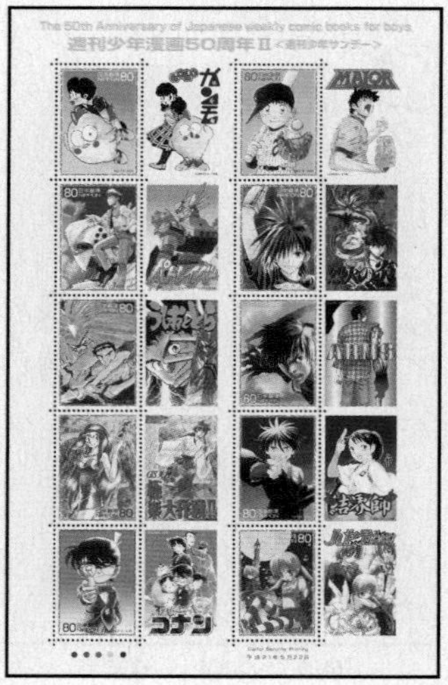

A2496

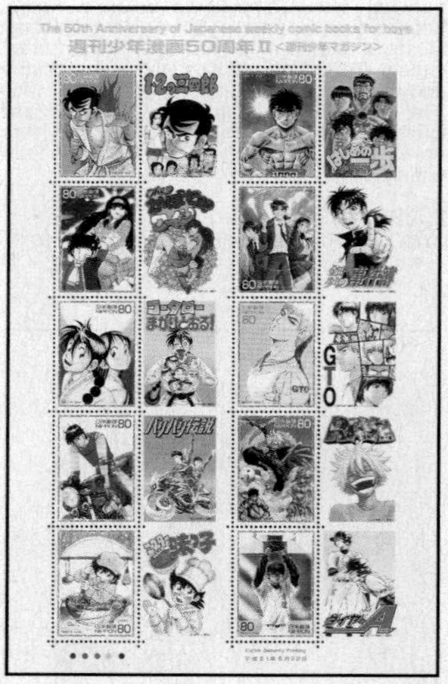

Weekly Comic Books For Boys, 50th Anniv — A2497

No. 3118: a, Gu-Gu Ganmo (child and chicken-like alien). b, Major (baseball player with bat, ball and glove). c, Patlabor Mobile Police (man standing on robot). d, Rekka no Hono (boy with gloved hand raised). e, Ushio to Tora (monster and boy holding torch). f, ARMS (boy with extended hand and slash marks in background). g, GS Mikami Gakuraku Daisakusen (woman with long red hair). h, Kekkaishi (magician pointing finger forward). i, Detective Conan (boy pointing forward wearing glasses and bow tie). j, Hayate no Gotoku (girl, boy and tower).

No. 3119: a, 1, 2 no Sanshiro (judo fighter with flame in background). b, Hajime no Ippo (boxer). c, Kabocha Wain (boy and tall girl). d, Kindaichi Shonen no Jikenbo (two boys and girl). e, Kotaro Makari Tooru (boy and girl in white clothes). f, GTO (boy with GTO tattoo). g, Bari Bari Densetsu (motorcyclist). h, RAVE (swordsman and other characters). i, Misuta Ajikko (chef). j, Daiya no A (baseball pitcher).

**2009, May 22 Litho. *Perf. 13***

| | | | | |
|---|---|---|---|---|
| **3118** | A2496 | Sheet of 10 | 17.50 | 17.50 |
| *a.-j.* | | 80y Any single | 1.40 | .60 |
| **3119** | A2497 | Sheet of 10 | 17.50 | 17.50 |
| *a.-j.* | | 80y Any single | 1.40 | .60 |

**Opening of Japanese Ports, 150th Anniv.**

Miniature Sheets

Nagasaki — A2498

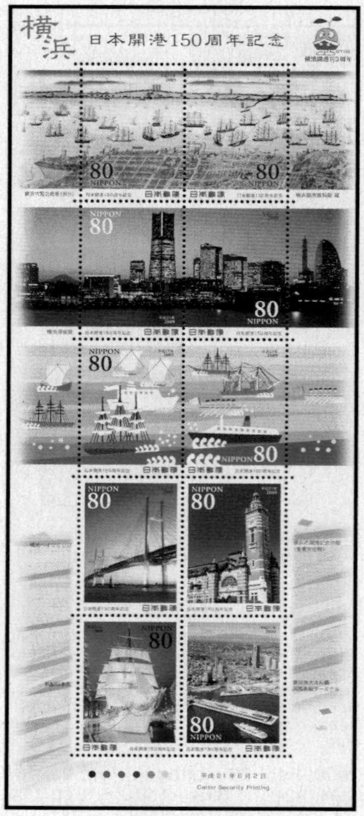


Yokohama — A2499

Hakodate — A2500

No. 3120: a, 19th century woodblock print of Nagasaki Port (denomination at left in black). b, 19th century woodblock print of Nagasaki Port (denomination at right in black). c, Nagasaki Port at night (denomination at UL in white). d, Nagasaki Port at night (denomination at UR in black). e, Drawing of boats and ships (denomination at UL in black). f, Drawing of boats and ships (denomination at LR in white). g, Nagasaki Port at night (denomination at LL in white). h, Oura Catholic Church. i, Goddess Great Bridge, Nippon Maru cruise ship. j, Glover Garden, Nagasaki Port (lamppost in foreground).

No. 3121: a, Woodblock print of Yokohama Port, 1871 (denomination at LL in black). b, Woodblock print of Yokohama Port, 1871 (denomination at LR in black). c, Yokohama Port at night (denomination at UL in white, tall building at right). d, Yokohama Port at night (denomination at LR in white). e, Yokohama Bay Bridge. f, Yokohama City Port Opening Memorial Hall. g, Sailing ship Nippon Maru. h, Yokohama International Passenger Boat Terminal and cruise ship.

No. 3122: a, Woodblock print of Hakodate Port, 1882 (denomination at LL in black). b, Woodblock print of Hakodate Port, 1882 (denomination at UL in black). c, Hakodate Port at night (denomination at UR in white). d, Hakodate Port at night (denomination at UL in white). e, Street on Hachiman Slope, Hakodate Port at night. f, Hakodate Orthodox Christian Church. g, Ship, lamppost at Old Pier at night. h, Hakodate Park, Hakodate Port (denomination at UL in black).

**2009, June 2 Litho. *Perf. 13***

| | | | | |
|---|---|---|---|---|
| 3120 | A2498 | Sheet of 10 | 17.50 | 17.50 |
| *a.-j.* | | 80y Any single | 1.40 | .60 |
| 3121 | A2499 | Sheet of 10, #3120e-3120f, 3121a-3121h | 17.50 | 17.50 |
| *a.-h.* | | 80y Any single | 1.40 | .60 |
| 3122 | A2500 | Sheet of 10, #3120e-3120f, 3122a-3122h | 17.50 | 17.50 |
| *a.-h.* | | 80y Any single | 1.40 | .60 |
| | | *Nos. 3120-3122 (3)* | 52.50 | 52.50 |

Miniature Sheet

National Afforestation Campaign — A2501

No. 3123 — Flora from Fukui Prefecture: a, Weeping cherry blossoms. b, Japanese zelkova tree. c, Japanese red pine tree. d, Japanese bird cherry tree. e, Magnolia blossoms. f, Camellia. g, Japanese horse chestnut tree. h, Kousa dogwood blossoms. i, Narcissi (denomination at UL). j, Narcissi (denomination at UR).

**2009, June 5 Litho. *Perf. 13***

| | | | | |
|---|---|---|---|---|
| 3123 | A2501 | Sheet of 10 | 11.00 | 11.00 |
| *a.-j.* | | 50y Any single | .90 | .50 |

Miniature Sheet

Home Towns — A2502

No. 3124 — Paintings by Taiji Harada of views of towns: a, Flowers Blooming in the Rain (mother and daughter under umbrellas on path by flower field, Tone District, Gumma prefecture). b, Potato Blossoms (train car near potato field, Nakagawa District, Hokkaido prefecture). c, High Country Flowers (people in flower field, Suwa, Nagano prefecture). d, Memories on the Wind (farmer with wheelbarrow on path near farmhouse, Hagi, Yamaguchi prefecture). e, Tranquility (people near stone wall in front of house, Sumoto, Hyogo prefecture). f, Sunset Skies (adult and child on hillside path near house, Nishiusuki District, Miyazaki prefecture). g, Island Post Office (people standing in front of post office, Yaeyama District, Okinawa prefecture). h, Lotus Blossoms (field of lotus with house and large tree in background, Hakusan, Ishikawa prefecture). i, Flower Garden (two women picking flowers with house and telephone pole in background, Minamiboso, Chiba prefecture). j, Peach Blossoms (adult and child picnicking under trees, Fuefuki, Yamanashi prefecture).

**2009, June 23 Photo. *Perf. 13***

| | | | | |
|---|---|---|---|---|
| 3124 | A2502 | Sheet of 10 | 17.50 | 17.50 |
| *a.-j.* | | 80y Any single | 1.40 | .60 |

Miniature Sheet

Intl. Polar Year — A2503

No. 3125: a, Polar bears. b, Weddell seal. c, Arctic fox. d, Adélie penguin.

**Litho. With Hologram Affixed**

**2009, June 30 *Die Cut Perf. 13***

**Self-Adhesive**

| | | | | |
|---|---|---|---|---|
| 3125 | A2503 | Sheet of 4 | 7.00 | 7.00 |
| *a.-d.* | | 80y Any single | 1.40 | .60 |

Gentian A2504

Chrysanthemums A2505

Miyagi Bush Clover — A2506

Black Lilies — A2507

Japanese Maple — A2508

Gentian — A2509

Chrysanthemums A2510

Miyagi Bush Clover A2511

Black Lilies — A2512

Japanese Maple — A2513

**2009, July 1 Photo. *Perf. 13¼***

| | | | | |
|---|---|---|---|---|
| 3126 | A2504 | 50y multi | .90 | .50 |
| 3127 | A2505 | 50y multi | .90 | .50 |
| 3128 | A2506 | 50y multi | .90 | .50 |
| 3129 | A2507 | 50y multi | .90 | .50 |
| 3130 | A2508 | 50y multi | .90 | .50 |
| *a.* | | Vert. strip of 5, #3126-3130 | 5.50 | 4.00 |
| 3131 | A2509 | 80y multi | 1.40 | .60 |
| 3132 | A2510 | 80y multi | 1.40 | .60 |
| 3133 | A2511 | 80y multi | 1.40 | .60 |
| 3134 | A2512 | 80y multi | 1.40 | .60 |
| 3135 | A2513 | 80y multi | 1.40 | .60 |
| *a.* | | Vert. strip of 5, #3131-3135 | 8.75 | 6.25 |
| | | *Nos. 3126-3135 (10)* | 11.50 | 5.50 |

Flora of Kumamoto, Hyogo, Miyagi, Ishikawa and Hiroshima prefectures.

Miniature Sheet

Niigata Prefecture Local Autonomy Law, 60th Anniv. — A2514

No. 3136: a, Japanese crested ibis over Sado Island (33x39mm). b, Cherry blossoms, Takada Castle (28x33mm). c, Fireworks over Nagaoka (28x33mm). d, Imori Pond, Mt. Myoko (28x33mm). e, Fireworks at Tokamichi Snow Festival (28x33mm).

***Perf. 13¼ (#3136a), 13x13¼***

**2009, July 8 Photo.**

| | | | | |
|---|---|---|---|---|
| 3136 | A2514 | Sheet of 5 | 8.75 | 8.75 |
| *a.-e.* | | 80y Any single | 1.40 | .60 |

Statue of Eki Doji — A2515

**2009, July 23 Photo.** ***Perf. 13x13½***

**3137** A2515 300y multi 6.25 4.75

Ono no Komachi, Poet — A2516

Ietaka Junii, Poet — A2517

Hoshi Jakuren, Poet — A2518

Sakanoue no Korenori, Poet — A2519

Daini no Sanmi, Poet — A2520

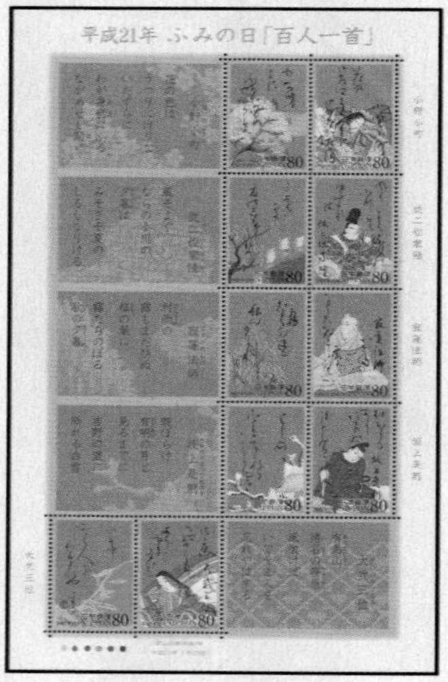

Poetry — A2521

No. 3143 — Poetry in Japanese calligraphy and: a, Tree with white blossoms. b, Ono no Komachi. c, Tree near pond. d, Ietaka Junii. e, Tree with green leaves. f, Hoshi Jakuren. g, House. h, Sakanoue no Korenori. i, Leaves. j, Daini no Sanmi.

**2009, July 23 Photo.** ***Perf. 13¼***

| | | | | |
|---|---|---|---|---|
| **3138** | A2516 | 50y multi | .90 | .50 |
| **3139** | A2517 | 50y multi | .90 | .50 |
| **3140** | A2518 | 50y multi | .90 | .50 |
| **3141** | A2519 | 50y multi | .90 | .50 |
| **3142** | A2520 | 50y multi | .90 | .50 |
| *a.* | | Vert. strip of 5, #3138-3142 | 5.50 | 5.50 |

***Perf. 12¾x13***

| | | | | |
|---|---|---|---|---|
| **3143** | A2521 | Sheet of 10 | 17.50 | 17.50 |
| *a.-j.* | | 80y Any single | 1.40 | .90 |

Letter Writing Day.

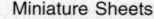

Miniature Sheets

A2522

Hello Kitty and Dear Daniel — A2523

No. 3144: a, Hello Kitty with envelope. b, Hello Kitty, Dear Daniel, birds in pond. c, Hello Kitty, Dear Daniel, two trees. d, Hello Kitty and Dear Daniel with envelopes. e, Hello Kitty, Dear Daniel, three trees.

No. 3145: a, Hello Kitty with envelope (35mm diameter). b, Hello Kitty, two birds (35x28mm, heart-shaped). c, Hello Kitty, tree, three birds. d, Bird carrying envelope flying over Hello Kitty. e, Hello Kitty, bird, two trees. f, Hello Kitty, Dear Daniel, bird, squirrel and rabbit.

***Die Cut Perf. 13½***

**2009, July 23 Litho.**

| | | | | |
|---|---|---|---|---|
| **3144** | A2522 | Sheet of 10, 2 each #a-e | 11.00 | |
| *a.-e.* | | 50y Any single | .90 | .50 |

***Die Cut Perf. (#3145a-3145b), Die Cut Perf. 13½***

| | | | | |
|---|---|---|---|---|
| **3145** | A2523 | Sheet of 10, #a-b, 2 each #c-f | 17.50 | |
| *a.-f.* | | 80y Any single | 1.40 | .90 |

Suwa Bluff, Nippori, by Hiroshige A2524

Pensive Love, by Utamaro A2525

Tokuji Otani as Yakko Sodesuke, by Sharaku A2526

Kumano Junisha Shrine, by Hiroshige A2527

Moon Promontory, by Hiroshige A2528

Woman Reading a Letter, by Utamaro A2529

Wadaemon Nakajima as Bodara Chozaemon and Konozo Nakamura as Funayado Kanagaway no Gon, by Sharaku A2530

Pagoda at Zojo Temple, by Hiroshige A2531

Clear Weather After Snowfall at Japan Bridge, by Hiroshige A2532

Kameikichi of Sodegaura, by Utamaro A2533

**2009, Aug. 3 Litho.** ***Perf. 13¼***

| | | | | |
|---|---|---|---|---|
| **3146** | | Sheet of 10 | 17.50 | 17.50 |
| *a.* | A2524 | 80y multi | 1.40 | .90 |
| *b.* | A2525 | 80y multi | 1.40 | .90 |
| *c.* | A2526 | 80y multi | 1.40 | .90 |
| *d.* | A2527 | 80y multi | 1.40 | .90 |
| *e.* | A2528 | 80y multi | 1.40 | .90 |
| *f.* | A2529 | 80y multi | 1.40 | .90 |
| *g.* | A2530 | 80y multi | 1.40 | .90 |
| *h.* | A2531 | 80y multi | 1.40 | .90 |
| *i.* | A2532 | 80y multi | 1.40 | .90 |
| *j.* | A2533 | 80y multi | 1.40 | .90 |

Life in Edo (Tokyo).

Gujo Dance (Gifu) — A2534

Fukagawa Hachiman Festival (Tokyo) — A2535

Denomination at: No. 3147, Right. No. 3148, Left. No. 3149, Right. No. 3150, Left.

**2009, Aug. 10**

| | | | |
|---|---|---|---|
| **3147** | 50y multi | .90 | .50 |
| **3148** | 50y multi | .90 | .50 |
| *a.* | A2534 Horiz. pair, #3147-3148 | 2.20 | 2.20 |
| **3149** | 50y multi | .90 | .50 |
| **3150** | 50y multi | .90 | .50 |
| *a.* | A2535 Horiz. pair, #3149-3150 | 2.20 | 2.20 |
| | *Nos. 3147-3150 (4)* | 3.60 | 2.00 |

Miniature Sheet

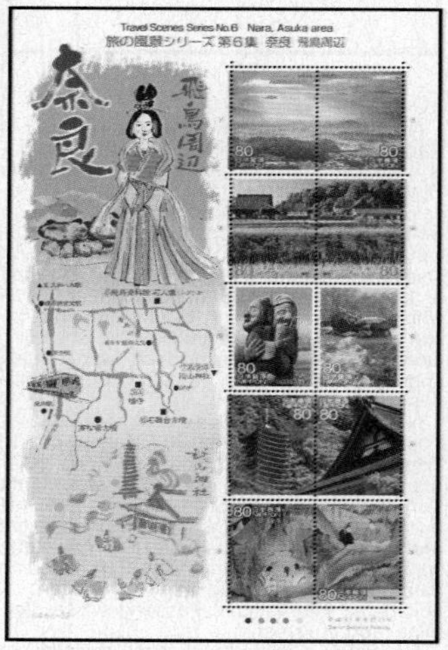

Travel Scenes — A2536

No. 3151: a, Asuka, denomination at LL (stamp 1). b, Asuka, denomination at LR (stamp 2). c, Tachibana Temple, denomination at LL (stamp 3). d, Tachibana Temple, denomination at LR (stamp 4). e, Sculpture, Asuka Historical Museum (stamp 5). f, Stone burial mound (stamp 6). g, Tanzan Shrine, denomination at UR (stamp 7). h, Tanzan Shrine, denomination at UL (stamp 8). i, Picture scroll, denomination at UL (stamp 9). j, Picture scroll, denomination at LL (stamp 10).

**2009, Aug. 21** ***Perf. 13x13¼***

| | | | | |
|---|---|---|---|---|
| **3151** | A2536 | Sheet of 10 | 17.50 | 17.50 |
| *a.-j.* | | 80y Any single | 1.40 | .90 |

Persimmons and Haiku by Shiki Masaoka — A2537

Roofs of Dogo Onsen and Haiku by Shiki Masaoka — A2538

Mountain, Field and Haiku by Kyoshi Takahama A2539

House and Haiku by Soseki Natsume — A2540

Cherry Blossoms and Haiku by Hekigoto Kawahigashi A2541

**2009, Sept. 1** **Litho.**

| | | | | |
|---|---|---|---|---|
| **3152** | A2537 80y multi | | 1.40 | .90 |
| **3153** | A2538 80y multi | | 1.40 | .90 |
| **3154** | A2539 80y multi | | 1.40 | .90 |
| **3155** | A2540 80y multi | | 1.40 | .90 |
| **3156** | A2541 80y multi | | 1.40 | .90 |
| *a.* | Vert. strip of 5, #3152-3156 | | 8.75 | 8.75 |

Miniature Sheet

National Athletic Meet (Niigata) — A2542

No. 3157: a, Tohoku Electric Power Big Swan Stadium. b, Soccer player. c, Boxer. d, Basketball player.

**2009, Sept. 25** ***Perf. 13x13¼***

| | | | | |
|---|---|---|---|---|
| **3157** | A2542 | Sheet of 10, 2 each #3157a-3157c, 4 #3157d | 11.00 | 11.00 |
| *a.-d.* | | 50y Any single | .90 | .50 |

Takayama Festival (Gifu) — A2543

Hakone Feudal Lord's Procession (Kanagawa) — A2544

Designs: No. 3158, Crowd at Night Festival. No. 3159, Shakkyo float puppet. No. 3160, Three men and box. No. 3161, Three men.

**2009, Oct. 1** ***Perf. 13¼***

| | | | |
|---|---|---|---|
| **3158** | 50y multi | .90 | .50 |
| **3159** | 50y multi | .90 | .50 |
| *a.* | A2543 Pair, #3158-3159 | 2.20 | 2.20 |
| **3160** | 50y multi | .90 | .50 |
| **3161** | 50y multi | .90 | .50 |
| *a.* | A2544 Horiz. pair, #3160-3161 | 2.20 | 2.20 |
| | *Nos. 3158-3161 (4)* | 3.60 | 2.00 |

Miniature Sheet

Home Towns — A2545

No. 3162 — Paintings by Taiji Harada of views of towns: a, Nagasaki Kunchi (palanquin in parade, Nagasaki, Nagasaki prefecture). b, Rice Paddy Spirit Festival (people in rice paddy, Satsumasendai, Kagoshima prefecture). c, Carp Streamers (people making carp streamers, Iwakura, Aichi prefecture). d, Doll Send-off (winter parade, Waga District, Iwate prefecture). e, Deer Dance (musicians, people in blue, white, red and yellow costumes holding poles with banners, Kitauwa District, Ehime prefecture). f, Business Success Festival (crowd in front of Ebisu Shrine, Naniwa Ward, Osaka prefecture). g, Amahage Festival (masked man visiting children and parents, Akumi District, Yamagata prefecture). h, Lion Dance (large crowd surrounding float with dancers on tower, Wakayama, Wakayama prefecture). i, Floating Doll Festival (women dropping dolls into Sendai River, Tottori, Tottori prefecture). j, Gruel Doll Festival (children at table near Kama River, Tano District, Gumma prefecture).

**2009, Oct. 8** **Photo.** ***Perf. 13***

| | | | | |
|---|---|---|---|---|
| **3162** | A2545 | Sheet of 10 | 17.50 | 17.50 |
| *a.-j.* | | 80y Any single | 1.40 | .90 |

**International Letter Writing Week Type of 2000**

Hiroshige paintings from 53 Stations of the Tokaido Highway: 90y, Fujisawa. 110y, Okitsu. 130y, Chiryu.

**2009, Oct. 9** **Photo.** ***Perf. 13¼***

| | | | |
|---|---|---|---|
| **3163** | A2119 90y multi | 1.60 | .80 |
| **3164** | A2119 110y multi | 1.90 | .90 |
| **3165** | A2119 130y multi | 2.10 | 1.00 |
| | *Nos. 3163-3165 (3)* | 5.60 | 2.70 |

Miniature Sheet

Diplomatic Relations Between Japan and Austria, 140th Anniv. — A2546

No. 3166: a, Portrait of Emilie Flöge, by Gustav Klimt (45x30mm). b, Autumn Clothing, by Shoen Uemura (45x30mm). c, Vienna Art History Museum and fountain (39x30mm). d, Empress Elizabeth of Austria, by Franz Winterhalter (39x30mm). e, Melk Abbey (steeple at right), Austria (39x30mm). f, Melk Abbey (steeple at left, 39x30mm). g, Wolfgang Amadeus Mozart and Salzburg (39x30mm). h, Salzburg (39x30mm). i, Hallstatt waterfront (39x30mm). j, Mountainside buildings, Hallstatt (39x30mm).

**2009, Oct. 16** **Litho.** ***Perf. 13¼x13***

| | | | | |
|---|---|---|---|---|
| **3166** | A2546 | Sheet of 10 | 17.50 | 17.50 |
| *a.-j.* | | 80y Any single | 1.40 | .90 |

See Austria No. 2227.

Miniature Sheet

Diplomatic Relations Between Japan and Hungary, 140th Anniv. — A2547

No. 3167: a, Hungarian flask. b, Mount Fuji, horiz. c, Jar from Japanese tea service. d, Hungarian Parliament (flag above building). e, Hungarian Parliament (building with dome). f, Matyo folk embroidery, Hungary. g, Elizabeth Bridge, Hungary, horiz. h, Crane and leaves fabric pattern from Japanese kimono. i, Herend porcelain figurine (Hussar examining sword blade). j, Herend porcelain vase.

***Perf. 13x13¼, 13¼x13***

**2009, Oct. 16** **Litho.**

| | | | | |
|---|---|---|---|---|
| **3167** | A2547 | Sheet of 10 | 17.50 | 17.50 |
| *a.-j.* | | 80y Any single | 1.40 | .90 |

See Hungary No. 4141.

**Animation**

Miniature Sheet

Naruto: Hurricane Chronicles — A2548

No. 3168: a, Naruto Uzumaki (yellow hair, black and orange shirt). b, Sasuke Uchiha (with open shirt). c, Sakura Haruno (girl with pink hair). d, Kakashi Hatake (with red spiral on sleeve). e, Sai (with sword). f, Shikamaru Nara (clasping hands). g, Deidara (girl with yellow hair and raised hand). h, Itachi Uchiha (with black hair and black and red robe). i, Jiraiya (with white hair). j, Fourth Hokage (yellow hair, white, gray and red robe).

**2009, Oct. 23** **Litho.** ***Perf. 13x13¼***

| | | | | |
|---|---|---|---|---|
| **3168** | A2548 | Sheet of 10 | 17.50 | 17.50 |
| *a.-j.* | | 80y Any single | 1.40 | .90 |

Miniature Sheet

Ibaraki Prefecture Local Autonomy Law, 60th Anniv. — A2549

No. 3169: a, H-2 rocket, Mt. Tsukuba (33x39mm). b, Fukuroda Falls (28x33mm). c, Mitsukuni Tokugawa (1628-1700), Mito daimyo (28x33mm). d, Boat on Kasumigaura (28x33mm). e, Fireworks over Tsuchiura (28x33mm).

***Perf. 13¼ (#3169a), 13x13¼***

**2009, Nov. 4** **Photo.**

| | | | | |
|---|---|---|---|---|
| **3169** | A2549 | Sheet of 5 | 9.00 | 9.00 |
| *a.-e.* | | 80y Any single | 1.40 | .90 |

A2550

A2551

New Year 2010 (Year of the Tiger)
A2552 A2553

**2009, Nov. 11 Photo. *Perf. 13x13½***

| | | | | |
|---|---|---|---|---|
| **3170** | A2550 50y multi | .95 | .40 |
| **3171** | A2551 80y multi | 1.40 | .50 |

***Perf. 13¼***

| | | | |
|---|---|---|---|
| **3172** | A2552 50y +3y multi | 1.10 | .50 |
| **3173** | A2553 80y +3y multi | 1.60 | .50 |
| | *Nos. 3170-3173 (4)* | 5.05 | 1.90 |

Sheets of two containing Nos. 3170-3171 were lottery prizes. Value, $4.

Phoenix — A2554

Kirin Facing Right
A2555

Kirin Facing Left
A2556

**2009, Nov. 12 Photo. *Perf. 13¼***

| | | | |
|---|---|---|---|
| **3174** | A2554 80y multi | 1.40 | .90 |
| **3175** | A2555 80y multi | 1.40 | .90 |
| **3176** | A2556 80y multi | 1.40 | .90 |
| *a.* | Souvenir sheet, #3175-3176 | 3.50 | 2.80 |
| | *Nos. 3174-3176 (3)* | 4.20 | 2.70 |

Enthronement of Emperor Akihito, 20th anniv. Nos. 3174-3176 were printed in sheets containing two each of Nos. 3175 and 3176 and six of No. 3174.

Miniature Sheet

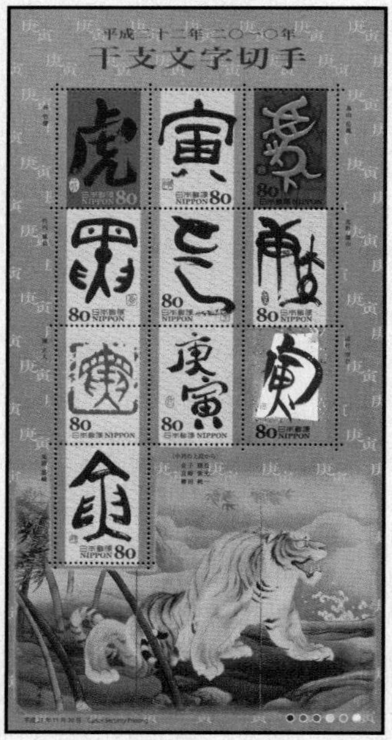


Calligraphy — A2557

No. 3177 — Characters for "tiger" by calligraphers: a, Chikusei Hayashi (character in running script with red background). b, Chosho Kneko (character in clerical style, with denomination at LR, and large red chop at LL). c, Gakufu Toriyama (character in kinbun style in gold with blue green background). d, Hosen Takeuchi (character in kinbun style with denomination at LL, red chop at LR). e, Shiko Miyazaki (character in hiragana script with denomination above Japanese characters and "Nippon" at LL). f, Setsuzan Kitano (character in kokotsubun style with denomination and red chop at LL). g, Masato Seki (character in kinbun style in red). h, Junichi Yanagida (characters in running script with denomination at LL above Japanese characters and "Nippon" at LR). i, Kukoku Tamura (character in clerical script in blue with light blue and white background). j, Bokushun Kito (character in kinbun style with denomination at LR and small red chop at LL).

**Litho. & Embossed**

**2009, Nov. 20 *Perf. 13x13¼***

| | | | |
|---|---|---|---|
| **3177** | A2557 Sheet of 10 | 17.50 | 17.50 |
| *a.-j.* | 80y Any single | 1.40 | .90 |

Miniature Sheets

A2558

Greetings Stamps — A2559

No. 3178: a, Girl and apples. b, Snowman and stars. c, Angel holding toy rabbit. d, Apple, ribbon, ring of roses. e, Figures with blue and pink faces, horiz.

No. 3179: a, Christmas wreath. b, Santa Claus playing violin on chimney. c, Oil lamp and flowers. d, Angel with gift. e, Figure made of fir branches, candle.

***Die Cut Perf. 12¾x13, 13x12¾***

**2009, Nov. 24 Litho.**

**Self-Adhesive**

| | | | |
|---|---|---|---|
| **3178** | A2558 Sheet of 5 | 5.50 | 5.50 |
| *a.-e.* | 50y Any single | .90 | .50 |

***Die Cut Perf. 12¾x13***

| | | | |
|---|---|---|---|
| **3179** | A2559 Sheet of 5 | 9.00 | 9.00 |
| *a.-e.* | 80y Any single | 1.40 | .90 |

Peach Blossoms
A2560

Rape Blossoms
A2561

Plum Blossoms and Primrose
A2562

Bayberry
A2563

Bungo Plum Blossoms
A2564

Peach Blossoms
A2565

Rape Blossoms
A2566

Plum Blossoms and Primrose
A2567

Bayberry
A2568

Bungo Plum Blossoms
A2569

**2009, Dec. 1 Photo. *Perf. 13¼***

| | | | |
|---|---|---|---|
| **3180** | A2560 50y multi | .90 | .50 |
| **3181** | A2561 50y multi | .90 | .50 |
| **3182** | A2562 50y multi | .90 | .50 |
| **3183** | A2563 50y multi | .90 | .50 |
| **3184** | A2564 50y multi | .90 | .50 |
| *a.* | Vert. strip of 5, #3180-3184 | 5.50 | 5.50 |
| **3185** | A2565 80y multi | 1.40 | .90 |
| **3186** | A2566 80y multi | 1.40 | .90 |
| **3187** | A2567 80y multi | 1.40 | .90 |
| **3188** | A2568 80y multi | 1.40 | .90 |
| **3189** | A2569 80y multi | 1.40 | .90 |
| *a.* | Vert. strip of 5, #3185-3189 | 8.75 | 8.75 |
| | *Nos. 3180-3189 (10)* | 11.50 | 7.00 |

Flowers of Okayama, Chiba, Osaka, Kochi and Oita prefectures.

**Prefecture Types of 1991-2007**

Designs as before.

***Die Cut Perf. 13¼ at T, L and R, Serpentine Die Cut 11¾ at B***

**2009 Litho. Self-Adhesive**

| | | | |
|---|---|---|---|
| **3189B** | ZA684 50y multi | .90 | .50 |

***Serpentine Die Cut 11¾ at T and B, Die Cut Perf. 13¼ at L and R***

| | | | |
|---|---|---|---|
| **3189C** | ZA685 50y multi | .90 | .50 |
| **3189D** | ZA686 50y multi | .90 | .50 |
| **3189E** | ZA687 50y multi | .90 | .50 |

***Serpentine Die Cut 11¾ at T, Die Cut Perf. 13¼ at L, R and B***

| | | | |
|---|---|---|---|
| **3189F** | ZA688 50y multi | .90 | .50 |
| *j.* | Vert. strip of 5, #3189B-3189F | 5.50 | |

***Serpentine Die Cut 11½ at T, Die Cut Perf. 13½ at L, R and B***

| | | | |
|---|---|---|---|
| **3189G** | ZA115 80y multi | 1.40 | .90 |

***Serpentine Die Cut 11¾***

| | | | |
|---|---|---|---|
| **3189H** | 80y Katsura Beach | 1.40 | .90 |
| **3189I** | 80y Sakamoto Ryoma | 1.40 | .90 |
| *k.* | ZA352 Horiz. pair, #3189H-3189I | 3.50 | |
| | *Nos. 3189B-3189I (8)* | 8.70 | 5.20 |

Issued: Nos. 3189B-3189F, Oct.; No. 3189G, 3/19; Nos. 3189H-3189I, Nov.

**Animation**

Miniature Sheet

Sergeant Keroro — A2570

No. 3190: a, Sergeant Keroro, wearing helmet, holding post card. b, Fuyuki Hinata holding post card. c, Natsumi Hinata holding gift. d, Corporal Giroro, wearing helmet, with arms crossed. e, Private Tamama holding gift above head. f, Momoka Nishizawa holding letter. g, Saburo holding stamps. h, Sergeant Major Kururu with stamp on forehead. i, Lance Corporal Dororo, with white helmet, holding scroll. j, Koyuki Azumaya, holding scroll.

**2010, Jan. 22 Litho. *Perf. 13***

| | | | |
|---|---|---|---|
| **3190** | A2570 Sheet of 10 | 17.50 | 17.50 |
| *a.-j.* | 80y Any single | 1.40 | .90 |

Miniature Sheets

A2571

Greetings Stamps — A2572

No. 3191: a, Fairy with watering can. b, Fairy giving letter to bird. c, Fairies holding flower basket. d, Fairy with horn on back of flying bird. e, Fairy with violin on flower leaf.

No. 3192: a, Flower bouquet in red wrapping paper, butterflies. b, Woman with flute. c, Flower bouquet in white wrapping paper, butterflies. d, Flowers, G clef. e, Flowers, rabbit.

***Die Cut Perf. 12¾x13***

**2010, Jan. 25 Litho.**

**Self-Adhesive**

| | | | |
|---|---|---|---|
| **3191** | A2571 Sheet of 5 | 5.50 | 5.50 |
| *a.-e.* | 50y Any single | .90 | .50 |
| **3192** | A2572 Sheet of 5 | 9.00 | 9.00 |
| *a.-e.* | 80y Any single | 1.40 | .90 |

Miniature Sheet

Travel Scenes — A2573

No. 3193: a, Matsushima, denomination at LL (stamp 1). b, Matsushima, denomination at LR (stamp 2). c, Sendai Castle ruins (stamp 3). d, Suit of armor and crested helmet (stamp 4). e, Sendai tourist bus (stamp 5). f, A Bathing Woman, sculpture by Venanzo Crocetti, Sendai (stamp 6). g, Tanabata Festival, Sendai (stamp 7). h, Zuihoden Mausoleum (stamp 8). i, Rinno Temple, denomination at LL (stamp 9). j, Garden and pond at Rinno Temple (stamp 10).

**2010, Jan. 29 Litho. *Perf. 13***

| | | | | |
|---|---|---|---|---|
| **3193** | A2573 | Sheet of 10 | 17.50 | 17.50 |
| *a.-j.* | | 80y Any single | 1.40 | .90 |

Tulips — A2574

Chinese Milk Vetch — A2575

Nijisseiki Pear Blossoms A2576

Coral Tree Blossoms A2577

Fuji Cherry Blossoms A2578

Tulips A2579

Chinese Milk Vetch A2580

Nijisseiki Pear Blossoms A2581

Coral Tree Blossoms A2582

Fuji Cherry Blossoms A2583

**2010, Feb. 1 Photo. *Perf. 13¼***

| | | | | |
|---|---|---|---|---|
| **3194** | A2574 50y multi | | .90 | .50 |
| **3195** | A2575 50y multi | | .90 | .50 |
| **3196** | A2576 50y multi | | .90 | .50 |
| **3197** | A2577 50y multi | | .90 | .50 |
| **3198** | A2578 50y multi | | .90 | .50 |
| *a.* | Vert. strip of 5, #3194-3198 | | 5.50 | 5.50 |
| **3199** | A2579 80y multi | | 1.40 | .90 |
| **3200** | A2580 80y multi | | 1.40 | .90 |
| **3201** | A2581 80y multi | | 1.40 | .90 |
| **3202** | A2582 80y multi | | 1.40 | .90 |
| **3203** | A2583 80y multi | | 1.40 | .90 |
| *a.* | Vert. strip of 5, #3199-3203 | | 8.75 | 8.75 |
| | *Nos. 3194-3203 (10)* | | 11.50 | 7.00 |

Flowers of Toyama, Gifu, Tottori, Okinawa and Yamanashi prefectures.

Miniature Sheet

Nara Prefecture Local Autonomy Law, 60th Anniv. — A2584

No. 3204: a, Great Hall of State, cherry blossoms, kemari players (33x39mm). b, Hase Temple, peonies (28x33mm). c, Ukimodo during Nara Candlelight Festival (28x33mm). d, Muro Temple pagoda (28x33mm). e, Mt. Yoshino and cherry blossoms (28x33mm).

***Perf. 13¼ (#3204a), 13x13¼***

**2010, Feb. 8 Photo.**

| | | | | |
|---|---|---|---|---|
| **3204** | A2584 | Sheet of 5 | 9.00 | 9.00 |
| *a.-e.* | | 80y Any single | 1.40 | .90 |

Miniature Sheet

Travel Scenes — A2585

No. 3205: a, Kurashiki District buildings, denomination at LL (stamp 1). b, Kurashiki District buildings, swans, denomination at UR (stamp 2). c, Ohara Museum of Art (stamp 3). d, Belgian Girl in Kimono, painting by Torajiro Kojima (stamp 4). e, Seto Great Bridge, from distance (stamp 5). f, Arches and roadway of Seto Great Bridge (stamp 6). g, Kotohira Shrine (stamp 7). h, Mt. Iino (stamp 8). i, Bridge, Ritsurin Park, Takamatsu, denomination at LL (stamp 9). j, Bridge, Ritsurin Park, and cherry blossoms, denomination at UR (stamp 10).

**2010, Mar. 1 Litho. *Perf. 13***

| | | | | |
|---|---|---|---|---|
| **3205** | A2585 | Sheet of 10 | 17.50 | 17.50 |
| *a.-j.* | | 80y Any single | 1.40 | .90 |

Miniature Sheet

Characters From Peanuts Comic Strip — A2586

No. 3206: a, Snoopy reading letter (33x32mm). b, Woodstock reading letter under lamp (33x32mm). c, Peppermint Patty reading letter (33x32mm). d, Snoopy hugging Woodstock (35mm diameter). e, Sally reading letter (33x32mm). f, Snoopy and Woodstock on doghouse (35x29mm heart-shaped). g, Snoopy giving letter to Woodstock (33x32mm). h, Charlie Brown writing letter (33x32mm).

***Die Cut Perf. 13½***

**2010, Mar. 3 Litho.**

**Self-Adhesive**

| | | | | |
|---|---|---|---|---|
| **3206** | A2586 | Sheet of 10, #3206c-3206h, 2 each #3206a-3206b | 17.50 | 17.50 |
| *a.-h.* | | 80y Any single | 1.40 | .90 |

Peony A2587

Sudachi Flowers A2588

Unzen Azalea Flowers A2589

Kakitsubata Irises A2590

Camphor Blossoms A2591

Peonies A2592

Sudachi Flowers A2593

Unzen Azalea Flowers A2594

Kakitsubata Irises A2595

Camphor Blossoms A2596

**2010, Mar. 8 Photo. *Perf. 13¼***

| | | | | |
|---|---|---|---|---|
| **3207** | A2587 50y multi | | .90 | .50 |
| **3208** | A2588 50y multi | | .90 | .50 |
| **3209** | A2589 50y multi | | .90 | .50 |
| **3210** | A2590 50y multi | | .90 | .50 |
| **3211** | A2591 50y multi | | .90 | .50 |
| *a.* | Vert. strip of 5, #3207-3211 | | 5.50 | 5.50 |
| **3212** | A2592 80y multi | | 1.40 | .90 |
| **3213** | A2593 80y multi | | 1.40 | .90 |
| **3214** | A2594 80y multi | | 1.40 | .90 |
| **3215** | A2595 80y multi | | 1.40 | .90 |
| **3216** | A2596 80y multi | | 1.40 | .90 |
| *a.* | Vert. strip of 5, #3212-3216 | | 8.75 | 8.75 |
| | *Nos. 3207-3216 (10)* | | 11.50 | 7.00 |

Flowers of Shimane, Tokushima, Nagasaki, Aichi and Saga prefectures.

Miniature Sheet

Friendship With San Marino — A2597

No. 3217: a, La Repubblica, statue by Vittorio Pocchini, San Marino (stamp 1). b, First Tower, San Marino (stamp 2). c, Saint Marinus, angel and crowd from Appearance of Saint Marinus to His People, mural by Emilio Retrosi (stamp 3). d, Angel and crowd from Appearance of Saint Marinus to His People (stamp 4). e, Statue of Liberty, San Marino Government Building (stamp 5). f, Basilica of Saint Marinus (stamp 6). g, Second Tower, San Marino (stamp 7). h, Bell tower, First Tower (stamp 8). i, St. Mary Magdalene, painting by Francesco Menzocchi (stamp 9). j, St. Marinus, painting by unknown artist (stamp 10).

**2010, Mar. 23 Litho. *Perf. 13***

| | | | | |
|---|---|---|---|---|
| **3217** | A2597 | Sheet of 10 | 17.50 | 17.50 |
| *a.-j.* | | 80y Any single | 1.40 | .90 |

See San Marino No. 1818.

Miniature Sheet

Hometown Festival — A2598

No. 3218 — Suwa Grand Shrine Sacred Pillar Festival, Nagano Prefecture: a, Honmiya Shrine, denomination in yellow. b, Maemiya Shrine, denomination in pink. c, Akimiya Shrine, denomination in greenish black. d, Harumiya Shrine, denomination in light blue. e, Men dragging logs to Miya River, denomination in pink. f, Nagamochi, denomination in black. g, Men dragging log down hill, denomination in blue.

**2010, Apr. 1 Litho. *Perf. 13¼***
**Self-Adhesive**

| | | | | |
|---|---|---|---|---|
| **3218** | A2598 | Sheet of 10, #3218a-3218d, 2 each #3218e-3218g | 11.00 | 11.00 |
| *a.-g.* | | 50y Any single | .90 | .50 |

Philately Week — A2599

No. 3219: a, Tiger from screen painting by Gaho Hashimoto, denomination at UL. b, Peonies from screen painting by Hashimoto, denomination at LL. c, Peonies and birds from screen painting by Hashimoto, denomination at UL. d, Tiger, by Zhang Shanzi, denomination at LR.

***Perf. 12¾x12½ Syncopated***
**2010, Apr. 20 Photo.**

| | | | | |
|---|---|---|---|---|
| **3219** | A2599 | Block of 4 | 7.00 | 7.00 |
| *a.-d.* | | 80y Any single | 1.40 | .90 |

Miniature Sheet

Treasures of Nara — A2600

No. 3220: a, Restored Heijo Palace (stamp 1). b, Inner gate, Kasuga Grand Shrine (stamp 2). c, Tanjo Shaka statue, denomination in white at UR (stamp 3). d, Aizen Myo-o statue, denomination in white at UL (stamp 4). e, Tentoki holding lantern, denomination in gold at UL (stamp 5). f, Buddha Yakushi, denomination in gold at UL (stamp 6). g, Thousand-armed Kannon statue, denomination in white at UR (stamp 7). h, Standing Bodhisattva statue, denomination in white at LR (stamp 8). i, Tamonten statue, denomination in gold at LL (stamp 9). j, Basara Taisho statue, denomination in gold at LR (stamp 10).

**2010, Apr. 23 Litho. *Perf. 14x13¾***

| | | | | |
|---|---|---|---|---|
| **3220** | A2600 | Sheet of 10 | 17.50 | 17.50 |
| *a.-j.* | | 80y Any single | 1.40 | .90 |

Move of Imperial capital to Nara, 1300th anniv.

Hanashobu Iris A2601

Olive Blossoms A2602

Azalea Flowers A2603

Paulownia Blossoms A2604

Crinum Flowers A2605

Hanashobu Irises A2606

Olive Blossoms A2607

Azalea Flowers A2608

Paulownia Blossoms A2609

Crinum Flowers A2610

**2010, Mar. 8 Photo. *Perf. 13¼***

| | | | | |
|---|---|---|---|---|
| **3221** | A2601 | 50y multi | .90 | .50 |
| **3222** | A2602 | 50y multi | .90 | .50 |
| **3223** | A2603 | 50y multi | .90 | .50 |
| **3224** | A2604 | 50y multi | .90 | .50 |
| **3225** | A2605 | 50y multi | .90 | .50 |
| *a.* | | Vert. strip of 5, #3221-3225 | 5.50 | 5.50 |
| **3226** | A2606 | 80y multi | 1.40 | .90 |
| **3227** | A2607 | 80y multi | 1.40 | .90 |
| **3228** | A2608 | 80y multi | 1.40 | .90 |
| **3229** | A2609 | 80y multi | 1.40 | .90 |
| **3230** | A2610 | 80y multi | 1.40 | .90 |
| *a.* | | Vert. strip of 5, #3226-3230 | 8.75 | 8.75 |
| | | *Nos. 3221-3230 (10)* | 11.50 | 7.00 |

Flowers of Mie, Kagawa, Gumma, Iwate and Miyazaki prefectures.

**Kobe-Awaji Expressway Prefecture Type of 1998**

***Die Cut Perf. 11½***
**2010, Aug. Self-Adhesive Litho.**

| | | | |
|---|---|---|---|
| **3230B** | ZA229 | 80y Like No. Z237 | — |
| **3230C** | ZA229 | 80y Like No. Z238 | — |

Miniature Sheet

A2611

Hello Kitty — A2612

No. 3231 — Hello Kitty: a, With butterflies and flowers (28x31mm heart-shaped). b, In kimono, flowers (28x31mm heart-shaped). c, With dragon (28x28mm). d, With mountain (28x28mm). e, With peonies (28x28mm). f, With origami cranes (28x28mm).

No. 3232 — Hello Kitty: a, And Shanghai skyline (30x32mm). b, And pagoda in Shanghai (30x32mm). c, And Tiger (30x32mm). d, With peonies (31x28mm heart-shaped). e, Holding fan (31mm diameter).

***Die Cut Perf. 13½***
**2010, May 6 Litho.**
**Self-Adhesive**

| | | | | |
|---|---|---|---|---|
| **3231** | A2611 | Sheet of 10, #3231a-3231b, 2 each #3231c-3231f | 11.00 | 11.00 |
| *a.-f.* | | 50y Any single | .90 | .50 |

***Die Cut Perf. 12½***

| | | | | |
|---|---|---|---|---|
| **3232** | A2612 | Sheet of 10, 2 each #3232a-3232e | 17.50 | 17.50 |
| *a.-e.* | | 80y Any single | 1.40 | .90 |

Miniature Sheet

Kochi Prefecture Local Autonomy Law, 60th Anniv. — A2613

No. 3233: a, Ryoma Sakamoto (1836-67), samurai, and Katsura Beach (33x39mm). b, Farmhouse clock, Aki (28x33mm). c, Harimaya Bridge, streetcar (28x33mm). d, Paper carp streamers (28x33mm). e, Cape Ashizuri Lighthouse (28x33mm).

***Perf. 13¼ (#3233a), 13x13¼***

**2010, May 14 Photo.**

| | | | | |
|---|---|---|---|---|
| **3233** | A2613 | Sheet of 5 | 8.75 | 8.75 |
| *a.-e.* | | 80y Any single | 1.40 | .90 |

Miniature Sheet

Kanagawa Prefecture Afforestation — A2614

No. 3234: a, Pinks. b, Japanese cedar. c, Sawtooth oak. d, Japanese maple. e, Golden-rayed lilies. f, Evergreen oak. g, Japanese chinquapin. h, Ginkgo. i, Beech. j, Gentians.

**2010, May 21 Litho. *Perf. 13***

| | | | | |
|---|---|---|---|---|
| **3234** | A2614 | Sheet of 10 | 11.00 | 11.00 |
| *a.-j.* | | 50y Any single | .90 | .50 |

Miniature Sheets

A2615

2010 World Cup Soccer Championships, South Africa — A2616

No. 3235: a, Soccer ball, African animals (33x39mm). b, World Cup trophy (29x38mm). c, Poster for 2010 World Cup tournament (29x38mm). d, Emblem of 2010 World Cup (29x38mm). e, Emblem of Japan Soccer Association (29x38mm).

No. 3236 — Posters for World Cup tournaments of: a, 1930. b, 1934. c, 1938. d, 1950. e, 1954. f, 1958. g, 1962. h, 1970. i, 1978. j, 1986. k, 1990. l, 1994. m, 1998. n, 2002. o, 2006. p, Jules Rimet Cup. q, Jules Rimet Cup and hand.

**Litho., Litho. & Embossed (#3235a)**

***Perf. 13, 14x13½ (#3235a)***

**2010, May 31**

| | | | | |
|---|---|---|---|---|
| **3235** | A2615 | Sheet of 5 | 8.75 | 8.75 |
| *a.-e.* | | 80y Any single | 1.40 | .90 |

**Litho.**

***Perf. 13***

| | | | | |
|---|---|---|---|---|
| **3236** | A2616 | Sheet of 20, #3236a-3236o, 3 #3236p, 2 #3236q | 35.00 | 35.00 |
| *a.-q.* | | 80y Any single | 1.40 | .90 |

Miniature Sheet

Asia-Pacific Economic Cooperation Economic Leader's Meeting, Yokohama — A2617

No. 3237: a, Flowers at top and left, denomination at LR. b, Flowers at top and right, denomination at LL. c, Purple flower at center right, denomination at UR. d, Purple flower at center left, denomination at UL. e, Pink rose at center right, denomination at LL. f, Pink rose at center left, denomination at LR. g, White flowers at center right, denomination at UR. h, White flowers at center left, denomination at UL. i, Flowers at bottom and left, red flowers at LR, denomination at UR. j, Flowers at bottom and right, red flowers at LL, denomination at UL.

**2010, June 4 Litho. *Perf. 13***

| | | | | |
|---|---|---|---|---|
| **3237** | A2617 | Sheet of 10 | 17.50 | 17.50 |
| *a.-j.* | | 80y Any single | 1.40 | .90 |

Emblem of Japan Academy A2618

Certificate and Photograph of First Awards Ceremony A2619

Venue of First Awards Ceremony A2620

Former Japan Academy Hall A2621

Rooster — A2622

**2010, June 7 Litho. *Perf. 13***

| | | | | |
|---|---|---|---|---|
| **3238** | A2618 80y multi | | 1.40 | .90 |
| **3239** | A2619 80y multi | | 1.40 | .90 |
| **3240** | A2620 80y multi | | 1.40 | .90 |
| **3241** | A2621 80y multi | | 1.40 | .90 |
| **3242** | A2622 80y multi | | 1.40 | .90 |
| *a.* | Vert. strip of 5, #3238-3242 | | 8.75 | 8.75 |
| | *Nos. 3238-3242 (5)* | | 7.00 | 4.50 |

Japan Academy Prizes, cent.

**Animation**

Miniature Sheet

Full Metal Alchemist — A2623

No. 3243: a, Edward Elric (with yellow hair and hand on his shoulder). b, Alphonse Elric (in black armor). c, Riza Hawkeye (holding gun). d, Roy Mustang with symbol on back of hand. e, Xiao Mei (panda). f, May Chang (with braided hair). g, Ling Yao holding sword. h, Lan Fan holding dagger. i, Winry Rockbell (girl in tank top). j, Edward Elric with dog, Den.

**2010, June 14 Litho. *Perf. 13x13¼***

| | | | | |
|---|---|---|---|---|
| **3243** | A2623 | Sheet of 10 | 19.00 | 19.00 |
| *a.-j.* | | 80y Any single | 1.40 | .90 |

Miniature Sheet

Gifu Local Autonomy Law, 60th Anniv. — A2624

No. 3244: a, Cormorant fishing on Nagara River (32x39mm). b, Gifu Castle (28x33mm). c, Yokokura Temple (28x33mm). d, Art exhibition, Mino (28x33mm). e, Restored buildings, Magome (28x33mm).

***Perf. 13¼ (#3244a), 13x13¼***

**2010, June 18** **Photo.**

| | | | | |
|---|---|---|---|---|
| **3244** | A2624 | Sheet of 5 | 9.50 | 9.50 |
| *a.-e.* | | 80y Any single | 1.40 | .90 |

Revision of Japan-United States Security Treaty, 50th Anniv. — A2625

Designs: No. 3245, Flags of U.S. and Japan, Japanese Prime Minister Nobusuke Kishi and U.S. President Dwight D. Eisenhower. No. 3246, Japanese Diet and U.S. Capitol.

**2010, June 23** **Litho.** ***Perf. 13***

| | | | | |
|---|---|---|---|---|
| **3245** | | 80y multi | 1.40 | .90 |
| **3246** | | 80y multi | 1.40 | .90 |
| *a.* | A2625 | Pair, #3245-3246 | 3.80 | 3.80 |

Miniature Sheet

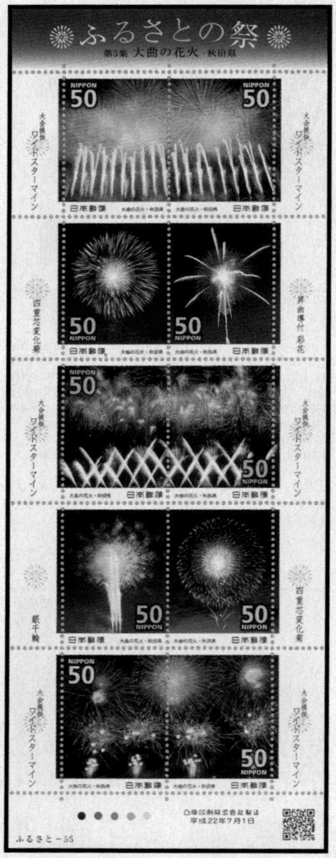

National Fireworks Competition, Omagari, Akita Prefecture — A2626

No. 3247 — Various fireworks with denomination in: a, Yellow green at UL, country name in Japanese characters at LL. b, Yellow green at UR. c, Pale orange at LL. d, Blue at LL. e, Rose at UL. f, Rose at LR, country name in Japanese characters at LR. g, Rose at LR, country name in Japanese characters at LL. h, Blue green at LR. i, Yellow green at UL, country name in Japanese characters at LR. j, Yellow green at LR.

**2010, July 1** **Litho.** ***Perf. 13¼***

| | | | | |
|---|---|---|---|---|
| **3247** | A2626 | Sheet of 10 | 11.50 | 11.50 |
| *a.-j.* | | 50y Any single | .90 | .50 |

Miniature Sheet

Travel Scenes — A2627

No. 3248: a, Kurushima-Kaikyo Great Bridge, denomination at LL (stamp 1). b, Kurushima-Kaikyo Great Bridge, denomination at LR (stamp 2). c, Jodo Temple, denomination at UR (stamp 3). d, Jodo Temple, denomination at UL (stamp 4). e, Bridge, sculptures on Mt. Shirataki (stamp 5). f, Kojoji three-story pagoda (stamp 6). g, Oyamazumi Shrine (stamp 7). h, Omishima Bridge, boat (stamp 8). i, Building with red window shutters at Imabari Castle (stamp 9). j, Six-story donjon at Imabari Castle (stamp 10).

**2010, July 8** **Litho.** ***Perf. 13x13¼***

| | | | | |
|---|---|---|---|---|
| **3248** | A2627 | Sheet of 10 | 19.00 | 19.00 |
| *a.-j.* | | 80y Any single | 1.40 | .90 |

Emperor Koko, Poet — A2628

Lady Ise, Poet — A2629

Saki no Daisojo Gyoson, Poet — A2630

Yushi Naishinno-ke no Kii, Poet — A2631

Sutoku In, Poet — A2632

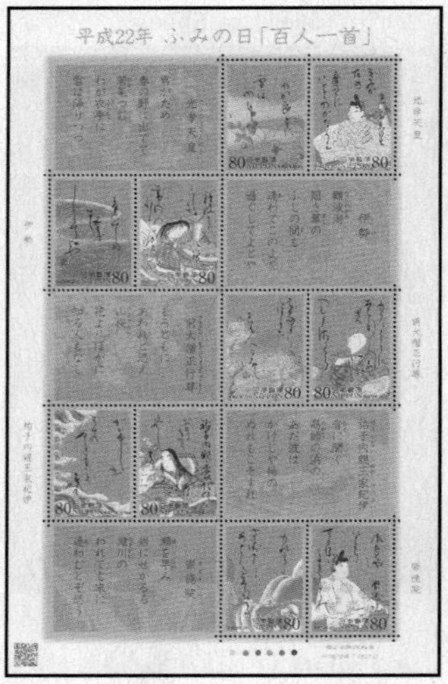

Poetry — A2633

No. 3254 — Poetry in Japanese calligraphy and: a, Purple flowers. b, Emperor Koko. c, Pond. d, Lady Ise. e, Hill and flowering trees. f, Saki no Daisojo Gyoson. g, Ocean waves. h, Yushi Naishinno-ke no Kii. i, Waterfall. j, Sutoku In.

**2010, July 23** **Photo.** ***Perf. 13¼***

| | | | | |
|---|---|---|---|---|
| **3249** | A2628 | 50y multi | .90 | .50 |
| **3250** | A2629 | 50y multi | .90 | .50 |
| **3251** | A2630 | 50y multi | .90 | .50 |
| **3252** | A2631 | 50y multi | .90 | .50 |
| **3253** | A2632 | 50y multi | .90 | .50 |
| *a.* | | Vert. strip of 5, #3249-3253 | 6.25 | 6.25 |

***Perf. 12¾x13***

| | | | | |
|---|---|---|---|---|
| **3254** | A2633 | Sheet of 10 | 19.00 | 19.00 |
| *a.-j.* | | 80y Any single | 1.40 | .90 |

Letter Writing Day.

Suruga Street, by Hiroshige A2634

Woman Reading a Letter, by Utamaro A2635

Dyer's Quarters, Kanda, by Hiroshige A2636

Sojuro Sawamura II as Kurando Ogishi, by Sharaku A2637

Asakusa Ricefields and Torinomachi Festival, by Hiroshige A2638

White Uchikake, by Utamaro A2639

Takinogawa, Oji, by Hiroshige A2640

Torazo Tanimura as Yaheiji Washizuka, by Sharaku A2641

Yamashita Park, Ueno, by Hiroshige A2642

Glass Goblet, by Utamaro A2643

**2010, Aug. 2** **Litho.** ***Perf. 13¼***

| | | | | |
|---|---|---|---|---|
| **3255** | | Sheet of 10 | 19.00 | 19.00 |
| *a.* | A2634 | 80y multi | 1.40 | .90 |
| *b.* | A2635 | 80y multi | 1.40 | .90 |
| *c.* | A2636 | 80y multi | 1.40 | .90 |
| *d.* | A2637 | 80y multi | 1.40 | .90 |
| *e.* | A2638 | 80y multi | 1.40 | .90 |
| *f.* | A2639 | 80y multi | 1.40 | .90 |
| *g.* | A2640 | 80y multi | 1.40 | .90 |
| *h.* | A2641 | 80y multi | 1.40 | .90 |
| *i.* | A2642 | 80y multi | 1.40 | .90 |
| *j.* | A2643 | 80y multi | 1.40 | .90 |

Life in Edo (Tokyo).

Miniature Sheet

Fukui Local Autonomy Law, 60th Anniv. — A2644

No. 3256: a, Dinosaur at Tojimbo (32x39mm). b, Narcissus (28x33mm). c, Lake and flowers (28x33mm). d, Ichijodani ruins, cherry tree (28x33mm). e, Crab, Echizen-Kaga Kaigan Quasi-National Park (28x33mm).

***Perf. 13¼ (#3256a), 13x13¼***

**2010, Aug. 9** **Photo.**

| | | | | |
|---|---|---|---|---|
| **3256** | A2644 | Sheet of 5 | 9.50 | 9.50 |
| *a.-e.* | | 80y Any single | 1.40 | .90 |

Miniature Sheet

Home Towns — A2645

No. 3257 — Paintings by Taiji Harada of views of Hokkaido prefecture towns: a, Shiranuka Line (Farmhouses, haystack, two cows, Shiranuka). b, Shiranuka Line (Train, three cows, Shiranuka). c, Red-crowned Cranes (Building near forest in snow, Tsurui). d, Red-crowned Cranes (Woman feeding cranes, Tsurui). e, Flowers of the Land (Houses, trees hills, Biei). f, Flowers of the Land (Tractor, hills, trees, Biei). g, Farm (Farm buildings, mail box cows, Ishikari). h, Farm (Farm buildings, silo, farmer tending cow, Ishikari). i, Hibernation (Building in snow, fishing boats, Wakkanai). j, Canal in Spring (Boats in canal, Otaru).

**2010, Sept. 10 Photo. *Perf. 13***

| | | | | |
|---|---|---|---|---|
| **3257** | A2645 | Sheet of 10 | 19.00 | 19.00 |
| *a.-j.* | | 80y Any single | 1.40 | .90 |

Biplane of Henri Farman A2646

Aeronautical Research Plane A2647

Asuka A2648

Boeing 747-400 A2649

Mitsubishi Regional Jet — A2650

Monoplane of Hans Grade A2651

YS-11 A2652

Kawasaki T-4 A2653

US-2 A2654

Supersonic Plane A2655

**2010, Sept. 21 Litho. *Perf. 13***

| | | | | |
|---|---|---|---|---|
| **3258** | | Sheet of 10 | 20.00 | 20.00 |
| *a.* | A2646 | 80y multi | 1.40 | .90 |
| *b.* | A2647 | 80y multi | 1.40 | .90 |
| *c.* | A2648 | 80y multi | 1.40 | .90 |
| *d.* | A2649 | 80y multi | 1.40 | .90 |
| *e.* | A2650 | 80y multi | 1.40 | .90 |
| *f.* | A2651 | 80y multi | 1.40 | .90 |
| *g.* | A2652 | 80y multi | 1.40 | .90 |
| *h.* | A2653 | 80y multi | 1.40 | .90 |
| *i.* | A2654 | 80y multi | 1.40 | .90 |
| *j.* | A2655 | 80y multi | 1.40 | .90 |

Aviation in Japan, cent.

**Animation**

Miniature Sheet

Chibi Maruko-chan — A2656

No. 3259: a, Sakura family members, Maruko, Sakiko, and mother Sumire (denomination in red at UL). b, Sakura family members father Hiroshi, grandfather Tomozo, and grandmother Kotake (denomination in white at LL). c, Maruko blowing bubbles (holding gun). d, Tomozo and bubbles. e, Hiroshi and Maruko with glow worm. f, Sakiko with glow worm. g, Sumire preparing food. h, Maruko and Kotake preparing food. i, Hamaji and Butaro (boys and snowflakes). j, Maruko and Tama-chan (and snowflakes).

**2010, Sept. 22 Litho. *Perf. 13x13¼***

| | | | | |
|---|---|---|---|---|
| **3259** | A2656 | Sheet of 10 | 20.00 | 20.00 |
| *a.-j.* | | 80y Any single | 1.40 | .90 |

Chiba Central Sports Center and Chiba Marine Stadium — A2657

Hammer Throw — A2658

Equestrian A2659

Rock Climbing A2660

Pole Vault — A2661

**2010, Sept. 24 Litho. *Perf. 13x13¼***

| | | | | |
|---|---|---|---|---|
| **3260** | | Sheet of 10, 2 each #a-e | 12.50 | 12.50 |
| *a.* | A2657 | 50y multi | .90 | .50 |
| *b.* | A2658 | 50y multi | .90 | .50 |
| *c.* | A2659 | 50y multi | .90 | .50 |
| *d.* | A2660 | 50y multi | .90 | .50 |
| *e.* | A2661 | 50y multi | .90 | .50 |

65th National Athletics Meet, Chiba.

Miniature Sheet

Travel Scenes — A2662

No. 3261: a, Akashi Strait Great Bridge, denomination in blue at UL (stamp 1). b, Akashi Strait Great Bridge, Sun Yat-sen Memorial Hall, Kobe, denomination at UR (stamp 2). c, Flowers, Awaji Island, denomination at UR to right of "Nippon" (stamp 3). d, Flowers, Awaji Island, denomination at UR below "Nippon" (stamp 4). e, Awaji puppet theater, denomination at UR (stamp 5). f, Awaji puppet theater, denomination at UL (stamp 6). g, Onaruto Bridge, denomination in white at LL (stamp 7). h, Onaruto Bridge, denomination in white at UR( stamp 8). i, Bridge, Naruto Whirlpools (stamp 9). j, Esaki Lighthouse (stamp 10).

**2010, Oct. 1 Litho. *Perf. 13x13¼***

| | | | | |
|---|---|---|---|---|
| **3261** | A2662 | Sheet of 10 | 20.00 | 20.00 |
| *a.-j.* | | 80y Any single | 1.40 | .90 |

Miniature Sheet

Aichi Local Autonomy Law, 60th Anniv. — A2663

No. 3262: a, Golden dolphin sculpture at Nagoya Castle, irises, Atsumi Peninsula (32x39mm). b, Eurasian scops owl (28x33mm). c, Ginkgo leaves (28x33mm). d, Seto ceramic jar (28x33mm). e, Cherry blossoms (28x33mm).

***Perf. 13¼ (#3262a), 13x13¼***

**2010, Oct. 4 Photo.**

| | | | | |
|---|---|---|---|---|
| **3262** | A2663 | Sheet of 5 | 10.00 | 10.00 |
| *a.-e.* | | 80y Any single | 1.40 | .90 |

Intl. Letter Writing Week — A2664

Painting details: 90y, Michitose, by Shinsui Ito. 110y, Nozaki Village, by Kiyokata Kaburagi. 130y, Botanyuki, by Shoen Uemura, horiz.

**2010, Oct. 8 Photo. *Perf. 13¼***

| | | | | |
|---|---|---|---|---|
| **3263** | A2664 | 90y multi | 1.60 | 1.00 |
| **3264** | A2664 | 110y multi | 2.00 | 1.40 |
| **3265** | A2664 | 130y multi | 2.50 | 1.60 |
| | | *Nos. 3263-3265 (3)* | 8.25 | 6.25 |

Miniature Sheet

Tenth Conference of Parties to the Convention on Biological Diversity, Nagoya — A2665

No. 3266: a, Lake Mashu, frost-covered trees. b, Spotted seal. c, Mt. Tsurugi. d, Japanese antelope. e, Buildings in mountains. f, Common tree frog and flowers. g, Banks of Shimanto River. h, Common kingfisher. i, Flowers at Cape Tamatori. j, False clownfish and sea anemone.

**2010, Oct. 18 Litho. *Perf. 13x13¼***

| | | | | |
|---|---|---|---|---|
| **3266** | A2665 | Sheet of 10 | 20.00 | 20.00 |
| *a.-j.* | | 80y Any single | 2.00 | 1.50 |

Miniature Sheet

Friendship Between Japan and Portugal, 150th Anniv. — A2666

No. 3267: a, Japanese screen painting depicting bow of Portuguese ship, denomination at LL (30x45mm, stamp 1). b, Japanese screen painting depicting stern of Portuguese ship, denomination at LR (30x45mm, stamp 2). c, Belém Tower, Lisbon (30x43mm, stamp 3). d, Statue of St. Vincent (30x43mm, stamp 4). e, Monastery of the Hieronymites, Lisbon (30x43mm, stamp 5). f, Ruins of Roman Temple of Evora, Portugal (30x43mm, stamp 6). g, Oporto, Portugal, and boat (30x43mm, stamp 7). h, Batalha Monastery, Batalha, Portugal (30x43mm, stamp 8). i, Portuguese decorative tiles (30x43mm, stamp 9). j, Puppet of St. Isabel of Portugal (30x43mm, stamp 10).

**2010, Oct. 22 Litho. *Perf. 13¼x13***

| | | | | |
|---|---|---|---|---|
| **3267** | A2666 | Sheet of 10 | 20.00 | 20.00 |
| *a.-j.* | | 80y Any single | 1.40 | .90 |

See Portugal No. 3271.

Seven People — A2667

Eight People — A2668

Congress Emblem A2669

Peace Statute, Nagasaki A2670

**2010, Nov. 5 Photo. *Perf. 13***

| | | | | |
|---|---|---|---|---|
| **3268** | | Sheet of 10, 2 each #3268a-3268c, 4 #3268d | 20.00 | 20.00 |
| *a.* | A2667 | 80y multi | 1.40 | .90 |
| *b.* | A2668 | 80y multi | 1.40 | .90 |
| *c.* | A2669 | 80y multi | 1.40 | .90 |
| *d.* | A2670 | 80y multi | 1.40 | .90 |

Third UNI Global Union World Congress, Nagasaki.

Miniature Sheets

A2671

A2672

Greetings — A2673

No. 3269: a, Star and Santa Claus with sack. b, Poinsettias, ribbon and bell. c, Sleigh of Santa Claus over church, horiz. d, Heart-shaped wreath. e, Reindeer and Aurora Borealis.

No. 3270: a, Santa Claus. b, Christmas tree. c, Sleigh of Santa Claus over mountain, horiz. d, Wreath with pine cones. e, Reindeer and Aurora Borealis, diff.

No. 3271: a, Fairy with horn flying above town. b, Snowman juggling snowballs. c, Children singing, horiz. d, Rose in box. e, Cakes.

***Die Cut Perf. 13***

**2010, Nov. 8 Litho.**

**Self-Adhesive**

| | | | | |
|---|---|---|---|---|
| **3269** | A2671 | Sheet of 5 | 6.25 | 6.25 |
| *a.-e.* | | 50y Any single | 1.25 | .50 |
| **3270** | A2672 | Sheet of 5 | 10.00 | 10.00 |
| *a.-e.* | | 80y Any single | 1.40 | .90 |
| **3271** | A2673 | Sheet of 5 | 11.50 | 11.50 |
| *a.-e.* | | 90y Any single | 1.60 | 1.00 |

A2674

A2675

New Year 2011 (Year of the Rabbit)

A2676 A2677

**2010, Nov. 10 Photo. *Perf. 13x13½***

| | | | | |
|---|---|---|---|---|
| **3272** | A2674 | 50y multi | .95 | .40 |
| **3273** | A2675 | 80y multi | 1.40 | .50 |

**Photo. & Typo.**

***Perf. 13¼***

| | | | | |
|---|---|---|---|---|
| **3274** | A2676 | 50y +3y multi | 1.10 | .50 |
| **3275** | A2677 | 80y +3y multi | 1.60 | .50 |
| | | *Nos. 3272-3275 (4)* | 6.75 | 5.15 |

Sheets of two containing Nos. 3272-3273 were lottery prizes. Value, $4.

Miniature Sheet

Aomori Local Autonomy Law, 60th Anniv. — A2678

No. 3276: a, Apples, Nebuta Festival floats (32x39mm). b, Hirosaki Castle and cherry blossoms (28x33mm). c, Three Shrines Festival, Hachinohe (28x33mm). d, Lake Towada (28x33mm). e, Horse and Shiriyazaki Lighthouse (28x33mm).

***Perf. 13¼ (#3276a), 13x13¼***

**2010, Nov. 15 Photo.**

| | | | | |
|---|---|---|---|---|
| **3276** | A2678 | Sheet of 5 | 10.00 | 10.00 |
| *a.-e.* | | 80y Any single | 1.40 | .90 |

Miniature Sheet

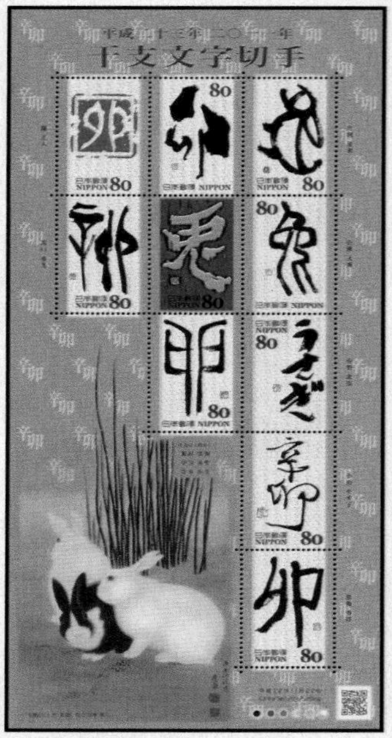

Edo Calligraphy — A2679

No. 3277 — Charcters for "rabbit": a, In Kinbun style (red character). b, In Six Dynasties style standard script (heavy black characters with red chop at LL, denomination at UR. c, In oracle bone script (single black character resembling animal with legs and tail, denomination at LR). d, In oracle bone script (three characters having horizontal line at UL, with red chop at LR, denomination at LR). e, In clerical script (silver character on green background). f, In small seal script (denomination at UL, "Nippon" at LR). g, In seal script (two black characters, with red chop, denomination and "Nippon" at LR). h, In Hirigana style (black character with denomination and "Nippon" at UL, red chop near center). i, In running script (black character with small dot at top, with denomination at LR and "Nippon" at LL). j, In standard script (two black characters with red chop and denomination at LR, "Nippon" at LL).

**Litho. & Embossed**

**2010, Dec. 3 *Perf. 13x13¼***

| | | | | |
|---|---|---|---|---|
| **3277** | A2679 | Sheet of 10 | 20.00 | 20.00 |
| *a.-j.* | | 80y Any single | 1.40 | .90 |

Japanese Diet, 120th Anniv. — A2680

Stained-glass window from Central Hall, old and new Diet buildings with entranceway of: No. 3278, New Diet. No. 3279, Old Diet.

**2010, Nov. 29 Litho. *Perf. 13***

| | | | | |
|---|---|---|---|---|
| **3278** | | 80y multi | 1.40 | .90 |
| **3279** | | 80y multi | 1.40 | .90 |
| *a.* | A2680 | Horiz. pair, #3278-3279 | 4.00 | 3.00 |

Miniature Sheet

Home Towns — A2681

No. 3280 — Paintings by Taiji Harada of views of Tohuku region towns: a, Paulownia Village (Cyclist near house, Mishima, Fukushima prefecture). b, Paulownia Village (Farmers and tree near water, Mishima). c, Bonnet Bus (White bus, Hiraizumi, Iwate prefecture). d, Bonnet Bus (Houses, people under umbrella, Hiraizumi). e, Bent House by the Sea (Mother with children near sea, Yurihonjo, Akita prefecture). f, After the Snowfall (Person and houses in snow, Akita, Akita prefecture). g, Railbus (Railbus and station, Kamikita District, Aomori prefecture ). h, Railbus (People at station, Kamikita District). i, Dear Home (People on path near house, Tsuruoka, Yamagata prefecture). j, Kokeshi Doll (Children and adults near doll vendor's stall, Shiroishi, Miyagi prefecture).

**2010, Dec. 1 Photo. *Perf. 13***

| | | | | |
|---|---|---|---|---|
| **3280** | A2681 | Sheet of 10 | 20.00 | 20.00 |
| *a.-j.* | | 80y Any single | 2.00 | 1.50 |

**Mandarin Duck Type of 2007**

***Perf. 13¾x13½ Syncopated***

**2010, Jan. Litho.**

| | | | | |
|---|---|---|---|---|
| **3281** | A2352 | 50y multi | 1.10 | .85 |

**Prefecture Type of 1990 Redrawn and Prefecture Types of 1991-96**

Designs as before.

***Serpentine Die Cut 10¾x11½***

**2010 Litho. Self-Adhesive**

| | | | | |
|---|---|---|---|---|
| **3282** | ZA85 | 80y multi | 1.40 | .90 |
| **3283** | ZA86 | 80y multi | 1.40 | .90 |
| **3284** | ZA87 | 80y multi | 1.40 | .90 |
| **3285** | ZA88 | 80y multi | 1.40 | .90 |
| *a.* | | Horiz. strip of 4, #3282-3285 | 7.00 | 7.00 |
| **3286** | ZA97 | 80y multi | 1.40 | .90 |
| **3287** | ZA98 | 80y multi | 1.40 | .90 |
| **3288** | ZA99 | 80y multi | 1.40 | .90 |
| **3289** | ZA100 | 80y multi | 1.40 | .90 |
| *a.* | | Horiz. strip of 4, #3286-3289 | 7.00 | 7.00 |

***Serpentine Die Cut 11½x11¾***

| | | | | |
|---|---|---|---|---|
| **3290** | ZA186 | 80y multi | 1.40 | .90 |
| | | *Nos. 3282-3290 (9)* | 12.60 | 8.10 |

Issued: Nos. 3282-3289, Mar.; No. 3290, Apr.

Hisoka Maeshima (1835-1919), Founder of Japanese Postal Service A2682

Little Cuckoo A2683

Mute Swan A2684

Silver Crane A2685

Burial Statue of Warrior, Ota A2686

Bazara-Taisho, c. 710-794 A2687

**2010-11 Photo. *Perf. 13x13½***

| | | | | |
|---|---|---|---|---|
| **3293** | A2682 | 1y brown | .25 | .25 |
| **3294** | A2683 | 3y green | .25 | .25 |
| **3295** | A2684 | 5y blue & lt bl | .25 | .25 |
| **3296** | A2685 | 100y multi | 1.75 | 1.20 |
| **3297** | A2686 | 200y vermilion | 3.75 | 2.50 |
| **3298** | A2687 | 500y dark green | 9.50 | 6.00 |
| | | *Nos. 3293-3298 (6)* | 15.75 | 10.45 |

Issued: 1y, 1/7/11; 3y, 12/8; 5y, 12/6; 100y, 12/27; 200y, 2/10/11; 500y, 12/15. Compare type A2682 with type A563a, types A2683-A2687 with types A713, A714, A718a, A718d, A1013 and A1207.

Miniature Sheet

Saga Local Autonomy Law, 60th Anniv. — A2688

No. 3299: a, Shigenobu Okuma (1838-1922), politician, and Arita porcelain (32x39mm). b, Yoshinogari ruins (28x33mm). c, Yutoku Inari shrine and bridge (28x33mm). d, Hot-air balloons, Saga International Balloon Festival (28x33mm). e, Sea bream float, Karatsu Festival (28x33mm).

***Perf. 13¼ (#3299a), 13x13¼***

**2011, Jan. 14 Photo.**

| | | | | |
|---|---|---|---|---|
| **3299** | A2688 | Sheet of 5 | 10.00 | 10.00 |
| *a.-e.* | | 80y Any single | 1.40 | .90 |

Miniature Sheet

Phila Nippon'11, Yokohama — A2689

No. 3300: a, Mighty Atom (blue background, 28x48mm). b, Doraemon (green background, 28x48mm). c, Pikachu (purple background, 28x48mm), d, Hello Kitty (red background, 28x48mm). e, Rabbit riding donkey from 11th cent. scroll (28x48mm). f, Mighty Atom, diff. (28x32mm). g, Doraemon, diff. (28x32mm). h, Pikachu, diff. (28x32mm). i, Hello Kitty, diff. (28x32mm). j, Rabbit riding donkey, diff. (28x32mm).

***Die Cut Perf. 12¾x13***

**2011, Jan. 21 Litho.**

**Self-Adhesive**

| | | | | |
|---|---|---|---|---|
| **3300** | A2689 | Sheet of 10 | 20.00 | 20.00 |
| *a.-j.* | | 80y Any single | 1.40 | .90 |

Miniature Sheet

Friendship Between Japan and Germany, 150th Anniv. — A2690

No. 3301 — UNESCO World Heritage Sites and other landmarks: a, Old Town, Regensburg, horiz. (45x26mm, stamp 1). b, Yakushi-ji, Historic Monuments of Ancient Nara, Japan, horiz. (45x26mm, stamp 2). c, Quadriga of Brandenburg Gate, Berlin (27x38mm, stamp 3). d, Frauenkirche, Dresden (27x38mm, stamp 4). e, Schwerin Castle (two tall spires, 27x38mm, stamp 5). f, Schwerin Castle (three tall spires, 27x38mm, stamp 6). g, Old Town, Bamberg (bridge at right, 27x38mm, stamp 7). h, Old Town, Bamberg (bridge at left, 27x38mm, stamp 8). i, Neuschwanstein Castle (27x38mm, stamp 9). j, Tower at Zollverein Coal Mine Industrial Complex, Essen (27x38mm, stamp 10).

**2011, Jan. 24 Litho. *Perf. 13***

| | | | | |
|---|---|---|---|---|
| **3301** | A2690 | Sheet of 10 | 20.00 | 20.00 |
| *a.-j.* | | 80y Any single | 1.40 | .90 |

Miniature Sheet

Travel Scenes — A2691

No. 3302: a, Snow sculpture of Frauenkirche of Dresden, Germany at Sapporo Snow Festival, German and Japanese flags (stamp 1). b, Penguins walking at Asahiyama Zoo (stamp 2). c, Lamp post along canal at Otaru Snow Light Path (stamp 3). d, Building along canal in Otaru (stamp 4). e, Lake Toya in winter (stamp 5). f, Hakodate Orthodox Christian Church (stamp 6). g, Lake and snow-capped mountains at Shiretoko UNESCO World Heritage Site, denomination at LL (stamp 7). h, Lake and snow-capped mountains at Shiretoko UNESCO World Heritage Site, denomination at LR (stamp 8). i, Red-crowned cranes (stamp 9). j, Ice on Sea of Okhotsk near Abashiri (stamp 10).

**2011, Feb. 1 Litho. *Perf. 13x13¼***

| | | | | |
|---|---|---|---|---|
| **3302** | A2691 | Sheet of 10 | 20.00 | 20.00 |
| *a.-j.* | | 80y Any single | 1.40 | .90 |

Miniature Sheets

A2692

Greetings Stamps — A2693

No. 3303: a, Fawn, yellow crocuses. b, Bluebird, blue lilies. c, Rose, butterfly made of pink violets. d, Swans, blue roses. e, Hares, strawberries and flowers.

No. 3304: a, Flowers trailing from fairy's hat. b, Fairy blowing horn in daffodils. c, Fairy on back of bird delivering mail, horiz. d, Fairy with letter on rainbow. e, Fairy writing in purple flowers.

**2011, Feb. 4 Litho. *Die Cut Perf.***

**Self-Adhesive**

| | | | | |
|---|---|---|---|---|
| **3303** | A2692 | Sheet of 5 | 6.25 | 6.25 |
| *a.-e.* | | 50y Any single | .90 | .50 |

***Die Cut Perf. 13***

| | | | | |
|---|---|---|---|---|
| **3304** | A2693 | Sheet of 5 | 10.00 | 10.00 |
| *a.-e.* | | 80y Any single | 1.40 | .90 |

Rose A2694

Apple Blossoms A2695

Primroses A2696

Japanese Grapefruit Blossoms A2697

Kyushu Azalea Flowers A2698

Roses A2699

Apple Blossoms A2700

Primroses A2701

Japanese Grapefruit Blossoms A2702

Kyushu Azalea Flowers A2703

**2011, Feb. 8 Photo. *Perf. 13¼***

| | | | | | |
|---|---|---|---|---|---|
| **3305** | A2694 | 50y | multi | .90 | .50 |
| **3306** | A2695 | 50y | multi | .90 | .50 |
| **3307** | A2696 | 50y | multi | .90 | .50 |
| **3308** | A2697 | 50y | multi | .90 | .50 |
| **3309** | A2698 | 50y | multi | .90 | .50 |
| *a.* | | | Vert. strip of 5, #3305-3309 | 6.25 | 6.25 |
| **3310** | A2699 | 80y | multi | 1.40 | .90 |
| **3311** | A2700 | 80y | multi | 1.40 | .90 |
| **3312** | A2701 | 80y | multi | 1.40 | .90 |
| **3313** | A2702 | 80y | multi | 1.40 | .90 |
| **3314** | A2703 | 80y | multi | 1.40 | .90 |
| *a.* | | | Vert. strip of 5, #3310-3314 | 10.00 | 10.00 |
| | *Nos. 3305-3314 (10)* | | | 11.50 | 7.00 |

Flowers of Ibaraki, Aomori, Saitama, Yamaguchi and Kagoshima prefectures.

Miniature Sheet

Home Towns — A2704

No. 3315 — Paintings by Taiji Harada of views of towns of Kanto region: a, Rice Nursery (farmers in rice field, Hitachi, Ibaraka prefecture, denomination at UL). b, Rice Nursery (farmers in rice field, Hitachi, denomination at LL). c, Spring Breeze (woman and child near farmhouse, Kumagaya, Saitama prefecture, denomination at LL). d, Spring Breeze (farm buildings, trees in bloom in orchard, Kumagaya, denomination at UL). e,Spring Garden (tall tree, farmer with pole near shed, Tone District, Gumma prefecture). f, Spring Garden (boy with dog near mailbox near farmhouse, Tone District). g, Wheat Field (farmer and dog in field, Haga District, Tochigi prefecture). h, Home Inside a Tree Grove (house amidst trees, Kisarazu, Chiba prefecture). i, Roadside Zelkova Trees (city street with trees, Shibuya Ward, Tokyo prefecture). j, Westernized Building (building with lamp post, Yokohama, Kanagawa prefecture).

**2011, Mar. 1 Photo. *Perf. 13***

| | | | | |
|---|---|---|---|---|
| **3315** | A2704 | Sheet of 10 | 20.00 | 20.00 |
| *a.-j.* | | 80y Any single | 1.40 | .90 |

Miniature Sheets

Characters From Children's Stories by Beatrix Potter — A2705

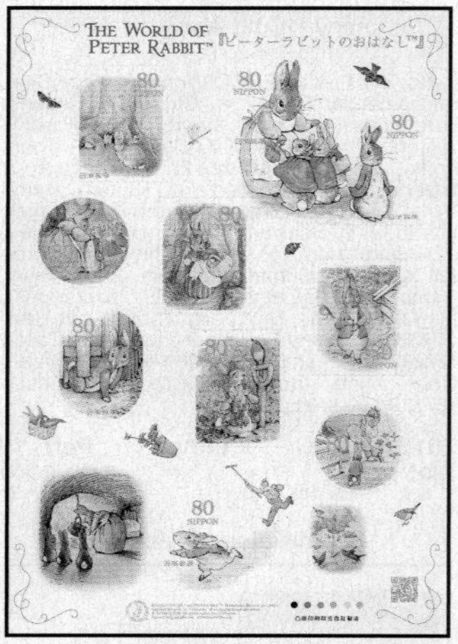


Scenes From *The Tale of Peter Rabbit,* by Beatrix Potter — A2706

No. 3316: a, Peter Rabbit running. b, Mouse of Gloucester. c, Peter Rabbit standing. d, Benjamin Bunny. e, Pigling Bland. f, Old Mr. Brown and Nutkin. g, Mrs. Tiggy-winkle. h, Jemima Puddle-duck. i, Squirrel Nutkin. j, Tom Kitten.

No. 3317: a, Rabbit family's home under fir tree. b, Mother and younger sisters (27x37mm oval). c, Peter Rabbit and back of sisters. d, Mother dressing Peter (29mm diameter) e, Mother holding basket. f, Peter near pots in garden, robin. g, Peter going under garden fence (27x37mm oval). h, Peter eating vegetables. i, Peter encountering Mr. McGregor (29mm diameter). j, Peter running from Mr. McGregor (29mm diameter).

**2011, Mar. 3 Litho. *Die Cut Perf.***
**Self-Adhesive**

| | | | | |
|---|---|---|---|---|
| **3316** | A2705 | Sheet of 10 | 12.50 | 12.50 |
| *a.-j.* | | 50y Any single | .90 | .50 |

***Die Cut Perf. 13¼x13¾, Die Cut Perf.***

| | | | | |
|---|---|---|---|---|
| **3317** | A2706 | Sheet of 10 | 20.00 | 20.00 |
| *a.-j.* | | 80y Any single | 1.40 | .90 |

**Animation**
Miniature Sheet

One Piece — A2707

No. 3318: a, Monkey D. Luffy wearing hat and red shirt. b, Chopper wearing large top hat. c, Sanji wearing blue shirt. d, Zoro wearing white shirt. e, Robin wearing red striped blouse. f, Nami wearing beige shirt. g, Usopp and Brook. h, Franky with chain on chest. i, D Successor 1 with fire coming from hand. j, D Successor 2 with clouds.

**2011, Mar. 23 Litho. *Perf. 13x13¼***

| | | | | |
|---|---|---|---|---|
| **3318** | A2707 | Sheet of 10 | 19.00 | 19.00 |
| *a.-j.* | | 80y Any single | 1.90 | 1.40 |

Samisen Player A2708

Samisen Player and Children A2709

Matsubashi Parade Participants, Decorated Bamboo A2710

Matsubashi Parade A2711

**2011, Apr. 4 Litho. *Perf. 13¼***

| | | | |
|---|---|---|---|
| **3319** | Block of 6, #3319c-3319d, 2 each #3319a-3319b | 7.50 | 7.50 |
| *a.* | A2708 50y green & multi | .90 | .50 |
| *b.* | A2709 50y red violet & multi | .90 | .50 |
| *c.* | A2710 50y blue & multi | .90 | .50 |
| *d.* | A2711 50y blue & multi | .90 | .50 |

Hakata Dontaku Port Festival, Fukuoka, Fukuoka prefecture. Printed in sheets of 10 containing Nos. 3319c-3319d and 4 each Nos. #3319a-3319b.

Administrative Counselors System, 50th Anniv. — A2712

**2011, Apr. 15 *Perf. 13***

| | | | | |
|---|---|---|---|---|
| **3320** | 80y | Denomination at LL | 1.40 | .90 |
| **3321** | 80y | Denomination at LR | 1.40 | .90 |
| *a.* | A2712 | Horiz. pair, #3320-3321 | 4.00 | 4.00 |

Digital Television Broadcasting Towers — A2713

Designs: No. 3322, Tokyo Sky Tree, emblem at LR. No. 3323, Tokyo Tower, emblem at LL.

**2011, Apr. 15 *Perf. 14x14¼***

| | | | | |
|---|---|---|---|---|
| **3322** | 80y | multi | 1.40 | .90 |
| **3323** | 80y | multi | 1.40 | .90 |
| *a.* | A2713 | Pair, #3322-3323 | 4.00 | 4.00 |

Kabuki Actor Kikugoro Onoe V as Postman, by Kunichika Toyohara A2714

Yokkaichi Postal Communications Bureau, by Hiroshige III — A2715

A Quick Primer on Modernization, by Kunimasa Baido — A2716

***Perf. 12½x12¾ Syncopated***
**2011, Apr. 20 Photo.**

| | | | | | |
|---|---|---|---|---|---|
| **3324** | A2714 | 80y | multi | 1.40 | .90 |
| **3325** | A2715 | 80y | multi | 1.40 | .90 |
| **3326** | A2716 | 80y | multi | 1.40 | .90 |
| *a.* | | | Vert. strip of 3, #3324-3326 | 6.00 | 6.00 |

Philately Week. Printed in sheets of 10 containing 4 No. 3325 and 3 each Nos. 3324, 3326.

Azalea Flowers A2717

Satsuma Orange Blossoms A2718

Azalea Flowers A2719

Satsuma Orange Blossoms A2720

**2011, May 2 Photo. *Perf. 13¼***

| | | | | |
|---|---|---|---|---|
| **3327** | A2717 | 50y multi | .90 | .50 |
| **3328** | A2718 | 50y multi | .90 | .50 |
| *a.* | | Horiz. pair, #3327-3328 | 2.50 | 2.50 |
| *b.* | | Sheet of 47 + label (see contents below) | 62.50 | 62.50 |
| **3329** | A2719 | 80y multi | 1.40 | .90 |
| **3330** | A2720 | 80y multi | 1.40 | .90 |
| *a.* | | Horiz. pair, #3329-3330 | 4.00 | 4.00 |
| *b.* | | Sheet of 47 + label (see contents below) | 100.00 | 100.00 |
| | | *Nos. 3327-3330 (4)* | 4.60 | 2.80 |

Flowers of Shizuoka and Ehime prefectures.

Issued: Nos. 3328b, 3330b, 7/15.

No. 3328b contains Nos. 3030-3034, 3079-3083, 3094-3098, 3126-3130, 3180-3184, 3194-3198, 3207-3211, 3221-3225, 3305-3309, 3327-3328 + label.

No. 3330b, contains Nos. 3035-3039, 3084-3088, 3099-3103, 3131-3135, 3185-3189, 3199-3203, 3212-3216, 3226-3230, 3310-3314, 3329-3330 + label.

Miniature Sheet

Kumamoto Local Autonomy Law, 60th Anniv. — A2721

No. 3331: a, Mt. Azo (32x39mm). b, Kumamoto Castle (28x33mm). c, Kikuchi Castle (octagonal tower, 28x33mm). d, Utasebune (sailboat, 28x33mm). e, Matsushima and Maejima Bridges (28x33mm).

***Perf. 13¼ (#3331a), 13x13¼***

**2011, May 13 Photo.**

| | | | | |
|---|---|---|---|---|
| **3331** | A2721 | Sheet of 5 | 10.00 | 10.00 |
| *a.-e.* | | 80y Any single | 1.40 | .90 |

Miniature Sheet

Intl. Year of Forests — A2722

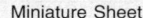

No. 3332: a, Japanese cypress (denomination in white at LL, Japanese text in green, date at UR). b, Cherry blossoms (denomination in white at UR, Japanese text in blue, date at LL). c, Persea thunbergii (denomination in white at LL, Japanese text in blue, date at LR). d, Japanese umbrella pine (denomination in blue at UR, Japanese text in green, date at UL). e, Plum blossoms (denomination in white at UR, Japanese text in green, date at LL). f, Boat oak (denomination in white at UR, Japanese text in blue, date at LL). g, Nageia nagi (denomination in white at LL, Japanese text in blue, date at UL). h, Michelia compressa blossom (denomination in white at UR, Japanese text in green, date at UL). i, Japanese Douglas fir (denomination in white at UL, Japanese text in green, date at LL). j, Intl. Year of Forests emblem.

**2011, May 20 Litho. *Perf. 13***

| | | | | |
|---|---|---|---|---|
| **3332** | A2722 | Sheet of 10 | 12.50 | 12.50 |
| *a.-j.* | | 50y Any single | .90 | .50 |

Miniature Sheet

Travel Scenes — A2723

No. 3333: a, Spotted seal (stamp 1). b, Wheat field, Biei (stamp 2). c, Lavender field, Furano, denomination at LR (stamp 3). d, Lavender field, Furano, denomination at LL (stamp 4). e, Statue of Dr. William Smith Clark, Hitsujigaoka (stamp 5). f, Cattle in pasture, Kamishihoro (stamp 6). g, Rugosa roses, Mt. Rishiri, denomination at UL (stamp 7). h, Rugosa roses, Mt. Rishiri, denomination at UR (stamp 8). i, Trees on hill at Higashimokoto Moss Pink Park, denomination at UL (stamp 9). j, Trees on hill at Higashimokoto Moss Pink Park, denomination at UR (stamp 10).

**2011, May 30 Litho. *Perf. 13x13¼***

| | | | | |
|---|---|---|---|---|
| **3333** | A2723 | Sheet of 10 | 20.00 | 20.00 |
| *a.-j.* | | 80y Any single | 1.40 | .90 |

**Animation**

Miniature Sheet

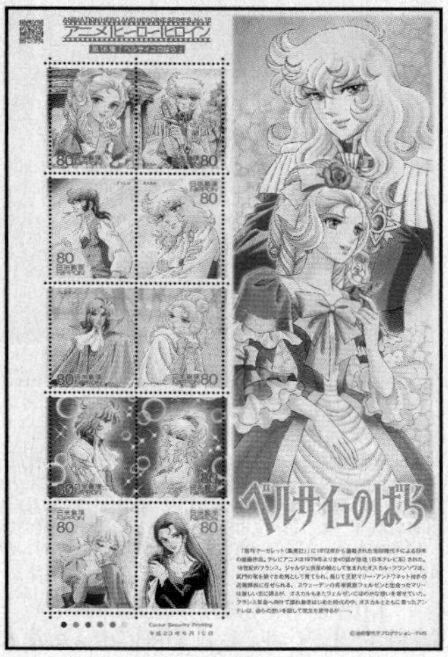
Rose of Versailles — A2724

No. 3334: a, Marie Antoinette holding rose (blue denomination at LL). b, Oscar François de Jarjayes holding sword (blue denomination at LR). c, André Grandier (pink denomination at LL). d, Jarjayes wearing green shirt (pink denomination at UR). e, Hans Axel von Fersen in brown cape (trees in background, blue denomination at LL). f, Marie Antoinette (pink denomination at LR). g, Von Fersen (bubbles in background, blue denomination at LL). h, Jarjayes in blue dress (bubbles in background, blue denomination at lR) i, Rosalie Lamorlière in pink dress ( blue denomination at UL). j, Jeanne de Valois-Saint Rémy (pink denomination at UR).

**2011, June 10 *Perf. 13x13¼***

| | | | | |
|---|---|---|---|---|
| **3334** | A2724 | Sheet of 10 | 20.00 | 20.00 |
| *a.-j.* | | 80y Any single | 1.40 | .90 |

Miniature Sheet

Toyama Local Autonomy Law, 60th Anniv. — A2725

No. 3335: a, Tateyama Mountains (32x39mm). b, Kurobe Dam (28x33mm). c, Japanese rock ptarmigan (28x33mm). d, Zuiryu Temple (28x33mm). e, Gokayama farmhouse (28x33mm).

***Perf. 13¼ (#3335a), 13x13¼***

**2011, June 15 Photo.**

| | | | | |
|---|---|---|---|---|
| **3335** | A2725 | Sheet of 5 | 10.00 | 10.00 |
| *a.-e.* | | 80y Any single | 1.40 | .90 |

A2726

A2727

A2728

A2729

A2730

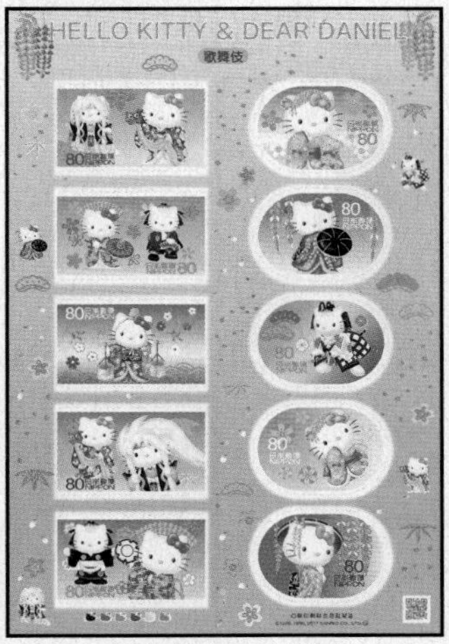

Hello Kitty — A2731

No. 3341: a, Dear Daniel at left, and Hello Kitty, rectangular stamp with green background, denomination in green at LL. b, Hello Kitty and Dear Daniel, rectangular stamp with pink background. c, Hello Kitty, rectangular stamp with blue gray background, denomination in white at UL. d, Hello Kitty and Dear Daniel, rectangular stamp with green background, denomination in purple at LL. e, Dear Daniel and Hello Kitty, rectangular stamp with purple background, denomination in gold at LL. f, Hello Kitty, oval stamp with pink background and gold denomination at right. g, Hello Kitty, oval stamp with blue gray background, denomination in white at UR. h, Dear Daniel, oval stamp with green background. i, Hello Kitty, oval stamp with pink background and white denomination at left. j, Hello Kitty, oval stamp with purple background, denomination in purple at LR.

***Die Cut Perf. 13½***

**2011, June 22** **Litho.**

**Self-Adhesive**

| | | | | | |
|---|---|---|---|---|---|
| **3336** | A2726 | 50y multi | | .90 | .50 |
| **3337** | A2727 | 50y multi | | .90 | .50 |
| **3338** | A2728 | 50y multi | | .90 | .50 |
| **3339** | A2729 | 50y multi | | .90 | .50 |
| **3340** | A2730 | 50y multi | | .90 | .50 |
| *a.* | Vert. strip of 5, #3336-3340 | | | 6.25 | 6.25 |

***Die Cut Perf. 11½x13¼ (#3341a-3341e), 12 (#3341f-3341j)***

| | | | | |
|---|---|---|---|---|
| **3341** | A2731 | Sheet of 10 | 20.00 | |
| *a.-j.* | 80y Any single | | 1.40 | .90 |

Nos. 3336-3340 were printed in sheets containing 2 of each stamp.

Adélie Penguin — A2732

Chinstrap Penguin — A2733

Gentoo Penguin — A2734

Emperor Penguin — A2735

Macaroni Penguin — A2736

Map of Antarctica and Snowflakes A2737

**2011, June 23** ***Perf. 13***

| | | | |
|---|---|---|---|
| **3342** | Sheet of 10, #3342a-3342e, 5 #3342f | 20.00 | 20.00 |
| *a.* | A2732 80y multi | 1.40 | .90 |
| *b.* | A2733 80y multi | 1.40 | .90 |
| *c.* | A2734 80y multi | 1.40 | .90 |
| *d.* | A2735 80y multi | 1.40 | .90 |
| *e.* | A2736 80y multi | 1.40 | .90 |
| *f.* | A2737 80y multi | 1.40 | .90 |

Antarctic Treaty, 50th Anniv.

Miniature Sheet

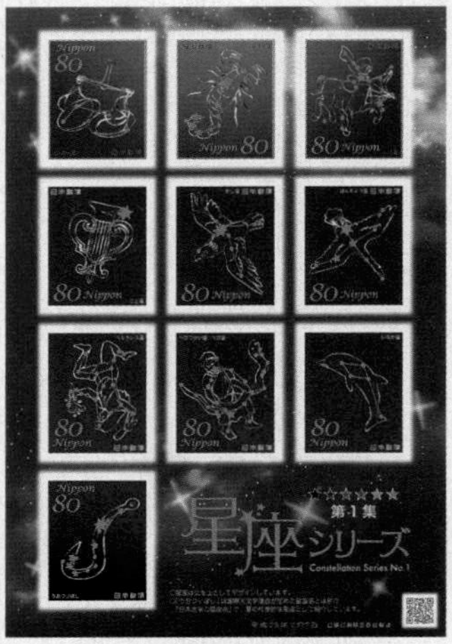


Constellations — A2738

No. 3343: a, Libra (scales). b, Scorpius (scorpion). c, Sagittarius (archer). d, Lyra (lyre). e, Aquila (eagle). f, Cygnus (swan). g, Hercules. h, Ophiuchus and Serpens (man and snake). i, Delphinus (dolphin). j, Fishhook asterism.

**Litho. With Foil Application**

**2011, July 7** ***Die Cut Perf. 13***

**Self-Adhesive**

| | | | | |
|---|---|---|---|---|
| **3343** | A2738 | Sheet of 10 | 20.00 | |
| *a.-j.* | 80y Any single | | 1.40 | .90 |

Miniature Sheet

Japan Sports Association, Cent. — A2739

No. 3344: a, Jigoro Kano (1860-1938), and Seiichi Kishi (1867-1933), presidents of Japan Amateur Sports Association (stamp 1). b, Athletes in parade at 1912 Stockholm Olympics (stamp 2). c, Women's volleyball, horse jumping, and emblem of National Athletic Meet (stamp 3). d, Hironoshin Furuhashi (1928-2009), swimmer (stamp 4). e, Baseball players and boy with martial arts stick (stamp 5). f, Weight lifter, gymnast and women's volleyball team members from 1964 Tokyo Summer Olympics (stamp 6). g, Skiers from 1972 Sapporo Winter Olympics (stamp 7). h, Skier and skater from 1998 Nagano Winter Olympics (stamp 8). i, Emblem of Sports Masters Japan Tournament (stamp 9). j, Woman wrestler, swimmer and women's softball team members from 2008 Beijing Summer Olympics (stamp 10).

**2011, July 8** **Litho.** ***Perf. 13***

| | | | | |
|---|---|---|---|---|
| **3344** | A2739 | Sheet of 10 | 20.00 | 20.00 |
| *a.-j.* | 80y Any single | | 1.40 | .90 |

A2740

A2741

PhilaNippon 2011 Intl. Philatelic Exhibition, Yokohama — A2742

No. 3345 — Woodblock prints by Hokusai depicting Mt. Fuji: a, Shower Below the Summit (Mt. Fuji and clouds, denomination in gold at LL). b, Fujimigahara in Owari Province (cooper making cask). c, Hodogaya on the Tokaido (people on road near Mt. Fuji). d, Mishima Pass in Kai Province (large tree and Mt. Fuji). e, The Surface of the Water at Misaka (boat and reflection of Mt. Fuji in lake). f, Clear Day with a Southern Breeze (Mt. Fuji and clouds, denomination in white at LR). g, The Village of Sekiya on the Sumida River (horsemen on road). h, Sea Route to Kazusa (sailing ship). i, Hongan Temple at Asakusa (kite and temple roof). j, Senju in Musashi Province (fishermen, man with horse).

No. 3346: a, Writing box depicting rabbit, bamboo and chrysanthemum. b, Japan #1.

No. 3347: a, Astro Boy (32x47mm). b, Doraemon (cat, 28x47mm). c, Pikachu (28x47mm). d, Hello Kitty (28x47mm). e, Emblem of PhilaNippon 2011, Mt. Fuji (28x47mm). f, Astro Boy, diff. (28x32mm). g, Doraemon, diff. (28x32mm). h, Pikachu, diff. (28x32mm). i, Hello Kitty, diff. (28x 32mm). j, Emblem, diff. (28x32mm).

**2011, July 28** **Litho.** ***Perf. 13***

| | | | | |
|---|---|---|---|---|
| **3345** | A2740 | Sheet of 10 + 10 labels | 21.00 | 21.00 |
| *a.-j.* | 80y Any single + label | | 1.40 | .90 |

**Souvenir Sheet**

**Litho. & Embossed With Foil Application**

***Perf. 14x13¾***

| | | | | |
|---|---|---|---|---|
| **3346** | A2741 | Sheet of 2 | 32.50 | 32.50 |
| *a.-b.* | 500y Either single | | 9.50 | 9.50 |

**Self-Adhesive**

**Litho. With Foil Application**

***Die Cut Perf. 13***

| | | | | |
|---|---|---|---|---|
| **3347** | A2742 | Sheet of 10 | 21.00 | 21.00 |
| *a.-j.* | 80y Any single | | 1.40 | .90 |

No. 3346 sold for 1200y inside a folder that was sealed in plastic.

Sazae Hall, by Hiroshige A2743

Kisegawa of Matsubaya, by Utamaro A2744

Tanabata Festival in a Prospering City, by Hiroshige A2745

Komazo Ishikawa III as Daishichi Shiga, by Sharaku A2746

Plum Garden at Kamata, by Hiroshige A2747

Three Beauties of the Present Day, by Utamaro A2748

Yatsukoji, Inside Sujikai Gate, by Hiroshige A2749

Tomisaburo Segawa II as Yadorigi, by Sharaku A2750

Old Man's Tea House, Meguro, by Hiroshige A2751

Hanaogi of Ogiya, by Utamaro A2752

**2011, Aug. 1** **Litho.** ***Perf. 13¼***

| | | | |
|---|---|---|---|
| **3348** | Sheet of 10 | 21.00 | 21.00 |
| *a.* | A2743 80y multi | 1.40 | .90 |
| *b.* | A2744 80y multi | 1.40 | .90 |
| *c.* | A2745 80y multi | 1.40 | .90 |
| *d.* | A2746 80y multi | 1.40 | .90 |
| *e.* | A2747 80y multi | 1.40 | .90 |
| *f.* | A2748 80y multi | 1.40 | .90 |
| *g.* | A2749 80y multi | 1.40 | .90 |
| *h.* | A2750 80y multi | 1.40 | .90 |
| *i.* | A2751 80y multi | 1.40 | .90 |
| *j.* | A2752 80y multi | 1.40 | .90 |

Life in Edo (Tokyo).

A2753

A2754

A2755

A2756

A2757

Lantern Float Festival, Aomori — A2758

**2011, Aug. 2**

| | | | |
|---|---|---|---|
| **3349** | Sheet of 10, #3349a-3349b, 3349e-3349f, 3 each #3349c-3349d | 13.00 | 13.00 |
| *a.* | A2753 50y multi | .90 | .50 |
| *b.* | A2754 50y multi | .90 | .50 |
| *c.* | A2755 50y multi | .90 | .50 |
| *d.* | A2756 50y multi | .90 | .50 |
| *e.* | A2757 50y multi | .90 | .50 |
| *f.* | A2758 50y multi | .90 | .50 |

Miniature Sheet

Tottori Local Autonomy Law, 60th Anniv. — A2759

No. 3350: a, Tottori Sand Dunes and San'in Coast (32x39mm). b, Japanese pear (28x33mm). c, Kirin lion mask (28x33mm). d, Nageire Hall, Sanbutsu Temple (28x33mm). e, Mt. Daisen (28x33mm).

***Perf. 13¼ (#3350a), 13x13¼***

**2011, Aug. 15 Photo.**

| | | | | |
|---|---|---|---|---|
| **3350** | A2759 | Sheet of 5 | 10.50 | 10.50 |
| *a.-e.* | | 80y Any single | 1.40 | .90 |

Tsushima Leopard Cat — A2760

Saunders's Gull — A2761

Rebun Large-flowered Cypripedium — A2762

Green Sea Turtle A2763

Shijimiaeoides Divinus — A2764

**2011, Aug. 23** ***Perf. 13¼***

| | | | | | |
|---|---|---|---|---|---|
| **3351** | A2760 | 80y multi | | 1.40 | .90 |
| **3352** | A2761 | 80y multi | | 1.40 | .90 |
| **3353** | A2762 | 80y multi | | 1.40 | .90 |
| **3354** | A2763 | 80y multi | | 1.40 | .90 |
| **3355** | A2764 | 80y multi | | 1.40 | .90 |
| *a.* | Vert strip of 5, #3351-3355 | | | 10.50 | 10.50 |

Endangered species. Nos. 3351-3355 printed in sheets containing two vertical strips.

Airplane and Old Control Tower — A2765

Airplane and New Control Tower — A2766

Airplane and Map of Airport — A2767

Airplane and New Control Tower — A2768

**2011, Aug. 25 Litho.** ***Perf. 13***

| | | | | |
|---|---|---|---|---|
| **3356** | A2765 | 80y multi | 1.40 | .90 |
| **3357** | A2766 | 80y multi | 1.40 | .90 |
| **3358** | A2767 | 80y multi | 1.40 | .90 |
| **3359** | A2768 | 80y multi | 1.40 | .90 |
| *a.* | Block of 4, #3356-3359 | | 8.50 | 8.50 |
| | *Nos. 3356-3359 (4)* | | 5.60 | 3.60 |

Nos. 3356-3359 were printed in a sheet of 10 containing Nos. 3356-3357, and 4 each Nos. 3358-3359.

Bellflower A2769

Pink A2770

Sweet Olive Flowers A2771

Cosmos A2772

Bush Clover A2773

Bellflowers A2774

Pinks A2775

Sweet Olive Flowers A2776

Cosmos A2777

Bush Clover A2778

**2011, Sept. 1 Photo.** ***Perf. 13¼***

| | | | | |
|---|---|---|---|---|
| **3360** | A2769 | 50y multi | .90 | .50 |
| **3361** | A2770 | 50y multi | .90 | .50 |
| **3362** | A2771 | 50y multi | .90 | .50 |
| **3363** | A2772 | 50y multi | .90 | .50 |
| **3364** | A2773 | 50y multi | .90 | .50 |
| *a.* | Vert. strip of 5, #3360-3364 | | 6.50 | 6.50 |
| **3365** | A2774 | 80y multi | 1.40 | .90 |
| **3366** | A2775 | 80y multi | 1.40 | .90 |
| **3367** | A2776 | 80y multi | 1.40 | .90 |
| **3368** | A2777 | 80y multi | 1.40 | .90 |
| **3369** | A2778 | 80y multi | 1.40 | .90 |
| *a.* | Vert. strip of 5, #3365-3369 | | 10.50 | 10.50 |
| | *Nos. 3360-3369 (10)* | | 11.50 | 7.00 |

Miniature Sheet

Travel Scenes — A2779

No. 3370: a, Midori Swamp, denomination at LL (stamp 1). b, Lake Mashu in autumn, denomination at LR (stamp 2). c, Old Hokkaido Central Government Building, denomination at UR (stamp 3). d, Sapporo Clock Tower, denomination at LR (stamp 4). e, Lake Toya, Nakajima and tree top in autumn, denomination at LL (stamp 5). f, Lake Toya, Nakajima and tree in autumn, denomination at LR (stamp 6). g, Hagoromo Falls (stamp 7). h, Glasswort in Lake Notoro (red plants in lake) (stamp 8). i, Ezo sable, denomination at UR (stamp 9). j, Ezo flying squirrel, denomination at UL (stamp 10).

**2011, Sept. 9 Litho.** ***Perf. 13x13¼***

| | | | | |
|---|---|---|---|---|
| **3370** | A2779 | Sheet of 10 | 21.00 | 21.00 |
| *a.-j.* | | 80y Any single | 1.40 | .90 |

Mt. Fuji A2780

Mt. Bandai A2781

Hakusan A2782

Mt. Hiei A2783

Mt. Ishizuchi A2784

Mt. Iwate A2785

Mt. Tanigawa A2786

Mt. Akaishi A2787

Hiruzen A2788

Mt. Aso A2789

**2011, Sept. 22** *Perf. 13*

| | | | |
|---|---|---|---|
| **3371** | Sheet of 10 | 21.00 | 21.00 |
| *a.* | A2780 80y multi | 1.40 | .90 |
| *b.* | A2781 80y multi | 1.40 | .90 |
| *c.* | A2782 80y multi | 1.40 | .90 |
| *d.* | A2783 80y multi | 1.40 | .90 |
| *e.* | A2784 80y multi | 1.40 | .90 |
| *f.* | A2785 80y multi | 1.40 | .90 |
| *g.* | A2786 80y multi | 1.40 | .90 |
| *h.* | A2787 80y multi | 1.40 | .90 |
| *i.* | A2788 80y multi | 1.40 | .90 |
| *j.* | A2789 80y multi | 1.40 | .90 |

66th National Athletic Meet — A2790

**2011, Sept. 30**

| | | | |
|---|---|---|---|
| **3372** | A2790 50y Sailing | .90 | .50 |
| **3373** | A2790 50y Wrestling | .90 | .50 |
| **3374** | A2790 50y Rock climbing | .90 | .50 |
| **3375** | A2790 50y Handball | .90 | .50 |
| **3376** | A2790 50y Softball | .90 | .50 |
| *a.* | Vert. strip of 5, #3372-3376 | 6.50 | 6.50 |

2011 Artistic Gymnastics World Championships, Tokyo — A2791

Designs: No. 3377, Female gymnast. No. 3378, Male gymnast.

**2011, Oct. 6** **Litho.** *Perf. 13*

| | | | |
|---|---|---|---|
| **3377** | A2791 80y red vio & multi | 1.40 | .90 |
| **3378** | A2791 80y blue & multi | 1.40 | .90 |
| *a.* | Horiz. pair, #3377-3378 | 4.25 | 4.25 |

Intl. Letter Writing Week A2792

Designs: 90y, Sound of the Tsuzumi, by Shoen Uemura. 110y, Backstage, by Shinsui Ito. 130y, Midori, Heroine of Takekurabe, by Kiyokata Kaburagi.

**2011, Oct. 7** **Photo.** *Perf. 13¼*

| | | | |
|---|---|---|---|
| **3379** | A2792 90y multi | 1.60 | 1.00 |
| **3380** | A2792 110y multi | 1.90 | 1.40 |
| **3381** | A2792 130y multi | 2.10 | 1.60 |
| | *Nos. 3379-3381 (3)* | 5.60 | 4.00 |

Miniature Sheet

Shiga Local Autonomy Law, 60th Anniv. — A2793

No. 3382: a, Ukimido Temple, grebes on Lake Biwa (32x39mm). b, Boats in canal, Omihachiman (28x33mm). c, Boat tied to tree limb (28x33mm). d, Ishiyama Temple, Japanese red maples (28x33mm). e, Hikone Castle in winter (28x33mm).

*Perf. 13¼ (#3382a), 13x13¼*

**2011, Oct. 14** **Photo.**

| | | | | |
|---|---|---|---|---|
| **3382** | A2793 | Sheet of 5 | 10.50 | 10.50 |
| *a.-e.* | | 80y Any single | 1.40 | .90 |

Miniature Sheet

Travel Scenes — A2794

No. 3383: a, Yoyogi National Gymnasium, denomination at UR (stamp 1). b, Bench in Yoyogi Park, denomination at LR (stamp 2). c, Illumination of Omotesando trees at left, denomination at LL (stamp 3). d, Illumination of Otmotesando, trees at right, denomination at LR (stamp 4). e, Sidewalk and buildings along Omotesando, denomination at UL (stamp 5). f, Meiji Memorial Picture Gallery, denomination at UL (stamp 6). g, Ginkgo trees in Meiji Shrine Outer Garden, trees at left, denomination in blue at UL (stamp 7). h, Ginkgo trees in Meiji Shrine Outer Garden, trees at right, denomination in blue at UR (stamp 8). i, Nezu Museum, denomination at UL (stamp 9). j, Irises, painted screen, by Korin Ogata, denomination at LR (stamp 10).

**2011, Oct. 21** **Litho.** *Perf. 13x13¼*

| | | | | |
|---|---|---|---|---|
| **3383** | A2794 | Sheet of 10 | 21.00 | 21.00 |
| *a.-j.* | | 80y Any single | 1.40 | .90 |

Tokyo Metropolitan Festival Hall, 50th Anniv. — A2795

No. 3384: a, Stage and seating of Main Hall. b, Piano on stage of Small Hall. c, Ballet slippers, reflection of swan. d, Opera glasses, camellia. e, Piano keyboard. f, Violin.

**2011, Oct. 31** **Litho.** *Perf. 13*

| | | | | |
|---|---|---|---|---|
| **3384** | A2795 | Block of 6 | 13.00 | 13.00 |
| *a.-f.* | | 80y Any single | 1.40 | .90 |

No. 3384 was pritned in a sheet of 10 containing Nos. 3384a, 3384b and 2 each Nos. 3384c-3384f.

Miniature Sheets

A2796

A2797

Greetings — A2798

No. 3385: a, Wreath and dog (29mm diameter). b, Children and three Christmas trees (28x36mm). c, Christmas tree (28x38mm, Christmas tree-shaped). d, Santa Claus (28x36mm). e, Wreath and cat (29mm diameter).

No. 3386: a, Children starting to decorate Christmas tree. b, Children and decorated Christmas tree. c, Santa Claus, Christmas tree, children in bed. d, Santa Claus at Christmas tree. e, Children with Christmas presents.

No. 3387: a, Dog in snow (28x34mm oval). b, Flower bouquet (28x34mm oval). c, Snowman and animals on child's hat (38x28mm). d, Fairy and flowers (28x34mm oval). e, Children and cat looking at rabbit in snow (28x34mm oval).

**2011, Nov. 10** ***Die Cut Perf. 13***

**Self-Adhesive**

| | | | | |
|---|---|---|---|---|
| **3385** | A2796 | Sheet of 5 | 6.50 | 6.50 |
| *a.-e.* | | 50y Any single | .90 | .50 |
| **3386** | A2797 | Sheet of 5 | 10.50 | 10.50 |
| *a.-e.* | | 80y Any single | 1.40 | .90 |
| **3387** | A2798 | Sheet of 5 | 12.00 | 12.00 |
| *a.-e.* | | 90y Any single | 1.60 | 1.00 |

A2799 A2800

New Year 2012 (Year of the Dragon)

A2801 A2802

**2011, Nov. 11** **Photo.** *Perf. 13x13½*

| | | | |
|---|---|---|---|
| **3388** | A2799 50y multi | .95 | .40 |
| **3389** | A2800 80y multi | 1.40 | .50 |

**Photo. & Typo.**

***Perf. 13¼***

| | | | |
|---|---|---|---|
| **3390** | A2801 50y +3y multi | 1.10 | .50 |
| **3391** | A2802 80y +3y multi | 1.75 | .50 |
| | *Nos. 3388-3391 (4)* | 5.20 | 1.90 |

Sheets of two containing Nos. 3388-3389 were lottery prizes. Value, $4.

Miniature Sheet

Iwate Local Autonomy Law, 60th Anniv. — A2803

No. 3392: a, Golden Hall, Chuson-ji, lotus flower (32x39mm). b, Cherry trees in bloom (28x33mm). c, Hayachine Kagura folk performers (28x33mm). d, Rocks at Jodogahama (28x33mm). e, Joboji lacquer trees (28x33mm).

***Perf. 13¼ (#3392a), 13x13¼***

**2011, Nov. 15** **Photo.**

**3392** A2803 Sheet of 5 10.50 10.50
*a.-e.* 80y Any single 1.40 .90

Miniature Sheet

Edo Calligraphy — A2804

No. 3393 — Characters for "dragon": a, In running script (black chracter with small red chop at LR). b, In Kinbun style (blue background). c, In Kinbun style (red background). d, In Sosho cursive style (black character with large dot, red chop at LL). e, In Kana (black character with five lines not touching each other, red chop at left). f, In Reisho script (complex black character, red chop of right angle and circle at lower left). g, In Reisho script (black character with thick diagonal line over denomination, red chop at left). h, In seal script form (black character with two thick parallel horizontal lines at top, red chop at LL). i, In Tensho seal style (in red). j, In Kana black character with thin curved line well above rest of character, red chop at left).

**Litho. & Embossed**

**2011, Nov. 21** ***Perf. 13x13¼***

**3393** A2804 Sheet of 10 21.00 21.00
*a.-j.* 80y Any single 1.40 .90

Ministry of Agriculture, Forestry and Fisheries Festival, 50th Anniv. — A2805

Designs: No. 3394, Rice, chickens, tomatoes, fruit trees. No. 3395, Rice and fish.

**2011, Nov. 22** **Litho.** ***Perf. 13***

**3394** 80y multi 1.40 .90
**3395** 80y multi 1.40 .90
*a.* A2805 Horiz. pair, #3394-3395 4.20 4.20

Miniature Sheet

Home Towns — A2806

No. 3396 — Paintings by Taiji Harada of views of towns of Shinetsu region: a, Excursion (children, farmhouse, field of flowers, Iiyama, Nagano prefecture, denomination at LL). b, Excursion (children, hosue, river, field of flowers, Iiyama, denomination at UL). c, Kite Flying (three children near houses, Oshino Hakkai, Yamanashi prefecture, denomination at UL). d, Kite Flying (women and children, kites in air, Oshino Hakkai, denomination at UL). e, Riverbank Homes (person with dog in front of house, Kashiwazaki, Niigata prefecture). f, Riverbank Homes (man on scooter in front of house, Kashiwazaki). g, Yamakoshi in Springtime (koi breeding pool and building, Nagaoka, Niigata prefecture, denomination at LL). h, Yamakoshi in Springtime (building, man along path beside breeding pool, Nagaoka, denomination at UR). i, Town with a View of Fuji (adult and child, building, Mount Fuji, Yamanashi, Yamanashi prefecture). j, Snow Removal (adults cleaning snow, children playing, Naganao, Nagano prefecture).

**2011, Dec. 1** **Photo.** ***Perf. 13***

**3396** A2806 Sheet of 10 21.00 21.00
*a.-j.* 80y Any single 1.40 .90

Miniature Sheet

Akita Local Autonomy Law, 60th Anniv. — A2807

No. 3397: a, Nobu Shirase (1861-1946), Antarctic explorer, and two namahage (32x39mm). b, Korakukan Theater, Kosaka (28x33mm). c, Weeping cherry trees, Kakunodate (28x33mm). d, Statue of Tatsuko, Lake Tazawa (28x33mm). e, Kamakura Snow Festival, Yokote (28x33mm).

***Perf. 13¼ (#3397a), 13x13¼***

**2012, Jan. 13**

**3397** A2807 Sheet of 5 10.50 10.50
*a.-e.* 80y Any single 1.40 .90

**Animation**

Miniature Sheet

Dragon Ball Kai — A2808

No. 3398: a, Vegeta on rock (white denomination at UL). b, Son Goku (purple denomination at LL). c, Son Gohan (red denomination at LL). d, Piccolo (purple denomination at LR). e, Trunks facing left(white denomination at LL). f, Vegeta facing right (white denomination at UR). g, Son Goku with fist extended(red denomination at LR). h, Piccolo flying (white denomination at LR) i, Son Gohan with white cape (white denomination at LL). j, Son Goku with brown tunic (white denomination at LR).

**2012, Jan. 23** **Litho.** ***Perf. 13x13¼***

**3398** A2808 Sheet of 10 21.00 21.00
*a.-j.* 80y Any single 1.40 .90

Miniature Sheets

A2809

Greetings Stamps — A2810

No. 3399: a, Child on bird. b, Child with boxes and pail, cat, flowers. c, Tree, bear, rabbit, bird, flowers. d, Swan, flower bouquet. e, Children on cherry blossom petals.

No. 3400: a, Cat and flowers in box. b, Dog, falling cherry blossom petals. c, Bouquet of cherry blossoms. d, Birds in basket of flowers. e, Girl with letter, mailbox.

***Die Cut Perf. 13¼x13½***

**2012, Feb. 1** **Litho.**

**Self-Adhesive**

**3399** A2809 Sheet of 5 7.00
*a.-e.* 50y Any single .90 .50

***Die Cut Perf. 13***

**3400** A2810 Sheet of 5 10.50
*a.-e.* 80y Any single 1.40 .90

Violets — A2811

Rose — A2812

Flowering Dogwood A2813

Muscari A2814

Poppy — A2815

Violets — A2816

Roses A2817

Flowering Dogwood A2818

Muscari A2819

Poppies A2820

**2012, Mar. 1 Photo. *Perf. 13¼***

| | | | | | |
|---|---|---|---|---|---|
| **3401** | A2811 | 50y multi | | .90 | .50 |
| **3402** | A2812 | 50y multi | | .90 | .50 |
| **3403** | A2813 | 50y multi | | .90 | .50 |
| **3404** | A2814 | 50y multi | | .90 | .50 |
| **3405** | A2815 | 50y multi | | .90 | .50 |
| *a.* | Vert. strip of 5, #3401-3405 | | | 6.25 | 6.25 |
| **3406** | A2816 | 80y multi | | 1.40 | .90 |
| **3407** | A2817 | 80y multi | | 1.40 | .90 |
| **3408** | A2818 | 80y multi | | 1.40 | .90 |
| **3409** | A2819 | 80y multi | | 1.40 | .90 |
| **3410** | A2820 | 80y multi | | 1.40 | .90 |
| *a.* | Vert. strip of 5, #3406-3410 | | | 10.00 | 10.00 |
| | *Nos. 3401-3410 (10)* | | | 11.50 | 7.00 |

Miniature Sheets

A2821

Disney Characters — A2822

No. 3411: a, Mickey and Minnie Mouse holding each other with arms extended (36x29mm heart-shaped stamp). b, Mickey with arm raised (27x28mm). c, Minnie with arms at side (27x28mm). d, Mickey with arms behind back (27x28mm). e, Minnie winking (27x28mm). f, Mickey with hands on hips (27x28mm). g, Minnie and Mickey, Minnie at left (36x29mm heart-shaped stamp). h, Mickey and Minnie not touching, Mickey's arm extended (36x29mm heart-shaped stamp). i, Mickey and Minnie, tails crossing (36x29mm heart-shaped stamp). j, Mickey and Minnie, Minnie's arms extended (36x29mm heart-shaped stamp).

No. 3412: a, Mickey (yellow background, 28mm diameter). b, Minnie (yellow background, 28mm diameter). c, Mickey, Minnie, Goofy, Pluto, Daisy Duck, Donald Duck (yellow background, 37mm diameter). d, Minnie and Daisy (pink background, 28mm diameter). e, Daisy (pink background, 28mm diameter). f, Donald (blue background, 28mm diameter). g, Mickey and Pluto (blue background, 28mm diameter). h, Mickey with arms raised (white, beige and blue background, oval). i, Goofy, Mickey and Donald (pink background, 37mm diameter). j, Minnie, Pluto and Mickey (blue background, 37mm diameter).

***Die Cut Perf., Die Cut Perf. 13¼x13½ (#3411b-3411f)***

**2012, Mar. 2 Litho.**

**Self-Adhesive**

| | | | | |
|---|---|---|---|---|
| **3411** | A2821 | Sheet of 10 | 12.50 | 12.50 |
| *a.-j.* | 50y Any single | | .90 | .50 |
| **3412** | A2822 | Sheet of 10 | 20.00 | 20.00 |
| *a.-j.* | 80y Any single | | 1.40 | .90 |

Miniature Sheet

U.S. Cherry Blossom Centennial — A2823

No. 3413: a, Cherry trees in bloom, Washington Monument. b, Cherry trees in bloom, Jefferson Memorial. c, Cherry blossoms, bright blue background. d, Cherry blossoms, dark green background. e, Cherry blossoms, gray blue background. f, Cherry blossoms, olive brown background. g, Cherry blossoms, pink background.

**2012, Mar. 27 *Perf. 13***

| | | | | |
|---|---|---|---|---|
| **3413** | A2823 | Sheet of 10, #3413a-3413f, 4 #3413g | 20.00 | 20.00 |
| *a.-g.* | 80y Any single | | 1.40 | .90 |

See U.S. Nos. 4651-4652.

Miniature Sheet

Okinawa Local Autonomy Law, 60th Anniv. — A2824

No. 3414: a, Shuri Castle and Kumiodori dancer (32x39mm). b, Shurei Gate, Shuri Castle (28x33mm). c, Ryukyuan bingata (28x33mm). d, Ryukyuan dancers (28x33mm). e, Coral tree blossoms (28x33mm).

***Perf. 13¼ (#3414a), 13x13¼***

**2012, Apr. 13 Photo.**

| | | | | |
|---|---|---|---|---|
| **3414** | A2824 | Sheet of 5 | 10.00 | 10.00 |
| *a.-e.* | 80y Any single | | 1.40 | .90 |

Fence with Grasses and Flowers, From Paper Partition by Unknown Artist — A2825

Dragon, From Screen by Sanraku Kano — A2826

Peonies, From Screen by Eino Kano — A2827

***Perf. 12¾ Syncopated***

**2012, Apr. 20 Photo.**

| | | | | |
|---|---|---|---|---|
| **3415** | A2825 | 80y multi | 1.40 | .90 |
| **3416** | A2826 | 80y multi | 1.40 | .90 |
| **3417** | A2827 | 80y multi | 1.40 | .90 |
| | *Nos. 3415-3417 (3)* | | 4.20 | 2.70 |

Philately Week. Nos. 3415-3417 were printed in a sheet of 10 containing 3 each Nos. 3415 and 3417 and 4 No. 3416.

Miniature Sheet

Travel Scenes — A2828

No. 3418: a, Giant panda with open mouth (stamp 1). b, Giant panda with closed mouth (stamp 2). c, Shinobazo Pond, Ueno Park, Tokyo, denomination at UL (stamp 3). d, Shinobazo Pond, Ueno Park and Tokyo Buildings in distance, denomination at UR (stamp 4). e, Thunder Gate, Senso-ji Temple, denomination at LL (stamp 5). f, Senso-ji pagodas, denomination at UL (stamp 6). g, Boat on Sumida River. buildings, denomination at UR (stamp 7). h, Asahi Beer Buildings along Sumida River, denomination at UR (stamp 8). i, Cherry blossoms, Sumida Park, denomination at UL (stamp 9). j, Fireworks display alomg Sumida River, denomination at LR (stamp 10).

**2012, Apr. 23 Litho. *Perf. 13x13¼***

| | | | | |
|---|---|---|---|---|
| **3418** | A2828 | Sheet of 10 | 20.00 | 20.00 |
| *a.-j.* | 80y Any single | | 1.40 | .90 |

Japanese Bush Cranberry A2829

Yellow-flowered Toad Lily — A2830

Phedimus Sikokianus A2831

Japanese Wild Orchid — A2832

Stigmatodactylus Sikokianus A2833

**2012, Apr. 24 *Perf. 12¾x13***

| | | | | |
|---|---|---|---|---|
| **3419** | A2829 | 80y multi | 1.40 | .90 |
| **3420** | A2830 | 80y multi | 1.40 | .90 |
| **3421** | A2831 | 80y multi | 1.40 | .90 |
| **3422** | A2832 | 80y multi | 1.40 | .90 |
| **3423** | A2833 | 80y multi | 1.40 | .90 |
| *a.* | Vert. strip of 5, #3419-3423 | | 10.00 | 10.00 |
| | *Nos. 3419-3423 (5)* | | 7.00 | 4.50 |

Plant illustrations by Tomitaro Makino (1862-1957), botanist.

Miniature Sheet

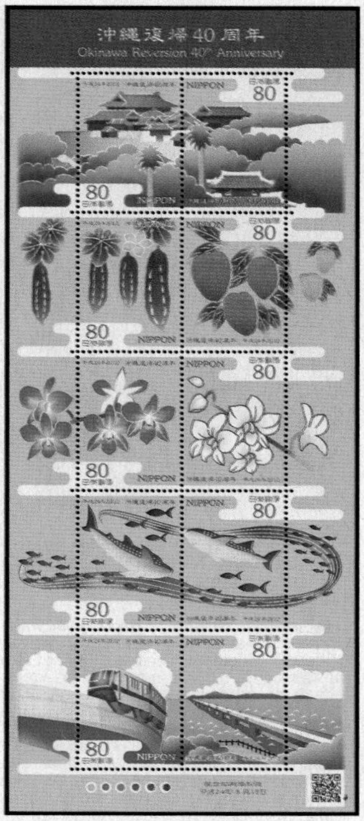


Return of Okinawa to Japanese Control, 40th Anniv. — A2834

No. 3424: a, Shuri Castle, denomination at LL. b, Shuri Castle, denomination at UR. c, Bitter melon, denomination at LL. d, Mangos, denomination at UR. e, Pink and white orchids, denomination at LL. f, White orchids, denomination at UR. g, Whale shark and fish, denomination at LL. h, Whale shark and fish, denomination at UR. i, Okinawa Urban Monorail, denomination at LL. j, Bridge between islands, denomination at UR.

**2012, May 15 Photo. *Perf. 13***

| | | | | |
|---|---|---|---|---|
| **3424** | A2834 | Sheet of 10 | 20.00 | 20.00 |
| ***a.-j.*** | | 80y Any single | 1.40 | .90 |

Miniature Sheet

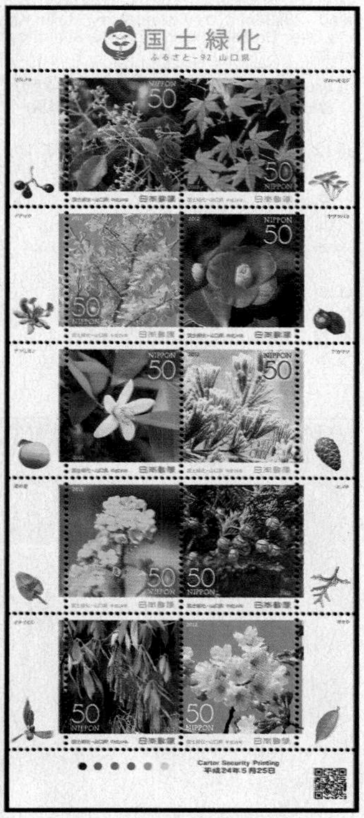


Yamaguchi Prefecture Afforestation — A2835

No. 3425: a, Camphor tree, denomination at UR. b, Japanese maple, denomination at LR in yellow. c, Ginkgo (yellow leaves on branch), denomination at LL in yellow. d, Wild camellia, denomination at UR. e, Citrus natsudaiidai (single white flower), denomination at UR. f, Japanese red pine, denomination at UR in green. g, Rape blossoms (yellow flowers), denomination at LR in yellow. h, Japanese cypress, denomination at LL. i, Boat oak, denomination at LL in green . j, Cherry blossoms, denomination at LL.

**2012, May 25 Litho.**

| | | | | |
|---|---|---|---|---|
| **3425** | A2835 | Sheet of 10 | 13.00 | 13.00 |
| ***a.-j.*** | | 50y Any single | .90 | .50 |

A2836

A2837

A2838

A2839

A2840

A2841

A2842

A2843

A2844

Ikebana, 550th Anniv. — A2845

**2012, May 31**

| | | | |
|---|---|---|---|
| **3426** | Sheet of 10 | 20.00 | 20.00 |
| ***a.*** | A2836 80y multi | 1.40 | .90 |
| ***b.*** | A2837 80y multi | 1.40 | .90 |
| ***c.*** | A2838 80y multi | 1.40 | .90 |
| ***d.*** | A2839 80y multi | 1.40 | .90 |
| ***e.*** | A2840 80y multi | 1.40 | .90 |
| ***f.*** | A2841 80y multi | 1.40 | .90 |
| ***g.*** | A2842 80y multi | 1.40 | .90 |
| ***h.*** | A2843 80y multi | 1.40 | .90 |
| ***i.*** | A2844 80y multi | 1.40 | .90 |
| ***j.*** | A2845 80y multi | 1.40 | .90 |

Miniature Sheet

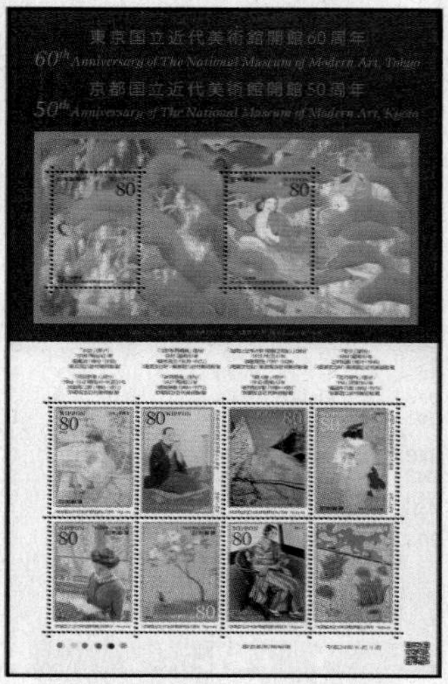

Modern Art — A2846

No. 3427: a, Bathhouse Girls, by Bakusen Tsuchida (detail of bird in tree). b, Bathouse Girls, by Tsuchida (detail of girl). c, Young Girl, by Kunzo Minami (girl at table writing). d, Portrait of Encho San'yutei, by Kiyokata Kaburagi (man kneeling on mat). e, Road, Cut Bank and Fence, by Ryusei Kishida. f, Mother and Child, by Shoen Uemura. g, Reading by the Window, by Kijiro Ota (woman reading book). h, Back Garden After the Rain, by Shinsen Tokuoka (bird under flowering bush). i, Portrait of a Lady, by Sotaro Yasui (woman seated in chair). j, Study of Flowers, by Heihachiro Fukuda (pond with iris shoots and fallen cherry blossoms).

**2012, June 1 Photo. *Perf. 13***

| | | | | |
|---|---|---|---|---|
| **3427** | A2846 | Sheet of 10 | 20.00 | 20.00 |
| ***a.-j.*** | | 80y Any single | 1.40 | .90 |

Wisteria A2847

Lily of the Valley A2848

Hydrangea A2849

Sunflower A2850

Morning Glories A2851

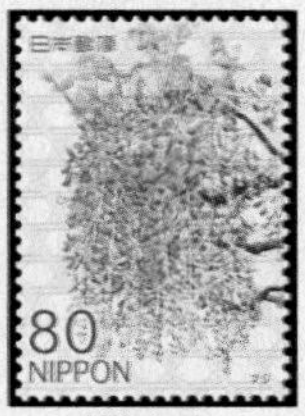

Wisteria A2852

Lily of the Valley A2853

Hydrangea A2854

Sunflowers
A2855

Morning Glories
A2856

**2012, June 7 Photo. *Perf. 13¼***

| | | | | |
|---|---|---|---|---|
| **3428** | A2847 50y multi | | .90 | .50 |
| **3429** | A2848 50y multi | | .90 | .50 |
| **3430** | A2849 50y multi | | .90 | .50 |
| **3431** | A2850 50y multi | | .90 | .50 |
| **3432** | A2851 50y multi | | .90 | .50 |
| *a.* | Vert. strip of 5, #3428-3432 | | 6.25 | 6.25 |
| **3433** | A2852 80y multi | | 1.40 | .90 |
| **3434** | A2853 80y multi | | 1.40 | .90 |
| **3435** | A2854 80y multi | | 1.40 | .90 |
| **3436** | A2855 80y multi | | 1.40 | .90 |
| **3437** | A2856 80y multi | | 1.40 | .90 |
| *a.* | Vert. strip of 5, #3433-3437 | | 10.00 | 10.00 |
| | *Nos. 3428-3437 (10)* | | 11.50 | 7.00 |

Tenjin Festival (Osaka) — A2857

**2012, June 15 Litho. *Perf. 13¼***

| | | | |
|---|---|---|---|
| **3438** | 50y Denomination at UR | .90 | .50 |
| **3439** | 50y Denomination at UL | .90 | .50 |
| *a.* | A2857 Horiz. pair, #3438-3439 | 2.50 | 2.50 |

Japanese Forces in United Nations Peacekeeping Operations, 20th Anniv. — A2858

**2012, June 19 *Perf. 13***

| | | | |
|---|---|---|---|
| **3440** | 80y pink & multi | 1.40 | .90 |
| **3441** | 80y blue & multi | 1.40 | .90 |
| *a.* | A2858 Pair, #3440-3441 | 4.00 | 4.00 |

Miniature Sheet

Ogaswara Islands UNESCO World Heritage Site — A2859

No. 3442: a, Bonin white-eye, denomination at UL (stamp 1). b, Bonin peonies, denomination at LR (stamp 2). c, Heart Rock, denomination at UL (stamp 3). d, Snail on leaf, denomination at LL (stamp 4). e, Ogi Pond and rock arch, denomination at LL (stamp 5). f, Semi-fossilized shells, denomination at UL (stamp 6). g, Bonin camellia, denomination at LL (stamp 7). h, Chichijima Forests, denomination at LR (stamp 8). i, Southern bottlenose dolphins, denomination at UR (stamp 9). j, Pandanus boninensis, denomination at UR (stamp 10).

**2012, June 20 Photo. *Perf. 13x13¼***

| | | | | |
|---|---|---|---|---|
| **3442** | A2859 | Sheet of 10 | 20.00 | 20.00 |
| *a.-j.* | | 80y Any single | 1.40 | .90 |

Miniature Sheets

A2860

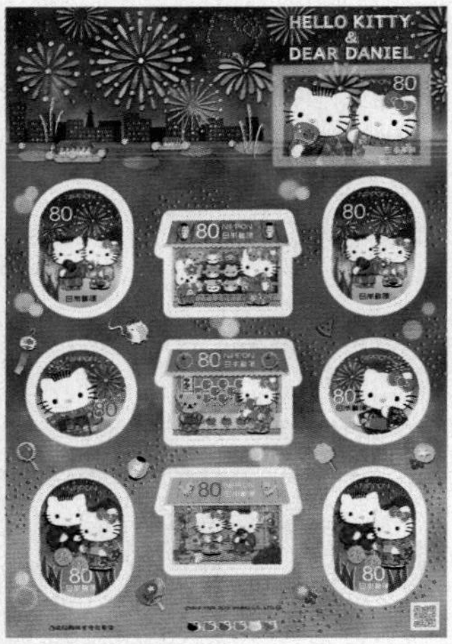


Hello Kitty — A2861

No. 3443: a, Hello Kitty and Dear Daniel (25x38mm fan-shaped stamp). b, Hello Kitty (25x38mm fan-shaped stamp). c, Hello Kitty, pink panel (25x25mm). d, Hello Kitty, lilac panel (25x25mm). e, Hello Kitty, yellow panel (25x25mm).

No. 3444: a, Hello Kitty and Dear Daniel (42x27mm rectangular stamp). b, Hello Kitty, rabbit, building with blue roof (40x29mm building-shaped stamp). c, Hello Kitty, denomination in red at R (29mm diameter). d, Hello Kitty, bear, building with red roof (40x29mm building shaped stamp). e, Hello Kitty, white denomination at L (29mm diameter). f, Hello Kitty and Dear Daniel, building with orange roof (40x29mm building-shaped stamp). g, Hello Kitty and Dear Daniel, fireworks overhead (28x38mm oval stamp). h, Hello Kitty and Dear Daniel holding fans (28x38mm oval stamp).

***Die Cut Perf. 13¼ (#3443a-3443b), Die Cut Perf. 13¼x13½ (#3443c-3443e)***

**2012, June 22 Litho.**

**Self-Adhesive**

| | | | | |
|---|---|---|---|---|
| **3443** | A2860 | Sheet of 10, 2 each #3443a-3443e | 12.50 | |
| *a.-e.* | | 50y Any single | .90 | .50 |

***Die Cut Perf. 13½***

| | | | | |
|---|---|---|---|---|
| **3444** | A2861 | Sheet of 10, #3444a-3444f, 2 each #3444g-3444h | 20.00 | |
| *a.-h.* | | 80y Any single | 1.40 | .90 |

Miniature Sheet

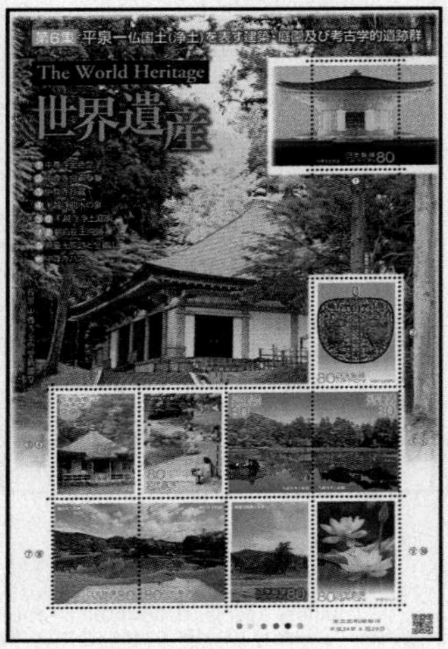


Hiraizumi UNESCO World Heritage Site — A2862

No. 3445: a, Golden Hall, Chuson-ji, denomination at LR in gold (stamp 1). b, Hanging ornament, denomination at LL (stamp 2). c, Kyozo buildings, Chuson-ji, denomination at UL (stamp 3). d, People under umbrellas at Motsuji, denomination at LL (stamp 4). e, Motsuji Jodo Garden and pond, denomination at UL (stamp 5). f, Motsuji Jodo Garden and pond, denomination at UR (stamp 6). g, Kanjizaio-in temple garden and pond, denomination at LR (stamp 7). h, Kanjizaio-in temple garden and pond, denomination at LL (stamp 8). i, Muryoko-in ruins, trees and mountain, denomination at LR (stamp 9). j, Lotus blossoms, denomination at LL (stamp 10).

**2012, June 29 Photo. *Perf. 13x13¼***

| | | | | |
|---|---|---|---|---|
| **3445** | A2862 | Sheet of 10 | 20.00 | 20.00 |
| *a.-j.* | | 80y Any single | 1.40 | .90 |

Adder's Tongue Lily
A2863

Bazara-Taisho (c. 710-794)
A2864

**2012, July 2 Photo. *Perf. 13x13¼***

| | | | |
|---|---|---|---|
| **3446** | A2863 350y multi | 7.00 | 6.00 |
| **3447** | A2864 500y multi | 9.50 | 8.00 |

No. 3446 has a vignette different from No. 2166.

Miniature Sheet

Season's Memories in My Heart — A2865

No. 3448: a, Woman on bench near water, denomination at UL (stamp 1). b, Street vendor booths at festival, denomination at LR in gold (stamp 2). c, Child running stick against fence posts, denomination at UR (stamp 3). d, Children and animals in fog, denomination at UR (stamp 4). e, Girl with flower, boy with fishing pole and bucket, denomination at UL (stamp 5). f, Children on steps near sea, denomination at LR (stamp 6). g, Children, boats on shore, flying gull, denomination at UL (stamp 7). h, Children on hill looking at boat, denomination at UL in gold (stamp 8). i, Boat on shore, children looking at jellyfish, denomination at UL (stamp 9). j, Cricket with leaf cello, child, bottle, denomination at UL in gold (stamp 10).

**2012, July 3 Photo. *Perf. 13***

| | | | | |
|---|---|---|---|---|
| **3448** | A2865 | Sheet of 10 | 20.00 | 20.00 |
| *a.-j.* | | 80y Any single | 1.40 | .90 |

Miniature Sheet

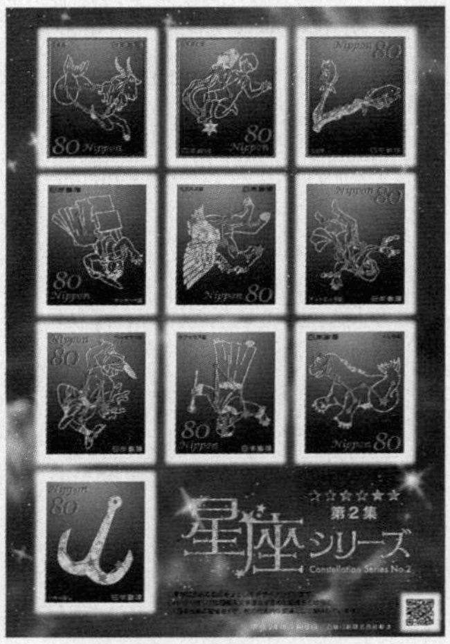


Constellations — A2866

No. 3449: a, Capricornus (goat). b, Aquarius (water bearer). c, Pisces (fish). d, Cassiopeia (woman in chair). e, Pegasus. f, Andromeda (woman in chains). g, Perseus (swordsman). h, Cepheus (king with scepter). i, Cetus (creature with two front legs and tail). j, Cassiopeia (anchor).

**Litho. With Foil Application**

**2012, July 6 *Die Cut Perf. 13***

**Self-Adhesive**

| | | | | |
|---|---|---|---|---|
| **3449** | A2866 | Sheet of 10 | 20.00 | |
| *a.-j.* | | 80y Any single | 1.40 | .90 |

Miniature Sheet

Kanagawa Local Autonomy Law, 60th Anniv. — A2867

No. 3450: a, Tsurugaoka Hachimangu, Kamakura, and mounted archer (32x39mm). b, Minato Mirai 21 buildings, Yokohama (28x33mm). c, Jogashima Lighthouse (28x33mm). d, Tanzawa Mountains and Lake Miyagase (28x33mm). e, Lake Ashi (28x33mm).

***Perf. 13¼ (#3450a), 13x13¼***

| | | | | | |
|---|---|---|---|---|---|
| **2012, July 13** | | | **Photo.** | | |
| **3450** | A2867 | Sheet of 5 | | 10.50 | 10.50 |
| *a.-e.* | | 80y Any single | | 1.40 | .90 |

Susanoo, Shinto God of the Sea — A2868

Legendary Princess Inada — A2869

Legendary Princess Konohanasakuya A2870

Legendary Prince Yamatotakeru A2871

| | | | | | |
|---|---|---|---|---|---|
| **2012, July 20** | | **Litho.** | ***Perf. 13*** | | |
| **3451** | A2868 | 80y multi | | 1.40 | .90 |
| **3452** | A2869 | 80y multi | | 1.40 | .90 |
| **3453** | A2870 | 80y multi | | 1.40 | .90 |
| **3454** | A2871 | 80y multi | | 1.40 | .90 |
| *a.* | | Block of 4, #3451-3454 | | 8.40 | 8.40 |
| | | *Nos. 3451-3454 (4)* | | 5.60 | 3.60 |

Nos. 3451-3454 were printed in sheets of 10 containing 3 each Nos. 3451-3452 and 2 each Nos. 3453-3454.

Inpumon In no Taifu, Poet — A2872

Fujiwara no Toshiyuki Ason, Poet — A2873

Shune-hoshi, Poet — A2874

Kokamon In no Betto, Poet — A2875

Sone no Yoshitada, Poet — A2876

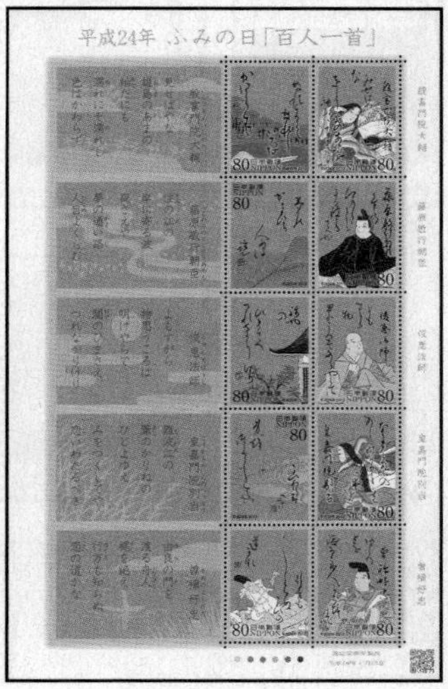

Poetry — A2877

No. 3460 — Poetry in Japanese calligraphy and: a, Boat in lake, denomination at LL. b, Inpumon In no Taifu. c, Hill near water, denomination at UL. d, Fujiwara no Toshiyuki Ason. e, Building and tree. f, Shune-hoshi. g, Eddies in river, denomination at UR. h, Kokamon In no Betto. i, Man rowing boat. j, Sone no Yoshitada.

| | | | | | |
|---|---|---|---|---|---|
| **2012, July 23** | | **Photo.** | ***Perf. 13¼*** | | |
| **3455** | A2872 | 50y multi | | .90 | .50 |
| **3456** | A2873 | 50y multi | | .90 | .50 |
| **3457** | A2874 | 50y multi | | .90 | .50 |
| **3458** | A2875 | 50y multi | | .90 | .50 |
| **3459** | A2876 | 50y multi | | .90 | .50 |
| *a.* | | Vert. strip of 5, #3455-3459 | | 6.50 | 6.50 |
| | | *Nos. 3455-3459 (5)* | | 4.50 | 2.50 |
| | | ***Perf. 12¾x13*** | | | |
| **3460** | A2877 | Sheet of 10 | | 21.00 | 21.00 |
| *a.-j.* | | 80y Any single | | 2.10 | 1.60 |

Hanaogi of the Ogi Establishment Going Elsewhere, by Eisho Chokosai A2878

The Moon Crossing Bridge at Arashiyama in Yamashiro Province, by Hiroshige A2879

Tosei Onna Fuzuoku Tsuu Hokkoku no Keisei, by Utamaro A2880

The Brocade Bridge at Iwakuni in Suo Province, by Hiroshige A2881

Furyu Setsugekka Tsuki, by Eizan Kikukawa A2882

Mt. Kyodai and the Moon Reflected in the Rice Fields at Sarashina in Shinano Province, by Hiroshige A2883

Ogiya Uchi Hanaogi Yoshino Tatsuta, by Utamaro A2884

Rough Sea at Naruto in Awa Province, by Hiroshige A2885

Furyu Mutamagawa Chofu no Tamagawa, by Eizan Kikukawa A2886

The Monkey Bridge in Kai Province, by Hiroshige A2887

| | | | | | |
|---|---|---|---|---|---|
| **2012, Aug. 1** | | **Litho.** | ***Perf. 13*** | | |
| **3461** | | Sheet of 10 | | 21.00 | 21.00 |
| *a.* | A2878 | 80y multi | | 1.40 | .90 |
| *b.* | A2879 | 80y multi | | 1.40 | .90 |
| *c.* | A2880 | 80y multi | | 1.40 | .90 |
| *d.* | A2881 | 80y multi | | 1.40 | .90 |
| *e.* | A2882 | 80y multi | | 1.40 | .90 |
| *f.* | A2883 | 80y multi | | 1.40 | .90 |
| *g.* | A2884 | 80y multi | | 1.40 | .90 |
| *h.* | A2885 | 80y multi | | 1.40 | .90 |
| *i.* | A2886 | 80y multi | | 1.40 | .90 |
| *j.* | A2887 | 80y multi | | 1.40 | .90 |

Miniature Sheet

Miyazaki Local Autonomy Law, 60th Anniv. — A2888

No. 3462: a, Miyazaki Prefectural Office and dancer (32x39mm). b, Koibitono-oka (hill with gazebo) (28x33mm). c, Yellow flowers, Saitobaru Burial Grounds (28x33mm). d, Pink flowers, Ebino-kogen Highlands (28x33mm). e, Terraced rice fields (28x33mm).

***Perf. 13¼ (#3462a), 13x13¼***

| | | | | | |
|---|---|---|---|---|---|
| **2012, Aug. 15** | | | **Photo.** | | |
| **3462** | A2888 | Sheet of 5 | | 10.50 | 10.50 |
| *a.-e.* | | 80y Any single | | 1.40 | .90 |

Sorex Minutissimus A2889

Aquila Chrysaetos A2890

Paeonia Obovata A2891

Oryzias Latipes A2892

Tachypleus Tridentatus A2893

| **2012, Aug. 23** | | | *Perf. 13¼* | |
|---|---|---|---|---|
| **3463** | A2889 | 80y multi | 1.40 | .90 |
| **3464** | A2890 | 80y multi | 1.40 | .90 |
| **3465** | A2891 | 80y multi | 1.40 | .90 |
| **3466** | A2892 | 80y multi | 1.40 | .90 |
| **3467** | A2893 | 80y multi | 1.40 | .90 |
| *a.* | | Vert. strip of 5, #3463-3467 | 10.50 | 10.50 |
| | | *Nos. 3463-3467 (5)* | 7.00 | 4.50 |

Normalization of Diplomatic Relations Between Japan and People's Republic of China, 40th Anniv. — A2894

| **2012, Sept. 4** | | | *Perf. 13* | |
|---|---|---|---|---|
| **3468** | A2894 | 80y multi | 1.40 | .90 |

Miniature Sheet

Travel Scenes — A2895

No. 3469 — Sites in Nagasaki: a, Urakami Cathedral, denomination at UR (stamp 1). b, Peace Statue, Nagasaki (stamp 2). c, Megane Bridge, denomination at LL (stamp 3). d, Megane Bridge, denomination at LR (stamp 4). e, Lantern Festival, denomination at UL below country name (stamp 5). f, Sofuku Temple, denomination at UL, to left of country name (stamp 6). g, Glover House, Glover Gardens, denomination at UR (stamp 7). h, Glover House , Glover Gardens, denomination at LR (stamp 8). i, People carrying dragon at Kunchi Festival, denomination at LL (stamp 9). j, Tall Ships Festival, denomination at UR (stamp 10).

| **2012, Sept. 11** | **Litho.** | | *Perf. 13x13¼* | |
|---|---|---|---|---|
| **3469** | A2895 | Sheet of 10 | 21.00 | 21.00 |
| *a.-j.* | | 80y Any single | 1.40 | .90 |

Miniature Sheets

A2896

Teddy Bears — A2897

No. 3470 — Teddy bear with: a, Blue cap, pink background, red bow at top (28x28mm). b, Blue cap, light blue background, blue bow at top (28x28mm). c, Blue and white box with red ribbon, pink background, pink bow at top (28x28mm). d, Gold box with yellow ribbon, yellow background, yellow bow at top (28x28mm). e, Card with red ribbon, lilac background, red bow at top(28x28mm). f, Card with blue ribbon, light green background, gray green bow at top (28x28mm). g, Red box with white ribbon, plaid bow around neck (26x30mm). h, Blue box with red ribbon, dark blue bow around neck (26x30mm). i, Card with red ribbon, green bow around neck (26x30mm). j, Blue and white box with red ribbon, blue bow around neck (26x30mm).

No. 3471: a, Bear with blue and white box with yellow ribbon (26x38mm). b, Bear with green box with red ribbon (26x38mm). c, Bear with card with red ribbon (26x38mm). d, Two bears, lilac denomination (42x27mm). e, Two bears, blue denomination (27x38mm oval). f, Two bears, red denomination (27x38mm oval). g, Bear with black and brown bow around neck, red denomination (27x38mm oval). h, Bear with card with red ribbon, red denomination (27x38mm oval). i, Bear with flower (27x38mm oval). j, Bear with cap, two boxes (42x27mm).

***Die Cut Perf. 14, Die Cut Perf. (#3470g-3470j)***

**2012, Sept. 21** **Litho.**

**Self-Adhesive**

| | | | | |
|---|---|---|---|---|
| **3470** | A2896 | Sheet of 10 | 13.00 | |
| *a.-j.* | | 50y Any single | .90 | .50 |

***Die Cut Perf. 14½x14 (#3471a-3471c), 11¼x13½ (#3471d, 3471j), 13¾***

| | | | | |
|---|---|---|---|---|
| **3471** | A2897 | Sheet of 10 | 21.00 | |
| *a.-j.* | | 80y Any single | 1.40 | .90 |

Badminton A2898

Rhythmic Gymnastics A2899

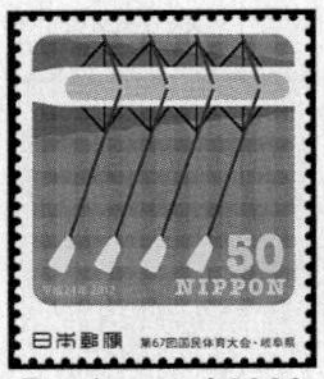


Rowing — A2900

Cycling — A2901

Field Hockey — A2902

| **2012, Sept. 28** | **Litho.** | | *Perf. 13* | |
|---|---|---|---|---|
| **3472** | A2898 | 50y multi | .90 | .50 |
| **3473** | A2899 | 50y multi | .90 | .50 |
| **3474** | A2900 | 50y multi | .90 | .50 |
| **3475** | A2901 | 50y multi | .90 | .50 |
| **3476** | A2902 | 50y multi | .90 | .50 |
| *a.* | | Vert. strip of 5, #3472-3476 | 6.50 | 6.50 |

67th National Athletic Meet, Gifu. Compare with type A2790.

Miniature Sheet

Horse Racing in Japan, 150th Anniv. — A2903

No. 3477: a, Orfevre (horse #9, jockey with green helmet). b, Apapane (horse #9, jockey with yellow helmet, blue and yellow silks). c, Deep Impact (horse #5, jockey with red helmet, yellow and gray silks). d, Still in Love (horse #9, jockey with yellow helmet, red and blue silks). e, Narita Brian (horse #4, jockey with red helmet). f, Mejiro l'Amone (horse #13). g, Symboli Rudolf (horse #5, jockey with red helmet, blue and red silks). h, Mr. C.B. (horse #12, jockey with green and white silks). i, Shinzan (horse #4, jockey with brown helmet). j, Saint Lite (horse #12, black-and-white photograph).

| **2012, Oct. 2** | **Photo.** | | *Perf. 13* | |
|---|---|---|---|---|
| **3477** | A2903 | Sheet of 10 | 21.00 | 21.00 |
| *a.-j.* | | 80y Any single | 1.40 | .90 |

Intl. Letter Writing Week A2904

Designs: 90y, Hatsugochi, by Kiyokata Kaburaki. 110y, Shunpo, by Shoen Uemura. 130y, Hubuki, by Shinsui Ito.

| **2012, Oct. 9** | **Photo.** | | *Perf. 13¼* | |
|---|---|---|---|---|
| **3478** | A2904 | 90y multi | 1.60 | 1.00 |
| **3479** | A2904 | 110y multi | 1.90 | 1.40 |
| **3480** | A2904 | 130y multi | 2.10 | 1.60 |
| | | *Nos. 3478-3480 (3)* | 5.60 | 4.00 |

Miniature Sheet

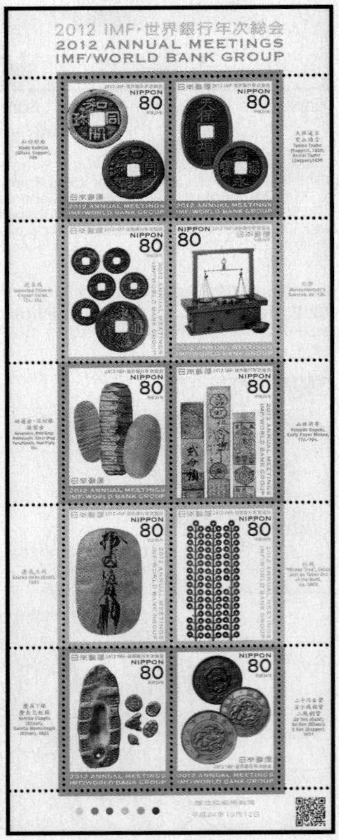


Annual Meeting of Intl. Monetary Fund and World Bank Group, Tokyo — A2905

No. 3481: a, Silver and copper Wado Kaichin coins, 708 (gold frame). b, Oval copper Tempo Tsuho coin, 1835, round Kanei Tsuho coin, 1636 (gold frame). c, Six round Chinese copper coins, 12th-15th cent. (silver frame) d, Moneychanger's balance, 19th cent. (silver frame). e, Hirumokin gold slug, Sekishugin silver slug, Yuzurihakin gold plate, 16th cent. (gold frame). f, Yamada Hagaki paper money, 17th-19th cent. (gold frame). g, Gold Keicho Oban, 1601 (silver frame). h, Molded coins attached to sprues, c. 1863 (silver frame). i, Silver Keicho Chogin coin and five Silver Keicho Mameitagin coins, 1601 (silver frame). j, 1871 gold 20-yen, silver 50-yen and copper 2-sen coins (gold frame).

| **2012, Oct. 12** | **Photo.** | | *Perf. 13* | |
|---|---|---|---|---|
| **3481** | A2905 | Sheet of 10 | 20.00 | 20.00 |
| *a.-j.* | | 80y Any single | 1.40 | .90 |

Miniature Sheet

Tochigi Local Autonomy Law, 60th Anniv. — A2906

No. 3482: a, Yomei Gate, Toshogu Shrine (32x39mm). b, Gate at Ashikaga School (28x33mm). c, Carp amulets on sticks (28x33mm). d, Moka Railway steam locomotive and flowers (28x33mm). e, Cherry blossoms and mountain, Nasu Kogen (28x33mm).

***Perf. 13¼ (#3482a), 13x13¼***

**2012, Oct. 15 Photo.**

| | | | | |
|---|---|---|---|---|
| **3482** | A2906 | Sheet of 5 | 10.00 | 10.00 |
| *a.-e.* | | 80y Any single | 1.40 | .90 |

**Animation**

Miniature Sheet

Rascal — A2907

No. 3483: a, Rascal the Raccoon on tree (white denomination at UR). b, Sterling and Alice (white denomination at UL). c, Rascal with book and lamp (white denomination at UL). d, Sterling and book (white denomination at UR). e, Three raccoon babies, butterflies (black denomination at UL). f, Rascal facing left (black denomination at UR). g, Rascal drinking from bottle (white denomination at UL). h, Sterling drinking from bottle (white denomination at UL). i, Rascal, Rascal in canoe (black denomination at UR). j, Sterling, Sterling in canoe (white denomination at UR).

**2012, Oct. 23 Litho. *Perf. 13x13¼***

| | | | | |
|---|---|---|---|---|
| **3483** | A2907 | Sheet of 10 | 20.00 | 20.00 |
| *a.-j.* | | 80y Any single | 1.40 | .90 |

Miniature Sheet

Traditional Crafts — A2908

No. 3484: a, Hakata doll depicting man holding fan (Fukuoka Prefecture). b, Black rectangular inkstone and lid (Miyagi Prefecture). c, Banana-fiber handbag (Okinawa Prefecture). d, Container and two cups (Fukushima Prefecture). e, Two lacquerware bowls (Aomori Prefecture). f, Folding fan (Kyoto Prefecture). g, Kaga dyed screen (Ishikawa Prefecture). h, Decorated Kutani plate (Ishikawa Prefecture). i, Cast-iron kettle (Iwate Prefecture). j, Tsuboya ceramic urn with handles (Okinawa Prefecture).

**2012, Oct. 25 Photo. *Perf. 13½***

| | | | | |
|---|---|---|---|---|
| **3484** | A2908 | Sheet of 10 | 20.00 | 20.00 |
| *a.-j.* | | 80y Any single | 1.40 | .90 |

Miniature Sheets

A2909

A2910

Greetings — A2911

No. 3485: a, Star, Santa Clauses, gift (29x39mm). b, Kitten in stocking (26x34mm). c, Wreath, children, squirrel (29mm diameter). d, Puppy in stocking (26x34mm). e, Christmas tree and cardinal (29x39mm).

No. 3486: a, Santa Claus and reindeer on building roof. b, Fireplace, Christmas tree, two children, cat and bird. c, Fireplace, three children, bird. d, Fireplace, Christmas tree, two children, two cats, bird. e, Fireplace, two children, Christmas tree being decorated, bird.

No. 3487: a, Cat on roof, envelope in night sky (37x28mm). b, Angel with violin, bird carrying letter (35x28mm ellipse). c, Snowman, squirrel, mailbox, child (28x37mm). d, Roses and open letter (35x28mm ellipse). e, three children in pajamas, candles (37x28mm).

**Self-Adhesive**

***Die Cut Perf. 13***

**2012, Nov. 9 Litho.**

| | | | | |
|---|---|---|---|---|
| **3485** | A2909 | Sheet of 5 | 6.25 | 6.25 |
| *a.-e.* | | 50y Any single | .90 | .50 |
| **3486** | A2910 | Sheet of 5 | 10.00 | 10.00 |
| *a.-e.* | | 80y Any single | 1.40 | .90 |
| **3487** | A2911 | Sheet of 5 | 11.50 | 11.50 |
| *a.-e.* | | 90y Any single | 1.60 | 1.00 |

A2912

A2913

New Year 2013 (Year of the Snake)

A2914 A2915

**2012, Nov. 12 Photo. *Perf. 13x13½***

| | | | | |
|---|---|---|---|---|
| **3488** | A2912 | 50y multi | .95 | .50 |
| **3489** | A2913 | 80y multi | 1.40 | .60 |

**Photo. & Typo.**

***Perf. 13¼***

| | | | | |
|---|---|---|---|---|
| **3490** | A2914 | 50y +3y multi | 1.25 | .60 |
| **3491** | A2915 | 80y +3y multi | 1.75 | .60 |
| | | *Nos. 3488-3491 (4)* | 5.35 | 2.30 |

Sheets of two containing Nos. 3488-3489 were lottery prizes. Value, $4.

Miniature Sheet

Oita Local Autonomy Law, 60th Anniv. — A2916

No. 3492: a, Usa Jingu Shrine, Oita, Futabayama (1912-68), sumo wrestler (32x39mm). b, Plum blossoms, Japanese white-eye (28x33mm). c, Fukiji Temple (28x33mm). d, Hita Gion Festival (28x33mm). e, Sunrise at Bungofutamigaura (28x33mm).

***Perf. 13¼ (#3492a), 13x13¼***

**2012, Nov. 15** **Photo.**

| | | | | |
|---|---|---|---|---|
| **3492** | A2916 | Sheet of 5 | 10.00 | 10.00 |
| *a.-e.* | | 80y Any single | 1.40 | .90 |

Miniature Sheets

A2917

Disney Characters — A2918

No. 3493: a, Winnie the Pooh (27x27mm). b, Piglet (27x27mm). c, Alice in Wonderland (27x38mm oval). d, Donald Duck (26x34mm). e, Daisy Duck (26x34mm). f, Cinderella (27x38mm oval). g, Dumbo (29mm diameter). h, Marie the Cat (26x34mm). i, Goofy (26x34mm). j, Three Dalmatians (29mm diameter).

No. 3494: a, Tinker Bell (27x27mm). b, Mickey Mouse (27x38mm oval). c, Minnie Mouse (27x38mm oval). d, Bambi (27x27mm). e, Pinocchio (27x35mm). f, Snow White (27x38mm oval). g, Pluto (27x35mm). h, Ariel (35x27mm). i, Stitch (29mm diameter). j, Three Little Pigs (35x27mm).

***Die Cut Perf. 13½, Die Cut Perf. 13 (#3493d, 3493e, 3493h, 3493i), Die Cut Perf. 13¼x13¾ (#3494e, 3494g), Die Cut Perf. 13¾x13¼ (#3494h, 3494j) Die Cut Perf. (#3493g, 3493j, 3494i)***

**2012, Nov. 20** **Litho.**

**Self-Adhesive**

| | | | | |
|---|---|---|---|---|
| **3493** | A2917 | Sheet of 10 | 12.50 | |
| *a.-j.* | | 50y Any single | .90 | .50 |
| **3494** | A2918 | Sheet of 10 | 20.00 | |
| *a.-j.* | | 80y Any single | 1.40 | .90 |

Miniature Sheet

Edo Calligraphy — A2919

No. 3495 — Characters for "snake": a, In Gyosho style (red background). b, In Reisho style (black character with red chop at bottom center). c, From Qing Dynaasty seal (black curved character with circle with small red chop at left). d, In Reisho style (pink background, red chop at bottom center). e, In Kana (black character similar to "3", red chop at LR). f, In Kaisho script (black character, red chop at LL). g, In Sosho stylet (black character with thick line similar to "2" and thin curved line, red chop at LR). h, In Gyosho style (green background). i, In small seal cutting (character in red). j, In Kinbun style (character in gold, brown background).

**Litho. & Embossed**

**2012, Nov. 21** ***Perf. 13x13¼***

| | | | | |
|---|---|---|---|---|
| **3495** | A2919 | Sheet of 10 | 20.00 | 20.00 |
| *a.-j.* | | 80y Any single | 1.40 | .90 |

Camellia
A2920

Plum Blossom
A2921

Adonis Flower
A2922

Cyclamen
A2923

Hellebore
A2924

Camellia
A2925

Plum Blossoms
A2926

Adonis Flowers
A2927

Cyclamen
A2928

Hellebores
A2929

**2012, Dec. 3** **Photo.** ***Perf. 13¼***

| | | | | |
|---|---|---|---|---|
| **3496** | A2920 | 50y multi | .90 | .50 |
| **3497** | A2921 | 50y multi | .90 | .50 |
| **3498** | A2922 | 50y multi | .90 | .50 |
| **3499** | A2923 | 50y multi | .90 | .50 |
| **3500** | A2924 | 50y multi | .90 | .50 |
| *a.* | | Vert. strip of 5, #3496-3500 | 6.25 | 6.25 |
| **3501** | A2925 | 80y multi | 1.40 | .90 |
| **3502** | A2926 | 80y multi | 1.40 | .90 |
| **3503** | A2927 | 80y multi | 1.40 | .90 |
| **3504** | A2928 | 80y multi | 1.40 | .90 |
| **3505** | A2929 | 80y multi | 1.40 | .90 |
| *a.* | | Vert. strip of 5, #3501-3505 | 10.00 | 10.00 |
| | | *Nos. 3496-3505 (10)* | 11.50 | 7.00 |

Miniature Sheet

Hyogo Local Autonomy Law, 60th Anniv. — A2930

No. 3506: a, Flying crane, Himeji Castle (32x39mm). b, Meriken Park, Kobe, and waterfront buildings (28x33mm). c, Shinkoro Tower, Izushi (28x33mm). d, Shinmaiko Beach (28x33mm). e, Narcissuses, Awaji-shima (28x33mm).

***Perf. 13¼ (#3506a), 13x13¼***

**2013, Jan. 15**

| | | | | |
|---|---|---|---|---|
| **3506** | A2930 | Sheet of 5 | 8.75 | 8.75 |
| *a.-e.* | | 80y Any single | 1.40 | .90 |

**Animation**
Miniature Sheet

Heidi, Girl of the Alps — A2931

No. 3507: a, Lamb and flowers. b, Heidi picking flowers). c, Dog and chalet. d, Heidi and chalet. e, Heidi's grandfather. f, Heidi pointing. g, Heidi and Peter on sled. h, Rabbits. i, Heidi running, mountain in background. j, Clara in blue dress.

**2013, Jan. 23** **Litho.** ***Perf. 13x13¼***

| | | | | |
|---|---|---|---|---|
| **3507** | A2931 | Sheet of 10 | 17.50 | 17.50 |
| *a.-j.* | | 80y Any single | 1.40 | .90 |

Miniature Sheets

A2932

Greetings — A2933

No. 3508: a, Cherry blossom, boy, birds with letter (30x29mm flower-shaped stamp). b, Wreath with strawberries (29mm diameter). c, Boy, girl, cat, wreath of cherry blossoms (29mm diameterl). d, Tulips, cats and rabbit (28x28mm). e, Girl carrying potted plant up stairs, cat with broom (28x28mm).

No. 3509: a, Gril with letter, cherry blossoms (30x29mm flower shaped stamp). b, Bouquet of red and pink flowerst (24x34mm oval). c, Bouquet of blue and white flowers (24x34mm oval). d, Bouquet of yellow and orange flowers (24x34mm oval). e, Teddy bear with letter and mail bag, mail box (23x30mm).

***Die Cut Perf., Die Cut Perf 13¼ (#3508d, 3508e, 3509b-3509d), Die Cut Perf. 13¼x12¾ (#3509e)***

**2013, Feb. 1**

**Self-Adhesive**

| | | | | | |
|---|---|---|---|---|---|
| **3508** | A2932 | Sheet of 5 | | 5.50 | 5.50 |
| *a.-e.* | | 50y Any single | | .90 | .50 |
| **3509** | A2933 | Sheet of 5 | | 8.75 | 8.75 |
| *a.-e.* | | 80y Any single | | 1.40 | .90 |

Dianthus Caryophyllus A2934

Tulip A2935

Cherry Blossoms A2936

Gerbera Daisy A2937

Myosotis Scorpioides A2938

Dianthus Caryophyllus A2939

Tulip A2940

Cherry Blossoms A2941

Gerbera Daisy A2942

Myosotis Scorpioides A2943

**2013, Feb. 8 Photo. *Perf. 13¼***

| | | | | | |
|---|---|---|---|---|---|
| **3510** | A2934 | 50y | multi | .90 | .50 |
| **3511** | A2935 | 50y | multi | .90 | .50 |
| **3512** | A2936 | 50y | multi | .90 | .50 |
| **3513** | A2937 | 50y | multi | .90 | .50 |
| **3514** | A2938 | 50y | multi | .90 | .50 |
| *a.* | Vert. strip of 5, #3510-3514 | | | 5.50 | 5.50 |
| **3515** | A2939 | 80y | multi | 1.40 | .90 |
| **3516** | A2940 | 80y | multi | 1.40 | .90 |
| **3517** | A2941 | 80y | multi | 1.40 | .90 |
| **3518** | A2942 | 80y | multi | 1.40 | .90 |
| **3519** | A2943 | 80y | multi | 1.40 | .90 |
| *a.* | Vert. strip of 5, #3515-3519 | | | 8.75 | 8.75 |
| | *Nos. 3510-3519 (10)* | | | 14.25 | 11.25 |

Mt. Fuji — A2944

Mt. Tsukuba A2945

Mt. Kasa A2946

Mt. Ibuki A2947

Mt. Iino — A2948

Mt. Zao — A2949

Mt. Gassan A2950

Mt. Ryokami A2951

Mt. Nijo — A2952

Mt. Kuju — A2953

**2013, Feb. 22 Litho. *Perf. 13¼x13***

| | | | |
|---|---|---|---|
| **3520** | Sheet of 10 | 17.50 | 17.50 |
| *a.* | A2944 80y multi | 1.40 | .90 |
| *b.* | A2945 80y multi | 1.40 | .90 |
| *c.* | A2946 80y multi | 1.40 | .90 |
| *d.* | A2947 80y multi | 1.40 | .90 |
| *e.* | A2948 80y multi | 1.40 | .90 |
| *f.* | A2949 80y multi | 1.40 | .90 |
| *g.* | A2950 80y multi | 1.40 | .90 |
| *h.* | A2951 80y multi | 1.40 | .90 |
| *i.* | A2952 80y multi | 1.40 | .90 |
| *j.* | A2953 80y multi | 1.40 | .90 |

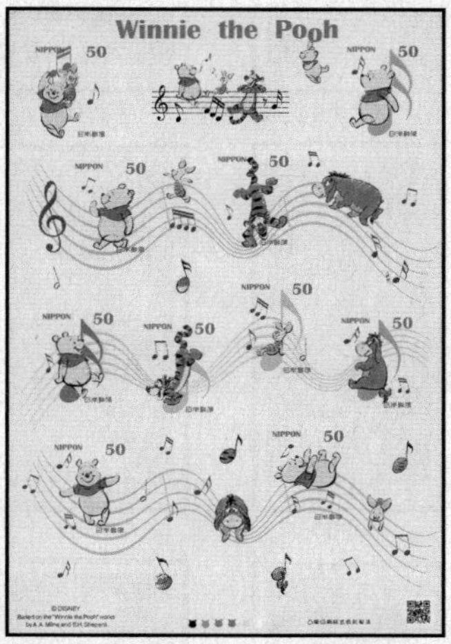


A2954

Winnie the Pooh — A2955

No. 3521: a, Winnie, Piglet, two beamed sixteenth notes in blue, eighth note in black. b, Winnie, sixteenth notes in black and green. c, Winnie, staff in pink, two beamed eighth notes in black. d, Tigger, staff in pink, eighth note in black. e, Winnie, staff in yellow, black and red sixteenth notes. f, Tigger, staff in yellow, two beamed eighth notes in black, eighth note in blue. g, Piglet, staff in yellow, three beamed sixteenth notes, eighth notes in black and pink, half note. h, Eeyore, staff in yellow, sixteenth note and two beamed sixteenth notes in black, eighth note in lilac. i, Winnie, staff in pink, sixteenth note and two beamed sixteenth notes in black. j, Winnie, staff in pink, eighth note, sixteenth note and two beamed sixteenth notes in black.

No. 3522, oval stamps: a, Winnie and Eeyore. b, Winnie seated, touching his nose and with arm wrapped over his head, vert. c, Winnie and Piglet standing, vert. d, Tigger, vert. e, Winnie and Tigger. f, Winnie and honey jar, vert. g, Eeyore and log. h, Winnie standing with arm near mouth. i, Tigger, Eeyore and Winnie. j, Winnie and Piglet walking, vert.

**2013, Mar. 1 *Die Cut Perf. 13x12¾***

**Self-Adhesive**

| | | | | |
|---|---|---|---|---|
| **3521** | A2954 | Sheet of 10 | 11.00 | |
| *a.-j.* | | 50y Any single | .90 | .50 |

***Die Cut Perf. 13***

| | | | | |
|---|---|---|---|---|
| **3522** | A2955 | Sheet of 10 | 17.50 | |
| *a.-j.* | | 80y Any single | 1.40 | .90 |

Grand Canyon, United States A2956

Pyramids, Egypt A2957

Mont-Saint-Michel, France — A2958

Macchu Picchu, Peru A2959

Angkor Wat, Cambodia
A2960

**2013, Mar. 14** ***Perf. 13¼x13***

| | | | | | |
|---|---|---|---|---|---|
| **3523** | A2956 | 80y | multi | 1.40 | .90 |
| **3524** | A2957 | 80y | multi | 1.40 | .90 |
| **3525** | A2958 | 80y | multi | 1.40 | .90 |
| **3526** | A2959 | 80y | multi | 1.40 | .90 |
| **3527** | A2960 | 80y | multi | 1.40 | .90 |
| *a.* | Horiz. strip of 5, #3523-3527 | | | 8.75 | 8.75 |
| | *Nos. 3523-3527 (5)* | | | 7.00 | 4.50 |

Foreign UNESCO World Heritage Sites.

Hirosaki Cherry Blossom Festival (Aomori) — A2961

Designs: No. 3528, Weeping cherry branch, Mt. Iwaki (denomination in green). No. 3529, Yoshino cherry blossoms, Hirosaki Castle (denomination in lilac).

**2013, Mar. 22** ***Perf. 13¼***

| | | | | |
|---|---|---|---|---|
| **3528** | 50y multi | | .90 | .50 |
| **3529** | 50y multi | | .90 | .50 |
| *a.* | A2961 | Horiz. pair, #3528-3529 | 2.20 | 2.20 |

Miniature Sheet

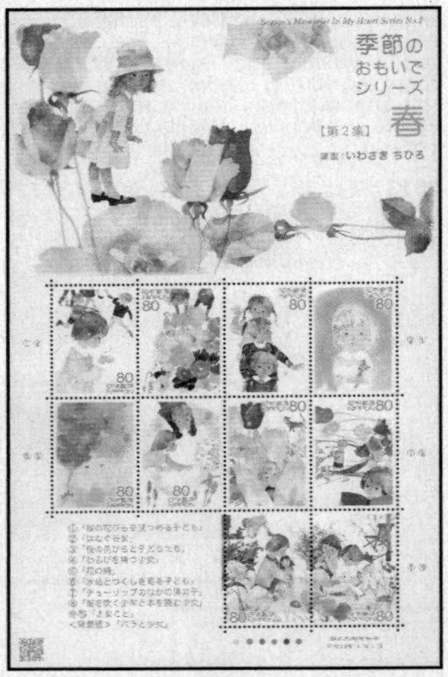


Season's Memories in My Heart — A2962

No. 3530: a, Girl in yellow dress staring at cherry blossom petals (stamp 1). b, Two children and flower cart (stamp 2). c, Three children, falling cherry blossom petals (stamp 3). d, Girl holding fiddlhead fern in field (stamp 4). e, Girl and flowers (stamp 5). f, Boy and girl looking at flowers (stamp 6). g, Boy in tulips, cat (stamp 7). h, Boy playing flute, girl reading book, flowers (stamp 8). i, Girl with doll, girl with dog, flowers (stamp 9). j, Girls playing house with doll, lawn chair (stamp 10).

**2013, Apr. 3** **Photo.** ***Perf. 13***

| | | | | |
|---|---|---|---|---|
| **3530** | A2962 | Sheet of 10 | 17.50 | 17.50 |
| *a.-j.* | 80y Any single | | 1.40 | .90 |

Miniature Sheet

Travel Scenes — A2963

No. 3531 — Sites in Tateyama and Kurobe areas of Toyama: a, Ptarmigan (stamp 1). b, Bus and tourists in Great Snow Valley (stamp 2). c, Shomyo Falls (stamp 3). d, Tateyama gentians, denomination at LL (stamp 4). e, Midagahara Wetlands, denomination at UL (stamp 5). f, Midagahara Wetlands, denomination at UR (stamp 6). g, Murodo Highland, yellow day lilies (stamp 7). h, Stoat (stamp 8). i, Aleutian avens flowers, denomination at LR (stamp 9). j, Cable car at Daikanbo (stamp 10).

**2013, Apr. 16** **Litho.** ***Perf. 13x13¼***

| | | | | |
|---|---|---|---|---|
| **3531** | A2963 | Sheet of 10 | 16.00 | 16.00 |
| *a.-j.* | 80y Any single | | 1.40 | .90 |

A2964

A2965

A2966

A2967

A2968

A2969

A2970

A2971

Sections of Painted Screen by Motonobu Kano (1476-1559)
A2972 A2973

**2013, Apr. 19** **Photo.** ***Perf. 13¼***

| | | | | |
|---|---|---|---|---|
| **3532** | | Sheet of 10 | 16.00 | 16.00 |
| *a.* | A2964 80y multi | | 1.40 | .90 |
| *b.* | A2965 80y multi | | 1.40 | .90 |
| *c.* | A2966 80y multi | | 1.40 | .90 |
| *d.* | A2967 80y multi | | 1.40 | .90 |
| *e.* | A2968 80y multi | | 1.40 | .90 |
| *f.* | A2969 80y multi | | 1.40 | .90 |
| *g.* | A2970 80y multi | | 1.40 | .90 |
| *h.* | A2971 80y multi | | 1.40 | .90 |
| *i.* | A2972 80y multi | | 1.40 | .90 |
| *j.* | A2973 80y multi | | 1.40 | .90 |

Philately Week.

Lily — A2974

Day Lily — A2975

Lilac
A2976

Clematis
A2977

Skunk Cabbage
A2978

Lilies
A2979

Day Lilies — A2980

Lilac — A2981

Clematis
A2982

Skunk Cabbages
A2983

**2013, Apr. 24** ***Perf. 13¼***

| | | | | | |
|---|---|---|---|---|---|
| **3533** | A2974 | 50y | multi | .90 | .50 |
| **3534** | A2975 | 50y | multi | .90 | .50 |
| **3535** | A2976 | 50y | multi | .90 | .50 |
| **3536** | A2977 | 50y | multi | .90 | .50 |
| **3537** | A2978 | 50y | multi | .90 | .50 |
| *a.* | Vert. strip of 5, #3533-3537 | | | 5.00 | 5.00 |
| **3538** | A2979 | 80y | multi | 1.40 | .90 |
| **3539** | A2980 | 80y | multi | 1.40 | .90 |
| **3540** | A2981 | 80y | multi | 1.40 | .90 |
| **3541** | A2982 | 80y | multi | 1.40 | .90 |
| **3542** | A2983 | 80y | multi | 1.40 | .90 |
| *a.* | Vert. strip of 5, #3538-3542 | | | 8.00 | 8.00 |

Miniature Sheet

Miyagi Local Autonomy Law, 60th Anniv. — A2984

No. 3543: a, Statue of Masamune Date, replica of Date Maru ship (32x39mm). b, Mt. Kurikoma and cherry tree (28x33mm). c, Sendai Tanabata Festival (28x33mm). d, Bridge, Narukokyo Gorge (28x33mm). e, Sendai Pageant of Starlight (28x33mm).

***Perf. 13¼ (#3543a), 13x13¼***

**2013, May 15** **Photo.**

| | | | | |
|---|---|---|---|---|
| **3543** | A2984 | Sheet of 5 | 8.75 | 8.75 |
| *a.-e.* | 80y Any single | | 1.75 | 1.40 |

Martes Zibellina Brachyura
A2985

Luscinia Komadori Namiyei
A2986

Primula Kisoana Miquel A2987

Neolucanus Insulicola Donan A2988

Meretrix Lusoria A2989

**2013, May 23** *Perf. 13¼*

| | | | | | |
|---|---|---|---|---|---|
| **3544** | A2985 | 80y multi | | 1.40 | .90 |
| **3545** | A2986 | 80y multi | | 1.40 | .90 |
| **3546** | A2987 | 80y multi | | 1.40 | .90 |
| **3547** | A2988 | 80y multi | | 1.40 | .90 |
| **3548** | A2989 | 80y multi | | 1.40 | .90 |
| *a.* | Vert. strip of 5, #3544-3548 | | | 8.75 | 8.75 |
| | *Nos. 3544-3548 (5)* | | | 7.00 | 4.50 |

Miniature Sheet

Tottori Prefecture Afforestation — A2990

No. 3549: a, Quercus serrata (tree), denomination at LL. b, Lilium japonicum (pink flower), denomination at LL. c, Prunus jamasakura (cherry blossoms), denomination at LR. d, Taxus cuspidata (Japanese yew with red arils), denomination at LR. e, Castanopsis sieboldii (tree), denomination at UR. f, Iris sanguinea (purple flowers), denomination at UL. g, Nijisseiki pear tree blossoms, denomination at LR. h, Japanese persimmons on branch, denomination at LR. i, Castanea crenata (Japanese chestnut), denomination at UR. j, Magnolia obovata flower, denomination at LL.

**2013, May 24** **Litho.** *Perf. 13*

| | | | | |
|---|---|---|---|---|
| **3549** | A2990 | Sheet of 10 | 11.00 | 11.00 |
| *a.-j.* | 50y Any single | | .90 | .50 |

Second Hideyo Noguchi Africa Prize — A2991

Noguchi (1876-1928), bacteriologist, and: No. 3550, Microscope and flowers. No. 3551, Globe.

**2013, May 31** **Photo.**

| | | | | |
|---|---|---|---|---|
| **3550** | 80y multicolored | | 1.40 | .90 |
| **3551** | 80y multicolored | | 1.40 | .90 |
| *a.* | A2991 Horiz. pair, #3550-3551 | | 3.50 | 3.50 |

**Animation**

Doraemon — A2992

No. 3552: a, Doraemon with wings, two children with wings. b, Three children with wings. c, Doraemon paddling raft. d, Children on fish. e, Doraemon, machine, woman near doorway carrying tray with bottles and glasses. f, Man and boy in indoor fountain. g, Three children with helicopter rotor on head flying. h, Doraemon and child with helicopter rotor on head flying. i, Boy and girl on orse, boy with smokestack on head, boy with umbrella in flight. j, Doraemon and cat on flying seahorses.

**2013, June 4** **Litho.** *Perf. 13x13¼*

| | | | | |
|---|---|---|---|---|
| **3552** | A2992 | Sheet of 10 | 17.50 | 17.50 |
| *a.-j.* | 80y Any single | | 1.40 | .90 |

Miniature Sheet

Hiroshima Local Autonomy Law, 60th Anniv. — A2993

No. 3553: a, Itsukushima Shrine, Bugaku dancer, maple leaves (32x39mm). b, Mibo no Hana Taue rice-planting ritual (28x33mm). c, Taishakukyo Valley (28x33mm). d, Lemons (28x33mm). e, Lighthouse and street, Tomonoura (28x33mm).

***Perf. 13¼ (#3553a), 13x13¼***

**2013, June 14** **Photo.**

| | | | | |
|---|---|---|---|---|
| **3553** | A2993 | Sheet of 5 | 8.75 | 8.75 |
| *a.-e.* | 80y Any single | | 1.40 | .90 |

Japan Women's Association for Rehabilitation Aid, 50th Anniv. — A2994

Designs: No. 3554, Two women. No. 3555, Three women.

**2013, June 18** **Litho.** *Perf. 13*

| | | | | |
|---|---|---|---|---|
| **3554** | 80y multicolored | | 1.40 | .90 |
| **3555** | 80y multicolored | | 1.40 | .90 |
| *a.* | A2994 Horiz. pair, #3554-3555 | | 3.50 | 3.50 |

Miniature Sheets

A2995

Greetings — A2996

No. 3556: a, Hello Kitty reading book (30x27mm heart-shaped stamp). b, Hello Kitty and house (27x30mm house-shaped stamp). c, Mimmy riding tricycle (23x23mm). d, Dear Daniel with letter at mailbox (22x30mm oval stamp). e, My Melody receiving kiss from mouse on tree stump (28mm diameter). f, Hello Kitty watering flowers (27x21mm). g, My Melody, bird in mailbox holding letter (21x27mm). h, My Melody and mouse jumping (30x27mm heart-shaped stamp). i, Little Twin Stars on crescent moon (28mm diameter). j, Little Twin Stars with music book and harp (23x23mm).

No. 3557: a, Little Twin Stars on cloud (27x21mm). b, Little Twin Stars, stars (24x28mm). c, Hello Kitty in airplane (28mm diameter). d, Hello Kitty holding teddy bear and letter (23x23mm). e, Hello Kitty on back of envelope (27x21mm). f, Hello Kitty and Mimmy on tricycles (27x21mm). g, Dear Daniel reaching to insert letter in mailbox (26x29mm). h, Hello Kitty holding apple (29x27mm heart-shaped stamp). i, My Melody receiving letter from bird in mailbox (29x26mm). j, My Melody receiving kiss from mouse (30x27mm oval stamp).

***Die Cut Perf. 13¼, Die Cut Perf. 14 (#3556c, 3556j, 3557d), Die Cut Perf. 13¼x14 (#3556f, 3557a, 3557e, 3557f), Die Cut Perf. 14x13¾ (#3556g), Die Cut Perf. (#3556e, 3556i, 3557b, 3557c)***

**2013, June 21** **Litho.**

**Self-Adhesive**

| | | | | |
|---|---|---|---|---|
| **3556** | A2995 | Sheet of 10 | 10.00 | |
| *a.-j.* | | 50y Any single | .90 | .50 |
| **3557** | A2996 | Sheet of 10 | 16.00 | |
| *a.-j.* | | 80y Any single | 1.40 | .90 |

Miniature Sheet

Travel Scenes — A2997

No. 3558 — Sites in Chiba: a, Narita-san Temple (stamp 1). b, Tourists in boat, flowers at Suigo Sarawa Aquatic Botanical Gardens (stamp 2). c, Chiba Port Tower (stamp 3). d, Nokogiriyama Cable Car (stamp 4). e, Yellow and red Kominato Railway train car (stamp 5). f, Waterfall, Yoro-keikoku Valley (stamp 6). g, Tsuki-no-Sabaku Statues, Onjuku Beach (stamp 7). h, Yellow and green Isumi Railway train car (stamp 8). i, Light green Choshi Electric Railway train car (stamp 9). j, Inubosaki Lighthouse (stamp 10).

**2013, June 25** **Litho.** ***Perf. 13x13¼***

| | | | | |
|---|---|---|---|---|
| **3558** | A2997 | Sheet of 10 | 16.00 | 16.00 |
| *a.-j.* | | 80y Any single | 1.40 | .90 |

Gion Festival, Kyoto — A2998

Various festival scenes with denomination in purple at: No. 3559, UL. No. 3560, UR. No. 3561, LL. No. 3562, LR.

**2013, July 1** ***Perf. 13¼***

| | | | | |
|---|---|---|---|---|
| **3559** | | 50y multi | .90 | .50 |
| **3560** | | 50y multi | .90 | .50 |
| **3561** | | 50y multi | .90 | .50 |
| **3562** | | 50y multi | .90 | .50 |
| *a.* | A2998 | Block of 4, #3559-3562 | 4.00 | 4.00 |
| | | *Nos. 3559-3562 (4)* | 3.60 | 2.00 |

Miniature Sheet

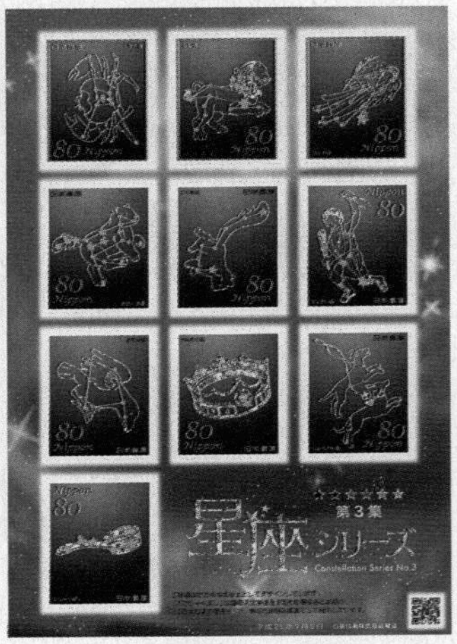


Constellations — A2999

No. 3563: a, Cancer (crab). b, Leo (lion). c, Virgo (virgin). d, Ursa Major (large bear, tail at left). e, Ursa Minor (small bear, tail at top). f, Boötes (herdsman). g, Corvus (crow). h, Corona Borealis (crown). i, Canes Venatici (hunting dogs). j, Big Dipper asterism.

**Litho. With Foil Application**

**2013, July 5** ***Die Cut Perf. 13***

**Self-Adhesive**

| | | | | |
|---|---|---|---|---|
| **3563** | A2999 | Sheet of 10 | 16.00 | |
| *a.-j.* | | 80y Any single | 1.40 | .90 |

Miniature Sheet

Gunma Local Autonomy Law, 60th Anniv. — A3000

No. 3564: a, Tomioka Silk Mill, woman (32x39mm). b, Red rhododendrons (28x33mm). c, Usui Railway Bridge (28x33mm). d, Fukiware Falls (28x33mm). e, Yellow day lilies (28x33mm).

***Perf. 13¼ (#3564a), 13x13¼***

**2013, July 12** **Photo.**

| | | | | |
|---|---|---|---|---|
| **3564** | A3000 | Sheet of 5 | 8.00 | 8.00 |
| *a.-e.* | | 80y Any single | 1.40 | .90 |

Boy Writing Postcard A3001

Goldfish in Bowl A3002

Mailbox, Dragonfly, Net — A3003

Japanese Morning Glories and Trellis — A3004

Cucumbers, Eggplants, and Tomatoes — A3005

A3006

No. 3570: a, Girl writing a letter. b, Mailbox, dragonfly, net, diff. c, Beans and bowl of rice. d, Tea kettle and glasses. e, Corn. f, Japanese morning glories and trellis, diff. g, Postal truck on bridge. h, Spiral mosquito repellent coils. i, Bowls of noodles and sauce. j, Tomatoes.

**2013, July 23** ***Perf. 13¼***

| | | | | |
|---|---|---|---|---|
| **3565** | A3001 | 50y multi | .90 | .50 |
| **3566** | A3002 | 50y multi | .90 | .50 |
| **3567** | A3003 | 50y multi | .90 | .50 |
| **3568** | A3004 | 50y multi | .90 | .50 |
| **3569** | A3005 | 50y multi | .90 | .50 |
| *a.* | | Vert strip of 5, #3565-3569 | 5.50 | 5.50 |
| | | *Nos. 3565-3569 (5)* | 4.50 | 2.50 |

***Perf. 13***

| | | | | |
|---|---|---|---|---|
| **3570** | A3006 | Sheet of 10 | 17.50 | 17.50 |
| *a.-j.* | | 80y Any single | 1.40 | .90 |

Letter Writing Day.

Kisegawa of Matsubaya, by Eishi Chobunsai A3007

Pine Grove at Miho, by Hiroshige A3008

Midorigi of the Wakamatsu House, by Eisho Chokosai A3009

Oyashirazu, by Hiroshige A3010

Woman Holding an Umbrella, by Eizan Kikukawa A3011

Waka Bay, by Hiroshige A3012

Koito of Itoya, by Utamaro A3013

Festival at the Itsukushima Shrine, by Hiroshige A3014

Geisha of Tachibana Street, by Kiyonaga Torii A3015

Amanohashidate, by Hiroshige A3016

**2013, Aug. 1** **Litho.** ***Perf. 13***

| | | | | |
|---|---|---|---|---|
| **3571** | | Sheet of 10 | 17.50 | 17.50 |
| *a.* | A3007 | 80y multi | 1.75 | 1.40 |
| *b.* | A3008 | 80y multi | 1.75 | 1.40 |
| *c.* | A3009 | 80y multi | 1.75 | 1.40 |
| *d.* | A3010 | 80y multi | 1.75 | 1.40 |
| *e.* | A3011 | 80y multi | 1.75 | 1.40 |
| *f.* | A3012 | 80y multi | 1.75 | 1.40 |
| *g.* | A3013 | 80y multi | 1.75 | 1.40 |
| *h.* | A3014 | 80y multi | 1.75 | 1.40 |
| *i.* | A3015 | 80y multi | 1.75 | 1.40 |
| *j.* | A3016 | 80y multi | 1.75 | 1.40 |

Miniature Sheets

A3017

Disney Characters — A3018

No. 3572: a, Mickey Mouse on blue box. b, Minnie Mouse on pink box. c, Donald Duck on blue box. d, Daisy Duck on pink box. e, Tinker Bell on pink box. f, Marie the Cat on blue box. g, Buzz Lightyear and Woody on pink box. h, Lightning McQueen on blue box. i, Winnie the Pooh on blue box. j, Alice on pink box.

No. 3573: a, Tinker Bell (29mm diameter). b, Winnie the Pooh and Piglet in balloon gondola (21x30mm oval). c, Alice in balloon gondola (29mm diameter). d, Marie the Cat in balloon gondola (21x30mm oval). e, Oswald the Rabbit in balloon gondola (23x23mm). f, Mike Wazowski and James P. Sullivan in balloon gondola (21x30mm oval). g, Goofy, Chip, Donald Duck, Pluto, Mickey Mouse, Minnie Mouse, Daisy Duck in balloon gondola (44x35mm). h, Woody and Buzz Lightyear in balloon gondola (21x30mm oval). i, Snow White, Rapunzel and Cinderella in balloon gondola (29mm diameter). j, Dumbo (30x21mm oval).

***Die Cut Perf. 13¼***

**2013, Aug. 8** **Litho.**

**Self-Adhesive**

| | | | | |
|---|---|---|---|---|
| **3572** | A3017 | Sheet of 10 | 10.00 | |
| *a.-j.* | | 50y Any single | 1.00 | .75 |

***Die Cut Perf., Die Cut Perf. 13¼ (oval stamps), Die Cut Perf. 14 (#3573e), Die Cut Perf. 13½ (#3573g)***

| | | | | |
|---|---|---|---|---|
| **3573** | A3018 | Sheet of 10 | 16.00 | |
| *a.-j.* | | 80y Any single | 1.60 | 1.25 |

Kayak on Tama River — A3019

Sailboats Near Tokyo Gate Bridge — A3020

Bonin Islands — A3021

Tokyo Skyline — A3022

Tokyo Stadium — A3023

**2013, Aug. 25** **Litho.** ***Perf. 13***

| | | | | | |
|---|---|---|---|---|---|
| **3574** | A3019 | 80y | multi | 1.60 | 1.25 |
| **3575** | A3020 | 80y | multi | 1.60 | 1.25 |
| **3576** | A3021 | 80y | multi | 1.60 | 1.25 |
| **3577** | A3022 | 80y | multi | 1.60 | 1.25 |
| **3578** | A3023 | 80y | multi | 1.60 | 1.25 |
| *a.* | Vert. strip of 5, #3574-3578 | | | 8.00 | 6.25 |
| | *Nos. 3574-3578 (5)* | | | 8.00 | 6.25 |

68th National Athletic Meet, Tokyo.

Persimmon A3024

Bok Choy A3025

Chestnut A3026

Sweet Potato A3027

Pear A3028

Apple A3029

Taro Roots A3030

Japanese Pears A3031

Turnip Greens A3032

Grapes A3033

***Die Cut Perf. 13x13¼, 13¼x13***

**2013, Aug. 30** **Photo.**

**Self-Adhesive**

| | | | |
|---|---|---|---|
| **3579** | Sheet of 10, 2 each #3579a-3579e | 10.00 | |
| *a.* | A3024 50y multi | 1.00 | .75 |
| *b.* | A3025 50y multi | 1.00 | .75 |
| *c.* | A3026 50y multi | 1.00 | .75 |
| *d.* | A3027 50y multi | 1.00 | .75 |
| *e.* | A3028 50y multi | 1.00 | .75 |
| **3580** | Sheet of 10, 2 each #3580a-3580e | 16.00 | |
| *a.* | A3029 80y multi | 1.60 | 1.25 |
| *b.* | A3030 80y multi | 1.60 | 1.25 |
| *c.* | A3031 80y multi | 1.60 | 1.25 |
| *d.* | A3032 80y multi | 1.60 | 1.25 |
| *e.* | A3033 80y multi | 1.60 | 1.25 |

Dahlia A3034

Chrysanthemum A3035

Cockscomb A3036

Asiatic Dayflower A3037

Rose A3038

Dahlias A3039

Chrysanthemums A3040

Cockscombs A3041

Asiatic Dayflowers A3042

Roses A3043

**2013, Sept. 13** **Photo.** ***Perf. 13¼***

| | | | | | |
|---|---|---|---|---|---|
| **3581** | A3034 | 50y | multi | 1.00 | .75 |
| **3582** | A3035 | 50y | multi | 1.00 | .75 |
| **3583** | A3036 | 50y | multi | 1.00 | .75 |
| **3584** | A3037 | 50y | multi | 1.00 | .75 |
| **3585** | A3038 | 50y | multi | 1.00 | .75 |
| *a.* | Vert. strip of 5, #3581-3585 | | | 5.00 | 3.75 |
| **3586** | A3039 | 80y | multi | 1.60 | 1.25 |
| **3587** | A3040 | 80y | multi | 1.60 | 1.25 |
| **3588** | A3041 | 80y | multi | 1.60 | 1.25 |
| **3589** | A3042 | 80y | multi | 1.60 | 1.25 |
| **3590** | A3043 | 80y | multi | 1.60 | 1.25 |
| *a.* | Vert. strip of 5, #3586-3590 | | | 8.00 | 6.25 |
| | *Nos. 3581-3590 (10)* | | | 13.00 | 10.00 |

Ambulance Service Legislation, 50th Anniv. — A3044

**2013, Sept. 9** **Litho.** ***Perf. 13***

| | | | | |
|---|---|---|---|---|
| **3591** | 80y | Helicopter ambulance | 1.60 | 1.25 |
| **3592** | 80y | Ambulance | 1.60 | 1.25 |
| *a.* | A3044 | Horiz. pair, #3591-3592 | 3.20 | 2.50 |

Miniature Sheets

A3045

Greetings — A3046

No. 3593 — Teddy bear wearing postman's cap: a, In bed (21x30mm oval). b, Alone at table (21x30mm oval). c, At right of pillar box (23x23mm). d, At left of pillar box (23x23mm). e, Delivering letter to large teddy bear (23x23mm). f, Delivering gift to large teddy bear (23x23mm). g, Holding flower bouquet with light blue ribbon (27x30mm). h, Holding flower bouquet with yellow ribbon (27x30mm). i, With two other teddy bears at table (21x30mm oval). j, Reading book in bed (21x30mm oval).

No. 3594: a, Teddy bear delivering letter to large teddy bear (27x21mm). b, Teddy bear walking on path, holding letter (21x30mm oval). c, Teddy bear delivering gift to large teddy bear (27x21mm). d, Teddy bear delivering letter to bird (21x30mm oval). e, Teddy bear on bicycle (27x21mm). f, Teddy bear delivering letter to bear with pail and fishing pole (27x21mm). g, Small teddy bear without cap holding letter near pillar box (21x30mm oval). h, Teddy bear with cap, small teddy bear with flower bouquet (27x21mm). i, Teddy bear with cap lifting small teddy bear to slot of pillar box (21x27mm). j, Small teddy bear behind teddy bear with cap (29mm diameter).

***Die Cut Perf. 13¼ (oval stamps), Die Cut Perf. 14 (square stamps), Die Cut Perf. (#3593g, 3593h)***

**2013, Sept. 19 — Litho.**

**Self-Adhesive**

| | | | | | |
|---|---|---|---|---|---|
| **3593** | A3045 | Sheet of 10 | | 10.00 | |
| *a.-j.* | | 50y Any single | | 1.00 | .75 |

***Die Cut Perf. 13¼x13¾, Die Cut Perf. 13¼ (oval stamps), Die Cut Perf. 13¾x13¼ (#3594i), Die Cut Perf. (#3594j)***

| | | | | | |
|---|---|---|---|---|---|
| **3594** | A3046 | Sheet of 10 | | 16.00 | |
| *a.-j.* | | 80y Any single | | 1.60 | 1.25 |

Baby Elephant A3047

Baby and Adult Killer Whales A3048

Black-tailed Prairie Dog A3049

Adult and Juvenile Gentoo Penguins A3050

Kangaroo A3051

Amur Tiger Cub A3052

Timber Wolf Pups — A3053

Ring-tailed Lemurs A3054

Polar Bear — A3055

White Oryx — A3056

***Die Cut Perf. 13¼***

**2013, Sept. 20 — Litho.**

**Self-Adhesive**

| | | | | |
|---|---|---|---|---|
| **3595** | | Sheet of 10, 2 each #3595a-3595e | 10.00 | |
| *a.* | A3047 | 50y multi | 1.00 | .75 |
| *b.* | A3048 | 50y multi | 1.00 | .75 |
| *c.* | A3049 | 50y multi | 1.00 | .75 |
| *d.* | A3050 | 50y multi | 1.00 | .75 |
| *e.* | A3051 | 50y multi | 1.00 | .75 |
| **3596** | | Sheet of 10, 2 each #3596a-3596e | 16.00 | |
| *a.* | A3052 | 80y multi | 1.60 | 1.25 |
| *b.* | A3053 | 80y multi | 1.60 | 1.25 |
| *c.* | A3054 | 80y multi | 1.60 | 1.25 |
| *d.* | A3055 | 80y multi | 1.60 | 1.25 |
| *e.* | A3056 | 80y multi | 1.60 | 1.25 |

Miniature Sheet

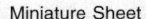

Diplomatic Relations Between Japan and Spain, 400th Anniv. — A3057

No. 3597: a, Potted geraniums on decorative shelf. b, Japanese bush clover. c, Guggenheim Museum, Bilbao, Spain (white denomination at UR, numeral to right of "Nippon.") d, Santiago de Compostela Cathedral (gold denomination at UR). e, Museum of Contemporary Art, León, Spain (white denomination at UR, numeral below "Nippon."). f, Alcazar of Segovia (castle with spires). g, Royal Palace, Madrid (building with dome). h, Arches and columns, Córdoba Cathedral, Spain. i, Courtyard and archway, Palace of Generalife, Granada, Spain. j, Field of sunflowers.

**2013, Oct. 1 — Litho. — *Perf. 13***

| | | | | |
|---|---|---|---|---|
| **3597** | A3057 | Sheet of 10 | 16.00 | 16.00 |
| *a.-j.* | | 80y Any single | 1.60 | 1.25 |

See Spain No. 3944.

Miniature Sheet

Okayama Local Autonomy Law, 60th Anniv. — A3058

No. 3598: a, Korakuen Gardens, Momotaro with animals (32x39mm). b, Bridge and buildings, Kurashiki Bikan (28x33mm). c, Shizutani School (28x33mm). d, Cattle grazing, Hiruzenkogen Highlands (28x33mm). e, Tsuyama Castle and cherry blossoms (28x33mm).

***Perf. 13¼ (#3598a), 13x13¼***

**2013, Oct. 4 — Photo.**

| | | | | |
|---|---|---|---|---|
| **3598** | A3058 | Sheet of 5 | 8.00 | 8.00 |
| *a.-e.* | | 80y Any single | 1.60 | 1.25 |

Intl. Letter Writing Week A3059

Posting stations from The Fifty-three Stations of the Tokaido, by Hiroshige: 70y, Shirasuka. 90y, Odawara. 110y, Hamamatsu. 130y, Ishiyakushi.

**2013, Oct. 9 — Photo. — *Perf. 13***

| | | | | |
|---|---|---|---|---|
| **3599** | A3059 | 70y multi | 1.50 | 1.10 |
| **3600** | A3059 | 90y multi | 1.90 | 1.50 |
| **3601** | A3059 | 110y multi | 2.25 | 1.75 |
| **3602** | A3059 | 130y multi | 2.60 | 2.00 |
| | *Nos. 3599-3602 (4)* | | 8.25 | 6.35 |

Tokyo Railroad Station A3060

Odakyu 3000 Series Locomotive A3061

JNR 151 Series Locomotive A3062

Kintetsu 10100 Series Locomotive A3063

JNR Kiha 81 Series Locomotive A3064

Meitetsu 7000 Series Locomotive A3065

Kintetsu 20100 Series Locomotive A3066

Odakyu 3100 Series Locomotive A3067

JNR Shinkansen 0 Series Locomotive A3068

Shinkansen E5 Series Locomotive A3069

**2013, Oct. 11 Photo. *Perf. 13¼x13***

| | | | |
|---|---|---|---|
| **3603** | Sheet of 10 | 16.00 | 16.00 |
| *a.* | A3060 80y multi | 1.60 | 1.25 |
| *b.* | A3061 80y multi | 1.60 | 1.25 |
| *c.* | A3062 80y multi | 1.60 | 1.25 |
| *d.* | A3063 80y multi | 1.60 | 1.25 |
| *e.* | A3064 80y multi | 1.60 | 1.25 |
| *f.* | A3065 80y multi | 1.60 | 1.25 |
| *g.* | A3066 80y multi | 1.60 | 1.25 |
| *h.* | A3067 80y multi | 1.60 | 1.25 |
| *i.* | A3068 80y multi | 1.60 | 1.25 |
| *j.* | A3069 80y multi | 1.60 | 1.25 |

Miniature Sheet

Shizuoka Local Autonomy Law, 60th Anniv. — A3070

No. 3604: a, Mount Fuji and clouds (32x39mm). b, Mount Fuji and yellow flowers (28x33mm). c, Mount Fuji reflected in Lake Tanuki (28x33mm). d, Mount Fuji and trees (28x33mm). e, Mount Fuji, ships and coastal rocks (28x33mm).

***Perf. 13¼ (#3604a), 13x13¼***

**2013, Oct. 15 Photo.**

| | | | |
|---|---|---|---|
| **3604** | A3070 Sheet of 5 | 8.00 | 8.00 |
| *a.-e.* | 80y Any single | 1.60 | 1.25 |

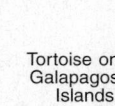

Tortoise on Galapagos Islands, Ecuador A3071

Taj Mahal, India A3072

Venice, Italy — A3073

Victoria Falls, Zambia and Zimbabwe A3074

Cologne Cathedral, Germany A3075

**2013, Oct. 23 Litho. *Perf. 13¼x13***

| | | | |
|---|---|---|---|
| **3605** | A3071 80y multi | 1.60 | 1.25 |
| **3606** | A3072 80y multi | 1.60 | 1.25 |
| **3607** | A3073 80y multi | 1.60 | 1.25 |
| **3608** | A3074 80y multi | 1.60 | 1.25 |
| **3609** | A3075 80y multi | 1.60 | 1.25 |
| *a.* | Horiz. strip of 5, #3605-3609 | 8.00 | 6.25 |
| | *Nos. 3605-3609 (5)* | 8.00 | 6.25 |

Foreign UNESCO World Heritage Sites.

Miniature Sheet

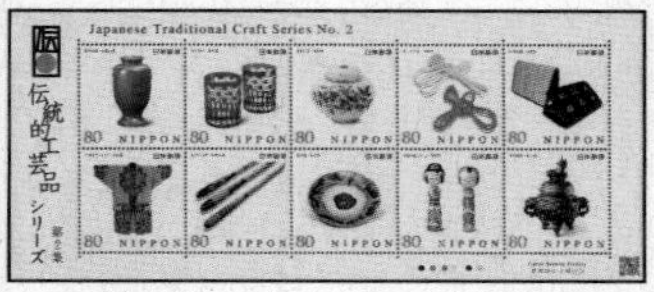


Traditional Crafts — A3076

No. 3610: a, Kishu lacquerware vase (Wakayama Prefecture). b, Two Edo Kiriko glasses (Tokyo Prefecture). c, Owari Shippo porcelain bowl with lid (Aichi Prefecture). d, Two Kyo Kumihimo braids (Kyoto Prefecture). e, Chibana Okinawa weavings (Okinawa Prefecture). f, Ainu ceremonial costume (Hokkaido Prefecture). g, Kishu lacquered utensil handles (Wakayama Prefecture). h, Mashiko-yaki pottery bowl (Tochigi Prefecture). i, Kokeshi dolls (Miyagi Prefecture). j, Takaoka copper vessel (Toyama Prefecture).

**2013, Oct. 25 Litho. *Perf. 13½***

| | | | |
|---|---|---|---|
| **3610** | A3076 Sheet of 10 | 16.00 | 16.00 |
| *a.-j.* | 80y Any single | 1.60 | 1.25 |

A3077 A3078

New Year 2014 (Year of the Horse)

A3079 A3080

**2013, Nov. 1 Photo. *Perf. 13x13½***

| | | | |
|---|---|---|---|
| **3611** | A3077 50y multi | 1.00 | .50 |
| **3612** | A3078 80y multi | 1.50 | .60 |

**Photo. & Typo.**

***Perf. 13¼***

| | | | |
|---|---|---|---|
| **3613** | A3079 50y +3y multi | 1.25 | .60 |
| **3614** | A3080 80y +3y multi | 1.75 | .60 |
| | *Nos. 3611-3614 (4)* | 5.50 | 2.30 |

Sheets of two containing Nos. 3611-3612 were lottery prizes. Value, $4.

Miniature Sheet

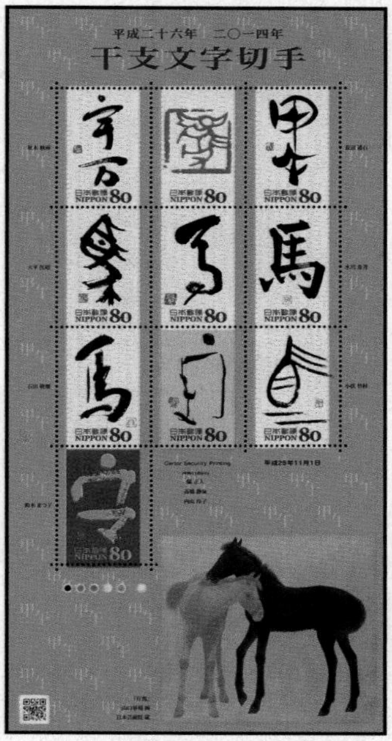


Edo Calligraphy — A3081

No. 3615 — Characters for "horse": a, In Manyo-kana style (black character with dot at top, red chop at center left). b, In oracle bone script (red character). c, In Qin Dynasty bamboo roll calligraphy (black character with curved arc crossing center line, red chop at center left). d, In Western Zhou Dynasty Kinbun style (black character with teardrop shaped top with dot in center, red chop at LL). e, In Sosho style (black character of one continuous curved line, red chop at LL). f, In Kaisho style (black character, red chop at bottom center). g, In Gyosho style (black character with red chop at LR. h, In Kana (black character with lilac background). i, In Seal style calligraphy (black character with two horizontal lines at bottom, red chop at center right). j, In Katakana (gold character on blue violet background).

**Litho. & Embossed**

**2013, Nov. 1 *Perf. 13x13¼***

| | | | |
|---|---|---|---|
| **3615** | A3081 Sheet of 10 | 16.00 | 16.00 |
| *a.-j.* | 80y Any single | 1.60 | 1.25 |

Two Snowmen A3082

Snowman With Broom A3083

Three Snowmen A3084

Snowman With Gift A3085

Snowman on Skis A3086

Snowflake Jewelry With Sapphires A3087

Snowflake Jewelry With Emeralds A3088

Snowflake Jewelry With Aquamarines A3089

Snowflake Jewelry With Peridots A3090

Snowflake Jewelry With Rubies A3091

Two Wine Glasses A3092

Two Candles A3093

Two Champagne Flutes A3094

Candle A3095

Two Martini Glasses — A3096

***Die Cut Perf. 13¼***

**2013, Nov. 7 Litho.**

**Self-Adhesive**

| | | | |
|---|---|---|---|
| **3616** | Sheet of 10, 2 each #3616a-3616e | 10.00 | |
| *a.* | A3082 50y multi | 1.00 | .75 |
| *b.* | A3083 50y multi | 1.00 | .75 |
| *c.* | A3084 50y multi | 1.00 | .75 |
| *d.* | A3085 50y multi | 1.00 | .75 |
| *e.* | A3086 50y multi | 1.00 | .75 |
| **3617** | Sheet of 10 | 16.00 | |
| *a.* | A3087 80y multi | 1.60 | 1.25 |
| *b.* | A3088 80y multi | 1.60 | 1.25 |
| *c.* | A3089 80y multi | 1.60 | 1.25 |
| *d.* | A3090 80y multi | 1.60 | 1.25 |
| *e.* | A3091 80y multi | 1.60 | 1.25 |
| *f.* | A3092 80y multi | 1.60 | 1.25 |
| *g.* | A3093 80y multi | 1.60 | 1.25 |
| *h.* | A3094 80y multi | 1.60 | 1.25 |
| *i.* | A3095 80y multi | 1.60 | 1.25 |
| *j.* | A3096 80y multi | 1.60 | 1.25 |

Miniature Sheet

Yamanashi Local Autonomy Law, 60th Anniv. — A3097

No. 3618: a, Mount Fuji, grapes, and maglev test train (32x39mm). b, Shosenkyo Gorges (28x33mm). c, Nishizawa Valley waterfalls (28x33mm). d, Pagoda and cherry blossoms (28x33mm). e, Saruhashi Bridge (28x33mm).

***Perf. 13¼ (#3618a), 13x13¼***

| | | | | |
|---|---|---|---|---|
| **2013, Nov. 15** | | **Photo.** | | |
| **3618** | A3097 | Sheet of 5 | 8.00 | 8.00 |
| *a.-e.* | | 80y Any single | 1.60 | 1.25 |

Mt. Iwakisan A3098

Mt. Tsurugidake A3099

Mt. Hirugatake A3100

Mt. Gozaishodake — A3101

Mt. Daisen A3102

Mt. Myokosan A3103

Mt. Aobasan A3104

Mt. Kaikomagatake — A3105

Mt. Oodaigahara A3106

Mt. Tenzan A3107

| | | | | |
|---|---|---|---|---|
| **2013, Nov. 19** | | **Litho.** | ***Perf. 13¼x13*** | |
| **3619** | | Sheet of 10 | 16.00 | 16.00 |
| *a.* | | A3098 80y multi | 1.60 | 1.25 |
| *b.* | | A3099 80y multi | 1.60 | 1.25 |
| *c.* | | A3100 80y multi | 1.60 | 1.25 |
| *d.* | | A3101 80y multi | 1.60 | 1.25 |
| *e.* | | A3102 80y multi | 1.60 | 1.25 |
| *f.* | | A3103 80y multi | 1.60 | 1.25 |
| *g.* | | A3104 80y multi | 1.60 | 1.25 |
| *h.* | | A3105 80y multi | 1.60 | 1.25 |
| *i.* | | A3106 80y multi | 1.60 | 1.25 |
| *j.* | | A3107 80y multi | 1.60 | 1.25 |

Volunteer Fire Service, 120th Anniv. — A3108

Paintings by Kunichida Toyohara of Kabuki actors wearing costumes of fire fighters: No. 3620, Jyuzaburo Nakamura (denomination at right). No. 3621, Hikosaburo Bando (denomination at left).

| | | | |
|---|---|---|---|
| **2013, Nov. 25** | **Litho.** | ***Perf. 13*** | |
| **3620** | 80y multi | 1.60 | 1.25 |
| **3621** | 80y multi | 1.60 | 1.25 |
| *a.* | A3108 Horiz. pair, #3620-3621 | 3.20 | 2.50 |

Japanese Allspice A3109

Snowdrop A3110

Christmas Camellia A3111

Narcissus A3112

Leopard Plant Flowers A3113

Japanese Allspice A3114

Snowdrops A3115

Christmas Camellias A3116

Narcissi A3117

Leopard Plant Flowers A3118

| | | | | |
|---|---|---|---|---|
| **2013, Dec. 3** | | **Photo.** | ***Perf. 13¼*** | |
| **3622** | A3109 | 50y multi | 1.00 | .75 |
| **3623** | A3110 | 50y multi | 1.00 | .75 |
| **3624** | A3111 | 50y multi | 1.00 | .75 |
| **3625** | A3112 | 50y multi | 1.00 | .75 |
| **3626** | A3113 | 50y multi | 1.00 | .75 |
| *a.* | | Vert. strip of 5, #3622-3626 | 5.00 | 3.75 |
| **3627** | A3114 | 80y multi | 1.60 | 1.25 |
| **3628** | A3115 | 80y multi | 1.60 | 1.25 |
| **3629** | A3116 | 80y multi | 1.60 | 1.25 |
| **3630** | A3117 | 80y multi | 1.60 | 1.25 |
| **3631** | A3118 | 80y multi | 1.60 | 1.25 |
| *a.* | | Vert. strip of 5, #3627-3631 | 8.00 | 6.25 |
| | | *Nos. 3622-3631 (10)* | 13.00 | 10.00 |

Miniature Sheet

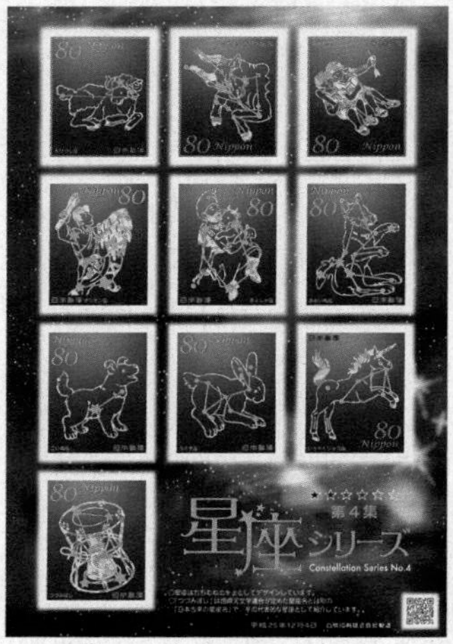


Constellations — A3119

No. 3632: a, Aries (ram). b, Taurus (bull). c, Gemini (twins). d, Orion (hunter with shield). e, Auriga (man holding goat). f, Canis Major (dog on hind legs). g, Canis Minor (dog on four legs). h, Lepus (rabbit). i, Monoceros (unicorn). j, Tsuzumiboshi (Japanese drum, Japanese version of Orion).

**Litho. With Foil Application**

**2013, Dec. 4** ***Die Cut Perf. 13***

**Self-Adhesive**

| | | | | |
|---|---|---|---|---|
| **3632** | A3119 | Sheet of 10 | 16.00 | |
| *a.-j.* | | 80y Any single | 1.60 | 1.25 |

Wakamatsu Castle — A3120

Odawara Castle — A3121

Hikone Castle — A3122

Nijo Castle — A3123

Okayama Castle — A3124

| | | | | |
|---|---|---|---|---|
| **2013, Dec. 10** | | **Litho.** | ***Perf. 13*** | |
| **3633** | A3120 | 80y multi | 1.60 | 1.25 |
| **3634** | A3121 | 80y multi | 1.60 | 1.25 |
| **3635** | A3122 | 80y multi | 1.60 | 1.25 |
| **3636** | A3123 | 80y multi | 1.60 | 1.25 |
| **3637** | A3124 | 80y multi | 1.60 | 1.25 |
| *a.* | | Vert. strip of 5, #3633-3637 | 8.00 | 6.25 |
| | | *Nos. 3633-3637 (5)* | 8.00 | 6.25 |

Diplomatic Relations Between Japan and Kenya, 50th Anniv. A3125

African wildlife: No. 3638, Giraffes. No. 3639, Cheetahs. No. 3640, Elephants. No. 3641, Zebras. No. 3642, Lion.

| | | | | |
|---|---|---|---|---|
| **2013, Dec. 12** | | **Litho.** | ***Perf. 13¼x13*** | |
| **3638** | A3125 | 80y multi | 1.60 | 1.25 |
| **3639** | A3125 | 80y multi | 1.60 | 1.25 |
| **3640** | A3125 | 80y multi | 1.60 | 1.25 |
| **3641** | A3125 | 80y multi | 1.60 | 1.25 |
| **3642** | A3125 | 80y multi | 1.60 | 1.25 |
| *a.* | | Horiz. strip of 5, #3638-3642 | 8.00 | 6.25 |
| | | *Nos. 3638-3642 (5)* | 8.00 | 6.25 |

Miniature Sheet

Kagoshima Local Autonomy Law, 60th Anniv. — A3126

No. 3643: a, Jomon Sugi tree, rhododendrons (32x39mm). b, Sakurajima Volcano (28x33mm). c, Kaimondake Volcano and coastal rocks (28x33mm). d, Flowers on Kirishima Mountains (28x33mm). e, Cranes (28x33mm).

***Perf. 13¼ (#3643a), 13x13¼***

**2013, Dec. 13** **Photo.**

| | | | | |
|---|---|---|---|---|
| **3643** | A3126 | Sheet of 5 | 8.00 | 8.00 |
| *a.-e.* | | 80y Any single | 1.60 | 1.25 |

Teddy Bear, Gift and Dog — A3127

Boy, Gift, Birds With Ribbon — A3128

Girl With Broom, Squirrel and Turtle A3129

Animals, Gift, Flowers and Strawberries A3130

Roses — A3131

Cherry Blossoms — A3132

Mt. Fuji and Cherry Blossoms A3133

Rose Bouquet A3134

Tulips and Girl With Letter and Flower Bouquet A3135

Teddy Bears, Flowers and Mailbox A3136

***Die Cut Perf., Die Cut Perf. 13 (#3644d, 3644e, 3645e)***

**2014, Jan. 16** **Litho.**

**Self-Adhesive**

| | | | | |
|---|---|---|---|---|
| **3644** | | Sheet of 10, 2 each #3644a-3644e | 10.00 | |
| *a.* | A3127 50y multi | | 1.00 | .75 |
| *b.* | A3128 50y multi | | 1.00 | .75 |
| *c.* | A3129 50y multi | | 1.00 | .75 |
| *d.* | A3130 50y multi | | 1.00 | .75 |
| *e.* | A3131 50y multi | | 1.00 | .75 |
| **3645** | | Sheet of 10, 2 each #3645a-3645e | 16.00 | |
| *a.* | A3132 80y multi | | 1.60 | 1.25 |
| *b.* | A3133 80y multi | | 1.60 | 1.25 |
| *c.* | A3134 80y multi | | 1.60 | 1.25 |
| *d.* | A3135 80y multi | | 1.60 | 1.25 |
| *e.* | A3136 80y multi | | 1.60 | 1.25 |

Miniature Sheet

Diplomatic Relations Between Japan and Switzerland, 150th Anniv. — A3137

No. 3646: a, Swiss mountains in spring. b, Mount Fuji and cherry blossoms. c, Aletsch Glacier, Switzerland. d, Bern, Switzerland. e, Lavaux Vineyard Terraces. f, Rhaetian Railway train on bridge. g, Jungfrau Railway train, flowers and mountains. h, Narcissus Path, Les Avants, Switzerland. i, Fluhalp Mountain Lodge. j, Meadow in Bernina Alps.

**2014, Feb. 6** **Litho.** ***Perf. 13***

| | | | | |
|---|---|---|---|---|
| **3646** | A3137 | Sheet of 10 | 16.00 | 16.00 |
| *a.-j.* | | 80y Any single | 1.60 | 1.25 |

See Switzerland Nos. 1507-1508.

Hokkaido Mountain Hare A3138

Cherry Blossoms A3139

Plum Blossoms A3140

Violets A3141

Cedar Tree — A3142

Nachi Falls — A3143

Rishiri Island — A3144

**2014, Mar. 3** **Photo.** ***Perf. 13x13¼***

| | | | | |
|---|---|---|---|---|
| **3647** | A3138 | 2y multi | .25 | .25 |
| **3648** | A3139 | 52y multi | 1.00 | .75 |
| **3649** | A3140 | 82y multi | 1.60 | 1.25 |
| **3650** | A3141 | 92y multi | 1.90 | 1.40 |
| **3651** | A3142 | 205y multi | 4.00 | 3.00 |
| **3652** | A3143 | 280y multi | 5.50 | 4.25 |
| **3653** | A3144 | 310y multi | 6.00 | 4.50 |
| | *Nos. 3647-3653 (7)* | | 20.25 | 15.40 |

Flowers For Mourning — A3145

**2014, Mar. 3** **Photo.** ***Perf. 13x13¼***

| | | | | |
|---|---|---|---|---|
| **3654** | A3145 | 52y multi | 1.00 | .75 |

Fan With Plum Blossoms A3146

Fan With Bamboo A3147

Fan With Tree Branches — A3148

**2014, Mar. 3** **Photo.** ***Perf. 13x13¼***

| | | | | |
|---|---|---|---|---|
| **3655** | A3146 | 52y multi | 1.00 | .75 |
| **3656** | A3147 | 82y multi | 1.60 | 1.25 |
| **3657** | A3148 | 92y multi | 1.90 | 1.40 |
| | *Nos. 3655-3657 (3)* | | 4.50 | 3.40 |

A3149

A3150

A3151

A3152

A3153

A3154

A3155

A3156

A3157

Takarazuka Revue, 100th Anniv. A3158

**2014, Apr. 1** **Litho.** ***Perf. 13***

| | | | |
|---|---|---|---|
| **3658** | Sheet of 10 | 16.00 | 16.00 |
| *a.* | A3149 82c multi | 1.60 | 1.25 |
| *b.* | A3150 82c multi | 1.60 | 1.25 |
| *c.* | A3151 82c multi | 1.60 | 1.25 |
| *d.* | A3152 82c multi | 1.60 | 1.25 |
| *e.* | A3153 82c multi | 1.60 | 1.25 |
| *f.* | A3154 82c multi | 1.60 | 1.25 |
| *g.* | A3155 82c multi | 1.60 | 1.25 |
| *h.* | A3156 82c multi | 1.60 | 1.25 |
| *i.* | A3157 82c multi | 1.60 | 1.25 |
| *j.* | A3158 82c multi | 1.60 | 1.25 |

Organization for Economic Cooperation, 50th Anniv. — A3159

Designs: No. 3659, Emblem, Organization Headquarters, Paris. No. 3660, Symbols for cooperation and development.

| **2014, Apr. 2** | **Litho.** | | ***Perf. 13*** | |
|---|---|---|---|---|
| **3659** | 82y multi | | 1.60 | 1.25 |
| **3660** | 82y multi | | 1.60 | 1.25 |
| *a.* | A3159 Pair, #3659-3660 | | 3.20 | 2.50 |

Daisy and Sweet Peas A3160

Lily A3161

Cherry Blossoms A3162

Water Lily A3163

Poppies and Ranunculus A3164

Peony A3165

Roses A3166

Magnolias A3167

| **2014, Apr. 3** | **Litho.** | | ***Perf. 14x14¼*** | |
|---|---|---|---|---|
| **3661** | A3160 | 52y multi | 1.00 | .75 |
| **3662** | A3161 | 52y multi | 1.00 | .75 |
| **3663** | A3162 | 52y multi | 1.00 | .75 |
| **3664** | A3163 | 52y multi | 1.00 | .75 |
| *a.* | Horiz. strip of 4, #3661-3664 | | 4.00 | 3.00 |
| **3665** | A3164 | 82y multi | 1.60 | 1.25 |
| **3666** | A3165 | 82y multi | 1.60 | 1.25 |
| **3667** | A3166 | 82y multi | 1.60 | 1.25 |
| **3668** | A3167 | 82y multi | 1.60 | 1.25 |
| *a.* | Horiz. strip of 4, #3665-3668 | | 6.40 | 5.00 |
| | *Nos. 3661-3668 (8)* | | 10.40 | 8.00 |

Miniature Sheet

Ehime Local Autonomy Law, 60th Anniv. — A3168

No. 3669: a, Oranges, Dogo Hot Springs Building (32x39mm). b, Matsuyama Castle (28x33mm). c, Mount Ichizuchi (28x33mm). d, Terraced fields, Yusumizugaura (28x33mm). e, Sadamisaki Lighthouse (28x33mm).

***Perf. 13¼ (#3669a), 13x13¼***

| **2014, Apr. 17** | | | **Photo.** | |
|---|---|---|---|---|
| **3669** | A3168 | Sheet of 5 | 8.00 | 8.00 |
| *a.-e.* | 82y Any single | | 1.60 | 1.25 |

Philatelic Week — A3169

Details from folding screens by Eishuku Kano: No. 3670, Seven small birds near tree. No. 3671, Two birds below tree branch. No. 3672, Three adult and three juvenile cranes, white and yellow flowers. No. 3673, Adult cranes and flowers.

| **2014, Apr. 18** | **Photo.** | | ***Perf. 13¼*** | |
|---|---|---|---|---|
| **3670** | 82y multi | | 1.60 | 1.25 |
| **3671** | 82y multi | | 1.60 | 1.25 |
| **3672** | 82y multi | | 1.60 | 1.25 |
| **3673** | 82y multi | | 1.60 | 1.25 |
| *a.* | A3169 Block of 4, #3670-3673 | | 6.40 | 5.00 |
| | *Nos. 3670-3673 (4)* | | 6.40 | 5.00 |

Nos. 3670-3673 were printed in sheets of 10 containing 3 each of Nos. 3670-3671 and 2 each of Nos. 3672-3673.

Mount Akita-Komagatake — A3170

Mount Iyo — A3171

Mount Oku-Hotakadake — A3172

Mount Fuji — A3173

Mount Rokko A3174

Mount Mikura A3175

Mount Tsurugi A3176

Mount Unzen A3177

Mount Okue A3178

Mount Tama A3179

| **2014, May 1** | **Litho.** | | ***Perf. 13¼x13*** | |
|---|---|---|---|---|
| **3674** | Sheet of 10 | | 16.00 | 16.00 |
| *a.* | A3170 82y multi | | 1.60 | 1.25 |
| *b.* | A3171 82y multi | | 1.60 | 1.25 |
| *c.* | A3172 82y multi | | 1.60 | 1.25 |
| *d.* | A3173 82y multi | | 1.60 | 1.25 |
| *e.* | A3174 82y multi | | 1.60 | 1.25 |
| *f.* | A3175 82y multi | | 1.60 | 1.25 |
| *g.* | A3176 82y multi | | 1.60 | 1.25 |
| *h.* | A3177 82y multi | | 1.60 | 1.25 |
| *i.* | A3178 82y multi | | 1.60 | 1.25 |
| *j.* | A3179 82y multi | | 1.60 | 1.25 |

Souvenir Sheets

A3180

A3181

2014 World Cup Soccer Championships, Brazil — A3182

No. 3675 — Trophy with: a, Denomination at UL, "Nippon" at UR. b, Denomination at LR. c, Denomination and "Nippon" at UL.

No. 3676: a, Emblem. b, Emblem, design with stylized soccer player dribbling ball at left. c, Emblem, design with stylized goalie making save at right.

No. 3677 — Mascot: a, Carrying flag. b, Holding soccer ball. c, Dribbling soccer ball.

| **2014, May 12** | **Litho.** | | ***Perf. 13*** | |
|---|---|---|---|---|
| **3675** | A3180 | Sheet of 3 | 5.00 | 5.00 |
| *a.-c.* | 82y Any single | | 1.60 | 1.25 |
| **3676** | A3181 | Sheet of 3 | 5.00 | 5.00 |
| *a.-c.* | 82y Any single | | 1.60 | 1.25 |
| **3677** | A3182 | Sheet of 3 | 5.00 | 5.00 |
| *a.-c.* | 82y Any single | | 1.60 | 1.25 |
| | *Nos. 3675-3677 (3)* | | 15.00 | 15.00 |

Miniature Sheet

Yamagata Local Autonomy Law, 60th Anniv. — A3183

No. 3678: a, Mogami River and cherries (32x39mm). b, Mt. Haguro five-story pagoda (28x33mm). c, Kubo cherry tree blossoming (28x33mm). d, Hayashi Family court dancer (28x33mm). e, Shinjo Festival (28x33mm).

***Perf. 13¼ (#3678a), 13x13¼***

| **2014, May 14** | | | **Photo.** | |
|---|---|---|---|---|
| **3678** | A3183 | Sheet of 5 | 8.00 | 8.00 |
| *a.-e.* | 82y Any single | | 1.60 | 1.25 |

Pentalagus Furnessi A3184

Lagopus Muta Japonica A3185

Polemonium Kiushianum A3186

Tanakia Tanago A3187

Cuora Flavomarginata Evelynae — A3188

**2014, May 15** **Litho.** ***Perf. 13¼***

| | | | | | |
|---|---|---|---|---|---|
| **3679** | A3184 | 82y multi | | 1.60 | 1.25 |
| **3680** | A3185 | 82y multi | | 1.60 | 1.25 |
| **3681** | A3186 | 82y multi | | 1.60 | 1.25 |
| **3682** | A3187 | 82y multi | | 1.60 | 1.25 |
| **3683** | A3188 | 82y multi | | 1.60 | 1.25 |
| *a.* | Vert. strip of 5, #3679-3683 | | | 8.00 | 6.25 |
| | *Nos. 3679-3683 (5)* | | | 8.00 | 6.25 |

Miniature Sheets

A3189

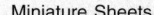

Characters From Disney Animated Films — A3190

No. 3684: a, Snow White and bird. b, Sleeping Beauty. c, Cinderella. d, Peter Pan with Wendy, John and Michael Darling. e, March Hare, Alice and Mad Hatter. f, Dumbo and Timothy. g, Thumper, Bambi and Flower. h, Lady and the Tramp. i, 101 Dalmatians. j, Geppetto and Pinocchio.

No. 3685: a, Winnie the Pooh seated, looking in honey jar. b, Winnie standing, looking in honey jar. c, Winnie and Eeyore. d, Winnie and Tigger. e, Winnie, Kanga and Roo. f, Winnie and Piglet. g, Winnie holding note. h, Winnie reaching for honey jar. i, Winnie turning over honey jar. j, Winnie standing in large honey pot.

***Die Cut Perf. 14***

**2014, May 23** **Litho.**

**Self-Adhesive**

| | | | | |
|---|---|---|---|---|
| **3684** | A3189 | Sheet of 10 | 10.00 | |
| *a.-j.* | | 52y Any single | 1.00 | .75 |
| **3685** | A3190 | Sheet of 10 | 16.00 | |
| *a.-j.* | | 82y Any single | 1.60 | 1.25 |

Miniature Sheet

National Afforestation — A3191

No. 3686: a, Tulipa gesneria. b, Magnolia salicifolia flowers. c, Magnolia obovata flowers. d, Erythronium japonicum. e, Fagus crenata leaves. f, Camellia rusticana. g, Maple leaves on branches. h, Hepatica nobilis. i, Narcissus tazetta. j, Azalea flowers.

**2014, May 30** **Litho.** ***Perf. 13***

| | | | | |
|---|---|---|---|---|
| **3686** | A3191 | Sheet of 10 | 10.00 | 10.00 |
| *a.-j.* | | 52y Any single | 1.00 | .75 |

Palace of Versailles, France A3192

Thebes, Egypt A3193

Roman Colosseum, Italy — A3194

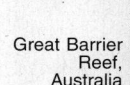

Great Barrier Reef, Australia A3195

La Pedrera, Barcelona, Spain A3196

**2014, June 3** **Litho.** ***Perf. 13¼x13***

| | | | | |
|---|---|---|---|---|
| **3687** | A3192 | 82y multi | 1.60 | 1.25 |
| **3688** | A3193 | 82y multi | 1.60 | 1.25 |
| **3689** | A3194 | 82y multi | 1.60 | 1.25 |
| **3690** | A3195 | 82y multi | 1.60 | 1.25 |
| **3691** | A3196 | 82y multi | 1.60 | 1.25 |
| *a.* | Horiz. strip of 5, #3687-3691 | | 8.00 | 6.25 |
| | *Nos. 3687-3691 (5)* | | 8.00 | 6.25 |

UNESCO World Heritage sites.

Cherries A3197

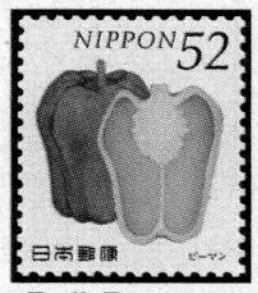
Bell Peppers A3198

Japanese Plums A3199

Corn A3200

Watermelons A3201

Tomato A3202

Japanese Apricots A3203

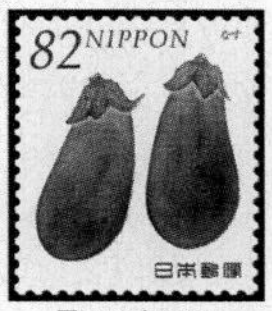
Eggplants A3204

Cucumbers A3205

Peach A3206

***Die Cut Perf. 13x13¼, 13¼x13***

**2014, June 4** **Litho.**

**Self-Adhesive**

| | | | | |
|---|---|---|---|---|
| **3692** | | Sheet of 10, 2 each #3692a-3692e | 10.00 | |
| *a.* | A3197 | 52y multi | 1.00 | .75 |
| *b.* | A3198 | 52y multi | 1.00 | .75 |
| *c.* | A3199 | 52y multi | 1.00 | .75 |
| *d.* | A3200 | 52y multi | 1.00 | .75 |
| *e.* | A3201 | 52y multi | 1.00 | .75 |
| **3693** | | Sheet of 10, 2 each #3693a-3693e | 16.00 | |
| *a.* | A3202 | 82y multi | 1.60 | 1.25 |
| *b.* | A3203 | 82y multi | 1.60 | 1.25 |
| *c.* | A3204 | 82y multi | 1.60 | 1.25 |
| *d.* | A3205 | 82y multi | 1.60 | 1.25 |
| *e.* | A3206 | 82y multi | 1.60 | 1.25 |

Miniature Sheet

Mie Local Autonomy Law, 60th Anniv. — A3207

No. 3694: a, Uji Bridge and Isuzu River (32x39mm). b, Iris ensata (28x33mm). c, Wedded Rocks, Ise-Shima National Park (28x33mm). d, Lion Rock and fireworks (28x33mm). e, Ago Bay (28x33mm).

***Perf. 13¼ (#3694a), 13x13¼***

**2014, June 19** **Photo.**

| | | | | | |
|---|---|---|---|---|---|
| **3694** | A3207 | Sheet of 5 | | 8.00 | 8.00 |
| ***a.-e.*** | | 82y Any single | | 1.60 | 1.25 |

Miniature Sheets

A3208

Sanrio Cartoon Characters — A3209

No. 3695: a, Hello Kitty on bicycle (29x26mm heart-shaped stamp). b, Hello Kitty on elephant (29mm diameter). c, Hello Kitty and Mimmy on telephone (23x23mm). d, Hello Kitty and Mimmy on see-saw (22x30mm oval stamp). e, Hello Kitty in airplane (23x23mm). f, Hello Kitty on scale (27x22mm). g, My Melody on swing with squirrel, Blanco (22x27mm). h, My Melody on ground with mouse, Flat (29x26mm heart-shaped stamp). i, Pompompurin and Macaroon (29mm diameter). j, Pompompurin and stuffed toys (23x23mm).

No. 3696: a, Hello Kitty, umbrella, cherries, pencils and candy bag (22x27mm). b, Hello Kitty with balloon (29x26mm heart-shaped stamp). c, Hello Kitty and Mimmy on telephone with apples (29mm diameter). d, Hello Kitty with watering can (27x22mm). e, Hello Kitty and Mimmy in go-karts (23x23mm). f, Hello Kitty with hair brush (22x30mm oval stamp). g, My Melody at mailbox (27x22mm). h, My Melody reading letter (30x22mm oval stamp). i, Pompompurin and Muffin (29x26mm heart-shaped stamp). j, Pompompurin and "PURIN" (27x22mm).

***Die Cut Perf. 14 (square stamps), 13¼x13¾, 13¾x13¼ (rectangular stamps), 13¼ (oval stamps), Die Cut Perf.***

**2014, June 23** **Litho.**

**Self-Adhesive**

| | | | | | |
|---|---|---|---|---|---|
| **3695** | A3208 | Sheet of 10 | | 10.00 | |
| ***a.-j.*** | | 52y Any single | | 1.00 | .75 |
| **3696** | A3209 | Sheet of 10 | | 16.00 | |
| ***a.-j.*** | | 82y Any single | | 1.60 | 1.25 |

Miniature Sheet

Mount Fuji UNESCO World Heritage Site — A3210

No. 3697 — Various views of Mount Fuji: a, Clouds above mountain, denomination at LL. b, Clouds obscuring base, denomination at LR. c, Framed by cherry trees in bloom, denomination at UL. d, With farm fields below, denomination at LL. e, With cherry blossoms at top, denomination at UL. f, In winter, with hills below, denomination at LL. g, With lake below, denomination at UL. h, With clouds and forest below, denomination at LL. i, With forest and waterfall below, denomination at LL. j, With swan on lake below, denomination at UR.

**2014, June 26** **Photo.** ***Perf. 13x13¼***

| | | | | | |
|---|---|---|---|---|---|
| **3697** | A3210 | Sheet of 10 | | 16.00 | 16.00 |
| ***a.-j.*** | | 82y Any single | | 1.60 | 1.25 |

Miniature Sheet

Constellations — A3211

No. 3698: a, Cancer. b, Leo. c, Virgo. d, Vega (without white frame).

**Litho. With Foil Application**

**2014, July 7** ***Die Cut Perf. 13x13¼***

**Self-Adhesive**

| | | | | | |
|---|---|---|---|---|---|
| **3698** | A3211 | Sheet of 10, 3 each #3698a-3698c, 1 #3698d | | 16.00 | |
| ***a.-d.*** | | 82y Any single | | 1.60 | 1.25 |

Matsumae Castle — A3212

Inuyama Castle — A3213

Matsue Castle — A3214

Takamatsu Castle — A3215

Kumamoto Castle — A3216

**2014, July 15** **Litho.** ***Perf. 13***

| | | | | | |
|---|---|---|---|---|---|
| **3699** | A3212 | 82y multi | | 1.60 | 1.25 |
| **3700** | A3213 | 82y multi | | 1.60 | 1.25 |
| **3701** | A3214 | 82y multi | | 1.60 | 1.25 |
| **3702** | A3215 | 82y multi | | 1.60 | 1.25 |
| **3703** | A3216 | 82y multi | | 1.60 | 1.25 |
| ***a.*** | | Vert. strip of 5, #3699-3703 | | 8.00 | 6.25 |
| | | *Nos. 3699-3703 (5)* | | 8.00 | 6.25 |

Irises A3217

Goldfish A3218

Flowers A3219

Rabbits A3220

Birds in Plum Tree A3221

Raspberries A3222

Morning Glories A3223

Gourds A3224

Cranes
A3225

Cherry Blossoms and Water Wheels
A3226

Geometric Pattern
A3227

Poppies
A3228

Grapevines
A3229

Flowers
A3230

Rape Blossoms
A3231

Loquats
A3232

Morning Glory and Fan
A3233

Leaves and Nuts
A3234

Pine Trees
A3235

Cherry Blossoms
A3236

***Die Cut Perf. 13x13½***

**2014, July 23 Litho.**

**Booklet Stamps**
**Self-Adhesive**

| | | | | |
|---|---|---|---|---|
| **3704** | A3217 | 52y multi | 1.00 | .75 |
| **3705** | A3218 | 52y multi | 1.00 | .75 |
| **3706** | A3219 | 52y multi | 1.00 | .75 |
| **3707** | A3220 | 52y multi | 1.00 | .75 |
| **3708** | A3221 | 52y multi | 1.00 | .75 |
| **3709** | A3222 | 52y multi | 1.00 | .75 |
| **3710** | A3223 | 52y multi | 1.00 | .75 |
| **3711** | A3224 | 52y multi | 1.00 | .75 |
| **3712** | A3225 | 52y multi | 1.00 | .75 |
| **3713** | A3226 | 52y multi | 1.00 | .75 |
| *a.* | Booklet pane of 10, #3704-3713 | | 10.00 | |
| **3714** | A3227 | 82y multi | 1.60 | 1.25 |
| **3715** | A3228 | 82y multi | 1.60 | 1.25 |
| **3716** | A3229 | 82y multi | 1.60 | 1.25 |
| **3717** | A3230 | 82y multi | 1.60 | 1.25 |
| **3718** | A3231 | 82y multi | 1.60 | 1.25 |
| **3719** | A3232 | 82y multi | 1.60 | 1.25 |
| **3720** | A3233 | 82y multi | 1.60 | 1.25 |
| **3721** | A3234 | 82y multi | 1.60 | 1.25 |
| **3722** | A3235 | 82y multi | 1.60 | 1.25 |
| **3723** | A3236 | 82y multi | 1.60 | 1.25 |
| *a.* | Booklet pane of 10, #3714-3723 | | 16.00 | |
| | *Nos. 3704-3723 (20)* | | 26.00 | 20.00 |

The Ide Tama River: Karuta of the Choji-ya, by Eizan Kikukawa
A3237

Karokoyama, by Hiroshige Utagawa
A3238

Hitomoto of the Mojiro, by Utamaro Kitagawa
A3239

Fishing Boats Netting Flounder, by Hiroshige Utagawa
A3240

Washing and Starching Fabric, by Eizan Kikukawa
A3241

Tsushima Tenno Festival, by Hiroshige Utagawa
A3242

Girl with a Fan, by Utamaro Kitagawa
A3243

Cherry Island, by Hiroshige Utagawa
A3244

The Doll Festival, by Eisho Chokosai
A3245

Basket Ferry, by Hiroshige Utagawa
A3246

**2014, Aug. 1 Litho. *Perf. 13½***

| | | | | |
|---|---|---|---|---|
| **3724** | Sheet of 10 | | 16.00 | 16.00 |
| *a.* | A3237 | 82y multi | 1.60 | 1.25 |
| *b.* | A3238 | 82y multi | 1.60 | 1.25 |
| *c.* | A3239 | 82y multi | 1.60 | 1.25 |
| *d.* | A3240 | 82y multi | 1.60 | 1.25 |
| *e.* | A3241 | 82y multi | 1.60 | 1.25 |
| *f.* | A3242 | 82y multi | 1.60 | 1.25 |
| *g.* | A3243 | 82y multi | 1.60 | 1.25 |
| *h.* | A3244 | 82y multi | 1.60 | 1.25 |
| *i.* | A3245 | 82y multi | 1.60 | 1.25 |
| *j.* | A3246 | 82y multi | 1.60 | 1.25 |

Mount Asahi
A3247

Mount Sanbe
A3248

Mount Nantai
A3249

Mount Tokusa
A3250

Mount Takao
A3251

Mount Hiko
A3252

Mount Mitsuse-Myojin — A3253

Mount Miune
A3254

Kumano Kodo
A3255

Mount Shinmoe
A3256

**2014, Aug. 11 Litho. *Perf. 13¼x13***

| | | | | |
|---|---|---|---|---|
| **3725** | Sheet of 10 | | 16.00 | 16.00 |
| *a.* | A3247 | 82y multi | 1.60 | 1.25 |
| *b.* | A3248 | 82y multi | 1.60 | 1.25 |
| *c.* | A3249 | 82y multi | 1.60 | 1.25 |
| *d.* | A3250 | 82y multi | 1.60 | 1.25 |
| *e.* | A3251 | 82y multi | 1.60 | 1.25 |
| *f.* | A3252 | 82y multi | 1.60 | 1.25 |
| *g.* | A3253 | 82y multi | 1.60 | 1.25 |
| *h.* | A3254 | 82y multi | 1.60 | 1.25 |
| *i.* | A3255 | 82y multi | 1.60 | 1.25 |
| *j.* | A3256 | 82y multi | 1.60 | 1.25 |

Miniature Sheets

A3257

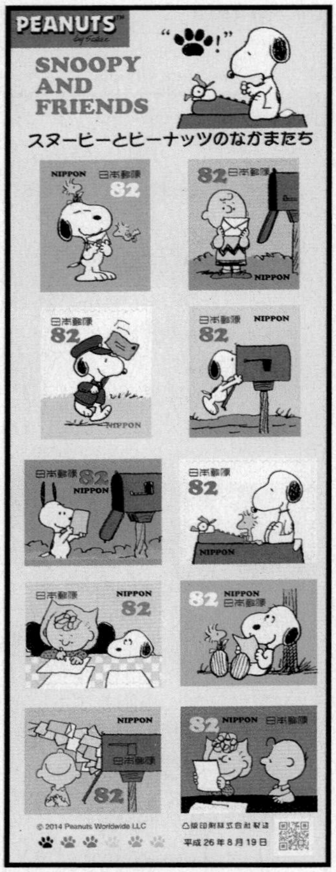


Characters From Peanuts Comic Strip — A3258

No. 3726: a, Sally, Woodstock and Snoopy drawing (26x22mm). b, Snoopy and heart (26x25mm). c, Snoopy holding slice of bread, Woodstock near mug (26x22mm). d, Snoopy, Linus, Woodstock and cookies (26x22mm). e, Snoopy on Charlie Brown's head, woodstock on books (26x22mm). f, Sally and Snoopy eating (26x22mm). g, Snoopy, Lucy and Woodstock with flowers (26x22mm). h, Woodstock flying, Snoopy attempting to fly (26x22mm). i, Snoopy and Woodstock on dog house roof (29x36mm). j, Snoopy, Woodstock, umbrella and musical notes (26x22mm).

No. 3727: a, Snoopy and Woodstock with letters, bird flying (22x27mm). b, Charlie Brown with letter near mailbox (22x27mm). c, Snoopy wearing mailman's uniform (22x27mm). d, Snoopy with nose in mailbox (22x27mm). e, Snoopy reading letter near mailbox (27x22mm). f, Snoopy and Woodstock at typewriter (27x22mm). g, Snoopy watching Sally write letter (27x22mm). h, Snoopy sitting and reading letter with Woodstock (27x22mm). i, Charlie Brown and stream of letters in mailbox (27x22mm). j, Charlie Brown and Sally looking at letter (27x22mm).

***Die Cut Perf. 14, 12¼ (#3726b, 3726i)***

**2014, Aug. 19** **Litho.**

**Self-Adhesive**

| | | | | |
|---|---|---|---|---|
| **3726** | A3257 | Sheet of 10 | 10.00 | |
| *a.-j.* | 52y Any single | | 1.00 | .75 |

***Die Cut Perf. 14x13½, 13½x14***

| | | | | |
|---|---|---|---|---|
| **3727** | A3258 | Sheet of 10 | 16.00 | |
| *a.-j.* | 52y Any single | | 1.60 | 1.25 |

Miniature Sheet

Japan Society of Civil Engineers, Cent. — A3259

No. 3728: a, Tunnel, sun over mountains. b, Dam. c, Ships and jetties, airport runway. d, Harbor and airport. e, Floodgate ar mouth of river. f, Bridges over river and interchange. g, Farm fields near coast, rocks in water. h, Small harbor and highway tunnel. i, Terraces and irrigation canal. j, Train and irrigation canal.

**2014, Sept. 1** **Litho.** ***Perf. 13***

| | | | | |
|---|---|---|---|---|
| **3728** | A3259 | Sheet of 10 | 16.00 | 16.00 |
| *a.-j.* | 82y Any single | | 1.60 | 1.25 |

Miniature Sheet

Season's Memories in My Heart — A3260

No. 3729: a, Houses near water, denomination in black at LL. b, Farm houses, denomination in white at LR. c, Farm house near river, denomination in white at UL. d, Sunset, denomination in white at UL. e, Village in mist, denomination in white at LL. f, Cars near church and building, denomination in black at UR. g, Church at end of path, denomination in white at left. h, Large cloud over church, flowers in air, denomination in white at UL. i, House near water, denomination in black at UR. j, Houses and path, denomination in black at UR.

**2014, Sept. 2** **Photo.** ***Perf. 13***

| | | | | |
|---|---|---|---|---|
| **3729** | A3260 | Sheet of 10 | 16.00 | 16.00 |
| *a.-j.* | 82y Any single | | 1.60 | 1.25 |

A3261

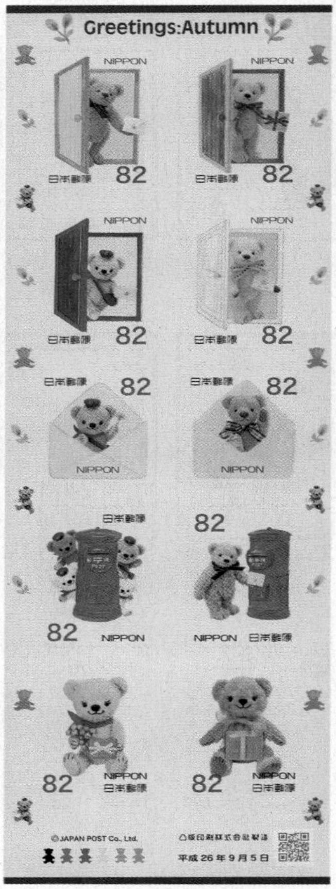


Teddy Bears — A3262

No. 3730: a, Bear with gray fur and pearl necklace, pink rose (22x30mm). b, Bear with brown fur and red ribbon, yellow flowers (22x30mm). c, Bear with light brown fur and blue bow tie, red rose (22x30mm). d, Bear with beige fur and yellow bow tie, pink flower (22x30mm). e, Bear with light brown fur, wearing cap and red ribbon, with flower bouquet (22x30mm). f, Bear with light brown fur and green ribbon, with pink lily (22x30mm). g, Three bears wearing caps, pink flowers (28x28mm). h, Five bears and yellow flowers (28x28mm). i, Two bears, pink flowers, red ribbon at top (28x28mm). j, Two bears, pink flowers, blue ribbon at top (28x28mm).

No. 3731: a, Bear with letter, yellow door (23x30mm). b, Bear with gift, green door (23x30mm). c, Bear with cap, mail bag and letter, blue door (23x30mm). d, Bear with letter, white door (23x30mm). e, Bear with cap in yellow envelope (25x25mm). f, Bear in light blue envelope (25x25mm). g, Four bears and mail box (23x30mm). h, Bear with letter at mail box (23x30mm). i, Pink bear with pink gift (27x30mm). j, Bear with blue gift (27x30mm).

***Die Cut Perf. 13¼x13¾, 13¾x13½***

**2014, Sept. 5** **Litho.**

**Self-Adhesive**

| | | | | |
|---|---|---|---|---|
| **3730** | A3261 | Sheet of 10 | 10.00 | |
| *a.-j.* | 52y Any single | | 1.00 | .75 |

***Die Cut Perf. 13x12¾, 13 (#3731e, 3731f)***

| | | | | |
|---|---|---|---|---|
| **3731** | A3262 | Sheet of 10 | 15.00 | |
| *a.-j.* | 82y Any single | | 1.50 | 1.10 |

Miniature Sheet

Kagawa Local Autonomy Law, 60th Anniv. — A3263

No. 3732: a, Ritsurin Koen Park (32x39mm). b, Gennai Hiraga and his electrostatic generator (28x33mm). c, Marugame Castle (28x33mm). d, Kotohiki Park (28x33mm). e, Olives (28x33mm).

***Perf. 13¼ (#3732a), 13x13¼***

**2014, Sept. 10** **Photo.**

| | | | | |
|---|---|---|---|---|
| **3732** | A3263 | Sheet of 5 | 7.50 | 7.50 |
| *a.-e.* | 82y Any single | | 1.50 | 1.10 |

Intl. Congress on Child Abuse and Neglect, Nagoya — A3264

**2014, Sept. 12** **Litho.** ***Perf. 13***

| | | | | |
|---|---|---|---|---|
| **3733** | A3264 | 82y multi | 1.50 | 1.10 |

Miniature Sheet

69th National Sports Festival — A3265

No. 3734: a, Gymnast on rings. b, Blue hydrangeas. c, Runner in starting blocks. d, Pink rhododendrons. e, Archer. f, Pink day lily. g, Soccer players. h, Lilac pink rhododendrons. i, Kendoka. j, Red camellias.

**2014, Sept. 12 Litho. *Perf. 13***

| | | | | |
|---|---|---|---|---|
| **3734** | A3265 82y Sheet of 10 | | 15.00 | 15.00 |
| | *a.-j.* | 82y Any single | 1.50 | 1.10 |

Tortoise
A3266

Spotted Seals
A3267

Tapir
A3268

Giraffes
A3269

Orangutans
A3270

Koalas
A3271

Giant Pandas
A3272

Capybara
A3273

Lion — A3274

Fennec Fox — A3275

***Die Cut Perf. 13x13¼***

**2014, Sept. 19 Litho.**

**Self-Adhesive**

| | | | | |
|---|---|---|---|---|
| **3735** | | Sheet of 10, 2 each #3735a-3735e | 10.00 | |
| | *a.* | A3266 52y multi | 1.00 | .75 |
| | *b.* | A3267 52y multi | 1.00 | .75 |
| | *c.* | A3268 52y multi | 1.00 | .75 |
| | *d.* | A3269 52y multi | 1.00 | .75 |
| | *e.* | A3270 52y multi | 1.00 | .75 |

***Die Cut Perf. 13¼***

| | | | | |
|---|---|---|---|---|
| **3736** | | Sheet of 10, 2 each #3736a-3736e | 15.00 | |
| | *a.* | A3271 82y multi | 1.50 | 1.10 |
| | *b.* | A3272 82y multi | 1.50 | 1.10 |
| | *c.* | A3273 82y multi | 1.50 | 1.10 |
| | *d.* | A3274 82y multi | 1.50 | 1.10 |
| | *e.* | A3275 82y multi | 1.50 | 1.10 |

Miniature Sheet

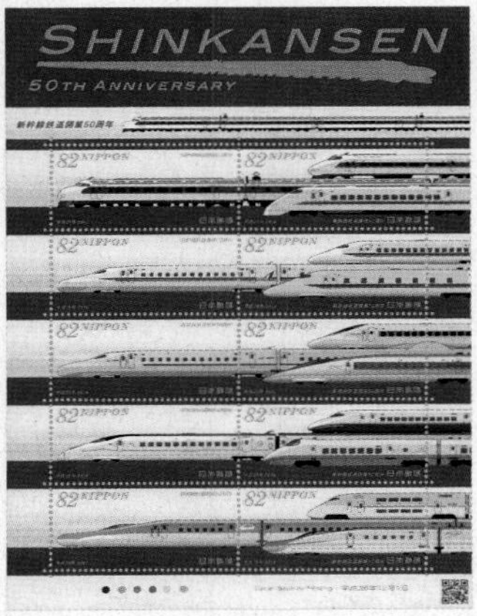


Shinkansen High-Speed Rail Lines, 50th Anniv. — A3276

No. 3737: a, Train with thick blue stripe (Tokaido and Sanyo 0 series). b, Three trains (Tokaido and Sanyo 100, 0 and 300 series), top train with thick blue stripe above thin blue stripe, bottom train with thin blue strip over thick blue stripe. c, Train with two thin blue stripes (Tokaido and Sanyo N700A). d, Three trains (Tokaido and Sanyo 700 series, N700A, and T4 model), top train with two thin blue stripes, bottom train yellow with two blue stripes. e, Light blue train with one blue stripe (Sanyo and Kyushu N700). f, Three trains (Sanyo 700 series Rail Star, Sanyo and Kyushu N700, Sanyo 500 series), top train with gray and yellow stripes along windows. g, Train with thin red stripe (Kyushu New 800 series). h, Three trains (Tohuku E2 series, Kyushu New 800 series, Yamagata 400 series), top train with red stripe under window above blue along bottom of train. i, Train with blue green top and red stripe (Tohuku E5 series). j, Three trains (Joetsu E1 series, Tohuku E5 series, Akita E6 series, light blue top train with blue green stripe.

**2014, Oct. 1 Litho. *Perf. 13½x13¼***

| | | | | |
|---|---|---|---|---|
| **3737** | A3276 Sheet of 10 | | 15.00 | 15.00 |
| | *a.-j.* | 82y Any single | 1.50 | 1.10 |

Miniature Sheet

Saitama Local Autonomy Law, 60th Anniv. — A3277

No. 3738: a, Eiichi Shibusawa, industrialist, Bell of Time (32x39mm). b, Saitama Stadium (28x33mm). c, Chichibu Night Festival (28x33mm). d, Shoden Hall, Kangi Temple (28x33mm). e, Stairway at Sakitama ancient tomb complex (28x33mm).

***Perf. 13¼ (#3738a), 13x13¼***

**2014, Oct. 8 Photo.**

| | | | | |
|---|---|---|---|---|
| **3738** | A3277 Sheet of 5 | | 7.50 | 7.50 |
| | *a.-e.* | 82y Any single | 1.50 | 1.10 |

A3278

International Letter Writing Week
A3279

Paintings by Hiroshige: 70y, Sparrows and Camellia in the Snow. 90y, The Fifty-three Stations of the Tokaido: Ejiri. 110y, The Fifty-three Stations of the Tokaido: Kanaya. 130y, The Fifty-three Stations of the Tokaido: Fukuroi.

**2014, Oct. 9 Photo. *Perf. 13¼***

| | | | |
|---|---|---|---|
| **3739** | A3278 70y multi | 1.25 | .95 |

***Perf. 13***

| | | | |
|---|---|---|---|
| **3740** | A3279 90y multi | 1.60 | 1.25 |
| **3741** | A3279 110y multi | 2.00 | 1.50 |
| **3742** | A3279 130y multi | 2.25 | 1.75 |
| | *Nos. 3739-3742 (4)* | 7.10 | 5.45 |

Fronts of Five Passenger Train Cars
A3280

Nagoya Railroad KiHa 8000 Series Locomotive
A3281

Kintetsu 18200 Series Locomotive
A3282

Japan National Railways 581 Series Locomotive
A3283

Japan National Railways Class EF66 Locomotive
A3284

Seibu Railways 5000 Series Locomotive
A3285

Japan National Railways 14 Series Sleeping Car — A3286

East Japan Railway E259 Series Locomotive
A3287

Keisei Electric Railway AE Series Locomotive
A3288

Tokyo Underground Railway 1000 Series Train
A3289

**2014, Oct. 10 Photo. *Perf. 13¼x13***

| | | | | |
|---|---|---|---|---|
| **3743** | | Sheet of 10 | 15.00 | 15.00 |
| | *a.* | A3280 82y multi | 1.50 | 1.10 |
| | *b.* | A3281 82y multi | 1.50 | 1.10 |
| | *c.* | A3282 82y multi | 1.50 | 1.10 |
| | *d.* | A3283 82y multi | 1.50 | 1.10 |
| | *e.* | A3284 82y multi | 1.50 | 1.10 |
| | *f.* | A3285 82y multi | 1.50 | 1.10 |
| | *g.* | A3286 82y multi | 1.50 | 1.10 |
| | *h.* | A3287 82y multi | 1.50 | 1.10 |
| | *i.* | A3288 82y multi | 1.50 | 1.10 |
| | *j.* | A3289 82y multi | 1.50 | 1.10 |

Sandalwood Go Game Board and Pieces — A3290

Gold and Silver Inlaid Lacquered Kin — A3291

Glass Goblet — A3292

Decorated Catapult Sticks — A3293

Sandalwood Lute — A3294

**2014, Oct. 17 Photo. *Perf. 13***

| | | | | |
|---|---|---|---|---|
| **3744** | A3290 | 82y multi | 1.50 | 1.10 |
| **3745** | A3291 | 82y multi | 1.50 | 1.10 |
| **3746** | A3292 | 82y multi | 1.50 | 1.10 |
| **3747** | A3293 | 82y multi | 1.50 | 1.10 |
| **3748** | A3294 | 82y multi | 1.50 | 1.10 |
| *a.* | | Vert. strip of 5, #3744-3748 | 7.50 | 5.50 |
| | | *Nos. 3744-3748 (5)* | 7.50 | 5.50 |

Treasures of the Shosoin.

Fish A3295

"Happy" and Stars A3296

**2014, Oct. 23 Litho. *Perf. 13x13¼***

| | | | | |
|---|---|---|---|---|
| **3749** | A3295 | 52y multi | .90 | .70 |

**Background Color**

| | | | | |
|---|---|---|---|---|
| **3750** | A3296 | 52y rose lilac | .90 | .70 |
| **3751** | A3296 | 52y orange | .90 | .70 |
| *a.* | | Vert. pair, #3750-3751 | 1.80 | 1.40 |
| | | *Nos. 3749-3751 (3)* | 2.70 | 2.10 |

Miniature Sheet

Traditional Crafts — A3297

No. 3752: a, Imari-Arita ceramic ware (Saga Prefecture). b, Inshu hand-made paper (Tottori Prefecture). c, Echizen chest of drawers (Fukui Prefecture). d, Chichibu-meisen silk textiles (Saitama Prefecture). e, Kagawa lacquered container (Kagawa Prefecture). f, Ise katagami paper stencils (Mie Prefecture). g, Yamaga lantern (Kumamoto Prefecture). h, Koshu carved crystal (Yamanashi Prefecture). i, Hakone parquet containers (Kanagawa Prefecture). j. Arimatsu-Narumi tie-dyed fabrics (Aichi Prefecture).

**2014, Oct. 24 Litho. *Perf. 13½***

| | | | | |
|---|---|---|---|---|
| **3752** | A3297 | Sheet of 10 | 15.00 | 15.00 |
| *a.-j.* | | 82y Any single | 1.50 | 1.10 |

Miniature Sheet

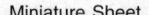

Edo Calligraphy — A3298

No. 3753 — Characters for "sheep": a, In Kobun style (blue character). b, In Han Dynasty document style (character in black with two red chops at left). c, In small seal script (character in black with thick lines, small red chop at LR. d, In cursive script (character in black with small red chop at LL). e, In running script (Black character on brown red background). f, In Kana characters (surved black character with dots with large red chop at LR). g, In oracle bone script (black character with curved and straight lines, large red chop at LR). h, In Chou Dyansty bronze vessel style (character in thick black lines with small red chop at LL). i, In seal script (character in red). j, In clerical script (character in thick black lines with large red chop at LL).

**Litho. & Embossed**

**2014, Oct. 30 *Perf. 13x13¼***

| | | | | |
|---|---|---|---|---|
| **3753** | A3298 | Sheet of 10 | 15.00 | 15.00 |
| *a.-j.* | | 82y Any single | 1.50 | 1.10 |

New Year 2014 Japanese Foods — A3299

Designs: No. 3754, Sushi (denomination at LL). No. 3755, Tempura (denomination at LR).

**2014, Oct. 30 Litho. *Perf. 13¼x13***

| | | | | |
|---|---|---|---|---|
| **3754** | | 18y multi | .35 | .30 |
| **3755** | | 18y multi | .35 | .30 |
| *a.* | A3299 | Horiz. pair, #3754-3755 | .90 | .90 |

A3300

A3301

New Year 2015 (Year of the Ram) A3302 A3303

**2014, Oct. 30 Photo. *Perf. 13x13¼***

| | | | | |
|---|---|---|---|---|
| **3756** | A3300 | 52y multi | 1.00 | .50 |
| **3757** | A3301 | 82y multi | 1.50 | .60 |

**Photo. & Typo.**

***Perf. 13¼***

| | | | | |
|---|---|---|---|---|
| **3758** | A3302 | 52y +3y multi | 1.25 | .60 |
| **3759** | A3303 | 82y +3y multi | 1.75 | .60 |
| | | *Nos. 3756-3759 (4)* | 5.50 | 2.30 |

Sheets of two containing Nos. 3756-3757 were lottery prizes. Value, $4.

Lady Shikibu Murasaki Scroll and Books — A3304

Flower Arrangement and Go Players — A3305

Noh and Bunraku Theater A3306

Lute Player and Entertainers A3307

Tale of the Genji Scroll — A3308

**2014, Oct. 31 Litho. *Perf. 13***

| | | | | |
|---|---|---|---|---|
| **3760** | A3304 | 82y multi | 1.50 | 1.10 |
| **3761** | A3305 | 82y multi | 1.50 | 1.10 |
| **3762** | A3306 | 82y multi | 1.50 | 1.10 |
| **3763** | A3307 | 82y multi | 1.50 | 1.10 |
| **3764** | A3308 | 82y multi | 1.50 | 1.10 |
| *a.* | | Vert. strip of 5, #3760-3764 | 7.50 | 5.50 |
| | | *Nos. 3760-3764 (5)* | 7.50 | 5.50 |

Classics Day.

Narcissus A3309

Plum Blossoms A3310

Adonis Ramosa A3311

Cyclamen A3312

Matthiola Incana A3313

Camellia Japonica A3314

Brassica Oleracea A3315

Poinsettia A3316

**2014, Nov. 6 Litho. *Perf. 14x14¼***

| | | | | |
|---|---|---|---|---|
| **3765** | A3309 | 52y multi | .90 | .70 |
| **3766** | A3310 | 52y multi | .90 | .70 |
| **3767** | A3311 | 52y multi | .90 | .70 |
| **3768** | A3312 | 52y multi | .90 | .70 |
| *a.* | | Horiz. strip of 4, #3765-3768 | 3.60 | 2.80 |
| **3769** | A3313 | 82y multi | 1.50 | 1.10 |
| **3770** | A3314 | 82y multi | 1.50 | 1.10 |
| **3771** | A3315 | 82y multi | 1.50 | 1.10 |
| **3772** | A3316 | 82y multi | 1.50 | 1.10 |
| *a.* | | Horiz. strip of 4, #3769-3772 | 6.00 | 4.40 |
| | | *Nos. 3765-3772 (8)* | 9.60 | 7.20 |

Miniature Sheets

A3317

Winter Greetings — A3318

No. 3773: a, Cookie with snowman design. b, Cookies in shape of man and woman. c, Cookie with mailbox design. d, Cookie with polar bear design. e, Cookie in shape of rabbit. f, Cookie with Christmas tree design. g, Cookie in shape of horse. h, Cookie in shape of woman. i, Cookie with poinsettia design. j, Cookie in shape of man.

No. 3774 — Needlepoint designs: a, House with brown door standing in front of trees. b, Post office with red mailbox at left. c, House with red door. d, House with brown door and shrubbery. e, Automobile. f, Snowman. g, One sheep. h, Two sheep. i, Boy and dog. j, Mailbox and fence.

***Die Cut Perf. 13x13¼***

**2014, Nov. 7 Litho.**

**Self-Adhesive**

| | | | | |
|---|---|---|---|---|
| **3773** | A3317 | Sheet of 10 | 9.00 | |
| *a.-j.* | | 52y Any single | .90 | .70 |
| **3774** | A3318 | Sheet of 10 | 15.00 | |
| *a.-j.* | | 82y Any single | 1.50 | 1.10 |

Miniature Sheet

Season's Memories in My Heart — A3319

No. 3775 — Illustrations from children's book *Guri and Gura*, by Yuriko Yamawaki: a, Guri, Gura and rabbits on sled. b, Child looking out of window. c, Guri and Gura making snowman. d, Guri and Gura reading near fireplace. e, Guri picking strawberries. f, Guri cooking. g, Guri and Gura looking at head-shaped cake. h, Guri and Gura holding basket. i, Stove and various animals. j, Guri, Gura, various animals and table.

**2014, Nov. 20 Litho.** ***Perf. 13½***

**3775** A3319 Sheet of 10 14.00 14.00
*a.-j.* 82y Any single 1.40 1.10

Miniature Sheet

Ishikawa Local Autonomy Law, 60th Anniv. — A3320

No. 3776: a, Stone lantern, trees in Kenrokuen Garden (32x39mm). b, Terraced rice fields at sunset (28x33mm). c, Mitsukejima (28x33mm). d, Mount Hakusan (28x33mm). e, Fritillaria cantschatcensis (28x33mm).

***Perf. 13¼ (#3776a), 13x13¼***

**2014, Nov. 26 Photo.**

**3776** A3320 Sheet of 5 7.00 7.00
*a.-e.* 82y Any single 1.40 1.10

Matsumoto Castle — A3321

Takeda Castle — A3322

Nagoya Castle — A3323

Bitchu-Matsuyama Castle — A3324

Shuri Castle — A3325

**2014, Dec. 10 Litho.** ***Perf. 12¾x13***

**3777** A3321 82y multi 1.40 1.10
**3778** A3322 82y multi 1.40 1.10
**3779** A3323 82y multi 1.40 1.10
**3780** A3324 82y multi 1.40 1.10
**3781** A3325 82y multi 1.40 1.10
*a.* Vert. strip of 5, #3777-3781 7.00 5.50
*Nos. 3777-3781 (5)* 7.00 5.50

Miniature Sheets

A3326

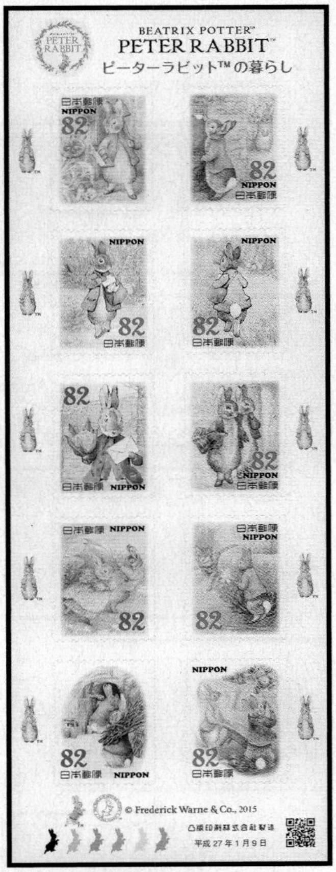


Illustrations From *Peter Rabbit,* by Beatrix Potter — A3327

No. 3782: a, Jemima Puddleduck. b, Peter Rabbit holding placard. c, Squirrel Nutkin. d, Owl reading "Squirrel Nutkin" book. e, Tom Kitten. f, Benjamin Bunny. g, Peter holding shovel. h, Peter and Benjamin Bunny. i, Mother Rabbit and young. j, Rabbits holding towel.

No. 3783: a, Peter with shovel and flower box. b, Peter posting letter. c, Rabbit with mail bag, facing forward. d, Rabbit with mail bag, facing backward. e, Rabbit holding letter and cauliflower. f, Rabbits with basket. g, Peter and female rabbit on windy day. h, Cat, Peter with daffodil. i, Peter and Benjamin carrying sticks. j, Peter and Benjamin harvesting apples.

**2015, Jan. 9 Litho.** ***Die Cut Perf. 14***

**Self-Adhesive**

**3782** A3326 Sheet of 10 9.00
*a.-j.* 52y Any single .90 .70

***Die Cut Perf. 14x13¼***

**3783** A3327 Sheet of 10 14.00
*a.-j.* 82y Any single 1.40 1.10

Flowers, Musical Notes, Clef and Staff — A3328

Flowers in Music Box — A3329

Four Teddy Bears — A3330

Musicians and Bird — A3331

Animals With Musical Instruments A3332

Cherry Blossoms and Bird A3333

Roses A3334

Violas A3335

Girl and Carnations A3336

Teddy Bear and Flowers A3337

***Die Cut Perf. 14***

**2015, Jan. 16 Litho.**

**Self-Adhesive**

**3784** Sheet of 10, 2 each #3784a-3784e 9.00
*a.* A3328 52y multi .90 .70
*b.* A3329 52y multi .90 .70
*c.* A3330 52y multi .90 .70
*d.* A3331 52y multi .90 .70
*e.* A3332 52y multi .90 .70

***Die Cut Perf. 14x13¼, 13¼x14***

**3785** Sheet of 10, 2 each #3785a-3785e 14.00
*a.* A3333 82y multi 1.40 1.10
*b.* A3334 82y multi 1.40 1.10
*c.* A3335 82y multi 1.40 1.10
*d.* A3336 82y multi 1.40 1.10
*e.* A3337 82y multi 1.40 1.10

Wombats A3338

Lamb A3339

Baby Rhinoceros A3340

Chick A3341

Porcupines A3342

Red Pandas A3343

Puppy A3344

Japanese Macaque A3345

Snow Leopard A3346

California Sea Lions A3347

***Die Cut Perf. 13¼***

**2015, Jan. 23 Litho.**

**Self-Adhesive**

**3786** Sheet of 10, 2 each #3786a-3786e 9.00
*a.* A3338 52y multi .90 .70
*b.* A3339 52y multi .90 .70
*c.* A3340 52y multi .90 .70
*d.* A3341 52y multi .90 .70
*e.* A3342 52y multi .90 .70

**3787** Sheet of 10, 2 each #3787a-3787e 14.00
*a.* A3343 82y multi 1.40 1.10
*b.* A3344 82y multi 1.40 1.10
*c.* A3345 82y multi 1.40 1.10
*d.* A3346 82y multi 1.40 1.10
*e.* A3347 82y multi 1.40 1.10

Hisoka Maejima (1835-1919), Founder of Japanese Postal Service A3348

Siberian Chipmunk A3349

Japanese Macaque A3350

Crested Ibis A3351

Sika Deer A3352 — Red Fox A3353

Japanese Serow A3354

Japanese Primrose A3355

Japanese Wisteria A3356

Kerria Japonica A3357

Stream, Towada-Hachimantai National Park — A3358

Mt. Fuji, by Chikuden Tanomura — A3359

**2015, Feb. 2 Photo. *Perf. 13x13¼***

| | | | | |
|---|---|---|---|---|
| **3788** | A3348 | 1y brown | .25 | .25 |
| **3789** | A3349 | 3y multi | .25 | .25 |
| *a.* | | Souvenir sheet of 2, #3648, 3789 | .50 | .50 |
| **3790** | A3350 | 5y multi | .25 | .25 |
| **3791** | A3351 | 10y multi | .25 | .25 |
| **3792** | A3352 | 20y multi | .35 | .25 |
| **3793** | A3353 | 30y multi | .50 | .40 |
| **3794** | A3354 | 50y multi | .85 | .65 |
| **3795** | A3355 | 100y multi | 1.75 | 1.40 |
| **3796** | A3356 | 120y multi | 2.10 | 1.60 |
| **3797** | A3357 | 140y multi | 2.40 | 1.90 |
| **3798** | A3358 | 500y multi | 8.50 | 6.50 |

**Photo. & Engr.**

***Perf. 13¼***

| | | | | |
|---|---|---|---|---|
| **3799** | A3359 | 1000y multi | 17.00 | 13.00 |
| *a.* | | Imperf. | 30.00 | 30.00 |
| *b.* | | Souvenir sheet of 2, #2485a, 3799a | 60.00 | 60.00 |
| | | *Nos. 3788-3799 (12)* | 34.45 | 26.70 |

Cabbage A3360

Satsuma Orange A3361

Peas A3362

Mango A3363

Onion A3364

Oranges A3365

Asparagus A3366

Strawberries A3367

Lettuce A3368

Pineapple A3369

***Die Cut Perf. 13¼x13, 13x13¼***

**2015, Feb. 23 Litho.**

**Self-Adhesive**

| | | | | |
|---|---|---|---|---|
| **3800** | | Sheet of 10, 2 each #3800a-3800e | 9.00 | |
| *a.* | A3360 | 52y multi | .90 | .70 |
| *b.* | A3361 | 52y multi | .90 | .70 |
| *c.* | A3362 | 52y multi | .90 | .70 |
| *d.* | A3363 | 52y multi | .90 | .70 |
| *e.* | A3364 | 52y multi | .90 | .70 |
| **3801** | | Sheet of 10, 2 each #3801a-3801e | 14.00 | |
| *a.* | A3365 | 82y multi | 1.40 | 1.10 |
| *b.* | A3366 | 82y multi | 1.40 | 1.10 |
| *c.* | A3367 | 82y multi | 1.40 | 1.10 |
| *d.* | A3368 | 82y multi | 1.40 | 1.10 |
| *e.* | A3369 | 82y multi | 1.40 | 1.10 |

United Nations World Conference on Disaster Risk Reduction, Sendai — A3370

No. 3802 — Arcs of color and map of Japan made of flowers, with denomination in: a, Orange. b, Carmine. c, Purple. d, Blue. e, Turquoise green.

***Perf. 13½x13¼***

**2015, Mar. 13 Photo.**

| | | | | |
|---|---|---|---|---|
| **3802** | | Horiz. strip of 5 | 7.00 | 7.00 |
| *a.-e.* | A3370 | 82y Any single | 1.40 | 1.10 |

Kanazawa Railroad Station A3371

Tateyama Mountain Range A3372

Takada Park — A3373

Zenkoji Temple A3374

Marunouchi Railroad Station, Tokyo A3375

Series W7, E2 and E7 Trains A3376

Series W7 Train A3377

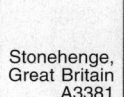

Series E7 Train — A3378

**2015, Mar. 13 Litho. *Perf. 13¼x13***

| | | | | |
|---|---|---|---|---|
| **3803** | | Sheet of 10, #3803a-3803f, 2 each #3803g-3803h | 14.00 | 14.00 |
| *a.* | A3371 | 82y multi | 1.40 | 1.10 |
| *b.* | A3372 | 82y multi | 1.40 | 1.10 |
| *c.* | A3373 | 82y multi | 1.40 | 1.10 |
| *d.* | A3374 | 82y multi | 1.40 | 1.10 |
| *e.* | A3375 | 82y multi | 1.40 | 1.10 |
| *f.* | A3376 | 82y multi | 1.40 | 1.10 |
| *g.* | A3377 | 82y multi | 1.40 | 1.10 |
| *h.* | A3378 | 82y multi | 1.40 | 1.10 |

Canadian Rocky Mountain Parks A3379

Historic Areas of Istanbul, Turkey A3380

Stonehenge, Great Britain A3381

Historic Center of Prague, Czech Republic A3382

Ha Long Bay, Viet Nam A3383

**2015, Mar. 26 Litho. *Perf. 13¼x13***

| | | | | |
|---|---|---|---|---|
| **3804** | A3379 | 82y multi | 1.40 | 1.10 |
| **3805** | A3380 | 82y multi | 1.40 | 1.10 |
| **3806** | A3381 | 82y multi | 1.40 | 1.10 |
| **3807** | A3382 | 82y multi | 1.40 | 1.10 |
| **3808** | A3383 | 82y multi | 1.40 | 1.10 |
| *a.* | | Horiz. strip of 5, #3804-3808 | 7.00 | 5.50 |
| | | *Nos. 3804-3808 (5)* | 7.00 | 5.50 |

UNESCO World Heritage Sites.

Hirosaki Castle — A3384

Kanazawa Castle — A3385

Himeji Castle — A3386

Fukuyama Castle — A3387

Fukuoka Castle — A3388

**2015, Apr. 3 Litho. *Perf. 13***

| | | | | |
|---|---|---|---|---|
| **3809** | A3384 | 82y multi | 1.40 | 1.10 |
| **3810** | A3385 | 82y multi | 1.40 | 1.10 |
| **3811** | A3386 | 82y multi | 1.40 | 1.10 |
| **3812** | A3387 | 82y multi | 1.40 | 1.10 |
| **3813** | A3388 | 82y multi | 1.40 | 1.10 |
| *a.* | | Vert. strip of 5, #3809-3813 | 7.00 | 5.50 |
| | | *Nos. 3809-3813 (5)* | 7.00 | 5.50 |

Japanese Diet, Tokyo, and Cherry Blossoms A3389

Clock Tower, Tokyo, and Dogwood Blossoms A3390

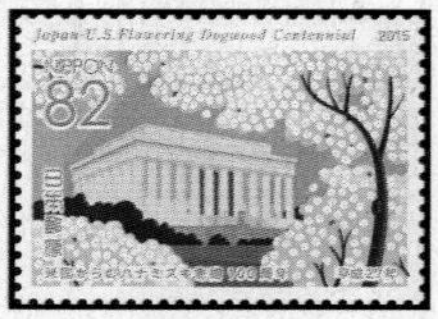

Lincoln Memorial and Cherry Blossoms A3391

U. S. Capitol and Dogwood Blossoms A3392

White Dogwood Blossoms
A3393

Cherry Blossoms
A3394

Red Dogwood Blossoms
A3395

**2015, Apr. 10 Photo. *Perf. 13x12¾***

| | | | |
|---|---|---|---|
| **3814** | Sheet of 10, #3814a-3814d, 2 each #3814e-3814g | 14.00 | 14.00 |
| *a.* | A3389 82y multi | 1.40 | 1.10 |
| *b.* | A3390 82y multi | 1.40 | 1.10 |
| *c.* | A3391 82y multi | 1.40 | 1.10 |
| *d.* | A3392 82y multi | 1.40 | 1.10 |
| *e.* | A3393 82y multi | 1.40 | 1.10 |
| *f.* | A3394 82y multi | 1.40 | 1.10 |
| *g.* | A3395 82y multi | 1.40 | 1.10 |

See United States Nos. 4982-4985.

Mount Rishiri
A3396

Mount Adatara
A3397

Mount Shibutu
A3398

Shirouma Sanzan
A3399

Mount Tateyama
A3400

Yarigatake
A3401

Yatsugatake
A3402

Mount Fuji — A3403

Kitadake
A3404

Miyanouradake — A3405

**2015, Apr. 17 Litho. *Perf. 13¼x13***

| | | | |
|---|---|---|---|
| **3815** | Sheet of 10 | 14.00 | 14.00 |
| *a.* | A3396 82y multi | 1.40 | 1.10 |
| *b.* | A3397 82y multi | 1.40 | 1.10 |
| *c.* | A3398 82y multi | 1.40 | 1.10 |
| *d.* | A3399 82y multi | 1.40 | 1.10 |
| *e.* | A3400 82y multi | 1.40 | 1.10 |
| *f.* | A3401 82y multi | 1.40 | 1.10 |
| *g.* | A3402 82y multi | 1.40 | 1.10 |
| *h.* | A3403 82y multi | 1.40 | 1.10 |
| *i.* | A3404 82y multi | 1.40 | 1.10 |
| *j.* | A3405 82y multi | 1.40 | 1.10 |

Japan Overseas Cooperation Volunteers, 50th Anniv. — A3406

**2015, Apr. 20 Litho. *Perf. 13***

**Denomination Color**

| | | | | |
|---|---|---|---|---|
| **3816** | 82y | blue | 1.40 | 1.10 |
| **3817** | 82y | crimson | 1.40 | 1.10 |
| *a.* | A3406 | Horiz. pair, #3816-3817 | 2.80 | 2.20 |

Phoenixes by Pawlonia Trees, Screen Painting by Kano Tan'yu — A3407

Designs: No. 3818, White phoenix facing left, denomination at LL. No. 3819, Phoenix facing left, denomination at UR. No. 3820, White phoenix facing right, denomination at UR. No. 3821, Phoenix with tail raised facing right, denomination at LL.

**2015, Apr. 20 Photo. *Perf. 13¼***

| | | | | |
|---|---|---|---|---|
| **3818** | 82y | multi | 1.40 | 1.10 |
| **3819** | 82y | multi | 1.40 | 1.10 |
| **3820** | 82y | multi | 1.40 | 1.10 |
| **3821** | 82y | multi | 1.40 | 1.10 |
| *a.* | A3407 | Block of 4, #3818-3821 | 5.60 | 4.40 |
| | *Nos. 3818-3821 (4)* | | 5.60 | 4.40 |

Philatelic Week.

Miniature Sheets

A3408

Moomins — A3409

No. 3822: a, Moomin standing, bright blue background. b, Little My, red background. c, Moomin, yellow background. d, Snufkin, green background. e, Moomin, red violet background. f, Moominpappa, dark blue background. g, Moomin running, bright blue background. h, Moominmamma, pink background. i, Moomin, yellow brown background. j, Snork Maiden, rose background.

No. 3823: a, Moomin characters, Snufkin with accordion. b, Moomin and Snufkin (29mm diameter). c, Moomin, Snork Maiden, ship, flowers. d, Moomin characters, Little My at left. e, Moomin characters and hammock. f, Moomin characters hugging. g, Little My in teapot. h, Moomin, Snork Maiden and Little My. i, Moominmamma and Moominpappa. j, Hattifatteners and top hat.

**2015, May 1 Litho. *Die Cut Perf. 14***

| | | | | |
|---|---|---|---|---|
| **3822** | A3408 | Sheet of 10 | 9.00 | |
| *a.-j.* | | 52y Any single | .90 | .70 |

***Die Cut Perf. 13¼x13¾***

| | | | | |
|---|---|---|---|---|
| **3823** | A3409 | Sheet of 10 | 14.00 | |
| *a.-j.* | | 82y Any single | 1.40 | 1.10 |

Miniature Sheet

Yamaguchi Local Autonomy Law, 60th Anniv. — A3410

No. 3824: a, Kintaikyo Bridge, Akiyoshidai (32x39mm). b, Goldfish lantern and buildings (28x33mm). c, Hooded crane (28x33mm). d, Shokasonjuku Academy and citrons (28x33mm). e, Misuzu Street (28x33mm).

***Perf. 13¼ (#3824a), 13x13¼***

**2015, May 12 Photo.**

| | | | | |
|---|---|---|---|---|
| **3824** | A3410 | Sheet of 5 | 7.00 | 7.00 |
| *a.-e.* | | 82y Any single | 1.40 | 1.10 |

Miniature Sheet

National Afforestation — A3411

No. 3825: a, Crepe myrtle blossoms. b, Ate cypress. c, Horse chestnut blossoms. d, Freesia. e, Japanese black pine. f, Plum blossoms. g, Wild cherry blossoms. h, Azalea blossoms. i, Zelkova tree. j, Chocolate lily.

**2015, May 15 Litho. *Perf. 13***

| | | | | |
|---|---|---|---|---|
| **3825** | A3411 | Sheet of 10 | 8.50 | 6.50 |
| *a.-j.* | | 52y Any single | .85 | .65 |

Crepe Myrtle A3412

Sunflowers A3413

Southern Stars A3414

Eustomas A3415

Gladiolus A3416

Marigolds A3417

Salvia A3418

Hydrangeas A3419

Gymnaster Savatieri A3420

Delphinium and Calla Lily A3421

***Die Cut Perf. 14***

**2015, May 29 Litho.**

**Self-Adhesive**

| | | | |
|---|---|---|---|
| **3826** | Sheet of 10, 2 each #3826a-3826e | 8.50 | |
| *a.* | A3412 52y multi | .85 | .65 |
| *b.* | A3413 52y multi | .85 | .65 |
| *c.* | A3414 52y multi | .85 | .65 |
| *d.* | A3415 52y multi | .85 | .65 |
| *e.* | A3416 52y multi | .85 | .65 |
| **3827** | Sheet of 10, 2 each #3827a-3827e | 14.00 | |
| *a.* | A3417 82y multi | 1.40 | 1.10 |
| *b.* | A3418 82y multi | 1.40 | 1.10 |
| *c.* | A3419 82y multi | 1.40 | 1.10 |
| *d.* | A3420 82y multi | 1.40 | 1.10 |
| *e.* | A3421 82y multi | 1.40 | 1.10 |

Miniature Sheet

Tokushima Local Autonomy Law, 60th Anniv. — A3422

No. 3828: a, Naruto Whirlpools, Naruto Bridge, Awa Dance Festival dancer, sudachi flower (32x39mm). b, Awa Puppet Theater (28x33mm). c, Yoshino River and Mount Bizan (28x33mm). d, Vine bridges in Iya Valley (28x33mm). e, Sea turtle on Ohama Beach (28x33mm).

***Perf. 13¼ (#3828a), 13x13¼***

**2015, June 2 Photo.**

| | | | | |
|---|---|---|---|---|
| **3828** | A3422 | Sheet of 5 | 7.00 | 7.00 |
| *a.-e.* | | 82y Any single | 1.40 | 1.10 |

Shells — A3423

No. 3829: a, Conus ammiralis (23x35mm). b, Mimachlamys nobilis (23x30mm). c, Terebridae (22x29mm). d, Babelomurex gemmatus (22x26mm). e, Scutarcopagia linguafelis (27x23mm).

No. 3830: a, Columbarium pagoda (22x36mm). b, Phalium flammiferum (22x30mm). c, Neocancilla papilio (22x30mm). d, Spondylus sanguineus (24x27mm). e, Architectonica perspectiva (29x25mm).

***Die Cut Perf. 13x13¼, 13¼x13 (#3829e, 3830e)***

**2015, June 5 Litho.**

| | | | |
|---|---|---|---|
| **3829** | Sheet of 10, 2 each #3829a-3829e | 8.50 | |
| *a.-e.* | A3423 52y Any single | .85 | .65 |
| **3830** | Sheet of 10, 2 each #3830a-3830e | 14.00 | |
| *a.-e.* | A3423 82y Any single | 1.40 | 1.10 |

Miniature Sheet

Fukuoka Local Autonomy Law, 60th Anniv. — A3424

No. 3831: a, Okinoshima Island, Munakata Taisha Shrine, gold ring (32x39mm). b, Kokura Castle (28x33mm). c, Triple water wheel, Asakura (28x33mm). d, Boat on Yanagawa River (28x33mm). e, Kane-no Torii and steps (28x33mm).

***Perf. 13¼ (#3831a), 13x13¼***

**2015, June 16 Photo.**

| | | | | |
|---|---|---|---|---|
| **3831** | A3424 | Sheet of 5 | 7.00 | 7.00 |
| *a.-e.* | | 82y Any single | 1.40 | 1.10 |

Normalization of Diplomatic Relations Between Japan and South Korea, 50th Anniv. — A3425

Designs: No. 3832, Japanese woman in kimono, Korean woman in hanbok. No. 3833, Rose of Sharon and cherry blossoms.

**2015, June 22 Litho. *Perf. 13½***

| | | | |
|---|---|---|---|
| **3832** | 82y multi | 1.40 | 1.10 |
| **3833** | 82y multi | 1.40 | 1.10 |
| *a.* | A3425 Vert. pair, #3832-3833 | 2.80 | 2.20 |

Miniature Sheet

Tomioka Silk Mill UNESCO World Heritage Site — A3426

No. 3834: a, Joshu Tomioka Silk Mill, woodblock print by Kuniteru Ichiyosai, denomination at UR (stamp 1). b, Joshu Tomioka Silk Mill, denomination at UL (stamp 2). c, The Diligence of Women Workers at Tomioka Spinning Mill, woodblock print by Asataka, denomination at LR (stamp 3). d, East Cocoon Warehouse, denomination at UL (stamp 4). e, Silk-reeling mill, denomination at UL (stamp 5). f, Illustration from Tomioka Diary, denomination at LL (stamp 6). g, Tajima Yahei Sericulture Farm, denomination at UR (stamp 7). h, Takayama-sha Sericulture School, denomination at LL (stamp 8). i, Arafune Cold Storage, denomination at LL (stamp 9). j, Keystone of Tomioka Silk Mill, denomination at UL (stamp 10).

**2015, June 25 Photo. *Perf. 13x13¼***

| | | | | |
|---|---|---|---|---|
| **3834** | A3426 | Sheet of 10 | 14.00 | 14.00 |
| *a.-j.* | | 82y Any single | 1.40 | 1.10 |

Yosemite National Park, United States A3427

Acropolis, Athens, Greece A3428

Chichen Itza, Mexico A3429

Saint Petersburg, Russia A3430

Borobudur Temple Compounds, Indonesia A3431

**2015, July 10 Litho. *Perf. 13¼x13***

| | | | | |
|---|---|---|---|---|
| **3835** | A3427 82y multi | 1.40 | 1.10 |
| **3836** | A3428 82y multi | 1.40 | 1.10 |
| **3837** | A3429 82y multi | 1.40 | 1.10 |
| **3838** | A3430 82y multi | 1.40 | 1.10 |

**3839** A3431 82y multi 1.40 1.10
*a.* Horiz. strip of 5, #3835-3839 7.00 5.50
*Nos. 3835-3839 (5)* 7.00 5.50

UNESCO World Heritage Sites.

Boy With Pencil and Postcard A3432

Penguins A3433

Squashes A3434

Snow on Camellias A3435

Cherry Blossoms and Birds A3436

Boy Putting Letter in Mailbox A3437

Hollyhocks A3438

Sparrows A3439

Chrysanthemums and Noshi — A3440

Carp Streamer A3441

Child Swimming A3442

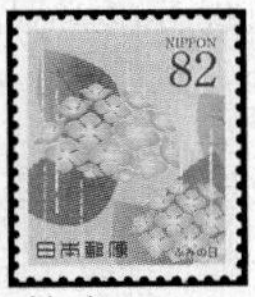
Hydrangeas A3443

Flowers A3444

Crane A3445

Cranes, Turtle and Flowers A3446

Child, Coins, Letter and Stamp A3447

Paper Balloons A3448

Dried Persimmons A3449

Ume Blossoms A3450

Horsetails — A3451

***Die Cut Perf. 13x13½***

**2015, July 23** **Litho.**

**Booklet Stamps**
**Self-Adhesive**

**3840** A3432 52y multi .85 .65
**3841** A3433 52y multi .85 .65
**3842** A3434 52y multi .85 .65
**3843** A3435 52y multi .85 .65
**3844** A3436 52y multi .85 .65
**3845** A3437 52y multi .85 .65
**3846** A3438 52y multi .85 .65
**3847** A3439 52y multi .85 .65
**3848** A3440 52y multi .85 .65
**3849** A3441 52y multi .85 .65
*a.* Booklet pane of 10, #3840-3849 8.50
**3850** A3442 82y multi 1.40 1.10
**3851** A3443 82y multi 1.40 1.10
**3852** A3444 82y multi 1.40 1.10
**3853** A3445 82y multi 1.40 1.10
**3854** A3446 82y multi 1.40 1.10
**3855** A3447 82y multi 1.40 1.10
**3856** A3448 82y multi 1.40 1.10
**3857** A3449 82y multi 1.40 1.10
**3858** A3450 82y multi 1.40 1.10
**3859** A3451 82y multi 1.40 1.10
*a.* Booklet pane of 10, #3850-3859 14.00
*Nos. 3840-3859 (20)* 22.50 17.50

Letter Writing Day.

23rd World Scout Jamboree, Kirara-hama — A3452

Designs: No. 3860, Three scouts, denomination at UL. No. 3861, Three scouts, denomination at UR. No. 3862, Male scout, denomination at UL. No. 3863, Female scout, denomination at UR.

**2015, July 28** **Litho.** ***Perf. 13¾x13½***

**3860** 82y multi 1.40 1.10
**3861** 82y multi 1.40 1.10
**3862** 82y multi 1.40 1.10
**3863** 82y multi 1.40 1.10
*a.* A3452 Block of 4, #3860-3863 5.60 4.40
*Nos. 3860-3863 (4)* 5.60 4.40

Roses A3453

Chrysanthemums A3454

Gerbera Daisies A3455

Ranunculus A3456

Freesias A3457

Cosmos and Dahlias A3458

Lilies and Baby's Breath A3459

Pansies A3460

Moth Orchids A3461

Christmas Cactus A3462

***Die Cut Perf. 14***

**2015, July 31** **Litho.**

**Self-Adhesive**

**3864** Sheet of 10, 2 each #3864a-3864e 8.50
*a.* A3453 52y multi .85 .65
*b.* A3454 52y multi .85 .65
*c.* A3455 52y multi .85 .65
*d.* A3456 52y multi .85 .65
*e.* A3457 52y multi .85 .65
**3865** Sheet of 10, 2 each #3865a-3865e 14.00
*a.* A3458 82y multi 1.40 1.10
*b.* A3459 82y multi 1.40 1.10
*c.* A3460 82y multi 1.40 1.10
*d.* A3461 82y multi 1.40 1.10
*e.* A3462 82y multi 1.40 1.10

Edo Castle — A3463

Maruoka Castle — A3464

Hiroshima Castle — A3465

Kochi Castle — A3466

Uwajima Castle — A3467

**2015, Aug. 7** **Litho.** ***Perf. 13***

**3866** A3463 82y multi 1.40 1.10
**3867** A3464 82y multi 1.40 1.10
**3868** A3465 82y multi 1.40 1.10
**3869** A3466 82y multi 1.40 1.10
**3870** A3467 82y multi 1.40 1.10
*a.* Vert. strip of 5, #3866-3870 7.00 5.50
*Nos. 3866-3870 (5)* 7.00 5.50

### Nagano Flora Prefecture Type of 2003

Designs: No. 3871, Dogtooth violet (pink flowers) and mountain. No. 3872, Skunk cabbage (white flower). No. 3873, Nikko daylily (yellow flower). No. 3874, Cosmos (white, pink and red flowers).

**2015, Aug. 21** **Photo.** ***Perf. 13¼***

**3871** 82y multi 1.40 1.10
**3872** 82y multi 1.40 1.10
**3873** 82y multi 1.40 1.10
**3874** 82y multi 1.40 1.10
*a.* ZA510 Horiz. strip of 4, #3871-3874 5.60 4.40
*Nos. 3871-3874 (4)* 5.60 4.40

### Owara Wind Festival Prefecture Type of 2007

No. 3875, Night Light. No. 3876, Lattice Door. No. 3877, Saotome Dancers. No. 3878, Limelight. No. 3879, Moonlight Night.

**2015, Aug. 21** **Litho.** ***Perf. 13¼***

**3875** ZA710 82y multi 1.40 1.10
**3876** ZA711 82y multi 1.40 1.10
**3877** ZA712 82y multi 1.40 1.10
**3878** ZA713 82y multi 1.40 1.10
**3879** ZA714 82y multi 1.40 1.10
*a.* Vert. strip of 5, #3875-3879 7.00 5.50

See Nos. Z807-Z811.

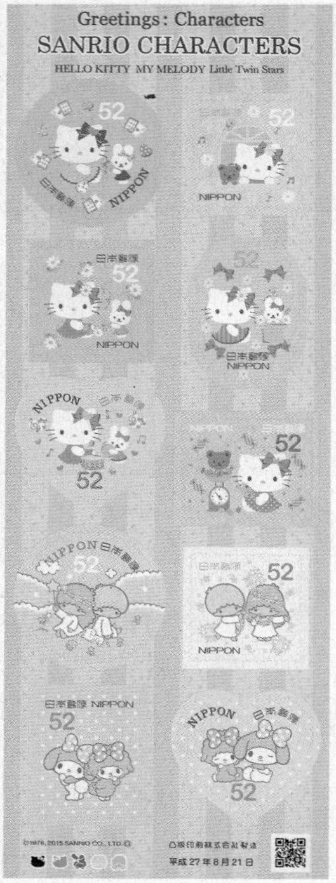

A3468

A3469

A3470

A3471

A3472

A3473

A3474

A3475

A3476

A3477

A3478

A3479

A3480

A3481

A3482

A3483

A3484

A3485

A3486

A3487

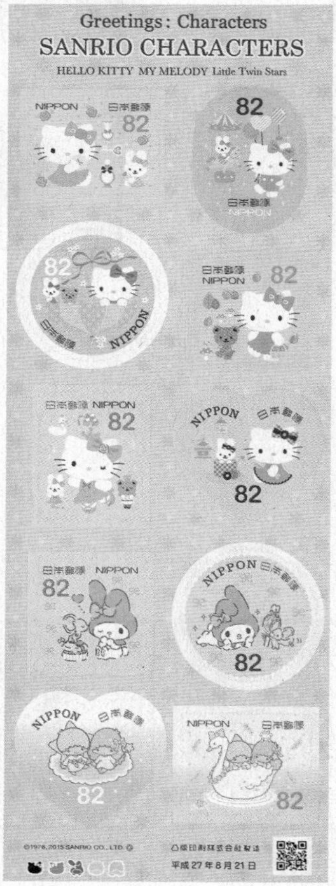

A3488

A3489

A3490

A3491

A3492

A3493

A3494

A3495

A3496

A3497

A3498

A3499

A3500

A3501

A3502

A3503

A3504

A3505

A3506

Sanrio Characters
A3507

No. 3880: a, Hello Kitty, Mimmy, playing cards, pink background (29mm diameter). b, Hello Kitty, Teddy bear in window, blue background (23x23mm). c, Hello Kitty, Mimmy, flowers, green background (23x23mm). d, Hello Kitty, Mimmy, bucket, flowers, bows, pink background (22x30mm oval). e, Hello Kitty, Mimmy, drum, cymbals, musical symbols, yellow background (29x26mm heart). f, Hello Kitty, Teddy bear, scale, blue background (27x22mm). g, Little Twin Stars, cat, blue & pink background (29mm diameter). h, Little Twin Stars, cream background (23x23mm). i, My Melody and Piano, yellow brown background with polka dots (22x27mm). j, My Melody and Piano, blue background with polka dots (29x26mm heart).

No. 3894: a, Hello Kitty, Mimmy, flowers, yellow background (27x22mm). b, Hello Kitty, Mimmy on carousel, pink background (22x30mm oval). c, Hello Kitty, Mimmy, Teddy bear in umbrella, pale lilac background (29mm diameter). d, Hello Kitty, Teddy bear, bird, berries and mushrooms, buff background (23x23mm). e, Hello Kitty, Mimmy, Teddy bear, swan, blue background (22x27mm). f, Hello Kitty, Mimmy in coffee mug, light green background (29x26mm heart). g, My Melody and mouse, pale sage green background (23x23mm). h, My Melody and mouse, pink background (29mm diameter). i, Little Twin Stars, white & rose background (29x26mm heart). j, Little Twin Stars on swan, blue & rose background (27x22mm).

***Die Cut Perf. 14 (#3880b, 3880c, 3880d, 3880h), Die Cut Perf. 13½x13¾ (#3880f), Die Cut Perf. 13¾x13½ (#3880i), Die Cut Perf.***

**2015, Aug. 21** **Litho.**

**Self-Adhesive**

| | | | | |
|---|---|---|---|---|
| **3880** | A3468 | Sheet of 10 | 9.00 | |
| *a.-j.* | | 52y Any single | .90 | .70 |

***Die Cut Perf. (A3469-A3474), Die Cut Perf. 13 (A3475-A3487)***

| | | | | |
|---|---|---|---|---|
| **3881** | | Sheet of 10, #3881a-3881f, 4 #3881g | 9.00 | |
| *a.* | A3469 52y multi | | .90 | .70 |
| *b.* | A3470 52y multi | | .90 | .70 |
| *c.* | A3471 52y multi | | .90 | .70 |
| *d.* | A3472 52y multi | | .90 | .70 |
| *e.* | A3473 52y multi | | .90 | .70 |
| *f.* | A3474 52y multi | | .90 | .70 |
| *g.* | A3475 52y multi | | .90 | .70 |
| **3882** | | Sheet of 10, #3881a-3881f, 4 #3882a | 9.00 | |
| *a.* | A3476 52y multi | | .90 | .70 |
| **3883** | | Sheet of 10, #3881a-3881f, 4 #3883a | 9.00 | |
| *a.* | A3477 52y multi | | .90 | .70 |
| **3884** | | Sheet of 10, #3881a-3881f, 4 #3884a | 9.00 | |
| *a.* | A3478 52y multi | | .90 | .70 |
| **3885** | | Sheet of 10, #3881a-3881f, 4 #3885a | 9.00 | |
| *a.* | A3479 52y multi | | .90 | .70 |
| **3886** | | Sheet of 10, #3881a-3881f, 4 #3886a | 9.00 | |
| *a.* | A3480 52y multi | | .90 | .70 |
| **3887** | | Sheet of 10, #3881a-3881f, 4 #3887a | 9.00 | |
| *a.* | A3481 52y multi | | .90 | .70 |
| **3888** | | Sheet of 10, #3881a-3881f, 4 #3888a | 9.00 | |
| *a.* | A3482 52y multi | | .90 | .70 |
| **3889** | | Sheet of 10, #3881a-3881f, 4 #3889a | 9.00 | |
| *a.* | A3483 52y multi | | .90 | .70 |
| **3890** | | Sheet of 10, #3881a-3881f, 4 #3890a | 9.00 | |
| *a.* | A3484 52y multi | | .90 | .70 |
| **3891** | | Sheet of 10, #3881a-3881f, 4 #3891a | 9.00 | |
| *a.* | A3485 52y multi | | .90 | .70 |
| **3892** | | Sheet of 10, #3881a-3881f, 4 #3892a | 9.00 | |
| *a.* | A3486 52y multi | | .90 | .70 |
| **3893** | | Sheet of 10, #3881a-3881f, 4 #3893a | 9.00 | |
| *a.* | A3487 52y multi | | .90 | .70 |

***Die Cut Perf. 13½x13¾ (#3894a, 3894j), Die Cut Perf. 14 (#3894b, #3894d, 3894g), Die Cut Perf. 13¾x13½ (#3894e), Die Cut Perf.***

| | | | | |
|---|---|---|---|---|
| **3894** | A3488 | Sheet of 10 | 14.00 | |
| *a.-j.* | | 82y Any single | 1.40 | 1.10 |

***Die Cut Perf. 14 (A3489-A3494), Die Cut Perf. 13½x13¾ (A3495-A3507)***

| | | | | |
|---|---|---|---|---|
| **3895** | | Sheet of 10, #3895a-3895f, 4 #3895g | 14.00 | |
| *a.* | A3489 82y multi | | 1.40 | 1.10 |
| *b.* | A3490 82y multi | | 1.40 | 1.10 |
| *c.* | A3491 82y multi | | 1.40 | 1.10 |
| *d.* | A3492 82y multi | | 1.40 | 1.10 |
| *e.* | A3493 82y multi | | 1.40 | 1.10 |
| *f.* | A3494 82y multi | | 1.40 | 1.10 |
| *g.* | A3495 82y multi | | 1.40 | 1.10 |
| **3896** | | Sheet of 10, #3895a-3985f, 4 #3896a | 14.00 | |
| *a.* | A3496 82y multi | | 1.40 | 1.10 |
| **3897** | | Sheet of 10, #3895a-3985f, 4 #3897a | 14.00 | |
| *a.* | A3497 82y multi | | 1.40 | 1.10 |
| **3898** | | Sheet of 10, #3895a-3985f, 4 #3898a | 14.00 | |
| *a.* | A3498 82y multi | | 1.40 | 1.10 |
| **3899** | | Sheet of 10, #3895a-3985f, 4 #3899a | 14.00 | |
| *a.* | A3499 82y multi | | 1.40 | 1.10 |
| **3900** | | Sheet of 10, #3895a-3985f, 4 #3900a | 14.00 | |
| *a.* | A3500 82y multi | | 1.40 | 1.10 |
| **3901** | | Sheet of 10, #3895a-3985f, 4 #3901a | 14.00 | |
| *a.* | A3501 82y multi | | 1.40 | 1.10 |
| **3902** | | Sheet of 10, #3895a-3985f, 4 #3902a | 14.00 | |
| *a.* | A3502 82y multi | | 1.40 | 1.10 |
| **3903** | | Sheet of 10, #3895a-3985f, 4 #3903a | 14.00 | |
| *a.* | A3503 82y multi | | 1.40 | 1.10 |
| **3904** | | Sheet of 10, #3895a-3985f, 4 #3904a | 14.00 | |
| *a.* | A3504 82y multi | | 1.40 | 1.10 |

| | | | | |
|---|---|---|---|---|
| 3905 | | Sheet of 10, #3895a-3985f, 4 #3905a | 14.00 | |
| a. | A3505 | 82y multi | 1.40 | 1.10 |
| 3906 | | Sheet of 10, #3895a-3985f, 4 #3906a | 14.00 | |
| a. | A3506 | 82y multi | 1.40 | 1.10 |
| 3907 | | Sheet of 10, #3895a-3985f, 4 #3907a | 14.00 | |
| a. | A3507 | 82y multi | 1.40 | 1.10 |
| | | *Nos. 3880-3907 (28)* | 322.00 | |

Miniature Sheet

70th National Sports Festival, Wakayama — A3508

No. 3908: a, Kayaking. b, Sailing. c, Basketball. d, Field hockey. e, Cycling. f, Gymnastics. g, Fencing. h, Soccer. i, Naginata. j, Volleyball.

**2015, Aug. 28 Litho. *Perf. 13***

| | | | | |
|---|---|---|---|---|
| 3908 | A3508 | Sheet of 10 | 14.00 | 14.00 |
| a.-j. | | 82y Any single | 1.40 | 1.10 |

### Niigata Flowers Prefecture Type of 2002

Designs: No. 3909, Red camellias, Kamoyama Kouen Park. No. 3910, Yellow daylilies, Oonogame. No. 3911, Irises, Ijimino Kouen Park. No. 3912, Pink iwakagami flowers, Mt. Myoukousan.

**2015, Aug. 28 Photo. *Perf. 13¼***

| | | | | |
|---|---|---|---|---|
| 3909 | | 82y multi | 1.40 | 1.10 |
| 3910 | | 82y multi | 1.40 | 1.10 |
| 3911 | | 82y multi | 1.40 | 1.10 |
| 3912 | | 82y multi | 1.40 | 1.10 |
| a. | ZA488 | Horiz. strip of 4, #3909-3912 | 5.60 | 4.40 |
| | | *Nos. 3909-3912 (4)* | 5.60 | 4.40 |

### Hokkaido Flowers Prefecture Type of 1991

Designs as before.

**2015, Aug. 28 Photo. *Perf. 13***

| | | | | |
|---|---|---|---|---|
| 3913 | ZA97 | 82y multi | 1.40 | 1.10 |
| 3914 | ZA98 | 82y multi | 1.40 | 1.10 |
| 3915 | ZA99 | 82y multi | 1.40 | 1.10 |
| 3916 | ZA100 | 82y multi | 1.40 | 1.10 |
| a. | | Horiz. strip of 4, #3913-3916 | 5.60 | 4.40 |
| | | *Nos. 3913-3916 (4)* | 5.60 | 4.40 |

### Hokkaido Flowers Prefecture Type of 2005

Designs as before.

**2015, Aug. 28 Photo. *Perf. 13¼***

| | | | | |
|---|---|---|---|---|
| 3917 | ZA569 | 82y multi | 1.40 | 1.10 |
| 3918 | ZA570 | 82y multi | 1.40 | 1.10 |
| 3919 | ZA571 | 82y multi | 1.40 | 1.10 |
| 3920 | ZA572 | 82y multi | 1.40 | 1.10 |
| a. | | Horiz. strip of 4, #3917-3920 | 5.60 | 4.40 |
| | | *Nos. 3917-3920 (4)* | 5.60 | 4.40 |

Plums A3509

Lemon and Lime A3510

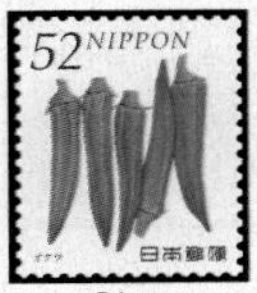

Okra A3511

Olives A3512

Mustard Spinach A3513

Celery A3514

Lotus Root A3515

Loquats A3516

Soybeans A3517

Fig A3518

***Die Cut Perf. 13¼x13, 13x13¼***

**2015, Aug. 31 Litho.**

**Self-Adhesive**

| | | | | |
|---|---|---|---|---|
| 3921 | | Sheet of 10, 2 each #3921a-3921e | 9.00 | |
| a. | A3509 | 52y multi | .90 | .70 |
| b. | A3510 | 52y multi | .90 | .70 |
| c. | A3511 | 52y multi | .90 | .70 |
| d. | A3512 | 52y multi | .90 | .70 |
| e. | A3513 | 52y multi | .90 | .70 |
| 3922 | | Sheet of 10, 2 each #3922a-3922e | 14.00 | |
| a. | A3514 | 82y multi | 1.40 | 1.10 |
| b. | A3515 | 82y multi | 1.40 | 1.10 |
| c. | A3516 | 82y multi | 1.40 | 1.10 |
| d. | A3517 | 82y multi | 1.40 | 1.10 |
| e. | A3518 | 82y multi | 1.40 | 1.10 |

Miniature Sheets

A3519

A3520

Greetings — A3521

No. 3923: a, Sea bream. b, Turtle and crane. c, Mount Fuji. d, Noshi. e, Clouds, rainbow and musical notes. f, Dove, horiz. g, "Happy" and shamrocks, horiz. h, Rose, horiz. i, Flowers and "For You," horiz. j, "Happy," birthday cake and candles, horiz.

No. 3924: a, Sea bream, diff. b, Gourds. c, Gift box with bow. d, Pine, bamboo and plum. e, Party hat, streamers and confetti. f, Bird, horiz. g, "Happy" and shamrocks, diff., horiz. h, Two roses, horiz. i, Bow and "For You," horiz. j, "Happy" and slice of birthday cake, horiz.

No. 3925: a, Sea bream, diff. b, Fans. c, Mount Fuji, diff. d, Mallet of luck. e, "Happy," heart with bow. f, Bird, diff., horiz. g, "Happy" and shamrocks, diff., horiz. h, Five roses, horiz. i, Envelope, "For You," feather, horiz. j, "Happy" and cup, horiz.

***Die Cut Perf. 13x13¼, 13¼x13***

**2015, Sept. 4 Litho.**

**Self-Adhesive**

| | | | | |
|---|---|---|---|---|
| 3923 | A3519 | Sheet of 10 | 9.00 | |
| a.-j. | | 52y Any single | .90 | .70 |
| 3924 | A3520 | Sheet of 10 | 14.00 | |
| a.-j. | | 82y Any single | 1.40 | 1.10 |
| 3925 | A3521 | Sheet of 10 | 16.00 | |
| a.-j. | | 92y Any single | 1.60 | 1.25 |
| | | *Nos. 3923-3925 (3)* | 39.00 | |

Miniature Sheet

Wakayama Local Autonomy Law, 60th Anniv. — A3522

No. 3926: a, Koyasan Danjo Garan (32x39mm). b, Wakayama Castle (28x33mm). c, Shirahama and beach (28x33mm). d, Hashikuiiwa Rocks (28x33mm). e, Nachi Waterfall and pagoda (28x33mm).

***Perf. 13¼ (#3926a), 13x13¼***

**2015, Sept. 8 Photo.**

| | | | | |
|---|---|---|---|---|
| 3926 | A3522 | Sheet of 5 | 7.00 | 7.00 |
| a.-e. | | 82y Any single | 1.40 | 1.10 |

Miniature Sheets

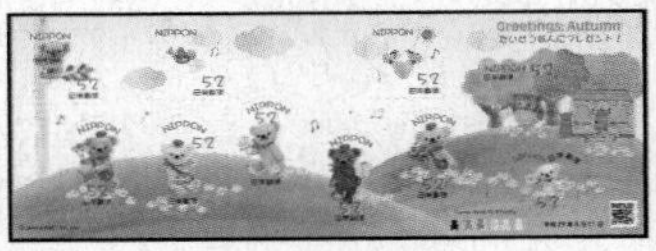

A3523

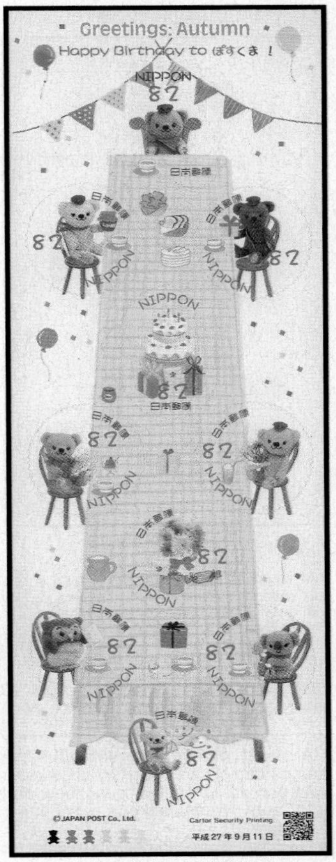


Greetings — A3524

No. 3927: a, Koala bear on tree (23x23mm). b, Bird with letter (23x23mm). c, Bees holding heart (23x23mm). d, Owl holding letter (23x23mm). e, Brown Teddy bear with mail bag and flowers (22x30mm oval). f, White Teddy bear with mail bag and gift box (22x30mm oval). g, Pink Teddy bear with flowers (22x30mm oval). h, Dark brown Teddy bear with mail bag and gift box (22x30mm oval). i, Light green Teddy bear with mail bag and flowers (22x30mm oval). j, Teddy bear with envelope (25x22mm heart).

No. 3928: a, Teddy bear, cup on table (26x29mm). b, Teddy bear holding honey jar (25mm diameter). c, Teddy bear holding gift box (25mm diameter). d, Birthday cake, gifts and envelope (22x30mm oval). e, Pink Teddy bear holding flowers, cup and dessert bowl on table (25mm diameter). f, Light greenTeddy bear holding flowers, drinking glass with straw on table (25mm diameter). g, Flowers, gifts and envelope (25mm diameter). h, Owl (25mm diameter). i, Gray Teddy bear holding lollipop (25mm diameter). j, Teddy bear with party hat, streamers and confetti (25mm diameter).

***Die Cut Perf. 14***

**2015, Sept. 11 Litho.**

**Self-Adhesive**

| | | | | |
|---|---|---|---|---|
| 3927 | A3523 | Sheet of 10 | 9.00 | |
| a.-j. | | 52y Any single | .90 | .70 |
| 3928 | A3524 | Sheet of 10 | 14.00 | |
| a.-j. | | 82y Any single | 1.40 | 1.10 |

### Okinawa Fish Prefecture Type of 2007

Designs as before.

**2015, Sept. 16 Litho. *Perf. 13¼***

| | | | | |
|---|---|---|---|---|
| 3929 | ZA704 | 82y multi | 1.40 | 1.10 |
| 3930 | ZA705 | 82y multi | 1.40 | 1.10 |
| 3931 | ZA706 | 82y multi | 1.40 | 1.10 |
| 3932 | ZA707 | 82y multi | 1.40 | 1.10 |
| 3933 | ZA708 | 82y multi | 1.40 | 1.10 |
| a. | | Horiz. strip of 5, #3929-3933 | 7.00 | 5.50 |
| | | *Nos. 3929-3933 (5)* | 7.00 | 5.50 |

Miniature Sheet

Children — A3525

No. 3934: a, Mother, girl and balloon. b, Girl and balloon. c, Child holding flowers. d, Boy with drum. e, Girl in raincoat looking at snail. f, Girl on beach. g, Children reading book. h, Child playing with blocks. i, Child in angel costume. j, Child sleeping with stuffed animal.

**2015, Sept. 18 Photo. *Perf. 13***

| | | | | |
|---|---|---|---|---|
| **3934** | A3525 | Sheet of 10 | 14.00 | 14.00 |
| *a.-j.* | | 82y Any single | 1.40 | 1.10 |

A sheet of five 82y self-adhesive stamps depicting Hello Kitty characters was printed in limited quantities and sold only in a package containing stationery.

Astronomy — A3526

No. 3935: a, Moon (25x34mm). b, Libra and scales (22x25mm). c, Scorpio and scorpion (22x25mm). d, Sagittarius, bow and arrow (22x25mm).

**Litho. With Foil Application**
***Die Cut Perf. 13x13¼***
**2015, Sept. 25 Self-Adhesive**

| | | | | |
|---|---|---|---|---|
| **3935** | A3526 | Sheet of 10, #3935a, 3 each #3935b-3935d | 14.00 | |
| *a.-d.* | | 82y Any single | 1.40 | 1.10 |

Miniature Sheet

Osaka Local Autonomy Law, 60th Anniv. — A3527

No. 3936: a, Bunraku puppet, Osaka Castle (32x39mm). b, Interior of Osaka Prefectural Government Building (28x33mm). c, Tower of the Sun (28x33mm). d, Jinai-machi Town, Tondabayashi (28x33mm). e, Eggplant (28x33mm).

***Perf. 13¼ (#3936a), 13x13¼***
**2015, Oct. 6 Photo.**

| | | | | |
|---|---|---|---|---|
| **3936** | A3527 | Sheet of 5 | 7.00 | 7.00 |
| *a.-e.* | | 82y Any single | 1.40 | 1.10 |

A3528

International Letter Writing Week A3529

Paintings by Hiroshige: 70y, Thoroughwort and Pink. 90y, The Fifty-three Stations of the Tokaido: Yoshiwara. 110y, The Fifty-three Stations of the Tokaido: Yoshida. 130y, The Fifty-three Stations of the Tokaido: Fujikawa.

**2015, Oct. 9 Photo. *Perf. 13¼***

| | | | | |
|---|---|---|---|---|
| **3937** | A3528 | 70y multi | 1.25 | .95 |

***Perf. 13***

| | | | | |
|---|---|---|---|---|
| **3938** | A3529 | 90y multi | 1.50 | 1.10 |
| **3939** | A3529 | 110y multi | 1.90 | 1.40 |
| **3940** | A3529 | 130y multi | 2.25 | 1.75 |
| | | *Nos. 3937-3940 (4)* | 6.90 | 5.20 |

Front Ends of Tokaido Shinkansen Rail Cars A3530

Japan National Railways 183 Series Locomotive A3531

Keisei Class AE Locomotive A3532

Hankyu 6300 Series Locomotive A3533

Meitetsu 6000 Series Locomotive A3534

Kintetsu 12400 Series Locomotive A3535

Japan Railways West 500 Series Locomotive A3536

Japan Railways Tokai and Japan Railways West N700 Series Locomotive A3537

Odakyu 60000 Series Locomotive A3538

Kintetsu 50000 Series Locomotive A3539

Front Ends of Tokaido Shinkansen Rail Cars A3540

Kintetsu 12400 Series Locomotive A3541

Japan National Railways 183 Series Locomotive A3542

Japan Railways West 500 Series Locomotive A3543

Keisei Class AE Locomotive A3544

Japan Railways Tokai and Japan Railways West N700 Series Locomotive A3545

Hankyu 6300 Series Locomotive A3546

Odakyu 60000 Series Locomotive A3547

Meitetsu 6000 Series Locomotive A3548

Kintetsu 50000 Series Locomotive A3549

**2015, Oct. 9 Photo. *Perf. 13¼x13***

| | | | | |
|---|---|---|---|---|
| **3941** | | Sheet of 10 | 14.00 | 14.00 |
| *a.* | A3530 | 82y multi | 1.40 | 1.10 |
| *b.* | A3531 | 82y multi | 1.40 | 1.10 |
| *c.* | A3532 | 82y multi | 1.40 | 1.10 |
| *d.* | A3533 | 82y multi | 1.40 | 1.10 |
| *e.* | A3534 | 82y multi | 1.40 | 1.10 |
| *f.* | A3535 | 82y multi | 1.40 | 1.10 |
| *g.* | A3536 | 82y multi | 1.40 | 1.10 |
| *h.* | A3537 | 82y multi | 1.40 | 1.10 |
| *i.* | A3538 | 82y multi | 1.40 | 1.10 |
| *j.* | A3539 | 82y multi | 1.40 | 1.10 |

***Perf. 13x13¼***

| | | | | |
|---|---|---|---|---|
| **3942** | | Sheet of 10 + 10 labels | 14.00 | 14.00 |
| *a.* | A3540 | 82y multi | 1.40 | 1.10 |
| *b.* | A3541 | 82y multi | 1.40 | 1.10 |
| *c.* | A3542 | 82y multi | 1.40 | 1.10 |
| *d.* | A3543 | 82y multi | 1.40 | 1.10 |
| *e.* | A3544 | 82y multi | 1.40 | 1.10 |
| *f.* | A3545 | 82y multi | 1.40 | 1.10 |
| *g.* | A3546 | 82y multi | 1.40 | 1.10 |
| *h.* | A3547 | 82y multi | 1.40 | 1.10 |
| *i.* | A3548 | 82y multi | 1.40 | 1.10 |
| *j.* | A3549 | 82y multi | 1.40 | 1.10 |

Chinese Style Sword — A3550

Folding Screen Depicting Lady of the Court — A3551

Circular Mirror With Inlaid Decorations A3552

Batik Folding Screen A3553

Lacquer Ewer — A3554

**2015, Oct. 16 Photo. *Perf. 13***

| | | | | | |
|---|---|---|---|---|---|
| **3943** | A3550 | 82y multi | | 1.40 | 1.10 |
| **3944** | A3551 | 82y multi | | 1.40 | 1.10 |
| **3945** | A3552 | 82y multi | | 1.40 | 1.10 |
| **3946** | A3553 | 82y multi | | 1.40 | 1.10 |
| **3947** | A3554 | 82y multi | | 1.40 | 1.10 |
| *a.* | Vert. strip of 5, #3943-3947 | | | 7.00 | 5.50 |
| | *Nos. 3943-3947 (5)* | | | 7.00 | 5.50 |

Treasures of the Shosoin.

Chihuahua A3555

Shiba A3556

Yorkshire Terrier A3557

French Bulldog A3558

Cavalier King Charles Spaniel A3559

Jack Russell Terriers A3560

Papillon A3561

Golden Retriever A3562

Beagles A3563

American Cocker Spaniel A3564

Toy Poodles A3565

Dachshund A3566

Pomeranians A3567

Maltese A3568

Miniature Schnauzer A3569

Shih Tzu A3570

Pembroke Welsh Corgi A3571

Pug A3572

Miniature Pinscher A3573

Bichon Frise A3574

***Die Cut Perf. 13x13¼***

**2015, Oct. 23 Litho.**

**Self-Adhesive**

| | | | |
|---|---|---|---|
| **3948** | Sheet of 10 | 9.00 | |
| *a.* | A3555 52y multi | .90 | .70 |
| *b.* | A3556 52y multi | .90 | .70 |
| *c.* | A3557 52y multi | .90 | .70 |
| *d.* | A3558 52y multi | .90 | .70 |
| *e.* | A3559 52y multi | .90 | .70 |
| *f.* | A3560 52y multi | .90 | .70 |
| *g.* | A3561 52y multi | .90 | .70 |
| *h.* | A3562 52y multi | .90 | .70 |
| *i.* | A3563 52y multi | .90 | .70 |
| *j.* | A3564 52y multi | .90 | .70 |
| **3949** | Sheet of 10 | 14.00 | |
| *a.* | A3565 82y multi | 1.40 | 1.10 |
| *b.* | A3566 82y multi | 1.40 | 1.10 |
| *c.* | A3567 82y multi | 1.40 | 1.10 |
| *d.* | A3568 82y multi | 1.40 | 1.10 |
| *e.* | A3569 82y multi | 1.40 | 1.10 |
| *f.* | A3570 82y multi | 1.40 | 1.10 |
| *g.* | A3571 82y multi | 1.40 | 1.10 |
| *h.* | A3572 82y multi | 1.40 | 1.10 |
| *i.* | A3573 82y multi | 1.40 | 1.10 |
| *j.* | A3574 82y multi | 1.40 | 1.10 |

Miniature Sheet

Edo Calligraphy — A3575

No. 3950 — Characters for "monkey": a, In Kinbun style of Western Zhou period (character with large red chop at LL). b, In Kinbuntai seal engraving style (red character). c, In Yin Dynasty oracle bone script style (white character with purple and black background). d, In Yin Dynasty oracle bone script style (character in black with light green background). e, In Shoten style (Black character with large central vertical line and large red chop at LL). f, In Hiragana style (black character, denomination at center left). g, In Gyosho style (black character with large central vertical line, small red chop at LR). h, In Gyosho style (black character with salmon pink background). i, In oracle bone script (black character with curved lines, small red chop at LL above denomination). j, In Tenreitai style (three-part black character with small red chop at LL).

**Litho. & Embossed**

**2015, Oct. 29 *Perf. 13x13¼***

| | | | | |
|---|---|---|---|---|
| **3950** | A3575 | Sheet of 10 | 14.00 | 14.00 |
| *a.-j.* | | 82y Any single | 1.40 | 1.10 |

Japanese Foods — A3576

Designs: No. 3951, Ramen noodles (denomination at LL). No. 3952, Sukiyaki (denomination at UL).

**2015, Oct. 29 Photo. *Perf. 13¼x13***

| | | | |
|---|---|---|---|
| **3951** | 18y multi | .30 | .25 |
| **3952** | 18y multi | .30 | .25 |
| *a.* | A3576 Horiz. pair, #3951-3952 | .60 | .45 |

A3577

A3578

A3579

A3580

New Year 2016 (Year of the Monkey)

A3579 A3580

**2015, Oct. 29 Photo. *Perf. 13x13¼***

| | | | | |
|---|---|---|---|---|
| **3953** | A3577 | 52y multi | 1.00 | .50 |
| **3954** | A3578 | 82y multi | 1.50 | .70 |

**Photo. & Typo.**

***Perf. 13¼***

| | | | | |
|---|---|---|---|---|
| **3955** | A3579 | 52y +3y multi | 1.25 | .60 |
| **3956** | A3580 | 82y +3y multi | 1.75 | .70 |
| | *Nos. 3953-3956 (4)* | | 5.50 | 2.50 |

Sheets of two containing Nos. 3953-3954 were lottery prizes. Value, $4.

Establishment of Tsunami Preparedness Day — A3581

**2015, Nov. 5 Litho. *Perf. 13***

| | | | | |
|---|---|---|---|---|
| **3957** | A3581 | 82y multi | 1.40 | 1.10 |

Miniature Sheet

Traditional Crafts — A3582

No. 3758: a, Takaoka Shikki lacquer box (Toyama Prefecture). b, Makabe Ishidoro stone lantern (Ibaraki Prefecture). c, Edo glassware (Tokyo Prefecture). d, Tokoname Yaki pottery (Aichi Prefecture). e, Mino Washi Japanese paper (Gifu Prefecture). f, Kyo Yuzen dyed fabric (Kyoto Prefecture). g, Osaka Naniwa Suzuki tin container (Osaka Prefecture). h, Kumano Fude brushes (Hiroshima Prefecture). i, Awa Sho-ai Shijira-ori weaving (Tokushima Prefecture). j, Beppu Takesaiku bamboo basket (Oita Prefecture).

**2015, Nov. 5 Litho. *Perf. 13½***

| | | | | |
|---|---|---|---|---|
| **3958** | A3582 | Sheet of 10 | 14.00 | 14.00 |
| *a.-j.* | | 82y Any single | 1.40 | 1.10 |

Miniature Sheets

A3583

Disney Characters — A3584

No. 3959: a, Winnie the Pooh, honey jar at his side. b, Winnie the pooh sticking snout in honey jar. c, Winnie the Pooh standing with head stuck in honey jar. d, Winnie the Pooh writing list. e, Winnie the Pooh in grass carrying honey jar. f, Winnie the Pooh scratching. g, Winnie the Pooh and Piglet. h, Christopher Robin draggin Winnie the Pooh down stairs. i, Winnie the Pooh next to Christopher Robin putting boots on feet. j, Christopher Robin and Winnie the Pooh reading sign.

No. 3960: a, Princess Aurora and pink roses (22x27mm). b, Princess Aurora and pink roses (27x22mm). c, Cinderella and lilies (22x27mm). d, Cinderella and lilies (27x22mm). e, Snow White and pink roses (22x27mm). f, Snow White, animals and pink roses (27x22mm). g, Ariel and red flowers (22x27mm). h, Rapunzel, lizard and pink flowers (27x22mm). i, Belle and pink rose (22x27mm). j, Jasmine and white flowers (27x22mm).

***Die Cut Perf. 11¼***

**2015, Nov. 6 Litho.**

**Self-Adhesive**

**3959** A3583 Sheet of 10 8.50

***Die Cut Perf. 14x13½, 13½x14***

| | | | | |
|---|---|---|---|---|
| *a.-j.* | | 52y Any single | .85 | .65 |
| **3960** | A3584 | Sheet of 10 | 14.00 | |
| *a.-j.* | | 82y Any single | 1.40 | 1.10 |

Miniature Sheet

Nagasaki Local Autonomy Law, 60th Anniv. — A3585

No. 3961: a, Oura Church and camellias (32x39mm). b, Nagasaki Kunchi Festival (28x33mm). c, Hashima (28x33mm). d, Mount Heisei-shinzan (28x33mm). e, Golden tiger lily (28x33mm).

***Perf. 13¼ (#3961a), 13x13¼***

**2015, Nov. 17 Photo.**

| | | | | |
|---|---|---|---|---|
| **3961** | A3585 | Sheet of 5 | 7.00 | 7.00 |
| *a.-e.* | | 82y Any single | 1.40 | 1.10 |

Iyokan Orange A3586

Carrot A3587

Yuzus A3588

Daikon Radish A3589

Green Onions A3590

Chinese Cabbage A3591

Broccoli A3592

Tangerines A3593

Spinach A3594

Kiwi A3595

***Die Cut Perf. 13¼***

**2015, Nov. 20 Litho.**

**Self-Adhesive**

| | | | | |
|---|---|---|---|---|
| **3962** | | Sheet of 10, 2 each #3962a-3962e | 8.50 | |
| *a.* | A3586 | 52y multi | .85 | .65 |
| *b.* | A3587 | 52y multi | .85 | .65 |
| *c.* | A3588 | 52y multi | .85 | .65 |
| *d.* | A3589 | 52y multi | .85 | .65 |
| *e.* | A3590 | 52y multi | .85 | .65 |
| **3963** | | Sheet of 10, 2 each #3963a-3963e | 14.00 | |
| *a.* | A3591 | 82y multi | 1.40 | 1.10 |
| *b.* | A3592 | 82y multi | 1.40 | 1.10 |
| *c.* | A3593 | 82y multi | 1.40 | 1.10 |
| *d.* | A3594 | 82y multi | 1.40 | 1.10 |
| *e.* | A3595 | 82y multi | 1.40 | 1.10 |

Miniature Sheet

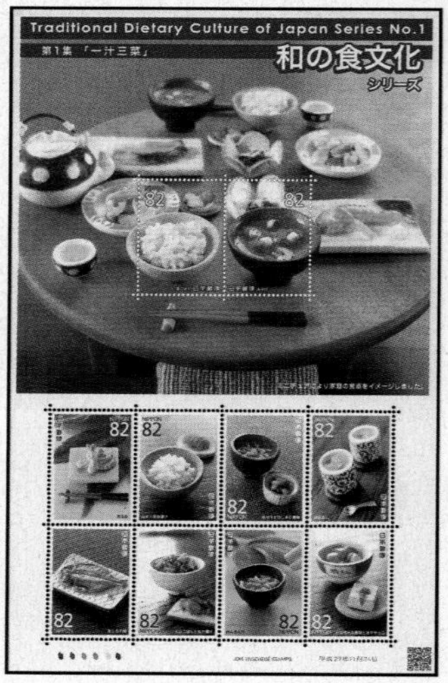

Japanese Foods — A3596

No. 3964: a, Chestnuts and rice. b, Miso soup. c, Shrimp tempura. d, Rice and Narazuke pickles. e, Miso soup and simmered seaweed. f, Steamed egg custard. g, Dried mackerel. h, Rice and Nukazuke pickles. i, Vegetable soup. j, Simmered pumpkin and cold tofu.

**2015, Nov. 24 Litho.** ***Perf. 13½***

| | | | | |
|---|---|---|---|---|
| **3964** | A3596 | Sheet of 10 | 14.00 | 14.00 |
| *a.-j.* | | 82y Any single | 1.40 | 1.10 |

Miniature Sheet

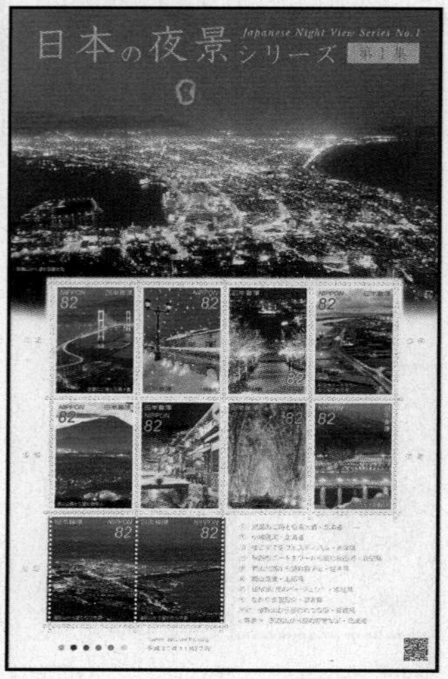

Japan at Night — A3597

No. 3965: a, Hakucho Bridge (stamp 1). b, Streetlight and buildings at Otaru Canal (stamp 2). c, Lighted trees at Hakodate Winter Festival, denomination at LR (stamp 3). d, Port of Akita and highway (stamp 4). e, Mount Iwate (stamp 5). f, Ginzan Onsen (stamp 6). g, Sendai Pageant of Starlight, denomination at UR (stamp 7). h, Nakayam Setsugekka (stamp 8). i, Center of Mutsu City (stamp 9). j, Mutsu City and harbor (stamp 10).

**2015, Nov. 27 Litho.** ***Perf. 13***

| | | | | |
|---|---|---|---|---|
| **3965** | A3597 | Sheet of 10 | 14.00 | 14.00 |
| *a.-j.* | | 82y Any single | 1.40 | 1.10 |

Miniature Sheet

Chiba Local Autonomy Law, 60th Anniv. — A3598

No. 3966: a, Tokyo Bay Aqua-line, rape blossoms (32x39mm). b, Character from Nanso Satomi Hakkenden (28x33mm). c, Inubosaki Lighthouse (28x33mm). d, Narita International Airport (28x33mm). e, Suigo Sawara Aquatic Botanical Garden (28x33mm).

***Perf. 13¼ (#3966a), 13x13¼***

**2015, Dec. 8 Photo.**

| | | | | |
|---|---|---|---|---|
| **3966** | A3598 | Sheet of 5 | 7.00 | 7.00 |
| *a.-e.* | | 82y Any single | 1.40 | 1.10 |

A3599

A3600

A3601

A3602

A3603

A3604

A3605

A3606

A3607

A3608

Candles
A3609

Girl Looking at Frosted Window
A3610

Snowglobe
A3611

House and Snowflakes
A3612

Snow-covered Trees
A3613

Bird in Cage
A3614

Poinsettia
A3615

Polar Bear
A3616

Reindeer in Forest
A3617

Ice Skater
A3618

***Die Cut Perf. 13x13¼***

**2015, Dec. 11** **Litho.**

**Self-Adhesive**

| | | | |
|---|---|---|---|
| **3967** | Sheet of 10 | 9.00 | |
| *a.* | A3599 52y multi | .90 | .70 |
| *b.* | A3600 52y multi | .90 | .70 |
| *c.* | A3601 52y multi | .90 | .70 |
| *d.* | A3602 52y multi | .90 | .70 |
| *e.* | A3603 52y multi | .90 | .70 |
| *f.* | A3604 52y multi | .90 | .70 |
| *g.* | A3605 52y multi | .90 | .70 |
| *h.* | A3606 52y multi | .90 | .70 |
| *i.* | A3607 52y multi | .90 | .70 |
| *j.* | A3608 52y multi | .90 | .70 |
| **3968** | Sheet of 10 | 14.00 | |
| *a.* | A3609 82y multi | 1.40 | 1.10 |
| *b.* | A3610 82y multi | 1.40 | 1.10 |
| *c.* | A3611 82y multi | 1.40 | 1.10 |
| *d.* | A3612 82y multi | 1.40 | 1.10 |
| *e.* | A3613 82y multi | 1.40 | 1.10 |
| *f.* | A3614 82y multi | 1.40 | 1.10 |
| *g.* | A3615 82y multi | 1.40 | 1.10 |
| *h.* | A3616 82y multi | 1.40 | 1.10 |
| *i.* | A3617 82y multi | 1.40 | 1.10 |
| *j.* | A3618 82y multi | 1.40 | 1.10 |

Phoenix Hall, Kyoto
A3619

State Guest House, Tokyo
A3620

**Photo. & Engr.**

**2016, Jan. 8** ***Perf. 13¼***

| | | | |
|---|---|---|---|
| **3969** | A3619 82y multi | 1.40 | 1.10 |
| **3970** | A3620 82y multi | 1.40 | 1.10 |
| *a.* | Vert. pair, #3969-3970 | 2.80 | 2.25 |

**Miniature Sheet**

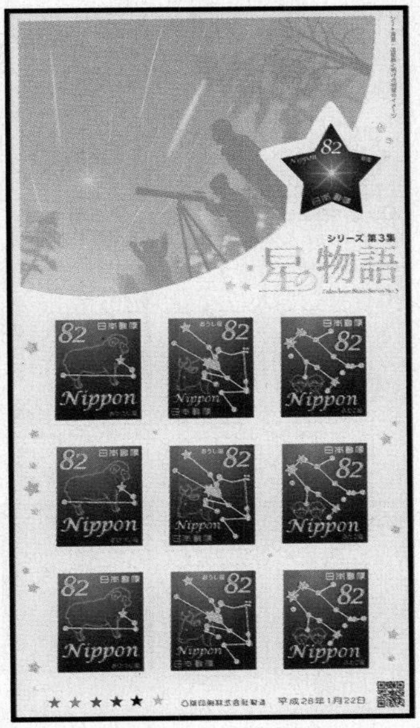
Astronomy — A3621

No. 3971: a, Morning star (26x36mm). b, Aries and ram (22x25mm). c, Taurus and bull (22x25mm). d, Gemini and twins (22x25mm).

***Die Cut Perf. 11 (#3971a), Die Cut Perf. 13x13¼***

**Litho. With Foil Application**

**2016, Jan. 22** **Self-Adhesive**

| | | | |
|---|---|---|---|
| **3971** | A3621 Sheet of 10, #3971a, 3 each #3971b-3971d | 14.00 | |
| *a.-d.* | 82y Any single | 1.40 | 1.10 |

**Souvenir Sheets**

Red Fuji, by Hokusai — A3622

Great Wave of Kanagawa, by Hokusai — A3623

No. 3972: a, Detail of Mount Fuji. b, Entire print.
No. 3973: a, Detail of wave. b, Entire print.

**Litho. & Embossed With Foil Application**

**2016, Jan. 29** ***Perf. 13¾x14***

| | | | |
|---|---|---|---|
| **3972** | A3622 Sheet of 2 | 65.00 | 65.00 |
| *a.-b.* | 1000y Either single | 32.50 | 32.50 |
| **3973** | A3623 Sheet of 2 | 65.00 | 65.00 |
| *a.-b.* | 1000y Either single | 32.50 | 32.50 |

Nos. 3972-3973 were only sold mounted in a booklet that sold for 8000y.

**Miniature Sheet**

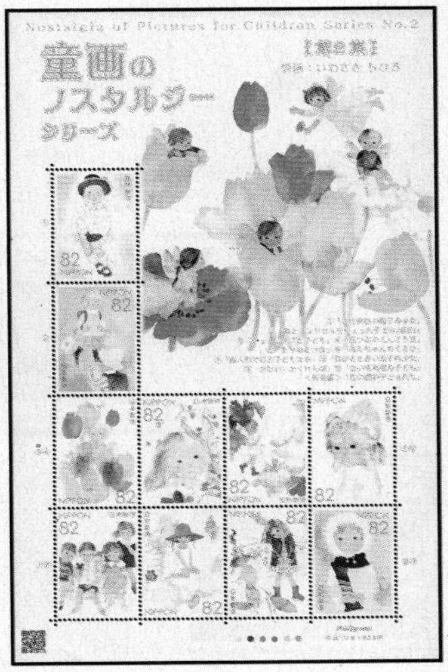
Children — A3624

No. 3974: a, Girl wearing dark brown hat. b, Cat and girl with red backpack. c, Child and tulips. d, Girl, peas and pea plant. e, Girl and irises. f, Child wearing blue bonnet. g, Four children with puppets. h, Girl wearing red hat, sea shells. i, Girl wearing red boots, hide and seek. j, Child wearing scarf and white knitted hat.

**2016, Jan. 29** **Litho.** ***Perf. 13***

| | | | |
|---|---|---|---|
| **3974** | A3624 Sheet of 10 | 14.00 | 14.00 |
| *a.-j.* | 82y Any single | 1.40 | 1.10 |

**Miniature Sheets**

A3625

Miffy — A3626

No. 3975: a, Miffy and Auntie Alice, plate of food (29x26mm). b, Miffy on bicycle (24x24mm). c, Miffy with hat over ears (23x29mm). d, Miffy with uncovered ears (23x29mm). e, Miffy and parents in car (24x24mm). f, Miffy writing letter (25mm diameter). g, Miffy and toys (24x24mm). h, Miffy and parent on chair (25mm diameter). i, Miffy holding plate of food (24x24mm). j, Miffy and other rabbits (35x20mm).

No. 3976: a, Miffy wearing orange dress (25x48mm). b, Miffy's father watering flowers (27x27mm). c, Miffy's mother with basket (27x27mm). d, Miffy wearing flowered dress (25mm diameter). e, Three rabbits and ball (25mm diameter). f, Angel (25mm diameter). g, Miffy wearing orange dress (25mm diameter). h, Miffy and father at dinner table (27x27mm). i, Miffy holding teddy bear (27x27mm). j, Miffy wearing flowered dress (25x48mm).

***Die Cut Perf. 12½ (#3975a, 3975j), Die Cut Perf. (3975c, 3975d, 3975f, 3975h), Die Cut Perf. 13¼x12½ (square stamps)***

**2016, Feb. 12** **Litho.**

**Self-Adhesive**

| | | | |
|---|---|---|---|
| **3975** | A3625 Sheet of 10 | 9.50 | |
| *a.-j.* | 52y Any single | .95 | .70 |

***Die Cut Perf. 12¼ (#3976a, 3976f), Die Cut Perf. (round stamps), Die Cut Perf. 13¼ (square stamps)***

| | | | |
|---|---|---|---|
| **3976** | A3626 Sheet of 10 | 15.00 | |
| *a.-j.* | 82y Any single | 1.50 | 1.10 |

Kototsuru of Nishizuchiya in Shinmachi, by Kiyonaga Torii
A3627

Idemi Beach at Sumiyoshi, Settsu Province, by Hiroshige Utagawa
A3628

Karakoto of the Chojiya, by Utamaro Kitagawa
A3629

Urami Waterfall at Nikko, Shimotsuke Province, by Hiroshige Utagawa
A3630

Eight Views of Genji: Komurasaki of the Tamaya, by Eizan Kikukawa
A3631

Cave Entrance at Enoshima, Sagami Province, by Hiroshige Utagawa
A3632

Hinazuru of Keizetsuro House, by Utamaro Kitagawa
A3633

Gokanosho, Higo Province, by Hiroshige Utagawa
A3634

Collection of Elegant Beauties: Mirror Stand, by Eizan Kikukawa
A3635

Maiko Beach, Harima Province, by Hiroshige Utagawa
A3636

**2016, Feb. 26** **Litho.** ***Perf. 13***

| | | | |
|---|---|---|---|
| **3977** | Sheet of 10 | 15.00 | 15.00 |
| *a.* | A3627 82y multi | 1.50 | 1.10 |
| *b.* | A3628 82y multi | 1.50 | 1.10 |
| *c.* | A3629 82y multi | 1.50 | 1.10 |
| *d.* | A3630 82y multi | 1.50 | 1.10 |
| *e.* | A3631 82y multi | 1.50 | 1.10 |
| *f.* | A3632 82y multi | 1.50 | 1.10 |
| *g.* | A3633 82y multi | 1.50 | 1.10 |
| *h.* | A3634 82y multi | 1.50 | 1.10 |
| *i.* | A3635 82y multi | 1.50 | 1.10 |
| *j.* | A3636 82y multi | 1.50 | 1.10 |

Cherry Blossom — A3637

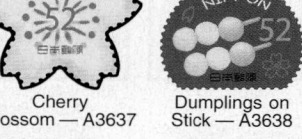

Dumplings on Stick — A3638

Blackberries and Blueberries
A3639

Blueberries and Raspberries
A3640

Teddy Bears — A3641

Cherry Blossom — A3642

Peach Blossoms — A3643

Letters and Bird — A3644

Strawberries
A3645

Owl and Teddy Bears
A3646

***Die Cut Perf. (#3978a), Die Cut Perf. 13 (#3978b); Die Cut Perf. 14***

**2016, Mar. 3** **Litho.**

**Self-Adhesive**

| | | | |
|---|---|---|---|
| **3978** | Sheet of 10, 2 each #3978a-3978e | 9.50 | |
| *a.* | A3637 52y multi | .95 | .70 |
| *b.* | A3638 52y multi | .95 | .70 |
| *c.* | A3639 52y multi | .95 | .70 |
| *d.* | A3640 52y multi | .95 | .70 |
| *e.* | A3641 52y multi | .95 | .70 |

***Die Cut Perf. (#3979a, 3979b, 3979d), Die Cut Perf. 14x13¼ (#3979c)***

| | | | |
|---|---|---|---|
| **3979** | Sheet of 10, 2 each #3979a-3979e | 15.00 | |
| *a.* | A3642 82y multi | 1.50 | 1.10 |
| *b.* | A3643 82y multi | 1.50 | 1.10 |
| *c.* | A3644 82y multi | 1.50 | 1.10 |
| *d.* | A3645 82y multi | 1.50 | 1.10 |
| *e.* | A3646 82y multi | 1.50 | 1.10 |

Hokkaido Shinkansen Train Facing Left — A3647

Port of Aomori, Hokkaido Shinkansen Train
A3648

Hirosaki Castle, Hokkaido Shinkansen Train
A3649

Cape Tappi, Hokkaido Shinkansen Train
A3650

Hokkaido Shinkansen Train Facing Right
A3651

Matsumae Castle, Hokkaido Shinkansen Train
A3652

Moss Phlox on Mt. Yakushi, Hokkaido Shinkansen Train
A3653

Tree-Lined Road and Trappist Monastery, Hokkaido Shinkansen Train
A3654

Hakodate, Hokkaido Shinkansen Train
A3655

Onuma Quasi-National Park, Hokkaido Shinkansen Train — A3656

***Perf. 13¼x12¾***

**2016, Mar. 25** **Litho.**

| | | | |
|---|---|---|---|
| **3980** | Sheet of 10 | 15.00 | 15.00 |
| *a.* | A3647 82y multi | 1.50 | 1.10 |
| *b.* | A3648 82y multi | 1.50 | 1.10 |
| *c.* | A3649 82y multi | 1.50 | 1.10 |
| *d.* | A3650 82y multi | 1.50 | 1.10 |
| *e.* | A3651 82y multi | 1.50 | 1.10 |
| *f.* | A3652 82y multi | 1.50 | 1.10 |
| *g.* | A3653 82y multi | 1.50 | 1.10 |
| *h.* | A3654 82y multi | 1.50 | 1.10 |
| *i.* | A3655 82y multi | 1.50 | 1.10 |
| *j.* | A3656 82y multi | 1.50 | 1.10 |

Opening of Hokkaido Shinkansen Line From Aomori to Hakodate

Columbines
A3657

Scabiosa
A3658

Moss Phlox
A3659

Cymbidium
A3660

Irises
A3661

Agapanthus
A3662

Carnations
A3663

Reeve's Spirea
A3664

Peruvian Lilies
A3665

Clematis
A3666

***Die Cut Perf. 14x14¼***

**2016, Apr. 1** **Litho.**

**Self-Adhesive**

| | | | |
|---|---|---|---|
| **3981** | Sheet of 10, 2 each #3981a-3981e | 9.50 | |
| *a.* | A3657 52y multi | .95 | .70 |
| *b.* | A3658 52y multi | .95 | .70 |
| *c.* | A3659 52y multi | .95 | .70 |
| *d.* | A3660 52y multi | .95 | .70 |
| *e.* | A3661 52y multi | .95 | .70 |
| **3982** | Sheet of 10, 2 each #3982a-3982e | 15.00 | |
| *a.* | A3662 82y multi | 1.50 | 1.10 |
| *b.* | A3663 82y multi | 1.50 | 1.10 |
| *c.* | A3664 82y multi | 1.50 | 1.10 |
| *d.* | A3665 82y multi | 1.50 | 1.10 |
| *e.* | A3666 82y multi | 1.50 | 1.10 |

Miniature Sheet

Castles — A3667

No. 3983: a, Goryokaku. b, Matsumoto Castle. c, Ueda Castle. d, Inuyama Castle. e, Osaka Castle. f, Hikone Castle. g, Marugame Castle. h, Himeji Castle. i, Matsuyama Castle. j, Matsue Castle.

**2016, Apr. 8** **Litho.** ***Perf. 13***

| | | | |
|---|---|---|---|
| **3983** | A3667 Sheet of 10 | 16.00 | 16.00 |
| *a.-j.* | 82y Any single | 1.60 | 1.25 |

Miniature Sheet

2016 G-7 Summit Ministers Meeting — A3668

No. 3984: a, Hiroshima Peace Memorial, Hiroshima. b, Shinano River and Bandai Bridge, Niigata. c, Ritsurin Garden, Takamatsu. d, Moji Port. e, Kurashiki Bikan Historical Quarter. f, Toyama Castle. g, Tsukuba Space Center. h, Equestrian statue, Sendai Castle Ruins. i, Port of Kobe. j, Shiraito Falls.

**2016, Apr. 8** **Photo.** ***Perf. 13***

| | | | |
|---|---|---|---|
| **3984** | A3668 Sheet of 10 | 16.00 | 16.00 |
| *a.-j.* | 82y Any single | 1.60 | 1.25 |

Miniature Sheet

Philately Week — A3669

No. 3985 — Various details of 16th century folding screen depicting Kyoto, by Eitoku Kano.

**2016, Apr. 20 Photo. *Perf. 13¼***

**3985** A3669 Sheet of 10 16.00 16.00
*a.-j.* 82y Any single 1.60 1.25

Miniature Sheets

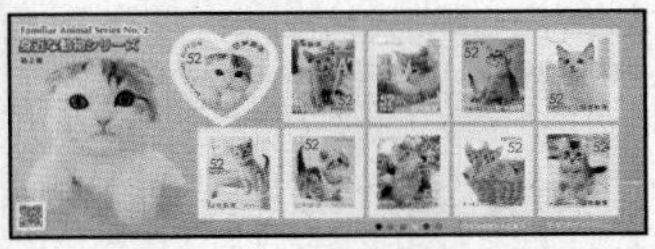

A3670

Cats — A3671

No. 3986: a, Scottish Fold cat (30x27mm). b, Russian Blue cat (22x26mm). c, Maine Coon cat (22x26mm). d, Abyssinian cat (22x26mm). e, Ragdoll cat (22x26mm). f, Ocicat (22x26mm). g, Munchkin cat (22x26mm). h, Persian cat (22x26mm). i, Two Tonkinese cats (22x26mm). j, American curl cat (22x26mm).

No. 3987: a, American shorthair cat (30x27mm). b, British shorthair cat (22x26mm). c, Norwegian Forest cat (22x26mm). d, Himalayan cat (22x26mm). e, Bengal cat (22x26mm). f, Singapura cats (22x26mm). g, Somali cat (22x26mm). h, Chartreux cat (22x26mm). i, Ragamuffin cat (22x26mm). j, Siamese cat (22x26mm).

***Die Cut Perf. (#3986a, 3987a), Die Cut Perf. 13x13¼***

**2016, Apr. 22 Litho.**

**Self-Adhesive**

**3986** A3670 Sheet of 10 10.00
*a.-j.* 52y Any single 1.00 .75
**3987** A3671 Sheet of 10 16.00
*a.-j.* 82y Any single 1.60 1.25

Miniature Sheet

2016 G-7 Summit — A3672

No. 3988: a, Pearls and Ago Bay, denomination at UL. b, Pearls and Ago Bay, denomination at UR. c, Snowy plover. d, Uji Bridge. e, Uji Bridge and Isuzu River. f, Japanese iris. g, Japanese spiny lobster. h, Wedded Rocks, Ise-Shima National Park. i, Cape Daio Lighthouse. j, Ise katagami and Iga kumihimo fabric crafting.

**2016, Apr. 26 Photo. *Perf. 13½***

**3988** A3672 Sheet of 10 16.00 16.00
*a.-j.* 82y Any single 1.60 1.25

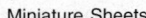

99th Lions Club International Convention, Fukuoka — A3673

**2016, May 6 Litho. *Perf. 13***

**3989** A3673 82y multi 1.50 1.10

Miniature Sheet

Fukushima Local Autonomy Law, 60th Anniv. — A3674

No. 3990: a, Hideyo Noguchi (1876-1928), bacteriologist, Mt. Bandai, Lake Inawashiro (32x39mm). b, Red cow and Okiagari-koboshi dolls (28x33mm). c, Waterfall cherry tree, Miharu (28x33mm). d, Obori Soma pottery (28x33mm). e, Aquamarine Fukushima (28x33mm).

***Perf. 13¼ (#3990a), 13x13¼***

**2016, May 11 Litho.**

**3990** A3674 Sheet of 5 7.50 7.50
*a.-e.* 82y Any single 1.50 1.10

Miniature Sheets

A3675

Sanrio Characters — A3676

No. 3991: a, Hello Kitty, lavender gray stripes (29x26mm heart). b, Hello Kitty, pale blue stripes (23x23mm). c, Hello Kitty, rose pink stripes (27x22mm). d, Hello Kitty, doily (29mm diameter). e, My Melody (22x30mm oval). f, My Melody, rose pink background (23x23mm). g, Little Twin Stars (22x28mm). h, Little Twin Stars, diff, (29x26mm heart). i, Pompompurin, rose pink background (29mm diameter). j, Pompompurin, pale blue background (23x23mm).

No. 3992: a, Hello Kitty, pale blue stripes (22x28mm). b, Hello Kitty, rose pink stripes (22x30mm oval). c, Hello Kitty, rose red background (29x26mm heart). d, Hello Kitty, rose pink stripes and pale blue circle (29mm diameter). e, My Melody, rose pink stripes (23x23mm). f, My Melody (29x26mm heart). g, Little Twin Stars, (27x22mm). h, Little Twin Stars (23x23mm). i, Pompompurin (29mm diameter). j, Pompompurin, pale orange stripes (27x22mm).

***Die Cut Perf. (#3991a, 3991c, 3991h, 3991i), Die Cut Perf. 14 (#3991b, 3991f, 3991j), Die Cut Perf. 12¼x11¾ (#3991c), Die Cut Perf. 13 (#3991e), Die Cut Perf12¾x13¼ (#3991g)***

**2016, May 13 Litho.**

**Self-Adhesive**

**3991** A3675 Sheet of 10 9.50
*a.-j.* 52y Any single .95 .70

***Die Cut Perf. 13¼x12¾ (#3992a), Die Cut Perf. 13 (#3992b), Die Cut Perf. 14 (#3992e), Die Cut Perf. 13¼x14 (#3992g, 3992j), Die Cut Perf. 13½ (#3992h), Die Cut Perf.***

**3992** A3676 Sheet of 10 15.00
*a.-j.* 82y Any single 1.50 1.10

Tangerine A3677

Japanese Ginger A3678

Perilla Leaf — A3679

Ginkgo Nuts — A3680

Potato A3681

Kabocha Squash A3682

Red and Yellow Peppers A3683

Fava Beans A3684

Kumquats A3685

Blueberries A3686

***Die Cut Perf, 13¼x13 (#3993a, 3994a, 3994b), Die Cut Perf. 13x13¼***

**2016, May 20 Litho.**

**Self-Adhesive**

**3993** Sheet of 10, 2 each #3993a-3993e 9.50
*a.* A3677 52y multi .95 .70
*b.* A3678 52y multi .95 .70
*c.* A3679 52y multi .95 .70
*d.* A3680 52y multi .95 .70
*e.* A3681 52y multi .95 .70

| | | | | |
|---|---|---|---|---|
| 3994 | Sheet of 10, 2 each #3994a-3994e | 15.00 | | |
| a. | A3682 82y multi | 1.50 | 1.10 |
| b. | A3683 82y multi | 1.50 | 1.10 |
| c. | A3684 82y multi | 1.50 | 1.10 |
| d. | A3685 82y multi | 1.50 | 1.10 |
| e. | A3686 82y multi | 1.50 | 1.10 |

Souvenir Sheet

2016 G-7 Summit — A3687

No. 3995 — Pearls and Ago Bay with denomination over: a, White area, b, Colored area.

**Litho. With Foil Application**

**2016, May 26** ***Perf. 14¼***

**Printed on Silk**

| | | | | |
|---|---|---|---|---|
| 3995 | A3687 Sheet of 2 | 24.00 | 24.00 |
| a.-b. | 500y Either single | 12.00 | 12.00 |

No. 3995 sold for 1300y.

Miniature Sheet

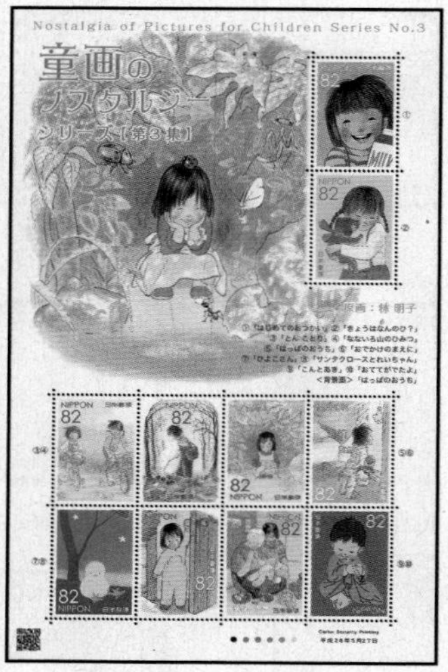


Children — A3688

No. 3996: a, Child with milk container. b, Girl hugging puppy. c, Children on bicycles with training wheels. d, Child poking mushrooms with stick. e, Girl crouched in foliage. f, Child holding doll opening curtain. g, Chick under tree. h, Child opening door. i, Grandmother repairing teddy bear for girl. j, Child in too-large orange kimono.

**2016, May 27** **Litho.** ***Perf. 12¾x13***

| | | | | |
|---|---|---|---|---|
| 3996 | A3688 Sheet of 10 | 15.00 | 15.00 |
| a.-j. | 82y Any single | 1.50 | 1.10 |

Miniature Sheet

National Afforestation — A3689

No. 3825: a, Takato winter-flowering cherry blossoms. b, Nikko fir. c, Chestnut. d, Gentian. e, Lisianthus. f, Japanese rowan. g, Japanese larch. h, Japanese white birch trees. i, Rape blossoms. j, Apple blossoms.

**2016, June 3** **Litho.** ***Perf. 13***

| | | | | |
|---|---|---|---|---|
| 3997 | A3689 Sheet of 10 | 10.00 | 10.00 |
| a.-j. | 52y Any single | 1.00 | .75 |

Miniature Sheet

Tokyo Local Autonomy Law, 60th Anniv. — A3690

No. 3998: a, Tokyo Tower, Rainbow Bridge and gulls (32x39mm). b, Eastern Sea Road 53 Stations, Morning Scene at Nihonbashi, by Hiroshige (28x33mm). c, Mt. Takao Yakuoin Izuna Gongen Hall (28x33mm). d, Camellia, Mt. Mihara (28x33mm). e, Ogasawara Islands and Ogi Pond (28x33mm).

***Perf. 13¼ (#3998a), 13x13¼***

**2016, June 7** **Litho.**

| | | | | |
|---|---|---|---|---|
| 3998 | A3690 Sheet of 5 | 8.00 | 8.00 |
| a.-e. | 82y Any single | 1.60 | 1.25 |

White Frangipani Flower A3695

White and Red Frangipani Flowers A3696

Sunlight Reflected Off Water A3697

Palm Trees A3698

Hibiscus — A3699

Sunflower A3700

Two Seashells A3701

Seashell A3702

Drink in Glass A3703

Palm Trees A3704

Hibiscus A3705

Clouds — A3706

***Die Cut Perf. 13¼, Die Cut Perf. 12 (#4000e, 4000f, 4001a, 4001b)***

**2016, June 10** **Litho.**

**Self-Adhesive**

| | | | | |
|---|---|---|---|---|
| 4000 | Sheet of 10, 2 each #4000a-4000d, 1 each #4000e, 4000f | 10.00 | | |
| a. | A3695 52y multi | 1.00 | .75 |
| b. | A3696 52y multi | 1.00 | .75 |
| c. | A3697 52y multi | 1.00 | .75 |
| d. | A3698 52y multi | 1.00 | .75 |
| e. | A3699 52y multi | 1.00 | .75 |
| f. | A3700 52y multi | 1.00 | .75 |
| 4001 | Sheet of 10, 1 each #4001a, 4001b, 2 each #4001c-4001f | 16.00 | |
| a. | A3701 82y multi | 1.60 | 1.25 |
| b. | A3702 82y multi | 1.60 | 1.25 |
| c. | A3703 82y multi | 1.60 | 1.25 |
| d. | A3704 82y multi | 1.60 | 1.25 |
| e. | A3705 82y multi | 1.60 | 1.25 |
| f. | A3706 82y multi | 1.60 | 1.25 |

Miniature Sheets

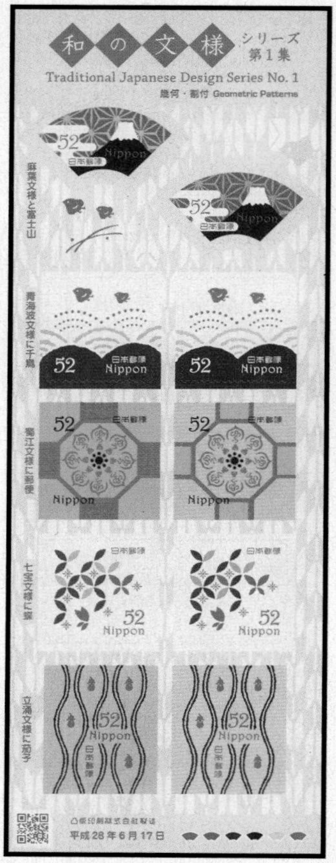


A3707

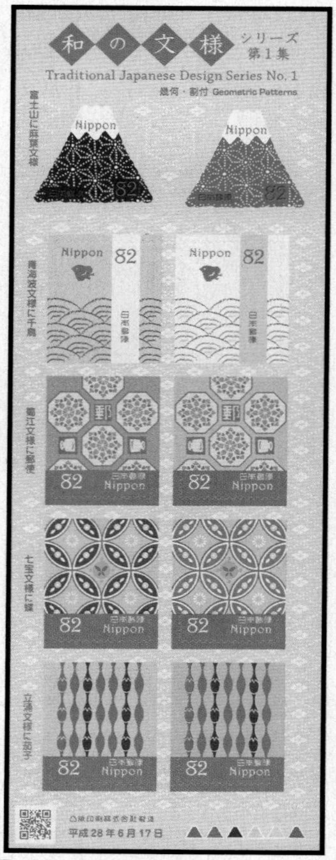


Traditional Japanese Designs — A3708

No. 4002: a, Fan with Mt. Fuji, dull green background (33x19mm). b, As "a", light purple background (33x19mm). c, Birds and waves, blue bottom panel (23x23mm). d, As "c," purple bottom panel (23x23mm). e, Octagon, apple green background (23x23mm). f, As "e," pale peach background (23x23mm). g, Flowers, blue green, light blue and gold petals (23x23mm). h, As "g," blue green, rose pink and gold petals (23x23mm). i, Eggplants and wavy lines, light blue background (22x26mm). j, As "i," lilac background (22x26mm).

No. 4003: a, Dark blue Mt. Fuji (30x25mm). b, Bright blue Mt. Fuji (30x25mm). c, Bird and waves, light blue background (22x26mm). d, As "c," pink panel (22x26mm). e, Octagons, sage green background (22x26mm). f, As "e," pink background (22x26mm). g, Interlocking circles, beige background (22x26mm). h, As "g," light blue background (22x26mm). i, Eggplants and wavy lines, pink background (22x26mm). j, As "i," orange yellow background (22x26mm).

***Die Cut Perf. 12¾ (#4002a, 4002b), Die Cut Perf. 14, Die Cut Perf. 13¼ (#4002i, 4002j)***

**2016, June 17** **Litho.**

**Self-Adhesive**

| | | | | |
|---|---|---|---|---|
| **4002** | A3707 Sheet of 10 | 10.00 | | |
| *a.-j.* | 52y Any single | 1.00 | .75 | |

***Die Cut Perf. 13 (#4003a, 4003b), Die Cut Perf. 13x13¼***

| | | | |
|---|---|---|---|
| **4003** | A3708 Sheet of 10 | 16.00 | |
| *a.-j.* | 82y Any single | 1.60 | 1.25 |

Miniature Sheets

A3709

Doraemon Characters — A3710

No. 4004: a, Doraemon carrying mailbox (19x27mm oval ). b, Doraemon holding stamp (20x23mm). c, Doraemon delivering letter (20x24mm). d, Dorami, yellow background with white polka dots (25mm diameter). e, Doraemon, Nobita and Shizuka (31x31mm). f, Doraemon eating (20x23mm). g, Dorami winking (20x23mm). h, Nobita writing letter (20x23mm). i, Shizuka reading letter (20x23mm). j, Doraemon licking lips (19x27mm oval).

No. 4005: a, Doraemon with bamboo helicopter on head (21x29mm oval). b, Doraemon and time cloth (21x29mm oval). c, Doraemon in pass-through loop (22x26mm). d, Doraemon shining light on Nobita (22x26mm). e, Doraemon and Nobita on time machine (31x28mm). f, Doraemon in Anywhere Door (30x37mm). g, Doraemon with open mouth (25mm diameter). h, Doraemon with closed mouth (25mm diameter). i, Doraemon with raised paws (25mm diameter). j, Doraemon licking lips (25mm diameter).

***Die Cut Perf. 13 (#4004a, 4004j), Die Cut Perf. 14¼x14½, Die Cut Perf. 12½ (#4004c, 4004e), Die Cut Perf. (#4004d)***

**2016, July 1** **Litho.**

**Self-Adhesive**

| | | | |
|---|---|---|---|
| **4004** | A3709 Sheet of 10 | 10.00 | |
| *a.-j.* | 52y Any single | 1.00 | .75 |

***Die Cut Perf. 13¾ (#4005a, 4005b), Die Cut Perf. 13x13¼ (#4005c, 4005d), Die Cut Perf. 13 (#4005e), Die Cut Perf. 12¾x13 (#4005f), Die Cut Perf.***

| | | | |
|---|---|---|---|
| **4005** | A3710 Sheet of 10 | 16.00 | |
| *a.-j.* | 82y Any single | 1.60 | 1.25 |

Miniature Sheet

Japan's Meiji Industrial Revolution Iron, Steel, Shipbuilding and Coal Mining UNESCO World Heritage Site — A3711

No. 4006: a, Former office of Yawata Steel Works, denomination at UR (stamp 1). b, Onga River Pumping Station, denomination at LL (stamp 2). c, Hagi Reverberatory Furnace, denomination at UL (stamp 3). d, Shuseikan Industrial Comples, denomination at LL (stamp 4). e, Nirayama Reverberatory Furnace, denomination at UR (stamp 5). f, Hashino Iron Mining and Smelting Site, denomination at UR (stamp 6). g, Mietsu Naval Dock Ruins, denomination at LL (stamp 7). h, Kosuge Slip Dock, denomination at LL (stamp 8). i, Misumi West Port, denomination at UL (stamp 9). j, Aerial view of Miike Port, denomination at UR (stamp 10).

**2016, July 8** **Litho.** ***Perf. 13***

| | | | |
|---|---|---|---|
| **4006** | A3711 Sheet of 10 | 16.00 | 16.00 |
| *a.-j.* | 82y Any single | 1.60 | 1.25 |

Amaryllises A3712

Narcissi A3713

Pine Tree, Sarcandra Glabra, and Ornamental Kale A3714

Statice and Dendrobium Orchids A3715

Dahlias A3716

Roses A3717

Cockscombs A3718

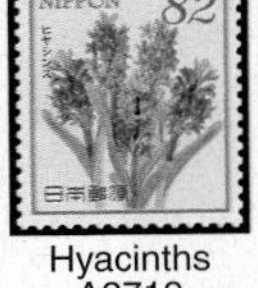

Hyacinths A3719

Chrysanthemums A3720

Nerines A3721

***Die Cut Perf. 14***

**2016, July 15** **Litho.**

**Self-Adhesive**

| | | | |
|---|---|---|---|
| **4007** | Sheet of 10, 2 each #4007a-4007e | 10.00 | |
| *a.* | A3712 52y multi | 1.00 | .75 |
| *b.* | A3713 52y multi | 1.00 | .75 |
| *c.* | A3714 52y multi | 1.00 | .75 |
| *d.* | A3715 52y multi | 1.00 | .75 |
| *e.* | A3716 52y multi | 1.00 | .75 |
| **4008** | Sheet of 10, 2 each #4008a-4008e | 16.00 | |
| *a.* | A3717 82y multi | 1.60 | 1.25 |
| *b.* | A3718 82y multi | 1.60 | 1.25 |
| *c.* | A3719 82y multi | 1.60 | 1.25 |
| *d.* | A3720 82y multi | 1.60 | 1.25 |
| *e.* | A3721 82y multi | 1.60 | 1.25 |

Letter Writing Day — A3722

Designs: No. 4009, Pen nibs. No. 4010, Tape rolls and strips. No. 4011, Erasers. No. 4012, Pencils. No. 4013, Paper clips. No. 4014, Three envelopes. No. 4015, Crayons. No. 4016, Fountain pens. No. 4017, Colored pencils. No. 4018, Two long envelopes.

***Die Cut Perf. 13x13¼***

**2016, July 22** **Litho.**

**Booklet Stamps**

**Self-Adhesive**

| | | | |
|---|---|---|---|
| **4009** | A3722 52y multi | 1.00 | .75 |
| **4010** | A3722 52y multi | 1.00 | .75 |
| **4011** | A3722 52y multi | 1.00 | .75 |
| **4012** | A3722 52y multi | 1.00 | .75 |
| **4013** | A3722 52y multi | 1.00 | .75 |
| *a.* | Booklet pane of 10, 2 each #4009-4013 | 10.00 | |
| **4014** | A3722 82y multi | 1.60 | 1.25 |
| **4015** | A3722 82y multi | 1.60 | 1.25 |
| **4016** | A3722 82y multi | 1.60 | 1.25 |
| **4017** | A3722 82y multi | 1.60 | 1.25 |
| **4018** | A3722 82y multi | 1.60 | 1.25 |
| *a.* | Booklet pane of 10, 2 each #4014-4018 | 16.00 | |
| | *Nos. 4009-4018 (10)* | 13.00 | 10.00 |

Toji of the Ogiya, Kamuro, Satoji and Uraji, by Kiyonaga Torii A3723

Mt. Otoko at Hirakata, Kawachi Province, by Hiroshige Utagawa A3724

The Maiden at the Dojo Temple, by Yukimaro Kitagawa A3725

Bonito Fishing at Sea, Tosa Province, by Hiroshige Utagawa A3726

The Brine Maidens, by Kiyonaga Torii A3727

Mt. Asama, Teahouse on the Mountain Pass, Ise Province, by Hiroshige Utagawa A3728

Tsukioka of the Hyogo House, by Eisui Ichirakutei A3729

The Takuhi Shrine, Oki Province, by Hiroshige Utagawa A3730

Good Relations Between Siblings, by Utamaro Kitagawa A3731

The Weir in the Shallows, Chikugo Province, by Hiroshige Utagawa A3732

**2016, July 29** **Litho.** ***Perf. 13***

| | | | |
|---|---|---|---|
| **4019** | Sheet of 10 | 16.00 | 16.00 |
| *a.* | A3723 82y multi | 1.60 | 1.25 |
| *b.* | A3724 82y multi | 1.60 | 1.25 |
| *c.* | A3725 82y multi | 1.60 | 1.25 |
| *d.* | A3726 82y multi | 1.60 | 1.25 |
| *e.* | A3727 82y multi | 1.60 | 1.25 |
| *f.* | A3728 82y multi | 1.60 | 1.25 |
| *g.* | A3729 82y multi | 1.60 | 1.25 |
| *h.* | A3730 82y multi | 1.60 | 1.25 |
| *i.* | A3731 82y multi | 1.60 | 1.25 |
| *j.* | A3732 82y multi | 1.60 | 1.25 |

Miniature Sheet

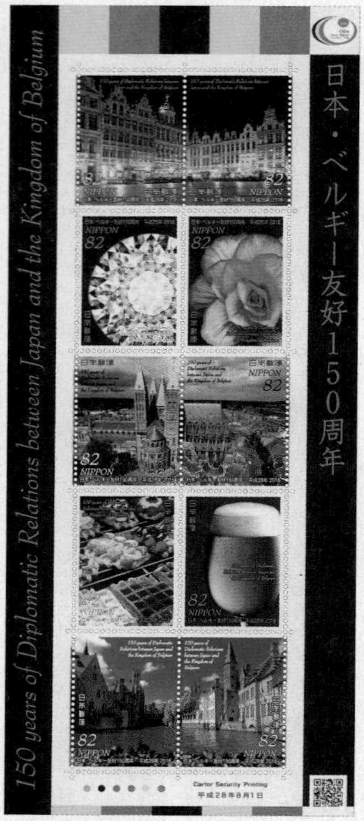


Diplomatic Relations Between Japan and Belgium, 150th Anniv. — A3733

No. 4006: a, Grand Place, Brussels, at night, denomination at LL. b, Grand Place, at night, denomination at LR. c, Cut diamond. d, Begonia. e, Notre Dame Cathedral, Tournai, Belgium, denomination at LL. f, Notre Dame Cathedral, Tournai, denomination at UR. g, Belgian waffles. h, Beer. i, Historic Center of Bruges, denomination at LL. j, Historic Center of Bruges, denomination at LR.

**2016, Aug. 1 Litho. *Perf. 13***

| | | | | |
|---|---|---|---|---|
| **4020** | A3733 | Sheet of 10 | 16.00 | 16.00 |
| *a.-j.* | | 82y Any single | 1.60 | 1.25 |

Miniature Sheets

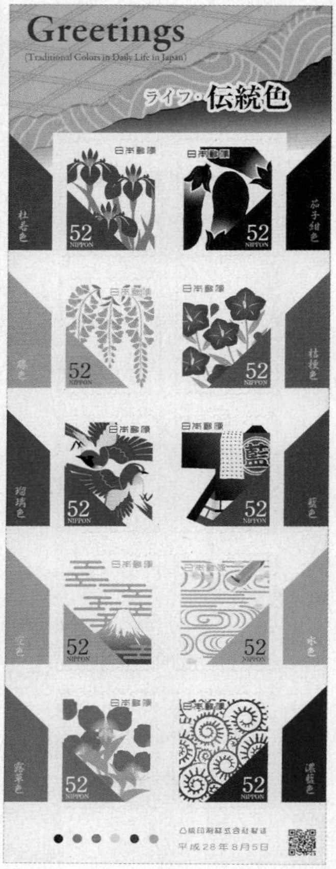


A3734

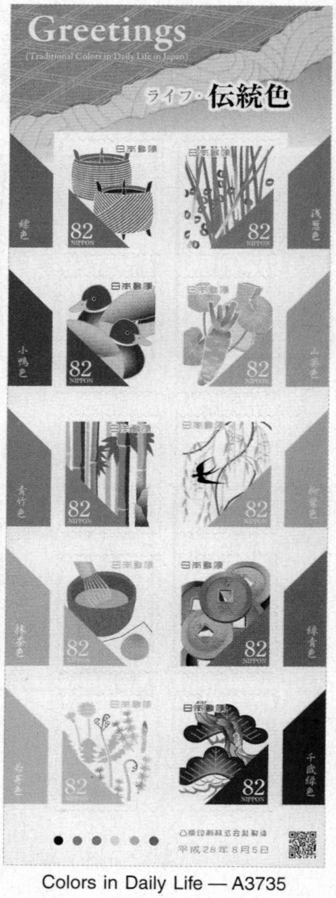


Colors in Daily Life — A3735

No. 4021: a, Japanese irises. b, Eggplants. c, Wisteria. d, Bellflowers. e, Blue birds. f, Hanten (short coat). g, Mt. Fuji. h, Bamboo boat and cherry blossoms in water. i, Asiatic dayflower. j, Octopus arabesque pattern.

No. 4022: a, Yarn on holders. b, Green onions. c, Mallards. d, Wasabi and grater. e, Bamboo. f, Bird and willow tree. g, Green tea and confection. h, Old Japanese coins. i, Dandelions, fiddleheads and horsetails. j, Pine tree.

***Die Cut Perf. 13x13¼***

**2016, Aug. 5 Litho.**

**Self-Adhesive**

| | | | | |
|---|---|---|---|---|
| **4021** | A3734 | Sheet of 10 | 10.00 | |
| *a.-j.* | | 52y Any single | 1.00 | .75 |
| **4022** | A3735 | Sheet of 10 | 16.00 | |
| *a.-j.* | | 82y Any single | 1.60 | 1.25 |

Miniature Sheet

Mountain Day — A3736

No. 4023: a, Daisetsuzan. b, Hokkaido crying rabbit. c, Mt. Iwate. d, Komakusa flowers. e, Mt. Yari. f, Yarigatake Eastern Blue butterfly. g, Daisen. h, Daisen yellow violet. i, Kuju Mountain Range. j, Hooaka bird.

**2016, Aug. 10 Litho. *Perf. 13x13¼***

| | | | | |
|---|---|---|---|---|
| **4023** | A3736 | Sheet of 10 | 16.00 | 16.00 |
| *a.-j.* | | 82y Any single | 1.60 | 1.25 |

Miniature Sheets

A3737

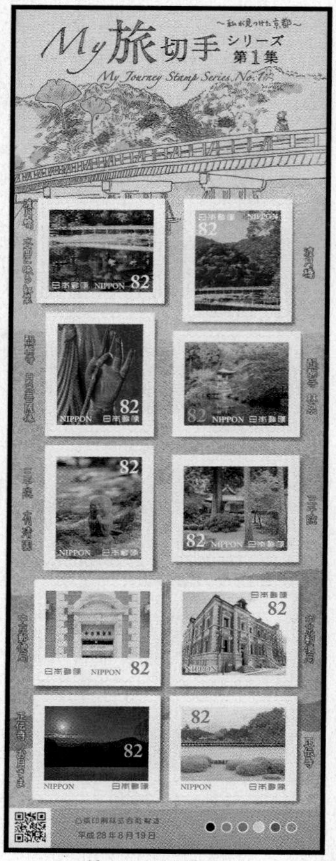


Kyoto Area Tourist Attractions — A3738

No. 4024: a, Kiyomizudera, denomination in white at LL. b, Kiyomizudera, denominaiton in white at LR, horiz. c, Sannenzaka, denomination in orange red at LL, horiz. d, Sannenzaka, denomination in white at LR, horiz. e, Nanzen-ji interior, denomination in pink at UR. f, Nanzen-ji exterior, denomination at LL, horiz. g, Shisen-do sands, denomination in magenta at LR, horiz. h, Shisen-do, denomination in yellow green at LR. i, Hanamikoji Dori, denomination in black at LL. j, Hanamikoji Dori at night, denomination in white at LL.

No. 4025: a, Togetsu-kyo, denomination in white at LR, horiz. b, Togetsu-kyo, denominaiton in white at UL. c, Daigo-ji statue of Buddha, denomination in white at LR. d, Daigo-ji hall, denomination in rose at LL, horiz. e, Sanzen-in, denomination in white at UR. f, Sanzen-in, denomination in white at LL, horiz. g, Nakagyo Post Office doorway, denomination in red at LR, horiz. h, Nakagyo Post Office, denomination in red at UR, horiz. i, Shoden-ji at night, denomination in azure at right, horiz. j, Shoden-ji, denomination in red at UL.

***Die Cut Perf. 13x13¼ (vert. stamps), Die Cut Perf. 13¼x13***

**2016, Aug. 19** **Litho.**

**Self-Adhesive**

| | | | | |
|---|---|---|---|---|
| **4024** | A3737 | Sheet of 10 | 10.00 | |
| *a.-j.* | | 52y Any single | 1.00 | .75 |
| **4025** | A3738 | Sheet of 10 | 16.00 | |
| *a.-j.* | | 82y Any single | 1.60 | 1.25 |

Miniature Sheet

Diplomatic Relations Between Japan and Italy, 150th Anniv. — A3739

No. 4026: a, Silkworm cocoons on mulberry leaves. b, Red silk. c, Madonna of the Yarnwinder, by Leonardo da Vinci. d, Maria de'Medici, by Agnolo Bronzino. e, Basil leaves and mozzarella cheese. f, Mozzarella cheese and tomatoes. g, Madonna of the Book, by Sandro Botticelli. h, Boy with a Basket of Fruit, by Caravaggio. i, Val d'Orcia, Trulli of Alberobello. j, Trulli of Alberobello, Florence Cathedral.

**2016, Aug. 25** **Litho.** ***Perf. 13***

| | | | | |
|---|---|---|---|---|
| **4026** | A3739 | Sheet of 10 | 16.00 | 16.00 |
| *a.-j.* | | 82y Any single | 1.60 | 1.25 |

Fish A3740

Crane and Tortoise A3741

Mt. Fuji in Blue A3742

Fish A3743

Owl A3744

Mt. Fuji in Gold A3745

Bird and Flowers A3746

Balloons A3747

Bird of Ribbon A3748

G Clef, Notes and Stars A3749

Rose A3750

Flower Bouquet A3751

Bells A3752

Lilies and Ribbon A3753

***Die Cut Perf. 14, Die Cut Perf. (#4030a, 4030c)***

**2016, Aug. 26** **Litho.**

**Self-Adhesive**

| | | | |
|---|---|---|---|
| **4027** | Sheet of 10, 4 each #4027a-4027b, 2 #4027c | 10.00 | |
| *a.* | A3740 52y multi | 1.00 | .75 |
| *b.* | A3741 52y multi | 1.00 | .75 |
| *c.* | A3742 52y multi | 1.00 | .75 |
| **4028** | Sheet of 10, 4 each #4028a-4028b, 2 #4028c | 16.00 | |
| *a.* | A3743 82y multi | 1.60 | 1.25 |
| *b.* | A3744 82y multi | 1.60 | 1.25 |
| *c.* | A3745 82y multi | 1.60 | 1.25 |
| **4029** | Sheet of 10, 4 #4029b, 2 each #4029a, 4029c, 4029d | 16.00 | |
| *a.* | A3746 82y multi | 1.60 | 1.25 |
| *b.* | A3747 82y multi | 1.60 | 1.25 |
| *c.* | A3748 82y multi | 1.60 | 1.25 |
| *d.* | A3749 82y multi | 1.60 | 1.25 |
| **4030** | Sheet of 10, 4 #4030a, 2 each #4030b, 4030c, 4030d | 16.00 | |
| *a.* | A3750 92y multi | 1.75 | 1.40 |
| *b.* | A3751 92y multi | 1.75 | 1.40 |
| *c.* | A3752 92y multi | 1.75 | 1.40 |
| *d.* | A3753 92y multi | 1.75 | 1.40 |

Miniature Sheet

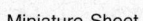

71st National Athletic Meet, Iwate — A3754

No. 4026: a, Rugby. b, Field hockey. c, Triathlon. d, Wrestling. e, Naginatajutsu. f, Boxing. g, Soccer. h, Tennis. i, Basketball. j, Baseball.

**2016, Sept. 1** **Litho.** ***Perf. 13***

| | | | | |
|---|---|---|---|---|
| **4031** | A3754 | Sheet of 10 | 16.00 | 16.00 |
| *a.-j.* | | 82y Any single | 1.60 | 1.25 |

Flower Pots on Trellis A3755

Potted Tree and Flowers A3756

Trellis, Potted Plants, Watering Can A3757

Seeds, Lantern, Gardening Tools A3758

Watering Can, Plant Labels, Shovel, Gloves A3759

Roses, Pastry Carrier, Tea Cup A3760

Hanging Flower Basket A3761

Garden A3762

Rose Trellis A3763

Potted Tree and Roses A3764

***Die Cut Perf. 14, Die Cut Perf. (#4033a, 4033b)***

**2016, Sept. 9** **Litho.**

**Self-Adhesive**

| | | | |
|---|---|---|---|
| **4032** | Sheet of 10, 2 each #4032a-4032e | 10.00 | |
| *a.* | A3755 52y multi | 1.00 | .75 |
| *b.* | A3756 52y multi | 1.00 | .75 |
| *c.* | A3757 52y multi | 1.00 | .75 |
| *d.* | A3758 52y multi | 1.00 | .75 |
| *e.* | A3759 52y multi | 1.00 | .75 |
| **4033** | Sheet of 10, 2 each #4033a-4033e | 16.00 | |
| *a.* | A3760 82y multi | 1.60 | 1.25 |
| *b.* | A3761 82y multi | 1.60 | 1.25 |
| *c.* | A3762 82y multi | 1.60 | 1.25 |
| *d.* | A3763 82y multi | 1.60 | 1.25 |
| *e.* | A3764 82y multi | 1.60 | 1.25 |

Teddy Bear Postman Delivering Letter A3765

Teddy Bear Holding Letter A3766

Owl at Table A3767

Teddy Bear at Table A3768

Two Teddy Bears — A3769

Beige Teddy Bear — A3770

Gray Teddy Bear — A3771

Brown Teddy Bear — A3772

Blue Teddy Bear A3773

Teddy Bears and Mailbox A3774

***Die Cut Perf. 12, Die Cut Perf. (#4034e)***

**2016, Sept. 16 — Litho.**

**Self-Adhesive**

| | | | |
|---|---|---|---|
| **4034** | Sheet of 10, 2 each #4034a-4034e | 10.00 | |
| *a.* | A3765 52y multi | 1.00 | .75 |
| *b.* | A3766 52y multi | 1.00 | .75 |
| *c.* | A3767 52y multi | 1.00 | .75 |
| *d.* | A3768 52y multi | 1.00 | .75 |
| *e.* | A3769 52y multi | 1.00 | .75 |

***Die Cut Perf. 12½, Die Cut Perf. 12x11¾ (#4035e)***

| | | | |
|---|---|---|---|
| **4035** | Sheet of 10, 2 each #4035a-4035e | 16.00 | |
| *a.* | A3770 82y multi | 1.60 | 1.25 |
| *b.* | A3771 82y multi | 1.60 | 1.25 |
| *c.* | A3772 82y multi | 1.60 | 1.25 |
| *d.* | A3773 82y multi | 1.60 | 1.25 |
| *e.* | A3774 82y multi | 1.60 | 1.25 |

A sheet of five self-adhesive stamps depicting teddy bears (three denominated 82y and two denominated 120y) was printed in limited quantities and sold only in a package containing stationery.

Miniature Sheet

Kamikochi Natural Monument — A3775

No. 4036: a, Japanese rock ptarmigan (stamp 1). b, Japanese robin (stamp 2). c, Japanese dormouse (stamp 3). d, Japanese serow (stamp 4). e, Lilium medeoloides (stamp 5). f, Trollius riederianus var. japonicus (stamp 6). g, Chickweed wintergreen (stamp 7). h, Poplar admiral butterfly (stamp 8). i, Orange tip butterfly (stamp 9). j, Moorland clouded yellow butterfly (stamp 10).

**2016, Sept. 23 — Litho. — *Perf. 13***

| | | | |
|---|---|---|---|
| **4036** | A3775 Sheet of 10 | 16.00 | 16.00 |
| *a.-j.* | 82y Any single | 1.60 | 1.25 |

Miniature Sheet

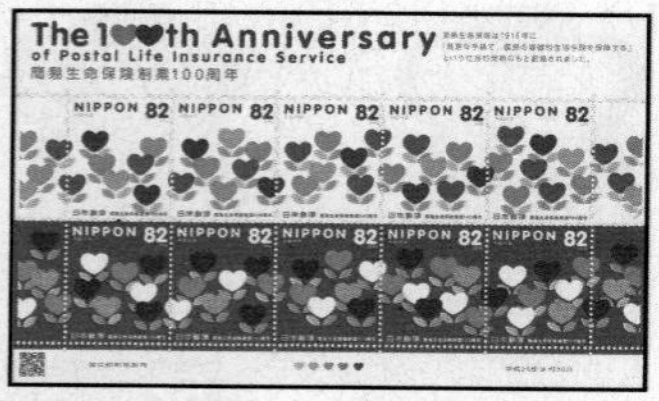

Postal Life Insurance Service, Cent. — A3776

No. 4037 — Heart-shaped flowers: a, Blue denomination, pink flower at bottom. b, Blue denomination, pink flower at top. c, Blue denomination, pink flower left of center. d, Blue denomination, pink flower at center. e, Blue denomination, pink flower at right. f, White denomination, pink flower at LL. below dark blue flower. g, White denomination, pink flower at bottom to right of white flower. h, White denomination, pink flower partly covered by dark blue flower. i, White denomination, pink flower at UR. j, White denomination, pink flower at LR.

**2016, Sept. 30 — Photo. — *Perf. 13***

| | | | |
|---|---|---|---|
| **4037** | A3776 Sheet of 10 | 16.00 | 16.00 |
| *a.-j.* | 82y Any single | 1.60 | 1.25 |

Fox A3777

Purple Grapes A3778

Rabbit A3779

Akebia A3780

Moose A3781

Bear A3782

Snake Gourds A3783

Squirrel A3784

White Grapes A3785

Japanese Raccoon Dog A3786

***Die Cut Perf. 13x13¼, Die Cut Perf. (#4038e, 4039e)***

**2016, Oct. 3 — Litho.**

**Self-Adhesive**

| | | | |
|---|---|---|---|
| **4038** | Sheet of 10, 2 each #4038a-4038e | 10.00 | |
| *a.* | A3777 52y multi | 1.00 | .75 |
| *b.* | A3778 52y multi | 1.00 | .75 |
| *c.* | A3779 52y multi | 1.00 | .75 |
| *d.* | A3780 52y multi | 1.00 | .75 |
| *e.* | A3781 52y multi | 1.00 | .75 |
| **4039** | Sheet of 10, 2 each #4039a-4039e | 16.00 | |
| *a.* | A3782 82y multi | 1.60 | 1.25 |
| *b.* | A3783 82y multi | 1.60 | 1.25 |
| *c.* | A3784 82y multi | 1.60 | 1.25 |
| *d.* | A3785 82y multi | 1.60 | 1.25 |
| *e.* | A3786 82y multi | 1.60 | 1.25 |

Map and Trains of Hokuriku Shinkansen Line — A3787

Kintetsu 30000 Series Locomotive A3788

Enoden 1000 Series Locomotive A3789

Odakyu Electric Railway 7000 Series Locomotive A3790

Hakone Tozan 1000 Series Locomotive A3791

Keikyu 2000 Series Locomotive A3792

Nankai Electric Railway 5000 Series Locomotive A3793

East Japan Railway E26 Series Locomotive A3794

Kyushu Railway 885 Series Locomotive A3795

Toyama Light Rail TLR0600 Series Train A3796

Hokuriku Shinkansen Line Locomotives A3797

Keikyu 2000 Series Locomotive A3798

Kintetsu 30000 Series Locomotive A3799

Nankai Electric Railway 5000 Series Locomotive A3800

Enoden 1000 Series Locomotive A3801

East Japan Railway E26 Series Locomotive A3802

Odakyu Electric Railway 7000 Series Locomotive A3803

Kyushu Railway 885 Series Locomotive A3804

Hakone Tozan 1000 Series Locomotive A3805

Toyama Light Rail TLR0600 Series Train A3806

**2016, Oct. 7 — Litho. — *Perf. 13¼x12¾***

| | | | |
|---|---|---|---|
| **4040** | Sheet of 10 | 16.00 | 16.00 |
| *a.* | A3787 82y multi | 1.60 | 1.25 |
| *b.* | A3788 82y multi | 1.60 | 1.25 |
| *c.* | A3789 82y multi | 1.60 | 1.25 |
| *d.* | A3790 82y multi | 1.60 | 1.25 |
| *e.* | A3791 82y multi | 1.60 | 1.25 |
| *f.* | A3792 82y multi | 1.60 | 1.25 |
| *g.* | A3793 82y multi | 1.60 | 1.25 |
| *h.* | A3794 82y multi | 1.60 | 1.25 |
| *i.* | A3795 82y multi | 1.60 | 1.25 |
| *j.* | A3796 82y multi | 1.60 | 1.25 |

***Perf. 12¾x13¼***

| | | | |
|---|---|---|---|
| **4041** | Sheet of 10 | 16.00 | 16.00 |
| *a.* | A3797 82y multi | 1.60 | 1.25 |
| *b.* | A3798 82y multi | 1.60 | 1.25 |
| *c.* | A3799 82y multi | 1.60 | 1.25 |
| *d.* | A3800 82y multi | 1.60 | 1.25 |
| *e.* | A3801 82y multi | 1.60 | 1.25 |
| *f.* | A3802 82y multi | 1.60 | 1.25 |
| *g.* | A3803 82y multi | 1.60 | 1.25 |
| *h.* | A3804 82y multi | 1.60 | 1.25 |
| *i.* | A3805 82y multi | 1.60 | 1.25 |
| *j.* | A3806 82y multi | 1.60 | 1.25 |

A3807

International Letter Writing Week A3808

Paintings by Hiroshige: 70y, Wild Duck Among Snow-Covered Reeds. 90y, Travelers Walking Towards Numazu. 110y, Changing of Horses and Porters at Fujieda Relay Station. 130y, Futagawa Station.

**2016, Oct. 7 — Photo. — *Perf. 13¼***

| | | | |
|---|---|---|---|
| **4042** | A3807 70y multi | 1.40 | 1.10 |

***Perf. 13***

| | | | |
|---|---|---|---|
| **4043** | A3808 90y multi | 1.75 | 1.40 |
| **4044** | A3808 110y multi | 2.10 | 1.60 |
| **4045** | A3808 130y multi | 2.50 | 1.90 |
| | *Nos. 4042-4045 (4)* | 7.75 | 6.00 |

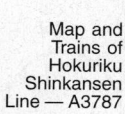

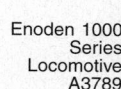

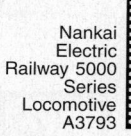

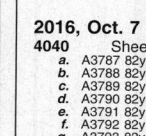

Miniature Sheet

Japan at Night — A3809

No. 4046: a, Rainbow Bridge (stamp 1). b, Tokyo Sky Tree (stamp 2). c, Tokyo tower (stamp 3). d, Yokohama Minata Mirai 21 (stamp 4). e, Kanto Plain (stamp 5). f, Chichibu Night Festival (stamp 6). g, Gunman Flower Park (stamp 7). h, Ashikaga Flower Park (stamp 8). i, Tokyo German Village (stamp 9). j, Fuefukigawa Fruit Park (stamp 10).

**2016, Oct. 14 Litho. *Perf. 13***

**4046** A3809 Sheet of 10 16.00 16.00
*a.-j.* 82y Any single 1.60 1.25

Banner Decoration A3810

Silver Platter A3811

Incense Burner — A3812

Lacquered Wooden Box — A3813

Detail of Incense Burner — A3814

**2016, Oct. 21 Photo. *Perf. 13***

**4047** A3810 82y multi 1.60 1.25
**4048** A3811 82y multi 1.60 1.25
**4049** A3812 82y multi 1.60 1.25
**4050** A3813 82y multi 1.60 1.25
**4051** A3814 82y multi 1.60 1.25
*a.* Vert. strip of 5, #4047-4051 8.00 6.25
*Nos. 4047-4051 (5)* 8.00 6.25

Miniature Sheet

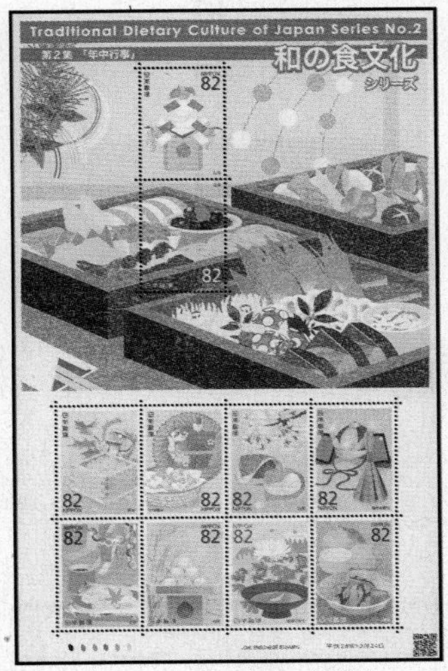


Japanese Foods — A3815

No. 4052: a, Rice cake in ceremonial display. b, Tray of New Year foods. c, Box of beans, hiirage and sardine heads. d, Dolls and crackers. e, Mochi wrapped in cherry leaves. f, Rice in bamboo leaves. g, Noodles. h, Tsukimi dumplings. i, Chrysanthemum petal in saki. j, Kabocha squash and yuzu.

**2016, Oct. 24 Litho. *Perf. 13½***

**4052** A3815 Sheet of 10 16.00 16.00
*a.-j.* 82y Any single 1.60 1.25

Miniature Sheet

Astronomy — A3816

No. 4053: a, Saturn (35x30mm). b, Capricorn and goat (22x25mm). c, Aquarius and water urn (22x25mm). d, Pisces and fish (22x25mm).

***Die Cut Perf. 9¾x10 (#4053a), Die Cut Perf. 13x13¼***
**Litho. With Foil Application**
**2016, Oct. 28 Self-Adhesive**

**4053** A3816 Sheet of 10, #4053a, 3 each #4053b-4053d 16.00
*a.-d.* 82y Any single 1.60 1.25

Miniature Sheet

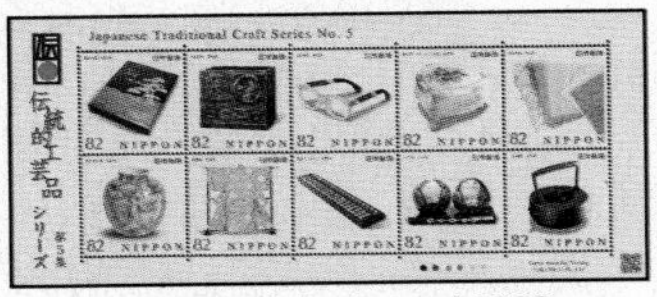


Traditional Crafts — A3822

No. 4060: a, Echizen lacquerware (Fukui Prefecture). b, Sendai storage cabinet (Miyagi Prefecture). c, Edo tortoiseshell eyeglasses (Tokyo Prefecture). d, Tokyo antimony jewelry box (Tokyo Prefecture). e, Tosa paper (Kochi Prefecture). f, Seto underglazed pottery (Aichi Prefecture). g, Nishijin textiles (Kyoto Prefecture). h, Banshu abacus (Hyogo Prefecture). i, Ouchi lacquerware (Yamaguchi Prefecture). j, Yamagata metal cast kettle (Yamagata Prefecture).

**2016, Nov. 4 Litho. *Perf. 13¼***

**4060** A3822 Sheet of 10 15.00 15.00
*a.-j.* 82y Any single 1.50 1.10

Miniature Sheet

World Tsunami Awareness Day — A3823

No. 4061: a, Earth and ocean. b, Man running from tsunami. c, Burning rice sheaves, man with torch. d, Miracle Pine of Rikuzentakata. e, Winning children's art in tsunami awareness poster contest.

**2016, Nov. 4 Litho. *Perf. 13***

**4061** A3823 Sheet of 10, 2 each #4053a-4053e 15.00 15.00
*a.-e.* 82y Any single 1.50 1.10

Miniature Sheets

A3824

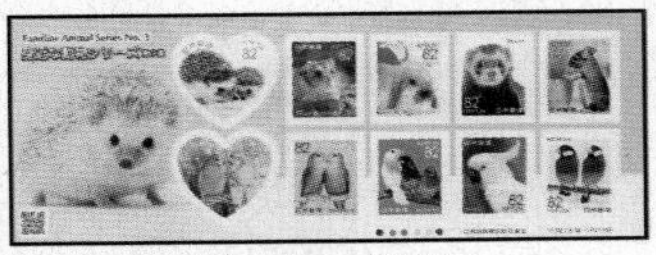

Animals — A3825

No. 4062: a, Netherland Dwarf rabbit (30x28mm heart). b, Flying squirrel (22x26mm). c, Hamster (22x26mm). d, Chipmunk (22x26mm). e, Guinea pig (22x26mm). f, White birds on fence (30x28mm heart). g, Zebra finches (22x26mm). h, Cockatiel (22x26mm). i, Canaries (22x26mm). j, Parakeets (22x26mm).

No. 4063: a, Hedgehogs (30x28mm heart). b, Djungarian hamster (22x26mm). c, Lop-eared rabbit (22x26mm). d, Ferret (22x26mm). e, Chinchilla (22x26mm). f, Budgerigars (30x28mm heart). g, Rosy-faced lovebirds (22x26mm). h, Society finches (22x26mm). i, Sulphur-crested cockatoo (22x26mm). j, Java sparrows (22x26mm).

***Die Cut Perf. 11¼x11, Die Cut Perf. (#4062a, 4062f, 4063a, 4063f)***
**2016, Nov. 11 Litho.**
**Self-Adhesive**

**4062** A3824 Sheet of 10 9.50
*a.-j.* 52y Any single .95 .70
**4063** A3825 Sheet of 10 15.00
*a.-j.* 82y Any single 1.50 1.10

Miniature Sheet

Illustrations From Children's Books by Mitsumasa Anno — A3826

No. 4064: a, People and horses on path (stamp 1). b, People gathered near buildings, man near tricycle, man with delivery bicycle (stamp 2). c, Anno's Counting house (stamp 3). d, Anno's medieval world (stamp 4). e, Anno's flea market (stamp 5). f, Anno's Aesop: A book of fables by Aesop & Mr. Fox (stamp 6). g, Anno's Journey, scene 15 (stamp 7). h, Anno's Journey III, scene 10 (stamp 8). i, Anno's Journey IV, scene 11 (stamp 9). j, Anno's Journey VIII, scene 2 (stamp 10).

**2016, Nov. 25 Photo. *Perf. 13***

**4064** A3826 Sheet of 10 15.00 15.00
*a.-j.* 82y Any single 1.50 1.10

Miniature Sheet

Diplomatic Relations Between Japan and Singapore, 50th Anniv. — A3827

No. 4065: a, Three Singaporean pots with handle. b, Two Japanese bowls. c, Merlion, Singapore. d, Gardens by the Bay, Singapore. e, Singapore at night. f, Singapore Art Museum. g, Plate of chili crab. h, Marina Bay at dusk. i, Orchid. j, Singapore Flyer Ferris Wheel and ArtScience Museum at night.

**2016, Nov. 29 Litho. *Perf. 13***

**4065** A3827 Sheet of 10 15.00 15.00
*a.-j.* 82y Any single 1.50 1.10

See Singapore Nos. 1812-1813.

Fireplace
A3828

Stew Pot and Bowl
A3829

Snow-Covered House
A3830

Snowman and Mailbox
A3831

Child Rolling Large Snowball
A3832

Trees
A3833

Concert, Bows on Instruments
A3834

Piano
A3835

Trees With Lights at Night
A3836

Shoppers With Packages
A3837

Concert, Bows Raised
A3838

Window and Door in Winter
A3839

***Die Cut Perf. 11¼x11¾, Die Cut Perf. 11½x11 (#4066c)***

**2016, Dec. 2** **Litho.**

**Self-Adhesive**

| | | | |
|---|---|---|---|
| **4066** | Sheet of 10, 2 each #4066a-4066d, 1 each #4066e, 4066f | 9.50 | |
| *a.* | A3828 52y multi | .95 | .70 |
| *b.* | A3829 52y multi | .95 | .70 |
| *c.* | A3830 52y multi | .95 | .70 |
| *d.* | A3831 52y multi | .95 | .70 |
| *e.* | A3832 52y multi | .95 | .70 |
| *f.* | A3833 52y multi | .95 | .70 |
| **4067** | Sheet of 10, #4067a, 4067e, 2 each #4067b-4067d, 4067f | 15.00 | |
| *a.* | A3834 82y multi | 1.50 | 1.10 |
| *b.* | A3835 82y multi | 1.50 | 1.10 |
| *c.* | A3836 82y multi | 1.50 | 1.10 |
| *d.* | A3837 82y multi | 1.50 | 1.10 |
| *e.* | A3838 82y multi | 1.50 | 1.10 |
| *f.* | A3839 82y multi | 1.50 | 1.10 |

A3840

A3841

A3842

A3843

A3844

A3845

A3846

A3847

A3848

A3849

A3850

A3851

A3852

A3853

Flowers — A3854

***Die Cut Perf. 13x13¼***

**2016, Dec. 9** **Litho.**

**Self-Adhesive**

| | | | |
|---|---|---|---|
| **4068** | Sheet of 10 | 9.00 | |
| *a.* | A3840 52y multi | .90 | .70 |
| *b.* | A3841 52y multi | .90 | .70 |
| *c.* | A3842 52y multi | .90 | .70 |
| *d.* | A3843 52y multi | .90 | .70 |
| *e.* | A3844 52y multi | .90 | .70 |
| *f.* | A3845 52y multi | .90 | .70 |
| *g.* | A3846 52y multi | .90 | .70 |
| *h.* | A3847 52y multi | .90 | .70 |
| *i.* | A3848 52y multi | .90 | .70 |
| *j.* | A3849 52y multi | .90 | .70 |
| **4069** | Sheet of 10, 2 each #4069a-4069e | 14.00 | |
| *a.* | A3850 82y multi | 1.40 | 1.10 |
| *b.* | A3851 82y multi | 1.40 | 1.10 |
| *c.* | A3852 82y multi | 1.40 | 1.10 |
| *d.* | A3853 82y multi | 1.40 | 1.10 |
| *e.* | A3854 82y multi | 1.40 | 1.10 |

Five-Story Pagoda at Kyo-o-gokoku-ji Temple, Kyoto — A3855

Tokyo Tower — A3856

**Photo. & Engr.**

**2017, Jan. 6** ***Perf. 13¼***

| | | | |
|---|---|---|---|
| **4070** | A3855 82y multi | 1.50 | 1.10 |
| **4071** | A3856 82y multi | 1.50 | 1.10 |
| *a.* | Horiz. pair, #4070-4071 | 3.00 | 2.25 |

Monocolor (green, red, orange brown and blue) engraved examples of Nos. 4070-4071 were printed in two sheets of ten that were in booklets produced in limited quantities that sold for 2500y.

**Miniature Sheets**

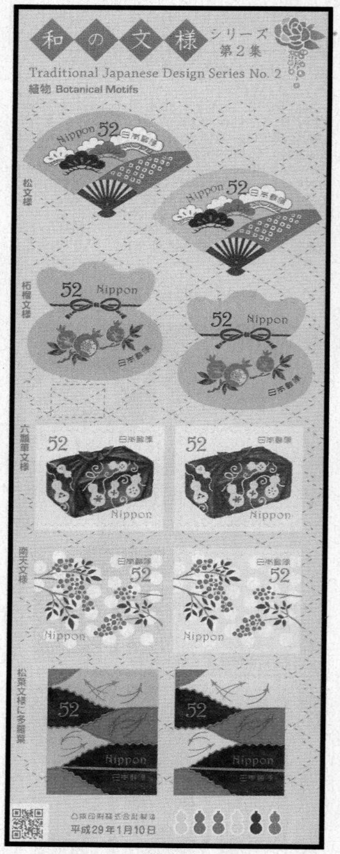

A3857

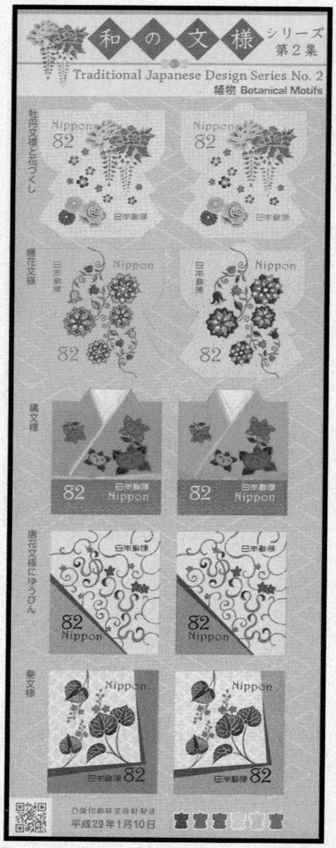

Traditional Japanese Designs — A3858

No. 4072: a, Fan with pine trees, lilac background (30x21mm). b, As "a," buff background (30x21mm). c, Pomegranates and tied rope, dull green background (27x24mm). d, As "c," rose background (27x24mm). e, Blue box with gourd pattern and bow (26x22mm). f, As "e," red violet box (26x22mm). g, Nandina berries, pink background (26x22mm). h, As "g," pale yellow background (26x22mm). i, Pine needles, dull green background (22x26mm). j, As "i," light yellow background (22x26mm).

No. 4073: a, Peonies, pink background (26x27mm). b, As "a," pale orange background (26x27mm). c, Flowers, yellow orange background (26x27mm). d, As "c," light blue background (26x27mm). e, Flowers on salmon kimono (22x23mm). f, As "e," pale green kimono (22x23mm). g, Flowers, mauve triangular panel (22x26mm). h, As "g," turquoise blue triangular panel (22x26mm). i, Flowers and leaves, light green background (22x26mm). j, As "i," lilac background (22x26mm).

***Die Cut Perf. 11 (#4072a, 4072b), Die Cut Perf. (#4072c, 4072d), Die Cut Perf. 11½x11, Die Cut Perf. 11¼x11¾ (#4072i, 4072j)***

**2017, Jan. 10** **Litho.**

**Self-Adhesive**

| | | | |
|---|---|---|---|
| **4072** | A3857 Sheet of 10 | 9.50 | |
| *a.-j.* | 52y Any single | .95 | .70 |
| **4073** | A3858 Sheet of 10 | 15.00 | |
| *a.-j.* | 82y Any single | 1.50 | 1.10 |

Skiing — A3860

Biathlon — A3861

Skating — A3862

Ice Hockey — A3863

Curling — A3864

**2017, Jan. 19 Photo. *Perf. 13***

| | | | |
|---|---|---|---|
| **4075** | A3860 82y multi | 1.50 | 1.10 |
| **4076** | A3861 82y multi | 1.50 | 1.10 |
| **4077** | A3862 82y multi | 1.50 | 1.10 |
| **4078** | A3863 82y multi | 1.50 | 1.10 |
| **4079** | A3864 82y multi | 1.50 | 1.10 |
| *a.* | Horiz. strip of 5, #4075-4079 | 7.50 | 5.50 |
| | *Nos. 4075-4079 (5)* | 7.50 | 5.50 |

2017 Sapporo Asian Winter Games.

A sheet of six heart-shaped self-adhesive stamps (three denominated 52y and three denominatied 82y) was printed in limited quantities and sold only in a package containing stationery that sold for 1200y.

Miniature Sheets

A3865

Disney Characters — A3866

No. 4080: a, Mickey Mouse, orange yellow background (23x23mm). b, Minnie Mouse, orange yellow background (23x23mm). c, Mickey Mouse, apple green background (23x23mm). d, Minnie Mouse, apple green background (23x23mm). e, Mickey Mouse, lilac background (23x23mm). f, Minnie Mouse, lilac background (23x23mm). g, Mickey Mouse, rose background (22x26mm). h, Minnie Mouse, rose background (22x26mm). i, Mickey Mouse, light blue background (22x26mm). j, Minnie Mouse, light blue background (22x26mm).

No. 4081: a, Winnie the Pooh and Piglet looking at book (23x23mm). b, Winnie the Pooh in light blue frame (23x23mm). c, Winnie the Pooh and Piglet reading books (23x23mm). d, Piglet and Winnie the Pooh holding butterfly (23x23mm). e, Piglet with Winnie the Pooh holding "A," "B" and "C" (23x23mm). f, Piglet sitting on Winnie the Pooh's leg (23x23mm). g, Winnie the Pooh and letter "P" (23x23mm). h, Winnie the Pooh and Tigger (23x23mm). i, Tigger, Winnie the Pooh and Eeyore sleeping (25x22mm). j Winnie the Pooh with toys and honey pot (22x25mm).

***Die Cut Perf. 14***

**2017, Feb. 9 Litho.**

**Self-Adhesive**

| | | | |
|---|---|---|---|
| **4080** A3865 | Sheet of 10 | 15.00 | |
| *a.-j.* | 82y Any single | 1.50 | 1.10 |
| **4081** A3866 | Sheet of 10 | 15.00 | |
| *a.-j.* | 82y Any single | 1.50 | 1.10 |

Cherry Blossoms A3867

Plum Blossoms A3868

Pansies and Sweet Alyssum A3869

Snapdragons A3870

Lupines A3871

Cherry Blossoms A3872

Mimosa Blossoms A3873

Bellflowers A3874

Ornithogalum A3875

Anemones A3876

***Die Cut Perf. 14***

**2017, Feb. 15 Litho.**

**Self-Adhesive**

| | | | |
|---|---|---|---|
| **4082** | Sheet of 10, 2 each #4082a-4082e | 9.50 | |
| *a.* | A3867 52y multi | .95 | .70 |
| *b.* | A3868 52y multi | .95 | .70 |
| *c.* | A3869 52y multi | .95 | .70 |
| *d.* | A3870 52y multi | .95 | .70 |
| *e.* | A3871 52y multi | .95 | .70 |
| **4083** | Sheet of 10, 2 each #4083a-4083e | 15.00 | |
| *a.* | A3872 82y multi | 1.50 | 1.10 |
| *b.* | A3873 82y multi | 1.50 | 1.10 |
| *c.* | A3874 82y multi | 1.50 | 1.10 |
| *d.* | A3875 82y multi | 1.50 | 1.10 |
| *e.* | A3876 82y multi | 1.50 | 1.10 |

Cherry Blossoms A3877

Dandelions and Clover A3878

Vegetables in Basket A3879

Bamboo Shoots A3880

Cherry Blossoms A3881

Strawberries and Mailbox A3882

Field Mustard A3883

Wreath of Flowers A3884

***Die Cut Perf. (#4085a-4085b, 4086a, 4086b), Die Cut Perf. 14***

**2017, Feb. 24 Litho.**

**Self-Adhesive**

| | | | |
|---|---|---|---|
| **4084** | Sheet of 10, 4 #4084a, 2 each #4084b-4084d | 9.50 | |
| *a.* | A3877 52y multi | .95 | .70 |
| *b.* | A3878 52y multi | .95 | .70 |
| *c.* | A3879 52y multi | .95 | .70 |
| *d.* | A3880 52y multi | .95 | .70 |
| **4085** | Sheet of 10, 4 #4085a, 2 each #4085b-4085d | 15.00 | |
| *a.* | A3881 82y multi | 1.50 | 1.10 |
| *b.* | A3882 82y multi | 1.50 | 1.10 |
| *c.* | A3883 82y multi | 1.50 | 1.10 |
| *d.* | A3884 82y multi | 1.50 | 1.10 |

Miniature Sheet

Southern Hemisphere Constellations — A3885

No. 4086: a, Grus and goose. b, Telescopium and telescope. c, Centaurus and centaur. d, Tucana and toucan. e, Pavo and peacock. f, Crux and cross. g, Volans and flying fish. h, Dorado and dolphinfish. i, Chamaeleon and chameleon. j, Carina and ship.

**Litho. With Foil Application**

**2017, Mar. 3 *Die Cut Perf. 13x13¼***

**Self-Adhesive**

| | | | |
|---|---|---|---|
| **4086** A3885 | Sheet of 10 | 15.00 | |
| *a.-j.* | 82y Any single | 1.50 | 1.10 |

Hydrangea A3890

Daisies A3891

Peony A3892

Lantana A3893

Hibiscus
A3894

Hydrangea
A3895

Sunflowers and Roses
A3896

Carnations
A3897

Gardenias
A3898

Tulips
A3899

***Die Cut Perf. 10¼***

**2017, Apr. 4 Litho.**

**Self-Adhesive**

| | | | |
|---|---|---|---|
| **4091** | Sheet of 10, 2 each #4091a-4091e | 9.50 | |
| *a.* | A3890 52y multi | .95 | .70 |
| *b.* | A3891 52y multi | .95 | .70 |
| *c.* | A3892 52y multi | .95 | .70 |
| *d.* | A3893 52y multi | .95 | .70 |
| *e.* | A3894 52y multi | .95 | .70 |
| **4092** | Sheet of 10, 2 each #4092a-4092e | 15.00 | |
| *a.* | A3895 82y multi | 1.50 | 1.10 |
| *b.* | A3896 82y multi | 1.50 | 1.10 |
| *c.* | A3897 82y multi | 1.50 | 1.10 |
| *d.* | A3898 82y multi | 1.50 | 1.10 |
| *e.* | A3899 82y multi | 1.50 | 1.10 |

Miniature Sheets

A3900

My Journey — A3901

No. 4093: a, Enoshima Lighthouse and sea gulls (27x26mm). b, Electric train (27x22mm). c, Enoshima (27x22mm). d, Electric train in station (27x22mm). e, Drink with lime and kiwifruit (22x26mm). f, Hamburger (22x26mm). g, Girl on beach, three sailboats (27x22mm). h, Dog on surfboard (27x22mm). i, Enoshima at night and shooting star (22x26mm). j, Rocky beach at sunset (27x22mm).

No. 4094: a, Great Buddha at Kamakura (25x31mm). b, Bicycle on sidewalk (26x22mm). c, Archer on horseback (26x22mm). d, Vegetables (25mm diameter). e, Mailbox and hydrangeas (25mm diameter). f, Hydrangeas (26x22mm). g, Bamboo grove (26x22mm). h, Bowl of anmitsu (26x22mm). i, Electric train and railroad crossing sign (26x22mm). j, Girl at Gokurakuji railroad station (26x22mm).

***Die Cut Perf. 10¾ (#4093a), Die Cut Perf. (#4093f), Die Cut Perf. 10¼***

**2017, Apr. 14 Litho.**

**Self-Adhesive**

| | | | |
|---|---|---|---|
| **4093** | A3900 Sheet of 10 | 9.50 | |
| *a.-j.* | 52y Any single | .95 | .70 |

***Die Cut Perf. (#4094a, 4094d, 4094e), Die Cut Perf. 10¼***

| | | | |
|---|---|---|---|
| **4094** | A3901 Sheet of 10 | 15.00 | |
| *a.-j.* | 82y Any single | 1.50 | 1.10 |

A sheet of seven self-adhesive stamps (five denominated 82y and two denominated 120y) was printed in limited quantities and sold only in a package containing stationery that sold for 1200y.

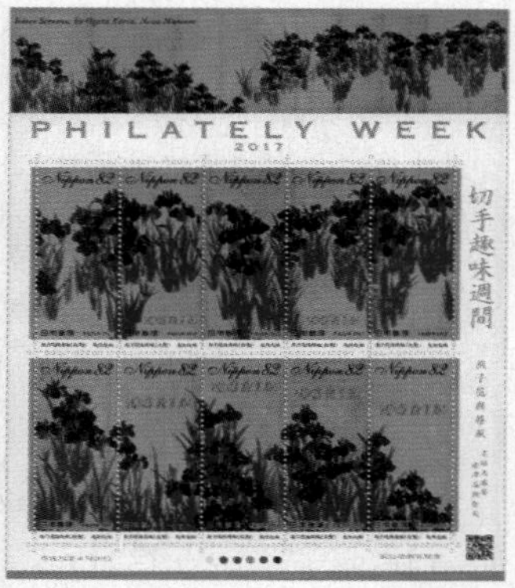

Irises, by Korin Ogata — A3902

Various details of the screen painting, as shown.

**2017, Apr. 20 Photo. *Perf. 13x13¼***

| | | | |
|---|---|---|---|
| **4095** | A3902 Sheet of 10 | 15.00 | 15.00 |
| *a.-j.* | 82y Any single | 1.50 | 1.10 |

Philately Week.

Products of Institute of Physical and Chemical Research
A3903

K Supercomputer
A3904

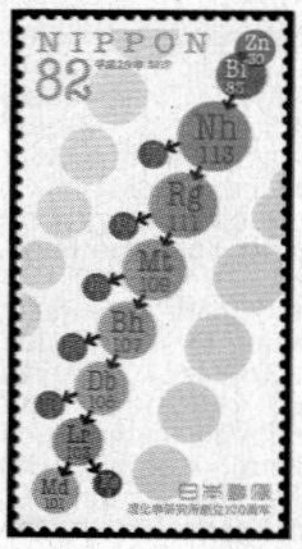

Discovery of Element 113 (Nihonium) — A3905

Photomicrographs of Plant and Animal Tissue — A3906

Cherry Blossom Mutations From Heavy Ion Beam Breeding Technique — A3907

**2017, Apr. 26 Photo. *Perf. 13¼***

| | | | |
|---|---|---|---|
| **4096** | A3903 82y multi | 1.50 | 1.10 |
| **4097** | A3904 82y multi | 1.50 | 1.10 |
| **4098** | A3905 82y multi | 1.50 | 1.10 |
| **4099** | A3906 82y multi | 1.50 | 1.10 |
| **4100** | A3907 82y multi | 1.50 | 1.10 |
| *a.* | Horiz. strip of 5, #4096-4100 | 7.50 | 5.50 |
| | *Nos. 4096-4100 (5)* | 7.50 | 5.50 |

Institute of Physical and Chemical Research (RIKEN), cent.

Miniature Sheet

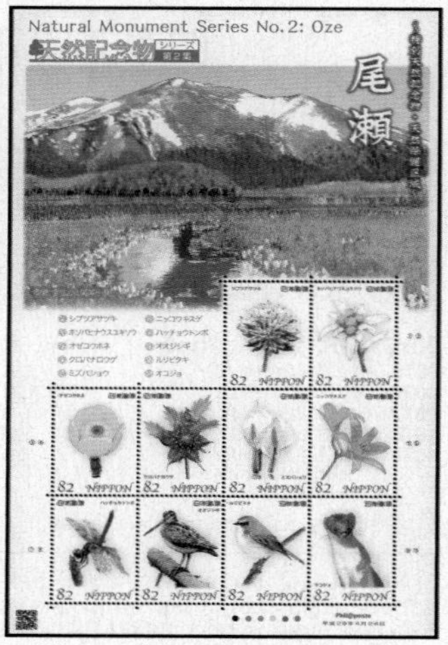

Flora and Fauna of Oze Natural Monument — A3908

No. 4101: a, Allium schoenoprasum var. shibutuense (purple flower, stamp 1). b, Leontopodium fauriei var. angustifolium (white flower, stamp 2). c, Nuphar pumilum var. ozeense (yellow flower, stamp 3). d, Potentilla palustris (red flower, stamp 4). e, Lysichiton camtschatcense (two white flowers, stamp 5). f, Hemerocallis dumortieri (orange flower, stamp 6). g, Dragonfly (stamp 7). h, Latham's snipe on thick branch (stamp 8). i, Red-flanked bluetail on thin branch (stamp 9). j, Stoat (stamp 10).

**2017, Apr. 28 Litho. *Perf. 13***

| | | | |
|---|---|---|---|
| **4101** | A3908 Sheet of 10 | 15.00 | 15.00 |
| *a.-j.* | 82y Any single | 1.50 | 1.10 |

Miniature Sheet

Diplomatic Relations Between Japan and Denmark, 150th Anniv. — A3909

No. 4102: a, Nyhavn, Copenhagen with red boat. b, Nyhavn with green boat. c, Tivoli Gardens and swans. d, Pigs and vegetables. e, Cyclists. f, Wind generators. g, Ship and Little Mermaid. h, Thumbelina in flower. i, Kronborg Castle. j, Amalienborg and guards.

**2017, May 2 Litho. *Perf. 13***

| | | | | |
|---|---|---|---|---|
| **4102** | A3909 | Sheet of 10 | 15.00 | 15.00 |
| *a.-j.* | | 82y Any single | 1.50 | 1.10 |

Miniature Sheets

A3910

Characters From *Peanuts* Comic Strip — A3911

No. 4103: a, Snoopy with blue box (29mm diameter). b, Snoopy driving truck facing left (24x26mm). c, Snoopy in gift box (26x25mm). d, Snoopy driving truck facing right (28x23mm). e, Charlie Brown and Snoopy exchanging gifts (26x22mm). f, Snoopy pushing gift on cart (26x22mm). g, Snoopy and Woodstock carrying boxes (26x22mm). h, Snoopy with red box (23x25mm). i, Snoopy on dog house (28x36mm). j, Snoopy holding red heart (25x30mm).

No. 4104: a, Snoopy reading Valentine's Day card (29x26mm). b, Snoopy holding yellow envelope (29mm diameter). c, Snoopy dancing (32x25mm). d, Woodstock and birds in hot air balloon (24x28mm). e, Woodstock on bicycle (26x24mm). f, Snoopy, Charlie Brown and mailbox (27x23mm). g, Snoopy, Woodstock and bird with umbrellas (22x26mm). h, Woodstock and Snoopy at mailbox (26x26mm). i, Snoopy typing (26x27mm). j, Snoopy delivering letter (22x26mm).

***Die Cut Perf. (#4103a), Die Cut Perf. 12¾x13 (#4103b, 4103h), Die Cut Perf. 13x12¾ (#4103c), Die Cut Perf. 13 (#4103d), Die Cut Perf. 14 (#4103e, 4103f, 4103g), Die Cut Perf. 12 (#4103i, 4103j)***

**2017, May 10 Litho.**

**Self-Adhesive**

| | | | | |
|---|---|---|---|---|
| **4103** | A3910 | Sheet of 10 | 15.00 | |
| *a.-j.* | | 82y Any single | 1.50 | 1.10 |

***Die Cut Perf. 12½ (#4104a, 4104h), Die Cut Perf, (#4104b, 4104d), Die Cut Perf. 12¾x12 (#4104c), Die Cut Perf 12½x12¼ (#4104e), Die Cut Perf. 13½x13 (#4104f), Die Cut Perf. 13¾x14 (#4104g), Die Cut Perf. 12¾ (#4104i), Die Cut Perf. 13¾x13½ (#4104j)***

| | | | | |
|---|---|---|---|---|
| **4104** | A3911 | Sheet of 10 | 15.00 | |
| *a.-j.* | | 82y Any single | 1.50 | 1.10 |

Volunteer Welfare Commisioners System, Cent. — A3912

**2017, May 12 Litho. *Perf. 13***

| | | | | |
|---|---|---|---|---|
| **4105** | A3912 | 82y multi | 1.50 | 1.10 |

A3916

A3917

A3918

A3919

Lions Clubs International, Cent. — A3920

Design: No. 4110, Logo of Lions Club International. No. 4111, Engaging our youth. No. 4112, Sharing the vision. No. 4113, Relieving the hunger. No. 4114, Protecting our environment.

**2017, May 24 Litho. *Perf. 13***

| | | | | |
|---|---|---|---|---|
| **4110** | A3916 | 82y multi | 1.50 | 1.10 |
| **4111** | A3917 | 82y multi | 1.50 | 1.10 |
| **4112** | A3918 | 82y multi | 1.50 | 1.10 |
| **4113** | A3919 | 82y multi | 1.50 | 1.10 |
| **4114** | A3920 | 82y multi | 1.50 | 1.10 |
| *a.* | | Vert. strip of 5, #4110-4114 | 7.50 | 5.50 |
| | | *Nos. 4110-4114 (5)* | 7.50 | 5.50 |

Miniature Sheet

National Afforestation — A3921

No. 4115: a, Cherry blossoms. b, North Kobushi magnolia flower. c, Gentian. d, Tulips. e, Japanese bigleaf magnolia. f, Cherry blossoms, diff. g, Adder's tongue lilies. h, Kanoko lily. i, Japanese bay tree, j, Tateyama cedar tree.

**2017, May 26 Litho. *Perf. 13***

| | | | | |
|---|---|---|---|---|
| **4115** | A3921 | Sheet of 10 | 11.00 | 11.00 |
| *a.-j.* | | 62y Any single | 1.10 | .85 |

Clouds A3922

Shells and Ramune Bottles A3923

Water Balloons A3924

Sunflowers A3925

Sunflowers A3926

Goldfish in Bowl A3927

Bowl of Shaved Ice A3928

Beach A3929

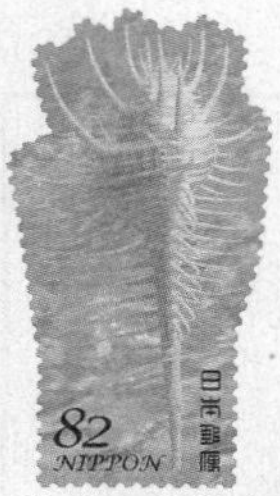
Shell — A3930

Shell — A3931

Marbles
A3932

Watermelon Slice
A3933

***Die Cut Perf. 13x13¼, Die Cut Perf. 13¼x13 (#4116d, 4116e), Die Cut Perf. (#4116f)***

**2017, June 2 Litho.**

**Self-Adhesive**

**4116** Sheet of 10, #4116d, 4116e, 2 each #4116a-4116c, 4116f 11.00
*a.* A3922 62y multi 1.10 .85
*b.* A3923 62y multi 1.10 .85
*c.* A3924 62y multi 1.10 .85
*d.* A3925 62y multi 1.10 .85
*e.* A3926 62y multi 1.10 .85
*f.* A3927 62y multi 1.10 .85

***Die Cut Perf. 13x13¼ (#4117a, 4117b), Die Cut Perf. 13 (#4117c, 4117d, 4117f), Die Cut Perf. 13¼ (#4117e)***

**4117** Sheet of 10, #4117c, 4117d, 2 each #4117a-4117b, 4117e-4117f 15.00
*a.* A3928 82y multi 1.50 1.10
*b.* A3929 82y multi 1.50 1.10
*c.* A3930 82y multi 1.50 1.10
*d.* A3931 82y multi 1.50 1.10
*e.* A3932 82y multi 1.50 1.10
*f.* A3933 82y multi 1.50 1.10

Miniature Sheet

Paintings — A3934

No. 4118: a, Sunflowers, by Chinami Nakajima (stamp 5, 32x39mm). b, Morning Glories, by Nakajima (stamp 6, 32x28mm). c, Chinese Bellflowers, by Fumiko Hori (stamp 7, 30x32mm). d, The Flow of Mountain Seasons, by Hori (stamp 8, 32x39mm). e, Angela and the Blue Sky II, by Koji Kinutani (stamp 1, 32x28mm). f, Celebration - Flying Dragon, Sacred Gateway of Fuji, by Kinutani (stamp 2, 32x39mm). g, Early Summer, by Rieko Morita (stamp 9, 32x39mm). h, Autumn Flowers, by Morita (stamp 10, 32x28mm). i, Nachi Waterfall in the Moonlight, by Yuji Tezuka (stamp 3, 32x39mm). j, Beautiful Sky, by Tezuka (stamp 4, 32x32mm).

***Die Cut Perf. 12½x13, Die Cut Perf. 13x12 (#4118b, 4118e, 4118h), Die Cut Perf. 12½ (#4118c, 4118j)***

**2017, June 7 Litho.**

**Self-Adhesive**

**4118** A3934 Sheet of 10 15.00
*a.-j.* 82y Any single 1.50 1.10

Miniature Sheet

Japan at Night — A3935

No. 4119: a, Sky Gate Bridge R, Osaka Prefecture (stamp 1). b, Meriken Park, Hyogo Prefecture (stamp 2). c, Kodaiji in autumn, Kyoto Prefecture (stamp 3). d, Nagoya Television Tower, Aichi Prefecture (stamp 4). e, Gifu Castle and Gifu, Gifu Prefecture (stamp 5). f, Shimizu Port and Mount Fuji, Shizuoka Prefecture (stamp 6). g, Lake Suwa Fireworks Festival, Nagano Prefecture (stamp 7). h, Ishiyama-dera Autumn Moon Viewing Festival, Shiga Prefecture (stamp 8). i, Echigo Hillside National Government Park, Niigata Prefecture (stamp 9). j, Seki-juku, Mie Prefecture (stamp 10).

**2017, June 9 Litho. *Perf. 13***

**4119** A3935 Sheet of 10 15.00 15.00
*a.-j.* 82y Any single 1.50 1.10

Dragées
A3936

Jordan
Almonds
A3937

Dragées
A3938

Macarons
A3939

Dragées
A3940

Konpeito
Candy
A3941

***Die Cut Perf. 13x13¼***

**2017, June 23 Photo.**

**Self-Adhesive**

**4120** Sheet of 10, 5 each #4120a-4120b 11.00
*a.* A3936 62y multi 1.10 .85
*b.* A3937 62y multi 1.10 .85

**4121** Sheet of 10, 5 each #4121a-4121b 15.00
*a.* A3938 82y multi 1.50 1.10
*b.* A3939 82y multi 1.50 1.10

**4122** Sheet of 10, 5 each #4122a-4122b 17.50
*a.* A3940 92y multi 1.75 1.40
*b.* A3941 92y multi 1.75 1.40
*Nos. 4120-4122 (3)* 43.50

Miniature Sheet

Characters From *Super Mario* Video Games — A3942

No. 4123: a, Mario with fist and leg raised (22x33mm). b, Mario mailing letter (24x25mm). c, Mario seated, reading letter (24x27mm). d, Princess Peach writing letter (23x25mm). e, Mario on Yoshi (25x23mm). f, Luigi removing letter from mailbox (23x25mm). g, Toad with mail bag (25x23mm). h, Mario pointing (24x24mm). i, Mario and Princess Peach (26x25mm). j, Princess Peach (24x24mm).

***Die Cut Perf. 11¾ (#4123a), Die Cut Perf. 11 (#4123b, 4123c), Die Cut Perf. 11½x11 (#4123d, 4123f, 4123i), Die Cut Perf. 11x11½ (#4123e, 4123g), Die Cut Perf. 11½ (#4123h, 4123j)***

**2017, June 28 Litho.**

**Self-Adhesive**

**4123** A3942 Sheet of 10 15.00
*a.-j.* 82y Any single 1.50 1.10

A3943

A3944

A3945

A3946

A3947

A3948

A3949

A3950

A3951

Penguins — A3952

**Litho. With Foil Application**

**2017, July 5 *Die Cut Perf. 10¼***

**Self-Adhesive**

**4124** Sheet of 10 15.00
*a.* A3943 82y multi 1.50 1.10
*b.* A3944 82y multi 1.50 1.10
*c.* A3945 82y multi 1.50 1.10
*d.* A3946 82y multi 1.50 1.10
*e.* A3947 82y multi 1.50 1.10
*f.* A3948 82y multi 1.50 1.10
*g.* A3949 82y multi 1.50 1.10
*h.* A3950 82y multi 1.50 1.10
*i.* A3951 82y multi 1.50 1.10
*j.* A3952 82y multi 1.50 1.10

Miniature Sheet

National Museum of Western Art UNESCO World Heritage Site — A3953

No. 4125: a, Entrance to Main building (stamp 1). b, 19th Century Hall (stamp 2). c, Aerial view of Main building (stamp 3). d, Main building's second-floor exhibition room (stamp 4). e, Entrance to Main building, diff (stamp 5). f, The Thinker, statue by Auguste Rodin (stamp 6). g, Roses, by Vincent van Gogh (stamp 7). h, Boy in Flowers (Jacques Hoschedé), by Edouard Manet (stamp 8). i, The Port of Saint-Tropez, by Paul Signac (stamp 9). j, Water Lilies, by Claude Monet (stamp 10).

**2017, July 14 Litho. *Perf. 13¾x14¼***

**4125** A3953 Sheet of 10 15.00 15.00
*a.-j.* 82y Any single 1.50 1.10

Flowers and "Thank You"
A3954

Cupcake
A3955

Tea Cup and Tea Pot
A3956

Stars
A3957

Swan Holding Letter — A3958

Stars — A3959

Dots and "Thank You" — A3960

Elephant and Flower — A3961

Gift — A3962

Ribbon With Bow — A3963

***Die Cut Perf. 13x13¼ (#4126), Die Cut Perf. 13x12¾ (#4127, 4129, 4132, 4134), Die Cut Perf. 13½x13¼ (#4128, 4130, 4133, 4135), Die Cut Perf. 10¾ (#4131)***

**2017, July 21** **Litho.**

**Booklet Stamps**
**Self-Adhesive**

| | | | | |
|---|---|---|---|---|
| **4126** | A3954 62y multi | | 1.10 | .85 |
| **4127** | A3955 62y multi | | 1.10 | .85 |
| **4128** | A3956 62y multi | | 1.10 | .85 |
| **4129** | A3957 62y multi | | 1.10 | .85 |
| **4130** | A3958 62y multi | | 1.10 | .85 |
| *a.* | Booklet pane of 5, #4126-4130 | | 5.50 | |
| **4131** | A3959 82y multi | | 1.50 | 1.10 |
| **4132** | A3960 82y multi | | 1.50 | 1.10 |
| **4133** | A3961 82y multi | | 1.50 | 1.10 |
| **4134** | A3962 82y multi | | 1.50 | 1.10 |
| **4135** | A3963 82y multi | | 1.50 | 1.10 |
| *a.* | Booklet pane of 5, #4131-4135 | | 7.50 | |
| | *Nos. 4126-4135 (10)* | | 13.00 | 9.75 |

Letter Writing Day.

Rilakkuma A3964

Kiiroitori and Korilakkuma A3965

Characters Picking Strawberries A3966

Kiiroitori, Korilakkuma and Rilakkuma A3967

Characters With Flowers A3968

Characters and Skerwered Dumplings A3969

Characters in Tub — A3970

Characters and Lemon — A3971

Chairoikoguma and Rilakkuma A3972

Characters With Toy A3973

Rilakkuma and Kiiroitori A3974

Korilakkuma A3975

Kiiroitori A3976

Rilakkuma A3977

Rilakkuma Holding Letter — A3978

Characters and Yellow Dots — A3979

Rilakkuma Eating A3980

Korilakkuma and Toys A3981

Rilakkuma and Kiiroitori A3982

Rilakkuma A3983

***Die Cut Perf. 13x13¼ (#4136a, 4136b, 4136d, 4136e), Die Cut Perf. (#4136c, 4136i, 4136j), Die Cut Perf. 11½x11¼ (#4136f), Die Cut Perf. 11½ (#4136g), Die Cut Perf. 13¼x13 (#4136h)***

**2017, July 26** **Litho.**

**Self-Adhesive**

| | | | | |
|---|---|---|---|---|
| **4136** | Sheet of 10 | | 11.00 | |
| *a.* | A3964 62y multi | | 1.10 | .85 |
| *b.* | A3965 62y multi | | 1.10 | .85 |
| *c.* | A3966 62y multi | | 1.10 | .85 |
| *d.* | A3967 62y multi | | 1.10 | .85 |
| *e.* | A3968 62y multi | | 1.10 | .85 |
| *f.* | A3969 62y multi | | 1.10 | .85 |
| *g.* | A3970 62y multi | | 1.10 | .85 |
| *h.* | A3971 62y multi | | 1.10 | .85 |
| *i.* | A3972 62y multi | | 1.10 | .85 |
| *j.* | A3973 62y multi | | 1.10 | .85 |

***Die Cut Perf. 13x13¼ (#4137a, 4137g, 4137h, 4137i), Die Cut Perf 11¾ (#4137b, 4137d), Die Cut Perf. 11 (#4132c), Die Cut Perf. 13¼x13 (#4137e, 4137j), Die Cut Perf. (#4137f)***

| | | | | |
|---|---|---|---|---|
| **4137** | Sheet of 10 | | 15.00 | |
| *a.* | A3974 82y multi | | 1.50 | 1.10 |
| *b.* | A3975 82y multi | | 1.50 | 1.10 |
| *c.* | A3976 82y multi | | 1.50 | 1.10 |
| *d.* | A3977 82y multi | | 1.50 | 1.10 |
| *e.* | A3978 82y multi | | 1.50 | 1.10 |
| *f.* | A3979 82y multi | | 1.50 | 1.10 |
| *g.* | A3980 82y multi | | 1.50 | 1.10 |
| *h.* | A3981 82y multi | | 1.50 | 1.10 |
| *i.* | A3982 82y multi | | 1.50 | 1.10 |
| *j.* | A3983 82y multi | | 1.50 | 1.10 |

Miniature Sheet

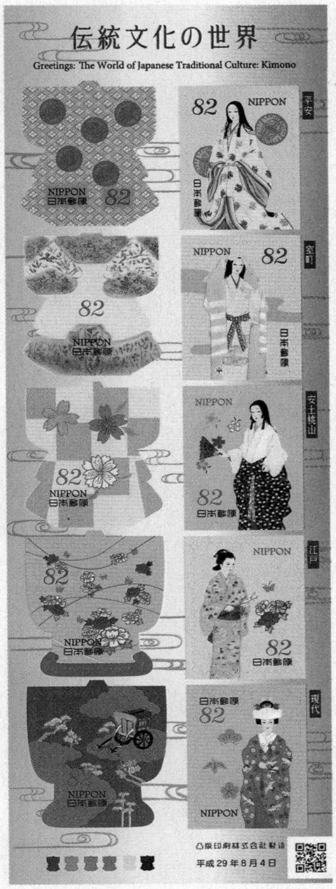


Kimonos — A3984

No. 4138: a, Green and red kimono (26x27mm). b, Woman in Heian era kimono (light green background, 22x28mm). c, Beige and brown kimono (26x27mm). d, Woman in Muromachi era kimono (light brown and brown background, 22x28mm). e, Beige and brown kimono with checkerboard pattern and flowers (26x27mm). f, Woman in Azuchi-Momoyama era kimono (pale orange background, 22x28mm). g, Blue and red kimono with flowers (26x27mm). h, Woman in Edo era kimono (light blue background, 22x28mm). i, Purple kimono with flowers and cart (26x27mm). j, Modern kimono (buff background, 22x28mm).

***Die Cut Perf. 11x10¼ (#4138a, 4138c, 4138e, 4138g, 4138i), Die Cut Perf. 11¾x11½ (#4138b, 4138d, 4138f, 4138h, 4138j)***

**2017, Aug. 4** **Litho.**

**Self-Adhesive**

| | | | | |
|---|---|---|---|---|
| **4138** | A3984 Sheet of 10 | | 15.00 | |
| *a.-j.* | 82y Any single | | 1.50 | 1.10 |

A3985

A3986

A3987

A3988

A3989

A3990

A3991

A3992

A3993

Women's Fashion — A3994

***Die Cut Perf. 11¼x11***

**2017, Aug. 9** **Litho.**

**Self-Adhesive**

| | | | | |
|---|---|---|---|---|
| **4139** | Sheet of 10 | | 15.00 | |
| *a.* | A3985 82y multi | | 1.50 | 1.10 |
| *b.* | A3986 82y multi | | 1.50 | 1.10 |
| *c.* | A3987 82y multi | | 1.50 | 1.10 |
| *d.* | A3988 82y multi | | 1.50 | 1.10 |
| *e.* | A3989 82y multi | | 1.50 | 1.10 |
| *f.* | A3990 82y multi | | 1.50 | 1.10 |
| *g.* | A3991 82y multi | | 1.50 | 1.10 |
| *h.* | A3992 82y multi | | 1.50 | 1.10 |
| *i.* | A3993 82y multi | | 1.50 | 1.10 |
| *j.* | A3994 82y multi | | 1.50 | 1.10 |

Butterflies A3995 — Deer A3996

Rabbits A3997 — Horses A3998

Dragonflies A3999 — Peacock and Peony A4000

Geese and Clover A4001 — Mandarin Ducks A4002

Egrets
A4003

Plovers
A4004

***Die Cut Perf. (#4140a), Die Cut Perf. 11¼x11¾ (#4140b, 4140e, 4141b, 4141d, 4141e), Die Cut Perf. 11¾x11¼ (#4140c, 4140d, 4141c), Die Cut Perf. 11¼ (#4141a)***

**2017, Aug. 18** **Litho.**

**Self-Adhesive**

| | | | |
|---|---|---|---|
| **4140** | Sheet of 10, 2 each #4140a-4140e | 12.50 | |
| *a.* | A3995 62y multi | 1.25 | .95 |
| *b.* | A3996 62y multi | 1.25 | .95 |
| *c.* | A3997 62y multi | 1.25 | .95 |
| *d.* | A3998 62y multi | 1.25 | .95 |
| *e.* | A3999 62y multi | 1.25 | .95 |
| **4141** | Sheet of 10, 2 each #4141a-4141e | 12.50 | |
| *a.* | A4000 82y multi | 1.50 | 1.10 |
| *b.* | A4001 82y multi | 1.50 | 1.10 |
| *c.* | A4002 82y multi | 1.50 | 1.10 |
| *d.* | A4003 82y multi | 1.50 | 1.10 |
| *e.* | A4004 82y multi | 1.50 | 1.10 |

Mailbox in Autumn
A4005

Girl and Mushrooms
A4006

Chestnuts
A4007

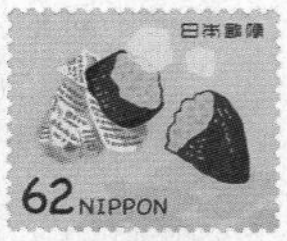
Baked Sweet Potato
A4008

Girl Raking Leaves
A4009

House and Trees
A4010

Rabbits Pounding Rice
A4011

Child Reading in Moonlight
A4012

Mushrooms on Brazier
A4013

Girl in Library
A4014

Dragonflies Over Rice Field
A4015

Mailbox in Autumn
A4016

Fish on Brazier — A4017

***Die Cut Perf. 13x13¼ (#4142a, 4142b, 4142e, 4142f, 4143b, 4143d, 4143f), Die Cut Perf. (#4142c, 4143a, 4143c), Die Cut Perf. 13¼x13 (#4142d, 4143e), Die Cut Perf. 12 (#4143g)***

**2017, Aug. 23** **Litho.**

**Self-Adhesive**

| | | | |
|---|---|---|---|
| **4142** | Sheet of 10, #4142a, 4142b, 2 each #4142c-4142f | 12.50 | |
| *a.* | A4005 62y multi | 1.25 | .95 |
| *b.* | A4006 62y multi | 1.25 | .95 |
| *c.* | A4007 62y multi | 1.25 | .95 |
| *d.* | A4008 62y multi | 1.25 | .95 |
| *e.* | A4009 62y multi | 1.25 | .95 |
| *f.* | A4010 62y multi | 1.25 | .95 |
| **4143** | Sheet of 10, #4143a, 4143c, 4143f, 4143g, 2 each #4143b, 4143d, 4143e | 15.00 | |
| *a.* | A4011 82y multi | 1.50 | 1.10 |
| *b.* | A4012 82y multi | 1.50 | 1.10 |
| *c.* | A4013 82y multi | 1.50 | 1.10 |
| *d.* | A4014 82y multi | 1.50 | 1.10 |
| *e.* | A4015 82y multi | 1.50 | 1.10 |
| *f.* | A4016 82y multi | 1.50 | 1.10 |
| *g.* | A4017 82y multi | 1.50 | 1.10 |

Miniature Sheet

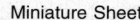

72nd National Athletic Meet, Ehime — A4018

No. 4144: a, Kendo. b, Mount Ishizuchi. c, Rowing. d, Shimanami Kaido and bridge. e, Weight lifting. f, Bathhouse at Dogo Onsen Hot Springs. g, Archery. h, Mikan oranges. i, Basketball. j, Red seabream.

**2017, Aug. 30** **Litho.** ***Perf. 13½***

| | | | | |
|---|---|---|---|---|
| **4144** | A4018 | Sheet of 10 | 15.00 | 15.00 |
| *a.-j.* | | 82y Any single | 1.50 | 1.10 |

The Koya Tama River, Kii Province, by Eizan Kikukawa
A4019

Mount Hiyori and Toba Bay, Shima Province, by Hiroshige Utagawa
A4020

Yosooi and Matsumura of the Matsubaya, by Utamaro Kitagawa
A4021

Mount Inasa at Nagasaki, Hizen Province, by Hiroshige Utagawa
A4022

Kisegawa of the Matsubaya, by Utamaro Kitagawa
A4023

Daijingu Shrine at Kashima, Hitachi Province, by Hiroshige Utagawa
A4024

Beauty with Ball and Fan, by Utamaro Kitagawa
A4025

Kanegasaka, Tanba Province, by Hiroshige Utagawa
A4026

Hanaogi of the Ogiya, by Eishi Chobunsai
A4027

Clear Evening on the Coast, Tsushima Province, by Hiroshige Utagawa
A4028

**2017, Sept. 6** **Litho.** ***Perf. 13½***

| | | | |
|---|---|---|---|
| **4145** | Sheet of 10 | 15.00 | 15.00 |
| *a.* | A4019 82y multi | 1.50 | 1.10 |
| *b.* | A4020 82y multi | 1.50 | 1.10 |
| *c.* | A4021 82y multi | 1.50 | 1.10 |
| *d.* | A4022 82y multi | 1.50 | 1.10 |
| *e.* | A4023 82y multi | 1.50 | 1.10 |
| *f.* | A4024 82y multi | 1.50 | 1.10 |
| *g.* | A4025 82y multi | 1.50 | 1.10 |
| *h.* | A4026 82y multi | 1.50 | 1.10 |
| *i.* | A4027 82y multi | 1.50 | 1.10 |
| *j.* | A4028 82y multi | 1.50 | 1.10 |

Miniature Sheets

A4029

Posukuma and Friends — A4030

No. 4146: a Two bears near mailbox. b, Two bears, one with letter, near mailbox. c, Three bears. d, Large bear delivering letter to small bear. e, Bear and flowers. f, Two bears, tree, letter in mailbox. g, Bear with violin. h, Mailbox, bear licking envelope. i, Two bears on swings. j, Crying bear and letter.

No. 4147 — Tree and: a, Two bears with raised arms, two beamed yellow sixteenth notes. b, Bear and owl, red orange eighth note. c, Two bears, one with mail bag, with arms crossed, green eighth note. d, Two bears, one with crossed arms, two beamed yellow sixteenth notes. e, Two bears waving, red orange eighth note. f, Two bears with mail bags waving, red eighth note. g, Two bears, one with mail bag, sitting, red eighth note. h, Two bears sitting, green eighth note. i, Two bears waving, two beamed blue sixteenth notes. j, Seven bears and owl, red orange eighth note and two beamed blue sixteenth notes.

***Die Cut Perf. 13½x13¼***

**2017, Sept. 15 Litho.**

**Self-Adhesive**

| | | | | |
|---|---|---|---|---|
| **4146** | A4029 | Sheet of 10 | 11.00 | |
| *a.-j.* | | 62y Any single | 1.10 | .85 |
| **4147** | A4030 | Sheet of 10 | 15.00 | |
| *a.-j.* | | 82y Any single | 1.50 | 1.10 |

**PREFECTURE ISSUES**

Japan has 47 prefectures (political subdivisions) and 13 postal regions (12 until 2004). Since 1989, the national postal ministry has issued stamps to publicize each prefecture. These prefectural stamps are valid throughout Japan and were issued not only in the prefecture named on the stamp but in all other prefectures in the postal region, and in one or more post offices in the other 11 or 12 postal regions. Prefectural stamps are distinguishable from other Japanese stamps by the style of the ideographic characters of "Nippon yubin" on each stamp:

日本郵便

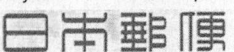

Inscr. on National Stamps since 1948

日本郵便

Inscr. on Prefectural Stamps

Monkeys (Nagano) — ZA1

Cherries on Tree (Yamagata) — ZA2

*Shurei-mon,* Gate of Courtesy (Okinawa) — ZA3

Dogo Hot Spa (Ehime) — ZA4

Blue-eyed Doll (Kanagawa) ZA5

Seto Inland Sea (Hiroshima) — ZA6

Memorial Hall and Mandai Bridge (Niigata) — ZA8

Nagoya Castle and *Shachihoko* (Aichi) — ZA9

Mt. Takasaki Monkey Holding Perilla Leaf, Fruit (Oita) — ZA10

City Hall, 1888 (Hokkaido) ZA11

Runner, Flower (Hokkaido) ZA12

Kumamoto Castle (Kumamoto) ZA13

Stone Lantern, Kenroku-en Park (Ishikawa) — ZA14

Bunraku Puppets and Theater (Osaka) — ZA15

Shigaraki Ware Raccoon Dog and Lake Biwa (Shiga) ZA16

Apples and Blossoms (Aomori) — ZA17

Raccoon Dogs Dancing (Chiba) — ZA18

Blowfish Lanterns (Yamaguchi) ZA19

Tokyo Station (Tokyo) — ZA20

2nd Asian Winter Olympics (Hokkaido) ZA21

Waterfalls (Toyama) ZA22

***Perf. 13, 13½ (#Z4, Z11, Z20), 13x13½ (#Z12-Z19)***

**1989-90 Photo., Litho. (#Z16-Z17)**

| | | | | | |
|---|---|---|---|---|---|
| **Z1** | ZA1 | 62y | multicolored | 1.10 | .70 |
| **Z2** | ZA2 | 62y | multicolored | 1.10 | .70 |
| **Z3** | ZA3 | 62y | multicolored | 1.10 | .70 |
| **Z4** | ZA4 | 62y | multicolored | 1.10 | .70 |
| **Z5** | ZA5 | 62y | multicolored | 1.10 | .70 |
| **Z6** | | 62y | sampan, bridge | 1.10 | .70 |
| **Z7** | | 62y | islands, stairs, starbursts | 1.10 | .70 |
| *a.* | ZA6 | | Pair, #Z6-Z7 | 2.25 | 2.25 |
| **Z8** | ZA8 | 62y | multicolored | 1.10 | .70 |
| **Z9** | ZA9 | 62y | multicolored | 1.10 | .70 |
| **Z10** | ZA10 | 62y | multicolored | 1.10 | .70 |
| **Z11** | ZA11 | 62y | multicolored | 1.10 | .70 |
| **Z12** | ZA12 | 62y | multicolored | 1.10 | .70 |
| **Z13** | ZA13 | 62y | multicolored | 1.10 | .70 |
| **Z14** | ZA14 | 62y | multicolored | 1.10 | .70 |
| **Z15** | ZA15 | 62y | multicolored | 1.10 | .70 |
| **Z16** | ZA16 | 62y | multicolored | 1.10 | .70 |
| **Z17** | ZA17 | 62y | multicolored | 1.10 | .70 |
| **Z18** | ZA18 | 62y | multicolored | 1.10 | .70 |
| **Z19** | ZA19 | 62y | multicolored | 1.10 | .70 |
| **Z20** | ZA20 | 62y | multicolored | 1.10 | .70 |
| **Z21** | ZA21 | 62y | multicolored | 1.10 | .70 |
| **Z22** | ZA22 | 62y | multicolored | 1.10 | .70 |
| | | | *Nos. Z1-Z22 (22)* | 24.20 | 15.40 |

Sheets containing 4 Nos. Z1, Z2, Z4, Z11 or 3 No. Z14 + label, 3 No. Z19 + label were lottery prizes.

Issued: Nos. Z1-Z2, 4/1; No. Z3, 5/15; No. Z4, 6/1; No. Z5, 6/2; NOs. Z6-Z7, 7/7; No. Z8, 7/14; No. Z9, 8/1; Nos. Z10-Z11, 8/15; No. Z12, 9/1; No. Z13, 9/29; Nos. Z14-Z17, 10/2; No. Z18, 10/27; Nos. Z19-Z20, 11/1; No. Z21, 3/1/90; No. Z22, 4/18/90.

See Nos. Z263, Z285, Z363.

Nos. Z23-Z69 were issued as one set. It is broken into sections for ease of reference. See No. Z69a for sheet containing all 47 stamps.

Hokkaido ZA23 — Aomori ZA24

Iwate — ZA25 — Miyagi — ZA26

Akita ZA27 — Yamagata ZA28

Fukushima ZA29 — Ibaraki ZA30

Flowers of the Prefectures: No. Z23, Sweet briar. No. Z24, Apple blossom. No. Z25, Paulowina. No. Z26, Japanese bush clover. No. Z27, Butterbur flower. No. Z28, Safflower. No. Z29, Alpine rose. No. Z30, Rose.

**1990, Apr. 27 Litho.** ***Perf. 13½***

| | | | | |
|---|---|---|---|---|
| **Z23** | ZA23 62y multicolored | | 3.50 | .70 |
| **Z24** | ZA24 62y multicolored | | 1.25 | .70 |
| **Z25** | ZA25 62y multicolored | | 1.25 | .70 |
| **Z26** | ZA26 62y multicolored | | 1.25 | .70 |
| **Z27** | ZA27 62y multicolored | | 1.25 | .70 |
| **Z28** | ZA28 62y multicolored | | 1.25 | .70 |
| **Z29** | ZA29 62y multicolored | | 1.25 | .70 |
| **Z30** | ZA30 62y multicolored | | 1.25 | .70 |
| | *Nos. Z23-Z30 (8)* | | 12.25 | 5.60 |

See Nos. Z190, Z614-Z619.

Tochigi — ZA31 — Gunma — ZA32

Saitama — ZA33 — Chiba — ZA34

Tokyo ZA35 — Kanagawa ZA36

Yamanashi ZA37 — Nagano ZA38

Niigata — ZA39 — Toyama — ZA40

No. Z31, Yashio azalea. No. Z32, Japanese azalea. No. Z33, Primrose. No. Z34, Rape blossom. No. Z35, Cherry blossom. No. Z36, Gold-banded lily. No. Z37, Cherry blossom. No. Z38, Autumn bellflower. No. Z39, Tulip. No. Z40, Tulip.

| | | | | |
|---|---|---|---|---|
| **Z31** | ZA31 62y multicolored | | 1.25 | .70 |
| **Z32** | ZA32 62y multicolored | | 1.25 | .70 |
| **Z33** | ZA33 62y multicolored | | 1.25 | .70 |
| **Z34** | ZA34 62y multicolored | | 1.25 | .70 |
| **Z35** | ZA35 62y multicolored | | 1.25 | .70 |
| **Z36** | ZA36 62y multicolored | | 1.25 | .70 |
| **Z37** | ZA37 62y multicolored | | 1.25 | .70 |
| **Z38** | ZA38 62y multicolored | | 3.50 | .70 |
| **Z39** | ZA39 62y multicolored | | 1.25 | .70 |
| **Z40** | ZA40 62y multicolored | | 1.25 | .70 |
| | *Nos. Z31-Z40 (10)* | | 14.75 | 7.00 |

See No. Z197.

Ishikawa ZA41 — Fukui ZA42

Gifu ZA43 — Shizuoka ZA44

Aichi — ZA45 — Mie — ZA46

Shiga — ZA47 — Kyoto — ZA48

Osaka — ZA49 — Hyogo — ZA50

No. Z41, Black lily. No. Z42, Daffodil. No. Z43, Chinese milk vetch. No. Z44, Azalea. No. Z45, Rabbit-ear iris. No. Z46, Iris. No. Z47, Alpine rose. No. Z48, Drooping cherry blossom. No. Z49, Japanese apricot and primrose. No. Z50, Chrysanthemum.

| | | | | |
|---|---|---|---|---|
| **Z41** | ZA41 62y multicolored | | 1.25 | .70 |
| **Z42** | ZA42 62y multicolored | | 1.25 | .70 |
| **Z43** | ZA43 62y multicolored | | 1.50 | .70 |
| **Z44** | ZA44 62y multicolored | | 2.00 | .70 |
| **Z45** | ZA45 62y multicolored | | 1.25 | .70 |
| **Z46** | ZA46 62y multicolored | | 1.25 | .70 |
| **Z47** | ZA47 62y multicolored | | 3.00 | .70 |
| **Z48** | ZA48 62y multicolored | | 3.00 | .70 |
| **Z49** | ZA49 62y multicolored | | 1.25 | .70 |
| **Z50** | ZA50 62y multicolored | | 1.25 | .70 |
| | *Nos. Z41-Z50 (10)* | | 17.00 | 7.00 |

Nara ZA51 — Wakayama ZA52

Tottori ZA53 — Shimane ZA54

Okayama ZA55 — Hiroshima ZA56

Yamaguchi ZA57 — Tokushima ZA58

Kagawa — ZA59 — Ehime — ZA60

No. Z51, Double cherry blossom. No. Z52, Japanese apricot. No. Z53, Pear blossom. No. Z54, Peony. No. Z55, Peach blossom. No. Z56, Japanese Maple. No. Z57, Summer orange blossom. No. Z58, Sudachi orange blossom. No. Z59, Olive blossom. No. Z60, Mandarin orange blossom.

| | | | | |
|---|---|---|---|---|
| **Z51** | ZA51 62y multicolored | | 2.00 | .70 |
| **Z52** | ZA52 62y multicolored | | 1.50 | .70 |
| **Z53** | ZA53 62y multicolored | | 1.25 | .70 |
| **Z54** | ZA54 62y multicolored | | 1.25 | .70 |
| **Z55** | ZA55 62y multicolored | | 1.25 | .70 |
| **Z56** | ZA56 62y multicolored | | 1.25 | .70 |
| **Z57** | ZA57 62y multicolored | | 1.25 | .70 |
| **Z58** | ZA58 62y multicolored | | 1.50 | .70 |
| **Z59** | ZA59 62y multicolored | | 5.00 | .70 |
| **Z60** | ZA60 62y multicolored | | 2.50 | .70 |
| | *Nos. Z51-Z60 (10)* | | 18.75 | 7.00 |

Kochi ZA61 — Fukuoka ZA62

Saga ZA63 — Nagasaki ZA64

Kumamoto ZA65 — Oita ZA66

Miyazaki ZA67 — Kagoshima ZA68

Okinawa — ZA69

No. Z61, Myrica. No. Z62, Japanese apricot. No. Z63, Laurel. No. Z64, Unzen azalea. No. Z65, Autumn bellflower. No. Z66, Japanese apricot of bungo. No. Z67, Crinum. No. Z68, Rosebay. No. Z69, Coral tree.

| | | | | |
|---|---|---|---|---|
| **Z61** | ZA61 62y multicolored | | 2.00 | .70 |
| **Z62** | ZA62 62y multicolored | | 1.25 | .70 |
| **Z63** | ZA63 62y multicolored | | 1.25 | .70 |
| **Z64** | ZA64 62y multicolored | | 1.25 | .70 |
| **Z65** | ZA65 62y multicolored | | 1.25 | .70 |
| **Z66** | ZA66 62y multicolored | | 1.25 | .70 |
| **Z67** | ZA67 62y multicolored | | 1.25 | .70 |
| **Z68** | ZA68 62y multicolored | | 1.25 | .70 |
| **Z69** | ZA69 62y multicolored | | 1.25 | .70 |
| *a.* | Sheet of 47 + 3 labels, #Z23-Z69 | | 110.00 | |
| | *Nos. Z61-Z69 (9)* | | 12.00 | 6.30 |

Nos. Z23-Z69 were issued in sheets of 20. No. Z69a was released in all prefectures.

Seven Baby Crows (Ibaraki) — ZA70

Inns of Tsumago & Magome (Nagano)

ZA71 ZA72

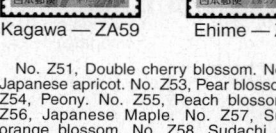

Mt. Fuji and Tea Picking (Shizuoka) ZA73

Two Peaches (Fukushima) ZA74

Mt. Sakurajima (Kagoshima) ZA75

Fireworks Festival of Omagari (Akita) ZA76

Travel Expo '90, Nagasaki (Nagasaki) — ZA77

Tokyo Shin Post Office (Tokyo) ZA78

Yasukibushi Folk Song (Shimane) ZA79

Ryukyu Dancer (Okinawa) ZA80

**Litho., Litho. & Engr. (#Z70-Z71)**

**1990** ***Perf. 13***

| | | | | |
|---|---|---|---|---|
| **Z70** | ZA70 62y multicolored | | 1.10 | .70 |
| **Z71** | ZA71 62y blk & buff | | 1.10 | .70 |
| **Z72** | ZA72 62y blk & pale grn | | 1.10 | .70 |
| *a.* | Pair, #Z71-Z72 | | 2.25 | 2.25 |
| **Z73** | ZA73 62y multicolored | | 1.10 | .70 |
| **Z74** | ZA74 62y multicolored | | 1.10 | .70 |
| **Z75** | ZA75 62y multicolored | | 1.10 | .70 |
| **Z76** | ZA76 62y multicolored | | 1.10 | .70 |
| **Z77** | ZA77 62y multicolored | | 1.10 | .70 |
| **Z78** | ZA78 62y multicolored | | 1.10 | .70 |
| **Z79** | ZA79 62y multicolored | | 1.10 | .70 |
| **Z80** | ZA80 62y multicolored | | 1.10 | .70 |
| | *Nos. Z70-Z80 (11)* | | 12.10 | 7.70 |

Issued: Nos. Z70-Z72, 5/1; No. Z73, 5/2; No. Z74, 6/1; Nos. Z75-Z76, 7/2; No. Z77, 8/1; No. Z78, 8/6; Nos. Z79-Z80, 8/15.

Sheets of 3 + label of Nos. Z70, Z73, Z80 were lottery prizes. Value, each $3.25.

See Nos. Z332-Z333.

Dancing Girl (Kyoto) ZA81

Old Path of Kumano (Wakayama) ZA82

45th Natl. Athletic Meet (Fukuoka) ZA83

Izu Swamp, Swans (Miyagi) ZA84

Spring (Gifu) — ZA85

Summer (Gifu) — ZA86

Autumn (Gifu) — ZA87

Winter (Gifu) — ZA88

Nursery Rhyme, Toryanse (Saitama) — ZA89

Japanese Cranes (Hokkaido) ZA90

**1990**

| | | | |
|---|---|---|---|
| **Z81** | ZA81 62y multicolored | 1.10 | .70 |
| **Z82** | ZA82 62y multicolored | 1.10 | .70 |
| **Z83** | ZA83 62y multicolored | 1.10 | .70 |
| **Z84** | ZA84 62y multicolored | 1.10 | .70 |
| **Z85** | ZA85 62y multicolored | 1.10 | .70 |
| **Z86** | ZA86 62y multicolored | 1.10 | .70 |
| **Z87** | ZA87 62y multicolored | 1.10 | .70 |
| **Z88** | ZA88 62y multicolored | 1.10 | .70 |
| *a.* | Strip of 4, #Z85-Z88 | 4.50 | 4.50 |
| **Z89** | ZA89 62y multicolored | 1.10 | .70 |
| **Z90** | ZA90 62y multicolored | 1.10 | .70 |
| | *Nos. Z81-Z90 (10)* | 11.00 | 7.00 |

Issued: Nos. Z81-Z83, 9/3; No. Z84, 10/1; Nos. Z85-Z88, 10/9; No. Z89, 10/12; No. Z90, 10/30.

Sheets of 3 No. Z82 + label were lottery prizes. Value, $3.25.

See Nos. 3282-3285, Z171-Z174.

Bizen Ware (Okayama) — ZA92

Battle of Yashima (Kagawa) — ZA91

Yoshinogari Ruins (Saga) — ZA94

Bride Under Cherry Blossoms (Yamanashi) ZA95

Carp (Niigata) ZA96

Lily of the Valley (Hokkaido) ZA97

Lilac (Hokkaido) ZA98

Daylily (Hokkaido) ZA99

Rowanberry (Hokkaido) ZA100

**Litho., Photo. (#Z94-Z95)**

**1991** ***Perf. 13***

| | | | | |
|---|---|---|---|---|
| **Z91** | ZA91 | 62y multicolored | 1.10 | .70 |
| **Z92** | | 62y pedestal | 1.10 | .70 |
| **Z93** | | 62y bowl | 1.10 | .70 |
| *a.* | ZA92 Pair, #Z92-Z93 | | 2.25 | 2.25 |
| **Z94** | ZA94 | 62y multicolored | 1.10 | .70 |
| **Z95** | ZA95 | 62y multicolored | 1.10 | .70 |
| **Z96** | ZA96 | 62y multicolored | 1.10 | .70 |
| **Z97** | ZA97 | 62y multicolored | 1.10 | .70 |
| **Z98** | ZA98 | 62y multicolored | 1.10 | .70 |
| **Z99** | ZA99 | 62y multicolored | 1.10 | .70 |
| **Z100** | ZA100 | 62y multicolored | 1.10 | .70 |
| *a.* | Strip of 4, #Z97-Z100 | | 4.50 | 4.50 |
| | *Nos. Z91-Z100 (10)* | | 11.00 | 7.00 |

Issued: No. Z91, 2/19; Nos. Z92-Z93, 4/5; No. Z94, 4/12; No. Z95, 4/18; No. Z96, 5/1; Nos. Z97-Z100, 5/31.

See Nos. 3286-3289, 3913-3916, Z304-Z307.

Nikkou Mountains (Tochigi) — ZA101

Mt. Iwate by Yaoji Hashimoto (Iwate) — ZA102

Wooden Puppet (Tokushima) ZA103

Whales (Kochi) ZA104

Fringed Orchids (Tokyo) ZA105

Cape Toi, Horses (Miyazaki) ZA106

Black Pearls of Kabira Bay (Okinawa) ZA107

Japanese Pears (Tottori) ZA108

Tsujun-kyo Bridge (Kumamoto) ZA109

**1991** **Photo.**

| | | | |
|---|---|---|---|
| **Z101** | ZA101 62y multicolored | 1.10 | .70 |
| **Z102** | ZA102 62y multicolored | 1.10 | .70 |
| *a.* | Booklet pane of 10 | 11.00 | |
| | Complete booklet, #Z102a | 11.00 | |
| **Z103** | ZA103 62y multicolored | 1.10 | .70 |
| *a.* | Pane of 10 | 11.00 | |
| **Z104** | ZA104 62y multicolored | 1.10 | .70 |
| *a.* | Pane of 10 | 11.00 | |
| **Z105** | ZA105 41y multicolored | 2.50 | 1.00 |
| *a.* | Booklet pane of 10 | 15.00 | |
| | Complete booklet, #Z105a | 15.00 | |
| **Z106** | ZA106 62y multicolored | 1.10 | .70 |
| *a.* | Booklet pane of 10 | 15.00 | |
| | Complete booklet, #Z106a | 15.00 | |
| **Z107** | ZA107 41y multicolored | .80 | .50 |
| **Z108** | ZA108 62y multicolored | 1.10 | .70 |
| **Z109** | ZA109 62y multicolored | 1.10 | .70 |
| *a.* | Booklet pane of 10 | 15.00 | |
| | Complete booklet, #Z108a | 15.00 | |
| | *Nos. Z101-Z109 (9)* | 11.00 | 6.40 |

Issued: No. Z101, 5/29; No. Z102, 6/10; Nos. Z103-Z104, 6/26; Nos. Z105-Z106, 7/1; Nos. Z107-Z108, 8/1; No. Z109, 8/26.

Sheets of 3 No. Z106 + label were lottery prizes. Value, $3.

Ninja, Iga Ueno Castle (Mie) ZA111

46th Natl. Athletic Meet (Ishikawa)
ZA110

Eyeglass Industry (Fukui)
ZA112

Nursery Rhyme, Tortoise and the Hare — ZA113

Kobe City Weathervane (Hyogo) — ZA114

Spring (Nara) — ZA115

Autumn (Nara, Gunma) — ZA116

**Litho., Photo. (#Z110, Z112)**

**1991** ***Perf. 13, 13½ (#Z110)***

| | | | |
|---|---|---|---|
| **Z110** | ZA110 41y multicolored | .80 | .50 |
| *a.* | Pane of 10 | 8.00 | |
| **Z111** | ZA111 62y multicolored | 1.10 | .70 |
| *a.* | Booklet pane of 10 | 14.00 | |
| | Complete booklet, #Z111a | 14.00 | |
| **Z112** | ZA112 62y multicolored | 1.10 | .70 |
| *a.* | Booklet pane of 10 | 14.00 | |
| | Complete booklet, #Z112a | 14.00 | |
| **Z113** | ZA113 62y multicolored | 1.10 | .70 |
| *a.* | Booklet pane of 10 | 14.00 | |
| | Complete booklet, #Z113a | 14.00 | |
| **Z114** | ZA114 62y multicolored | 1.10 | .70 |
| *a.* | Booklet pane of 10 | 14.00 | |
| | Complete booklet, #Z114a | 14.00 | |
| **Z115** | ZA115 62y multicolored | 1.10 | .70 |
| **Z116** | ZA116 62y multicolored | 1.10 | .70 |
| *a.* | Pair, #Z115-Z116 | 2.25 | 2.25 |
| *b.* | Booklet pane, 5 #Z116a | 14.00 | |
| | Complete booklet, #Z116b | 14.00 | |
| | *Nos. Z110-Z116 (7)* | 7.40 | 4.70 |

Issued: No. Z110, 9/2; No. Z111, 9/10; No. Z112, 10/1; No. Z113, 10/23; Nos. Z114-Z116, 10/25.

See Nos. 3189G, Z177-Z178.

Gogo-An Temple, Sea of Japan (Niigata)
ZA117

Natl. Land Afforestation Campaign (Fukuoka)
ZA118

Arctic Fox (Hokkaido)
ZA119

Tateyama Mountain Range (Toyama)
ZA120

Rikuchu Coast (Iwate) — ZA121

Kurushima Strait (Ehime)
ZA122

Tsurusaki Dance (Oita)
ZA123

Tanabata Lantern Festival (Yamaguchi)
ZA124

Shasui-no-taki Waterfall (Kanagawa)
ZA125

Kurodabushi Dance (Fukuoka)
ZA126

Boat Race (Okinawa)
ZA127

Osaka Castle, Business Park (Osaka)
ZA128

Owl, Mt. Horaiji (Aichi) — ZA129

**1992** **Litho.** ***Perf. 13½***

| | | | |
|---|---|---|---|
| **Z117** | ZA117 41y multicolored | .80 | .50 |
| *a.* | Pane of 10 | 8.00 | |
| | **Photo.** | | |
| **Z118** | ZA118 41y multicolored | .80 | .50 |
| **Z119** | ZA119 62y multicolored | 1.10 | .70 |
| *a.* | Souvenir sheet of 3 | 3.50 | 3.50 |
| | **Litho.** | | |
| **Z120** | ZA120 62y multicolored | 1.10 | .70 |
| *a.* | Pane of 10 | 11.00 | |
| | **Photo.** | | |
| **Z121** | ZA121 62y multicolored | 1.10 | .70 |
| *a.* | Pane of 10 | 11.00 | |
| **Z122** | ZA122 62y multicolored | 1.10 | .70 |
| *a.* | Pane of 10 | 11.00 | |
| **Z123** | ZA123 62y multicolored | 1.10 | .70 |
| **Z124** | ZA124 62y multicolored | 1.10 | .70 |
| **Z125** | ZA125 62y multicolored | 1.10 | .70 |
| *a.* | Pane of 10 | 11.00 | |
| *b.* | Souvenir sheet of 3 | 3.50 | 3.50 |
| | **Litho.** | | |
| **Z126** | ZA126 62y multicolored | 1.10 | .70 |
| **Z127** | ZA127 62y multicolored | 1.10 | .70 |
| **Z128** | ZA128 41y multicolored | .80 | .60 |
| | **Photo.** | | |
| **Z129** | ZA129 62y multicolored | 1.10 | .70 |
| *a.* | Souvenir sheet of 3 | 3.50 | 3.50 |
| *b.* | Pane of 10 | 11.00 | |
| | *Nos. Z117-Z129 (13)* | 13.40 | 8.60 |

Issued: No. Z117, 5/1; No. Z118, 5/8; No. Z119, 5/29; No. Z120, 6/10; Nos. Z121-Z122, 6/23; No. Z124, 7/7; No. Z123, 7/23; No. Z125, 7/24; No. Z126, 8/3; No. Z127, 8/17; No. Z129, 10/15.

See also No. Z320.

Oga Peninsula (Akita)
ZA130

Fukuroda Waterfall (Ibaraki)
ZA131

Notojima Bridge, Nanao Bay (Ishikawa)
ZA132

Tama District Mountains (Metropolitan Tokyo)
ZA133

Harbor Seal (Hokkaido) — ZA134

Peace Statue (Kagawa)
ZA135

Hana Ta'ue Rice Planting Festival (Hiroshima)
ZA136

Paradise Flycatcher and Mt. Fuji (Shizuoka)
ZA137

Sailboats on Lake Biwa (Shiga)
ZA138

Matumoto Castle & Japan Alps (Nagano)
ZA139

Ohara Festival (Kagoshima)
ZA140

Oirase Mountain Stream (Aomori)
ZA141

Yourou Valley (Chiba) — ZA142

**1993** **Litho.** ***Perf. 13½***

| | | | |
|---|---|---|---|
| **Z130** | ZA130 41y multicolored | .80 | .50 |
| *a.* | Pane of 10 | 8.00 | |
| **Z131** | ZA131 62y multicolored | 1.10 | .70 |
| *a.* | Pane of 10 | 11.00 | |
| | **Photo.** | | |
| **Z132** | ZA132 62y multicolored | 1.10 | .70 |
| *a.* | Pane of 10 | 11.50 | |
| **Z133** | ZA133 62y multicolored | 1.10 | .70 |
| *a.* | Booklet pane of 10 | 11.50 | |
| | Complete booklet, #Z133a | 11.50 | |
| **Z134** | ZA134 62y multicolored | 1.10 | .70 |
| **Z135** | ZA135 62y multicolored | 1.10 | .70 |
| *a.* | Pane of 10 | 11.50 | |
| **Z136** | ZA136 62y multicolored | 1.25 | .70 |
| **Z137** | ZA137 41y multicolored | .80 | .50 |
| *a.* | Pane of 10 | 12.00 | |
| **Z138** | ZA138 62y multicolored | 1.25 | .70 |
| *a.* | Pane of 10 | 12.00 | |
| **Z139** | ZA139 62y multicolored | 1.25 | .70 |
| *a.* | Pane of 10 | 12.00 | |
| **Z140** | ZA140 41y multicolored | .80 | .50 |
| *a.* | Pane of 10 | 8.00 | |
| | ***Perf. 13x13½*** | | |
| **Z141** | ZA141 62y multicolored | 1.10 | .70 |
| *a.* | Pane of 10 | 11.00 | |
| | ***Perf. 13½*** | | |
| **Z142** | ZA142 41y multicolored | .80 | .50 |
| *a.* | Pane of 10 | 8.00 | |
| | *Nos. Z130-Z142 (13)* | 13.55 | 8.30 |

Issued: No. Z130, 2/12; No. Z131, 3/26; No. Z132, 4/2; No. Z133, 4/23; No. Z134, 5/17; No. Z135, 5/21; No. Z136, 6/4; No. Z137, 6/23; No. Z138, 7/1; No. Z139, 7/16; No. Z140, 9/1; No. Z141, 9/22; No. Z142, 10/1.

See also No. Z321.

Dream Bridge (Metropolitan Tokyo)
ZA143

Kurobe Canyon & Dam (Toyama)
ZA144

Haiku, Storehouse of Poet Issa (1763-1827) (Nagano)
ZA145

Okuni, Izumo Great Shrine, Taisha (Shimane)
ZA146

Fukiwari Falls (Gunma) ZA147

Ezoshika (Hokkaido) ZA148

Watch Tower, Festival in Tajima (Hyogo) ZA149

Wakura Coast (Wakayama) ZA150

**1994** **Photo.** ***Perf. 13***

| | | | |
|---|---|---|---|
| **Z143** | ZA143 50y multicolored | .90 | .50 |
| *a.* | Pane of 10 | 9.50 | |
| **Z144** | ZA144 80y multicolored | 1.40 | .90 |
| *a.* | Pane of 10 | 15.00 | |
| **Z145** | ZA145 80y multicolored | 1.40 | .90 |
| *a.* | Pane of 10 | 15.00 | |
| **Z146** | ZA146 80y multicolored | 1.40 | .90 |
| *a.* | Pane of 10 | 15.00 | |

**Litho.**

| | | | |
|---|---|---|---|
| **Z147** | ZA147 80y multicolored | 1.40 | .90 |
| *a.* | Pane of 10 | 15.00 | |
| **Z148** | ZA148 50y multicolored | .90 | .50 |
| *a.* | Pane of 10 | 10.00 | |
| **Z149** | ZA149 50y multicolored | .90 | .50 |
| *a.* | Pane of 10 | 10.00 | |
| **Z150** | ZA150 80y multicolored | 1.40 | .90 |
| *a.* | Pane of 10 | 15.00 | |
| | *Nos. Z143-Z150 (8)* | 9.70 | 6.00 |

Issued: No. Z143, 3/23; No. Z144, 4/25; Nos. Z145-Z146, 5/2; No. Z147, 6/6; No. Z148, 6/7; No. Z149, 6/23; No. Z150, 7/15.

Kentish Plovers (Mie) ZA151

Awaodori Dance (Tokushima) ZA152

Tug-of-War (Okinawa) ZA153

Kehi Pine Wood (Fukui) ZA154

Matsushima (Miyagi) ZA155

Kunchi Festival (Nagasaki) ZA156

**1994** **Photo.** ***Perf. 13***

| | | | |
|---|---|---|---|
| **Z151** | ZA151 80y multicolored | 1.40 | .90 |
| *a.* | Pane of 10 | 15.00 | |
| **Z152** | ZA152 50y multicolored | .90 | .50 |
| *a.* | Pane of 10 | 10.00 | |
| **Z153** | ZA153 50y multicolored | .90 | .50 |
| **Z154** | ZA154 50y multicolored | .90 | .50 |
| *a.* | Pane of 10 | 10.00 | |
| **Z155** | ZA155 80y multicolored | 1.40 | .90 |
| *a.* | Pane of 10 | 16.50 | |
| **Z156** | ZA156 80y multicolored | 1.40 | .90 |
| *a.* | Pane of 10 | 16.50 | |
| | *Nos. Z151-Z156 (6)* | 6.90 | 4.20 |

Issued: No. Z151, 7/22; Nos. Z152-Z153, 8/1; No. Z154, 9/1; No. Z155, 9/20; No. Z156, 10/3.

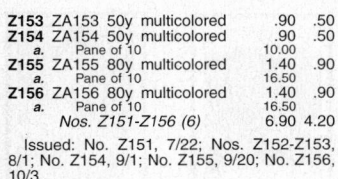

Hokkaido Chipmunks (Hokkaido) — ZA157

Ushiwakamaru and Benkei (Kyoto) — ZA158

Utopia Flower (Gifu) ZA159

Jade Bead, Gyofu Soma (1883-1950), Lyricist (Niigata) ZA160

Cape Ashizuri-Misaki Lighthouse (Kochi) ZA161

Ishikawamon Gate, Kanazawa Castle (Ishikawa) ZA162

Akamon Gate, University of Tokyo (Tokyo) ZA163

Three Waterfalls, Kuroyama (Saitama) ZA164

Lady's Slipper, Rebun Island (Hokkaido) ZA165

Street with Zelkova Trees (Miyagi) ZA166

Eisa Festival (Okinawa) — ZA167

**1995** **Photo.** ***Perf. 13***

| | | | |
|---|---|---|---|
| **Z157** | ZA157 80y multicolored | 1.40 | .90 |
| *a.* | Pane of 10 | 19.00 | |

***Perf. 13½***

| | | | |
|---|---|---|---|
| **Z158** | ZA158 80y multicolored | 1.40 | .90 |
| *a.* | Pane of 10 | 19.00 | |
| **Z159** | ZA159 80y multicolored | 1.40 | .90 |
| *a.* | Pane of 10 | 19.00 | |
| **Z160** | ZA160 80y multicolored | 1.40 | .90 |
| *a.* | Pane of 10 | 19.00 | |
| **Z161** | ZA161 80y multicolored | 1.40 | .90 |
| *a.* | Pane of 10 | 19.00 | |
| **Z162** | ZA162 80y multicolored | 1.40 | .90 |
| *a.* | Pane of 10 | 19.00 | |
| **Z163** | ZA163 50y multicolored | .90 | .50 |
| *a.* | Pane of 10 | 11.00 | |
| **Z164** | ZA164 80y multicolored | 1.40 | .90 |
| *a.* | Pane of 10 | 17.50 | |
| **Z165** | ZA165 80y multicolored | 1.40 | .90 |
| *a.* | Pane of 10 | 17.50 | |
| **Z166** | ZA166 50y multicolored | .90 | .50 |
| *a.* | Pane of 10 | 10.00 | |
| **Z167** | ZA167 80y multicolored | 1.40 | .90 |
| | *Nos. Z157-Z167 (11)* | 14.40 | 9.10 |

Issued: No. Z157, 3/3; No. Z158, 4/3; No. Z159, 4/26; No. Z160, 5/1; Nos. Z161-Z162, 6/1; Nos. Z163-Z165, 7/7; Nos. Z166-Z167, 8/1.

**Seasons Types of 1990-91 Redrawn and**

Kishiwada Danjiri Festival (Osaka) ZA168

Yamadera Temple (Yamagata) ZA169

Karatsu Kunchi Festival (Saga) ZA170

Niimi-No-Shou Festival (Okayama) ZA171

Kirifuri Waterfall (Tochigi) ZA172

10th All-Japan Holstein Show (Chiba) ZA173

Nos. Z171-Z174: (Gifu).
No. Z177, (Nara). No. Z178, (Nara, Gunma).

**1995** **Photo.** ***Perf. 13½***

| | | | |
|---|---|---|---|
| **Z168** | ZA168 80y multicolored | 1.40 | .90 |
| *a.* | Pane of 10 | 16.00 | |
| **Z169** | ZA169 80y multicolored | 1.40 | .90 |
| *a.* | Pane of 10 | 16.00 | |
| **Z170** | ZA170 80y multicolored | 1.40 | .90 |
| *a.* | Pane of 10 | 16.00 | |

***Perf. 13***

| | | | |
|---|---|---|---|
| **Z171** | ZA85 80y Spring | 1.40 | .90 |
| **Z172** | ZA86 80y Summer | 1.40 | .90 |
| **Z173** | ZA87 80y Autumn | 1.40 | .90 |
| **Z174** | ZA88 80y Winter | 1.40 | .90 |
| *a.* | Strip of 4, #Z171-Z174 | 6.50 | 6.50 |

***Perf. 13½***

| | | | |
|---|---|---|---|
| **Z175** | ZA171 80y multicolored | 1.40 | .90 |
| **Z176** | ZA172 50y multicolored | .90 | .50 |
| *a.* | Pane of 10 | 10.00 | |
| **Z177** | ZA115 80y Spring | 1.40 | .90 |
| **Z178** | ZA116 80y Autumn | 1.40 | .90 |
| *a.* | Pair, #Z177-Z178 | 3.00 | 3.00 |
| **Z179** | ZA173 80y multicolored | 1.40 | .90 |
| *a.* | Pane of 10 | 15.00 | |
| | *Nos. Z168-Z179 (12)* | 16.30 | 10.40 |

Issued: No. Z168, 9/1; No. Z169, 9/15; Nos. Z170-Z174, 10/2; No. Z175, 10/13; No. Z176, 10/27; Nos. Z177-Z178, 11/6; No. Z179, 11/21.

For self-adhesives, see Nos. 3282-3285.

Clione Limancia (Hokkaido) ZA174

Ushibuka Haiya Festival (Kumamoto) ZA175

Peony of Sukagawa (Fukushima) ZA176

Hamayu (Mie) ZA177

Ama Divers (Mie) — ZA178

World Ceramics Expo '96 (Saga) — ZA179

Shosenkyo Gorge (Yamanashi) ZA180

Murasaki Shikibu of Takefu (Fukui) ZA181

**1996** **Litho.** ***Perf. 13½x13***

| | | | |
|---|---|---|---|
| **Z180** | ZA174 80y multicolored | 1.40 | .90 |
| *a.* | Pane of 10 | 11.50 | |

**Photo.**

| | | | |
|---|---|---|---|
| **Z181** | ZA175 80y multicolored | 1.40 | .90 |
| *a.* | Pane of 10 | 15.00 | |
| **Z182** | ZA176 80y multicolored | 1.40 | .90 |
| *a.* | Pane of 10 | 15.00 | |
| **Z183** | ZA177 80y multicolored | 1.40 | .90 |
| **Z184** | ZA178 80y multicolored | 1.40 | .90 |
| *a.* | Pair, #Z183-Z184 | 3.00 | 3.00 |
| *b.* | Pane, 5 #Z184a | 15.00 | |
| **Z185** | ZA179 80y multicolored | 1.40 | .90 |

***Perf. 13½***

| | | | |
|---|---|---|---|
| **Z186** | ZA180 50y multicolored | .90 | .50 |
| *a.* | Pane of 10 | 9.50 | |
| **Z187** | ZA181 80y multicolored | 1.40 | .90 |
| *a.* | Pane of 10 | 15.00 | |
| | *Nos. Z180-Z187 (8)* | 10.70 | 6.80 |

Issued: No. Z180, 2/6; No. Z181, 4/1; No. Z182, 4/26; Nos. Z183-Z184, 5/1; No. Z185, 5/17; No. Z186, 6/3; No. Z187, 6/24.

**Flower Types of 1990 and**

Ancient Trees, Kompon-chudo of Mt. Hiei (Shiga)
ZA182

Nishiumi Marine Park (Ehime)
ZA183

Nebuta Festival (Aomori)
ZA184

Main Palace, Shuri Castle (Okinawa)
ZA186

Shimozuru Usudaiko Odori Folk Dance (Miyazaki)
ZA185

Asakusa Kaminarimon Gate (Metropolitan Tokyo)
ZA187

Tottori Shanshan Festival (Tottori)
ZA188

Saito Kinen Festival Matsumoto (Nagano)
ZA189

No. Z190, (Hokkaido). No. Z197, (Nagano).

**1996 Photo. Perf. 13½**

| | | | |
|---|---|---|---|
| Z188 | ZA182 80y multicolored | 1.40 | .90 |
| a. | Pane of 10 | 15.00 | |
| Z189 | ZA183 80y multicolored | 1.40 | .90 |
| a. | Pane of 10 | 15.00 | |
| Z190 | ZA23 80y Sweetbriar | 1.40 | .90 |
| Z191 | ZA184 80y multicolored | 1.40 | .90 |
| a. | Pane of 10 | 15.00 | |
| Z192 | ZA185 80y multicolored | 1.40 | .90 |
| a. | Pane of 10 | 15.00 | |
| Z193 | ZA186 80y multicolored | 1.40 | .90 |
| Z194 | ZA187 80y multicolored | 1.40 | .90 |
| a. | Pane of 10 | 15.00 | |
| Z195 | ZA188 80y multicolored | 1.40 | .90 |
| Z196 | ZA189 80y multicolored | 1.40 | .90 |
| a. | Pane of 10 | 15.00 | |
| Z197 | ZA38 80y Autumn bell-flower | 1.40 | .90 |
| | *Nos. Z188-Z197 (10)* | 14.00 | 9.00 |

Issued: Nos. Z188-Z189, 7/1; No. Z190, 7/5; No. Z191, 7/23; Nos. Z192-Z193, 8/1; No. Z194, 8/8; No. Z195, 8/16; Nos. Z196-Z197, 8/22.

For self-adhesive, see No. 3290.

Sengokubara Marsh (Kanagawa)
ZA190

Nagoya Festival (Aichi) — ZA191

Grass-burning Rite on Mt. Wakakusa (Nara)
ZA193

1997 Men's Handball World Championships (Kumamoto)
ZA194

Tea Picking (Shizuoka)
ZA195

Dahurian Rhododendron (Hokkaido)
ZA196

Mt. Fuji (Shizuoka) — ZA197

**1996-97 Photo. Perf. 13½**

| | | | |
|---|---|---|---|
| Z198 | ZA190 80y multicolored | 1.40 | .90 |
| a. | Pane of 10 | 15.00 | |
| Z199 | 80y horse, rider | 1.40 | .90 |
| Z200 | 80y two floats | 1.40 | .90 |
| a. | ZA191 Pair, #Z199-Z200 | 3.00 | 3.00 |
| b. | Pane, 5 #Z200a | 15.00 | |
| Z201 | ZA193 50y multicolored | .90 | .50 |
| a. | Pane of 10 | 9.50 | |
| Z202 | ZA194 80y multicolored | 1.40 | .90 |
| a. | Pane of 10 | 15.00 | |
| Z203 | ZA195 50y multicolored | .90 | .50 |
| a. | Pane of 10 | 9.50 | |
| Z204 | ZA196 80y multicolored | 1.40 | .90 |
| a. | Pane of 10 | 15.00 | |
| Z205 | 80y cattle | 1.40 | .90 |
| Z206 | 80y orange grasses | 1.40 | .90 |
| a. | ZA197 Pair, #Z205-Z206 | 2.50 | 2.50 |
| b. | Pane, 5 #Z206a | 12.50 | |
| | *Nos. Z198-Z206 (9)* | 11.60 | 7.30 |

Issued: No. Z198, 9/6; Nos. Z199-Z200, 10/1; No. Z201, 11/15; No. Z202, 4/17/97; Nos. Z203-Z206, 4/25/97.

Marugame Castle (Kagawa)
ZA199

Hokkaido Ermine (Hokkaido)
ZA200

Okayama Castle (Okayama)
ZA201

Okinawan Fruits (Okinawa)
ZA202

ZA204 ZA205

ZA206 ZA207

Nagasaki Kaido Highway (Nagasaki, Saga, Fukuoka)

Fukiya Koji's Hanayome Ningyo, Doll of Bride (Niigata)
ZA208

The Clock Tower of Kyoto University (Kyoto)
ZA209

**1997 Photo. Perf. 13½**

| | | | |
|---|---|---|---|
| Z207 | ZA199 80y multicolored | 1.40 | .90 |
| a. | Pane of 10 | 15.00 | |
| Z208 | ZA200 50y multicolored | .90 | .50 |
| a. | Pane of 10 | 9.50 | |
| Z209 | ZA201 80y multicolored | 1.40 | .90 |
| a. | Pane of 10 | 15.00 | |
| Z210 | ZA202 50y pineapple | .90 | .50 |
| Z211 | ZA202 50y mango | .90 | .50 |
| a. | Pair, #Z210-Z211 | 1.90 | 1.90 |
| Z212 | ZA204 80y multicolored | 1.40 | .90 |
| Z213 | ZA205 80y multicolored | 1.40 | .90 |
| Z214 | ZA206 80y multicolored | 1.40 | .90 |
| Z215 | ZA207 80y multicolored | 1.40 | .90 |
| a. | Strip of 4, #Z212-Z215 | 6.00 | 6.00 |
| Z216 | ZA208 50y multicolored | .90 | .50 |
| a. | Pane of 10 | 9.50 | |
| Z217 | ZA209 80y multicolored | 1.40 | .90 |
| a. | Pane of 10 | 15.00 | |
| | *Nos. Z207-Z217 (11)* | 13.40 | 8.30 |

Issued: No. Z207, 5/15; Nos. Z208-Z209, 5/30; Nos. Z210-Z211, 6/2; Nos. Z212-Z215, 6/3; Nos. Z216-Z217, 6/18.

Kanto Festival (Akita)
ZA210

San-in Yume Minato Exposition (Tottori)
ZA211

Waterwheel Plant, Hozoji-numa Pond (Saitama)
ZA212

Lake Kasumigaura (Ibaraki)
ZA215

Bon Wind Festival, Owara (Toyama) — ZA213

Tokyo Big Site (Tokyo)
ZA216

Telecom Center (Tokyo)
ZA217

Rainbow Bridge (Tokyo)
ZA218

Intl. Forum (Tokyo)
ZA219

Tokyo Museum (Tokyo)
ZA220

First World Walking Festival (Saitama)
ZA221

**1997 Photo. Perf. 13½**

| | | | |
|---|---|---|---|
| Z218 | ZA210 80y multicolored | 1.40 | .90 |
| a. | Pane of 10 | 15.00 | |
| Z219 | ZA211 80y multicolored | 1.40 | .90 |
| a. | Pane of 10 | 15.00 | |
| Z220 | ZA212 50y multicolored | .90 | .50 |
| a. | Pane of 10 | 9.50 | |
| Z221 | 80y woman | 1.40 | .90 |
| Z222 | 80y man | 1.40 | .90 |
| a. | ZA213 Pair, #Z221-Z222 | 3.00 | 3.00 |
| b. | Pane, 5 #Z222a | 15.00 | |
| Z223 | ZA215 80y multicolored | 1.40 | .90 |
| a. | Pane of 10 | 15.00 | |

| | | | | | |
|---|---|---|---|---|---|
| **Z224** | ZA216 | 80y multicolored | 1.40 | .90 |
| **Z225** | ZA217 | 80y multicolored | 1.40 | .90 |
| **Z226** | ZA218 | 80y multicolored | 1.40 | .90 |
| **Z227** | ZA219 | 80y multicolored | 1.40 | .90 |
| **Z228** | ZA220 | 80y multicolored | 1.40 | .70 |
| *a.* | | Strip of 5, #Z224-Z228 | 7.50 | 7.50 |
| *b.* | | Pane, 2 #Z228a | 15.00 | |
| **Z229** | ZA221 | 80y multicolored | 1.40 | .70 |
| *a.* | | Pane of 10 | 15.00 | |
| | | *Nos. Z218-Z229 (12)* | 16.30 | 10.00 |

Issued: No. Z218, 7/7; No. Z219, 7/11; No. Z220, 8/1; Nos. Z221-Z222, 8/20; No. Z223, 9/1; Nos. Z224-Z228, 10/1; No. Z229, 10/28.

Kanagawa-Chiba Bridge Tunnel (Chiba, Kanagawa) — ZA222

Snow-Covered Tree (Hokkaido) ZA224

Flower in a Dream (Hokkaido) ZA225

Hiyoshi Dam (Kyoto) ZA226

Sanshin (Okinawa) ZA227

Okoshi Daiko (Gifu) ZA228

Kobe-Awaji Expressway (Tokushima, Hyogo) — ZA229

| **1997-98** | **Litho.** | | ***Perf. 13½*** | |
|---|---|---|---|---|
| **Z230** | | 80y denomination upper right | 1.40 | .90 |
| **Z231** | | 80y denomination lower left | 1.40 | .90 |
| *a.* | ZA222 | Pair, #Z230-Z231 | 3.00 | 3.00 |
| *b.* | | Pane, 5 #Z231a | 15.00 | |
| **Z232** | ZA224 | 80y multicolored | 1.40 | .90 |
| **Z233** | ZA225 | 80y multicolored | 1.40 | .90 |
| *a.* | | Pair, #Z232-Z233 | 3.00 | 3.00 |
| *b.* | | Pane, 5 #Z233a | 15.00 | |

**Photo.**

***Perf. 13***

| | | | | |
|---|---|---|---|---|
| **Z234** | ZA226 | 80y multicolored | 1.40 | .90 |
| *a.* | | Pane of 10 | 15.00 | |

***Perf. 13½***

| | | | | |
|---|---|---|---|---|
| **Z235** | ZA227 | 80y multicolored | 1.40 | .90 |
| *a.* | | Pane of 10 | 15.00 | |
| **Z236** | ZA228 | 80y multicolored | 1.40 | .90 |
| *a.* | | Pane of 10 | 15.00 | |
| **Z237** | | 80y bridge, whirlpool | 1.40 | .90 |
| **Z238** | | 80y bridge, flowers | 1.40 | .90 |
| *a.* | ZA229 | Pair, #Z237-Z238 | 3.00 | 3.00 |
| *b.* | | Pane, 5 #Z238a | 15.00 | |

Issued: Nos. Z230-Z231, 12/18; Nos. Z232-Z233, 2/5/98; No. Z234, 3/2/98; No. Z235, 3/4/98; No. Z236, 3/19/98; Nos. Z237-Z238, 3/20/98.

See Nos. 3230B-3230C.

Jomon Figurine (Nagano) ZA231

Chaguchagu Umakko, Mt. Iwate (Iwate) ZA232

Tokyo '98 Business Show (Tokyo) ZA233

Mt. Heisei Shinzan (Nagasaki) ZA234

Oze (Gunma) — ZA235

Hanagasa Matsuri (Yamagata) ZA237

9th Women's World Softball Championships (Shizuoka) ZA238

| **1998** | **Photo.** | | ***Perf. 13½*** | |
|---|---|---|---|---|
| **Z239** | ZA231 | 80y multicolored | 1.40 | .90 |
| *a.* | | Pane of 10 | 15.00 | |
| **Z240** | ZA232 | 80y multicolored | 1.40 | .90 |
| *a.* | | Pane of 10 | 15.00 | |
| **Z241** | ZA233 | 80y multicolored | 1.40 | .90 |
| *a.* | | Pane of 10 | 15.00 | |
| **Z242** | ZA234 | 80y multicolored | 1.40 | .90 |
| *a.* | | Pane of 10 | 15.00 | |
| **Z243** | | 80y blue & multi | 1.40 | .90 |
| **Z244** | | 80y brown & multi | 1.40 | .90 |
| *a.* | ZA235 | Pair, #Z243-Z244 | 3.00 | 3.00 |
| *b.* | | Pane, 5 #Z244a | 15.00 | |
| **Z245** | ZA237 | 50y multicolored | .90 | .50 |
| *a.* | | Pane of 10 | 9.50 | |
| **Z246** | ZA238 | 80y multicolored | 1.40 | .90 |
| *a.* | | Pane of 10 | 15.00 | |
| | | *Nos. Z239-Z246 (8)* | 10.70 | 6.80 |

Issued: No. Z239, 4/1; No. Z240, 4/24; No. Z241, 5/19; No. Z242, 5/20/98; Nos. Z243-Z244, 5/21; No. Z245, 6/5; No. Z246, 6/22.

Mt. Hakusan (Ishikawa) ZA239

Hita Gion (Ohita) ZA240

World Puppetry Festival (Nagano) — ZA241

Views of Seto (Hiroshima) — ZA243

First Postage Stamps of Ryukyu Islands, 50th Anniv. (Ryukyu Islands) — ZA245

| **1998** | **Photo.** | | ***Perf. 13½*** | |
|---|---|---|---|---|
| **Z247** | ZA239 | 50y multicolored | .90 | .50 |
| *a.* | | Pane of 10 | 9.50 | |
| **Z248** | ZA240 | 50y multicolored | .90 | .50 |
| *a.* | | Pane of 10 | 9.50 | |
| **Z249** | | 50y stage left | .90 | .50 |
| **Z250** | | 50y stage right | .90 | .50 |
| *a.* | ZA241 | Pair, #Z249-Z250 | 1.90 | 1.90 |
| *b.* | | Pane, 5 #Z250a | 9.50 | |
| **Z251** | | 80y harbor | 1.40 | .90 |
| **Z252** | | 80y highway | 1.40 | .90 |
| *a.* | ZA243 | Pair, #Z251-Z252 | 3.00 | 3.00 |
| *b.* | | Pane, 5 #Z252a | 15.00 | |
| **Z253** | | 80y Ryukyu Islands #1 | 1.40 | .90 |
| **Z254** | | 80y Ryukyu Islands #228 | 1.40 | .90 |
| *a.* | ZA245 | Pair, #Z253-Z254 | 3.00 | 3.00 |
| | | *Nos. Z247-Z254 (8)* | 9.20 | 5.60 |

Issued: Nos. Z247-Z248, 7/1; Nos. Z249-Z252, 7/17; Nos. Z253-Z254, 7/23.

Satsuma Pottery, 400th Anniv. (Kogoshima) — ZA247

Seto Ohashi Bridge (Kagawa) ZA249

Kobe Luminaries (Hyogo) ZA250

Apples (Aomori) ZA251

Kumano Path (Wakayama) ZA252

Tama Monorail (Tokyo) — ZA253

| **1998** | **Photo.** | | ***Perf. 13½*** | |
|---|---|---|---|---|
| **Z255** | | 80y bowl | 1.40 | .90 |
| **Z256** | | 80y vase | 1.40 | .90 |
| *a.* | ZA247 | Pair, #Z255-Z256 | 3.00 | 3.00 |
| *b.* | | Pane, 5 #Z256a | 15.00 | |
| **Z257** | ZA249 | 80y multicolored | 1.40 | .90 |
| *a.* | | Pane of 10 | 15.00 | |
| **Z258** | ZA250 | 80y multicolored | 1.40 | .90 |
| *a.* | | Pane of 10 | 15.00 | |

***Perf. 13***

| | | | | |
|---|---|---|---|---|
| **Z259** | ZA251 | 80y multicolored | 1.40 | .90 |
| *a.* | | Pane of 10 | 15.00 | |
| **Z260** | ZA252 | 80y multicolored | 1.40 | .90 |

***Perf. 13½***

| | | | | |
|---|---|---|---|---|
| **Z261** | ZA253 | 80y multicolored | 1.40 | .90 |
| *a.* | | Pane of 10 | 15.00 | |
| | | *Nos. Z255-Z261 (7)* | 9.80 | 6.30 |

Issued: Nos. Z255-Z256, 10/1; Nos. Z257-Z258, 11/9; Nos. Z259-Z260, 11/13; No. Z261, 11/26.

**Dogo Hot Spa (Ehime) Type of 1989 and**

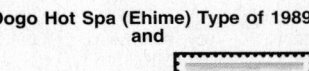

Ibara Line (Okayama, Hiroshima) — ZA254

ZA255

Ao-no-Domon (Oita) — ZA256

ZA257

ZA258

Snow World (Hokkaido)

ZA259 ZA260

Tokamachi Snow Festival (Niigata) — ZA261

Orchids (Tokyo) — ZA262

Dinosaurs (Fukui) — ZA264

**1999 Photo. *Perf. 13½***

**Z262** ZA254 80y multicolored 1.40 .70
*a.* Pane of 10 15.00
**Z263** ZA4 80y multicolored 1.40 .70
**Z264** ZA255 80y multicolored 1.40 .70
**Z265** ZA256 80y multicolored 1.40 .70
*a.* Vert. pair, #Z264-Z265 3.00 3.00
*b.* Pane, 5 #Z265a 15.00
**Z266** ZA257 50y multicolored .90 .50
**Z267** ZA258 50y multicolored .90 .50
**Z268** ZA259 80y multicolored 1.40 .70
**Z269** ZA260 80y multicolored 1.40 .70
*a.* Strip of 4, #Z266-Z269 5.00 3.50
**Z270** ZA261 80y multicolored 1.40 .70
*a.* Pane of 10 15.00
**Z271** 80y white flowers 1.40 .70
**Z272** 80y purple flowers 1.40 .70
*a.* ZA262 Pair, #Z271-Z272 3.00 3.00
*b.* Pane, 5 #Z272a 15.00
**Z273** 80y denomination upper left 1.40 .70
**Z274** 80y denomination lower left 1.40 .70
*a.* ZA264 Pair, #Z273-Z274 3.00 3.00
*b.* Pane, 5 #Z274a 15.00
*Nos. Z262-Z274 (13)* 17.20 8.70

Issued: No. Z262, 1/1; Nos. Z263-Z265, 2/1; Nos. Z266-Z269, 2/5; Nos. Z270-Z272, 2/12; Nos. Z273-Z274, 2/22.

Lake Chuzenji (Tochigi) — ZA266

Renowned Cherry Tree (Gifu) ZA268

Kiso Observatory, Mt. Ontake (Nagano) ZA271

Postal Service in Okinawa, 125th Anniv. (Okinawa) — ZA269

ZA272

ZA273

ZA274

The Old Path for Kumano (Mie) — ZA275

No. Z275, Spring. No. Z276, Fall. No. Z278, Traditional costume. No. Z279, Laughing lions. No. Z281, Tsuzurato Pass. No. Z282, Matsumoto Pass. No. Z283, Umagoshi Pass. No. Z284, Touri Pass.

**1999 Photo. *Perf. 13½***

**Z275** 80y multicolored 1.40 .90
**Z276** 80y multicolored 1.40 .90
*a.* ZA266 Pair, #Z275-Z276 3.00 3.00
*b.* Pane, 5 #Z276a 15.00
**Z277** ZA268 80y multicolored 1.40 .90
*a.* Pane of 10 15.00
**Z278** 80y multicolored 1.40 .90
**Z279** 80y multicolored 1.40 .90
*a.* ZA269 Pair, #Z278-Z279 3.00 3.00
*b.* Pane, 5 #Z279a 15.00
**Z280** ZA271 80y multicolored 1.40 .90
*a.* Pane of 10 15.00
**Z281** ZA272 80y multicolored 1.40 .70
**Z282** ZA273 80y multicolored 1.40 .70
**Z283** ZA274 80y multicolored 1.40 .70
**Z284** ZA275 80y multicolored 1.40 .70
*a.* Strip of 4, #Z281-Z284 6.00 6.00
*Nos. Z275-Z284 (10)* 14.00 8.20

Issued: Nos. Z275-Z276, 3/1. No. Z277, 3/16. Nos. Z278-Z279, 3/23. No. Z280, 4/9. Nos. Z281-Z284, 4/16.

**Cherries (Yamagata) Type of 1989 and**

Taiko-Mon Gate, Matsumoto Castle (Nagano) ZA276

Firefly Squid (Toyama) ZA277

ZA278

ZA279

Four Seasons, Kenrokuen Garden (Ishikawa)

ZA280 ZA281

No. Z288, Kaisekitou Pagoda, Spring. No. Z289, Fountain, Summer. No. Z290, Kinjoureitaku spring, Autumn. No. Z291, Kotoji stone lantern and yukitsuri, Winter.

**1999, Apr. 26 Photo. *Perf. 13***

**Z285** ZA2 80y like #Z2 1.40 .90

***Perf. 13½***

**Z286** ZA276 80y multicolored 1.40 .90
*a.* Pane of 10 15.00
**Z287** ZA277 80y multicolored 1.40 .90
*a.* Pane of 10 15.00
**Z288** ZA278 80y multicolored 1.40 .90
**Z289** ZA279 80y multicolored 1.40 .90
**Z290** ZA280 80y multicolored 1.40 .90
**Z291** ZA281 80y multicolored 1.40 .90
*a.* Strip of 4, #Z288-Z291 6.00 6.00
*b.* Souvenir sheet, #Z288-Z291 6.00 6.00
*Nos. Z285-Z291 (7)* 9.80 6.30

ZA282 ZA283

ZA284 ZA285

ZA286 ZA287

ZA288 ZA289

Opening of Shimanami Seaside Highway (Hiroshima & Ehime)

ZA290 ZA291

Designs: No. Z292, Onomichi-suido Channel. No. Z293, Kurushima-kaikyo Straits. No. Z294, Old, new Onomichi-oohashi Bridges. No. Z295, Kurushima-kaikyo-oohashi Bridge. No. Z296, Innoshima-oohashi Bridge. No. Z297, Kurushima-kaikyo-oohashi Bridge, diff. No. Z298, Ikuchibashi Bridge. No. Z299, Hakatabashi, Ooshima-oohashi Bridges. No. Z300, Tatara-oohashi Bridge. No. Z301, Oomishimabashi Bridge.

**1999, Apr. 26 Photo. *Perf. 13½***

**Z292** ZA282 80y multicolored 1.40 .90
**Z293** ZA283 80y multicolored 1.40 .90
**Z294** ZA284 80y multicolored 1.40 .90
**Z295** ZA285 80y multicolored 1.40 .90
**Z296** ZA286 80y multicolored 1.40 .90
**Z297** ZA287 80y multicolored 1.40 .90
**Z298** ZA288 80y multicolored 1.40 .90
**Z299** ZA289 80y multicolored 1.40 .90
**Z300** ZA290 80y multicolored 1.40 .90
**Z301** ZA291 80y multicolored 1.40 .90
*a.* Block of 10, #Z292-Z301 15.00 15.00
*b.* Sheet of 8, # Z294-Z301 12.00 12.00

**Flora (Hokkaido) Type of 1991 and**

Southern Kii Peninsula (Wakayama) — ZA292

Designs: No. Z302, Nachi-no-taki Falls. No. Z303, Engetsutou Island.

**1999, Apr. 28 Photo. *Perf. 13½***

**Z302** 80y multicolored 1.40 .90
**Z303** 80y multicolored 1.40 .90
*a.* ZA292 Pair, #Z302-Z303 3.00 3.00
*b.* Pane, 5 #Z303a 15.00

***Perf. 13***

**Z304** ZA97 80y Lily bell 1.40 .90
**Z305** ZA98 80y Lilac 1.40 .90
**Z306** ZA99 80y Daylily 1.40 .90
**Z307** ZA100 80y Rowanberry 1.40 .90
*a.* Strip of 4, #Z304-Z307 6.00 6.00

Sendai Tanabata Festival (Miyagi) ZA294

Souma Nomaoi Festival (Fukushima) ZA295

**1999, May 14 Photo. *Perf. 13½***

**Z310** ZA294 80y multicolored 1.40 .90
**Z311** ZA295 80y multicolored 1.40 .90
*a.* Pair, #Z310-Z311 3.00 3.00
*b.* Pane, 5 #Z311a 15.00

Ryukyu Dance (Okinawa) — ZA296

**1999, May 14**

**Z312** ZA296 80y multicolored 1.40 .90
*a.* Pane of 10 15.00

ZA297

Northern Paradise (Hokkaido) ZA298

**1999, May 25**

**Z313** ZA297 50y Lavender field .90 .50
**Z314** ZA298 80y Wheat field 1.40 .90

Kurashiki Sightseeing District (Okayama) — ZA299

**1999, May 25 Photo. *Perf. 13½***

Z316 ZA299 80y multicolored 1.40 .90
*a.* Pane of 10 15.00

Shirone Big Kite Battle (Niigata)
ZA300 ZA301

**1999, June 1 Litho. *Perf. 13½***

Z317 ZA300 80y multicolored 1.40 .90
Z318 ZA301 80y multicolored 1.40 .90
*a.* Pair, #Z317-Z318 3.00 3.00
*b.* Pane, 5 #Z318a 15.00

Noto Kiriko Festival (Ishikawa) — ZA302

**1999, June 11**

Z319 ZA302 80y multicolored 1.40 .90
*a.* Pane of 10 15.00

**Hokkaido Types of 1992-93**

**1999, June 25 Photo. *Perf. 13½***

Z320 ZA119 80y Arctic fox 1.40 .90

**Litho.**

Z321 ZA134 80y Largha seals 1.40 .90

ZA303

Tokyo: No. Z323, morning glories. No. Z324, starburst fireworks over Sumida River. No. Z325, flower burst fireworks.

**1999, July 1 Photo. *Perf. 13½***

Z323 80y multicolored 1.40 .90
Z324 80y multicolored 1.40 .90
Z325 80y multicolored 1.40 .90
*a.* ZA303 Block of 3, #Z323-Z325 4.50 4.50
*b.* Souv. sheet of 2, #Z324-Z325 3.00 3.00

Hakata Gion Yamagasa Festival (Fukuoka) — ZA306

**1999, July 1 Litho.**

Z326 ZA306 80y multicolored 1.40 .90
*a.* Pane of 10 15.00

ZA307 ZA308

ZA309 ZA310

Five Fuji Lakes (Yamanashi) ZA311

**1999, July 1**

Z327 ZA307 80y Yamanakako 1.40 .90
Z328 ZA308 80y Kawaguchiko 1.40 .90
Z329 ZA309 80y Saiko 1.40 .90
Z330 ZA310 80y Shoujiko 1.40 .90
Z331 ZA311 80y Motosuko 1.40 .90
*a.* Strip of 5, #Z327-Z331 7.70 7.50
*b.* Pane, 2 #Z331a 15.00

**Inns of Tsumago, Magome Types of 1990**

**Photo. & Engr.**

**1999, July 16 *Perf. 13***

Z332 ZA71 80y like #Z71 1.40 .90
Z333 ZA72 80y like #Z72 1.40 .90
*a.* Pair, #Z332-Z333 3.00 3.00

ZA312

Toki (Japanese Crested Ibis) (Niigata) ZA313

No. Z334, Youyou, Yangyang. No. Z335, Kin.

**1999, July 16 Litho. *Perf. 13½***

Z334 ZA312 80y multicolored 1.40 .90
Z335 ZA313 80y multicolored 1.40 .90
*a.* Pair, #Z334-Z335 3.00 3.00
*b.* Pane, 5 #Z335a 15.00

ZA314

Design: Amanohashidate sandbar, Miyatsu Bay (Kyoto).

**1999, July 16**

Z336 ZA314 80y multicolored 1.40 .90

ZA315

Design: Ooga lotus (Chiba).

**1999, July 16**

Z337 ZA315 80y multicolored 1.40 .90
*a.* Pane of 10 15.00

ZA316 ZA317

ZA318 ZA319

Birds (Hokkaido): No. Z338, Steller's sea-eagle. No. Z339, Tufted puffin. No. Z340, Blakiston's fish owl. No. Z341, Red-crowned crane.

**1999, July 23 Photo. *Perf. 13½***

Z338 ZA316 50y multicolored .90 .50
Z339 ZA317 50y multicolored .90 .50
Z340 ZA318 50y multicolored .90 .50
Z341 ZA319 50y multicolored .90 .50
*a.* Strip of 4, #Z337-Z340 4.00 4.00

Hill on Ie Island, Sabani Boat (Okinawa) — ZA320

**1999, July 23 Litho. *Perf. 13¼***

Z343 ZA320 80y multicolored 1.40 .90
*a.* Pane of 10 15.00

National Treasures (Wakayama) — ZA321

No. Z344, Kouyasan, Buddhist monastic complex. No. Z345, Natl. treasure, Kongara-douji.

**1999, July 26 *Perf. 13½***

Z344 80y multicolored 1.40 .90
Z345 80y multicolored 1.40 .90
*a.* ZA321 Pair, #Z344-Z345 3.00 3.00
*b.* Pane, 5 #Z345a 15.00

Autumn Bellflowers (Iwate) — ZA323

**1999, July 30**

Z346 ZA323 50y multicolored .90 .50
*a.* Pane of 10 9.50

Shimizu Port, Cent. (Shizuoka) ZA324 Fishing Boat (Kumamoto) ZA325

**1999, Aug. 2 Litho. *Perf. 13¼***

Z347 ZA324 80y multi 1.40 .90
*a.* Pane of 10 15.00
Z348 ZA325 80y multi 1.40 .90
*a.* Pane of 10 15.00

Ritsurin Park (Kagawa) — ZA326

**1999, Aug. 2 *Perf. 13¼***

Z349 ZA326 80y multi 1.40 .90
*a.* Pane of 10 15.00

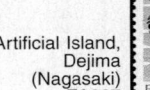

Artificial Island, Dejima (Nagasaki) ZA327

**1999, Sept. 1 Photo.**

Z350 ZA327 80y multi 1.40 .90
*a.* Pane of 10 15.00

Yoritomo Minamotono (1174-99), Shogun (Kanagawa) ZA328

**1999, Sept. 2 Litho.**

Z351 ZA328 80y multi 1.40 .90
*a.* Pane of 10 15.00

Shirakami Mountains (Aomori) ZA329

**1999, Sept. 6**

Z352 ZA329 80y multi 1.40 .90
*a.* Pane of 10 15.00

Gassho-zukuri Farmhouses and Kokiriko Dance (Toyama) — ZA330

**1999, Sept. 14 Photo.**

Z353 ZA330 80y multi 1.40 .90
*a.* Pane of 10 15.00

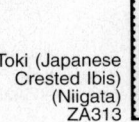

Corn (Hokkaido)
ZA331

Potatoes
(Hokkaido)
ZA332

Asparagus
(Hokkaido)
ZA333

Muskmelon
(Hokkaido)
ZA334

**1999, Sept. 17** **Litho.**

| | | | | |
|---|---|---|---|---|
| **Z354** | ZA331 50y multi | | .90 | .50 |
| **Z355** | ZA332 50y multi | | .90 | .50 |
| **Z356** | ZA333 50y multi | | .90 | .50 |
| **Z357** | ZA334 50y multi | | .90 | .50 |
| *a.* | Strip, #Z354-Z357 | | 4.00 | 4.00 |

(Gumma) — ZA335

**1999, Sept. 17** ***Perf. 13¼***

| | | | |
|---|---|---|---|
| **Z358** | ZA335 80y multi | 1.40 | .90 |
| *a.* | Pane of 10 | 15.00 | |

Iwajuku Paleolithic Site Excavations, 50th anniv.

(Osaka) — ZA336

**1999, Sept. 27**

| | | | |
|---|---|---|---|
| **Z359** | ZA336 80y multi | 1.40 | .90 |

23rd Rhythmic Gymnastics World Championships.

Nihonmatsu
Chrysanthemum
Exhibition
(Fukushima)
ZA337

**1999, Oct. 1**

| | | | |
|---|---|---|---|
| **Z360** | ZA337 80y multi | 1.40 | .90 |

Town of Obi (Miyazaki) — ZA338

Designs: No. Z361, Taihei dance, front gate of Obi Castle. No. Z362, Shintokudou School, Komura Jutarou (1855-1911).

**1999, Oct. 1** ***Perf. 13¼***

| | | | |
|---|---|---|---|
| **Z361** | 80y multi | 1.40 | .90 |
| **Z362** | 80y multi | 1.40 | .90 |
| *a.* | ZA338 Pair, #Z361-Z362 | 3.00 | 3.00 |
| *b.* | Pane, 5 #Z362a | 15.00 | |

### Nagano Monkey Type of 1989

**1999, Oct. 13** **Photo.** ***Perf. 12¾x13***

| | | | |
|---|---|---|---|
| **Z363** | ZA1 80y multi | 1.50 | .75 |

(Aichi) — ZA340

No. Z364, Ichiei Sato. No. Z365, "Beautiful Yamato."

**1999, Oct. 13** **Photo.** ***Perf. 13¼***

| | | | |
|---|---|---|---|
| **Z364** | 80y multi | 1.40 | .90 |
| **Z365** | 80y multi | 1.40 | .90 |
| *a.* | ZA340 Pair, #Z364-Z365 | 3.00 | 3.00 |
| *b.* | Pane, 5 #Z365a | 15.00 | |

ZA342

No. Z366, Hagi (Yamaguchi). No. Z367, Tsuwano (Shimane).

**1999, Oct. 13**

| | | | |
|---|---|---|---|
| **Z366** | 80y multi | 1.40 | .90 |
| **Z367** | 80y multi | 1.40 | .90 |
| *a.* | ZA342 Vert. pair, #Z366-Z367 | 3.00 | 3.00 |
| *b.* | Pane, 5 #Z367a | 15.00 | |

(Nara) — ZA344

No. Z368, Yamato Three Mountains. No. Z369, Ishibutai Tomb.

**1999, Oct. 28** **Litho.** ***Perf. 13¼***

| | | | |
|---|---|---|---|
| **Z368** | 80y multi | 1.40 | .90 |
| **Z369** | 80y multi | 1.40 | .90 |
| *a.* | ZA344 Pair, #Z368-Z369 | 3.00 | 3.00 |
| *b.* | Pane, 5 #Z369a | 15.00 | |

Shikina-en Garden
(Okinawa) — ZA346

**1999, Oct. 28**

| | | | |
|---|---|---|---|
| **Z370** | 50y multi | .90 | .50 |
| **Z371** | 50y multi | .90 | .50 |
| *a.* | ZA346 Pair, #Z370-Z371 | 1.90 | 1.90 |
| *b.* | Pane, 5 #Z371a | 9.50 | |

(Fukui) — ZA348

No. Z372, Echizen Crab. No. Z373, Tojinbou Cliff.

**1999, Nov. 4**

| | | | |
|---|---|---|---|
| **Z372** | 80y multi | 1.40 | .90 |
| **Z373** | 80y multi | 1.40 | .90 |
| *a.* | ZA348 Pair, #Z372-Z373 | 3.00 | 3.00 |
| *b.* | Pane, 5 #Z373a | 15.00 | |

Children in
Santa's Sleigh
(Hokkaido)
ZA350

Yoshinogari Dig
Site (Saga)
ZA351

**1999, Nov. 11** ***Perf. 13¼***

| | | | |
|---|---|---|---|
| **Z374** | ZA350 80y multi | 1.40 | .90 |
| *a.* | Pane of 10 | 15.00 | |
| **Z375** | ZA351 80y multi | 1.40 | .90 |
| *a.* | Pane of 10 | 15.00 | |

(Kochi) — ZA352

No. Z376, Katsura Beach. No. Z377, Sakamoto Ryoma.

**1999, Nov. 15** **Photo.**

| | | | |
|---|---|---|---|
| **Z376** | 80y multi | 1.40 | .90 |
| **Z377** | 80y multi | 1.40 | .90 |
| *a.* | ZA352 Pair, #Z376-Z377 | 3.00 | 3.00 |
| *b.* | Pane, 5 #Z377a | 15.00 | |

For self-adhesives, see Nos. 3189H-3189I.

Samurai House,
Kakunodate
(Akita) — ZA354

**1999, Dec. 17** **Litho.** ***Perf. 13¼***

| | | | |
|---|---|---|---|
| **Z378** | ZA354 80y multi | 1.40 | .90 |
| *a.* | Pane of 10 | 15.00 | |

ZA355

ZA356

ZA357

ZA358

Tokyo Scenes
(Tokyo) — ZA359

**2000, Jan. 12** **Litho.** ***Perf. 13¼***

| | | | |
|---|---|---|---|
| **Z379** | ZA355 50y multi | .90 | .50 |
| **Z380** | ZA356 50y multi | .90 | .50 |
| **Z381** | ZA357 50y multi | .90 | .50 |
| **Z382** | ZA358 50y multi | .90 | .50 |
| **Z383** | ZA359 50y multi | .90 | .50 |
| *a.* | Horiz. strip, #Z379-Z383 | 4.75 | 4.75 |
| *b.* | Pane, 2 each #Z379-Z383 | 9.50 | |

ZA360 ZA361

ZA362 ZA363
Snow World (Hokkaido)

**2000, Feb. 7** **Photo.**

| | | | |
|---|---|---|---|
| **Z384** | ZA360 80y multi | 1.40 | .90 |
| **Z385** | ZA361 80y multi | 1.40 | .90 |
| **Z386** | ZA362 80y multi | 1.40 | .90 |
| **Z387** | ZA363 80y multi | 1.40 | .90 |
| *a.* | Strip, #Z384-Z387 | 6.00 | 6.00 |

ZA364

Japan Flora 2000
(Hyogo) — ZA365

**2000, Mar. 1** **Litho.** ***Perf. 13¼***

| | | | |
|---|---|---|---|
| **Z388** | ZA364 50y multi | .90 | .50 |
| **Z389** | ZA365 80y multi | 1.40 | .90 |
| *a.* | Pane, 5 each #Z388-Z389 | 12.50 | |

ZA366 ZA367

ZA368 ZA369

Korakuen Gardens, 300th Anniv. (Okayama)

**2000, Mar. 2** **Photo.**

**Z390** ZA366 80y multi 1.40 .70
**Z391** ZA367 80y multi 1.40 .70
**Z392** ZA368 80y multi 1.40 .70
**Z393** ZA369 80y multi 1.40 .70
*a.* Strip, #Z390-Z393 6.00 6.00
*b.* Souvenir sheet, #Z390-Z393 6.00 6.00

Cherry Blossoms in Takato (Nagano) — ZA370

**2000, Mar. 3**

**Z394** ZA370 80y multi 1.40 .90
*a.* Pane of 10 15.00

Dyed Fabrics (Okinawa) ZA371

**2000, Mar. 17** **Litho.**

**Z395** ZA371 50y multi .90 .50
*a.* Pane of 10 9.50

Azumino (Nagano) — ZA372

**2000, Mar. 23** **Photo.**

**Z396** ZA372 80y multi 1.40 .90
*a.* Pane of 10 15.00

Cherry Blossoms (Aomori) ZA373

Cherry Blossoms (Fukushima) ZA374

Cherry Blossoms (Iwate) — ZA375

Cherry Blossoms (Miyagi) — ZA376

Cherry Blossoms (Akita) — ZA377

Cherry Blossoms (Yamagata) ZA378

**2000, Apr. 3** **Litho.**

**Z397** ZA373 80y multi 1.40 .90
*a.* Pair, #Z397, Z399 3.00 3.00
*b.* Pair, #Z397, Z400 3.00 3.00
*c.* Pair, #Z397, Z401 3.00 3.00
*d.* Pair, #Z397, Z402 3.00 3.00
**Z398** ZA374 80y multi 1.40 .90
*a.* Pair, #Z398, Z399 3.00 3.00
*b.* Pair, #Z398, Z400 3.00 3.00
*c.* Pair, #Z398, Z401 3.00 3.00
*d.* Pair, #Z398, Z402 3.00 3.00
**Z399** ZA375 80y multi 1.40 .90
**Z400** ZA376 80y multi 1.40 .90
**Z401** ZA377 80y multi 1.40 .90
**Z402** ZA378 80y multi 1.40 .90
*a.* Vert. strip, #Z399-Z402 6.00 6.00
*Nos. Z397-Z402 (6)* 8.40 5.40

Printed in sheets containing one column of four stamps of Nos. Z397 and Z398 at left and right respectively with 3 No. Z402a between.

Tulips (Toyama) — ZA379

**2000, Apr. 28** **Photo.** ***Perf. 13¼***

**Z403** 50y multi .90 .50
**Z404** 80y multi 1.40 .90
*a.* ZA379 Pair, #Z403-Z404 2.50 2.50
*b.* Pane, 5 #Z404a 12.50

Uwajima Castle (Ehime) — ZA381

**2000, Apr. 28** ***Perf. 13½x13¼***

**Z405** ZA381 80y multi 1.40 .90

New Urban Center (Saitama) — ZA382

**2000, May 1** ***Perf. 13¼***

**Z406** 50y multi .90 .50
**Z407** 50y multi .90 .50
*a.* ZA382 Pair, #Z406-Z407 1.90 1.90
*b.* Pane, 5 #Z407a 9.50

### Flowers of the Chugoku Region

(Tottori) ZA384

(Shimane) ZA385

(Okayama) ZA386

(Hiroshima) ZA387

(Yamaguchi) ZA388

**2000, May 1** **Litho.** ***Perf. 13¼***

**Z408** ZA384 50y multi .90 .50
**Z409** ZA385 50y multi .90 .50
**Z410** ZA386 50y multi .90 .50
**Z411** ZA387 50y multi .90 .50
**Z412** ZA388 50y multi .90 .50
*a.* Vert. strip, #Z408-Z412 4.75 4.75
*b.* Pane, 2# Z412a 9.50

Cosmos (Tokyo) ZA389

Roses (Tokyo) ZA390

Bird of Paradise Flowers (Tokyo) ZA391

Sasanquas (Tokyo) ZA392

Freesias (Tokyo) — ZA393

**2000, June 1** **Photo.** ***Perf. 13¼***

**Z413** ZA389 50y multi .90 .50
**Z414** ZA390 50y multi .90 .50
**Z415** ZA391 50y multi .90 .50
**Z416** ZA392 50y multi .90 .50
**Z417** ZA393 50y multi .90 .50
*a.* Vert. strip of 5, #Z413-Z417 4.75 4.75
*b.* Pane, 2 #Z417a 9.50

Shonan Hiratsuka Tanabata Festival (Kanagawa) — ZA394

**2000, June 2** **Litho.**

**Z418** 50y multi .90 .50
**Z419** 50y multi .90 .50
*a.* ZA394 Pair, #Z418-Z419 1.90 1.90
*b.* Pane, 5 #Z419a 9.50

Bankoku Shinryokan (Okinawa) — ZA396

**2000, June 21** **Photo.** ***Perf. 13¼***

**Z420** ZA396 80y multi 1.40 .90
*a.* Pane of 10 15.00

World Performing Arts Festival (Osaka) — ZA397

**2000, June 28** **Litho.**

**Z421** ZA397 80y multi 1.40 .90
*a.* Pane of 10 15.00

Kujuku Islands (Akita) — ZA398

**2000, July 7** **Photo.**

**Z422** ZA398 80y multi 1.40 .90
*a.* Pane of 10 15.00

Potato Field (Hokkaido) — ZA399

Hillside and Hay Rolls (Hokkaido) — ZA400

**2000, July 19**

**Z423** 50y Flowers, barn .90 .50
**Z424** 50y Barn, silo .90 .50
*a.* ZA399 Pair, #Z423-Z424 1.90 1.90

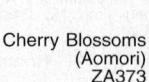

**Z425** 80y + 20y Hayrolls, houses 1.90 1.00
**Z426** 80y + 20y Hayrolls, barns 1.90 1.00
*a.* ZA400 Pair, #Z425-Z426 4.00 4.00
*Nos. Z423-Z426 (4)* 5.60 3.00

Surtax on Nos. Z425-Z426 for refugees of eruption of Mt. Usu.

Awa-odori (Tokushima) ZA401

**2000, July 31** **Litho.**
**Z427** ZA401 80y multi 1.40 .90
*a.* Pane of 10 15.00

Golden Hall of Chusonji Temple (Iwate) — ZA402

**2000, Aug. 1**
**Z428** ZA402 80y multi 1.40 .90
*a.* Pane of 10 15.00

Hakata Doll (Fukuoka) — ZA403

**2000, Aug. 2**
**Z429** ZA403 80y multi 1.40 .90
*a.* Pane of 10 15.00

55th Natl. Athletic Meet (Toyama) — ZA404

**2000, Sept. 1** **Photo.**
**Z430** ZA404 50y multi .90 .50
*a.* Pane of 10 9.50

25th World Parachuting Championships (Mie) — ZA405

No. Z431, 2 skydivers. No. Z432, 3 skydivers.

**2000, Sept. 13**
**Z431** 80y multicolored 1.40 .90
**Z432** 80y multicolored 1.40 .90
*a.* ZA405 Pair, #Z431-Z432 3.00 3.00
*b.* Pane, 5 #Z432a 15.00

Friendly Tokyo (Tokyo) — ZA406

**2000, Sept. 29** **Litho.**
**Z433** ZA406 80y multi 1.40 .90
*a.* Pane of 10 15.00

Iwakuni Kintaikyo Bridge (Yamaguchi) ZA407

**2000, Oct. 10**
**Z434** ZA407 80y multi 1.40 .90
*a.* Pane of 10 15.00

Intl. Wheelchair Marathon (Oita) — ZA408

**2000, Oct. 11**
**Z435** ZA408 80y multi 1.40 .90
*a.* Pane of 10 15.00

Willow and Frog (Aichi) — ZA409

**2000, Oct. 20** **Photo.**
**Z436** ZA409 80y multi 1.40 .90
*a.* Pane of 10 15.00

ZA410 ZA411

ZA412 ZA413

Four Seasons (Kyoto)

**2000, Oct. 20** **Litho.**
**Z437** ZA410 80y multi 1.40 .90
**Z438** ZA411 80y multi 1.40 .90
*a.* Pane, 5 each #Z437-Z438 15.00
**Z439** ZA412 80y multi 1.40 .90
**Z440** ZA413 80y multi 1.40 .90
*a.* Horiz. strip, #Z437-Z440 6.00 3.50
*b.* Pane, 5 each #Z439-Z440 15.00

Odawarajo Castle (Kanagawa) — ZA414

**2000, Oct. 27** ***Perf. 13¼***
**Z441** 50y multi .90 .50
**Z442** 50y multi .90 .50
*a.* ZA414 Pair, #Z441-Z442 1.90 1.90
*b.* Pane, 5 #Z442a 9.50

Intl. Balloon Festival (Saga) — ZA415

**2000, Nov. 1** **Litho.** ***Perf. 13¼***
**Z443** ZA415 80y multi 1.40 .90
*a.* Pane of 10 15.00

Chichibu Night Festival (Saitama) — ZA416

**2000, Nov. 1** **Photo.**
**Z444** 80y Yatai, fireworks 1.40 .90
**Z445** 80y Kasahoko 1.40 .90
*a.* ZA416 Pair, #Z444-Z445 3.00 3.00
*b.* Pane, 5 #Z445a 15.00

Scenic Izu (Shizuoka) — ZA417

**2000, Nov. 29** **Litho.**
**Z446** 50y Garden .90 .50
**Z447** 50y Waterfall .90 .50
*a.* ZA417 Pair, #Z446-Z447 1.90 1.90
*b.* Pane, 5 #Z447a 9.50

Hata Festival, Kohata (Fukushima) ZA418

**2000, Dec. 1** **Photo.**
**Z448** ZA418 80y multi 1.40 .90
*a.* Pane of 10 15.00

Sekino'o-taki Falls and Kirishima (Miyazaki) — ZA419

**2000, Dec. 12** **Photo.**
**Z449** 80y Waterfall 1.40 .90
**Z450** 80y Mountain 1.40 .90
*a.* ZA419 Pair, #Z449-Z450 3.00 3.00
*b.* Pane, 5 #Z450a 15.00

Megane-bashi Bridge (Gunma) — ZA420

**2000, Dec. 15** **Litho.**
**Z451** 50y Bridge .90 .50
**Z452** 50y Transformer substation .90 .50
*a.* ZA420 Pair, #Z451-Z452 1.90 1.90

Song "Shinano-no Kuni" (Nagano) — ZA421

**2000, Dec. 15** **Photo.**
**Z453** 50y Denom. at L .90 .50
**Z454** 50y Denom. at R .90 .50
*a.* ZA421 Pair, #Z453-Z454 1.90 1.90

Kobe Earthquake Restoration (Hyogo) — ZA422

**2001, Jan. 17** **Photo.** ***Perf. 13¼***
**Z455** 50y Pandas .90 .50
**Z456** 80y Kobe Port 1.40 .90
*a.* ZA422 Pair, #Z455-Z456 2.50 2.50
*b.* Pane, 5 #Z456a 12.50

Ooe Kouwaka-mai (Fukuoka) — ZA423

**2001, Jan. 19** **Litho.**
**Z457** ZA423 80y multi 1.40 .90
*a.* Pane of 10 15.00

Kairakuen Garden (Ibaraki) — ZA424

Designs: No. Z458, Koubuntei Pavilion, tree blossoms. No. Z459, Path, Chumon Gate. No. Z460, Togyokusen Spring, path. No. Z461, Koubuntei Pavilion in winter.

**2001, Feb. 1** **Photo.**
**Z458** 50y multi .90 .50
**Z459** 50y multi .90 .50
**Z460** 50y multi .90 .50
**Z461** 50y multi .90 .50
*a.* ZA424 Horiz. strip, #Z458-Z461 4.00 4.00
*b.* Souvenir sheet, #Z461a 4.00 4.00

Ezo Sable (Hokkaido) — ZA425

**2001, Feb. 6** **Litho.**

**Z462** ZA425 80y multi 1.40 .90
*a.* Pane of 10 15.00
*b.* Horiz. pair, #Z321, Z462 3.00 3.00

Issued: No. Z462b, Sept. 2007.

Kochi Castle and Sunday Market (Kochi) — ZA426

**2001, Mar. 1** **Photo.** ***Perf. 13¼***

**Z463** 80y multi 1.40 .90
**Z464** 80y multi 1.40 .90
*a.* ZA426 Pair, #Z463-Z464 3.00 3.00
*b.* Pane, 5 #Z464a 15.00

Takarazuka Revue Dancers (Hyogo) — ZA427

Violets (Hyogo) — ZA428

**2001, Mar. 21** **Litho.**

**Z465** ZA427 80y multi 1.40 .90
**Z466** ZA428 80y multi 1.40 .90
*a.* Pane, 5 each #Z465-Z466 15.00

Matsue Castle and Meimei-an Teahouse (Shimane) — ZA429

**2001, Mar. 21**

**Z467** 80y multi 1.40 .90
**Z468** 80y multi 1.40 .90
*a.* ZA429 Pair, #Z467-Z468 3.00 3.00
*b.* Pane, 5 #Z468a 15.00

Grapes, Jewelry and Mt. Fuji (Yamanashi) ZA430

**2001, Mar. 30** **Photo.**

**Z469** ZA430 80y multi 1.40 .90
*a.* Pane of 10 15.00

Sports Paradise (Osaka) — ZA431

Designs: No. Z470, Thunder god (red) playing table tennis. No. Z471, Wing god (green) playing table tennis. No. Z472, Bowling. No. Z473, Taekwondo.

**2001, Apr. 3**

**Z470** 50y multi .90 .50
**Z471** 50y multi .90 .50
**Z472** 50y multi .90 .50
**Z473** 50y multi .90 .50
*a.* ZA431 Horiz. strip, #Z470-Z473 4.00 4.00

Beautiful Fukushima Future Expo (Fukushima) ZA432

**2001, Apr. 10**

**Z474** ZA432 80y multi 1.40 .90
*a.* Pane of 10 15.00

Cherry Blossoms at Takada Castle (Niigata) — ZA433

**2001, Apr. 10** **Litho.**

**Z475** ZA433 80y multi 1.40 .90
*a.* Pane of 10 15.00

Hamamatsu Festival (Shizuoka) — ZA434

Designs: No. Z476, Palace Festival. No. Z477, Kite fighting.

**2001, May 1**

**Z476** 80y multi 1.40 .90
**Z477** 80y multi 1.40 .90
*a.* ZA434 Pair, #Z476-Z477 3.00 3.00
*b.* Pane, 5 #Z477a 15.00

Ashikaga School Gate (Tochigi) ZA435

Ashikaga School (Tochigi) ZA436

**2001, May 11** **Photo.**

**Z478** ZA435 80y multi 1.40 .90
**Z479** ZA436 50y multi 1.40 .90
*a.* Pane, 5 each #Z478-Z479 15.00

Natl. Afforestation Campaign (Yamanashi) ZA437

**2001, May 18**

**Z480** ZA437 50y multi .90 .50
*a.* Pane of 10 9.50

Sendai, 400th Anniv. (Miyagi) — ZA438

**2001, May 18** **Litho.**

**Z481** ZA438 80y multi 1.40 .90
*a.* Pane of 10 15.00

Zenkoji Temple and Mt. Iizunayama (Nagano) — ZA439

**2001, May 23**

**Z482** 80y multi 1.40 .90
**Z483** 80y multi 1.40 .90
*a.* ZA439 Pair, #Z482-Z483 3.00 3.00
*b.* Pane, 5 #Z483a 15.00

Ducks (Yamaguchi) ZA440

Kirara Band, Japan Expo Site (Yamaguchi) ZA441

**2001, May 25**

**Z484** ZA440 50y multi .90 .50
**Z485** ZA441 80y multi 1.40 .90
*a.* Pane, 5 each #Z484-Z485 12.25

Cherry Blossoms (Tokyo) — ZA442

Hydrangea (Tokyo) — ZA443

Salvia (Tokyo) — ZA444

Chrysanthemums (Tokyo) — ZA445

Camellias (Tokyo) — ZA446

**2001, June 1** **Photo.**

**Z486** ZA442 50y multi .90 .50
**Z487** ZA443 50y multi .90 .50
**Z488** ZA444 50y multi .90 .50
**Z489** ZA445 50y multi .90 .50
**Z490** ZA446 50y multi .90 .50
*a.* Vert. strip, #Z486-Z490 4.75 4.75
*b.* Pane, 2 #Z490a 9.50

ZA447

Sites (Tottori) — ZA448

Designs: No. Z491, Snow crab, Uradome Coast. No. Z492, Tottori Dunes. No. Z493, Paper Hina dolls in river. No. Z494, Mt. Daisen. No. Z495, Nageiredo Hall. No. Z496, Mukibanda Yayoi Period.

Illustration ZA447 reduced.

**2001, June 1**

**Z491** 50y multi .90 .50
**Z492** 50y multi .90 .50
**Z493** 50y multi .90 .50
**Z494** 50y multi .90 .50
*a.* ZA447 Horiz. strip, #Z491-Z494 4.00 4.00
**Z495** 80y multi 1.40 .90
**Z496** 80y multi 1.40 .90
*a.* ZA448 Horiz. pair, #Z495-Z496 3.00 3.00
*Nos. Z491-Z496 (6)* 6.40 3.80

Prosperity in Kaga (Ishikawa) — ZA449

**2001, June 4** **Litho.**

**Z497** ZA449 80y multi 1.40 .90
*a.* Pane of 10 15.00

Poppies (Hokkaido) ZA450

Calanthe (Hokkaido) ZA451

**2001, June 22** **Litho.**

**Z498** ZA450 50y multi .90 .50
*a.* Pane of 10 9.50
**Z499** ZA451 50y multi .90 .50
*a.* Pane of 10 9.50

Cornerstone of Peace (Okinawa) — ZA452

**2001, June 22** **Photo.**

**Z500** ZA452 80y multi 1.40 .90

Peach Blossoms, Shirane-sanzan Mountains (Yamanashi) ZA453

Irises, Mt. Kitadake (Yamanashi) ZA454

Horses. Mt. Yatsugatake (Yamanashi) ZA455

Oshino-hakkai Pond (Yamanashi) ZA456

Cherry Blossoms, Minobu (Yamanashi) ZA457

**2001, July 2**

**Z501** ZA453 50y multi .90 .50
**Z502** ZA454 50y multi .90 .50
**Z503** ZA455 50y multi .90 .50
**Z504** ZA456 50y multi .90 .50
**Z505** ZA457 50y multi .90 .50
*a.* Vert. strip, #Z501-Z505 4.75 4.75
*b.* Pane, 2 #Z505a 9.50

Automobile City, Toyota (Aichi) — ZA458

Designs: No. Z506, Toyota-oohashi Bridge. No. Z507, Toyota Stadium.

**2001, July 2**

**Z506** 50y multi .90 .50
**Z507** 50y multi .90 .50
*a.* ZA458 Pair, #Z506-Z507 1.90 1.90
*b.* Pane, 5 #Z507a 9.50

Kitakyushu Expo Festival (Fukuoka) — ZA459

**2001, July 4**

**Z508** ZA459 80y multi 1.40 .90
*a.* Pane of 10 15.00

World Trade Organization, 14th General Assembly (Osaka) — ZA460

Designs: No. Z509, Namdaemun, Seoul, and Doton-bori, Osaka. No. Z510, Bunraku, Nong-ak.

**2001, July 6** **Litho.**

**Z509** 80y multi 1.40 .90
**Z510** 80y multi 1.40 .90
*a.* ZA460 Pair, #Z509-Z510 3.00 3.00

Grand Fireworks of Nagaoka (Niigata) — ZA461

**2001, July 23**

**Z511** 50y yel & multi .90 .50
**Z512** 50y pink & multi .90 .50
*a.* ZA461 Pair, #Z511-Z512 1.90 1.90
*b.* Pane, 5 #Z512a 9.50

Poplars (Hokkaido) ZA462

Statue, Sheep (Hokkaido) ZA463

**2001, Sept. 3** **Litho.** ***Perf. 13¼***

**Z513** ZA462 80y multi 1.40 .90
**Z514** ZA463 80y multi 1.40 .90
*a.* Pane, 5 each #Z513-Z514 15.00

56th Natl. Athletic Meets (Miyagi) — ZA464

**2001, Sept. 7** **Photo.**

**Z515** ZA464 50y multi .90 .50
*a.* Pane of 10 9.50

Matsuyama Castle, Masaoki Shiki (1867-1902), Poet (Ehime) — ZA465

**2001, Sept. 12**

**Z516** 50y Castle .90 .50
**Z517** 50y Poet .90 .50
*a.* ZA465 Horiz. pair, #Z516-Z517 1.90 1.90

Ibi Traditions (Gifu) — ZA466

Designs: No. Z518, Tanigumi-Odori dance. No. Z519, Train, persimmons.

**2001, Sept. 28** **Photo.** ***Perf. 13¼***

**Z518** 50y multi .90 .50
**Z519** 50y multi .90 .50
*a.* ZA466 Horiz. pair, #Z518-Z519 1.90 1.90
*b.* Pane, 5 #Z519a 9.50

Kamakura Igloo (Akita) — ZA467

**2001, Oct. 1** **Litho.**

**Z520** ZA467 80y multi 1.40 .90
*a.* Pane of 10 15.00

9th Intl. Conference on Lake Conservation & Management (Shiga) — ZA468

**2001, Oct. 1**

**Z521** ZA468 50y multi .90 .50
*a.* Pane of 10 9.50

World Indoor Cycling Championships (Kagoshima) ZA469

**2001, Oct. 1**

**Z522** ZA469 80y multi 1.40 .90

Okuma Auditorium, Waseda University (Tokyo) — ZA470

**2001, Oct. 19**

**Z523** ZA470 80y multi 1.40 .90
*a.* Pane of 10 15.00

Wild Narcissi (Fukui) ZA471

Echizen Coast and Wild Narcissi (Fukui) ZA472

**2001, Nov. 6**

**Z524** ZA471 50y multi .90 .50
*a.* Pane of 10 9.50
**Z525** ZA472 80y multi 1.40 .90
*a.* Pane of 10 15.00

Tokyo Millenalio (Tokyo) — ZA473

**2001, Dec. 3** **Photo.**

**Z526** ZA473 80y multi 1.40 .90
*a.* Pane of 10 15.00

Ezo Flying Squirrels (Hokkaido) — ZA474

**2002, Feb. 5**

**Z527** ZA474 80y multi 1.40 .90

Scenes North of Hiroshima (Hiroshima) — ZA475

Designs: No. Z528, Nukui Dam. No. Z529, On-bashi Bridge.

**2002, Feb. 22** **Litho.**

**Z528** 80y multi 1.40 .90
**Z529** 80y multi 1.40 .90
*a.* ZA475 Horiz. pair, #Z528-Z529 3.00 3.00

Azaleas (Wakayama) ZA476

**2002, Mar. 1** **Photo.** ***Perf. 13¼***

**Z530** ZA476 80y multi 1.40 .90

Glover Garden (Nagasaki) — ZA477

Designs: No. Z531, Houses, fountain, roses. No. Z532, House, tulips.

**2002, Mar. 1** **Litho.**

**Z531** 50y multi .90 .50
**Z532** 50y multi .90 .50
*a.* ZA477 Horiz. pair, #Z531-Z532 1.90 1.90

Cherry Blossoms, Hiikawa River (Shimane) ZA478

Cherry Blossoms, Bicchu-Kokubunji Temple (Okayama) ZA479

**2002, Mar. 18**

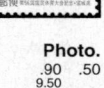

**Z533** ZA478 50y multi .90 .50
**Z534** ZA479 50y multi .90 .50
*a.* Horiz. pair, #Z533-Z534 1.90 1.90
*b.* Pane, 5 #Z534a 9.50 —

Tangerine, Sata Cape (Ehime) ZA480

Citrus Fruit, Mt. Tsurugisan (Tokushima) ZA481

Bayberry, Tengu Highlands (Kochi) ZA482

Olives, Shodo Island (Kagawa) ZA483

**2002, Mar. 20** **Photo.**

| | | | |
|---|---|---|---|
| **Z535** | ZA480 50y multi | .90 | .50 |
| **Z536** | ZA481 50y multi | .90 | .50 |
| **Z537** | ZA482 50y multi | .90 | .50 |
| **Z538** | ZA483 50y multi | .90 | .50 |
| *a.* | Horiz. strip of 4, #Z535-Z538 | 4.00 | 4.00 |

Flowers (Hokkaido) — ZA484

No. Z539, Tulips, windmills. No. Z540, Sunflowers, field.

**2002, Apr. 25** **Litho.**

| | | | |
|---|---|---|---|
| **Z539** | 80y multicolored | 1.40 | .90 |
| **Z540** | 80y multicolored | 1.40 | .90 |
| *a.* | ZA484 Horiz. pair, #Z539-Z540 | 3.00 | 3.00 |

54th Intl. Whaling Commission (Yamaguchi) ZA485

**2002, Apr. 25**

| | | | |
|---|---|---|---|
| **Z541** | ZA485 80y multi | 1.40 | .90 |

Bonsai Village (Saitama) — ZA486

**2002, Apr. 26** **Photo.**

| | | | |
|---|---|---|---|
| **Z542** | ZA486 80y multi | 1.40 | .90 |

Yokohama (Kanagawa) — ZA487

Designs: No. Z543, Sailing ships. No. Z544, Modern ship, skyline, woman.

**2002, May 1**

| | | | |
|---|---|---|---|
| **Z543** | 50y multi | .90 | .50 |
| **Z544** | 50y multi | .90 | .50 |
| *a.* | ZA487 Horiz. pair, #Z543-Z544 | 1.90 | 1.90 |
| *b.* | Pane, 5 #Z544a | 9.50 | |

Flowers (Niigata) — ZA488

Designs: No. Z545, Red camellias. No. Z546, Yellow daylilies. No. Z547, Purple and pink irises. No. Z548, Pink iwakagami flowers.

**2002, May 1** **Litho.**

| | | | |
|---|---|---|---|
| **Z545** | 50y multi | .90 | .50 |
| **Z546** | 50y multi | .90 | .50 |
| **Z547** | 50y multi | .90 | .50 |
| **Z548** | 50y multi | .90 | .50 |
| *a.* | ZA488 Horiz. strip of 4, #Z545-Z548 | 4.00 | 4.00 |

See Nos. 3909-3912.

Natl. Afforestation Campaign (Yamagata) — ZA489

**2002, May 31** **Photo.**

| | | | |
|---|---|---|---|
| **Z549** | ZA489 50y multi | .90 | .50 |
| *a.* | Pane of 10 | 9.50 | — |

Oze (Fukushima) — ZA490

Designs: No. Z550, Flowers, bare trees, walkway. No. Z551, Flowers, evergreens.

**2002, June 28** **Litho.**

| | | | |
|---|---|---|---|
| **Z550** | 50y multi | .90 | .50 |
| **Z551** | 50y multi | .90 | .50 |
| *a.* | ZA490 Horiz. pair, #Z550-Z551 | 1.90 | 1.90 |

Mt. Tanigawadake (Gunma) — ZA491

Mountains and: No. Z552, Rhododendrons. No. Z553, Trees in autumn.

**2002, June 28**

| | | | |
|---|---|---|---|
| **Z552** | 80y multi | 1.40 | .90 |
| **Z553** | 80y multi | 1.40 | .90 |
| *a.* | ZA491 Horiz. pair, #Z552-Z553 | 3.00 | 3.00 |

Tokyo Fair and Market (Tokyo) — ZA492

Designs: No. Z554, Morning Glory Fair. No. Z555, Hozuki Fair.

**2002, June 28** **Photo.**

| | | | |
|---|---|---|---|
| **Z554** | 80y multi | 1.40 | .90 |
| **Z555** | 80y multi | 1.40 | .90 |
| *a.* | ZA492 Horiz. pair, #Z554-Z555 | 3.00 | 3.00 |

Alpine Flora (Ishikawa) — ZA493

**2002, July 1** **Flower Color**

| | | | |
|---|---|---|---|
| **Z556** | 50y Purple | .90 | .50 |
| **Z557** | 50y Brown | .90 | .50 |
| **Z558** | 50y Bright pink | .90 | .50 |
| **Z559** | 50y White | .90 | .50 |
| *a.* | ZA493 Horiz. strip of 4, #Z556-Z559 | 4.00 | 4.00 |

Gujou-odori Dance (Gifu) — ZA494

**2002, July 1**

| | | | |
|---|---|---|---|
| **Z560** | ZA494 50y multi | .90 | .50 |

85th Lions Club Intl. Convention (Osaka) — ZA495

**2002, July 1**

| | | | |
|---|---|---|---|
| **Z561** | ZA495 80y multi | 1.40 | .90 |

23rd Asia-Pacific Scout Jamboree (Osaka) — ZA496

**2002, July 15**

| | | | |
|---|---|---|---|
| **Z562** | ZA496 50y multi | .90 | .50 |

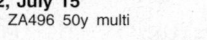

Yachiyoza Theater (Kumamoto) — ZA497

**2002, July 15** **Litho.**

| | | | |
|---|---|---|---|
| **Z563** | ZA497 80y multi | 1.40 | .90 |

Hikan-zakura, Iejima (Okinawa) ZA498

Hibiscus, Kaichudouro Highway (Okinawa) ZA499

Bougainvillea, House in Tsuboya (Okinawa) ZA500

Lily, Higashihennazaki (Okinawa) ZA501

Seishika Flower, Seishika Bridge (Okinawa) — ZA502

**2002, Aug. 23** **Photo.** ***Perf. 13¼***

| | | | |
|---|---|---|---|
| **Z564** | ZA498 50y multi | .90 | .50 |
| **Z565** | ZA499 50y multi | .90 | .50 |
| **Z566** | ZA500 50y multi | .90 | .50 |
| **Z567** | ZA501 50y multi | .90 | .50 |
| **Z568** | ZA502 50y multi | .90 | .50 |
| *a.* | Vert. strip of 5, #Z564-Z568 | 4.75 | 4.75 |

Printed in sheets containing two No. Z568a.

Flora (Tokyo) — ZA503

Designs: No. Z569, Azalea (pink flower, blue denomination). No. Z570, Lily. No. Z571, Crape myrtle (pink flower and denomination). No. Z572, Ginkgo leaves.

**2002, Sept. 2**

| | | | |
|---|---|---|---|
| **Z569** | 50y multi | .90 | .50 |
| **Z570** | 50y multi | .90 | .50 |
| **Z571** | 50y multi | .90 | .50 |
| **Z572** | 50y multi | .90 | .50 |
| *a.* | ZA503 Horiz. strip of 4, #Z569-Z572 | 4.00 | 4.00 |

57th Natl. Athletic Meet (Kochi) — ZA504

**2002, Sept. 5**

| | | | |
|---|---|---|---|
| **Z573** | ZA504 50y multi | .90 | .50 |

Iga-Ueno (Mie) — ZA505

Designs: No. Z574, Basho Matsuo, Iga-Ueno Castle. No. Z575, Iga-Ueno Castle, Haisei-den Hall.

**2002, Sept. 10** **Litho.**

| | | | |
|---|---|---|---|
| **Z574** | 80y multi | 1.40 | .90 |
| **Z575** | 80y multi | 1.40 | .90 |
| *a.* | ZA505 Horiz. pair, #Z574-Z575 | 3.00 | 3.00 |

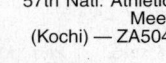

Tohoku's Four Season Story (Aomori) — ZA506

**2002, Oct. 23 Photo. *Perf. 13¼***
**Z576** ZA506 80y multi 1.40 .90

Fifth Winter Asian Games (Aomori) — ZA507

**2003, Jan. 24 Photo. *Perf. 13¼***
**Z577** ZA507 50y multi 1.40 .90

Nobeoka, City of Noh Theater (Miyazaki) — ZA508

Designs: No. Z578, Actor on stage, audience. No. Z579, Actor with red kimono.

**2003, Feb. 3**
**Z578** 80y multi 1.40 .90
**Z579** 80y multi 1.40 .90
*a.* ZA508 Horiz. pair, #Z578-Z579 3.00 3.00

Hokkaido Heritage (Hokkaido) — ZA509

**2003, Feb. 5 Photo. *Perf. 13¼***
**Z580** 80y Ainu design 1.40 .90
**Z581** 80y Lake Mashuko 1.40 .90
*a.* ZA509 Horiz. pair, #Z580-Z581 3.00 3.00

Flora (Nagano) — ZA510

Designs: No. Z582, Dogtooth violet (pink flowers) and mountain. No. Z583, Skunk cabbage (white flower). No. Z584, Nikko day lily (yellow flower. No. Z585, Cosmos (white, pink and red flowers).

**2003, Mar. 5 Photo. *Perf. 13¼***
**Z582** 50y multi .85 .50
**Z583** 50y multi .85 .50
**Z584** 50y multi .85 .50
**Z585** 50y multi .85 .50
*a.* ZA510 Horiz. strip of 4, #Z582-Z585 3.50 3.50

See Nos. 3871-3874.

Kibitsu Shrine (Okayama) — ZA511

**2003, Mar. 5**
**Z586** ZA511 80y multi 1.40 .90

Kompira-Ohshibai Theater (Kagawa) — ZA512

**2003, Mar. 24 Litho.**
**Z587** ZA512 80y multi 1.40 .90

Imari-Arita Ceramics (Saga) — ZA513

**2003, Apr. 10**
**Z588** ZA513 80y multi 1.40 .90

Kaneko Misuzu and Poem "Tairyo" (Yamaguchi) — ZA514

**2003, Apr. 11 Photo.**
**Z589** 80y Misuzu 1.40 .90
**Z590** 80y Poem 1.40 .90
*a.* ZA514 Horiz. pair, #Z589-Z590 2.80 2.80

Cormorant Fishing and Gifu Castle (Gifu) — ZA515

**2003, May 1 *Perf. 13¼***
**Z591** 50y Fishermen .85 .50
**Z592** 50y Castle .85 .50
*a.* ZA515 Horiz. pair, #Z591-Z592 1.75 1.75

Traditional Events (Kyoto) — ZA516

Designs: No. Z593, Aoi-matsuri (wagon decorated with flowers). No. Z594, Gion-matsuri festival float (tower on wheels). No. Z595, Okuribi (fire on mountain). No. Z596, Jidai-matsuri (parade procession).

**2003, May 1 Litho.**
**Z593** 50y multi .85 .50
**Z594** 50y multi .85 .50
**Z595** 50y multi .85 .50
**Z596** 50y multi .85 .50
*a.* ZA516 Horiz. strip of 4, #Z593-Z596 3.50 3.50

Natl. Afforestation Campaign (Chiba) — ZA517

**2003, May 16 Photo.**
**Z597** ZA517 50y multi .85 .50

Mt. Tsukuba and Iris (Ibaraki) — ZA518

**2003, May 20 Litho.**
**Z598** ZA518 80y multi 1.40 .90

Tsurugajou Castle, Persimmons (Fukushima) ZA519

**2003, July 1 Photo. *Perf. 13¼***
**Z599** ZA519 80y multi 1.40 .90

Kyuya Fukada, Mountineer, Birth Cent. (Ishikawa) — ZA520

**2003, July 1 Litho.**
**Z600** ZA520 80y multi 1.40 .90

Okinawa Urban Monorail (Okinawa) — ZA521

**2003, Aug. 8**
**Z601** 50y Shurijo Castle .85 .50
**Z602** 50y Naha Airport .85 .50
*a.* ZA521 Horiz. pair, #Z601-Z602 1.75 1.75

58th Natl. Athletics Meets (Shizuoka) — ZA522

**2003, Aug. 29 Photo.**
**Z603** ZA522 50y multi .85 .65

Sweet Briar (Tokyo) ZA523

Wisterias (Tokyo) ZA524

Irises (Tokyo) ZA525

Tea Blossoms (Tokyo) ZA526

**2003, Sept. 1**
**Z604** ZA523 50y multi .85 .50
**Z605** ZA524 50y multi .85 .50
**Z606** ZA525 50y multi .85 .50
**Z607** ZA526 50y multi .85 .50
*a.* Horiz. strip, #Z604-Z607 3.50 3.50

Chiyojo, Haiku Poet (Ishikawa) — ZA527

**2003, Oct. 3 Litho.**
**Z608** 80y Haiku text 1.40 .90
**Z609** 80y Chiyojo 1.40 .90
*a.* ZA527 Horiz. pair, #Z608-Z609 3.00 3.00

Yasujiro Ozu (1903-63), Film Director (Mie) — ZA528

**2003, Oct. 23 Photo.**
**Z610** ZA528 80y multi 1.40 .90

Kiritappu Wetland and Wakka Primeval Garden (Hokkaido) — ZA529

**2004, Feb. 5 Litho. *Perf. 13¼***
**Z611** 80y Yellow flowers 1.40 .90
**Z612** 80y Orange flowers 1.40 .90
*a.* ZA529 Horiz. pair, #Z611-Z612 3.00 3.00

Kyushu Bullet Train (Kagoshima) ZA530

**2004, Mar. 12 Photo. *Perf. 13¼***
**Z613** ZA530 50y multi .90 .65

### Flower Types of 1990

Designs as before.

**2004, Mar. 19**
**Z614** ZA24 50y multi .90 .50
**Z615** ZA25 50y multi .90 .50
**Z616** ZA26 50y multi .90 .50
**Z617** ZA27 50y multi .90 .50
**Z618** ZA28 50y multi .90 .50
**Z619** ZA29 50y multi .90 .50
*Nos. Z614-Z619 (6)* 5.40 3.00

Zuiryuji Temple (Toyama) — ZA531

**2004, Mar. 19** **Litho.**

**Z620** ZA531 80y multi 1.40 .90

Hana-Kairou Flower Park (Tottori) — ZA532

**2004, Mar. 23**

**Z621** ZA532 80y multi 1.40 .90

Gerbera (Shizuoka) ZA533

Carnation (Shizuoka) ZA534

Rose (Shizuoka) ZA535

Lisianthus (Shizuoka) ZA536

**2004, Apr. 8**

**Z622** ZA533 80y multi 1.40 .90
**Z623** ZA534 80y multi 1.40 .90
**Z624** ZA535 80y multi 1.40 .90
**Z625** ZA536 80y multi 1.40 .90
*a.* Horiz. strip of 4, #Z622-Z625 6.00 6.00

Pacific Flora 2004.

National Afforestation Campaign (Miyazaki) — ZA537

**2004, Mar. 23** **Photo.**

**Z626** ZA537 50y multi .90 .50

Murouji's Five Story Pagoda (Nara) — ZA538

**2004, Apr. 26**

**Z627** ZA538 80y multi 1.40 .90

Rotary International Convention (Osaka) — ZA539

**2004, May 21**

**Z628** ZA539 80y multi 1.40 .90

Ice Breaker Garinko-go, Steller's Sea Eagle (Hokkaido) — ZA540

**2004, May 28**

**Z629** ZA540 80y multi 1.40 .90

Kanto Festival Performer, Namahage (Akita) — ZA541

**2004, June 1** **Litho.**

**Z630** 50y blue & multi .90 .50
**Z631** 50y red & multi .90 .50
*a.* ZA541 Horiz. pair, #Z630-Z631 1.80 1.80

Akita City, 400th anniv.

Magnolia (Tokyo) — ZA542

Azalea (Tokyo) — ZA543

Wildflower (Tokyo) — ZA544

Bush Clover (Tokyo) — ZA545

**2004, June 1** **Photo.**

**Z632** ZA542 50y multi .90 .50
**Z633** ZA543 50y multi .90 .50
**Z634** ZA544 50y multi .90 .50
**Z635** ZA545 50y multi .90 .50
*a.* Horiz. strip of 4, #Z632-Z635 3.75 3.75

Roses and Buildings (Kanagawa) ZA546

Gold-banded Lily and Buildings (Kanagawa) ZA547

Wisteria and Enoshima Island (Kanagawa) ZA548

Hydrangea and Lake Ashinoko (Kanagawa) ZA549

**2004, June 1**

**Z636** ZA546 50y multi .90 .50
**Z637** ZA547 50y multi .90 .50
**Z638** ZA548 50y multi .90 .50
**Z639** ZA549 50y multi .90 .50
*a.* Horiz. strip of 4, #Z636-Z639 3.75 3.75

Daimyo Processions of Lord Takachika Mouri (Yamaguchi) — ZA550

**2004, June 21** **Litho.**

**Z640** 80y red & multi 1.40 .90
**Z641** 80y green & multi 1.40 .90
*a.* ZA550 Horiz. pair, #Z640-Z641 3.00 3.00

Rose, Mt. Tsukubasan (Ibaraki) ZA551

Yashio-tsutsuji and Lake Chuzenjiko (Tochigi) ZA552

Renge-tsutsuji and Mt. Akagisan (Gunma) ZA553

Primrose and Tajimagahara Native Primrose Field (Saitama) ZA554

Rape Blossoms and Nojimazaki Lighthouse (Chiba) — ZA555

**2004, June 23** **Photo.**

**Z642** ZA551 50y multi .90 .50
**Z643** ZA552 50y multi .90 .50
**Z644** ZA553 50y multi .90 .50
**Z645** ZA554 50y multi .90 .50
**Z646** ZA555 50y multi .90 .50
*a.* Vert. strip of 5, #Z642-Z646 4.75 4.75

Owara Dance (Toyama) — ZA556

Designs: No. Z647, Children. No. Z648, Dancers in pink kimonos. No. Z649, Dancers in black clothes. No. Z650, Dancers in blue kimonos.

**2004, Aug. 20** **Litho.**

**Z647** 50y multi .90 .50
**Z648** 50y multi .90 .50
**Z649** 50y multi .90 .50
**Z650** 50y multi .90 .50
*a.* ZA556 Horiz. strip of 4, #Z647-Z650 3.75 3.75

59th National Athletic Meets (Saitama) — ZA557

**2004, Sept. 10** **Photo.** ***Perf. 13¼***

**Z651** ZA557 50y multi .90 .50

Miniature Sheet

88 Temples (Shikoku) — ZA558

No. Z652: a, Ryozenji (Temple 1). b, Gokurakuji (Temple 2). c, Konsenji (Temple 3). d, Dainchiji (Temple 4). e, Tatsueji (Temple 19). f, Kakurinji (Temple 20). g, Tairyuji (Temple 21). h, Byoudouji (Temple 22). i, Iwamotoji (Temple 37). j, Kongoufukuji (Temple 38). k, Enkouji (Temple 39). l, Kanjizaiji (Temple 40). m, Nankoubou (Temple 55). n, Taizanji (Temple 56). o, Eifukuji (Temple 57). p, Senyuji (Temple 58). q, Shusshakaji (Temple 73). r, Kouyamaji (Temple 74). s, Zentsuji (Temple 75). t, Kouzouji (Temple 76).

**2004, Nov. 5**

**Z652** ZA558 Sheet of 20 30.00 30.00
*a.-t.* 80y Any single 1.40 .90

Temple numbers are found in the first group of small Japanese characters on each stamp. The numbers used are the same as those found under "China" in the Illustrated Identifier at the back of the book. The left and right Japanese characters in this first group of small characters, which ranges from 3 to 5 characters in length, are the same on each stamp. The characters between these two constant characters represent the temple number. As there is no character for zero, the number "20" will show the character for "2" (=) to the left of the character for "10" (+). Numbers 11-19 will have the unit's character to the right of the character for "10." Thus, the numbers "12" and "20" will have the same characters, just in a different order. Two-digit numbers beginning with 21 that are not divisible by 10 will be three characters long. Number 21, as an example, will show the characters for "2," "10," and "1" reading from left to right ( = + - ).

National Theater (Okinawa) ZA559

**2005, Jan. 21** **Litho.** ***Perf. 13¼***

**Z653** ZA559 50y multi .90 .50

Apple Blossoms (Nagano) ZA560

Renge Azalea (Nagano) ZA561

Lily of the Valley (Nagano) ZA562

Gentian (Nagano) ZA563

**2005, Apr. 1 Litho. *Perf. 13¼***

| | | | | | |
|---|---|---|---|---|---|
| **Z654** | ZA560 | 50y multi | | .90 | .50 |
| **Z655** | ZA561 | 50y multi | | .90 | .50 |
| **Z656** | ZA562 | 50y multi | | .90 | .50 |
| **Z657** | ZA563 | 50y multi | | .90 | .50 |
| *a.* | | Horiz. strip of 4, #Z654-Z657 | | 3.75 | 3.75 |

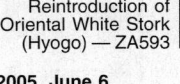

Tulip (Toyama, Ishikawa, Fukui) — ZA564

Hydrangea (Toyama, Ishikawa, Fukui) — ZA565

Rhododendron (Toyama, Ishikawa, Fukui) — ZA566

Lily (Toyama, Ishikawa, Fukui) — ZA567

**2005, Apr. 1**

| | | | | | |
|---|---|---|---|---|---|
| **Z658** | ZA564 | 50y multi | | .90 | .50 |
| **Z659** | ZA565 | 50y multi | | .90 | .50 |
| **Z660** | ZA566 | 50y multi | | .90 | .50 |
| **Z661** | ZA567 | 50y multi | | .90 | .50 |
| *a.* | | Horiz. strip of 4, #Z658-Z661 | | 3.75 | 3.75 |

Peace Memorial Park (Hiroshima) — ZA568

Designs: No. Z662, Birds, Cenotaph for Atomic Bomb Victims. No. Z663, Fountains, Hiroshima Peace Memorial Museum.

**2005, Apr. 22**

| | | | | |
|---|---|---|---|---|
| **Z662** | 50y multi | | .90 | .50 |
| **Z663** | 50y multi | | .90 | .50 |
| *a.* | ZA568 Horiz. pair, #Z662-Z663 | | 1.90 | 1.90 |

Sweetbrier (Hokkaido) ZA569

Lavender (Hokkaido) ZA570

Cowslip (Hokkaido) ZA571

Lily of the Valley (Hokkaido) ZA572

**2005, Apr. 26**

| | | | | | |
|---|---|---|---|---|---|
| **Z664** | ZA569 | 50y multi | | .90 | .50 |
| **Z665** | ZA570 | 50y multi | | .90 | .50 |
| **Z666** | ZA571 | 50y multi | | .90 | .50 |
| **Z667** | ZA572 | 50y multi | | .90 | .50 |
| *a.* | | Horiz. strip of 4, #Z664-Z667 | | 3.75 | 3.75 |

See Nos. 3917-3920.

Momordica Charantia (Okinawa) — ZA573

**2005, May 6**

| | | | | | |
|---|---|---|---|---|---|
| **Z668** | ZA573 | 50y multi | | .90 | .50 |

Sunflower, Mt. Yatsugatake (Yamanashi) ZA574

Gentian, Mt. Kitadake (Yamanashi) ZA575

Evening Primrose, Mt. Fuji (Yamanashi) ZA576

Lady's Slipper, Mt. Fuji (Yamanashi) ZA577

**2005, May 16 Litho. *Perf. 13¼***

| | | | | | |
|---|---|---|---|---|---|
| **Z669** | ZA574 | 80y multi | | 1.40 | .90 |
| **Z670** | ZA575 | 80y multi | | 1.40 | .90 |
| **Z671** | ZA576 | 80y multi | | 1.40 | .90 |
| **Z672** | ZA577 | 80y multi | | 1.40 | .90 |
| *a.* | | Horiz. strip of 4, #Z669-Z672 | | 6.00 | 6.00 |

National Afforestation Campaign (Ibaraki) ZA578

**2005, May 27 Photo.**

| | | | | | |
|---|---|---|---|---|---|
| **Z673** | ZA578 | 50y multi | | .90 | .50 |

Orchid (Tokyo) — ZA579

Crinum (Tokyo) — ZA580

Kerria (Tokyo) — ZA581

Azalea (Tokyo) — ZA582

**2005, June 1**

| | | | | | |
|---|---|---|---|---|---|
| **Z674** | ZA579 | 50y multi | | .90 | .50 |
| **Z675** | ZA580 | 50y multi | | .90 | .50 |
| **Z676** | ZA581 | 50y multi | | .90 | .50 |
| **Z677** | ZA582 | 50y multi | | .90 | .50 |
| *a.* | | Horiz. strip of 4, #Z674-Z677 | | 3.75 | 3.75 |

Une, Dazaifu-Tenmangu (Fukuoka) ZA583

Cherry Blossoms, Kanmon Bridge (Fukuoka) ZA584

Camphor Blossoms, Ariake Sea (Saga) ZA585

Azaleas, Mt. Fugendake (Nagasaki) ZA586

Tulips, Huis Ten Bosch (Nagasaki) ZA587

Gentians, Mt. Aso (Kumamoto) ZA588

Bungo-ume, Mt. Takasaki (Oita) ZA589

Crinums, Nichinan Beach (Miyazaki) ZA590

Azaleas, Kirishima Mountains (Kagoshima) ZA591

Hibiscus, Screw Pine (Kagoshima) ZA592

**2005, June 1**

| | | | | | |
|---|---|---|---|---|---|
| **Z678** | ZA583 | 50y multi | | .90 | .50 |
| **Z679** | ZA584 | 50y multi | | .90 | .50 |
| **Z680** | ZA585 | 50y multi | | .90 | .50 |
| **Z681** | ZA586 | 50y multi | | .90 | .50 |
| **Z682** | ZA587 | 50y multi | | .90 | .50 |
| **Z683** | ZA588 | 50y multi | | .90 | .50 |
| **Z684** | ZA589 | 50y multi | | .90 | .50 |
| **Z685** | ZA590 | 50y multi | | .90 | .50 |
| **Z686** | ZA591 | 50y multi | | .90 | .50 |
| **Z687** | ZA592 | 50y multi | | .90 | .50 |
| *a.* | | Block of 10, #Z678-Z687 | | 9.50 | 9.50 |

Reintroduction of Oriental White Stork (Hyogo) — ZA593

**2005, June 6 Litho.**

| | | | | | |
|---|---|---|---|---|---|
| **Z688** | ZA593 | 80y multi | | 1.40 | .90 |

Azaleas, Tsutsujigaoka Park (Gunma) ZA594

Nikko Day Lily, Kirifuri Heights (Tochigi) ZA595

Sunflowers, Hana-hotaru (Chiba) ZA596

Bush Clover, Kairakuen Garden (Ibaraki) ZA597

Allspice, Mt. Bukosan (Saitama) — ZA598

**2005, June 23**

| | | | | | |
|---|---|---|---|---|---|
| **Z689** | ZA594 | 50y multi | | .90 | .50 |
| **Z690** | ZA595 | 50y multi | | .90 | .50 |
| **Z691** | ZA596 | 50y multi | | .90 | .50 |
| **Z692** | ZA597 | 50y multi | | .90 | .50 |
| **Z693** | ZA598 | 50y multi | | .90 | .50 |
| *a.* | | Vert. strip of 5, #Z689-Z693 | | 4.50 | 4.50 |

Apples (Aomori) ZA599

Apples (Iwate) ZA600

Cherries (Yamagata) ZA601

Peaches (Fukushima) ZA602

**2005, June 28** **Litho.**

| | | | | |
|---|---|---|---|---|
| **Z694** | ZA599 | 50y multi | .90 | .50 |
| **Z695** | ZA600 | 50y multi | .90 | .50 |
| **Z696** | ZA601 | 50y multi | .90 | .50 |
| **Z697** | ZA602 | 50y multi | .90 | .50 |
| *a.* | | Horiz. strip of 4, #Z694-Z697 | 3.75 | 3.75 |

Miniature Sheet

88 Temples (Shikoku) — ZA603

No. Z698: a, Zizouji (Temple 5). b, Anrakuji (Temple 6). c, Juurakuji (Temple 7). d, Kumadaniji (Temple 8). e, Yakuooji (Temple 23). f, Hotsumisakiji (Temple 24). g, Shinjouji (Temple 25). h, Kongouchouji (Temple 26). i, Ryukouji (Temple 41). j, Butsumokuji (Temple 42). k, Meisekiji (Temple 43). l, Daihouji (Temple 44). m, Kokubunji (Temple 59). n, Yokomineji (Temple 60). o, Kouonji (Temple 61). p, Houjuji (Temple 62). q, Douryuji (Temple 77). r, Goushouji (Temple 78). s, Tennouji (Temple 79). t, Kokubunji (Temple 80).

**2005, July 8** **Photo.**

| | | | | |
|---|---|---|---|---|
| **Z698** | ZA603 | Sheet of 20 | 30.00 | 30.00 |
| *a.-t.* | | 80y Any single | 1.40 | .90 |

See note under No. Z652 for information on identifying temple numbers.

Swwtbriar, Old Shana Post Office (Hokkaido) ZA604

Sea Otter (Hokkaido) ZA605

Cherry Blossoms (Hokkaido) ZA606

Tufted Puffins (Hokkaido) ZA607

**2005, Aug. 22**

| | | | | |
|---|---|---|---|---|
| **Z699** | ZA604 | 80y multi | 1.40 | .90 |
| **Z700** | ZA605 | 80y multi | 1.40 | .90 |
| **Z701** | ZA606 | 80y multi | 1.40 | .90 |
| **Z702** | ZA607 | 80y multi | 1.40 | .90 |
| *a.* | | Horiz. strip of 4, #Z699-Z702 | 6.00 | 6.00 |

60th Natl. Athletic Meets (Okayama) — ZA608

**2005, Sept. 1**

| | | | | |
|---|---|---|---|---|
| **Z703** | ZA608 | 50y multi | .90 | .50 |

Kobe Luminarie (Hyogo) — ZA609

**2005, Dec. 9** **Litho.**

| | | | | |
|---|---|---|---|---|
| **Z704** | | 50y Yellow denomination | .85 | .50 |
| **Z705** | | 50y Blue denomination | .85 | .50 |
| *a.* | ZA609 | Horiz. pair, #Z704-Z705 | 1.75 | 1.75 |

Kawazu Cherry Blossoms (Shizuoka) — ZA610

**2006, Feb. 1** **Photo.** ***Perf. 13¼***

| | | | | |
|---|---|---|---|---|
| **Z706** | | 50y With bird | .85 | .50 |
| **Z707** | | 50y Without bird | .85 | .50 |
| *a.* | ZA610 | Horiz. pair, #Z706-Z707 | 1.75 | 1.75 |

Japanese Characters (Fukui) — ZA611

Maruoka Castle, Hills (Fukui) — ZA612

Maruoka Castle, Clouds (Fukui) — ZA613

Maruoka Castle, Sun (Fukui) — ZA614

Maruoka Castle, Moon (Fukui) — ZA615

**2006, Apr. 3** **Litho.**

| | | | | |
|---|---|---|---|---|
| **Z708** | ZA611 | 80y multi | 1.40 | .90 |
| **Z709** | ZA612 | 80y multi | 1.40 | .90 |
| **Z710** | ZA613 | 80y multi | 1.40 | .90 |
| **Z711** | ZA614 | 80y multi | 1.40 | .90 |
| **Z712** | ZA615 | 80y multi | 1.40 | .90 |
| *a.* | | Horiz. strip of 4, #Z709-Z712 | 5.75 | 5.75 |
| | | *Nos. Z708-Z712 (5)* | 7.00 | 4.50 |

Printed in sheets of 20 consisting of 12 No. ZA708, and 2 each Nos. Z709-Z712.

Primroses (Osaka) ZA616

Cherry Blossoms (Nara) ZA617

Wild Chrysanthemums (Hyogo) ZA618

Rhododendrons (Shiga) ZA619

Ume Blossoms (Wakayama) ZA620

Weeping Cherry Blossoms (Kyoto) ZA621

**2006, Apr. 3**

| | | | | |
|---|---|---|---|---|
| **Z713** | ZA616 | 50y multi | .85 | .50 |
| **Z714** | ZA617 | 50y multi | .85 | .50 |
| **Z715** | ZA618 | 50y multi | .85 | .50 |
| **Z716** | ZA619 | 50y multi | .85 | .50 |
| **Z717** | ZA620 | 50y multi | .85 | .50 |
| *a.* | | Horiz. strip of 4, #Z714-Z717 | 3.50 | 3.50 |
| **Z718** | ZA621 | 50y multi | .85 | .50 |
| | | *Nos. Z713-Z718 (6)* | 5.10 | 3.00 |

Printed in sheets containing 4 each nos. Z713, Z718, 3 each Nos. Z714-Z717.

Pear Blossoms, Yumigahama Beach (Tottori) ZA622

Peonies, Hinomisaki Lighthouse (Shimane) ZA623

Peach Blossoms, Seto-oohashi Bridge (Okayama) ZA624

Scarlet Maple Leaves, Miyajima Shrine (Hiroshima) ZA625

Citron Blossoms, Oomi Island (Yamaguchi) ZA626

**2006, May 1** **Photo.**

| | | | | |
|---|---|---|---|---|
| **Z719** | ZA622 | 50y multi | .90 | .50 |
| **Z720** | ZA623 | 50y multi | .90 | .50 |
| **Z721** | ZA624 | 50y multi | .90 | .50 |
| **Z722** | ZA625 | 50y multi | .90 | .50 |
| **Z723** | ZA626 | 50y multi | .90 | .50 |
| *a.* | | Vert. strip of 5, #Z719-Z723! | 4.50 | 4.50 |
| | | *Nos. Z719-Z723 (5)* | 4.50 | 2.50 |

National Afforestation Campaign (Gifu) — ZA627

**2006, May 19**

| | | | | |
|---|---|---|---|---|
| **Z724** | ZA627 | 50y multi | .90 | .50 |

Mt. Echigo (Niigata, Nagano) ZA628

Sankayou Flowers (Niigata, Nagano) ZA629

Mt. Asama (Niigata, Nagano) ZA630

Sakurasou Flowers (Niigata, Nagano) ZA631

**2006, June 1** **Litho.**

| | | | | |
|---|---|---|---|---|
| **Z725** | ZA628 | 80y multi | 1.40 | .90 |
| **Z726** | ZA629 | 80y multi | 1.40 | .90 |
| **Z727** | ZA630 | 80y multi | 1.40 | .90 |
| **Z728** | ZA631 | 80y multi | 1.40 | .90 |
| *a.* | | Horiz. strip of 4, #Z725-Z728 | 6.00 | 6.00 |
| | | *Nos. Z725-Z728 (4)* | 5.60 | 3.60 |

Daffodils, Nokonoshima Island (Fukuoka) ZA632

Bellflowers, Hirodai (Fukuoka) ZA633

Hydrangeas, Mikaerinotaki Falls (Saga) ZA634

Cosmos, Kujukushima Islands (Nagasaki) ZA635

Camellias, Amakusa Bridges (Kumamoto) ZA636

Flowers, Mt. Aso (Kumamoto) ZA637

Primroses, Mt. Yufudake (Oita) — ZA638

Lavender, Kujurenzan (Oita) — ZA639

Poppies, Mt. Hinamoridake (Miyazaki) ZA640

Nanohana, Mt. Kaimondake (Kagoshima) ZA641

**2006, June 1** **Photo.**

| | | | | | |
|---|---|---|---|---|---|
| **Z729** | ZA632 | 80y | multi | 1.40 | .90 |
| **Z730** | ZA633 | 80y | multi | 1.40 | .90 |
| **Z731** | ZA634 | 80y | multi | 1.40 | .90 |
| **Z732** | ZA635 | 80y | multi | 1.40 | .90 |
| **Z733** | ZA636 | 80y | multi | 1.40 | .90 |
| **Z734** | ZA637 | 80y | multi | 1.40 | .90 |
| **Z735** | ZA638 | 80y | multi | 1.40 | .90 |
| **Z736** | ZA639 | 80y | multi | 1.40 | .90 |
| **Z737** | ZA640 | 80y | multi | 1.40 | .90 |
| **Z738** | ZA641 | 80y | multi | 1.40 | .90 |
| *a.* | Block of 10, #Z729-Z738 | | | 15.00 | 15.00 |
| | *Nos. Z729-Z738 (10)* | | | 14.00 | 9.00 |

Fox (Hokkaido) ZA642

Bears (Hokkaido) ZA643

Squirrel (Hokkaido) ZA644

Owl (Hokkaido) ZA645

**2006, June 3**

| | | | | | |
|---|---|---|---|---|---|
| **Z739** | ZA642 | 50y | multi | .90 | .50 |
| **Z740** | ZA643 | 50y | multi | .90 | .50 |
| **Z741** | ZA644 | 50y | multi | .90 | .50 |
| **Z742** | ZA645 | 50y | multi | .90 | .50 |
| *a.* | Horiz. strip of 4, #Z739-Z742 | | | 3.75 | 3.75 |
| | *Nos. Z739-Z742 (4)* | | | 3.60 | 2.00 |

Aomori Nebuta Festival (Aomori) ZA646

Akita Kanto Festival (Akita) ZA647

Yamagata Hanagasa Festival (Yamagata) ZA648

Sendai Tanabata Festival (Miyagi) ZA649

**2006, June 3** **Litho.**

| | | | | | |
|---|---|---|---|---|---|
| **Z743** | ZA646 | 80y | multi | 1.40 | .90 |
| **Z744** | ZA647 | 80y | multi | 1.40 | .90 |
| **Z745** | ZA648 | 80y | multi | 1.40 | .90 |
| **Z746** | ZA649 | 80y | multi | 1.40 | .90 |
| *a.* | Horiz. strip of 4, #Z743-Z746 | | | 5.75 | 5.75 |
| | *Nos. Z743-Z746 (4)* | | | 5.60 | 3.60 |

Azaleas, Eboshi-iwa, Mt. Fuji (Kanagawa) ZA650

Daffodils, Sakawagawa River (Kanagawa) ZA651

Pinks, Tanzawa Mountains (Kanagawa) ZA652

Balloon Flowers, Mt. Fuji (Kanagawa) ZA653

**2006, Aug. 1** **Photo.**

| | | | | | |
|---|---|---|---|---|---|
| **Z747** | ZA650 | 80y | multi | 1.40 | .90 |
| **Z748** | ZA651 | 80y | multi | 1.40 | .90 |
| **Z749** | ZA652 | 80y | multi | 1.40 | .90 |
| **Z750** | ZA653 | 80y | multi | 1.40 | .90 |
| *a.* | Horiz. strip of 4, #Z747-Z750 | | | 5.75 | 5.75 |
| | *Nos. Z747-Z750 (4)* | | | 5.60 | 3.60 |

Miniature Sheet

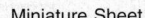

88 Temples (Shikoku) — ZA654

No. Z751: a, Hourinji (Temple 9). b, Kirihata (Temple 10). c, Fujiidera (Temple 11). d, Shouzanji (Temple 12). e, Kounomineji (Temple 27). f, Dainichiji (Temple 28). g, Kokubunji (Temple 29). h, Zenrakuji (Temple 30). i, Iwayaji (Temple 45). j, Joururiji (Temple 46). k, Yasakaji (Temple 47). l, Sairinji (Temple 48). m, Kichijouji (Temple 63). n, Maegamiji (Temple 64). o, Sankakuji (Temple 65). p, Unbenji (Temple 66). q, Shiromineji (Temple 81). r, Negoroji (Temple 82). s, Ichinomiyaji (Temple 83). t, Yashimaji (Temple 84).

**2006, Aug. 1**

| | | | | |
|---|---|---|---|---|
| **Z751** | ZA654 | Sheet of 20 | 28.00 | 28.00 |
| *a.-t.* | 80y Any single | | 1.40 | .90 |

See note under No. Z652 for information on identifying temple numbers.

61st National Athletic Meets (Hyogo) — ZA655

**2006, Sept. 1**

| | | | | | |
|---|---|---|---|---|---|
| **Z752** | ZA655 | 50y | multi | .85 | .50 |

Loquats, Byobugaura (Chiba) ZA656

Umes, Fukuroda Waterfall (Ibaraki) ZA657

Apples, Oze (Gunma) ZA658

Japanese Pears, Nagatoro (Saitama) ZA659

Strawberries, Kegon Waterfall (Tochigi) — ZA660

**2006, Sept. 1**

| | | | | | |
|---|---|---|---|---|---|
| **Z753** | ZA656 | 80y | multi | 1.40 | .90 |
| **Z754** | ZA657 | 80y | multi | 1.40 | .90 |
| **Z755** | ZA658 | 80y | multi | 1.40 | .90 |
| **Z756** | ZA659 | 80y | multi | 1.40 | .90 |
| **Z757** | ZA660 | 80y | multi | 1.40 | .90 |
| *a.* | Vert. strip of 5, #Z753-Z757 | | | 7.00 | 7.00 |
| | *Nos. Z753-Z757 (5)* | | | 7.00 | 4.50 |

Roses (Aichi) — ZA661

Chrysanthemums (Aichi) — ZA662

Orchids (Aichi) — ZA663

Cyclamen (Aichi) — ZA664

**2006, Oct. 2** **Litho.**

| | | | | | |
|---|---|---|---|---|---|
| **Z758** | ZA661 | 50y | multi | .85 | .50 |
| **Z759** | ZA662 | 50y | multi | .85 | .50 |
| **Z760** | ZA663 | 50y | multi | .85 | .50 |
| **Z761** | ZA664 | 50y | multi | .85 | .50 |
| *a.* | Horiz. strip of 4, #Z758-Z761 | | | 3.50 | 3.50 |
| | *Nos. Z758-Z761 (4)* | | | 3.40 | 2.00 |

Cherry Blossoms, Chidorigafuchi (Tokyo) — ZA665

Roses, Akasaka Palace (Tokyo) — ZA666

Cosmos, Shouwa Kinen Park (Tokyo) — ZA667

Japanese Apricot Blossoms, Yushima Tenjin Shrine (Tokyo) — ZA668

**2006, Oct. 2** **Photo.**

| | | | | | |
|---|---|---|---|---|---|
| **Z762** | ZA665 | 80y | multi | 1.40 | .90 |
| **Z763** | ZA666 | 80y | multi | 1.40 | .90 |
| **Z764** | ZA667 | 80y | multi | 1.40 | .90 |
| **Z765** | ZA668 | 80y | multi | 1.40 | .90 |
| *a.* | Horiz. strip of 4, #Z762-Z765 | | | 5.75 | 5.75 |
| | *Nos. Z762-Z765 (4)* | | | 5.60 | 3.60 |

Iris, Takeshima (Aichi, Mie, Gifu, Shizuoka) ZA669

Chinese Milk Vetch, Shirakawa Village (Aichi, Mie, Gifu, Shizuoka) ZA670

Lily, Nagoya Castle (Aichi, Mie, Gifu, Shizuoka) ZA671

Japanese Iris, Couple Rock (Aichi, Mie, Gifu, Shizuoka) ZA672

Azalea, Jogasaki Coast (Aichi, Mie, Gifu, Shizuoka) — ZA673

**2007, Apr. 2 Photo. *Perf. 13¼***

| | | | | | |
|---|---|---|---|---|---|
| **Z766** | ZA669 | 80y multi | | 1.40 | .90 |
| **Z767** | ZA670 | 80y multi | | 1.40 | .90 |
| **Z768** | ZA671 | 80y multi | | 1.40 | .90 |
| **Z769** | ZA672 | 80y multi | | 1.40 | .90 |
| **Z770** | ZA673 | 80y multi | | 1.40 | .90 |
| *a.* | | Vert. strip of 5, #Z766-Z770 | | 7.00 | 7.00 |

Cherry Blossom, Yatsugatake (Yamanashi) ZA674

Grapes, Katsunuma Vineyard (Yamanashi) ZA675

Azalea, Syosenkyo (Yamanashi) ZA676

Lavender, Mt. Fuji (Yamanashi) ZA677

Peaches, Southern Japanese Alps (Yamanashi) ZA678

**2007, Apr. 2**

| | | | | | |
|---|---|---|---|---|---|
| **Z771** | ZA674 | 80y multi | | 1.40 | .90 |
| **Z772** | ZA675 | 80y multi | | 1.40 | .90 |
| **Z773** | ZA676 | 80y multi | | 1.40 | .90 |
| **Z774** | ZA677 | 80y multi | | 1.40 | .90 |
| **Z775** | ZA678 | 80y multi | | 1.40 | .90 |
| *a.* | | Vert. strip of 5, #Z771-Z775 | | 7.00 | 7.00 |

Tulips (Niigata) ZA679

Rice (Niigata) ZA680

Pears (Niigata) ZA681

Mealy Primrose (Niigata) ZA682

Iris (Niigata) — ZA683

**2007, Apr. 2 Litho.**

| | | | | | |
|---|---|---|---|---|---|
| **Z776** | ZA679 | 80y multi | | 1.40 | .90 |
| **Z777** | ZA680 | 80y multi | | 1.40 | .90 |
| **Z778** | ZA681 | 80y multi | | 1.40 | .90 |
| **Z779** | ZA682 | 80y multi | | 1.40 | .90 |
| **Z780** | ZA683 | 80y multi | | 1.40 | .90 |
| *a.* | | Vert. strip of 5, #Z776-Z780 | | 7.00 | 7.00 |

Cherry Blossom (Saitama) ZA684

Japanese Rose (Ibaraki) ZA685

Skunk Cabbage (Gunma) ZA686

Adder's Tongue Lily (Tochigi) ZA687

Poppies (Chiba) — ZA688

**2007, May 1 Photo. *Perf. 13¼***

| | | | | | |
|---|---|---|---|---|---|
| **Z781** | ZA684 | 50y multi | | .85 | .50 |
| **Z782** | ZA685 | 50y multi | | .85 | .50 |
| **Z783** | ZA686 | 50y multi | | .85 | .50 |
| **Z784** | ZA687 | 50y multi | | .85 | .50 |
| **Z785** | ZA688 | 50y multi | | .85 | .50 |
| *a.* | | Vert. strip of 5, #Z781-Z785 | | 4.25 | 4.25 |

For self-adhesives, see Nos. 3189B-3189F.

Mandarin Ducks (Tottori) ZA689

Swans (Shimane) ZA690

Pheasants (Okayama) ZA691

Red-throated Loons (Hiroshima) ZA692

Hooded Cranes (Yamaguchi) ZA693

**2007, May 1 Litho.**

| | | | | | |
|---|---|---|---|---|---|
| **Z786** | ZA689 | 80y multi | | 1.40 | .90 |
| **Z787** | ZA690 | 80y multi | | 1.40 | .90 |
| **Z788** | ZA691 | 80y multi | | 1.40 | .90 |
| **Z789** | ZA692 | 80y multi | | 1.40 | .90 |
| **Z790** | ZA693 | 80y multi | | 1.40 | .90 |
| *a.* | | Vert. strip of 5, #Z786-Z790 | | 7.00 | 7.00 |

Japanese Cranes (Hokkaido) ZA694

Hokkaido Mountain Hares (Hokkaido) ZA695

Flying Squirrels (Hokkaido) ZA696

Hokkaido Deer (Hokkaido) ZA697

Spotted Seals (Hokkaido) ZA698

**2007, May 1 Litho.**

| | | | | | |
|---|---|---|---|---|---|
| **Z791** | ZA694 | 80y multi | | 1.40 | .90 |
| **Z792** | ZA695 | 80y multi | | 1.40 | .90 |
| **Z793** | ZA696 | 80y multi | | 1.40 | .90 |
| **Z794** | ZA697 | 80y multi | | 1.40 | .90 |
| **Z795** | ZA698 | 80y multi | | 1.40 | .90 |
| *a.* | | Horiz. strip of 5, #Z791-Z795 | | 7.00 | 7.00 |

Koriyama Castle (Nara) — ZA699

Hikone Castle (Shiga) — ZA700

Himeji Castle (Hyogo) — ZA701

Osaka Castle (Osaka) — ZA702

Wakayama Castle (Wakayama) ZA703

**2007, June 1 Photo.**

| | | | | | |
|---|---|---|---|---|---|
| **Z796** | ZA699 | 50y multi | | .85 | .50 |
| **Z797** | ZA700 | 50y multi | | .85 | .50 |
| **Z798** | ZA701 | 50y multi | | .85 | .50 |
| **Z799** | ZA702 | 50y multi | | .85 | .50 |
| **Z800** | ZA703 | 50y multi | | .85 | .50 |
| *a.* | | Vert. strip of 5, #Z796-Z800 | | 4.25 | 4.25 |

Whale Shark (Okinawa) ZA704

Longfin Bannerfish (Okinawa) ZA705

False Clownfish (Okinawa) ZA706

Blue Damselfish (Okinawa) ZA707

Manta Ray (Okinawa) ZA708

**2007, June 1 Photo.**

| | | | | | |
|---|---|---|---|---|---|
| **Z801** | ZA704 | 80y multi | | 1.40 | .90 |
| **Z802** | ZA705 | 80y multi | | 1.40 | .90 |
| **Z803** | ZA706 | 80y multi | | 1.40 | .90 |
| **Z804** | ZA707 | 80y multi | | 1.40 | .90 |
| **Z805** | ZA708 | 80y multi | | 1.40 | .90 |
| *a.* | | Horiz. strip of 5, #Z801-Z805 | | 7.00 | 7.00 |

See Nos. 3929-3933.

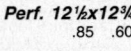

National Afforestation Campaign (Hokkaido) ZA709

**2007, June 22** ***Perf. 12½x12¾***

| | | | | |
|---|---|---|---|---|
| **Z806** | ZA709 | 50y multi | .85 | .60 |

Dancers, Owara Wind Festival (Toyama) ZA710

Dancers, Owara Wind Festival (Toyama) ZA711

Dancers, Owara Wind Festival (Toyama) ZA712

Dancers, Owara Wind Festival (Toyama) ZA713

Dancers, Owara Wind Festival (Toyama) — ZA714

**2007, July 2** **Litho.** ***Perf. 13¼***

| | | | | |
|---|---|---|---|---|
| **Z807** | ZA710 | 80y multi | 1.40 | .90 |
| **Z808** | ZA711 | 80y multi | 1.40 | .90 |
| **Z809** | ZA712 | 80y multi | 1.40 | .90 |
| **Z810** | ZA713 | 80y multi | 1.40 | .90 |
| **Z811** | ZA714 | 80y multi | 1.40 | .90 |
| *a.* | | Vert. strip of 5, #Z807-Z811 | 7.00 | 7.00 |

See Nos. 3875-3879.

Tokyo Tower, Japanese Allspice (Tokyo) — ZA715

Double Bridge, Chinese Violet Cress (Tokyo) — ZA716

Meiji shrine Outer Garden, Sweet Olive (Tokyo) — ZA717

Lake Okutama, Gentian (Tokyo) — ZA718

Japan Bridge, Camellia (Tokyo) — ZA719

**2007, July 2** **Photo.**

| | | | | |
|---|---|---|---|---|
| **Z812** | ZA715 | 80y multi | 1.40 | .90 |
| **Z813** | ZA716 | 80y multi | 1.40 | .90 |
| **Z814** | ZA717 | 80y multi | 1.40 | .90 |
| **Z815** | ZA718 | 80y multi | 1.40 | .90 |
| **Z816** | ZA719 | 80y multi | 1.40 | .90 |
| *a.* | | Vert. strip of 5, #Z812-Z8161 | 7.00 | 7.00 |

Oirase Mountain Stream (Aomori) ZA720

Hirosaki Castle (Aomori) ZA721

Chuson Temple (Iwate) — ZA722

Jodogahama (Iwate) — ZA723

Matsushima (Miyagi) ZA724

Mt. Zao Crater Lake (Miyagi, Yamagata) ZA725

Oga Peninsula (Akita) ZA726

Mt. Chokai (Akita, Yamagata) ZA727

Oze (Fukushima) ZA728

Gassan Volcano (Yamagata) ZA729

**2007, July 2**

| | | | |
|---|---|---|---|
| **Z817** | Sheet of 10 | 14.00 | 14.00 |
| *a.* | ZA720 80y multi | 1.40 | .90 |
| *b.* | ZA721 80y multi | 1.40 | .90 |
| *c.* | ZA722 80y multi | 1.40 | .90 |
| *d.* | ZA723 80y multi | 1.40 | .90 |
| *e.* | ZA724 80y multi | 1.40 | .90 |
| *f.* | ZA725 80y multi | 1.40 | .90 |
| *g.* | ZA726 80y multi | 1.40 | .90 |
| *h.* | ZA727 80y multi | 1.40 | .90 |
| *i.* | ZA728 80y multi | 1.40 | .90 |
| *j.* | ZA729 80y multi | 1.40 | .90 |

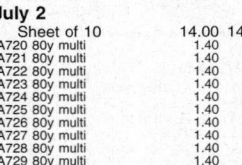

Main Tower, Kumamoto Castle, Cherry Blossoms (Kumamoto) ZA730

Uto Turret, Kumamoto Castle, in Summer (Kumamoto) ZA731

Main Tower, Kumamoto Castle, Gingko Trees (Kumamoto) ZA732

Uto Turret, Kumamoto Castle, in Winter (Kumamoto) ZA733

Three Towers, Kumamoto Castle (Kumamoto) ZA734

**2007, Aug. 1** **Litho.**

| | | | | |
|---|---|---|---|---|
| **Z818** | ZA730 | 80y multi | 1.40 | .90 |
| **Z819** | ZA731 | 80y multi | 1.40 | .90 |
| **Z820** | ZA732 | 80y multi | 1.40 | .90 |
| **Z821** | ZA733 | 80y multi | 1.40 | .90 |
| **Z822** | ZA734 | 80y multi | 1.40 | .90 |
| *a.* | | Vert. strip of 5, #Z818-Z822 | 7.00 | 7.00 |

Edo Bridge from Japan Bridge, by Hiroshige (Tokyo) — ZA735

Ohisa Takashima, by Utamaro (Tokyo) — ZA736

Yaozo Ichikawa II as Bunzo Tanabe, by Sharaku (Tokyo) — ZA737

Horikiri Irises, by Hiroshige (Tokyo) — ZA738

Kinryuzan Temple, by Hiroshige (Tokyo) — ZA739

Seven Women Applying Makeup Using a Full Length Mirror, by Utamaro (Tokyo) — ZA740

Ryuzo Arashi II as Kinkichi Ishibe, Moneylender, by Sharaku (Tokyo) — ZA741

Suido Bridge and Surugadai, by Hiroshige (Tokyo) — ZA742

Moon Pine, Ueno Temple, by Hiroshige (Tokyo) — ZA743

Hanaogi from Ogiya, No. 1 District, Edo Town, by Utamaro (Tokyo) — ZA744

**2007, Aug. 1**

| | | | |
|---|---|---|---|
| **Z823** | Sheet of 10 | 14.00 | 14.00 |
| *a.* | ZA735 80y multi | 1.40 | .90 |
| *b.* | ZA736 80y multi | 1.40 | .90 |
| *c.* | ZA737 80y multi | 1.40 | .90 |
| *d.* | ZA738 80y multi | 1.40 | .90 |
| *e.* | ZA739 80y multi | 1.40 | .90 |
| *f.* | ZA740 80y multi | 1.40 | .90 |
| *g.* | ZA741 80y multi | 1.40 | .90 |
| *h.* | ZA742 80y multi | 1.40 | .90 |
| *i.* | ZA743 80y multi | 1.40 | .90 |
| *j.* | ZA744 80y multi | 1.40 | .90 |

ZA745

88 Temples (Shikoku) — ZA746

No. Z824: a, Dainchiji (Temple 13). b, Jorakuji (Temple 14). c, Kokubunji (Temple 15). d, Kanonji (Temple 16). e, Chikurinji (Temple 31). f, Zenjibuji (Temple 32). g, Sekkeiji (Temple 33). h, Tanemaji (Temple 34). i, Jodoji (Temple 49). j, Hantaji (Temple 50). k, Ishiteji (Temple 51). l, Taisanji (Temple 52). m, Daikoji (Temple 67). n, Jinnein (Temple 68). o, Kannonji (Temple 69). p, Motoyamaji (Temple 70). q, Yakuriji (Temple 85). r, Shidoji (Temple 86). s, Nagaoji (Temple 87). t, Okuboji (Temple 88).

No. Z825: a, Idoji (Temple 17). b, Onzanji (Temple 18). c, Kiyotakiji (Temple 35). d, Shoryuji (Temple 36). e, Emmyoji (Temple 53). f, Emmeiji (Temple 54). g, Iyadaniji (Temple 71). h, Mandaraji (Temple 72). i, Deities Cave (no temple number). j, Painting of Daishi Kobo (no temple number).

**2007, Aug. 1 Photo. *Perf. 13¼***

**Z824** ZA745 Sheet of 20 28.00 28.00
*a.-t.* 80y Any single 1.40 .90
**Z825** ZA746 Sheet of 10 14.00 14.00
*a.-j.* 80y Any single 1.40 .90

See note under No. Z652 for information on identifying temple numbers.

62nd National Athletic Meet (Akita) — ZA747

**2007, Sept. 3 Litho.**

**Z826** ZA747 50y multi .90 .50

Miniature Sheet

Nagoya Port (Aichi) — ZA748

No. Z827: a, Hibiscus and Antarctic survey. b, Hibiscus and Port Tower. c, Azaleas, killer whale at Nagoya Aquarium. d, Azaleas, dolphins at Nagoya Aquarium. e, Yellow chrysanthemums, Meiko Triton Bridge. f, Orange and yellow chrysanthemums, two bridges. g, Snapdragons and fireworks. h, Sailing ship and snapdragons. i, Azaleas, bridge, Nagoya Aquarium and half of Ferris wheel. j, Azaleas, Port Tower, Nagoya Castle, and half of Ferris wheel.

**2007, Nov. 5 Litho. *Perf. 13¼***

**Z827** ZA748 Sheet of 10 15.00 15.00
*a.-j.* 80y Any single 1.40 .90

Beginning in 2008 the planning and design of prefecture stamps, previously done by regional postal authorities, was taken over by national postal authorities. The national authorities planned issues for 2008 that would be available in more of postal regions, thus making prefectural issues more nationwide and less local in scope. Additionally, the style of the "Nippon yubin" ideographic characters that had been used solely for prefecture stamps reverted to the style used on the national issues for most issues. Because of these changes, prefecture stamps will be listed in the regular postage listings starting with the 2008 issues.

## PREFECTURE SEMI-POSTAL STAMPS

Earthquake and Volcano Eruption Refugee Relief (Tokyo) — ZSP1

**2000, Nov. 15 Photo.**

**ZB1** 80y +20y Pink ribbon 1.75 1.25
**ZB2** 80y +20y Blue ribbon 1.75 1.25
*a.* ZSP1 Pair, #ZB1-ZB2 4.00 4.00

## SEMI-POSTAL STAMPS

Douglas Plane over Japan Alps — SP1

**Wmk. Zigzag Lines (141)**

**1937, June 1 Photo. *Perf. 13***

**B1** SP1 2s + 2s rose carmine 1.75 .80
**B2** SP1 3s + 2s purple 1.75 1.40
**B3** SP1 4s + 2s green 3.00 1.25
*Nos. B1-B3 (3)* 6.50 3.45
Set, never hinged 8.50

The surtax was for the Patriotic Aviation Fund to build civil airports.

Nos. 259 and 261 Surcharged in Blue or Red

**1942, Feb. 16 Wmk. 257 *Perf. 13***

**B4** A84 2s +1s crimson (Bl) 1.25 1.00
**B5** A86 4s +2s dk grn (R) 1.25 1.00
Set, never hinged 3.75

Fall of Singapore to Japanese forces.

Tank Corps Attack, Bataan — SP2

Pearl Harbor Under Japanese Attack — SP3

**Unwmk.**

**1942, Dec. 8 Photo. *Perf. 12***

**B6** SP2 2s +1s rose brown 2.00 1.10
**B7** SP3 5s +2s sapphire 2.25 1.60
Set, never hinged 7.00

1st anniv. of the "Greater East Asia War." The surtax was for national defense.

**Catalogue values for unused stamps in this section, from this point to the end of the section, are for Never Hinged items.**

SP4

**1947, Nov. 25 Wmk. 257 *Perf. 12½***

**B8** SP4 1.20y + 80s dk rose red 1.00 .85

Japan's 1st Community Chest drive. The surtax was for charitable purposes.

Nurse — SP5

Bird Feeding Young — SP6

**1948, Oct. 1 Unwmk. *Perf. 12½***

**B9** SP5 5y + 2.50y bright red 10.00 9.00
**B10** SP6 5y + 2.50y emerald 10.00 9.00

**Souvenir Sheet**

**Wmk. 257**

***Imperf***

**Without Gum**

**B11** Sheet of 2 85.00 *85.00*

The surtax on Nos. B9-B11 was divided between the Red Cross and Community Chest organizations.

No. B11 contains Nos. B9-B10, imperf.

Javelin Thrower SP8

No. B13, Wrestlers. No. B14, Diver. No. B15, Water polo. No. B16, Woman gymnast. No. B17, Judo. No. B18, Fencing. No. B19, Basketball. No. B20, Rowing. No. B21, Sailing. No. B22, Boxing. No. B23, Volleyball. No. B24, Bicyclist. No. B25, Equestrian. No. B26, Field hockey. No. B27, Pistol shooting. No. B28, Modern pentathlon. No. B29, Weight lifter. No. B30, Women's kayak doubles. No. B31, Soccer.

***Perf. 13½***

**1961, Oct. 11 Unwmk. Engr.**

**B12** SP8 5y + 5y bister .75 1.00
**B13** SP8 5y + 5y dk green .75 1.00
**B14** SP8 5y + 5y carmine .75 1.00
*a.* Souvenir sheet of 3 ('64) 4.00 4.75

**1962, June 23**

**B15** SP8 5y + 5y green .45 .75
**B16** SP8 5y + 5y dk purple .45 .75
**B17** SP8 5y + 5y dk carmine .45 .75
*a.* Souvenir sheet of 3 ('64) 2.75 3.25

**1962, Oct. 10**

**B18** SP8 5y + 5y brick red .25 .40
**B19** SP8 5y + 5y slate grn .25 .40
**B20** SP8 5y + 5y violet .25 .40
*a.* Souvenir sheet of 3 ('64) 2.25 2.50

**1963, June 23**

**B21** SP8 5y + 5y blue .25 .40
**B22** SP8 5y + 5y dk brown .25 .40
**B23** SP8 5y + 5y brown .25 .40
*a.* Souvenir sheet of 3 ('64) 4.50 5.25

**1963, Nov. 11**

**B24** SP8 5y + 5y dk blue .25 .25
**B25** SP8 5y + 5y olive .25 .25
**B26** SP8 5y + 5y black .25 .25
**B27** SP8 5y + 5y claret .25 .25
*a.* Souvenir sheet of 4 ('64) 4.50 5.25

**1964, June 23**

**B28** SP8 5y + 5y bluish vio .25 .25
**B29** SP8 5y + 5y dp olive .25 .25
**B30** SP8 5y + 5y grnsh blue .25 .25
**B31** SP8 5y + 5y rose claret .25 .25
*a.* Souvenir sheet of 4 ('64) 4.50 5.25
*Nos. B12-B31 (20)* 7.10 9.65

Issued to raise funds for the 1964 Olympic Games in Tokyo.

The souvenir sheets were issued Aug. 20, 1964. Each contains one each of the stamps in the set it follows. Nos. B14a, B20a, B23a and B27a, exist imperf.

Cobalt Treatment Unit — SP9

Early Cancer Detection with X-rays — SP10

**1966, Oct. 21 Photo. *Perf. 13***

**B32** SP9 7y + 3y yel org & blk .25 .25
**B33** SP10 15y + 5y multicolored .40 .25

9th Intl. Anticancer Congress, Tokyo, Oct. 23-29. The surtax was for the fight against cancer and for research.

EXPO '70 Emblem and Globe — SP11

Cherry Blossoms, Screen, Chishakuin Temple — SP12

**1969, Mar. 15 Photo. *Perf. 13***

**B34** SP11 15y + 5y bl, ocher & ver .60 .60
**B35** SP12 50y + 10y gold, brn & grn 1.25 1.25

Issued to publicize EXPO '70, International Exhibition, Osaka, 1970.

Ice Hockey, Sapporo Olympic Emblem SP13

Design: No. B37, Ski jump and Sapporo Olympic Games emblem, vert.

**1971, Feb. 6 Photo. *Perf. 13***

**B36** SP13 15y + 5y multi .40 .25
**B37** SP13 15y + 5y multi .40 .25

To promote the 11th Winter Olympic Games, Sapporo, Japan, 1972.

Blue Dragon, East Wall — SP14

Murals from ancient tomb mound: No. B39, Two men, east wall, vert. 50y+10y, Four women, west wall, vert.

**1973, Mar. 26 Photo. *Perf. 13***

**Size: 48x27mm, 27x48mm**

**B38** SP14 20y + 5y multi .50 .50
**B39** SP14 20y + 5y multi .50 .40

**Photogravure and Engraved**

**Size: 33x48mm**

**B40** SP14 50y + 10y multi 1.10 .75
*Nos. B38-B40 (3)* 2.10 1.65

Surtax was for restoration work on the murals of the Takamatsu-zuka tomb mound, discovered in March, 1972, and excavated in Nara Prefecture.

Reefs, by Hyakusui Hirafuku — SP15

**1974, Mar. 2 Photo. *Perf. 13***

**B41** SP15 20y + 5y multi .50 .30

The surtax was for the International Ocean Exposition, Okinawa, 1975.

Intl. Year of the Disabled — SP16

**Photogravure and Embossed**

**1981, Sept. 1 *Perf. 13½***

**B42** SP16 60y + 10y multi 1.25 .25

Surtax was for education of the disabled.

TSUKUB'85 Intl. Exposition, Mar. 17-Sept. 16, 1985 — SP17

**1984, Feb. 19 Photo. *Perf. 13½***

**B43** SP17 60y + 10y multi 1.25 .45

Intl. Garden and Greenery Exposition, Osaka — SP18

**1989, June 1 Photo. *Perf. 13***

**B44** SP18 62y +10y multi 1.40 .75

Surtax for the preparation and management of the exposition.

Intl. Garden and Greenery Exposition, Osaka SP19

**1990, Mar. 30**

**B45** SP19 41y +4y multi .85 .45

SP20

**1991, July 5 Photo. *Perf. 13***

**B46** SP20 62y +10y multi 1.40 .85

11th World Congress of the World Federation of the Deaf.

SP21

**1995, Apr. 20 Photo. *Perf. 13***

**B47** SP21 80y +20y multi 2.40 1.75

Philately week. Surtax for benefit of victims of Kobe earthquake.

1998 Winter Olympic Games, Nagano — SP22

**1997, Feb. 7 Photo. *Perf. 13***

**B48** 80y +10y Emblem 1.75 1.10
**B49** 80y +10y Stylized owls 1.75 1.10
*a.* SP22 Pair, #B48-B49 3.50 2.25

2002 Soccer World Cup, Japan and Korea — SP23

Colors of mascots: No. B50, Purple, yellow and blue. No. B51, Purple. No. B52, Blue.

**2001, May 31 Photo. *Perf. 13x13¼***

**B50** SP23 80y +10y multi 1.75 1.10
**B51** SP23 80y +10y multi 1.75 1.10
**B52** SP23 80y +10y multi 1.75 1.10
*a.* Horiz. pair, #B51-B52 3.50 2.20

Wall Paintings, Kitora Tumulus, Asuka — SP24

Designs: No. B53, White Tiger of the West. No. B54, Red Bird fo the South.

**2003, Oct. 15 Photo. *Perf. 13***

**B53** 80y +10y multi 1.75 1.25
**B54** 80y +10y multi 1.75 1.25
*a.* SP24 Horiz. pair, #B53-B54 3.50 2.50

2005 World Exposition, Aichi — SP25

Exposition mascots and: No. B55, Earth. No. B56, Cherry blossoms.

**2004, Mar. 25 Photo. *Perf. 13x13¼***

**B55** 80y +10y multi 1.75 1.75
**B56** 80y +10y multi 1.75 1.75
*a.* SP25 Horiz. pair, #B55-B56 3.50 3.50

Miniature Sheet

Be Kind to Animals Week — SP26

No. B57: a, Dog, flower background. b, White cat, red background. c, White Yorkshire terrier, green curtain. d, Cat, bubbles in background. e, Black Labrador retriever puppy sitting. f, Cat, brown striped background. g, Shiba puppy standing. h, Scottish Fold cat, dots and stripes in background. i, Dog in doorway. j, Cat, crescent moon.

**2009, Sept. 18 Litho. *Perf. 13¼***

**B57** SP26 Sheet of 10 11.00 11.00
*a.-j.* 50y+5y Any single 1.00 1.00

Surtax for animal welfare organizations.

SP27

SP28

SP29

SP30

Mar. 11, 2011 Earthquake and Tsunami Relief — SP31

**2011, June 21 Photo. *Perf. 13***

| | | | | | |
|---|---|---|---|---|---|
| **B58** | SP27 | 80y+20y multi | | 2.50 | 2.50 |
| **B59** | SP28 | 80y+20y multi | | 2.50 | 2.50 |
| **B60** | SP29 | 80y+20y multi | | 2.50 | 2.50 |
| **B61** | SP30 | 80y+20y multi | | 2.50 | 2.50 |
| **B62** | SP31 | 80y+20y multi | | 2.50 | 2.50 |
| *a.* | | Vert. strip of 5, #B58-B62 | | 12.50 | 12.50 |

Nos. B58-B62 were printed in sheets containing two strips.

## AIR POST STAMPS

Regular Issue of 1914 Overprinted in Red or Blue

**Wmk. Zigzag Lines (141)**

**1919, Oct. 3 *Perf. 13x13½***

**Granite Paper**

| | | | | |
|---|---|---|---|---|
| **C1** | A34 | 1½s blue (R) | 240.00 | 67.50 |
| **C2** | A34 | 3s rose (Bl) | 425.00 | 185.00 |

Excellent counterfeits exist.

Passenger Plane over Lake Ashi — AP1

**Granite Paper**

**1929-34 Engr. *Perf. 13½x13***

| | | | | |
|---|---|---|---|---|
| **C3** | AP1 | 8½s orange brn | 27.50 | 14.00 |
| **C4** | AP1 | 9½s rose | 9.00 | 3.75 |
| **C5** | AP1 | 16½s yellow grn | 9.00 | 4.00 |
| **C6** | AP1 | 18s ultra | 10.00 | 3.75 |
| **C7** | AP1 | 33s gray | 20.00 | 3.25 |
| | | *Nos. C3-C7 (5)* | 75.50 | 28.75 |
| | | Set, never hinged | 170.00 | |

**Souvenir Sheet**

| | | | | |
|---|---|---|---|---|
| **C8** | AP1 | Sheet of 4, #C4-C7 | 1,300. | 1,300. |
| | | Never hinged | 2,000. | |

Issued: 9½s, 3/1/34; No. C8, 4/20/34; others, 10/6/29. No. C8 for Communications Commemoration Day (1st observance of establishment of the postal service and issuance of #1-4). Sold only at Phil. Exhib. p.o., Tokyo, 4/20-27. Size: 110x100mm.

**Catalogue values for unused stamps in this section, from this point to the end of the section, are for Never Hinged items.**

Southern Green Pheasant AP3

***Perf. 13x13½***

**1950, Jan. 10 Engr. Unwmk.**

| | | | | |
|---|---|---|---|---|
| **C9** | AP3 | 16y gray | 35.00 | 10.00 |
| **C10** | AP3 | 34y brown violet | 50.00 | 12.00 |
| **C11** | AP3 | 59y carmine | 70.00 | 7.00 |
| **C12** | AP3 | 103y orange yellow | 45.00 | 20.00 |
| **C13** | AP3 | 144y olive | 55.00 | 22.50 |
| | | *Nos. C9-C13 (5)* | 255.00 | 71.50 |
| | | Set, hinged | 125.00 | |

Pagoda and Plane — AP4

Plane and Mt. Tsurugi-dake — AP5

**1951-52 Photo.**

| | | | | |
|---|---|---|---|---|
| **C14** | AP4 | 15y purple | 3.50 | 2.75 |
| **C15** | AP4 | 20y blue | 27.50 | 1.25 |
| **C16** | AP4 | 25y yellow grn | 25.00 | .45 |
| **C17** | AP4 | 30y brown red | 10.00 | .45 |
| **C18** | AP4 | 40y gray blk | 8.00 | .55 |
| **C19** | AP5 | 55y brt blue | 230.00 | 60.00 |
| **C20** | AP5 | 75y brnsh red | 150.00 | 35.00 |
| **C21** | AP5 | 80y magenta | 20.00 | 3.00 |
| **C22** | AP5 | 85y black | 25.00 | 7.25 |
| **C23** | AP5 | 125y olive bis | 12.00 | 3.25 |
| **C24** | AP5 | 160y Prus green | 27.50 | 3.75 |
| | | *Nos. C14-C24 (11)* | 538.50 | 117.70 |
| | | Set, hinged | 300.00 | |

Issue dates: 25y, 30y, Dec. 20; 15y, 20y, 40y, Sept. 1; 55y-160y, Feb. 11, 1952.

**Redrawn; Underlined Zeros Omitted**

**1952-62**

| | | | | |
|---|---|---|---|---|
| **C25** | AP4 | 15y purple ('62) | 1.75 | .60 |
| **C26** | AP4 | 20y blue | 55.00 | 1.00 |
| **C27** | AP4 | 25y yel grn ('53) | 1.25 | .35 |
| **C28** | AP4 | 30y brown red | 7.25 | .45 |
| **C29** | AP4 | 40y gray blk ('53) | 5.25 | .45 |
| **C30** | AP5 | 55y brt blue | 70.00 | 4.00 |
| **C32** | AP5 | 75y brnsh red | 140.00 | 9.00 |
| **C33** | AP5 | 80y magenta | 100.00 | 3.00 |
| **C34** | AP5 | 85y black | 6.25 | 1.50 |
| **C36** | AP5 | 125y olive bis | 9.00 | 1.75 |
| **C38** | AP5 | 160y Prus green | 37.50 | 2.00 |
| | | *Nos. C25-C38 (11)* | 433.25 | 24.10 |
| | | Set, hinged | 185.00 | |

See No. C43.

Great Buddha of Kamakura — AP6

**1953, Aug. 15 *Perf. 13½***

| | | | | |
|---|---|---|---|---|
| **C39** | AP6 | 70y red brown | 5.00 | .25 |
| **C40** | AP6 | 80y blue | 7.00 | .25 |
| **C41** | AP6 | 115y olive green | 3.50 | .50 |
| **C42** | AP6 | 145y Prus green | 22.50 | 3.00 |
| | | *Nos. C39-C42 (4)* | 38.00 | 4.00 |

**Redrawn Type of 1952-62**

**Coil Stamp**

**1961, Oct. 2 *Perf. 13 Horiz.***

| | | | | |
|---|---|---|---|---|
| **C43** | AP4 | 30y brown red | 35.00 | 27.50 |

## MILITARY STAMPS

Nos. 98, 119, 131 Overprinted

**1910-14 Unwmk. *Perf. 11½ to 13½***

| | | | | |
|---|---|---|---|---|
| **M1** | A26 | 3s rose | 200.00 | 35.00 |
| **M2** | A34 | 3s rose ('13) | 325.00 | 140.00 |

**Wmk. 141**

| | | | | |
|---|---|---|---|---|
| **M3** | A34 | 3s rose ('14) | 30.00 | 16.00 |
| | | *Nos. M1-M3 (3)* | 555.00 | 191.00 |

Nos. M1-M3 overprint type I has 3.85mm between characters; type II, 4-4.5mm (movable type).

**1921 On Offices in China No. 37**

| | | | | |
|---|---|---|---|---|
| **M4** | A34 | 3s rose | *5,750.* | *4,750.* |

No. M4 is a provisional military stamp issued at the Japanese Post Office, Tsingtao, China. The overprint differs from the illustration, being 12mm high with thicker characters. Counterfeits are plentiful.

**Overprint 16mm High**

**1924 On No. 131**

| | | | | |
|---|---|---|---|---|
| **M5** | A34 | 3s rose | 90.00 | 72.50 |
| *a.* | | 3s rose (#131b) | 90.00 | 75.00 |

Excellent forgeries exist of Nos. M1-M5.

## JAPANESE OFFICES ABROAD

### Offices in China

1899-1907 Regular Issues of Japan Overprinted in Red or Black

***Perf. 11½, 12, 12½, 13½, 13x13½***

**1900-06 Unwmk.**

| | | | | |
|---|---|---|---|---|
| **1** | A26 | 5r gray (R) | 3.25 | 2.50 |
| **2** | A26 | ½s gray (R) ('01) | 2.00 | .70 |
| **3** | A26 | 1s lt red brn (R) | 2.00 | .70 |
| **4** | A26 | 1½s ultra | 9.00 | 2.00 |
| **5** | A26 | 1½s vio ('06) | 5.00 | .95 |
| **6** | A26 | 2s lt grn (R) | 5.00 | .70 |
| **7** | A26 | 3s violet brn | 5.50 | .70 |
| **8** | A26 | 3s rose ('06) | 4.00 | .50 |
| **9** | A26 | 4s rose | 4.50 | 1.25 |
| **10** | A26 | 5s org yel (R) | 9.00 | 1.25 |
| **11** | A27 | 6s maroon ('06) | 16.00 | 11.00 |
| **12** | A27 | 8s ol grn (R) | 9.00 | 5.50 |
| **13** | A27 | 10s deep blue | 9.00 | 1.00 |
| **14** | A27 | 15s purple | 18.00 | 1.75 |
| **15** | A27 | 20s red org | 16.00 | 1.00 |
| **16** | A28 | 25s blue grn (R) | 32.50 | 3.50 |
| **17** | A28 | 50s red brown | 35.00 | 2.50 |
| **18** | A29 | 1y carmine | 55.00 | 2.50 |
| | | *Nos. 1-18 (18)* | 239.75 | 40.00 |

No. 6 with black overprint is bogus.

Nos. 5, 6, 8, 9 and 13 exist as booklet panes of 6, made from sheet stamps. They are rare.

**1900**

| | | | | |
|---|---|---|---|---|
| **19** | A30 | 3s carmine | 25.00 | 15.00 |

Wedding of Crown Prince Yoshihito and Princess Sadako.

Japan Nos. 113 & 114 Overprinted

**1908**

| | | | | |
|---|---|---|---|---|
| **20** | A33 | 5y green | 400.00 | 47.50 |
| **21** | A33 | 10y dark violet | 700.00 | 110.00 |

On #20-21 the space between characters of the overprint is 6½mm instead of 1½mm.

Stamps of 1913-33 Issues Overprinted

**1913 *Perf. 12, 12x13, 13x13½***

| | | | | |
|---|---|---|---|---|
| **22** | A34 | ½s brown | 14.00 | 14.00 |
| **23** | A34 | 1s orange | 15.00 | 15.00 |
| **24** | A34 | 1½s lt blue | 40.00 | 18.00 |
| **25** | A34 | 2s green | 45.00 | 20.00 |
| **26** | A34 | 3s rose | 22.50 | 8.00 |
| **27** | A35 | 4s red | 62.50 | 62.50 |
| **28** | A35 | 5s violet | 62.50 | 50.00 |
| **29** | A35 | 10s deep blue | 62.50 | 21.00 |
| **30** | A35 | 20s claret | 250.00 | 140.00 |
| **31** | A35 | 25s olive green | 90.00 | 21.00 |
| **32** | A36 | 1y yel grn & mar | 750.00 | 500.00 |
| | | *Nos. 22-32 (11)* | 1,414. | 869.50 |

Nos. 24, 25, 26, 27 and 29 exist in booklet panes of 6, made from sheet stamps. The No. 26 pane is very rare.

**Japan Nos. 127-137, 139-147 Overprinted**

**1914-21 Wmk. 141**

**Granite Paper**

| | | | | |
|---|---|---|---|---|
| **33** | A34 | ½s brown | 3.25 | .80 |
| **34** | A34 | 1s orange | 3.75 | .80 |
| **35** | A34 | 1½s blue | 4.25 | .80 |
| **36** | A34 | 2s green | 2.75 | .95 |
| **37** | A34 | 3s rose | 2.40 | .80 |
| **38** | A35 | 4s red | 10.00 | 4.75 |
| **39** | A35 | 5s violet | 17.50 | 1.75 |
| **40** | A35 | 6s brown ('20) | 30.00 | 18.00 |
| **41** | A35 | 8s gray ('20) | 37.50 | 20.00 |
| **42** | A35 | 10s dp blue | 12.00 | 1.25 |
| **43** | A35 | 20s claret | 42.50 | 3.25 |
| **44** | A35 | 25s olive grn | 50.00 | 3.50 |
| **45** | A36 | 30s org brn ('20) | 75.00 | 27.50 |
| **46** | A36 | 50s dk brn ('20) | 90.00 | 30.00 |
| **47** | A36 | 1y yel grn & mar ('18) | 130.00 | 6.75 |
| **48** | A33 | 5y green | 1,850. | 525.00 |
| **49** | A33 | 10y violet ('21) | 2,650. | 1,600. |
| | | *Nos. 33-49 (17)* | 5,011. | 2,246. |

On Nos. 48-49 the space between characters of overprint is 4½mm, instead of 6½mm on Nos. 20-21 and 1½mm on all lower values. See No. M4.

No. 42 exists as a booklet pane of 6, made from sheet stamps. It is very rare.

Counterfeit overprints exist of Nos. 1-49.

### Offices in Korea

Regular Issue of Japan Overprinted in Red or Black

**1900 Unwmk. *Perf. 11½, 12, 12½***

| | | | | |
|---|---|---|---|---|
| **1** | A26 | 5r gray (R) | 19.00 | 8.75 |
| **2** | A26 | 1s lt red brn (R) | 20.00 | 5.00 |
| **3** | A26 | 1½s ultra | 250.00 | 130.00 |
| **4** | A26 | 2s lt green (R) | 19.00 | 10.00 |
| **5** | A26 | 3s violet brn | 17.00 | 4.75 |
| **6** | A26 | 4s rose | 65.00 | 27.50 |
| **7** | A26 | 5s org yel (R) | 67.50 | 27.50 |
| **8** | A27 | 8s ol grn (R) | 250.00 | 120.00 |
| **9** | A27 | 10s deep blue | 35.00 | 9.00 |
| **10** | A27 | 15s purple | 62.50 | 6.00 |
| **11** | A27 | 20s red orange | 62.50 | 5.00 |
| **12** | A28 | 25s blue grn (R) | 220.00 | 55.00 |
| **13** | A28 | 50s red brown | 175.00 | 18.00 |
| **14** | A29 | 1y carmine | 475.00 | 14.00 |
| | | *Nos. 1-14 (14)* | 1,738. | 440.50 |

**1900**

| | | | | |
|---|---|---|---|---|
| **15** | A30 | 3s carmine | 125.00 | 55.00 |

Wedding of Crown Prince Yoshihito and Princess Sadako.

Counterfeit overprints exist of Nos. 1-15.

### Taiwan (Formosa)

Numeral of Value and Imperial Crest — A1

**1945 Unwmk. Litho. *Imperf.***

**Without Gum**

| | | | | |
|---|---|---|---|---|
| **1** | A1 | 3s carmine | 30.00 | 30.00 |
| **2** | A1 | 5s blue green | 24.00 | 24.00 |
| **3** | A1 | 10s pale blue | 35.00 | 35.00 |
| | | *Nos. 1-3 (3)* | 89.00 | 89.00 |

Additional values, prepared, but not issued, were: 30s, 40s, 50s, 1y, 5y and 10y. The entire set of nine was overprinted by Chinese authorities after World War II and issued for use in Taiwan.

For overprints see China-Taiwan Nos. 1-7.

# JORDAN

'jor-dən

## Trans-Jordan

LOCATION — In the Near East, separated from the Mediterranean Sea by Israel
GOVT. — Kingdom
AREA — 38,400 sq. mi.
POP. — 4,561,147 (1999 est.)
CAPITAL — Amman

The former Turkish territory was mandated to Great Britain following World War I. It became an independent state in 1946.

10 Milliemes = 1 Piaster
1000 Mils = 1 Palestine Pound (1930)
1000 Fils = 100 piasters = 1 Jordan Dinar (1951)

**Catalogue values for unused stamps in this country are for Never Hinged items, beginning with Scott 221 in the regular postage section, Scott B13 in the semi-postal section, Scott C1 in the air post section, Scott J47 in the postage due section, Scott RA1 in the postal tax section, Scott N1 in the occupation section, Scott NJ1 in the occupation postage due section, and Scott NRA1 in the occupation postal tax section.**

### Watermarks

Wmk. 305 — Roman and Arabic Initials

Wmk. 328 — UAR

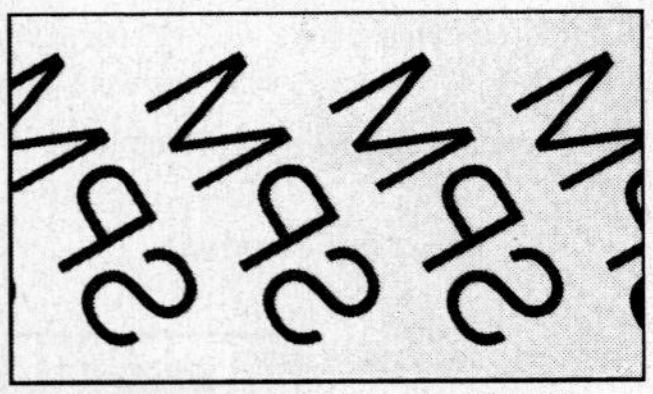

Wmk. 388 — Multiple "SPM"

### British Mandate

Stamps and Type of Palestine 1918 Overprinted in Black or Silver

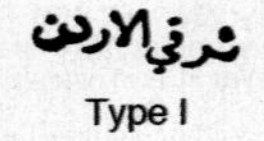

Type I

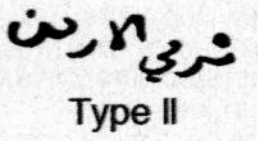

Type II

**1920, Nov. Wmk. 33 *Perf. 15x14***

1 A1 1m dark brown 3.75 6.00
a. Inverted overprint 150.00 300.00
2 A1 2m blue green 25.00 27.50
3 A1 3m light brown (I) 3.75 4.75
a. Overprint type II 1,200.
4 A1 4m scarlet 4.50 4.50
a. Arabic "40" 82.50
5 A1 5m orange 10.00 3.50
6 A1 1pi dark blue (S) 2,200.
7 A1 2pi olive green (I) 14.00 16.00
a. Overprint type II 950.00
8 A1 5pi plum 55.00 82.50
a. Overprint type II 1,500.
9 A1 9pi bister 100.00 120.00
*Nos. 1-9 (9)* 2,416. 264.75

***Perf. 14***

1B A1 1m dark brown 1.40 5.00
a. Inverted overprint 190.00
2B A1 2m blue green 3.00 4.50
a. Silver overprint 625.00 675.00
3B A1 3m light brown 22.50 30.00
4B A1 4m scarlet 19.00 50.00
a. Arabic "40" 160.00
5B A1 5m orange 2.75 3.50
6B A1 1pi dark blue (S) 3.75 4.25
7B A1 2pi olive green 13.00 13.00
8B A1 5pi plum 8.00 16.00
9B A1 9pi bister 8.00 55.00
10 A1 10pi ultramarine 22.50 60.00
11 A1 20pi gray 25.00 100.00
*Nos. 1B-11 (11)* 128.90 341.25

The overprint reads "Sharqi al-ardan" (East of Jordan).
For overprints see Nos. 12-73, 83A.

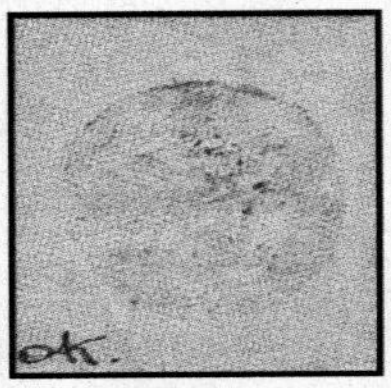

Moab District Seal

**1920, Nov. Handstamped *Imperf.***

12 A2 (1p) pale blue 3,750. 4,250.

No. 12 was issued at Kerak by the political officer for the Moab District and was used until March 1921 pending the arrival of Nos. 1//11.

Stamps of 1920 Issue Handstamp Surcharged "Ashir el qirsh" (tenth of piaster) and numeral in Black, Red or Violet

**On Nos. 1-9 (Perf. 15x14)**

**1922, Nov.**

13 A1 1/10pi on 1m dk brn 32.50 *55.00*
14 A1 1/10pi on 1m dk brn (R) 77.50 77.50
15 A1 1/10pi on 1m dk brn (V) 77.50 77.50
16 A1 2/10pi on 2m bl grn 37.50 37.50
a. 3/10pi on 2m bl grn (error) 130.00 120.00
17 A1 2/10pi on 2m bl grn (R) 87.50 87.50
18 A1 2/10pi on 2m bl grn (V) 110.00 110.00
19 A1 3/10pi on 3m lt brn 16.00 16.00
a. Pair, one without surcharge 875.00
b. On #3a (type II) 1,300. 1,300.
20 A1 3/10pi on 3m lt brn (V) 160.00 160.00
a. On #3a (type II) 3,000.
21 A1 4/10pi on 4m scar 65.00 70.00
22 A1 5/10pi on 5m org 200.00 110.00
23 A1 5/10pi on 5m dp org (V) 275.00 275.00

Handstamp Surcharged "El qirsh" (piaster) and numeral in Black, Red or Violet

24 A1 2pi on 2pi ol grn 275.00 82.50
a. On #7a (type II) 1,400.
25 A1 2pi on 2pi ol grn (R) 350.00 87.50
26 A1 2pi on 2pi ol grn (V) 325.00 100.00
27 A1 5pi on 5pi plum 70.00 87.50
a. On #8a (type II) 1,750.
28 A1 9pi on 9pi bister 325.00 375.00
29 A1 9pi on 9pi bister (R) 140.00 150.00

For overprint see No. 83B.

**On Nos. 1B-11 (Perf. 14)**

13C A1 1/10pi on 1m dk brn 27.50 32.50
a. Pair, one without surcharge 1,600.
14C A1 1/10pi on 1m dk brn (R) 65.00 65.00
15C A1 1/10pi on 1m dk brn (V) 275.00 325.00
16C A1 2/10pi on 2m bl grn 32.50 32.50
a. Pair, one without surcharge 1,600.
b. 3/10pi on 2m bl grn (error) 120.00 120.00
17C A1 2/10pi on 2m bl grn (R) 87.50 87.50
18C A1 2/10pi on 2m bl grn (V) 87.50 87.50
22C A1 5/10pi on 5m org 250.00 110.00
a. Pair, one without surcharge 2,250.
23C A1 5/10pi on 5m org (V) 300.00
23D A1 1pi on 1pi dk blue (R) 225.00 65.00
a. Pair, one without surcharge 2,000.
23E A1 1pi on 1pi dk blue (V) 450.00
29C A1 9pi on 9pi bister 600.00 600.00
31 A1 10pi on 10pi ultra 925.00 1,100.
32 A1 20pi on 20pi gray 700.00 825.00
33 A1 20pi on 20pi gray (V) 1,000. 1,050.

**Surcharge in Black on Palestine Nos. 13-14**

34 A1 10pi on 10pi ultra 2,000. 2,750.
35 A1 20pi on 20pi gray 2,750. 3,250.

Nos. 13-35 are handstamped, and the overprints exist double on most values. They have been extensively forged. Values above are for expertized examples.

Stamps of 1920 Handstamped in Violet, Black or Red

**1922, Dec. *Perf. 14***
**On Nos. 1-5, 7-9 (Perf. 15x14)**

36 A1 1m dk brn (R) 32.50 32.50
37 A1 1m dk brn (V) 32.50 37.50
38 A1 1m dk brn (Blk) 27.50 27.50
39 A1 2m bl grn (R) 30.00 30.00
40 A1 2m bl grn (V) 26.00 26.00
41 A1 2m bl grn (Blk) 25.00 25.00
42 A1 3m lt brn (R) 52.50 *52.50*
a. On #3a (type II) 1,750.
43 A1 3m lt brn (V) 10.00 10.00
a. Pair, one without surcharge 1,400.
b. On #3a (type II) 1,600. 1,600.
44 A1 3m lt brn (Blk) 11.00 11.00
45 A1 4m scar (R) 65.00 70.00
46 A1 4m scar (V) 65.00 70.00
47 A1 4m scar (Blk) 65.00 70.00
48 A1 5m orange (R) 50.00 13.00
49 A1 5m orange (V) 20.00 13.00
50 A1 2pi ol grn (R) 65.00 50.00
a. On #7a (type II) 1,600.
52 A1 2pi ol grn (V) 27.50 20.00
a. On #7a (type II) 1,600. 1,400.
53 A1 2pi ol grn (Blk) 18.00 13.00
54 A1 5pi plum (R) 110.00 130.00
a. Pair, one without surcharge 1,750.
55 A1 5pi plum (V) 70.00 90.00
56 A1 9pi bister (R) 450.00 500.00
57 A1 9pi bister (V) 225.00 275.00
a. Type II overprint 2,500.
58 A1 9pi bister (Blk) 75.00 90.00

**On #1B//11 (Perf. 14)**

36C A1 1m dk brn (R) 17.50 22.00
a. Pair, one without ovpt. 1,400.
37C A1 1m dk brn (V) 27.50 25.00
38C A1 1m dk brn (Blk) 25.00 25.00
39C A1 2m bl grn (R) 35.00 35.00
40C A1 2m bl grn (V) 11.00 11.00
41C A1 2m bl grn (Blk) 17.50 17.50
43C A1 3m lt brn (V) 850.00 375.00
48C A1 5m orange (R) 325.00 80.00
49C A1 5m orange (V) 35.00 25.00
51 A1 1pi dark blue (R) 40.00 19.00
51C A1 1pi dark blue (V) 25.00 12.50
52C A1 2pi ol grn (R) 85.00 90.00
54C A1 5pi plum (R) 110.00 120.00
55C A1 5pi plum (V) 110.00 130.00
57C A1 9pi bister (V) 1,000. 1,100.
59 A1 10pi ultra (R) 2,000. 2,100.
60 A1 10pi ultra (V) 1,200. 1,750.
61 A1 20pi gray (R) 1,750. 2,200.
62 A1 20pi gray (V) 1,200. 2,000.

The overprint reads "Hukumat al Sharqi al Arabia" (Arab Government of the East) and date, 1923. The surcharges or overprints on Nos. 12 to 61 inclusive are handstamped and, as usual, are found inverted and double.

Ink pads of several colors were in use at the same time and the surcharges and overprints frequently show a mixture of two colors.

For overprints see Nos. 84, 87, 89, 92-93, 95-96.

Stamps of 1920 Overprinted in Gold or Black

**1923, Mar. 1 *Perf. 15x14***

63 A1 1m dark brn (G) 1,600. 1,900.
64 A1 2m blue grn (G) 25.00 27.50
65 A1 3m lt brn (G) 19.00 20.00
a. Double overprint 550.00
b. Inverted overprint 600.00
c. Black overprint 82.50 92.50
66 A1 4m scarlet (Blk) 22.50 20.00
67 A1 5m orange (Blk) 65.00 55.00
a. Original ovpt. albino 1,300. 1,500.
69 A1 2pi ol grn (G) 25.00 22.50
a. On #7a (type II) 1,300. 1,100.
b. Black overprint 275.00 275.00
70 A1 5pi plum (G) 80.00 110.00
a. Inverted overprint 240.00
b. On #8a (type II) 2,200.
c. As "b," inverted ovpt. 2,750.
d. Black overprint inverted 1,600.

**Perf. 14**

63E A1 1m dark brn (G) 21.00 35.00
a. Inverted overprint 800.00
64E A1 2m blue grn (G) 20.00 22.50
a. Double overprint 325.00
b. Inverted overprint 375.00 375.00
c. Black overprint 325.00
d. As "c," inverted overprint 1,600.
67E A1 5m orange (Blk) 15.00 15.00
68 A1 1pi dk blue (G) 15.00 20.00
a. Double overprint 550.00 *600.00*
b. Black overprint *850.00* *900.00*
71 A1 9pi bister (Blk) 100.00 *140.00*
a. Gold overprint 3,250.
72 A1 10pi ultra (G) 90.00 140.00
73 A1 20pi gray (G) 90.00 140.00
a. Inverted overprint 400.00
b. Double overprint 500.00
c. Double ovpt., one inverted 500.00
d. Double ovpt., one inverted, one gold, one black, black ovpt. inverted 800.00
e. Triple overprint, one inverted 1,200.
f. Black overprint 900.00
g. As "f," inverted overprint 1,200.
h. As "f," double overprint, one inverted 1,400.

The overprint reads "Hukumat al Sharqi al Arabia, Nissan Sanat 921" (Arab Government of the East, April, 1921).
For overprints see Nos. 85, 99, 100, 102.

**Stamps of Hejaz, 1922, Overprinted in Black**

Coat of Arms (Hejaz A7)

**1923, Apr. Unwmk. *Perf. 11½***

74A A7 1/8pi orange brn 5.75 *4.50*
a. Double overprint 225.00
b. Inverted overprint 120.00
74B A7 1/2pi red 5.75 4.50
a. Inverted overprint *125.00*
74C A7 1pi dark blue 4.50 1.50
a. Inverted overprint 140.00 140.00
74D A7 1 1/2pi violet 4.75 *2.75*
a. Double overprint 160.00
b. Pair, one without overprint 250.00
c. Pair, imperf. between 175.00
74E A7 2pi orange 6.00 *8.50*
74F A7 3pi olive brn 15.00 *20.00*
a. Inverted overprint 250.00
b. Double overprint 250.00 250.00
c. Pair, one without overprint *400.00*
74G A7 5pi olive green 35.00 *47.50*
*Nos. 64-70 (7)* 76.75 *89.25*

The overprint is similar to that on the preceding group but is differently arranged. There are numerous varieties in the Arabic letters.
For overprints see Nos. 71-72, 91, J1-J5.

**With Additional Surcharge of New Value in Arabic**

a

b

74H A7(a) 1/4pi on 1/8pi 16.00 *11.00*
a. Inverted surcharge 175.00
b. Surcharge doubled — 200.00
74I A7(b) 10pi on 5pi 37.50 *42.50*

### Independence Issue

Palestine Stamps and Type of 1918 Overprinted Vertically in Black or Gold

**1923, May** **Wmk. 33** ***Perf. 15x14***

| | | | | |
|---|---|---|---|---|
| **74J** | A1 | 1m dark brn (Bk) | 24.00 | *24.00* |
| *a.* | | Double ovpt., one reversed | 725.00 | 650.00 |
| **74K** | A1 | 1m dark brn (G) | 175.00 | 175.00 |
| *c.* | | Double ovpt., one reversed | 1,000. | |
| **74** | A1 | 2m blue grn | 42.50 | *50.00* |
| **75** | A1 | 3m lt brown | 14.00 | *17.50* |
| **76** | A1 | 4m scarlet | 14.00 | *17.50* |
| **77** | A1 | 5m orange | 70.00 | *80.00* |
| **78** | A1 | 1pi dk blue (G) | 95.00 | *110.00* |
| *a.* | | Double overprint | *750.00* | *850.00* |
| **79** | A1 | 2pi olive grn | 70.00 | *90.00* |
| **80** | A1 | 5pi plum (G) | 80.00 | *90.00* |
| *a.* | | Double overprint (G) | *725.00* | |
| *b.* | | Double overprint (Bk) | *1,500.* | |
| **81** | A1 | 9pi bis, perf. 14 | 70.00 | *85.00* |
| **82** | A1 | 10pi ultra, perf. 14 | 80.00 | *100.00* |
| **83** | A1 | 20pi gray | 85.00 | *110.00* |
| | | *Nos. 73-83 (12)* | 819.50 | 949.00 |

The overprint reads, "Arab Government of the East (abbreviated), Souvenir of Independence, 25th, May, 1923 ('923')."

There were printed 480 complete sets and a larger number of the 1, 2, 3 and 4m. A large number of these sets were distributed to high officials. The overprint was in a setting of twenty-four and the error "933" instead of "923" occurs once in the setting. Value about five times the "923" stamps.

The overprint exists reading downward on all values, as illustrated, and reading upward on all except the 5m and 2pi.

Forged overprints exist.

For overprint see No. 101.

Stamps of Preceding Issues, Handstamp Surcharged

| | | | | |
|---|---|---|---|---|
| **83A** | A1 | 2½/ 10ths pi on 5m dp org | 240.00 | *240.00* |
| **83B** | A1 | 5/10pi on 3m (#17) | — | *120.00* |
| **84** | A1 | 5/10pi on 3m (#36) | 100.00 | 60.00 |
| **85** | A1 | 5/10pi on 3m (#55) | 27.50 | 40.00 |
| **86** | A1 | 5/10pi on 5pi (#23) | 85.00 | *100.00* |
| **87** | A1 | 5/10pi on 5pi (#48) | 10.00 | *17.50* |
| **88** | A1 | 1pi on 5pi (#23) | 75.00 | *140.00* |
| **89** | A1 | 1pi on 5pi (#48) | *2,500.* | *2,750.* |

### Same Surcharge on Palestine Stamp of 1918

| | | | | |
|---|---|---|---|---|
| **90** | A1 | 5/10pi on 3m lt brn | *17,000.* | |

No. 90 is valued in the grade of fine-very fine. Very fine examples are not known.

As is usual with handstamped surcharges these are found double, inverted, etc.

No. 67 Surcharged by Handstamp

**Unwmk.** ***Perf. 11½***

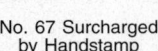

| | | | | |
|---|---|---|---|---|
| **91** | A7 | ½pi on 1½pi vio | 12.00 | *14.00* |
| *a.* | | Surcharge typographed | 55.00 | *55.00* |
| *b.* | | As "a," inverted surcharge | 150.00 | |
| *c.* | | As "a," double surcharge | 180.00 | |
| *d.* | | As "a," pair, one with surcharge | 500.00 | |

The surcharge reads: "Nusf el qirsh" (half piastre). See note after No. 90.

Handstamped surcharge exists double; inverted; double, one inverted, etc.

### Stamps of Preceding Issues Surcharged by Handstamp

No. 92

***Perf. 14, 15x14***

**1923, Nov.** **Wmk. 33**

| | | | | |
|---|---|---|---|---|
| **92** | A1 | ½pi on 2pi (#45) | 70.00 | *85.00* |
| **93** | A1 | ½pi on 2pi (#47) | 110.00 | *125.00* |
| **94** | A1 | ½pi on 5pi (#23) | 75.00 | *85.00* |
| **95** | A1 | ½pi on 5pi (#48) | 3,000. | 2,000. |
| **96** | A1 | ½pi on 5pi (#49) | 2,000. | *2,750.* |
| **97** | A1 | ½pi on 9pi (#24) | *6,500.* | |
| **98** | A1 | ½pi on 9pi (#25) | 95.00 | *160.00* |
| **99** | A1 | ½pi on 9pi (#61) | 200.00 | 160.00 |

Surcharged by Handstamp

No. 102

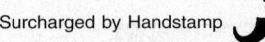

| | | | | |
|---|---|---|---|---|
| **100** | A1 | 1pi on 10pi (#62) | *2,250.* | *2,500.* |
| **101** | A1 | 1pi on 10pi (#82) | *3,000.* | *3,000.* |
| **102** | A1 | 2pi on 20pi (#63) | 65.00 | *87.50* |

Of the 25 examples of No. 100, a few were handstamped in violet. Value, unused $2,750.

Stamp of Hejaz, 1922, Overprinted by Handstamp

**1923, Dec.** **Unwmk.** ***Perf. 11½***

| | | | | |
|---|---|---|---|---|
| **103** | A7 | ½pi red | 8.00 | *4.25* |

Two settings of No. 103 exist. They differ in the spacing of the characters and the position of the bottom line of the overprint, either to the left or centered.

Nos. 92-103 handstamps exist inverted, doubled, etc.

Stamp of Hejaz, 1922, Overprinted

**1924** **Typo.**

| | | | | |
|---|---|---|---|---|
| **104** | A7 | ½pi red | 14.00 | *15.00* |

### King Hussein Issue

Stamps of Hejaz, 1922, Overprinted

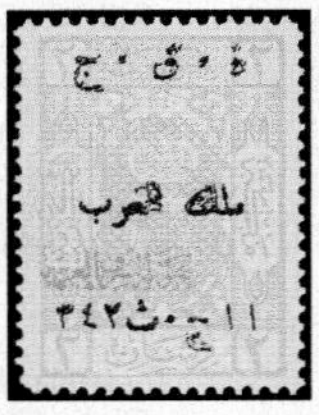

**1924** **Gold Overprint**

| | | | | |
|---|---|---|---|---|
| **105** | A7 | ½pi red | 4.00 | 4.00 |
| **106** | A7 | 1pi dark blue | 4.25 | 3.25 |
| **107** | A7 | 1½pi violet | 5.00 | *4.50* |
| **108** | A7 | 2pi orange | 12.00 | *13.00* |

**Black Overprint**

| | | | | |
|---|---|---|---|---|
| **109** | A7 | ½pi red | 3.00 | 3.00 |
| **110** | A7 | 1pi dark blue | 3.75 | 3.75 |
| **111** | A7 | 1½pi violet | 5.50 | 5.50 |
| **112** | A7 | 2pi orange | 13.00 | 13.00 |
| | | *Nos. 105-112 (8)* | 50.50 | 50.00 |

The overprint reads: "Arab Government of the East. In commemoration of the visit of H. M. the King of the Arabs, 11 Jemad el Than i 1342 (17th Jan. 1924)." The overprint was in a setting of thirty-six and the error "432" instead of "342" occurs once in the setting and is found on all values. Value, $75 each.

### Stamps of Hejaz, 1922-24, Overprinted in Black or Red

Coat of Arms (Hejaz A8)

**1924**

| | | | | |
|---|---|---|---|---|
| **113** | A7 | ⅛pi red brown | 2.00 | 1.75 |
| *a.* | | Inverted overprint | 130.00 | — |
| **114** | A7 | ¼pi yellow green | 2.00 | 1.00 |
| *a.* | | Tête bêche pair | 9.00 | 12.00 |
| *b.* | | As "a," one overprint inverted | 300.00 | — |
| *c.* | | Inverted overprint | 85.00 | — |
| **115** | A7 | ½pi red | 2.00 | .90 |
| **116** | A7 | 1pi dark blue | 11.00 | 1.50 |
| *a.* | | Inverted overprint | — | — |
| **117** | A7 | 1½pi violet | 7.00 | 7.00 |
| **118** | A7 | 2pi orange | 5.00 | 3.50 |
| *a.* | | Double overprint | — | — |
| **119** | A7 | 3pi red brown | 5.00 | 5.00 |
| *a.* | | Double overprint | 100.00 | — |
| *b.* | | Inverted overprint | 100.00 | — |
| **120** | A7 | 5pi olive green | 7.00 | *7.00* |
| **121** | A8 | 10pi vio & dk brn (R) | 15.00 | *17.50* |
| *a.* | | Pair, one without overprint | | |
| *b.* | | Black overprint | 250.00 | — |
| | | *Nos. 113-121 (9)* | 56.00 | 45.15 |

The overprint reads: "Hukumat al Sharqi al Arabia, 1342." (Arab Government of the East, 1924).

### Stamps of Hejaz, 1925, Overprinted in Black or Red

(Hejaz A9)

(Hejaz A10)

(Hejaz A11)

**1925, Aug.**

| | | | | |
|---|---|---|---|---|
| **122** | A9 | ⅛pi chocolate | 1.25 | *2.75* |
| *a.* | | Inverted overprint | 70.00 | — |
| **123** | A9 | ¼pi ultramarine | 2.25 | *4.25* |
| *a.* | | Inverted overprint | 70.00 | — |
| **124** | A9 | ½pi carmine rose | 1.75 | 1.25 |
| *a.* | | Inverted overprint | 70.00 | — |
| **125** | A10 | 1pi yellow green | 1.75 | 3.00 |
| **126** | A10 | 1½pi orange | 4.00 | *5.50* |
| *a.* | | Inverted overprint | 70.00 | — |
| **127** | A10 | 2pi deep blue | 5.00 | *7.50* |
| **128** | A11 | 3pi dark green (R) | 5.50 | *11.00* |
| *a.* | | Inverted overprint | 90.00 | — |
| **129** | A11 | 5pi orange brn | 8.00 | *18.00* |
| *a.* | | Inverted overprint | 85.00 | — |
| | | *Nos. 122-129 (8)* | 29.50 | *53.25* |

The overprint reads: "Hukumat al Sharqi al Arabi. 1343 Sanat." (Arab Government of the East, 1925). Nos. 122-129 exist imperforate, and with overprint double.

Type of Palestine, 1918

**1925, Nov. 1** **Wmk. 4** ***Perf. 14***

| | | | | |
|---|---|---|---|---|
| **130** | A1 | 1m dark brown | .60 | *3.50* |
| **131** | A1 | 2m yellow | .85 | .65 |
| **132** | A1 | 3m Prussian bl | 2.75 | 1.60 |
| **133** | A1 | 4m rose | 2.75 | *3.75* |
| **134** | A1 | 5m orange | 3.25 | .60 |
| **135** | A1 | 6m blue green | 2.75 | *2.75* |
| **136** | A1 | 7m yel brown | 2.75 | *2.75* |
| **137** | A1 | 8m red | 2.75 | 1.60 |
| **138** | A1 | 1pi gray | 2.75 | .75 |
| **139** | A1 | 13m ultramarine | 3.50 | *3.50* |
| **140** | A1 | 2pi olive green | 4.50 | *5.00* |
| **141** | A1 | 5pi plum | 9.50 | *10.00* |
| **142** | A1 | 9pi bister | 14.00 | *27.50* |
| **143** | A1 | 10pi light blue | 30.00 | *40.00* |
| **144** | A1 | 20pi violet | 50.00 | *90.00* |
| | | *Nos. 130-144 (15)* | 132.70 | *193.95* |

This overprint reads: "Sharqi al-ardan" (East of Jordan).

For overprints see Nos. J12-J23.

***Perf. 15x14***

| | | | | |
|---|---|---|---|---|
| *142a* | A1 | 9pi | 950. | *1,500.* |
| *143a* | A1 | 10pi | 100. | *110.* |
| *144a* | A1 | 20pi | 1,100. | 1,100. |
| | | *Nos. 142a-144a (3)* | 2,150. | *2,710.* |

Amir Abdullah ibn Hussein

A1 A2

**1927-29** **Engr.** ***Perf. 14***

| | | | | |
|---|---|---|---|---|
| **145** | A1 | 2(m) Prus blue | 2.50 | 1.25 |
| **146** | A1 | 3(m) rose | 3.75 | 3.00 |
| **147** | A1 | 4(m) green | 4.50 | *6.50* |
| **148** | A1 | 5(m) orange | 2.75 | .35 |
| **149** | A1 | 10(m) red | 3.75 | *6.50* |
| **150** | A1 | 15(m) ultra | 3.50 | .50 |
| **151** | A1 | 20(m) olive grn | 3.75 | *4.00* |
| **152** | A2 | 50(m) claret | 3.75 | *12.00* |
| **153** | A2 | 90(m) bister | 9.00 | *27.50* |
| **154** | A2 | 100(m) lt blue | 10.00 | *22.50* |
| **155** | A2 | 200(m) violet | 17.50 | *45.00* |
| **156** | A2 | 500(m) dp brn ('29) | 70.00 | *100.00* |
| **157** | A2 | 1000(m) gray ('29) | 165.00 | *190.00* |
| | | *Nos. 145-157 (13)* | 299.75 | *419.10* |

For overprints see Nos. 158-168, B1-B12, J24-J29.

Stamps of 1927 Overprinted in Black

**1928, Sept. 1**

| | | | | |
|---|---|---|---|---|
| **158** | A1 | 2(m) Prus blue | 3.00 | *3.50* |
| **159** | A1 | 3(m) rose | 3.50 | *4.50* |
| **160** | A1 | 4(m) green | 3.50 | *5.25* |
| **161** | A1 | 5(m) orange | 3.50 | *2.50* |
| **162** | A1 | 10(m) red | 3.75 | *5.75* |
| **163** | A1 | 15(m) ultra | 3.75 | 2.75 |
| **164** | A1 | 20(m) olive grn | 8.50 | *14.00* |
| **165** | A2 | 50(m) claret | 12.00 | *15.00* |
| **166** | A2 | 90(m) bister | 22.50 | *45.00* |
| **167** | A2 | 100(m) lt blue | 27.50 | *65.00* |
| **168** | A2 | 200(m) violet | 85.00 | *160.00* |
| | | *Nos. 158-168 (11)* | 176.50 | *323.25* |

The overprint is the Arabic word "Dastour," meaning "Constitution." The stamps were in commemoration of the enactment of the law setting forth the Constitution.

A3

"MILS" or "L. P." at lower right and Arabic equivalents at upper left.

**1930-36** **Engr.** ***Perf. 14***

**Size: 17¼x21mm**

| | | | | |
|---|---|---|---|---|
| **169** | A3 | 1m red brn ('34) | 2.00 | *1.00* |
| **170** | A3 | 2m Prus blue | 1.00 | *.60* |
| **171** | A3 | 3m rose | 1.75 | 1.00 |
| **172** | A3 | 3m green ('34) | 2.50 | 1.25 |
| **173** | A3 | 4m green | 2.00 | *4.00* |
| **174** | A3 | 4m rose ('34) | 4.00 | 1.50 |
| **175** | A3 | 5m orange | 1.50 | .45 |
| *a.* | | Perf. 13½x14 (coil) ('36) | 34.00 | 20.00 |
| **176** | A3 | 10m red | 2.25 | .25 |
| **177** | A3 | 15m ultra | 2.25 | .30 |
| *a.* | | Perf. 13½x14 (coil) ('36) | 32.50 | 17.50 |
| **178** | A3 | 20m olive grn | 3.25 | .55 |

**Size: 19¼x23½mm**

| | | | | |
|---|---|---|---|---|
| **179** | A3 | 50m red violet | 4.50 | 2.25 |
| **180** | A3 | 90m bister | 4.25 | *6.25* |
| **181** | A3 | 100m light blue | 5.00 | *6.00* |
| **182** | A3 | 200m violet | 17.50 | *18.00* |
| **183** | A3 | 500m deep brown | 32.50 | *57.50* |
| **184** | A3 | £1 gray | 77.50 | *120.00* |
| | | *Nos. 169-184 (16)* | 163.75 | *220.90* |

See Nos. 199-220, 230-235. For overprint see No. N15a.

**1939** *Perf. 13½x13*

**Size: 17¼x21mm**

| | | | | | |
|---|---|---|---|---|---|
| *169a* | A3 | 1m | red brown | 6.50 | 4.50 |
| *170a* | A3 | 2m | Prussian blue | 16.00 | 4.00 |
| *172a* | A3 | 3m | green | 25.00 | 7.00 |
| *174a* | A3 | 4m | rose | 90.00 | 29.00 |
| *175b* | A3 | 5m | orange | 75.00 | 4.50 |
| *176a* | A3 | 10m | red | 150.00 | 5.75 |
| *177b* | A3 | 15m | ultramarine | 47.50 | 6.00 |
| *178a* | A3 | 20m | olive green | 72.50 | 17.50 |
| | | | *Nos. 169a-178a (8)* | 482.50 | 78.25 |

For overprint see No. N3a.

Mushetta — A4

Nymphaeum, Jerash — A5

Kasr Kharana — A6

Kerak Castle — A7

Temple of Artemis, Jerash — A8

Aijalon Castle — A9

Khazneh, Rock-hewn Temple, Petra — A10

Allenby Bridge, River Jordan — A11

Ancient Threshing Floor — A12

Amir Abdullah ibn Hussein — A13

**1933, Feb. 1** *Perf. 12*

| | | | | | |
|---|---|---|---|---|---|
| **185** | A4 | 1m | dk brn & blk | 1.75 | 1.40 |
| **186** | A5 | 2m | claret & blk | 4.00 | 1.10 |
| **187** | A6 | 3m | blue green | 4.25 | 1.50 |
| **188** | A7 | 4m | bister & blk | 6.50 | 3.75 |
| **189** | A8 | 5m | orange & blk | 4.50 | 3.75 |
| **190** | A9 | 10m | brown red | 7.00 | 3.50 |
| **191** | A10 | 15m | dull blue | 4.75 | 1.75 |
| **192** | A11 | 20m | ol grn & blk | 6.75 | 5.50 |
| **193** | A12 | 50m | brn vio & blk | 20.00 | 17.50 |
| **194** | A6 | 90m | yel & black | 25.00 | *27.50* |
| **195** | A8 | 100m | blue & blk | 27.50 | *35.00* |
| **196** | A9 | 200m | dk vio & blk | 60.00 | *80.00* |
| **197** | A10 | 500m | brn & ver | 190.00 | *275.00* |
| **198** | A13 | £1 | green & blk | 650.00 | *950.00* |
| | | | *Nos. 185-198 (14)* | 1,012. | *1,407.* |

Nos. 194-197 are larger than the lower values in the same designs.

Amir Abdullah ibn Hussein — A14

*Perf. 13x13½*

**1942, May 18 Litho. Unwmk.**

| | | | | | |
|---|---|---|---|---|---|
| **199** | A14 | 1m | dull red brn | 1.10 | *4.00* |
| **200** | A14 | 2m | dull green | 2.00 | *2.25* |
| **201** | A14 | 3m | dp yel green | 2.50 | *4.50* |
| **202** | A14 | 4m | rose pink | 2.50 | *4.50* |
| **203** | A14 | 5m | orange yel | 4.25 | 1.00 |
| **204** | A14 | 10m | dull ver | 6.00 | 3.25 |
| **205** | A14 | 15m | deep blue | 12.50 | 4.00 |
| **206** | A14 | 20m | dull ol grn | 22.50 | 22.50 |
| | | | *Nos. 199-206 (8)* | 53.35 | 46.00 |

Type A14 differs from A3 in the redrawn inscription above the head and in the form of the "millieme" character at upper left.

For overprint see No. N1.

**Abdullah Type of 1930-39**

White Paper

**1943-44 Engr. Wmk. 4** *Perf. 12*

**Size: 17¾x21½mm**

| | | | | | |
|---|---|---|---|---|---|
| **207** | A3 | 1m | red brown | .30 | .70 |
| **208** | A3 | 2m | Prussian grn | 1.50 | 1.25 |
| **209** | A3 | 3m | blue green | 1.25 | 1.25 |
| **210** | A3 | 4m | deep rose | 1.25 | 1.25 |
| **211** | A3 | 5m | orange | 1.25 | .30 |
| **212** | A3 | 10m | scarlet | 2.25 | 1.25 |
| **213** | A3 | 15m | blue | 2.25 | 1.50 |
| **214** | A3 | 20m | olive ('44) | 2.25 | 1.00 |

**Size: 20x24mm**

| | | | | | |
|---|---|---|---|---|---|
| **215** | A3 | 50m | red lil ('44) | 2.50 | 1.25 |
| **216** | A3 | 90m | ocher | 5.00 | 6.00 |
| **217** | A3 | 100m | dp bl ('44) | 6.50 | 3.00 |
| **218** | A3 | 200m | dk vio ('44) | 8.00 | 10.00 |
| **219** | A3 | 500m | dk brn ('44) | 11.00 | 12.50 |
| **220** | A3 | £1 | black ('44) | 20.00 | 27.50 |
| | | | *Nos. 207-220 (14)* | 65.30 | 68.75 |

See Nos. 230-235. For overprints see Nos. 255-256, 259, 264-269, RA23, N2-N4, N7, N12-N17.

**Catalogue values for unused stamps in this section, from this point to the end of the section, are for Never Hinged items.**

**Independent Kingdom**

Symbols of Peace and Liberty — A15

*Perf. 11½*

**1946, May 25 Unwmk. Litho.**

| | | | | | |
|---|---|---|---|---|---|
| **221** | A15 | 1m | sepia | .30 | .25 |
| **222** | A15 | 2m | yel orange | .30 | .25 |
| **223** | A15 | 3m | dl ol grn | .30 | .25 |
| **224** | A15 | 4m | lt violet | .30 | .25 |
| **225** | A15 | 10m | orange brn | .30 | .25 |
| **226** | A15 | 12m | rose red | .30 | .25 |
| **227** | A15 | 20m | dark blue | .35 | .25 |
| **228** | A15 | 50m | ultra | .90 | .75 |
| **229** | A15 | 200m | green | 3.00 | 3.00 |
| | | | *Nos. 221-229 (9)* | 6.05 | 5.50 |

Independence of the Kingdom of Trans-Jordan.

Nos. 221-229 exist imperforate.

**Abdullah Type of 1930-39**

**1947 Wmk. 4 Engr.** *Perf. 12*

| | | | | | |
|---|---|---|---|---|---|
| **230** | A3 | 3m | rose carmine | .40 | .30 |
| **231** | A3 | 4m | deep yel green | .40 | .30 |
| **232** | A3 | 10m | violet | .60 | .30 |
| **233** | A3 | 12m | deep rose | 1.10 | .80 |
| **234** | A3 | 15m | dull olive grn | 1.25 | .90 |
| **235** | A3 | 20m | deep blue | 1.40 | 1.00 |
| | | | *Nos. 230-235 (6)* | 5.15 | 3.60 |

For overprints see Nos. 257-258, 260-263, RA24-RA25, N5-N6, N8-N11.

Parliament Building, Amman A16

**1947, Nov. 1 Engr. Unwmk.**

| | | | | | |
|---|---|---|---|---|---|
| **236** | A16 | 1m | purple | .40 | .25 |
| **237** | A16 | 3m | red orange | .40 | .25 |
| **238** | A16 | 4m | yel green | .40 | .25 |
| **239** | A16 | 10m | dk vio brn | .40 | .25 |
| **240** | A16 | 12m | carmine | .40 | .25 |
| **241** | A16 | 20m | deep blue | .50 | .25 |
| **242** | A16 | 50m | red vio | .80 | .35 |
| **243** | A16 | 100m | rose | 1.00 | .65 |
| **244** | A16 | 200m | dark green | 1.60 | 1.50 |
| | | | *Nos. 236-244 (9)* | 5.90 | 4.00 |

Founding of the new Trans-Jordan parliament, 1947.

Nos. 236-244 exist imperforate.

Symbols of the UPU A17

King Abdullah ibn Hussein A18

**1949, Aug. 1 Wmk. 4** *Perf. 13*

| | | | | | |
|---|---|---|---|---|---|
| **245** | A17 | 1m | brown | .40 | .40 |
| **246** | A17 | 4m | green | .75 | .75 |
| **247** | A17 | 10m | red | .95 | .95 |
| **248** | A17 | 20m | ultramarine | 1.60 | 1.60 |
| **249** | A18 | 50m | dull green | 2.50 | 2.50 |
| | | | *Nos. 245-249 (5)* | 6.20 | 6.20 |

UPU, 75th anniv. For overprints see Nos. N18-N22.

Nos. 207-208, 211, 215-220, 230-235 Surcharged in Carmine, Black or Green

**1952 Wmk. 4** *Perf. 12*

**Size: 17¾x21½mm**

| | | | | |
|---|---|---|---|---|
| **255** | A3 | 1f on 1m red brn (Bk) | .50 | .50 |
| **256** | A3 | 2f on 2m Prus grn | .50 | .50 |
| **257** | A3 | 3f on 3m rose car (Bk) | .50 | .50 |
| **258** | A3 | 4f on 4m dp yel grn | .50 | .50 |
| **259** | A3 | 5f on 5m org (G) | .75 | .75 |
| **260** | A3 | 10f on 10m vio | 1.10 | 1.00 |
| **261** | A3 | 12f on 12m dp rose (Bk) | 1.10 | 1.00 |
| **262** | A3 | 15f on 15m dl ol grn | 1.40 | .75 |
| **263** | A3 | 20f on 20m dp bl | 2.25 | 1.10 |

**Size: 20x24mm**

| | | | | |
|---|---|---|---|---|
| **264** | A3 | 50f on 50m red lil (G) | 2.25 | 1.75 |
| **265** | A3 | 90f on 90m ocher (G) | 16.00 | 11.50 |
| **266** | A3 | 100f on 100m dp bl | 9.00 | 3.75 |
| **267** | A3 | 200f on 200m dk vio | 14.00 | 4.75 |
| **268** | A3 | 500f on 500m dk brn | 30.00 | 15.00 |
| **269** | A3 | 1d on £1 black | 75.00 | 17.50 |
| | | *Nos. 255-269 (15)* | 154.85 | 60.85 |

This surcharge also exists on Nos. 199-203, 205, 209-210, 212-214. Numerous inverted, double and wrong color surcharges exist.

Relief Map — A19

*Perf. 13½x13*

**1952, Apr. 1 Engr. Wmk. 4**

| | | | | | |
|---|---|---|---|---|---|
| **270** | A19 | 1f | red brn & yel grn | .45 | .45 |
| **271** | A19 | 2f | dk bl grn & red | .45 | .45 |
| **272** | A19 | 3f | car & gray blk | .45 | .45 |
| **273** | A19 | 4f | green & orange | .50 | .50 |
| **274** | A19 | 5f | choc & rose vio | .55 | .55 |
| **275** | A19 | 10f | violet & brown | .55 | .55 |
| **276** | A19 | 20f | dark bl & blk | 1.50 | .80 |
| **277** | A19 | 100f | dp blue & brn | 5.50 | 3.50 |
| **278** | A19 | 200f | purple & orange | 13.00 | 6.75 |
| | | | *Nos. 270-278 (9)* | 22.95 | 14.00 |

Unity of Jordan, Apr. 24, 1950.

For overprints see Nos. 297-305.

Amir Abdullah ibn Hussein — A20

**1952 Wmk. 4** *Perf. 11½*

| | | | | | |
|---|---|---|---|---|---|
| **279** | A20 | 5f | orange | .50 | .50 |
| **280** | A20 | 10f | violet | .50 | .50 |
| **281** | A20 | 12f | carmine | 2.00 | 1.25 |
| **282** | A20 | 15f | olive | 1.25 | .50 |
| **283** | A20 | 20f | deep blue | 1.25 | .60 |

**Size: 20x24½mm**

*Perf. 12x12½*

| | | | | | |
|---|---|---|---|---|---|
| **284** | A20 | 50f | plum | 2.75 | 1.00 |
| **285** | A20 | 90f | brn orange | 7.50 | 3.75 |
| **286** | A20 | 100f | deep blue | 8.00 | 2.50 |
| | | | *Nos. 279-286 (8)* | 23.75 | 10.60 |

Nos. RA5-RA7 Overprinted in Black or Carmine

*Perf. 11½x12½*

**1953 Unwmk. Engr.**

| | | | | | |
|---|---|---|---|---|---|
| **286A** | PT1 | 10m | carmine | 57.50 | 47.50 |
| **286B** | PT1 | 15m | gray (C) | 4.00 | 2.00 |
| **286C** | PT1 | 20m | dark brown | 125.00 | 95.00 |

**Same Overprint on Nos. NRA4-NRA7**

| | | | | | |
|---|---|---|---|---|---|
| **286D** | PT1 | 5m | plum | 80.00 | 47.50 |
| **286E** | PT1 | 10m | carmine | 80.00 | 47.50 |
| **286F** | PT1 | 15m | gray (C) | 80.00 | 47.50 |
| **286G** | PT1 | 20m | dk brn (C) | 80.00 | 47.50 |
| | | | *Nos. 286A-286G (7)* | 506.50 | 334.50 |

In addition a few sheets of Nos. RA9, NRA1, NRA3, NRA8-NRA9 and RA37-RA41 have been reported with this overprint. It is doubtful whether they were regularly issued. See Nos. 344-347.

**Nos. RA28-RA31 Overprinted in Black or Carmine**

**1953 Wmk. 4** *Perf. 11½x12½*

| | | | | | |
|---|---|---|---|---|---|
| **287** | PT1 | 5f | plum | .45 | .25 |
| **288** | PT1 | 10f | carmine | .55 | .25 |
| **289** | PT1 | 15f | gray (C) | 1.25 | 1.00 |
| **290** | PT1 | 20f | dark brown (C) | 2.75 | 1.50 |
| | | | *Nos. 287-290 (4)* | 5.00 | 3.00 |

King Hussein A21

**Unwmk.**

**1953, Oct. 1 Engr.** *Perf. 12*

**Portrait in Black**

| | | | | | |
|---|---|---|---|---|---|
| **291** | A21 | 1f | dark green | .35 | .25 |
| **292** | A21 | 4f | deep plum | .35 | .25 |
| **293** | A21 | 15f | deep ultra | 2.00 | .40 |
| **294** | A21 | 20f | dark purple | 3.25 | .40 |

| | | | | |
|---|---|---|---|---|
| **295** | A21 | 50f dark blue grn | 7.00 | 3.25 |
| **296** | A21 | 100f dark blue | 12.50 | 9.00 |
| | | *Nos. 291-296 (6)* | 25.45 | 13.55 |

Accession of King Hussein, May 2, 1953.

Nos. 270-278 Overprinted in Black

½mm Spacing

**1953 Wmk. 4 *Perf. 13½x13***

| | | | | |
|---|---|---|---|---|
| **297** | A19 | 1f red brn & yel grn | .40 | .40 |
| **298** | A19 | 2f dk bl grn & red | .40 | .40 |
| **299** | A19 | 3f car & gray blk | .40 | .40 |
| **300** | A19 | 4f green & orange | .40 | .40 |
| **301** | A19 | 5f choc & rose vio | .40 | .40 |
| **302** | A19 | 10f violet & brown | 1.25 | .75 |
| **303** | A19 | 20f dark bl & blk | 1.25 | .95 |
| **304** | A19 | 100f dp blue & brn | 7.25 | 1.75 |
| **305** | A19 | 200f purple & org | 10.00 | 6.50 |
| | | *Nos. 297-305 (9)* | 21.75 | 11.95 |

Two main settings of the bars exist on Nos. 297-300 and 304 — the "normal" 1½mm spacing, and the "narrow" ½mm spacing. Values above are for normal spacing. Value of set with narrow spacing, $150.

El Deir Temple, Petra — A22

Dome of the Rock — A23

Designs: 2f, 4f, 500f, 1d, King Hussein. 3f, 5f, Treasury Bldg., Petra. 12f, 50f, 100f, 200f, Al Aqsa Mosque. 20f, as 10f.

**1954 Unwmk. Engr. *Perf. 12½***

| | | | | |
|---|---|---|---|---|
| **306** | A22 | 1f dk bl grn & red brn | .35 | .25 |
| **307** | A22 | 2f red & black | .35 | .25 |
| **308** | A22 | 3f dp plum & vio bl | .35 | .25 |
| **309** | A22 | 4f org brn & dk grn | .50 | .30 |
| **310** | A22 | 5f vio & dk grn | .50 | .30 |
| **311** | A23 | 10f pur & dk grn | .75 | .75 |
| **312** | A23 | 12f car rose & sep | 1.75 | .70 |
| **313** | A23 | 20f dp bl & dk grn | 1.75 | .35 |
| **314** | A23 | 50f dk bl & dp rose | 3.75 | 1.25 |
| **315** | A23 | 100f dk grn & dp bl | 3.25 | .75 |
| **316** | A23 | 200f dp cl & pck bl | 13.00 | 2.25 |
| **317** | A22 | 500f choc & purple | 37.50 | 12.50 |
| **318** | A22 | 1d dk ol grn & rose brn | 55.00 | 22.50 |
| | | *Nos. 306-318 (13)* | 118.80 | 42.40 |

See Nos. 324-337. For overprint see No. 425.

Globe — A23a

***Perf. 13½x13***

**1955, Jan. 1 Photo. Wmk. 195**

| | | | | |
|---|---|---|---|---|
| **319** | A23a | 15f green | .60 | .45 |
| **320** | A23a | 20f violet | .60 | .45 |
| **321** | A23a | 25f yellow brown | .75 | .70 |
| | | *Nos. 319-321 (3)* | 1.95 | 1.60 |

Founding of the APU, July 1, 1954.

Princess Dina Abdul Hamid and King Hussein — A24

**1955, Apr. 19 *Perf. 11x11½***

| | | | | |
|---|---|---|---|---|
| **322** | A24 | 15f ultramarine | 2.25 | .95 |
| **323** | A24 | 100f rose brown | 8.50 | 3.75 |

Marriage of King Hussein and Princess Dina Abdul Hamid.

### Types of 1954

Design: 15f, Dome of the Rock.

**Wmk. 305**

**1955-64 Engr. *Perf. 12½***

| | | | | |
|---|---|---|---|---|
| **324** | A22 | 1f dk bl grn & red brn ('57) | .40 | .25 |
| **325** | A22 | 2f red & blk ('57) | .40 | .25 |
| **326** | A22 | 3f dp plum & vio bl ('56) | .40 | .25 |
| **327** | A22 | 4f org brn & dk grn ('56) | .40 | .25 |
| **328** | A22 | 5f vio & dk grn ('56) | .40 | .25 |
| **329** | A23 | 10f pur & grn ('57) | 3.75 | 2.25 |
| **330** | A23 | 12f car rose & sep | 1.50 | 1.00 |
| **331** | A23 | 15f dp brn & rose red | .90 | .25 |
| **332** | A23 | 20f dp bl & dk grn ('57) | .75 | .25 |
| **333** | A23 | 50f dk bl & dp rose | 1.40 | .35 |
| **334** | A23 | 100f dk grn & dp bl ('62) | 3.50 | 1.25 |
| **335** | A23 | 200f dp cl & pck bl ('65) | 9.50 | 2.25 |
| **336** | A22 | 500f choc & pur ('65) | 32.50 | 12.00 |
| **337** | A22 | 1d dk ol grn & rose brn ('65) | 57.50 | 20.00 |
| | | *Nos. 324-337 (14)* | 113.30 | 40.85 |

Envelope A25

**Wmk. 305**

**1956, Jan. 15 Engr. *Perf. 14***

**"Postmarks" in Black**

| | | | | |
|---|---|---|---|---|
| **338** | A25 | 1f light brown | .35 | .30 |
| **339** | A25 | 4f dark car rose | .35 | .30 |
| **340** | A25 | 15f blue | .35 | .30 |
| **341** | A25 | 20f yellow olive | .35 | .30 |
| **342** | A25 | 50f slate blue | .75 | .40 |
| **343** | A25 | 100f vermilion | 1.10 | .70 |
| | | *Nos. 338-343 (6)* | 3.25 | 2.30 |

1st Arab Postal Congress in Amman.

Nos. RA1, RA3, RA8 and RA33 Overprinted in Carmine or Black

***Perf. 11½x12½***

**1956, Jan. 5 Unwmk.**

| | | | | |
|---|---|---|---|---|
| **344** | PT1 | 1m ultramarine | .45 | .45 |
| **345** | PT1 | 3m emerald | .45 | .45 |
| **346** | PT1 | 50m purple | 1.10 | 1.00 |

**Wmk. 4**

| | | | | |
|---|---|---|---|---|
| **347** | PT1 | 100f orange (Bk) | 6.75 | 3.50 |
| | | *Nos. 344-347 (4)* | 8.75 | 5.40 |

Numerous inverted, double and wrong color surcharges exist.

Torch of Liberty — A26

**1958 Wmk. 305 Engr. *Perf. 12½***

| | | | | |
|---|---|---|---|---|
| **348** | A26 | 5f blue & red brown | .35 | .35 |
| **349** | A26 | 15f bister brn & blk | .45 | .40 |
| **350** | A26 | 35f blue grn & plum | 1.00 | .90 |
| **351** | A26 | 45f car & olive grn | 3.25 | 1.00 |
| | | *Nos. 348-351 (4)* | 5.05 | 2.65 |

10th anniv. of the Universal Declaration of Human Rights.

King Hussein — A27

***Perf. 12x11½***

**1959 Wmk. 305 Engr.**

**Centers in Black**

| | | | | |
|---|---|---|---|---|
| **352** | A27 | 1f deep green | .35 | .25 |
| **353** | A27 | 2f violet | .35 | .25 |
| **354** | A27 | 3f deep carmine | .40 | .25 |
| **355** | A27 | 4f brown black | .45 | .25 |
| **356** | A27 | 7f dark green | .55 | .25 |
| **357** | A27 | 12f deep carmine | .75 | .25 |
| **358** | A27 | 15f dark red | .80 | .25 |
| **359** | A27 | 21f green | .90 | .25 |
| **360** | A27 | 25f ocher | 1.10 | .25 |
| **361** | A27 | 35f dark blue | 1.75 | .30 |
| **362** | A27 | 40f olive green | 2.50 | .30 |
| **363** | A27 | 50f red | 3.00 | .30 |
| **364** | A27 | 100f blue green | 4.00 | .75 |
| **365** | A27 | 200f rose lake | 11.00 | 3.00 |
| **366** | A27 | 500f gray blue | 26.00 | 12.00 |
| **367** | A27 | 1d dark purple | 50.00 | 30.00 |
| | | *Nos. 352-367 (16)* | 103.90 | 48.90 |

For overprints see Nos. 423-424, 425a, 426-427.

Arab League Center, Cairo, and King Hussein A28

***Perf. 13x13½***

**1960, Mar. 22 Photo. Wmk. 328**

| | | | | |
|---|---|---|---|---|
| **368** | A28 | 15f dull green & blk | .35 | .25 |

Opening of the Arab League Center and the Arab Postal Museum in Cairo.

World Refugee Year Emblem A29

**Wmk. 305**

**1960, Apr. 7 Litho. *Perf. 13½***

| | | | | |
|---|---|---|---|---|
| **369** | A29 | 15f pale blue & red | .35 | .25 |
| **370** | A29 | 35f bister & blue | .60 | .45 |

World Refugee Year, 7/1/59-6/30/60.
For overprints see Nos. 377-378.

Shah of Iran, King Hussein and Flags A30

***Perf. 13x13½***

**1960, May 15 Wmk. 305**

**Flags in Green, Red & Black**

| | | | | |
|---|---|---|---|---|
| **371** | A30 | 15f yellow & black | .55 | .55 |
| **372** | A30 | 35f blue & black | .80 | .80 |
| **373** | A30 | 50f salmon & black | 1.10 | 1.10 |
| | | *Nos. 371-373 (3)* | 2.45 | 2.45 |

Visit of Mohammed Riza Pahlavi, Shah of Iran, to Jordan, Nov. 2, 1959.

Oil Refinery, Zarka A31

**1961, May 1 Engr. *Perf. 14x13***

| | | | | |
|---|---|---|---|---|
| **374** | A31 | 15f dull vio & blue | .35 | .25 |
| **375** | A31 | 35f dl vio & brick red | .55 | .40 |

Opening of oil refinery at Zarka.

Urban and Nomad Families and Chart A32

***Perf. 13x13½***

**1961, Oct. 15 Photo. Unwmk.**

| | | | | |
|---|---|---|---|---|
| **376** | A32 | 15f orange brown | .30 | .25 |

First Jordanian census, 1961.

**Nos. 369-370 Overprinted in English and Arabic, "In Memorial of Dag Hammarskjoeld 1904-1961," and Laurel Leaf Border**

**1961 Wmk. 305 Litho. *Perf. 13½***

| | | | | |
|---|---|---|---|---|
| **377** | A29 | 15f pale blue & red | 4.00 | 3.75 |
| **378** | A29 | 35f bister & blue | 4.50 | 4.00 |

Dag Hammarskjold, Secretary General of the UN, 1953-1961.

Malaria Eradication Emblem — A33

***Perf. 11x11½***

**1962, Apr. 15 Unwmk.**

| | | | | |
|---|---|---|---|---|
| **379** | A33 | 15f bright pink | .35 | .25 |
| **380** | A33 | 35f blue | .45 | .30 |

WHO drive to eradicate malaria. A souvenir sheet exists with one each of Nos. 379-380. Value $5.50.

Dial and Exchange Building, Amman A34

**1962, Dec. 11 Engr. Wmk. 305**

| | | | | |
|---|---|---|---|---|
| **381** | A34 | 15f blue & lilac | .30 | .25 |
| **382** | A34 | 35f lilac & emer | .35 | .25 |

Telephone automation in Amman (in 1960).

Opening of the Port of 'Aqaba A35

**1962, Dec. 11**

| | | | | |
|---|---|---|---|---|
| **383** | A35 | 15f lilac & blk | .40 | .25 |
| **384** | A35 | 35f violet bl & blk | .60 | .30 |
| *a.* | | Souvenir sheet of 2, #383-384 | 5.00 | 5.00 |

No. 384a imperf., same value.

Dag Hammarskjold and UN Headquarters, NY — A36

***Perf. 14x14½***

**1963, Jan. 24 Photo. Unwmk.**

| | | | |
|---|---|---|---|
| **385** | A36 15f ultra, ol grn & brn red | .45 | .25 |
| **386** | A36 35f ol, brn red & ultra | .80 | .45 |
| **387** | A36 50f brn red, ol & ultra | 1.25 | .80 |
| | *Nos. 385-387 (3)* | 2.50 | 1.50 |

17th anniv. of the UN and in memory of Dag Hammarskjold, Secretary General of the UN, 1953-61. An imperf. souvenir sheet contains one each of Nos. 385-387 with simulated perforations. Value $9.

Imperforates

Starting with No. 385, imperforates exist of many Jordanian stamps.

Church of St. Virgin's Tomb, Jerusalem — A37

Designs: No. 389, Basilica of the Agony, Gethsemane. No. 390, Church of the Holy Sepulcher, Jerusalem. No. 391, Church of the Nativity, Bethlehem. No. 392, Haram el-Khalil (tomb of Abraham), Hebron. No. 393, Dome of the Rock, Jerusalem. No. 394, Mosque of Omar el-Khatab, Jerusalem. No. 395, Al Aqsa Mosque, Jerusalem.

**1963, Feb. 5** ***Perf. 14½x14***

**Center Multicolored**

| | | | |
|---|---|---|---|
| **388** | A37 50f blue | 1.50 | 1.00 |
| **389** | A37 50f dull red | 1.50 | 1.00 |
| **390** | A37 50f bright blue | 1.50 | 1.00 |
| **391** | A37 50f olive green | 1.50 | 1.00 |
| *a.* | Vert. strip of 4, #388-391 | 15.00 | |
| **392** | A37 50f gray | 1.50 | 1.00 |
| *a.* | Yellow (in center) omitted | — | |
| **393** | A37 50f purple | 1.50 | 1.00 |
| *a.* | Yellow (in center) omitted | — | |
| **394** | A37 50f dull red | 1.50 | 1.00 |
| *a.* | Yellow (in center) omitted | — | |
| **395** | A37 50f light purple | 1.50 | 1.00 |
| *a.* | Vert. strip of 4, #392-395 | 15.00 | |
| *b.* | Yellow (in center) omitted | — | |
| | *Nos. 388-395 (8)* | 12.00 | 8.00 |

Arab League Building, Cairo — A38

**1963, July 16 Photo.** ***Perf. 13½x13***

| | | | |
|---|---|---|---|
| **396** | A38 15f slate blue | .45 | .25 |
| **397** | A38 35f orange red | .65 | .25 |

Arab League.

Wheat and UN Emblem — A39

***Perf. 11½x12½***

**1963, Sept. 15 Litho. Wmk. 305**

| | | | |
|---|---|---|---|
| **398** | A39 15f lt bl, grn & black | .30 | .25 |
| **399** | A39 35f lt grn, grn & blk | .30 | .25 |
| *a.* | Souvenir sheet of 2, #398-399 | 1.50 | 1.50 |

FAO "Freedom from Hunger" campaign. No. 399a imperf., same value.

East Ghor Canal, Pylon, Gear Wheel and Wheat A40

**1963, Sept. 20** ***Perf. 14½x14***

| | | | |
|---|---|---|---|
| **400** | A40 1f dull yel & black | .35 | .25 |
| **401** | A40 4f blue & black | .35 | .25 |
| **402** | A40 5f lilac & black | .35 | .25 |
| **403** | A40 10f brt yel grn & blk | .40 | .25 |
| **404** | A40 35f orange & black | 1.25 | .50 |
| | *Nos. 400-404 (5)* | 2.70 | 1.50 |

East Ghor Canal Project.

UNESCO Emblem, Scales and Globe A41

***Perf. 13½x13***

**1963, Dec. 10 Unwmk.**

| | | | |
|---|---|---|---|
| **405** | A41 50f pale vio bl & red | .70 | .60 |
| **406** | A41 50f rose red & blue | .70 | .60 |

15th anniv. of the Universal Declaration of Human Rights.

Red Crescent and King Hussein — A42

**1963, Dec. 24 Photo.** ***Perf. 14x14½***

| | | | |
|---|---|---|---|
| **407** | A42 1f red & red lilac | .30 | .25 |
| **408** | A42 2f red & bl green | .30 | .25 |
| **409** | A42 3f red & dk blue | .30 | .25 |
| **410** | A42 4f red & dk green | .30 | .25 |
| **411** | A42 5f red & dk brown | .30 | .25 |
| **412** | A42 85f red & dp green | 1.10 | .95 |

**Design: Red Cross at right, no portrait**

| | | | |
|---|---|---|---|
| **413** | A42 1f red lilac & red | .30 | .25 |
| **414** | A42 2f blue grn & red | .30 | .25 |
| **415** | A42 3f dk blue & red | .30 | .25 |
| **416** | A42 4f dk green & red | .30 | .25 |
| **417** | A42 5f dk brown & red | .30 | .25 |
| **418** | A42 85f dp green & red | 4.00 | 1.50 |
| | *Nos. 407-418 (12)* | 8.10 | 4.95 |

Centenary of the Intl. Red Cross. Two 100f imperf. souvenir sheets, red and red lilac, exist in the Red Crescent and Red Cross designs. Value, pair of sheets $50.

Hussein ibn Ali and King Hussein A43

***Perf. 11x11½***

**1963, Dec. 25 Litho. Unwmk.**

| | | | |
|---|---|---|---|
| **419** | A43 15f yellow & multi | .50 | .25 |
| **420** | A43 25f multicolored | .75 | .35 |
| **421** | A43 35f brt pink & multi | 1.75 | .85 |
| **422** | A43 50f lt blue & multi | 2.75 | 2.00 |
| | *Nos. 419-422 (4)* | 5.75 | 3.45 |

Arab Renaissance Day, June 10, 1916. Perf. and imperf. souvenir sheets exist containing one each of Nos. 419-422. Value: perf, $6.50; imperf, $9.

Nos. 359, 312, 357 and 361 Surcharged

**Wmk. 305, Unwmk.**

***Perf. 12x11½, 12½***

**1963, Dec. 16 Engr.**

| | | | |
|---|---|---|---|
| **423** | A27 1f on 21f grn & blk | .40 | .30 |
| **424** | A27 2f on 21f grn & blk | .40 | .30 |
| **425** | A23 4f on 12f car rose & sepia | .45 | .40 |
| *a.* | 4f on 12f dp car & blk (#357) | 19.00 | 22.50 |
| **426** | A27 5f on 21f grn & blk | .85 | .50 |
| **427** | A27 25f on 35f dk bl & blk | 3.25 | 1.50 |
| | *Nos. 423-427 (5)* | 5.35 | 3.00 |

Pope Paul VI, King Hussein and Al Aqsa Mosque, Jerusalem — A44

Portraits and: 35f, Dome of the Rock. 50f, Church of the Holy Sepulcher. 80f, Church of the Nativity, Bethlehem.

**1964, Jan. 4 Litho.** ***Perf. 13x13½***

| | | | |
|---|---|---|---|
| **428** | A44 15f emerald & blk | .80 | .30 |
| **429** | A44 35f car rose & blk | 1.00 | .40 |
| *a.* | Black omitted | — | |
| **430** | A44 50f brown & black | 1.75 | .90 |
| **431** | A44 80f vio bl & blk | 3.25 | 2.00 |
| | *Nos. 428-431 (4)* | 6.80 | 3.60 |

Visit of Pope Paul VI to the Holy Land, Jan. 4-6. An imperf. souvenir sheet contains 4 stamps similar to Nos. 428-431. Value $27.50

A45

Crown Prince Abdullah ben Al-Hussein — A46

Design: 5f, Crown Prince standing, vert.

**1964, Mar. 30 Photo.** ***Perf. 14***

| | | | |
|---|---|---|---|
| **432** | A46 5f multicolored | .55 | .25 |
| **433** | A45 10f multicolored | .65 | .50 |
| **434** | A46 35f multicolored | 1.50 | 1.00 |
| | *Nos. 432-434 (3)* | 2.70 | 1.75 |

2nd birthday of Crown Prince Abdullah ben Al-Hussein (b. Jan. 30, 1962).

Nos. 433 and 434 exist with gold color omitted.

A47

Mercury Astronauts, Spacecraft — A48

Designs: b, M. Scott Carpenter. c, Entering space. d, Alan Shepard. e, At launch pad. f, Virgil Grissom. g, After separation. h, Walter Schirra. i, Lift-off. j, John Glenn. Stamp has point down on b, d, f, h, j.

**1964, Mar. 25 Photo.** ***Perf. 14***

| | | | |
|---|---|---|---|
| **435** | A47 20f Block of 10, #a.-j. | 12.00 | 6.50 |

***Imperf***

**Size: 111x80mm**

| | | | |
|---|---|---|---|
| **436** | A48 100f multicolored | 20.00 | 20.00 |

Table Tennis A49

Designs: 1f, 2f, 3f, 5f vertical.

***Perf. 14½x14, 14x14½***

**1964, June 1 Litho. Unwmk.**

| | | | |
|---|---|---|---|
| **446** | A49 1f Basketball | .50 | .25 |
| **447** | A49 2f Volleyball | .50 | .25 |
| **448** | A49 3f Soccer | .50 | .25 |
| **449** | A49 4f shown | .50 | .25 |
| **450** | A49 5f Running | .50 | .25 |
| **451** | A49 35f Bicycling | 1.75 | 1.10 |
| **452** | A49 50f Fencing | 2.50 | 1.50 |
| **453** | A49 100f Pole vault | 4.50 | 2.75 |
| | *Nos. 446-453 (8)* | 11.25 | 6.60 |

1964 Olympic Games, Tokyo, Oct. 10-25. An imperf. 200f greenish blue souvenir sheet in design of 100f exists. Value $35.

Mother and Child — A50

**1964, June 1 Wmk. 305** ***Perf. 14***

| | | | |
|---|---|---|---|
| **454** | A50 5f multicolored | .30 | .25 |
| **455** | A50 10f multicolored | .30 | .25 |
| **456** | A50 25f multicolored | .30 | .25 |
| | *Nos. 454-456 (3)* | .90 | .75 |

Social Studies Seminar, fourth session.

Pres. John F. Kennedy — A51

**1964, July 15 Unwmk.**

| | | | |
|---|---|---|---|
| **457** | A51 1f brt violet | .50 | .40 |
| **458** | A51 2f carmine rose | .50 | .40 |
| **459** | A51 3f ultramarine | .50 | .40 |
| **460** | A51 4f orange brown | .50 | .40 |
| **461** | A51 5f bright green | .50 | .40 |
| **462** | A51 85f rose red | 18.50 | 11.00 |
| | *Nos. 457-462 (6)* | 21.00 | 13.00 |

President John F. Kennedy (1917-1963). An imperf. 100f brown souvenir sheet exists. Size of stamp: 58x83mm. Value $18.50.

Ramses II
A52

*Perf. 14½x14*

**1964, July Litho. Wmk. 305**

| | | | | |
|---|---|---|---|---|
| **463** | A52 | 4f lt blue & dark brn | .30 | .25 |
| **464** | A52 | 15f yellow & violet | .30 | .25 |
| **465** | A52 | 25f lt yel grn & dk red | .30 | .25 |
| | | *Nos. 463-465 (3)* | .90 | .75 |

UNESCO world campaign to save historic monuments in Nubia.

King Hussein and Map of Jordan and Israel — A53

**1964, Sept. 5 Unwmk. *Perf. 12***

| | | | | |
|---|---|---|---|---|
| **466** | A53 | 10f multicolored | .40 | .25 |
| **467** | A53 | 15f multicolored | .40 | .25 |
| **468** | A53 | 25f multicolored | .40 | .25 |
| **469** | A53 | 50f multicolored | .70 | .25 |
| **470** | A53 | 80f multicolored | 1.00 | .45 |
| | | *Nos. 466-470 (5)* | 2.90 | 1.45 |

Council of the Heads of State of the Arab League (Arab Summit Conference), Cairo, Jan. 13, 1964. An imperf. souvenir sheet contains Nos. 466-470 with simulated perforations. Value $4.

Pope Paul VI, King Hussein and Patriarch Athenagoras; Church of St. Savior, Church of the Holy Sepulcher and Dome of the Rock — A54

**1964, Aug. 17 Litho.**

| | | | | |
|---|---|---|---|---|
| **471** | A54 | 10f dk grn, sep & org | .50 | .25 |
| **472** | A54 | 15f claret, sep & org | .50 | .25 |
| **473** | A54 | 25f choc, sepia & org | .50 | .25 |
| **474** | A54 | 50f blue, sepia & org | 1.00 | .70 |
| **475** | A54 | 80f brt grn, sep & org | 2.25 | .60 |
| | | *Nos. 471-475 (5)* | 4.75 | 2.05 |

Meeting between Pope Paul VI and Patriarch Athenagoras of the Greek Orthodox Church in Jerusalem, Jan. 5, 1964. An imperf. souvenir sheet contains Nos. 471-475 with simulated perforations. Value $12.

A two-line bilingual overprint, "Papa Paulus VI World Peace Visit to United Nations 1965", was applied to Nos. 471-475 and the souvenir sheet. These overprints were issued Apr. 27, 1966. Value, unused: set, $6; souvenir sheet, $12.

Pagoda, Olympic Torch and Emblem — A55

**1964, Nov. 21 Litho. *Perf. 14***

| | | | | |
|---|---|---|---|---|
| **476** | A55 | 1f dark red | .45 | .25 |
| **477** | A55 | 2f bright violet | .55 | .25 |
| **478** | A55 | 3f blue green | .65 | .25 |
| **479** | A55 | 4f brown | .75 | .30 |
| **480** | A55 | 5f henna brown | .85 | .35 |
| **481** | A55 | 35f indigo | 1.25 | 1.00 |
| **482** | A55 | 50f olive | 2.00 | 1.50 |
| **483** | A55 | 100f violet blue | 4.25 | 3.00 |
| | | *Nos. 476-483 (8)* | 10.75 | 6.90 |

18th Olympic Games, Tokyo, Oct. 10-25. An imperf. 100f carmine rose souvenir sheet exists. Size of stamp: 82mm at the base. Value $20.

Scouts Crossing Stream on Log Bridge — A56

Designs: 2f, First aid. 3f, Calisthenics. 4f, Instruction in knot tying. 5f, Outdoor cooking. 35f, Sailing. 50f, Campfire.

**1964, Dec. 7 Unwmk.**

| | | | | |
|---|---|---|---|---|
| **484** | A56 | 1f brown | .70 | .25 |
| **485** | A56 | 2f bright violet | .70 | .25 |
| **486** | A56 | 3f ocher | .70 | .25 |
| **487** | A56 | 4f maroon | .70 | .25 |
| **488** | A56 | 5f yellow green | .70 | .25 |
| **489** | A56 | 35f bright blue | 2.00 | 1.25 |
| **490** | A56 | 50f dk slate green | 3.50 | 1.75 |
| | | *Nos. 484-490 (7)* | 9.00 | 4.25 |

Jordanian Boy Scouts. An imperf. 100f dark blue souvenir sheet in campfire design exists. Size of stamp: 104mm at the base. Value $22.50.

Russian Cosmonauts — A57

Designs: No. 491, Yuri Gagarin. No. 492, Gherman Titov. No. 493, Andrian G. Nikolayev. No. 494, Pavel R. Popovich. No. 495, Valeri Bykovski. No. 496, Valentina Tereshkova.

**1965, Jan. 20 Litho. *Perf. 14***

| | | | | |
|---|---|---|---|---|
| **491** | A57 | 40f sepia & vio bl | 1.25 | .75 |
| **492** | A57 | 40f pink & dk grn | 1.25 | .75 |
| **493** | A57 | 40f lt bl & vio blk | 1.25 | .75 |
| **494** | A57 | 40f olive & dk vio | 1.25 | .75 |
| **495** | A57 | 40f lt grn & red brn | 1.25 | .75 |
| **496** | A57 | 40f chlky bl & blk | 1.25 | .75 |
| | | *Nos. 491-496 (6)* | 7.50 | 4.50 |

Russian cosmonauts. A blue 100f souvenir sheet exists showing portraits of the 6 astronauts and space-ship circling globe. This sheet received later an additional overprint honoring the space flight of Komarov, Feoktistov and Yegorov. Value $20, each.

For overprints see Nos. 527-527E.

UN Headquarters and Emblem — A58

**1965, Feb. 15 *Perf. 14x15***

| | | | | |
|---|---|---|---|---|
| **497** | A58 | 30f yel brn, pur & lt bl | .60 | .25 |
| **498** | A58 | 70f vio, lt bl & yel brn | 1.00 | .70 |

19th anniv. of the UN (in 1964). A souvenir sheet contains Nos. 497-498, imperf. Value $14.

Dagger in Map of Palestine — A59

**1965, Apr. 9 Photo. *Perf. 11x11½***

| | | | | |
|---|---|---|---|---|
| **499** | A59 | 25f red & olive | 4.50 | 1.25 |
| *a.* | | Red omitted | — | |

Deir Yassin massacre, Apr. 9, 1948.

See Iraq Nos. 372-373 and Kuwait Nos. 281-282.

Volleyball Player and Cup — A60

**1965, June Litho. *Perf. 14½x14***

| | | | | |
|---|---|---|---|---|
| **500** | A60 | 15f lemon | 1.25 | .25 |
| **501** | A60 | 35f rose brown | 1.50 | .25 |
| **502** | A60 | 50f greenish blue | 2.25 | .75 |
| | | *Nos. 500-502 (3)* | 5.00 | 1.25 |

Arab Volleyball Championships. An imperf. 100f orange brown souvenir sheet exists. Size of stamp: 33x57mm. Value $22.50.

Cavalry Horsemanship A61

Army Day: 10f, Tank. 35f, King Hussein and aides standing in army car.

**1965, May 24**

| | | | | |
|---|---|---|---|---|
| **503** | A61 | 5f green | .50 | .25 |
| **504** | A61 | 10f violet blue | .55 | .25 |
| **505** | A61 | 35f brown red | 1.50 | .55 |
| | | *Nos. 503-505 (3)* | 2.55 | 1.05 |

John F. Kennedy — A62

**1965, June 1 Wmk. 305 *Perf. 14***

| | | | | |
|---|---|---|---|---|
| **506** | A62 | 10f black & brt green | .30 | .25 |
| **507** | A62 | 15f violet & orange | .50 | .25 |
| **508** | A62 | 25f brown & lt blue | .50 | .30 |
| **509** | A62 | 50f deep claret & emer | 1.50 | .60 |
| | | *Nos. 506-509 (4)* | 2.80 | 1.40 |

John F. Kennedy (1917-63). An imperf. 50f salmon and dark blue souv. sheet exists. Value $17.50.

Pope Paul VI, King Hussein and Dome of the Rock — A63

*Perf. 13½x14*

**1965, June 15 Litho. Wmk. 305**

| | | | | |
|---|---|---|---|---|
| **510** | A63 | 5f brown & rose lil | .50 | .25 |
| **511** | A63 | 10f vio brn & lt yel grn | .90 | .40 |
| **512** | A63 | 15f ultra & salmon | 1.10 | .50 |
| **513** | A63 | 50f black & rose | 3.25 | 1.60 |
| | | *Nos. 510-513 (4)* | 5.75 | 2.75 |

1st anniversary of the visit of Pope Paul VI to the Holy Land. An imperf. 50f violet and light blue souvenir sheet exists with simulated perforations. Value $25.

Jordan's Pavilion and Unisphere — A64

*Perf. 14x13½*

**1965, Aug. Unwmk. Photo.**

| | | | | |
|---|---|---|---|---|
| **514** | A64 | 15f silver & multi | .45 | .25 |
| **515** | A64 | 25f bronze & multi | .45 | .25 |
| **516** | A64 | 50f gold & multi | .85 | .40 |
| *a.* | | Souvenir sheet of 1, 100f | 3.25 | 3.00 |
| | | *Nos. 514-516 (3)* | 1.75 | .90 |

New York World's Fair, 1964-65.

No. 516a contains a 100f gold and multicolored stamp, type A64, imperf.

Library Aflame and Lamp A64a

**1965, Aug. Wmk. 305 *Perf. 11½x11***

| | | | | |
|---|---|---|---|---|
| **517** | A64a | 25f black, grn & red | .50 | .25 |

Burning of the Library of Algiers, 6/7/62.

ITU Emblem, Old and New Telecommunication Equipment — A65

**1965, Aug. Litho. *Perf. 14x13½***

| | | | | |
|---|---|---|---|---|
| **518** | A65 | 25f lt blue & dk bl | .40 | .25 |
| **519** | A65 | 45f grnsh gray & blk | .60 | .35 |

ITU, centenary. An imperf. 100f salmon and carmine rose souvenir sheet exists with carmine rose border. Size of stamp: 39x32mm. Value $3.

Syncom Satellite over Pagoda — A66

Designs: 10f, 20f, Rocket in space. 15f, Astronauts in cabin.

**1965, Sept. *Perf. 14***

| | | | | |
|---|---|---|---|---|
| **521** | A66 | 5f multicolored | .30 | .25 |
| **521A** | A66 | 10f multicolored | .30 | .25 |
| **521B** | A66 | 15f multicolored | .50 | .25 |

| | | | | | |
|---|---|---|---|---|---|
| 521C | A66 | 20f | multicolored | .60 | .30 |
| 521D | A66 | 50f | multicolored | 1.50 | .75 |
| | | | *Nos. 521-521D (5)* | 3.20 | 1.80 |

Achievements in space research. A 50f multicolored imperf. souvenir sheet shows earth and Syncom satellite. Value $17.50.

Dead Sea A66a

Designs: b, Qumran Caves. c, Dead Sea. d, Dead Sea Scrolls.

**1965, Sept. 23 Photo. *Perf. 14***

| | | | | |
|---|---|---|---|---|
| 522 | A66a | 35f Strip of 4, #a.-d. | 6.00 | 6.00 |

Visit of King Hussein to France and U.S. — A66b

10f, With Charles DeGaulle. 20f, With Lyndon Johnson.

**Wmk. 305**

**1965, Oct. 5 Litho. *Perf. 14***

| | | | | | |
|---|---|---|---|---|---|
| 523 | A66b | 5f | shown | .30 | .25 |
| 523A | A66b | 10f | multicolored | .30 | .25 |
| 523B | A66b | 20f | multicolored | .65 | .50 |
| 523C | A66b | 50f | like #523 | 1.50 | 1.10 |
| | | | *Nos. 523-523C (4)* | 2.75 | 2.10 |

No. 523C exists in a 50f imperf. souvenir sheet. Value $12.

Intl. Cooperation Year — A66c

**1965, Oct. 24 *Perf. 14x13½***

| | | | | | |
|---|---|---|---|---|---|
| 524 | A66c | 5f | brt org & dk org | .40 | .25 |
| 524A | A66c | 10f | brt bl & dk bl | .75 | .35 |
| 524B | A66c | 45f | brt grn & dk violet | 2.10 | 1.40 |
| | | | *Nos. 524-524B (3)* | 3.25 | 2.00 |

Arab Postal Union, 10th Anniv. — A66d

**1965, Nov. 5 *Perf. 15x14***

| | | | | | |
|---|---|---|---|---|---|
| 525 | A66d | 15f | violet bl & blk | .30 | .25 |
| 525A | A66d | 25f | brt yel grn & blk | .50 | .35 |

Dome of the Rock A66e

**1965, Nov. 20 *Perf. 14x15***

| | | | | | |
|---|---|---|---|---|---|
| 526 | A66e | 15f | multicolored | 1.10 | 1.10 |
| 526A | A66e | 25f | multicolored | 1.60 | 1.60 |

**Nos. 491-496 with Spaceship & Bilingual Ovpt. in Blue**

**1966, Jan. 15 Litho. *Perf. 14***

| | | | | | |
|---|---|---|---|---|---|
| 527 | A57 | 40f | on No. 491 | 3.75 | 3.50 |
| 527A | A57 | 40f | on No. 492 | 3.75 | 3.50 |
| 527B | A57 | 40f | on No. 493 | 3.75 | 3.50 |
| 527C | A57 | 40f | on No. 494 | 3.75 | 3.50 |
| 527D | A57 | 40f | on No. 495 | 3.75 | 3.50 |
| 527E | A57 | 40f | on No. 496 | 3.75 | 3.50 |
| | | | *Nos. 527-527E (6)* | 22.50 | 21.00 |

Both souvenir sheets mentioned after No. 496 exist overprinted in red violet. Value, $50 each.

King Hussein A67

***Perf. 14½x14***

**1966, Jan. 15 Photo. Unwmk.**

**Portrait in Slate Blue**

| | | | | | |
|---|---|---|---|---|---|
| 528 | A67 | 1f | orange | .40 | .25 |
| 528A | A67 | 2f | ultramarine | .40 | .25 |
| 528B | A67 | 3f | dk purple | .40 | .25 |
| 528C | A67 | 4f | plum | .40 | .25 |
| 528D | A67 | 7f | brn orange | .40 | .25 |
| 528E | A67 | 12f | cerise | .40 | .25 |
| 528F | A67 | 15f | olive brn | .40 | .25 |

**Portrait in Violet Brown**

| | | | | | |
|---|---|---|---|---|---|
| 528G | A67 | 21f | green | .55 | .25 |
| 528H | A67 | 25f | greenish bl | .55 | .25 |
| 528I | A67 | 35f | yel bister | .80 | .35 |
| 528J | A67 | 40f | orange yel | 1.00 | .35 |
| 528K | A67 | 50f | olive grn | 1.10 | .25 |
| 528L | A67 | 100f | lt yel grn | 2.10 | .40 |
| 528M | A67 | 150f | violet | 3.00 | 1.00 |
| | | | *Nos. 528-528M,C43-C45 (17)* | 46.90 | 27.10 |

Anti-tuberculosis Campaign — A67a

**1966, May 17 Photo. *Perf. 14x15***

**Blue Overprint**

| | | | | | |
|---|---|---|---|---|---|
| 529 | A67a | 15f | multicolored | .65 | .50 |
| 529A | A67a | 35f | multicolored | 1.10 | .95 |
| 529B | A67a | 50f | multicolored | 1.50 | 1.25 |
| | | | *Nos. 529-529B (3)* | 3.25 | 2.70 |

Unissued Freedom from Hunger stamps overprinted. Two imperf. souvenir sheets exist, one with simulated perforations. Value, each $10.

**Nos. 529-529B with Added Surcharge Obliterated with Black Bars**

**1966, May 17 Photo. *Perf. 14x15***

| | | | | |
|---|---|---|---|---|
| 530 | A67a | 15f on 15f + 15f | .75 | .30 |
| 530A | A67a | 35f on 35f + 35f | 1.50 | .75 |
| 530B | A67a | 50f on 50f + 50f | 2.75 | 1.25 |
| | | *Nos. 530-530B (3)* | 5.00 | 2.30 |

A67b

Stations on Jesus' walk to Calvary along Via Dolorosa (Stations of the Cross): 1f, Condemned to death. 2f, Takes up cross. 3f, Falls the 1st time. 4f, Meets His mother. 5f, Simon helps carry cross. 6f, Woman wipes Jesus' brow. 7f, Falls 2nd time. 8f, Tells women not to weep. 9f, Falls 3rd time. 10f, Stripped of His garment. 11f, Nailed to cross. 12f, Death on cross. 13f, Removal from cross. 14f, Burial.

Denominations expressed in Roman numerals.

**1966, Sept. 14 Photo. *Perf. 15x14***

| | | | | | |
|---|---|---|---|---|---|
| 531 | A67b | 1f | multi | .40 | .25 |
| 531A | A67b | 2f | multi | .40 | .25 |
| 531B | A67b | 3f | multi | .40 | .25 |
| 531C | A67b | 4f | multi | .50 | .25 |
| 531D | A67b | 5f | multi | .60 | .30 |
| 531E | A67b | 6f | multi | .60 | .30 |
| 531F | A67b | 7f | multi | .80 | .40 |
| 531G | A67b | 8f | multi | .90 | .45 |
| 531H | A67b | 9f | multi | 1.00 | .50 |
| 531I | A67b | 10f | multi | 1.10 | .55 |
| 531J | A67b | 11f | multi | 1.25 | .60 |
| 531K | A67b | 12f | multi | 1.40 | .65 |
| 531L | A67b | 13f | multi | 1.50 | .70 |
| 531M | A67b | 14f | multi | 1.60 | .75 |
| | | | *Nos. 531-531M (14)* | 12.45 | 6.20 |

**Souvenir Sheet**

***Imperf***

| | | | | |
|---|---|---|---|---|
| 531N | A67b | 100f like #531 | *30.00* | *27.50* |

A67c

Astronauts and spacecraft from Gemini Missions 6-8: 1f, Walter M. Schirra. 2f, Thomas P. Stafford. 3f, Frank Borman. 4f, James A. Lovell. 30f, Neil Armstrong. 60f, David R. Scott.

100f, Gemini 6-8 astronauts.

**1966, Nov. 15 Photo. *Perf. 15x14***

| | | | | | |
|---|---|---|---|---|---|
| 532 | A67c | 1f | multi | .35 | .25 |
| 532A | A67c | 2f | multi | .35 | .25 |
| 532B | A67c | 3f | multi | .35 | .25 |
| 532C | A67c | 4f | multi | .35 | .25 |
| 532D | A67c | 30f | multi | 1.50 | .70 |
| 532E | A67c | 60f | multi | 2.10 | 1.50 |
| | | | *Nos. 532-532E (6)* | 5.00 | 3.20 |

***Imperf***

**Size: 119x89mm**

| | | | | |
|---|---|---|---|---|
| 532F | A67c | 100f multi | *22.50* | *20.00* |

Christmas — A67d

5f, Magi following star. 10f, Adoration of the Magi. 35f, Flight to Egypt, vert.

***Perf. 14x15, 15x14***

**1966, Dec. 21 Photo.**

| | | | | | |
|---|---|---|---|---|---|
| 533 | A67d | 5f | multi | .35 | .25 |
| 533A | A67d | 10f | multi | .35 | .25 |
| 533B | A67d | 35f | multi | 3.25 | 1.10 |
| | | | *Nos. 533-533B (3)* | 3.95 | 1.60 |

**Souvenir Sheet**

***Imperf***

| | | | | |
|---|---|---|---|---|
| 533C | A67d | 50f like #533A | *22.50* | *20.00* |

King Hussein — A67e

Builders of World Peace: No. 534, Dag Hammarskjold. No. 534A, U Thant. No. 534B, Jawaharlal Nehru. No. 534C, Charles DeGaulle. No. 534D, John F. Kennedy. No. 534E, Lyndon B. Johnson. No. 534F, Pope John XXIII. No. 534G, Pope Paul VI. No. 534H, King Abdullah of Jordan.

**1967, Jan. 5 Photo. *Perf. 15x14***

**Background Color**

| | | | | | |
|---|---|---|---|---|---|
| 534 | A67e | 5f | gray | .35 | .25 |
| 534A | A67e | 5f | brt yel grn | .35 | .25 |
| 534B | A67e | 10f | rose lilac | .35 | .25 |
| *a.* | | | "FILS" omitted | — | |
| 534C | A67e | 10f | red brown | .35 | .25 |
| 534D | A67e | 35f | olive green | .95 | .70 |
| 534E | A67e | 35f | orange | .95 | .70 |
| *a.* | | | Gold (frame) omitted | — | |
| 534F | A67e | 50f | rose claret | 1.10 | 1.00 |
| 534G | A67e | 50f | yel bister | 1.10 | 1.00 |
| 534H | A67e | 100f | brt blue | 2.50 | 2.10 |
| 534I | A67e | 100f | dull blue | 2.50 | 2.10 |
| | | | *Nos. 534-534I (10)* | 10.50 | 8.60 |

***Imperf***

**Size: 99x64mm**

| | | | | |
|---|---|---|---|---|
| 534J | A67e | 100f Kennedy, etc. | *22.50* | *22.50* |
| 534K | A67e | 100f DeGaulle, etc. | *22.50* | *22.50* |

King Hussein A67f

**Photo. & Embossed**

**1967, Feb. 7 *Imperf.***

**Gold Portrait and Border**

**Diameter: 50f, 100f, 48mm; 200f, 54mm**

**Portrait of King Hussein**

| | | | | | |
|---|---|---|---|---|---|
| 535 | A67f | 5f | dk bl & sal | .75 | .75 |
| 535A | A67f | 10f | pur & sal | .75 | .75 |
| 535B | A67f | 50f | blk brn & vio | 4.25 | 4.25 |
| 535C | A67f | 100f | dk ol grn & pink | 5.00 | 5.00 |
| 535D | A67f | 200f | dp bl & bl | 7.75 | 7.75 |

**Portrait of Crown Prince Hassan**

| | | | | | |
|---|---|---|---|---|---|
| 536 | A67f | 5f | brt yel grn & blk | .75 | .75 |
| 536A | A67f | 10f | vio & blk | .75 | .75 |
| 536B | A67f | 50f | bl & blk | 4.25 | 4.25 |
| 536C | A67f | 100f | bister & blk | 5.00 | 5.00 |
| 536D | A67f | 200f | brt pink & blk | 7.75 | 7.75 |

### Portrait of John F. Kennedy

**537** A67f 5f brt bl & lt grn .75 .75
**537A** A67f 10f dp grn & pink .75 .75
**537B** A67f 50f brt rose & org yel 3.25 3.25
**537C** A67f 100f brn & app grn 4.25 4.25
**537D** A67f 200f dk pur & pale grn 5.00 5.00
*Nos. 535-537D (15)* 51.00 51.00

1968 Summer Olympic Games, Mexico — A67g

Olympic torch and: 1f, Natl. University Library with O'Gormans mosaics, statue, Mexico City. 2f, Fishermen on Lake Patzcuaro. 3f, Natl. University buildings. 4f, Paseo de la Reforma, Mexico City. 30f, Guadalajara Cathedral. 60f, 100f, Palace of Fine Arts, Mexico City.

***Perf. 14x15***

**1967, Mar. Photo. Unwmk.**
**538** A67g 1f lake, dk bl vio & blk .30 .25
**538A** A67g 2f blk, lake & dk bl vio .30 .25
**538B** A67g 3f dark bl vio, blk & lake .30 .25
**538C** A67g 4f bl, grn & brn .30 .25
**538D** A67g 30f grn, brn & bl .60 .60
**538E** A67g 60f brn, bl & grn 1.10 1.10
*Nos. 538-538E (6)* 2.90 2.70

**Souvenir Sheet**

***Imperf***

**538F** A67g 100f brn, dark bl & grn 22.50 22.50

Symbolic Water Cycle A68

***Perf. 14½x14***

**1967, Mar. 1 Litho. Wmk. 305**
**539** A68 10f dp org, blk & gray .50 .25
**540** A68 15f grnsh bl, blk & gray .50 .35
**541** A68 25f brt rose lil, blk & gray .75 .50
*Nos. 539-541 (3)* 1.75 1.10

Hydrological Decade (UNESCO), 1965-74.

UNESCO Emblem — A69

**1967, Mar. 16**
**542** A69 100f multicolored 1.10 1.10

20th anniv. of UNESCO.

Dromedary — A70

Animals: 2f, Karakul. 3f, Angora goat.

***Perf. 14x15***

**1967, Feb. 11 Photo. Unwmk.**
**543** A70 1f dark brn & multi 1.10 .25
**544** A70 2f yellow & multi 1.10 .25
**545** A70 3f lt blue & multi 1.10 .25
*Nos. 543-545,C46-C48 (6)* 12.30 3.15

A souvenir sheet exists with a 100f in design and colors of No. C47, simulated perforation and marginal animal design. Value $35.

Inauguration of WHO Headquarters, Geneva — A71

**1967, Apr. 7 Wmk. 305**
**546** A71 5f emerald & blk .40 .25
**547** A71 45f dl orange & blk .50 .30

Arab League Emblem and Hands Reaching for Knowledge — A72

**1968, May 5 Unwmk. *Perf. 11***
**548** A72 20f org & slate grn .45 .25
**549** A72 20f brt pink & dk bl .45 .25

Issued to publicize the literacy campaign.

"20" and WHO Emblem A73

***Perf. 14½x14***

**1968, Aug. 10 Wmk. 305**
**550** A73 30f multicolored .60 .25
**551** A73 100f multicolored 1.75 1.10

20th anniv. of the WHO.

European Goldfinch — A74

Protected Game: 10f, Rock partridge, vert. 15f, Ostriches, vert. 20f, Sand partridge. 30f, Dorcas gazelle. 40f, Oryxes. 50f, Houbara bustard.

**1968, Oct. 5 Unwmk. *Perf. 13½***
**552** A74 5f multicolored 3.25 1.25
**553** A74 10f multicolored 6.50 1.25
**554** A74 15f multicolored 8.50 1.50
**555** A74 20f multicolored 8.50 1.75
**556** A74 30f multicolored 5.25 1.25
**557** A74 40f multicolored 8.00 1.50
**558** A74 50f multicolored 12.50 3.00
*Nos. 552-558,C49-C50 (9)* 77.00 25.50

Human Rights Flame — A75

**1968, Dec. 10 Litho. *Perf. 13***
**559** A75 20f dp org, lt org & blk .40 .25
**560** A75 60f grn, lt blue & blk .75 .45

International Human Rights Year.

Dome of the Rock, Jerusalem A76

5f, 45f, Holy Kaaba, Mecca, & Dome of the Rock.

**1969, Oct. 8 Photo. *Perf. 12***

**Size: 56x25mm**

**561** A76 5f dull vio & multi .80 .25

**Size: 36x25mm**

**562** A76 10f vio blue & multi .80 .50
**563** A76 20f Prus bl & multi 1.25 .60

**Size: 56x25mm**

**564** A76 45f Prus bl & multi 2.10 .70
*Nos. 561-564 (4)* 4.95 2.05

ILO Emblem A77

**1969, June 10 *Perf. 13½x14***
**565** A77 10f blue & black .35 .25
**566** A77 20f bister brn & blk .35 .25
**567** A77 25f lt olive & black .35 .25
**568** A77 45f lil rose & black .50 .30
**569** A77 60f orange & black .75 .35
*Nos. 565-569 (5)* 2.30 1.40

ILO, 50th anniversary.

Horses A78

20f, White stallion. 45f, Mare and foal.

**1969, July 6 Unwmk. *Perf. 13½***
**570** A78 10f dark bl & multi 1.50 .25
**571** A78 20f dl green & multi 3.50 .60
**572** A78 45f red & multi 6.50 1.75
*Nos. 570-572 (3)* 11.50 2.60

Prince Hassan and Princess Tharwat A79

Designs: 60f, 100f, Prince Hassan and bride in western bridal gown.

**1969, Dec. 2 Photo. *Perf. 12½***
**573** A79 20f gold & multi .50 .25
**573A** A79 60f gold & multi 1.00 .65
**573B** A79 100f gold & multi 1.50 1.25
*c.* Strip of 3, #573-573B 3.25 3.25

Wedding of Crown Prince Hassan, 11/14/68.

The Tragedy and the Flight of the Refugees — A79a

Different design on each stamp. Each strip of 5 has five consecutive denominations.

***Perf. 14½x13½***

**1969, Dec. 10 Photo.**
**574** A79a 1f-5f Strip of 5 11.00 11.00
*f.-j.* 1f-5f Any single
**574A** A79a 6f-10f Strip of 5 11.00 11.00
*a.-e.* 6f-10f Any single
**574B** A79a 11f-15f Strip of 5 11.00 11.00
*a.-e.* 11f-15f Any single
**574C** A79a 16f-20f Strip of 5 11.00 11.00
*a.-e.* 16f-20f Any single
**574D** A79a 21f-25f Strip of 5 11.00 11.00
*a.-e.* 21f-25f Any single
**574E** A79a 26f-30f Strip of 5 11.00 11.00
*a.-e.* 26f-30f Any single

For surcharges see Nos. 870-875.

### Inscribed: Tragedy in the Holy Lands

Different design on each stamp. Each strip of 5 has five consecutive denominations.

***Perf. 14½x13½***

**1969, Dec. 10 Photo.**
**575** A79a 1f-5f Strip of 5 5.00 5.00
*f.-j.* 1f-5f Any single
**575A** A79a 6f-10f Strip of 5 5.00 5.00
*a.-e.* 6f-10f Any single
**575B** A79a 11f-15f Strip of 5 5.00 5.00
*a.-e.* 11f-15f Any single
**575C** A79a 16f-20f Strip of 5 5.00 5.00
*a.-e.* 16f-20f Any single
**575D** A79a 21f-25f Strip of 5 5.00 5.00
*a.-e.* 21f-25f Any single
**575E** A79a 26f-30f Strip of 5 5.00 5.00
*a.-e.* 26f-30f Any single

For surcharges see Nos. 876-881.

Pomegranate Flower (inscribed "Desert Scabius") — A80

Oranges — A81

Black Bush Robin — A82

Designs: 15f, Wattle flower ("Caper"). 20f, Melon. 25f, Caper flower ("Pomegranate"). 30f, Lemons. 35f, Morning glory. 40f, Grapes. 45f, Desert scabius ("Wattle"). 50f, Olive-laden branch. 75f, Black iris. 100f, Apples. 180f, Masked shrike. 200f, Palestine sunbird. (Inscriptions incorrect on 5f, 15f, 25f and 45f.)

***Perf. 14x13½ (flowers), 12 (fruit), 13½x14 (birds)***

**1969-70 Photo.**
**576** A80 5f yel & multi ('70) .40 .25
**577** A81 10f blue & multi .40 .25
**578** A80 15f tan & multi ('70) .70 .25
**579** A81 20f sepia & multi .60 .25
**580** A80 25f multi ('70) 1.00 .25
**581** A81 30f vio bl & multi 1.00 .25
**582** A80 35f multi ('70) 1.50 .25
**583** A81 40f dull yel & multi 1.50 .25
**584** A80 45f gray & multi ('70) 2.00 .25
**585** A81 50f car rose & multi 2.00 .40
**586** A80 75f multi ('70) 3.00 1.00
**587** A81 100f dk gray & multi 3.25 1.25
**588** A82 120f org & multi ('70) 10.00 2.00
**589** A82 180f multi ('70) 17.50 4.75
**590** A82 200f multi ('70) 20.00 7.00
*Nos. 576-590 (15)* 64.85 18.65

Issued: Fruits, 11/22; flowers, 3/21; birds, 9/1.

Soccer A83

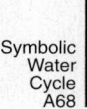

Designs: 10f, Diver. 15f, Boxers. 50f, Runner. 100f, Bicyclist, vert. 150f, Basketball, vert.

**1970, Aug.** ***Perf. 13½x14, 14x13½***

**651** A83 5f green & multi 1.00 .25
**652** A83 10f lt bl & multi 1.00 .25
**653** A83 15f gray & multi 1.00 .25
**654** A83 50f gray & multi 1.50 .65
**655** A83 100f yellow & multi 2.25 1.25
**656** A83 150f multicolored 3.25 2.25
*Nos. 651-656 (6)* 10.00 4.90

Refugee Children A84

Emblems and: 10F, Boy Fetching Water, UNICEF and Refugee Emblems. 15f, Girl and tents. 20f, Boy in front of tent.

**1970, Aug.**

**657** A84 5f multicolored .30 .25
**658** A84 10f multicolored .40 .25
**659** A84 15f multicolored .50 .25
**660** A84 20f multicolored .70 .25
*Nos. 657-660 (4)* 1.90 1.00

Issued for Childhood Day.

Nativity Grotto, Bethlehem A85

Church of the Nativity, Bethlehem: 10f, Manger. 20f, Altar. 25f, Interior.

**1970, Dec. 25** **Photo.** ***Perf. 13½***

**661** A85 5f blue & multi .45 .25
**662** A85 10f scarlet & multi .45 .25
**663** A85 20f rose lilac & multi .80 .30
**664** A85 25f green & multi 1.00 .35
*Nos. 661-664 (4)* 2.70 1.15

Christmas.

Flag and Map of Arab League Countries A85a

**1971, May 10** **Photo.** ***Perf. 11½x11***

**665** A85a 10f orange & multi .40 .25
**666** A85a 20f lt blue & multi .40 .25
**667** A85a 30f olive & multi .40 .25
*Nos. 665-667 (3)* 1.20 .75

25th anniversary of the Arab League.

Emblem and Doves — A86

Designs: 5f, Emblem and 4 races, vert. 10f, Emblem as flower, vert.

**1971, July**

**668** A86 5f green & multi .35 .30
**669** A86 10f brick red & multi .40 .30
**670** A86 15f dk blue & multi .50 .30
*Nos. 668-670 (3)* 1.25 .90

Intl. Year Against Racial Discrimination.

Dead Sea A87

Views of the Holy Land: 30f, Excavated building, Petra. 45f, Via Dolorosa, Jerusalem, vert. 60f, Jordan River. 100f, Christmas bell, Bethlehem, vert.

**1971, Aug.** ***Perf. 14x13½, 13½x14***

**671** A87 5f blue & multi .90 .30
**672** A87 30f pink & multi 1.75 .60
**673** A87 45f blue & multi 2.25 .90
**674** A87 60f gray & multi 3.75 1.50
**675** A87 100f gray & multi 5.50 3.00
*Nos. 671-675 (5)* 14.15 6.30

Tourist publicity.

Opening of UPU Headquarters, Bern in 1970 — A88

**1971, Oct.** ***Perf. 11***

**676** A88 10f brn, brn & yel grn .40 .25
**677** A88 20f dk vio, grn & yel grn .70 .25

Averroes (1126-1198) A89

Arab Scholars: 5f, Avicenna (980-1037). 20f, ibn-Khaldun (1332-1406). 25f, ibn-Tufail (?-1185). 30f, Alhazen (965?-1039?).

**1971, Sept.** ***Perf. 12***

**678** A89 5f gold & multi .35 .25
**679** A89 10f gold & multi .35 .25
**680** A89 20f gold & multi .65 .25
**681** A89 25f gold & multi 1.00 .35
**682** A89 30f gold & multi 1.50 .75
*Nos. 678-682 (5)* 3.85 1.85

Child Learning to Write — A90

**1972, Feb. 9** **Photo.** ***Perf. 11***

**683** A90 5f ultra, brn & grn .35 .25
**684** A90 15f mag, brn & blue .35 .25
**685** A90 20f grn, brn & blue .35 .25
**686** A90 30f org, brn & blue .75 .30
*Nos. 683-686 (4)* 1.80 1.05

International Education Year.

Arab Mother and Child — A91

Mother's Day: 10f, Mothers and children, horiz. 20f, Mother and child.

**1972, Mar.** ***Perf. 14x13½***

**687** A91 10f lt grn & multi .50 .25
**688** A91 20f red brown & blk .50 .25
**689** A91 30f blue, brn & blk .75 .25
*Nos. 687-689 (3)* 1.75 .75

Pope Paul VI and Holy Sepulcher — A92

**1972, Apr.** **Photo.** ***Perf. 14x13½***

**690** A92 30f black & multi 1.00 .25

Easter. See Nos. C51-C52.

UNICEF Emblem, Children A93

UNICEF Emblem and: 20f, Child playing with blocks spelling "UNICEF," vert. 30f, Mother and child.

**1972, May** ***Perf. 11½x11, 11x11½***

**691** A93 10f bl, vio bl & blk .40 .25
**692** A93 20f multicolored .40 .25
**693** A93 30f blue & multi .50 .25
*Nos. 691-693 (3)* 1.30 .75

25th anniv. (in 1971) of UNICEF.

UN Emblem, Dove and Grain — A94

**1972, July** ***Perf. 11x11½***

**694** A94 5f vio & multi .50 .25
**695** A94 10f multicolored .50 .25
**696** A94 15f black & multi .50 .25
**697** A94 20f green & multi .50 .25
**698** A94 30f multicolored .85 .50
*Nos. 694-698 (5)* 2.85 1.50

25th anniv. (in 1970) of the UN.

Al Aqsa Mosque, Jerusalem — A95

Designs: 60f, Al Aqsa Mosque on fire. 100f, Al Aqsa Mosque, interior.

**1972, Aug. 21** **Litho.** ***Perf. 14½***

**699** A95 30f green & multi 1.60 .25
**700** A95 60f blue & multi 3.50 .85
**701** A95 100f ocher & multi 5.50 1.50
*Nos. 699-701 (3)* 10.60 2.60

3rd anniversary of the burning of Al Aqsa Mosque, Jerusalem.

House in Desert A96

5f, Falconer, vert. 15f, Man on camel. 20f, Pipe line construction. 25f, Shepherd. 30f, Camels at water trough. 35f, Chicken farm. 45f, Irrigation canal.

**1972, Nov.** ***Perf. 14x13½, 13½x14***

**702** A96 5f multicolored .55 .25
**703** A96 10f shown .55 .25
**704** A96 15f multicolored .55 .25
**705** A96 20f multicolored .95 .25
**706** A96 25f multicolored .95 .25
**707** A96 30f multicolored 1.25 .45
**708** A96 35f multicolored 1.50 .65
**709** A96 45f multicolored 2.00 1.10
*Nos. 702-709 (8)* 8.30 3.45

Life in the Arab desert.

Wasfi el Tell and Dome of the Rock A97

Wasfi el Tell, Map of Palestine and Jordan — A98

***Perf. 13x13½, 13½x13***

**1972, Dec.** **Photo.**

**710** A97 5f citron & multi .45 .25
**711** A98 10f red & multi .50 .25
**712** A97 20f dl blue & multi 1.00 .25
**713** A98 30f green & multi 1.10 .85
*Nos. 710-713 (4)* 3.05 1.60

In memory of Prime Minister Wasfi el Tell, who was assassinated in Cairo by Black September terrorists.

Trapshooting A99

Designs: 75f, Trapshooter facing right, horiz. 120f, Trapshooter facing left, horiz.

**1972, Dec.** ***Perf. 14x13½, 13½x14***

**714** A99 25f multicolored .80 .25
**715** A99 75f multicolored 1.10 .80
**716** A99 120f multicolored 2.10 1.00
*Nos. 714-716 (3)* 4.00 2.05

World Trapshooting Championships.

Aero Club Emblem A100

**1973, Jan.** **Photo.** ***Perf. 13½x14***

**717** A100 5f blue, blk & yel .50 .25
**718** A100 10f blue, blk & yel .50 .25
*Nos. 717-718,C53-C55 (5)* 4.10 2.05

Royal Jordanian Aero Club.

Peace Dove and Jordanian Flag A101

10f, Emblem. 15f, King Hussein. 30f, Map of Jordan.

**1973, Mar.** *Perf. 11½*

| | | | | |
|---|---|---|---|---|
| **719** | A101 | 5f blue & multi | .45 | .25 |
| **720** | A101 | 10f pale grn & multi | .45 | .25 |
| **721** | A101 | 15f olive & multi | .45 | .25 |
| **722** | A101 | 30f yel grn & multi | .90 | .45 |
| | | *Nos. 719-722 (4)* | 2.25 | 1.20 |

Hashemite Kingdom of Jordan, 50th anniv.

Battle, Flag and Map of Palestine — A102

10f, 2 soldiers in combat, map of Palestine. 15f, Map of Palestine, olive branch, soldier on tank.

**1973, Apr. 10** **Photo.** *Perf. 11*

| | | | | |
|---|---|---|---|---|
| **723** | A102 | 5f crimson & multi | 1.00 | .40 |
| **724** | A102 | 10f crimson & multi | 1.50 | .60 |
| **725** | A102 | 15f grn, blue & brn | 2.25 | 1.25 |
| | | *Nos. 723-725 (3)* | 4.75 | 2.25 |

5th anniversary of Karama Battle.

Father and Child — A103

Father's Day: 20f, Father & infant. 30f, Family.

**1973, Apr. 20** *Perf. 13½*

| | | | | |
|---|---|---|---|---|
| **726** | A103 | 10f citron & multi | .50 | .25 |
| **727** | A103 | 20f lt blue & multi | .75 | .25 |
| **728** | A103 | 30f multicolored | 1.25 | .55 |
| | | *Nos. 726-728 (3)* | 2.50 | 1.05 |

Phosphate Mine A104

10f, Cement factory. 15f, Sharmasil Dam. 20f, Kafrein Dam.

**1973, June 25** **Litho.** *Perf. 13½x14*

| | | | | |
|---|---|---|---|---|
| **729** | A104 | 5f shown | .40 | .25 |
| **730** | A104 | 10f multicolored | .40 | .25 |
| **731** | A104 | 15f multicolored | .50 | .25 |
| **732** | A104 | 20f multicolored | .70 | .25 |
| | | *Nos. 729-732 (4)* | 2.00 | 1.00 |

Development projects.

Camel Racer A105

Designs: Camel racing.

**1973, July 21**

| | | | | |
|---|---|---|---|---|
| **733** | A105 | 5f multicolored | .80 | .25 |
| **734** | A105 | 10f multicolored | .80 | .25 |
| **735** | A105 | 15f multicolored | .80 | .25 |
| **736** | A105 | 20f multicolored | .80 | .25 |
| | | *Nos. 733-736 (4)* | 3.20 | 1.00 |

Book Year Emblem — A106

**1973, Aug. 25** **Photo.** *Perf. 13x13½*

| | | | | |
|---|---|---|---|---|
| **737** | A106 | 30f dk grn & multi | .75 | .25 |
| **738** | A106 | 60f purple & multi | 1.00 | .35 |

Intl. Book Year. For overprints see Nos. 781-782.

Family A107

Family Day: 30f, Family around fire. 60f, Large family outdoors.

**1973, Sept. 18** **Litho.** *Perf. 13½*

| | | | | |
|---|---|---|---|---|
| **739** | A107 | 20f multicolored | .50 | .25 |
| **740** | A107 | 30f multicolored | .50 | .25 |
| **741** | A107 | 60f multicolored | 1.00 | .35 |
| | | *Nos. 739-741 (3)* | 2.00 | .85 |

Kings of Iran and Jordan, Tomb of Cyrus the Great and Mosque of Omar — A108

**1973, Oct.** **Litho.** *Perf. 13*

| | | | | |
|---|---|---|---|---|
| **742** | A108 | 5f ver & multi | .50 | .25 |
| **743** | A108 | 10f brown & multi | .50 | .25 |
| **744** | A108 | 15f gray & multi | .75 | .25 |
| **745** | A108 | 30f blue & multi | 1.00 | .40 |
| | | *Nos. 742-745 (4)* | 2.75 | 1.15 |

2500th anniversary of the founding of the Persian Empire by Cyrus the Great.

Palestine Week Emblem A109

Palestine Week: 10f, Torch and laurel. 15f, Refugee family behind barbed wire, vert. 30f, Children, Map of Palestine, globe. Sizes: 5f, 10f, 30f; 38½x22mm. 15f, 25x46mm.

**1973, Nov. 17** **Photo.** *Perf. 11*

| | | | | |
|---|---|---|---|---|
| **746** | A109 | 5f multicolored | .50 | .25 |
| **747** | A109 | 10f dl bl & multi | .65 | .25 |
| **748** | A109 | 15f yel grn & multi | .85 | .25 |
| **749** | A109 | 30f brt grn & multi | 1.50 | .40 |
| | | *Nos. 746-749 (4)* | 3.50 | 1.15 |

Traditional Harvest A110

Traditional and modern agricultural methods: 10f, Harvesting machine. 15f, Traditional seeding. 20f, Seeding machine. 30f, Ox plow. 35f, Plowing machine. 45f, Pest control. 60f, Horticulture.

**1973, Dec. 25** *Perf. 13½*

| | | | | |
|---|---|---|---|---|
| **750** | A110 | 5f shown | .65 | .25 |
| **751** | A110 | 10f multicolored | .65 | .25 |
| **752** | A110 | 15f multicolored | .65 | .25 |
| **753** | A110 | 20f multicolored | .65 | .25 |
| **754** | A110 | 30f multicolored | 1.00 | .25 |
| **755** | A110 | 35f multicolored | 1.10 | .25 |
| **756** | A110 | 45f multicolored | 1.25 | .25 |
| **757** | A110 | 60f multicolored | 1.75 | 1.10 |
| | | *Nos. 750-757,C56 (9)* | 10.20 | 4.60 |

Red Sea Fish A111

Designs: Various Red Sea fishes.

**1974, Feb. 15** **Photo.** *Perf. 14*

| | | | | |
|---|---|---|---|---|
| **758** | A111 | 5f multicolored | .50 | .25 |
| **759** | A111 | 10f multicolored | .60 | .25 |
| **760** | A111 | 15f multicolored | .75 | .25 |
| **761** | A111 | 20f multicolored | .90 | .35 |
| **762** | A111 | 25f multicolored | 1.25 | .40 |
| **763** | A111 | 30f multicolored | 2.00 | .50 |
| **764** | A111 | 35f multicolored | 2.25 | .80 |
| **765** | A111 | 40f multicolored | 2.75 | 1.00 |
| **766** | A111 | 45f multicolored | 3.00 | 1.10 |
| **767** | A111 | 50f multicolored | 5.00 | 1.25 |
| **768** | A111 | 60f multicolored | 6.25 | 1.75 |
| | | *Nos. 758-768 (11)* | 25.25 | 7.90 |

Battle of Muta, 1250 A112

20f, Yarmouk Battle, 636. 30f, Hitteen Battle, 1187.

**1974, Mar. 15** **Photo.** *Perf. 13½*

| | | | | |
|---|---|---|---|---|
| **769** | A112 | 10f shown | .65 | .25 |
| **770** | A112 | 20f multicolored | 1.25 | .40 |
| **771** | A112 | 30f multicolored | 1.60 | .65 |
| | | *Nos. 769-771 (3)* | 3.50 | 1.30 |

Clubfooted Boy, by Murillo — A113

Paintings: 10f, Praying Hands, by Dürer. 15f, St. George and the Dragon, by Paolo Uccello. 20f, Mona Lisa, by Da Vinci. 30f, Hope, by Frederic Watts. 40f, Angelus, by Jean F. Millet, horiz. 50f, The Artist and her Daughter, by Angelica Kauffmann. 60f, Portrait of my Mother, by James Whistler, horiz. 100f, Master Hare, by Reynolds.

***Perf. 14x13½, 13½x14***

**1974, Apr. 15** **Litho.**

| | | | | |
|---|---|---|---|---|
| **772** | A113 | 5f black & multi | 1.50 | .25 |
| **773** | A113 | 10f black & gray | 1.50 | .25 |
| **774** | A113 | 15f black & multi | 1.50 | .25 |
| **775** | A113 | 20f black & multi | 1.50 | .25 |
| **776** | A113 | 30f black & multi | 1.50 | .25 |
| **777** | A113 | 40f black & multi | 1.75 | .25 |
| **778** | A113 | 50f black & multi | 2.00 | .95 |
| **779** | A113 | 60f black & multi | 2.50 | 1.00 |
| **780** | A113 | 100f black & multi | 3.50 | 1.75 |
| | | *Nos. 772-780 (9)* | 17.25 | 5.20 |

**Nos. 737-738 Overprinted**

**1974, Apr. 20** **Photo.** *Perf. 13x13½*

| | | | | |
|---|---|---|---|---|
| **781** | A106 | 30f dk grn & multi | .70 | .25 |
| **782** | A106 | 60f purple & multi | 1.00 | .50 |

Intl. Conf. for Damascus History, Apr. 20-25.

UPU Emblem — A114

**1974** *Perf. 13x12½*

| | | | | |
|---|---|---|---|---|
| **783** | A114 | 10f yel grn & multi | .40 | .25 |
| **784** | A114 | 30f blue & multi | .50 | .25 |
| **785** | A114 | 60f multicolored | .85 | .30 |
| | | *Nos. 783-785 (3)* | 1.75 | .80 |

Centenary of Universal Postal Union.

Camel Caravan at Sunset A115

3f, 30f, Palm at shore of Dead Sea. 4f, 40f, Hotel at shore. 5f, 50f, Jars from Qumran Caves. 6f, 60f, Copper scrolls, vert. 10f, 100f, Cracked cistern steps, vert. 20f, like 2f.

**1974, June 25** **Photo.** *Perf. 14*

| | | | | |
|---|---|---|---|---|
| **786** | A115 | 2f multicolored | .50 | .25 |
| **787** | A115 | 3f multicolored | .50 | .25 |
| **788** | A115 | 4f multicolored | .50 | .25 |
| **789** | A115 | 5f multicolored | .75 | .25 |
| **790** | A115 | 6f multicolored | .75 | .25 |
| **791** | A115 | 10f multicolored | .75 | .25 |
| **792** | A115 | 20f multicolored | .50 | .25 |
| **793** | A115 | 30f multicolored | .65 | .25 |
| **794** | A115 | 40f multicolored | .75 | .50 |
| **795** | A115 | 50f multicolored | 1.75 | .40 |
| **796** | A115 | 60f multicolored | 2.25 | .50 |
| **797** | A115 | 100f multicolored | 3.50 | .85 |
| | | *Nos. 786-797 (12)* | 13.15 | 4.25 |

WPY Emblem — A116

**1974, Aug. 20** **Photo.** *Perf. 11*

| | | | | |
|---|---|---|---|---|
| **798** | A116 | 5f lt green, blk & pur | .30 | .25 |
| **799** | A116 | 10f lt green, blk & car | .30 | .25 |
| **800** | A116 | 20f lt green, blk & org | .40 | .25 |
| | | *Nos. 798-800 (3)* | 1.00 | .75 |

World Population Year.

Water Skiing — A117

Water Skiing: 10f, 100f, Side view, horiz. 20f, 200f, Turning, horiz. 50f, like 5f.

***Perf. 14x13½, 13½x14***

**1974, Sept. 20**

| | | | | |
|---|---|---|---|---|
| **801** | A117 | 5f multicolored | .50 | .25 |
| **802** | A117 | 10f multicolored | .50 | .25 |
| **803** | A117 | 20f multicolored | .50 | .25 |
| **804** | A117 | 50f multicolored | .65 | .25 |
| **805** | A117 | 100f multicolored | 1.25 | .50 |
| **806** | A117 | 200f multicolored | 2.10 | .95 |
| | | *Nos. 801-806 (6)* | 5.50 | 2.45 |

Holy Kaaba, Mecca, and Pilgrims — A118

**1974, Nov. Photo. *Perf. 11***

**807** A118 10f blue & multi .75 .25
**808** A118 20f yellow & multi .80 .25

Pilgrimage season.

Amrah Palace A119

Ruins: 20f, Hisham Palace. 30f, Kharraneh Castle.

**1974, Nov. 25 Photo. *Perf. 14x13½***

**809** A119 10f black & multi .50 .25
**810** A119 20f black & multi .75 .30
**811** A119 30f black & multi 1.25 .50
*Nos. 809-811 (3)* 2.50 1.05

Jordanian Woman — A120

Designs: Various women's costumes.

**1975, Feb. 1 Photo. *Perf. 12***

**812** A120 5f lt green & multi .45 .25
**813** A120 10f yellow & multi .50 .25
**814** A120 15f lt blue & multi .75 .30
**815** A120 20f ultra & multi 1.10 .40
**816** A120 25f green & multi 1.50 .85
*Nos. 812-816 (5)* 4.30 2.05

Treasury, Petra — A121

Ommayyad Palace, Amman A122

Designs: 30f, Dome of the Rock, Jerusalem. 40f, Columns, Forum of Jerash.

***Perf. 14x13½, 13½x14***

**1975, Mar. 1 Photo.**

**824** A121 15f lt blue & multi 1.00 .25
**825** A122 20f pink & multi 1.00 .25
**826** A122 30f yellow & multi 1.25 .25
**827** A122 40f lt blue & multi 1.60 .25
*Nos. 824-827,C59-C61 (7)* 10.25 3.25

King Hussein — A123

**1975, Apr. 8 Photo. *Perf. 14***
**Size: 19x23mm**

**831** A123 5f green & ind .50 .25
**832** A123 10f vio & indigo .50 .25
**833** A123 15f car & indigo .50 .25
**834** A123 20f brn ol & ind .50 .25
**835** A123 25f vio bl & ind .50 .25
**836** A123 30f brown & ind .50 .25
**837** A123 35f vio & indigo .50 .25
**838** A123 40f orange & ind .50 .25
**839** A123 45f red lil & ind .50 .25
**840** A123 50f bl green & ind .65 .25
*Nos. 831-840,C62-C68 (17)* 21.00 13.00

Globe, "alia" and Plane — A125

Designs: 30f, Boeing 727 connecting Jordan with world, horiz. 60f, Globe and "alia."

**1975, June 15 Photo. *Perf. 11***

**853** A125 10f multicolored .70 .25
**854** A125 30f multicolored .75 .25
**855** A125 60f multicolored 1.40 .85
*Nos. 853-855 (3)* 2.85 1.35

Royal Jordanian Airline, 30th anniversary.

Satellite Transmission System, Map of Mediterranean — A126

**1975, Aug. 1 Photo. *Perf. 11***

**856** A126 20f vio bl & multi .90 .25
**857** A126 30f green & multi 1.10 .75

Opening of satellite earth station.

Chamber of Commerce Emblem — A127

**1975, Oct. 15 Photo. *Perf. 11***

**858** A127 10f yellow & blue .35 .25
**859** A127 15f yel, red & blue .35 .25
**860** A127 20f yel, grn & blue .35 .25
*Nos. 858-860 (3)* 1.05 .75

Amman Chamber of Commerce, 50th anniv.

Hand Holding Wrench, Wall and Emblem — A128

**1975, Nov. Photo. *Perf. 11½***

**861** A128 5f green, car & blk .35 .25
**862** A128 10f car, green & blk .35 .25
**863** A128 20f blk, green & car .35 .25
*Nos. 861-863 (3)* 1.05 .75

Three-year development plan.

Family and IWY Emblem A129

IWY Emblem and: 25f, Woman scientist with microscope. 60f, Woman graduate.

**1976, Apr. 27 Litho. *Perf. 14x13½***

**864** A129 5f multicolored .50 .25
**865** A129 25f multicolored .50 .25
**866** A129 60f multicolored 1.00 .40
*Nos. 864-866 (3)* 2.00 .90

International Women's Year.

Salt Industry — A130

Arab Labor Organization Emblem and: 30f, Welders. 60f, Ship at 'Aqaba.

**1976, June 1 Litho. *Perf. 13½x14***

**867** A130 10f gray & multi .50 .25
**868** A130 30f bister & multi .50 .25
**869** A130 60f brown & multi .75 .40
*Nos. 867-869 (3)* 1.75 .90

Arab Labor Organization.

Nos. 574-574E Srchd.

***Perf. 14½x13½***

**1976, July 18 Strips of 5 Photo.**

**870** A79a 25f on 1f-5f 32.50 32.50
*a.-e.* Any single, 1f-5f
**871** A79a 25f on 6f-10f 32.50 32.50
*a.-e.* Any single, 6f-10f
**872** A79a 40f on 11f-15f 32.50 32.50
*a.-e.* Any single, 11f-15f
**873** A79a 50f on 16f-20f 32.50 32.50
*a.-e.* Any single, 16f-20f
**874** A79a 75f on 21f-25f 32.50 32.50
*a.-e.* Any single, 21f-25f
**875** A79a 125f on 26f-30f 32.50 32.50
*a.-e.* Any single, 26f-30f

**Nos. 575-575E Surcharged Same as Nos. 870-875**

**876** A79a 25f on 1f-5f 32.50 32.50
*a.-e.* Any single, 1f-5f
**877** A79a 25f on 6f-10f 32.50 32.50
*a.-e.* Any single, 6f-10f
**878** A79a 40f on 11f-15f 32.50 32.50
*a.-e.* Any single, 11f-15f
**879** A79a 50f on 16f-20f 32.50 32.50
*a.-e.* Any single, 16f-20f
**880** A79a 75f on 21f-25f 32.50 32.50
*a.-e.* Any single, 21f-25f
**881** A79a 125f on 26f-30f 32.50 32.50
*a.-e.* Any single, 26f-30f

Tennis — A132

Designs: 10f, Athlete and wreath. 15f, Soccer. 20f, Equestrian and Jordanian flag. 30f, Weight lifting. 100f, Stadium, Amman.

**1976, Nov. 1 Litho. *Perf. 14x13½***

**990** A132 5f buff & multi .75 .25
**991** A132 10f lt bl & multi .75 .25
**992** A132 15f green & multi .75 .25
**993** A132 20f green & multi .75 .25
**994** A132 30f green & multi 1.00 .25
**995** A132 100f multicolored 2.00 1.25
*Nos. 990-995 (6)* 6.00 2.50

Sports and youth.

Dam — A133

Designs: Various dams.

**1976, Dec. 7 Litho. *Perf. 14x13½***

**996** A133 30f multicolored 1.00 .25
**997** A133 60f multicolored 1.25 .70
**998** A133 100f multicolored 2.25 1.10
*Nos. 996-998 (3)* 4.50 2.05

Telephones, 1876 and 1976 — A134

125f, 1876 telephone and 1976 receiver.

**1977, Feb. 17 Litho. *Perf. 11½x12***

**999** A134 75f rose & multi 1.50 .95
**1000** A134 125f blue & multi 2.00 1.25

Centenary of first telephone call by Alexander Graham Bell, Mar. 10, 1876.

Street Crossing, Traffic Light — A135

Designs: 75f, Traffic circle and light. 125f, Traffic light and signs, motorcycle policeman.

**1977, May 4 Litho. *Perf. 11x12***

**1001** A135 5f rose & multi .55 .25
**1002** A135 75f black & multi 1.50 .85
**1003** A135 125f yellow & multi 2.25 1.40
*Nos. 1001-1003 (3)* 4.30 2.50

International Traffic Day.

Plane over Ship — A136

Coat of Arms and: 25f, Factories and power lines. 40f, Fertilizer plant and trucks. 50f, Ground to air missile. 75f, Mosque and worshippers. 125f, Radar station and TV emblem.

**1977, Aug. 11 Photo. *Perf. 11½x12***

**1004** A136 10f sil & multi .40 .25
**1005** A136 25f sil & multi .40 .25
**1006** A136 40f sil & multi .70 .35
**1007** A136 50f sil & multi .80 .40
**1008** A136 75f sil & multi .95 .60
**1009** A136 125f sil & multi 1.75 1.00
*Nos. 1004-1009 (6)* 5.00 2.85

***Imperf***
**Size: 100x70mm**

**1009A** A136 100f multicolored 8.50 8.50

25th anniv. of the reign of King Hussein.

Child with Toy Bank — A137

Postal Savings Bank: 25f, Boy with piggy bank. 50f, Postal Savings Bank emblem. 75f, Boy talking to teller.

**1977, Sept. 1 Litho. *Perf. 11½x12***

| | | | | | |
|---|---|---|---|---|---|
| **1010** | A137 | 10f | multicolored | .40 | .25 |
| **1011** | A137 | 25f | multicolored | .60 | .25 |
| **1012** | A137 | 50f | multicolored | .75 | .40 |
| **1013** | A137 | 75f | multicolored | 1.10 | .65 |
| | | | *Nos. 1010-1013 (4)* | 2.85 | 1.55 |

King Hussein and Queen Alia — A138

**1977, Nov. 1 Litho. *Perf. 11½x12***

| | | | | | |
|---|---|---|---|---|---|
| **1014** | A138 | 10f | lt grn & multi | .40 | .25 |
| **1015** | A138 | 25f | rose & multi | .40 | .25 |
| **1016** | A138 | 40f | yellow & multi | .50 | .25 |
| **1017** | A138 | 50f | blue & multi | .70 | .25 |
| | | | *Nos. 1014-1017 (4)* | 2.00 | 1.00 |

Queen Alia — A139

**1977, Dec. 1 Litho. *Perf. 11½x12***

| | | | | | |
|---|---|---|---|---|---|
| **1018** | A139 | 10f | green & multi | .50 | .25 |
| **1019** | A139 | 25f | brown & multi | .50 | .25 |
| **1020** | A139 | 40f | blue & multi | .70 | .25 |
| **1021** | A139 | 50f | yellow & multi | .95 | .25 |
| | | | *Nos. 1018-1021 (4)* | 2.65 | 1.00 |

Queen Alia, died in 1977 air crash.

Jinnah, Flags of Pakistan and Jordan — A140

**1977, Dec. 20 *Perf. 11½***

| | | | | | |
|---|---|---|---|---|---|
| **1022** | A140 | 25f | multicolored | .30 | .25 |
| **1023** | A140 | 75f | multicolored | .70 | .40 |

Mohammed Ali Jinnah (1876-1948), 1st Governor General of Pakistan.

APU Emblem, Members' Flags — A141

**1978, Apr. 12 Litho. *Perf. 12x11½***

| | | | | | |
|---|---|---|---|---|---|
| **1024** | A141 | 25f | yellow & multi | .75 | .50 |
| **1025** | A141 | 40f | buff & multi | 1.25 | .75 |

25th anniv. (in 1977), of Arab Postal Union.

Copper Coffee Set — A142

Handicraft: 40f, Porcelain plate and ashtray. 75f, Vase and jewelry. 125f, Pipe holder.

**1978, May 30 Photo. *Perf. 11½x12***

| | | | | | |
|---|---|---|---|---|---|
| **1026** | A142 | 25f | olive & multi | .50 | .25 |
| **1027** | A142 | 40f | lilac & multi | .65 | .25 |
| **1028** | A142 | 75f | ultra & multi | 1.10 | .65 |
| **1029** | A142 | 125f | orange & multi | 1.75 | 1.00 |
| | | | *Nos. 1026-1029 (4)* | 4.00 | 2.15 |

Roman Amphitheater, Jerash A143

Tourist Views: 20f, Roman Columns, Jerash. 40f, Goat, grapes and man, Roman mosaic, Madaba. 75f, Rock formations, Rum, and camel rider.

**1978, July 30 Litho. *Perf. 12***

| | | | | | |
|---|---|---|---|---|---|
| **1030** | A143 | 5f | multicolored | .55 | .25 |
| **1031** | A143 | 20f | multicolored | .55 | .25 |
| **1032** | A143 | 40f | multicolored | 1.00 | .25 |
| **1033** | A143 | 75f | multicolored | 1.40 | .75 |
| | | | *Nos. 1030-1033 (4)* | 3.50 | 1.50 |

King Hussein and Pres. Sadat — A144

Designs: No. 1035, King Hussein and Pres. Assad, Jordanian and Syrian flags, horiz. No. 1036, King Hussein, King Khalid, Jordanian and Saudi Arabian flags, horiz.

**1978, Aug. 20 *Perf. 11½x12***

| | | | | | |
|---|---|---|---|---|---|
| **1034** | A144 | 40f | multicolored | .90 | .50 |
| **1035** | A144 | 40f | multicolored | .90 | .50 |
| **1036** | A144 | 40f | multicolored | .90 | .50 |
| | | | *Nos. 1034-1036 (3)* | 2.70 | 1.50 |

Visits of Arab leaders to Jordan.

Cement Factory A145

Designs: 10f, Science laboratory. 25f, Printing press. 75f, Artificial fertilizer plant.

**1978, Sept. 25 Litho. *Perf. 12***

| | | | | | |
|---|---|---|---|---|---|
| **1037** | A145 | 5f | multicolored | .60 | .25 |
| **1038** | A145 | 10f | multicolored | .60 | .25 |
| **1039** | A145 | 25f | multicolored | .80 | .25 |
| **1040** | A145 | 75f | multicolored | 1.60 | .90 |
| | | | *Nos. 1037-1040 (4)* | 3.60 | 1.65 |

Industrial development.

"UNESCO" Scales and Globe — A146

**1978, Dec. 5 Litho. *Perf. 12x11½***

| | | | | | |
|---|---|---|---|---|---|
| **1041** | A146 | 40f | multicolored | .75 | .35 |
| **1042** | A146 | 75f | multicolored | 1.25 | .70 |

30th anniversary of UNESCO.

1976-1980 Development Plan — A147

**1979, Oct. 25 Litho. *Perf. 12½x12***

| | | | | | |
|---|---|---|---|---|---|
| **1043** | A147 | 25f | multicolored | .30 | .25 |
| **1044** | A147 | 40f | multicolored | .70 | .25 |
| **1045** | A147 | 50f | multicolored | .95 | .25 |
| | | | *Nos. 1043-1045 (3)* | 1.95 | .75 |

IYC Emblem, Flag of Jordan — A148

**1979, Nov. 15 Litho. *Perf. 12x12½***

| | | | | | |
|---|---|---|---|---|---|
| **1046** | A148 | 25f | multicolored | .50 | .25 |
| **1047** | A148 | 40f | multicolored | .75 | .25 |
| **1048** | A148 | 50f | multicolored | 1.25 | .35 |
| | | | *Nos. 1046-1048 (3)* | 2.50 | .85 |

International Year of the Child.

1979 Population and Housing Census A149

**1979, Dec. 25 Litho. *Perf. 12½x12***

| | | | | | |
|---|---|---|---|---|---|
| **1049** | A149 | 25f | multicolored | .50 | .25 |
| **1050** | A149 | 40f | multicolored | .70 | .25 |
| **1051** | A149 | 50f | multicolored | .80 | .30 |
| | | | *Nos. 1049-1051 (3)* | 2.00 | .80 |

King Hussein — A150

**1980 Litho. *Perf. 13½x13***

| | | | | | |
|---|---|---|---|---|---|
| **1052** | A150 | 5f | multicolored | .30 | .25 |
| *b.* | | | Inscribed 1981 | .30 | .25 |
| **1053** | A150 | 10f | multicolored | .30 | .25 |
| *b.* | | | Inscribed 1981 | .30 | .25 |
| **1055** | A150 | 20f | multicolored | .30 | .25 |
| *b.* | | | Inscribed 1981 | .30 | .25 |
| **1056** | A150 | 25f | multicolored | .30 | .25 |
| *a.* | | | Inscribed 1979 | .30 | .25 |
| *b.* | | | Inscribed 1981 | .30 | .25 |
| **1058** | A150 | 40f | multicolored | .60 | .25 |
| *a.* | | | Inscribed 1979 | .50 | .25 |
| *b.* | | | Inscribed 1981 | .60 | .25 |
| **1059** | A150 | 50f | multicolored | .80 | .25 |
| **1060** | A150 | 75f | multicolored | 1.00 | .30 |
| **1061** | A150 | 125f | multicolored | 1.50 | .35 |
| *a.* | | | Complete booklet, 4 each #1056, 1058-1061 | 17.50 | |
| | | | *Nos. 1052-1061 (8)* | 5.10 | 2.15 |

International Nursing Day — A151

**1980, May 12 Litho. *Perf. 12x12½***

| | | | | | |
|---|---|---|---|---|---|
| **1062** | A151 | 25f | multicolored | .50 | .25 |
| **1063** | A151 | 40f | multicolored | .70 | .25 |
| **1064** | A151 | 50f | multicolored | .85 | .25 |
| | | | *Nos. 1062-1064 (3)* | 2.05 | .75 |

El Deir Temple, Petra — A152

**1980 Litho. *Perf. 14½***

| | | | | | |
|---|---|---|---|---|---|
| **1065** | A152 | 25f | multicolored | .60 | .25 |
| **1066** | A152 | 40f | multicolored | .90 | .50 |
| **1067** | A152 | 50f | multicolored | 1.25 | .60 |
| | | | *Nos. 1065-1067 (3)* | 2.75 | 1.35 |

World Tourism Conf., Manila, Sept. 27.

Hegira (Pilgrimage Year) — A153

**1980, Nov. 11 Litho. *Perf. 14½***

| | | | | | |
|---|---|---|---|---|---|
| **1068** | A153 | 25f | multicolored | .30 | .25 |
| **1069** | A153 | 40f | multicolored | .45 | .25 |
| **1070** | A153 | 50f | multicolored | .75 | .30 |
| **1071** | A153 | 75f | multicolored | 1.50 | .40 |
| **1072** | A153 | 100f | multicolored | 1.50 | .70 |
| | | | *Nos. 1068-1072 (5)* | 4.50 | 1.90 |

**Souvenir Sheet**

***Imperf***

| | | | | | |
|---|---|---|---|---|---|
| **1073** | A153 | 290f | multicolored | 6.50 | 6.50 |

No. 1073 contains designs of Nos. 1068-1071.

11th Arab Summit Conference, Amman — A153a

**1980, Nov. 25 Litho. *Perf. 14½***

| | | | | | |
|---|---|---|---|---|---|
| **1073A** | A153a | 25f | multi | .40 | .25 |
| **1073B** | A153a | 40f | multi | .60 | .25 |
| **1073C** | A153a | 50f | multi | .80 | .30 |
| **1073D** | A153a | 75f | multi | 1.00 | .45 |
| **1073E** | A153a | 100f | multi | 1.10 | .65 |
| *f.* | | | Souv. sheet of 5, #1073A-1073E, imperf. | 6.50 | 6.50 |
| | | | *Nos. 1073A-1073E (5)* | 3.90 | 1.90 |

A154

**1981, May 8 Litho. *Perf. 14½***

| | | | | | |
|---|---|---|---|---|---|
| **1074** | A154 | 25f | multicolored | .50 | .25 |
| **1075** | A154 | 40f | multicolored | .80 | .60 |
| **1076** | A154 | 50f | multicolored | .95 | .70 |
| | | | *Nos. 1074-1076 (3)* | 2.25 | 1.55 |

Red Crescent Society.

A155

**1981, June 17 Litho. *Perf. 14x14½***

| | | | | | |
|---|---|---|---|---|---|
| **1077** | A155 | 25f | multicolored | .75 | .25 |
| **1078** | A155 | 40f | multicolored | .90 | .90 |
| **1079** | A155 | 50f | multicolored | 1.25 | .90 |
| | | | *Nos. 1077-1079 (3)* | 2.90 | 2.05 |

13th World Telecommunications Day.

Nos. 174 and 832 — A156

40f, Nos. 313, 189, vert. 50f, Nos. 272, 222.

***Perf. 13½x14½, 14½x13½***

**1981, July 1 Litho.**

| | | | | | |
|---|---|---|---|---|---|
| **1080** | A156 | 25f | shown | .55 | .25 |
| **1081** | A156 | 40f | multicolored | 1.00 | .65 |
| **1082** | A156 | 50f | multicolored | 1.10 | .90 |
| | | | *Nos. 1080-1082 (3)* | 2.65 | 1.80 |

Postal Museum opening.

A157

Arab Women: 25f, Khawla Bint El-Azwar, Ancient Warrior. 40f, El-Khansa (d.645), writer. 50f, Rabia El-Adawiyeh, religious leader.

**1981, Aug. 25 Litho. *Perf. 14½x14***

| | | | | | |
|---|---|---|---|---|---|
| **1083** | A157 | 25f | multicolored | .25 | .25 |
| **1084** | A157 | 40f | multicolored | 2.00 | 1.25 |
| **1085** | A157 | 50f | multicolored | 3.00 | 1.50 |
| | | | *Nos. 1083-1085 (3)* | 5.25 | 3.00 |

A158

**1981, Oct. 16 Litho. *Perf. 14x14½***

| | | | | | |
|---|---|---|---|---|---|
| **1086** | A158 | 25f | multicolored | .25 | .25 |
| **1087** | A158 | 40f | multicolored | .80 | .55 |
| **1088** | A158 | 50f | multicolored | 1.00 | .65 |
| | | | *Nos. 1086-1088 (3)* | 2.05 | 1.45 |

World Food Day.

Intl. Year of the Disabled A159

**1981, Nov. 14 Litho. *Perf. 14½x14***

| | | | | | |
|---|---|---|---|---|---|
| **1089** | A159 | 25f | multicolored | .25 | .25 |
| **1090** | A159 | 40f | multicolored | 1.00 | .70 |
| **1091** | A159 | 50f | multicolored | 1.40 | .90 |
| | | | *Nos. 1089-1091 (3)* | 2.65 | 1.85 |

Hands Reading Braille — A160

**1981, Nov. 14 *Perf. 14x14½***

| | | | | | |
|---|---|---|---|---|---|
| **1092** | A160 | 25f | multicolored | .25 | .25 |
| **1093** | A160 | 40f | multicolored | 1.00 | .70 |
| **1094** | A160 | 50f | multicolored | 1.40 | .90 |
| | | | *Nos. 1092-1094 (3)* | 2.65 | 1.85 |

A161

Design: Hand holding jug and stone tablet.

**1982, Mar. 10 Litho. *Perf. 14x14½***

| | | | | | |
|---|---|---|---|---|---|
| **1095** | A161 | 25f | multicolored | .50 | .25 |
| **1096** | A161 | 40f | multicolored | 1.10 | .60 |
| **1097** | A161 | 50f | multicolored | 1.25 | .80 |
| | | | *Nos. 1095-1097 (3)* | 2.85 | 1.65 |

Nos. 1095-1097 inscribed 1981.

A162

**1982, Apr. 12 Litho. *Perf. 14x14½***

| | | | | | |
|---|---|---|---|---|---|
| **1098** | A162 | 10f | multicolored | .25 | .25 |
| **1099** | A162 | 25f | multicolored | .65 | .25 |
| **1100** | A162 | 40f | multicolored | .90 | .65 |
| **1101** | A162 | 50f | multicolored | 1.10 | .80 |
| **1102** | A162 | 100f | multicolored | 2.40 | 1.60 |
| | | | *Nos. 1098-1102 (5)* | 5.30 | 3.55 |

30th anniv. of Arab Postal Union.

King Hussein and Rockets A163

25f, Tanks crossing bridge. 40f, Jet. 50f, Tanks, diff. 100f, Raising flag.

**1982, May 25 Litho. *Perf. 14½x14***

| | | | | | |
|---|---|---|---|---|---|
| **1103** | A163 | 10f | shown | .25 | .25 |
| **1104** | A163 | 25f | multicolored | .65 | .25 |
| **1105** | A163 | 40f | multicolored | .90 | .65 |
| **1106** | A163 | 50f | multicolored | 1.25 | .75 |
| **1107** | A163 | 100f | multicolored | 2.25 | 1.50 |
| | | | *Nos. 1103-1107 (5)* | 5.30 | 3.40 |

Independence and Army Day; 30th anniv. of King Hussein's accession to the throne.

Salt Secondary School A164

**1982, Sept. 12 Litho. *Perf. 14½x14***

| | | | | | |
|---|---|---|---|---|---|
| **1108** | A164 | 10f | multicolored | .25 | .25 |
| **1109** | A164 | 25f | multicolored | .60 | .25 |
| **1110** | A164 | 40f | multicolored | .85 | .60 |
| **1111** | A164 | 50f | multicolored | 1.10 | .65 |
| **1112** | A164 | 100f | multicolored | 2.25 | 1.25 |
| | | | *Nos. 1108-1112 (5)* | 5.05 | 3.00 |

International Heritage of Jerusalem — A165

10f, Gate to Old City. 25f, Minaret. 40f, Al Aqsa. 50f, Dome of the Rock. 100f, Dome of the Rock, diff.

**1982, Nov. 14 Litho. *Perf. 14x14½***

| | | | | | |
|---|---|---|---|---|---|
| **1113** | A165 | 10f | multicolored | .25 | .25 |
| **1114** | A165 | 25f | multicolored | 1.00 | .45 |
| **1115** | A165 | 40f | multicolored | 1.25 | .80 |
| **1116** | A165 | 50f | multicolored | 1.60 | .90 |
| **1117** | A165 | 100f | multicolored | 3.25 | 1.75 |
| | | | *Nos. 1113-1117 (5)* | 7.35 | 4.15 |

Yarmouk Forces A166

No. 1123, Armed Forces emblem.

**1982, Nov. 14 *Perf. 14½x14***

| | | | | | |
|---|---|---|---|---|---|
| **1118** | A166 | 10f | pink & multi | .25 | .25 |
| **1119** | A166 | 25f | buff & multi | .45 | .25 |
| **1120** | A166 | 40f | yel & multi | .80 | .45 |
| **1121** | A166 | 50f | lt blue & multi | .95 | .60 |
| **1122** | A166 | 100f | pale grn & multi | 2.10 | 1.40 |
| | | | *Nos. 1118-1122 (5)* | 4.55 | 2.95 |

**Size: 71x51mm**

***Imperf***

| | | | | | |
|---|---|---|---|---|---|
| **1123** | A166 | 100f | tan & multi | 15.00 | 15.00 |

2nd UN Conf. on Peaceful Uses of Outer Space, Vienna, Aug. 9-21 — A167

**1982, Dec. 1 *Perf. 14½x14***

| | | | | | |
|---|---|---|---|---|---|
| **1124** | A167 | 10f | multicolored | .25 | .25 |
| **1125** | A167 | 25f | multicolored | .50 | .25 |
| **1126** | A167 | 40f | multicolored | .75 | .50 |
| **1127** | A167 | 50f | multicolored | .95 | .60 |
| **1128** | A167 | 100f | multicolored | 2.00 | 1.25 |
| | | | *Nos. 1124-1128 (5)* | 4.45 | 2.85 |

Birth Centenary of Amir Abdullah ibn Hussein — A168

**1982, Dec. 13 Litho. *Perf. 14½***

| | | | | | |
|---|---|---|---|---|---|
| **1129** | A168 | 10f | multicolored | .25 | .25 |
| **1130** | A168 | 25f | multicolored | .40 | .25 |
| **1131** | A168 | 40f | multicolored | .60 | .45 |
| **1132** | A168 | 50f | multicolored | .95 | .80 |
| **1133** | A168 | 100f | multicolored | 2.25 | 1.40 |
| | | | *Nos. 1129-1133 (5)* | 4.45 | 3.15 |

Roman Ruins of Jerash A169

10f, Temple colonnade. 25f, Arch. 40f, Columns. 50f, Ampitheater. 100f, Hippodrome.

**1982, Dec. 29 Litho. *Perf. 15***

| | | | | | |
|---|---|---|---|---|---|
| **1134** | A169 | 10f | multicolored | .25 | .25 |
| **1135** | A169 | 25f | multicolored | .90 | .25 |
| **1136** | A169 | 40f | multicolored | 1.40 | .90 |
| **1137** | A169 | 50f | multicolored | 1.75 | 1.00 |
| **1138** | A169 | 100f | multicolored | 3.25 | 2.10 |
| | | | *Nos. 1134-1138 (5)* | 7.55 | 4.50 |

King Hussein — A170

**1983 Litho. *Perf. 14½x14***

| | | | | | |
|---|---|---|---|---|---|
| **1139** | A170 | 10f | multicolored | .25 | .25 |
| **1140** | A170 | 25f | multicolored | .25 | .25 |
| **1141** | A170 | 40f | multicolored | .40 | .30 |
| **1142** | A170 | 60f | multicolored | .60 | .40 |
| **1143** | A170 | 100f | multicolored | 1.00 | .65 |
| **1144** | A170 | 125f | multicolored | 1.25 | .70 |
| | | | *Nos. 1139-1144 (6)* | 3.75 | 2.55 |

Issue dates: 10f, 60f, Feb. 1; 40f, Feb. 8; 25f, 100f, 125f, Mar. 3. Inscribed 1982.

Massacre at Shatilla and Sabra Palestinian Refugee Camps A171

10f, 25f, 50f, No. 1149, Various victims. 40f, Children. No. 1150, Wounded child.

**1983, Apr. 9 Litho. *Perf. 14½***

| | | | | | |
|---|---|---|---|---|---|
| **1145** | A171 | 10f | multicolored | *.50* | *.25* |
| **1146** | A171 | 25f | multicolored | *1.00* | *.70* |
| **1147** | A171 | 40f | multicolored | *1.50* | *.90* |
| **1148** | A171 | 50f | multicolored | *2.00* | *1.25* |
| **1149** | A171 | 100f | multicolored | *3.00* | *2.00* |
| | | | *Nos. 1145-1149 (5)* | *8.00* | *5.10* |

**Souvenir Sheet**

***Imperf***

| | | | | | |
|---|---|---|---|---|---|
| **1150** | A171 | 100f | multicolored | *18.00* | |

Opening of Queen Alia Intl. Airport A172

10f, Aerial view. 25f, Terminal buildings. 40f, Hangar. 50f, Terminal buildings, diff. 100f, Embarkation Bridge.

**1983, May 25 Litho. *Perf. 12½***

| | | | | | |
|---|---|---|---|---|---|
| **1151** | A172 | 10f | multicolored | .25 | .25 |
| **1152** | A172 | 25f | multicolored | .80 | .25 |
| **1153** | A172 | 40f | multicolored | 1.10 | .80 |
| **1154** | A172 | 50f | multicolored | 1.40 | .90 |
| **1155** | A172 | 100f | multicolored | 2.75 | 1.75 |
| | | | *Nos. 1151-1155 (5)* | 6.30 | 3.95 |

Royal Jordanian Radio Amateurs' Society A173

**1983, Aug. 11 Litho. *Perf. 12***

| | | | | | |
|---|---|---|---|---|---|
| **1156** | A173 | 10f | multicolored | .25 | .25 |
| **1157** | A173 | 25f | multicolored | .65 | .25 |
| **1158** | A173 | 40f | multicolored | .90 | .65 |
| **1159** | A173 | 50f | multicolored | 1.25 | .75 |
| **1160** | A173 | 100f | multicolored | 2.40 | 1.50 |
| | | | *Nos. 1156-1160 (5)* | 5.45 | 3.40 |

Royal Academy for Islamic Cultural Research A174

10f, Academy Building. 25f, Silk carpet. 40f, Mosque, Amman. 50f, Dome of the Rock. 100f, Islamic city views.

**1983, Sept. 16 Litho. *Perf. 12***

| | | | | | |
|---|---|---|---|---|---|
| **1161** | A174 | 10f | multicolored | .25 | .25 |
| **1162** | A174 | 25f | multicolored | .70 | .50 |
| **1163** | A174 | 40f | multicolored | 1.10 | .70 |
| **1164** | A174 | 50f | multicolored | 1.50 | .90 |
| **1165** | A174 | 100f | multicolored | 2.75 | 1.75 |
| | | | *Nos. 1161-1165 (5)* | 6.30 | 4.10 |

A 100f souvenir sheet shows letter from Mohammed. Value $15.

World Food Day A175

10f, Irrigation canal. 25f, Greenhouses. 40f, Light-grown crops. 50f, Harvest. 100f, Sheep farm.

**1983, Oct. 16 Litho. *Perf. 12***

| | | | | | |
|---|---|---|---|---|---|
| **1166** | A175 | 10f | multicolored | .25 | .25 |
| **1167** | A175 | 25f | multicolored | .60 | .25 |
| **1168** | A175 | 40f | multicolored | 1.00 | .60 |
| **1169** | A175 | 50f | multicolored | 1.25 | .70 |
| **1170** | A175 | 100f | multicolored | 2.50 | 1.40 |
| | | | *Nos. 1166-1170 (5)* | 5.60 | 3.20 |

World Communications Year — A176

10f, Radio switchboard operators. 25f, Earth satellite station. 40f, Symbols of communication. 50f, Emblems. 100f, Airmail letter.

**1983, Nov. 14**

| | | | | |
|---|---|---|---|---|
| **1171** | A176 | 10f multicolored | .25 | .25 |
| **1172** | A176 | 25f multicolored | 1.00 | .25 |
| **1173** | A176 | 40f multicolored | 1.25 | 1.00 |
| **1174** | A176 | 50f multicolored | 1.50 | 1.00 |
| **1175** | A176 | 100f multicolored | 3.25 | 1.75 |
| | | *Nos. 1171-1175 (5)* | 7.25 | 4.25 |

Intl. Palestinian Solidarity Day A177

Dome of the Rock, Jerusalem.

**1983, Nov. 29** ***Perf. 12***

| | | | | |
|---|---|---|---|---|
| **1176** | A177 | 5f multicolored | .90 | .45 |
| **1177** | A177 | 10f multicolored | 1.50 | .70 |

35th Anniv. of UN Declaration of Human Rights A178

**1983, Dec. 10**

| | | | | |
|---|---|---|---|---|
| **1178** | A178 | 10f multicolored | .25 | .25 |
| **1179** | A178 | 25f multicolored | .65 | .25 |
| **1180** | A178 | 40f multicolored | .75 | .65 |
| **1181** | A178 | 50f multicolored | 1.25 | .75 |
| **1182** | A178 | 100f multicolored | 2.50 | 1.50 |
| | | *Nos. 1178-1182 (5)* | 5.40 | 3.40 |

Anti-Paralysis — A179

**1984, Apr. 7** ***Perf. 13½x11½***

| | | | | |
|---|---|---|---|---|
| **1183** | A179 | 40f multicolored | 1.10 | .70 |
| **1184** | A179 | 60f multicolored | 1.60 | .95 |
| **1185** | A179 | 100f multicolored | 2.75 | 1.60 |
| | | *Nos. 1183-1185 (3)* | 5.45 | 3.25 |

Anti-Polio Campaign.

Israeli Bombing of Iraq Nuclear Reactor — A180

Various designs.

**1984, June 7 Litho.** ***Perf. 13½x11½***

| | | | | |
|---|---|---|---|---|
| **1186** | A180 | 40f multicolored | 1.60 | .55 |
| **1187** | A180 | 60f multicolored | 2.00 | .70 |
| **1188** | A180 | 100f multicolored | 3.25 | 1.25 |
| | | *Nos. 1186-1188 (3)* | 6.85 | 2.50 |

Independence and Army Day — A181

King Hussein and various armed forces.

**1984, June 10**

| | | | | |
|---|---|---|---|---|
| **1189** | A181 | 10f multicolored | .25 | .25 |
| **1190** | A181 | 25f multicolored | .65 | .25 |
| **1191** | A181 | 40f multicolored | 1.00 | .65 |
| **1192** | A181 | 60f multicolored | 1.60 | .90 |
| **1193** | A181 | 100f multicolored | 2.75 | 1.60 |
| | | *Nos. 1189-1193 (5)* | 6.25 | 3.65 |

1984 Summer Olympics, Los Angeles — A182

40f, Swimming. 60f, Shooting, archery. 100f, Gymnastics.

**1984, July 28**

| | | | | |
|---|---|---|---|---|
| **1194** | A182 | 25f shown | .30 | .25 |
| **1195** | A182 | 40f multicolored | .50 | .30 |
| **1196** | A182 | 60f multicolored | 1.10 | .45 |
| **1197** | A182 | 100f multicolored | 1.60 | .75 |
| | | *Nos. 1194-1197 (4)* | 3.50 | 1.75 |

An imperf. 100f souvenir sheet exists picturing pole vaulting. Value $14.

Water and Electricity Year — A183

25f, Power lines, factory. 40f, Amman Power Station. 60f, Irrigation. 100f, Hydro-electric dam.

**1984, Aug. 11**

| | | | | |
|---|---|---|---|---|
| **1198** | A183 | 25f multicolored | .45 | .25 |
| **1199** | A183 | 40f multicolored | .70 | .45 |
| **1200** | A183 | 60f multicolored | 1.10 | .60 |
| **1201** | A183 | 100f multicolored | 1.75 | 1.10 |
| | | *Nos. 1198-1201 (4)* | 4.00 | 2.40 |

Coins A184

40f, Omayyad gold dinar. 60f, Abbasid gold dinar. 125f, Hashemite silver dinar.

**1984, Sept. 26 Photo.** ***Perf. 13***

| | | | | |
|---|---|---|---|---|
| **1202** | A184 | 40f multicolored | 1.10 | .60 |
| **1203** | A184 | 60f multicolored | 1.40 | .80 |
| **1204** | A184 | 125f multicolored | 3.00 | 1.75 |
| | | *Nos. 1202-1204 (3)* | 5.50 | 3.15 |

Royal Society for the Conservation of Nature — A185

25f, Four antelopes. 40f, Grazing. 60f, Three antelopes. 100f, King Hussein, Queen Alia, Duke of Edinburgh.

**1984, Oct. 18**

| | | | | |
|---|---|---|---|---|
| **1205** | A185 | 25f multicolored | .70 | .25 |
| **1206** | A185 | 40f multicolored | 1.10 | .70 |
| **1207** | A185 | 60f multicolored | 1.60 | .95 |
| **1208** | A185 | 100f multicolored | 2.75 | 1.60 |
| | | *Nos. 1205-1208 (4)* | 6.15 | 3.50 |

Natl. Universities — A186

Designs: 40f, Mu'ta Military University, Karak. 60f, Yarmouk University, Irbid. 125f, Jordan University, Amman.

**1984, Nov. 14** ***Perf. 13x13½***

| | | | | |
|---|---|---|---|---|
| **1209** | A186 | 40f multicolored | .55 | .40 |
| **1210** | A186 | 60f multicolored | .95 | .55 |
| **1211** | A186 | 125f multicolored | 2.00 | 1.10 |
| | | *Nos. 1209-1211 (3)* | 3.50 | 2.05 |

Al Sahaba Tombs A187

Designs: 10f, El Harath bin Omier el-Azdi and Derer bin El-Azwar. 25f, Sharhabil bin Hasna and Abu Obaidah Amer bin el-Jarrah. 40f, Muath bin Jabal. 50f, Zaid bin Haretha and Abdullah bin Rawaha. 60f, Amer bin Abi Waqqas. 100f, Jafar bin Abi Taleb.

**1984, Dec. 5 Litho.** ***Perf. 13½x11½***

| | | | | |
|---|---|---|---|---|
| **1212** | A187 | 10f multicolored | .25 | .25 |
| **1213** | A187 | 25f multicolored | .50 | .25 |
| **1214** | A187 | 40f multicolored | .75 | .50 |
| **1215** | A187 | 50f multicolored | .95 | .55 |
| **1216** | A187 | 60f multicolored | 1.25 | .65 |
| **1217** | A187 | 100f multicolored | 2.00 | 1.25 |
| | | *Nos. 1212-1217 (6)* | 5.70 | 3.45 |

Independence and Army Day — A188

Designs: 25f, King Hussein, soldier descending mountain. 40f, King Hussein, Arab revolt flag, globe, Sharif Hussein. 60f, Flag, natl. arms, equestrian. 100f, Natl. flag, arms, Sharif Hussein.

**1985, June 10** ***Perf. 13x13½***

| | | | | |
|---|---|---|---|---|
| **1218** | A188 | 25f multicolored | .45 | .25 |
| **1219** | A188 | 40f multicolored | .90 | .45 |
| **1220** | A188 | 60f multicolored | 1.40 | .75 |
| **1221** | A188 | 100f multicolored | 2.25 | 1.40 |
| | | *Nos. 1218-1221 (4)* | 5.00 | 2.85 |

Men in Postal History A189

40f, Sir Rowland Hill. 60f, Heinrich von Stephan. 125f, Yacoub al-Sukkar.

**1985, July 1**

| | | | | |
|---|---|---|---|---|
| **1222** | A189 | 40f multicolored | .75 | .45 |
| **1223** | A189 | 60f multicolored | 1.10 | .65 |
| **1224** | A189 | 125f multicolored | 2.40 | 1.40 |
| | | *Nos. 1222-1224 (3)* | 4.25 | 2.50 |

1st Convention of Jordanian Expatriates A190

Various designs.

**1985, July 20** **Photo.**

| | | | | |
|---|---|---|---|---|
| **1225** | A190 | 40f multicolored | .75 | .45 |
| **1226** | A190 | 60f multicolored | 1.10 | .65 |
| **1227** | A190 | 125f multicolored | 2.40 | 1.40 |
| | | *Nos. 1225-1227 (3)* | 4.25 | 2.50 |

Intl. Youth Year — A191

Various designs.

**1985, Aug. 11 Litho.** ***Perf. 13½x13***

| | | | | |
|---|---|---|---|---|
| **1228** | A191 | 10f multicolored | .25 | .25 |
| **1229** | A191 | 25f multicolored | .50 | .25 |
| **1230** | A191 | 40f multicolored | .80 | .50 |
| **1231** | A191 | 60f multicolored | 1.25 | .70 |
| **1232** | A191 | 125f multicolored | 2.50 | 1.50 |
| | | *Nos. 1228-1232 (5)* | 5.30 | 3.20 |

World Tourism Organization, 10th Anniv. — A192

10f, Ruins of the Treasury, Petra. 25f, Jerash Temple. 40f, Roman baths. 50f, Jordanian valley town. 60f, Aqaba Bay. 125f, Roman amphitheater.

**1985, Sept. 13** ***Perf. 13½x13***

| | | | | |
|---|---|---|---|---|
| **1233** | A192 | 10f multicolored | .25 | .25 |
| **1234** | A192 | 25f multicolored | .50 | .25 |
| **1235** | A192 | 40f multicolored | .80 | .50 |
| **1236** | A192 | 50f multicolored | 1.00 | .60 |
| **1237** | A192 | 60f multicolored | 1.25 | .70 |
| **1238** | A192 | 125f multicolored | 2.50 | 1.40 |
| | | *Nos. 1233-1238 (6)* | 6.30 | 3.70 |

An imperf. 100f souvenir sheet exists picturing flower, 10 and natl. flag. Value $6.50.

UN Child Survival Campaign A193

Various designs.

**1985, Oct. 7**

| | | | | |
|---|---|---|---|---|
| **1239** | A193 | 25f multicolored | .50 | .25 |
| **1240** | A193 | 40f multicolored | .75 | .50 |
| **1241** | A193 | 60f multicolored | 1.25 | .70 |
| **1242** | A193 | 125f multicolored | 2.50 | 1.50 |
| | | *Nos. 1239-1242 (4)* | 5.00 | 2.95 |

An imperf. 100f souvenir sheet exists picturing campaign emblem and the faces of healthy children. Value $12.

5th Jerash Festival A194

10f, Opening ceremony, 1980. 25f, Folk dancers. 40f, Dancers. 60f, Choir, Roman theater. 100f, King and Queen.

**1985, Oct. 21**

| | | | | | |
|---|---|---|---|---|---|
| 1243 | A194 | 10f | multicolored | .25 | .25 |
| 1244 | A194 | 25f | multicolored | .45 | .25 |
| 1245 | A194 | 40f | multicolored | .90 | .45 |
| 1246 | A194 | 60f | multicolored | 1.50 | .75 |
| 1247 | A194 | 100f | multicolored | 2.40 | 1.50 |
| | | | *Nos. 1243-1247 (5)* | 5.50 | 3.20 |

UN, 40th Anniv. A195

**1985, Oct. 25 Photo. *Perf. 13x13½***

| | | | | | |
|---|---|---|---|---|---|
| 1248 | A195 | 60f | multicolored | 1.25 | 1.00 |
| 1249 | A195 | 125f | multicolored | 2.50 | 2.00 |

King Hussein, 50th Birthday A196

Various photos of King.

**1985, Nov. 14 Litho. *Perf. 14½***

| | | | | | |
|---|---|---|---|---|---|
| 1250 | A196 | 10f | multicolored | .25 | .25 |
| 1251 | A196 | 25f | multicolored | .50 | .25 |
| 1252 | A196 | 40f | multicolored | .90 | .50 |
| 1253 | A196 | 60f | multicolored | 1.50 | .75 |
| 1254 | A196 | 100f | multicolored | 2.40 | 1.50 |
| | | | *Nos. 1250-1254 (5)* | 5.55 | 3.25 |

An imperf. 200f souvenir sheet exists picturing flags, King Hussein and Dome of the Rock. Value $15.

Restoration of Al Aqsa Mosque, Jerusalem A196a

**1985, Nov. 25 Litho. *Perf. 13x13½***

| | | | | | |
|---|---|---|---|---|---|
| 1254A | A196a | 5f | multicolored | *1.10* | *1.10* |
| 1254B | A196a | 10f | multicolored | *2.40* | *2.25* |

Police A197

**1985, Dec. 18**

| | | | | | |
|---|---|---|---|---|---|
| 1255 | A197 | 40f | Patrol car | 1.10 | .25 |
| 1256 | A197 | 60f | Crossing guard | 1.40 | 1.10 |
| 1257 | A197 | 125f | Police academy | 3.00 | 2.00 |
| | | | *Nos. 1255-1257 (3)* | 5.50 | 3.35 |

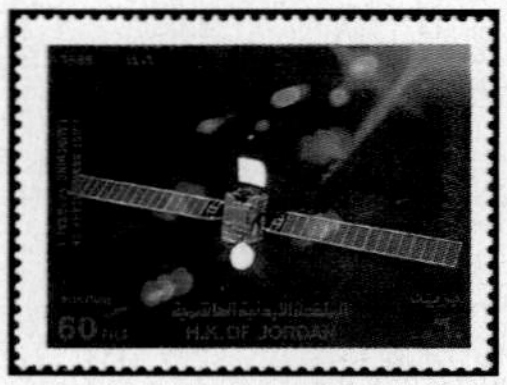


Launch of ARABSAT-1, 1st Anniv. — A198

60f, Satellite in orbit. 100f, Over map of Arab countries.

**1986, Feb. 8 Litho. *Perf. 13½x13***

| | | | | | |
|---|---|---|---|---|---|
| 1258 | A198 | 60f | multicolored | .85 | .25 |
| 1259 | A198 | 100f | multicolored | 1.40 | .85 |

Arabization of the Army, 30th Anniv. A199

40f, King Hussein presenting flag. 60f, Greeting army sergeant. 100f, Hussein addressing army.

**1986, Mar. 1 *Perf. 11½x12½***

| | | | | | |
|---|---|---|---|---|---|
| 1260 | A199 | 40f | multicolored | .75 | .25 |
| 1261 | A199 | 60f | multicolored | .90 | .25 |
| 1262 | A199 | 100f | multicolored | 1.60 | .90 |
| | | | *Nos. 1260-1262 (3)* | 3.25 | 1.40 |

An imperf. souvenir sheet exists with design of 100f. Value $10.

Natl. Independence, 40th Anniv. — A200

Design: King Abdullah decorating soldier.

**1986, May 25 *Perf. 12½x11½***

| | | | | | |
|---|---|---|---|---|---|
| 1263 | A200 | 160f | multicolored | 2.75 | 2.10 |

Arab Revolt against Turkey, 70th Anniv. — A201

Unattributed paintings (details): 40f, The four sons of King Hussein, Prince of Mecca, vert. 60f, Sharif Hussein, retainers and bodyguard. 160f, Abdullah and followers on horseback.

***Perf. 12½x11½, 11½x12½***

**1986, June 10**

| | | | | | |
|---|---|---|---|---|---|
| 1264 | A201 | 40f | multicolored | .65 | .25 |
| 1265 | A201 | 60f | multicolored | .85 | .25 |
| 1266 | A201 | 160f | multicolored | 2.50 | 1.25 |
| | | | *Nos. 1264-1266 (3)* | 4.00 | 1.75 |

An imperf. 200f souvenir sheet exists picturing the Arab Revolt flag, Sharif Hussein and text from independence declaration. Value $9.

Intl. Peace Year A202

**1986, July 1 Litho. *Perf. 13½x13***

| | | | | | |
|---|---|---|---|---|---|
| 1267 | A202 | 160f | multicolored | 2.25 | 1.25 |
| 1268 | A202 | 240f | multicolored | 3.25 | 1.90 |

King Hussein Medical City Cardiac Center A203

**1986, Aug. 11**

| | | | | | |
|---|---|---|---|---|---|
| 1269 | A203 | 40f | Cardiac Center | .90 | .25 |
| 1270 | A203 | 60f | Surgery | 1.10 | .90 |
| 1271 | A203 | 100f | Surgery, diff. | 1.75 | .95 |
| | | | *Nos. 1269-1271 (3)* | 3.75 | 2.10 |

UN, 40th Anniv. — A204

Excerpts from King Hussein's speech: 40f, In Arabic. 80f, Arabic, diff. 100f, English.

**1986, Sept. 27 *Perf. 12½x11½***

| | | | | | |
|---|---|---|---|---|---|
| 1272 | A204 | 40f | multicolored | .75 | .25 |
| 1273 | A204 | 80f | multicolored | 1.25 | .85 |
| 1274 | A204 | 100f | multicolored | 1.60 | .85 |
| | | | *Nos. 1272-1274 (3)* | 3.60 | 1.95 |

An imperf. 200f stamp 90x70mm exists picturing speech in Arabic and English, King Hussein at podium. Value $8.50.

Arab Postal Union, 35th Anniv. A205

**1987, Apr. 12 Litho. *Perf. 13½x13***

| | | | | | |
|---|---|---|---|---|---|
| 1275 | A205 | 80f | Old post office | .85 | .60 |
| 1276 | A205 | 160f | New post office | 1.90 | 1.10 |

Chemical Soc. Emblem and Chemists — A206

Designs: 60f, Jaber ibn Hayyan al-Azdi (720-813). 80f, Abu-al-Qasem al-Majreeti (950-1007). 240f, Abu-Bakr al-Razi (864-932).

**1987, Apr. 24**

| | | | | | |
|---|---|---|---|---|---|
| 1277 | A206 | 60f | multicolored | .75 | .50 |
| 1278 | A206 | 80f | multicolored | 1.00 | .60 |
| 1279 | A206 | 240f | multicolored | 2.75 | 1.60 |
| | | | *Nos. 1277-1279 (3)* | 4.50 | 2.70 |

SOS Children's Village — A207

80f, Village in Amman. 240f, Child, bird mural.

**1987, May 7**

| | | | | | |
|---|---|---|---|---|---|
| 1280 | A207 | 80f | multicolored | 1.25 | .70 |
| 1281 | A207 | 240f | multicolored | 3.25 | 1.90 |

4th Brigade, 40th Anniv. A208

80f, Soldiers in armored vehicle. 160f, Four veterans.

**1987, June 10**

| | | | | | |
|---|---|---|---|---|---|
| 1282 | A208 | 60f | shown | 1.40 | .95 |
| 1283 | A208 | 80f | multicolored | 1.60 | 1.10 |

**Size: 70x91mm**

***Imperf***

| | | | | | |
|---|---|---|---|---|---|
| 1284 | A208 | 160f | multicolored | 8.00 | 7.50 |
| | | | *Nos. 1282-1284 (3)* | 11.00 | 9.55 |

Indigenous Birds — A209

10f, Hoopoe. 40f, Palestine sunbird. 50f, Black-headed bunting. 60f, Spur-winged plover. 80f, Greenfinch. 100f, Black-winged stilt.

**1987, June 24**

| | | | | | |
|---|---|---|---|---|---|
| 1285 | A209 | 10f | multicolored | 1.60 | .55 |
| 1286 | A209 | 40f | multicolored | 1.60 | .55 |
| 1287 | A209 | 50f | multicolored | 2.00 | .60 |
| 1288 | A209 | 60f | multicolored | 2.50 | .90 |
| 1289 | A209 | 80f | multicolored | 3.00 | 1.25 |
| 1290 | A209 | 100f | multicolored | 4.00 | 1.75 |
| | | | *Nos. 1285-1290 (6)* | 14.70 | 5.60 |

King Hussein — A210

**1987, June 24 Litho. *Perf. 13x13½***

| | | | | | |
|---|---|---|---|---|---|
| 1291 | A210 | 60f | multicolored | .40 | .30 |
| 1292 | A210 | 80f | multicolored | .85 | .40 |
| 1293 | A210 | 160f | multicolored | 1.75 | 1.10 |
| 1294 | A210 | 240f | multicolored | 2.50 | 1.75 |
| | | | *Nos. 1291-1294 (4)* | 5.50 | 3.55 |

Battle of Hittin, 800th Anniv. A211

Dome of the Rock and Saladin (1137-1193), Conqueror of Jerusalem — A212

60f, Battle, Jerusalem. 80f, Horseman, Jerusalem, Dome of the Rock. No. 1297, 100f, Saladin.

**1987, July 4**

**1295** A211 60f multicolored .75 .70
**1296** A211 80f multicolored 1.50 .85
**1297** A211 100f multicolored 2.25 1.50
*Nos. 1295-1297 (3)* 4.50 3.05

**Souvenir Sheet**

***Perf. 12x12½***

**1298** A212 100f shown 8.00 7.75

No. 1298 exists imperf.

Natl. Coat of Arms — A213

***Perf. 11½x12½***

**1987, Aug. 11** **Litho.**

**1299** A213 80f multicolored 1.00 .65
**1300** A213 160f multicolored 2.00 1.25

Amman Industrial Park at Sahab — A214

**1987, Aug. 11** ***Perf. 13½x13***

**1301** A214 80f multicolored 1.00 .80

University Crest A215

University Entrance — A216

***Perf. 11½x11, 12½x11½***

**1987, Sept. 2**

**1302** A215 60f multicolored .80 .50
**1303** A216 80f multicolored .95 .65

University of Jordan, 25th anniv.

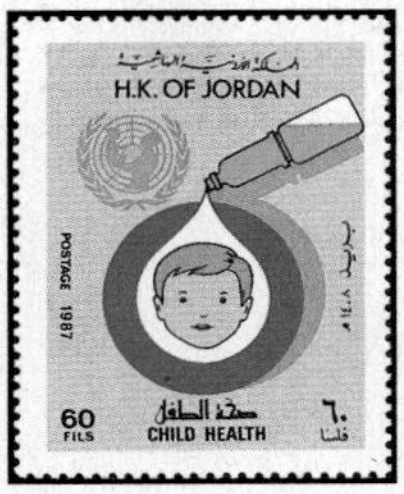


UN Child Survival Campaign A217

60f, Oral vaccine. 80f, Natl. flag, child. 160f, Growth monitoring.

**1987, Oct. 5** **Litho.** ***Perf. 13x13½***

**1304** A217 60f multicolored .75 .60
**1305** A217 80f multicolored 1.25 .80
**1306** A217 160f multicolored 2.50 1.60
*Nos. 1304-1306 (3)* 4.50 3.00

Parliament, 40th Anniv. — A218

60f, Opening ceremony, 1947. 80f, In session, 1987.

**1987, Oct. 20** ***Perf. 13½x13***

**1307** A218 60f dp mag & gold 1.00 .60
**1308** A218 80f multi & gold 1.25 .80

A219

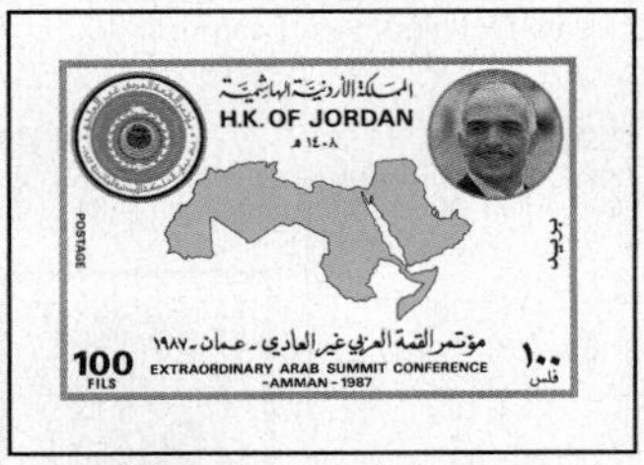


Special Arab Summit Conference, Amman — A220

**1987, Nov. 8**

**1309** A219 60f multicolored .55 .50
**1310** A219 80f multicolored .90 .55
**1311** A219 160f multicolored 2.00 1.25
**1312** A219 240f multicolored 2.75 2.00
*Nos. 1309-1312 (4)* 6.20 4.30

**Size: 90x66mm**

***Imperf***

**1313** A220 100f multicolored 7.50 7.50

King Hussein, Dag Hammarskjold Peace Prize Winner for 1987 — A221

80f, Hussein, woman, vert.

**1988, Feb. 6** **Litho.** ***Perf. 12½***

**1314** A221 80f multicolored .95 .75
**1315** A221 160f shown 1.90 1.25

Natl. Victory at the 1987 Arab Military Basketball Championships — A222

60f, Golden Sword Award. 80f, Hussein congratulating team. 160f, Jump ball.

**1988, Mar. 1** ***Perf. 13½x13***

**1316** A222 60f multicolored .80 .50
**1317** A222 80f multicolored 1.10 .65
**1318** A222 160f multicolored 2.10 1.25
*Nos. 1316-1318 (3)* 4.00 2.40

WHO, 40th Anniv. — A223

**1988, Apr. 7** **Photo.** ***Perf. 13x13½***

**1319** A223 60f multicolored 1.00 .70
**1320** A223 80f multicolored 1.25 .90

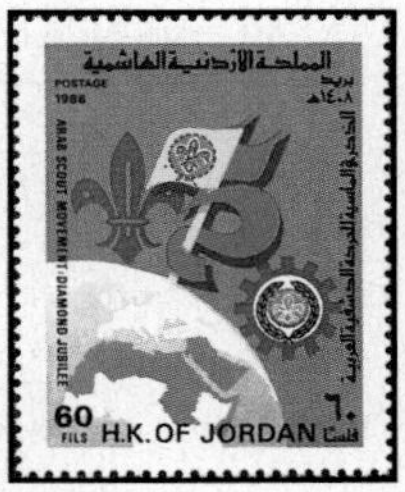


Arab Scouts, 75th Anniv. — A224

**1988, July 2** **Litho.** ***Perf. 13x13½***

**1321** A224 60f multicolored 1.00 .90
**1322** A224 80f multicolored 1.25 1.10

Birds A225

10f, Crested lark. 20f, Stone curlew. 30f, Redstart. 40f, Blackbird. 50f, Rock dove. 160f, Smyrna kingfisher.
310f, Six species.

**1988, July 21** **Litho.** ***Perf. 11½x12***

**1323** A225 10f multi 2.25 .70
**1324** A225 20f multi 2.25 .80
**1325** A225 30f multi 2.25 .90
**1326** A225 40f multi 3.25 1.00
**1327** A225 50f multi 4.00 1.10
**1328** A225 160f multi 11.00 1.75
*Nos. 1323-1328 (6)* 25.00 6.25

**Size: 71x90mm**

***Imperf***

**1328A** A225 310f multi 17.50 15.00

Restoration of San'a, Yemen Arab Republic A226

**1988, Aug. 11** **Litho.** ***Perf. 12x11½***

**1329** A226 80f multicolored .95 .70
**1330** A226 160f multicolored 1.90 1.50

Historic Natl. Sites A227

**1988, Aug. 11** ***Perf. 13½x13***

**1331** A227 60f Umm Al-rasas .70 .50
**1332** A227 80f Umm Qais .90 .70
**1333** A227 160f Iraq Al-amir 1.90 1.50
*Nos. 1331-1333 (3)* 3.50 2.70

An imperf. souvenir sheet of 3 exists containing one each Nos. 1331-1333. Value $5.

1988 Summer Olympics, Seoul — A228

10f, Tennis. 60f, Character trademark. 80f, Running, swimming. 120f, Basketball. 160f, Soccer.
100f, Emblems.

**1988, Sept. 17** **Litho.** ***Perf. 13x13½***

**1334** A228 10f multi .25 .25
**1335** A228 60f multi .90 .70
**1336** A228 80f multi 1.40 .90
**1337** A228 120f multi 1.75 1.50
**1338** A228 160f multi 2.50 1.75
*Nos. 1334-1338 (5)* 6.80 5.10

**Size: 70x91mm**

***Imperf***

**1339** A228 100f multi 17.50 17.50

Royal Jordanian Airlines, 25th Anniv. — A229

60f, Ruins of Petra. 80f, Aircraft, world map.

**1988, Dec. 15** **Litho.** ***Perf. 11½x12***

**1340** A229 60f multicolored 1.00 .75
**1341** A229 80f multicolored 1.25 1.00

UN Declaration of Human Rights, 40th Anniv. — A230

**1988, Dec. 10**

**1342** A230 80f multicolored .75 .60
**1343** A230 160f multicolored 1.75 1.10

Arab Cooperation Council, Feb. 16 — A231

**1989** **Litho.** ***Perf. 13½x13***

**1344** A231 10f shown .25 .25
**1345** A231 30f multi, diff. .25 .25
**1346** A231 40f multi, diff. .25 .25
**1347** A231 60f multi, diff. 1.00 .95
*Nos. 1344-1347 (4)* 1.75 1.70

Martyrs of Palestine and Their Families — A232

**1989** ***Perf. 14½***
**1348** A232 5f multicolored .90 .30
**1349** A232 10f multicolored .90 .30

Interparliamentary Union, Cent. — A233

**1989** **Litho.** ***Perf. 12***
**1350** A233 40f multicolored .35 .25
**1351** A233 60f multicolored .55 .35

Arab Housing Day and World Refuge Day A234

Designs: 5f, Housing complex, emblems, vert. 60f, Housing complex, emblem.

**1989**
**1352** A234 5f multicolored .25 .25
**1353** A234 40f shown .55 .25
**1354** A234 60f multicolored .75 .55
*Nos. 1352-1354 (3)* 1.55 1.05

Ministry of Agriculture, 50th Anniv. — A235

40f, Tree, anniv. emblem. 60f, Fruit tree, emblem, apiary.

**1989** **Litho.** ***Perf. 12***
**1355** A235 5f shown .25 .25
**1356** A235 40f multicolored .25 .25
**1357** A235 60f multicolored 2.25 .25
*Nos. 1355-1357 (3)* 2.75 .75

Arabian Horse Festival A236

40f, Horse, building facade. 60f, Horse's head, vert. 100f, Mare and foal.

**1989** ***Perf. 12***
**1358** A236 5f shown .40 .25
**1359** A236 40f multicolored .85 .25
**1360** A236 60f multicolored 2.40 .25
*Nos. 1358-1360 (3)* 3.65 .75

**Size: 90x70mm**

***Imperf***

**1361** A236 100f multicolored *25.00 22.50*

Natl. Library Assoc. A237

**1989** ***Perf. 12***
**1362** A237 40f multicolored .25 .25
**1363** A237 60f multicolored 1.00 .25

Mosque of the Martyr King Abdullah — A238

**1989** ***Perf. 12***
**1364** A238 40f multicolored .25 .25
**1365** A238 60f multicolored 1.00 .25

**Size: 90x70mm**

***Imperf***

**1366** A238 100f multicolored *6.75 6.75*

Mosaics A239

5f, Man with Basket. 10f, Building. 40f, Deer. 60f, Man with stick. 80f, Town, horiz.

**1989, Dec. 23** **Litho.** ***Perf. 12***
**1367** A239 5f multi .60 .30
**1368** A239 10f multi .60 .30
**1369** A239 40f multi 1.50 .50
**1370** A239 60f multi 2.00 .65
**1371** A239 80f multi 2.50 .90
*Nos. 1367-1371 (5)* 7.20 2.65

**Size: 90x70mm**

***Imperf***

**1372** A239 100f like #1371, horiz. *17.50 17.50*

Arab Cooperation Council, 1st Anniv. — A240

**1990, Feb. 16** ***Perf. 13***
**1373** A240 5f multicolored .25 .25
**1374** A240 20f multicolored .25 .25
**1375** A240 60f multicolored .75 .45
**1376** A240 80f multicolored 1.00 .65
*Nos. 1373-1376 (4)* 2.25 1.60

Nature Conservation — A241

**1990, Apr. 22**
**1377** A241 40f Horses .25 .25
**1378** A241 60f Mountain .50 .25
**1379** A241 80f Oasis .65 .35
*Nos. 1377-1379 (3)* 1.40 .85

Prince Abdullah's Arrival in Ma'an, 70th Anniv. — A243

**1990** **Litho.** ***Perf. 13½x13***
**1382** A243 40f org & multi .25 .25
**1383** A243 60f grn & multi .40 .25

**Size: 90x70mm**

***Imperf***

**1384** A243 200f multicolored *7.00 7.00*

UN Development Program, 40th Anniv. — A244

**1990** ***Perf. 13***
**1385** A244 60f multicolored .25 .25
**1386** A244 80f multicolored .55 .25

King Hussein — A245

**1990-92** **Litho.** ***Perf. 12x13½***
**1387** A245 5f yel org & multi .25 .25
*a.* Slightly larger vignette, inscr. 1991 .25 .25
**1390** A245 20f bl grn & multi .25 .25
**1391** A245 40f orange & multi .25 .25
**1393** A245 60f blue & multi .45 .45
**1395** A245 80f pink & multi .70 .70
*a.* Slightly larger vignette, inscr. 1991 .70 .70
**1397** A245 240f brown & multi 1.25 .90
**1398** A245 320f red lilac & multi 1.75 1.25
**1399** A245 1d yel green & multi 2.75 2.40
*Nos. 1387-1399 (8)* 7.65 6.45

No. 1390 dated 1991.
Issued: 20f, 1992; 5f, 60f, 80f 1990; others 1991.

Endangered Animals A246

**1991, Sept. 1** **Litho.** ***Perf. 13x13½***
**1401** A246 5f Nubian ibex .25 .25
**1402** A246 40f Onager .50 .25
**1403** A246 80f Arabian gazelle 2.25 .40
**1404** A246 160f Arabian oryx 1.60 1.10
*Nos. 1401-1404 (4)* 4.60 2.00

Energy Rationalization Program — A247

Designs: 5f, Light bulbs. 40f, Solar panels, sun, vert. 80f, Electric table lamp, vert.

***Perf. 13½x13, 13x13½***
**1991, Oct. 3** **Litho.**
**1405** A247 5f multicolored .25 .25
**1406** A247 40f multicolored .25 .25
**1407** A247 80f multicolored .70 .25
*Nos. 1405-1407 (3)* 1.20 .75

Grain Production for Food Security — A248

5f, Different grains. 80f, Wheat stalk, kernels.

**1991, Oct. 16** ***Perf. 13½x13***
**1408** A248 5f multicolored .25 .25
**1409** A248 40f shown .25 .25
**1410** A248 80f multicolored .70 .25
*Nos. 1408-1410 (3)* 1.20 .75

Palestinian Uprising — A249

**1991, Nov. 29** **Litho.** ***Perf. 11***
**1411** A249 20f multicolored 2.00 .75

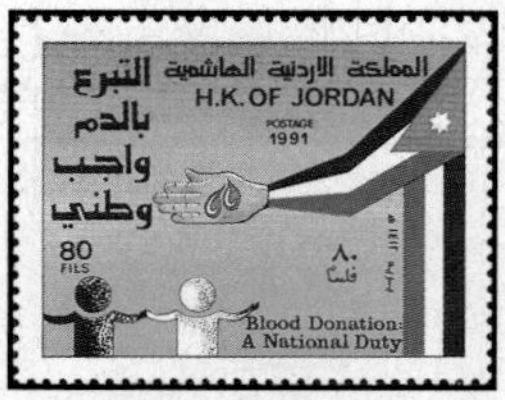


Blood Donation Campaign — A250

**1991, Nov. 14** **Litho.** ***Perf. 13½x13***
**1412** A250 80f multicolored .75 .25
**1413** A250 160f multicolored 1.50 .75

Expo '92, Seville A251

**1992, Feb. 20**
**1414** A251 80f multicolored .65 .25
**1415** A251 320f multicolored 1.60 .95

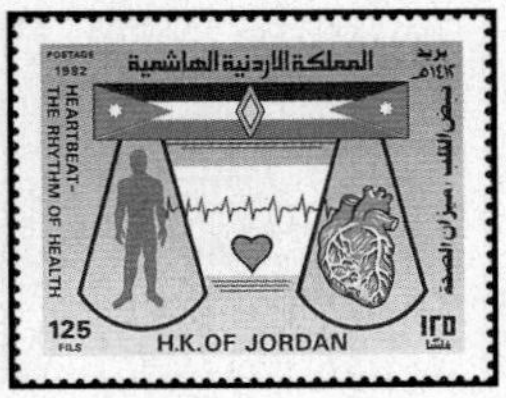


Healthy Hearts A252

80f, Man & woman, heart at center of scale, vert.

*Perf. 13x13½, 13½x13*

**1992, Apr. 7** **Litho.**

**1416** A252 80f multicolored .70 .25
**1417** A252 125f multicolored .80 .50

SOS Children's Village, 'Aqaba — A253

**1992, Apr. 30** **Litho.** *Perf. 13½x13*

**1418** A253 80f shown .70 .25
**1419** A253 125f Village .80 .50

1992 Summer Olympics, Barcelona — A254

Stylized designs with Barcelona Olympic emblem: 5fr, Judo, 40f, Runner, vert. 80f, Diver. 125f, Flag, Cobi, map, vert. 160f, Table tennis.

100f, Incorporates all designs of set.

*Perf. 13½x13, 13x13½*

**1992, July 25** **Litho.**

**1420** A254 5f multicolored .25 .25
**1421** A254 40f multicolored .25 .25
**1422** A254 80f multicolored .50 .25
**1423** A254 125f multicolored .75 .35
**1424** A254 160f multicolored 1.10 .50
*Nos. 1420-1424 (5)* 2.85 1.60

**Size: 70x90mm**

***Imperf***

**1425** A254 100f multicolored *15.00 12.00*

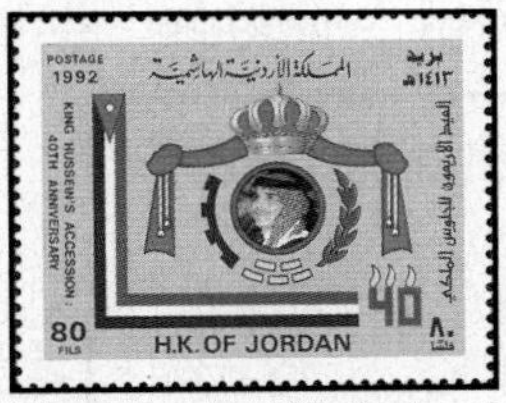


King Hussein, 40th Anniv. of Accession — A255

Designs: 40f, Flags, King in full dress uniform, vert. 125f, King wearing headdress, flags. 160f, King in business suit, crown. 200f, Portrait.

**1992, Aug. 11** *Perf. 13x13½*

**1426** A255 40f multicolored .25 .25

*Perf. 13½x13*

**1427** A255 80f shown .45 .25
**1428** A255 125f multicolored .75 .35
**1429** A255 160f multicolored 1.10 .50
*Nos. 1426-1429 (4)* 2.55 1.35

**Size: 90x70mm**

***Imperf***

**1430** A255 200f multicolored *7.25 7.25*

Butterflies — A256

5f, Danaus chrysippus. 40f, Aporia cartaegi. 80f, Papilio machaon. 160f, Pseudochazara telephassa. 200f, Same as Nos. 1431-1434.

**1992, Dec. 20** **Litho.** *Perf. 13½x13*

**1431** A256 5f multicolored .50 .25
**1432** A256 40f multicolored 1.00 .25
**1433** A256 80f multicolored 2.00 .50
**1434** A256 160f multicolored 4.50 1.25
*Nos. 1431-1434 (4)* 8.00 2.25

***Imperf***

**Size: 90x70mm**

**1435** A256 200f multicolored *17.50 17.50*

See Nos. 1448-1452.

Intl. Customs Day — A257

**1993, Jan. 26** **Litho.** *Perf. 13½x13*

**1436** A257 80f green & multi .60 .25
**1437** A257 125f pale org & multi .90 .45

Royal Scientific Society — A258

**1993, June 10** **Litho.** *Perf. 12½x13*

**1438** A258 80f multicolored .50 .25

Es Salt Municipality, Cent. — A259

**1993, Sept. 1** **Litho.** *Perf. 12*

**1439** A259 80f pink & multi .60 .25
**1440** A259 125f green & multi .90 .45
*a.* Souvenir sheet of 2, #1439-1440, imperf. *6.25 6.25*

No. 1440a sold for 200f.

Great Arab Revolt and Army Day A260

Designs: 5f, Rockets, planes, tank, King Hussein, 40f, King Hussein, military activities. 80f, Amir Abdullah ibn Hussein, Dome of the Rock, map, flags. 125f, Amir Abdullah ibn Hussein, Dome of the Rock, riders. 100f, King Hussein, flags.

**1993, June 10**

**1441** A260 5f multicolored .25 .25
**1442** A260 40f multicolored .25 .25
**1443** A260 80f multicolored .50 .25
**1444** A260 125f multicolored .85 .35
*Nos. 1441-1444 (4)* 1.85 1.10

**Size: 90x70mm**

***Imperf***

**1445** A260 100f multicolored *6.00 6.00*

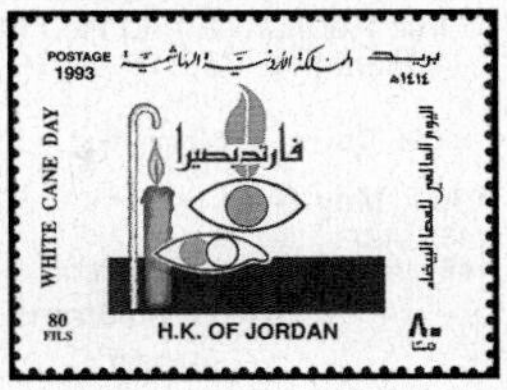


White Cane Day A261

Design: 125f, Lighted world, cane, eye, vert.

**1993, Oct. 23** **Litho.** *Perf. 12*

**1446** A261 80f shown .60 .25
**1447** A261 125f multicolored .90 .45

**Butterfly Type of 1992**

Designs: 5f, Lampides boeticus. 40f, Melanargria titea. 80f, Allancastria deyrollei. 160f, Gonepteryx cleopatra. 100f, Same designs as Nos. 1448-1451.

**1993, Oct. 10** *Perf. 12*

**1448** A256 5f multicolored .40 .25
**1449** A256 40f multicolored .75 .30
**1450** A256 80f multicolored 1.00 .40
**1451** A256 160f multicolored 2.50 1.00
*Nos. 1448-1451 (4)* 4.65 1.95

**Size: 83x65mm**

***Imperf***

**1452** A256 100f multicolored *25.00 25.00*

UN Declaration of Human Rights, 45th Anniv. — A262

**1993, Dec. 10** *Perf. 12*

**1453** A262 40f yellow & multi .25 .25
**1454** A262 160f red & multi 1.10 .75

Recovery & Homecoming, 1st Anniv. — A263

King Hussein: 80f, Crowd. 125f, Waving to people. 160f, Embracing woman. 100f, Standing on airplane ramp.

**1993, Nov. 25**

**1455** A263 80f multicolored .50 .25
**1456** A263 125f multicolored .85 .40
**1457** A263 160f multicolored 1.00 .50
*Nos. 1455-1457 (3)* 2.35 1.15

**Size: 85x65**

***Imperf***

**1458** A263 100f multicolored *5.50 3.75*

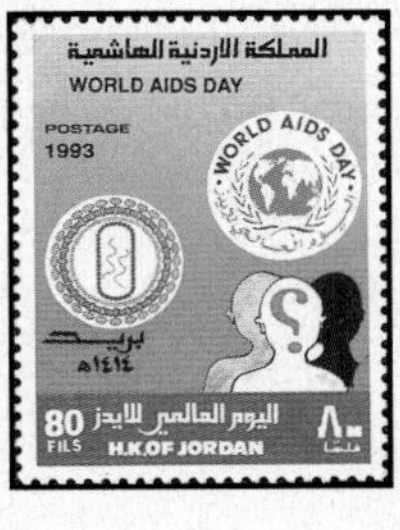


World AIDS Day — A264

**1993, Dec. 1** *Perf. 12*

**1459** A264 80f red & multi .50 .25
**1460** A264 125f green & multi .85 .45

**Size: 83x70mm**

***Imperf***

**1461** A264 200f like #1459-1460 *6.25 4.50*

King Hussein A265

King Hussein wearing: 40f, Military uniform. 80f, Traditional costume. 125f, Business suit. 160f, 100f, Dress uniform in portrait with Queen Noor.

**1993, Nov. 14** *Perf. 12*

**1462** A265 40f multicolored .25 .25
**1463** A265 80f multi, horiz. .50 .25
**1464** A265 125f multi, horiz. .80 .35
**1465** A265 160f multicolored 1.25 .50
*Nos. 1462-1465 (4)* 2.80 1.35

**Size: 82x68mm**

***Imperf***

**1466** A265 100f multicolored *8.00 5.75*

Assumption of Constitutional Powers by King Hussein, 40th anniv.

Saladin (1138-1193), Dome of the Rock — A266

**1993, Nov. 25** *Perf. 12*

**1467** A266 40f blue & multi .25 .25
**1468** A266 80f gray & multi .55 .25
**1469** A266 125f yellow & multi .75 .40
*Nos. 1467-1469 (3)* 1.55 .90

Triumphal Arch, Jerash — A267

***Perf. 12x13½ (5f, No. 80f, 1473A, 1475, 160f, 320f, 1d), 12 (25f, 40f, 50f, #1474C, 240f, No. 1478C, No. 1479), 14x13½ (75f, No. 1474, 150f, 200f, 300f, 400f), 13½x14 (#120f), 12¾x13¼ (#1479B)***

**1993-2003** **Litho.**

**1470** A267 5f blue & multi .25 .25
**1471** A267 25f pale vio & multi .25 .25
*b.* Perf 12¾x13¼, inscr. "2003" .25 .25
**1471A** A267 40f grn & multi .25 .25
**1472** A267 50f yel & multi .25 .25
*a.* Perf 12, inscr. "1996" .25 .25
*b.* Perf 12¾x13¼ .25 .25
*c.* Perf 13½x14 .25 .25
*d.* As "b," inscr. "2003" .25 .25
**1472E** A267 75f buff & multi .40 .40
**1473** A267 80f grn & multi .35 .25
**1473A** A267 100f red & multi .40 .25
*b.* Perf. 12 .40 .40
*c.* As "b," inscribed "1996" .40 .25
**1474** A267 100f apple grn & multi .50 .50
*a.* Perf. 12 .50 .50
*d.* As "a," inscr. "1996" .50 .50
**1474B** A267 120f bl grn & multi .65 .65
**1474C** A267 125f lt bl & multi .60 .60
**1475** A267 125f buff & multi .50 .25
*a.* Perf. 12 .50 .25
**1475B** A267 150f sal pink & multi .90 .90
**1476** A267 160f yel & multi .65 .25
*b.* Perf. 12 .75 .25
*c.* As "b," inscribed "1994" .75 .25
**1476A** A267 200f gray & multi 1.10 1.10
*d.* Perf. 12 1.10 1.10

| | | | | |
|---|---|---|---|---|
| **1477** | A267 240f pink & multi | 1.00 | .25 |
| *b.* | Perf. 12x13½ | .90 | .25 |
| *c.* | perf 12, inscribed "1994" | 1.25 | 1.25 |
| **1477A** | A267 300f pink & multi | 1.75 | 1.75 |
| *d.* | Perf. 12 | 1.75 | 1.75 |
| **1478** | A267 320f brn & multi | 1.25 | .35 |
| **1478A** | A267 320f sal & multi | 1.25 | .35 |
| **1478C** | A267 400f brt blue & multi | 2.50 | 2.50 |
| *b.* | Perf. 13x13¼ | 2.50 | 2.50 |
| **1479** | A267 500f bister & multi | 2.00 | .85 |
| *a.* | Perf. 12x13½ | 2.00 | .85 |
| **1479B** | A267 500f yel & multi | 2.50 | 2.50 |
| **1480** | A267 1d olive & multi | 4.00 | 1.25 |
| *a.* | Perf. 12¾x13¼ | 5.00 | 1.25 |
| | *Nos. 1470-1480 (22)* | 23.30 | 15.95 |

Nos. 1472E, 1473, 1473A , 1477b, 1479a are dated 1992; Nos. 1471A, 1473Ab, 1476b, 1993; No. 1474, 1994; No. 1477Ac, 1995; Nos. 1478Ab, 1479B, 1480a, 1997.

Issued: 5f, 320f, 1/13/93 (dated 1992); 25f, 1/18/96 (dated 1995); 40f, 1994; 100f, 200f, 300f, 5/15/96; 1d, 1/13/93; 125f, 160f, 1/13/93; 240f, 3/23/94; 50f, 1995; 150f, 400f, 5/15/96; 500f, 10/25/96; 75f, 5/15/96; No. 1478Ab, 5/10/98. 80f, Nos. 1473A, 1477b, 1479a, 1/13/93; Nos. 1473Ab, 1476b, 3/23/94; 120f, 5/15/96; No. 1474C, 2/13/95; Nos. 1476Ad, 1477Ad, 1/18/96; No. 1478C, 1993; Nos. 1479B, 1480a, 5/10/98.

For surcharges, see Nos. 2305-2314.

Hashemite Charity Organization — A268

Designs: 80f, Loading supplies into plane. 125f, People gathering at plane.

**1994, Mar. 20 Litho. *Perf. 12***

| | | | |
|---|---|---|---|
| **1481** | A268 80f multicolored | .55 | .25 |
| **1482** | A268 125f multicolored | .80 | .50 |

Third Hashemite Restoration of Al Aqsa Mosque, Dome of the Rock — A269

King Hussein with various scenes of restoration.

**1994, Apr. 18 Litho. *Perf. 12x12½***

| | | | |
|---|---|---|---|
| **1483** | A269 80f yellow & multi | .40 | .25 |
| **1484** | A269 125f lt orange & multi | .70 | .35 |
| **1485** | A269 240f lilac & multi | 1.25 | .60 |
| | *Nos. 1483-1485 (3)* | 2.35 | 1.20 |

***Imperf***

**Size: 90x70mm**

| | | | |
|---|---|---|---|
| **1486** | A269 100f green & multi | *8.00* | *5.50* |

ILO, 75th Anniv. A270

**1994, June 13 Litho. *Perf. 12***

| | | | |
|---|---|---|---|
| **1487** | A270 80f yellow & multi | .45 | .25 |
| **1488** | A270 125f brt pink & multi | .70 | .35 |

Intl. Red Cross and Red Crescent Societies, 75th Anniv. — A271

160f, Doves, emblems, vert.

**1994, May 8 *Perf. 12***

| | | | |
|---|---|---|---|
| **1489** | A271 80f shown | .45 | .25 |
| **1490** | A271 160f multicolored | .80 | .45 |

**Size: 61x78mm**

***Imperf***

| | | | |
|---|---|---|---|
| **1491** | A271 200f #1489-1490 | *11.00* | *8.25* |

Intl. Year of the Family A272

**1994, Aug. 11 Litho. *Perf. 12***

| | | | |
|---|---|---|---|
| **1492** | A272 80f green & multi | .45 | .25 |
| **1493** | A272 125f pink & multi | .80 | .40 |
| **1494** | A272 160f yellow & multi | 1.00 | .45 |
| | *Nos. 1492-1494 (3)* | 2.25 | 1.10 |

Intl. Olympic Committee, Cent. — A273

Olympic rings and: 80f, Globe, venue symbols, vert. 100f, Jordanian colors. 125f, Venue symbols, diff., vert. 160f, shown. 240f, Torch.

**1994, June 23**

| | | | |
|---|---|---|---|
| **1495** | A273 80f blue & multi | .40 | .25 |
| **1496** | A273 125f multicolored | .65 | .30 |
| **1497** | A273 160f multicolored | 1.10 | .40 |
| **1498** | A273 240f multicolored | 1.60 | .65 |
| | *Nos. 1495-1498 (4)* | 3.75 | 1.60 |

**Size: 90x70mm**

***Imperf***

| | | | |
|---|---|---|---|
| **1499** | A273 100f multicolored | *8.50* | *8.50* |

Jordanian Participation in UN Peacekeeping Forces — A274

Designs: 80f, King Hussein greeting troops. 125f, King inspecting troops. 160f, Checkpoint.

**1994, Aug. 11 Litho. *Perf. 12***

| | | | |
|---|---|---|---|
| **1500** | A274 80f multicolored | .45 | .25 |
| **1501** | A274 125f multicolored | .70 | .35 |
| **1502** | A274 160f multicolored | .85 | .45 |
| | *Nos. 1500-1502 (3)* | 2.00 | 1.05 |

Water Conservation Day — A275

80f, Hands, water droplet. 125f, Water faucet, foods, factory. 160f, Child, rain drops.

**1994, Nov. 14 Litho. *Perf. 14***

| | | | |
|---|---|---|---|
| **1503** | A275 80f multicolored | .60 | .25 |
| **1504** | A275 125f multicolored | 1.00 | .55 |
| **1505** | A275 160f multicolored | 1.25 | .60 |
| | *Nos. 1503-1505 (3)* | 2.85 | 1.40 |

ICAO, 50th Anniv. A276

**1994, Oct. 25 *Perf. 12***

| | | | |
|---|---|---|---|
| **1506** | A276 80f green & multi | .45 | .25 |
| **1507** | A276 125f red & multi | .70 | .35 |
| **1508** | A276 160f blue & multi | .85 | .45 |
| | *Nos. 1506-1508 (3)* | 2.00 | 1.05 |

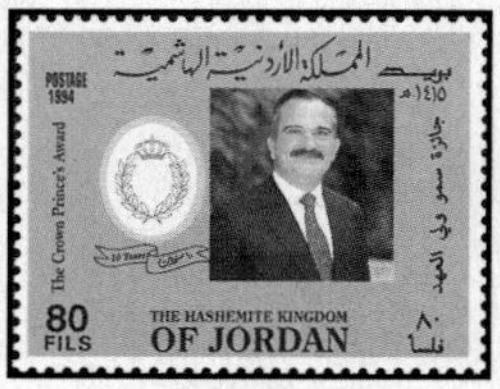

Crown Prince's Award, 10th Anniv. A277

**1994, Dec. 11 Litho. *Perf. 12***

| | | | |
|---|---|---|---|
| **1509** | A277 80f yel grn & multi | .70 | .25 |
| **1510** | A277 125f org brn & multi | .90 | .55 |
| **1511** | A277 160f vio bl & multi | 1.25 | .70 |
| | *Nos. 1509-1511 (3)* | 2.85 | 1.50 |

UN, 50th Anniv. A278

**1995, Apr. 1 Litho. *Perf. 14***

| | | | |
|---|---|---|---|
| **1512** | A278 80f green & multi | .65 | .25 |
| **1513** | A278 125f pink & multi | .95 | .55 |

May Day A279

80f, Emblem, workers, flag. 125f, Emblem, world map, worker. 160f, Hands holding wrench, torch, Jordanian map, emblem.

**1995, May 1**

| | | | |
|---|---|---|---|
| **1514** | A279 80f multicolored | .45 | .25 |
| **1515** | A279 125f multicolored | .65 | .40 |
| **1516** | A279 160f multicolored | .90 | .45 |
| | *Nos. 1514-1516 (3)* | 2.00 | 1.10 |

Jordan Week in Japan A280

Globe in two hemispheres with olive branches and: 125f, Japanese, Jordanian flags. 160f, Flags above wall.

**1995, May 22 Litho. *Perf. 14***

| | | | |
|---|---|---|---|
| **1517** | A280 80f green & multi | .45 | .25 |
| **1518** | A280 125f pink & multi | .70 | .30 |
| **1519** | A280 160f gray & multi | .85 | .45 |
| | *Nos. 1517-1519 (3)* | 2.00 | 1.00 |

Opening of Al al-Bayt University A281

**1995, Feb. 8 Litho. *Perf. 12***

| | | | |
|---|---|---|---|
| **1520** | A281 80f aqua & multi | .50 | .25 |
| **1521** | A281 125f ol grn & multi | .75 | .40 |
| *a.* | Souvenir sheet, #1520-1521, imperf. | 3.75 | 3.25 |

No. 1521a sold for 200f. Nos. 1520-1521 are dated 1994.

Petra, the Rose City A282

Archaeological discoveries: 50f, Amphitheater. 75f, Facial carvings, bowl, pitcher. 80f, Columns of building, vert. 160f, Front of building with columns, vert. 200f, Building in side of mountain.

**1995, Aug. 11 Litho. *Perf. 14***

| | | | |
|---|---|---|---|
| **1524** | A282 50f multicolored | .25 | .25 |
| **1525** | A282 75f multicolored | .85 | .25 |
| **1526** | A282 80f multicolored | .95 | .25 |
| **1527** | A282 160f multicolored | 1.75 | .95 |
| | *Nos. 1524-1527 (4)* | 3.80 | 1.70 |

**Size: 90x70mm**

***Imperf***

| | | | |
|---|---|---|---|
| **1528** | A282 200f multicolored | *20.00* | *20.00* |

Arab League, 50th Anniv. A283

**1995, Sept. 20 Litho. *Perf. 14***

| | | | |
|---|---|---|---|
| **1529** | A283 80f green & multi | .45 | .25 |
| **1530** | A283 125f pink & multi | .70 | .25 |
| **1531** | A283 160f gray & multi | .85 | .45 |
| | *Nos. 1529-1531 (3)* | 2.00 | .95 |

FAO, 50th Anniv. A284

Designs: 125f, "50," FAO emblem, shafts of grain. 160f, UN, FAO emblems, "50."

**1995, Oct. 16 Litho. *Perf. 14***

| | | | | | |
|---|---|---|---|---|---|
| **1532** | A284 | 80f shown | .50 | .25 |
| **1533** | A284 | 125f multicolored | .85 | .40 |
| **1534** | A284 | 160f multicolored | 1.00 | .50 |
| | | *Nos. 1532-1534 (3)* | 2.35 | 1.15 |

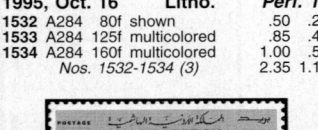

Middle East and North Africa Economic Summit, Amman — A285

**1995, Oct. 29 *Perf. 12***

| | | | | |
|---|---|---|---|---|
| **1535** | A285 | 80f brt pink & multi | .50 | .25 |
| **1536** | A285 | 125f org yel & multi | .75 | .40 |

The Deaf A286

125f, Emblems, hand sign.

**1995, Nov. 30 *Perf. 14***

| | | | | |
|---|---|---|---|---|
| **1537** | A286 | 80f shown | .50 | .25 |
| **1538** | A286 | 125f multicolored | .75 | .35 |

King Hussein, 60th Birthday A287

Designs: 40f, Crown over King's picture in business suit. 80f, Crown, flag, dove, ruins of Petra, King in traditional head wear, military uniform. 100f, King dress uniform, crown, "60." 125f, King in traditional head wear, business suit, crown, flag, olive branch. 160f, Flag, King in business suit. 200f, "60," Dome of the Rock, King in dress uniform, olive branch.

**1995, Nov. 14**

| | | | | |
|---|---|---|---|---|
| **1539** | A287 | 25f multicolored | .25 | .25 |
| **1540** | A287 | 40f multicolored | .25 | .25 |
| **1541** | A287 | 80f multicolored | .45 | .25 |
| **1542** | A287 | 100f multicolored | .50 | .25 |
| **1543** | A287 | 125f multicolored | 1.00 | .35 |
| **1544** | A287 | 160f multicolored | 1.25 | .45 |
| | | *Nos. 1539-1544 (6)* | 3.70 | 1.80 |

**Size: 83x63mm**

***Imperf***

| | | | | |
|---|---|---|---|---|
| **1545** | A287 | 200f multicolored | *6.25* | *6.25* |

Independence, 50th Anniv. — A288

King Hussein and: No. 1547, Outline map of Jordan, crown, dove of peace, Amir Abdullah ibn Hussein. 300f, Jordanian monuments, flag.
No. 1549, Map of Jordan surrounded by wreath, dove, national flags.

**1996, May 25 Litho. *Perf. 12***

| | | | | |
|---|---|---|---|---|
| **1546** | A288 | 100f multicolored | .55 | .25 |
| **1547** | A288 | 200f multicolored | 1.10 | .40 |
| **1548** | A288 | 300f multicolored | 1.75 | .65 |
| | | *Nos. 1546-1548 (3)* | 3.40 | 1.30 |

**Size: 86x66mm**

| | | | | |
|---|---|---|---|---|
| **1549** | A288 | 200f multicolored | *7.50* | *7.50* |

1996 Summer Olympic Games, Atlanta A289

1996 Olympic Games Emblem and: 50f, Natl. flag, Olympic rings, sports pictograms. 100f, Sports pictograms. 200f, Hands. 300f, Torch, Olympic rings, natl. flag.

**1996, July 19 Litho. *Perf. 12***

| | | | | |
|---|---|---|---|---|
| **1550** | A289 | 50f multicolored | .25 | .25 |
| **1551** | A289 | 100f multicolored | .70 | .25 |
| **1552** | A289 | 200f multicolored | 1.60 | .70 |
| **1553** | A289 | 300f multicolored | 2.50 | 1.10 |
| | | *Nos. 1550-1553 (4)* | 5.05 | 2.30 |

Protection of the Ozone Layer — A290

**1996, Sept. 16**

| | | | | |
|---|---|---|---|---|
| **1554** | A290 | 100f multicolored | 1.25 | .25 |

UNICEF, 50th Anniv. — A291

**1996, Dec. 11 Litho. *Perf. 12***

| | | | | |
|---|---|---|---|---|
| **1555** | A291 | 100f green & multi | .60 | .25 |
| **1556** | A291 | 200f gray lilac & multi | 1.00 | .60 |

Crown Prince El-Hassan, 50th Birthday — A292

Designs: 50f, On horseback. 100f, Wearing suit & tie, vert. No. 1559, Natl. flag, wearing traditional attire.
No. 1560, Wearing graduation cap.

**1997, Mar. 20 Litho. *Perf. 12***

| | | | | |
|---|---|---|---|---|
| **1557** | A292 | 50f multicolored | .25 | .25 |
| **1558** | A292 | 100f multicolored | .70 | .25 |
| **1559** | A292 | 200f multicolored | 1.10 | .70 |
| | | *Nos. 1557-1559 (3)* | 2.05 | 1.20 |

**Size: 84x64mm**

***Imperf***

| | | | | |
|---|---|---|---|---|
| **1560** | A292 | 200f multicolored | *8.25* | *8.25* |

Heinrich von Stephan (1831-97) A293

**1997, Apr. 8 Litho. *Perf. 12***

| | | | | |
|---|---|---|---|---|
| **1561** | A293 | 100f multicolored | .90 | .25 |
| **1562** | A293 | 200f multicolored | 1.60 | .80 |

Discovery of the Madeba Mosaic Map, Cent. — A294

100f, Karak, vert. 200f, River Jordan. 300f, Jerusalem, vert.
No. 1566, Entire map.

**1997, Apr. 7**

| | | | | |
|---|---|---|---|---|
| **1563** | A294 | 100f multicolored | .75 | .35 |
| **1564** | A294 | 200f multicolored | 1.50 | .50 |
| **1565** | A294 | 300f multicolored | 2.50 | .90 |
| | | *Nos. 1563-1565 (3)* | 4.75 | 1.75 |

**Size: 86x67mm**

***Imperf***

| | | | | |
|---|---|---|---|---|
| **1566** | A294 | 100f multi | *15.00* | *15.00* |

Jordanian Rosefinch — A295

**1997, May 25 Litho. *Perf. 12***

| | | | | |
|---|---|---|---|---|
| **1567** | A295 | 50f multicolored | .25 | .25 |
| **1568** | A295 | 100f multi, diff. | .65 | .25 |
| **1569** | A295 | 150f multi, diff. | 1.00 | .45 |
| **1570** | A295 | 200f multi, diff. | 1.50 | .65 |
| | | *Nos. 1567-1570 (4)* | 3.40 | 1.60 |

Jerash Festival, 15th Anniv. A296

Designs: 50f, Couples in traditional costumes, ruins. 100f, Symphony orchestra, silhouettes of buildings. 150f, Pillars, parade of dignitaries. 200f, Women in traditional costumes, crowd, ruins.
15d, Queen Noor lighting torch.

**1997, July 23 Litho. *Perf. 12***

| | | | | |
|---|---|---|---|---|
| **1571** | A296 | 50f multicolored | .25 | .25 |
| **1572** | A296 | 100f multicolored | .60 | .25 |
| **1573** | A296 | 150f multicolored | .95 | .45 |
| **1574** | A296 | 200f multicolored | 1.50 | .65 |
| | | *Nos. 1571-1574 (4)* | 3.30 | 1.60 |

**Size: 90x70mm**

***Imperf***

| | | | | |
|---|---|---|---|---|
| **1575** | A296 | 15d multicolored | 8.50 | 8.50 |

Natl. Forum for Women A297

Emblem and: 50f, Women in tradtional and modern dress, vert. 100f, Natl. flag, flame, book. 150fr, Natl. flag, women seated at conference table.

**1997, Dec. 20 Litho. *Perf. 12***

| | | | | |
|---|---|---|---|---|
| **1576** | A297 | 50f multicolored | .25 | .25 |
| **1577** | A297 | 100f multicolored | .50 | .25 |
| **1578** | A297 | 150f multicolored | .80 | .35 |
| | | *Nos. 1576-1578 (3)* | 1.55 | .85 |

Jordanian Team, 1997 Arab Soccer Champions — A298

Designs: 50f, Team parading in stadium. 75f, Team in red uniforms. 100f, Team in white uniforms, ceremony.
200f, Formal presentation to King Hussein, motorcade.

**1997, Dec. 15**

| | | | | |
|---|---|---|---|---|
| **1579** | A298 | 50f multicolored | .25 | .25 |
| **1580** | A298 | 75f multicolored | .40 | .25 |
| **1581** | A298 | 100f multicolored | .55 | .25 |
| | | *Nos. 1579-1581 (3)* | 1.20 | .75 |

**Size: 91x70mm**

***Imperf***

| | | | | |
|---|---|---|---|---|
| **1582** | A298 | 200f multicolored | *9.00* | *7.50* |

House of Parliament, 50th Anniv. — A299

100f, Outside view of building, drawing. 200f, Speaker, members assembled in chamber.

**1997, Nov. 1 *Perf. 12½***

| | | | | |
|---|---|---|---|---|
| **1583** | A299 | 100f multicolored | .60 | .25 |
| **1584** | A299 | 200f multicolored | .90 | .60 |

53rd General Meeting of Intl. Air Transport Association A300

**1997, Nov. 3 Litho. *Perf. 13x13½***

| | | | | |
|---|---|---|---|---|
| **1585** | A300 | 100f lt blue & multi | 1.00 | 1.00 |
| **1586** | A300 | 200f red & multi | 1.00 | 1.00 |
| **1587** | A300 | 300f gray & multi | 1.00 | 1.00 |

Two additional stamps were issued in this set. The editors would like to examine them.

King Hussein II, 62nd Birthday A301

**1997, Nov. 14 Litho. *Perf. 13x13½***

**Frame Color**

| | | | | |
|---|---|---|---|---|
| **1588** | A301 | 100f red | 1.00 | 1.00 |
| **1589** | A301 | 200f gold | 1.00 | 1.00 |
| **1590** | A301 | 300f blue | 1.00 | 1.00 |

**Souvenir Sheet**

***Perf. 12***

| | | | | |
|---|---|---|---|---|
| **1590A** | A301 | 200f gold | 8.50 | 8.50 |

No. 1590A contains one 44x60mm stamp.

Earth Day A302

Children's drawings: 50f, Various ways of polluting air and water. 100f, Pollution from factory smoke, automobiles. 150f, Earth chained to various methods of pollution, vert.

**1998, Apr. 29 Litho. *Perf. 14***

| | | | | |
|---|---|---|---|---|
| **1591** | A302 | 50f multicolored | .25 | .25 |
| **1592** | A302 | 100f multicolored | .50 | .25 |
| **1593** | A302 | 150f multicolored | .80 | .50 |
| | | *Nos. 1591-1593 (3)* | 1.55 | 1.00 |

Trans-Jordan Emirate, 75th Anniv. — A303

Designs: 100f, Camel rider holding flag, Amir Abdullah ibn Hussein. 200f, Camel rider holding flag, King Hussein. 300f, King Hussein, arms, #81, Amir Abdullah ibn Hussein.

**1998, May 25 *Perf. 12***

| | | | | |
|---|---|---|---|---|
| **1594** | A303 | 100f multicolored | .50 | .50 |
| **1595** | A303 | 200f multicolored | 1.00 | 1.00 |
| **1596** | A303 | 300f multicolored | 1.75 | 1.75 |
| | | *Nos. 1594-1596 (3)* | 3.25 | 3.25 |

**Size: 80x70mm**

***Imperf***

| | | | | |
|---|---|---|---|---|
| **1597** | A303 | 300f like #1596 | *8.50* | *8.50* |

Mosaics, Um Ar-Rasas A304

**1998, July 22 Litho. *Perf. 14***

| | | | | |
|---|---|---|---|---|
| **1598** | A304 | 100f multicolored | .50 | .50 |
| **1599** | A304 | 200f multi, diff. | 1.00 | 1.00 |
| **1600** | A304 | 300f multi, diff. | 1.75 | 1.75 |
| | | *Nos. 1598-1600 (3)* | 3.25 | 3.25 |

Flowers A305

50f, Purple & white, thorns. 100f, Poppies. 200f, Flower, map of Jordan.

**1998, July 7**

| | | | | |
|---|---|---|---|---|
| **1601** | A305 | 50f multicolored | .30 | .25 |
| **1602** | A305 | 100f multicolored | .60 | .55 |
| **1603** | A305 | 150f shown | 1.00 | .75 |
| | | *Nos. 1601-1603 (3)* | 1.90 | 1.55 |

**Size: 60x80mm**

***Imperf***

| | | | | |
|---|---|---|---|---|
| **1604** | A305 | 200f multicolored | *8.50* | *8.50* |

2nd Arab Beekeepers Conference — A306

Various pictures of bees, flowers, honeycomb.

**1998, Aug. 3 Litho. *Perf. 14***

| | | | | |
|---|---|---|---|---|
| **1605** | A306 | 50f multicolored | .50 | .40 |
| **1606** | A306 | 100f multi, vert. | .85 | .50 |
| **1607** | A306 | 150f multicolored | 1.25 | .60 |
| | | *Nos. 1605-1607 (3)* | 2.60 | 1.50 |

**Size: 80x60mm**

***Imperf***

| | | | | |
|---|---|---|---|---|
| **1608** | A306 | 200f Bees, flowers, emblem | *9.00* | *9.00* |

World Stamp Day A307

100f, World map, emblems. 150f, Globe, stamps.

**1998, Oct. 9 Litho. *Perf. 14***

| | | | | |
|---|---|---|---|---|
| **1609** | A307 | 50f shown | .25 | .25 |
| **1610** | A307 | 100f multicolored | .90 | .90 |
| **1611** | A307 | 150f multicolored | 1.75 | 1.75 |
| | | *Nos. 1609-1611 (3)* | 2.90 | 2.90 |

Universal Declaration of Human Rights, 50th Anniv. — A308

200f, Emblems, people.

**1998, Dec. 10**

| | | | | |
|---|---|---|---|---|
| **1612** | A308 | 100f shown | .60 | .60 |
| **1613** | A308 | 200f multicolored | 1.00 | 1.00 |

King Hussein, 63rd Birthday A309

**1998, Nov. 14 Litho. *Perf. 14x14½***

| | | | | |
|---|---|---|---|---|
| **1614** | A309 | 100f green & multi | .65 | .45 |
| **1615** | A309 | 200f violet & multi | 1.25 | 1.00 |
| **1616** | A309 | 300f vio blue & multi | 2.25 | 1.50 |
| | | *Nos. 1614-1616 (3)* | 4.15 | 2.95 |

**Size: 90x70mm**

***Imperf***

| | | | | |
|---|---|---|---|---|
| **1617** | A309 | 300f gold & multi | *8.50* | *8.50* |

Arab Police and Security Chiefs Meeting, 25th Anniv. (in 1997) A310

Map of Arab world and: 100f, King Hussein, emblem. 200f, Flags of Arab countries, emblem, flame, vert. 300f, Beret.

**1998, Nov. 18 *Perf. 14***

| | | | | |
|---|---|---|---|---|
| **1618** | A310 | 100f multicolored | .65 | .65 |
| **1619** | A310 | 200f multicolored | 1.10 | 1.10 |
| **1620** | A310 | 300f multicolored | 2.00 | 1.75 |
| | | *Nos. 1618-1620 (3)* | 3.75 | 3.50 |

Mustafa Wahbi (1899-1949), Poet — A311

**1999, May 25 Litho. *Perf. 14¼***

| | | | | |
|---|---|---|---|---|
| **1621** | A311 | 100f multicolored | .90 | .90 |

Environmental Protection — A312

Designs: 100f, Children, bandaged Earth. 200f, Earth as fruit in hands.

**1999, Oct. 14 Litho. *Perf. 13¼x13¾***

| | | | | |
|---|---|---|---|---|
| **1622** | A312 | 100f multi | .50 | .50 |
| **1623** | A312 | 200f multi | 1.00 | 1.00 |

Hijazi Railway Museum A313

Train and: 100f, 200f, Map of Jordan, museum building. 300f, Museum building.

**1999, Sept. 7 Litho. *Perf. 13½x13¾***

| | | | | |
|---|---|---|---|---|
| **1624-1626** | A313 | Set of 3 | 6.00 | 6.00 |

9th Arab Sports Tournament — A314

Bird mascot, emblem and: 50f, Weight lifting, tennis, wrestling, soccer. 100f, Torch. No. 1629, Shooting, fencing, swimming, track & field, vert. 300f, Flag, map, discus thrower, tennis player.

No. 1631, Basketball, volleyball, boxing, swimming.

***Perf. 13¼x13¾, 13¾x13¼***

**1999, Aug. 15 Litho.**

| | | | | |
|---|---|---|---|---|
| **1627** | A314 | 50f multi | .25 | .25 |
| **1628** | A314 | 100f multi | .65 | .65 |
| **1629** | A314 | 200f multi | 1.40 | 1.40 |
| **1630** | A314 | 300f multi | 2.25 | 2.25 |
| | | *Nos. 1627-1630 (4)* | 4.55 | 4.55 |

***Imperf***

**Size: 90x70mm**

| | | | | |
|---|---|---|---|---|
| **1631** | A314 | 200f multi | 3.25 | 3.25 |

UPU, 125th Anniv. A315

Designs: 100f, "125," UPU emblems, stripes of airmail envelope. No. 1633, Airmail envelope with UPU emblem.

No. 1634, Like No. 1633, yellow background.

**1999, Oct. 9 *Perf. 13¼x13¾***

| | | | | |
|---|---|---|---|---|
| **1632** | A315 | 100f multi | .65 | .65 |
| **1633** | A315 | 200f multi | 1.10 | 1.10 |

***Imperf***

**Size: 90x70mm**

| | | | | |
|---|---|---|---|---|
| **1634** | A315 | 200f multi | 2.50 | 2.50 |

Gulf of Aqaba Corals A316

Designs: 50f, Pachyseris speciosa. 100f, Acropora digitifera. No. 1637, 200f, Oxypora lacera. 300f, Fungia echinata.

No. 1639, 200f, Gorgonia.

**1999, Oct. 2 Litho. *Perf. 13½x13¾***

| | | | | |
|---|---|---|---|---|
| **1635-1638** | A316 | Set of 4 | 4.00 | 4.00 |

***Imperf***

**Size: 90x70mm**

| | | | | |
|---|---|---|---|---|
| **1639** | A316 | 200f multi | *12.00* | *12.00* |

Cradle of Civilizations — A317

Archaeological sites — Petra: No. 1640, 100f, Al-Deir. No. 1641, 200f, Khazneh. No. 1642, 300f, Obelisk tomb.

Jerash: No. 1643, 100f, Cardo Maximus. No. 1644, 200f, Temple of Artemis. No. 1645, 300f, Nymphaeum.

Amman: No. 1646, 100f, Roman Theater. No. 1647, 200f, Citadel. No. 1648, 300f, Ain Ghazal statues.

Wadi Rum and Aqaba: No. 1649, 100f, Camel riders, Wadi Rum. No. 1650, 200f, House, Aqaba. No. 1651, Ruins, Aqaba.

Madaba: No. 1652, 100f, Mosaic. No. 1653, 200f, Church. No. 1654, 300f, Mosaic map of Jerusalem.

Baptism Site (Bethany): No. 1655, Plant life near water. No. 1656, 200f, Aerial view. No. 1657, 300f, Excavation site.

Aljoun: No. 1658, 100f, Ruins. No. 1659, 200f, Ruins diff. No. 1660, 300f, Ruins, diff.

Pella: No. 1661, 100f, Ruins of Byzantine cathedral. No. 1662, 200f, Three large pillars. No. 1663, 300f, Ruins.

**1999-2000 Litho. *Perf. 13½x14***

| | | | | |
|---|---|---|---|---|
| **1640-1663** | A317 | Set of 24 | 23.00 | 23.00 |

Issued: Nos. 1640-1645, 10/24; Nos. 1646-1651, 10/31; Nos. 1652-1654, 12/22; Nos. 1655-1657, 12/23; Nos. 1658-1663, 3/7/00.

See Nos. 1688-1693. For surcharges, see Nos. 2317-2321, 2324-2325.

Museum of Political History — A318

100f, Building interior. 200f, Museum entrance and plaza. 300f, Museum entrance.

**1999, Nov. 14 Litho. *Perf. 13½x14***

**1664-1666** A318 Set of 3 3.75 3.75

Jordan Philatelic Club, 20th Anniv. — A318a

Designs: 100f, #534H and other stamps. 200f, #284 and other stamps.

**1999, Nov. 14 *Perf. 14¼***

**1666A-1666B** A318a Set of 2 1.50 1.50

SOS Children's Village, Irbid — A318b

100f, SOS Children's Village 50th anniv. emblem, Jordanian flag. 200f, Woman, children.

**1999, Nov. 23**

**1666C-1666D** A318b Set of 2 1.50 1.50

Coronation of King Abdullah II — A319

**1999, Dec. 27 Litho. *Perf. 11¾***

**Frame Color**

**1667** A319 100f red .90 .90
**1668** A319 200f green .90 .90
**1669** A319 300f blue .90 .90

**Souvenir Sheet**

**1670** A319 200f gold 1.00 1.00

King Abdullah II and Queen Rania A319a

**1999, Dec. 27 Litho. *Perf. 11¾***

**1670A** A319a 100f red .95 .95
**1670B** A319a 200f green .95 .95
**1670C** A319a 300f blue .95 .95

**Souvenir Sheet**

**1670D** A319a 200f gold *5.25 5.25*

Issued: 1670D, 12/27/99.

Numbers have been reserved for three additional stamps in this set. The editors would like to examine any examples of them.

King Abdullah II, 38th Birthday A320

King, crown and: 100f, Olive branches. 200f, Nos. #1672 #1674, Flag, "38," horiz. 300f, Flag, "38," eagle, olive branch, horiz.

***Perf 12, Imperf (#1674)***

**2000, Jan. 30 Litho.**

**1671-1673** A320 Set of 3 3.00 3.00

**Size: 90x74mm**

**1674** A320 200f multi *3.50 3.50*

Geneva Convention, 50th Anniv. — A321

***Perf. 13½x13¾***

**2000, Feb. 15 Litho.**

**1675** Horiz. strip of 3 3.50 3.50
*a.* A321 100f lt bl & multi .50 .50
*b.* A321 200f ocher & multi 1.00 1.00
*c.* A321 300f gray & multi 1.50 1.50

Dated 1999.

Millennium A322

No. 1678: a, Jordanian flag, "Jordan, The River & The Land of the Baptism" in English. b, Fish in river. c, As "a," with Arabic inscription.

***Perf. 13¼x13¾***

**2000, Feb. 22 Litho.**

**1678** Strip of 3 3.25 3.25
*a.* A322 100f multi .45 .45
*b.* A322 200f multi .90 .90
*c.* A322 300f multi 1.25 1.25

King Abdullah II, Houses of Worship and Pope John Paul II — A323

Color of lower panel: 100f, Dull blue green. 200f, Lilac. 300f, Bright yellow green.

**2000, Mar. 20 Litho. *Perf. 12***

**1679-1681** A323 Set of 3 3.25 3.25

Visit of Pope Paul VI to Jordan, 36th anniv.

Visit of Pope John Paul II to Jordan A324

Pope John Paul II, King Abdullah II and: 100f, "2000." 200f, River. 300f, Vatican and Jordanian flags, map of Jordan. No. 1685, Pope, baptism of Christ, vert.

***Perf 12, Imperf (#1685)***

**2000, Mar. 20**

**1682-1684** A324 Set of 3 3.25 3.25

**Size: 70x90mm**

**1685** A324 200f multi *17.50 17.50*

World Meteorological Organization, 50th Anniv. — A325

Designs: 100f, Globe, emblem, anniversary emblem. 200f, Globe with arrows, emblem, anniversary emblem.

**2000, Mar. 23 Litho. *Perf. 12***

**1686** A325 100f multi .75 .75
**1687** A325 200f multi 1.25 1.25

**Cradle of Civilizations Type of 1999**

Archaeological sites — Palaces: No. 1688, 100f, Mushatta. No. 1689, 200f, Kharaneh. No. 1690, 300f, Amra.

Um Qais: No. 1691, 100f, Decumanus. No. 1692, 200f, Amphitheater. No. 1693, 300f, Ruins.

**2000, Apr. 7 Litho. *Perf. 13½x14***

**Palaces**

**1688-1690** A317 Set of 3 4.00 4.00

**Um Qais**

**1691-1693** A317 Set of 3 4.00 4.00
*a.* Sheet, #1640-1663, 1688-1693 40.00 —

For surcharges, see Nos. 2322-2323.

Scouting in Jordan, 90th Anniv. A326

"90" and: 100f, Emblem, Jordanian flag. 200f, Tents. 300f, Tents, Jordanian flag. No. 1697, Like No. 1694.

***Perf 12, Imperf (#1697)***

**2000, May 11 Litho.**

**1694-1696** A326 Set of 3 5.00 5.00

**Size: 90x70mm**

**1697** A326 200f multi *7.50 7.50*

Expo 2000, Hanover — A327

Designs: No. 1698, 200f, Inscribed clay tablet. 300f, Artifact with two heads.

No. 1700, 200f, King, Queen, Jordan pavilion interior.

**2000, June 1 Litho. *Perf. 11¾***

**Granite Paper**

**1698-1699** A327 Set of 2 3.50 3.50

***Imperf***

**Size: 90x70mm**

**1700** A327 200f multi 3.00 3.00

Palace of Justice A328

Palace and: 100f, Scales of justice. 200f, Scales, Jordanian flag.

**2000, June 25 Unwmk. *Perf. 12***

**1701** A328 100f multi .75 .75

**Wmk. 388**

**1702** A328 200f multi 1.25 1.25

A number has been reserved for an additional stamp in this set. The editors would like to examine it.

Al-Amal Cancer Center — A329

Emblem and: 200f, Building. 300f, Family.

***Perf. 11¾***

**2000, July 17 Litho. Unwmk.**

**Granite Paper**

**1704-1705** A329 Set of 2 3.75 3.75

Flora and Fauna — A330

Designs: 50f, Dove. 100f, Arabian oryx. 150f, Caracal. 200f, Red fox. 300f, Jal'ad iris. 400f, White broom.

**2000, Sept. 28 *Perf. 14¼***

**Booklet Stamps**

**1706** A330 50f multi .35 .30
**1707** A330 100f multi .75 .50
*a.* Booklet pane, 2 each #1706-1707 4.00 —
**1708** A330 150f multi 1.25 .60
**1709** A330 200f multi 1.50 .80
*a.* Booklet pane, 2 each #1708-1709 7.00 —
**1710** A330 300f multi 2.50 1.75
**1711** A330 400f multi 3.00 1.90
*a.* Booklet pane, 2 each #1710-1711 13.00 —
Booklet, #1707a, 1709a, 1711a 30.00

World Conservation Union — A331

Background color: 200f, Green. 300f, Blue.

**2000, Oct. 4** ***Perf. 11¾***

**Granite Paper**

**1712-1713** A331 Set of 2 3.50 3.50

Tourist Sites A332

Designs: 50f, Petra. 100f, Jerash. 150f, Mount Nebo. 200f, Dead Sea. 300f, Aqaba. 400f, Wadi Rum.

**2000, Oct. 9** ***Perf. 14¼***

**Booklet Stamps**

**1714** A332 50f multi .35 .35
**1715** A332 100f multi .75 .60
*a.* Booklet pane, 2 each #1714-1715 2.25 —
**1716** A332 150f multi 1.25 .90
**1717** A332 200f multi 1.75 1.10
*a.* Booklet pane, 2 each #1716-1717 6.00 —
**1718** A332 300f multi 2.25 1.50
**1719** A332 400f multi 2.75 2.25
*a.* Booklet pane, 2 each #1718-1719 10.00 —
Booklet, #1715a, 1717a, 1719a 22.50

King Hussein (1935-99) A333

Designs: 50f, King, vert. No. 1721, 150f, No. 1723, 200f, King and wreath. No. 1722, 200f, King, symbols of industry and agriculture.

**2000, Nov. 14 Litho.** ***Perf. 11¾***

**Granite Paper**

**1720-1722** A333 Set of 3 *2.75 2.75*

**Size: 90x70mm**

***Imperf***

**1723** A333 200f multi *4.50 4.50*

UN High Commissioner for Refugees, 50th Anniv. — A334

Designs: 200f, Man, women, child. 300f, Emblem.

**2000, Dec. 3 Litho.** ***Perf. 11¾***

**Granite Paper**

**1724-1725** A334 Set of 2 3.50 3.50

13th Arab Summit Conference A335

Emblem, map of Middle East and: 50f, Jordanian flag. 200f, Jordanian flags. 250f, King Abdullah II.

**2001, Aug. 1** ***Perf. 14***

**1726-1728** A335 Set of 3 3.00 3.00

Palestinian Intifada A336

Dome of the Rock and: 200f, Rock throwers, man carrying flag. 300f, Rock throwers, Israeli troops.

**2001, Aug. 5**

**1729-1730** A336 Set of 2 3.00 3.00

Mohammed Al-Dorra, Boy Killed in Intifada Crossfire A337

Designs: 200f, Al-Dorra and father, Dome of the Rock. 300f, Close-up of Al-Dorra, Al-Dorra dead on father's lap.

**2001, Aug. 5**

**1731-1732** A337 Set of 2 3.00 3.00

Healthy Non-smoking Students — A338

Designs: 200f, Students. 300f, Cartoon character, vert.

**2001, Sept. 1**

**1733-1734** A338 Set of 2 3.00 3.00

Sports For People With Special Needs — A339

Stylized figures and: 200f, Man in wheelchair. 300f, Woman.

**2001, Sept. 15**

**1735-1736** A339 Set of 2 3.00 3.00

Olive Trees A340

Designs: 200f, Olives on branch, tree, map of Jordan. 300f, Woman picking olives, vert.

**2001, Oct. 1**

**1737-1738** A340 Set of 2 3.00 3.00

Year of Dialogue Among Civilizations A341

Emblem and: 200f, Family, handshake, world map. 300f, Other stylized drawings.

**2001, Oct. 21**

**1739-1740** A341 Set of 2 3.00 3.00

Cooperation Between Jordan and Japan — A342

Designs: 200f, Sheikh Hussein Bridge, flags. 300f, King Hussein Bridge, handshake.

**2001, Nov. 12 Litho.** ***Perf. 14¼***

**1741-1742** A342 Set of 2 3.00 3.00

Jordan - People's Republic of China Diplomatic Relations, 25th Anniv. A343

Designs: 200f, Dove with envelope. 300f, King Abdullah II and Chinese Pres. Jiang Zemin.

**2002** ***Perf. 12***

**1743-1744** A343 Set of 2 2.25 2.25

Amman, 2002 Arab Cultural Capital A344

Designs: 100f, Arabic script, star. 200f, Pen, torch. 300f, Amphitheater.

**2002** ***Perf. 14¼***

**1745-1747** A344 Set of 3 3.00 3.00

Paintings A345

Paintings by, 100f, Rafiq Laham. 150f, Mahmoud Taha, horiz. 200f, Mohanna Durra. 300f, Wijdan, horiz.

**2002, July 2** ***Perf. 13¼***

**1748-1751** A345 Set of 4 4.50 4.50

Vision 2020 — A346

Designs: 200f, Symbols of business and technology. 300f, Fingers, electronic device.

**2002 Litho.** ***Perf. 13¼***

**1752-1753** A346 Set of 2 2.25 2.25

Migratory Birds A347

Designs: 100f, Goldfinch. No. 1755, 200f, Rufous bush robin. 300f, White stork.

No. 1757, 200f, Golden oriole, goshawk, ortolan bunting, hoopoe.

**2002** ***Perf. 13¼***

**1754-1756** A347 Set of 3 4.00 4.00

***Imperf***

**Size: 70x90mm**

**1757** A347 200f multi *8.50 8.50*

Hashemite Rulers A348

No. 1758: a, Sherif Hussein bin Ali. b, King Abdullah. c, King Talal bin Abdullah. d, King Hussein bin Talal. e, King Abdullah II.

**2003, July 2 Litho.** ***Perf. 14***

**1758** Miniature sheet of 5 4.50 4.50
*a.-e.* A348 200f Any single .75 .75

Salt Museum A349

Views of building exterior: 150f, 250f.

**2003, July 2**

**1759-1760** A349 Set of 2 1.75 1.75

Trees A350

Designs: 50f, Cupressus sempervirens. 100f, Pistacia atlantica. 200f, Quercus aegilops.

**2003, Aug. 7**

**1761-1763** A350 Set of 3 2.25 2.25

Flowers A351

Designs: 50f, Cistanche tubulosa. 100f, Ophioglossum polyphyllum, vert. 150f, Narcissus tazetta. 200f, Gynandriris sisyrinchium, vert.

**2003, Aug. 7**

**1764-1767** A351 Set of 4 3.00 3.00

Birds of Prey — A352

Designs: 100f, Ciraetus gallicus. No. 1769, 200f, Falco peregrinus. 300f, Accipiter nisus.
No. 1771, 200f, Ciraetus gallicus, diff.

**2003, Dec. 9 Litho. *Perf. 14***
**1768-1770** A352 Set of 3 3.50 3.50

**Size: 70x90mm**

***Imperf***

**1771** A352 200f multi 6.00 6.00

Royal Cars Museum A353

Designs: 100f, Red sports car. 150f, Black limousine. 300f, White limousine.
200f, Three automobiles.

**2003, Dec. 23 Litho. *Perf. 14***
**1772-1774** A353 Set of 3 3.50 3.50

**Size: 90x70mm**

***Imperf***

**1775** A353 200f multi 4.50 4.50

Jordan Post Company A354

Emblem and: 50f, Arch. 100f, Pillars, vert.

**2003, Dec. 23 Litho. *Perf. 14***
**1776-1777** A354 Set of 2 1.00 1.00

**Triumphal Arch Type of 1993-98**

**2003 Litho. *Perf. 12¾x13¼***

**Granite Paper**

**1777A** A267 25f gray & multi — —

Arabian Horses A355

Various horses: 5pi, 7.50pi, 12.50pi, 15pi, 25pi.
10pi, Two horses, horiz.

**2004, Dec. 27 Litho. *Perf. 14¼***

**Granite Paper**

**1778-1782** A355 Set of 5 3.25 3.25

***Imperf***

**Size: 90x70mm**

**1783** A355 10pi multi *8.50 8.50*

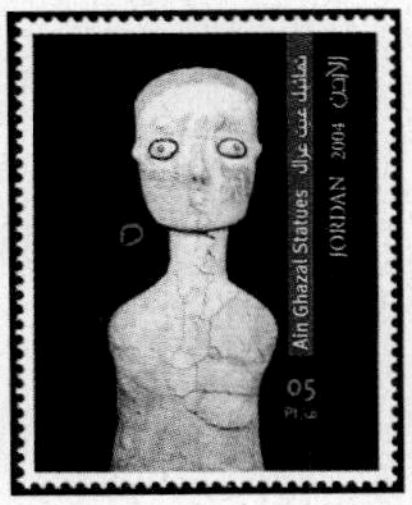


Ain Ghazal Statues A356

Various statues: 5pi, 7.50pi, 12.50pi, 15pi, 25pi.
10pi, Two statues.

**2004, Dec. 29 Granite Paper**
**1784-1788** A356 Set of 5 3.00 3.00

***Imperf***

**Size: 70x90mm**

**1789** A356 10pi multi *5.00 5.00*

Children's Paintings — A357

Various paintings: 5pi, 7.50pi, 12.50pi, 15pi, 25pi.
10pi, Parts of various paintings.

**2004, Dec. 27 Granite Paper**
**1790-1794** A357 Set of 5 2.75 2.75

***Imperf***

**Size: 90x70mm**

**1795** A357 10pi multi *5.50 5.50*

Miniature Sheet

Nazareth Iris — A358

No. 1796 — Various photographs of Nazareth Iris: a, 5pi. b, 7.50pi. c, 10pi (70x90mm). d, 12.50pi. e, 15pi. f, 25pi.

**2004, Dec. 29 *Perf. 14¼***

**Granite Paper**

**1796** A358 Sheet of 6, #a-f *6.00 6.00*

Miniature Sheet

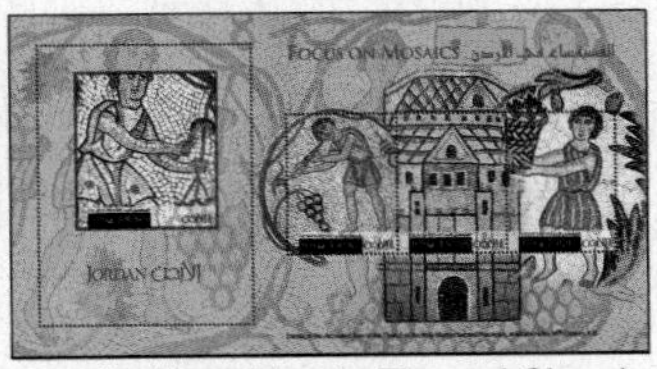


Details From Mosaic Floor of Church of the Holy Martyrs Lot and Procopius, Mount Nebo — A359

No. 1797: a, 10pi, Man with scythe (68x90mm). b, 10pi, Man with flute, grapes. c, 15pi, Building. d, 25pi, Man with Basket.

**2004, Dec. 27 Litho.**

**Granite Paper**

**1797** A359 Sheet of 4, #a-d *6.00 6.00*

Expo 2005, Aichi, Japan A360

No. 1798: a, Dead Sea salt crystal. b, Dead Sea salt crystal, diff. c, Dead Sea salt crystal, diff. d, Dead Sea (70x70mm).

**2005, Aug. 7 Litho. *Perf. 13¾***

| | | | |
|---|---|---|---|
| **1798** | Sheet of 4 | 3.25 | 3.25 |
| *a.* | A360 5pi multi | .30 | .30 |
| *b.* | A360 7.50pi multi | .45 | .45 |
| *c.* | A360 12.50pi multi | .75 | .75 |
| *d.* | A360 20pi multi | .90 | .90 |

Fish — A361

Various Red Sea fish: 5f, 5pi, 7.50pi, 12.50pi.

***Perf. 13½x13¾***

**2005, Dec. 27 Litho.**
**1799-1802** A361 Set of 4 2.50 2.50

**Souvenir Sheet**

**1803** A361 20pi Lionfish *5.00 5.00*

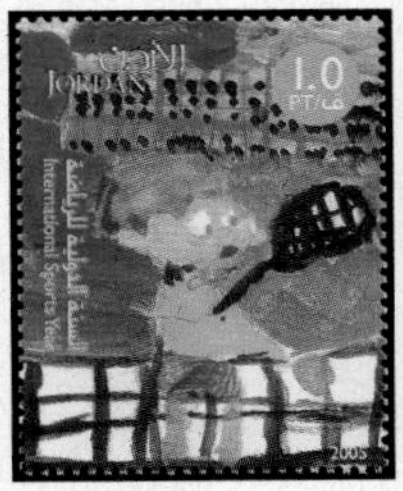


Intl. Sports Year — A362

Children's drawings of: 1pi, Tennis player. 10pi, Medal winner. 15pi, Soccer game, horiz. No. 1807, 20pi, Swimmer, horiz.
No. 1808, Basketball player.

***Perf. 13½x13¾, 13¾x13½***

**2005, Dec. 27**
**1804-1807** A362 Set of 4 3.50 3.50

**Size: 71x90mm**

***Imperf***

**1808** A362 20pi multi *6.00 6.00*

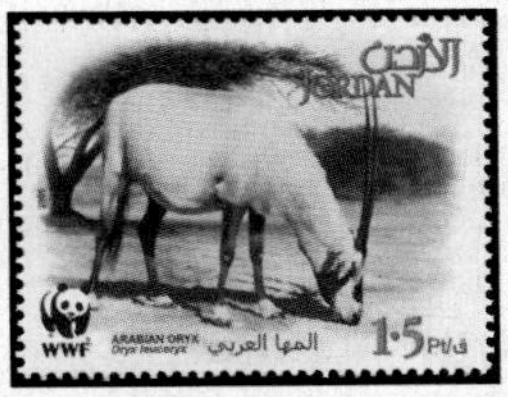


Worldwide Fund for Nature — A363

Arabian oryx: 1.50pi, Grazing. 5pi, Three oryx. 7.50pi, Adults and juvenile. 12.50pi, Two adults.
20pi, Adult, three oryx in background.

**2005, Dec. 27 *Perf. 13¾x13½***
**1809-1812** A363 Set of 4 *7.25 7.25*

**Souvenir Sheet**

**1813** A363 20pi multi *22.50 22.50*

Child Protection — A364

Designs: 7.50pi, Hands of adult and child. 10pi, Mother holding infant. 12.50pi, Adult hugging child.
20pi, Child.

**2005, Dec. 27 *Perf. 13¾***
**1814-1816** A364 Set of 3 3.00 3.00

**Size: 70x90mm**

***Imperf***

**1817** A364 20pi multi *6.50 6.50*

Friendship of Jordan and Japan — A365

Design: 7.50pi, Gallery of Japanese calligraphy. 12.50pi, Building. 15pi, Building at night.
20pi, Pottery in museum gallery.

**2005, Dec. 27 *Perf. 13¾x13½***
**1818-1820** A365 Set of 3 2.75 2.75

**Size: 70x90mm**

***Imperf***

**1821** A365 20pi multi *5.75 5.75*

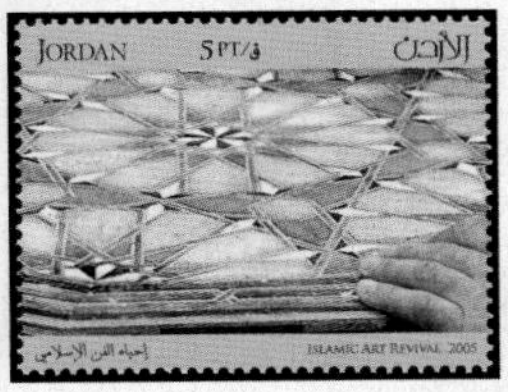


Islamic Art Revival A366

Designs: 5pi, Woodworker. 7.50pi, Engraver. 10pi, Calligrapher. 15pi, Woodworker, diff.
20pi, Calligrapher, diff.

**2005, Dec. 27 *Perf. 13¾x13½***
**1822-1825** A366 Set of 4 3.00 3.00

**Size: 90x71mm**

***Imperf***

**1826** A366 20pi multi *6.00 6.00*

Modern Architecture A367

Various buildings with panel color of: 7.50pi, Green. 10pi, Lemon, horiz. 12.50pi, Red brown.
20pi, Brown, horiz.

**2006, Jan. 1 Litho. *Perf. 14***
**1827-1829** A367 Set of 3 3.50 3.50

***Imperf***

**Size: 90x70mm**

**1830** A367 20pi multi *4.50 4.50*

Government Vehicles — A368

Designs: 10pi, Police car. 12.50pi, Fire truck. 17.50pi, Garbage truck. No. 1834, 20pi, Mail vans.
No. 1835, 20pi, Ambulance.

**2006, Jan. 1** *Perf. 14*
**1831-1834** A368 Set of 4 3.75 3.75

***Imperf***

**Size: 90x70mm**

**1835** A368 20pi multi *4.50 4.50*

Ancient Coins — A369

Various coins with background color of: 5pi, Purple. 7.50pi, Yellow brown. 10pi, Gray. 12.50pi, Blue. 15pi, Dark red.
30pi, Dark blue, horiz.

**2006, Jan. 1** *Perf. 13¾*
**1836-1840** A369 Set of 5 4.50 4.50

***Imperf***

**Size: 90x70mm**

**1841** A369 30pi multi *6.50 6.50*

2006 World Cup Soccer Championships, Germany A370

Background color: 5pi, Light blue. 7.50pi, Yellow. 10pi, Tan. 12.50pi, Green. 15pi, Blue.
30pi, Yellow green, horiz.

**2006, Jan. 1** *Perf. 14*
**1842-1846** A370 Set of 5 4.50 4.50

***Imperf***

**Size: 90x70mm**

**1847** A370 30pi multi *5.50 5.50*

Art — A371

Various works of art by unnamed artists: 5pi, 10pi, 15pi. 20pi.
No. 1852, Four works of art, horiz.

**2006, Oct. 21** **Litho.** *Perf. 14¼*

**Granite Paper**

**1848-1851** A371 Set of 4 3.50 3.50

***Imperf***

**Size: 90x70mm**

**1852** A371 20pi multi *6.00 6.00*

Desert Reptiles A372

Designs: 5pi, Lizard. 7.50pi, Snake. 10pi, Lizards. 12.50pi, Lizard, diff. 15pi, Lizard, horiz. 20pi, Snake, diff.
No. 1859, Lizard, diff., horiz.

**2006, Oct. 21** *Perf. 14¼*

**Granite Paper**

**1853-1858** A372 Set of 6 3.25 3.25

***Imperf***

**Size: 90x70mm**

**1859** A372 20pi multi *5.25 5.25*

Information and Communications Technology in Education — A373

Design: 7.50pi, Man at computer. 12.50pi, Woman punching keys on keypad. 15pi, Man and computer screen. 20pi, Man using cellular phone.
No. 1864, Circuit board, design of unissued 50f stamp showing finger punching keypad.

**2006, Nov. 11** *Perf. 14¼*

**Granite Paper**

**1860-1863** A373 Set of 4 2.75 2.75

***Imperf***

**Size: 70x90mm**

**1864** A373 20pi multi *5.50 5.50*

National Symbols A374

Designs: 5pi, King Abdullah II in dress uniform. 7.50pi, King Abdullah II in suit and tie. 10pi, Jordanian soldiers, horiz. 12.50pi, King Abdullah II in camouflage uniform. 15pi, Flag, horiz. 20pi, Men in army uniforms and native garb, horiz. 25pi, Parade of tanks, horiz. 30pi, Flag and rose, horiz.

**2006, Nov. 11** *Perf. 14¼*

**Granite Paper**

**1865-1872** A374 Set of 8 6.25 6.25

Pitchers and Spouted Pots — A375

Designs: 10pi, Spouted pot. 20pi, Spouted pot with legs. 30pi, Pitcher.
25pi, Spouted pot, horiz.

*Perf. 13½x13¾*

**2007, Dec. 31** **Litho.**
**1873-1875** A375 Set of 3 1.75 1.75

***Imperf***

**Size: 90x70mm**

**1876** A375 25pi multi *2.25 2.25*

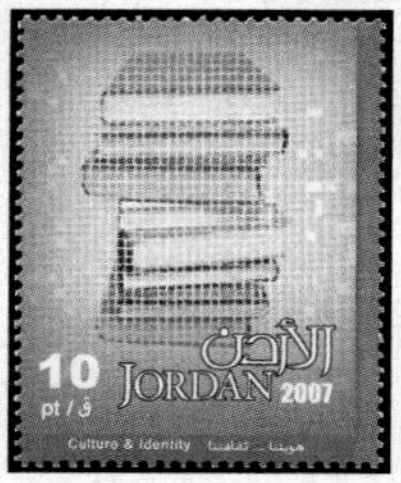

Culture and Identity A376

Designs: 10pi, Books. No. 1878, 20pi, Lute. 25pi, Bottle. 30pi, Arabic text.
No. 1881, 20pi, Arabic text, paint brushes, bottle, lute, books.

**2007, Dec. 31** *Perf. 13½x13¾*
**1877-1880** A376 Set of 4 2.40 2.40

***Imperf***

**Size: 70x90mm**

**1881** A376 20pi multi *1.50 1.50*

Butterflies A377

Various butterflies with denomination color of: 10pi, Orange. 15pi, Yellow green. 20pi, Gray. 25pi, Olive gray, horiz. 30pi, Orange, horiz.
40pi, Olive green, horiz.

*Perf. 13½x13¾, 13¼x13½*

**2007, Dec. 31**
**1882-1886** A377 Set of 5 3.00 3.00

***Imperf***

**Size: 90x70mm**

**1887** A377 40pi multi *4.50 4.50*

Aqaba A378

Designs: 10pi, Arch and beach. 15pi, Scuba diver. 20pi, Motor boats. 30pi, Double-masted ship.

**2008, July 16** **Litho.** *Perf. 14¼*

**Granite Paper**

**1888-1891** A378 Set of 4 2.10 2.10

Traditional Women's Clothing A379

Designs: 10pi, Mafraq. 15pi, Ma'an. 20pi, Amman. 25pi, Jerash. 30pi, Salt.

**2008, July 16** **Granite Paper**
**1892-1896** A379 Set of 5 3.00 3.00

Fruit — A380

Designs: 10pi, Oranges. 15pi, Cherries. 20pi, Figs. 25pi, Pomegranates. 30pi, Grapes.

**2008, July 16** **Granite Paper**
**1897-1901** A380 Set of 5 3.00 3.00

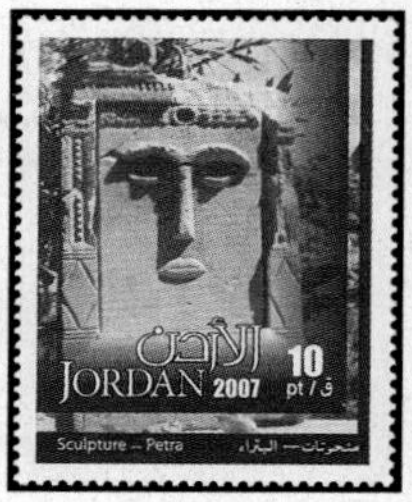

Petra — A381

Designs: 10pi, Sculpture of face. 15pi, Ceramic plate. 20pi, Sculpture of grapevine. 25pi, Siq al Barid fresco. 30pi, Rock formations. 40pi, Treasury.

**2008, July 16** **Litho.** *Perf. 14¼*

**Granite Paper**

**1902-1906** A381 Set of 5 3.00 3.00

**Size: 66x86mm**

**1907** A381 40pi multi 1.25 1.25

***Imperf***

**1908** A381 40pi multi 1.25 1.25

Bridge A382

50th Anniversary Emblem of Engineer's Association A383

**2008, Sept. 22** **Litho.** *Perf. 14¼*

**Granite Paper**

| | | | | |
|---|---|---|---|---|
| **1909** | A382 | 15pi shown | .45 | .45 |
| **1910** | A383 | 20pi shown | .60 | .60 |
| **1911** | A382 | 25pi Power station | .70 | .70 |
| | | *Nos. 1909-1911 (3)* | 1.75 | 1.75 |

2008 Summer Olympics, Beijing A384

Desings: 20pi, Taekwondo. 30pi, Equestrian. 40pi, Table tennis. 50pi, Running.

**2008, Sept. 22** **Litho.**

**Granite Paper**

**1912-1915** A384 Set of 4 4.00 4.00

Musical Instruments
A385

Designs: 20pi, Oud. 40pi, Rebab. 60pi, Zither. 80pi, Flutes. 100pi, Tambourine and drum.

50pi, Oud, rebab, zither, flutes, tambourine and drum, horiz.

**2008, Sept. 22** ***Perf. 14¼***

**Granite Paper**

**1916-1920** A385 Set of 5 8.50 8.50

***Imperf***

**Size: 90x70mm**

**1921** A385 50pi multi 1.40 1.40

Flowers
A386

Designs: 5pi, Egyptian catchfly. 10pi, Lupine. 15pi, Judean viper's bugloss. 20pi, Pimpernel. 30pi, Asiatic crowfoot. 40pi, Grape hyacinth. No. 1928, 50pi, Large flowered sage. 60pi, Star of Bethlehem. 80pi, Pyramidalis. 100pi, Calotropis.

No. 1932, 50pi, Cyclamen, horiz.

**2008, Nov. 25** **Litho.** ***Perf. 14¼***

**Granite Paper**

**1922-1931** A386 Set of 10 12.00 12.00

***Imperf***

**Size: 90x70mm**

**1932** A386 50pi multi 1.40 1.40

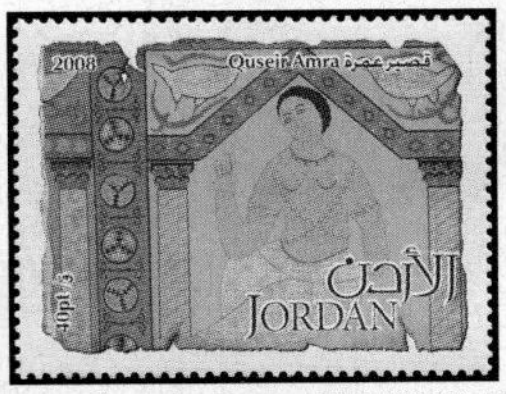


Art From Quseir Amra UNESCO World Heritage Site — A387

Designs: 40pi, Woman with arm raised. 60pi, Grapes. 80pi, Hunters on horseback, bath. 100pi, Face of woman.

50pi, Quseir Amra Palace.

**2008, Nov. 25** ***Perf. 14¼x14***

**Granite Paper**

**1933-1936** A387 Set of 4 8.00 8.00

***Imperf***

**Size: 90x69mm**

**1937** A387 50pi multi 1.40 1.40

Hejaz Railway, Cent.
A388

Designs: 20pi, Train on bridge. 30pi, Locomotive and tender. 50pi, Station and road.

**2009, Feb. 1** **Litho.** ***Perf. 14¼***

**Granite Paper**

**1938-1940** A388 Set of 3 3.00 3.00

Dated 2008.

Birds
A389

Designs: 10pi, Mallard duck. 15pi, Saker. 20pi, Crouser cream. 30pi, Palestine sunbird. 40pi, Hoopoe. No. 1946, 50pi, Black francolin. 60pi, Little green bee-eater. 80pi, Sinai rosefinch.

No. 1949, 50pi, Kingfisher.

**2009, Feb. 1** ***Perf. 14¼***

**Granite Paper**

**1941-1948** A389 Set of 8 8.75 8.75

***Imperf***

**Size: 90x70mm**

**1949** A389 50pi multi *4.75 4.75*

Dated 2008.

Arabian Coffee Tools — A390

Designs: 40pi, Mortar and pestle. 60pi, Coffee pots and roasting pan. 80pi, Coffee pot and cups. 100pi, Bowl, roasting pan and shovel.

50pi, Mortar, pestle, coffee pot, bowl, roasting pan and shovel.

**2009, Mar. 1** ***Perf. 14¼***

**Granite Paper**

**1950-1953** A390 Set of 4 8.00 8.00

***Imperf***

**Size: 70x90mm**

**1954** A390 50pi multi *4.25 4.25*

Dated 2008.

Traditional Costumes
A391

Close-ups of costumes and: 40pi, Woman. 60pi, Woman, diff. 80pi, Woman, diff. 100pi, Man and woman.

50pi, Woman only.

**2009, Mar. 1** ***Perf. 14¼***

**Granite Paper**

**1955-1958** A391 Set of 4 8.00 8.00

***Imperf***

**Size: 70x90mm**

**1959** A391 50pi multi *4.25 4.25*

Visit of Pope Benedict XVI to Jordan
A392

Designs: 20pi, Pope Benedict XVI, King Abdullah II, walkway to river. 30pi, Pope Benedict XVI. 40pi, Pope and King shaking hands.

50pi, Pope and King shaking hands, walkway to river, crucifix.

**2009, May 8** ***Perf. 14¼***

**Granite Paper**

**1960-1962** A392 Set of 3 2.60 2.60

***Imperf***

**Size: 90x70mm**

**1963** A392 50pi multi *4.75 4.75*

King Abdullah II, 10th Anniv. of Accession to Throne — A393

**2009, June 9** ***Perf. 13¾***

**Granite Paper**

**Background Color**

| | | | | | |
|---|---|---|---|---|---|
| **1964** | A393 | 10pi | maroon | .30 | .30 |
| **1965** | A393 | 15pi | dark blue | .45 | .45 |
| **1966** | A393 | 20pi | bright blue | .60 | .60 |
| **1967** | A393 | 25pi | tan | .70 | .70 |
| **1968** | A393 | 30pi | dark green | .85 | .85 |
| **1969** | A393 | 35pi | blue | 1.00 | 1.00 |
| **1970** | A393 | 40pi | purple | 1.10 | 1.10 |
| **1971** | A393 | 45pi | black | 1.25 | 1.25 |
| **1972** | A393 | 50pi | brown | 1.40 | 1.40 |
| **1973** | A393 | 1d | blue gray | 3.00 | 3.00 |
| | | | *Nos. 1964-1973 (10)* | 10.65 | 10.65 |

E-Government
A394

Designs: 20pi, Computer cables. 30pi, Spiral emblem. 40pi, Internet address of Jordanian government. 50pi, Letter, compass, Earth.

**2009, Aug. 25** **Litho.** ***Perf. 13¼***

**Granite Paper**

**1974-1977** A394 Set of 4 4.00 4.00

A395

A396

A397

A398

A399

University emblems: No. 1983, Al-Hussein Bin Jalal University. No. 1984, Tafila Technical University. No. 1985, German-Jordanian University. No. 1986, Al-Balqa Applied University. No. 1987, Yarmouk University.

**2009, Aug. 25** ***Perf. 13¼***

**Granite Paper**

| | | | | | |
|---|---|---|---|---|---|
| **1978** | A395 | 20pi | multi | .60 | .60 |
| **1979** | A396 | 20pi | multi | .60 | .60 |
| **1980** | A397 | 20pi | multi | .60 | .60 |
| **1981** | A398 | 20pi | multi | .60 | .60 |
| **1982** | A399 | 20pi | multi | .60 | .60 |
| **1983** | A399 | 20pi | multi | .60 | .60 |
| **1984** | A399 | 20pi | multi | .60 | .60 |
| **1985** | A399 | 20pi | multi | .60 | .60 |
| **1986** | A399 | 20pi | multi | .60 | .60 |
| **1987** | A399 | 20pi | multi | .60 | .60 |
| | | | *Nos. 1978-1987 (10)* | 6.00 | 6.00 |

Waterfalls, Ma'een — A400

Designs: 10pi, Waterfall, orange brown panel. 20pi, Building and mountain, fawn panel. 30pi, Waterfall, black panel. 40pi, Waterfall, gray green panel. 50pi, Waterfall, olive brown panel.

60pi, Waterfall, blue panel.

**2009, Aug. 25** **Litho.**

**Granite Paper**

**1988-1992** A400 Set of 5 4.25 4.25

**Size: 70x91mm**

***Imperf***

**1993** A400 60pi multi 1.75 1.75

Animals
A401

Designs: 10pi, Horse. 20pi, Rabbits. 30pi, Fox. 40pi, Maha gazelle. 50pi, Gazelle.

60pi, Camel.

**2009, Aug. 25** **Litho.**

**Granite Paper**

**1994-1998** A401 Set of 5 4.25 4.25

**Size: 70x91mm**

***Imperf***

**1999** A401 60pi multi 1.75 1.75

Vegetables
A402

No. 2000: a, Corn. b, Onions, garlic. c, Beans, peas, okra. d, Cabbages. e, Eggplants. f, Pumpkins. g, Bell peppers. h, Hot peppers. i, Radishes, turnips, beets. j, Tomatoes, zucchini.

**2009, Aug. 25** ***Perf. 13¼***

**Granite Paper**

**2000** Sheet of 10 6.00 6.00

*a.-j.* A402 20pi Any single .60 .60

Environmental Protection — A403

Designs: 20pi, Tree, shrub, flower. 30pi, Man and fire. 40pi, Animals grazing. 50pi, Litter in stream.

**2009** **Granite Paper** **Litho.**

**2001-2004** A403 Set of 4 4.00 4.00

Insects — A404

Designs: 10pi, Beetle. 15pi, Butterfly. 20pi, Ladybug. 25pi, Bee. 30pi, Mantis. 40pi, Moth. 50pi, Dragonfly. 60pi, Fly. 80pi, Grasshopper. 100pi, Dragonflies.

**2009, Dec. 13 Litho. *Perf. 13¼***
**Granite Paper**

**2005-2014** A404 Set of 10 12.50 12.50

Nos. 588-590 Surcharged

**Methods and Perfs As Before**

**2009, Dec. 20**

**2015** A82 80pi on 120f #588 2.25 2.25
**2016** A82 80pi on 180f #589 2.25 2.25
**2017** A82 80pi on 200f #590 2.25 2.25
*Nos. 2015-2017 (3)* 6.75 6.75

No. 1471b Surcharged

***Perf. 12¾x13¼***

**2009, Dec. 20 Litho.**

**2018** A267 80pi on 25f multi 2.25 2.25

Tourism A405

Sites in: 10pi, Ajlun. 20pi, Amman. 30pi, Karak. 40pi, Showbak.
50pi, Jerash.

**2010, Oct. 3 *Perf. 14***

**2019-2022** A405 Set of 4 3.00 3.00

**Size: 90x70mm**

***Imperf***

**2023** A405 50pi multi 1.50 1.50

Miniature Sheet

Mushrooms — A406

No. 2024: a, Cortinarius balteatus. b, Russula bicolor. c, Red fly agaric. d, Amanita muscaria. e, Boletus edulis. f, Amanita albocreata. g, Agaricus anderwij. h, Agaricus bisporus.

**2010, Oct. 3 *Perf. 14***

**2024** A406 20pi Sheet of 8, #a-h 4.50 4.50

Mosques in Jordan A407

Designs: 10pi, Jordan University Mosque. 20pi, Abu-Darwiesh Mosque. 30pi, Al Hussainy Mosque. 40pi, King Abdullah Mosque. 50pi, King Hussein bin Talal Mosque.

**2010, Nov. 30**

**2025-2029** A407 Set of 5 4.25 4.25

Sports — A408

Designs: 10pi, Skydiving. 20pi, Swimming. 30pi, Hot-air ballooning. 40pi, Racing boats. 50pi, Jordan Rally.

**2010, Nov. 30 *Perf. 14***

**2030-2033** A408 Set of 4 3.00 3.00

**Size: 70x90mm**

***Imperf***

**2034** A408 50pi multi 1.50 1.50

Old Farming Tools A409

Designs: 20pi, Millstone. 30pi, Flail. 40pi, Pitchfork. 50pi, Olive crushing wheel.

**2011, Feb. 27 *Perf. 14***

**2035-2038** A409 Set of 4 4.00 4.00

Dated 2010.

Development Zones — A410

Emblem of: No. 2039, 20pi, Dead Sea Development Zone. No. 2040, 20pi, Irbid Development Area. No. 2041, 20pi, Jabal Ajloun Development Area. No. 2042, 20pi, King Hussein Bin Talal Development Area. No. 2043, 20pi, Ma'an Development Area.

**2011, Feb. 27**

**2039-2043** A410 Set of 5 3.00 3.00

Dated 2010.

Wild Herbs — A411

Designs: No. 2044, 20pi, Artemisia herba alba. No. 2045, 20pi, Capparis spinosa. No. 2046, 20pi, Lavandula vera. No. 2047, 20pi, Matricaria chamomilla. No. 2048, 20pi, Ocimum basilicum. No. 2049, 20pi, Salvia officinalis. No. 2050, 20pi, Thymus serpyllum. No. 2051, 20pi, Trigonella foenum-graecum.

**2011, Feb. 27**

**2044-2051** A411 Set of 8 4.50 4.50

Dated 2010. Latin names of plants are misspelled on Nos. 2044, 2045, 2046, 2050 and 2051.

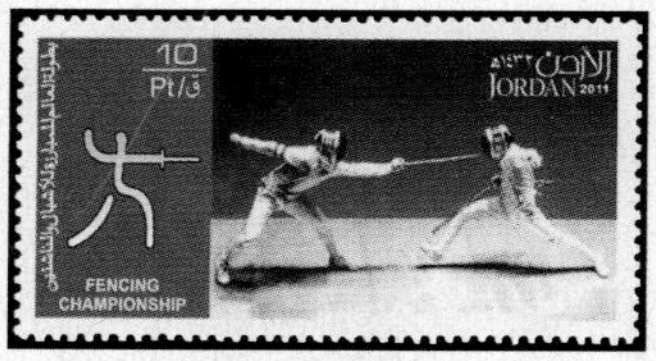


Junior and Cadet World Fencing Championships, Jordan — A412

Fencers and stylized fencer in panel in: 10pi, Red brown. 20pi, Blue violet. 30pi, Greenish blue. 40pi, Olive green. No. 2056, 50pi, Gray.
No. 2057, 50pi, Fencers, vert.

**2011, Apr. 6 *Perf. 13x12¾***

**2052-2056** A412 Set of 5 4.25 4.25

**Size: 75x94mm**

***Imperf***

**2057** A412 50pi multi *6.00 6.00*

Jordan Rally — A413

Various race cars: 10pu, 20pi, 30pi, 40pi, 50pi.
No. 2063, 50pi, Race car, ruins, helicopter.

**2011, Apr. 14 *Perf. 13x12¾***

**2058-2062** A413 Set of 5 4.25 4.25

**Size: 95x74mm**

***Imperf***

**2063** A413 50pi multi *5.75 5.75*

Jewelry — A414

Designs: 20pi, Pendant on necklace. No. 2065, 30pi, Pendants, necklace and bracelet. 40pi, Ring. 50i, Necklace with pendants.
No. 2068, 30pi, Ring, diff.

**2011, May 10 *Perf. 13¼x13***

**Granite Paper**

**2064-2067** A414 Set of 4 4.00 4.00

**Size: 77x77mm**

***Imperf***

**2068** A414 30pi multi *5.00 5.00*

Dated 2010.

A415

A416

A417

A418

A419

A420

A421

A422

A423

Dams A424

**2011, May 10 *Perf. 13x13¼***

**Granite Paper**

**2069** A415 20pi multi .60 .60
**2070** A416 20pi multi .60 .60
**2071** A417 20pi multi .60 .60
**2072** A418 20pi multi .60 .60
**2073** A419 20pi multi .60 .60
**2074** A420 20pi multi .60 .60
**2075** A421 20pi multi .60 .60
**2076** A422 20pi multi .60 .60
**2077** A423 20pi multi .60 .60
**2078** A424 20pi multi .60 .60
*Nos. 2069-2078 (10)* 6.00 6.00

**Size: 90x70mm**

***Imperf***

**2079** A424 30pi multi *6.75 6.75*

Dated 2010.

Red Sea Coral Reefs A425

Designs: 20pi, Brain coral. 30pi, Coral, fish. No. 2082, 40pi, Coral. 50pi, Coral, diff. 60pi, Coral, diff. No. 2085, 40p, Coral, fish, diff.

**2011, Sept. 28 Litho. *Perf. 14***
**2080-2084** A425 Set of 5 5.75 5.75

**Size: 90x70mm**

***Imperf***

**2085** A425 40pi multi 1.25 1.25

Ceramics A426

Designs: 10pi, Jug with handle, head. 20pi, Item on pedestal. No. 2088, 30pi, Jug with handle. 40pi, Item with Arabic script. 50pi, Item with Arabic script and people. 60pi, Sphere on pedestal. No. 2092, 30p, Abstract tile designs.

**2011, Sept. 28 *Perf. 14***
**2086-2091** A426 Set of 5 6.00 6.00

**Size: 70x90mm**

***Imperf***

**2092** A426 30pi multi .85 .85

A427

A428

A429

A430

A431

A432

A433

A434

A435

Historical Path — A436

**2011, Sept. 28 *Perf. 14***
**2093** A427 20pi multi .60 .60
**2094** A428 20pi multi .60 .60
**2095** A429 20pi multi .60 .60
**2096** A430 20pi multi .60 .60
**2097** A431 20pi multi .60 .60
**2098** A432 20pi multi .60 .60
**2099** A433 20pi multi .60 .60
**2100** A434 20pi multi .60 .60
**2101** A435 20pi multi .60 .60
**2102** A436 20pi multi .60 .60
*Nos. 2093-2102 (10)* 6.00 6.00

Crown Prince Hussein A437

Denominations: 20pi, 30pi, 50pi.

**2011 *Perf. 13½x13¼***
**Granite Paper**
**2103-2105** A437 Set of 3 3.00 3.00

Old Astronomical Instruments A438

Designs: 10pi, Astrolabe. 20pi, Telescope. 30pi, Sextant. 40pi, Sundial.

**2011 *Perf. 13½x13¼***
**Granite Paper**
**2106-2109** A438 Set of 4 3.00 3.00

Royal Jordanian Falcons Aerobatic Squad — A439

Designs: 10pi, Line of four airplanes. 20pi, Pilot in cockpit, three other airplanes. 30pi, Three airplanes. 40pi, Four airplanes in formation.
50pi, Four airplanes, Jordanian flag.

**2011 *Perf. 13¼x13½***
**Granite Paper**
**2110-2113** A439 Set of 4 3.00 3.00

**Size: 90x70mm**

***Imperf***

**2114** A439 50pi multi 1.40 1.40

Souvenir Sheet

Preervation of Polar Regions and Glaciers — A440

No. 2115: a, 80pi, Penguins. b, 1d, Polar bear.

**2012, Jan. 23 *Perf. 13½***
**Granite Paper**
**2115** A440 Sheet of 2, #a-b 5.25 5.25
Dated 2011.

A441

A442

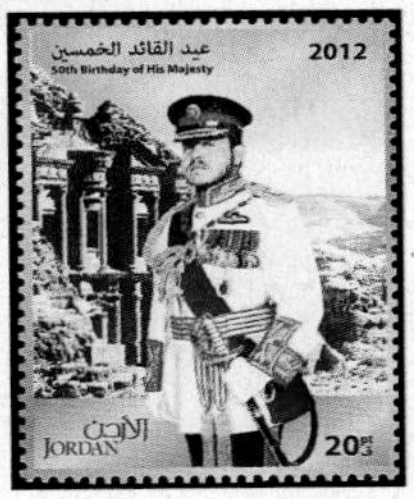

A443

A444

A445

King Abdullah II — A446

Design: 50pi, King Abdullah II and mosque, horiz.

**2012, Jan. 30 *Perf. 13½x13¼***
**Granite Paper**
**2116** A441 20pi multi .60 .60
**2117** A442 20pi multi .60 .60
**2118** A443 20pi multi .60 .60
**2119** A444 20pi multi .60 .60
**2120** A445 20pi multi .60 .60
**2121** A446 20pi multi .60 .60
*Nos. 2116-2121 (6)* 3.60 3.60

**Size: 90x70mm**

***Imperf***

**2122** A446 50pi multi 1.40 1.40

Labor Day — A447

Designs: 20pi, Raised fists. 30pi, Man with shovel. 40pi, Man with pick, woman and child. 50pi, Man with hard hat.

**2012 *Perf. 13½x13¼***
**Granite Paper**
**2123-2126** A447 Set of 4 4.00 4.00

World Telecommunications Day — A448

Designs: 30pi, Hands holding Earth. 40pi, Dish antennas. 50pi, Computer.

**2012 Granite Paper Litho.**
**2127-2129** A448 Set of 3 3.50 3.50

2012 Summer Olympics, London
A449

Designs: 20pi, Equestrian. 30pi, Soccer. 40pi, Tennis. 50pi, Kayaking.

**2012** **Granite Paper**
**2130-2133** A449 Set of 4 4.00 4.00

Chess
A450

Various chess pieces: 30pi, 40pi, 50pi.

**2012** **Litho.** ***Perf. 11¾***
**2134-2136** A450 Set of 3 3.50 3.50

Citrus Fruits — A451

Designs: 10pi, Kumquats. 20pi, Oranges. 30pi, Lemons. 40pi, Oranges, diff. 50pi, Pomelos.

**2012** **Litho.** ***Perf. 11¾***
**2137-2141** A451 Set of 5 4.25 4.25

Miniature Sheets

A452

Prehistoric Animals — A453

No. 2142: a, Pteranodon in flight, back of Apatosaurus. b, Tyrannosaurus Rex and volcano. c, Triceratops and Stegosaurus. d, Horned dinosaur, legs of Tyrannosaurus Rex.
No. 2143: a, Head of Tyrannosaurus rex, waterfall. b, Apatosauruses. c, Raptors on shore. d, Three dinosaurs in water.

**2012** **Litho.** ***Perf. 11¾***
**2142** A452 20pi Sheet of 4, #a-d 2.25 2.25
**2143** A453 20pi Sheet of 4, #a-d 2.25 2.25

A454

A454a

A454b

A454c

A454d

A454e

A454f

Artists — A454g

**2012** **Litho.** ***Perf. 11¾***
**2144** A454 20pi multi .60 .60
**2145** A454a 20pi multi .60 .60
**2146** A454b 20pi multi .60 .60
**2147** A454c 20pi multi .60 .60
**2148** A454d 20pi multi .60 .60
**2149** A454e 20pi multi .60 .60
**2150** A454f 20pi multi .60 .60
**2151** A454g 20pi multi .60 .60
*Nos. 2144-2151 (8)* 4.80 4.80

Jordan Library and Information Association, 50th Anniv. — A455

Designs: 40pi, Association emblem. 50pi, 50th anniversary emblem.

**2013** **Litho.** ***Perf. 14***
**2152-2153** A455 Set of 2 2.60 2.60

Horses — A456

Designs: 10pi, Two horses. 20pi, One horse, horiz. 30pi, Two horses, horiz. 40pi, Head of horse, horiz. No. 2158, 50pi, Horse in water, horiz.
No. 2159, 50pi, Six horses, horiz.

**2013, Dec. 2** **Litho.** ***Perf. 11¾***
**2154-2158** A456 Set of 5 4.25 4.25
**Size: 90x70mm**
***Imperf***
**2159** A456 50pi multi 1.40 1.40
Dated 2012.

Ships
A457

Various ships, 20pi, 30pi, 40pi, 50pi.
No. 2164, 50pi, Fleet of ships.

**2013, Dec. 2** **Litho.** ***Perf. 11¾***
**2160-2163** A457 Set of 4 4.00 4.00
**Size: 90x70mm**
***Imperf***
**2164** A457 50pi multi 1.40 1.40
Dated 2012.

Nature Reserves — A458

Designs: 10pi, Rocks. 20pi, Flowers, horiz. 30pi, Lake, horiz. 40pi, Plateaus, horiz. No. 2169, 50pi, Antelopes, horiz.
No. 2170, 50pi, Hillside village, horiz.

**2014, Feb. 9** **Litho.** ***Perf. 14***
**2165-2169** A458 Set of 5 4.25 4.25
**Size: 90x70mm**
***Imperf***
**2170** A458 50pi multi 1.40 1.40
Dated 2013.

Doors and Windows
A459

Designs: No. 2171, 20pi, Door, King Hussein's Mosque. No. 2172, 20pi, Door and window, Umayyad Palace. No. 2173, 20pi, Door, Royal Hashemite Court, vert. No. 2174, 20pi, Door and windows, Justice Palace, vert. No. 2175, 20pi, Window, Raghadan Palace, vert. No. 2176, 20pi, Door, Al-Salt School, vert. No. 2177, 20pi, Window, Al-Salt, vert.

**2014, Feb. 9** **Litho.** ***Perf. 14***
**2171-2177** A459 Set of 7 4.00 4.00
Dated 2013.

A460

A461

A462

A463

A464

A465

A466

Birds — A467

**2014, Feb. 9** **Litho.** ***Perf. 14***

| | | | | | |
|---|---|---|---|---|---|
| 2178 | A460 | 20pi | multi | .60 | .60 |
| 2179 | A461 | 20pi | multi | .60 | .60 |
| 2180 | A462 | 20pi | multi | .60 | .60 |
| 2181 | A463 | 20pi | multi | .60 | .60 |
| 2182 | A464 | 20pi | multi | .60 | .60 |
| 2183 | A465 | 20pi | multi | .60 | .60 |
| 2184 | A466 | 20pi | multi | .60 | .60 |
| 2185 | A467 | 20pi | multi | .60 | .60 |
| | *Nos. 2178-2185 (8)* | | | 4.80 | 4.80 |

Dated 2013.

1933 Stamps and Map of Jordan — A468

Map of Jordan and stamp: No. 2186, 80pi, Jordan #191. No. 2187, 80pi, Jordan #197.

**2014, Feb. 9** **Litho.** ***Imperf.***
**2186-2187** A468 Set of 2 4.50 4.50

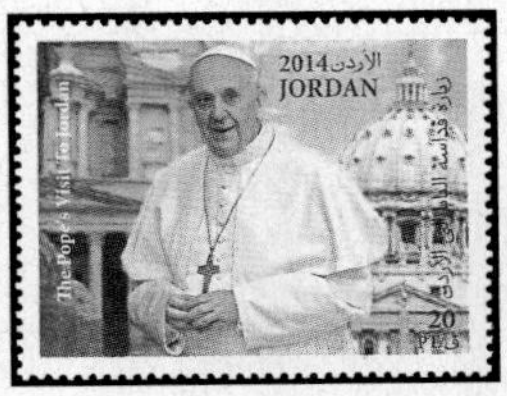


Visit of Pope Francis to Jordan A469

Designs: 20pi, Pope Francis. 30pi, Pope Francis and King Abdullah II. 40pi, Pope Francis and dove, vert.

50pi, Flags of Vatican City and Jordan, Jordan #474, 1683, 1961, 2188.

**2014, May 24** **Litho.** ***Perf. 14¼***
**2188-2190** A469 Set of 3 2.60 2.60

***Imperf***

**Size: 90x70mm**

**2191** A469 50pi multi 1.40 1.40

First Papal visit to Jordan, 50th anniv. (No. 2191).

A470

A471

A472

A473

A474

Cartoons — A475

**2014, July 1** **Litho.** ***Perf. 14***

| | | | | | |
|---|---|---|---|---|---|
| 2192 | A470 | 20pi | multi | .60 | .60 |
| 2193 | A471 | 20pi | multi | .60 | .60 |
| 2194 | A472 | 20pi | multi | .60 | .60 |
| 2195 | A473 | 20pi | multi | .60 | .60 |
| 2196 | A474 | 20pi | multi | .60 | .60 |
| 2197 | A475 | 20pi | multi | .60 | .60 |
| | *Nos. 2192-2197 (6)* | | | 3.60 | 3.60 |

Dated 2013.

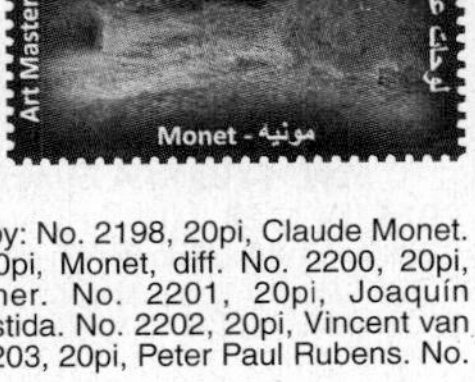


Paintings A476

Paintings by: No. 2198, 20pi, Claude Monet. No. 2199, 20pi, Monet, diff. No. 2200, 20pi, J.M.W. Turner. No. 2201, 20pi, Joaquín Sorolla y Bastida. No. 2202, 20pi, Vincent van Gogh. No. 2203, 20pi, Peter Paul Rubens. No. 2204, 20pi, Monet, diff., vert. No. 2205, 20pi, Johannes Vermeer, vert.

**2014** **Litho.** ***Perf. 11¾***
**2198-2205** A476 Set of 8 4.50 4.50

Dated 2013.

**Miniature Sheet**

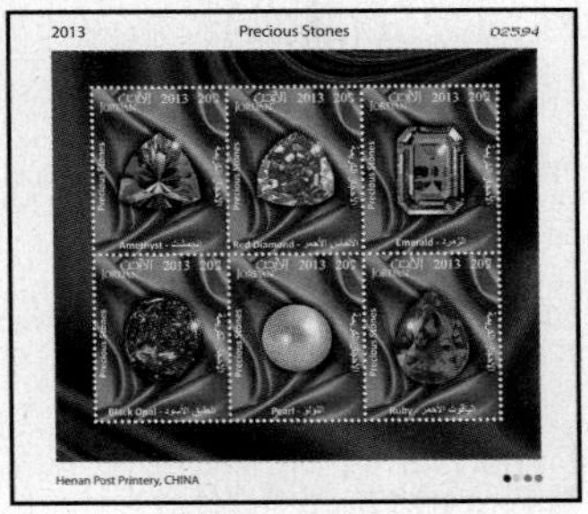


Gems — A477

No. 2206: a, Amethyst. b, Red diamond. c, Emerald. d, Black opal. e, Pearl. f, Ruby.

**2014** **Litho.** ***Perf. 11¾***
**2206** A477 20pi Sheet of 6, #a-f 3.50 3.50

Dated 2013.

Euromed Postal Emblem and Mediterranean Sea — A478

**2014, July 9**
**2207** A478 80pi multi 2.25 2.25

Amman Chamber of Commerce, 90th Anniv. — A479

**2014** **Litho.** ***Perf. 14¼***
**2208** A479 40pi multi 1.25 1.25

Economic and Social Foundation for Military Retirees and Veterans — A480

**2014** **Litho.** ***Perf. 14¼***
**2209** A480 40pi multi 1.25 1.25

Arab Lawyers Union A481

**2014** **Litho.** ***Perf. 14¼***
**2210** A481 40pi multi 1.25 1.25

Jordanian Deaf Women's Association — A482

**2015** **Litho.** ***Perf. 14¼***
**2211** A482 40pi multi 1.25 1.25

United Nations, 70th Anniv. A483

***Perf. 14¼x14½ Syncopated***
**2015, Dec. 13** **Litho.**
**2212** A483 80pi multi 2.25 2.25

Jordanian Banknotes — A484

Designs: 10pi, 1-dinar note. 20pi, 5-dinar note. 40pi, 10-dinar note. 60pi, 20-dinar note. 80pi, 50-dinar note.

***Perf. 14¼x14½ Syncopated***
**2015, Dec. 13** **Litho.**
**2213-2217** A484 Set of 5 6.00 6.00

Order of the Renaissance — A485

Order of the Renaissance — A486

Order of Independence — A487

Al-Hussein Order of Military Merit — A488

Order of the Star of Jordan A489

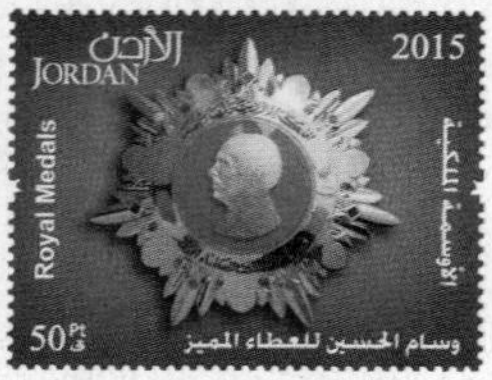

Al-Hussein Decoration for Distinguished Service — A490

Order of Hussein ibn Ali — A491

Medal of Honor — A492

Order of the Hashemite Star — A493

Royal Medal — A494

***Perf. 14¼x14½ Syncopated***

**2015, Dec. 13** **Litho.**

**2218** A485 50pi multi 1.40 1.40
**2219** A486 50pi multi 1.40 1.40
**2220** A487 50pi multi 1.40 1.40
**2221** A488 50pi multi 1.40 1.40
**2222** A489 50pi multi 1.40 1.40
**2223** A490 50pi multi 1.40 1.40

***Perf. 14½x14¼ Syncopated***

**2224** A491 50pi multi 1.40 1.40
**2225** A492 50pi multi 1.40 1.40
**2226** A493 50pi multi 1.40 1.40
**2227** A494 50pi multi 1.40 1.40
*Nos. 2218-2227 (10)* 14.00 14.00

Decapolis — A495

Designs: No. 2228, 50pi, Beit Ras. No. 2229, 50pi, Gerasa. No. 2230, 50pi, Quwayliba. No. 2231, 50pi, Umm Aljemal. No. 2232, 50pi, Umm Qais.

***Perf. 14¼x14½ Syncopated***

**2015, Dec. 28** **Litho.**

**2228-2232** A495 Set of 5 7.00 7.00

A496

A497

A498

Mosaics A499

Design: 60pi, Thalassa.

***Perf. 14¼x14½ Syncopated***

**2015, Dec. 28** **Litho.**

**2233** A496 30pi multi .85 .85
**2234** A497 30pi multi .85 .85
**2235** A498 30pi multi .85 .85
**2236** A499 30pi multi .85 .85
*Nos. 2233-2236 (4)* 3.40 3.40

**Size: 90x70mm**

***Imperf***

**2237** A499 60pi multi 1.75 1.75

A500

A501

A502

A503

Handicrafts — A504

Design: 60pi, Sand bottles.

***Perf. 14¼x14½ Syncopated***

**2015, Dec. 28** **Litho.**

**2238** A500 30pi multi .85 .85
**2239** A501 30pi multi .85 .85
**2240** A502 30pi multi .85 .85
**2241** A503 30pi multi .85 .85
**2242** A504 30pi multi .85 .85
*Nos. 2238-2242 (5)* 4.25 4.25

**Size: 90x70mm**

***Imperf***

**2243** A504 60pi multi 1.75 1.75

Traditional Women's Clothing A505

Woman from: No. 2244, 20pi, Ajloun. No. 2245, 20pi, Amman. No. 2246, 20pi, Badawi. No. 2247, 20pi, Jerash. No. 2248, 20pi, Karak. No. 2249, 20pi, Ma'an. No. 2250, 20pi, Madaba. No. 2251, 20pi, Mafraq. No. 2252, 20pi, Salt. No. 2253, 20pi, Tafilah. No. 2254, 20pi, Um Qais. No. 2255, 20pi, Wadi Rum.

***Perf. 14½x14¼ Syncopated***

**2015, Dec. 28** **Litho.**

**2244-2255** A505 Set of 12 6.75 6.75

Miniature Sheet

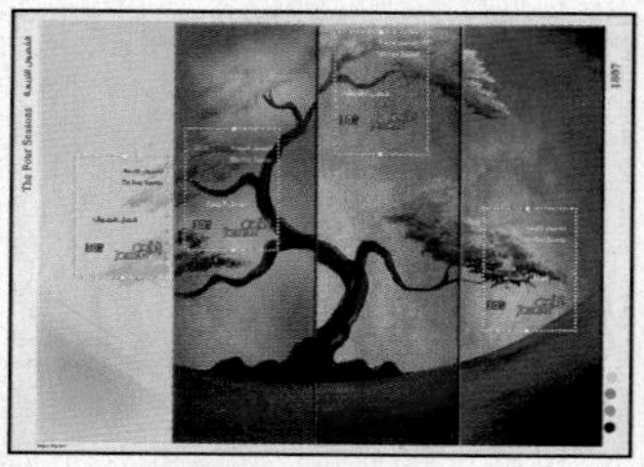
Four Seasons — A506

No. 2256 — Tree leaves in: a, Spring (yellow background). b, Summer (green background). c, Autumn (orange brown background). d, Winter (blue background).

***Perf. 14½x14¼ Syncopated***

**2015, Dec. 28** **Litho.**

**2256** A506 30pi Sheet of 4, #a-d 3.50 3.50

Great Arab Revolt, Cent. A507

Centenary emblem and: 10pi, Soldiers on camels. 20pi, Soldier on horse. 30pi, Jordanian kings. 50pi, Kingh Abdullah II. 100pi, Sharif Hussein.
40pi, Centenary emblem, vert.

***Perf. 14¼x14½ Syncopated***

**2016, June 10** **Litho.**

**2257-2261** A507 Set of 5 6.00 6.00

**Size: 70x90mm**

***Imperf***

**2262** A507 40pi multi 1.25 1.25

Fish of the Mediterranean Sea — A508

Designs: No. 2263, 40pi, Axillary wrasse. No. 2264, 40pi, Blackback butterflyfish. No. 2265, 40pi, Butterfly blenny. No. 2266, 40pi, Lionfish. No. 2267, 40pi, Scorpionfish.

***Perf. 14¼x14½ Syncopated***

**2016, June 30** **Litho.**

**2263-2267** A508 Set of 5 5.75 5.75

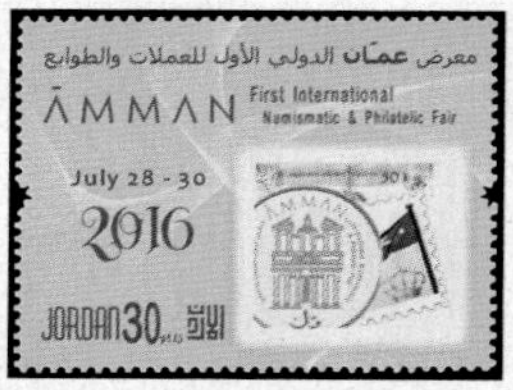

First International Numismatic and Philatelic Fair, Amman — A509

Background colors: 30pi, Yellow. 50pi, Dark red and red.

***Perf. 14¼x14½ Syncopated***

**2016, July 28** **Litho.**

**2268-2269** A509 Set of 2 2.25 2.25

Hiking Destinations — A510

Designs: No. 2270, 40pi, Karak. No. 2271, 40pi, Ma'in. No. 2272, 40pi, Madaba. No. 2273, 40pi, Wadi Rum. No. 2274, 40pi, Ajlun, vert. No. 2275, 40pi, Madaba, vert. No. 2276, 40pi, Wadi Al Dab, vert.

***Perf. 14¼x14½ Syncopated, 14½x14¼ Syncopated***

**2016, July 28** **Litho.**

**2270-2276** A510 Set of 7 8.00 8.00

Arab Postal Day A511

Background color: No. 2277, 40pi, Blue, denomination at LR. No. 2278, 40pi, Green, denomination at LL.

***Perf. 14¼x14½ Syncopated***

**2016, Aug. 3** **Litho.**

| | | | | |
|---|---|---|---|---|
| **2277-2278** | A511 | Set of 2 | 2.25 | 2.25 |

Women's Under-17 World Cup Soccer Tournament, Jordan — A512

Jordanian flag and silhouettes of players: 40pi, Dribbling ball (white silhouette). 50pi, Chasing ball (gray and white silhouettes). 60pi, Dribbling ball (black silhouette). 70pi, Kicking ball (black silhouette).

***Perf. 14¼x14½ Syncopated***

**2016, Sept. 25** **Litho.**

| | | | | |
|---|---|---|---|---|
| **2279-2282** | A512 | Set of 4 | 3.25 | 3.25 |

Ancient Castles and Palaces A513

Designs: No. 2283, 30pi, Ajlun Castle. No. 2284, 30pi, Al-azraq Castle. No. 2285, 30pi, Umayyad Palace. No. 2286, 40pi, Aqaba Castle. No. 2287, 40pi, Karak Castle. No. 2288, 40pi, Shobak Castle.

***Perf. 14¼x14½ Syncopated***

**2016, Oct. 20** **Litho.**

| | | | | |
|---|---|---|---|---|
| **2283-2288** | A513 | Set of 6 | 6.00 | 6.00 |

Museum of Parliamentary Life, Amman — A514

Designs: 20pi, Emblem. 30pi, Museum gate and entrance. 40pi, Room. 50pi, Dais. 60pi, King Abdullah II.

***Perf. 14¼x14½ Syncopated***

**2016, Nov. 7** **Litho.**

| | | | | |
|---|---|---|---|---|
| **2289-2293** | A514 | Set of 5 | 5.75 | 5.75 |

28th Arab League Summit, Amman A515

Designs: 10pi, Map and flags of Arab League countries. 20pi, Summit venue. 30pi, Umayyad Palace, map and flag of Jordan. 40pi, "28th."
50pi, King Abdullah II.

**2017, Mar. 29** **Litho.** ***Perf. 10***

**Granite Paper**

| | | | | |
|---|---|---|---|---|
| **2294-2297** | A515 | Set of 4 | 3.00 | 3.00 |

**Size: 96x80mm**

***Imperf***

| | | | | |
|---|---|---|---|---|
| **2298** | A515 | 50pi multi | 1.40 | 1.40 |

1996 Half-Piaster Coin — A516

1978 10-Fils Coin A517

1949 100-Fils Coin — A518

2000 10-Piaster Coin — A519

1970 Quarter-Dinar Coin — A520

1977 Quarter-Dinar Coin — A521

**2017, May 4** **Litho.** ***Perf. 10***

**Granite Paper**

| | | | | |
|---|---|---|---|---|
| **2299** | A516 | 40pi multi | 1.10 | 1.10 |
| **2300** | A517 | 40pi multi | 1.10 | 1.10 |
| **2301** | A518 | 40pi multi | 1.10 | 1.10 |
| **2302** | A519 | 40pi multi | 1.10 | 1.10 |
| **2303** | A520 | 40pi multi | 1.10 | 1.10 |
| **2304** | A521 | 40pi multi | 1.10 | 1.10 |
| | | *Nos. 2299-2304 (6)* | 6.60 | 6.60 |

No. 1472d Surcharged in Red Brown and Gray

**Methods and Perfs. As Before**

**2017, July 20**

**Granite Paper**

| | | | | |
|---|---|---|---|---|
| **2305** | A267 | 10pi on 50f #1472d | .30 | .30 |
| **2306** | A267 | 15pi on 50f #1472d | .45 | .45 |
| **2307** | A267 | 20pi on 50f #1472d | .60 | .60 |
| **2308** | A267 | 25pi on 50f #1472d | .70 | .70 |
| **2309** | A267 | 30pi on 50f #1472d | .85 | .85 |
| **2310** | A267 | 35pi on 50f #1472d | 1.00 | 1.00 |
| **2311** | A267 | 40pi on 50f #1472d | 1.10 | 1.10 |
| **2312** | A267 | 45pi on 50f #1472d | 1.25 | 1.25 |
| **2313** | A267 | 50pi on 50f #1472d | 1.40 | 1.40 |
| **2314** | A267 | 60pi on 50f #1472d | 1.75 | 1.75 |
| | | *Nos. 2305-2314 (10)* | 9.40 | 9.40 |

Trees — A522

Designs: 30pi, Spanish fir. 50pi, Turkey oak.

***Perf. 14¾x14¼ Syncopated***

**2017, July 10** **Litho.**

| | | | | |
|---|---|---|---|---|
| **2315-2316** | A522 | Set of 2 | 2.25 | 2.25 |

**Nos. 1640, 1643, 1649, 1658, 1661, 1688, 1691 Surcharged in Black and Red and No. 1648 Surcharged in Black, Red and Green**

c

d

**Methods and Perfs. As Before**

**2017, Oct. 12**

| | | | | |
|---|---|---|---|---|
| **2317** | A317(c) | 20pi on 100f #1640 | .60 | .60 |
| **2318** | A317(c) | 20pi on 100f #1643 | .60 | .60 |
| **2319** | A317(c) | 20pi on 100f #1649 | .60 | .60 |
| **2320** | A317(c) | 20pi on 100f #1658 | .60 | .60 |
| **2321** | A317(c) | 20pi on 100f #1661 | .60 | .60 |
| **2322** | A317(c) | 20pi on 100f #1688 | .60 | .60 |
| **2323** | A317(c) | 20pi on 100f #1691 | .60 | .60 |
| **2324** | A317(d) | 30pi on 300f #1648 | .85 | .85 |
| **2325** | A317(d) | 50pi on 300f #1648 | 1.40 | 1.40 |
| | | *Nos. 2317-2325 (9)* | 6.45 | 6.45 |

Fruit A523

Designs: No. 2326, 20pi, Plums. No. 2327, 20pi, Pomegranate. No. 2328, 20pi, Peaches. No. 2329, 20pi, Figs. No. 2330, 20pi, Cactus fruit. No. 2331, 20pi, Grapes. No. 2332, 20pi, Blackberries. No. 2333, 20pi, Strawberries. No. 2334, 20pi, Cantaloupe. No. 2335, 20pi, Watermelon.

***Perf. 14¼x14¾ Syncopated***

**2017, Oct. 12** **Litho.**

| | | | | |
|---|---|---|---|---|
| **2326-2335** | A523 | Set of 10 | 5.75 | 5.75 |

Miniature Sheet

Birds — A524

No. 2336: a, Carrier pigeon. b, Goldfinch. c, Buteo rufinus. d, Blackbird. e, Shunnarbird (rock partridge). f, Sinai rosefinch.

***Perf. 14¼x14¾ Syncopated***

**2017, Oct. 12** **Litho.**

| | | | | |
|---|---|---|---|---|
| **2336** | A524 | 30pi Sheet of 6, #a-f | 5.25 | 5.25 |

Medical Tourism Sites A525

Designs: No. 2337, 40pi, Maeen Baths. No. 2338, 40pi, Afra Baths. No. 2339, 40pi, Dead Sea. No. 2340, 40pi, Jordan's Springs.

***Perf. 14¼x14¾ Syncopated***

**2017, Nov. 21** **Litho.**

| | | | | |
|---|---|---|---|---|
| **2337-2340** | A525 | Set of 4 | 4.50 | 4.50 |

UNESCO World Heritage Sites in Jordan — A526

Designs: No. 2341, 40pi, Baptism Site. No. 2342, 40pi, Petra. No. 2343, 40pi, Qusayr Amra. No. 2344, 40pi, Um er-Rasas. No. 2345, 40pi, Wadi Rum.

***Perf. 14¼x14¾ Syncopated***

**2017, Nov. 21** **Litho.**

| | | | | |
|---|---|---|---|---|
| **2341-2345** | A526 | Set of 5 | 5.75 | 5.75 |

A527

A528

A529

A530

A531

A532

Military Uniforms of Jordan A533

*Perf. 14¼x14¾ Syncopated*

**2017, Nov. 21 Litho.**

| | | | | |
|---|---|---|---|---|
| **2346** A527 | 30pi multi | | .85 | .85 |
| **2347** A528 | 30pi multi | | .85 | .85 |
| **2348** A529 | 30pi multi | | .85 | .85 |
| **2349** A530 | 30pi multi | | .85 | .85 |
| **2350** A531 | 30pi multi | | .85 | .85 |
| **2351** A532 | 30pi multi | | .85 | .85 |
| **2352** A533 | 30pi multi | | .85 | .85 |
| | *Nos. 2346-2352 (7)* | | 5.95 | 5.95 |

## SEMI-POSTAL STAMPS

### Locust Campaign Issue

Nos. 145-156 Overprinted

**1930, Apr. 1 Wmk. 4 *Perf. 14***

| | | | |
|---|---|---|---|
| **B1** A1 | 2(m) Prus blue | 2.50 | *4.00* |
| *a.* | Inverted overprint | 200.00 | |
| **B2** A1 | 3(m) rose | 2.00 | *4.00* |
| **B3** A1 | 4(m) green | 2.75 | *5.00* |
| **B4** A1 | 5(m) orange | 22.50 | 17.50 |
| *a.* | Double overprint | 300.00 | |
| **B5** A1 | 10(m) red | 2.25 | *3.75* |
| **B6** A1 | 15(m) ultra | 2.25 | *3.50* |
| *a.* | Inverted overprint | 200.00 | |
| **B7** A1 | 20(m) olive grn | 2.75 | *4.50* |
| **B8** A2 | 50(m) claret | 5.50 | *11.00* |
| **B9** A2 | 90(m) bister | 16.00 | *47.50* |
| **B10** A2 | 100(m) lt blue | 17.50 | *50.00* |
| **B11** A2 | 200(m) violet | 37.50 | *100.00* |
| **B12** A2 | 500(m) brown | 100.00 | *160.00* |
| *a.* | "C" of "Locust" omitted | 750.00 | |
| | *Nos. B1-B12 (12)* | 213.50 | *410.75* |

These stamps were issued to raise funds to help combat a plague of locusts.

**Catalogue values for unused stamps in this section, from this point to the end of the section, are for Never Hinged items.**

Jerusalem — SP1

**1997, Nov. 29 Litho. *Perf. 13½x13***

| | | | |
|---|---|---|---|
| **B13** SP1 | 100f +10f bl & multi | .90 | .75 |
| **B14** SP1 | 200f +20f yel & multi | 1.90 | 1.75 |
| **B15** SP1 | 300f +30f bl grn & multi | 2.75 | 2.50 |
| | *Nos. B13-B15 (3)* | 5.55 | 5.00 |

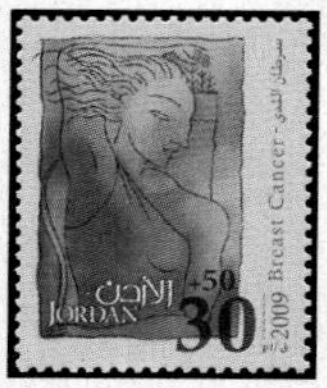
Breast Cancer Prevention — SP2

**2009, Aug. 25 Litho. *Perf. 13¼***
**Granite Paper**

| | | | |
|---|---|---|---|
| **B16** SP2 | 30pi +50pi multi | 3.75 | 3.75 |

Jerusalem, Capital of Arab Culture — SP3

Panel color: 20pi+25pi, Orange. 30pi+25pi, Purple. 40pi+25pi, Red. 50pi+25pi, Gray green.

**2009, Dec. 13 *Perf. 13¼***
**Granite Paper**

| | | | |
|---|---|---|---|
| **B17-B20** SP3 | Set of 4 | 8.00 | 8.00 |

## AIR POST STAMPS

**Catalogue values for unused stamps in this section are for Never Hinged items.**

Plane and Globe — AP1

***Perf. 13½x13***
**1950, Sept. 16 Engr. Wmk. 4**

| | | | |
|---|---|---|---|
| **C1** AP1 | 5f org & red vio | 1.00 | .80 |
| **C2** AP1 | 10f pur & brown | 1.00 | .80 |
| **C3** AP1 | 15f ol grn & rose car | 1.00 | .80 |
| **C4** AP1 | 20f deep blue & blk | 1.25 | 1.25 |
| **C5** AP1 | 50f rose pink & dl grn | 1.75 | 1.25 |
| **C6** AP1 | 100f blue & brown | 3.00 | 3.00 |
| **C7** AP1 | 150f blk & red org | 4.50 | 4.25 |
| | *Nos. C1-C7 (7)* | 13.50 | 12.15 |

Temple of Artemis, Jerash — AP2

**1954 Unwmk. *Perf. 12***

| | | | |
|---|---|---|---|
| **C8** AP2 | 5f blue blk & org | .45 | .25 |
| **C9** AP2 | 10f vio brn & ver | .80 | .75 |
| **C10** AP2 | 25f bl grn & ultra | .90 | .80 |
| **C11** AP2 | 35f dp plum & grnsh bl | 1.00 | .80 |
| **C12** AP2 | 40f car rose & blk | 1.25 | .80 |
| **C13** AP2 | 50f dp ultra & org yel | 1.50 | 1.00 |
| **C14** AP2 | 100f dk bl & vio brn | 1.75 | 1.75 |
| **C15** AP2 | 150f stl bl & red brn | 3.00 | 2.25 |
| | *Nos. C8-C15 (8)* | 10.65 | 8.40 |

**1958-59 Wmk. 305 *Perf. 12***

| | | | |
|---|---|---|---|
| **C16** AP2 | 5f blue blk & org | .45 | .25 |
| **C17** AP2 | 10f vio brn & ver | .75 | .25 |
| **C18** AP2 | 25f bl grn & ultra | .90 | .40 |
| **C19** AP2 | 35f dp plum grnsh bl | .90 | .60 |
| **C20** AP2 | 40f car rose & blk | 1.10 | .75 |
| **C21** AP2 | 50f dp ultra & org yel ('59) | 2.00 | 1.00 |
| | *Nos. C16-C21 (6)* | 6.10 | 3.25 |

Stadium and Torch AP3

***Perf. 11x11½***
**1964, July 12 Litho. Wmk. 305**

| | | | |
|---|---|---|---|
| **C22** AP3 | 1f yellow & multi | .40 | .30 |
| **C23** AP3 | 4f red & multi | .40 | .30 |
| **C24** AP3 | 10f blue & multi | .40 | .30 |
| **C25** AP3 | 35f yel grn & multi | .80 | .60 |
| *a.* | Souvenir sheet of 4, #C22-C25 | 2.75 | 2.25 |
| | *Nos. C22-C25 (4)* | 2.00 | 1.50 |

Opening of Hussein Sports City. No. C25a also exists imperf.

Gorgeous Bush-Shrike — AP4

Birds: 500f, Ornate hawk-eagle, vert. 1d, Gray-headed kingfisher, vert.

***Perf. 14x14½***
**1964, Dec. 18 Photo. Unwmk.**
**Birds in Natural Colors**

| | | | |
|---|---|---|---|
| **C26** AP4 | 150f lt grn, blk & car | 30.00 | 13.00 |
| **C27** AP4 | 500f brt bl, blk & grn | 70.00 | 35.00 |
| **C28** AP4 | 1d lt ol grn & blk | 135.00 | 75.00 |
| | *Nos. C26-C28 (3)* | 235.00 | 123.00 |

Pagoda, Olympic Torch and Emblem — AP5

**1965, Mar. 5 Litho. *Perf. 14***

| | | | |
|---|---|---|---|
| **C29** AP5 | 10f deep rose | .40 | .40 |
| **C30** AP5 | 15f violet | .40 | .40 |
| **C31** AP5 | 20f blue | .45 | .45 |
| **C32** AP5 | 30f green | .45 | .45 |
| **C33** AP5 | 40f brown | .60 | .60 |
| **C34** AP5 | 60f carmine rose | .85 | .85 |
| | *Nos. C29-C34 (6)* | 3.15 | 3.15 |

18th Olympic Games, Tokyo, Oct. 10-25, 1964. An imperf. 100f violet blue souvenir sheet exists. Size of stamp: 60x60mm. Value $12.50.

For overprints see Nos. C42A-C42F.

Forum, Jerash — AP6

Antiquities of Jerash: No. C36, South Theater. No. C37, Triumphal arch. No. C38, Temple of Artemis. No. C39, Cathedral steps. No. C40, Artemis Temple, gate. No. C41, Columns. No. C42, Columns and niche, South Theater. Nos. C39-C42 are vertical.

**1965, June 22 Photo. *Perf. 14x15***
**Center Multicolored**

| | | | |
|---|---|---|---|
| **C35** AP6 | 55f bright pink | 1.40 | 1.40 |
| **C36** AP6 | 55f light blue | 1.40 | 1.40 |
| **C37** AP6 | 55f green | 1.40 | 1.40 |
| **C38** AP6 | 55f black | 1.40 | 1.40 |
| **C39** AP6 | 55f light green | 1.40 | 1.40 |
| **C40** AP6 | 55f carmine rose | 1.40 | 1.40 |
| **C41** AP6 | 55f gray | 1.40 | 1.40 |
| **C42** AP6 | 55f blue | 1.40 | 1.40 |
| | *Nos. C35-C42 (8)* | 11.20 | 11.20 |

Nos. C35-C38 are printed in horizontal rows of 4; Nos. C39-C42 in vertical rows of 4; sheets of 16.

**Nos. C29-C34 with Bilingual Ovpt. and Rocket in Black**

**1965, Sept. 25 Litho. *Perf. 14***

| | | | |
|---|---|---|---|
| **C42A** AP5 | 10f deep rose | 1.50 | 1.50 |
| **C42B** AP5 | 15f violet | 2.00 | 2.00 |
| **C42C** AP5 | 20f blue | 2.75 | 2.75 |
| **C42D** AP5 | 30f green | 4.25 | 4.00 |
| **C42E** AP5 | 40f brown | 5.50 | 5.50 |
| **C42F** AP5 | 60f carmine rose | 7.50 | 7.50 |
| | *Nos. C42A-C42F (6)* | 23.50 | 23.25 |

The imperf. 100f blue souvenir sheet exists overprinted. Value $21.50.

**King Hussein Type of Regular Issue**

**1966, Jan. 15 Photo. *Perf. 14½x14***
**Portrait in Brown**

| | | | |
|---|---|---|---|
| **C43** A67 | 200f brt blue grn | 5.00 | 2.00 |
| **C44** A67 | 500f light green | 11.00 | 8.00 |
| **C45** A67 | 1d light ultra | 19.00 | 12.50 |
| | *Nos. C43-C45 (3)* | 35.00 | 22.50 |

**Animal Type of Regular Issue, 1967**

Animals: 4f, Striped hyena. 30f, Arabian stallion. 60f, Persian gazelle.

**1967, Feb. 11 Photo. *Perf. 14x15***

| | | | |
|---|---|---|---|
| **C46** A70 | 4f dk brn & multi | 2.00 | .30 |
| **C47** A70 | 30f lt bl & multi | 2.50 | .60 |
| **C48** A70 | 60f yellow & multi | 4.50 | 1.50 |
| | *Nos. C46-C48 (3)* | 9.00 | 2.40 |

**Game Type of Regular Issue, 1968**

Protected Game: 60f, Nubian ibex, vert. 100f, Wild ducks.

**1968, Oct. 5 Litho. *Perf. 13½***

| | | | |
|---|---|---|---|
| **C49** A74 | 60f multicolored | 9.50 | 5.00 |
| **C50** A74 | 100f multicolored | 15.00 | 9.00 |

**Easter Type of Regular Issue**

Designs: 60f, Altar, Holy Sepulcher. 100f, Feet Washing, Holy Gate, Jerusalem.

**1972, Apr. Photo. *Perf. 14x13½***

| | | | |
|---|---|---|---|
| **C51** A92 | 60f dk bl & multi | 1.40 | .70 |
| **C52** A92 | 100f multicolored | 2.00 | 1.10 |

### Aero Club Type of Regular Issue

15f, Two Piper 140s. 20f, R.J.A.C. Beechcraft. 40f, Aero Club emblem with winged horse.

**1973, Jan. Photo. *Perf. 13½x14***

| | | | | |
|---|---|---|---|---|
| **C53** | A100 | 15f blue, blk & red | .70 | .35 |
| **C54** | A100 | 20f blue, blk & red | .80 | .40 |
| **C55** | A100 | 40f mag, blk & yel | 1.60 | .80 |
| | | *Nos. C53-C55 (3)* | 3.10 | 1.55 |

### Agriculture Type of Regular Issue

Design: 100f, Soil conservation.

**1973, Dec. 25 *Perf. 13½***

| | | | | |
|---|---|---|---|---|
| **C56** | A110 | 100f multicolored | 2.50 | 1.75 |

King Hussein Driving Car — AP7

**1974, Dec. 20 *Perf. 12***

| | | | | |
|---|---|---|---|---|
| **C57** | AP7 | 30f multicolored | .60 | .25 |
| **C58** | AP7 | 60f multicolored | 1.50 | 1.00 |

Royal Jordanian Automobile Club.

### Building Type of Regular Issue

Designs: 50f, Palms, Aqaba. 60f, Obelisk tomb. 80f, Fort of Wadi Rum.

**1975, Mar. 1 Photo. *Perf. 13½x14***

| | | | | |
|---|---|---|---|---|
| **C59** | A121 | 50f pink & multi | 1.40 | .65 |
| **C60** | A121 | 60f lt bl & multi | 1.75 | .80 |
| **C61** | A121 | 80f yellow & multi | 2.25 | .80 |
| | | *Nos. C59-C61 (3)* | 5.40 | 2.25 |

### Hussein Type of Regular Issue

**1975, Apr. 8 Photo. *Perf. 14x13½***

**Size: 22x27mm**

| | | | | |
|---|---|---|---|---|
| **C62** | A123 | 60f dk grn & brn | 1.25 | .35 |
| **C63** | A123 | 100f org brn & brn | 2.00 | .40 |
| **C64** | A123 | 120f dp bl & brn | 1.10 | .65 |
| **C65** | A123 | 180f brt mag & brn | 1.75 | 1.10 |
| **C66** | A123 | 200f grnsh bl & brn | 2.25 | 1.50 |
| **C67** | A123 | 400f pur & brown | 3.25 | 2.50 |
| **C68** | A123 | 500f orange & brn | 4.25 | 4.00 |
| | | *Nos. C62-C68 (7)* | 15.85 | 10.50 |

## POSTAGE DUE STAMPS

Stamps of Regular Issue (Nos. 69, 66-68 Surcharged with New Value like No. 91) Overprinted

This overprint reads: "Mustahaq" (Tax or Due)

### Typo. Ovpt. "Mustahaq" 10mm long

**1923 Unwmk. *Perf. 11½***

| | | | | |
|---|---|---|---|---|
| **J1** | A7 | ½pi on 3pi ol brn | 57.50 | 60.00 |
| | | a. Inverted overprint | 200.00 | 200.00 |
| | | b. Double overprint | 200.00 | 200.00 |

### Handstamped Overprint 12mm long

| | | | | |
|---|---|---|---|---|
| **J2** | A7 | ½pi on 3pi ol brn | 27.50 | 35.00 |
| | | a. Inverted overprint | 55.00 | — |
| | | b. Double overprint | 55.00 | — |
| **J3** | A7 | 1pi dark blue | 18.00 | 21.00 |
| | | a. Inverted overprint | 50.00 | — |
| | | b. Double overprint | 52.50 | — |
| **J4** | A7 | 1½pi violet | 21.00 | 22.50 |
| | | a. Inverted overprint | 50.00 | — |
| | | b. Double overprint | 52.50 | — |
| **J5** | A7 | 2pi orange | 25.00 | 27.50 |
| | | a. Inverted overprint | 65.00 | 60.00 |
| | | b. Double overprint | 70.00 | — |
| | | *Nos. J1-J5 (5)* | 149.00 | 166.00 |

Stamps of Hejaz Handstamped

| | | | | |
|---|---|---|---|---|
| **J6** | A7 | ½pi red | 2.50 | 6.00 |
| **J7** | A7 | 1pi dark blue | 6.00 | 6.50 |
| **J8** | A7 | 1½pi violet | 5.00 | 7.50 |
| **J9** | A7 | 2pi orange | 8.00 | 8.00 |
| **J10** | A7 | 3pi olive brown | 12.50 | 17.50 |
| **J11** | A7 | 5pi olive green | 15.00 | 30.00 |
| | | *Nos. J6-J11 (6)* | 49.00 | 75.50 |

Type of Palestine, 1918, Overprinted

**1925 Wmk. 4 *Perf. 14***

| | | | | |
|---|---|---|---|---|
| **J12** | A1 | 1m dark brown | 2.50 | 6.00 |
| **J13** | A1 | 2m yellow | 4.25 | 4.25 |
| **J14** | A1 | 4m rose | 4.75 | 6.75 |
| **J15** | A1 | 8m red | 6.50 | 12.00 |
| **J16** | A1 | 13m ultramarine | 9.50 | 12.00 |
| **J17** | A1 | 5pi plum | 11.00 | 19.00 |
| | | a. Perf. 15x14 | 67.50 | 85.00 |
| | | *Nos. J12-J17 (6)* | 38.50 | 60.00 |

The overprint reads: "Mustahaq. Sharqi al'Ardan." (Tax. Eastern Jordan).

Stamps of Palestine, 1918, Surcharged

**1926**

| | | | | |
|---|---|---|---|---|
| **J18** | A1 | 1m on 1m dk brn | 10.00 | 12.00 |
| **J19** | A1 | 2m on 1m dk brn | 9.00 | 12.00 |
| **J20** | A1 | 4m on 3m Prus bl | 10.00 | 15.00 |
| **J21** | A1 | 8m on 3m Prus bl | 10.00 | 15.00 |
| **J22** | A1 | 13m on 13m ultra | 13.00 | 17.00 |
| **J23** | A1 | 5pi on 13m ultra | 16.00 | 25.00 |
| | | *Nos. J18-J23 (6)* | 68.00 | 96.00 |

The surcharge reads "Tax — Eastern Jordan" and New Value.

Stamps of Regular Issue, 1927, Overprinted

**1929**

| | | | | |
|---|---|---|---|---|
| **J24** | A1 | 2m Prussian bl | 2.50 | 6.00 |
| **J25** | A1 | 10m red | 2.50 | 6.50 |
| **J26** | A2 | 50m claret | 7.50 | 22.50 |
| | | *Nos. J24-J26 (3)* | 12.50 | 35.00 |

### With Additional Surcharge

| | | | | |
|---|---|---|---|---|
| **J27** | A1 | 1(m) on 3(m) rose | 1.75 | 7.00 |
| **J28** | A1 | 4(m) on 15(m) ultra | 3.00 | 8.50 |
| | | a. Inverted surch. and ovpt. | 200.00 | 350.00 |
| **J29** | A2 | 20(m) on 100(m) lt bl | 7.00 | 20.00 |
| | | *Nos. J27-J29 (3)* | 11.75 | 35.50 |

D1

**Size: 17¼x21mm**

**1929 Engr. *Perf. 14***

| | | | | |
|---|---|---|---|---|
| **J30** | D1 | 1m brown | 1.40 | 6.50 |
| | | a. Perf. 13½x13 | 160.00 | 130.00 |
| **J31** | D1 | 2m orange | 2.75 | 7.00 |
| **J32** | D1 | 4m green | 4.00 | 11.00 |
| **J33** | D1 | 10m carmine | 7.00 | 10.00 |
| **J34** | D1 | 20m olive green | 13.00 | 21.00 |
| **J35** | D1 | 50m blue | 16.00 | 32.50 |
| | | *Nos. J30-J35 (6)* | 44.15 | 88.00 |

See Nos. J39-J43 design with larger type. For surcharge see No. J52. For overprints see Nos. NJ1a, NJ3, NJ5a, NJ6-NJ7.

D2

**1942 Unwmk. Litho. *Perf. 13x13½***

| | | | | |
|---|---|---|---|---|
| **J36** | D2 | 1m dull red brn | 3.00 | 24.00 |
| **J37** | D2 | 2m dl orange yel | 9.00 | 13.00 |
| **J38** | D2 | 10m dark carmine | 12.00 | 7.50 |
| | | *Nos. J36-J38 (3)* | 24.00 | 44.50 |

For overprints see Nos. NJ8-NJ10.

### Type of 1929

**1943-44 Engr. Wmk. 4 *Perf. 12***

**Size: 17¾x21¼mm**

| | | | | |
|---|---|---|---|---|
| **J39** | D1 | 1m orange brn | .60 | 6.00 |
| **J40** | D1 | 2m yel orange | .80 | 6.50 |
| **J41** | D1 | 4m yel green | .80 | 8.00 |
| **J42** | D1 | 10m rose carmine | 2.00 | 11.00 |
| **J43** | D1 | 20m olive green | 45.00 | 90.00 |
| | | *Nos. J39-J43 (5)* | 49.20 | 121.50 |

For overprints see Nos. J47-J51, NJ1-NJ2, NJ3a, NJ5, NJ6a.

**Catalogue values for unused stamps in this section, from this point to the end of the section, are for Never Hinged items.**

Nos. J39-J43, J35 Srchd. "FILS" & its Arabic Equivalent in Black, Green or Carmine

**1952 Wmk. 4 *Perf. 12***

| | | | | |
|---|---|---|---|---|
| **J47** | D1 | 1f on 1m org brn (Bk) | 1.75 | 1.75 |
| **J48** | D1 | 2f on 2m yel org (G) | 1.75 | 1.75 |
| **J49** | D1 | 4f on 4m yel grn | 2.25 | 2.25 |
| **J50** | D1 | 10f on 10m rose car (Bk) | 4.00 | 4.50 |
| **J51** | D1 | 20f on 20m ol grn | 9.50 | 9.50 |

***Perf. 14***

| | | | | |
|---|---|---|---|---|
| **J52** | D1 | 50f on 50m blue | 9.00 | 9.50 |
| | | *Nos. J47-J52 (6)* | 28.25 | 29.25 |

This overprint exists on Nos. J34, J36-J38. Exists inverted, double and in wrong color.

D3

Inscribed: "The Hashemite Kingdom of the Jordan"

**1952 Engr. *Perf. 11½***

| | | | | |
|---|---|---|---|---|
| **J53** | D3 | 1f orange brown | .65 | .85 |
| **J54** | D3 | 2f yel orange | .65 | .85 |
| **J55** | D3 | 4f yel green | .65 | .85 |
| **J56** | D3 | 10f rose carmine | 1.25 | 1.50 |
| **J57** | D3 | 20f yel brown | 1.25 | 1.75 |
| **J58** | D3 | 50f blue | 3.50 | 4.00 |
| | | *Nos. J53-J58 (6)* | 7.95 | 9.80 |

### Type of 1952 Redrawn

Inscribed: "The Hashemite Kingdom of Jordan"

**1957 Wmk. 305 *Perf. 11½***

| | | | | |
|---|---|---|---|---|
| **J59** | D3 | 1f orange brown | 1.00 | .40 |
| **J60** | D3 | 2f yel orange | 1.00 | .40 |
| **J61** | D3 | 4f yel green | 1.00 | .60 |
| **J62** | D3 | 10f rose carmine | 1.25 | .55 |
| **J63** | D3 | 20f yel brown | 1.75 | 1.25 |
| | | *Nos. J59-J63 (5)* | 6.00 | 3.20 |

## OFFICIAL STAMP

Saudi Arabia No. L34 Overprinted

**1924, Jan. Typo. *Perf. 11½***

| | | | | |
|---|---|---|---|---|
| **O1** | A7 | ½pi red | 100.00 | 150.00 |

Overprint reads: "(Government) the Arabian East 1342."

## POSTAL TAX STAMPS

**Catalogue values for unused stamps in this section are for Never Hinged items.**

Mosque at Hebron — PT1

Designs: 10m, 15m, 20m, 50m, Dome of the Rock. 100m, 200m, 500m, £1, Acre.

***Perf. 11½x12½***

**1947 Unwmk. Engr.**

| | | | | |
|---|---|---|---|---|
| **RA1** | PT1 | 1m ultra | .60 | .40 |
| **RA2** | PT1 | 2m carmine | .70 | .50 |
| **RA3** | PT1 | 3m emerald | .80 | .75 |
| **RA4** | PT1 | 5m plum | 1.00 | .85 |
| **RA5** | PT1 | 10m carmine | 1.10 | 1.00 |
| **RA6** | PT1 | 15m gray | 1.75 | 1.25 |
| **RA7** | PT1 | 20m dk brown | 3.00 | 1.50 |
| **RA8** | PT1 | 50m purple | 4.50 | 3.50 |
| **RA9** | PT1 | 100m orange red | 14.00 | 9.00 |
| **RA10** | PT1 | 200m dp blue | 37.50 | 22.50 |
| **RA11** | PT1 | 500m green | 80.00 | 60.00 |
| **RA12** | PT1 | £1 dk brown | 140.00 | 130.00 |
| | | *Nos. RA1-RA12 (12)* | 284.95 | 231.25 |

Issued to help the Welfare Fund for Arabs in Palestine. Required on foreign-bound letters to the amount of half the regular postage.

For overprints and surcharges see Nos. 286A-286C, 344-346, RA37-RA46, NRA1-NRA12.

Nos. 211, 232 and 234 Overprinted in Black

**1950 Wmk. 4 *Perf. 12***

| | | | | |
|---|---|---|---|---|
| **RA23** | A3 | 5m orange | 19.00 | 20.00 |
| **RA24** | A3 | 10m violet | 27.50 | 29.00 |
| **RA25** | A3 | 15m dull olive grn | 32.50 | 32.50 |
| | | *Nos. RA23-RA25 (3)* | 79.00 | 81.50 |

Arch and Colonnade, Palmyra, Syria — PT2

Two types of 5m:

Type I — "A" with serifs. Arabic ovpt. 8mm wide.

Type II — "A" without serifs. Arabic ovpt. 5mm wide.

### Black or Carmine Overprint

**1950-51 Engr. *Perf. 13½x13***

| | | | | |
|---|---|---|---|---|
| **RA26** | PT2 | 5m orange (I) | 22.50 | 17.50 |
| | | a. Type II ('51) | 27.50 | 2.75 |
| **RA27** | PT2 | 10m violet (C) | 22.50 | 20.00 |

The overprint on No. RA27 is similar to that on RA23-RA25 but slightly bolder.

### Type of 1947

Designs: 5f, Hebron Mosque. 10f, 15f, 20f, Dome of the Rock. 100f, Acre.

**1951 Wmk. 4 *Perf. 11½x12½***

| | | | | |
|---|---|---|---|---|
| **RA28** | PT1 | 5f plum | .85 | .85 |
| **RA29** | PT1 | 10f carmine | .85 | .85 |
| **RA30** | PT1 | 15f gray | 1.00 | 1.00 |
| **RA31** | PT1 | 20f dk brown | 1.25 | 1.25 |
| **RA33** | PT1 | 100f orange | 6.25 | 6.25 |
| | | *Nos. RA28-RA33 (5)* | 10.20 | 10.20 |

The tax on Nos. RA1-RA33 was for Arab aid in Palestine.

For overprints see Nos. 287-290, 347.

Postal Tax Stamps of 1947 Srchd. "FILS" or "J.D." & Their Arabic Equivalents & Bars in Carmine or Black

**1952 Unwmk.**

| | | | | |
|---|---|---|---|---|
| **RA37** | PT1 | 1f on 1m ultra | .50 | .45 |
| **RA38** | PT1 | 3f on 3m emer | .80 | .45 |
| **RA39** | PT1 | 10f on 10m car | 1.30 | .55 |
| **RA40** | PT1 | 15f on 15m gray | 1.75 | 1.25 |
| **RA41** | PT1 | 20f on 20m dk brown | 2.50 | 1.75 |
| **RA42** | PT1 | 50f on 50m pur | 5.00 | 3.75 |
| **RA43** | PT1 | 100f on 100m org red | 17.50 | 10.00 |
| **RA44** | PT1 | 200f on 200m dp blue | 45.00 | 27.50 |
| **RA45** | PT1 | 500f on 500m grn | 100.00 | 75.00 |
| **RA46** | PT1 | 1d on £1 dk brn | 150.00 | 140.00 |
| | | *Nos. RA37-RA46 (10)* | 324.35 | 260.70 |

"J.D." stands for Jordanian Dinar.

---

### OCCUPATION STAMPS

**Catalogue values for unused stamps in this section are for Never Hinged items.**

### For Use in Palestine

Stamps of Jordan Overprinted in Red, Black, Dark Green, Green or Orange Red

### On No. 200

**1948 Unwmk. *Perf. 13x13½***

| | | | | |
|---|---|---|---|---|
| **N1** | A14 | 2m dull green (R) | 8.00 | 8.00 |

### On #207-209, 211, 230-235, 215-220

**1948 Wmk. 4 *Perf. 12, 13½x13, 14***

| | | | | |
|---|---|---|---|---|
| **N2** | A3 | 1m red brown | 1.00 | .80 |
| **N3** | A3 | 2m Prus grn (R) | 1.00 | .80 |
| *a.* | | 2m Prussian blue, perf. 13½x13 (R) (#170a) | 2.50 | *2.50* |
| **N4** | A3 | 3m blue grn (R) | 1.00 | 1.00 |
| **N5** | A3 | 3m rose carmine | .65 | .65 |
| **N6** | A3 | 4m dp yel grn (R) | .65 | .65 |
| **N7** | A3 | 5m orange (G) | .65 | .65 |
| **N8** | A3 | 10m violet (OR) | 1.50 | 1.50 |
| **N9** | A3 | 12m deep rose | 1.50 | .90 |
| **N10** | A3 | 15m dl ol grn (R) | 2.25 | 2.25 |
| **N11** | A3 | 20m dp blue (R) | 3.00 | 1.50 |
| **N12** | A3 | 50m red lil (Dk G) | 3.25 | 3.25 |
| **N13** | A3 | 90m ocher (Dk G) | 15.00 | 3.25 |
| **N14** | A3 | 100m dp blue (R) | 17.50 | 10.00 |
| **N15** | A3 | 200m dk vio (R) | 9.00 | *15.00* |
| *a.* | | 200m vio, perf. 14 (R) (#182) | 75.00 | 50.00 |
| **N16** | A3 | 500m dk brn (R) | 60.00 | 25.00 |
| **N17** | A3 | £1 black (R) | 110.00 | 60.00 |
| | | *Nos. N2-N17 (16)* | 227.95 | 127.20 |

The first overprinting of these stamps include Nos. N1-N6, N9-N17. The second overprinting includes Nos. N1, N3, N5-N17, in inks differing in shade from the originals.

Many values exist with inverted or double overprint.

### Jordan Nos. 245-249 Overprinted in Black or Red

**1949, Aug. Wmk. 4 *Perf. 13***

| | | | | |
|---|---|---|---|---|
| **N18** | A17 | 1m brown (Bk) | 1.50 | 1.75 |
| **N19** | A17 | 4m green | 1.50 | 1.75 |
| *a.* | | "PLAESTINE" | 80.00 | |
| **N20** | A17 | 10m red | 1.75 | 1.75 |
| **N21** | A17 | 20m ultra | 1.75 | 1.75 |
| **N22** | A18 | 50m dull green | 3.50 | 3.50 |
| *a.* | | "PLAESTINE" | 75.00 | |
| | | *Nos. N18-N22 (5)* | 10.00 | 10.50 |

The overprint is in one line on No. N22.

UPU, 75th anniversary.

---

### OCCUPATION POSTAGE DUE STAMPS

**Catalogue values for unused stamps in this section are for Never Hinged items.**

Jordan Nos. J39, J30a, J40, J32, J41-J43, J34 and J35 Overprinted in Black, Red or Carmine

**1948-49 Wmk. 4 *Perf. 12, 14***

| | | | | |
|---|---|---|---|---|
| **NJ1** | D1 | 1m org brn, perf. 12 | 3.50 | *4.50* |
| *a.* | | Perf. 13½x13 (#J30a) | 75.00 | 50.00 |
| **NJ2** | D1 | 2m yel orange | 4.00 | *5.50* |
| **NJ3** | D1 | 4m grn (R) (#J32) | 4.00 | *5.50* |
| *a.* | | 4m yel grn (C) (#J41) | 15.00 | *18.00* |
| **NJ5** | D1 | 10m rose car (#J42) ('49) | 4.00 | *5.00* |
| *a.* | | Perf. 14 (#J33) | 325.00 | |
| **NJ6** | D1 | 20m ol grn (R), perf. 14 | 3.75 | *4.50* |
| *a.* | | Perf. 12 (R) (#J43) | 95.00 | 95.00 |
| **NJ7** | D1 | 50m blue (R) | 4.25 | *5.50* |
| | | *Nos. NJ1-NJ3,NJ5-NJ7 (6)* | 23.50 | *30.50* |

The second overprinting of these stamps includes Nos. NJ1-NJ3, NJ3a and NJ5-NJ7, in inks differing in shade from the originals.

Double and inverted overprints exist.

### Same Overprint in Black on Jordan Nos. J36-J38

**1948-49 Unwmk. *Perf. 13x13½***

| | | | | |
|---|---|---|---|---|
| **NJ8** | D2 | 1m dl red brn | *175.00* | *175.00* |
| **NJ9** | D2 | 2m dl org yel ('49) | 20.00 | *22.50* |
| **NJ10** | D2 | 10m dark car | 17.50 | *19.00* |

---

### OCCUPATION POSTAL TAX STAMPS

**Catalogue values for unused stamps in this section are for Never Hinged items.**

Postal Tax Stamps of 1947 Overprinted in Red or Black

**1950**

| | | | | |
|---|---|---|---|---|
| **NRA1** | PT1 | 1m ultra (R) | .40 | .75 |
| **NRA2** | PT1 | 2m carmine | .45 | .75 |
| **NRA3** | PT1 | 3m emer (R) | .75 | .85 |
| **NRA4** | PT1 | 5m plum | 1.00 | .75 |
| **NRA5** | PT1 | 10m carmine | 1.25 | .75 |
| **NRA6** | PT1 | 15m gray (R) | 2.75 | .90 |
| **NRA7** | PT1 | 20m dk brn (R) | 4.50 | 1.50 |
| **NRA8** | PT1 | 50m purple (R) | 6.50 | 3.00 |
| **NRA9** | PT1 | 100m org red | 11.00 | 4.50 |
| **NRA10** | PT1 | 200m dp blue (R) | 27.50 | 14.50 |
| **NRA11** | PT1 | 500m green (R) | 75.00 | 42.50 |
| **NRA12** | PT1 | £1 dk brn (R) | 140.00 | 75.00 |
| | | *Nos. NRA1-NRA12 (12)* | 271.10 | 145.75 |

For overprints see Nos. 286D-286G.

---

## KARELIA

kə-'rē-lə-ə

LOCATION — In northwestern Soviet Russia

GOVT. — An autonomous republic of the Soviet Union

AREA — 55,198 sq. mi. (approx.)

POP. — 270,000 (approx.)

CAPITAL — Petrozavodsk (Kalininsk)

In 1921 the Karelians rebelled and for a short period a form of sovereignty independent of Russia was maintained.

100 Pennia = 1 Markka

Bear — A1

**1922 Unwmk. Litho. *Perf. 11½, 12***

| | | | | |
|---|---|---|---|---|
| 1 | A1 | 5p dark gray | 15.00 | *55.00* |
| 2 | A1 | 10p light blue | 15.00 | *55.00* |
| 3 | A1 | 20p rose red | 15.00 | *55.00* |
| 4 | A1 | 25p yellow brown | 15.00 | *55.00* |
| 5 | A1 | 40p magenta | 15.00 | *55.00* |
| 6 | A1 | 50p gray green | 15.00 | *55.00* |
| 7 | A1 | 75p orange yellow | 20.00 | *55.00* |
| 8 | A1 | 1m pink & gray | 20.00 | *55.00* |
| 9 | A1 | 2m yel grn & gray | 27.50 | *110.00* |
| 10 | A1 | 3m lt blue & gray | 27.50 | *140.00* |
| 11 | A1 | 5m red lil & gray | 27.50 | *175.00* |
| 12 | A1 | 10m lt brn & gray | 27.50 | *275.00* |
| 13 | A1 | 15m green & car | 27.50 | *275.00* |
| 14 | A1 | 20m rose & green | 27.50 | *275.00* |
| 15 | A1 | 25m yellow & blue | 30.00 | *275.00* |
| | | *Nos. 1-15 (15)* | 325.00 | *1,965.* |
| | | Set, never hinged | 450.00 | |

Nos. 1-15 were valid Jan. 31-Feb. 16, 1922. Use probably ended Feb. 3, although cancellations of the 4th and 5th exist.

Nos. 7, 8, 10, 13, 14 and 15 exist imperf. Value, each pair $250 hinged; $500 never hinged. Other denominations may exist imperf.

Counterfeits abound.

---

### OCCUPATION STAMPS

### Issued under Finnish Occupation

Issued in the Russian territory of Eastern Karelia under Finnish military administration.

### Types of Finland Stamps, 1930 Overprinted in Black

On A26

On A27-A28

**1941 Unwmk. *Perf. 14***

| | | | | |
|---|---|---|---|---|
| **N1** | A26 | 50p brt yel grn | .45 | *1.00* |
| **N2** | A26 | 1.75m dk gray | 1.25 | *1.75* |
| **N3** | A26 | 2m dp org | 1.75 | *4.50* |
| **N4** | A26 | 2.75m yel org | .85 | *1.25* |
| **N5** | A26 | 3½m lt ultra | 2.50 | *4.50* |
| **N6** | A27 | 5m rose vio | 6.00 | *10.00* |
| **N7** | A28 | 10m pale brn | 6.75 | *12.00* |
| | | *Nos. N1-N7 (7)* | 19.55 | *35.00* |
| | | Set, never hinged | 32.00 | |

### Types of Finland Stamps, 1930 Overprinted in Green

On A26

On A27-A29

| | | | | |
|---|---|---|---|---|
| **N8** | A26 | 50p brt yel grn | .55 | *.90* |
| **N9** | A26 | 1.75m dk gray | .70 | *1.00* |
| **N10** | A26 | 2m dp org | 1.00 | *2.40* |
| **N11** | A26 | 2.75m yel org | .65 | *1.25* |
| **N12** | A26 | 3½m lt ultra | 1.25 | *2.25* |
| **N13** | A27 | 5m rose vio | 2.00 | *5.00* |
| **N14** | A28 | 10m pale brown | 4.25 | *8.50* |
| **N15** | A29 | 25m green | 4.50 | *9.00* |
| | | *Nos. N8-N15 (8)* | 14.90 | *30.30* |
| | | Set, never hinged | 35.00 | |

Mannerheim Type of Finland Overprinted

**1942**

| | | | | |
|---|---|---|---|---|
| **N16** | A48 | 50p dk yel grn | .95 | *2.25* |
| **N17** | A48 | 1.75m slate bl | .95 | *2.25* |
| **N18** | A48 | 2m red org | .95 | *2.25* |
| **N19** | A48 | 2.75m brn org | .80 | *2.25* |
| **N20** | A48 | 3.50m brt ultra | .80 | *2.25* |
| **N21** | A48 | 5m brn vio | .80 | *2.25* |
| | | *Nos. N16-N21 (6)* | 5.25 | *13.50* |
| | | Set, never hinged | 10.00 | |

### Same Overprint on Ryti Type of Finland

| | | | | |
|---|---|---|---|---|
| **N22** | A49 | 50p dk yel grn | .80 | *2.25* |
| **N23** | A49 | 1.75m slate bl | .80 | *2.25* |
| **N24** | A49 | 2m red org | .80 | *2.25* |
| **N25** | A49 | 2.75m brn org | .95 | *2.25* |
| **N26** | A49 | 3.50m brt ultra | .95 | *2.25* |
| **N27** | A49 | 5m brn vio | .95 | *2.25* |
| | | *Nos. N22-N27 (6)* | 5.25 | *13.50* |
| | | Set, never hinged | 10.00 | |

The overprint translates, "East Karelia Military Administration."

---

### OCCUPATION SEMI-POSTAL STAMP

Arms of East Karelia — SP1

**1943 Unwmk. Engr. *Perf. 14***

| | | | | |
|---|---|---|---|---|
| **NB1** | SP1 | 3.50m + 1.50m dk ol | .90 | *2.50* |
| | | Never hinged | 2.50 | |

This surtax aided war victims in East Karelia.

# KATANGA

kə-ˈtäŋ-gə

LOCATION — Central Africa
GOVT. — Republic
CAPITAL — Elisabethville

Katanga province seceded from the Congo (ex-Belgian) Republic in July, 1960, but established nations did not recognize it as an independent state. The UN declared the secession ended in Sept, 1961. The last troops surrendered Sept. 1963.

During the secession Katanga stamps were tolerated in the international mails, but the government authorizing them was not recognized.

100 Centimes = 1 Franc

**Catalogue values for all unused stamps in this country are for Never Hinged items.**

### Belgian Congo Nos. 318-322 Overprinted "KATANGA"

*Perf. 11½*

**1960, Sept. 12 Photo. Unwmk.**

| | | | | |
|---|---|---|---|---|
| 1 | A94 | 50c golden brn, ocher & red brn | | |
| 2 | A94 | 1fr dk bl, pur & red brn | | |
| 3 | A94 | 2fr gray, brt bl & red brn | | |
| | | *Nos. 1-3 (3)* | .65 | .65 |

**Inscription in French**

| | | | | |
|---|---|---|---|---|
| 4 | A95 | 3fr gray & red | 6.50 | 6.50 |

**Inscription in Flemish**

| | | | | |
|---|---|---|---|---|
| 5 | A95 | 3fr gray & red | 6.50 | 6.50 |

Inverted overprints exist on No. 1-5. Values: 1-3 $9 each; 4-5 $15 each.

For surcharges see Nos. 50-51.

### Animal Type of Belgian Congo, Nos. 306-317, Overprinted "KATANGA"

**1960, Sept. 19 Granite Paper**

| | | | | |
|---|---|---|---|---|
| 6 | A92 | 10c bl & brn | | |
| 7 | A93 | 20c red org & slate | | |
| 8 | A92 | 40c brn & bl | | |
| 9 | A93 | 50c brt ultra, red & sep | | |
| 10 | A92 | 1fr brn, grn & blk | | |
| 11 | A93 | 1.50fr blk & org yel | | |
| 12 | A92 | 2fr crim, blk & brn | | |
| 13 | A93 | 3fr blk, gray & lil rose | | |
| 14 | A92 | 5fr brn, dk brn & brt grn | | |
| 15 | A93 | 6.50fr bl, brn & org yel | | |
| 16 | A92 | 8fr org brn, ol bis & lil | | |
| 17 | A93 | 10fr multi | | |
| | | *Nos. 6-17 (12)* | 52.50 | 27.50 |

Inverted overprints exist. Value $17.50 each.

### Flower Type of Belgian Congo, Nos. 263-271, 274-281, Overprinted "KATANGA"

**Flowers in Natural Colors**

**1960, Sept. 22 Granite Paper**

| | | | | |
|---|---|---|---|---|
| 18 | A86 | 10c dp plum & ocher | | |
| 19 | A86 | 15c red & yel grn | | |
| 20 | A86 | 20c grn & gray | | |
| 21 | A86 | 25c dk grn & dl org | | |
| 22 | A86 | 40c grn & sal | | |
| 23 | A86 | 50c dk car & aqua | | |
| 24 | A86 | 60c bl grn & pink | | |
| 25 | A86 | 75c dp plum & gray | | |
| 26 | A86 | 1fr car & yel | | |
| 27 | A86 | 2fr ol grn & buff | | |
| 28 | A86 | 3fr ol grn & pink | | |
| 29 | A86 | 4fr choc & lil | | |
| 30 | A86 | 5fr dp plum & lt bl grn | | |
| 31 | A86 | 6.50fr dk car & lil | | |
| 32 | A86 | 7fr dk grn & fawn | | |
| 33 | A86 | 8fr grn & lt yel | | |
| 34 | A86 | 10fr dp plum & pale ol | | |
| | | *Nos. 18-34 (17)* | 75.00 | 27.50 |

Inverted overprints exist. Value $24 each.

Carving and Mask Type of Belgian Congo, Nos. 241, 246, 254-256, Surcharged or Overprinted

**1960, Sept. 22** *Perf. 12½*

| | | | | |
|---|---|---|---|---|
| 35 | A82 | 1.50fr on 1.25fr | 1.75 | .60 |
| 36 | A82 | 3.50fr on 2.50fr | 1.60 | .75 |
| 37 | A82 | 20fr red org & vio brn | 5.75 | 4.00 |
| 38 | A82 | 50fr dp org & blk | 12.50 | 10.00 |
| 39 | A82 | 100fr crim & blk brn | 80.00 | 30.00 |
| | | *Nos. 35-39 (5)* | 101.60 | 45.35 |

Inverted surcharges and overprints exist. Values: No. 37, $60; No. 38, $70; No. 39, $110.

### Map Type of Congo Democratic Republic, Nos. 356-365, Overprinted "11 / JUILLET / DE / L'ETAT DU KATANGA"

**1960, Oct. 26** *Perf. 11½*

**Granite Paper**

| | | | | |
|---|---|---|---|---|
| 40 | A93a | 20c brown | .25 | .25 |
| 41 | A93a | 50c rose red | .25 | .25 |
| 42 | A93a | 1fr green | .25 | .25 |
| 43 | A93a | 1.50fr red brn | .25 | .25 |
| 44 | A93a | 2fr rose car | .25 | .25 |
| 45 | A93a | 3.50fr lilac | .25 | .25 |
| 46 | A93a | 5fr brt bl | .25 | .25 |
| 47 | A93a | 6.50fr gray | .25 | .25 |
| 48 | A93a | 10fr orange | .30 | .25 |
| 49 | A93a | 20fr ultra | .40 | .25 |
| | | *Nos. 40-49 (10)* | 2.70 | 2.50 |

Inverted and double surcharges exist.

### Belgian Congo Nos. 321-322 Surcharged

**1961, Jan. 16**

| | | | | |
|---|---|---|---|---|
| 50 | A95 | 3.50fr on 3fr #321 | 3.50 | 3.50 |
| 51 | A95 | 3.50fr on 3fr #322 | 3.50 | 3.50 |

Inverted surcharges exist. Value $6.50 each.

A1

Katangan Wood Carvings: 3.50fr-8fr, Preparing meal. 10fr-100fr, Family group.

**1961, Mar. 1** *Perf. 11½*

**Granite Paper**

| | | | | |
|---|---|---|---|---|
| 52 | A1 | 10c grn & lt grn | .25 | .25 |
| 53 | A1 | 20c purple & lil | .25 | .25 |
| 54 | A1 | 50c blue & lt bl | .25 | .25 |
| 55 | A1 | 1.50fr ol grn & lt ol grn | .25 | .25 |
| 56 | A1 | 2fr red brn & lt brn | .25 | .25 |
| 57 | A1 | 3.50fr dk blue & lt bl | .25 | .25 |
| 58 | A1 | 5fr bl grn & lt bl grn | .25 | .25 |
| 59 | A1 | 6fr org brn & tan | .25 | .25 |
| 60 | A1 | 6.50fr bl vio & gray vio | .25 | .25 |
| 61 | A1 | 8fr claret & pink | .25 | .25 |
| 62 | A1 | 10fr dk brn & lt brn | .25 | .25 |
| 63 | A1 | 20fr dk ol & lt grn | .25 | .25 |
| 64 | A1 | 50fr brn & lt brn | .60 | .35 |
| 65 | A1 | 100fr Prus bl & lt bl | 1.10 | .75 |
| | | *Nos. 52-65 (14)* | 4.70 | 4.10 |

A2

1fr, 5fr, Abstract vehicle. 2.50fr, 6.50fr, Gear.

**Granite Paper**

**1961, July 8** *Perf. 11½*

| | | | | |
|---|---|---|---|---|
| 66 | A2 | 50c blk, grn & red | .25 | .25 |
| 67 | A2 | 1fr blk & blue | .25 | .25 |
| 68 | A2 | 2.50fr blk & yellow | .25 | .25 |
| 69 | A2 | 3.50fr blk, brn & scar | .30 | .25 |
| 70 | A2 | 5fr blk & purple | .40 | .35 |
| 71 | A2 | 6.50fr blk & orange | 1.00 | .60 |
| | | *Nos. 66-71 (6)* | 2.45 | 1.95 |

Katanga International Fair.

Imperfs exist. Value, set $45.

Air Katanga A3

Design: 6.50fr, 10fr, Plane on ground.

**1961, Aug. 1** *Perf. 11½*

**Granite Paper**

| | | | | |
|---|---|---|---|---|
| 72 | A3 | 3.50fr multicolored | | |
| 73 | A3 | 6.50fr multicolored | | |
| 74 | A3 | 8fr multicolored | | |
| 75 | A3 | 10fr multicolored | | |
| | | *Nos. 72-75 (4)* | 6.00 | 6.00 |

Imperfs exist. Value, set $60.

Katanga Gendarmerie — A4

**1962, Oct. 1** *Perf. 11½*

**Granite Paper**

| | | | | |
|---|---|---|---|---|
| 76 | A4 | 6fr multicolored | | |
| 77 | A4 | 8fr multicolored | | |
| 78 | A4 | 10fr multicolored | | |
| | | *Nos. 76-78 (3)* | 4.25 | 4.25 |

Imperfs exist.Value, set $40.

## SEMI-POSTAL STAMPS

Pres. Moise Tshombe — SP1

**1961, July 11** *Perf. 11½*

**Granite Paper**

| | | | | |
|---|---|---|---|---|
| B1 | SP1 | 6.50fr + 5fr multi | | |
| B2 | SP1 | 8fr + 5fr multi | | |
| B3 | SP1 | 10fr + 5fr multi | | |
| | | *Nos. B1-B3 (3)* | 7.00 | 5.00 |

Nos. B1-B3 exist imperf. Value, set $80.

## POSTAGE DUE STAMPS

### Belgian Congo Nos. J8a-J10a, J16-J19 Handstamped "KATANGA" in Blue

**1960, Dec. 30 Unwmk.** *Perf. 12½*

| | | | | |
|---|---|---|---|---|
| J1 | D2 | 10c olive green | | |
| J2 | D2 | 20c dark ultra | | |
| J3 | D2 | 50c green | | |

*Perf. 11½*

| | | | | |
|---|---|---|---|---|
| J4 | D3 | 1fr light blue | | |
| J5 | D3 | 2fr vermilion | | |
| J6 | D3 | 4fr purple | | |
| J7 | D3 | 6fr violet blue | | |
| | | *Nos. J1-J7 (7)* | 30.00 | 30.00 |

This overprint also exists on Belgian Congo Nos. J11a-J12a, J13-J15. Value, set $180.

# KAZAKHSTAN

ˌka-ˌzak-ˈstan

(Kazakstan)

LOCATION — Bounded by southern Russia, Uzbekistan, Kyrgyzstan, and China.
GOVT. — Independent republic, member of the Commonwealth of Independent States.
AREA — 1,049,155 sq. mi.
POP. — 16,824,825 (1999 est.)
CAPITAL — Astana

With the breakup of the Soviet Union on Dec. 26, 1991, Kazakhstan and ten former Soviet republics established the Commonwealth of Independent States.

100 Kopecks = 1 Ruble
100 Tijn = 1 Tenge (1993)

**Catalogue values for all unused stamps in this country are for Never Hinged items.**

Overprinted Stamps

The Philatelic Club of Alma Ata, Kazakhstan, has announced that various overprinted stamps of the USSR were not generally available nor were they in values reflecting actual postal rates.

A1

*Perf. 12x12½*

**1992, Mar. 23 Litho. Unwmk.**

| | | | | |
|---|---|---|---|---|
| 1 | A1 | 50k multicolored | .40 | .30 |

For surcharge, see No. 667.

Saiga Tatarica A2

**1992, Sept. 11 Litho.** *Perf. 12*

| | | | | |
|---|---|---|---|---|
| 2 | A2 | 75k multicolored | .40 | .30 |

Camels and Train, by K. Kasteev — A3

**1992, Sept. 11 Litho.** *Perf. 12½x12*

| | | | | |
|---|---|---|---|---|
| 3 | A3 | 1r multicolored | .40 | .30 |

Day of the Republic A3a

**1992, Dec. 16 Litho.** *Perf. 12*

| | | | | |
|---|---|---|---|---|
| 4 | A3a | 5r multicolored | .50 | .50 |

Space Ship and Yurt — A4

Natl. Flag — A5

**1993, Jan. 24 Litho. *Perf. 13x12½***

22 A4 1r green .25 .25
23 A4 3r red .25 .25
24 A4 10r golden brown .30 .30
25 A4 25r purple .70 .70

***Perf. 14***

26 A5 50r multicolored 1.25 1.25
*Nos. 22-26 (5)* 2.75 2.75

See Nos. 64, 69, 108-115.

Space Mail A6

**1993, Mar. 5 Litho. *Perf. 13½***

35 A6 100r multicolored 1.50 1.50

New Year 1993 (Year of the Rooster) — A7

**1993, Mar. 22 Litho. *Perf. 13x13½***

36 A7 60r yellow, black & red 1.60 1.60

See Nos. 54, 98, 141, 187A, 220, 268.

Cosmonauts' Day — A8

**1993, Apr. 12 *Perf. 13½x13***

37 A8 90r multicolored 2.00 2.00

Pres. Nursultan Nazarbayev — A9

**1993, Aug. 2 Litho. *Perf. 14***

38 A9 50r multicolored 1.00 1.00

Bukar Zhirav Kalkaman (1668-1781), Poet — A10

**1993, Aug. 18 *Perf. 13½x13***

39 A10 15r multicolored .50 .50

Map, Pres. Nursultan Nazarbayev — A11

**1993, Sept. 24 Litho. *Perf. 13***

40 A11 100r multicolored 1.60 1.25

Wildlife A12

Designs: 5r, Selevinia betpakdalensis. 10r, Hystrix leucura. 15r, Vormela peregusna. 20r, Equis hemionus onager. 25r, Ovis orientalis. 30r, Acinonyx jubatus venaticus.

**1993, Nov. 11 *Perf. 12x12½***

41 A12 5r multicolored .30 .30
42 A12 10r multicolored .35 .35
43 A12 15r multicolored .40 .40
44 A12 20r multicolored .45 .45
45 A12 25r multicolored .50 .50
46 A12 30r multicolored .55 .55
*Nos. 41-46 (6)* 2.55 2.55

Nos. 1-46 were sold after the currency changeover as stamps denominated in one or both of the new currency units. Nos. 47-50, 54, 64 and 69 were sold as stamps denominated in tijn, and later as tenge.

1994 Winter Olympics, Lillehammer A13

**1994, Jan. 24 Litho. *Perf. 13½x13***

47 A13 15te Ice hockey .30 .30
48 A13 25te Slalom skiing .45 .45
49 A13 90te Ski jumping 1.25 1.25
50 A13 150te Speed skating 2.00 2.00
*Nos. 47-50 (4)* 4.00 4.00

1994 Winter Olympics, Lillehammer — A14

No. 53 With 2 Line Cyrillic Inscription

Designs: 2te, Skiers Vladimir Smirnov, Kazakhstan; Bjorn Daehlie, Norway. 6.80te, 12te, Smirnov.

**1994, Feb. 19 Litho. *Perf. 13x13½***

51 2te multicolored .30 .30
52 6.80te multicolored .70 .70
a. A14 Pair, #51-52 1.50 1.50
53 A14 12te like No. 52 1.10 1.10
*Nos. 51-53 (3)* 2.10 2.10

No. 53 has an additional two line Cyrillic inscription.

**New Year Type of 1993**

**Size: 26x38mm**

**1994, Mar. 22 *Perf. 12***

54 A7 30te green, black & blue .75 .50

New Year 1994 (Year of the Dog).

Space Program A15

**1994, Apr. 12 *Perf. 13½x13***

55 A15 2te multicolored .50 .50

**Souvenir Sheet**

Russian Space Shuttle, Cosmonaut — A16

**1994, July 12 *Perf. 13***

56 A16 6.80te Sheet of 4 3.50 3.50

**Space Ship and Yurt Type of 1993**

**1994, July 12 Litho. *Perf. 11½***

64 A4 15ti blue 1.10 .95
69 A4 80ti lake 2.40 1.90

For surcharges see Nos. 70-76, 122.

Nos. 64, 69 Surcharged in Lake or Purple

**1995-2004 Litho. *Perf. 11½***

70 A4 1te on 15ti #64 .30 .30
71 A4 2te on 15ti #64 .40 .40
72 A4 3te on 80ti #69 (P) .40 .40
73 A4 4te on 80ti #69 (P) .50 .50
74 A4 6te on 80ti #69 (P) .60 .60
75 A4 8te on 80ti #69 (P) 1.10 1.10
76 A4 12te on 80ti #69 (P) .90 .90
77 A4 20te on 80ti #69 (P) 1.10 1.10
78 A4 200te on 80ti #69 (P) 10.00 10.00
*Nos. 70-78 (9)* 15.30 15.30

Issued: 1te, 2te, 12te, 2/2/95. 3te, 4te, 6te, 20te, 2/10/95. 8te, 9/25/95. 200te, 1/29/04.
Inverted surcharges exist.

Music Competition Festival A18

Designs: 10te, Snow-covered mountain top. 15te, Aerial view of stadium at night.

**1994, Aug. 1 *Perf. 13½***

81 A18 10te multicolored .55 .55
82 A18 15te multicolored .80 .80

For surcharges see Nos. 119A-119B.

Reptiles A19

Designs: 1te, Agrionemys horsfieldi. 1.20te, Phrynocephalus mystaceus. 2te, Agkistrodon halys. 3te, Teratoscincus scincus. 5te, Trapelus sanguinolenta. 7te, Ophisaurus apodus. 10te, Varanus griseus.

**1994, Oct. 10 *Perf. 12½x12***

83 A19 1te multicolored .25 .25
84 A19 1.20te multicolored .25 .25
85 A19 2te multicolored .30 .30
86 A19 3te multicolored .30 .30
87 A19 5te multicolored .40 .40
88 A19 7te multicolored .50 .50
*Nos. 83-88 (6)* 2.00 2.00

**Souvenir Sheet**

89 A19 10te multicolored 1.25 1.25

Prehistoric Animals A20

1te, Entelodon. 1.20te, Saurolophus. 2te, Plesiosaurus. 3te, Sordes pilosus. 5te, Mosasaurus. 7te, Megaloceros giganteum. 10te, Koelodonta antiquitatis.

**1994, Nov. 24 Litho. *Perf. 12½x12***

90 A20 1te multicolored .25 .25
91 A20 1.20te multicolored .25 .25
92 A20 2te multicolored .25 .25
93 A20 3te multicolored .30 .30
94 A20 5te multicolored .40 .40
95 A20 7te multicolored .50 .50
*Nos. 90-95 (6)* 1.95 1.95

**Souvenir Sheet**

96 A20 10te multicolored 1.40 1.40

Day of the Republic A21

**1994, Oct. 25 *Perf. 11½***

97 A21 2te multicolored .60 .60

For surcharge see No. 160B.

**New Year Type of 1993**

**1995, Mar. 22 Litho. *Perf. 14***

**Size: 27x32mm**

98 A7 10te blue, black & ultra 1.25 1.25

New Year 1995 (Year of the Boar).

Abai (Ibraghim) Kynanbaev (1845-1904), Poet — A22

**1995, Mar. 31**

99 A22 4te Portrait .30 .30
100 A22 9te Portrait, diff. .60 .60

Nos. 99-100 exist with "Kazakstan" spelled "Kazakstah." Value, set $9.

Space Day — A23

Designs: 10te, Cosmonauts Malenchenko, Musabaev and Merbold.

**1995, Apr. 12 Litho. *Perf. 14***

101 A23 2te multicolored 3.50 3.50
102 A23 10te multicolored 13.50 13.50

Mahatma Gandhi (1869-1948) — A24

**1995, Oct. 2**

| | | | | |
|---|---|---|---|---|
| 103 | A24 | 9te multicolored | 2.50 | 2.50 |
| 104 | A24 | 22te multicolored | 6.00 | 6.00 |

End of World War II, 50th Anniv. A25

Designs: 1te, Hero, battle scene. 3te, Heroine, tank. 5te, Dove, monument.

**1995, May 9 Litho. *Perf. 14***

| | | | | |
|---|---|---|---|---|
| 105 | A25 | 1te multicolored | 1.10 | 1.10 |
| 106 | A25 | 3te multicolored | 3.25 | 3.25 |
| 107 | A25 | 5te multicolored | 5.50 | 5.50 |
| | | *Nos. 105-107 (3)* | 9.85 | 9.85 |

**Spaceship and Yurt Type of 1993**

**1995, Mar. 24 Litho. *Perf. 14x14½***

| | | | | |
|---|---|---|---|---|
| 108 | A4 | 20ti orange | .30 | .25 |
| 109 | A4 | 25ti yellow brown | .35 | .25 |
| 110 | A4 | 50ti gray | .40 | .25 |
| 111 | A4 | 1te green | .50 | .25 |
| 112 | A4 | 2te blue | .65 | .25 |
| 113 | A4 | 4te bright pink | .85 | .50 |
| 114 | A4 | 6te gray green | 1.00 | .75 |
| 115 | A4 | 12te lilac | 2.10 | 1.50 |
| | | *Nos. 108-115 (8)* | 6.15 | 4.00 |

Nos. 108-115 are inscribed "1995."

Paintings — A26

Designs: 4te, "Springtime," by S. Mambeev. 9te, "Mountains," by Z. Shchardenov. 15te, "Kulash Baiseitova in role of Kyz Zhibek," by G. Ismailova, vert. 28te, "Kokpar," by K. Telzhanov.

**1995, June 23 Litho. *Perf. 14***

| | | | | |
|---|---|---|---|---|
| 116 | A26 | 4te multicolored | .75 | .75 |
| 117 | A26 | 9te multicolored | 1.25 | 1.25 |
| 118 | A26 | 15te multicolored | 2.50 | 2.50 |
| 119 | A26 | 28te multicolored | 4.50 | 4.50 |
| | | *Nos. 116-119 (4)* | 9.00 | 9.00 |

Nos. 81-82 Ovptd.

**1995, July 25 Litho. *Perf. 13½***

| | | | | |
|---|---|---|---|---|
| 119A | A18 | 10te multicolored | 1.10 | 1.10 |
| 119B | A18 | 15te multicolored | 1.50 | 1.50 |

Dauletkerey (1820-87), Composer — A27

**1995, Sept. 1 Litho. *Perf. 14***

| | | | | |
|---|---|---|---|---|
| 120 | A27 | 2te yellow & multi | .50 | .50 |
| 121 | A27 | 28te lake & multi | 6.00 | 6.00 |

UN, 50th Anniv. — A28

**1995, Nov. 24 Litho. *Perf. 14***

| | | | | |
|---|---|---|---|---|
| 123 | A28 | 10te multicolored | 1.25 | 1.25 |
| 124 | A28 | 36te gold & lt blue | 4.75 | 4.75 |

Resurrection Cathedral A29

Circus A29a

Buildings in Alma-Ata: 2te, Culture Palace. 3te, Opera and Ballet House. 6te, Kazakh Science Academy. 48te, Dramatics Theatre.

***Perf. 14, 13x12 (#126, 129)***

**1995-96 Litho.**

| | | | | |
|---|---|---|---|---|
| 125 | A29 | 1te green | .50 | .40 |
| 126 | A29a | 1te green | .25 | .25 |
| 127 | A29 | 2te blue | .75 | .65 |
| 128 | A29 | 3te red | .90 | .80 |
| 129 | A29a | 6te olive | .60 | .60 |
| 130 | A29 | 48te brown | 8.00 | 7.50 |
| | | *Nos. 125-130 (6)* | 11.00 | 10.20 |

Issued: Nos. 125, 127-128, 130, 10/25/95; Nos. 126, 129, 7/5/96.

Raptors A30

1te, Haliaeetus albicilla. 3te, Pandion haliaetus. 5te, Gypaetus barbatus. 6te, Gyps himalayensis. 30te, Falco cherrug. 50te, Aquila chrysaetus.

**1995, Dec. 20 Litho. *Perf. 14***

| | | | | |
|---|---|---|---|---|
| 131 | A30 | 1te multicolored | .25 | .25 |
| 132 | A30 | 3te multicolored | .30 | .30 |
| 133 | A30 | 5te multicolored | .50 | .50 |
| 134 | A30 | 6te multicolored | .60 | .60 |
| 135 | A30 | 30te multicolored | 2.00 | 2.00 |
| 136 | A30 | 50te multicolored | 3.50 | 3.50 |
| | | *Nos. 131-136 (6)* | 7.15 | 7.15 |

**New Year Type of 1993**

Size: 27x32mm

**1996, Mar. 21 Litho. *Perf. 14***

| | | | | |
|---|---|---|---|---|
| 141 | A7 | 25te lil, blk & red | 2.25 | 2.25 |

New Year 1996 (Year of the Rat).

Space Day — A32

6te, Earth. 15te, Cosmonaut. 20te, Space station Mir.

**1996, Apr. 12**

| | | | | |
|---|---|---|---|---|
| 142 | A32 | 6te multicolored | 1.75 | 1.75 |
| 143 | A32 | 15te multicolored | 2.75 | 2.75 |
| 144 | A32 | 20te multicolored | 4.50 | 4.50 |
| | | *Nos. 142-144 (3)* | 9.00 | 9.00 |

**Souvenir Sheet**

Save the Aral Sea — A33

Designs: a, Felis caracal. b, Salmo trutta aralensis. c, Hyaena hyaena. d, Pseudoscaphirhynchus kaufmanni. e, Aspiolucius esocinus.

**1996, Apr. 20 Litho. *Perf. 14***

| | | | | |
|---|---|---|---|---|
| 145 | A33 | 20te Sheet of 5, #a.-e. | 4.25 | 4.25 |

See Kyrgyzstan No. 107, Tadjikistan No. 91, Turkmenistan No. 52, Uzbekistan No. 113.

1996 Summer Olympic Games, Atlanta — A34

**1996, June 19 Litho. *Perf. 14***

| | | | | |
|---|---|---|---|---|
| 146 | A34 | 4te Cycling | .60 | .60 |
| 147 | A34 | 6te Wrestling | 1.50 | 1.50 |
| 148 | A34 | 30te Boxing | 5.75 | 5.75 |
| | | *Nos. 146-148 (3)* | 7.85 | 7.85 |

**Souvenir Sheet**

| | | | | |
|---|---|---|---|---|
| 149 | A34 | 50te Hurdles | 4.00 | 4.00 |

Issued: Nos. 146-148, 6/19/96; No. 149, 7/19/96.

Architectural Sites — A35

1te, Tomb, 8-9th cent. 3te, Mausoleum, 11-12th cent. 6te, Mausoleum, 13th cent. 30te, Hadji Ahmet Yassauy's Mausoleum, 14th cent.

**1996, Sept. 27 Litho. *Perf. 14***

| | | | | |
|---|---|---|---|---|
| 150 | A35 | 1te multicolored | .50 | .50 |
| 151 | A35 | 3te multicolored | 1.50 | 1.50 |
| 152 | A35 | 6te multicolored | 3.00 | 3.00 |
| | | *Nos. 150-152 (3)* | 5.00 | 5.00 |

**Souvenir Sheet**

| | | | | |
|---|---|---|---|---|
| 153 | A35 | 30te multicolored | 2.75 | 2.75 |

World Post Day — A37

**1996, Oct. 9 Litho. *Perf. 14***

| | | | | |
|---|---|---|---|---|
| 156 | A37 | 9te shown | .85 | .85 |
| 157 | A37 | 40te UPU emblem | 2.75 | 2.75 |

A38

**1996, Aug. 21**

| | | | | |
|---|---|---|---|---|
| 158 | A38 | 12te multicolored | 1.40 | 1.40 |

Schambyl Schabaev (1846-1945).

Space Station Mir — A39

**1996, Oct. 2**

| | | | | |
|---|---|---|---|---|
| 159 | A39 | 46te multicolored | 3.00 | 2.75 |
| 160 | A39 | 46te T. Aubakirov | 3.00 | 2.75 |
| a. | | Pair, #159-160 | 6.00 | 6.00 |

T. Aubakirov, 1st Kazak cosmonaut.

No. 97 Surcharged

**1997, Oct. 25 Litho. *Perf. 11½***

| | | | | |
|---|---|---|---|---|
| 160B | A21 | 21te on 2te multi | 1.25 | 1.25 |

Surcharge adds numeral 1 to existing value to appear as 21, obliterates original date and adds new date.

Butterflies A40

4te, Saturnia schenki. 6te, Parnassius patricius. 12te, Parnassius ariadne. 46te, Colias draconis.

**1996, Nov. 21 Litho. *Perf. 14***

| | | | | |
|---|---|---|---|---|
| 161 | A40 | 4te multicolored | .30 | .25 |
| 162 | A40 | 6te multicolored | .35 | .30 |
| 163 | A40 | 12te multicolored | .50 | .45 |
| 164 | A40 | 46te multicolored | 1.75 | 1.50 |
| a. | | Sheet of 10, 2 ea. #161-162, 3 ea. #163-164 | 9.00 | 9.00 |
| | | *Nos. 161-164 (4)* | 2.90 | 2.50 |

Hunting Dogs A41

**1996, Nov. 29**

| | | | | |
|---|---|---|---|---|
| 165 | A41 | 5te multicolored | .55 | .55 |

**Souvenir Sheet**

| | | | | |
|---|---|---|---|---|
| 166 | A41 | 100te like #165 | 4.00 | 4.00 |

No. 166 is a continuous design.

A42

Traditional Costumes, Furnishings: a, 10te, Woman outside tent. b, 16te, Man outside tent. c, 45te, Interior view of furnishings.

**1996, Dec. 5**

| | | | | |
|---|---|---|---|---|
| 167 | A42 | Strip of 3, #a.-c. | 6.00 | 6.00 |

Nos. 167a-167b have continuous design.

A43

Archives, Bicent.: 4te, Quill pen, candle, documents. 68te, Scroll, papers, book.

**1996, Dec. 24**

**168** A43 4te brown .35 .35
**169** A43 68te purple 2.40 2.40

Motion Pictures, Cent. — A44

Film scenes: a, Man in hat holding up fingers. b, Horse, woman, man. c, Two men, from "His Time Arrives." d, Woman holding paper, boy holding hat.

**1996, Dec. 25 Litho. *Perf. 14***

**170** A44 24te Sheet of 4, #a.-d. 9.50 9.50

Vormela Peregusna — A45

**1997, Feb. 12 Litho. *Perf. 14***

**171** A45 6te shown .65 .65
**172** A45 10te Adult .75 .75
**173** A45 32te Two young 2.00 2.00
**174** A45 46te Adult, tail up 2.50 2.50
*a.* Vert. strip of 4, #171-174, with horiz. gutters 10.00 10.00
*b.* Souv. sheet of 8, 2 ea. #171-174 12.00 12.00
*Nos. 171-174 (4)* 5.90 5.90

World Wildlife Fund.

Nos. 171-174 each printed in sheets of 10. No. 174b has no gutters between stamps.

Zodiac Constellations A47

**1997, Mar. 26 Litho. *Perf. 14***

**176** A47 1te Aries .25 .25
**177** A47 2te Taurus .25 .25
**178** A47 3te Gemini .25 .25
**179** A47 4te Cancer .25 .25
**180** A47 5te Leo .25 .25
**181** A47 6te Virgo .25 .25
**182** A47 7te Libra .25 .25
**183** A47 8te Scorpio .25 .25
**184** A47 9te Sagittarius .30 .30
**185** A47 10te Capricorn .35 .35
**186** A47 12te Aquarius .45 .45
**187** A47 20te Pisces .70 .70
*b.* Sheet of 12, #176-187 5.50 5.50

### New Year Type of 1993 With Kazakhstan Inscribed in Both Cyrillic & Roman Letters

**1997, Mar. 22 Litho. *Perf. 14***

**187A** A7 40te multicolored 1.75 1.75

New Year 1997 (Year of the Ox).

A48

Cosmonauts' Day: a, Earth, Sputnik. b, Space vehicle, Saturn. c, Space shuttle, space station.

**1997, Apr. 12**

**188** A48 10te Strip of 3, #a.-c. 3.25 3.25

No. 188 has continuous design.

A49

**1997, Apr. 23**

**189** A49 15te org yel & grn .50 .50
**190** A49 60te org yel & grn 2.10 2.10

UNESCO World Book Day.

Mukhtar Auezov (1897-1961), Writer — A50

**1997, May**

**191** A50 25te House 1.00 1.00
**192** A50 40te Auezov at his desk 1.50 1.50

Orders and Medals — A51

Various medals.

**1997, June 30 Litho. *Perf. 14***

**193** A51 15te grn & yel ribbon .50 .50
**194** A51 15te grn, red & pink ribbon .50 .50
**195** A51 20te grn bl & multi .75 .75
**196** A51 30te grn yel & multi 1.00 1.00
*Nos. 193-196 (4)* 2.75 2.75

Tulips — A52

15te, Tulipa regelii. No. 198, Tulipa greigii. No. 199, Tulipa alberti.

**1997, Aug. 7 Litho. *Perf. 13½***

**197** A52 15te multicolored .50 .50
**198** A52 35te multicolored 1.40 1.40
**199** A52 35te multicolored 1.40 1.40
*Nos. 197-199 (3)* 3.30 3.30

Paintings — A53

Designs: No. 200, Roping of a Wild Horse, by Moldakhmet S. Kenbaev. No. 201, Shepherd, by Sh. T. Sariev, vert. No. 202, Fantastic Still Life, by Sergei I. Kalmykov, vert.

**1997, Sept. 10 Litho. *Perf. 14***

**200** A53 25te multicolored 1.10 1.10
**201** A53 25te multicolored 1.10 1.10
**202** A53 25te multicolored 1.10 1.10
*Nos. 200-202 (3)* 3.30 3.30

Agate — A54

Azurite — A55

**1997, Oct. 15 Litho. *Perf. 14***

**203** A54 15te shown .70 .70
**204** A54 15te Chalcedony .70 .70
**205** A55 20te shown 1.10 1.10
**206** A55 20te Malachite 1.10 1.10
*a.* Souvenir sheet, #203-206 3.75 3.75
*Nos. 203-206 (4)* 3.60 3.60

Desert Fauna — A56

Designs: No. 207, Gylippus rickmersi. No. 208, Anemelobathus rickmersi. No. 209, Latrodectus pallidus. No. 210, Oculicosa supermirabilis.

**1997, Nov. 26 Litho. *Perf. 14***

**207** A56 30te multicolored 1.15 1.15
**208** A56 30te multicolored 1.15 1.15
**209** A56 30te multicolored 1.15 1.15
**210** A56 30te multicolored 1.15 1.15
*Nos. 207-210 (4)* 4.60 4.60

### Souvenir Sheet

Nature Park — A57

Designs: a, Mountain goat. b, Trees on side of mountain. c, Rock formations, wildflowers.

**1997, Dec. 22**

**211** A57 30te Sheet of 3, #a.-c. 3.00 3.00

See No. 257A.

A58

Sports A59

Designs: No. 212, Woman, man riding horses. No. 213, Wrestling match. No. 214, Group of men on galloping horses.

**1997, Dec. 30 Litho. *Perf. 14***

**212** A58 20te multicolored 1.75 1.75
**213** A58 20te multicolored 1.75 1.75
**214** A58 20te multicolored 1.75 1.75
**215** A59 20te multicolored 1.75 1.75
*Nos. 212-215 (4)* 7.00 7.00

1998 Winter Olympic Games, Nagano — A60

**1998, Mar. 13 Litho. *Perf. 14***

**216** A60 15te Figure skating .70 .50
**217** A60 30te Biathlon 1.25 1.00

Children's Paintings — A61

**1998, Mar. 20**

**218** A61 15te shown .55 .55
**219** A61 15te Outdoor scene, horiz. .55 .55

### New Year Type of 1993 with "Kazakhstan" inscribed in both Cyrillis and Roman letters

**1998, Mar. 22 Litho. *Perf. 14***

**220** A7 30te yel, blk & brn 1.75 1.75

New Year 1998 (Year of the Tiger).

Kurmangazy (1823-96), Composer — A62

No. 222, Ahmet Baitursynov (1873-1937), poet.

**1998 Litho. *Perf. 14***

**221** A62 30te multicolored 1.00 1.00
**222** A62 30te multicolored 1.00 1.00

Issued: No. 221, 4/10/98. No. 222, 4/28/98.

Ancient Gold Folk Art A63

15te, Ram's heads. 30te, Jeweled pendants, vert. 40te, Animal filigree diadem fragment.

**1998, Apr. 30**

**223** A63 15te multicolored .55 .55
**224** A63 30te multicolored .95 .95
**225** A63 40te multicolored 2.00 2.00
*Nos. 223-225 (3)* 3.50 3.50

Cosmonaut's Day — A64

No. 226, Apollo 8, moon, sun. No.227, Apollo 8, moon, Earth. 50te, Vostok 6, Earth.

**1998, May 4**

| | | | |
|---|---|---|---|
| **226** | A64 30te multi, vert. | 1.10 | 1.10 |
| **227** | A64 30te multi, vert. | 1.10 | 1.10 |
| *a.* | Pair, #226-227, with tabs | 4.25 | 4.25 |
| **228** | A64 50te multi | 1.75 | 1.75 |
| | *Nos. 226-228 (3)* | 3.95 | 3.95 |

Astana, New Capital City — A64a

A65

Buildings: 10te, Mosque. 15te, Govt., vert. 20te, Parliament, vert. 25te, Office. 100te, Presidential office.

**1998 Litho. *Perf. 13½***

| | | | | |
|---|---|---|---|---|
| **229** | A64a | 10te brown | .45 | .45 |
| **230** | A64a | 15te dark blue | .65 | .65 |
| **231** | A64a | 15te blue | .65 | .65 |
| **232** | A64a | 20te green blue | .80 | .80 |
| **232A** | A64a | 25te purple | 1.50 | 1.50 |
| | | *Nos. 229-232A (5)* | 4.05 | 4.05 |

**Souvenir Sheet**

| | | | | |
|---|---|---|---|---|
| **233** | A65 | 100te multicolored | 3.25 | 3.25 |

Issued: Nos. 229-232, 233, 6/10; 25te, 12/98. No. 230 is inscribed "AKMOLA" in Cyrillic. No. 231 is inscribed "ACTANA."

**Souvenir Sheet**

Climbing Mt. Everest — A67

**1998, July 29 Litho. *Perf. 14***

| | | | |
|---|---|---|---|
| **239** | A67 100te multicolored | 4.25 | 4.25 |

Fauna — A68

Birds: No. 240, Ciconia nigra. No. 241, Phoenicopterus roseus. No. 242, Grus leucogeranus.

Wild cats: No. 243, Lynx lynx isabellinus. No. 244, Felis margarita. No. 245, Uncia uncia.

**1998**

| | | | |
|---|---|---|---|
| **240** | A68 15te multicolored | .70 | .70 |
| **241** | A68 30te multicolored | 1.25 | 1.25 |
| **242** | A68 50te multicolored | 2.10 | 2.10 |
| | *Nos. 240-242 (3)* | 4.05 | 4.05 |
| **243** | A68 15te multicolored | .70 | .70 |
| **244** | A68 30te multicolored | 1.25 | 1.25 |
| **245** | A68 50te multicolored | 2.10 | 2.10 |
| | *Nos. 243-245 (3)* | 4.05 | 4.05 |

Issued: Nos. 240-242, 7/31; Nos. 243-245, 8/8.

**Souvenir Sheet**

Admission of Kazakhstan to UPU — A69

**1998, Oct. 9 Litho. *Perf. 14***

| | | | |
|---|---|---|---|
| **246** | A69 50te multicolored | 4.00 | 4.00 |

Natl. Arms A70

World Stamp Day A71

Republic, 5th Anniv. — A72

**1998 Litho. *Perf. 13½***

**Inscribed "1998"**

| | | | | |
|---|---|---|---|---|
| **247** | A70 | 1te green | .25 | .25 |
| *a.* | | Inscribed "1999" | .25 | .25 |
| **248** | A70 | 2te blue | .25 | .25 |
| *a.* | | Inscribed "1999" | .25 | .25 |
| **249** | A70 | 3te red | .25 | .25 |
| **250** | A70 | 4te bright pink | .30 | .30 |
| **251** | A70 | 5te orange yellow | .30 | .30 |
| *a.* | | Inscribed "1999" | .30 | .30 |
| **252** | A70 | 8te orange | .50 | .50 |
| **253** | A71 | 30te olive | 1.40 | 1.40 |
| **254** | A72 | 40te orange | 1.60 | 1.60 |
| | | *Nos. 247-254 (8)* | 4.85 | 4.85 |

Issued; 1te-5te, 6/29; 8te-40te, 11/12. "1999" varieties issued: 1te, 1/28/00; 2te, 9/7/99; 5te, 11/12/99.

See Nos. 296, 299. Compare with Nos. 444-455.

Natl. Epic A73

Horseman: 20te, Holding sword. 30te, Shooting bow and arrow. 40te, Charging with spear.

**1998, Dec. *Perf. 14***

| | | | |
|---|---|---|---|
| **255** | A73 20te multicolored | 1.50 | 1.50 |
| **256** | A73 30te multicolored | 2.25 | 2.25 |
| **257** | A73 40te multicolored | 2.75 | 2.75 |
| | *Nos. 255-257 (3)* | 6.50 | 6.50 |

**Souvenir Sheet**

**Nature Park Type of 1997**

Designs: a, Island in middle of lake, mountains. b, Lake, mountain peaks.

**1998, Dec. Litho. *Perf. 14***

| | | | |
|---|---|---|---|
| **257A** | A57 30te Sheet of 2, #a.-b. | 3.00 | 3.00 |

1999 Census A74

Space Communications A77

K. Satpayev (1899-1964)
A75 A76

**1999 Litho. *Perf. 13½***

| | | | |
|---|---|---|---|
| **258** | A74 1te green | .25 | .25 |
| **259** | A75 15te rose lake | .50 | .50 |
| **260** | A76 20te brown | .65 | .65 |
| **261** | A77 30te olive | 1.25 | 1.25 |
| | *Nos. 258-261 (4)* | 2.65 | 2.65 |

Issued: 1te, 2/5/99; 30te, 3/19/99.

See Nos. 270, 272.

Trains — A78

Map showing Orenburg-Tashkent Rail Line, 1890-1906, and: 40te, Steam train. 50te, Diesel locomotive. 60te, Bullet train. 80te, Interurban train.

**1999 *Perf. 14***

| | | | |
|---|---|---|---|
| **262** | A78 40te yel & multi | 1.50 | 1.50 |
| **263** | A78 50te pink & multi | 2.10 | 2.10 |
| **264** | A78 60te grn & multi | 2.50 | 2.50 |
| **265** | A78 80te blue & multi | 3.00 | 3.00 |
| | *Nos. 262-265 (4)* | 9.10 | 9.10 |

Space Achievements — A79

50te, Soviet spacecraft, vert. 90te, Apollo 11 mission.

**1999**

| | | | |
|---|---|---|---|
| **266** | A79 50te multicolored | 7.00 | 7.00 |
| **267** | A79 90te multicolored | 14.00 | 14.00 |

Cosmonaut Day (No. 266), first manned lunar landing, 30th anniv. (No. 267).

**New Year Type of 1993**

**with "Kazakhstan" inscribed in both Cyrillis and Roman letters**

**1999, Mar. 19 Litho. *Perf. 14***

| | | | |
|---|---|---|---|
| **268** | A7 40te multicolored | 3.50 | 3.50 |

New Year 1999 (Year of the Rabbit).

**Space Communications Type of 1999 and**

A79a

A79b

**1999 Litho. *Perf. 13½***

| | | | | |
|---|---|---|---|---|
| **270** | A77 | 3te red | .30 | .30 |
| **271** | A79a | 4te bright pink | .30 | .30 |
| **272** | A77 | 9te bright green | .50 | .50 |
| **273** | A79b | 10te purple | .75 | .75 |
| **274** | A79a | 30te olive green | 1.10 | 1.10 |
| | | *Nos. 270-274 (5)* | 2.95 | 2.95 |

No. 273 is for the UPU, 125th Anniv.

Flowers — A80

Designs: 20te, Pseudoeremostachys severzowii. 30te, Rhaphidophyton regelii. 90te, Niedzwedkia semiretscenskia.

**1999, June 28 Litho. *Perf. 14¼x14***

| | | | |
|---|---|---|---|
| **276** | A80 20te multicolored | 1.25 | 1.25 |
| **277** | A80 30te multicolored | 1.50 | 1.50 |
| **278** | A80 90te multicolored | 4.00 | 4.00 |
| | *Nos. 276-278 (3)* | 6.75 | 6.75 |

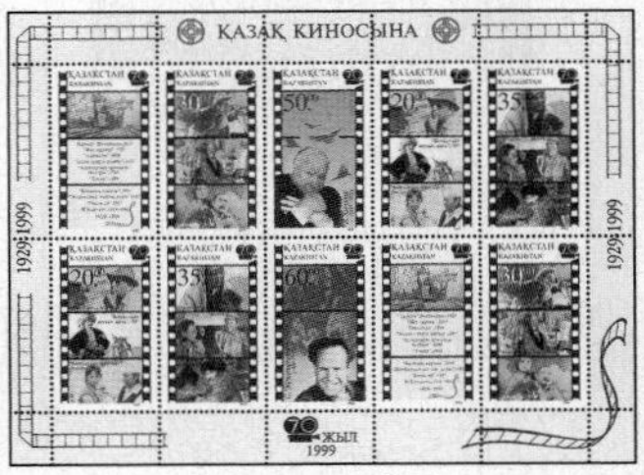

Movies — A81

No. 279: a, 15te, Film scene from 1929. b, 20te, Scenes from 1988, 1997, M. Berkovich. c, 30te, Scenes from 1935, 1938, 1957. d, 35te, Scenes from 1989, 1994, 1997. e, 50te, Alfred Hitchcock. f, 60te, Sergei Eisenstein.

**1999 Litho. *Perf. 14***

| | | | |
|---|---|---|---|
| **279** | A81 Sheet of 10, #e.-f., 2 each #a.-d. | 9.00 | 9.00 |

Foxes A82

Designs: 20te, Vulpes vulpes. 30te, Cuon alpinus. 90te, Vulpes corsac.

**1999 Litho. *Perf. 14x 14¼***

| | | | |
|---|---|---|---|
| **280** | A82 20te multicolored | 1.50 | 1.10 |
| **281** | A82 30te multicolored | 2.25 | 1.90 |
| **282** | A82 90te multicolored | 6.00 | 5.25 |
| | *Nos. 280-282 (3)* | 9.75 | 8.25 |

**Souvenir Sheet**

Environmental Protection — A83

Designs: a, 15te, Cessation of nuclear tests at Semipalatinsk, 10th anniv. b, 45te, Save the ozone layer. c, 60te, Save nature.

**1999 Litho. *Perf. 14x13¾***

| | | | |
|---|---|---|---|
| **283** | A83 Sheet of 3, #a.-c. | 4.00 | 4.00 |

Kazakhstan Hockey Team — A84

**1999 Litho. *Perf. 14***

| | | | | |
|---|---|---|---|---|
| **284** | A84 | 20te Face-off | 1.40 | 1.40 |
| **285** | A84 | 30te Team photo | 1.75 | 1.75 |

10th Gusman Kosanov Memorial Track & Field Meet — A85

**1999**

| | | | | |
|---|---|---|---|---|
| **286** | A85 | 40te multi | 2.00 | 2.00 |

Cosmonauts — A86

40te, Talgat Musabayev. 50te, Toktar Aubakirov, vert.

**1999 *Perf. 14***

| | | | | |
|---|---|---|---|---|
| **287** | A86 | 40te multicolored | 1.60 | 1.60 |
| **288** | A86 | 50te multicolored | 1.90 | 1.90 |

Souvenir Sheet

UPU, 125th Anniv. — A87

**1999, Dec. 20 Litho. *Perf. 14x13¾***

| | | | | |
|---|---|---|---|---|
| **289** | A87 | 20te multi | 1.75 | 1.75 |

**Arms Type of 1998 and**

Spireanthus Schrenhianus A88

Echo Satellite A89

Oil Rig A90

Mukhammed Khaidar Dulati (1499-1551), Historian A91

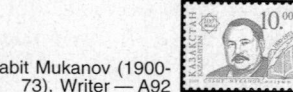

Sabit Mukanov (1900-73), Writer — A92

**2000 Litho. *Perf. 13½***

| | | | | |
|---|---|---|---|---|
| **290** | A88 | 1te green | .25 | .25 |
| **291** | A88 | 2te bright blue | .25 | .25 |
| **291A** | A89 | 5te orange yellow | .25 | .25 |
| **292** | A90 | 7te red | .40 | .40 |
| **293** | A91 | 8te dark blue | .30 | .30 |
| **294** | A92 | 10te olive green | .40 | .40 |
| **295** | A89 | 15te violet blue | .50 | .50 |
| **296** | A70 | 20te orange | .75 | .75 |
| **297** | A89 | 20te indigo | .80 | .80 |
| **299** | A70 | 50te blue | 1.90 | 1.90 |
| **300** | A88 | 50te blue | 1.75 | 1.60 |
| | | *Nos. 290-300 (11)* | 7.55 | 7.40 |

Issued: 7te, 20te, 50te, 1/18/00; 1te, 2te, No. 300, 11/24; 5te, 15te, No. 297, 9/28; 8te, 8/25; 10te, 6/30. 20te and 50te are dated 1999.

Navruz Bayram — A93

**2000, Mar. 21 Litho. *Imperf.***

| | | | | |
|---|---|---|---|---|
| **301** | A93 | 20te multi | 4.00 | 4.00 |

Millennium — A94

**2000, Mar. 24 Litho. *Perf. 13½***

| | | | | |
|---|---|---|---|---|
| **302** | A94 | 30te org & blue green | 2.50 | 2.50 |

Victory in World War II, 55th Anniv. — A95

**2000, May 8 Litho. *Perf. 13½***

| | | | | |
|---|---|---|---|---|
| **303** | A95 | 3te brown & red | .30 | .30 |

Souvenir Sheet

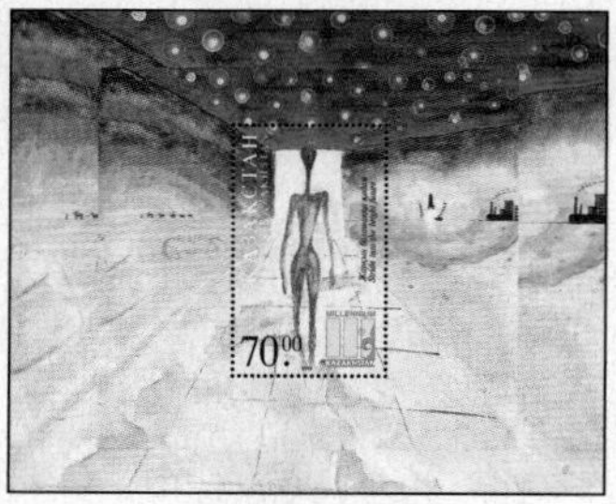

Millennium — A96

**2000, June 1 *Perf. 14x13¾***

| | | | | |
|---|---|---|---|---|
| **304** | A96 | 70te multi | 3.00 | 3.00 |

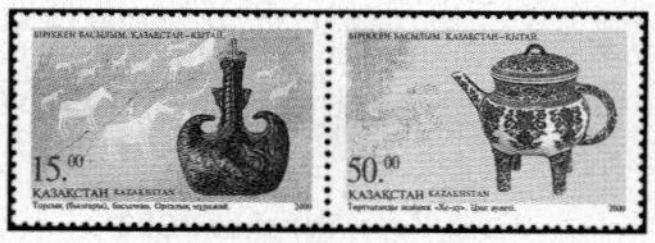

Containers — A97

No. 305: a, 15te, Leather vessel for koumiss, Kazakhstan. b, 50te, Teapot, China.

**2000, June 28 *Perf. 12½x12***

| | | | | |
|---|---|---|---|---|
| **305** | A97 | Horiz. pair, #a-b | 3.00 | 3.00 |

See China (PRC) Nos. 3042-3043.

2000 Summer Olympics, Sydney — A98

Designs: 35te, Rowing. No. 307, 40te, Taekwondo. No. 308, 40te, Men's gymnastics. 50te, Triathlon.

**2000, Sept. 15 *Perf. 12***

| | | | | |
|---|---|---|---|---|
| **306-309** | A98 | Set of 4 | 7.50 | 7.50 |

Souvenir Sheet

Turkistan, 1500th Anniv. — A99

Mausoleums of: a, 50te, Arystan Bab, 12th-20th cents. b, 50te, Karashash Ana, 12th-18th cents. c, 70te, Hadji Ahmet Yassauy, 14th cent.

**2000, Oct. 19 *Perf. 13½***

| | | | | |
|---|---|---|---|---|
| **310** | A99 | Sheet of 3, #a-c | 9.00 | 9.00 |
| | | Complete booklet, #310 | *16.00* | |

Bourzhan Momush-Uly (1910-82), Hero of the Soviet Union — A100

**2000, Dec. 22 *Perf. 13½***

| | | | | |
|---|---|---|---|---|
| **311** | A100 | 4te black & brown | .60 | .60 |

**No. B1 Surcharged in Dark Blue**

**Method and Perf. as Before**

**2001, Jan. 26**

**Block of 3, #a-c, + Label**

| | | | | |
|---|---|---|---|---|
| **312** | SP1 | 10te on 1te+30ti multi | 1.00 | 1.00 |

No. 312 exists with double surcharge and inverted surcharge.

**New Year Type of 1993 with "Kazakhstan" Inscribed in Both Cyrillic and Roman Letters**

**2001, Mar. 2 Litho. *Perf. 13¾x14***

| | | | | |
|---|---|---|---|---|
| **313** | A7 | 40te org, blk & blue | 1.60 | 1.60 |

Dated 2000. New Year 2000 (Year of the Snail).

Cosmonaut's Day — A101

Designs: 40te, Dogs Belka and Strelka. 70te, Rocket launch, vert.

**2001, Mar. 6 *Perf. 14***

| | | | | |
|---|---|---|---|---|
| **314-315** | A101 | Set of 2 | *5.00* | *5.00* |

Dated 2000. Spaceflight of Belka and Strelka, 40th anniv., Baikonur Cosmodrome, 45th anniv.

**New Year Type of 1993 with "Kazakhstan" Inscribed in Both Cyrillic and Roman Letters**

**2001, Mar. 21 Litho. *Perf. 13¾x14***

| | | | | |
|---|---|---|---|---|
| **316** | A7 | 40te grn, blk & brn | 1.40 | 1.40 |

New Year 2001 (Year of the Snake).

Souvenir Sheet

Ministry of Communications, 10th Anniv. — A102

**2001, Apr. 4 *Perf. 11½***

| | | | | |
|---|---|---|---|---|
| **317** | A102 | 100te multi | *14.00* | *14.00* |

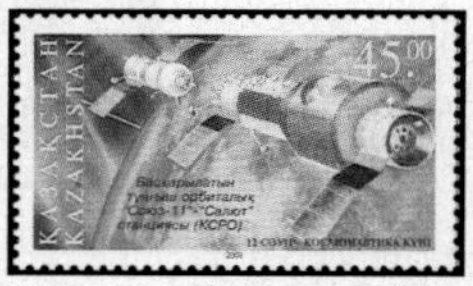

Cosmonaut's Day — A103

Designs: 45te, Soyuz 11 and Salyut. 60te, Yuri Gagarin, Earth.

**2001, Apr. 12 *Perf. 14***

| | | | | |
|---|---|---|---|---|
| **318-319** | A103 | Set of 2 | 4.00 | 4.00 |

Aquilegia Karatavica A104

School, Almaty A105

Phodopus Roborovskii — A106

***Perf. 13½, 14 (#321, 326)***

**2001 Litho.**

| | | | | |
|---|---|---|---|---|
| **320** | A104 | 3te olive green | .30 | .30 |
| **321** | A105 | 7te red violet | .30 | .30 |
| **322** | A106 | 8te orange | .35 | .35 |
| **323** | A104 | 10te yellow green | .40 | .40 |
| **324** | A106 | 15te dark blue | .55 | .55 |
| **325** | A106 | 20te deep blue | .65 | .65 |
| **326** | A105 | 30te greenish gray | .85 | .85 |
| **327** | A106 | 50te brown | 1.40 | 1.40 |
| | | *Nos. 320-327 (8)* | 4.80 | 4.80 |

See Nos. 399, 403-405.

Issued: 7te, 30te, 10/19/01.

Kazakh State Khans — A107

Designs: 50te, Abulkhair Khan (1693-1748). 60te, Abylai Khan (1711-81).

**2001, May 24 Litho. *Perf. 13¾x14***

| | | | | |
|---|---|---|---|---|
| **328-329** | A107 | Set of 2 | 3.75 | 3.75 |

Dated 2000.

Owls A108

Designs: 30te, Bubo bubo. 40te, Asio otus. 50te, Surnia ulula.

**2001, June 7 *Perf. 14***

| | | | | |
|---|---|---|---|---|
| **330-332** | A108 | Set of 3 | *7.75* | *7.75* |

Dated 2000.

Communications Program 2030 — A109

**2001, June 21** *Perf. 14x13¾*
**333** A109 40te multi 1.40 1.40

Dated 2000.

Souvenir Sheet

Lake Markakol — A110

No. 334: a, Cervus elaphus. b, Ursus arctos. c, Brachymystax lenok.

**2001, July 5** *Perf. 13¾x14*
**334** A110 30te Sheet of 3, #a-c *8.50 8.50*

Souvenir Sheet

Flora & Fauna — A111

No. 335: a, 9te, Marmota bobac. b, 12te, Otis tarda. c, 25te, Larus relictus. d, 60te, Felis libyca. e, 90te, Nymphaea alba. f, 100te, Pelecanus crispus.

**2001, July 19** *Perf. 14x14¼*
**335** A111 Sheet of 6, #a-f 6.00 6.00

Souvenir Sheet

Kazakh Railways, 10th Anniv. — A112

No. 336: a, 15te, Building. b, 20te, Turkestan-Siberia locomotive. c, 50te, Railroad workers.

**2001, Aug. 4** *Perf. 14x13¾*
**336** A112 Sheet of 3, #a-c *22.50 22.50*

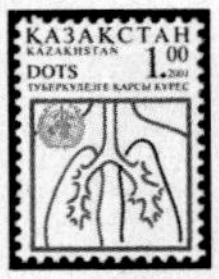

Medicine — A113

Designs: 1te, WHO emblem, lungs (tuberculosis prevention). 5te, Ribbon, book (AIDS prevention).

**2001, Aug. 9** *Perf. 13½*
**337-338** A113 Set of 2 .60 .60

Intl. Year of Mountains (in 2002) — A114

Various mountains: 35te, 60te.

**2001, Sept. 26** *Perf. 14*
**339-340** A114 Set of 2 3.50 3.50

Space Achievements A115

Designs: 50te, Alexei Leonov's walk in space, 1965, vert. 70te, Apollo-Soyuz mission, 1975.

**2001, Oct. 2**
**341-342** A115 Set of 2 *7.50 7.50*

Dated 2000.

Year of Dialogue Among Civilizations A116

**2001, Oct. 9** *Perf. 13¾x14*
**343** A116 45te multi 1.75 1.75

Worldwide Fund for Nature (WWF) — A117

Various views of Equus hemionus kulan: 9te, 12te, 25te, 50te.

**2001, Nov. 1** *Perf. 14*
**344-347** A117 Set of 4 3.25 3.25

Commonwealth of Independent States, 10th Anniv. — A118

**2001, Dec. 12** **Litho.** *Perf. 14*
**348** A118 40te multi 1.75 1.75

Visit of Pope John Paul II — A119

No. 349: a, 20te, Pres. Nazarbayev, Pope. b, 50te, Pope, Pres. Nazarbayev.

**2001, Dec. 14** *Perf. 11½*
**349** A119 Horiz. pair, #a-b *5.50 5.50*

A120

Independence, 10th Anniv. — A121

No. 351: a, 9te, Monument of Independence, Almaty. b, 25te, Parliament, Astana. c, 35te, Pres. Nazarbayev.

**2001** *Perf. 13½*
**350** A120 40te multi 1.75 1.75

**Souvenir Sheet**

*Perf. 13¾x14*

**351** A121 Sheet of 3, #a-c *5.50 5.50*

Issued: 40te, 12/18; No. 351, 12/16.

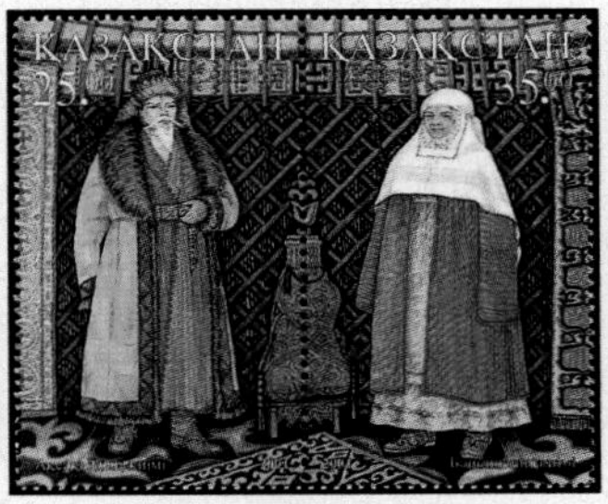

Native Attire — A122

No. 352: a, 25te, Male attire. b, 35te, Female attire.

**2001, Dec. 25** *Perf. 14x13¾*
**352** A122 Horiz. pair, #a-b 2.75 2.75

2002 Winter Olympics, Salt Lake City A123

Designs: 50te, Women's ice hockey. 150te, Freestyle skiing.

**2002, Feb. 14** *Perf. 14*
**353-354** A123 Set of 2 7.00 7.00

Most often collected with colored Olympic rings margin tab. Value, set $10.

**New Year Type of 1993 With "Kazakhstan" Inscribed in Both Cyrillic and Roman Letters**

**2002, Mar. 21** *Perf. 11½*
**355** A7 50te multi 2.00 2.00

New Year 2002 (Year of the Horse).

Horses A124

Horses: 9te, English. 25te, Kustenai. 60te, Akhalteka.

**2002, Mar. 28**
**356-358** A124 Set of 3 4.75 4.75

Pterygostemon Spathulatus A125

Gani Muratbaev (1902-25), Political Leader A126

Salpingotus Pallidus A127

Trade House, Petropavlovsk A128

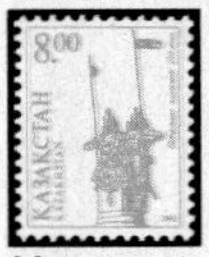

Monument, Petropavlovsk A129

Gabiden Mustafin (1902-85), Writer A130

**2002** **Litho.** *Perf. 13½*

| | | | | | |
|---|---|---|---|---|---|
| **359** | A125 | 1te | blue green | .30 | .30 |
| **360** | A125 | 2te | blue | .35 | .35 |
| **361** | A125 | 3te | green | .40 | .40 |
| **362** | A126 | 3te | brown | .25 | .25 |
| **363** | A127 | 5te | rose lilac | .25 | .25 |
| **364** | A128 | 6te | red | .25 | .25 |
| **365** | A128 | 7te | lilac | .25 | .25 |
| **366** | A129 | 8te | orange | .30 | .30 |
| **367** | A125 | 10te | violet | .60 | .60 |
| **368** | A130 | 10te | blue | .30 | .30 |
| **369** | A125 | 12te | pink | .70 | .70 |
| **370** | A127 | 15te | dark blue | .40 | .40 |
| **371** | A129 | 23te | gray blue | .70 | .70 |
| **372** | A125 | 25te | purple | .90 | .90 |
| **373** | A125 | 35te | olive green | 1.10 | 1.10 |
| **374** | A127 | 40te | bister brown | 1.25 | 1.25 |
| **375** | A127 | 50te | brown | 1.60 | 1.60 |
| | | | *Nos. 359-375 (17)* | 9.90 | 9.90 |

Petropavlovsk, 250th anniv. (Nos. 364-366, 371). Issued: 1te, 2te, 5/7; Nos. 361, 367, 35te, 4/30; 5te, 15te, 40te, 50te, 4/4; 6te, 7te, 8te, 23te, 7/9; 12te, 25te, 5/14; No. 362, 12/19; No. 368, 12/18.

Cosmonauts Day — A131

Designs: 30te, Cosmonauts Yuri Baturin, Talgat Musabaev and first space tourist Dennis Tito. 70te, Globe, rocket, flags of US, Kazakhstan and Russia.

**2002, Apr. 10** **Litho.** *Perf. 11¾*
**376-377** A131 Set of 2 3.50 3.50

2002 World Cup Soccer Championships, Japan and Korea — A132

Two players, one with: No. 378, 10te, Jersey No. 8. No. 379, 10te, Jersey No. 7.

**2002, May 31**
**378-379** A132 Set of 2 1.50 1.50

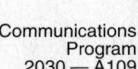

Transeurasia 2002 Conference — A133

**2002, June 6** ***Perf. 13½***

**380** A133 30te multi 1.10 1.10

Souvenir Sheet

Flora and Fauna — A134

No. 381: a, Leontopodium fedtschenkoanum. b, Mustela erminea. c, Aport Alexander apples.

**2002, June 6** ***Perf. 11¾x11½***

**381** A134 30te Sheet of 3, #a-c 3.25 3.25

Art — A135

Designs: 8te, Kazakh Folk Epos, by E. Sidorkin, 1961. 9te, Makhambet, by M. Kisamedinov, 1973. 60te, Batyr, by Sidorkin, 1979.

**2002, July 19** ***Perf. 11¾***

**382-384** A135 Set of 3 3.00 3.00

Birds — A136

No. 385: a, 10te, Larus ichthyaetus pallas. b, 15te, Anthropoides virgo.

**2002, Aug. 29** ***Perf. 12***

**385** A136 Horiz. pair, #a-b 2.00 2.00

See Russia No. 6709.

Marine Life — A137

No. 386: a, 20te, Huso huso ponticus. b, 35te, Phoca caspica.

**2002, Sept. 6**

**386** A137 Horiz. pair, #a-b 2.25 2.25

See Ukraine No. 483.

Souvenir Sheet

Taraz, 2000th Anniv. — A138

**2002, Sept. 25**

**387** A138 70te multi 2.25 2.25

Souvenir Sheet

International Year of Mountains — A139

**2002, Oct. 4** ***Perf. 11½x11¾***

**388** A139 50te multi 1.60 1.60

Gabit Musrepov (1902-85) A140

**2002, Dec. 30** **Litho.** ***Perf. 11½***

**389** A140 20te multi .75 .75

Airplanes A141

Designs: 20te, Ilyushin-86. 40te, Tupolev-144 and map.

***Perf. 11½x11¾***

**2002, Dec. 23** **Litho.**

**390-391** A141 Set of 2 2.40 2.40

First Moscow to Alma Ata flight of Tupolev-144, 25th anniv. (No. 391).

**Type of 1999, Types of 2000-01 Redrawn and**

Monument to Victims of Political Reprisals A142

Selevinia Betpakdalensis A143

**2003** **Litho.** ***Perf. 13½***

| | | | | | |
|---|---|---|---|---|---|
| **392** | A88 | 1te | green | .25 | .25 |
| **393** | A142 | 1te | red violet | .25 | .25 |
| **394** | A88 | 2te | bright blue | .25 | .25 |
| **394A** | A77 | 3te | red | .25 | .25 |
| **395** | A143 | 4te | brown | .35 | .35 |
| **396** | A143 | 5te | bister | .40 | .40 |
| **397** | A143 | 6te | gray green | .40 | .40 |
| **398** | A143 | 7te | dull green | .40 | .40 |
| **399** | A106 | 8te | orange | .25 | .25 |
| **400** | A142 | 8te | red brown | .25 | .25 |
| **401** | A77 | 9te | dark blue | .35 | .35 |
| **402** | A143 | 10te | blue | .25 | .25 |
| **403** | A106 | 15te | deep blue | .45 | .45 |
| **404** | A106 | 20te | gray blue | .55 | .55 |
| **405** | A106 | 35te | dark green | 1.40 | 1.40 |
| **406** | A143 | 63te | fawn | 2.25 | 2.25 |
| **407** | A77 | 84te | purple | 2.40 | 2.40 |
| **408** | A77 | 100te | orange | 2.75 | 2.75 |
| **409** | A143 | 150te | claret | 5.00 | 5.00 |
| | *Nos. 392-409 (19)* | | | 18.45 | 18.45 |

Issued: No. 392, 2te, 2/24; Nos. 393, 400, 4/17; 4te, 5te, 6te, 7te, 10te, 63te, 150te, 1/31; No. 399, 15te, 20te, 35te, 3/28; 84te, 100te, 5/30; 3te, 9te, 9/12.

Nos. 392 and 394 are dated "2003" and have smaller Cyrillic inscription of country name, and longer Roman inscription of country name than Nos. 290-291.

Nos. 394A is dated "2003" and has a smaller denomination with thinner zeroes than No. 270.

Nos. 399, 403 and 404 are dated "2003" and have taller Cyrillic inscription of country name than Nos. 322, 324-325.

Domestic and Wild Sheep — A144

Various rams, ewes and lambs: 20te, 40te, 50te.

**2003, Feb. 26** ***Perf. 11½x11¾***

**410-412** A144 Set of 3 3.50 3.50

**New Year Type of 1993 With "Kazakhstan" Inscribed in Both Cyrillic and Roman Letters**

**2003, Mar. 21** ***Perf. 11½***

**413** A7 40te lt bl, blk & dk bl 1.50 1.50

New Year 2003 (Year of the Ram).

Cosmonaut's Day — A145

Designs: 40te, Pioneer 10 and Jupiter. 70te, Mir Space Station, vert.

**2003, Apr. 12** ***Perf. 11¾***

**414-415** A145 Set of 2 3.50 3.50

Intl. Association of Academies of Science, 10th Anniv. — A146

**2003, Apr. 23** **Litho.** ***Perf. 11½***

**416** A146 50te multi 1.60 1.60

Souvenir Sheet

Ethnic Groups in Kazakhstan — A147

No. 417: a, Kazakhs (woman with red vest). b, Russians (woman with yellow blouse). c, Ukrainians (woman with blue vest).

**2003, Apr. 29** **Litho.** ***Perf. 11¾x11½***

**417** A147 35te Sheet of 3, #a-c 3.50 3.50

Musical Instruments A148

Designs: 25te, Dombra. 50te, Kobyz.

**2003, May 26**

**418-419** A148 Set of 2 2.25 2.25

Fairy Tales A149

Designs: 30te, Aldar Kose and Alasha Khan. 40te, Aldar Kose and Karynbaj.

**2003, June 27** ***Perf. 11½***

**420-421** A149 Set of 2 2.00 2.00

Art — A150

Designs: 20te, Chess Match, by Arturo Ricci (1854-1919). 35te, Portrait of the Shepherd, sculpture by H. Nauryzbaev. 45te, Bowls of Koumiss, by Aisha Galimbaeva (1917- ).

**2003, July 7** ***Perf. 11¾***

**422-424** A150 Set of 3 3.75 3.75

Famous Men — A151

Designs: No. 425, 60te, Tole Bey (1663-1756). No. 426, 60te, Kazybek Bey (1667-1763). No. 427, 60te, Aiteke Bey (1689-1766).

**2003, Aug. 11** ***Perf. 11¾x11½***

**425-427** A151 Set of 3 4.25 4.25

Halyk Bank, 80th Anniv. A152

**2003, Aug. 15** ***Perf. 11½x11¾***

**428** A152 23te multi .70 .70

International Transit Conference, Almaty — A153

**2003, Aug. 28**

**429** A153 40te multi 1.35 1.35

World Post Day — A154

**2003, Oct. 9** ***Perf. 13½***
**430** A154 23te pur & blue .65 .65

Houses of Worship, Almaty — A155

Designs: No. 431, 50te, Cathedral. No. 432, 50te, Mosque.

**2003, Oct. 10** ***Perf. 11¾x11½***
**431-432** A155 Set of 2 2.50 2.50

Tenge Currency, 10th Anniv. — A156

**2003, Nov. 15** ***Perf. 13½***
**433** A156 25te blue & yel org .65 .65

Paintings — A157

No. 434: a, Baxt, by S. Ayitbaev, 1966. b, Tong. Onalik, by R. Ahmedov, 1962.

**2003, Nov. 25** ***Perf. 12***
**434** A157 100te Horiz. pair, #a-b *4.75 4.75*

See Uzbekistan No. 385.

Populus Diversifolia A158

**2003, Dec. 10** ***Perf. 11½***
**435** A158 100te multi 2.10 2.10

Petroglyphs, Tamgaly — A159

Designs. 25te, Cows. 30te, Man as sun on bull, vert.

***Perf. 11½x11¾, 11¾x11½***
**2003, Dec. 19**
**436-437** A159 Set of 2 2.10 2.10

Abylkhan Kasteev (1904-73), Artist — A160

**2004, Feb. 28 Litho.** ***Perf. 11¾***
**439** A160 115te multi 3.25 3.25

**New Year Type of 1993 With "Kazakhstan" Inscribed in Both Cyrillic and Roman Letters**

**2004, Mar. 23** ***Perf. 11½***
**440** A7 35te lt bl, dk bl & org 1.00 1.00

New Year 2004 (Year of the Monkey).

Cosmonaut's Day — A161

Designs: 40te, Mariner 10, vert. 50te, Luna 3.

***Perf. 11¾x11½, 11½x11¾***
**2004, Apr. 12**
**441-442** A161 Set of 2 *2.00 2.00*

Kazakhstan Flag — A162

**2004, Apr. 19** ***Perf. 13½***
**443** A162 25te yel & brt blue .75 .75

**Arms Type of 1998 Redrawn**

| **2004** | | **Litho.** | ***Perf. 13½*** | |
|---|---|---|---|---|
| **444** | A70 | 1te green | .25 | .25 |
| **445** | A70 | 2te bright blue | .25 | .25 |
| **446** | A70 | 4te bright pink | .25 | .25 |
| **447** | A70 | 5te orange yellow | .30 | .30 |
| **448** | A70 | 10te olive green | .40 | .40 |
| **449** | A70 | 16te brt purple | .50 | .50 |
| **450** | A70 | 20te purple | .60 | .60 |
| **451** | A70 | 35te bright yellow | 1.00 | 1.00 |
| **452** | A70 | 50te brt green | 1.40 | 1.40 |
| **453** | A70 | 72te orange | 1.90 | 1.90 |
| **454** | A70 | 100te greenish blue | 2.75 | 2.75 |
| **455** | A70 | 200te vermilion | 5.25 | 5.25 |
| | | *Nos. 444-455 (12)* | 14.85 | 14.85 |

Issued: 1te, 2te, 4te, 4/19; 20te, 35te, 72te, 100te, 200te, 5/11; 5te, 10te, 16te, 50te, 6/10.

Nos. 444-455 are dated "2004," arms and "Kazakhstan" in Roman letters are larger and denominations are smaller than those features on Nos. 247-254.

No. 447 is dated "2004," arms and "Kazakhstan" in Roman letters are larger and denomination is smaller than those features on No. 251.

Souvenir Sheet

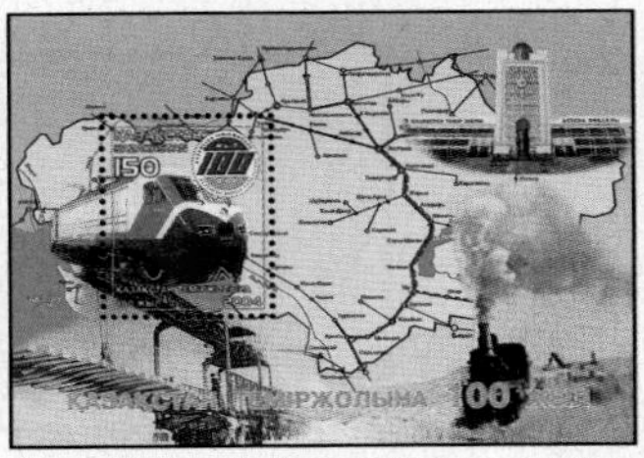

Kazakhstan Railways, Cent. — A163

**2004, Apr. 22 Litho.** ***Perf. 11¾x11½***
**456** A163 150te multi 3.00 3.00

Souvenir Sheet

Ethnic Groups in Kazakhstan — A164

No. 457: a, Uzbeks (denomination at left). b, Germans (denomination at right).

**2004, May 12**
**457** A164 65te Sheet of 2, #a-b 3.25 3.25

FIFA (Fédération Internationale de Football Association), Cent. — A165

FIFA emblem, soccer player and soccer ball at: No. 458, 100te, Left. No. 459, 100te, Center.

**2004, May 21 Litho. & Embossed**
**458-459** A165 Set of 2 5.00 5.00

Children's Art — A166

Designs: No. 460, 45te, Yurts and sheep, by A. Sadykov. No. 461, 45te, Woman, by D. Iskhanova, vert.

**2004, June 20 Litho.** ***Perf. 11½***
**460-461** A166 Set of 2 2.25 2.25

Souvenir Sheet

2004 Summer Olympics, Athens — A167

No. 462: a, 70te, Boxing. b, 115te, Shooting.

**Litho., Margin Embossed**

**2004, June 28**
**462** A167 Sheet of 2, #a-b 3.75 3.75

Souvenir Sheet

Fauna in Altyn Emel Reserve — A168

No. 463: a, Acgypius monacus. b, Capra sibirica. c, Gazella subgutturosa.

**2004, Aug. 11** ***Perf. 11½x11¾***
**463** A168 50te Sheet of 3, #a-c 4.00 4.00

Souvenir Sheet

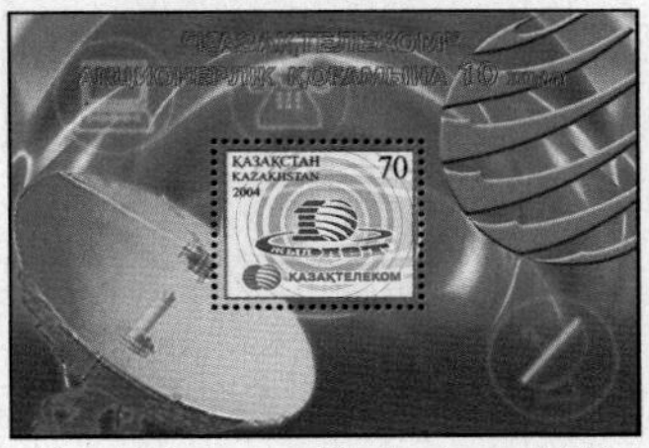

Kazaktelecom, 10th Anniv. — A169

***Perf. 11½x11¾***
**2004, Aug. 18 Litho.**
**464** A169 70te multi 2.00 2.00

Alkei Khakan Margulan (1904-85), Archaeologist A170

**2004, Sept. 23**
**465** A170 115te multi 2.25 2.25

Flowers — A171

**2004, Oct. 4** ***Perf. 12¼x11½***
**466** A171 25te multi + label .75 .75

Printed in sheets of 12 + 12 labels.

**World Post Day Type of 2003**

**2004, Oct. 9** ***Perf. 13½***
**467** A154 3te red vio & blue .30 .30
**468** A154 30te yel org & blue .80 .80

New Year 2005 — A172

**2004, Nov. 23** ***Perf. 13¼***
**469** A172 65te multi 1.40 1.40

Musical Instruments — A173

No. 470: a, Adyma. b, Gizhak and bow.

**2004, Nov. 29** ***Perf. 11½x11¾***
**470** A173 100te Horiz. pair, #a-b 4.50 4.50

See Tajikistan No. 248.

Saken Seifullin (1894-1939), Writer — A174

**2004, Dec. 28**
**471** A174 35te multi .75 .75

Women's Headdresses — A175

No. 472: a, Kazakh headdress, denomination at left. b, Mongol headdress, denomination at right.

**2004, Dec. 30**
**472** A175 72te Horiz. pair, #a-b 3.25 3.25

See Mongolia No. 2590.

Veterinary Research Institute, Cent. — A176

**2005, Jan. 14** ***Perf. 13½***
**473** A176 7te multi .40 .40

Constitution, 10th Anniv. — A177

**2005, Apr. 8** **Litho.** ***Perf. 13½***

| | | | | |
|---|---|---|---|---|
| **474** | A177 | 1te blue & brn | .25 | .25 |
| **475** | A177 | 2te vio & brn | .25 | .25 |
| **476** | A177 | 3te brt grn & brn | .25 | .25 |
| **477** | A177 | 8te brt bl & brn | .25 | .25 |
| **478** | A177 | 10te red & brn | .25 | .25 |
| **479** | A177 | A red vio & brn | .70 | .70 |
| **480** | A177 | 50te olive & brn | 1.10 | 1.10 |
| **481** | A177 | 65te bl grn & brn | 1.40 | 1.40 |
| | | *Nos. 474-481 (8)* | 4.45 | 4.45 |

No. 479 sold for 25te on day of issue.

Europa — A178

**2005, Apr. 14** **Litho.** ***Perf. 11½x12¼***
**482** A178 90te multi 5.00 5.00

End of World War II, 60th Anniv. — A179

**2005, Apr. 28** **Litho.** ***Perf. 13¼x13***
**483** A179 72te multi 1.75 1.75

Souvenir Sheet

Baikonur Space Complex, 50th Anniv. — A180

No. 484: a, Rocket. b, Buran space shuttle. c, Capsule and parachute.

**2005, June 2** ***Perf. 11½x11¾***
**484** A180 72te Sheet of 3, #a-c 4.50 4.50

Peace and Harmony Palace — A181

**Litho. & Embossed**

**2005, July 6** ***Perf. 13¼***
**485** A181 65te multi 1.50 1.50

Minerals — A182

Designs: 50te, Azurite. 70te, Agate.

**2005, July 12** **Litho.** ***Perf. 11¾x11½***
**486-487** A182 Set of 2 3.00 3.00

**Fairy Tales Type of 2003**

Designs: 35te, Aldar Kose and the Musician. 45te, Aldar Kose and the Raiser of Asses.

**2005, Aug. 11**
**488-489** A149 Set of 2 1.90 1.90

Constitution, 10th Anniv. — A183

**2005, Aug. 26**
**490** A183 72te multi 1.60 1.60

Souvenir Sheet

Olympic Gold Medalists — A184

No. 491: a, Zaksylik Ushkempirov, 1980, 48kg Greco-Roman wrestling. b, Vitaly Savin, 1988, 4x100m relay. c, Vasily Zhirov, 1996, light heavyweight boxing. d, Bekzat Sattarkhanov, 2000, featherweight boxing.

**2005, Sept. 22** **Litho.** ***Perf. 11¾***
**491** A184 100te Sheet of 4, #a-d *9.00 9.00*

Akhmet Baitursynov (1873-1937), Writer — A185

**Litho. with Foil Application**

**2005, Oct. 6** ***Perf. 13¾x14***
**492** A185 30te multi .80 .80

No. 492 not issued without gold overprint.

World Post Day — A186

**2005, Oct. 8** **Litho.** ***Perf. 13½***
**493** A186 35te blue & pur .80 .80
**494** A186 40te pur & red .95 .95

Dogs — A187

No. 495: a, Kazakh hound (dog with curled tail). b, Estonian hound (white, black and brown dog).

**2005, Oct. 19** ***Perf. 11½x11¾***
**495** A187 138te Horiz. pair, #a-b 4.75 4.75

See Estonia No. 523.

United Nations, 60th Anniv. — A188

**2005, Oct. 31** ***Perf. 13½***
**496** A188 150te multi 3.00 3.00

New Year 2006 — A189

**2005, Nov. 10** **Litho.** ***Perf. 13¼***
**497** A189 65te multi 1.50 1.50

Evgeny Brusilovsky (1905-81), Composer — A190

**2005, Nov. 18** ***Perf. 11½x11¾***
**498** A190 150te multi 2.75 2.75

Assembly of Peoples of Kazakhstan, 10th Anniv. — A191

**2005, Nov. 24** ***Perf. 13½***
**499** A191 80te multi 1.75 1.75

Souvenir Sheet

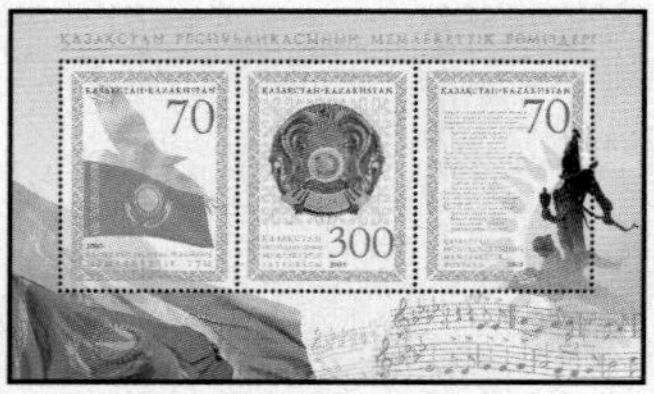


National Symbols — A192

No. 500: a, 70te, Flag and eagle. b, 70te, National anthem. c, 300te, Arms.

**Litho. & Embossed**

**2005, Dec. 22** ***Perf. 13¼***
**500** A192 Sheet of 3, #a-c 7.00 7.00

Turgen Waterfall A193

Mountain Lake A194

**2005, Dec. 23** **Litho.** ***Perf. 13½***
**501** A193 12te multi .50 .50
**502** A194 100te multi 3.00 3.00

Hans Christian Andersen (1805-75), Author — A195

**2005, Dec. 30** ***Perf. 11¾x11½***
**503** A195 200te multi 3.75 3.75

Parliament, 10th Anniv. — A196

**2006, Jan. 17** **Litho.** ***Perf. 11½x11¾***
**504** A196 50te multi 1.25 1.25

Abylai Khan, by Aubakir Ismailov A197

**Litho. With Foil Application**

**2006, Jan. 27** *Perf. 13x13¼*
**505** A197 94te multi 1.90 1.90

2006 Winter Olympics, Turin — A198

*Perf. 11½x11¾*

**2006, Feb. 20** **Litho.**
**506** A198 138te multi 2.50 2.50

Cosmonaut's Day — A199

Paintings of cosmonauts by: 100te, P. M. Popov. 120te, A. M. Stepanov.

**2006, Apr. 12** *Perf. 11¾x11½*
**507-508** A199 Set of 2 4.50 4.50

Traditional Jewelry — A200

No. 509: a, Bracelet, Kazakhstan. b, Brooch, Latvia.

**2006, Apr. 19** *Perf. 11½x11¾*
**509** A200 110te Horiz. pair, #a-b 4.50 4.50

See Latvia No. 650.

Saksaul Tree — A201

**2006, Apr. 27** *Perf. 11¾x11½*
**510** A201 25te multi .60 .60

Europa — A202

**2006, May 3**
**511** A202 210te multi 3.50 3.50
*a.* Tete-beche pair 10.00 10.00

Turkestan-Siberia Railway, 75th Anniv. — A203

**2006, May 31** *Perf. 13x13¼*
**512** A203 200te multi 4.00 4.00

2006 World Cup Soccer Championships, Germany — A204

**2006, June 2** *Perf. 11½x11¾*
**513** A204 150te multi 2.75 2.75

Intl. Year of Deserts and Desertification — A205

**2006, July 7** *Perf. 13¼*
**514** A205 110te multi 2.10 2.10

Mosque, Astana — A206

**2006** **Litho.** *Perf. 13½x13¾*

| | | | | | |
|---|---|---|---|---|---|
| **515** | A206 | 5te | emerald | .30 | .25 |
| **516** | A206 | 8te | Prus blue | .40 | .25 |
| **517** | A206 | 10te | olive grn | .50 | .25 |
| **518** | A206 | A | purple | .90 | .90 |
| **518A** | A206 | 100te | dark blue | 2.25 | 1.75 |
| **519** | A206 | 110te | brown | 2.50 | 2.00 |
| **520** | A206 | 120te | green | 2.75 | 2.25 |
| **521** | A206 | 200te | red violet | 4.50 | 3.50 |
| | | *Nos. 515-521 (8)* | | 14.10 | 11.15 |

No. 518 sold for 25te on day of issue.
Issued: 100te, 10/10/06; rest, 7/20/06.

Akzhan Mashani, Geologist, Cent. of Birth — A207

**2006, July 21** **Litho.** *Perf. 11½x11¾*
**522** A207 85te multi 2.00 2.00

Houses of Worship in Almaty — A208

Designs: No. 523, 25te, Catholic Church (denomination in orange). No. 524, 25te, Synagogue (denomination in white).

**2006, Aug. 17** *Perf. 11¾x11½*
**523-524** A208 Set of 2 1.10 1.10

Souvenir Sheet

Famous Men — A209

No. 525: a, Chokan Valikhanov (1835-65), diplomat. b, Saken Sejfullin (1894-1938), poet. c, Nazir Tjurjakulov (1893-1937). d, Kanysh Satpaev (1899-1964), geologist.

**2006, Aug. 20** *Perf. 11½*
**525** A209 90te Sheet of 4, #a-d 6.00 6.00

Third Meeting of Economic Cooperation Organization Postal Authorities, Turkey — A210

**2006, Sept. 15** *Perf. 12*
**526** A210 210te multi 3.50 3.50

See Iran No. 2917, Pakistan No. 1101 and Turkey No. 3041.

**No. 526 Overprinted in Gold**

**2006, Sept. 22**
**527** A210 210te multi 3.50 3.50

Overprint corrects site of meeting from Istanbul to Ankara.

Ahmet Zhubanov (1906-68), Composer A211

**2006, Oct. 13** *Perf. 11½*
**528** A211 85te multi 1.75 1.75

Coats of Arms — A212

Arms of: 17te, Almaty. 80te, Astana.

**2006, Oct. 20** **Litho.** *Perf. 13½x13¾*
**529-530** A212 Set of 2 2.00 2.00

New Year 2007 — A213

**2006, Nov. 1** Litho. *Perf. 13¼*
**531** A213 25te multi .75 .75

Latif Khamidi (1906-83), Composer A214

**2006, Nov. 9** *Perf. 11½x11¾*
**532** A214 110te multi 2.00 2.00

Mukagali Makataev (1931-76), Writer — A215

**2006, Nov. 29** *Perf. 13½x13¾*

| | | | | | |
|---|---|---|---|---|---|
| **533** | A215 | 1te | dark blue | .25 | .25 |
| **534** | A215 | 4te | olive grn | .25 | .25 |
| **535** | A215 | 7te | rose claret | .25 | .25 |
| **536** | A215 | 15te | red brown | .30 | .30 |
| | | *Nos. 533-536 (4)* | | 1.05 | 1.05 |

Manash Kozybaev (1931-2002), Historian — A216

**2006, Nov. 29**
**537** A216 20te brown .45 .45
**538** A216 30te brn lake .65 .65

Character From Opera *Silk Girl* — A217

**2006, Dec. 15** *Perf. 13¼*
**539** A217 80te multi 1.25 1.25

Values are for stamps with surrounding selvage.

18th Century Helmet — A218

**2006, Dec. 15** *Perf. 13x12¾*
**540** A218 85te multi 1.75 1.75

Nikolai Repinsky (1906-69), Architect — A219

**2006, Dec. 20** *Perf. 13½x13¾*

**541** A219 2te brown .25 .25
**542** A219 3te yel brn .25 .25
**543** A219 105te gray grn 2.00 2.00
**544** A219 150te blue 3.00 3.00
**545** A219 500te rose claret 9.00 9.00
*Nos. 541-545 (5)* 14.50 14.50

Miniature Sheet

Kurgalzhinsky Nature Reserve — A220

No. 546: a, 25te, Phoenicopterus roseus. b, 100te, Cygnus cygnus. c, 120te, Meles meles.

**2006, Dec. 29** *Perf. 11½x11¾*

**546** A220 Sheet of 3, #a-c 5.50 5.50

KazTransOil, 10th Anniv. — A221

**2007, Apr. 12** **Litho.** *Perf. 12¾*

**547** A221 25te multi .60 .60

Cosmonaut's Day — A222

Designs: 80te, Konstantin E. Tsiolkovsky (1857-1935), rocket pioneer. 110te, Sergei P. Korolev (1906-66), aeronautical engineer.

**2007, Apr. 12** *Perf. 12¼x11¾*

**548-549** A222 Set of 2 3.50 3.50

Europa — A223

No. 550 — Children's art: a, 25te, Scout bugler and tents. b, 65te, Scouts with backpacks, dog.

**2007, May 8** *Perf. 11½x11¾*

**550** A223 Pair, #a-b 2.40 2.40

Scouting, cent.

63rd Session of UN Economic and Social Commission for Asia and the Pacific, Almaty — A224

**2007, May 17** *Perf. 12¾*

**551** A224 25te multi .55 .55

Gali Ormanov (1907-78), Poet — A225

**2007, Sept. 28** **Litho.** *Perf. 11½*

**552** A225 25te multi .55 .55

Conference on Interaction and Confidence-Building Measures in Asia, 15th Anniv. — A226

**2007, Oct. 17** *Perf. 13½*

**553** A226 80te multi 1.75 1.75

Maulen Balakaev (1907-95), Philologist — A227

**2007, Oct. 29** **Litho.** *Perf. 13½*

**554** A227 1te red brown .25 .25
**555** A227 4te green .25 .25
**556** A227 5te dk brown .25 .25
*Nos. 554-556 (3)* .75 .75

Almaty Zoo Animals — A228

No. 557: a, 25te, Zebras. b, 110te, Elephant.

**2007, Oct. 31** **Litho.** *Perf. 11½*

**557** A228 Pair, #a-b 2.75 2.75

Printed in sheets containing 4 each of Nos. 557a and 557b, with a central label.

Hirundo Rustica — A229

**2007, Nov. 15** *Perf. 13½*

**558** A229 20te multi .65 .40
**559** A229 25te multi .75 .50
**560** A229 50te multi 1.40 1.00
**561** A229 100te multi 3.25 2.00
*Nos. 558-561 (4)* 6.05 3.90

Saddle A230

**2007, Nov. 27** *Perf. 12*

**562** A230 80te multi 1.75 1.75

Launch of Sputnik 1, 50th Anniv. — A231

**2007, Nov. 27** *Perf. 12½x12¾*

**563** A231 500te multi 8.00 8.00

Karagand Arms — A232

Pavlodar Arms — A233

**2007, Dec. 10** *Perf. 13½x13¼*

**564** A232 10te multi .55 .55
**565** A233 10te multi .55 .55

Miniature Sheet

Olympic Gold Medalists — A234

No. 566: a, Vladimir Smirnov, 1994, 50-kilometer skiing. b, Yuri Melinichenko, 1996, Greco-Roman wrestling. c, Olga Shishigina, 2000, 100-meter hurdles. d, Ermahan Ibraimov, 2000, boxing.

**2007, Dec. 28** *Perf. 12x11½*

**566** A234 150te Sheet of 4, #a-d 11.00 11.00

Souvenir Sheet

Peoples of Kazakhstan — A235

No. 567: a, Uighur man and woman (denomination at left). b, Tatar man and woman (denomination at right).

**2007, Dec. 28** *Perf. 11½*

**567** A235 105te Sheet of 2, #a-b 4.25 4.25

New Year — A236

**2008, Jan. 23** **Litho.** *Perf. 13¼*

**568** A236 25te multi .75 .75

Printed in sheets of 8 + central label.

Miniature Sheet

Women's Day — A237

No. 569 — Various flowers with: a, Denomination at LL. b, Denomination at LR. c, Denomination and country name at UL. d, Denomination and country name at UR, Kazakh text in lower panel justified at right. e, Denomination at L, country name at LL. f, Denomination and country name at UR, Kazakh text in lower panel justified at left.

**2008, Mar. 14** *Perf. 13¼*

**569** A237 25te Sheet of 6, #a-f, + 3 labels 5.25 5.25

Navruz Bayram — A238

**2008, Mar. 21** *Perf. 12¾*

**570** A238 25te multi .70 .70

2008 Summer Olympics, Beijing — A239

**2008, Apr. 2** *Perf. 14x14¼*

**571** A239 25te multi .70 .70

Kazakhstan Postal Service, 15th Anniv. — A240

**2008, Apr. 4** *Perf. 12¾*

**572** A240 25te multi .70 .70

Cosmonaut's Day — A241

Designs: 100te, Space Station Mir. 150te, International Space Station.

**2008, Apr. 10** *Perf. 14x14¼*

**573-574** A241 Set of 2 5.50 5.50

Europa — A242

No. 575 — Color of dove: a, Blue. b, Red.

**2008, May 6** *Perf. 14x14¼*
**575** A242 150te Horiz. pair, #a-b 5.25 5.25

2008 Summer Olympics, Beijing — A243

No. 576: a, Judo. b, Handball.

**2008, Aug. 10 Litho.** *Perf. 14x14¼*
**576** A243 100te Horiz. pair, #a-b 4.00 4.00

Deer — A244

No. 577: a, Cervus elaphus sibiricus. b, Cervus nippon.

**2008, Sept. 18**
**577** A244 110te Horiz. pair, #a-b 4.00 4.00

See Moldova No. 596.

Ancient Jewelry From Iran and Kazakhstan — A245

No. 578: a, Buckle depicting snow leopard and mountains, 4th-5th cent. B.C., Kazakhstan. b, Gold medal depicting lions, 7th cent. B.C., Iran.

**2008, Oct. 3** *Perf. 14x14¼*
**578** Horiz. pair + flanking label 4.50 4.50
*a.* A245 25te multi .55 .55
*b.* A245 150te multi 3.50 3.50

See Iran No. 2965.

Universal Declaration of Human Rights, 60th Anniv. — A246

*Perf. 11¾x11½*

**2008, Dec. 10** **Litho.**
**579** A246 25te multi .70 .70

Taiyr Zharakov (1908-65), Poet — A247

**2008, Dec. 12** *Perf. 11½*
**580** A247 25te multi .70 .70

Shakarim Kudaiberdyuly (1859-1931), Poet — A248

**2008, Dec. 12**
**581** A248 25te multi .70 .70

Alash Movement, 90th Anniv. — A249

**2008, Dec. 18**
**582** A249 25te multi .70 .70

Musical Instruments — A250

No. 583: a, 25te, Zhelbuaz. b, 100te, Dauylpaz.

**2008, Dec. 19**
**583** A250 Pair, #a-b 2.25 2.25

Paintings — A251

No. 584: a, 25te, Portrait of Kenesary, by A. Kasteev. b, 100te, Guest, by S. Aitbayev.

**2008, Dec. 19**
**584** A251 Pair, #a-b 2.50 2.50

Insects — A252

No. 585: a, 25te, Callisthenes semenovi. b, 100te, Dorcadion acharlense.

**2008, Dec. 22**
**585** A252 Pair, #a-b 2.50 2.50

Peter Aravin (1908-79), Musicologist A253

*Perf. 13¾x13½*

**2008, Dec. 25** **Litho.**
**586** A253 10te multi .75 .75

Eagle — A254

**2008, Dec. 25**
**587** A254 20te multi 1.00 1.00

Arms of Atyrau — A255

Arms of Taraz — A256

**2008, Dec. 25 Litho.** *Perf. 14x13½*
**588** A255 A multi .80 .80
**589** A256 A multi .80 .80

On day of issue, Nos. 588-589 each sold for 25te.

Preservation of Polar Regions and Glaciers — A257

**2009, Mar. 12 Litho.** *Perf. 12¾*
**590** A257 230te multi 3.75 3.75

Navruz Bayram — A258

**2009, Mar. 20**
**591** A258 25te multi .50 .50

Louis Braille (1809-52), Educator of the Blind — A259

**2009, Mar. 26** *Perf. 11½*
**592** A259 230te multi 4.00 4.00

Europa — A260

Telescopes and: No. 593, 230te, Galileo Galilei, Moon. No. 594, 230te, Taurus constellation, Kazakhs looking at sky.

**2009, Apr. 3**
**593-594** A260 Set of 2 8.00 8.00

Intl. Year of Astronomy.

Earrings — A261

No. 595 — Earring from: a, Korea, 5th-6th cent. b, Mongolia, 18th-19th cent. c, Kazakhstan, 2nd-1st cent, B.C.

**2009, June 12 Litho.** *Perf. 13x12¾*
**595** A261 Horiz. strip of 3 9.00 9.00
*a.-c.* 180te Any single 2.75 2.75

See South Korea No. 2313, Mongolia No. 2674.

Astronomy A262

Designs: 180te, Telescope. 230te, Observatories.

**2009, June 25** *Perf. 13*
**596-597** A262 Set of 2 6.25 6.25

Horsemen and Shield — A263

**2009, July 9** *Perf. 12¾x12½*
**598** A263 190te multi 3.50 3.50
*a.* Tête bêche pair 8.50 8.50

Maria Lizogub (1909-98), Painter — A264

**2009, Aug. 25** *Perf. 11½*
**599** A264 180te multi 3.00 3.00

Kenen Azerbaev (1884-1976), Composer
A265

**2009, Sept. 2**
**600** A265 180te multi 3.00 3.00

Garifolla Kurmangaliev (1909-93), Singer — A266

**2009, Sept. 8**
**601** A266 180te multi 3.00 3.00

18th Session of World Tourism Organization, Astana — A267

**2009, Oct. 5**
**602** A267 140te multi 2.10 2.10

Miniature Sheet

Ballet — A268

No. 603: a, 180te, Dancers from Giselle (woman in white, man in black). b, 180te, Dancers from Don Quixote (woman in red, man in black and white). c, 180te, Dancers from Swan Lake (man and woman in white). d, 180te, Dancer from Tilep and Sarykyz. e, 230te, Dancer in red from Legend About Love. f, 230te, Dancer in blue from Bahchisarayski Fountain.

**2009, Oct. 8** ***Perf. 13¼***
**603** A268 Sheet of 6, #a-f 18.00 18.00

National Games — A269

No. 604: a, 140te, Blindfolded man on horseback. b, 180te, Horsemen in competition.

**2009, Nov. 16** ***Perf. 12***
**604** A269 Pair, #a-b 5.00 5.00

Abdilda Tazhibaev (1909-98), Writer — A270

**2009, Nov. 16** ***Perf. 11½***
**605** A270 180te multi 3.00 3.00

Flora and Fauna
A271

Designs: No. 606, 180te, Crataegus ambigua. No. 607, 180te, Mellivora capensis.

**2009, Dec. 3** **Litho.** ***Perf. 13***
**606-607** A271 Set of 2 5.50 5.50

Iskander Tynyshpaev (1909-95), Cinematographer — A272

**2009, Dec. 9** ***Perf. 11½x11¾***
**608** A272 25te multi .60 .60

Tuleu Basenov (1909-76), Architect
A273

**2009, Dec. 30**
**609** A273 25te multi .60 .60

Birzhan Sal Kozhaguluiy (1834-97), Composer
A274

**2009, Dec. 30**
**610** A274 25te multi .60 .60

Construction of Central Asian Gas Pipeline — A275

***Perf. 12½x12¾***
**2009, Dec. 30** **Litho.**
**611** A275 25te multi .60 .60

Kazakhstan Chairmanship of Organization for Security and Cooperation in Europe — A276

**2010, Jan. 6** **Litho.** ***Perf. 12***
**612** A276 230te multi 4.00 4.00

Navruz Bayram — A277

**2010, Apr. 15** ***Perf. 12¾***
**613** A277 32te multi .75 .75

Victory in World War II, 65th Anniv.
A278

**2010, Apr. 15** ***Perf. 12***
**614** A278 32te multi .75 .75

2010 Winter Olympics, Vancouver
A279

Designs: 32te, Ski jumper. 190te, Alpine skier.

**2010, Apr. 29** **Litho.** ***Perf. 12***
**615-616** A279 Set of 2 3.75 3.75

Europa — A280

**2010, May 5** ***Perf. 12¾***
**617** A280 240te multi 3.75 3.75

Temirtau, 50th Anniv.
A281

**2010, June 1** **Litho.** ***Perf. 14x14¼***
**618** A281 32te multi .65 .65

Khan Shatyr Entertainment Center, Astana — A282

**2010, July 1**
**619** A282 32te multi .65 .65

2010 World Cup Soccer Championships, South Africa — A283

**2010, July 12**
**620** A283 240te multi 4.00 4.00

Arms of Chimkent
A284

Arms of Aktyubinsk
A285

**2010** ***Perf. 14¼ Syncopated***
**621** A284 5te multi .25 .25
**622** A285 10te multi .25 .25

Issued: 5te, 8/17; 10te, 7/27.

Constitution, 15th Anniv. — A286

**2010, Aug. 20** ***Perf. 14x14¼***
**623** A286 32te multi .60 .60

Musa Baijanuly (1835-1929), Composer
A287

***Perf. 13¾x13½ Syncopated***
**2010, Aug. 24**
**624** A287 (32te) multi .60 .60

Baikonur Cosmodrome, 55th Anniv. — A288

**2010, Aug. 27** ***Perf. 13x13¼***
**625** A288 190te multi 3.25 3.25

Mukhamedzhan Karataev (1910-95), Encyclopedia Editor — A289

***Perf. 13¾x13½ Syncopated***
**2010, Sept. 22**
**626** A289 20te multi .45 .45

Souvenir Sheet

Baurjan Momasuhly (1910-82), World War II Hero — A290

**2010, Sept. 24** ***Perf. 14x14¼***
**627** A290 140te multi 2.50 2.50

Shokan Valikhanov (1835-65), Diplomat, Engineer — A291

**2010, Oct. 21** *Perf. 14¼x14*

**628** A291 140te multi 2.50 2.50

See Russia No. 7246.

Frédéric Chopin (1810-49), Composer — A292

**2010, Oct. 28** *Perf. 14¼x14*

**629** A292 240te multi 4.00 4.00

Water Agreement Between Kazakhstan and Kyrgyzstan, 10th Anniv. — A293

**2010, Nov. 17** *Perf. 14x14¼*

**630** A293 32te multi .65 .65

Souvenir Sheet

Organization for Security and Cooperation in Europe Summit, Astana — A294

No. 631: a, 32te, Independence Monument and Kazakhstan flag. b, 140te, Pyramid of Peace. c, 190te, Ak Orda (Presidential Palace), Pyramid of Peace.

**2010, Nov. 23** *Perf. 14¼x14*

**631** A294 Sheet of 3, #a-c 6.25 6.25

Birds of the Caspian Sea — A295

No. 632: a, Phoenicopterus roseus. b, Ardeola ralloides.

**2010, Nov. 24** **Litho.**

**632** A295 140te Pair, #a-b 5.00 5.00

See Azerbaijan No. 938.

Seventh Asian Winter Games, Astana and Almaty — A296

No. 633: a, 190te, Games emblem. b, 190te, Mascot freestyle skiing. c, 240te, Mascot ski jumping. d, 240te, Mascot ice skating.

**2010, Dec. 21**

**633** A296 Block or horiz. strip of 4, #a-d 12.00 12.00

Mirzhakyp Dulatov (1885-1935), Poet — A297

***Perf. 13½x13¾ Syncopated***

**2010, Dec. 28**

**634** A297 50te multi .80 .80

Fish in Astana Oceanarium — A298

No. 635: a, 32te, Rhinecanthus aculeatus. b, 190te, Zebrasoma veliferum.

**2010, Dec. 30** *Perf. 13½x13¾*

**635** A298 Pair, #a-b 3.75 3.75

Souvenir Sheet

Fauna of Bayanaul Nature Reserve — A299

No. 636: a, 32te, Tadorna ferruginea. b, 140te, Mustela nivalis. c, 190te, Capreolus pygargus.

**2010, Dec. 30** *Perf. 14x14¼*

**636** A299 Sheet of 3, #a-c 8.00 8.00

On Nos. 636a-636c, country name is misspelled "Kazakhstah."

Souvenir Sheet

Peoples of Kazakhstan — A300

No. 637: a, 32te, Korean man and woman. b, 190te, Belarussian man and woman.

**2010, Dec. 30** *Perf. 14¼x14*

**637** A300 Sheet of 2, #a-b 3.50 3.50

First Man in Space, 50th Anniv. A301

**2011, Feb. 28** *Perf. 14x14¼*

**638** A301 190te multi 3.00 3.00

Europa A302

**2011, Apr. 21** **Litho.**

**639** A302 250te multi 4.00 4.00

Intl. Year of Forests.

Shanghai Cooperation Organization, 10th Anniv. — A303

**2011, May 5** *Perf. 14¼x14*

**640** A303 210te multi 3.25 3.25

Campaign Against AIDS, 30th Anniv. — A304

**2011, June 3** **Litho.** *Perf. 14x13½*

**641** A304 32te multi .70 .70

Eurasian Economic Community, 10th Anniv. — A305

**2011, June 14** *Perf. 14¼x14*

**642** A305 32te multi .70 .70

Kasym Amanzholov (1911-55), Poet — A306

**2011, July 14** *Perf. 13½x14*

**643** A306 32te multi .65 .65

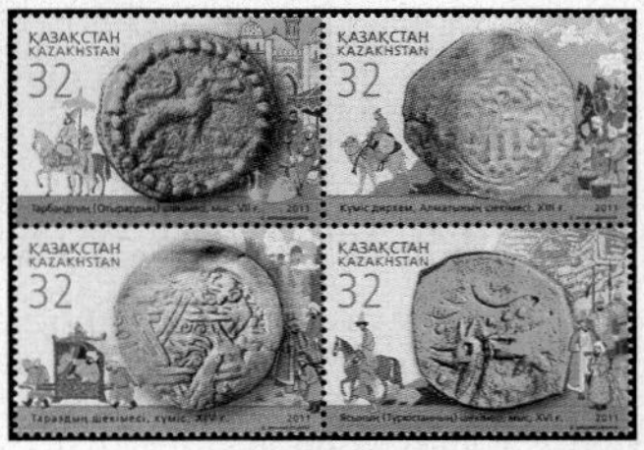

Coins — A307

No. 644 — Coin from: a, 7th cent. b, 13th cent. c, 14th cent. d, 16th cent.

**2011, Sept. 7** *Perf. 14x14¼*

**644** A307 32te Block of 4, #a-d 2.00 2.00

Orymbek Zhautykov (1911-89), Mathematician A308

**2011, Sept. 15**

**645** A308 32te multi .65 .65

Customs Union of Eurasian Economic Community A309

**2011, Sept. 22** *Perf. 14¼x14*

**646** A309 32te multi .65 .65

Regional Communications Commonwealth, 20th Anniv. — A310

**2011, Sept. 22** *Perf. 14x13½*

**647** A310 150te multi 2.25 2.25

Gabdol Slanov (1911-69), Writer — A311

**2011, Sept. 30** *Perf. 14x14¼*

**648** A311 32te multi .65 .65

National Coat of Arms — A312

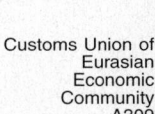

***Perf. 14x14¼ Syncopated***

**2011, Oct. 5**

| | | | | |
|---|---|---|---|---|
| **649** | A312 | A multi | .50 | .50 |
| **650** | A312 | 50te multi | .85 | .85 |
| **651** | A312 | 80te multi | 1.25 | 1.25 |
| **652** | A312 | 100te multi | 1.50 | 1.50 |
| **653** | A312 | 200te multi | 3.00 | 3.00 |
| **654** | A312 | 500te multi | 8.00 | 8.00 |
| | | *Nos. 649-654 (6)* | 15.10 | 15.10 |

No. 649 sold for 32te on day of issue.

Umirzak Sultangazin (1936-2005), Director of Kazakhstan Space Reseach Institute — A313

**2011, Oct. 20** ***Perf. 14x14¼***
**655** A313 32te multi .65 .65

Dina Nurpeisova (1861-1955), Musician — A314

**2011, Oct. 25** ***Perf. 14x14¼***
**656** A314 32te multi .65 .65

Commonwealth of Independent States, 20th Anniv. — A315

**2011, Nov. 10** ***Perf. 14¼x14***
**657** A315 150te multi 2.50 2.50

Independence, 20th Anniv. — A316

**2011, Dec. 5**
**658** A316 32te multi .65 .65

Isatai Isabayev (1936-2007), Painter — A317

**2011, Dec. 14** ***Perf. 14x14¼***
**659** A317 32te multi .65 .65

Miniature Sheet

Birds — A318

No. 660: a, Turdus merula. b, Acridotheres tristis. c, Parus major. d, Corvus frugilegus. e, Pica pica. f, Columba livia. g, Corvus cornix. h, Passer domesticus.

**2011, Dec. 14**
**660** A318 250te Sheet of 8, #a-h 30.00 30.00

Independence, 20th Anniv. — A319

**2011, Dec. 15**
**661** A319 20te multi .45 .45

First Kazakh Antarctic Expedition A320

**2011, Dec. 16**
**662** A320 190te multi 3.50 3.50

Petro Kazakhstan Kumkol Resources, 25th Anniv. — A321

**2011, Dec. 22**
**663** A321 150te multi 2.25 2.25

Kazakhstan E-Government — A322

**2011, Dec. 31**
**664** A322 32te multi .65 .65

Dinmukhamed Konayev (1912-93), Politician — A323

**2012, Jan. 27** ***Perf. 14¼x14***
**665** A323 100te multi 1.60 1.60

Katynkaragay National Park — A324

**2012, Mar. 20** ***Perf. 13½x13¾***
**666** A324 110te multi 2.00 2.00

No. 1 Surcharged in Gold

**Method and Perf. As Before**

**2012, Apr. 4**
**667** A1 50te on 50k #1 1.10 1.10

Europa A325

**2012, Apr. 11** **Litho.** ***Perf. 14x14¼***
**668** A325 250te multi 3.50 3.50

Hedgehogs — A326

No. 669: a, Erinaceus europaeus. b, Hemiechinus auritus.

**2012, June 20**
**669** A326 190te Pair, #a-b 6.50 6.50

See Belarus Nos. 827-828.

Navruz Bayram A327

**2012, July 25**
**670** A327 190te multi 3.00 3.00

Space Vehicle A328

**2012, July 25**
**671** A328 250te multi 3.50 3.50

Ufa Ahmedsafin (1912-84), Hydrogeologist A329

**2012, Aug. 9** ***Perf. 14¼x14***
**672** A329 150te multi 2.25 2.25

Conference on a Nuclear Weapons-Free World, Astana — A330

**2012, Aug. 27**
**673** A330 50te multi 1.00 1.00

Mezhit Begalin (1922-78), Film Director — A331

**2012, Oct. 4** ***Perf. 14x14¼***
**674** A331 90te multi 1.40 1.40

Lev Gumilev (1912-92), Anthropologist A332

**2012, Oct. 11**
**675** A332 100te multi 1.50 1.50

Dmitri Snegin (1912-2001), Writer — A333

**2012, Oct. 17** ***Perf. 13¾ Syncopated***
**676** A333 80te multi 1.50 1.50

Shara Zhienkulova (1912-91), Dancer — A334

**2012, Oct. 17**
**677** A334 100te multi 1.75 1.75

Paintings — A335

No. 678: a, Warriors, by P. Zaltsman, 1973. b, Milking a Red Camel, by A. Sadykhanov, 1986-87.

**2012, Oct. 17** ***Perf. 14¼x14***
**678** A335 250te Vert. pair, #a-b 7.25 7.25

Mir Broadcasting Company, 20th Anniv. — A336

**2012, Oct. 25**
**679** A336 10te multi .35 .35

Collective Security Treaty Organization, 10th Anniv. — A337

**2012, Oct. 25**
**680** A337 80te multi 1.25 1.25

Zein Shashkin (1912-66), Writer — A338

Zhamal Omarova (1912-76), Singer — A339

Zhumagali Sain (1912-61), Poet — A340

***Perf. 13¾ Syncopated***
**2012, Nov. 12**
**681** A338 5te multi .30 .30
**682** A339 10te multi .30 .30
**683** A340 20te multi .45 .45
*Nos. 681-683 (3)* 1.05 1.05

Kulyash Baiseitova (1912-57), Opera Singer — A341

Denominations: 2te, 50te, A.

***Perf. 13¾ Syncopated***
**2012, Nov. 12**
**684-686** A341 Set of 3 2.00 2.00
No. 686 sold for 60te on day of issue.

Coat of Arms and Flag of Kazakhstan, 20th Anniv. — A342

**2012, Nov. 20** ***Perf. 14¼x14***
**687** A342 190te multi 2.75 2.75

Union of Designers, 25th Anniv. — A343

**2012, Nov. 22**
**688** A343 80te multi 1.40 1.40

Diplomatic Relations Between Kazakhstan and Bulgaria, 20th Anniv. — A344

No. 689: a, Gold buckle depicting bird and deer, 8th-7th cent. B.C. b, Gold rhyton with design of deer's head, 4th cent. B.C.

**2012, Dec. 14** ***Perf. 14¼x14***
**689** A344 250te Horiz. pair, #a-b 7.25 7.25

Printed in sheets containing 4 pairs. See Bulgaria No. 4622.

Raoul Wallenberg (1912-47), Swedish Diplomat Who Saved Jews During World War II — A345

**2012, Dec. 19** ***Perf. 14x14¼***
**690** A345 250te multi 4.00 4.00

School, Astana — A346

Lev N. Gumilev University, Astana — A347

Mangylik El Triumphal Arch, Astana — A348

**2012, Dec. 20**
**691** A346 100te multi 1.50 1.50
**692** A347 100te multi 1.50 1.50
**693** A348 100te multi 1.50 1.50
*Nos. 691-693 (3)* 4.50 4.50

Traditional Costumes — A349

Designs: 150te, Man and woman, emblem of Regional Communications Commonwealth. 250te, Man and woman, no emblem.

**2013, Jan. 23** ***Perf. 14¼x14***
**694-695** A349 Set of 2 6.00 6.00

Miniature Sheet

2012 Summer Olympics Gold Medalists — A350

No. 696: a, Ilya Ilin, weight lifting (wearing blue and white uniform). b, Serik Sapiyev, boxing. c, Olga Rypakova, triple jump. d, Alexander Vinokourov, cycling. e, Svetlana Podobedova, weight lifting (wearing yellow uniform, with hand over heart). f, Zulfiya Chinshanlo, weight lifting (holding medal around neck, denomination at left). g, Maiya Maneza, weight lifting (holding medal around neck, denomination at right).

**2013, Jan. 23**
**696** A350 150te Sheet of 7, #a-g, + label 17.50 17.50

Postman, by Nikolai Khludov — A351

**2013, Apr. 25**
**697** A351 200te multi 3.00 3.00
*a.* Tête bêche pair 7.00 7.00

Miniature Sheet

Lunar Calendar Animals — A352

No. 698: a, Mouse. b, Calf. c, Snow leopard. d, Rabbit. e, Snail. f, Snake. g, Horse. h, Sheep. i, Monkey. j, Chicks. k, Dog. l, Pig.

**2013, Apr. 25** ***Perf. 14x14¼***
**698** A352 100te Sheet of 12, #a-l 17.50 17.50

Rocket, Gull, Space Capsule and Parachute A353

Cosmonaut Valentina Tereshkova A354

***Perf. 13½x13¾ Syncopated***
**2013, July 2** **Litho.**
**699** A353 150te multi 2.00 2.00
**700** A354 200te multi 3.00 3.00
*a.* Pair, #699-700 6.00 6.00

Space flight of Tereshkova (first woman in space), 50th anniv. Nos. 699-700 each were printed in sheets of 6. No. 700a is from sheet containing three each of Nos. 699-700.

Souvenir Sheets

Pres. Nursultan Nazarbayev, Map of Kazakhstan — A355

***Perf. 13½x13¾ Syncopated***
**2013, July 2** **Litho.**
**701** A355 250te multi 4.00 4.00

**Litho. With Foil Application**
***Perf. 14***
**Granite Paper**
**702** A355 900te multi 13.00 13.00

Establishment of diplomatic relations with various countries, 20th anniv. No. 701 contains one 55x33mm stamp. No. 702 contains one 50x30mm stamp.

Miniature Sheets

A356

Renaming of Akmola to Astana, 15th Anniv. — A357

No. 703: a, Presidential Palace. b, Palace of Independence and fountain. c, Bayterek Tower. d, Kazakh Eli Monument. No. 704: a, Pres. Nursultan Nazarbayev. b, Emblem of Astana with "1998." c, New cost of arms. d, Emblem of Expo 2017.

***Perf. 13¾x13½ Syncopated***

**2013, July 4** **Litho.**

**703** A356 100te Sheet of 4, #a-d 6.50 6.50
**704** A357 100te Sheet of 4, #a-d 6.50 6.50

Miniature Sheet

Navruz Bayram — A358

No. 705: a, Emblem of People's Assembly of Kazakhstan. b, Pres. Nursultan Nazarbayev waving at Navruz celebrations. c, Pres. Nazarbayev playing stringed instrument at Navruz celebrations. d, Emblem of Congress of Leaders of World and Traditional Religions, Astana.

***Perf. 13¾x13½ Syncopated***

**2013, July 5** **Litho.**

**705** A358 150te Sheet of 4, #a-d 8.00 8.00

Miniature Sheet

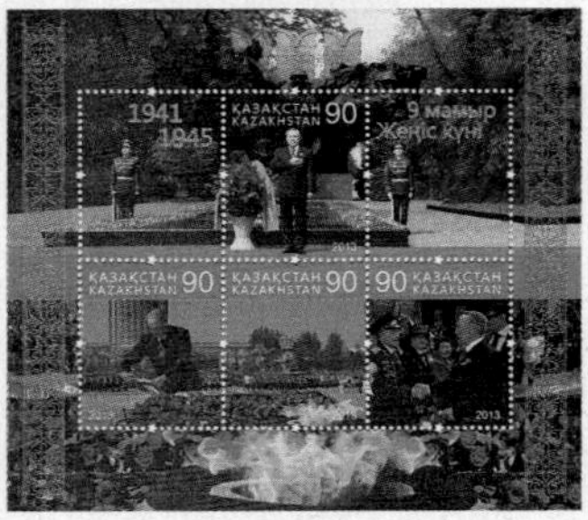


Victory Day — A359

No. 706: a, Pres. Nursultan Nazarbayev with hand over heart, floral bouquet. b, Flowers, Pres. Nazarbayev folding Kazakhstan flag. c, Eternal flame, flowers, parade. d, Pres. Nazarbayev shaking hands with veteran.

***Perf. 13½ Syncopated***

**2013, July 5** **Litho.**

**706** A359 90te Sheet of 4, #a-d, + 2 labels 5.25 5.25

Souvenir Sheet

Olympic Champions — A360

No. 707 — Kazakhstan flag and: a, Bakhtiyar Artayev, boxing, 2004 (denomination at UR). b, Alexander Parygin, pentathlon, 1996 (denomination at UL, Parygin not touching medal). c, Bakhyt Sarsekbayev, boxing, 2008 (denomination at UL, Sarsekbayev touching medal).

***Perf. 13½x13¾ Syncopated***

**2013, July 16** **Litho.**

**707** A360 150te Sheet of 3, #a-c, + label 6.75 6.75

Souvenir Sheet

Kazakhstan's Participation in 2010 and 2012 Nuclear Security Summits — A361

No. 708: a, Pres. Nursultan Nazarbayev at lectern at 2010 summit. b, U.S. Pres. Barack Obama, Pres. Nazarbayev, and Russian Pres. Dmitry Medvedev at 2012 summit.

***Perf. 13¾x13½ Syncopated***

**2013, Aug. 28** **Litho.**

**708** A361 150te Sheet of 2, #a-b 5.00 5.00

Miniature Sheet

Flowers — A362

No. 709: a, 60te, Tulipa behmiana. b, 60te, Tulipa ostrowskiana. c, 100te, Papaver tianschanicum. d, 100te, Papaver pavoninum.

***Perf. 13¼x13¾ Syncopated***

**2013, Oct. 4** **Litho.**

**709** A362 Sheet of 4, #a-d 5.25 5.25

Souvenir Sheet

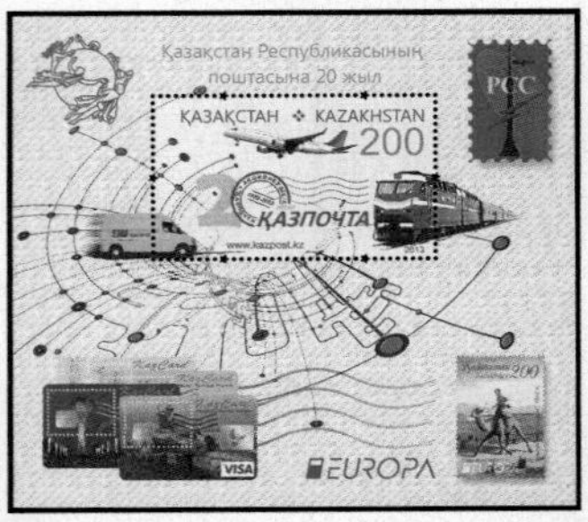


Kazakhstan Postal Service, 20th Anniv. — A363

***Perf. 13½x13¾ Syncopated***

**2013, Oct. 9** **Litho.**

**710** A363 200te multi 3.25 3.25

Miniature Sheet

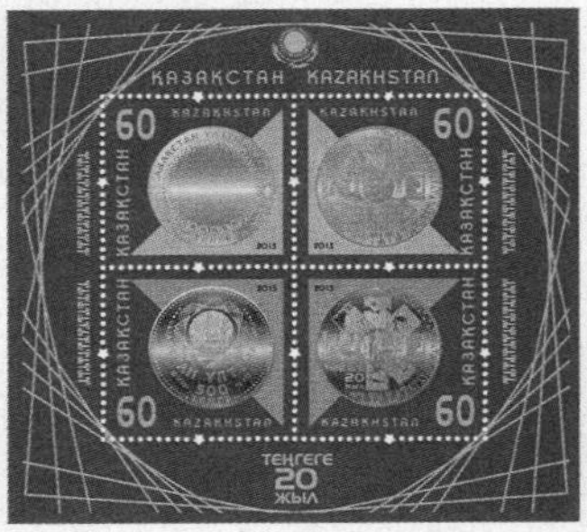


Kazakhstan Coins — A364

No. 711: a, Obverse of 100,000-tenge gold coin. b, Reverse of 100,000-tenge gold coin of 2013. c, Obverse of 500-tenge silver coin. d, Reverse of 500-tenge silver coin of 2013.

***Perf. 13¾x13¼ Syncopated***

**2013, Nov. 29** **Litho.**

**711** A364 60te Sheet of 4, #a-d 4.25 4.25

Introduction of tenge currency, 20th anniv.

Miniature Sheet

Birds — A365

No. 712: a, Chettusia gregaria. b, Tetrax tetrax. c, Aquila nipalensis. d, Numenius arquata. e, Oxyura leucocephala. f, Melanocorypha yeltoniensis.

***Perf. 13½x14 Syncopated***

**2013, Dec. 25** **Litho.**

**712** A365 150te Sheet of 6, #a-f 14.00 14.00

Souvenir Sheet

Wildlife of the Ustyurt Game Reserve — A366

No. 713: a, 60te, Acinonyx jubatus. b, 150e, Saga pedo. c, 190te, Circaetus gallicus.

***Perf. 13½x14 Syncopated***

**2013, Dec. 25** **Litho.**

**713** A366 Sheet of 3, #a-c 6.00 6.00

Mukan Tolebayev (1913-60), Composer A367

Amre Kashaubayev (1888-1938), Singer A368

Valentina Tereshkova, First Woman in Space A369

Saiga A370

***Perf. 13½x14½ Syncopated***

**2013, Dec. 27** **Litho.**

**714** A367 1te pale yel & blk .35 .35
**715** A368 3te lt grn & blk .35 .35
**716** A369 5te lt bl & blk .35 .35

***Perf. 14½x13½ Syncopated***

**717** A370 10te yel & blk .35 .35
*Nos. 714-717 (4)* 1.40 1.40

Tereshkova's space flight, 50th anniv. (No. 716).

Souvenir Sheet

Yurt Furnishings — A371

No. 718: a, Pillows and blankets on chest, edge of table. b, Trunks and chests, table with bowls and tureen. c, Curtains above bed with pillows.

***Perf. 13½ Syncopated***

**2014, Jan. 15** **Litho.**

**718** A371 200te Sheet of 3, #a-c 8.50 8.50

Souvenir Sheet

Communications History — A372

***Perf. 13½x13¾ Syncopated***

**2014, Jan. 15** **Litho.**

**719** A372 200te multi 3.25 3.25

Kulakhmet Khodzhikov (1914-86), Artist A373

Sabira Maykanovoy (1914-95), Actress A374

Ilyas Dzhansugurov (1894-1938), Poet — A375

2014 World Weight Lifting Championships, Almaty — A376

***Perf. 14x14¼ Syncopated***

**2014** **Litho.**

| | | | | | |
|---|---|---|---|---|---|
| **720** | A373 | 50te blk & lt bl | | .50 | .50 |
| **721** | A374 | 100te yel & blk | | 1.00 | 1.00 |
| **722** | A375 | 100te yel & blk | | 1.00 | 1.00 |
| **723** | A376 | 200te rose & blk | | 2.00 | 2.00 |
| | | *Nos. 720-723 (4)* | | 4.50 | 4.50 |

Issued: 50te, 12/31; Nos. 721-722, 12/26; 200te, 12/29.

Souvenir Sheet

New Year 2014 (Year of the Horse) — A377

**2015, Jan. 12** **Litho.** ***Perf.***

**724** A377 200te multi 3.00 3.00

Dated 2014.

Anna Akhmatova (1889-1966), Poet — A378

Mikhail Lermontov (1814-41), Writer — A379

**2015, Jan. 12** **Litho.** ***Perf. 13x13½***

**725** A378 60te multi .90 .90

**726** A379 60te multi .90 .90

Dated 2014.

Employment Roadmap 2020 Emblem — A380

**2015, Jan. 12** **Litho.** ***Perf. 12***

**727** A380 150te multi 2.25 2.25

Dated 2014.

2013 Soyuz TMA-11M Flight — A381

Voskhod Spacecraft, 50th Anniv. (in 2014) — A382

Space Flight of Talgat Musabayev, 20th Anniv. (in 2014) — A383

Space Communications, 10th Anniv. — A384

**2015, Jan. 12** **Litho.** ***Perf. 13x13½***

| | | | | | |
|---|---|---|---|---|---|
| **728** | A381 | 150te multi | | 2.25 | 2.25 |
| **729** | A382 | 150te multi | | 2.25 | 2.25 |
| **730** | A383 | 150te multi | | 2.25 | 2.25 |
| | | *Nos. 728-730 (3)* | | 6.75 | 6.75 |

**Souvenir Sheet**

**731** A384 300te multi 4.25 4.25

Dated 2014.

Souvenir Sheet

Statue of Batyr Zhanibek Berdauletuly (1714-92) — A385

**2015, Jan. 12** **Litho.** ***Perf. 13½x13***

**732** A385 200te multi 3.00 3.00

Dated 2014.

Souvenir Sheet

Shaken Aimanov (1914-70), Actor — A386

**2015, Jan. 12** **Litho.** ***Perf. 13½x13***

**733** A386 200te multi 3.00 3.00

Dated 2014.

Miniature Sheet

Traditional Women's Headdresses — A387

No. 734 — Woman from: a, Shygys, 1955. b, Almaty, 1970. c, Karagandy, 19th cent. d, Pavlodar, 20th cent.

**2015, Jan. 12** **Litho.** ***Perf. 12***

**734** A387 50te Sheet of 4, #a-d 3.00 3.00

Dated 2014.

Souvenir Sheet

Naurzum Nature Reserve — A388

No. 735: a, Nymphaea candida. b, Haliaeetus albicilla. c, Alces alces.

**2015, Jan. 12** **Litho.** ***Perf. 13½x13***

**735** A388 200te Sheet of 3, #a-c 8.75 8.75

Dated 2014.

Miniature Sheet

2014 Winter Olympics, Sochi, Russia — A389

No. 736: a, Short track speed skating. b, Figure skating. c, Snowboarding. d, Skeleton.

**2015, Jan. 12** **Litho.** ***Perf. 12***

**736** A389 200te Sheet of 4, #a-d 11.50 11.50

Dated 2014.

Miniature Sheet

2014 Winter Paralympics, Sochi, Russia — A390

No. 737: a, Alpine skiing. b, Cross-country skiing. c, Sled hockey. d, Wheelchair curling.

**2015, Jan. 12** **Litho.** ***Perf. 13½x13***

**737** A390 250te Sheet of 4, #a-d 14.00 14.00

Dated 2014.

Kazakhstan Chairmanship of Energy Charter Conference A391

**2015, Jan. 15** **Litho.** ***Perf. 13½x13***

**738** A391 100te multi 1.40 1.40

Dated 2014.

Ice Hockey — A392

**2015, Jan. 15** **Litho.** ***Perf. 12***

**739** A392 100te multi 1.40 1.40

Dated 2014.

Nowruz — A393

**2015, Jan. 15** **Litho.** ***Perf. 13***

**740** A393 190te multi 3.00 3.00

No. 740 is printed in sheets of 7 + label and is dated 2014.

Europa — A394

No. 741: a, Kobyz and bow, b, Dombra.

**2015, Jan. 15** **Litho.** ***Perf. 12***

**741** A394 200te Pair, #a-b 5.25 5.25

No. 741 was printed in sheets containing 4 pairs + 2 labels, and is dated 2014.

Children's Art — A395

No. 742 — Drawings depicting scenes from Kazakh fairy tales: a, Maktakyz and the Cat (yellow panels). b, Aldar-Koze (green panels). c, Beautiful Kunekey (blue panels). d, Alpamys Batyr (red panels).

**2015, Jan. 15** **Litho.** ***Perf. 12***

**742** A395 50te Block or horiz. strip of 4, #a-d 3.00 3.00

Dated 2014.

Souvenir Sheet

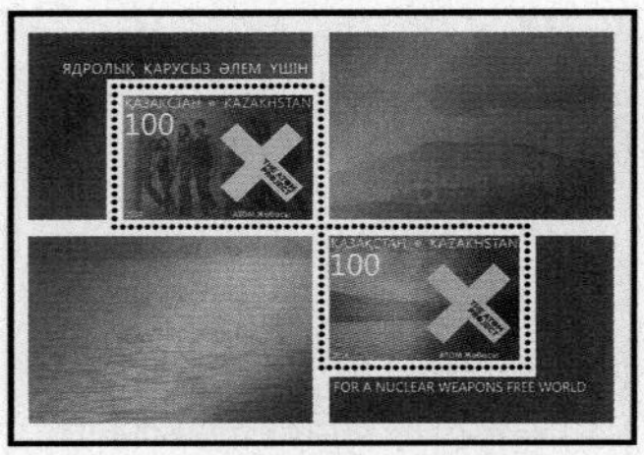


Campaign to End Nuclear Testing — A396

No. 744 — ATOM Project emblem and: a, People. b, Landscape.

**2015, Jan. 15** **Litho.** ***Perf. 13½x13***

**743** A396 100te Sheet of 2, #a-b 3.00 3.00

Dated 2014.

Souvenir Sheet

Charlie Chaplin (1889-1977), Actor — A397

No. 744 — Chaplin with: a, 60te, Child actor (30x26mm). b, 100te, Dog (37x26mm). c, 200te, Camera (37x52mm).

**2015, Jan. 15** **Litho.** ***Perf. 13½x13***

**744** A397 Sheet of 3, #a-c 5.25 5.25

Dated 2014.

Miniature Sheet

Zhoshy Khan Mausoleum — A398

No. 745: a, Interior of dome. b, Mausoleum, stone wall in foreground. c, Mausoleum, decorative fence in front of arch. d, Mausoleum, grass field in foreground.

**2015, Jan. 15** **Litho.** ***Perf. 13½x13***

**745** A398 200te Sheet of 4, #a-d 11.00 11.00

Dated 2014.

Vaccines in Kazakhstan, Cent. — A399

**2015, Jan. 15** **Litho.** ***Perf. 13x13½***

**746** A399 60te multi .80 .80

Souvenir Sheet

Victory in World War II, 70th Anniv. — A400

No. 747: a, Rakhymzhan Koshkarbayev (1924-88), damaged Reichstag Building, medal at LL. b, Manshuk Mametova (1922-43), gun, medal at LR. c, Ivan Panfilov (1893-1941), Moscow buildings, medal at LL.

***Perf. 14¼x14 Syncopated***

**2015, May 6** **Litho.**

**747** A400 200te Sheet of 3, #a-c, + label 5.50 5.50

Eurasian Economic Union — A401

***Perf. 14¼x14 Syncopated***

**2015, May 22** **Litho.**

**748** A401 100te multi 1.40 1.40

Ilyas Yesenberlin (1915-83), Writer A402

Malik Gabdullin (1915-73), Writer A403

Emblem of Expo 2017, Astana A404

Space Walking, 50th Anniv. A405

***Perf. 13½x14½ Syncopated***

**2015, June 18** **Litho.**

| | | | | |
|---|---|---|---|---|
| **749** A402 | 5te | lt bl & blk | .60 | .60 |
| **750** A403 | 10te | blk & stone | .60 | .60 |
| **751** A404 | 20te | blk & pink | .60 | .60 |
| **752** A405 | (112te) | red & blue | 1.25 | 1.25 |
| | *Nos. 749-752 (4)* | | 3.05 | 3.05 |

See No. 780.

Souvenir Sheet

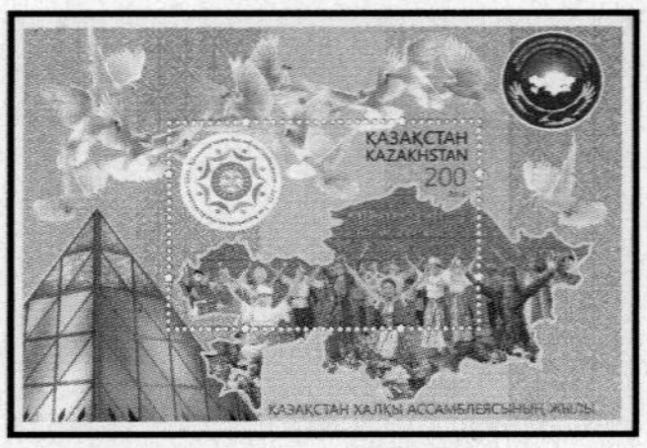


Assembly of the People of Kazakhstan, 20th Anniv. — A406

***Perf. 14¼x14 Syncopated***

**2015, June 25** **Litho.**

**753** A406 200te multi 2.00 2.00

Constitution, 20th Anniv. — A407

***Perf. 14¼x14 Syncopated***

**2015, Aug. 25** **Litho.**

**754** A407 (112te) multi 1.40 1.40

Kazakh Khanate, 550th Anniv. — A408

***Perf. 14¼x14 Syncopated***

**2015, Sept. 8** **Litho.**

**755** A408 550te multi 7.00 7.00

Navruz Bayram A409

***Perf. 13¼ Syncopated***

**2015, Oct. 28** **Litho.**

**756** A409 140te multi 1.75 1.75

Europa — A410

No. 757: a, 200te, Asyk Atu game pieces. b, 300te, Asyk Atu players and game pieces.

***Perf. 13x13¼ Syncopated***

**2015, Oct. 28** **Litho.**

**757** A410 Pair, #a-b 5.75 5.75

Diplomatic Relations Between Kazakhstan and United Arab Emirates — A411

No. 758: a, Sheikh Khalifa, flag of United Arab Emirates. b, Pres. Nursultan Nazarbayev, flag of Kazakhstan.

***Perf. 13¼x13 Syncopated***

**2015, Oct. 28** **Litho.**

**758** A411 200te Horiz. pair, #a-b 5.00 5.00

See United Arab Emirates No. 1137.

Postcrossing A412

***Perf. 13x13¼ Syncopated***

**2015, Nov. 7** **Litho.**

**759** A412 (140te) multi 1.75 1.75

Souvenir Sheet

Year of the Sheep — A413

***Perf. Syncopated***

**2015, Nov. 7** **Litho.**

**760** A413 300te multi 3.25 3.25

Cosmonaut Aidyn Aimbetov — A414

***Perf. 13¼ Syncopated***

**2015, Dec. 11** **Litho.**

**761** A414 300te multi 2.50 2.50

First Spacewalk, 50th Anniv. — A415

No. 762: a, 200te, Alexei A. Leonov, first spacewalker. b, (200te), Leonov spacewalking, Voskhod 2.

***Perf. 13½x13¼ Syncopated***

**2015, Dec. 11** **Litho.**

**762** A415 Horiz. pair, #a-b 3.50 3.50

Expo 2017, Astana A416

***Perf. 13¼x13½ Syncopated***

**2015, Dec. 25** **Litho.**

**763** A416 300te multi 2.50 2.50

Kenesary Street M. K. Kubrin Supermarket, Astana — A417

No. 764: a, (200te), Building in color. b, 200te, Building in Sepia.

***Perf. 13¾x13 Syncopated***

**2015, Dec. 25** **Litho.**

**764** A417 Pair, #a-b 3.25 3.25

Printed in sheets of 3 horizontal pairs of Nos. 764a-764b, + 3 flanking labels.

Souvenir Sheet

Aktobe Region — A418

No. 765: a, 140te, Koblandy Batyr Memorial. b, 200te, Aliya Moldagulova Monument.

***Perf. 13½x13¼ Syncopated***

**2015, Dec. 30** **Litho.**

**765** A418 Sheet of 2, #a-b, + 2 labels 2.75 2.75

Kazhymukan Munaitpasov (1871-1948), Wrestler — A419

No. 766: a, 60te, Munaitpasov. b, 200te, Soviet warplane paid for by Munaitpasov, letter to Munaitpasov from Joseph Stalin.

***Perf. 13¼x13 Syncopated***

**2016, Jan. 18** **Litho.**

**766** A419 Pair. #a-b 2.00 2.00

Souvenir Sheet

Aksu-Zhabagly Nature Reserve — A420

No. 767: a, Tulipa greigii. b, Capra sibirica. c, Gypaetus barbatus.

***Perf. 13¼x13 Syncopated***

**2016, Apr. 8** **Litho.**

**767** A420 200te Sheet of 3, #a-c 5.25 5.25

Miniature Sheet

Tobet Dogs — A421

No. 768: a, 60te, Two puppies (34x26mm). b, 140te, Dog, sheep, horses (37x26mm). c, 200te, Three dogs (37x26mm). d, 400te, Dog and sheep (37x52mm).

***Perf. 13¼x13 Syncopated***

**2016, Apr. 27** **Litho.**

**768** A421 Sheet of 4, #a-d 7.00 7.00

Regional Communications Commonwealth, 25th Anniv. — A422

***Perf. 13¼x13 Syncopated***

**2016, Apr. 29** **Litho.**

**769** A422 60te multi .60 .60

L. N. Gumilev Eurasian National University, 20th Anniv. — A423

***Perf. 13¼x13 Syncopated***

**2016, May 23** **Litho.**

**770** A423 60te multi .60 .60

Souvenir Sheet

Paintings by Yerbolat Tolepbay — A424

No. 771: a, 250te, Kazakh Khans (country name at UL, 56x40mm). b, 250te, Seven Rules (country name at UR, 56x40mm). c, 500te, Pres. Nursultan Nazarbayev (28x40mm).

***Perf. 13¼ Syncopated***

**2016, May 26** **Litho.**

**771** A424 Sheet of 3, #a-c 8.75 8.75

Souvenir Sheet

Pres. Nursultan Nazarbayev — A425

***Perf. 14x14¼ Syncopated***

**2016, June 13** **Litho.**

**772** A425 (121te) multi 1.25 1.25

Miniature Sheet

Orders of Kazakhstan — A426

No. 773: a, Order of the Golden Eagle. b, Order of the Fatherland. c, Order of the First President of Kazakhstan Nursultan Nazarbayev. d, Order of the Leopard. e, Order of Glory. f, Order of Valor. g, Order of Nobility. h, Order of Friendship. i, Order of Honor.

***Perf. 13½x13 Syncopated***

**2016, June 17** **Litho.**

**773** A426 100te Sheet of 9, #a-i 7.75 7.75

Souvenir Sheet

Akmola Region — A428

No. 775: a, 140te, Mountain and lake. b, 200te, Mosque.

***Perf. 13½ Syncopated***

**2016, June 24** **Litho.**

**775** A428 Sheet of 2, #a-b, + 2 labels 2.75 2.75

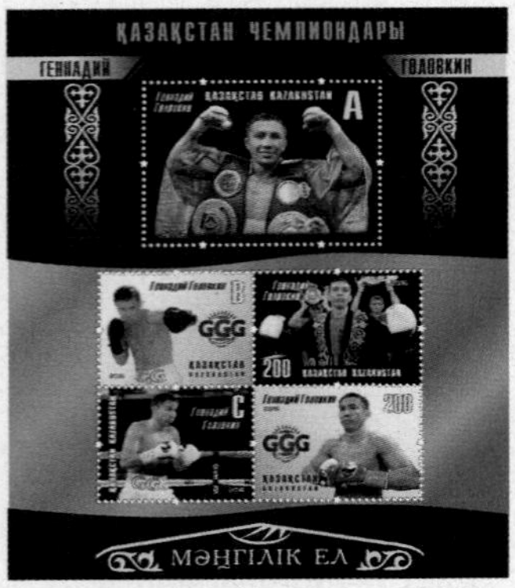


Gennady Golovkin, Boxer — A429

No. 776 — Golovkin with: a, (121te), Championship belts (52x37mm). b, (200te), Black boxing gloves and white trunks (37x21mm). c, 200te, Black robe, assistants holding belts (37x21mm). d, 200te, Blue and red boxing gloves (37x21mm) e, (218te), Ring ropes in background (37x21mm).

***Perf. 12¾x13¼ Syncopated (#776a), Perf. 13¼x12¾ Syncopated***

**2016, July 11 Litho.**

**776** A429 Sheet of 5, #a-e 8.25 8.25

**Expo 2017 Emblem Type of 2015 and**

Alikhan Bukeikhanov (1866-1937), Statesman A430

Morali Shamenov (1916-74), Union Leader A431

Ybyrai Altynsarin (1841-89), Educator — A432

Kayim Mukhmedzhanov (1916-2004), Poet — A433

***Perf. 13½x14½ Syncopated***

**2016 Litho.**

| | | | | |
|---|---|---|---|---|
| **777** | A430 | 5te pale bl & black | .25 | .25 |
| **778** | A431 | 50te blk & lt blue | .60 | .60 |
| **779** | A432 | (121te) red & blue | 1.25 | 1.25 |
| **780** | A404 | 200te pink & blk | 1.75 | 1.75 |
| **781** | A433 | (218te) blk & lilac | 2.25 | 2.25 |
| | | *Nos. 777-781 (5)* | 6.10 | 6.10 |

Issued: Nos. 777, 779, 781, 7/12; Nos. 778, 780, 7/22.

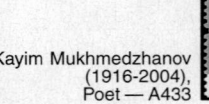

100 Concrete Steps for Mangilik El National Goals A434

***Perf. 13¼ Syncopated***

**2016, Aug. 18 Litho.**

**782** A434 100te multi 1.00 1.00

A435

***Perf. 12¾x13¼ Syncopated***

**2016, Aug. 18 Litho.**

**783** A435 60te multi .50 .50
*a.* Tete-beche pair 1.00 1.00

No. 783 was printed in sheets containing two tete-beche pairs.

Souvenir Sheet

Expo 2017, Astana — A436

***Perf. 13¼ Syncopated***

**2016, Aug. 19 Litho.**

**784** A436 300te multi 2.60 2.60

Traditional Foods A437

***Perf. 13¼ Syncopated***

**2016, Aug. 26 Litho.**

**785** A437 200te multi 1.75 1.75

Souvenir Sheet

Almaty Region — A438

No. 786: a, 140te, Medeu skating rink. b, 200te, Tamgaly Gorge petroglyphs.

***Perf. 13½ Syncopated***

**2016, Sept. 23 Litho.**

**786** A438 Sheet of 2, #a-b, + 2 labels 2.75 2.75

New Year A439

***Perf. Syncopated***

**2016, Oct. 21 Litho.**

**787** A439 100te multi .85 .85

No. 787 was printed in sheets of 4.

Souvenir Sheet

New Year 2016 (Year of the Monkey) — A440

***Perf. Syncopated***

**2016, Oct. 21 Litho.**

**788** A440 300te multi 2.60 2.60

Kerey Khan (c.1428-70) and Zhanibek Khan (1428-80), Founders of Kazakh Khanate — A442

No. 790 — Khans: a, On scroll. b, On monument.

***Perf. 13¼ Syncopated***

**2016, Nov. 2 Litho.**

**790** A442 200te Horiz. pair, #a-b 3.50 3.50

Printed in sheets of 8, containing 4 each Nos. 790a-790b.

2016 European Soccer Championships, France — A443

No. 791 — Soccer players, with player in red uniform at: a, Left. b, Right.

***Perf. 13¼ Syncopated***

**2016, Nov. 2 Litho.**

**791** A443 (218te) Horiz. pair, #a-b 4.00 4.00

World Post Day — A444

***Perf. 13¼ Syncopated***

**2016, Nov. 16 Litho.**

**792** A444 100te multi .85 .85

No. 792 was printed in sheets of 8 + central label.

Fourth National Sports Festival — A445

No. 793: a, 100te, Kyz kuu. b, 200te, Kekpar.

***Perf. 13¼ Syncopated***

**2016, Nov. 16 Litho.**

**793** A445 Horiz. pair, #a-b 2.60 2.60

Souvenir Sheet

Atyrau Region — A447

No. 795: a, 140te, Kurmangazy Palace of Culture. b, 200te, Biplane, medal and Hiuaz Dospanova Monument.

***Perf. 13½ Syncopated***

**2016, Nov. 16 Litho.**

**795** A447 Sheet of 2, #a-b, + 2 labels 2.75 2.75

Miniature Sheet

Sharks in Astana Aquarium — A448

No. 796: a, Carcharhinus melanopterus. b, Triaenodon obesus. c, Chiloscyllium plagiosum. d, Negaprion brevirostris.

***Perf. 13½ Syncopated***

**2016, Nov. 16 Litho.**

**796** A448 100te Sheet of 4, #a-d 3.50 3.50

Miniature Sheet

Gold and Silver Medalists at 2016 Summer Olympics — A449

No. 797: a, Gold medalist boxer Daniyar Yeleussinov. b, Gold medalist swimmer Dmitriy Balandin. c, Gold medalist weight lifter Nijat Rahimov. d, Silver medalist boxer Vasiliy Levit. e, Silver medalist boxer Adilbek Niyazymbetov. f, Silver medalist wrestler Guzel Manyurova. g, Silver medalist judo Yeldos Smetov. h, Silver medalist weight lifter Zhazira Zhapparkul.

***Perf. 13¼ Syncopated***

**2016, Nov. 16 Litho.**

**797** A449 200te Sheet of 8, #a-h 13.50 13.50

Endangered Mammals — A451

No. 799: a, Martes martes. b, Martes foina.

***Perf. 13¼ Syncopated***

**2016, Dec. 5** **Litho.**

**799** A451 200te Pair, #a-b 3.50 3.50

Printed in sheets of 8, 4 each of Nos. 799a-799b.

Souvenir Sheet

Alakol Nature Reserve — A452

No. 800: a, Larus relictus. b, Pelecanus crispus. c, Perca schrenki.

***Perf. 12¾x13¼ Syncopated***

**2016, Dec. 8** **Litho.**

**800** A452 200te Sheet of 3, #a-c 5.00 5.00

Souvenir Sheet

28th Winter Universiade, Almaty — A453

***Perf. 13¼ Syncopated***

**2016, Dec. 8** **Litho.**

**801** A453 300te multi 2.60 2.60

Sauran Ruins A454

***Perf. 13¼ Syncopated***

**2016, Dec. 27** **Litho.**

**802** A454 100te multi .95 .95

No. 802 was printed in sheets of 8 + label.

Astana Circus A455

***Perf. 13¼ Syncopated***

**2016, Dec. 27** **Litho.**

**803** A455 150te multi 1.40 1.40

Souvenir Sheet

Endangered Flora — A456

No. 804: a, Iridodictyum kolpokowskianum. b, Malus sieversii. c, Crocus altavicus.

***Perf. 13¼ Syncopated***

**2016, Dec. 27** **Litho.**

**804** A456 200te Sheet of 3, #a-c 5.00 5.00

Fayzulla Galimzhanov (1891-1942) A457

***Perf. 13¼ Syncopated***

**2016, Dec. 30** **Litho.**

**805** A457 100te multi .95 .95

Alash Orda Provisional Government, cent. (in 2017).

Gold and Silver Medalists at the 2016 Summer Paralympics — A458

No. 806: a, Gold medalist swimmer Zulfiya Gabidullina. b, Silver medalist power lifter Raushan Koyshibayeva.

***Perf. 13½ Syncopated***

**2016, Dec. 30** **Litho.**

**806** A458 200te Horiz. pair, #a-b 3.50 3.50

Souvenir Sheet

New Year — A459

***Perf. 13½ Syncopated***

**2016, Dec. 30** **Litho.**

**807** A459 (218te) multi 1.90 1.90

28th Winter Universiade, Almaty — A460

***Perf. 13½ Syncopated***

**2017, Jan. 30** **Litho.**

**808** A460 200te multi 1.90 1.90

Kazakhstan Olympic Committee, 25th Anniv. — A461

***Perf. 13½ Syncopated***

**2017, Mar. 2** **Litho.**

**809** A461 100te multi 1.00 1.00

**Expo 2017 Emblem Type of 2015 and**

Expo 2017 Emblem
A462 A463

**2017, Mar. 7** **Litho.** ***Perf. 13½x13***

| | | | | | |
|---|---|---|---|---|---|
| **810** | A404 | 10te | blk & orange | .25 | .25 |
| **811** | A404 | 50te | blk & green | .25 | .25 |
| **812** | A462 | (130te) | red & blue | 1.25 | 1.25 |
| **813** | A463 | (218te) | blk & ultra | 2.10 | 2.10 |
| | | *Nos. 810-813 (4)* | | 3.85 | 3.85 |

Nazir Tyuryakulov (1892-1937), Diplomat — A464

Kazybek (1667-1764), Bey
A465 A466

**2017, Mar. 14** **Litho.** ***Perf. 13½x13***

| | | | | | |
|---|---|---|---|---|---|
| **814** | A464 | 1te | yel & blk | .25 | .25 |
| **815** | A465 | 5te | lt bl & blk | .25 | .25 |
| **816** | A466 | 100te | org yel & blk | 1.00 | 1.00 |
| | | *Nos. 814-816 (3)* | | 1.50 | 1.50 |

Expo 2017, Astana A467

**2017, July 12** **Litho.** ***Perf. 13¼***

**817** A467 300te multi 2.75 2.75

Souvenir Sheet

New Year 2017 (Year of the Rooster) — A468

**2017, Aug. 7** **Litho.** ***Perf.***

**818** A468 300te multi 2.75 2.75

KazEOSat-1 — A469

**2017, Aug. 14** **Litho.** ***Perf. 12***

**819** A469 (220te) multi 2.10 2.10

Kazakhstan No. 1 — A470

**2017, Aug. 21** **Litho.** ***Perf. 12***

**820** A470 C multi 2.00 2.00

Kazakhstan postage stamps, 25th anniv. No. 820 sold for 220te on day of issue.

Souvenir Sheet

Uncia Uncia — A471

No. 821: a, Head of adult snow leopard. b, Snow leopard on rock ledge. c, Snow leopard kittens.

**2017, Aug. 28** **Litho.** ***Perf. 12***

**821** A471 300te Sheet of 3, #a-c 8.50 8.50

Novruz A472

**2017, Aug. 31** **Litho.** ***Perf.***

**822** A472 300te multi 2.75 2.75

No. 822 was printed in sheets of 4.

Mausoleum of Khoja Ahmed Yasawi, Turkestan — A473

**2017, Aug. 31 Litho. *Perf. 13x13¼***
**823** A473 750te multi 7.00 7.00

Europa.

KazTransOil, 20th Anniv. — A474

**2017, Sept. 8 Litho. *Perf. 12***
**824** A474 50te multi .50 .50

Diplomatic Relations Between Kazakhstan and Belarus, 25th Anniv. A475

**2017, Sept. 16 Litho. *Perf. 12***
**825** A475 (140te) multi 1.40 1.40

See Belarus No. 1061.

Souvenir Sheet

Flora — A476

No. 826: a, Berberis iliensis. b, Juniperus sabina.

**2017, Sept. 25 Litho. *Perf. 12***
**826** A476 200te Sheet of 2, #a-b 3.75 3.75

Miniature Sheet

2017 Automobiles — A477

No. 827: a, JAC S3. b, Hyundai Elantra. c, Peugeot 301. d, Skoda Superb. e, Lada Vesta. f, Kia Sportage.

**2017, Oct. 2 Litho. *Perf. 12***
**827** A477 100te Sheet of 6, #a-f 5.75 5.75

Ministry of Foreign Affairs, 25th Anniv. — A478

**2017, Oct. 10 Litho. *Perf. 13x13½***
**828** A478 100te pale blue & dk blue .95 .95

Mir Interstate Television and Radio Company, 25th Anniv. A480

**2017, Oct. 31 Litho. *Perf. 13½x13***
**830** A480 (130te) multi 1.25 1.25

Joint issue between Russia, Belarus and Kazakhstan.

See Belarus No. 1065, Russia No.

Souvenir Sheet

Attractions of East Kazakhstan Region — A481

No. 831: a, 140te, Khalifa Altai Mosque, Oskemen. b, 200te, Kozy Korpesh and Bayan Sulu Mausoleum, Tansyk.

**2017, Nov. 3 Litho. *Perf. 12***
**831** A481 Sheet of 2, #a-b, + 2 labels 3.25 3.25

Souvenir Sheet

Karatau Nature Reserve — A482

No. 832: a, Ovis ammon nigrimontana. b, Mustela erminea. c, Hedysarum mind-shelkense bajt.

**2017, Nov. 6 Litho. *Perf. 13x13½***
**832** A482 200te Sheet of 2, #a-b 5.75 5.75

Souvenir Sheet

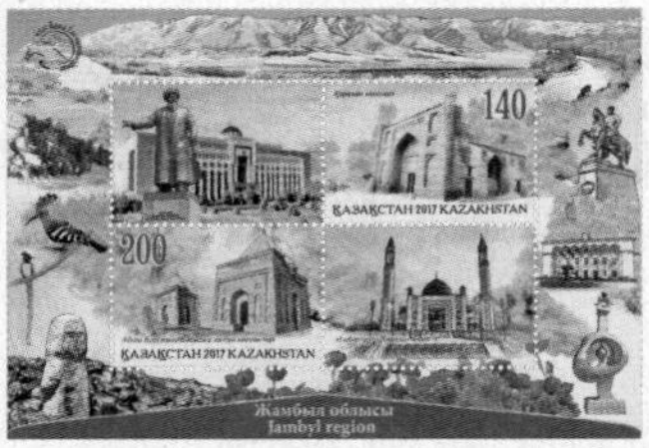


Attractions of Jambyl Region — A483

No. 833: a, 140te, Karakhan Mausoleum, Taraz. b, 200te, Aisha Bibi and Babaji Khatun Mausoleums, Taraz.

**2017, Nov. 15 Litho. *Perf. 12***
**833** A483 Sheet of 2, #a-b, + 2 labels 3.25 3.25

Diplomatic Relations Between Kazakhstan and France, 25th Anniv. — A484

No. 834: a, (220te), Eagle and rooster. b, 500te, Bayterek Tower, Astana, and Eiffel Tower, Paris.

**2017, Nov. 20 Litho. *Perf. 13½x13***
**834** A484 Horiz. pair, #a-b 6.75 6.75

Yurt and Decorated Chest — A485

**2017, Nov. 23 Litho. *Perf. 13¼***
**835** A485 300te multi 2.75 2.75

## SEMI-POSTAL STAMP

Cartoons — SP1

a, Mother and child. b, Cow, rabbit. c, Horses.

**1994, Nov. 3 Litho. *Perf. 12½x12***
**B1** SP1 1te +30ti Block of 3 + label .75 .75

# KENYA

ˈke-nyə

LOCATION — East Africa, bordering on the Indian Ocean
GOVT. — Republic
AREA — 224,960 sq. mi.
POP. — 28,808,658 (1999 est.)
CAPITAL — Nairobi

Formerly a part of the British colony of Kenya, Uganda, Tanganyika, Kenya gained independence Dec. 12, 1963.

100 Cents = 1 Shilling

**Catalogue values for all unused stamps in this country are for Never Hinged items.**

Treetop Hotel and Elephants — A1

Designs: 5c, Cattle ranching. 10c, Wood carving. 15c, Riveter. 20c, Timber industry. 30c, Jomo Kenyatta facing Mt. Kenya. 40c, Fishing industry. 50c, Flag and emblem. 65c, Pyrethrum industry (daisies). 1sh, National Assembly bldg. 2sh, Harvesting coffee. 5sh, Harvesting tea. 10sh, Mombasa port. 20sh, Royal College, Nairobi.

***Perf. 14x14½***

**1963, Dec. 12 Photo. Unwmk.**

**Size: 21x17½mm**

| | | | | |
|---|---|---|---|---|
| 1 | A1 | 5c bl, buff & dk brn | .25 | *.50* |
| 2 | A1 | 10c brown | .25 | .25 |
| *a.* | | Booklet pane of 4 | .30 | |
| 3 | A1 | 15c deep magenta | 1.00 | .25 |
| *a.* | | Booklet pane of 4 | 4.00 | |
| 4 | A1 | 20c yel grn & dk brn | .25 | .25 |
| *a.* | | Booklet pane of 4 | .40 | |
| 5 | A1 | 30c yel & black | .25 | .25 |
| *a.* | | Booklet pane of 4 | .55 | |
| 6 | A1 | 40c blue & brown | .25 | .30 |
| 7 | A1 | 50c grn, blk & dp car | .60 | .25 |
| *a.* | | Booklet pane of 4 | 2.50 | |
| 8 | A1 | 65c steel blue & yel | .55 | .70 |

***Perf. 14½***

**Size: 41½x25½mm**

| | | | | |
|---|---|---|---|---|
| 9 | A1 | 1sh multicolored | .25 | .25 |
| 10 | A1 | 1.30sh grn, brn & blk | 5.25 | .30 |
| 11 | A1 | 2sh multicolored | 1.25 | .40 |
| 12 | A1 | 5sh ultra, yel grn & brn | 1.25 | 1.00 |
| 13 | A1 | 10sh brn & dark brn | 9.00 | 2.75 |
| 14 | A1 | 20sh pink & grnsh blk | 4.00 | *10.00* |
| | | *Nos. 1-14 (14)* | 24.40 | 17.45 |

President Jomo Kenyatta and Flag of Kenya — A2

Flag and: 15c, Cockerel. 50c, African lion. 1.30sh, Hartlaub's touraco. 2.50sh, Nandi flame flower.

**1964, Dec. 12 Photo. *Perf. 13x12½***

| | | | | |
|---|---|---|---|---|
| 15 | A2 | 15c lt violet & multi | .25 | .25 |
| 16 | A2 | 30c dk blue & multi | .25 | .25 |
| 17 | A2 | 50c dk brown & multi | .25 | .25 |
| 18 | A2 | 1.30sh multicolored | 2.75 | .50 |
| 19 | A2 | 2.50sh multicolored | .40 | *3.25* |
| | | *Nos. 15-19 (5)* | 3.90 | *4.50* |

Establishment of the Republic of Kenya, Dec. 12, 1964.

Greater Kudu A3

Animals: 5c, Thomson's gazelle. 10c, Sable antelope. 15c, Aardvark. 20c, Senegal bush baby. 30c, Warthog. 40c, Zebra. 50c, Buffalo. 65c, Black rhinoceros. 70c, Ostrich. 1.30sh, Elephant. 1.50sh, Bat-eared fox. 2.50sh, Cheetah. 5sh, Vervet monkey. 10sh, Giant pangolin. 20sh, Lion.

**1966-69 Unwmk. *Perf. 14x14½***

**Size: 21x17mm**

| | | | | |
|---|---|---|---|---|
| 20 | A3 | 5c gray, blk & org | .30 | .25 |
| 21 | A3 | 10c blk & yel grn | .25 | .25 |
| 22 | A3 | 15c dp org & blk | .25 | .25 |
| 23 | A3 | 20c ultra, lt brn & blk | .25 | .25 |
| 24 | A3 | 30c lt ultra & blk | .25 | .25 |
| 25 | A3 | 40c ocher & blk | .50 | .25 |
| 26 | A3 | 50c dp orange & blk | .50 | .25 |
| 27 | A3 | 65c dp yel grn & blk | 1.00 | *2.00* |
| 28 | A3 | 70c rose lake & blk | 3.75 | 1.75 |

***Perf. 14½***

**Size: 41x25mm**

| | | | | |
|---|---|---|---|---|
| 29 | A3 | 1sh gray bl, ol & blk | 1.00 | .25 |
| 30 | A3 | 1.30sh yel grn & blk | 3.50 | .35 |
| 31 | A3 | 1.50sh brn org, brn & black | 2.50 | *3.00* |
| 32 | A3 | 2.50sh ol bis, yel & blk | 3.50 | 1.25 |
| 33 | A3 | 5sh brt grn, ultra & black | .75 | .75 |
| 34 | A3 | 10sh red brn, bis & black | 2.75 | *3.00* |
| 35 | A3 | 20sh ocher, bis, gold & black | 8.00 | *12.00* |
| | | *Nos. 20-35 (16)* | 29.05 | 26.10 |

Issued: No. 28, 31, 9/15/69; others, 12/12/66.

Branched Murex — A4

Sea shells: 5c, Morning pink. 10c, Episcopal miter. 15c, Strawberry-top shell. 20c, Humpback cowrie. 30c, variable abalone. 40c, Flame-top shell. 50c, Violet sailor. 60c, Bull's-mouth helmet. 70c, Pearly nautilus. 1.50sh, Neptune's trumpet. 2.50sh, Mediterranean tulip shell. 5sh, Fluctuating turban. 10sh, Textile cone. 20sh, Scorpion shell.

**1971 Dec. 13 Photo. *Perf. 14½x14***

**Size: 17x21mm**

**36** A4 5c bister & multi .25 *.45*
**37** A4 10c dull grn & multi .25 .25
*a.* Booklet pane of 4 .60
**38** A4 15c tan & multi .25 .25
*a.* Booklet pane of 4 .60
**39** A4 20c tan & multi .25 .25
*a.* Booklet pane of 4 .75
**40** A4 30c yellow & multi .25 .25
*a.* Booklet pane of 4 2.25
**41** A4 40c gray & multi .25 .25
*a.* Booklet pane of 4 2.25
**42** A4 50c buff & multi (*Janthina globosa*) .40 .30
*a.* Booklet pane of 4 3.50
**43** A4 60c lilac & multi .40 *1.75*
**44** A4 70c gray grn & multi (Nautilus pompileus) .55 *1.50*
*a.* Booklet pane of 4 5.00

***Perf. 14½***

**Size: 25x41mm**

**45** A4 1sh ocher & multi .40 .35
**46** A4 1.50sh pale grn & multi 1.25 .30
**47** A4 2.50sh vio gray & multi 1.75 .30
**48** A4 5sh lemon & multi 2.00 *.25*
**49** A4 10sh multicolored 2.25 *.25*
**50** A4 20sh gray & multi 3.25 *.25*
*Nos. 36-50 (15)* 13.75 *6.95*

Used values of Nos. 48-50 are for stamps with printed cancellations.

For surcharges see Nos. 53-55.

**Nos. 42, 44 with Revised Inscription**

**1974, Jan. 20 *Perf. 14½x14***

**51** A4 50c (Janthina janthina) 15.00 3.75
**52** A4 70c (Nautilus pompilius) 13.00 7.00

**Nos. 46-47, 50 Surcharged with New Value and 2 Bars**

**1975, Nov. 17 Photo. *Perf. 14½***

**53** A4 2sh on 1.50sh multi 8.00 *5.75*
**54** A4 3sh on 2.50sh multi 12.00 *22.50*
**55** A4 40sh on 20sh multi 8.00 *14.00*
*Nos. 53-55 (3)* 28.00 *42.25*

Microwave Tower — A5

Designs: 1sh, Cordless switchboard and operators, horiz. 2sh, Telephones of 1880, 1930 and 1976. 3sh, Message switching center, horiz.

**1976, Apr. 15 Litho. *Perf. 14½***

**56** A5 50c blue & multi .25 .25
**57** A5 1sh red & multi .25 .25
**58** A5 2sh yellow & multi .25 .35
**59** A5 3sh multicolored .45 .45
*a.* Souvenir sheet of 4 2.00 2.00
*Nos. 56-59 (4)* 1.20 1.30

Telecommunication development in East Africa. No. 59a contains 4 stamps similar to Nos. 56-59 with simulated perforations.

Akii Bua, Ugandan Hurdler — A6

Designs: 1sh, Filbert Bayi, Tanzanian runner. 2sh, Steve Muchoki, Kenyan boxer. 3sh, Olympic torch, flags of Kenya, Tanzania and Uganda.

**1976, July 5 Litho. *Perf. 14½***

**60** A6 50c blue & multi .25 .25
**61** A6 1sh red & multi .25 .25
**62** A6 2sh yellow & multi .40 .35
**63** A6 3sh blue & multi .80 .55
*a.* Souv. sheet of 4, #60-63, perf. 13 7.25 7.25
*Nos. 60-63 (4)* 1.70 1.40

21st Olympic Games, Montreal, Canada, July 17-Aug. 1.

Tanzania-Zambia Railway — A7

Designs: 1sh, Nile Bridge, Uganda. 2sh, Nakuru Station, Kenya. 3sh, Class A locomotive, 1896.

**1976, Oct. 4 Litho. *Perf. 14½***

**64** A7 50c lilac & multi .40 .25
**65** A7 1sh emerald & multi .70 .25
**66** A7 2sh brt rose & multi 1.40 1.00
**67** A7 3sh yellow & multi 1.50 1.40
*a.* Souv. sheet of 4, #64-67, perf. 13 9.00 9.00
*Nos. 64-67 (4)* 4.00 2.90

Rail transport in East Africa.

No. 67a exists imperf., value $22.50.

Nile Perch — A8

Game Fish: 1sh, Tilapia. 3sh, Sailfish. 5sh, Black marlin.

**1977, Jan. 10 Litho. *Perf. 14½***

**68** A8 50c multicolored .25 .25
**69** A8 1sh multicolored .40 .25
**70** A8 3sh multicolored 1.25 .60
**71** A8 5sh multicolored 1.40 1.00
*a.* Souvenir sheet of 4, #68-71 11.00 11.00
*Nos. 68-71 (4)* 3.30 2.10

Festival Emblem and Masai Tribesmen Bleeding Cow — A9

Festival Emblem and: 1sh, Dancers from Uganda. 2sh, Makonde sculpture, Tanzania. 3sh, Tribesmen skinning hippopotamus.

**1977, Jan. 15 *Perf. 13½x14***

**72** A9 50c multicolored .25 .25
**73** A9 1sh multicolored .30 .30
**74** A9 2sh multicolored .65 .65
**75** A9 3sh multicolored .80 .80
*a.* Souvenir sheet of 4, #72-75 5.00 5.00
*Nos. 72-75 (4)* 2.00 2.00

2nd World Black and African Festival, Lagos, Nigeria, Jan. 15-Feb. 12.

Automobile Passing through Village — A10

Safari Rally Emblem and: 1sh, Winner at finish line. 2sh, Car going through washout. 5sh, Car, elephants and Mt. Kenya.

**1977, Apr. 5 Litho. *Perf. 14***

**76** A10 50c multicolored .25 .25
**77** A10 1sh multicolored .35 .35
**78** A10 2sh multicolored .55 .55
**79** A10 5sh multicolored 2.10 2.10
*a.* Souvenir sheet of 4, #76-79 4.50 4.50
*Nos. 76-79 (4)* 3.25 3.25

25th Safari Rally, Apr. 7-11.

Rev. Canon Apolo Kivebulaya — A11

1sh, Uganda Cathedral. 2sh, Early grass-topped Cathedral. 5sh, Early tent congregation, Kigezi.

**1977, June 20 Litho. *Perf. 14***

**80** A11 50c multicolored .25 .25
**81** A11 1sh multicolored .25 .25
**82** A11 2sh multicolored .40 .40
**83** A11 5sh multicolored 1.25 1.25
*a.* Souvenir sheet of 4, #80-83 1.75 1.75
*Nos. 80-83 (4)* 2.15 2.15

Church of Uganda, centenary.

Elizabeth II and Prince Philip at Sagana Lodge — A12

Designs: 5sh, "Treetops" observation hut, Aberdare Forest, and elephants, vert. 10sh, Pres. Jomo Kenyatta, Elizabeth II, crossed spears and shield. 15sh, Elizabeth II and Pres. Kenyatta in open automobile. 50sh, Elizabeth II and Prince Philip at window in Treetops.

**1977, July 20 Litho. *Perf. 14***

**84** A12 2sh multicolored .25 .25
**85** A12 5sh multicolored .25 .25
**86** A12 10sh multicolored .55 .55
**87** A12 15sh multicolored .65 .65
*a.* Souvenir sheet of 1 1.25 1.25
*Nos. 84-87 (4)* 1.70 1.70

**Souvenir Sheet**

**88** A12 50sh multicolored 3.50 3.50

Reign of Queen Elizabeth II, 25th anniv.

Pancake Tortoise — A13

Wildlife Fund Emblem and; 1sh, Nile crocodile. 2sh, Hunter's hartebeest. 3sh, Red colobus monkey. 5sh, Dugong.

**1977, Sept. 26 Litho. *Perf. 14x13½***

**89** A13 50c multicolored .50 .25
**90** A13 1sh multicolored .70 .30
**91** A13 2sh multicolored 1.75 1.75
**92** A13 3sh multicolored 2.50 2.50
**93** A13 5sh multicolored 2.75 2.75
*a.* Souvenir sheet of 4, #90-93 9.00 9.00
*Nos. 89-93 (5)* 8.20 7.55

Endangered species.

Kenya-Ethiopia Border Point — A14

Designs: 1sh, Station wagon at Archer's Post. 2sh, Thika overpass. 5sh, Marsabit Game Lodge and elephant.

**1977, Nov. 10 Litho. *Perf. 14***

**94** A14 50c multicolored .25 .25
**95** A14 1sh multicolored .25 .25
**96** A14 2sh multicolored .40 .40
**97** A14 5sh multicolored .80 .80
*a.* Souvenir sheet of 4, #94-97 2.25 2.25
*Nos. 94-97 (4)* 1.70 1.70

Opening of Nairobi-Addis Ababa highway.

Minerals Found in Kenya — A15

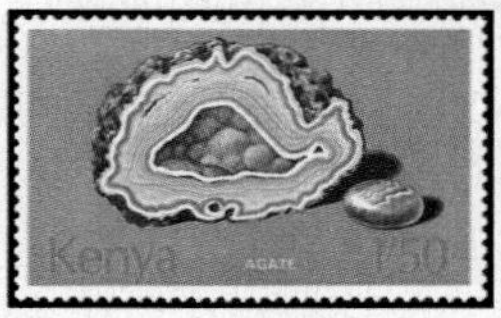


A16

10c, Gypsum. 20c, Trona. 30c, Kyanite. 40c, Amazonite. 50c, Galena. 70c, Silicified wood. 80c, Fluorite. 1sh, Amethyst. 1.50sh, Agate. 2sh, Tourmaline. 3sh, Aquamarine. 5sh, Rhodolite garnet. 10sh, Sapphire. 20sh, Ruby. 40sh, Green grossular garnet.

***Perf. 14½x14, 14½ (A16)***

**1977, Dec. 13 Photo.**

**98** A15 10c multicolored 1.25 .25
**99** A15 20c multicolored 2.00 .25
**100** A15 30c multicolored 2.00 .25
**101** A15 40c multicolored 1.50 .25
**102** A15 50c multicolored 1.50 .25
**103** A15 70c multicolored 7.50 .90
**104** A15 80c multicolored 7.50 .75
**105** A16 1sh multicolored 1.50 .25
**106** A16 1.50sh multicolored 1.50 .40
**107** A16 2sh multicolored 1.50 .35
**108** A16 3sh multicolored 1.75 1.00
**109** A16 5sh multicolored 1.75 1.25
**110** A16 10sh multicolored 2.00 2.00
**111** A16 20sh multicolored 4.50 3.00
**112** A16 40sh multicolored 17.50 *20.00*
*Nos. 98-112 (15)* 55.25 31.15

The 10c, 20c, 40c, 50c and 80c were also issued in booklet panes of 4. The 50c was also issued in a booklet pane of 2.

For surcharge see No. 242.

Soccer, Joe Kadenge and World Cup — A17

World Cup and: 1sh, Mohammed Chuma receiving trophy, and his portrait. 2sh, Shot on goal and Omari S. Kidevu. 3sh, Backfield defense and Polly Ouma.

**1978, Apr. 10 Litho. *Perf. 14x13½***

**113** A17 50c green & multi .25 .25
**114** A17 1sh lt brown & multi .25 .25
**115** A17 2sh lilac & multi .30 *.70*
**116** A17 3sh dk blue & multi .50 *1.00*
*a.* Souvenir sheet of 4, #113-116 3.75 3.75
*Nos. 113-116 (4)* 1.30 2.20

World Soccer Cup Championships, Argentina 78, June 1-25.

Boxing and Games' Emblem A18

Games Emblem and: 1sh, Pres. Kenyatta welcoming 1968 Olympic team. 3sh, Javelin. 5sh, Pres. Kenyatta, boxing team and trophy.

**1978, July 15 Photo. *Perf. 13x14***

| | | | | |
|---|---|---|---|---|
| **117** | A18 | 50c multicolored | .25 | .25 |
| **118** | A18 | 1sh multicolored | .25 | .25 |
| **119** | A18 | 3sh multicolored | .70 | .70 |
| **120** | A18 | 5sh multicolored | .85 | .85 |
| | | *Nos. 117-120 (4)* | 2.05 | 2.05 |

Commonwealth Games, Edmonton, Canada, Aug. 3-12.

Overloaded Truck — A19

Road Safety: 1sh, Observe speed limit. 1.50sh, Observe traffic lights. 2sh, School crossing. 3sh, Passing. 5sh, Railroad crossing.

**1978, Sept. 18 Litho. *Perf. 13½x14***

| | | | | |
|---|---|---|---|---|
| **121** | A19 | 50c multicolored | .50 | .25 |
| **122** | A19 | 1sh multicolored | .75 | .25 |
| **123** | A19 | 1.50sh multicolored | 1.10 | 1.00 |
| **124** | A19 | 2sh multicolored | 1.75 | 1.50 |
| **125** | A19 | 3sh multicolored | 2.00 | *2.25* |
| **126** | A19 | 5sh multicolored | 2.25 | *2.50* |
| | | *Nos. 121-126 (6)* | 8.35 | 7.75 |

Pres. Kenyatta at Harambee Water Project Opening — A20

Kenyatta Day: 1sh, Prince Philip handing over symbol of independence, 1963. 2sh, Pres. Jomo Kenyatta addressing independence rally. 3sh, Stage at 15th independence anniversary celebration. 5sh, Handcuffed Kenyatta led by soldiers, 1952.

**1978, Oct. 16 Litho. *Perf. 14***

| | | | | |
|---|---|---|---|---|
| **127** | A20 | 50c multicolored | .35 | .35 |
| **128** | A20 | 1sh multicolored | .35 | .35 |
| **129** | A20 | 2sh multicolored | .45 | .45 |
| **130** | A20 | 3sh multicolored | .75 | .75 |
| **131** | A20 | 5sh multicolored | 1.00 | 1.00 |
| | | *Nos. 127-131 (5)* | 2.90 | 2.90 |

Soldiers and Emblem A21

Anti-Apartheid Emblem and: 1sh, Anti-Apartheid Conference. 2sh, Stephen Biko, South African Anti-Apartheid leader. 3sh, Nelson Mandela, jailed since 1961. 5sh, Bishop Lamont, expelled from Rhodesia in 1977.

**1978, Dec. 11 Litho. *Perf. 14x14½***

| | | | | |
|---|---|---|---|---|
| **132** | A21 | 50c multicolored | .30 | .30 |
| **133** | A21 | 1sh multicolored | .30 | .30 |
| **134** | A21 | 2sh multicolored | .45 | .45 |
| **135** | A21 | 3sh multicolored | .65 | .65 |
| **136** | A21 | 5sh multicolored | .75 | .75 |
| | | *Nos. 132-136 (5)* | 2.45 | 2.45 |

Anti-Apartheid Year and Namibia's struggle for independence.

Children on School Playground — A22

Children's Year Emblem and: 2sh, Boy catching fish. 3sh, Children dancing and singing. 5sh, Children and camel caravan.

**1979, Feb. 5 Litho. *Perf. 14***

| | | | | |
|---|---|---|---|---|
| **137** | A22 | 50c multicolored | .35 | .35 |
| **138** | A22 | 2sh multicolored | .55 | .55 |
| **139** | A22 | 3sh multicolored | .70 | .70 |
| **140** | A22 | 5sh multicolored | 1.00 | 1.00 |
| | | *Nos. 137-140 (4)* | 2.60 | 2.60 |

International Year of the Child.

"The Lion and the Jewel" A23

National Theater: 1sh, Dancers and drummers. 2sh, Programs of various productions. 3sh, View of National Theater. 5sh, "Genesis," performed by Nairobi City Players.

**1979, Apr. 6 Litho. *Perf. 13½x14***

| | | | | |
|---|---|---|---|---|
| **141** | A23 | 50c multicolored | .25 | .25 |
| **142** | A23 | 1sh multicolored | .30 | .30 |
| **143** | A23 | 2sh multicolored | .45 | .45 |
| **144** | A23 | 3sh multicolored | .75 | .75 |
| **145** | A23 | 5sh multicolored | 1.00 | 1.00 |
| | | *Nos. 141-145 (5)* | 2.75 | 2.75 |

Village Workshop — A24

Salvation Army Emblem and: 50c, Blind telephone operator, vert. 1sh, Care for the aged, vert. 5sh, Vocational training (nurse).

**1979, June 4 *Perf. 13½x13, 13x13½***

| | | | | |
|---|---|---|---|---|
| **146** | A24 | 50c multicolored | .30 | .30 |
| **147** | A24 | 1sh multicolored | .40 | .40 |
| **148** | A24 | 3sh multicolored | .75 | .75 |
| **149** | A24 | 5sh multicolored | 1.25 | 1.25 |
| | | *Nos. 146-149 (4)* | 2.70 | 2.70 |

Salvation Army Social Services, 50th anniv.

Funeral Procession — A25

Kenyatta: 1sh, Taking oath of office. 3sh, Addressing crowd. 5sh, As young man with wooden trying plane.

**1979, Aug. 22 Litho. *Perf. 13½x14***

| | | | | |
|---|---|---|---|---|
| **150** | A25 | 50c multicolored | .25 | .25 |
| **151** | A25 | 1sh multicolored | .35 | .35 |
| **152** | A25 | 3sh multicolored | .50 | .50 |
| **153** | A25 | 5sh multicolored | .75 | .75 |
| | | *Nos. 150-153 (4)* | 1.85 | 1.85 |

Jomo Kenyatta (1893-1978), first president of Kenya.

British East Africa No. 2, Hill, Signature — A26

Hill, Signature and: 1sh, Kenya, Uganda and Tanzania #54. 2sh, Penny Black. 5sh, Kenya #19.

**1979, Nov. 27 Litho. *Perf. 14***

| | | | | |
|---|---|---|---|---|
| **154** | A26 | 50c multicolored | .25 | .25 |
| **155** | A26 | 1sh multicolored | .25 | .25 |
| **156** | A26 | 2sh multicolored | .35 | .35 |
| **157** | A26 | 5sh multicolored | .65 | .65 |
| | | *Nos. 154-157 (4)* | 1.50 | 1.50 |

Sir Rowland Hill (1795-1879), originator of penny postage.

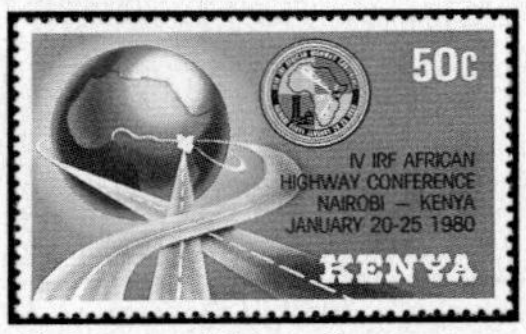


Highways, Globe, Conference Emblem — A27

Conference Emblem and: 1sh, Truck at Athi River, New Weighbridge. 3sh, New Nyali Bridge, Mombasa. 5sh, Jomo Kenyatta Airport Highway.

**1980, Jan. 10 Litho. *Perf. 14***

| | | | | |
|---|---|---|---|---|
| **158** | A27 | 50c multicolored | .25 | .25 |
| **159** | A27 | 1sh multicolored | .25 | .25 |
| **160** | A27 | 3sh multicolored | .60 | .60 |
| **161** | A27 | 5sh multicolored | .85 | .85 |
| | | *Nos. 158-161 (4)* | 1.95 | 1.95 |

4th IRF African Highway Conference, Nairobi, Jan. 20-25.

Patient Airlift A28

50c, Outdoor clinic. 1sh, Mule transport of patient, vert.. 3sh, Surgery, vert.

**1980, Mar. 20 Litho. *Perf. 14½***

| | | | | |
|---|---|---|---|---|
| **162** | A28 | 50c multicolored | .25 | .25 |
| **163** | A28 | 1sh multicolored | .35 | .35 |
| **164** | A28 | 3sh multicolored | .65 | .65 |
| **165** | A28 | 5sh shown | 1.00 | 1.00 |
| *a.* | | Souvenir sheet of 4, #162-165 | 3.00 | 3.00 |
| | | *Nos. 162-165 (4)* | 2.25 | 2.25 |

Flying doctor service.

Hill Statue, Kidderminster and Mt. Kenya — A29

**1980, May 6 Litho. *Perf. 14***

| | | | | |
|---|---|---|---|---|
| **166** | A29 | 25sh multicolored | 1.40 | 1.40 |
| *a.* | | Souvenir sheet | 1.75 | *2.00* |

London 1980 International Stamp Exhibition, May 6-14.

Pope John Paul II and Crowd A30

Visit of Pope John Paul II to Kenya: 1sh, Pope, Nairobi Cathedral, papal flag and arms, vert. 5sh, Pope, papal and Kenya flags, dove, vert. 10sh, Pres. arap Moi of Kenya, Pope, flag of Kenya on map of Africa.

**1980, May 8 *Perf. 13½***

| | | | | |
|---|---|---|---|---|
| **167** | A30 | 50c multicolored | .35 | .25 |
| **168** | A30 | 1sh multicolored | .45 | .45 |
| **169** | A30 | 5sh multicolored | 1.00 | 1.00 |
| **170** | A30 | 10sh multicolored | 1.75 | 1.75 |
| | | *Nos. 167-170 (4)* | 3.55 | 3.45 |

Sting Ray — A31

**1980, June 27 Litho. *Perf. 14½***

| | | | | |
|---|---|---|---|---|
| **171** | A31 | 50c shown | .50 | .25 |
| **172** | A31 | 2sh Alkit snapper | 1.25 | .60 |
| **173** | A31 | 3sh Sea slug | 1.40 | 1.40 |
| **174** | A31 | 5sh Hawksbill turtle | 2.50 | 2.50 |
| | | *Nos. 171-174 (4)* | 5.65 | 4.75 |

National Archives, 1904 A32

1sh, Commissioner's Office, Nairobi, 1913. 1.50sh, Nairobi House, 1913. 2sh, Norfolk Hotel, 1904. 3sh, McMillan Library, 1929. 5sh, Kipande House, 1913.

**1980, Oct. 9 Litho. *Perf. 14***

| | | | | |
|---|---|---|---|---|
| **175** | A32 | 50c shown | .25 | .25 |
| **176** | A32 | 1sh multicolored | .25 | .25 |
| **177** | A32 | 1.50sh multicolored | .30 | .25 |
| **178** | A32 | 2sh multicolored | .35 | *.45* |
| **179** | A32 | 3sh multicolored | .50 | *.95* |
| **180** | A32 | 5sh multicolored | .60 | *1.50* |
| | | *Nos. 175-180 (6)* | 2.25 | *3.65* |

Woman in Wheelchair and Child — A33

1sh, Pres. arap Moi, team captain. 3sh, Blind mountain climbers, Mt. Kenya, 1965. 5sh, Disabled artist.

**1981, Feb. 10 Litho. *Perf. 14x13½***

| | | | | |
|---|---|---|---|---|
| **181** | A33 | 50c shown | .25 | .25 |
| **182** | A33 | 1sh multicolored | .25 | .25 |
| **183** | A33 | 3sh multicolored | .55 | .55 |
| **184** | A33 | 5sh multicolored | 1.00 | 1.00 |
| | | *Nos. 181-184 (4)* | 2.05 | 2.05 |

International Year of the Disabled.

Longonot Earth Station Complex — A34

**1981, Apr. 4 Litho. *Perf. 14x14½***

185 A34 50c shown .30 .30
186 A34 2sh Intelsat V .40 .40
187 A34 3sh Longonot I .50 .50
188 A34 5sh Longonot II .85 .85
*Nos. 185-188 (4)* 2.05 2.05

Conference Center, OAU Flag — A35

18th Organization for African Unity Conference, Nairobi: 1sh, Map of Africa showing Panaftel earth stations. 3sh, Parliament Building, Nairobi. 5sh, Jomo Kenyatta Intl. Airport. 10sh, OAU flag.

**1981, June 24 Wmk. 373 *Perf. 13½***

189 A35 50c multicolored .25 .25
190 A35 1sh multicolored .25 .25
191 A35 3sh multicolored .55 .55
192 A35 5sh multicolored .70 .70
193 A35 10sh multicolored 1.40 1.40
*a.* Souvenir sheet of 1, perf. 14½ 2.25 2.25
*Nos. 189-193 (5)* 3.15 3.15

St. Paul's Cathedral — A36

50c, Charles, Pres. arap Moi. 5sh, Britannia. 10sh, Charles.
25sh, Couple.

**1981, July 29 Litho. *Perf. 14, 12***

194 A36 50c multicolored .25 .25
195 A36 3sh shown .25 .25
196 A36 5sh multicolored .25 .30
197 A36 10sh multicolored .25 *.60*
*Nos. 194-197 (4)* 1.00 1.40

**Souvenir Sheet**

198 A36 25sh multicolored 1.50 1.50

Royal Wedding.
Perf. 12 comes from minisheets of 5 + label. Value, set of 4 sheets $7.50.

Reticulated Giraffe — A37

**1981, Aug. 31 Litho. *Perf. 14½***

199 A37 50c shown .30 .30
200 A37 2sh Bongo .40 .40
201 A37 5sh Roan antelope .90 .90
202 A37 10sh Mangabey 2.60 2.60
*Nos. 199-202 (4)* 4.20 4.20

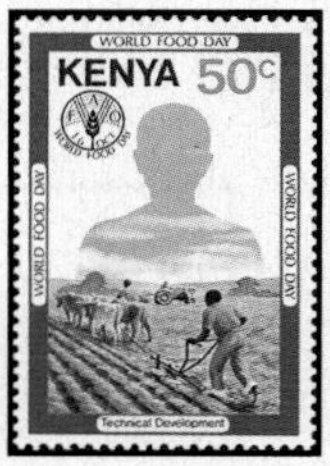


World Food Day — A38

**1981, Oct. 16 Litho. *Perf. 14***

203 A38 50c Plowing .25 .25
204 A38 1sh Rice field .25 .25
205 A38 2sh Irrigation .40 .40
206 A38 5sh Cattle .90 .90
*Nos. 203-206 (4)* 1.80 1.80

Ceremonial Tribal Costumes A39

***Perf. 14½x13½***

**1981, Dec. 18 Litho.**

207 A39 50c Kamba .45 .25
208 A39 1sh Turkana .55 .25
209 A39 2sh Giriama 1.25 .80
210 A39 3sh Masai 1.75 *2.25*
211 A39 5sh Luo 2.00 *4.00*
*Nos. 207-211 (5)* 6.00 7.55

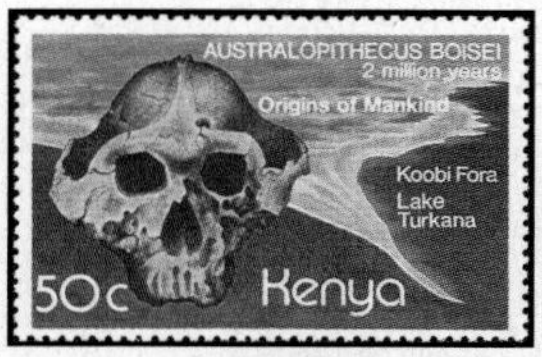


Australopithecus Boisei — A40

2sh, Homo erectus. 3sh, Homo habilis. 5sh, Proconsul africanus.

**1982, Jan. 16 Litho. *Perf. 14***

212 A40 50c shown 1.75 .40
213 A40 2sh multicolored 2.75 1.50
214 A40 3sh multicolored 3.00 *3.50*
215 A40 5sh multicolored 3.50 *5.00*
*Nos. 212-215 (4)* 11.00 *10.40*

Scouting Year A41

No. 216, Tree planting. No. 217, Paying homage. No. 218, Be Prepared. No. 219, Intl. friendship. No. 220, Helping disabled. No. 221, Community service. No. 222, Paxtu Cottage. No. 223, Lady Baden-Powell.

**1982, June 2 Litho. *Perf. 14½***

216 A41 70c multicolored .50 .50
217 A41 70c multicolored .50 .50
*a.* Pair, #216-217 1.25 1.25
218 A41 3.50sh multicolored 1.25 1.25
219 A41 3.50sh multicolored 1.25 1.25
*a.* Pair, #218-219 3.00 3.00
220 A41 5sh multicolored 1.60 1.60
221 A41 5sh multicolored 1.60 1.60
*a.* Pair, #220-221 4.50 4.50
222 A41 6.50sh multicolored 2.25 2.25
223 A41 6.50sh multicolored 2.25 2.25
*a.* Pair, #222-223 6.25 6.25
*Nos. 216-223 (8)* 11.20 11.20

**Souvenir Sheet**

224 Sheet of 4 6.00 6.00
*a.* A41 70c like #216 .25 .25
*b.* A41 3.50sh like #218 1.00 1.00
*c.* A41 5sh like #220 1.50 1.50
*d.* A41 6.50sh like #222 2.00 2.00

1982 World Cup — A42

Various soccer players on world map.

**1982, July 5 Litho. *Perf. 12½***

225 A42 70c multicolored 1.25 .50
226 A42 3.50sh multicolored 2.75 2.50
227 A42 5sh multicolored 3.25 4.25
228 A42 10sh multicolored 4.75 *6.50*
*Nos. 225-228 (4)* 12.00 13.75

**Souvenir Sheet**

***Perf. 13½x14***

229 A42 20sh multicolored 6.00 6.00

A43

**1982, Sept. 28 Litho. *Perf. 14½***

230 A43 70c Cattle judging .70 .25
231 A43 2.50sh Farm machinery 1.25 1.25
232 A43 3.50sh Musical ride 2.00 2.00
233 A43 6.50sh Emblem 3.00 *4.00*
*Nos. 230-233 (4)* 6.95 7.50

Agricultural Society, 80th anniv.

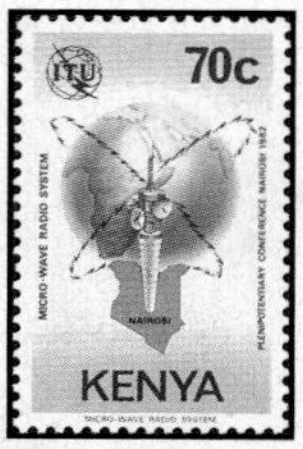


A44

70c, Microwave radio system. 3.50sh, Ship-to-shore communication. 5sh, Rural telecommunication. 6.50sh, Emblem.

**1982, Oct. 27 Photo. *Perf. 11½***
**Granite Paper**

234 A44 70c multicolored .50 .25
235 A44 3.50sh multicolored 1.75 1.75
236 A44 5sh multicolored 2.25 2.25
237 A44 6.50sh multicolored 3.00 3.00
*Nos. 234-237 (4)* 7.50 7.25

ITU Plenipotentiaries Conf., Nairobi, Sept.

5th Anniv. of Kenya Ports Authority A45

70c, Container cranes. 2sh, Cranes, diff. 3.50sh, Cranes, diff. 5sh, Mombasa Harbor map.

**1983, Jan. 20 Litho. *Perf. 14***

238 A45 70c multicolored .75 .25
239 A45 2sh multicolored 1.75 1.60
240 A45 3.50sh multicolored 2.50 2.50
241 A45 5sh multicolored 3.25 3.25
*a.* Souvenir sheet of 4, #238-241 9.00 9.00
*Nos. 238-241 (4)* 8.25 7.60

**No. 104 Surcharged**

**1983, Jan. Photo. *Perf. 14½x14***

242 A15 70c on 80c multicolored 2.00 2.00

A45a

70c, Coffee picking, vert. 2sh, Pres. arap Moi, vert. 5sh, Globe. 10sh, Masai dance.

**1983, Mar. 14 Litho. *Perf. 14½***

243 A45a 70c multicolored .25 .25
244 A45a 2sh multicolored .25 .25
245 A45a 5sh multicolored .40 .40
246 A45a 10sh multicolored .85 .85
*Nos. 243-246 (4)* 1.75 1.75

Commonwealth Day.

Dichrostachys Cinerea A46

Dombeya Burgessiae A47

20c, Rhamphicarpa montana. 30c, Barleria eranthemoides. 40c, Commelina. 50c, Canarina abyssinica. 70c, Aspilia mossambicensis. 1sh, Dombeya burgessiae. 1.50sh, Lantana trifolia. 2sh, Adenium obesum. 2.50sh, Terminalia orbicularis. 3.50sh, Ceropegia ballyana. 5sh, Ruttya fruticosa. 10sh, Pentanisia ouranogyne. 20sh, Brillantaisia nyanzarum. 40sh, Crotalaria axillaris.

***Perf. 14½x14, 14x14½***

**1983, Feb. 15 Photo.**

247 A46 10c shown .50 .40
248 A46 20c multicolored .70 .40
249 A46 30c multicolored .70 .40
250 A46 40c multicolored .70 .40
251 A46 50c multicolored .70 .30
252 A46 70c multicolored .80 .25
253 A47 1sh multicolored .90 .25
254 A47 1.50sh multicolored 2.00 .65
255 A47 2sh multicolored 2.00 .65
256 A47 2.50sh multicolored 2.25 .65
257 A47 3.50sh multicolored 2.00 1.60
258 A47 5sh multicolored 1.60 1.50
259 A47 10sh multicolored 1.60 1.50
260 A47 20sh multicolored 1.75 *2.75*
261 A47 40sh multicolored 2.75 *8.00*
*Nos. 247-261 (15)* 20.95 *19.70*

See Nos. 350-354.

30th Anniv. of Customs Cooperation Council — A48

70c, Parcel check. 2.50sh, Headquarters, Mombasa. 3.50sh, Headquarters, Brussels. 10sh, Patrol boat.

**1983, May 11 Litho. *Perf. 14½***

262 A48 70c multicolored .30 .25
263 A48 2.50sh multicolored .65 .30
264 A48 3.50sh multicolored .75 .40
265 A48 10sh multicolored 2.50 2.50
*Nos. 262-265 (4)* 4.20 3.45

World Communications Year — A49

70c, Satellite, dish antenna, vert. 2.50sh, Mailbox, birthday card, telephone, vert. 3.50sh, Jet, ship. 5sh, Railroad bridge, highway.

**1983, July 4 Litho. *Perf. 14½***

266 A49 70c multicolored .65 .25
267 A49 2.50sh multicolored 1.50 1.50
268 A49 3.50sh multicolored 2.25 2.25
269 A49 5sh multicolored 2.50 2.50
*Nos. 266-269 (4)* 6.90 6.50

Intl. Maritime Organization, 25th Anniv. — A50

70c, Kilindini Harbor. 2.50sh, Life preserver. 3.50sh, Mombasa Container Terminal. 10sh, Marine Park.

**1983, Sept. 22 Litho. *Perf. 14½***

| | | | | | |
|---|---|---|---|---|---|
| **270** | A50 | 70c | multicolored | 1.00 | .25 |
| **271** | A50 | 2.50sh | multicolored | 2.00 | 1.50 |
| **272** | A50 | 3.50sh | multicolored | 2.50 | 2.50 |
| **273** | A50 | 10sh | multicolored | 3.00 | *3.75* |
| | | | *Nos. 270-273 (4)* | 8.50 | 8.00 |

29th Commonwealth Parliamentary Conference — A51

2.50sh, Parliament Bldg., vert. 5sh, State Opening, vert.

**1983, Oct. 31 Litho. *Perf. 14***

| | | | | | |
|---|---|---|---|---|---|
| **274** | A51 | 70c | shown | .35 | .25 |
| **275** | A51 | 2.50sh | multicolored | 1.25 | 1.25 |
| **276** | A51 | 5sh | multicolored | 1.75 | *2.25* |
| *a.* | | | Souv. sheet of 3, #274-276 + label | 4.00 | 4.00 |
| | | | *Nos. 274-276 (3)* | 3.35 | 3.75 |

Royal Visit A52

70c, Flags. 3.50sh, Sagana State Lodge. 5sh, Tree Tops Hotel. 10sh, Elizabeth II and Daniel arap Moi.

**1983, Nov. 10 Litho. *Perf. 14***

| | | | | | |
|---|---|---|---|---|---|
| **277** | A52 | 70c | multicolored | .60 | .25 |
| **278** | A52 | 3.50sh | multicolored | 2.00 | 1.50 |
| **279** | A52 | 5sh | multicolored | 2.25 | 2.25 |
| **280** | A52 | 10sh | multicolored | 3.50 | 4.50 |
| | | | *Nos. 277-280 (4)* | 8.35 | 8.50 |

**Souvenir Sheet**

| | | | | | |
|---|---|---|---|---|---|
| **281** | A52 | 25sh | multicolored | 6.25 | 6.25 |

No. 281 contains Nos. 277-280 without denominations showing simulated perforations.

President Daniel arap Moi, Monument — A53

2sh, Tree planting. 3.50sh, Map, flag, emblem. 5sh, School, milk program. 10sh, People, flag, banner.

**1983, Dec. 9 Litho. *Perf. 14½***

| | | | | | |
|---|---|---|---|---|---|
| **282** | A53 | 70c | shown | .25 | .25 |
| **283** | A53 | 2sh | multicolored | .25 | .25 |
| **284** | A53 | 3.50sh | multicolored | .35 | .35 |
| **285** | A53 | 5sh | multicolored | .55 | .55 |
| **286** | A53 | 10sh | multicolored | .95 | .95 |
| | | | *Nos. 282-286 (5)* | 2.35 | 2.35 |

**Souvenir Sheet**

***Imperf***

| | | | | | |
|---|---|---|---|---|---|
| **287** | A53 | 25sh | multicolored | 2.25 | 2.25 |

Independence, 20th Anniv. No. 287 contains Nos. 282, 284-286 without denominations.

Rare Local Birds — A54

70c, White-backed night heron. 2.50sh, Quail plover. 3.50sh, Heller's ground thrush. 5sh, Papyrus gonolek. 10sh, White-winged Apalis.

**1984, Feb. 6 Litho. *Perf. 14½x13½***

| | | | | | |
|---|---|---|---|---|---|
| **288** | A54 | 70c | multicolored | 2.00 | .40 |
| **289** | A54 | 2.50sh | multicolored | 2.50 | 2.50 |
| **290** | A54 | 3.50sh | multicolored | 3.75 | 3.75 |
| **291** | A54 | 5sh | multicolored | 4.50 | 4.50 |
| **292** | A54 | 10sh | multicolored | 5.75 | *6.75* |
| | | | *Nos. 288-292 (5)* | 18.50 | 17.90 |

Intl. Civil Aviation Org., 40th Anniv. A55

70c, Radar, vert. 2.50sh, Kenya School of Aviation. 3.50sh, Jet, Moi Intl. Airport. 5sh, Air traffic control center, vert.

**1984, Apr. 2 Litho. *Perf. 14***

| | | | | | |
|---|---|---|---|---|---|
| **293** | A55 | 70c | multicolored | .25 | .25 |
| **294** | A55 | 2.50sh | multicolored | .50 | .50 |
| **295** | A55 | 3.50sh | multicolored | .80 | .80 |
| **296** | A55 | 5sh | multicolored | 1.25 | 1.25 |
| | | | *Nos. 293-296 (4)* | 2.80 | 2.80 |

1984 Summer Olympics — A56

**1984, May 21 *Perf. 14½***

| | | | | | |
|---|---|---|---|---|---|
| **297** | A56 | 70c | Running | .40 | .40 |
| **298** | A56 | 2.50sh | Hurdles | .75 | .75 |
| **299** | A56 | 5sh | Boxing | 1.25 | 1.25 |
| **300** | A56 | 10sh | Field Hockey | 4.00 | 4.00 |
| | | | *Nos. 297-300 (4)* | 6.40 | 6.40 |

**Souvenir Sheet**

***Imperf***

| | | | | | |
|---|---|---|---|---|---|
| **301** | A56 | 25sh | Torch bearers | 5.00 | 5.00 |

No. 301 contains designs of Nos. 297-300.

Bookmobile — A57

70c, Emblem. 5sh, Adult library. 10sh, Children's library.

**1984, Aug. 10 Litho. *Perf. 14½***

| | | | | | |
|---|---|---|---|---|---|
| **302** | A57 | 70c | multicolored | .25 | .25 |
| **303** | A57 | 3.50sh | shown | .45 | .45 |
| **304** | A57 | 5sh | multicolored | .65 | .65 |
| **305** | A57 | 10sh | multicolored | .95 | .95 |
| | | | *Nos. 302-305 (4)* | 2.30 | 2.30 |

Intl. Fed. of Library Associations, 50th Conf.

Kenya Export Year (KEY) A58

**1984, Oct. 1 Litho. *Perf. 14***

| | | | | | |
|---|---|---|---|---|---|
| **306** | A58 | 70c | Emblem, vert. | .35 | .35 |
| **307** | A58 | 3.50sh | Airport | 1.75 | 1.75 |
| **308** | A58 | 5sh | Harbor, vert. | 2.75 | 2.75 |
| **309** | A58 | 10sh | Exports | 3.75 | 3.75 |
| | | | *Nos. 306-309 (4)* | 8.60 | 8.60 |

A59

70c, Doves, cross. 2.50sh, Doves, Hinduism symbol. 3.50sh, Doves, Sikhism symbol. 6.50sh, Doves, Islam symbol.

**1984, Aug. 23 Litho. *Perf. 14x14½***

| | | | | | |
|---|---|---|---|---|---|
| **310** | A59 | 70c | multicolored | .30 | .30 |
| **311** | A59 | 2.50sh | multicolored | 1.00 | 1.00 |
| **312** | A59 | 3.50sh | multicolored | 1.50 | 1.50 |
| **313** | A59 | 6.50sh | multicolored | 2.75 | 2.75 |
| | | | *Nos. 310-313 (4)* | 5.55 | 5.55 |

World Conference on Religion and Peace, Nairobi, Aug. 23-31, 1984.

Tribal Costumes A60

**1984, Nov. 5 Litho. *Perf. 14½x13½***

| | | | | | |
|---|---|---|---|---|---|
| **314** | A60 | 70c | Luhya | .75 | .30 |
| **315** | A60 | 2sh | Kikuyu | 2.00 | 1.75 |
| **316** | A60 | 3.50sh | Pokomo | 2.25 | 2.00 |
| **317** | A60 | 5sh | Nandi | 2.75 | 2.75 |
| **318** | A60 | 10sh | Rendile | 3.50 | *4.25* |
| | | | *Nos. 314-318 (5)* | 11.25 | 11.05 |

60th Anniv., World Chess Federation — A61

70c, Nyayo Stadium, knight. 2.50sh, Fort Jesus, rook. 3.50sh, National Monument, bishop. 5sh, Parliament, queen. 10sh, Nyayo Fountain, king.

**1984, Dec. 21 Litho. *Perf. 14½***

| | | | | | |
|---|---|---|---|---|---|
| **319** | A61 | 70c | multicolored | 1.75 | .50 |
| **320** | A61 | 2.50sh | multicolored | 2.50 | 1.75 |
| **321** | A61 | 3.50sh | multicolored | 3.00 | 2.00 |
| **322** | A61 | 5sh | multicolored | 3.50 | 3.50 |
| **323** | A61 | 10sh | multicolored | 5.50 | *7.00* |
| | | | *Nos. 319-323 (5)* | 16.25 | 14.75 |

Energy Conservation — A62

70c, Stove, fire pit. 2sh, Solar panel. 3.50sh, Biogas tank. 10sh, Plowing field. 20sh, Energy conservation.

**1985, Jan. 22 Litho. *Perf. 13½***

| | | | | | |
|---|---|---|---|---|---|
| **324** | A62 | 70c | multicolored | .30 | .25 |
| **325** | A62 | 2sh | multicolored | .65 | .65 |
| **326** | A62 | 3.50sh | multicolored | .80 | .80 |
| **327** | A62 | 10sh | multicolored | 2.40 | 2.40 |
| **328** | A62 | 20sh | multicolored | 4.25 | 4.25 |
| | | | *Nos. 324-328 (5)* | 8.40 | 8.35 |

No. 328 contains Nos. 324-327 without denominations.

Girl Guides, 75th Anniv. A63

1sh, Girl Guide, handicrafts. 3sh, Community service. 5sh, Lady Baden-Powell, Kenyan leader. 7sh, Food project.

**1985, Mar. 27 Litho. *Perf. 13½***

| | | | | | |
|---|---|---|---|---|---|
| **329** | A63 | 1sh | multicolored | .75 | .25 |
| **330** | A63 | 3sh | multicolored | 1.50 | 1.00 |
| **331** | A63 | 5sh | multicolored | 2.00 | 2.00 |
| **332** | A63 | 7sh | multicolored | 3.00 | *4.00* |
| | | | *Nos. 329-332 (4)* | 7.25 | 7.25 |

Intl. Red Cross Day A64

**1985, May 8 *Perf. 14½***

| | | | | | |
|---|---|---|---|---|---|
| **333** | A64 | 1sh | Emblem | .75 | .25 |
| **334** | A64 | 4sh | First Aid | 2.25 | 2.25 |
| **335** | A64 | 5sh | Blood donation | 2.75 | 2.75 |
| **336** | A64 | 7sh | Famine relief, cornucopia | 3.75 | *4.25* |
| | | | *Nos. 333-336 (4)* | 9.50 | 9.50 |

A65

Diseases caused by microorganisms carried by insects.

**1985, June 25**

| | | | | | |
|---|---|---|---|---|---|
| **337** | A65 | 1sh | Malaria | 1.25 | .25 |
| **338** | A65 | 3sh | Leishmaniasis | 2.25 | 2.25 |
| **339** | A65 | 5sh | Trypanosomiasis | 2.50 | 2.50 |
| **340** | A65 | 7sh | Babesiosis | 4.00 | *5.00* |
| | | | *Nos. 337-340 (4)* | 10.00 | 10.00 |

7th Intl. Congress on Protozoology, Nairobi, June 22-29.

UN Decade for Women — A66

1sh, Repairing water pipes. 3sh, Traditional food processing. 5sh, Basket weaving. 7sh, Dress making.

**1985, July 15**

| | | | | | |
|---|---|---|---|---|---|
| **341** | A66 | 1sh | multicolored | .35 | .25 |
| **342** | A66 | 3sh | multicolored | .85 | .70 |
| **343** | A66 | 5sh | multicolored | .95 | .95 |
| **344** | A66 | 7sh | multicolored | 1.50 | 1.50 |
| | | | *Nos. 341-344 (4)* | 3.65 | 3.40 |

43rd Intl. Eucharistic Congress, Nairobi, Aug. 11-18 — A67

1sh, The Last Supper. 3sh, Afro-Christian family. 5sh, Congress altar, Uhuru Park. 7sh, St. Peter Claver's Church.

25sh, Pope John Paul II.

**1985, Aug. 15** *Perf. 13½*

| | | | | |
|---|---|---|---|---|
| **345** A67 | 1sh multicolored | .70 | .30 |
| **346** A67 | 3sh multicolored | 2.00 | 1.50 |
| **347** A67 | 5sh multicolored | 2.25 | 2.25 |
| **348** A67 | 7sh multicolored | 2.50 | *3.25* |
| | *Nos. 345-348 (4)* | 7.45 | 7.30 |

**Souvenir Sheet**

**349** A67 25sh multicolored 8.50 8.50

**Flower Types of 1983**

1sh, Dombeya burgessiae. 3sh, Calotropis procera. 4sh, Momordica foetida. 7sh, Oncoba spinosa.

**1985 Photo.** *Perf. 14½x14, 14½*

| | | | |
|---|---|---|---|
| **350** A46 | 80c like #250 | 3.00 | *4.00* |
| **351** A46 | 1sh multicolored | 3.00 | .80 |
| **352** A47 | 3sh multicolored | 9.00 | 8.00 |
| **353** A47 | 4sh multicolored | 3.00 | *6.00* |
| **354** A47 | 7sh multicolored | 4.00 | *7.50* |
| | *Nos. 350-354 (5)* | 22.00 | *26.30* |

Endangered Wildlife — A68

1sh, Diceros bicornis. 3sh, Acinonyx jubatus. 5sh, Cercopithecus neglectus. 10sh, Equus greyvi. 25sh, Hunter pursuing game.

**1985, Dec. 10 Litho.** *Perf. 14½*

| | | | |
|---|---|---|---|
| **355** A68 | 1sh multicolored | 2.00 | .50 |
| **356** A68 | 3sh multicolored | 2.25 | 2.00 |
| **357** A68 | 5sh multicolored | 2.75 | 2.75 |
| **358** A68 | 10sh multicolored | 5.25 | *6.50* |
| | *Nos. 355-358 (4)* | 12.25 | 11.75 |

**Size: 130x122mm**

***Imperf***

**359** A68 25sh multicolored 9.50 9.50

Trees A69

1sh, Borassus aethiopum. 3sh, Acacia xanthophloea. 5sh, Ficus natalensis. 7sh, Spathodea nilotica. 25sh, Glade.

**1986, Jan. 24** *Perf. 14½*

| | | | |
|---|---|---|---|
| **360** A69 | 1sh multicolored | 1.40 | .25 |
| **361** A69 | 3sh multicolored | 3.50 | 2.75 |
| **362** A69 | 5sh multicolored | 4.75 | 4.75 |
| **363** A69 | 7sh multicolored | 6.75 | 6.75 |
| | *Nos. 360-363 (4)* | 16.40 | 14.50 |

**Size: 117x97mm**

***Imperf***

**364** A69 25sh multicolored 6.50 6.50

Intl. Peace Year — A70

1sh, Dove, UN emblem. 3sh, UN General Assembly, horiz. 7sh, Mushroom cloud. 10sh, Isaiah 2:4, horiz.

**1986, Apr. 17** *Perf. 14½*

| | | | |
|---|---|---|---|
| **365** A70 | 1sh multicolored | .55 | .55 |
| **366** A70 | 3sh multicolored | 1.25 | 1.25 |
| **367** A70 | 7sh multicolored | 2.40 | 2.40 |
| **368** A70 | 10sh multicolored | 3.75 | 3.75 |
| | *Nos. 365-368 (4)* | 7.95 | 7.95 |

1986 World Cup Soccer Championships, Mexico — A71

**1986, May 9**

| | | | |
|---|---|---|---|
| **369** A71 | 1sh Dribbling | 1.10 | .55 |
| **370** A71 | 3sh Penalty shot | 2.25 | 1.10 |
| **371** A71 | 5sh Tackling | 3.50 | 2.25 |
| **372** A71 | 7sh Champions | 4.50 | 4.50 |
| **373** A71 | 10sh Heading the ball | 5.75 | 5.75 |
| | *Nos. 369-373 (5)* | 17.10 | 14.15 |

**Size: 110x86mm**

***Imperf***

**374** A71 30sh Harambee Stars 6.50 6.50

EXPO '86, Vancouver — A72

1sh, Rural post office. 3sh, Container depot, Embakasi. 5sh, Plane landing. 7sh, Shipping exports. 10sh, Goods transport.

**1986, June 11** *Perf. 13½x13*

| | | | |
|---|---|---|---|
| **375** A72 | 1sh multicolored | 1.25 | .60 |
| **376** A72 | 3sh multicolored | 2.40 | 1.25 |
| **377** A72 | 5sh multicolored | 3.75 | 2.40 |
| **378** A72 | 7sh multicolored | 4.75 | 4.75 |
| **379** A72 | 10sh multicolored | 6.25 | 6.25 |
| | *Nos. 375-379 (5)* | 18.40 | 15.25 |

TELECOM '86, Nairobi, Sept. 16-23 — A73

1sh, Telephone-computer links. 3sh, Telephones, 1876-1986. 5sh, Satellite communications. 7sh, Switchboards.

**1986, Sept. 16 Litho.** *Perf. 14½*

| | | | |
|---|---|---|---|
| **380** A73 | 1sh multicolored | .30 | .30 |
| **381** A73 | 3sh multicolored | 1.25 | 1.25 |
| **382** A73 | 5sh multicolored | 2.10 | 2.10 |
| **383** A73 | 7sh multicolored | 3.50 | 3.50 |
| | *Nos. 380-383 (4)* | 7.15 | 7.15 |

A74

Dhows (Ships) — A75

**1986, Oct. 30 Litho.** *Perf. 14½*

| | | | |
|---|---|---|---|
| **384** A74 | 1sh Mashua | .90 | .25 |
| **385** A74 | 3sh Mtepe | 2.25 | 1.50 |
| **386** A74 | 5sh Dau La Mwao | 3.25 | 3.00 |
| **387** A74 | 10sh Jahazi | 6.75 | 6.75 |
| | *Nos. 384-387 (4)* | 13.15 | 11.50 |

**Souvenir Sheet**

**388** A75 25sh Lamu, map 8.00 8.00

Christmas A76

**1986, Dec. 5** *Perf. 12*

| | | | |
|---|---|---|---|
| **389** A76 | 1sh Nativity, vert. | .35 | .25 |
| **390** A76 | 3sh Shepherd boy, vert. | 1.75 | 1.75 |
| **391** A76 | 5sh Angel, map | 2.50 | 2.50 |
| **392** A76 | 7sh Magi | 3.75 | 3.75 |
| | *Nos. 389-392 (4)* | 8.35 | 8.25 |

UNICEF, 40th Anniv. — A77

Child Survival Campaign: 1sh, Universal immunization by 1990. 3sh, Food and nutrition. 4sh, Oral rehydration. 5sh, Family planning. 10sh, Literacy of women.

**1987, Jan. 6 Litho.** *Perf. 14½*

| | | | |
|---|---|---|---|
| **393** A77 | 1sh multicolored | .60 | .60 |
| **394** A77 | 3sh multicolored | 1.25 | 1.25 |
| **395** A77 | 4sh multicolored | 1.75 | 1.75 |
| **396** A77 | 5sh multicolored | 2.25 | 2.25 |
| **397** A77 | 10sh multicolored | 3.50 | 3.50 |
| | *Nos. 393-397 (5)* | 9.35 | 9.35 |

A78

Tourism — A79

**1987, Mar. 25 Litho.** *Perf. 14½*

| | | | |
|---|---|---|---|
| **398** A78 | 1sh Akamba carvers | .60 | .25 |
| **399** A78 | 3sh Beach | 3.25 | 2.00 |
| **400** A78 | 5sh Escarpment | 4.00 | 4.00 |
| **401** A78 | 7sh Pride of lions | 6.00 | 6.00 |
| | *Nos. 398-401 (4)* | 13.85 | 12.25 |

**Souvenir Sheet**

**402** A79 30sh Kenya geysers 14.00 14.00

Ceremonial Costumes A80

**1987, May 20** *Perf. 14½x13½*

| | | | |
|---|---|---|---|
| **403** A80 | 1sh Embu | 1.25 | .60 |
| **404** A80 | 3sh Kisii | 2.75 | 1.40 |
| **405** A80 | 5sh Samburu | 4.25 | 2.40 |
| **406** A80 | 7sh Taita | 4.75 | 4.75 |
| **407** A80 | 10sh Boran | 5.00 | 5.00 |
| | *Nos. 403-407 (5)* | 18.00 | 14.15 |

See Nos. 505-509.

Posts & Telecommunications Corp., 10th Anniv. — A81

1sh, Telecommunications satellite. 3sh, Rural post office, Kajiado. 4sh, Athletics. 5sh, Rural communication. 7sh, Speedpost.
25sh, Natl. Flag.

**1987, July 1 Litho.** *Perf. 13½*

| | | | |
|---|---|---|---|
| **408** A81 | 1sh multicolored | .75 | .30 |
| **409** A81 | 3sh multicolored | 1.75 | 1.75 |
| **410** A81 | 4sh multicolored | 2.25 | 2.25 |
| **411** A81 | 5sh multicolored | 2.40 | 2.40 |
| **412** A81 | 7sh multicolored | 3.25 | 3.25 |
| | *Nos. 408-412 (5)* | 10.40 | 9.95 |

**Souvenir Sheet**

**413** A81 25sh multicolored 4.50 4.50

A82

1sh, Volleyball. 3sh, Cycling. 4sh, Boxing. 5sh, Swimming. 7sh, Steeple chase.
30sh, Kasarani Sports Complex.

**1987, Aug. 5** *Perf. 14½x14*

| | | | |
|---|---|---|---|
| **414** A82 | 1sh multicolored | .25 | .25 |
| **415** A82 | 3sh multicolored | .55 | .55 |
| **416** A82 | 4sh multicolored | .75 | .75 |
| **417** A82 | 5sh multicolored | .90 | .90 |
| **418** A82 | 7sh multicolored | 1.25 | 1.25 |
| | *Nos. 414-418 (5)* | 3.70 | 3.70 |

**Souvenir Sheet**

***Perf. 14x14½***

**419** A82 30sh multicolored 5.00 5.00

4th All Africa Games, Nairobi, Aug. 1-12. Nos. 414-418, vert.

A83

Medicinal herbs: 1sh, Aloe volkensii. 3sh, Cassia didymobotrya. 5sh, Erythrina abyssinica. 7sh, Adenium obesum. 10sh, Herbalist's clinic.

**1987, Oct. 27 Litho.** *Perf. 13½x14*

| | | | |
|---|---|---|---|
| **420** A83 | 1sh multicolored | 1.10 | .65 |
| **421** A83 | 3sh multicolored | 2.25 | 1.50 |
| **422** A83 | 5sh multicolored | 3.00 | 2.40 |
| **423** A83 | 7sh multicolored | 3.75 | 3.75 |
| **424** A83 | 10sh multicolored | 5.00 | 5.00 |
| | *Nos. 420-424 (5)* | 15.10 | 13.30 |

Butterflies — A84

10c, Cyrestis camillus. 20c, Iolaus sidus. 40c, Vanessa cardui. 50c, Colotis euippe omphale. 70c, Precis westermanni. 80c, Colias electo. 1sh, Eronia leda. 1.50sh, Papilio dardanus planemoides. 2sh, Papilio rex. 2.50sh, Colotis phisadia. 3sh, Papilio desmondi teita. 3.50sh, Papilio demodocus. 4sh, Papilio phorcas. 5sh, Charaxes druceanus teita. 7sh, Cymothoe teita. 10sh,

Charaxes zoolina. 20sh, Papilio dardanus. 40sh, Charaxes cithaeron kennethi.

**1988-90 Photo. *Perf. 15x14***

| | | | | |
|---|---|---|---|---|
| **424A** | A84 | 10c multicolored | 1.25 | 1.25 |
| **425** | A84 | 20c multicolored | .35 | .40 |
| **426** | A84 | 40c multicolored | .50 | .40 |
| **427** | A84 | 50c multicolored | .50 | .40 |
| **428** | A84 | 70c multicolored | .50 | .40 |
| **429** | A84 | 80c multicolored | .50 | .40 |
| **430** | A84 | 1sh multicolored | .50 | .30 |
| **430A** | A84 | 1.50sh multicolored | 5.00 | 1.25 |

**Size: 25x41mm**

***Perf. 14½***

| | | | | |
|---|---|---|---|---|
| **431** | A84 | 2sh multicolored | .75 | .95 |
| **432** | A84 | 2.50sh multicolored | .80 | .95 |
| **433** | A84 | 3sh multicolored | .80 | .95 |
| **434** | A84 | 3.50sh multicolored | .85 | .95 |
| **435** | A84 | 4sh multicolored | .90 | *1.75* |
| **436** | A84 | 5sh multicolored | 1.25 | .70 |
| **437** | A84 | 7sh multicolored | 1.50 | *2.50* |
| **438** | A84 | 10sh multicolored | 2.50 | 1.75 |
| **439** | A84 | 20sh multicolored | 4.00 | *3.50* |
| **440** | A84 | 40sh multicolored | 7.25 | *8.00* |
| | | *Nos. 424A-440 (18)* | 29.70 | 26.80 |

Issued: 10c, 9/1/89; 1.50sh, 5/18/90; others, 2/14/88.

Game Lodges A85

1sh, Samburu. 3sh, Naro Moru River. 4sh, Mara Serena. 5sh, Voi Safari. 7sh, Kilimanjaro Buffalo Lodge. 10sh, Meru Mulika.

**1988, May 31 Litho. *Perf. 14½***

| | | | | |
|---|---|---|---|---|
| **441** | A85 | 1sh multicolored | .75 | .35 |
| **442** | A85 | 3sh multicolored | 1.10 | 1.10 |
| **443** | A85 | 4sh multicolored | 1.75 | 1.75 |
| **444** | A85 | 5sh multicolored | 1.90 | 1.90 |
| **445** | A85 | 7sh multicolored | 2.25 | 2.25 |
| **446** | A85 | 10sh multicolored | 2.75 | 2.75 |
| | | *Nos. 441-446 (6)* | 10.50 | 10.10 |

World Expo '88, Brisbane A86

EXPO '88 and Australia bicentennial emblems plus: 1sh, Stadium, site of the 1982 Commonwealth Games, and runners. 3sh, Flying Doctor Service aircraft. 4sh, HMS Sirius, a 19th cent. immigrant ship. 5sh, Ostrich and emu. 7sh, Pres. Daniel arap Moi, Queen Elizabeth II and Robert Hawke, prime minister of Australia. 30sh, Kenya Pavilion at EXPO '88.

**1988, June 10**

| | | | | |
|---|---|---|---|---|
| **447** | A86 | 1sh multicolored | .60 | .60 |
| **448** | A86 | 3sh multicolored | 1.75 | 1.75 |
| **449** | A86 | 4sh multicolored | 3.00 | 3.00 |
| **450** | A86 | 5sh multicolored | 4.00 | 4.00 |
| **451** | A86 | 7sh multicolored | 5.00 | 5.00 |
| | | *Nos. 447-451 (5)* | 14.35 | 14.35 |

**Souvenir Sheet**

| | | | | |
|---|---|---|---|---|
| **452** | A86 | 30sh multicolored | 4.50 | 4.50 |

World Health Organization, 40th Anniv. — A87

**1988, July 1 Litho. *Perf. 14½***

| | | | | |
|---|---|---|---|---|
| **453** | A87 | 1sh shown | .35 | .35 |
| **454** | A87 | 3sh Nutrition | 1.40 | 1.40 |
| **455** | A87 | 5sh Immunization | 2.50 | 2.50 |
| **456** | A87 | 7sh Water supply | 3.75 | 3.75 |
| | | *Nos. 453-456 (4)* | 8.00 | 8.00 |

1988 Summer Olympics, Seoul — A88

**1988, Aug. 1 Litho. *Perf. 14½x14***

| | | | | |
|---|---|---|---|---|
| **457** | A88 | 1sh Handball | .50 | .25 |
| **458** | A88 | 3sh Judo | 1.00 | .80 |
| **459** | A88 | 5sh Weight lifting | 1.50 | 1.50 |
| **460** | A88 | 7sh Javelin | 2.00 | 2.00 |
| **461** | A88 | 10sh 400-meter relay | 2.50 | 2.50 |
| | | *Nos. 457-461 (5)* | 7.50 | 7.05 |

**Souvenir Sheet**

| | | | | |
|---|---|---|---|---|
| **462** | A88 | 30sh Tennis | 5.00 | 5.00 |

Utensils A89

1sh, Calabashes, vert. 3sh, Milk gourds, vert. 5sh, Cooking pots. 7sh, Winnowing trays. 10sh, Reed baskets.
25sh, Gourds, calabash, horn.

***Perf. 14½x14, 14x14½***

**1988, Sept. 20 Litho.**

| | | | | |
|---|---|---|---|---|
| **463** | A89 | 1sh multicolored | .55 | .25 |
| **464** | A89 | 3sh multicolored | 1.10 | .65 |
| **465** | A89 | 5sh multicolored | 1.50 | 1.10 |
| **466** | A89 | 7sh multicolored | 1.90 | 1.90 |
| **467** | A89 | 10sh multicolored | 2.50 | 2.50 |
| | | *Nos. 463-467 (5)* | 7.55 | 6.40 |

**Souvenir Sheet**

| | | | | |
|---|---|---|---|---|
| **468** | A89 | 25sh multicolored | 4.50 | 4.50 |

10-Year Presidency of Daniel arap Moi — A90

Designs: 1sh, Swearing-in ceremony, 1978. 3sh, Promoting soil conservation. 3.50sh, Public transportation (bus), Nairobi. 4sh, Jua Kali artisans at market. 5sh, Moi University, Eldoret, established in 1985. 7sh, Hospital ward expansion. 10sh, British Prime Minister Margaret Thatcher and Pres. Moi inaugurating the Kapsabet Telephone Exchange, Jan. 6, 1988.

**1988, Oct. 13 Litho. *Perf. 13½x14½***

| | | | | |
|---|---|---|---|---|
| **469** | A90 | 1sh multicolored | .70 | .70 |
| **470** | A90 | 3sh multicolored | 1.75 | 1.75 |
| **471** | A90 | 3.50sh multicolored | 2.00 | 2.00 |
| **472** | A90 | 4sh multicolored | 2.25 | 2.25 |
| **473** | A90 | 5sh multicolored | 2.75 | 2.75 |
| **474** | A90 | 7sh multicolored | 3.50 | 3.50 |
| **475** | A90 | 10sh multicolored | 5.50 | 5.50 |
| | | *Nos. 469-475 (7)* | 18.45 | 18.45 |

Independence, 25th Anniv. — A91

1sh, Natl. flag. 3sh, Coffee picking. 5sh, Model of postal headquarters. 7sh, Harambee Star Airbus A310-300. 10sh, Locomotive 9401.

**1988, Dec. 9 Litho. *Perf. 11½***

| | | | | |
|---|---|---|---|---|
| **476** | A91 | 1sh multicolored | .35 | .35 |
| **477** | A91 | 3sh multicolored | 1.90 | 1.90 |
| **478** | A91 | 5sh multicolored | 3.25 | 3.25 |
| **479** | A91 | 7sh multicolored | 4.75 | 4.75 |
| **480** | A91 | 10sh multicolored | 6.50 | 6.50 |
| | | *Nos. 476-480 (5)* | 16.75 | 16.75 |

Natl. Monuments — A92

1.20sh, Gedi Ruins, Malindi. 3.40sh, Vasco Da Gama Pillar, Malindi, vert. 4.40sh, Ishiakani Monument, Kiunga. 5.50sh, Ft. Jesus, Mombasa. 7.70sh, She Burnan Omwe, Lamu, vert.

**1989, Mar. 15 Litho. *Perf. 14½***

| | | | | |
|---|---|---|---|---|
| **481** | A92 | 1.20sh multicolored | .40 | .40 |
| **482** | A92 | 3.40sh multicolored | 1.00 | 1.00 |
| **483** | A92 | 4.40sh multicolored | 2.00 | 2.00 |
| **484** | A92 | 5.50sh multicolored | 2.50 | 2.50 |
| **485** | A92 | 7.70sh multicolored | 3.00 | 3.00 |
| | | *Nos. 481-485 (5)* | 8.90 | 8.90 |

Red Cross, 125th Anniv. A93

1.20sh, Anniv. and natl. soc. emblems. 3.40sh, First aid. 4.40sh, Disaster relief. 5.50sh, Jean-Henri Dunant. 7.70sh, Blood donation.

**1989, May 8 Litho. *Perf. 14x13½***

| | | | | |
|---|---|---|---|---|
| **486** | A93 | 1.20sh multicolored | .35 | .35 |
| **487** | A93 | 3.40sh multicolored | 1.25 | 1.25 |
| **488** | A93 | 4.40sh multicolored | 1.75 | 1.75 |
| **489** | A93 | 5.50sh multicolored | 2.40 | 2.40 |
| **490** | A93 | 7.70sh multicolored | 3.75 | 3.75 |
| | | *Nos. 486-490 (5)* | 9.50 | 9.50 |

World Wildlife Fund — A94

Giraffes, Giraffa Camelopardalis Reticulata.

**1989, July 12 Litho. *Perf. 14½***

| | | | | |
|---|---|---|---|---|
| **491** | A94 | 1.20sh multicolored | 2.50 | 2.25 |
| **492** | A94 | 3.40sh multicolored | 5.25 | 5.00 |
| **493** | A94 | 4.40sh multicolored | 6.00 | 6.00 |
| **494** | A94 | 5.50sh multicolored | 7.25 | *8.00* |
| | | *Nos. 491-494 (4)* | 21.00 | 21.25 |

**Size: 80x110mm**

***Imperf***

| | | | | |
|---|---|---|---|---|
| **495** | A94 | 30sh multicolored | 15.00 | 15.00 |

No. 495 contains four labels like Nos. 491-494, perf. 14½, without denominations or WWF emblem.

Mushrooms — A95

**1989, Sept. 6 Litho. *Perf. 14½***

| | | | | |
|---|---|---|---|---|
| **496** | A95 | 1.20sh Oyster | 2.40 | .65 |
| **497** | A95 | 3.40sh Chestnut | 3.50 | 2.40 |
| **498** | A95 | 4.40sh White button | 4.00 | 3.25 |
| **499** | A95 | 5.50sh Termite | 4.75 | 3.75 |
| **500** | A95 | 7.70sh Shiitake | 6.50 | 6.50 |
| | | *Nos. 496-500 (5)* | 21.15 | 16.55 |

Jawaharlal Nehru, 1st Prime Minister of Independent India — A96

1.20sh, Independence struggle. 3.40sh, Education. 5.50sh, Portrait. 7.70sh, Industry.

**1989, Nov. 9 Litho. *Perf. 13½x14***

| | | | | |
|---|---|---|---|---|
| **501** | A96 | 1.20sh multicolored | 2.00 | 1.50 |
| **502** | A96 | 3.40sh multicolored | 2.50 | 2.00 |
| **503** | A96 | 5.50sh multicolored | 4.50 | 4.50 |
| **504** | A96 | 7.70sh multicolored | 7.50 | 7.50 |
| | | *Nos. 501-504 (4)* | 16.50 | 15.50 |

**Costume Type of 1980**

**1989, Dec. 8 Litho. *Perf. 14½x13½***

| | | | | |
|---|---|---|---|---|
| **505** | A80 | 1.20sh Kipsigis | 1.25 | .45 |
| **506** | A80 | 3.40sh Rabai | 2.50 | 2.50 |
| **507** | A80 | 5.50sh Duruma | 3.25 | 2.40 |
| **508** | A80 | 7.70sh Kuria | 4.50 | 3.75 |
| **509** | A80 | 10sh Bajuni | 5.50 | 5.50 |
| | | *Nos. 505-509 (5)* | 17.00 | 14.60 |

Pan-African Postal Union, 10th Anniv. — A97

1.20sh, EMS Speedpost. 3.40sh, Mail runner. 5.50sh, Mandera P.O.. 7.70sh, EMS, diff., vert. 10sh, PAPU emblem, vert.

***Perf. 14x13½, 13½x14***

**1990, Jan. 31 Litho.**

| | | | | |
|---|---|---|---|---|
| **510** | A97 | 1.20sh multicolored | .30 | .30 |
| **511** | A97 | 3.40sh multicolored | .90 | .90 |
| **512** | A97 | 5.50sh multicolored | 1.10 | 1.10 |
| **513** | A97 | 7.70sh multicolored | 1.40 | 1.40 |
| **514** | A97 | 10sh multicolored | 1.75 | 1.75 |
| | | *Nos. 510-514 (5)* | 5.45 | 5.45 |

Soccer Trophies — A98

Designs:1.50sh, Moi Golden Cup. 4.50sh, East & Central Africa Challenge Cup. 6.50sh, East & Central Africa Club Championship Cup. 9sh, World Cup.

**1990, May 21 Litho. *Perf. 14½***

| | | | | |
|---|---|---|---|---|
| **515** | A98 | 1.50sh multicolored | .50 | .50 |
| **516** | A98 | 4.50sh multicolored | 3.00 | 3.00 |
| **517** | A98 | 6.50sh multicolored | 4.00 | 4.00 |
| **518** | A98 | 9sh multicolored | 5.00 | 5.00 |
| | | *Nos. 515-518 (4)* | 12.50 | 12.50 |

Penny Black 150th Anniv., Stamp World London '90 — A99

4.50sh, Great Britain No. 1. 6.50sh, Early British cancellations. 9sh, Main P.O.

**1990, Apr. 27 Litho. *Perf. 11½***

| | | | | |
|---|---|---|---|---|
| **519** | A99 | 1.50sh shown | .45 | .35 |
| **520** | A99 | 4.50sh multicolored | 1.60 | 1.60 |
| **521** | A99 | 6.50sh multicolored | 2.40 | 2.40 |
| **522** | A99 | 9sh multicolored | 3.50 | 3.50 |
| *a.* | | Souvenir sheet of 4, #519-522 | 8.50 | 8.50 |
| | | *Nos. 519-522 (4)* | 7.95 | 7.85 |

No. 522a sold for 30 shillings.

ITU, 125th Anniv. A100

Designs: 4.50sh, Telephone assembly. 6.50sh, ITU Anniv. emblem. 9sh, Telecommunications development.

**1990, July 12**

| | | | | | |
|---|---|---|---|---|---|
| 523 | A100 | 1.50sh | multicolored | .45 | .25 |
| 524 | A100 | 4.50sh | multicolored | .90 | .65 |
| 525 | A100 | 6.50sh | multicolored | 1.25 | 1.10 |
| 526 | A100 | 9sh | multicolored | 1.60 | 1.60 |
| | | | *Nos. 523-526 (4)* | 4.20 | 3.60 |

Common Design Types pictured following the introduction.

**Queen Mother, 90th Birthday**
Common Design Types

10sh, Queen Mother. 40sh, At garden party, 1947.

***Perf. 14x15***

**1990, Aug. 4 Litho. Wmk. 384**

| | | | | | |
|---|---|---|---|---|---|
| 527 | CD343 | 10sh | multicolored | 1.50 | 1.50 |

***Perf. 14½***

| | | | | | |
|---|---|---|---|---|---|
| 528 | CD344 | 40sh | multicolored | 5.50 | 5.50 |

Kenya African National Union (KANU), 50th Anniv. A101

1.50sh, KANU flag. 2.50sh, Nyayo Monument. 4.50sh, KICC Party Headquarters. 5sh, Jomo Kenyatta. 6.50sh, Daniel T. arap Moi. 9sh, KANU mass meeting. 10sh, Voters.

**1990, June 11**

| | | | | | |
|---|---|---|---|---|---|
| 529 | A101 | 1.50sh | multicolored | .35 | .25 |
| 530 | A101 | 2.50sh | multicolored | .40 | .35 |
| 531 | A101 | 4.50sh | multicolored | .85 | .85 |
| 532 | A101 | 5sh | multicolored | 1.00 | 1.00 |
| 533 | A101 | 6.50sh | multicolored | 1.10 | 1.10 |
| 534 | A101 | 9sh | multicolored | 1.75 | 1.75 |
| 535 | A101 | 10sh | multicolored | 1.75 | 1.75 |
| | | | *Nos. 529-535 (7)* | 7.20 | 7.05 |

Kenya Postage Stamps, Cent. — A102

Designs: 1.50sh, Kenya #431. 4.50sh, East Africa and Uganda Protectorates #2. 6.50sh, British East Africa #1. 9sh, Kenya and Uganda #25. 20sh, Kenya, Uganda, Tanzania #232.

**1990, Sept. 5 Litho. *Perf. 14x14½***

| | | | | | |
|---|---|---|---|---|---|
| 536 | A102 | 1.50sh | multicolored | 1.50 | .45 |
| 537 | A102 | 4.50sh | multicolored | 3.00 | 2.50 |
| 538 | A102 | 6.50sh | multicolored | 4.00 | 3.75 |
| 539 | A102 | 9sh | multicolored | 5.25 | 4.75 |
| 540 | A102 | 20sh | multicolored | 8.50 | 8.50 |
| | | | *Nos. 536-540 (5)* | 22.25 | 19.95 |

Intl. Literacy Year — A103

1.50sh, Adult literacy class. 4.50sh, Radio teaching program. 6.50sh, Technical training. 9sh, Literacy year emblem.

**1990, Nov. 30 Litho. *Perf. 13½x14***

| | | | | | |
|---|---|---|---|---|---|
| 541 | A103 | 1.50sh | multicolored | .65 | .65 |
| 542 | A103 | 4.50sh | multicolored | 1.60 | 1.60 |
| 543 | A103 | 6.50sh | multicolored | 2.25 | 2.25 |
| 544 | A103 | 9sh | multicolored | 3.50 | 3.50 |
| | | | *Nos. 541-544 (4)* | 8.00 | 8.00 |

1992 Summer Olympics, Barcelona — A106

**1991, Nov. 29 Litho. *Perf. 14x13½***

| | | | | | |
|---|---|---|---|---|---|
| 554 | A106 | 2sh | National flag | .45 | .45 |
| 555 | A106 | 6sh | Basketball | 1.90 | 1.90 |
| 556 | A106 | 7sh | Field hockey | 2.50 | 2.50 |
| 557 | A106 | 8.50sh | Table tennis | 3.00 | 3.00 |
| 558 | A106 | 11sh | Boxing | 4.50 | 4.50 |
| | | | *Nos. 554-558 (5)* | 12.35 | 12.35 |

Fight AIDS — A107

2sh, You too can be infected. 6sh, Has no cure. 8.50sh, Casual sex is unsafe. 11sh, Sterilize syringe before use.

**1991, Oct. 31 Litho. *Perf. 13½x14***

| | | | | | |
|---|---|---|---|---|---|
| 559 | A107 | 2sh | multicolored | 1.25 | .25 |
| 560 | A107 | 6sh | multicolored | 2.50 | 2.25 |
| 561 | A107 | 8.50sh | multicolored | 3.50 | 3.00 |
| 562 | A107 | 11sh | multicolored | 4.75 | 4.75 |
| | | | *Nos. 559-562 (4)* | 12.00 | 10.25 |

**Queen Elizabeth II's Accession to the Throne, 40th Anniv.**
Common Design Type

**1992, Feb. 6 Litho. *Perf. 14x13½***

| | | | | | |
|---|---|---|---|---|---|
| 563 | CD349 | 3sh | multicolored | .25 | .25 |
| 564 | CD349 | 8sh | multicolored | 1.10 | 1.10 |
| 565 | CD349 | 11sh | multicolored | 1.40 | 1.40 |
| 566 | CD349 | 14sh | multicolored | 1.60 | 1.60 |
| 567 | CD349 | 40sh | multicolored | 4.75 | 4.75 |
| | | | *Nos. 563-567 (5)* | 9.10 | 9.10 |

Wildlife — A108

**1992, May 8 *Perf. 14½***

| | | | | | |
|---|---|---|---|---|---|
| 568 | A108 | 3sh | Leopard | 2.00 | .35 |
| 569 | A108 | 8sh | Lion | 2.75 | 2.00 |
| 570 | A108 | 10sh | Elephant | 5.75 | 3.00 |
| 571 | A108 | 11sh | Buffalo | 3.50 | 3.00 |
| 572 | A108 | 14sh | Rhinoceros | 9.50 | 5.00 |
| | | | *Nos. 568-572 (5)* | 23.50 | 13.35 |

Vintage Cars A109

Designs: 3sh, Intl. Harvester S.S. motor truck, 1926. 8sh, Fiat 509, 1924. 10sh, "R" Hupmobile, 1923. 11sh, Chevrolet Box Body, 1928. 14sh, Bentley Parkward, 1934.

**1992, June 24 *Perf. 14½***

| | | | | | |
|---|---|---|---|---|---|
| 573 | A109 | 3sh | multicolored | 2.25 | .70 |
| 574 | A109 | 8sh | multicolored | 3.00 | 1.90 |
| 575 | A109 | 10sh | multicolored | 3.50 | 2.50 |
| 576 | A109 | 11sh | multicolored | 4.00 | 3.50 |
| 577 | A109 | 14sh | multicolored | 5.50 | 5.50 |
| | | | *Nos. 573-577 (5)* | 18.25 | 14.10 |

1992 Summer Olympics, Barcelona — A110

3sh, Runners. 8sh, Judo. 10sh, Women's volleyball. 11sh, 4x100-meter relay. 14sh, 10,000-meter run.

**1992, July 24 Litho. *Perf. 14½***

| | | | | | |
|---|---|---|---|---|---|
| 578 | A110 | 3sh | multicolored | .60 | .60 |
| 579 | A110 | 8sh | multicolored | 2.10 | 2.10 |
| 580 | A110 | 10sh | multicolored | 3.50 | 3.50 |
| 581 | A110 | 11sh | multicolored | 3.50 | 3.50 |
| 582 | A110 | 14sh | multicolored | 4.75 | 4.75 |
| | | | *Nos. 578-582 (5)* | 14.45 | 14.45 |

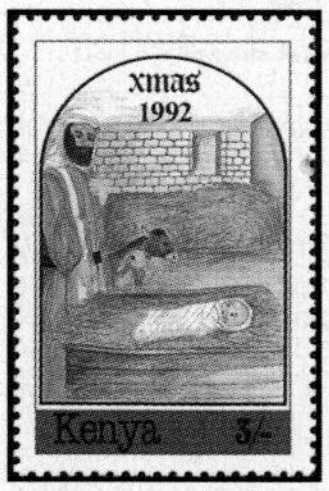


Christmas — A111

Designs: 3sh, Joseph, Jesus & animals in stable. 8sh, Mary holding Jesus in stable. 11sh, Map of Kenya, Christmas tree. 14sh, Adoration of the Magi.

**1992, Dec. 14 Litho. *Perf. 13½x14***

| | | | | | |
|---|---|---|---|---|---|
| 583 | A111 | 3sh | multicolored | .50 | .50 |
| 584 | A111 | 8sh | multicolored | 1.25 | 1.25 |
| 585 | A111 | 11sh | multicolored | 1.75 | 1.75 |
| 586 | A111 | 14sh | multicolored | 2.00 | 2.00 |
| | | | *Nos. 583-586 (4)* | 5.50 | 5.50 |

Lighthouses A112

Designs: 3sh, Asembo Bay, Lake Victoria. 8sh, Ras Serani, Mombasa. 11sh, Ras Serani, Mombasa, diff. 14sh, Gingira, Lake Victoria.

**1993, Jan. 25 *Perf. 14½***

| | | | | | |
|---|---|---|---|---|---|
| 587 | A112 | 3sh | multicolored | 2.75 | 1.10 |
| 588 | A112 | 8sh | multicolored | 4.75 | 3.25 |
| 589 | A112 | 11sh | multicolored | 6.00 | 5.25 |
| 590 | A112 | 14sh | multicolored | 8.00 | 8.00 |
| | | | *Nos. 587-590 (4)* | 21.50 | 17.60 |

Birds — A113

Designs: 50c, Superb starling. 1sh, Red and yellow barbet. 1.50sh, Ross's turaco. 3sh, Greater honeyguide. 5sh, African fish eagle. 6sh, Vulturine guineafowl. 7sh, Malachite kingfisher. 8sh, Speckled pigeon. 10sh, Cinnamon-chested bee-eater. 11sh, Scarlet-chested sunbird. 14sh, Reichenow's weaver. 50sh, Yellow-billed hornbill. 80sh, Lesser flamingo. 100sh, Hadada ibis.

**1993-99 Photo. *Perf. 15x14***
**Granite Paper**

| | | | | | |
|---|---|---|---|---|---|
| 594 | A113 | 50c | multi | .25 | .25 |
| 597 | A113 | 1sh | multi | .25 | .25 |
| 598 | A113 | 1.50sh | multi | .25 | .25 |
| 600 | A113 | 3sh | multi | .25 | .25 |
| 601 | A113 | 5sh | multi | .25 | .25 |
| 601A | A113 | 6sh | multi | *5.00* | 1.00 |
| 602 | A113 | 7sh | multi | .45 | .45 |
| 603 | A113 | 8sh | multi | .55 | .55 |
| 604 | A113 | 10sh | multi | .65 | .65 |
| 605 | A113 | 11sh | multi | .70 | .70 |
| 606 | A113 | 14sh | multi | .90 | .90 |

**Size: 25x42mm**

***Perf. 14½***

| | | | | | |
|---|---|---|---|---|---|
| 608 | A113 | 50sh | multi | 3.25 | 3.25 |
| 609 | A113 | 80sh | multi | 5.00 | 5.00 |
| 610 | A113 | 100sh | multi | 6.50 | 6.50 |
| | | | *Nos. 594-610 (14)* | 24.25 | 20.25 |

Issued: 1.50sh, 5sh, 2/14/94; 6sh, 1999; others, 2/22/93.

This is an expanding set. Numbers may change.

17th World Congress of Rehabilatation Intl. — A114

3sh, Health care, vert. 8sh, Recreation. 10sh, Vocational training. 11sh, Recreation & sports. 14sh, Emblem, vert.

**1993, July 1 Litho. *Perf. 14½***

| | | | | | |
|---|---|---|---|---|---|
| 611 | A114 | 3sh | multicolored | .90 | .25 |
| 612 | A114 | 8sh | multicolored | 1.40 | .75 |
| 613 | A114 | 10sh | multicolored | 1.75 | 1.75 |
| 614 | A114 | 11sh | multicolored | 1.75 | 1.75 |
| 615 | A114 | 14sh | multicolored | 2.10 | 2.10 |
| | | | *Nos. 611-615 (5)* | 7.90 | 6.60 |

Maendeleo ya Wanawake Organization, 42th Anniv. — A115

Designs: 3.50sh, Maendeleo House. 9sh, Planting trees. 11sh, Rural family planning services, vert. 12.50sh, Water nearer the people. 15.50sh, Maendeleo improved wood cookstove, vert.

***Perf. 14x13½, 13½x14***

**1994, Mar. 17 Litho.**

| | | | | | |
|---|---|---|---|---|---|
| 616 | A115 | 3.50sh | multicolored | 1.10 | .25 |
| 617 | A115 | 9sh | multicolored | 1.60 | .60 |
| 618 | A115 | 11sh | multicolored | 1.25 | 1.25 |
| 619 | A115 | 12.50sh | multicolored | 2.25 | 2.25 |
| 620 | A115 | 15.50sh | multicolored | 2.50 | 2.50 |
| | | | *Nos. 616-620 (5)* | 8.70 | 6.85 |

Orchids — A116

Designs: 3.50sh, Ansellia africana. 9sh, Aerangis lutecalba. 12.50sh, Polystachya bella. 15.50sh, Brachycorythis kalbreyeri. 20sh, Eulophia guineensis.

**1994, June 27 Litho. *Perf. 13½x14***

| | | | | | |
|---|---|---|---|---|---|
| 621 | A116 | 3.50sh | multicolored | 2.40 | .25 |
| 622 | A116 | 9sh | multicolored | 3.25 | 1.00 |
| 623 | A116 | 12.50sh | multicolored | 3.50 | 2.50 |
| 624 | A116 | 15.50sh | multicolored | 4.25 | 4.25 |
| 625 | A116 | 20sh | multicolored | 5.50 | 5.50 |
| | | | *Nos. 621-625 (5)* | 18.90 | 13.50 |

African Development Bank, 30th Anniv. — A117

**1994, Nov. 21 Litho. *Perf. 14½***

**626** A117 6sh KICC, Nairobi 1.25 .25
**627** A117 25sh Isinya, Kajiado 4.50 4.50

Intl. Year of the Family — A118

6sh, Family planning. 14.50sh, Health. 20sh, Education, horiz. 25sh, Emblem, horiz.

**1994, Dec. 22**

**628** A118 6sh multi 1.00 .25
**629** A118 14.50sh multi 3.50 1.50
**630** A118 20sh multi 4.00 4.00
**631** A118 25sh multi 4.00 4.00
*Nos. 628-631 (4)* 12.50 9.75

Rotary, 50th Anniv. — A119

Designs: 6sh, Paul P. Harris, founder. 14.50sh, Rotary Club of Mombasa. 17.50sh, Polio plus vaccine. 20sh, Water projects. 25sh, Emblem, motto.

**1994, Dec. 29 *Perf. 13½x14***

**632** A119 6sh multicolored .60 .25
**633** A119 14.50sh multicolored 1.60 .75
**634** A119 17.50sh multicolored 2.00 2.00
**635** A119 20sh multicolored 2.25 2.25
**636** A119 25sh multicolored 2.75 2.75
*Nos. 632-636 (5)* 9.20 8.00

SPCA — A120

**1995, Jan. 13 Litho. *Perf. 14½***

**637** A120 6sh Donkey .55 .25
**638** A120 14.50sh Cattle 1.50 .55
**639** A120 17.50sh Sheep 1.90 1.10
**640** A120 20sh Dog 2.10 2.10
**641** A120 25sh Cat 2.60 2.60
*Nos. 637-641 (5)* 8.65 6.60

Kenya Society for Prevention of Cruelty to Animals.

Golf — A121

6sh, Man in vest. 17.50sh, Woman. 20sh, Man in red shirt. 25sh, Golf club.

**1995, Feb. 28 Litho. *Perf. 14½***

**642** A121 6sh multicolored 1.10 .25
**643** A121 17.50sh multicolored 3.50 1.10
**644** A121 20sh multicolored 3.75 1.80
**645** A121 25sh multicolored 5.00 1.60
*Nos. 642-645 (4)* 13.35 4.75

Traditional Crafts — A122

6sh, Perfume containers. 14.50sh, Basketry. 17.50sh, Preservation pots. 20sh, Gourds. 25sh, Wooden containers.

**1995, Mar. 24 Litho. *Perf. 14x13½***

**646** A122 6sh multicolored .50 .25
**647** A122 14.50sh multicolored 1.00 .95
**648** A122 17.50sh multicolored 1.40 1.40
**649** A122 20sh multicolored 1.75 1.75
**650** A122 25sh multicolored 2.40 2.40
*Nos. 646-650 (5)* 7.05 6.75

UN, 50th Anniv. A123

Designs: 23sh, UN Headquarters, Nairobi. 26sh, People holding UN emblem. 32sh, UN Peacekeeper's helmet. 40sh, UN emblem.

**1995, Oct. 24 Litho. *Perf. 13½***

**651** A123 23sh multicolored 1.40 .70
**652** A123 26sh multicolored 1.50 .90
**653** A123 32sh multicolored 2.10 2.10
**654** A123 40sh multicolored 2.25 2.25
*Nos. 651-654 (4)* 7.25 5.95

ICIPE, 25th Anniv. — A124

**1995, Sept. 29 Litho. *Perf. 13½***

**655** A124 14sh Tse-tse fly .75 .35
**656** A124 26sh Tick 1.40 .90
**657** A124 32sh Wild silk moth 1.75 1.25
**658** A124 33sh Maize borer 1.90 1.90
**659** A124 40sh Locust 2.25 2.25
*Nos. 655-659 (5)* 8.05 6.65

FAO, 50th Anniv. — A125

14sh, Maize production. 28sh, Cattle rearing. 32sh, Poultry keeping. 33sh, Fishing. 40sh, Fruits.

**1995, Oct. 16**

**660** A125 14sh multicolored .90 .35
**661** A125 28sh multicolored 2.00 1.00
**662** A125 32sh multicolored 2.25 2.00
**663** A125 33sh multicolored 2.25 2.25
**664** A125 40sh multicolored 2.75 2.75
*Nos. 660-664 (5)* 10.15 8.35

### Miniature Sheets

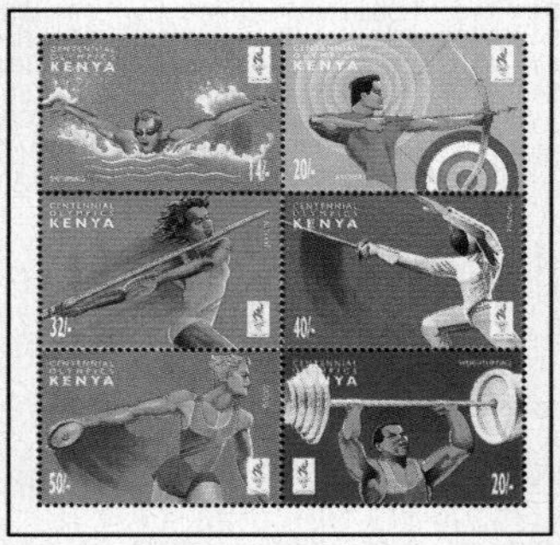


1996 Summer Olympics, Atlanta — A126

No. 665: a, 14sh, Swimming. b, 20sh, Archery. c, 32sh, Javelin. d, 40sh, Fencing. e, 50sh, Discus. f, 20sh, Weight lifting.

No. 666: a, Pole vault. b, Equestrian. c, Diving. d, Track e, Torch bearer. f, Hurdles. g, Kayak. h, Boxing. i, Gymnastics.

No. 667 — Medal winners: a, Greg Louganis, diving. b, Muhammed Ali, boxing. c, Nadia Comaneci, gymnastics. d, Daley Thompson, decathlon. e, Kipchoge "Kip" Keino, track and field. f, Kornelia Enders, swimming. g, Jackie Joyner-Kersee, track and field. h, Michael Jordan, basketball. i, Shun Fujimoto, gymnastics.

No. 668, 100sh, Torch bearer. No. 669, 100sh, Gold medalist.

**1996, Jan. 5 Litho. *Perf. 14***

**665** A126 Sheet of 6, #a.-f. 11.50 11.50
**666** A126 20sh Sheet of 9, #a.-i. 12.50 12.50
**667** A126 25sh Sheet of 9, #a.-i. 13.50 13.50

### Souvenir Sheets

**668-669** A126 Set of 2 11.00 11.00

World Tourism Organization, 20th Anniv. — A127

**1996, Jan. 31 Litho. *Perf. 13½***

**670** A127 6sh Lions .50 .25
**671** A127 14sh Mount Kenya 1.00 .35
**672** A127 20sh Water sports 1.50 .80
**673** A127 25sh Hippopotomus 2.00 2.00
**674** A127 40sh Culture 3.00 3.00
*Nos. 670-674 (5)* 8.00 6.40

***Perf. 13x13½***

**675** A127 50sh Giraffes, vert. 5.00 5.00

Wild Animals A128

No. 676, Water buck. No. 677, Rhinoceros. No. 678, Cheetah. No. 679, Oryx. No. 680, Reticulated giraffe. No. 681, Bongo.

### Booklet Stamps

**1996 *Perf. 13x13½***

**676** A128 20sh multicolored 1.40 1.10
**677** A128 20sh multicolored 1.40 1.10
**678** A128 20sh multicolored 1.40 1.10
**679** A128 20sh multicolored 1.40 1.10
**680** A128 20sh multicolored 1.40 1.10
**681** A128 20sh multicolored 1.40 1.10
*a.* Booklet pane of 6, #676-681 11.00
Complete booklet, 4 #681a 45.00

Nos. 676-681 appear in No. 681a in two different orders. Complete booklet contains 2 of each type of pane.

1996 Summer Olympic Games, Atlanta — A129

**1996, July 18 Litho. *Perf. 13½x14***

**682** A129 6sh Woman running .30 .30
**683** A129 14sh Steeple chase .60 .60
**684** A129 20sh Victory lap .90 .90
**685** A129 25sh Boxing 1.10 1.10
**686** A129 40sh Man running 1.90 1.90
*Nos. 682-686 (5)* 4.80 4.80

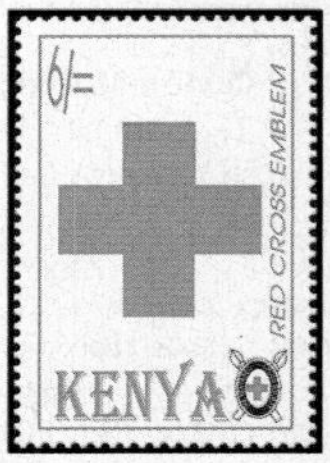


Red Cross — A130

6sh, Emblem. 14sh, Blood donation. 20sh, Immunization. 25sh, Refugees. 40sh, Clean environment.

**1996, Aug. 30 Litho. *Perf. 14***

**687** A130 6sh multicolored .40 .40
**688** A130 14sh multicolored .80 .80
**689** A130 20sh multicolored 1.25 1.25
**690** A130 25sh multicolored 1.50 1.50
**691** A130 40sh multicolored 2.50 2.50
*Nos. 687-691 (5)* 6.45 6.45

East African Wildlife Society — A131

**1996, Sept. 10 Litho. *Perf. 14½***

**693** A131 6sh Impala .45 .45
**694** A131 20sh Colobus monkey 1.60 1.60
**695** A131 25sh Elephant 2.00 2.00
**696** A131 40sh Black rhino 3.75 3.75
*Nos. 693-696 (4)* 7.80 7.80

Lions Club Intl. — A132

**1996, Oct. 31 Litho. *Perf. 13½***

**697** A132 6sh Logo .30 .30
**698** A132 14sh Eye camps .95 .95
**699** A132 20sh Wheel chair 1.50 1.50
**700** A132 25sh Ambulance 1.75 1.75
*Nos. 697-700 (4)* 4.50 4.50

COMESA (Common Market for Eastern and Southern Africa — A133

**1997, Jan. 15 Litho. *Perf. 13½x14***

**701** A133 6sh COMESA logo .25 .25
**702** A133 20sh Natl. flag 1.40 1.40

Fish of Lake Victoria A134

Haplochromis: No. 703, Orange rock hunter. No. 704, Chilotes. No. 705, Cinctus. No. 706, Nigricans.

**1997, Jan. 31 *Perf. 14x13½***

**703** A134 25sh multicolored *3.00 1.75*
**704** A134 25sh multicolored *3.00 1.75*
**705** A134 25sh multicolored *3.00 1.75*
**706** A134 25sh multicolored *3.00 1.75*
*Nos. 703-706 (4)* 12.00 *7.00*

World Wildlife Fund.

Locomotives — A135

**1997, Feb. 20 Litho. *Perf. 14x13½***

**707** A135 6sh Class 94, 1981 .80 .25
**708** A135 14sh Class 87, 1964 1.25 .45
**709** A135 20sh Class 59, 1955 1.60 .70
**710** A135 25sh Class 57, 1939 1.60 1.25
**711** A135 30sh Class 23, 1923 2.00 2.00
**712** A135 40sh Class 10, 1914 2.25 2.25
*Nos. 707-712 (6)* 9.50 6.90

Dated 1996.

Fruits — A136

**1997, Feb. 28 *Perf. 14½***

**713** A136 6sh Orange .25 .25
**714** A136 14sh Pineapple 2.10 .50
**715** A136 20sh Mango 3.00 2.00
**716** A136 25sh Papaya 3.75 2.50
*Nos. 713-716 (4)* 9.10 5.25

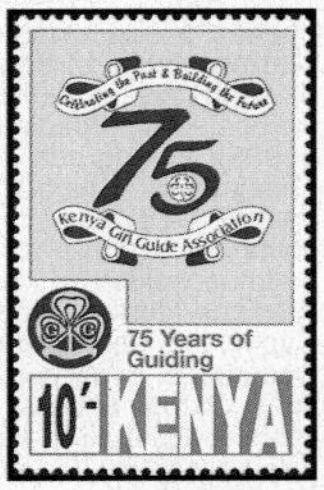


A137

Scouting Organizations: No. 717, Girl Guides, 75th anniv. No. 718, Lord Baden Powell. No. 719, Girl scouts hiking. No. 720, Rangers camping. No. 721, Girl Guides planting trees. No. 722, Boy Scouts first aid. No. 723, Boy Scouts camping. No. 724, Brownies.

**1997, Sept. 1 Litho. *Perf. 14½***

**717** A137 10sh multicolored .35 .35
**718** A137 10sh multicolored .35 .35
*a.* Pair, #717-718 .75 .75
**719** A137 27sh multicolored .90 .90
**720** A137 27sh multicolored .90 .90
*a.* Pair, #719-720 2.25 2.25
**721** A137 33sh multicolored 1.25 1.25
**722** A137 33sh multicolored 1.25 1.25
*a.* Pair, #721-722 3.00 3.00
**723** A137 42sh multicolored 1.50 1.50
**724** A137 42sh multicolored 1.50 1.50
*a.* Pair, #723-724 3.50 3.50
*Nos. 717-724 (8)* 8.00 8.00

Tourist Attractions — A138

Designs: 10sh, Crocodile. 27sh, Hot Springs, Lake Bogoria. 30sh, Warthogs. 33sh, Wind surfing. 42sh, Traditional huts.

**1997, Oct. 9 *Perf. 13½***

**725** A138 10sh multicolored 1.25 .25
**726** A138 27sh multicolored 2.00 1.60
**727** A138 30sh multicolored 2.00 1.90
**728** A138 33sh multicolored 2.25 2.25
**729** A138 42sh multicolored 2.50 2.50
*Nos. 725-729 (5)* 10.00 8.50

Vasco da Gama's Stop in Malindi, 500th Anniv. A139

Designs: 10sh, Residents greeting ships as they arrive. 24sh, Three ships. 33sh, Map of voyage. 42sh, Ships in bay, monument.

**1998, Apr. 4 Litho. *Perf. 13***

**730** A139 10sh multicolored .60 .30
**731** A139 24sh multicolored 1.40 .75
**732** A139 33sh multicolored 2.00 2.00
**733** A139 42sh multicolored 2.50 2.50
*Nos. 730-733 (4)* 6.50 5.55

Pan African Postal Union (PAPU) A140

**1998, June 10 Litho. *Perf. 14½***

**734** A140 10sh Lion 2.10 .30
**735** A140 24sh Buffalo 2.75 .85
**736** A140 33sh Grant's gazelle 3.75 3.75
**737** A140 42sh Cheetah 5.00 5.00
*Nos. 734-737 (4)* 13.60 9.90

**Souvenir Sheet**

**738** A140 50sh Hirola gazelle 4.50 4.50

Pres. Daniel arap Moi Taking Oath of Office, 1998 A141

**1998, Dec. 8 Litho. *Perf. 13½***

**739** A141 14sh multicolored 1.50 .80

Turtles A142

Designs: 17sh, Leatherback. 20sh, Green sea. 30sh, Hawksbill. 47sh, Olive Ridley. 59sh, Loggerhead.

**2000, Apr. 13 Litho. *Perf. 13½x13¾***

**740** A142 17sh multi 1.00 .35
**741** A142 20sh multi 1.25 .40
**742** A142 30sh multi 1.75 1.00
**743** A142 47sh multi 2.50 2.50
**744** A142 59sh multi 3.00 3.00
*Nos. 740-744 (5)* 9.50 7.25

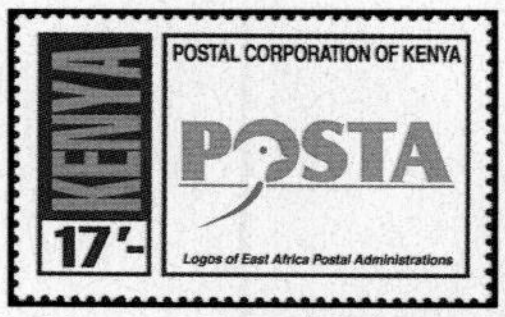


Emblems of East African Postal Administrations — A143

Designs: 17sh, Postal Corporation of Kenya. 35sh, Uganda Posta Limited. 50sh, Tanzania Posts Corporation. 70sh, Postal Corporation of Kenya.

**2000, May 31 *Perf. 13¾x13½***

**745** A143 17sh multi .85 .35
**746** A143 35sh multi 1.60 1.25
**747** A143 50sh multi 2.25 2.25
*Nos. 745-747 (3)* 4.70 3.85

**Souvenir Sheet**

***Perf. 13¼x13***

**748** A143 70sh multi 4.50 4.50

Crops — A144

**2001, Feb. 28 Photo. *Perf. 14½x14***

**749** A144 2sh Cotton .25 .25
**750** A144 4sh Bananas .25 .25
**751** A144 5sh Avocados .25 .25
**752** A144 6sh Cassava .25 .25
**753** A144 8sh Arrowroot .25 .25
**754** A144 10sh Papayas .25 .25
**755** A144 19sh Oranges .50 .35
**756** A144 20sh Pyrethrum .50 .35
**757** A144 30sh Peanuts .75 .60
**758** A144 35sh Coconuts .90 .60
**759** A144 40sh Sisal 1.00 .75
**760** A144 50sh Cashews 1.25 .90

**Size: 25x42mm**

***Perf. 14¼***

**761** A144 60sh Tea 1.50 1.00
**762** A144 80sh Corn 2.00 1.50
**763** A144 100sh Coffee 2.50 1.75
**764** A144 200sh Finger millet 5.00 3.50
**765** A144 400sh Sorghum 10.00 7.00
**766** A144 500sh Sugar cane 12.50 8.50
*Nos. 749-766 (18)* 39.90 28.30

**2001 Photo. *Perf. 14¾ Horiz.***

**Coil Stamps**

**766A** A144 5sh Avocados — —
**766B** A144 10sh Papayas — —

Historic Sites of East Africa A145

Designs: 19sh, Source of Nile River, Jinja, Uganda. 35sh, Lamu Fort, Kenya (28x28mm). 40sh, Olduvai Gorge, Tanzania. 50sh, Thimlich Ohinga, Kenya (28x28mm).

***Perf. 14¼, 13½ (35sh, 50sh)***

**2002 Litho.**

**767-770** A145 Set of 4 9.50 9.50

Kenya - People's Republic of China Diplomatic Relations, 40th Anniv. — A146

Flags of Kenya and People's Republic of China and: 21sh, Section of Mombasa Road. 66sh, Kasarani Stadium.

**2003, Dec. 14 Litho. *Perf. 12***

**771-772** A146 Set of 2 6.00 6.00

Mammals — A147

Designs: 21sh, Lioness and baby oryx. 60sh, Leopard and cub. 66sh, Zebra and calf. 88sh, Bongo and calf.

**2004, Nov. 19 Litho. *Perf. 14½***

**773-776** A147 Set of 4 11.00 11.00

Easter — A148

Designs: 25sh, Jesus with hand raised. 65sh, Jesus condemned to death. 75sh, Crucifixion. 95sh, Jesus praying.

**2005, Apr. 1 Litho. *Perf. 13½***

**777-780** A148 Set of 4 10.50 10.50

Rotary International, Cent. — A149

Rotary emblem and: 25sh, Polio vaccination. 65sh, Donation of Jaipur feet. 75sh, Don Bosco Center, Nairobi. 95sh, Donation of sewing machine.

**2005, May 26**

**781-784** A149 Set of 4 12.00 12.00

Native Costumes A150

Designs: 21sh, Gabbra. 60sh, Pokot. 66sh, Meru. 88sh, Digo.

**2005, Dec. 6 Litho. *Perf. 14½***

**785-788** A150 Set of 4 8.00 8.00

Fish A151

Designs: 25sh, Elephant snout fish. 55sh, Sudan catfish. 75sh, Nile perch. 95sh, Redbreast tilapia.

**2006, May 4 Litho. *Perf. 13½x13***

**789** A151 25sh multi — —
**790** A151 55sh multi — —
**791** A151 75sh multi — —
**792** A151 95sh multi —

24th Universal Postal Union Congress, Nairobi — A152

**2006, Oct. 11 Litho. *Perf. 13½***

**793** A152 25sh multi 1.25 1.25

Values are for stamps with surrounding selvage. Due to political unrest in Kenya, the UPU Congress was moved to Geneva, Switzerland.

Hippopotamus and Tortoise — A153

**2006, Dec. 15 Litho. *Perf. 12½x13***

**794** A153 25sh multi 2.00 2.00

Tourism A155

**2006, Dec. 15 *Perf. 13***

**Booklet Stamps**

| | | | |
|---|---|---|---|
| **795** | A155 25sh Roan antelope | 2.60 | 2.60 |
| **796** | A155 25sh Weaver bird | 2.60 | 2.60 |
| **797** | A155 25sh Monkey | 2.60 | 2.60 |
| *a.* | Booklet pane of 3, #795-797 | 8.00 | — |
| **798** | A155 25sh Turkana hut | 2.60 | 2.60 |
| **799** | A155 25sh Sports | 2.60 | 2.60 |
| **800** | A155 25sh Golf course | 2.60 | 2.60 |
| *a.* | Booklet pane of 3, #798-800 | 8.00 | — |
| **801** | A155 25sh Abadares Waterfall | 2.60 | 2.60 |
| **802** | A155 25sh Balloon safari | 2.60 | 2.60 |
| **803** | A155 25sh Bull fighting | 2.60 | 2.60 |
| *a.* | Booklet pane of 3, #801-803 | 8.00 | — |
| **804** | A155 25sh Chimpanzee | 2.60 | 2.60 |
| **805** | A155 25sh Maasai | 2.60 | 2.60 |
| **806** | A155 25sh Kit Mikaye | 2.60 | 2.60 |
| *a.* | Booklet pane of 3, #804-806 | 8.00 | — |
| | Complete booklet, #797a, 800a, 803a, 806a | 32.00 | |
| | *Nos. 795-806 (12)* | *31.20* | *31.20* |

Mountains — A156

Designs: 25sh, Mt. Kenya, Kenya. 75sh, Mt. Ruwenzori, Uganda. 95sh, Mt. Kilimanjaro, Tanzania.

**2007, Feb. 28 Litho. *Perf. 13½***

**807-809** A156 Set of 3 6.25 6.25

Breast Cancer Awareness A157

**2007, Oct. 28 *Perf. 13¼***

**810** A157 25sh multi 1.25 1.25

Ceremonial Costumes — A158

Men's and women's costumes: 25sh, Ogiek. 65sh, Sabaot. 75sh, Ribe. 95sh, Elmolo.

**2007, Nov. 21 *Perf. 14½***

**811-814** A158 Set of 4 8.25 8.25

National Arboretum, Cent. — A159

Designs: 25sh, Cape chestnut tree and blossom. 65sh, Bhutan cypress tree, Tree Center. 75sh, Nandi flame tree and blossom. 95sh, Calabash nutmeg tree and blossom.

**2007, Dec. 13 Litho. *Perf. 13¾***

**815-818** A159 Set of 4 8.25 8.25

24th UPU Congress — A160

Design: 25sh, Sitalunga gazelle in Saiwa Swamp. 65sh, Jackson's hartebeest at Ruma Park. 75sh, Steeplechase runner. 95sh, Kenyatta Intl. Conference Center, Nairobi.

**2008, Feb. 7 Litho. *Perf. 14½***

| | | | |
|---|---|---|---|
| **819** | A160 25sh multi | 1.00 | .50 |
| **820** | A160 65sh multi | 2.50 | 1.50 |
| **821** | A160 75sh multi | 3.00 | 2.25 |
| **822** | A160 95sh multi | 3.75 | 3.75 |
| | *Nos. 819-822 (4)* | 10.25 | 8.00 |

Because of political turmoil in Kenya, the 24th UPU Congress was moved from Nairobi to Geneva, Switzerland.

2008 Summer Olympics, Beijing — A161

Designs: 25sh, Kenyan athletes holding Kenyan flag. 65sh, Women's volleyball, vert. 75sh, Women runners. 95sh, Boxing.

**2008, Aug. 21 Litho. *Perf. 14½***

**823-826** A161 Set of 4 7.50 7.50

Heroes of Kenya — A162

Designs: 25sh, Vice-president Oginga Odinga (c. 1911-94), Pio Gama Pinto (1927-65), politician, Tom Mboya (1930-69), politician, Ronald Ngala (1923-72), politician. 65sh, The Kapenguria Six. 75sh, Dedan Kimathi (1920-57), rebel leader, Elijah Masinde (c. 1910-87), Bukusu tribal leader, Mekatilili Wa Menza, female leader of 1914 rebellion, Koitalel Samoei (1860-1905), Nandi chief. 95sh, Kenya Army Peacekeeping Force.

**2008, Oct. 17 *Perf. 12¾x13¼***

**827-830** A162 Set of 4 8.50 8.50

Theosophical Order of Service, Cent. — A163

**2008, Nov. 17 Litho. *Perf. 14x13¾***

**831** A163 25sh multi 1.25 1.25

Aga Khan, 50th Anniv.of Reign A164

Designs: 25sh, Madrasa program (40x40mm). 65sh, Coastal rural support program (40x40mm). 75sh, Aga Khan Academy, Mombasa (44x30mm). 95sh, Aga Khan University Hospital, Nairobi (44x30mm).

***Perf. 13, 14½ (75sh, 95sh)***

**2008, Dec. 13**

**832-835** A164 Set of 4 7.50 7.50

Blind Man — A165

**2009, July 20 *Perf. 14½***

**836** A165 25sh multi .65 .65

Louis Braille (1809-52), educator of the blind.

Postal Services — A166

Designs: No. 837, 25sh, Man greeting woman, PostaPay emblem. No. 838, 25sh, Parcels, Posta Parcel emblem. No. 839, 25sh, Mailman and trucks, Posta Dispatch emblem. No. 840, 25sh, Stamp collector and stamps, Posta Philately emblem. No. 841, 25sh, Open post office box, Posta Direct Mail emblem. No. 842, 25sh, Agency services, Posta Kenya emblem. No. 843, 25sh, Woman reading letter, Posta Mail emblem. No. 844, 25sh, Man at open post office box, Posta Kenya emblem. No. 845, 25sh, Financial Services clerk and client, computer, Posta Money Order emblem. No. 846, 65sh, Postal worker with package at airport, EMS Kenya emblem. No. 847, 75sh, Narok Post Office, Posta Kenya emblem. No. 848, 95sh, People at water spigot, Posta Kenya emblem.

**2009, Dec. 9 *Perf. 14x13¾***

**837-848** A166 Set of 12 12.50 12.50

*845a* Sheet of 9, #837-845 6.00 6.00

East Africa Natural History Society, Cent. A167

Bird on branch and: 25sh, Taita African violet, Amegilla bee. 65sh, Reed frog. 75sh, Great blue turaco. 95sh, Golden-rumped sengi.

**2010, Mar. 25 *Perf. 13***

**Granite Paper**

**849-852** A167 Set of 4 6.75 6.75

Pan-African Postal Union, 30th Anniv. — A167a

**2010, Nov. 30 Litho. *Perf. 14x13¾***

**852A** A167a 25sh multi .65 .65

Insects A168

No. 853: a, Danaus chrysippus (African monarch). b, Pontia helice. c, Junonia hierta (Yellow pansy). d, Chiasmia subcurvaria. e, Catopsilia florella (African migrant). f, Belenois thysa (False dotted border). g, Leucinodes orbonalis sp. h, Gelechioidea sp. i, Eupithecia sp. cf. festiva. j, Nymphalidae. k, Paraccra mimesa. l, Hodebertia testalis. m, Alucitidae sp. n, Anthozela sp. n. o, Eucosmini gen. n. sp. n. p, Eucosmini sp. q, Zalaca snelleni. r, Yponomeuta strigillata. s, Tortrix dinota. t, Parotis sp. nr. prasinalis. u, Precis hierta. v, Colotis antevippe. w, Cryptophlebia semilunana. x, Hypolimnas misippus. y, Yponomeuta fumigatus.

No. 854: a, Oplostomus haroldi (Large hive beetle). b, Cartoblatta sp. (Cockroaches). c, Mormotomyia hirsuta. d, Cicindellidae. e, Nosognatha ruficollis. f, Hetrodinae sp. g, Helopeltis schoutedeni. h, Ceroctis sp. (Blister beetle). i, Bagrada cruciferarum. j, Popillia aeneipennis (Chafer). k, Lampetis sp. (Jewel beetle). l, Oryctes sp. (Rhinoceros beetle). m, Homoderus mellyi. n, Zonocerus variegatus. o, Leucospidae. p, Agnoscelis versicolor. q, Hispinae (Tortoise beetle). r, Curculionidae. s, Cypholoba perspicillaris. t, Lycidae. u, Milkweed bugs. v, Mylabris tristigma. w, Paederus sp. x, Pyrops turritus. y, Tenebrionidae.

No. 855: a, Fig wasp in flight. b, Ptyelus flavescens (Rain tree bug). c, Phlebotomus feeding. d, Fig wasp, head at bottom. e, Trithemis annulata (Dragonfly). f, Braconid wasp. g, Polistes sp. (Paper wasps). h, Helopeltis schoutedeni. i, Trithemis sp. (Dragonfly). j, Cicada. k, Silverfish. l, Stingless bee. m, Lipotriches sp. n, Bombyliidae. o, Bromophila caffra. p, Schistocerca gregaria. q, Plagiotryptus hippiscus. r, Reduviidae. s, Diopsidae (Stalk-eyed fly). t, Lamyra gulo and wasp prey. u, Dictyopharidae. v, Rhiniidae cf. Fainia sp. w, Locust. x, Megastigmus sp. m. y, Glossina morsitans feeding.

No. 856: a, Bactrocera invadens, head at top. b, Trirhithrum culcasiae. c, Trirhithrum coffeae. d, Bactrocera invadens, head at bottom. e, Bactrocera munroi. f, Caprophthoromyia dimidiata. g, Celidodacus obnubilus. h, Ceratitis caetrata. i, Ceratitis captiata. j, Ceratitis copelandi. k, Ceratitis cosyra. l, Ceratitis cuthbertsoni. m, Ceratitis rosa. n, Ceratitis stictica. o, Ceratitis whartoni. p, Conradtina acroleuca. q, Dacus apostata. r, Dacus frontalis. s, Dacus sphaeristicus. t, Dacus telfairae. u, Munromyia whartoni. v, Craspedoxantha sp. w, Taomyia marshalli. x, Themarictera laticeps. y, Trirhithrum albomaculatum.

**2011, Nov. 16** *Perf. 13x13¼*

| | | | |
|---|---|---|---|
| **853** | Sheet of 25 | 14.00 | 14.00 |
| *a.-y.* | A168 25sh Any single | .55 | .55 |
| **854** | Sheet of 25 | 37.50 | 37.50 |
| *a.-y.* | A168 65sh Any single | 1.50 | 1.50 |
| **855** | Sheet of 25 | 44.00 | 44.00 |
| *a.-y.* | A168 75sh Any single | 1.75 | 1.75 |
| **856** | Sheet of 25 | 52.50 | 52.50 |
| *a.-y.* | A168 95sh Any single | 2.10 | 2.10 |
| | *Nos. 853-856 (4)* | 148.00 | 148.00 |

Intl. Center of Insect Physiology and Endocrinology, 40th anniv.

Promulgation of New Constitution A169

**2011** *Perf. 14½*
**857** A169 25sh multi .60 .60

United Nations Environment Program, 40th Anniv. — A170

Designs: 30sh, Flags at UNEP regional office, Nairobi. 90sh, Buildings in Stockholm, Sweden. 110sh, Christ the Redeemer Statue, Rio de Janeiro.

**2012** *Perf. 14*
**858-860** A170 Set of 3 5.50 5.50

United Nations Environment Program, 40th Anniv. — A171

United Nations Environment Program emblem and emblem for: 30sh, Convention on International Trade in Endangered Species of Wild Fauna and Flora. 90sh, Montreal Protocol on Substances that Deplete the Ozone Layer. 110sh, Green Economy,

**2012, June 22** **Litho.** *Perf. 14*
**861-863** A171 Set of 3 5.50 5.50

Wangari Muta Maathai (1940-2011), 2004 Nobel Peace Laureate — A173

**2012, Sept. 25** **Litho.** *Perf. 14*
**867** A173 30sh multi .70 .70

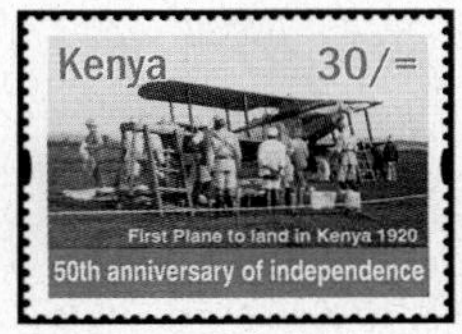

Independence, 50th Anniv. — A174

No. 868: a, First airplane to land in Kenya, 1920. b, 1904 locomotive. c, East Africa Railway & Harbor train car. d, Jamhuri High School. e, Prince of Wales School. f, Machakos Girls School. g, Royal Technical College, University of Nairobi. h, Kenyatta University. i, Jomo Kenyatta University of Agriculture & Technology. j, Nairobi skyline. k, King George VI Hospital. l, Kenyatta National Hospital. m, Jomo Kenyatta International Airport. n, Mobile library. o, Kenya National Library, Nairobi. p, Horticulture. q, Poultry farming. r, Corn farming (maize). s, Beef farming. t, Dairy farming. u, Compulsory free primary education. v, Kenya National Adult Literacy Survey. w, Murang's Road Junction. x, Globe Cinema Complex. y, Oil prospecting.

No. 869: a, Pres. Uhuru Kenyatta and Deputy Pres. William Ruto. b, Queen Elizabeth II and Prince Philip, 1953. c, Lancaster House Conference, 1963. d, Dedan Kimathi. e, Mau Mau movement. f, Kapenguria Six. g, Kapenguria cells. h, Lowering of the Union Jack, 1963. i, Munyao Kisol hoisting Kenyan flag on Mt. Kenya, 1963. j, Promulgation of new constitution. k, First transition. l, Second transition. m, Third transition. n, Fourth transition. o, Parliament Building. p, First Cabinet, 1963. q, Colonial and current coats of arms. r, Colonial and current flags. s, Maps showing the eight provinces and 47 counties. t, Judiciary Building. u, Kenyatta Mausoleum. v, Old Provincial Commissioner's Office, 1913. w, Nyayo House. x, Baron Delamere, first governor of Nairobi. y, Kenya Defense Forces in Somalia.

No. 870: a, Fort Jesus, 1565. b, Kenya-Uganda railway line, 1896. c, Nyall Bridge, 1900. d, Gedi Ruins, 13th cent. e, First Post Office in Mombasa, 1902. f, First General Post Office in Mombasa, 1920. g, First General Post Office in Nairobi, 1944. h, Kenya National Archives, 1944. i, Macmillan Library, 1925. j, Nairobi National Museum, 1890. k, 1885 Mombasa coins. l, Maasai Morans. m, Luo traditional homestead. n, Karen Blixen Museum. o, Kipande House, 1913. p, Laikipia camel caravan. q, East Africa and Uganda Protectorates #53, Kenya #8. r, Chaka drummers. s, Obokano musical instrument. t, Vasco da Gama Pillar, Malindi. u, Naftali Temu, first Kenyan Olympic gold medalist. v, Pamela Jelimo, Janeth Jepkosgei, runners. w, Ezekiel Kemboi, 2004 Olympic steeplechase gold medalist. x, David Rudisha, 2012 Olympic 800-meter gold medalist. y, Kenya Rugby Union national team.

No. 871: a, Lion. b, Elephant. c, Leopard. d, Rhinoceros. e, Buffalo. f, Hippopotamus. g, Cheetah. h, Giraffe. i, Zebra. j, Warthog. k, Wildebeest migration. l, Bongo. m, Impala. n, Hyena. o, Jackal. p, Crocodiles on Tana River. q, Flamingos at Lake Nakuru. r, Ostriches. s, Colobus monkey. t, Falcon. u, Longonot Crater. v, Thompson Falls, Nyahururu. w, Mt. Kenya. x, Lake Turkana. y, Solar eclipse.

*Perf. 13½x13¼ Syncopated*

**2013, Dec. 13** **Litho.**

| | | | |
|---|---|---|---|
| **868** | Sheet of 25 | 17.50 | 17.50 |
| *a.-y.* | A174 30sh Any single | .70 | .70 |
| **869** | Sheet of 25 | 44.00 | 44.00 |
| *a.-y.* | A174 75sh Any single | 1.75 | 1.75 |
| **870** | Sheet of 25 | 52.50 | 52.50 |
| *a.-y.* | A174 90sh Any single | 2.10 | 2.10 |
| **871** | Sheet of 25 | 65.00 | 65.00 |
| *a.-y.* | A174 110sh Any single | 2.60 | 2.60 |
| | *Nos. 868-871 (4)* | 179.00 | 179.00 |

Diplomatic Relations Between Kenya and People's Republic of China, 50th Anniv. — A175

Flags of Kenya and People's Republic of China and: 30sh, Ship, Kenyan and Chinese containers. 110sh, Cranes, Kenyan Pres. Uhuru Kenyatta, Chinese Pres. Xi Jinping.
150sh, Like 110sh.

**2013, Dec. 20** **Litho.** *Perf. 12*
**875-876** A175 Set of 2 3.25 3.25

**Souvenir Sheet**

**877** A175 150sh multi 3.50 3.50

No. 877 contains one 76x50mm stamp.

Birds — A176

Designs: 30sh, Red and yellow barbet. 35sh, Scarlet-chested sunbird. 50sh, Yellow-billed hornbill. 55sh, Greater honeyguide. 65sh, Superb starling. 70sh, African fish eagle. 80sh, Lesser flamingo. 100sh, Hadada ibis. 110sh, Ross's turaco.

*Perf. 13x13¼ Syncopated*

**2014** **Litho.**

| | | | | |
|---|---|---|---|---|
| **878** | A176 | 30sh multi | .70 | .70 |
| **879** | A176 | 35sh multi | .80 | .80 |
| **880** | A176 | 50sh multi | 1.10 | 1.10 |
| **881** | A176 | 55sh multi | 1.25 | 1.25 |
| **882** | A176 | 65sh multi | 1.50 | 1.50 |
| **883** | A176 | 70sh multi | 1.60 | 1.60 |
| **884** | A176 | 80sh multi | 1.90 | 1.90 |
| **885** | A176 | 100sh multi | 2.25 | 2.25 |
| **886** | A176 | 110sh multi | 2.50 | 2.50 |
| | | *Nos. 878-886 (9)* | 13.60 | 13.60 |

Nos. 878-886 have three punched holes at lower left.

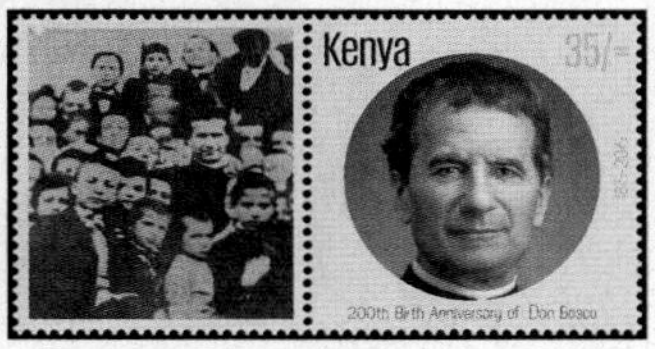

St. John Bosco (1815-88) — A177

**2015, Feb. 1** **Litho.** *Perf. 14¼x14½*
**887** A177 35sh multi + label .80 .80

No. 887 was printed in sheets of 20 + 20 labels. An additional stamp was issued in this set, The editors would like to examine any example.

United Nations, 70th Anniv. — A178

*Perf. 13¾ Syncopated*

**2015, Oct. 2** **Litho.**
**888** A178 35sh multi .70 .70

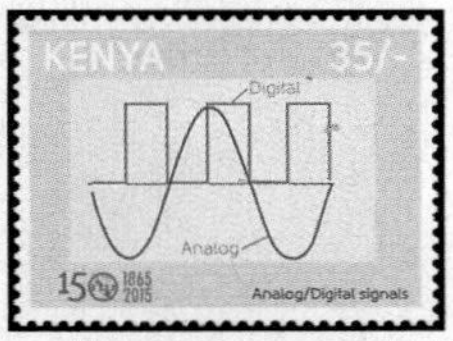

International Telecommunication Union, 150th Anniv. — A179

Designs: 35sh, Digital and analog signals. 90sh, Terrestrial services. 105sh, 150th anniv. emblem. 130sh, Space services.

**2015** **Litho.** *Perf. 13x13¼*
**889-892** A179 Set of 4 7.25 7.25

No. 892 the country name and denomination are smaller than on Nos. 889-891.

Big Game Animals — A180

Designs: 35sh, Elephant. 80sh, Lion, horiz. 90sh, Buffalo, horiz. 105sh, Leopard, horiz. 130sh, Rhinoceros.
175sh, Buffalo, lion, leopard, elephant and rhinoceros, horiz.

*Perf. 13¼ Syncopated*

**2017, May 10** **Litho.**
**893-897** A180 Set of 5 8.50 8.50

**Size: 110x80mm**

***Imperf***

**898** A180 175sh multi 3.50 3.50

Mombasa-Nairobi Standard Gauge Railway — A181

Designs: 35sh, Mombasa Terminus. 50sh, Man standing on railroad track. 110sh, Train on bridge. 130sh, Locomotive. 150sh, Nairobi Terminus.
200sh, Like 50sh.

**2017, May 31** **Litho.** *Perf. 14*
**899-903** A181 Set of 5 9.25 9.25

**Souvenir Sheet**

*Perf. 13¼x13*

**904** A181 200sh multi 4.00 4.00

No. 904 contains one 45x35mm stamp.

Kenya Pres. Uhuru Kenyatta and U.S. Pres. Barack Obama — A182

*Perf. 13½x13¼*

**2017, Sept. 13** **Litho.**
**905** A182 50sh multi + label 1.00 1.00

Visit of Pres. Obama to Kenya, 2nd anniv.

United Nations Sustainable Development Goals — A183

Designs: 50sh, Goal 7. 90sh, Goal 14. 105sh, Goal 13. 130sh, Goal 15.

*Perf. 13½x13¼ Syncopated*

**2017, Oct. 9** **Litho.**
**906-909** A183 Set of 4 7.25 7.25

## POSTAGE DUE STAMPS

D1

*Perf. 14x13½*

**1967-85** **Litho.** **Unwmk.**

**"POSTAGE DUE" 12½mm long**

| | | | | |
|---|---|---|---|---|
| **J1** | D1 | 5c dark red | .25 | 2.75 |
| **J2** | D1 | 10c green | .35 | 2.75 |
| **J3** | D1 | 20c dark blue | .70 | 3.25 |
| **J4** | D1 | 30c reddish brown | 1.00 | 4.00 |
| **J5** | D1 | 40c brt red lilac | 1.25 | 6.75 |

*Perf. 14*

| | | | | |
|---|---|---|---|---|
| **J6** | D1 | 80c brick red | 1.00 | 6.25 |

*Perf. 14x13½*

**J7** D1 1sh orange 1.75 *7.00*

**"POSTAGE DUE" 11½mm long**

***Perf. 14¾x14***

**J8** D1 2sh pale violet 2.25 *4.00*
*Nos. J1-J8 (8)* 8.55 *36.75*

Issued: 80c, 1978. 2sh, 1985; others, 1/3/67.
See Nos. J9-J14.

**1969-70** ***Perf. 14***

*J1a* D1 5c .25 5.25
*J2a* D1 10c .25 5.25
*J3a* D1 20c .45 5.75
*J4a* D1 30c .70 6.75
*J5a* D1 40c .80 *22.50*
*J7a* D1 1sh 2.00 *13.50*
*Nos. J1a-J7a (6)* 4.45 *59.00*

Issued: 1sh, 2/18/70; others, 12/16/69.

**1971-73** ***Perf. 14x15***

*J1b* D1 5c 1.75 5.25
*J2b* D1 10c 8.50 5.25
*J3b* D1 20c 11.00 11.00
*J4b* D1 30c 10.50 15.00
*J5b* D1 40c 1.25 15.00
*J7b* D1 1sh 17.00 *40.00*
*Nos. J1b-J7b (6)* 50.00 91.50

Issued: 30c, 7/13/71; others, 2/20/73. The 10c, 20c, 1sh on chalky paper were issued 7/13/71.

**1973, Dec. 12** ***Perf. 15***

*J1c* D1 5c .45 4.00
*J2c* D1 10c .45 4.00
*J3c* D1 20c .45 5.00
*J4c* D1 30c .45 5.75
*J5c* D1 40c 5.25 10.00
*J7c* D1 1sh 1.75 *12.50*
*Nos. J1c-J7c (6)* 8.80 41.25

**1983 Wmk. 373** ***Perf. 14x14¼***

*J2d* D1 10c .45 *2.00*
*J3d* D1 20c .45 *2.00*
*J5d* D1 40c 8.50 *10.00*

**Nos. J5, J7-J8 Redrawn**

***Perf. 14¾x14***

**1987-98 Litho. Unwmk.**

**J8A** D1 30c brown .25 .25
**J9** D1 40c bright red lilac .25 .25
**J10** D1 50c dark green .25 .25
**J10A** D1 80c red brown .25 .25
**J11** D1 1sh bright orange .80 .80
***a.*** light orange .25 .25
**J12** D1 2sh pale violet .25 .25
**J13** D1 3sh dark blue .45 .45
**J14** D1 5sh red brown .45 .45
**J15** D1 10sh brown .45 .45
**J16** D1 20sh red lilac .80 .80
*Nos. J8A-J16 (10)* 4.20 4.20

"KENYA" is 9mm wide on Nos. J9, J11. "CENTS" is 4½mm wide and "SHILLING" has cross bar on "G"; both are in a new font.

"KENYA" is 8½mm wide on No. J12. "POSTAGE DUE" is 11mm wide on Nos. J10, J11a, J15, J16.

Issued: 40c, 1sh, 1987; 10sh, 20sh, 1998; others, Dec. 6, 1993.

## OFFICIAL STAMPS

Nos. 1-5 and 7 Overprinted

***Perf. 14x14½***

**1964, Oct. 1 Photo. Unwmk.**

**Size: 21x17½mm**

**O1** A1 5c blue, buff & dk brn .25 .25
**O2** A1 10c brown .25 .25
**O3** A1 15c dp magenta 1.25 .30
**O4** A1 20c yel green & dk brn .30 .45
**O5** A1 30c yellow & black .35 .65
**O6** A1 50c green, blk & dp car 2.75 1.10
*Nos. O1-O6 (6)* 5.15 3.00

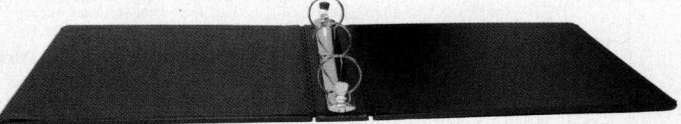

# KENYA, UGANDA, & TANZANIA

ˈke-nyə, ü-ˈgan-də, ˌtan-zə-ˈnē-ə

LOCATION — East Africa, bordering on the Indian Ocean
GOVT. — States in British Commonwealth
AREA — 679,802 sq. mi.
POP. — 42,760,000 (est. 1977)
CAPITAL — Nairobi (Kenya), Kampala (Uganda), Dar es Salaam (Tanzania)

Kenya became a crown colony in 1906, including the former East Africa Protectorate leased from the Sultan of Zanzibar and known as the Kenya Protectorate. In 1963 the colony became independent. Its stamps are listed under "Kenya."

The inland Uganda Protectorate, lying west of Kenya Colony, was declared a British Protectorate in 1894. Uganda became independent in 1962.

Tanganyika, a trust territory larger than Kenya or Uganda, was grouped with them postally from 1935 under the East African Posts & Telecommunications Administration. Tanganyika became independent in 1961. When it merged with Zanzibar in 1964, "Zanzibar" was added to the inscriptions on stamps issued under the E.A.P. & T. Administration. In 1965 the multiple inscription was changed to "Kenya, Uganda, Tanzania," variously arranged.

Zanzibar withdrew its own stamps in 1968, and K., U. & T. stamps became valid Jan. 1, 1968.

100 Cents = 1 Rupee
100 Cents = 1 Shilling (1922)
20 Shillings = 1 Pound

**Catalogue values for unused stamps in this country are for Never Hinged items, beginning with Scott 90.**

## East Africa and Uganda Protectorates

King George V
A1 A2

**1921 Typo. Wmk. 4 *Perf. 14***

**Ordinary Paper**

| | | | | |
|---|---|---|---|---|
| **1** | A1 | 1c black | .90 | *1.90* |
| **2** | A1 | 3c green | 6.75 | *16.50* |
| **3** | A1 | 6c rose red | 11.00 | *22.50* |
| **4** | A1 | 10c orange | 9.75 | 1.40 |
| **5** | A1 | 12c gray | 11.00 | *140.00* |
| **6** | A1 | 15c ultramarine | 12.50 | *22.50* |

**Chalky Paper**

| | | | | |
|---|---|---|---|---|
| **7** | A1 | 50c gray lilac & blk | 16.50 | *125.00* |
| **8** | A2 | 2r blk & red, *blue* | 82.50 | *190.00* |
| **9** | A2 | 3r green & violet | 150.00 | *425.00* |
| **10** | A2 | 5r gray lil & ultra | 190.00 | *350.00* |
| **11** | A2 | 50r gray grn & red | 3,750. | *9,000.* |
| | | Revenue cancel | | 425.00 |
| | | *Nos. 1-10 (10)* | 490.90 | *1,295.* |

The name of the colony was changed to Kenya in August, 1920, but stamps of the East Africa and Uganda types were continued in use. Stamps of types A1 and A2 watermarked Multiple Crown and C A (3) are listed under East Africa and Uganda Protectorates. Used values for Nos. 8-11 are for postally used stamps. Examples with court cancels are worth considerably less.

For stamps of Kenya and Uganda overprinted "G. E. A." used in parts of former German East Africa occupied by British forces, see Tanganyika Nos. 1-9.

## Kenya and Uganda

King George V
A3 A4

**1922-27 Wmk. 4**

| | | | | |
|---|---|---|---|---|
| **18** | A3 | 1c brown | 1.10 | *4.75* |
| **19** | A3 | 5c violet | 6.50 | 1.00 |
| **20** | A3 | 5c grn ('27) | 2.40 | .55 |
| **21** | A3 | 10c green | 1.75 | .35 |
| **22** | A3 | 10c blk ('27) | 4.50 | .25 |
| **23** | A3 | 12c black | 16.00 | *29.00* |
| **24** | A3 | 15c car rose | 1.40 | .25 |
| **25** | A3 | 20c orange | 3.75 | .25 |
| **26** | A3 | 30c ultra | 4.50 | .60 |
| **27** | A3 | 50c gray | 2.75 | .25 |
| **28** | A3 | 75c ol bister | 11.00 | *12.00* |
| **29** | A4 | 1sh green | 7.25 | 3.00 |
| **30** | A4 | 2sh gray lil | 10.00 | *21.00* |
| **31** | A4 | 2sh50c brn ('25) | 24.00 | *125.00* |
| **32** | A4 | 3sh gray blk | 20.00 | 7.50 |
| **33** | A4 | 4sh gray ('25) | 37.50 | *135.00* |
| **34** | A4 | 5sh carmine | 27.50 | 27.50 |
| **35** | A4 | 7sh50c org ('25) | 140.00 | *325.00* |
| **36** | A4 | 10sh ultra | 82.50 | *77.50* |
| **37** | A4 | £1 org & blk | 230.00 | *340.00* |
| | | Revenue cancel | | 30.00 |
| **38** | A4 | £2 brn vio & grn ('25) | 1,150. | *2,100.* |
| | | Revenue cancel | | 170.00 |
| **39** | A4 | £3 yel & dl vio ('25) | 1,850. | — |
| | | Revenue cancel | | 275.00 |
| **40** | A4 | £4 rose lil & blk ('25) | 5,000. | — |
| | | Revenue cancel | | 300.00 |
| **41** | A4 | £5 blue & blk | 5,500. | — |
| | | Revenue cancel | | 375.00 |
| **41A** | A4 | £10 grn & blk | *15,000.* | |
| | | Revenue cancel | | 475.00 |
| **41B** | A4 | £20 grn & red ('25) | *34,500.* | |
| | | Revenue cancel | | 850.00 |
| **41C** | A4 | £25 red & blk | *43,500.* | |
| | | Revenue cancel | | 800.00 |
| **41D** | A4 | £50 brn & blk | *85,000.* | |
| | | Revenue cancel | | 900.00 |
| **41E** | A4 | £75 gray & purple | *140,000.* | |
| | | Revenue cancel | | 3,500. |
| **41F** | A4 | £100 blk & red | *160,000.* | |
| | | Revenue cancel | | 2,250. |
| | | *Nos. 18-37 (20)* | 634.40 | *1,111.* |

High face value stamps are known with revenue cancellations removed and forged postal cancellations added.

Common Design Types pictured following the introduction.

## Kenya, Uganda, Tanganyika Silver Jubilee Issue

Common Design Type

**1935, May Engr. *Perf. 13½x14***

| | | | | |
|---|---|---|---|---|
| **42** | CD301 | 20c ol grn & lt bl | 2.00 | .25 |
| **43** | CD301 | 30c blue & brown | 2.75 | *3.00* |
| **44** | CD301 | 65c indigo & green | 1.75 | *2.75* |
| **45** | CD301 | 1sh brt vio & indigo | 2.25 | *5.00* |
| | | *Nos. 42-45 (4)* | 8.75 | *11.00* |
| | | Set, never hinged | 23.00 | |
| | | Set, perf. "SPECIMEN" | 175.00 | |

Kavirondo Cranes — A5

Dhow on Lake Victoria — A6

Lion — A7

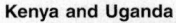

Mount Kilimanjaro — A8

Jinja Bridge by Ripon Falls — A9

Mount Kenya — A10

Lake Naivasha A11

Type I

FIVE CENTS
Type I — Left rope does not touch sail.
Type II — Left rope touches sail.

***Perf. 13, 14, 11½x13, 13x11½***
**Engr.; Typo. (10c, £1)**

**1935, May 1**

| | | | | |
|---|---|---|---|---|
| **46** | A5 | 1c red brn & blk | 1.00 | *2.00* |
| **47** | A6 | 5c grn & blk (I) | 3.50 | .50 |
| *a.* | | Type II | *40.00* | 9.00 |
| *b.* | | Perf. 13x11½ (I) | *9,750.* | *1,000.* |
| *c.* | | Perf. 13x11½ (II) | *875.00* | *250.00* |
| **48** | A7 | 10c black & yel | 7.50 | 1.00 |
| **49** | A8 | 15c red & black | 4.00 | .25 |
| **50** | A5 | 20c red org & blk | 4.00 | .25 |
| **51** | A9 | 30c dk ultra & blk | 5.25 | 1.25 |
| **52** | A6 | 50c blk & red vio (I) | 6.00 | .25 |
| **53** | A10 | 65c yel brn & blk | 8.75 | *2.25* |
| **54** | A11 | 1sh grn & black | 5.75 | 1.50 |
| *a.* | | Perf. 13x11½ ('36) | *1,600.* | 150.00 |
| **55** | A8 | 2sh red vio & rose brn | 13.00 | 4.75 |
| **56** | A11 | 3sh blk & ultra | 20.00 | *17.50* |
| *a.* | | Perf. 13x11½ | *2,600.* | |
| **57** | A9 | 5sh car & black | 26.00 | *35.00* |
| **58** | A5 | 10sh ultra & red vio | 110.00 | *135.00* |
| **59** | A7 | £1 blk & scar | 325.00 | *425.00* |
| | | *Nos. 46-59 (14)* | 539.75 | 626.50 |
| | | Set, never hinged | 900.00 | |
| | | Set, perf. "SPECIMEN" | 550.00 | |

## Coronation Issue

Common Design Type

**1937, May 12 Engr. *Perf. 13½x14***

| | | | | |
|---|---|---|---|---|
| **60** | CD302 | 5c deep green | .25 | .25 |
| **61** | CD302 | 20c deep orange | .30 | .35 |
| **62** | CD302 | 30c brt ultra | .45 | *1.75* |
| | | *Nos. 60-62 (3)* | 1.00 | 2.35 |
| | | Set, never hinged | 1.75 | |
| | | Set, perf. "SPECIMEN" | 150.00 | |

Kavirondo Cranes — A12

Dhow on Lake Victoria — A13

Lake Naivasha — A14

Jinja Bridge, Ripon Falls — A16

Mt. Kilimanjaro A15

Lion — A17

Type II

FIFTY CENTS:
Type I — Left rope does not touch sail.
Type II — Left rope touches sail.

**1938-54 Engr. *Perf. 13x13½***

| | | | | |
|---|---|---|---|---|
| **66** | A12 | 1c vio brn & blk ('42) | .25 | *.50* |
| *a.* | | 1c red brown & gray black, perf. 13 | 3.00 | .90 |
| | | ***Perf. 13x11½*** | | |
| **67** | A13 | 5c grn & blk | 3.25 | .55 |
| **68** | A13 | 5c red org & brn ('49) | 1.40 | *7.50* |
| *a.* | | Perf. 13x12½ ('50) | 2.50 | *4.75* |
| **69** | A14 | 10c org & brn | 1.60 | .25 |
| *a.* | | Perf. 14 ('41) | 95.00 | 10.00 |
| **70** | A14 | 10c grn & blk ('49) | .35 | *2.00* |
| *a.* | | Perf. 13x12½ ('50) | 2.75 | .25 |
| | | ***Perf. 13x12½*** | | |
| **71** | A14 | 10c gray & red brn ('52) | 1.00 | .60 |
| | | ***Perf. 13½x13, 13x13½*** | | |
| **72** | A15 | 15c car & gray blk ('43) | 4.25 | 2.00 |
| *a.* | | Booklet pane of 4 | 17.50 | |
| *b.* | | Perf. 13 | 22.50 | .60 |
| **73** | A15 | 15c grn & blk ('52) | 1.90 | *6.25* |
| **74** | A12 | 20c org & gray blk ('42) | 5.75 | .25 |
| *a.* | | Booklet pane of 4 | 24.00 | |
| *b.* | | Imperf., pair | | |
| *c.* | | Perf. 13 | *35.00* | .30 |
| *d.* | | Perf. 14 ('41) | *45.00* | 3.00 |
| | | ***Perf. 13x12½*** | | |
| **75** | A13 | 25c car & blk ('52) | 1.25 | *2.40* |
| | | ***Perf. 13x13½*** | | |
| **76** | A16 | 30c dp bl & gray blk ('42) | 2.00 | .35 |
| *a.* | | Perf. 14 ('41) | *130.00* | 12.50 |
| *b.* | | Perf. 13 | *40.00* | .45 |
| **77** | A16 | 30c brn & pur ('52) | 1.25 | .45 |
| **78** | A12 | 40c brt bl & gray blk ('52) | 1.50 | *5.00* |
| | | ***Perf. 13x12½*** | | |
| **79** | A13 | 50c gray blk & red vio (II) ('49) | 7.25 | .60 |
| *a.* | | Perf. 13x11½ (II) | 14.00 | 1.10 |
| *b.* | | Perf. 13x11½ (I) | 175.00 | *250.00* |
| | | ***Perf. 13x11½*** | | |
| **80** | A14 | 1sh yel brn & gray blk | 18.00 | .30 |
| *a.* | | Perf. 13x12½ ('49) | 12.00 | .65 |
| | | ***Perf. 13½x13*** | | |
| **81** | A15 | 2sh red vio & org brn ('44) | 30.00 | .30 |
| *a.* | | Perf. 13 | *110.00* | 9.00 |
| *b.* | | Perf. 14 ('41) | *62.50* | 19.00 |
| | | ***Perf. 13x12½*** | | |
| **82** | A14 | 3sh gray blk & ultra ('50) | 30.00 | 9.00 |
| *a.* | | Perf. 13x11½ | 50.00 | 9.00 |
| | | ***Perf. 13x13½*** | | |
| **83** | A16 | 5sh car rose & gray blk ('44) | 30.00 | 2.00 |
| *a.* | | Perf. 13 | *125.00* | 21.00 |
| *b.* | | Perf. 14 ('41) | *35.00* | 3.25 |

**84** A12 10sh ultra & red vio ('44) 40.00 8.50
*a.* Perf. 13 110.00 30.00
*b.* Perf. 14 ('41) 32.50 25.00

**Typo.**
***Perf. 14***

**85** A17 £1 blk & scar ('41) 25.00 *27.50*
*a.* Perf. 11½x13 300.00 170.00
*b.* Perf. 12½ ('54) 12.00 *42.50*
*Nos. 66-85 (20)* 206.00 *76.30*
Set, never hinged 330.00

Nos. 85-85b were printed on chalky paper. No. 85 also exists on ordinary paper, from a 1944 printing. Values are the same.
See Nos. 98-99.

South Africa Nos. 48, 57, 60 and 62 Surcharged

Basic stamps of Nos. 86-89 are inscribed alternately in English and Afrikaans.

**1941-42 Wmk. 201 *Perf. 15x14, 14***

**86** A6 5c on 1p car & gray, pair 1.10 *3.00*
*a.* Single, English .25 .25
*b.* Single, Afrikaans .25 .25
**87** A17 10c on 3p ultra, pair 3.50 *10.00*
*a.* Single, English .30 .35
*b.* Single, Afrikaans .30 .35
**88** A7 20c on 6p org & grn, pair 2.50 *3.75*
*a.* Single, English .25 .25
*b.* Single, Afrikaans .25 .25
**89** A11 70c on 1sh lt bl & ol brn, pair 15.00 *7.00*
*a.* Single, English .50 .45
*b.* Single, Afrikaans .50 .45
*Nos. 86-89 (4)* 22.10 23.75
Set, never hinged 30.00

Issued: Nos. 86-88, 7/1/41; No. 89, 4/20/42.
Values are for horizontal pairs. Vertical pairs are worth substantially less.

**Catalogue values for unused stamps in this section, from this point to the end of the section, are for Never Hinged items.**

### Peace Issue
Common Design Type
***Perf. 13½x14***

**1946, Nov. 11 Engr. Wmk. 4**
**90** CD303 20c red orange .25 .25
**91** CD303 30c deep blue .40 .40

### Silver Wedding Issue
Common Design Types

**1948, Dec. 1 Photo. *Perf. 14x14½***
**92** CD304 20c orange .25 .25

**Engr.; Name Typo.**
***Perf. 11½x11***
**93** CD305 £1 red 50.00 *67.50*

### UPU Issue
Common Design Types
**Engr.; Typo. on Nos. 95 and 96**

**1949, Oct. 10 *Perf. 13, 11x11½***
**94** CD306 20c red orange .25 .25
**95** CD307 30c indigo 1.75 *2.25*
**96** CD308 50c gray .40 .40
**97** CD309 1sh red brown .50 .50
*Nos. 94-97 (4)* 2.90 3.40

### Type of 1949 with Added Inscription: "Royal Visit 1952"

**1952, Feb. 1 Engr. *Perf. 13x12½***
**98** A14 10c green & black .30 *1.60*
**99** A14 1sh yel brn & gray blk 1.25 *2.25*

Visit of Princess Elizabeth, Duchess of Edinburgh, and the Duke of Edinburgh, 1952.

### Coronation Issue
Common Design Type

**1953, June 2 *Perf. 13½x13***
**101** CD312 20c red orange & blk .40 .25

Owen Falls Dam — A18

**Inscribed "ROYAL VISIT 1954"**

**1954, Apr. 28 *Perf. 12½x13***
**102** A18 30c dp ultra & black .50 .25

Visit of Queen Elizabeth II and the Duke of Edinburgh, 1954.

Owen Falls Dam — A18a

Giraffe — A19

Mt. Kilimanjaro A20

Elizabeth II — A21

5c, 30c, Owen Falls Dam (without "Royal Visit 1954"). 20c, 40c, 1sh, Lion. 15c, 1.30sh, 5sh, Elephants. 10sh, Royal Lodge, Sagana.

**1954-59 *Perf. 12½x13, 13x12½***
**103** A18a 5c choc & blk 1.75 .65
*a.* Booklet pane of 4 7.00
*b.* Vignette (dam) inverted *67,500.*
**104** A19 10c carmine 1.75 .25
*a.* Booklet pane of 4 7.00
**105** A20 15c lt blue & blk (no period below "c") ('58) 1.00 1.40
*a.* Booklet pane of 4 4.00
**106** A20 15c lt blue & blk (period below "c") ('59) 1.00 1.40
*a.* Booklet pane of 4 4.00
**107** A19 20c org & black 2.00 .25
*a.* Booklet pane of 4 8.00
*b.* Imperf., pair *1,300.* 1,500.
**108** A18a 30c ultra & black 1.25 .25
*a.* Booklet pane of 4 6.00
*b.* Vignette (dam) inverted *32,500.*
**109** A19 40c brown ('58) 1.50 .80
**110** A19 50c dp red lilac 3.00 .25
*a.* Booklet pane of 4 14.00
**111** A20 65c brn car & grn ('55) 3.00 1.50
**112** A19 1sh dp mag & blk 3.00 .25
**113** A20 1.30sh pur & red org ('55) 15.00 .25
**114** A20 2sh dp grn & gray 14.00 1.25
**115** A20 5sh black & org 20.00 3.25
**116** A20 10sh ultra & black 35.00 5.75
**117** A21 £1 black & ver 18.00 19.00
*Nos. 103-117 (15)* 121.25 36.50

No. 103b is unique.
For "Official" overprints see Tanganyika Nos. O1-O12.

Map Showing Lakes Victoria and Tanganyika A22

***Perf. 12½x13***

**1958, July 30 Engr. Wmk. 314**
**118** A22 40c green & blue .70 .40
**119** A22 1.30sh violet & green .70 *1.00*

Cent. of the discovery of Lakes Victoria and Tanganyika by Sir Richard F. Burton and Capt. J. H. Speke.

Sisal — A23

A25

Mount Kenya and Giant Plants A24

10c, Cotton. 15c, Coffee. 20c, Gnu. 25c, Ostriches. 30c, Thompson's gazelles. 40c, Manta ray. 50c, Zebras. 65c, Cheetah. 1.30sh, Murchison Falls & hippopotamuses. 2sh, Mt. Kilimanjaro & giraffes. 2.50sh, Candelabra tree & black rhinoceroses. 5sh, Crater Lake & Mountains of the Moon. 10sh, Ngorongoro Crater & buffaloes.

***Perf. 14½x14***

**1960, Oct. 1 Photo. Wmk. 314**
**120** A23 5c dull blue .25 .25
**121** A23 10c lt olive green .25 .25
*a.* Booklet pane of 4 .60
**122** A23 15c dull purple .45 .25
*a.* Booklet pane of 4 1.75
**123** A23 20c brt lilac rose .25 .25
*a.* Booklet pane of 4 1.20
**124** A23 25c olive gray 3.25 1.25
**125** A23 30c brt vermilion .25 .25
*a.* Booklet pane of 4 .90
**126** A23 40c bright blue .25 .25
**127** A23 50c dull violet .30 .25
*a.* Booklet pane of 4 1.90
**128** A23 65c lemon .50 *1.75*

**Engr.**
***Perf. 14***

**129** A24 1sh vio & red lilac 1.50 .25
**130** A24 1.30sh choc & dk car 5.75 .25
**131** A24 2sh dk bl & dull bl 7.50 .45
**132** A24 2.50sh ol grn & dull bl 9.80 2.50
**133** A24 5sh rose red & lil 4.25 .60
**134** A24 10sh sl bl & ol grn 13.00 6.00

***Perf. 13½x13***

**135** A25 20sh lake & bluish violet 25.00 *25.00*
*Nos. 120-135 (16)* 72.55 39.80

Booklets issued in 1961.
On Nos. 120-134, positions of "Kenya," "Uganda" and "Tanganyika" are rotated.
For "Official" overprints see Tanganyika Nos. O13-O20.

Agricultural Development — A26

Design: 30c, 1.30sh, Farmer picking corn.

**Unwmk.**

**1963, Mar. 21 Photo. *Perf. 14***
**136** A26 15c lt ol grn & ultra .25 .25
**137** A26 30c yel & red brown .30 .25
**138** A26 50c dp org & ultra .40 .25
**139** A26 1.30sh lt blue & red brn .80 *1.00*
*Nos. 136-139 (4)* 1.75 1.75

FAO "Freedom from Hunger" campaign.

Scholars and Open Book A27

**1963, June 28 Unwmk. *Perf. 14***
**140** A27 30c multicolored .25 .25
**141** A27 1.30sh multicolored .25 .25

Inauguration of University of East Africa.

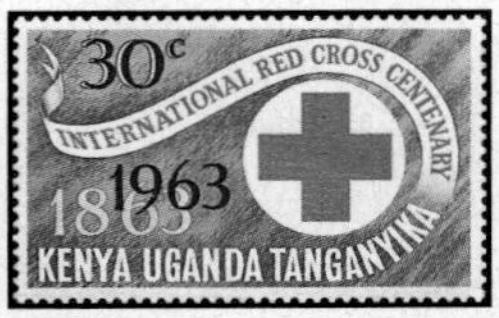

Red Cross A28

**1963, Sept. 2**
**142** A28 30c blue & red 1.25 .30
**143** A28 50c bister brown & red 1.50 1.25

Centenary of International Red Cross.

### Kenya, Uganda, Tanganyika and Zanzibar

Issued by the East African Common Services Organization. Not used in Zanzibar.

Japanese Crest and Olympic Rings — A29

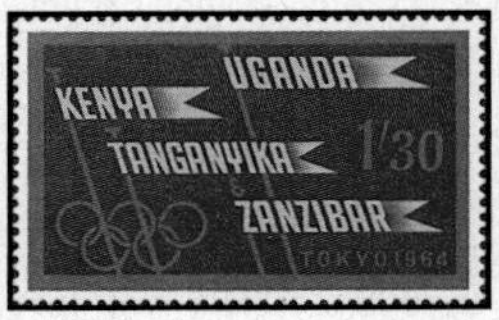

Olympic Rings and Banners A30

**Unwmk.**

**1964, Oct. 25 Photo. *Perf. 14***
**144** A29 30c org & dk purple .25 .25
**145** A29 50c dk purple & org .25 .25
**146** A30 1.30sh blue, grn & org .35 .25
**147** A30 2.50sh blue, vio & lil rose .40 *.75*
*Nos. 144-147 (4)* 1.25 1.50

18th Olympic Games, Tokyo, Oct. 10-25.

### Kenya, Uganda, Tanzania

Issued by the East African Common Services Organization.

Safari Rally Emblem and Leopard — A31

1.30sh, 2.50sh, Car on road through national park & emblem of the East African Safari Rally.

**1965, Apr. 15 Unwmk. *Perf. 14***
**148** A31 30c blue grn, yel & blk .25 .25
**149** A31 50c brown, yel & blk .25 .25
**150** A31 1.30sh lt ultra, ocher & green .25 .25
**151** A31 2.50sh blue, dk grn & dull red .45 *1.10*
*Nos. 148-151 (4)* 1.20 1.85

13th East African Safari Rally, 4/15-19/65.

ITU Emblem, Old and Modern Communication Equipment — A32

**1965, May 17** **Photo.**

| | | | | | |
|---|---|---|---|---|---|
| 152 | A32 | 30c | lilac rose, gold & brn | .25 | .25 |
| 153 | A32 | 50c | gray, gold & brown | .25 | .25 |
| 154 | A32 | 1.30sh | lt vio bl, gold & brn | .40 | .25 |
| 155 | A32 | 2.50sh | brt bl grn, gold & brn | 1.25 | 1.25 |
| | | | *Nos. 152-155 (4)* | 2.15 | 2.00 |

Cent. of the ITU.

ICY Emblem — A33

**1965, Aug. 4** **Unwmk.** ***Perf. 14***

| | | | | | |
|---|---|---|---|---|---|
| 156 | A33 | 30c | green & gold | .25 | .25 |
| 157 | A33 | 50c | slate blk & gold | .25 | .25 |
| 158 | A33 | 1.30sh | ultra & gold | .40 | .25 |
| 159 | A33 | 2.50sh | car & gold | 1.00 | 1.00 |
| | | | *Nos. 156-159 (4)* | 1.90 | 1.75 |

International Cooperation Year.

Game Park Lodge A34

Tourist Publicity: 50c, Murchison Falls, Uganda. 1.30sh, Lake Nakuru, Kenya. 2.50sh, Deep-sea fishing, Tanzania.

**1966, Apr. 4** **Photo.** ***Perf. 14***

| | | | | | |
|---|---|---|---|---|---|
| 160 | A34 | 30c | ocher & multi | .45 | .25 |
| 161 | A34 | 50c | green & multi | .55 | .25 |
| *a.* | | | Blue omitted | *425.00* | |
| 162 | A34 | 1.30sh | multicolored | 2.75 | .35 |
| 163 | A34 | 2.50sh | gray & multi | 1.75 | *2.25* |
| | | | *Nos. 160-163 (4)* | 5.50 | 3.10 |

Javelin Thrower and Games' Emblem A35

**1966, Aug. 2** **Unwmk.** ***Perf. 14***

| | | | | | |
|---|---|---|---|---|---|
| 164 | A35 | 30c | multicolored | .25 | .25 |
| 165 | A35 | 50c | multicolored | .25 | .25 |
| 166 | A35 | 1.30sh | multicolored | .25 | .25 |
| 167 | A35 | 2.50sh | multicolored | .30 | *1.25* |
| | | | *Nos. 164-167 (4)* | 1.05 | 2.00 |

8th British Commonwealth and Empire Games, Jamaica, Aug. 4-13, 1966.

UNESCO Emblem — A36

**1966, Oct. 3** **Photo.** ***Perf. 14***

| | | | | | |
|---|---|---|---|---|---|
| 168 | A36 | 30c | rose red, brt grn & blk | .45 | .25 |
| 169 | A36 | 50c | lt brn, brt grn & blk | .50 | .25 |
| 170 | A36 | 1.30sh | gray, brt grn & blk | 1.25 | .25 |
| 171 | A36 | 2.50sh | yel, brt grn & blk | 1.60 | *4.25* |
| | | | *Nos. 168-171 (4)* | 3.80 | 5.00 |

20th anniv. of UNESCO.

Dragon Rapide A37

Planes: 50c, Super VC10. 1.30sh, Comet 4. 2.50sh, F.27 Friendship.

**1967, Jan. 23** **Unwmk.**

| | | | | | |
|---|---|---|---|---|---|
| 172 | A37 | 30c | multicolored | .30 | .25 |
| 173 | A37 | 50c | multicolored | .40 | .25 |
| 174 | A37 | 1.30sh | multicolored | .85 | .30 |
| 175 | A37 | 2.50sh | multicolored | 1.40 | *3.00* |
| | | | *Nos. 172-175 (4)* | 2.95 | 3.80 |

21st anniversary of East African Airways.

Pillar Tomb, East African Coast — A38

Designs: 50c, Man hunting elephant, petroglyph, Tanzania. 1.30sh, Clay head, Luzira, Uganda. 2.50sh, Proconsul skull, Rusinga Island, Kenya.

**1967, May 2** **Photo.** ***Perf. 14***

| | | | | | |
|---|---|---|---|---|---|
| 176 | A38 | 30c | rose lake, blk & yel | .25 | .25 |
| 177 | A38 | 50c | gray, black & ver | .60 | .25 |
| 178 | A38 | 1.30sh | green, yel & blk | .85 | .25 |
| 179 | A38 | 2.50sh | cop red, yel & blk | 1.25 | *2.50* |
| | | | *Nos. 176-179 (4)* | 2.95 | 3.25 |

Archaeological relics of East Africa.

Emblems of Kenya, Tanzania and Tanganyika — A39

**Photo.; Gold Impressed**

**1967, Dec. 1** ***Perf. 14½x14***

| | | | | | |
|---|---|---|---|---|---|
| 180 | A39 | 5sh | gray, black & gold | .50 | *1.00* |

Establishment of East African Community.

Mountain climber A40

30c Mountain climber. 50c, Mount Kenya. 1.30sh, Mount Kilimanjaro. 2.50sh, Ruwenzori Mountains.

**1968, Mar. 4** **Photo.** ***Perf. 14½***

| | | | | | |
|---|---|---|---|---|---|
| 181 | A40 | 30c | multicolored | .25 | .25 |
| 182 | A40 | 50c | multicolored | .35 | .25 |
| 183 | A40 | 1.30sh | multicolored | .60 | .25 |
| 184 | A40 | 2.50sh | multicolored | 1.10 | *2.00* |
| | | | *Nos. 181-184 (4)* | 2.30 | 2.75 |

Family and Rural Hospital A41

Family and: 50c, Student nurse. 1.30sh, Microscope. 2.50sh, Mosquito and hand holding hypodermic.

**1968, May 13** **Photo.** ***Perf. 13½***

| | | | | | |
|---|---|---|---|---|---|
| 185 | A41 | 30c | multicolored | .25 | .25 |
| 186 | A41 | 50c | rose vio, blk & brt pink | .25 | .25 |
| 187 | A41 | 1.30sh | brn org, blk & brt pink | .25 | .25 |
| 188 | A41 | 2.50sh | gray, blk & brt pink | .30 | *1.25* |
| | | | *Nos. 185-188 (4)* | 1.05 | 2.00 |

20th anniv. of the WHO.

Stadium A42

Designs: 50c, Diving tower. 1.30sh, Pylons and tracks. 2.50sh, Boxing ring, vert.

***Perf. 14½x14, 14x14½***

**1968, Oct. 14** **Photo.**

| | | | | | |
|---|---|---|---|---|---|
| 189 | A42 | 30c | dull pur & gray grn | .25 | .25 |
| 190 | A42 | 50c | brt grn, blk & gray | .25 | .25 |
| 191 | A42 | 1.30sh | gray grn, blk & dk car | .25 | .25 |
| 192 | A42 | 2.50sh | buff, brn org & brn blk | .30 | *1.00* |
| | | | *Nos. 189-192 (4)* | 1.05 | 1.75 |

19th Olympic Games, Mexico City, 10/12-27.

Railroad Ferry MV Umoja A43

Water Transport: 50c, Transatlantic liner S.S. Harambee. 1.30sh, Lake motor vessel Victoria. 2.50sh, Ferry St. Michael.

**1969, Jan. 20** **Photo.** ***Perf. 14***

| | | | | | |
|---|---|---|---|---|---|
| 193 | A43 | 30c | blue, gray & dk bl | .40 | .25 |
| 194 | A43 | 50c | blue, gray & scar | .45 | .25 |
| 195 | A43 | 1.30sh | bl, dk bl & dk green | .75 | .25 |
| 196 | A43 | 2.50sh | bl, dk bl & org | 1.40 | *2.50* |
| | | | *Nos. 193-196 (4)* | 3.00 | 3.25 |

Farm Workers and ILO Emblem A44

ILO Emblem and: 50c, Construction. 1.30sh, Industry. 2.50sh, Shipping.

**1969, Apr. 14** **Photo.** ***Perf. 14***

| | | | | | |
|---|---|---|---|---|---|
| 197 | A44 | 30c | green, blk & yel | .25 | .25 |
| 198 | A44 | 50c | car rose, blk & car | .25 | .25 |
| 199 | A44 | 1.30sh | dp org, blk & org | .25 | .25 |
| 200 | A44 | 2.50sh | grnsh bl, blk & ultra | .25 | *.75* |
| | | | *Nos. 197-200 (4)* | 1.00 | 1.50 |

50th anniv. of the ILO.

Pope Paul VI, Mountains of the Moon, Papal Arms, Crested Crane — A45

**1969, July 31** **Photo.** ***Perf. 14***

| | | | | | |
|---|---|---|---|---|---|
| 201 | A45 | 30c | dk blue, blk & gold | .25 | .25 |
| 202 | A45 | 70c | plum, blk & gold | .25 | .25 |
| 203 | A45 | 1.50sh | gray bl, blk & gold | .25 | .25 |
| 204 | A45 | 2.50sh | dp vio, blk & gold | .30 | *.90* |
| | | | *Nos. 201-204 (4)* | 1.05 | 1.65 |

Visit of Pope Paul VI to Uganda, 7/31-8/2.

Euphorbia Tree in Shape of Africa, Development Bank Emblem — A46

***Perf. 14x13½***

**1969, Dec. 8** **Litho.** **Unwmk.**

| | | | | | |
|---|---|---|---|---|---|
| 205 | A46 | 30c | brt grn, dk grn & gold | .25 | .25 |
| 206 | A46 | 70c | plum, dk grn & gold | .25 | .25 |
| 207 | A46 | 1.50sh | grnsh bl, dk grn & gold | .25 | .25 |
| 208 | A46 | 2.50sh | brn org, dk grn & gold | .35 | *.60* |
| | | | *Nos. 205-208 (4)* | 1.10 | 1.35 |

African Development Bank, 5th anniv.

Amadinda, Uganda — A47

Musical Instruments: 30c, Marimba, Tanzania. 1.50sh, Nzomari (trumpet), Kenya. 2.50sh, Adeudeu, Kenya.

**1970, Feb. 16** **Litho.** ***Perf. 11x12***

| | | | | | |
|---|---|---|---|---|---|
| 209 | A47 | 30c | multicolored | .25 | .25 |
| 210 | A47 | 70c | multicolored | .30 | .25 |
| 211 | A47 | 1.50sh | dk rose brn & org | .50 | .25 |
| 212 | A47 | 2.50sh | multicolored | .90 | *1.50* |
| | | | *Nos. 209-212 (4)* | 1.95 | 2.25 |

Satellite Earth Station A48

Designs: 70c, Radar station by day. 1.50sh, Radar station by night. 2.50sh, Satellite transmitting communications to and from earth.

**1970, May 18** **Litho.** ***Perf. 14½***

| | | | | | |
|---|---|---|---|---|---|
| 213 | A48 | 30c | multicolored | .25 | .25 |
| 214 | A48 | 70c | multicolored | .25 | .25 |
| 215 | A48 | 1.50sh | org, blk & vio | .30 | .25 |
| 216 | A48 | 2.50sh | dull bl & multi | .40 | *2.00* |
| | | | *Nos. 213-216 (4)* | 1.20 | 2.75 |

Opening of the East African Satellite Earth Station, Mt. Margaret, Kenya.

Runner — A49

**1970, July 16** **Litho.** ***Perf. 14½***

| | | | | | |
|---|---|---|---|---|---|
| 217 | A49 | 30c | org brn, dk brn & blk | .25 | .25 |
| 218 | A49 | 70c | grn, dk brn & blk | .25 | .25 |
| 219 | A49 | 1.50sh | dull pur, dk brn & blk | .25 | .25 |
| 220 | A49 | 2.50sh | grnsh bl, dk brn & blk | .25 | *.80* |
| | | | *Nos. 217-220 (4)* | 1.00 | 1.55 |

9th British Commonwealth Games, Edinburgh, July 16-25.

UN Emblem and People
A50

**1970, Oct. 19 Photo. *Perf. 14½***

| | | | | | |
|---|---|---|---|---|---|
| 221 | A50 | 30c | org brn, gold & black | .25 | .25 |
| 222 | A50 | 70c | bl grn, gold & black | .25 | .25 |
| 223 | A50 | 1.50sh | dull red brn, gold & blk | .25 | .25 |
| 224 | A50 | 2.50sh | olive, gold & blk | .35 | *1.50* |
| | | | *Nos. 221-224 (4)* | 1.10 | 2.25 |

25th anniversary of the United Nations.

Conversion from Pounds to Kilograms — A51

Designs: 70c, Conversion from Fahrenheit to centigrade. 1.50sh, Conversion from gallons to liters. 2.50sh, Conversion from miles to kilometers.

**1971, Jan. 4 Photo. *Perf. 14½***

| | | | | | |
|---|---|---|---|---|---|
| 225 | A51 | 30c | silver & multi | .25 | .25 |
| 226 | A51 | 70c | silver & multi | .25 | .25 |
| 227 | A51 | 1.50sh | silver & multi | .25 | .25 |
| 228 | A51 | 2.50sh | silver & multi | .25 | *.80* |
| | | | *Nos. 225-228 (4)* | 1.00 | 1.55 |

Conversion to metric system of weights and measures.

Locomotive — A52

Designs: Various locomotives.

**1971, Apr. 19 Photo. *Perf. 14½***

| | | | | | |
|---|---|---|---|---|---|
| 229 | A52 | 30c | gold & multi | .30 | .25 |
| 230 | A52 | 70c | gold & multi | .35 | .25 |
| 231 | A52 | 1.50sh | gold & multi | .80 | .25 |
| 232 | A52 | 2.50sh | gold & multi | 1.00 | *2.00* |
| *a.* | | | Souvenir sheet of 4, #229-232 | 8.50 | 8.50 |
| | | | *Nos. 229-232 (4)* | 2.45 | 2.75 |

70th anniversary of the completion of the Mombasa to Kisumu line.

Campaign Emblem and Cow — A53

Designs: 1.50sh, Like 30c. 70c, 2.50sh, Bull and Campaign Emblem.

**1971, July 5 Photo. *Perf. 14½***

| | | | | | |
|---|---|---|---|---|---|
| 233 | A53 | 30c | yel grn, blk & bis | .25 | .25 |
| 234 | A53 | 70c | gray bl, blk & bis | .25 | .25 |
| 235 | A53 | 1.50sh | mag, blk & bis | .25 | .25 |
| 236 | A53 | 2.50sh | red org, blk & bis | .25 | *.65* |
| | | | *Nos. 233-236 (4)* | 1.00 | 1.40 |

Rinderpest campaign by the Organization for African Unity.

Meeting of Stanley and Livingstone — A54

**1971, Oct. 28 Litho. *Perf. 14***

| | | | | | |
|---|---|---|---|---|---|
| 237 | A54 | 5sh | multicolored | .40 | .40 |

Centenary of the meeting at Ujiji of Dr. David Livingstone, missionary, and Henry M. Stanley, journalist, who had been sent to find Livingstone.

Modern Farming Village — A55

Designs: 30c, Pres. Julius K. Nyerere carried in triumph, 1961, vert. 1.50sh, University of Dar es Salaam. 2.50sh, Kilimanjaro International Airport.

**1971, Dec. 9 *Perf. 14***

| | | | | | |
|---|---|---|---|---|---|
| 238 | A55 | 30c | bister & multi | .25 | .25 |
| 239 | A55 | 70c | lt blue & multi | .25 | .25 |
| 240 | A55 | 1.50sh | lt green & multi | .25 | .25 |
| 241 | A55 | 2.50sh | yel & multi | .50 | *1.75* |
| | | | *Nos. 238-241 (4)* | 1.25 | 2.50 |

10th anniv. of independence of Tanzania.

Flags of African Nations and Fair Emblem — A56

**1972, Feb. 23 *Perf. 13½x14***

| | | | | | |
|---|---|---|---|---|---|
| 242 | A56 | 30c | lt bl & multi | .25 | .25 |
| 243 | A56 | 70c | gray & multi | .25 | .25 |
| 244 | A56 | 1.50sh | yel & multi | .25 | .25 |
| 245 | A56 | 2.50sh | multicolored | .25 | *.75* |
| | | | *Nos. 242-245 (4)* | 1.00 | 1.50 |

First All-Africa Trade Fair, Nairobi, Kenya, Feb. 23-Mar. 5.

Child Drinking Milk, UNICEF Emblem
A57

25th Anniv. (in 1971) of UNICEF: 70c, Children playing ball. 1.50sh, Child writing on blackboard. 2.50sh, Boy playing with tractor.

**1972, Apr. 24 Litho. *Perf. 14½x14***

| | | | | | |
|---|---|---|---|---|---|
| 246 | A57 | 30c | brn org & multi | .25 | .25 |
| 247 | A57 | 70c | lt ultra & multi | .25 | .25 |
| 248 | A57 | 1.50sh | yel & multi | .25 | .25 |
| 249 | A57 | 2.50sh | green & multi | .25 | *.75* |
| | | | *Nos. 246-249 (4)* | 1.00 | 1.50 |

Hurdles, Olympic and Motion Emblems — A58

**1972, Aug. 28**

| | | | | | |
|---|---|---|---|---|---|
| 250 | A58 | 40c | shown | .25 | .25 |
| 251 | A58 | 70c | Running | .25 | .25 |
| 252 | A58 | 1.50sh | Boxing | .25 | .25 |
| 253 | A58 | 2.50sh | Hockey | .30 | *1.50* |
| *a.* | | | Souvenir sheet of 4, #250-253 | 6.75 | 6.75 |
| | | | *Nos. 250-253 (4)* | 1.05 | 2.25 |

20th Olympic Games, Munich, 8/26-9/11.

Uganda Kob, Semliki Game Reserve — A59

70c, Intl. Conf. Center. 1.50sh, Makerere Univ., Kampala. 2.50sh, Uganda arms.

**1972, Oct. 9 Litho. *Perf. 14***

| | | | | | |
|---|---|---|---|---|---|
| 254 | A59 | 40c | shown | .25 | .25 |
| 255 | A59 | 70c | multicolored | .30 | .25 |
| 256 | A59 | 1.50sh | multicolored | .60 | .30 |
| 257 | A59 | 2.50sh | multicolored | 1.00 | *2.00* |
| *a.* | | | Souvenir sheet of 4, #254-257, perf. 13x14 | 4.50 | 4.50 |
| | | | *Nos. 254-257 (4)* | 2.15 | 2.80 |

Uganda's independence, 10th anniv. No. 256 also for 50th anniv. of Makerere University, Kampala.

Flag of East Africa — A60

**1972, Dec. 1 Litho. *Perf. 14½x14***

| | | | | | |
|---|---|---|---|---|---|
| 258 | A60 | 5sh | multicolored | .85 | .85 |

5th anniv. of the East African Community.

Anemometer, Lake Victoria Station — A61

WMO Emblem and: 70c, Release of weather balloon, vert. 1.50sh, Hail suppression by meteorological rocket. 2.50sh, Meteorological satellite receiving antenna.

**1973, Mar. 5 Litho. *Perf. 14***

| | | | | | |
|---|---|---|---|---|---|
| 259 | A61 | 40c | multicolored | .25 | .25 |
| 260 | A61 | 70c | ultra & multi | .25 | .25 |
| 261 | A61 | 1.50sh | emer & multi | .25 | .25 |
| 262 | A61 | 2.50sh | multicolored | .35 | *1.00* |
| | | | *Nos. 259-262 (4)* | 1.10 | 1.75 |

Cent. of intl. meteorological cooperation.

Scouts Laying Bricks — A62

Designs: 70c, Baden-Powell's gravestone, Nyeri, Kenya. 1.50sh, World Scout emblem. 2.50sh, Lord Baden-Powell.

**1973, July 16 Litho. *Perf. 14***

| | | | | | |
|---|---|---|---|---|---|
| 263 | A62 | 40c | ocher & multi | .25 | .25 |
| 264 | A62 | 70c | multicolored | .30 | .25 |
| 265 | A62 | 1.50sh | multicolored | .50 | .30 |
| 266 | A62 | 2.50sh | grn & ultra | 1.25 | *1.60* |
| | | | *Nos. 263-266 (4)* | 2.30 | 2.40 |

24th Boy Scout World Conference (1st in Africa), Nairobi, Kenya, July 16-21.

International Bank for Reconstruction and Development and Affiliates' Emblems — A63

Designs: 40c, Arrows dividing 4 bank affiliate emblems. 70c, Vert. lines dividing 4 emblems. 1.50sh, Kenyatta Conference Center, Nairobi, vert.

**1973, Sept. 24 Litho. *Perf. 14x13½***

| | | | | | |
|---|---|---|---|---|---|
| 267 | A63 | 40c | gray, blk & grn | .25 | .25 |
| 268 | A63 | 70c | brn, gray & blk | .25 | .25 |
| 269 | A63 | 1.50sh | lem, gray & blk | .25 | *.30* |
| 270 | A63 | 2.50sh | blk, org & gray | .25 | *1.50* |
| *a.* | | | Souvenir sheet of 4 | 2.50 | *2.50* |
| | | | *Nos. 267-270 (4)* | 1.00 | 2.30 |

Intl. Bank for Reconstruction and Development and Affiliate Intl. Monetary Fund Meetings, Nairobi.

No. 270a contains stamps similar to Nos. 267-270 with simulated perforations.

INTERPOL Emblem, Policeman and Dog — A64

Designs: 70c, East African policemen and emblem. 1.50sh, INTERPOL emblem. 2.50sh, INTERPOL Headquarters, St. Cloud, France.

**1973-74 Litho. *Perf. 14x14½***

| | | | | | |
|---|---|---|---|---|---|
| 271 | A64 | 40c | yellow & multi | .55 | .25 |
| 272 | A64 | 70c | multicolored | .75 | .25 |
| 273 | A64 | 1.50sh | violet & multi | 1.25 | .85 |
| 274 | A64 | 2.50sh | lemon & multi *(St. Clans)* | 3.50 | *4.75* |
| 275 | A64 | 2.50sh | lemon & multi *(St. Cloud)* ('74) | 5.25 | *5.75* |
| | | | *Nos. 271-275 (5)* | 11.30 | 11.85 |

50th anniv. of Intl. Criminal Police Org. Issued: Nos. 271-274, Oct. 24, 1973.

Tea Factory, Nandi Hills — A65

**1973, Dec. 12 Photo. *Perf. 13x14***

| | | | | | |
|---|---|---|---|---|---|
| 276 | A65 | 40c | shown | .25 | .25 |
| 277 | A65 | 70c | Kenyatta Hospital | .25 | .25 |
| 278 | A65 | 1.50sh | Nairobi Airport | .50 | .25 |
| 279 | A65 | 2.50sh | Kindaruma hydroelectric plant | .75 | *1.50* |
| | | | *Nos. 276-279 (4)* | 1.75 | 2.25 |

10th anniversary of independence.

Afro-Shirazi Party Headquarters — A66

Designs: 70c, Michenzani housing development. 1.50sh, Map of East Africa and television screen with flower. 2.50sh, Amaan Stadium.

**1974, Jan. 12 Litho. *Perf. 13½x14***

| | | | | |
|---|---|---|---|---|
| **280** | A66 | 40c multicolored | .25 | .25 |
| **281** | A66 | 70c multicolored | .25 | .25 |
| **282** | A66 | 1.50sh black & multi | .35 | .25 |
| **283** | A66 | 2.50sh black & multi | .65 | *2.25* |
| | | *Nos. 280-283 (4)* | 1.50 | 3.00 |

10th anniversary of Zanzibar revolution.

Symbol of Union A67

Designs: 70c, Map of Tanganyika and Zanzibar, and handshake. 1.50sh, Map of Tanganyika and Zanzibar, and communications symbols. 2.50sh, Flags of Tanu, Tanzania and Afro-Shirazi Party.

**1974, Apr. 24 Litho. *Perf. 14½***

| | | | | |
|---|---|---|---|---|
| **284** | A67 | 40c sepia & multi | .25 | .25 |
| **285** | A67 | 70c blue grn & multi | .25 | .25 |
| **286** | A67 | 1.50sh ultra & multi | .35 | .25 |
| **287** | A67 | 2.50sh multicolored | .65 | *2.25* |
| | | *Nos. 284-287 (4)* | 1.50 | 3.00 |

Union of Tanganyika and Zanzibar, 10th anniv.

Family and Home A68

Designs: 70c, Drummer at dawn. 1.50sh, Family hoeing, and livestock. 2.50sh, Telephonist, train, plane, telegraph lines.

**1974, July 15 Litho. *Perf. 14½***

| | | | | |
|---|---|---|---|---|
| **288** | A68 | 40c multicolored | .25 | .25 |
| **289** | A68 | 70c multicolored | .25 | .25 |
| **290** | A68 | 1.50sh multicolored | .25 | .25 |
| **291** | A68 | 2.50sh multicolored | .70 | *1.10* |
| | | *Nos. 288-291 (4)* | 1.45 | 1.85 |

17th Intl. Conf. on Social Welfare, 7/14-20.

Post and Telegraph Headquarters, Kampala — A69

Cent. of the UPU: 70c, Mail train and truck. 1.50sh, UPU Headquarters, Bern. 2.50sh, Loading mail on East African Airways VC-10.

**1974, Oct. 9 Litho. *Perf. 14***

| | | | | |
|---|---|---|---|---|
| **292** | A69 | 40c lt green & multi | .25 | .25 |
| **293** | A69 | 70c gray & multi | .25 | .25 |
| **294** | A69 | 1.50sh yel & multi | .25 | .25 |
| **295** | A69 | 2.50sh lt blue & multi | .40 | *1.10* |
| | | *Nos. 292-295 (4)* | 1.15 | 1.85 |

Family Planning Clinic A70

World Population Year: 70c, "Tug of War." 1.50sh, Scales and world population figures. 2.50sh, World Population Year emblem.

**1974, Dec. 16 Litho. *Perf. 14½***

| | | | | |
|---|---|---|---|---|
| **296** | A70 | 40c multicolored | .25 | .25 |
| **297** | A70 | 70c purple & multi | .25 | .25 |
| **298** | A70 | 1.50sh multicolored | .25 | .25 |
| **299** | A70 | 2.50sh blue blk & multi | .30 | *1.25* |
| | | *Nos. 296-299 (4)* | 1.05 | 2.00 |

Seronera Wild Life Lodge, Tanzania — A71

Game lodges of East Africa: 70c, Mweya Safari Lodge, Uganda. 1.50sh, Ark-Aberdare Forest Lodge, Kenya. 2.50sh, Paraa Safari Lodge, Uganda.

**1975, Feb. 24 Litho. *Perf. 14½***

| | | | | |
|---|---|---|---|---|
| **300** | A71 | 40c multicolored | .25 | .25 |
| **301** | A71 | 70c multicolored | .25 | .25 |
| **302** | A71 | 1.50sh multicolored | .25 | .30 |
| **303** | A71 | 2.50sh multicolored | .75 | *1.75* |
| | | *Nos. 300-303 (4)* | 1.50 | 2.55 |

Wooden Comb, Bajun, Kenya — A72

African Artifacts: 1sh, Earring, Chaga, Tanzania. 2sh, Armlet, Acholi, Uganda. 3sh, Kamba gourd, Kenya.

**1975, May 5 Litho. *Perf. 13½***

| | | | | |
|---|---|---|---|---|
| **304** | A72 | 50c gray & multi | .25 | .25 |
| **305** | A72 | 1sh gray & multi | .25 | .25 |
| **306** | A72 | 2sh multicolored | .30 | .35 |
| **307** | A72 | 3sh multicolored | .60 | *1.25* |
| | | *Nos. 304-307 (4)* | 1.40 | 2.10 |

Map Showing OAU Members, Ugandan Flag — A73

OAU Emblem and: 50c, Entebbe Airport, horiz. 2sh, Nile Hotel, Kampala, horiz. 3sh, Ugandan Martyrs' Shrine, Namugongo.

***Perf. 11½x11, 11x11½***

**1975, July 28 Litho.**

| | | | | |
|---|---|---|---|---|
| **308** | A73 | 50c multicolored | .35 | .25 |
| **309** | A73 | 1sh multicolored | .35 | .25 |
| **310** | A73 | 2sh multicolored | .35 | .50 |
| **311** | A73 | 3sh multicolored | .55 | *1.25* |
| | | *Nos. 308-311 (4)* | 1.60 | 2.25 |

Organization for African Unity (OAU), Summit Conf., Kampala, July 28 - Aug. 1.

Elephant, Kenya — A74

Protected animals: 1sh, Albino buffalo, Uganda. 2sh, Elephant, exhibit in National Museum, Kenya. 3sh, Abbott's duiker, Tanzania.

**1975, Sept. 11 Litho. *Perf. 11x11½***

| | | | | |
|---|---|---|---|---|
| **312** | A74 | 50c multicolored | .60 | .25 |
| **313** | A74 | 1sh brown & multi | .65 | .25 |
| **314** | A74 | 2sh yel green & multi | 1.60 | 1.50 |
| **315** | A74 | 3sh blue grn & multi | 2.25 | 2.25 |
| | | *Nos. 312-315 (4)* | 5.10 | 4.25 |

Masai Villagers Bleeding Cow, Masai, Kenya — A75

Festival Emblem and: 1sh, Ugandan dancers. 2sh, Family, Makonde sculpture, Tanzania. 3sh, Skinning hippopotamus, East Africa.

**1975, Nov. 3 Litho. *Perf. 13½x14***

| | | | | |
|---|---|---|---|---|
| **316** | A75 | 50c org brown & multi | .25 | .25 |
| **317** | A75 | 1sh brt green & multi | .25 | .25 |
| **318** | A75 | 2sh dk blue & multi | .55 | *.80* |
| **319** | A75 | 3sh lilac & multi | .85 | *1.25* |
| | | *Nos. 316-319 (4)* | 1.90 | 2.55 |

2nd World Black and African Festival of Arts and Culture, Lagos, Nigeria, Jan. 5 - Feb. 12.

Fokker Friendship, Nairobi Airport — A76

East African Airways, 30th anniv.: 1sh, DC-9 Kilimanjaro Airport. 2sh, Super VC10, Entebbe Airport. 3sh, East African Airways emblem.

**1976, Jan. 2 Litho. *Perf. 11½***

| | | | | |
|---|---|---|---|---|
| **320** | A76 | 50c ultra & multi | 1.10 | .75 |
| **321** | A76 | 1sh rose & multi | 1.25 | .75 |
| **322** | A76 | 2sh orange & multi | 3.25 | 3.25 |
| **323** | A76 | 3sh black & multi | 3.75 | 4.00 |
| | | *Nos. 320-323 (4)* | 9.35 | 8.75 |

## POSTAGE DUE STAMPS

### Kenya and Uganda

D1

***Perf. 14½x14***

**1928-33 Typo. Wmk. 4**

| | | | | |
|---|---|---|---|---|
| **J1** | D1 | 5c deep violet | 2.25 | 1.00 |
| **J2** | D1 | 10c orange red | 2.25 | .60 |
| **J3** | D1 | 20c yel green | 3.50 | 4.25 |
| **J4** | D1 | 30c ol brn ('31) | 22.50 | 20.00 |
| **J5** | D1 | 40c dull blue | 6.00 | *15.00* |
| **J6** | D1 | 1sh grnsh gray ('33) | 60.00 | *145.00* |
| | | *Nos. J1-J6 (6)* | 96.50 | *185.85* |
| | | Set, never hinged | 160.00 | |

### Kenya, Uganda, Tanganyika

D2

**1935, May 1 *Perf. 13½x14***

| | | | | |
|---|---|---|---|---|
| **J7** | D2 | 5c violet | 2.50 | 1.75 |
| **J8** | D2 | 10c red | .35 | .45 |
| **J9** | D2 | 20c green | .50 | .45 |
| **J10** | D2 | 30c brown | 1.50 | .45 |
| **J11** | D2 | 40c ultramarine | 1.60 | *3.00* |
| **J12** | D2 | 1sh gray | 17.50 | 17.50 |
| | | *Nos. J7-J12 (6)* | 23.95 | *23.60* |
| | | Set, never hinged | 40.00 | |

## OFFICIAL STAMPS

The 1959-60 "OFFICIAL" overprints on Nos. 103-104, 106-108, 110, 112-117, 120-123, 125, 127, 129, 133 are listed under Tanganyika, as they were used by the Tanganyika government.

# KIAUCHAU

(Kiautschou)

LOCATION — A district of China on the south side of the Shantung peninsula.
GOVT. — German colony
AREA — 200 sq. mi.
POP. — 192,000 (approx. 1914).

The area was seized by Germany in 1897 and through negotiations that followed was leased to Germany by China.

100 Pfennig = 1 Mark
100 Cents = 1 Dollar (1905)

## TSINGTAU ISSUES

### Stamps of Germany, Offices in China 1898, with Additional Surcharge

a

b

c

On Nos. 1-9, a blue or violet line is drawn through "PF. 10 PF." All exist without this line. All examples of Nos. 1b, 2b and 3b lack the colored line.

The three surcharge types can most easily be distinguished by the differences in the lower loop of the "5."

### "China" Overprint at 56 degree Angle

**1900**

| | | | | |
|---|---|---|---|---|
| **1** | A10(a) | 5pfg on 10pf car | 45.00 | *52.50* |
| *c.* | | Dbl. surch., one inverted | 750.00 | |
| **2** | A10(b) | 5pfg on 10pf car | 45.00 | *52.50* |
| *c.* | | Dbl. surch., one inverted | 750.00 | |
| **3** | A10(c) | 5pfg on 10pf car | 45.00 | *52.50* |
| *c.* | | Dbl. surch., one inverted | 750.00 | |
| | | *Nos. 1-3 (3)* | 135.00 | 157.50 |

### "China" Overprint at 45 degree Angle

| | | | | |
|---|---|---|---|---|
| *1a* | A10(a) | 5pfg on 10pf car | 145.00 | *130.00* |
| *b.* | | Double surcharge | 450.00 | *575.00* |
| *2a* | A10(b) | 5pfg on 10pf car | 145.00 | *130.00* |
| *b.* | | Double surcharge | 450.00 | *575.00* |
| *3a* | A10(c) | 5pfg on 10pf car | 145.00 | *130.00* |
| *b.* | | Double surcharge | 450.00 | *575.00* |
| | | *Nos. 1a-3a (3)* | 435.00 | 390.00 |

### Surcharged

d

e

**5 Pf.**

f

### "China" Overprint at 48 degree Angle on Nos. 4-9

| | | | | |
|---|---|---|---|---|
| **4** | A10(d) | 5pf on 10pf car | 3,250. | 4,000. |
| *a.* | | Double surcharge | *8,250.* | *18,000.* |
| **5** | A10(e) | 5pf on 10pf car | *3,250.* | *4,000.* |
| *a.* | | Double surcharge | *8,250.* | *18,000.* |
| **6** | A10(f) | 5pf on 10pf car | *3,250.* | *4,000.* |
| *a.* | | Double surcharge | *8,250.* | *18,000.* |
| *b.* | | 5fP | | *18,000.* |
| *c.* | | As "b," double surcharge | — | — |

With Add'l Handstamp **5**

| | | | | |
|---|---|---|---|---|
| **7** | A10(d) | 5pf on 10pf car | *40,000.* | *50,000.* |
| **8** | A10(f) | 5pf on 10pf car | *40,000.* | *50,000.* |
| *a.* | | On No. 6b | — | — |

With Additional Handstamp

| | | | | |
|---|---|---|---|---|
| 9 | A10(f) | 5pf on 10pf car | *8,250.* | *12,500.* |
| *a.* | | Double surcharge | *37,500.* | |
| *b.* | | On No. 6a | | |
| *c.* | | On No. 6b | | |
| *d.* | | On No. 6c | | |

Kaiser's Yacht "Hohenzollern"
A1 A2

**1901, Jan. Unwmk. Typo.** ***Perf. 14***

| | | | | |
|---|---|---|---|---|
| **10** | A1 | 3pf brown | 2.00 | 2.00 |
| **11** | A1 | 5pf green | 2.00 | 1.75 |
| **12** | A1 | 10pf carmine | 2.50 | 2.10 |
| **13** | A1 | 20pf ultra | 7.50 | 8.50 |
| **14** | A1 | 25pf org & blk, *yel* | 13.50 | *17.00* |
| **15** | A1 | 30pf org & blk, *sal* | 13.50 | *16.50* |
| **16** | A1 | 40pf lake & blk | 16.00 | *21.00* |
| **17** | A1 | 50pf pur & blk, *sal* | 16.00 | *22.50* |
| **18** | A1 | 80pf lake & blk, *rose* | 30.00 | *52.50* |
| | | **Engr.** ***Perf. 14½x14*** | | |
| **19** | A2 | 1m carmine | 50.00 | *92.50* |
| **20** | A2 | 2m blue | 75.00 | *110.00* |
| **21** | A2 | 3m blk vio | 75.00 | *200.00* |
| **22** | A2 | 5m slate & car | 210.00 | *650.00* |
| | | *Nos. 10-22 (13)* | 513.00 | *1,196.* |
| | | Set, never hinged | 1,350. | |

A3

A4

**1905** **Typo.**

| | | | | |
|---|---|---|---|---|
| **23** | A3 | 1c brown | 1.25 | 1.75 |
| **24** | A3 | 2c green | 2.00 | 1.75 |
| **25** | A3 | 4c carmine | 4.50 | 1.75 |
| **26** | A3 | 10c ultra | 8.50 | 5.50 |
| **27** | A3 | 20c lake & blk | 34.00 | 20.00 |
| **28** | A3 | 40c lake & blk, *rose* | 100.00 | *100.00* |
| | | **Engr.** | | |
| **29** | A4 | $½ carmine | 72.50 | *85.00* |
| **30a** | A4 | $1 blue | 150.00 | 130.00 |
| **31** | A4 | $1½ blk vio, 26x17 holes | 1,200. | *1,700.* |
| *a.* | | blk vio, 25x16 holes | *24,000.* | |
| **32** | A4 | $2½ slate & car, 26x17 holes | 1,500. | *5,000.* |
| *a.* | | $2½ slate & car, 25x16 holes | 2,100. | *3,500.* |
| | | *Nos. 23-32 (10)* | 3,073. | *7,041.* |
| | | Set, never hinged | 8,000. | |

**1905-16 Wmk. 125 Typo.**

| | | | | |
|---|---|---|---|---|
| **33** | A3 | 1c brown ('06) | 1.25 | 1.50 |
| *a.* | | 1c yellow brown ('16) | .50 | — |
| **34** | A3 | 2c green ('09) | 1.10 | *1.10* |
| *a.* | | 2c dark green ('14) | .50 | *1.75* |
| **35** | A3 | 4c carmine ('09) | 1.00 | *1.10* |
| **36** | A3 | 10c ultra ('09) | 1.10 | *3.25* |
| *a.* | | 10c blue | 12.00 | 5.00 |
| **37** | A3 | 20c lake & blk ('08) | 3.00 | *16.00* |
| **38** | A3 | 40c lake & blk, *rose* | 3.75 | *52.50* |
| | | **Engr.** | | |
| **39** | A4 | $½ car, 26x17 holes ('07) | 9.50 | *65.00* |
| **40** | A4 | $1 blue, 26x17 holes ('06) | 12.50 | *67.50* |
| **41** | A4 | $1½ blk violet | 11.00 | *225.00* |
| **42** | A4 | $2½ slate & car | 50.00 | *475.00* |
| | | *Nos. 33-42 (10)* | 94.20 | 907.95 |
| | | Set, never hinged | 550.00 | |

Four values of the design A3 and A4 stamps in recognizably different shades were printed and released in 1918, but by then Germany had lost control of Kiauchau, and these stamps are not known used. The four stamps and their unused values are: 20c red & black, $1.75; $½ pale rose, $5.50; $1 bright blue, $6.75; $1½ gray violet, $20.

## KIONGA

'kyoŋ-gə

LOCATION — Southeast Africa and northeast Mozambique, on Indian Ocean south of Rovuma River
GOVT. — Part of German East Africa
AREA — 400 sq. mi.

This territory, occupied by Portuguese troops during World War I, was allotted to Portugal by the Treaty of Versailles. Later it became part of Mozambique.

100 Centavos = 1 Escudo

Lourenco Marques No. 149 Surcharged in Red

**1916, May 29 Unwmk.** ***Perf. 11½***

| | | | | |
|---|---|---|---|---|
| **1** | A2 | ½c on 100r bl, *bl* | 30.00 | 20.00 |
| **2** | A2 | 1c on 100r bl, *bl* | 25.00 | 17.00 |
| **3** | A2 | 2½c on 100r bl, *bl* | 25.00 | 17.00 |
| **4** | A2 | 5c on 100r bl, *bl* | 25.00 | 17.00 |
| | | *Nos. 1-4 (4)* | 105.00 | 71.00 |

Most of the stock of Lourenço Marques No. 149 used for these surcharges lacked gum. Unused examples with original gum are worth approximately 50% more than the values shown.

## KIRIBATI

'kir-ə-ˌbas

LOCATION — A group of islands in the Pacific Ocean northeast of Australia
GOVT. — Republic
AREA — 277 sq. mi.
POP. — 85,501 (1999 est.)
CAPITAL — Tarawa

100 Cents = 1 Australian Dollar

Kiribati, former Gilbert Islands, consists of the Gilbert, Phoenix, Ocean and Line Islands.

**Catalogue values for all unused stamps in this country are for Never Hinged items.**

**Watermark**

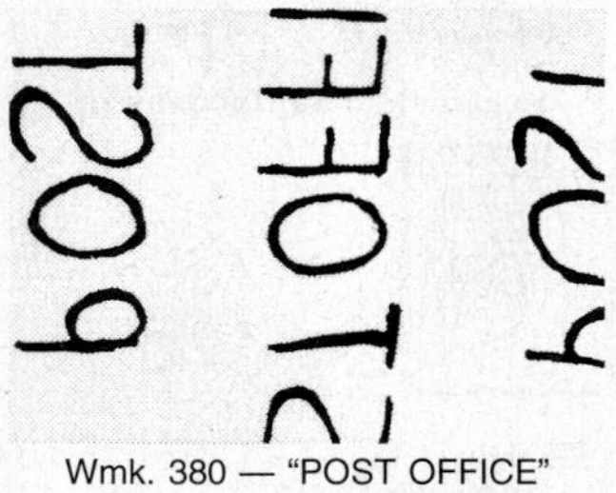

Wmk. 380 — "POST OFFICE"

Kiribati Flag A50

Parliament, London, Assembly, Tarawa — A51

**Wmk. 373**

**1979, July 12 Litho.** ***Perf. 14***

| | | | | |
|---|---|---|---|---|
| **325** | A50 | 10c multicolored | .25 | .30 |
| **326** | A51 | 45c multicolored | .25 | .50 |

Independence.

Training Ship Teraaka A52

Designs: 3c, Passenger launch Tautunu. 5c, Hibiscus. 7c, Cathedral, Tarawa. 10c, House of Assembly, Bikenibeu Island. 12c, Betio harbor. 15c, Reef egret. 20c, Flamboyant tree. 25c, Moorish idol (fish). 30c, Frangipani blossoms. 35c, Chapel, Tangintebu Island. 50c, Hypolimnas bolina elliciana (butterfly). $1, Tarawa Lagoon ferry, Tabakea. $2, Sunset over lagoon. $5, Natl. flag.

**1979-80** **Wmk. 373**

| | | | | |
|---|---|---|---|---|
| **327** | A52 | 1c multicolored | .25 | .65 |
| **328** | A52 | 3c multicolored | .25 | .35 |
| **329** | A52 | 5c multicolored | .25 | .25 |
| **330** | A52 | 7c multicolored | .25 | .25 |
| **331** | A52 | 10c multicolored | .25 | .25 |
| **332** | A52 | 12c multicolored | .25 | *.25* |
| **333** | A52 | 15c multicolored | .30 | .30 |
| **334** | A52 | 20c multicolored | .25 | *.30* |
| **335** | A52 | 25c multicolored | .25 | *.30* |
| **336** | A52 | 30c multicolored | .25 | .30 |
| **337** | A52 | 35c multicolored | .25 | .30 |
| **338** | A52 | 50c multicolored | .70 | .55 |
| **339** | A52 | $1 multicolored | .55 | .60 |
| **340** | A52 | $2 multicolored | .55 | .70 |
| **340A** | A52 | $5 multicolored | 1.25 | *3.00* |
| | | *Nos. 327-340A (15)* | 5.85 | 8.35 |

Issued: $5, 8/27/80; others, 7/12/79.

**1980-81** **Unwmk.**

| | | | | |
|---|---|---|---|---|
| *327a* | A52 | 1c multi ('81) | .25 | .35 |
| *328a* | A52 | 3c multi ('81) | .25 | .35 |
| *329a* | A52 | 5c multi | .25 | .35 |
| *330a* | A52 | 7c multi | .25 | .35 |
| *331a* | A52 | 10c multi | .25 | .35 |
| *332a* | A52 | 12c multi | .25 | .35 |
| *333a* | A52 | 15c multi | .65 | .35 |
| *334a* | A52 | 20c multi ('81) | .25 | .35 |
| *335a* | A52 | 25c multi | .35 | .35 |
| *336a* | A52 | 30c multi ('81) | .25 | .75 |
| *337a* | A52 | 35c multi ('81) | .25 | .75 |
| *338a* | A52 | 50c multi ('81) | .90 | 1.10 |
| *339a* | A52 | $1 multi | .75 | .75 |
| *340b* | A52 | $2 multi | 1.40 | 1.05 |
| *340c* | A52 | $5 multi ('80) | 2.25 | 3.75 |
| | | *Nos. 327a-340c (15)* | 8.55 | 11.30 |

For overprints see Nos. O1-O15.

Gilbert and Ellice Islands No. 1 — A53

Simulated Cancel and: 20c, Gilbert and Ellice No. 70. 25c, Great Britain No. 139. 45c, Gilbert and Ellice No. 31.

**Wmk. 373**

**1979, Oct. 4 Litho.** ***Perf. 14***

| | | | | |
|---|---|---|---|---|
| **341** | A53 | 10c multicolored | .25 | .25 |
| **342** | A53 | 20c multicolored | .25 | .25 |
| **343** | A53 | 25c multicolored | .25 | .25 |
| **344** | A53 | 45c multicolored | .25 | .25 |
| *a.* | | Souvenir sheet of 4, #341-344 | 1.25 | 1.25 |
| | | *Nos. 341-344 (4)* | 1.00 | 1.00 |

Sir Rowland Hill (1795-1879), originator of penny postage.

Boy Climbing Coconut Palm, IYC Emblem — A54

IYC Emblem, Coat of Arms and: 10c, Boy and giant clam shell. 45c, Girl reading book. $1, Boy wearing garlands. All vert.

***Perf. 14x13½, 13½x14***

**1979, Nov. 28** **Litho.**

| | | | | |
|---|---|---|---|---|
| **345** | A54 | 10c multicolored | .25 | .25 |
| **346** | A54 | 20c multicolored | .25 | .25 |
| **347** | A54 | 45c multicolored | .25 | .25 |
| **348** | A54 | $1 multicolored | .25 | .25 |
| | | *Nos. 345-348 (4)* | 1.00 | 1.00 |

International Year of the Child.

Downrange Station — A55

National Space Development Agency of Japan (NASDA) Satellite Tracking: 45c, Experimental satellite trajectory (map). $1, Rocket launch, Tanegashima, Japan, vert.

**1980, Feb. 20 Litho.** ***Perf. 14½***

| | | | | |
|---|---|---|---|---|
| **349** | A55 | 25c multicolored | .25 | .25 |
| **350** | A55 | 45c multicolored | .25 | .25 |
| **351** | A55 | $1 multicolored | .25 | .25 |
| | | *Nos. 349-351 (3)* | .75 | .75 |

T.S. Teraaka, London 1980 Emblem A56

25c, Air Tungaru plane, Bonriki Airport. 30c, Radio operator. $1, Bairiki post office.

**1980, Apr. 30 Litho. Unwmk.**

| | | | | |
|---|---|---|---|---|
| **352** | A56 | 12c shown | .25 | .25 |
| **353** | A56 | 25c multicolored | .25 | .25 |
| **354** | A56 | 30c multicolored | .25 | .25 |
| **355** | A56 | $1 multicolored | .25 | .35 |
| *a.* | | Souvenir sheet of 4, #352-355 | .75 | .85 |
| | | *Nos. 352-355 (4)* | 1.00 | 1.10 |

London 1980 Intl. Stamp Exhib., May 6-14.

Achaea Janata A57

25c, Ethmia nigroapicella. 30c, Utetheisa pulchelloides. 50c, Anua coronata.

**1980, Aug. 27 Litho.** ***Perf. 14***

| | | | | |
|---|---|---|---|---|
| **356** | A57 | 12c shown | .25 | .25 |
| **357** | A57 | 25c multicolored | .25 | .25 |
| **358** | A57 | 30c multicolored | .30 | .30 |
| **359** | A57 | 50c multicolored | .45 | .45 |
| | | *Nos. 356-359 (4)* | 1.25 | 1.25 |

Capt. Cook Hotel A58

**1980, Nov. 19 Wmk. 373** ***Perf. 13½***

| | | | | |
|---|---|---|---|---|
| **360** | A58 | 10c shown | .25 | .25 |
| **361** | A58 | 20c Stadium | .25 | .25 |
| **362** | A58 | 25c Intl. Airport, Bonriki | .25 | .25 |

**363** A58 35c National Library .25 .25
**364** A58 $1 Otintai Hotel .25 .25
*Nos. 360-364 (5)* 1.25 1.25

Acalypha Godseffiana A59

30c, Hibiscus schizopetalus. 35c, Calotropis gigantea. 50c, Euphorbia pulcherrima.

***Perf. 14x13½***

**1981, Feb. 18 Litho. Wmk. 373**

**365** A59 12c shown .25 .25
**366** A59 30c multicolored .25 .25
**367** A59 35c multicolored .25 .25
**368** A59 50c multicolored .25 .25
*Nos. 365-368 (4)* 1.00 1.00

Abaiang and Marakei Islands, String Figures — A60

30c, Butaritari, Little Makin, house. 35c, Maiana, Coral Road. $1, Christmas Island, Resolution.

**Wmk. 380**

**1981, May 6 Litho. *Perf. 14***

**369** A60 12c shown .25 .25
**370** A60 30c multicolored .25 .25
**371** A60 35c multicolored .25 .25
**372** A60 $1 multicolored .45 .45
*Nos. 369-372 (4)* 1.20 1.20

Prince Charles, Lady Diana, Royal Yacht Charlotte A60a

Prince Charles and Lady Diana — A60b

No. 373, Couple, The Katherine. No. 374, Couple. No. 375, The Osborne. No. 377, Britannia.

**Wmk. 380**

**1981, July 29 Litho. *Perf. 14***

**373** A60a 12c multi .25 .25
***a.*** Bklt. pane of 4, perf. 12, unwmkd. .75
**374** A60b 12c multi .30 .25
**375** A60a 50c multi .85 .50
**376** A60b 50c like #374 .90 .50
***a.*** Bklt. pane of 2, perf. 12, unwmkd. 2.25
**377** A60a $2 multi 2.25 1.60
**378** A60b $2 like #374 2.25 1.60
*Nos. 373-378 (6)* 6.80 4.70

**Souvenir Sheet**

***Perf. 12***

**379** A60b $1.20 like #374 3.00 3.00

Royal wedding.

Stamps of the same denomination issued in sheets of 7 (6 type A60a and 1 type A60b).

Bonriki Tuna Fish Bait Breeding Center A61

**1981, Nov. 19**

**380** A61 12c shown .25 .25
**381** A61 30c Fishing boat .25 .25
**382** A61 35c Cold storage, Betio .25 .25
**383** A61 50c Nei Manganibuka .25 .25
***a.*** Souvenir sheet of 4, #380-383 1.25 1.25
*Nos. 380-383 (4)* 1.00 1.00

Pomarine Jaegers A62

2c, Mallards. 4c, Collared petrels. 5c, Blue-faced boobies. 7c, Friendly quail dove. 8c, Shovelers. 12c, Christmas Island warblers. 15c, Pacific plovers. 20c, Reef herons. 25c, Brown noddies. 30c, Brown boobies. 35c, Audubon's shearwaters. 40c, White-throated storm petrels, vert. 50c, Bristle-thighed curlews, vert. 55c, Fairy tern. $1, Scarlet-breasted lorikeets, vert. $2, Long-tailed cuckoo, vert. $5, Great frigate birds, vert.

**1982-85 Litho. *Perf. 14***

**384** A62 1c shown .25 .25
**385** A62 2c multicolored .25 .25
**386** A62 4c multicolored .25 .25
**387** A62 5c multicolored .25 .25
**388** A62 7c multicolored .25 .25
**389** A62 8c multicolored .25 .25
**390** A62 12c multicolored .30 .25
**391** A62 15c multicolored .35 .35
**392** A62 20c multicolored .40 .50
**392A** A62 25c multi ('83) 2.75 1.75
**393** A62 30c multicolored .55 .60
**394** A62 35c multicolored .75 .70
**395** A62 40c multicolored .70 .80
**396** A62 50c multicolored .75 .65
**396A** A62 55c multi ('85) 12.50 *17.00*
**397** A62 $1 multicolored 1.60 .85
**398** A62 $2 multicolored 2.25 1.10
**399** A62 $5 multicolored 4.50 4.00
*Nos. 384-399 (18)* 28.90 30.05

Issued: 25c, 1/31/83; 55c, 11/19/85; others, 2/18/82.

For overprints see Nos. O16-O20.

Air Tungaru A63

12c, De Havilland DH114 Heron. 30c, Britten-Norman Trislander. 35c, Casa 212 Aviocar. 50c, Boeing 727.

**1982, Feb. 18 Wmk. 380**

**400** A63 12c multicolored .25 .25
**401** A63 30c multicolored .25 .25
**402** A63 35c multicolored .25 .25
**403** A63 50c multicolored .40 .40
*Nos. 400-403 (4)* 1.15 1.15

21st Birthday of Princess Diana, July 1 — A64

**1982, May 19**

**404** A64 12c Mary of Teck, 1893 .25 .25
**405** A64 50c Teck arms .40 .40
**406** A64 $1 Diana .60 .60
*Nos. 404-406 (3)* 1.25 1.25

**Nos. 404-406 Overprinted: "ROYAL BABY"**

**1982, July 14**

**407** A64 12c multicolored .25 .25
**408** A64 50c multicolored .40 .40
**409** A64 $1 multicolored .60 .60
*Nos. 407-409 (3)* 1.25 1.25

Birth of Prince William of Wales, June 21.

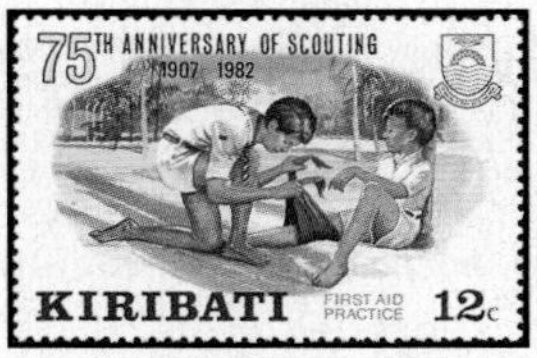


Scouting Year — A65

**1982, Aug. 12**

**410** A65 12c First aid .25 .25
**411** A65 25c Repairing boat .25 .25
**412** A65 30c Saluting .30 .30
**413** A65 50c Gilbert Islds. #304 .40 .40
*Nos. 410-413 (4)* 1.20 1.20

Visit of Queen Elizabeth II and Prince Philip A66

**Wmk. 380**

**1982, Oct. 23 Litho. *Perf. 14***

**414** A66 12c Couple, dancer .25 .25
**415** A66 25c Couple, boat .25 .25
**416** A66 35c Philatelic Bureau .45 .45
*Nos. 414-416 (3)* .95 .95

**Souvenir Sheet**

**417** A66 50c Queen Elizabeth II, vert. 1.30 1.30

Nos. 414-416 also issued in sheets of 6.

A67

12c, Obaia the Feathered legend. 30c, Robert Louis Stevenson Hotel, Abemama. 50c, Betio Harbor. $1, Map.

**1983, Mar. 14 Wmk. 380 *Perf. 14***

**418** A67 12c multicolored .25 .25
**419** A67 30c multicolored .25 .25
**420** A67 50c multicolored .25 .25
**421** A67 $1 multicolored .30 .30
*Nos. 418-421 (4)* 1.05 1.05

Commonwealth day.

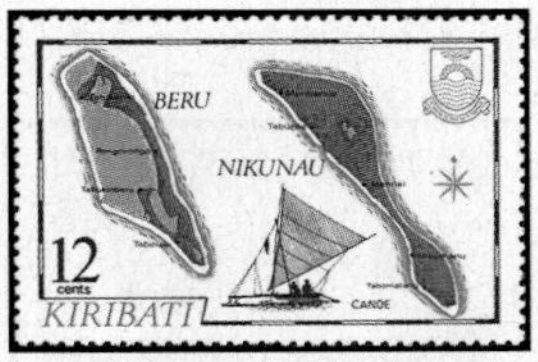


Map of Beru and Nikunau Islds., Canoe — A68

25c, Abemama, Kuria, Aranuka. 35c, Nonouti, vert. 50c, Tarawa, vert.

**1983, May 19 Litho. *Perf. 14***

**422** A68 12c shown .25 .25
**423** A68 25c multicolored .25 .25
**424** A68 35c multicolored .25 .25
**425** A68 50c multicolored .25 .25
*Nos. 422-425 (4)* 1.00 1.00

See Nos. 436-439, 456-459, 475-479, 487-490.

Copra Industry A69

Designs: 12c, Collecting fallen Coconuts. 25c, Selecting Coconuts for Copra. 30c, Removing Husk from Coconuts. 35c, Drying Copra in the Sun. 50c, Loading Copra, Betio Harbor.

**1983, Aug. 8 Litho. *Perf. 14***

**426** A69 12c multicolored .25 .25
**427** A69 25c multicolored .40 .35
**428** A69 30c multicolored .50 .45
**429** A69 35c multicolored .55 .55
**430** A69 50c multicolored .70 .70
*Nos. 426-430 (5)* 2.40 2.30

Battle of Tarawa, 40th Anniv. A70

12c, War memorials. 30c, Battle map. 35c, Defense gun. 50c, Scenes, 1943, 1983. $1, Amphibious Assault Ship USS Tarawa.

**1983, Nov. 17 Litho. Wmk. 380**

**431** A70 12c multicolored .25 .25
**432** A70 30c multicolored .25 .25
**433** A70 35c multicolored .25 .25
**434** A70 50c multicolored .30 .30
**435** A70 $1 multicolored .45 .45
*Nos. 431-435 (5)* 1.50 1.50

**Map Type of 1983**

**1984, Feb. 14 Wmk. 380 *Perf. 14***

**436** A68 12c Teraina .25 .25
**437** A68 30c Nikumaroro .35 .35
**438** A68 35c Kanton .40 .40
**439** A68 50c Banaba .60 .60
*Nos. 436-439 (4)* 1.60 1.60

Local Ships A71

12c, Tug boat. 35c, Ferry landing craft. 50c, Ferry. $1, Cargo and passanger boat.

**1984, May 9 Litho. Wmk. 380**

**440** A71 12c multicolored .45 .25
**441** A71 35c multicolored .65 .50
**442** A71 50c multicolored 1.00 .75
**443** A71 $1 multicolored 1.50 1.50
***a.*** Souvenir sheet of 4, #440-443, perf. 13½ 4.00 4.00
*Nos. 440-443 (4)* 3.60 3.00

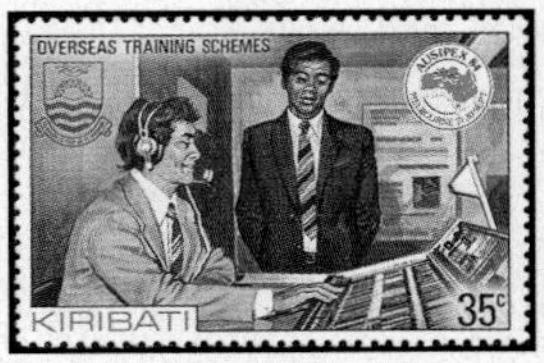


Ausipex '84 — A72

12c, South Tarawa sewer & water system. 30c, Fishing boat Nouamake. 35c, Overseas communications training. 50c, Intl. telecommunications link.

**1984, Aug. 21 Litho. *Perf. 14***

**444** A72 12c multicolored .25 .25
**445** A72 30c multicolored .25 .25
**446** A72 35c multicolored .25 .25
**447** A72 50c multicolored .35 .35
*Nos. 444-447 (4)* 1.10 1.10

Legends
A73

Designs: 12c, Tabakea supporting Banaba on his back. 30c, Nakaa, Judge of the Dead. 35c, Naareau and Tiku-Tiku-Tamoamoa. 50c, Whistling Ghosts.

**1984, Nov. 21 Wmk. 380 *Perf. 14***
**448** A73 12c multicolored .25 .25
**449** A73 30c multicolored .25 .25
**450** A73 35c multicolored .25 .25
**451** A73 50c multicolored .25 .25
*Nos. 448-451 (4)* 1.00 1.00

See Nos. 464-467.

Reef Fish
A74

12c, Tang. 25c, White-barred triggerfish. 35c, Surgeon fish. 80c, Squirrel fish.

**1985, Feb. 19 Litho. *Perf. 14***
**452** A74 12c multicolored .65 .30
**453** A74 25c multicolored 1.10 .70
**454** A74 35c multicolored 1.25 .90
**455** A74 80c multicolored 2.00 2.00
*a.* Souvenir sheet of 4, #452-455 5.50 5.50
*Nos. 452-455 (4)* 5.00 3.90

See Nos. 540-554, 567.

**Map Type of 1983**

12c, Tabuaeran, frigate bird. 35c, Rawaki, coconuts. 50c, Arorae, xanthid crab. $1, Tamana, fish hook.

**1985, May 9 Litho. *Perf. 13½***
**456** A68 12c multicolored 1.00 .35
**457** A68 35c multicolored 1.25 .50
**458** A68 50c multicolored 1.50 .70
**459** A68 $1 multicolored 2.00 1.50
*Nos. 456-459 (4)* 5.75 3.05

Intl. Youth Year
A76

15c, Boys playing soccer. 35c, Emblems. 40c, Girl processing fruit, vert. 55c, Intl. youth exchange.

**1985, Aug. 5**
**460** A76 15c multicolored .75 .50
**461** A76 35c multicolored 1.00 1.00
**462** A76 40c multicolored 1.10 1.10
**463** A76 55c multicolored 1.50 1.50
*Nos. 460-463 (4)* 4.35 4.10

**Legends Type of 1984**

15c, Nang Kineia & the Tickling Ghosts. 35c, Myth of Auriaria & Tituabine. 40c, First Coming of Babai at Arorae. 55c, Riiki & the Milky Way.

**1985, Nov. 19 Wmk. 380 *Perf. 14***
**464** A73 15c multicolored .50 .50
**465** A73 35c multicolored .75 .75
**466** A73 40c multicolored .90 .90
**467** A73 55c multicolored 1.10 1.10
*Nos. 464-467 (4)* 3.25 3.25

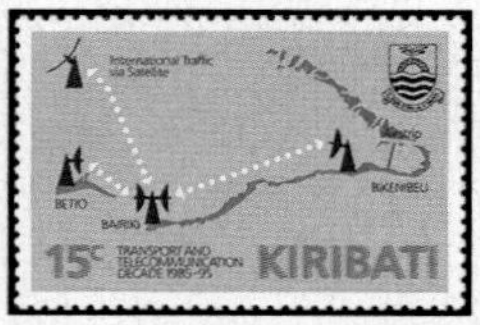

Transport and Telecommunications Decade 1985-95 — A77

15c, Satellite network. 40c, Tarawa-Suva feeder service.

**1985, Dec. 9 Litho. *Perf. 14***
**468** A77 15c multicolored 2.25 2.00
**469** A77 40c multicolored 3.25 3.00

Common Design Types pictured following the introduction.

**Queen Elizabeth II 60th Birthday**
Common Design Type

15c, Review of Girl Guides, Windsor Castle, 1938. 35c, Birthday parade, Buckingham Palace, 1980. 40c, With Prince Philip during royal tour, 1982. 55c, Banquet, Austrian embassy in London, 1966. $1, Visiting Crown Agents' offices, 1983.

**1986, Apr. 21 *Perf. 14½x14***
**470** CD337 15c scar, black & sil .25 .25
**471** CD337 35c ultra & multi .25 .25
**472** CD337 40c green & multi .25 .25
**473** CD337 55c violet & multi .40 .40
**474** CD337 $1 rose vio & multi .95 .95
*Nos. 470-474 (5)* 2.10 2.10

For overprints see Nos. 495-499.

**Map Type of 1983**

**1986, June 17 Wmk. 380 *Perf. 14***
**475** A68 15c Manra 2.50 1.50
**476** A68 30c Birnie, McKean 3.25 1.75
**477** A68 35c Orona 3.50 2.25
**478** A68 40c Malden 4.00 2.75
**479** A68 55c Vostok, Caroline, Flint 4.25 3.00
*Nos. 475-479 (5)* 17.50 11.25

Lizards
A79

15c, Lepidodactylus lugubris. 35c, Gehyra mutilata. 40c, Hemidactylus frenatus. 55c, Gehyra oceanica.

**1986, Aug. 26 Unwmk. *Perf. 14***
**480** A79 15c multicolored 1.50 .75
**481** A79 35c multicolored 2.25 1.75
**482** A79 40c multicolored 2.75 2.25
**483** A79 55c multicolored 3.50 2.75
*Nos. 480-483 (4)* 10.00 7.50

See Nos. 491-494.

America's Cup — A80

***Perf. 14x14½***
**1986, Dec. 29 Unwmk.**
**484** A80 Strip of 3 2.25 2.25
*a.* 15c Map of Australia .25 .25
*b.* 55c Course, trophy .55 .55
*c.* $1.50 Australia II 1.30 1.30

No. 484 has a continuous design.

Transport and Telecommunications Decade (1985-1995) — A81

Designs: 30c, Nei Moamoa, flagship of Kiribati overseas shipping line. 55c, Manual and electronic telephone switching systems.

**1987, Mar. 31 Litho. *Perf. 14***
**485** A81 30c multicolored 2.75 2.50
**486** A81 55c multicolored 3.50 3.50

**Map Type of 1983**

15c, Starbuck, red-tailed tropicbird. 30c, Enderbury, white tern. 55c, Tabiteuea, pandanus. $1, Onotoa, Okai house.

**1987, Sept. 22 Litho. Unwmk.**
**487** A68 15c multicolored .50 .45
**488** A68 30c multicolored .60 .45
**489** A68 55c multicolored .75 .50
**490** A68 $1 multicolored 1.25 *1.75*
*Nos. 487-490 (4)* 3.10 3.15

Nos. 487-490 vert.

**Lizard Type of 1986**

**1987, Oct. 27 *Perf. 15***
**491** A79 15c Emoia nigra .25 .25
**492** A79 35c Cryptoblepharus .25 .25
**493** A79 40c Emoia cyanura .50 .50
**494** A79 $1 Lipinia noctua .90 *1.50*
*a.* Souvenir sheet of 4, #491-494 2.00 2.00
*Nos. 491-494 (4)* 1.90 2.50

Nos. 470-474 Overprinted in Silver

***Perf. 14½x14***
**1987, Nov. 30 Litho. Unwmk.**
**495** CD337 15c scar, black & sil .25 .25
**496** CD337 35c ultra & multi .25 .30
**497** CD337 40c green & multi .35 .35
**498** CD337 55c violet & multi .45 .40
**499** CD337 $1 rose vio & multi .90 *1.25*
*Nos. 495-499 (5)* 2.20 2.55

Intl. Red Cross and Red Crescent Organizations, 125th Annivs. — A83

15c, Jean Henri Dunant (1828-1910), founder. 35c, Red Cross volunteers on parade. 40c, Stretcher bearers. 55c, Gilbert and Ellice Islands #159.

***Perf. 14½x14***
**1988, May 8 Litho. Unwmk.**
**500** A83 15c multicolored .75 .60
**501** A83 35c multicolored 1.00 *1.25*
**502** A83 40c multicolored 1.25 *1.40*
**503** A83 55c multicolored 2.25 *3.25*
*Nos. 500-503 (4)* 5.25 *6.50*

A84

SYDPEX '88, Australia Bicentennial — A85

Emblem and: 15c, Australia-assisted causeway construction. 35c, Capt. Cook, map of Australia and Kiribati. No. 506, Australia bicentennial banknote obverse. No. 507, Bank note reverse. $2, "Logistic Ace."

**1988, July 30 Litho. *Perf. 14½***
**504** A84 15c multicolored .30 .30
**505** A84 35c multicolored .60 .60
**506** A84 $1 multicolored 1.50 1.50
**507** A84 $1 multicolored 1.50 1.50
*a.* Pair, #506-507 3.50 3.50
*Nos. 504-507 (4)* 3.90 3.90

**Souvenir Sheet**
***Perf. 13½x14***
**508** A85 $2 multicolored 6.00 6.00

Robert F. Stockton, 1st propeller-driven steamship, 150th anniv.

Transport and Telecommunications Decade (1985-1995) — A86

35c, Telephone operator, map. 45c, Betio-Bairiki Causeway.

**Wmk. 373**
**1988, Dec. 28 Litho. *Perf. 14***
**509** A86 35c multicolored 1.25 1.25
**510** A86 45c multicolored 1.75 1.75

Ships
A87

15c, Brigantine Hound, 1835. 30c, Brig Phantom, 1854. 40c, HMS Alacrity, 1873. $1, Whaler Charles W. Morgan, 1851.

**Wmk. 384**
**1989, May 26 Litho. *Perf. 14½***
**511** A87 15c multicolored 1.25 .90
**512** A87 30c multicolored 2.00 1.50
**513** A87 40c multicolored 2.40 2.40
**514** A87 $1 multicolored 3.75 3.75
*Nos. 511-514 (4)* 9.40 8.55

See Nos. 557-561, 687-690.

A88

***Perf. 13½x14***
**1989, July 12 Litho. Wmk. 384**
**515** A88 15c House of Assembly .40 .40
**516** A88 $1 Constitution 2.60 2.60

Natl. Independence, 10th anniv.

**Moon Landing, 20th Anniv.**
Common Design Type

Apollo 10: 20c, Service and command modules, launch escape system. 50c, Eugene A. Cernan, Thomas P. Stafford and John W. Young. 60c, Mission emblem. 75c, Splashdown, Honolulu. $2.50, Apollo 11 command module in space.

**1989, July 20 *Perf. 14***
**Size of Nos. 518-519: 29x29mm**
**517** CD342 20c multicolored .50 .50
**518** CD342 50c multicolored .90 .90
**519** CD342 60c multicolored 1.10 1.10
**520** CD342 75c multicolored 1.25 1.25
*Nos. 517-520 (4)* 3.75 3.75

**Souvenir Sheet**
**521** CD342 $2.50 multicolored 8.75 8.75

Birds — A89

No. 522, Eastern reef heron. No. 523, Brood in nest. No. 524, White-tailed tropicbird in flight. No. 525, Seated tropicbird.

*Perf. 14½x14*

**1989, June 28 Litho. Wmk. 384**

| | | | |
|---|---|---|---|
| 522 A89 15c multicolored | 1.60 | 1.60 |
| 523 A89 15c multicolored | 1.60 | 1.60 |
| a. Pair, #522-523 | 3.75 | 3.75 |
| 524 A89 $1 multicolored | 3.00 | 3.00 |
| 525 A89 $1 multicolored | 3.00 | 3.00 |
| a. Pair, #524-525 | 6.50 | 6.50 |
| *Nos. 522-525 (4)* | 9.20 | 9.20 |

Nos. 523a, 525a have continuous designs. For overprints see Nos. 534-535.

Souvenir Sheets

A90

*Perf. 14x13½*

**1989, Aug. 7 Litho. Wmk. 384**

| | | |
|---|---|---|
| 526 A90 $2 Gilbert & Ellice Isls. #58 | 6.00 | 6.00 |

A91

Workmen renovating the Statue of Liberty: a, Torch. b, Drilling copper sheeting. c, Glancing at a sketch of the statue.

*Perf. 14x13½*

**1989, Sept. 25 Litho. Unwmk.**

| | | |
|---|---|---|
| 527 A91 Sheet of 3 | 5.50 | 5.50 |
| a.-c. 35c any single | 1.60 | 1.60 |

World Stamp Expo '89, Washington, DC, PHILEXFRANCE '89, Paris. No. 526 margin pictures #435, France #634 and US #2224.

Transport and Telecommunications Decade, 1985-95 — A92

**1989, Oct. 16 Wmk. 384 *Perf. 14***

| | | |
|---|---|---|
| 528 A92 30c shown | 2.50 | 2.25 |
| 529 A92 75c MV *Mataburo* | 3.75 | 3.25 |

Christmas — A93

Paintings: 10c, *Adoration of the Holy Child* (detail), by Denys Calvert. 15c, *Adoration of the Holy Child* (entire painting). 55c, *The Holy Family and St. Elizabeth*, by Rubens. $1, *Madonna with Child and Mary Magdalene*, School of Corregio.

**1989, Dec. 1**

| | | |
|---|---|---|
| 530 A93 10c multicolored | 1.00 | .60 |
| 531 A93 15c multicolored | 1.25 | .75 |
| 532 A93 55c multicolored | 2.50 | 1.25 |
| 533 A93 $1 multicolored | 3.75 | *6.50* |
| *Nos. 530-533 (4)* | 8.50 | 9.10 |

Nos. 524-525 Ovptd.

**1989, Oct. 21 Litho. *Perf. 14½x14***

| | | |
|---|---|---|
| 534 A89 $1 on No. 524 | 4.00 | 4.00 |
| 535 A89 $1 on No. 525 | 4.00 | 4.00 |
| a. Pair, #534-535 | 9.50 | 9.50 |

STAMPSHOW '89, Melbourne.

Penny Black 150th Anniv., Stamp World London '90 — A94

Stamps on stamps: 15c, Gilbert & Ellice #15, Great Britain #2. 50c, Gilbert & Ellice #8, Great Britain #1 canceled. 60c, Kiribati #384, Great Britain #58. $1, Gilbert Islands #269, Great Britain #3.

**1990, May 1 Litho. *Perf. 14***

| | | |
|---|---|---|
| 536 A94 15c multicolored | 1.00 | 1.00 |
| 537 A94 50c multicolored | 2.50 | 2.50 |
| 538 A94 60c multicolored | 2.60 | 2.60 |
| 539 A94 $1 multicolored | 2.75 | 2.75 |
| *Nos. 536-539 (4)* | 8.85 | 8.85 |

### Fish Type of 1985

Fish: 1c, Blue-barred orange parrotfish. 5c, Honeycomb rock cod. 10c, Bluefin jack. 15c, Paddle tail snapper. 20c, Variegated emperor. 25c, Rainbow runner. 30c, Black saddled coral trout. 35c, Great barracuda. 40c, Convict surgeonfish. 50c, Violet squirrelfish. 60c, Freckled hawkfish. 75c, Pennant coral fish. $1, Yellow and blue sea perch. $2, Pacific sailfish. $5, Whitetip reef shark.

**Wmk. 373**

**1990, July 12 Litho. *Perf. 14***

| | | |
|---|---|---|
| 540 A74 1c multicolored | .40 | .40 |
| 541 A74 5c multicolored | .50 | .50 |
| 542 A74 10c multicolored | .65 | .65 |
| 543 A74 15c multicolored | .75 | .75 |
| 544 A74 20c multicolored | .90 | .90 |
| 545 A74 25c multicolored | 1.00 | .95 |
| 546 A74 30c multicolored | 1.10 | 1.00 |
| 547 A74 35c multicolored | 1.25 | 1.10 |
| 548 A74 40c multicolored | 1.50 | 1.25 |
| 549 A74 50c multicolored | 1.75 | 1.75 |
| 550 A74 60c multicolored | 2.00 | 2.00 |
| 551 A74 75c multicolored | 2.25 | 2.25 |
| 552 A74 $1 multicolored | 3.00 | 2.50 |
| 553 A74 $2 multicolored | 4.50 | 4.50 |
| 554 A74 $5 multicolored | 7.75 | *9.00* |
| *Nos. 540-554 (15)* | 29.30 | 29.50 |

Dated 1990. See No. 567. For overprints see Nos. 587-590.

### Queen Mother 90th Birthday
Common Design Types

75c, Queen Mother. $2, King, Queen & WWII bombing victim, 1940.

**1990, Aug. 4 Wmk. 384 *Perf. 14x15***

| | | |
|---|---|---|
| 555 CD343 75c multicolored | 1.50 | 1.50 |

***Perf. 14½***

| | | |
|---|---|---|
| 556 CD344 $2 multicolored | 3.25 | 3.25 |

### Ships Type of 1989

15c, Whaling ship Herald, 1851. 50c, Bark Belle, 1849. 60c, Schooner Supply, 1851. 75c, Whaling ship Triton, 1848.
$2, Convict transport Charlotte, 1789.

**1990, Nov. 5 Litho. *Perf. 14½***

| | | |
|---|---|---|
| 557 A87 15c multicolored | 1.00 | .75 |
| 558 A87 50c multicolored | 1.60 | 1.50 |
| 559 A87 60c multicolored | 1.75 | 1.75 |
| 560 A87 75c multicolored | 2.25 | 2.25 |
| *Nos. 557-560 (4)* | 6.60 | 6.25 |

**Souvenir Sheet**

| | | |
|---|---|---|
| 561 A87 $2 multicolored | 8.00 | 8.00 |

Manta Ray A95

**1991, Jan. 17 Wmk. 373 *Perf. 14***

| | | |
|---|---|---|
| 562 A95 15c shown | 1.25 | .60 |
| 563 A95 20c Manta ray, diff. | 1.50 | 1.00 |
| 564 A95 30c Whale shark | 1.75 | 1.75 |
| 565 A95 35c Whale shark, diff. | 2.25 | 2.25 |
| *Nos. 562-565 (4)* | 6.75 | 5.60 |

World Wildlife Fund.

### Fish Type of 1985

Design: 23c, Bennett's pufferfish.

**1991, Apr. 30 Wmk. 384**

| | | |
|---|---|---|
| 567 A74 23c multicolored | 2.00 | 2.00 |

For overprint see No. 587.

### Elizabeth & Philip, Birthdays
Common Design Types

**1991, June 17 *Perf. 14½***

| | | |
|---|---|---|
| 571 CD345 65c multicolored | 1.75 | 1.75 |
| 572 CD346 70c multicolored | 1.75 | 1.75 |
| a. Pair, #571-572 + label | 4.00 | 4.00 |

Phila Nippon '91 — A96

Opening of new Tungaru Central Hospital: 23c, Aerial view. 50c, Traditional dancers. 60c, Main entrance. 75c, Foundation stone, plaque. $5, Ambulance, nursing staff.

**1991, Nov. 16 *Perf. 13½x14***

| | | |
|---|---|---|
| 573 A96 23c multicolored | .50 | .50 |
| 574 A96 50c multicolored | 1.00 | 1.00 |
| 575 A96 60c multicolored | 1.40 | 1.40 |
| 576 A96 75c multicolored | 1.60 | 1.60 |
| *Nos. 573-576 (4)* | 4.50 | 4.50 |

**Souvenir Sheet**

| | | |
|---|---|---|
| 577 A96 $5 multicolored | 9.00 | 9.00 |

Christmas A97

Designs: 23c, Island mother and child. 50c, Family in island hut. 60c, Nativity Scene. 75c, Adoration of the Shepherds.

**1991, Dec. 2 Wmk. 373**

| | | |
|---|---|---|
| 578 A97 23c multicolored | .75 | .60 |
| 579 A97 50c multicolored | 1.25 | 1.25 |
| 580 A97 60c multicolored | 1.75 | 1.75 |
| 581 A97 75c multicolored | 2.25 | 2.25 |
| *Nos. 578-581 (4)* | 6.00 | 5.85 |

### Queen Elizabeth II's Accession to the Throne, 40th Anniv.
Common Design Type

**Wmk. 373**

**1992, Feb. 6 Litho. *Perf. 14***

| | | |
|---|---|---|
| 582 CD349 23c multicolored | .35 | .35 |
| 583 CD349 30c multicolored | .50 | .50 |
| 584 CD349 50c multicolored | .80 | .80 |
| 585 CD349 60c multicolored | 1.00 | 1.00 |
| 586 CD349 75c multicolored | 1.20 | 1.20 |
| *Nos. 582-586 (5)* | 3.85 | 3.85 |

Nos. 550-551, 553, & 567 Ovptd.

**Wmk. 384, 373**

**1992, June 1 Litho. *Perf. 14***

| | | |
|---|---|---|
| 587 A74 23c on No. 567 | 1.00 | .85 |
| 588 A74 60c on No. 550 | 2.25 | 2.25 |
| 589 A74 75c on No. 551 | 2.75 | 2.75 |
| 590 A74 $2 on No. 553 | 3.00 | 3.50 |
| *Nos. 587-590 (4)* | 9.00 | 9.35 |

Marine Training Center, 25th Anniv. A98

23c, Entrance. 50c, Cadets at morning parade. 60c, Fire school. 75c, Lifeboat training.

**1992, Aug. 28 *Perf. 14***

| | | |
|---|---|---|
| 591 A98 23c multicolored | .65 | .65 |
| 592 A98 50c multicolored | 1.00 | 1.00 |
| 593 A98 60c multicolored | 1.20 | 1.20 |
| 594 A98 75c multicolored | 1.50 | 1.50 |
| *Nos. 591-594 (4)* | 4.35 | 4.35 |

FAO, WHO A99

23c, Children running. 50c, Night fishing. 60c, Fruit. 75c, Ship.

**Wmk. 373**

**1992, Dec. 1 Litho. *Perf. 14***

| | | |
|---|---|---|
| 595 A99 23c multicolored | 1.10 | 1.10 |
| 596 A99 50c multicolored | 1.30 | 1.30 |
| 597 A99 60c multicolored | 1.75 | 1.75 |
| 598 A99 75c multicolored | 3.00 | 3.00 |
| *Nos. 595-598 (4)* | 7.15 | 7.15 |

Water Birds — A100

No. 599, Phoenix petrel. No. 600, Cooks petrel. No. 601, Northern pintail. No. 602, Eurasian widgeon. No. 603, Spectacled tern. No. 604, Black naped tern. No. 605, Stilt wader. No. 606, Wandering tattler.

**Wmk. 373**

**1993, May 28 Litho. *Perf. 14½***

| | | |
|---|---|---|
| 599 A100 23c multicolored | .70 | .70 |
| 600 A100 23c multicolored | .70 | .70 |
| a. Pair, #599-600 | 1.50 | 1.50 |
| 601 A100 60c multicolored | 1.30 | 1.30 |
| 602 A100 60c multicolored | 1.30 | 1.30 |
| a. Pair, #601-602 | 2.75 | 2.75 |
| 603 A100 75c multicolored | 1.60 | 1.60 |
| 604 A100 75c multicolored | 1.60 | 1.60 |
| a. Pair, #603-604 | 3.50 | 3.50 |
| 605 A100 $1 multicolored | 1.75 | 1.75 |
| 606 A100 $1 multicolored | 1.75 | 1.75 |
| a. Pair, #605-606 | 4.00 | 4.00 |
| *Nos. 599-606 (8)* | 10.70 | 10.70 |

Insects — A101

23c, Chilocorus nigritus. 60c, Rodolia pumila. 75c, Rodolia cardinalis. $1, Cryptolaemus montrouzieri.

*Perf. 14½x14*

**1993, Aug. 23 Litho. Wmk. 373**

| | | |
|---|---|---|
| 607 A101 23c multicolored | 1.25 | 1.25 |
| 608 A101 60c multicolored | 2.00 | 2.00 |
| 609 A101 75c multicolored | 2.50 | 2.50 |
| 610 A101 $1 multicolored | 3.00 | *3.50* |
| *Nos. 607-610 (4)* | 8.75 | 9.25 |

Liberation of Kiribati, 50th Anniv. — A102

No. 611: a, Air reconnaissance of Tarawa Atoll. b, USS Nautilus surveys Tarawa. c, USS Indianapolis. d, USS Pursuit leads seaborne assault. e, Kingfisher spotter plane. f, Destroyers USS Ringgold and USS Dashiell. g, Sherman tank on seabed. h, Fighter plane in lagoon. i, Naval gun on seabed. j, First US aircraft to land on Betio Island.

No. 612: a, Transports disembark landing craft. b, Marines assault Betio Island. c, Sea and air assault of Betio. d, Marines pinned down in surf. e, USS Maryland firing broadside. f, Betio from the air. g, Memorial to US Navy dead. h, Memorial to expatriates. i, Memorial to Japanese dead. j, Battle map of Betio.

**Wmk. 373**

**1993, Nov. 1 Litho. *Perf. 14***

**Sheets of 10**

| | | | |
|---|---|---|---|
| **611** A102 23c #a.-j. + label | | 8.50 | 8.50 |
| **612** A102 75c #a.-j. + label | | 22.50 | 22.50 |

Christmas — A103

23c, Shepherds. 40c, Three kings. 60c, Holy Family. 75c, Mother, children.
$3, Madonna and Child.

***Perf. 13½x14***

**1993, Dec. 1 Litho. Wmk. 373**

| | | |
|---|---|---|
| **613** A103 23c multicolored | .65 | .40 |
| **614** A103 40c multicolored | 1.00 | 1.00 |
| **615** A103 60c multicolored | 1.40 | *1.75* |
| **616** A103 75c multicolored | 1.75 | *2.10* |
| *Nos. 613-616 (4)* | 4.80 | 5.25 |

**Souvenir Sheet**

| | | |
|---|---|---|
| **617** A103 $3 multicolored | 6.50 | 6.50 |

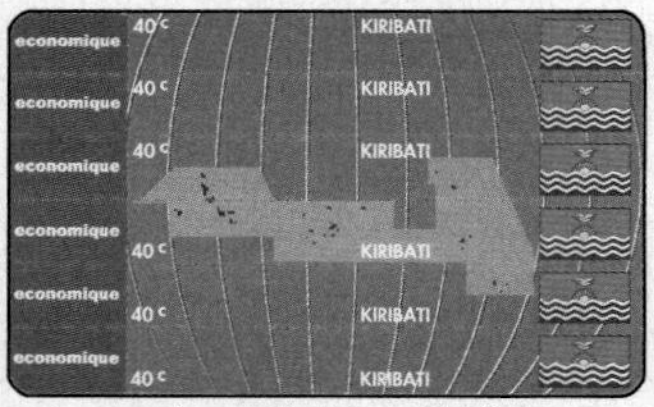

Stampcards — A104

***Rouletted 6 on 2 or 3 Sides***

**1993, Nov. 1 Litho.**

**Self-Adhesive**

**Cards of 6 + 6 labels**

| | |
|---|---|
| **618** A104 40c #a.-f. | *5.00* |
| **619** A104 $1 #a.-f. | *12.00* |
| **620** A104 $1.20 #a.-f. | *15.00* |
| **621** A104 $1.60 #a.-f. | *22.50* |
| *Nos. 618-621 (4)* | *54.50* |

Nos. 619-621 are airmail. Individual stamps measure 70x9mm and have a card backing. Se-tenant labels on No. 618 inscribed "economique." Se-tenant labels on Nos. 619-621 inscribed "prioritaire AIR MAIL."

It has been stated that these stamps were available only from the Philatelic Bureau and were not accepted by local post offices as valid for postage, though this is contradicted by the Controller of Postal Services.

Souvenir Sheet

New Year 1994 (Year of the Dog) — A105

**Wmk. 373**

**1994, Feb. 18 Litho. *Perf. 14***

| | | |
|---|---|---|
| **622** A105 $3 multicolored | 7.00 | 7.00 |

Hong Kong '94.

Whales A106

Designs: 23c, Bryde's whale. 40c, Blue whale. 60c, Humpback whale. 75c, Killer whale.

**1994, May 2**

| | | |
|---|---|---|
| **623** A106 23c multicolored | 1.25 | 1.25 |
| **624** A106 23c multicolored | 1.25 | 1.25 |
| *a.* Pair, #623-624 | 2.75 | 2.75 |
| **625** A106 40c multicolored | 1.50 | 1.50 |
| **626** A106 40c multicolored | 1.50 | 1.50 |
| *a.* Pair, #625-626 | 3.25 | 3.25 |
| **627** A106 60c multicolored | 2.00 | 2.00 |
| **628** A106 60c multicolored | 2.00 | 2.00 |
| *a.* Pair, #627-628 | 5.00 | 5.00 |
| **629** A106 75c multicolored | 2.25 | 2.25 |
| **630** A106 75c multicolored | 2.25 | 2.25 |
| *a.* Pair #629-630 | 5.50 | 5.50 |
| *Nos. 623-630 (8)* | 14.00 | 14.00 |

Value at UL on Nos. 623, 625, 627, 629; at UR on others.

Nos. 624a-630a have continuous designs.

Environmental Protection — A107

Designs: 40c, Family on beach at sunset. 60c, Fish. 75c, Frigate birds.

**1994, July 12**

| | | |
|---|---|---|
| **631** A107 40c multicolored | 1.00 | .90 |
| **632** A107 60c multicolored | 1.10 | 1.10 |
| **633** A107 75c multicolored | 1.60 | 1.60 |
| *Nos. 631-633 (3)* | 3.70 | 3.60 |

Independence, 15th anniv.

Butterflies A108

Designs: 1c, Diaphania indica. 5c, Herpetogamma licarsisalis. 10c, Parotis suralis. 12c, Sufetula sunidesalis. 20c, Aedia sericea. 23c, Anomis vitiensis. 30c, Anticarsia irrorata. 35c, Spodoptera litura. 40c, Mocis frugalis. 45c, Agrius convolvuli. 50c, Cephonodes picus. 55c, Gnathothlibus erotus. 60c, Macroglossum hirundo. 75c, Badamia exclamationis. $1, Precis villida. $2, Danaus plexippus. $3, Hypolimnas bolina (male). $5, Hypolimnas bolina (female).

**1994, Aug. 19 *Perf. 14½x14***

| | | |
|---|---|---|
| **634** A108 1c multicolored | .25 | .25 |
| **635** A108 5c multicolored | .25 | .25 |
| **636** A108 10c multicolored | .25 | .25 |
| **637** A108 12c multicolored | .25 | .25 |
| **638** A108 20c multicolored | .35 | .35 |
| **639** A108 23c multicolored | .45 | .45 |
| **640** A108 30c multicolored | .60 | .55 |
| **641** A108 35c multicolored | .70 | .65 |
| **642** A108 40c multicolored | .80 | .70 |
| **643** A108 45c multicolored | .85 | .80 |
| **644** A108 50c multicolored | .90 | .85 |
| **645** A108 55c multicolored | 1.10 | .95 |
| **646** A108 60c multicolored | 1.10 | 1.00 |
| **647** A108 75c multicolored | 1.25 | 1.25 |
| **648** A108 $1 multicolored | 1.75 | 1.75 |
| *a.* Souvenir sheet of 1 | 2.75 | 2.75 |
| **649** A108 $2 multicolored | 3.25 | *4.00* |
| **650** A108 $3 multicolored | 5.25 | *6.00* |
| **651** A108 $5 multicolored | 9.00 | *10.00* |
| *Nos. 634-651 (18)* | 28.35 | 30.30 |

No. 648a issued 2/12/97 for Hong Kong '97.

For overprints see Nos. 763-767.

Flowers — A109

23c, Nerium oleander. 60c, Catharanthus roseus. 75c, Ipomea pes-caprae. $1, Calophyllum mophyllum.

**1994, Oct. 31**

| | | |
|---|---|---|
| **652** A109 23c multicolored | .65 | .65 |
| **653** A109 60c multicolored | 1.10 | 1.10 |
| **654** A109 75c multicolored | 1.50 | 1.50 |
| **655** A109 $1 multicolored | 2.00 | 2.00 |
| *Nos. 652-655 (4)* | 5.25 | 5.25 |

A110

Constellations.

**1995, Jan. 31**

| | | |
|---|---|---|
| **656** A110 50c Gemini | 1.20 | 1.20 |
| **657** A110 60c Cancer | 1.30 | 1.30 |
| **658** A110 75c Cassiopeia | 1.50 | 1.50 |
| **659** A110 $1 Southern cross | 2.00 | 2.00 |
| *Nos. 656-659 (4)* | 6.00 | 6.00 |

A111

Scenes of Kiribati: No. 660: a, Architecture. b, Men, canoe, sailboat. c, Gun emplacement, Tarawa. d, Children, shells. e, Outdoor sports.

No. 661: a, Women traditionally attired. b, Windsurfing. c, Filleting fish. d, Snorkeling, scuba diving. e, Weaving.

**Wmk. 384**

**1995, Apr. 3 Litho. *Perf. 14½***

| | | |
|---|---|---|
| **660** A111 30c Strip of 5, #a.-e. | 4.50 | 4.50 |
| **661** A111 40c Strip of 5, #a.-e. | 6.50 | 6.50 |
| *f.* Booklet pane, #660, #661 + 5 labels | 12.00 | *12.00* |
| Complete booklet, #661f | 13.00 | |

Visit South Pacific Year.

**End of World War II, 50th Anniv.**

Common Design Type

Designs: 23c, Grumman TBM-3E Avenger. 40c, Curtiss SOC. 3-1 seagull. 50c, Consolidated B-24J Liberator. 60c, Grumman Goose. 75c, Martin B-26 Marauder. $1, Northrop P-61B Black Widow. $2, Reverse of War Medal 1939-45.

***Perf. 14x13½***

**1995, May 8 Wmk. 373**

| | | |
|---|---|---|
| **662** CD351 23c multicolored | 1.10 | 1.10 |
| **663** CD351 40c multicolored | 1.30 | 1.30 |
| **664** CD351 50c multicolored | 1.50 | 1.50 |
| **665** CD351 60c multicolored | 1.75 | 1.75 |
| **666** CD351 75c multicolored | 2.40 | 2.40 |
| **667** CD351 $1 multicolored | 3.25 | 3.25 |
| *Nos. 662-667 (6)* | 11.30 | 11.30 |

**Souvenir Sheet**

***Perf. 14***

| | | |
|---|---|---|
| **668** CD352 $2 multicolored | 5.00 | 5.00 |

For overprints see Nos. 691-697.

Souvenir Sheet

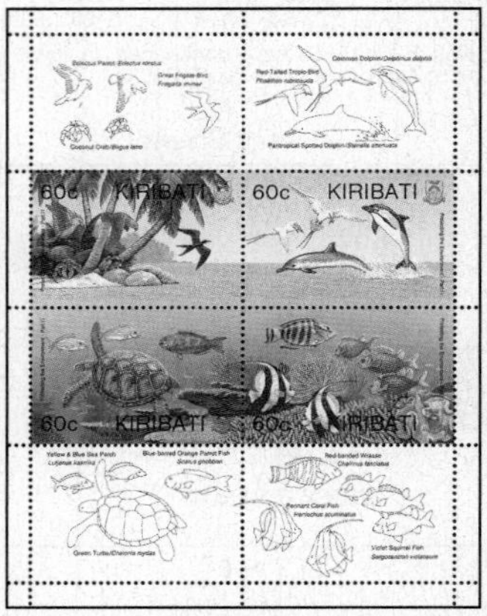


Environmental Protection — A112

Marine life: a, Electus parrot, great frigate bird, coconut crab. b, Red-tailed tropic bird, common dolphin, pantropical spotted dolphin. c, Yellow & blue sea perch, green turtle, blue-barred orange parrot fish. d, Pennant coral fish, red-banded wrasse, violet squirrel fish.

**Wmk. 373**

**1995, July 12 Litho. *Perf. 14***

| | | |
|---|---|---|
| **669** A112 60c #a.-d. + 4 labels | 5.00 | 5.00 |

For overprint see No. 672.

Souvenir Sheet

New Year 1995 (Year of the Boar) — A113

$2, Sow, piglets.

**1995, Sept. 1 Litho. *Perf. 13***

| | | |
|---|---|---|
| **670** A113 $2 multicolored | 4.75 | 4.75 |

Singapore '95.

Souvenir Sheet

Beijing '95 — A114

Design: $2, like #670.

**1995, Sept. 14**

| | | |
|---|---|---|
| **671** A114 $2 multicolored | 4.75 | 4.75 |

**No. 669 Overprinted for Jakarta '95**

**Wmk. 373**

**1995, Aug. 19 Litho. *Perf. 14***
**672** A112 60c #a.-d. + 4 labels 10.00 10.00

Police Maritime Unit — A115

Patrol boat RKS Teanoai: No. 673, In harbor. No. 674, Under way.

**Wmk. 373**

**1995, Nov. 30 Litho. *Perf. 13***
**673** 75c multicolored 2.25 2.25
**674** 75c multicolored 2.25 2.25
*a.* A115 Pair, #673-674 4.75 4.75

Dolphins A116

Designs: 23c, Pantropical spotted. 60c, Spinner. 75c, Fraser's. $1, Rough-toothed.

**Wmk. 384**

**1996, Jan. 15 Litho. *Perf. 14***
**675** A116 23c multicolored 1.60 .90
**676** A116 60c multicolored 2.25 1.30
**677** A116 75c multicolored 3.00 2.25
**678** A116 $1 multicolored 3.50 *3.75*
*Nos. 675-678 (4)* 10.35 8.20

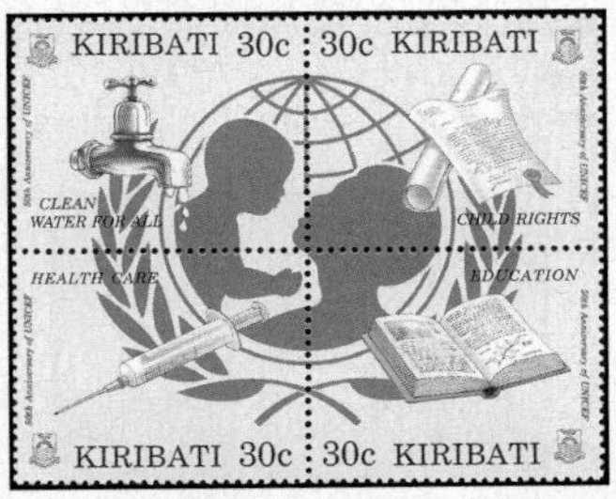


UNICEF, 50th Anniv. — A117

Portion of UNICEF emblem and: a, Water faucet, clean water. b, Documents, chilren's rights. c, Hypodermic, health care. d, Open book, education.

**Wmk. 373**

**1996, Apr. 22 Litho. *Perf. 13***
**679** A117 30c Block of 4, #a.-d. 2.75 2.75

No. 679 is a continuous design.

Souvenir Sheet

CHINA '96, 9th Intl. Philatelic Exhibition — A118

**1996, Apr. 30 Wmk. 384 *Perf. 13½***
**680** A118 50c multicolored 2.00 2.00

New Year 1996, Year of the Rat.

Souvenir Sheet

No. 5609 Gilbert and Ellice Islands LMS Jubilee Class 4-6-0 Locomotive — A119

**Wmk. 373**

**1996, June 8 Litho. *Perf. 12***
**681** A119 $2 multicolored 4.25 4.25

CAPEX '96.

Sea Crabs A120

23c, Rathbun red. 60c, Red & white painted. 75c, Red spotted. $1, Red spotted white.

**Wmk. 373**

**1996, Aug. 6 Litho. *Perf. 14***
**682** A120 23c multicolored .65 .50
**683** A120 60c multicolored 1.50 1.10
**684** A120 75c multicolored 1.75 1.75
**685** A120 $1 multicolored 2.25 *2.75*
*Nos. 682-685 (4)* 6.15 6.10

Souvenir Sheet

Taipei '96 — A121

**Wmk. 384**

**1996, Oct. 21 Litho. *Perf. 14½***
**686** A121 $1.50 Outrigger canoe 4.25 4.25

**Ships Type of 1989**

23c, Whaling ship, "Potomac," 1843. 50c, Barkentine "Southern Cross IV," 1891. 60c, Bark "John Williams III," 1890. $1, HMS Dolphin, 1765.

**Wmk. 384**

**1996, Dec. 2 Litho. *Perf. 14½***
**687** A87 23c multicolored .70 .55
**688** A87 50c multicolored 1.10 1.10
**689** A87 60c multicolored 1.30 1.30
**690** A87 $1 multicolored 2.25 2.25
*Nos. 687-690 (4)* 5.35 5.20

Nos. 662-668 Ovptd.

***Perf. 14x13½***

**1997, May 29 Litho. Wmk. 373**
**691** CD351 23c multicolored .70 .50
**692** CD351 40c multicolored .95 .80
**693** CD351 50c multicolored 1.25 1.10
**694** CD351 60c multicolored 1.50 1.50
**695** CD351 75c multicolored 1.75 1.75
**696** CD351 $1 multicolored 2.25 2.25
*Nos. 691-696 (6)* 8.40 7.90

**Souvenir Sheet**

**697** CD351 $2 multicolored 5.00 5.00

Queen Elizabeth II and Prince Philip, 50th Wedding Anniv. — A122

No. 698, Queen Elizabeth II. No. 699, Horse team going down river bank. No. 700, Queen in open carriage. No. 701, Prince Philip. No. 702, Prince, Queen. No. 703, Riding horse. $2, Queen, Prince in open carriage, horiz.

***Perf. 14½x14***

**1997, July 10 Litho. Wmk. 373**
**698** 50c multicolored 1.40 1.40
**699** 50c multicolored 1.40 1.40
*a.* A122 Pair, #698-699 3.00 3.00
**700** 60c multicolored 1.60 1.60
**701** 60c multicolored 1.60 1.60
*a.* A122 Pair, #700-701 3.50 3.50
**702** 75c multicolored 2.40 2.40
**703** 75c multicolored 2.40 2.40
*a.* A122 Pair, #702-703 5.25 5.25
*Nos. 698-703 (6)* 10.80 10.80

**Souvenir Sheet**

**704** A122 $2 multicolored 6.50 6.50

Birds — A123

Nos. 705-706, Rock dove. Nos. 707-708, Pacific pigeon. Nos. 709-710, Micronesian pigeon.

**Wmk. 373**

**1997, Dec. 1 Litho. *Perf. 14***
**705** 50c Immature 1.10 1.10
**706** 50c Adult 1.10 1.10
*a.* A123 Pair, #705-706 2.40 2.40
**707** 60c Adult 1.50 1.50
**708** 60c Immature 1.50 1.50
*a.* A123 Pair, #707-708 3.25 3.25
**709** 75c Adult 1.75 1.75
**710** 75c Immature 1.75 1.75
*a.* A123 Pair, #709-710 3.75 3.75
*Nos. 705-710 (6)* 8.70 8.70

Nos. 705-706, 709-710 With Added Inscription

**Wmk. 373**

**1997, Dec. 5 Litho. *Perf. 14***
**711** 50c on #705 1.25 1.25
**712** 50c on #706 1.25 1.25
*a.* A123 Pair, #711-712 2.75 2.75
**713** 75c on #709 2.00 2.00
**714** 75c on #710 2.00 2.00
*a.* A123 Pair, #713-714 4.25 4.25
*Nos. 711-714 (4)* 6.50 6.50

Asia '97.

Spiny Lobster A124

No. 716, Crawling right. No. 717, Crawling left. No. 718, Looking upward. No. 719, Looking straight forward.

**Wmk. 373**

**1998, Feb. 2 Litho. *Perf. 14***
**715** A124 25c shown .70 .70
**716** A124 25c multicolored .70 .70
**717** A124 25c multicolored .70 .70
**718** A124 25c multicolored .70 .70
*a.* Strip of 4, #715-718 3.00 3.00

**Souvenir Sheet**

**719** A124 $1.50 multicolored 3.50 3.50

World Wildlife Fund.

**Diana, Princess of Wales (1961-97)**

Common Design Type

Various portraits — No. 720: a, 50c. b, 60c. c, 75c.

***Perf. 14½x14***

**1998, Mar. 31 Litho. Wmk. 373**
**719A** CD355 25c multicolored .60 .60

**Sheet of 4**

**720** CD355 #a.-c., 719A 4.25 4.25

No. 720 sold for $2.10 + 50c, with surtax from international sales being donated to the Princess Diana Memorial Fund, and surtax from national sales being donated to designated local charity.

Intl. Year of the Ocean — A125

Whales and dolphins: No. 721, Indo-Pacific humpbacked dolphin. No. 722, Bottlenose dolphin. No. 723, Short-snouted spinner dolphin. No. 724, Risso's dolphin. No. 725, Striped dolphin. No. 726, Sei whale. No. 727, Fin whale. No. 728, Minke whale.

**Wmk. 373**

**1998, Oct. 1 Litho. *Perf. 14***
**721** 25c multicolored .60 .60
**722** 25c multicolored .60 .60
*a.* A125 Pair, #721-722 1.50 1.50
**723** 60c multicolored 1.25 1.25
**724** 60c multicolored 1.25 1.25
*a.* A125 Pair, #723-724 2.75 2.75
**725** 75c multicolored 1.75 1.75
**726** 75c multicolored 1.75 1.75
*a.* A125 Pair, #725-726 3.75 3.75
**727** $1 multicolored 2.00 2.00
**728** $1 multicolored 2.00 2.00
*a.* A125 Pair, #727-728 4.50 4.50
*Nos. 721-728 (8)* 11.20 11.20

Souvenir Sheet

Children of Kiribati — A125a

**1998, Sept. 15**
**729** A125a $1 multicolored 2.25 2.25

Souvenir Sheet

Reuben K. Uatioa Stadium — A126

**Wmk. 373**

**1998, Oct. 23 Litho. *Perf. 14***

**730** A126 $2 multicolored 3.75 3.75

Italia '98 World Philatelic Exhibition.

Greenhouse Effect — A127

Designs: 25c, Contributors to Greenhouse gases. 50c, Explanation of the Greenhouse Effect. 60c, Greenhouse Effect on Tarawa Atoll. 75c, Greenhouse Effect on Kiritimati Island.

$1.50, People in sailboat, "Kiribati way of life."

**Wmk. 373**

**1998, Dec. 1 Litho. *Perf. 13½***

| | | | | |
|---|---|---|---|---|
| **731** | A127 | 25c multicolored | .60 | .60 |
| **732** | A127 | 50c multicolored | .90 | .90 |
| **733** | A127 | 60c multicolored | 1.25 | 1.25 |
| **734** | A127 | 75c multicolored | 1.75 | 1.75 |
| | | *Nos. 731-734 (4)* | 4.50 | 4.50 |

**Souvenir Sheet**

**735** A127 $1.50 multicolored 4.75 4.75

Souvenir Sheet

HMS Resolution at Christmas Island — A128

**Wmk. 373**

**1999, Mar. 19 Litho. *Perf. 14***

**736** A128 $2 multicolored 4.25 4.25

Australia '99 World Stamp Expo.

IBRA '99, Philatelic Exhibition, Nuremberg — A129

Ducks: 25c, Northern shoveller, male. 50c, Northern shoveller, female. 60c, Green-winged teal, male. 75c, Green-winged teal, female and ducklings.

$3, Green winged teal, male, duckling.

**Wmk. 373**

**1999, Apr. 27 Litho. *Perf. 14***

| | | | | |
|---|---|---|---|---|
| **737** | A129 | 25c multicolored | .65 | .50 |
| **738** | A129 | 50c multicolored | 1.25 | .80 |
| **739** | A129 | 60c multicolored | 1.40 | 1.40 |
| **740** | A129 | 75c multicolored | 1.75 | *2.00* |
| | | *Nos. 737-740 (4)* | 5.05 | 4.70 |

**Souvenir Sheet**

**741** A129 $3 multicolored 6.00 6.00

Independence, 20th Anniv. — A130

Designs: 25c, Millennium Island. 60c, Map of Kiribati. 75c, Map of Nikumaroro. $1, Amelia Earhart, Lockheed 10E Electra airplane.

**Wmk. 373**

**1999, July 12 Litho. *Perf. 13½***

| | | | | |
|---|---|---|---|---|
| **742** | A130 | 25c multicolored | .60 | .60 |
| **743** | A130 | 60c multicolored | 1.10 | 1.10 |
| **744** | A130 | 75c multicolored | 1.40 | 1.40 |
| **745** | A130 | $1 multicolored | 3.00 | 3.00 |
| *a.* | | Souvenir sheet, #744-745 | 4.00 | 4.00 |
| | | *Nos. 742-745 (4)* | 6.10 | 6.10 |

**1st Manned Moon Landing, 30th Anniv.**

Common Design Type

Designs: 25c, Edwin Aldrin. 60c, Service module docks with lander. 75c, Apollo 11 on lunar surface. $1, Command module separates from service module.

$2, Earth as seen from moon.

***Perf. 14x13¾***

**1999, July 20 Litho. Wmk. 384**

| | | | | |
|---|---|---|---|---|
| **746** | CD357 | 25c multicolored | .60 | .60 |
| **747** | CD357 | 60c multicolored | 1.10 | 1.10 |
| **748** | CD357 | 75c multicolored | 1.40 | 1.40 |
| **749** | CD357 | $1 multicolored | 1.75 | 1.75 |
| | | *Nos. 746-749 (4)* | 4.85 | 4.85 |

**Souvenir Sheet**

***Perf. 14***

**750** CD357 $2 multicolored 4.00 4.00

No. 750 contains one 40mm circular stamp 40mm.

UPU, 125th Anniv., Christmas A131

**Wmk. 373**

**1999, Oct. 9 Litho. *Perf. 13½***

| | | | | |
|---|---|---|---|---|
| **751** | A131 | 25c Santa in canoe | .55 | .45 |
| **752** | A131 | 60c Santa on dock | 1.00 | .85 |
| **753** | A131 | 75c Santa in sleigh | 1.25 | 1.25 |
| **754** | A131 | $1 Santa at computer | 1.50 | 1.50 |
| | | *Nos. 751-754 (4)* | 4.30 | 4.05 |

Millennium A132

***Perf. 13¼x13***

**2000, Jan. 1 Litho. Wmk. 373**

| | | | | |
|---|---|---|---|---|
| **755** | A132 | 25c Faith | .55 | .45 |
| **756** | A132 | 40c Harmony | .80 | .70 |
| **757** | A132 | 60c Hope | 1.10 | 1.10 |
| **758** | A132 | 75c Enlightenment | 1.75 | 1.75 |
| **759** | A132 | $1 Peace | 2.00 | 2.00 |
| | | *Nos. 755-759 (5)* | 6.20 | 6.00 |

Sesame Street Characters — A133

No. 760: a, Bert. b, Baby Bear. c, Grover. d, Elmo, Cookie Monster. e, Telly Monster. f. Zoe. g, Ernie. h, Big Bird, Rosita. i, Oscar the Grouch.

No. 761, Grover as mailman.

***Perf. 14½x14¾***

**2000, Mar. 22 Litho. Wmk. 373**

**760** A133 20c Sheet of 9, #a-i 3.75 3.75

**Souvenir Sheet**

**761** A133 $1.50 multi 2.75 2.75

Souvenir Sheet

The Stamp Show 2000, London — A134

**2000, May 8 Wmk. 373 *Perf. 13¾***

**762** A134 $5 Queen Elizabeth II 7.50 7.50

Nos. 635, 636, 638, 648 and 650 Ovptd.

***Perf. 14½x14***

**2000, June 1 Wmk. 373**

| | | | | |
|---|---|---|---|---|
| **763** | A108 | 5c multi | .40 | .40 |
| **764** | A108 | 10c multi | .40 | .40 |
| **765** | A108 | 20c multi | .50 | .50 |
| **766** | A108 | $1 multi | 1.50 | 1.50 |
| **767** | A108 | $3 multi | 4.00 | 4.00 |
| | | *Nos. 763-767 (5)* | 6.80 | 6.80 |

Prince William, 18th Birthday A135

Various views of Prince William with Prince Charles.

**Wmk. 373**

**2000, July 24 Litho. *Perf. 12¾***

| | | | | |
|---|---|---|---|---|
| **768** | A135 | 25c multi | .40 | .40 |
| **769** | A135 | 60c multi | .90 | .90 |
| **770** | A135 | 75c multi | 1.25 | 1.25 |
| **771** | A135 | $1 multi | 1.50 | 1.50 |
| | | *Nos. 768-771 (4)* | 4.05 | 4.05 |

Ducks A136

Designs: No. 772, 25c, Blue duck. No. 773, 25c, Green-winged teal. No. 774, 25c, Mallard. No. 775, 25c, Northern shoveler. No. 776, 25c, Pacific black duck. No. 777, 25c, Wandering whistling duck.

**Wmk. 373**

**2001, Jan. 22 Litho. *Perf. 14***

**772-777** A136 Set of 6 9.00 9.00

**Souvenir Sheet**

**778** A136 $1 Gray teal 8.50 8.50

Water Conservation A137

Children's art by: 25c, Tiare Hongkai. 50c, Gilbert Z. Tluanga. 60c, Mantokataake Tebaiuea, vert. 75c, Tokaman Karanebo, vert. $2, Taom Simon.

**2001, July 12 Litho. *Perf. 13¼***

**779-783** A137 Set of 5 6.25 6.25

Phila Nippon '01 A138

Development projects: 75c, Betio Port. $2, New Parliament House.

**2001, Aug. 1**

**784-785** A138 Set of 2 5.00 5.00

Tourism — A139

Designs: 75c, Norwegian Cruise Line ship, map of cruise to Fanning Island. $3, The Betsey, map of Fanning Island.

***Perf. 13¼***

**2001, Nov. 14 Litho. Unwmk.**

**786-787** A139 Set of 2 5.75 5.75

Fish — A140

Designs: 5c, Paracanthurus hepatus. 10c, Centropyge flavissimus. 15c, Anthias squamipinnis. 20c, Centropyge loriculus. 25c, Acanthurus lineatus. 30c, Oxycirrhites typus. 40c, Dascyllus trimaculatus. 50c, Acanthurus achilles. 60c, Pomacentrus coeruleus. 75c, Acanthurus glaucopareus. 80c, Thalassoma lunare. 90c, Arothron meleagris. $1, Odonus niger. $2, Cephalopholis miniatus. $5, Pomacanthus imperator. $10, Balistoides conspicillum.

**2002, Feb. 28 Unwmk. *Perf. 13***

| | | | | |
|---|---|---|---|---|
| **788** | A140 | 5c multi | .25 | .25 |
| **789** | A140 | 10c multi | .30 | .30 |
| **790** | A140 | 15c multi | .35 | .35 |
| **791** | A140 | 20c multi | .40 | .40 |
| **792** | A140 | 25c multi | .45 | .45 |
| **793** | A140 | 30c multi | .50 | .50 |
| **794** | A140 | 40c multi | .70 | .70 |
| **795** | A140 | 50c multi | .80 | .80 |
| **796** | A140 | 60c multi | .90 | .90 |
| **797** | A140 | 75c multi | 1.00 | 1.00 |
| **798** | A140 | 80c multi | 1.25 | 1.25 |
| **799** | A140 | 90c multi | 1.60 | 1.60 |
| **800** | A140 | $1 multi | 1.75 | 1.75 |
| **801** | A140 | $2 multi | 3.50 | 3.50 |
| **802** | A140 | $5 multi | 8.00 | 8.00 |
| **803** | A140 | $10 multi | 14.50 | 14.50 |
| | | *Nos. 788-803 (16)* | 36.25 | 36.25 |

For overprints, see Nos. 988-990.

Pacific Explorers A141

Designs: 25c, Adm. Fabian von Bellingshausen and the Vostok, 1820. 40c, Capt. Charles Wilkes and the Vincennes, 1838-42. 60c, Capt. Edmund Fanning and the Betsey, 1798. 75c, Capt. Coffin and the Transit, 1823. $1, Commodore John Byron and the Dolphin, 1765. $2, Capt. Broughton and HMS Providence, 1795.

$5, Capt. James Cook, 1777, vert.

**2002, Mar. 25 Wmk. 373 *Perf. 14***

**804-809** A141 Set of 6 9.00 9.00

**Souvenir Sheet**

**810** A141 $5 multi 9.00 9.00

In Remembrance of Sept. 11, 2001 Terrorist Attacks — A142

No. 811: a, 25c. b, $2.

**2002, May 3 Wmk. 373 *Perf. 13¾***

**811** A142 Vert. pair, #a-b 5.00 5.00

Issued in sheets of 2 pairs.

Reign of Queen Elizabeth II, 50th Anniv. — A143

Various photographs by Dorothy Wilding. Panel colors: 25c, Purple.

No. 812: a, Maroon. b, Purple.

**2002, June 3 Wmk. 373 *Perf. 14***

**812** A143 25c multi 1.25 1.25

**Souvenir Sheet**

**813** A143 $2 Sheet of 2, #a-b 10.00 10.00

Christmas A144

Ribbons and bow with various basketry weaves: 25c, 60c, 75c, $1, $2.50.

**2002, Dec. 2 Litho. *Perf. 13x13¼***

**814-818** A144 Set of 5 7.00 7.00

Cowrie Shells — A145

Designs: 25c, Cypraea mappa. 50c, Cypraea eglantina. 60c, Cypraea mauritiana. 75c, Cypraea cribaria. $1, Cypraea talpa. $2.50, Cypraea depressa.

***Perf. 14½x14¼***

**2003, May 12 Litho. Unwmk.**

**819-824** A145 Set of 6 8.50 8.50

*824a* Souvenir sheet, #819-824 8.50 8.50

**Coronation of Queen Elizabeth II, 50th Anniv.**

Common Design Type

Designs: Nos. 825, 25c, 827a, $2, Queen and Prince Philip waving. Nos. 826, $3, 827b, $5, Prince Philip paying homage to Queen at coronation.

***Perf. 14¼x14½***

**2003, June 2 Litho. Wmk. 373**

**Vignettes Framed, Red Background**

**825** CD363 $2 multicolored 1.75 1.75

**826** CD363 $3 multicolored 2.50 2.50

**Souvenir Sheet**

**Vignettes Without Frame, Purple Panel**

**827** CD363 Sheet of 2, #a-b 9.25 9.25

Powered Flight, Cent. — A146

Designs: 25c, Sopwith Camel. 50c, Northrop Alpha. No. 830, 60c, DeHavilland Comet. 75c, Boeing 727. $1, English Electric Canberra. $2.50, Lockheed Martin F-22.

No. 834: a, 40c, Mitsubishi A6M-5 Zero. b, 60c, Grumman F6F Hellcat.

**Wmk. 373**

**2003, Aug. 29 Litho. *Perf. 14***

**Stamp + Label**

**828-833** A146 Set of 6 10.00 10.00

**Souvenir Sheet**

**834** A146 Sheet of 2, #a-b 3.50 3.50

Christmas — A147

Christmas Island scenes: 25c, Teareba Taomeka, Tabwakea. 40c, Seventh Day Adventist Church, London. 50c, St. Teresa Catholic Church, Tabakea Village. 60c, Betaera Fou, London. 75c, Children, church bells, London. $1.50, Emanuira Church, London. $2.50, Church of Christ (60x24mm).

**2003, Dec. 20 Unwmk. *Perf. 13¼***

**835-841** A147 Set of 7 10.00 10.00

*841a* Souvenir sheet, #835-841 10.00 10.00

Road Safety — A148

No. 842: a, Accident. b, Automobile. c, Beverage can, drink, cigarette. d, Children.

**2004, Apr. 7 Litho. *Perf. 13x13¼***

| | | | | |
|---|---|---|---|---|
| **842** | A148 | Horiz. strip of 4 | 6.50 | 6.50 |
| *a.* | | 30c multi | .75 | .75 |
| *b.* | | 40c multi | 1.10 | 1.10 |
| *c.* | | 50c multi | 1.30 | 1.10 |
| *d.* | | 60c multi | 1.60 | 1.40 |
| *e.* | | Souvenir sheet, #842 | 6.50 | 6.50 |

World Health Day.

Bird Life International A149

Designs: 25c, Pacific golden plover. 40c, Whimbrel. 50c, Wandering tattler. 60c, Sanderling. 75c, Bar-tailed godwit. $2.50, Ruddy turnstone.

No. 849 — Bristle-thighed curlew: a, One in tree, one at water's edge. b, Head of bird. c, Front of bird, head facing right, vert. d, Back of bird, head facing left, vert. e, Two birds at water's edge.

***Perf. 14¼x13¾***

**2004, Apr. 29 Litho. Unwmk.**

**843-848** A149 Set of 6 11.00 11.00

**Souvenir Sheet**

***Perf. 14¼x14½***

**849** A149 $1 Sheet of 5, #a-e 13.00 13.00

2004 Summer Olympics, Athens — A150

Designs: 25c, Runners. 50c, Taekwondo. 60c, Weight lifting. 75c, Women's running.

**2004, July 12 Wmk. 373 *Perf. 14***

**850-853** A150 Set of 4 3.75 3.75

Souvenir Sheet

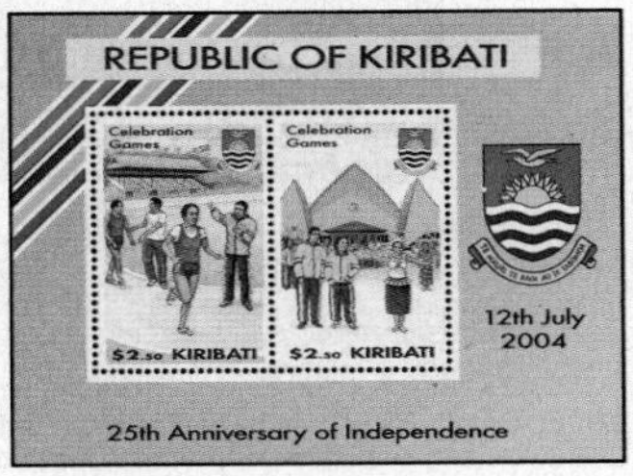


Celebration Games — A151

No. 854: a, Runners on track. b, Athletes, dancer, building.

**2004, July 12**

**854** A151 $2.50 Sheet of 2, #a-b 9.00 9.00

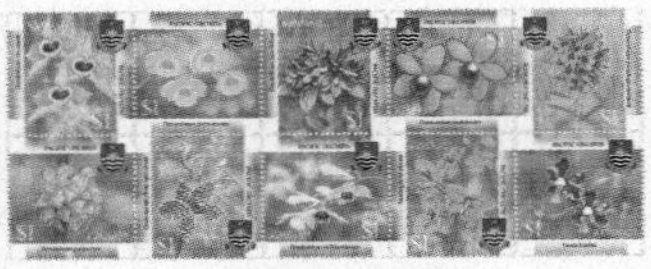

Orchids — A152

No. 855: a, Dendrobium anosmum. b, Dendrobium chrysotoxum. c, Dendrobium laevifolium. d, Dendrobium mohlianum. e, Dendrobium pseudoglomeratum. f, Dendrobium purpureum. g, Grammatophyllum speciosum. h, Dendrobium williamsianum. i, Spathoglottis plicata. j, Vanda hindsii.

**2004, Aug. 28 Unwmk. *Perf. 13½***

**855** A152 Block of 10 18.00 18.00

*a.-j.* $1 Any single 1.60 1.50

Merchant Ships A153

Designs: 50c, MV Montelucia. 75c, MS Pacific Princess. $2.50 MS Prinsendam. $5, MS Norwegian Wind.

**2004, Oct. 25 Litho. *Perf. 13¼***

**856-859** A153 Set of 4 14.50 14.50

Battle of Trafalgar, Bicent. — A154

Designs: 25c, French 16-pounder cannon. 50c, San Ildefonso in action against HMS Defence. 75c, HMS Victory lashed to the Redoubtable. $1, Emperor Napoleon Bonaparte, vert. $1.50, HMS Victory. No. 865, $2.50, Vice-admiral Sir Horatio Nelson, vert.

No. 866: a, Admiral Federico Gravina. b, Santissima Trinidad.

**2005, Mar. 29 Litho. *Perf. 13¼***

**860-865** A154 Set of 6 12.00 12.00

**Souvenir Sheet**

**866** A154 $2.50 Sheet of 2, #a-b 8.25 8.25

No. 864 has particles of wood from the HMS Victory embedded in the areas covered by a thermographic process that produces a raised, shiny effect.

End of World War II, 60th Anniv. — A155

No. 867: a, Japanese Type 95 Ha-Go tank invading Gilbert Islands. b, Japanese A6M Zero fighter on Gilbert Islands. c, USS Argonaut and Nautilus land Marines at Butaritari in Carlson Raid. d, Pacific Fleet Admiral Chester W. Nimitz. e, USS Liscome Bay sunk by Japanese submarine. f, US Higgins landing craft approaching Tarawa Red Beach. g, F6F-3 Hellcats provide air cover over Tarawa Red Beach. h, LVTs hit the shore at Tarawa Red Beach. i, Sherman tank at Tarawa Red Beach. j, US Marines take cover on Tarawa Red Beach.

$5, Australian Prime Minister John Curtin, British Prime Minister Winston Churchill.

**2005, Apr. 21 *Perf. 13¾***

**867** A155 75c Sheet of 10, #a-j 14.50 14.50

**Souvenir Sheet**

**868** A155 $5 multi 13.00 13.00

Pacific Explorer 2005 World Stamp Expo, Sydney (No. 868).

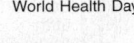

BirdLife International — A156

No. 869, 25c — Birds of Christmas Island: a, Lesser frigatebird. b, Red-tailed tropicbird. c, Blue noddy. d, Christmas shearwater. e, Sooty tern. f, Masked booby.

No. 870, $2 — Birds of Kiribati: a, White-tailed tropicbird. b, Black noddy. c, Red-footed booby. d, Wedge-tailed shearwater. e, White tern. f, Great frigatebird.

**2005, Aug. 15** *Perf. 13¼x13*

**Sheets of 6, #a-f**

**869-870** A156 Set of 2 25.00 25.00

Pope John Paul II (1920-2005) A157

**2005, Aug. 18 Litho.** *Perf. 14*

**871** A157 $1 multi 3.00 3.00

Battle of Trafalgar, Bicent. — A158

Designs: 25c, HMS Victory. 50c, Ships, horiz. $5, Admiral Horatio Nelson

**2005, Oct. 18 Litho.** *Perf. 13½*

**872-874** A158 Set of 3 12.50 12.50

Worldwide Fund for Nature (WWF) — A159

Various depictions of harlequin shrimp: 50c, 60c, 75c, $5.

**2005, Dec. 1** *Perf. 14*

**875-878** A159 Set of 4 13.00 13.00

*878a* Miniature sheet, 2 each #875-878 22.50 22.50

Queen Elizabeth II, 80th Birthday A160

Queen: 50c, As young woman. 75c, Wearing tiara, sepia photograph. $1, Wearing tiara, color photograph. $2, Wearing pink hat.

No. 883: a, $1.50, Like $1. b, $2.50, Like 75c.

**2006, Apr. 21 Litho.** *Perf. 14*

**Stamps With White Frames**

**879-882** A160 Set of 4 9.50 9.50

**Souvenir Sheet**

**Stamps Without White Frames**

**883** A160 Sheet of 2, #a-b 10.00 10.00

For footnotes, see Nos. 991-994.

Europa Stamps, 50th Anniv. — A161

Flags of European Union and Kiribati with gradiating background colors of: $2, Gray green. $2.50, Purple. $3, Yellowish brown. $5, Blue.

**2006, May 4** *Perf. 13¼*

**884-887** A161 Set of 4 20.00 20.00

*887a* Souvenir sheet, #884-887 20.00 20.00

Anniversaries — A162

No. 888, 25c: a, Charles Darwin and marine life. b, Fish and marine life.

No. 889, 50c: a, Isambard Kingdom Brunel. b, Glowing rivet.

No. 890, 75c: a, Christopher Columbus. b, Ship.

No. 891, $1: a, Thomas Alva Edison. b, Tin foil phonograph.

No. 892, $1.25: a, Wolfgang Amadeus Mozart. b, Violin and quill pen.

No. 893, $1.50: a, Concorde. b, Wing of Concorde, Concorde in flight.

**2006, May 27** *Perf. 13x12½*

**Horiz. Pairs, #a-b**

**888-893** A162 Set of 6 22.50 22.50

Darwin's voyage on the Beagle, 250th anniv., Birth of Brunel, bicent., Death of Columbus, 500th anniv., Death of Edison, 75th anniv., Birth of Mozart, 250th anniv., Inaugural Concorde flights, 30th anniv.

Dinosaurs A163

Designs: 25c, Ultrasaurus. 50c, Rhamphorhynchus. 60c, Dilophosaurus. 75c, Brachiosaurus. No. 898, $1, Minmi paravertebra. No. 899, $1, Eoraptor. $1.25, Stegosaurus. $1.50, Gigantosaurus.

**2006, Sept. 15** *Perf. 13¼x13½*

**894-901** A163 Set of 8 11.50 11.50

Miniature Sheet

Victoria Cross, 150th Anniv. — A164

No. 902: a. Troop Sergeant Major John Berryman with Captain Webb at Balaclava. b, Private W. Norman bringing in two Russian prisoners. c, Sergeant Major John Greive saving officer's life at Balaclava. d, Private Thomas Beach rescuing Colonel Carpenter at Inkerman. e, Brevet Major C. H. Lumley engaged with Russian gunners in the Redan. f, Major F. C. Elton working in trenches.

**2006, Oct. 20 Litho.** *Perf. 13¼x12½*

**902** A164 $1.50 Sheet of 6, #a-f, + 6 labels 17.50 17.50

60th Wedding Anniversary of Queen Elizabeth II and Prince Philip — A165

Designs: 50c, Portrait of Elizabeth and Philip. 75c, Wedding procession. $1, Bride and groom waving. $1.50, Queen reading. $5, Wedding portrait.

**2007, Jan. 31 Litho.** *Perf. 13¾*

**903-906** A165 Set of 4 6.00 6.00

**Souvenir Sheet**

***Perf. 14***

**907** A165 $5 multi 7.75 7.75

No. 907 contains one 42x56mm stamp

Scouting, Cent. A166

Designs: 25c, Scouts with Kiribati flag, hands tying neckerchief. 50c, Scouts learning about AIDS, Scout saluting. 75c, Scout leaders, hand with compass. $2, 1962 Scout shelter, hands lashing rope.

No. 912, vert.: a, $1, Emblem of Kiribati Scouts. b, $1.50, Lord Robert Baden-Powell.

***Perf. 13x13¼***

**2007, Sept. 21 Litho. Wmk. 373**

**908-911** A166 Set of 4 7.50 7.50

**Souvenir Sheet**

***Perf. 13¼x13***

**912** A166 Sheet of 2, #a-b 5.25 5.25

Princess Diana (1961-97) A167

Designs: No. 913, 25c, Wearing white dress, facing right. No. 914, 25c, Wearing pink dress, facing left. 50c, Wearing pink dress, diff. No. 916, 75c, Wearing emerald necklace. No. 917, 75c, Wearing black and white dress. $1, Wearing red dress.

***Perf. 13¼x12½***

**2007, Nov. 1 Litho. Unwmk.**

**913-918** A167 Set of 6 7.00 7.00

Military Uniforms — A168

Uniforms of: 25c, Royal Engineers. 40c, 95th Rifles. 50c, 24th Regiment of Foot. 60c, New Zealand soldiers. 75c, 93rd Sutherland Highlanders. 90c, Irish Guard. $1, Japanese soldiers. $1.50, United States Marine Corps.

**2007, Nov. 20 Wmk. 373** *Perf. 14*

**919-926** A168 Set of 8 12.00 12.00

Birds — A169

Designs: 5c, Great crested tern. 10c Eurasian teal. 15c, Laughing gull. 20c, Black-tailed godwit. 25c, Pectoral sandpiper. 50c, Band-rumped storm petrel. 60c, Sharp-tailed sandpiper. 75c, Gray-tailed tattler. 90c, Red phalarope. $1, Pink-footed shearwater. $2, Ring-billed gull. $5, Bonin petrel.

**Wmk. 373**

**2008, Feb. 9 Litho.** *Perf. 13¾*

| | | | | |
|---|---|---|---|---|
| **927** | A169 | 5c multi | .25 | .25 |
| **928** | A169 | 10c multi | .25 | .25 |
| **929** | A169 | 15c multi | .30 | .30 |
| **930** | A169 | 20c multi | .40 | .40 |
| **931** | A169 | 25c multi | .45 | .45 |
| **932** | A169 | 50c multi | .95 | .95 |
| **933** | A169 | 60c multi | 1.10 | 1.10 |
| **934** | A169 | 75c multi | 1.40 | 1.40 |
| **935** | A169 | 90c multi | 1.75 | 1.75 |
| **936** | A169 | $1 multi | 2.00 | 2.00 |
| **937** | A169 | $2 multi | 4.25 | 4.25 |
| *a.* | | Souvenir sheet, #929, 933-937 | 10.00 | 10.00 |
| **938** | A169 | $5 multi | 10.50 | 10.50 |
| *a.* | | Souvenir sheet, #927-928, 930-932, 938 | 12.50 | 12.50 |
| | | *Nos. 927-938 (12)* | 23.60 | 23.60 |

For surcharges, see Nos. 984-987.

A170

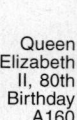

Royal Air Force, 90th Anniv. — A171

Designs: 25c, Avro Shackleton. 50c, Harrier GR3. 75c, Eurofighter Typhoon. $1, Vickers Valiant.
$2.50, Dambusters Raid.

**Wmk. 373**

**2008, Apr. 1 Litho. *Perf. 14***
**939-942** A170 Set of 4 5.50 5.50

**Souvenir Sheet**

**943** A171 $2.50 multi 4.75 4.75

Phoenix Island Protected Area A172

Designs: 40c, Huts. 75c, Map of Kanton Island. 80c, Map of various islands. 85c, Phoenix petrel. $1.25, Acropora nobilis and reef fish. $1.75, Blacktip reef shark.

**2008, July 12 *Perf. 13¾***
**944-949** A172 Set of 6 11.50 11.50
*949a* Souvenir sheet of 6, #944-949 11.50 11.50

2008 Summer Olympics, Beijing A173

Designs: 25c, Bamboo, weight lifting. 50c, Dragon, running. 60c, Lanterns, cycling. 75c, Fish, javelin.

**Wmk. 373**

**2008, Aug. 8 Litho. *Perf. 13½***
**950-953** A173 Set of 4 3.75 3.75

Christmas — A174

No. 954, 25c: a, Lady Sacred Heart Church, Bairiki. b, Kiribati Protestant Church, Bikenibeu.
No. 955, 40c: a, Kaotitaeka Roman Catholic Church, Betio. b, Mormon Church, Iesu Kristo.
No. 956, 50c: a, Moaningaina Church, Eita. b, Sacred Heart Cathedral, Tarawa.
No. 957, 75c: a, St. Paul's Millennium Church, Betio. b, Kainkatikun Kristo Church, Naninimo.

**Wmk. 406**

**2008, Dec. 8 Litho. *Perf. 13***

**Pairs, #a-b**

**954-957** A174 Set of 4 5.00 5.00
*957c* Souvenir sheet, #954a-954b, 955a-955b, 956a-956b, 957a-957b 5.00 5.00

Explorers — A175

Designs: 25c, Sir Ernest Shackleton (1874-1922). 40c, Robert Falcon Scott (1868-1912). 50c, Captain James Cook (1728-79). 75c, Marco Polo (1254-1324). $1.50, Matthew Flinders (1774-1814). $1.75, John Cabot (c. 1450-99).

**Wmk. 406**

**2009, Mar. 9 Litho. *Perf. 14***
**958-963** A175 Set of 6 9.00 9.00

Naval Aviation, Cent. A176

Aircraft: 40c, Grumman Avenger. 50c, Chance Vought Corsair. 75c, Westland Whirlwind helicopter. $1.25, McDonnell Douglas Phantom.
$3, Helicopter on deck of HMS Ark Royal.

**Wmk. 406**

**2009, May 12 Litho. *Perf. 14***
**964-967** A176 Set of 4 4.75 4.75

**Souvenir Sheet**

**968** A176 $3 multi 4.75 4.75

Nos. 964-968 each were printed in sheets of 8 + central label.

Space Exploration A177

Designs: 40c, Mars Science Laboratory. 50c, International Space Station. 75c, Space Shuttle Endeavour and Boeing transporter plane. $1.25, Launch of Apollo 12. No. 973, $3, Luna 16.
No. 974, $3, Astronaut on Moon, painting by Capt. Alan Bean, vert.

**Wmk. 406**

**2009, July 20 Litho. *Perf. 13¼***
**969-973** A177 Set of 5 9.25 9.25

**Souvenir Sheet**

***Perf. 13x13½***

**974** A177 $3 multi 4.75 4.75

First man on the Moon, 40th anniv. No. 974 contains one 40x60mm stamp.

Battle of Britain, 70th Anniv. — A178

Stained-glass windows of Biggin Hill Memorial Chapel depicting: 25c, Aircraft servicing. 40c, Knight, English flag, airplanes. 50c, Parachute packing. 75c, Ground control. $1, Rescue services. $1.50, Royal Air Force emblem.
$3, Photograph of Sir Douglas Bader.

**Wmk. 406**

**2010, Apr. 14 Litho. *Perf. 13***
**975-980** A178 Set of 6 8.25 8.25

**Souvenir Sheet**

**981** A178 $3 multi 5.75 5.75

Souvenir Sheet

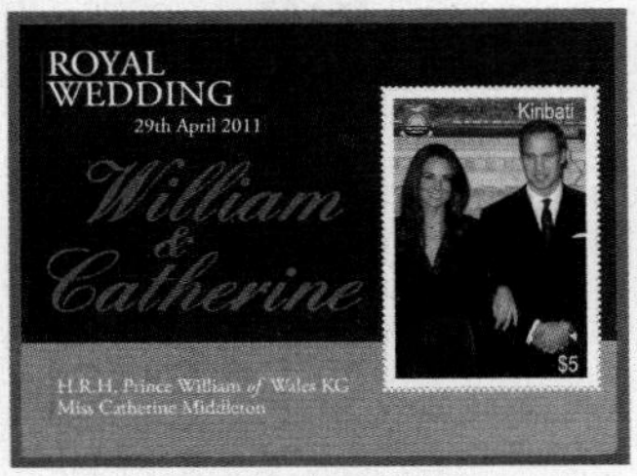


Wedding of Prince William and Catherine Middleton — A179

***Perf. 14¾x14¼***

**2011, Apr. 29 Litho. Wmk. 406**
**982** A179 $5 multi 11.00 11.00

No. 871 Overprinted

**Unwmk.**

**2011, June 13 Litho. *Perf. 14***
**983** A157 $1 multi 2.10 2.10

Nos. 927-930 Surcharged

**Methods, Perfs and Watermarks As Before**

**2011, July**
**984** A169 25c on 5c #927 .50 .50
**985** A169 30c on 10c #928 .60 .60
**986** A169 50c on 20c #930 .95 .95
**987** A169 75c on 15c #929 1.40 1.40
*Nos. 984-987 (4)* 3.45 3.45

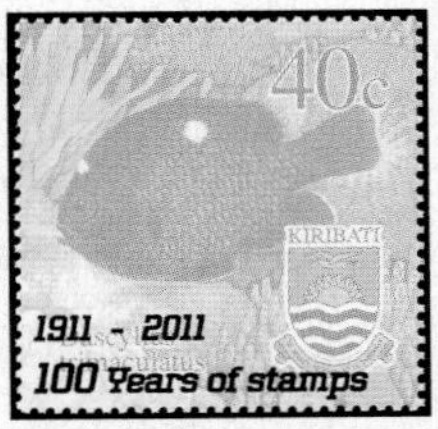


Nos. 794, 801 & 803 Ovptd.

**Methods and Perfs As Before**

**2011, July**
**988** A140 40c on #794 .75 .75
**989** A140 $2 on #801 3.75 3.75
**990** A140 $10 on #803 19.00 19.00
*Nos. 988-990 (3)* 23.50 23.50

**Nos. 879-882 Overprinted in Silver**

**Methods and Perfs. As Before**

**2012, June 4**
**991** A160 50c on #879 1.00 1.00
**992** A160 75c on #880 1.50 1.50
**993** A160 $1 on #881 2.00 2.00
**994** A160 $2 on #882 4.00 4.00
*Nos. 991-994 (4)* 8.50 8.50

Worldwide Fund for Nature (WWF) A180

Various views of Giant trevally.

**2012, July 11 Litho. *Perf. 14¼x14***
**995** Horiz. strip of 4 11.50 11.50
*a.* A180 80c multi 1.75 1.75
*b.* A180 $1 multi 2.10 2.10
*c.* A180 $1.50 multi 3.25 3.25
*d.* A180 $2 multi 4.25 4.25

Printed in sheets containing two each Nos. 995a-995d.

Miniature Sheet

Marine Life of Phoenix Islands Protected Area — A181

No. 996: a, 40c, Manta ray. b, 50c, Napoleon wrasse. c, 60c, Yellow and blueback fusiliers. d, 75c, Rainbow runners. e, $1, Green turtle. f, $1.50, Ornate butterflyfish. g, $2, Chrysiptera albata. h, $2.50, Small giant clam.

**2012, Sept. 12 *Perf. 14¼x14***
**996** A181 Sheet of 8, #a-h 19.00 19.00

Watercraft A182

Designs: 5c, Christmas Island outrigger. 10c, Ferry to shore. 15c, Inter-island ferries. 20c, Fishing boats. 25c, Inter-island ferry. 30c, Te Tia Awaka and cargo boat. 35c, Bwaan Tetangira II. 40c, Passengers diving off outrigger Te Okarsi. 45c, Akenraoi in Abaiang Lagoon. 50c, Native house with outrigger. 55c, Moamoa. 60c, Container ship Kiribati Chief. 75c, Cruise liner Pride of Aloha. $1, Kiribati 36 yacht. $2, Pilot boat Teeitei. $5, Traditional outrigger.

***Perf. 13¾***

**2013, Oct. 5 Litho. Unwmk.**
**997** A182 5c multi .25 .25
**998** A182 10c multi .25 .25
**999** A182 15c multi .30 .30
**1000** A182 20c multi .40 .40
**1001** A182 25c multi .50 .50
**1002** A182 30c multi .60 .60
**1003** A182 35c multi .65 .65
**1004** A182 40c multi .75 .75
**1005** A182 45c multi .85 .85
**1006** A182 50c multi .95 .95
**1007** A182 55c multi 1.00 1.00
**1008** A182 60c multi 1.10 1.10
**1009** A182 75c multi 1.40 1.40
**1010** A182 $1 multi 1.90 1.90
**1011** A182 $2 multi 3.75 3.75
**1012** A182 $5 multi 9.50 9.50
*a.* Souvenir sheet of 16, #997-1012 24.50 24.50
*Nos. 997-1012 (16)* 24.15 24.15

Mangroves — A183

Designs: 45c, Building and mangroves. 75c, Man and boys on beach near mangroves. $1, People near mangroves. $3, People planting mangroves.

**2014, June 16 Litho. *Perf. 14x14½***

| | | | | |
|---|---|---|---|---|
| **1013-1016** | A183 | Set of 4 | 10.00 | 10.00 |

2014 Commonwealth Games, Glasgow — A184

Designs: 25c, Weight lifter Davia Katoatau. 75c, Katoatau with medal.

No. 1019, horiz.: a, Kiribati team and flag-bearer. b, Scottish terrier wearing sweater with "Kiribati" sign.

**2014, Sept. 8 Litho. *Perf. 14½***

| | | | | |
|---|---|---|---|---|
| **1017-1018** | A184 | Set of 2 | 1.75 | 1.75 |

**Souvenir Sheet**

| | | | | |
|---|---|---|---|---|
| **1019** | A184 $2.50 | Sheet of 2, #a-b | 8.75 | 8.75 |

Souvenir Sheet

Butterflies — A185

No. 1020: a, $2, Meadow argus. b, $3, Blue moon.

***Perf. 14¼x14***

**2015, May 27 Litho. Unwmk.**

| | | | | |
|---|---|---|---|---|
| **1020** | A185 | Sheet of 2, #a-b | 7.75 | 7.75 |

Nos. 935, 938 Surcharged

Nos. 936-937 Overprinted

**Methods, Perfs and Watermarks As Before**

**2015, July 17**

| | | | | | |
|---|---|---|---|---|---|
| **1021** | A169 | 40c on 90c #935 | | .60 | .60 |
| **1022** | A169 | 60c on $5 #938 | | .90 | .90 |
| **1023** | A169 | $1 on #936 | | 1.50 | 1.50 |
| **1024** | A169 | $2 on #937 | | 3.00 | 3.00 |
| | | *Nos. 1021-1024 (4)* | | 6.00 | 6.00 |

Queen Elizabeth II, 90th Birthday — A186

Queen Elizabeth II wearing: 25c, Blue green dress and hat. 75c, Beige jacket and hat. $1, Floral dress and white hat. $2.50, Tweed jacket and hat. $3.75, Blue jacket and hat.

$5, Queen Elizabeth II and Prince Philip in Kiribati, 1982.

***Perf. 13¼x13***

**2016, Apr. 21 Litho. Unwmk.**

| | | | | |
|---|---|---|---|---|
| **1025-1029** | A186 | Set of 5 | 13.00 | 13.00 |

**Souvenir Sheet**

| | | | | |
|---|---|---|---|---|
| **1030** | A186 | $5 multi | 7.75 | 7.75 |

2016 World Stamp Show, New York City A187

Show emblem and: 25c, Participants in Independence celebrations. 75c, Participants in Independence celebrations, diff. $1.25, Boats on ground and in water. $3, Betio War Memorial.

***Perf. 13x13¼***

**2016, May 28 Litho. Unwmk.**

| | | | | |
|---|---|---|---|---|
| **1031-1034** | A187 | Set of 4 | 7.75 | 7.75 |

**POSTAGE DUE STAMPS**

Natl. Arms — D1

**1981, Aug. 27 Litho. *Perf. 14***

| | | | | | |
|---|---|---|---|---|---|
| **J1** | D1 | 1c | brt pink & black | .25 | .25 |
| **J2** | D1 | 2c | greenish blue & blk | .25 | .25 |
| **J3** | D1 | 5c | brt yel grn & black | .25 | .25 |
| **J4** | D1 | 10c | lt red brown & blk | .25 | .25 |
| **J5** | D1 | 20c | ultra & black | .25 | .25 |
| **J6** | D1 | 30c | yel bister & black | .25 | .35 |
| **J7** | D1 | 40c | brt pur & black | .25 | .45 |
| **J8** | D1 | 50c | green & black | .25 | .50 |
| **J9** | D1 | $1 | red orange & blk | .25 | .90 |
| | | | *Nos. J1-J9 (9)* | 2.25 | 3.45 |

Imperfs exist from the liquidation of Format International. They are not errors.

**OFFICIAL STAMPS**

**Nos. 327a-340c Overprinted "O.K.G.S."**

**1981, May Litho. Unwmk. *Perf. 14***

| | | | | | |
|---|---|---|---|---|---|
| **O1** | A52 | 1c | multicolored | .25 | .25 |
| **O2** | A52 | 3c | multicolored | .25 | .25 |
| **O3** | A52 | 5c | multicolored | .25 | .25 |
| **O4** | A52 | 7c | multicolored | .25 | .25 |
| **O5** | A52 | 10c | multicolored | .25 | .25 |
| **O6** | A52 | 12c | multicolored | .25 | .25 |
| **O7** | A52 | 15c | multicolored | .25 | .25 |
| **O8** | A52 | 20c | multicolored | .25 | .25 |
| **O9** | A52 | 25c | multicolored | .25 | .25 |
| **O10** | A52 | 30c | multicolored | .25 | .25 |
| **O11** | A52 | 35c | multicolored | .30 | .30 |
| **O12** | A52 | 50c | multicolored | .40 | .40 |
| **O13** | A52 | $1 | multicolored | .70 | .70 |
| **O14** | A52 | $2 | multicolored | 1.20 | 1.20 |
| **O15** | A52 | $5 | multicolored | 3.00 | 3.00 |
| | | | *Nos. O1-O15 (15)* | 8.10 | 8.10 |

Nos. O1-O15 have thick overprint.

**1981 Wmk. 373**

| | | | | | |
|---|---|---|---|---|---|
| *O1a* | A52 | 1c | multi | 4.00 | 4.25 |
| *O5a* | A52 | 10c | multi | 20.00 | 21.00 |
| *O6a* | A52 | 12c | multi | 6.00 | 6.00 |
| *O7a* | A52 | 15c | multi | 20.00 | 20.00 |
| *O8a* | A52 | 20c | multi | 13.00 | 13.00 |
| *O10a* | A52 | 30c | multi | 8.00 | 9.00 |
| *O12a* | A52 | 50c | multi | 7.50 | 7.50 |
| *O13a* | A52 | $1 | multi | 14.00 | 14.00 |
| *O14a* | A52 | $2 | multi | 16.00 | 17.00 |
| *O15a* | A52 | $5 | multi | 4.50 | 4.50 |
| | | | *Nos. O1a-O15a (10)* | 113.00 | 116.25 |

**Nos. 390, 393-394, 396, 398 Overprinted "O.K.G.S."**

**1983, June 28 Litho. *Perf. 14***

| | | | | | |
|---|---|---|---|---|---|
| **O16** | A62 | 12c | multicolored | .45 | .45 |
| **O17** | A62 | 30c | multicolored | .80 | .80 |
| **O18** | A62 | 35c | multicolored | .90 | .90 |
| **O19** | A62 | 50c | multicolored | 1.25 | 1.25 |
| **O20** | A62 | $2 | multicolored | 3.75 | 3.75 |
| | | | *Nos. O16-O20 (5)* | 7.15 | 7.15 |

This overprint has shorter, thinner letters than the one used for Nos. O1-O15. It also exists on Nos. 327, 331-334, 336-340. These have been questioned.

# KOREA

kə-ˈrē-ə

(Corea)

(Chosen, Tyosen, Tae Han)

LOCATION — Peninsula extending from Manchuria between the Yellow Sea and the Sea of Japan (East Sea)
GOVT. — Republic
AREA — 38,221 sq. mi.
POP. — 48,860,500 (2011 est.)
CAPITAL — Seoul

Korea (or Corea) an independent monarchy for centuries under Chinese influence, came under Japanese influence in 1876. Chinese and Japanese stamps were used there as early as 1877. Administrative control was assumed by Japan in 1905 and annexation followed in 1910. Postage stamps of Japan were used in Korea from 1905 to early 1946.

At the end of World War II, American forces occupied South Korea and Russian forces occupied North Korea, with the 38th parallel of latitude as the dividing line. A republic was established in 1948 following an election in South Korea. North Korea issues its own stamps.

100 Mon = 1 Poon
5 Poon = 1 Cheun
1000 Re = 100 Cheun = Weun
100 Weun = 1 Hwan (1953)
100 Chun = 1 Won (1962)

**Catalogue values for unused stamps in this country are for Never Hinged items, beginning with Scott 283 in the regular postage section, Scott B5 in the semi-postal section, and Scott C23 in the airpost section.**

**Watermarks**

Wmk. 257 — Curved Wavy Lines

Wmk. 312 — Zigzag Lines

Wmk. 317 — Communications Department Emblem

Stylized Yin Yang
A1 A2

***Perf. 8½ to 11½***

**1884 Typo. Unwmk.**

| | | | | |
|---|---|---|---|---|
| **1** | A1 | 5m rose | 52.50 | *10,000.* |
| **2** | A2 | 10m blue | 52.50 | *10,000.* |

Reprints and counterfeits of Nos. 1-2 exist.

These stamps were never placed in use. Values: 25 $5; 50 mon $6.50; 100 mon $9.

Counterfeits exist.

Yin Yang — A6

***Perf. 10¾, 11½, 11¾ 12, 13, 13¼ and Compound***

**1895 Litho.**

| | | | | |
|---|---|---|---|---|
| **6** | A6 | 5p green (II) | 30.00 | 16.00 |
| | *b.* | Vert. pair, imperf horiz. | 425.00 | — |
| | *c.* | Horiz. pair, imperf. vert. | 425.00 | — |
| | *d.* | Vertical pair, imperf. between | 425.00 | — |
| | *e.* | Horiz. pair, imperf. btwn. | 425.00 | — |
| **7** | A6 | 10p blue (II) | 110.00 | 37.50 |
| | *a.* | Horiz. pair, imperf. between | 425.00 | — |
| | *b.* | Vert. pair, imperf. horiz. | 425.00 | — |
| **8** | A6 | 25p maroon (II) | 70.00 | 30.00 |
| | *a.* | Horiz. pair, imperf. between | 375.00 | 375.00 |
| | *b.* | Vert. pair, imperf. horiz. | 375.00 | 375.00 |
| **9** | A6 | 50p purple (II) | 22.50 | 16.00 |
| | *a.* | Horiz. pair, imperf. between | 400.00 | 400.00 |
| | *b.* | Vert, pair, imperf. horiz. | 400.00 | 400.00 |
| | *c.* | Horiz. pair, imperf. vert. | 400.00 | 400.00 |
| | | *Nos. 6-9 (4)* | 232.50 | 99.50 |

No. 6a exists with sewing machine perforations vertically.

For overprints and surcharges see Nos. 10-17C, 35-38.

Counterfeits exist of Nos. 6-9 and all surcharges and overprints.

Overprinted "Tae Han" in Korean and Chinese Characters

**1897** **Red Overprint**

| | | | |
|---|---|---|---|
| 10 | A6 5p green | 87.50 | 35.00 |
| a. | 5p pale yellow green | 200.00 | 150.00 |
| b. | Inverted overprint | 160.00 | 160.00 |
| c. | Without ovpt. at bottom | 150.00 | 130.00 |
| d. | Without overprint at top | 150.00 | 130.00 |
| f. | Double overprint at top | 140.00 | 140.00 |
| g. | Overprint at bottom in blk | 160.00 | 160.00 |
| h. | Pair, one without overprint | 450.00 | 450.00 |
| i. | Double overprint at top, inverted at bottom | 550.00 | |
| 11 | A6 10p deep blue | 115.00 | 65.00 |
| a. | Without ovpt. at bottom | 150.00 | 150.00 |
| b. | Without overprint at top | 150.00 | 150.00 |
| c. | Double overprint at top | 150.00 | 150.00 |
| d. | Bottom overprint inverted | 140.00 | 140.00 |
| e. | Top ovpt. dbl., one in blk | 210.00 | 210.00 |
| f. | Top overprint omitted, bottom overprint inverted | 450.00 | |
| 12 | A6 25p maroon | 130.00 | 65.00 |
| a. | Overprint at bottom invtd. | 150.00 | 150.00 |
| b. | Overprint at bottom in blk | 210.00 | 210.00 |
| c. | Bottom overprint omitted | 150.00 | 150.00 |
| e. | Top ovpt. dbl., one in blk | 225.00 | 225.00 |
| f. | Top and bottom overprints double, one of each in blk | 250.00 | 250.00 |
| g. | Pair, one without overprint | 425.00 | 425.00 |
| 13 | A6 50p purple | 82.50 | 50.00 |
| a. | Without ovpt. at bottom | 120.00 | 110.00 |
| b. | Without overprint at top | 120.00 | 110.00 |
| c. | Bottom overprint double | 120.00 | 110.00 |
| e. | Pair, one without overprint | 275.00 | 275.00 |
| | *Nos. 10-13 (4)* | 415.00 | 215.00 |

**1897** **Black Overprint**

| | | | |
|---|---|---|---|
| 13F | A6 5p green | 500.00 | 160.00 |
| 13G | A6 10p deep blue | 650.00 | 200.00 |
| h. | Without ovpt. at bottom | 450.00 | |
| 14 | A6 25p maroon | 825.00 | 200.00 |
| a. | Without ovpt. at bottom | 450.00 | |
| b. | Without overprint at top | 450.00 | |
| c. | Double overprint at bottom | 450.00 | |
| 15 | A6 50p purple | 650.00 | 160.00 |
| a. | Without ovpt. at bottom | 450.00 | |
| | *Nos. 13F-15 (4)* | 2,625. | |

These stamps with black overprint, also No. 16A, are said not to have been officially authorized.

Nos. 6, 6a and 8 Surcharged in Red or Black

**1900**

| | | | |
|---|---|---|---|
| 15B | A6 1p on 5p grn (R) | *6,000.* | *2,500.* |
| c. | Yellow green | | |
| 16 | A6 1p on 25p mar | 260.00 | 65.00 |

**Same Surcharge in Red or Black on Nos. 10, 10a, 12, 12c and 14**

| | | | |
|---|---|---|---|
| 16A | A6 1p on 5p grn (R) | 975.00 | 550.00 |
| b. | 1p on 5p pale yellow green | 1,050. | |
| 17 | A6 1p on 25p (#12) | 65.00 | 40.00 |
| a. | Figure "1" omitted | 100.00 | |
| b. | On #12c | 90.00 | 70.00 |
| 17C | A6 1p on 25p (#14) | 750.00 | 650.00 |

Counterfeit overprints and surcharges of Nos. 10-17C exist. See note after No. 15.

A8

A9

A10

A11

A12

A13

A14

A15

A16

A17

A18

A19

A20

A21

**1900-01** **Typo.** ***Perf. 11***

| | | | | |
|---|---|---|---|---|
| 18 | A8 | 2re gray | 9.75 | 8.00 |
| 19 | A9 | 1ch yellow grn | 19.50 | 10.00 |
| 20B | A11 | 2ch pale blue | 23.00 | 11.00 |
| 21 | A12 | 3ch org red | 19.50 | 16.00 |
| a. | | Vert. pair, imperf. horiz. | 200.00 | 200.00 |
| b. | | Horiz. pair, imperf. btwn. | | 500.00 |
| c. | | 3c brnsh org | 21.00 | 17.50 |
| d. | | As "c," vert. pair, imperf. btwn. | | 500.00 |
| 22 | A13 | 4ch carmine | 34.00 | 16.00 |
| 23 | A14 | 5ch pink | 27.50 | 20.00 |
| 24 | A15 | 6ch dp blue | 34.00 | 20.00 |
| 25 | A16 | 10ch pur ('01) | 40.00 | 24.00 |
| 26 | A17 | 15ch gray vio | 62.50 | 40.00 |
| 27 | A18 | 20ch red brown | 110.00 | 52.50 |
| 31 | A19 | 50ch ol grn & pink | 500.00 | 190.00 |
| 32 | A20 | 1wn rose, blk & bl | 1,050. | 325.00 |
| 33 | A21 | 2wn pur & yel grn | 1,300. | 600.00 |
| | | *Nos. 18-33 (13)* | 3,230. | 1,333. |

Nos. 22, 23, 25, 26, 33 exist imperf.

Some examples of Nos. 18-27 exist with forged Tae Han overprints in red. It is believed that Nos. 18 and 21 exist with genuine Tae Han overprints.

*Reprints of No. 24 were made in light blue, perf. 12x13, in 1905 for a souvenir booklet. Value $135. See note after No. 54.*

See Nos. 52-54.

***Perf. 10***

| | | | | |
|---|---|---|---|---|
| 18a | A8 | 2re | 17.00 | 5.25 |
| 19a | A9 | 1ch | 17.00 | 5.50 |
| 20 | A10 | 2ch blue | 75.00 | 45.00 |
| a. | | Horiz. pair, imperf. btwn. | *725.00* | |
| 20Ba | A11 | 2ch pale blue | 50.00 | 45.00 |
| 21e | A12 | 3ch | 15.50 | 9.00 |
| 22a | A13 | 4ch | 45.00 | 20.00 |
| 23a | A14 | 5ch | 40.00 | 10.00 |
| 24a | A15 | 6ch | 47.50 | 12.00 |
| 26a | A17 | 15ch | 160.00 | 140.00 |
| 27a | A18 | 20ch | 225.00 | 225.00 |
| | | *Nos. 18a-27a (10)* | 692.00 | 516.75 |

Emperor's Crown — A22

**1902, Oct. 18** ***Perf. 11½***

| | | | |
|---|---|---|---|
| 34 | A22 3ch orange | 65.00 | 35.00 |

40th year of the reign of Emperor Kojong. An imperf. single was part of the 1905 souvenir booklet. Value $325. See note following No. 54.

Counterfeits exist.

**Nos. 8 and 9 Handstamp Surcharged in Black**

1ch

2ch

3ch

***Perf. 11½, 12, 12½, 13 and Compound***

**1902**

| | | | |
|---|---|---|---|
| 35 | A6 1ch on 25p maroon | 26.00 | 20.00 |
| b. | Horiz. pair, imperf. btwn. | 275.00 | |
| c. | Imperf. | 90.00 | |
| d. | Vert. pair, imperf. horiz. | 275.00 | |
| e. | On No. 12 | — | — |
| 36 | A6 2ch on 25p maroon | 32.50 | 30.00 |
| b. | Imperf. | 75.00 | |
| d. | On No. 12 | 90.00 | 90.00 |
| 36E | A6 2ch on 50p purple | 175.00 | 175.00 |
| f. | Character "cheun" unabbreviated (in two rows instead of one) | 250.00 | 175.00 |
| 37 | A6 3ch on 50p purple | 27.50 | 20.00 |
| b. | With character "cheun" unabbreviated (in two rows instead of one) | 2,400. | 950.00 |
| d. | Horiz. pair, imperf. btwn. | | 200.00 |
| e. | Vert. pair, imperf. btwn. | | 200.00 |
| g. | On No. 13 | | 240.00 |
| 38 | A6 3ch on 25p maroon | 65.00 | 62.50 |
| | *Nos. 35-38 (5)* | 326.00 | 307.50 |

There are several sizes of these surcharges. Being handstamped, inverted and double surcharges exist.

Counterfeit surcharges exist.

Falcon — A23

**1903** ***Perf. 13½x14***

| | | | | |
|---|---|---|---|---|
| 39 | A23 | 2re slate | 10.00 | 10.00 |
| 40 | A23 | 1ch violet brn | 13.50 | 10.00 |
| 41 | A23 | 2ch green | 14.00 | 10.00 |
| 42 | A23 | 3ch orange | 12.50 | 10.00 |
| 43 | A23 | 4ch rose | 20.00 | 10.00 |
| 44 | A23 | 5ch yellow brn | 20.00 | 10.00 |
| 45 | A23 | 6ch lilac | 24.00 | 11.00 |
| 46 | A23 | 10ch blue | 29.00 | 13.50 |
| 47 | A23 | 15ch red, *straw* | 40.00 | 20.00 |
| 48 | A23 | 20ch vio brn, *straw* | 57.50 | 25.00 |
| 49 | A23 | 50ch red, *grn* | 170.00 | 100.00 |
| 50 | A23 | 1wn vio, *lav* | 425.00 | 210.00 |
| 51 | A23 | 2wn vio, *org* | 425.00 | 210.00 |
| | | *Nos. 39-51 (13)* | 1,261. | 649.50 |

Values are for stamps with perfs touching the design.

**Types of 1901**

**1903** ***Perf. 12½***

**Thin, Semi-Transparent Paper**

| | | | | |
|---|---|---|---|---|
| 52 | A19 | 50ch pale ol grn & pale pink | *400.00* | *160.00* |
| 53 | A20 | 1wn rose, blk & bl | *600.00* | *200.00* |
| 54 | A21 | 2wn lt vio & lt grn | *875.00* | *250.00* |
| | | *Nos. 52-54 (3)* | *1,875.* | 610.00 |

No. 24, perf. 12x13, No. 34 imperf. and most examples of Nos. 52-54 unused are from souvenir booklets made up in 1905 when the Japanese withdrew all Korean stamps from circulation.

**WARNING**

In 1957 the Ministry of Communications issued 4000 presentation booklets containing Nos. 1-54 reproduced on watermark 312 paper.

Other presentation booklets included full-color reproductions of Nos. 1-54 and Japan No. 110 printed on the pages. Beware of wide-margined imperfs cut from these booklets.

**Issued under US Military Rule**

Stamps of Japan Nos. 331, 268, 342, 332, 339 and 337 Surcharged in Black

**1946, Feb. 1** **Wmk. 257** ***Perf. 13***

| | | | | |
|---|---|---|---|---|
| 55 | A86 | 5ch on 5s brn lake | 8.00 | *17.50* |
| 56 | A93 | 5ch on 14s rose lake & pale rose | 1.20 | *3.00* |
| a. | | 5ch on 40s dark violet (error) | 125.00 | |
| 57 | A154 | 10ch on 40s dk vio | 1.20 | *3.00* |
| 58 | A147 | 20ch on 6s lt ultra | 1.20 | *3.00* |
| a. | | 20ch on 27s rose brown (error) | 125.00 | |
| b. | | Double surcharge | 30.00 | |
| 59 | A151 | 30ch on 27s rose brn | 1.20 | *3.00* |
| a. | | 30ch on 6s light ultra (error) | 125.00 | |
| b. | | Double surcharge | 25.00 | |
| 60 | A151 | 5wn on 17s gray vio | 7.25 | *17.50* |
| | | *Nos. 55-60 (6)* | 20.05 | *47.00* |
| | | Set, never hinged | 33.00 | |

Five essays for this provisional issue exist both with and without additional overprint of two Chinese characters ("specimen") in vermilion. The essays are: 20ch on Japan No. 269; 50ch on No. 272; 1wn on No. 336; 1wn on No. 273; 10wn on No. 265. Values, each: $1,200 never hinged, $750 hinged. Other denominations have been reported.

Korean Family and Flag — A24

Arms of Korea — A25

**Wmk. 257**

**1946, May 1** **Litho.** ***Perf. 10½***

| | | | | |
|---|---|---|---|---|
| 61 | A24 | 3ch orange yellow | .75 | 1.60 |
| 62 | A24 | 5ch green | .75 | 1.60 |
| 63 | A24 | 10ch carmine | .75 | 1.60 |
| 64 | A24 | 20ch dark blue | .75 | 1.60 |
| 65 | A25 | 50ch brown violet | 3.00 | *2.50* |
| 66 | A25 | 1wn lt brown | 5.00 | *3.25* |
| | | *Nos. 61-66 (6)* | 11.00 | *12.15* |
| | | Set, never hinged | 18.50 | |

Liberation from Japan.

Imperfs., Part Perfs.

Imperforate and part-perforate examples of a great many Korean stamps from No. 61 onward exist.

The imperfs. include Nos. 61-90, 93-97, 116-117, 119-126, 132-173, 182-186, 195, 197-199, 202A, 203, 204-205, 217, etc.

The part-perfs. include Nos. 62-65, 69, 72-73, 109, 111-113, 132, etc.

Printers waste includes printed on both sides, etc.

As the field is so extensive, the editors believe that they belong more properly in a specialized catalogue.

Dove — A26

**1946, Aug. 15** **Unwmk.**

| | | | | |
|---|---|---|---|---|
| **67** | A26 50ch deep violet | | 7.50 | *5.25* |
| | Never hinged | | 12.50 | |

First anniversary of liberation.

Perforations often are rough on stamps issued between Aug. 1946 and the end of 1954. This is not considered a defect.

Flags of US and Korea A27

**1946, Sept. 9** ***Perf. 11***

| | | | | |
|---|---|---|---|---|
| **68** | A27 10wn carmine | | 5.75 | *4.50* |
| | Never hinged | | 9.50 | |

Resumption of postal communication with the US.

Astronomical Observatory, Kyongju — A28

Hibiscus with Rice — A29

Map of Korea — A30

Gold Crown of Silla Dynasty — A31

Admiral Li Sun-sin — A32

**1946** ***Rouletted 12***

| | | | | |
|---|---|---|---|---|
| **69** | A28 | 50ch dark blue | .95 | *1.90* |
| **70** | A29 | 1wn buff | .90 | *2.00* |
| **71** | A30 | 2wn indigo | 1.60 | 2.75 |
| **72** | A31 | 5wn magenta | 10.00 | *20.00* |
| **73** | A32 | 10wn emerald | 11.00 | *18.50* |
| | | *Nos. 69-73 (5)* | 24.45 | *45.15* |
| | | Set, never hinged | 37.50 | |

***Perf. 11***

| | | | | |
|---|---|---|---|---|
| *70a* | A29 | 1wn | 1.75 | *3.25* |
| *71a* | A30 | 2wn | 62.50 | *120.00* |
| *72a* | A31 | 5wn | 62.50 | *120.00* |
| | | *Nos. 70a-72a (3)* | 126.75 | *243.25* |
| | | Set, never hinged | 240.00 | |

Korean Phonetic Alphabet — A33

**1946, Oct. 9** ***Perf. 11***

| | | | | |
|---|---|---|---|---|
| **74** | A33 50ch deep blue | | 4.50 | 4.50 |
| | Never hinged | | 8.50 | |

500th anniv. of the introduction of the Korean phonetic alphabet (Hangul).

Li Jun — A34

Admiral Li Sun-sin — A35

***Perf. 11½x11, 11½***

**1947, Aug. 1** **Litho.** **Wmk. 257**

| | | | | |
|---|---|---|---|---|
| **75** | A34 | 5wn lt blue green | 6.75 | *8.75* |
| **76** | A35 | 10wn light blue | 7.25 | *8.75* |
| | | Set, never hinged | 25.00 | |

Presentation Sheets

Starting in 1947 with No. 75, nearly 100 Korean stamps were printed in miniature or souvenir sheets and given to government officials and others. These sheets were released in quantities of 300 to 4,000. In 1957 the Ministry of Communications began to sell the souvenir sheets at post offices at face value to be used for postage. They are listed from No. 264a onward.

Letter-encircled Globe — A36

**1947, Aug. 1** ***Perf. 11½x11***

| | | | | |
|---|---|---|---|---|
| **77** | A36 10wn light blue | | 10.50 | *9.25* |
| | Never hinged | | 18.00 | |

Resumption of international mail service between Korea and all countries of the world.

Granite Paper

Starting with No. 77, most Korean stamps through No. 751, except those on Laid Paper, are on Granite Paper. Granite Paper is noted above listing if the issue was printed on both ordinary and Granite Paper, such as Nos. 360a-374A.

Arch of Independence, Seoul — A37

Tortoise Ship, First Ironclad War Vessel — A38

**1948, Apr.**

| | | | | |
|---|---|---|---|---|
| **78** | A37 | 20wn rose | 5.00 | *4.00* |
| **79** | A38 | 50wn dull red brown | 80.00 | 40.00 |
| | | Set, never hinged | 150.00 | |

## Republic

Flag and Ballot — A39

Woman and Man Casting Ballots — A40

***Perf. 11x11½***

**1948, May 10** **Litho.** **Wmk. 257**

| | | | | |
|---|---|---|---|---|
| **80** | A39 | 2wn orange | 11.00 | 8.25 |
| **81** | A39 | 5wn lilac rose | 18.50 | 11.50 |
| **82** | A39 | 10wn lt violet | 29.00 | 20.00 |
| **83** | A40 | 20wn carmine | 65.00 | 30.00 |
| **84** | A40 | 50wn blue | 32.50 | 22.50 |
| | | *Nos. 80-84 (5)* | 156.00 | 92.25 |
| | | Set, never hinged | 220.00 | |

South Korea election of May 10, 1948.

Korean Flag and Olive Branches — A41

Olympic Torchbearer and Map of Korea — A42

**1948, June 1** ***Perf. 11x11½, 11½x11***

| | | | | |
|---|---|---|---|---|
| **85** | A41 | 5wn green | 120.00 | 60.00 |
| **86** | A42 | 10wn purple | 37.50 | 22.50 |
| | | Set, never hinged | 270.00 | |

Korea's participation in the 1948 Olympic Games.

National Assembly — A43

**1948, July 1** **Wmk. 257** ***Perf. 11½***

| | | | | |
|---|---|---|---|---|
| **87** | A43 4wn orange brown | | 22.50 | *12.00* |
| | Never hinged | | 37.50 | |

Opening of the Assembly July 1, 1948.
Exists without period between "5" and "31."

Korean Family and Capitol — A44

Flag of Korea A45

**1948, Aug. 1** **Litho.**

| | | | | |
|---|---|---|---|---|
| **88** | A44 | 4wn emerald | 82.50 | 50.00 |
| **89** | A45 | 10wn orange brown | 32.50 | *24.00* |
| | | Set, never hinged | 200.00 | |

Signing of the new constitution, 7/17/48.

Pres. Syngman Rhee — A46

**1948, Aug. 5**

| | | | | |
|---|---|---|---|---|
| **90** | A46 5wn deep blue | | 260.00 | 200.00 |
| | Never hinged | | 450.00 | |

Inauguration of Korea's first president, Syngman Rhee.

Dove — A47

Hibiscus — A48

Two types of 5wn:

I — "1948" 3mm wide; top inscription 9mm wide; periods in "8.15." barely visible.

II — "1948" 4mm wide; top inscription 9½mm; periods in "8.15." bold and strong.

**1948** ***Perf. 11, 11x11½***

| | | | | |
|---|---|---|---|---|
| **91** | A47 | 4wn blue | 29.00 | *30.00* |
| **92** | A48 | 5wn rose lilac (II) | 65.00 | 50.00 |
| ***a.*** | | Type I | *120.00* | 100.00 |
| | | Set, never hinged | 160.00 | |

Issued to commemorate the establishment of Korea's republican government.

Li Jun — A49

Observatory, Kyongju — A50

**1948, Oct. 1** ***Perf. 11½x11***

| | | | | |
|---|---|---|---|---|
| **93** | A49 | 4wn rose carmine | .75 | 1.20 |
| **94** | A50 | 14wn deep blue | .75 | 1.20 |
| ***a.*** | | 14wn light blue | 140.00 | 100.00 |
| | | Never Hinged | 320.00 | |
| | | Set, never hinged | 3.50 | |

For surcharges see Nos. 127, 174, 176.

Doves over UN Emblem — A51

**1949, Feb. 12 Wmk. 257 *Perf. 11***

| | | | | |
|---|---|---|---|---|
| **95** | A51 10wn blue | | *30.00* | *25.00* |
| | Never hinged | | *52.50* | |

Arrival of the UN Commission on Korea, Feb. 12, 1949.

Korean Citizen and Census Date — A52

**1949, Apr. 25**

| | | | |
|---|---|---|---|
| **96** | A52 15wn purple | 40.00 | 30.00 |
| | Never hinged | 72.50 | |

Census of May 1, 1949.

Korean Boy and Girl A53

**1949, May 5**

| | | | |
|---|---|---|---|
| **97** | A53 15wn purple | 22.50 | 20.00 |
| | Never hinged | 40.00 | |

20th anniv. of Children's Day, May 5, 1949.

Postman — A54

Worker and Factory — A55

Rice Harvesting A56

Japanese Cranes A57

Diamond Mountains A58

Ginseng Plant A59

South Gate, Seoul — A60

Tabo Pagoda, Kyongju — A61

**1949 Litho. *Perf. 11***

| | | | | |
|---|---|---|---|---|
| **98** | A54 | 1wn rose | 3.25 | 3.25 |
| **99** | A55 | 2wn dk blue gray | 3.00 | 3.00 |
| **100** | A56 | 5wn yellow green | 14.00 | 9.50 |
| **101** | A57 | 10wn blue green | 1.20 | 1.20 |
| **102** | A58 | 20wn orange brown | .80 | 1.20 |
| **103** | A59 | 30wn blue green | .80 | 1.20 |
| **104** | A60 | 50wn violet blue | .80 | 1.20 |
| **105** | A61 | 100wn dull yellow grn | .80 | 1.20 |
| | | *Nos. 98-105 (8)* | 24.65 | 21.75 |
| | | Set, never hinged | 47.50 | |

For surcharges see Nos. 129-131, 175, 177B-179, 181.

Phoenix and Yin Yang — A62

**1949, Aug. 25**

| | | | |
|---|---|---|---|
| **106** | A62 15wn deep blue | 27.50 | 22.50 |
| | Never hinged | 52.50 | |

1st anniv. of Korea's independence.

Express Train "Sam Chun Li" A63

**1949, Sept. 18 *Perf. 11½x12***

| | | | |
|---|---|---|---|
| **107** | A63 15wn violet blue | 105.00 | 55.00 |
| | Never hinged | 190.00 | |

50th anniversary of Korean railroads.

Korean Flag — A64

***Perf. 11½x11***

**1949, Oct. 15 Wmk. 257**

| | | | |
|---|---|---|---|
| **108** | A64 15wn red org, yel & dk bl | 14.00 | *15.00* |
| | Never hinged | 30.00 | |

75th anniv. of the UPU.

No. 108 exists unwatermarked. These are counterfeit.

Hibiscus — A65

Magpies and Map of Korea — A66

Stylized Bird and Globe — A67

Diamond Mountains A68

Admiral Li Sun-sin A69

**1949 Wmk. 257 Litho. *Perf. 11***

| | | | | |
|---|---|---|---|---|
| **109** | A65 | 15wn vermilion | .60 | *1.10* |
| **110** | A66 | 65wn deep blue | 2.10 | *2.10* |
| **111** | A67 | 200wn green | .60 | *1.10* |
| **112** | A68 | 400wn brown | .60 | *1.10* |
| **113** | A69 | 500wn deep blue | .60 | *1.10* |
| | | *Nos. 109-113 (5)* | 4.50 | *6.50* |
| | | Set, never hinged | 7.50 | |

For surcharges see Nos. 128, 177, 180.

Canceled to Order

More than 100 Korean stamps and souvenir sheets were canceled to order, the cancellation incorporating the date "67.9.20." These include 81 stamps between Nos. 111 and 327, 18 airmail stamps between Nos. C6 and C26, and 5 souvenir sheets between Nos. 313 and 332, etc.

Also exists with later dates and on other stamps.

These c-t-o stamps and souvenir sheets are sold for much less than the values shown below, which are for postally used examples.

A70

Ancient postal medal (Ma-Pae).

**1950, Jan. 1**

| | | | |
|---|---|---|---|
| **114** | A70 15wn yellow green | 22.50 | *20.00* |
| **115** | A70 65wn red brown | 11.50 | *8.00* |
| | Set, never hinged | 65.00 | |

50th anniv. of Korea's entrance into the UPU.

Revolutionists — A71

**1950, Mar. 10 *Perf. 11½***

| | | | |
|---|---|---|---|
| **116** | A71 15wn olive | 23.00 | *20.00* |
| **117** | A71 65wn light violet | 11.50 | 8.00 |
| | Set, never hinged | 65.00 | |

41st anniversary of Korea's declaration of Independence.

Korean Emblem and National Assembly — A72

**1950, May 30**

| | | | |
|---|---|---|---|
| **118** | A72 30wn bl, red, brn & grn | 15.00 | 10.00 |
| | Never hinged | 26.00 | |

2nd natl. election of the Korean Republic.

Syngman Rhee — A73

Korean Flag and White Mountains — A74

Flags of UN and Korea, Map of Korea A75

**1950, Nov. 20 Wmk. 257 *Perf. 11***

| | | | |
|---|---|---|---|
| **119** | A73 100wn blue | 4.50 | *4.00* |
| **120** | A74 100wn green | 4.50 | *3.25* |
| **121** | A75 200wn dark green | 3.25 | *2.50* |
| | *Nos. 119-121 (3)* | 12.25 | 9.75 |
| | Set, never hinged | 22.00 | |

Crane — A76

Tiger Mural — A77

Dove and Flag — A78

Postal Medal — A79

Mural from Ancient Tomb — A80

**1951 Unwmk. *Perf. 11***

**Ordinary Paper**

| | | | | |
|---|---|---|---|---|
| **122** | A76 | 5wn org brn | 1.60 | *2.00* |
| **123** | A77 | 20wn purple | 2.10 | *2.75* |
| **124** | A78 | 50wn green | 14.50 | *13.50* |
| **125** | A79 | 100wn deep blue | 27.00 | 13.50 |
| **126** | A80 | 1000wn green | 31.00 | 12.00 |
| | | *Nos. 122-126 (5)* | 76.20 | 43.75 |
| | | Set, never hinged | 125.00 | |

***Rouletted 12***

| | | | | |
|---|---|---|---|---|
| *122a* | A76 | 5wn orange brown | 1.00 | *1.50* |
| *123a* | A77 | 20wn purple | 1.00 | *1.50* |
| *124a* | A78 | 50wn green | 2.75 | *4.00* |
| *125a* | A79 | 100wn blue | 4.25 | 5.00 |
| | | *Nos. 122a-125a (4)* | 9.00 | *12.00* |
| | | Set, never hinged | 16.50 | |

No. 126 also exists perforated 12½. See Nos. 187-189.

**No. 93 Surcharged with New Value and Wavy Lines in Blue**

**1951 Wmk. 257 *Perf. 11½x11***

| | | | |
|---|---|---|---|
| **127** | A49 100wn on 4wn rose car | 3.25 | 5.00 |
| *a.* | Inverted surcharge | 32.50 | *65.00* |
| | Never hinged | 65.00 | |

Nos. 109, 101, 102 and 104 Surcharged in Blue or Brown

*Perf. 11*

| | | | |
|---|---|---|---|
| 128 | A65 200wn on 15wn | 3.75 | 7.00 |
| a. | Inverted surcharge | 32.50 | *65.00* |
| | Never hinged | 65.00 | |
| 129 | A57 300wn on 10wn (Br) | 5.25 | 6.00 |
| a. | Inverted surcharge | 32.50 | |
| | Never hinged | 65.00 | |
| 130 | A58 300wn on 20wn | 4.00 | 4.50 |
| a. | Inverted surcharge | 35.00 | |
| | Never hinged | 75.00 | |
| 131 | A60 300wn on 50wn (Br) | 45.00 | 4.00 |
| | *Nos. 127-131 (5)* | 61.25 | 26.50 |
| | Set, never hinged | 92.50 | |

Size and details of surcharge varies. Numeral upright on Nos. 129 and 131; numeral slanted on Nos. 175 and 179. See Nos. 174-181.

On No. 130, the zeros in "300" are octagonal; on No. 177B they are oval.

Flags of US and Korea and Statue of Liberty — A81

Design (blue stamps): Flag of same country as preceding green stamp, UN emblem and doves.

**1951-52 Wmk. 257 *Perf. 11***

**Flags in Natural Colors, Participating Country at Left**

| | | | |
|---|---|---|---|
| 132 | A81 500wn green | 4.50 | 8.50 |
| 133 | A81 500wn blue | 4.50 | 8.50 |
| 134 | A81 500wn grn *(Australia)* | 5.00 | 10.00 |
| 135 | A81 500wn blue | 5.00 | 10.00 |
| 136 | A81 500wn grn *(Belgium)* | 5.00 | 10.00 |
| 137 | A81 500wn blue | 5.00 | 10.00 |
| 138 | A81 500wn grn *(Britain)* | 5.00 | 10.00 |
| 139 | A81 500wn blue | 5.00 | 10.00 |
| 140 | A81 500wn grn *(Canada)* | 5.00 | 10.00 |
| 141 | A81 500wn blue | 5.00 | 10.00 |
| 142 | A81 500wn grn *(Colombia)* | 5.00 | 10.00 |
| 143 | A81 500wn blue | 5.00 | 10.00 |
| 144 | A81 500wn grn *(Denmark)* | 25.00 | *35.00* |
| 145 | A81 500wn blue | 25.00 | *35.00* |
| 146 | A81 500wn grn *(Ethiopia)* | 5.00 | 10.00 |
| 147 | A81 500wn blue | 5.00 | 10.00 |
| 148 | A81 500wn grn *(France)* | 5.00 | 10.00 |
| 149 | A81 500wn blue | 5.00 | 10.00 |
| 150 | A81 500wn grn *(Greece)* | 5.00 | 10.00 |
| 151 | A81 500wn blue | 5.00 | 10.00 |
| 152 | A81 500wn grn *(India)* | 20.00 | 35.00 |
| 153 | A81 500wn blue | 20.00 | 35.00 |
| 154 | A81 500wn grn *(Italy)* | 5.50 | 20.00 |
| a. | Flag without crown ('52) | 30.00 | 45.00 |
| 155 | A81 500wn blue | 5.50 | 20.00 |
| a. | Flag without crown ('52) | 30.00 | 45.00 |
| 156 | A81 500wn grn *(Luxembourg)* | 20.00 | 35.00 |
| 157 | A81 500wn blue | 20.00 | 35.00 |
| 158 | A81 500wn grn *(Netherlands)* | 5.00 | 10.00 |
| 159 | A81 500wn blue | 5.00 | 10.00 |
| 160 | A81 500wn grn *(New Zealand)* | 5.00 | 10.00 |
| 161 | A81 500wn blue | 5.00 | 10.00 |
| 162 | A81 500wn grn *(Norway)* | 20.00 | 35.00 |
| 163 | A81 500wn blue | 20.00 | 35.00 |
| 164 | A81 500wn grn *(Philippines)* | 5.00 | 10.00 |
| 165 | A81 500wn blue | 5.00 | 10.00 |
| 166 | A81 500wn grn *(Sweden)* | 5.00 | 10.00 |
| 167 | A81 500wn blue | 5.00 | 10.00 |
| 168 | A81 500wn grn *(Thailand)* | 5.00 | 10.00 |
| 169 | A81 500wn blue | 5.00 | 10.00 |
| 170 | A81 500wn grn*(Turkey)* | 5.00 | 10.00 |
| 171 | A81 500wn blue | 5.00 | 10.00 |
| 172 | A81 500wn grn *(Union of So. Africa)* | 5.00 | 10.00 |
| 173 | A81 500wn blue | 5.00 | 10.00 |
| | *Nos. 132-173 (42)* | 340.00 | 637.00 |
| | Set, never hinged | 850.00 | |

Twenty-two imperf. souvenir sheets of two, containing the green and the blue stamps for each participating country (including both types of Italy) were issued. Size: 140x90mm. Value, set hinged $875; never hinged $1,400.

**Nos. 93-94, 101-105, 109-110 Surcharged Like Nos. 128-131 in Blue or Brown**

**1951 Wmk. 257 *Perf. 11½x11, 11***

| | | | |
|---|---|---|---|
| 174 | A49 300wn on 4wn | 3.00 | *4.50* |
| a. | Inverted surcharge | 32.50 | *65.00* |
| | Never hinged | 65.00 | |
| 175 | A57 300wn on 10wn (Br) | 7.25 | *5.50* |
| a. | Inverted surcharge | 32.50 | *65.00* |
| | Never hinged | 65.00 | |
| 176 | A50 300wn on 14wn (Br) | 5.50 | *4.50* |
| a. | 300wn on 14wn lt bl | 2,250. | 1,500. |
| | Never hinged | 4,000. | |
| b. | Inverted surcharge | 32.50 | *65.00* |
| | Never hinged | 65.00 | |
| 177 | A65 300wn on 15wn | 3.00 | *4.50* |
| a. | Inverted surcharge | 32.50 | *65.00* |
| | Never hinged | 65.00 | |
| 177B | A58 300wn on 20wn | 5.25 | 5.25 |
| 178 | A59 300wn on 30wn (Br) | 3.25 | *4.50* |
| a. | Inverted surcharge | 32.50 | *65.00* |
| | Never hinged | 65.00 | |
| 179 | A60 300wn on 50wn (Br) | 2.75 | 4.00 |
| 180 | A66 300wn on 65wn (Br) | 3.25 | *4.50* |
| a. | Inverted monad | 47.50 | 95.00 |
| | Never hinged | 95.00 | |
| 181 | A61 300wn on 100wn | 3.00 | 4.50 |
| a. | Inverted surcharge | 45.00 | *90.00* |
| | Never hinged | 90.00 | |
| | *Nos. 174-181 (9)* | 36.25 | 41.75 |
| | Set, never hinged | 67.50 | |

"300" slanted on Nos. 175, 177B and 179; "300" upright on Nos. 129 and 131. The surcharge exists double on several of these stamps.

No. 177B differs from No. 130 in detail noted after No. 131.

Syngman Rhee and "Happiness" — A82

**1952, Sept. 10 Litho. *Perf. 12½***

| | | | |
|---|---|---|---|
| 182 | A82 1000wn dark green | 7.50 | *7.50* |
| | Never hinged | 14.00 | |

Second inauguration of President Syngman Rhee, Aug. 15, 1952.

Sok Kul Am, Near Kyongju — A83

Bool Gook Temple, Kyongju — A84

Tombstone of Mu Yal Wang — A85

Choong Yul Sa Shrine, Tongyung — A86

**1952 Wmk. 257 Typo. *Perf. 12½***

| | | | |
|---|---|---|---|
| 183 | A83 200wn henna brown | 1.60 | *1.40* |
| 184 | A84 300wn green | 1.35 | 1.00 |
| 185 | A85 500wn carmine | 2.10 | *1.60* |
| 186 | A86 2000wn deep blue | 1.60 | 1.00 |

***Rough Perf. 10-11, 11½x11 and Compound***

**Litho.**

| | | | |
|---|---|---|---|
| 186A | A83 200wn henna brown | 1.75 | *1.35* |
| 186B | A84 300wn green | 1.60 | *1.00* |
| | *Nos. 183-186B (6)* | 10.00 | 7.35 |
| | Set, never hinged | 19.50 | |

**Types of 1951**

**Designs slightly smaller**

**1952-53 *Rough Perf. 10-11***

| | | | |
|---|---|---|---|
| 187 | A77 20wn purple | 10.50 | *5.00* |
| 187A | A78 50wn green | 25.00 | *23.00* |
| 187B | A79 100wn deep blue | 2.10 | 1.50 |
| 187C | A80 1000wn green | 135.00 | 27.00 |
| | *Nos. 187-187C (4)* | 172.60 | 56.50 |
| | Set, never hinged | 340.00 | |

**Designs slightly larger**

***Perf. 12½***

| | | | |
|---|---|---|---|
| 187D | A78 50wn green | 2.50 | 2.40 |
| 188 | A79 100wn deep blue | 1.75 | *1.90* |
| 189 | A80 1000wn green ('53) | 5.50 | 1.10 |
| | *Nos. 187D-189 (3)* | 9.75 | 5.40 |
| | Set, never hinged | 20.00 | |

**Type of 1952**

**1953**

| | | | |
|---|---|---|---|
| 189A | A85 500wn deep blue | 24.00 | *160.00* |
| | Never hinged | 42.50 | |

All examples of No. 189A were affixed to postal cards before sale. Values are for stamps removed from the cards.

See Nos. 191-192, 203B, 248.

**Types of 1952 and**

Planting Trees — A87

**Wmk. 257**

**1953, Apr. 5 Litho. *Perf. 12½***

| | | | |
|---|---|---|---|
| 190 | A87 1h aqua | .80 | *.65* |
| 191 | A85 2h aqua | .80 | .50 |
| 192 | A85 5h bright green | 1.00 | .50 |
| 193 | A87 10h bright green | 2.75 | 1.50 |
| 194 | A86 20h brown | 3.75 | *2.00* |
| | *Nos. 190-194 (5)* | 9.10 | 5.15 |
| | Set, never hinged | 17.00 | |

See Nos. 203A, 247.

Map and YMCA Emblem — A88

**1953, Oct. 25 *Perf. 13½***

| | | | |
|---|---|---|---|
| 195 | A88 10h dk slate bl & red | 4.75 | *3.25* |
| | Never hinged | 9.00 | |

50th anniv. of the Korean YMCA.

Tombstone of Mu Yal Wang — A88a

A89

Sika Deer — A90

**1954, Apr. *Perf. 12½***

| | | | |
|---|---|---|---|
| 196 | A88a 5h dark green | 1.10 | *1.20* |
| 197 | A89 100h brn car | 7.50 | 2.60 |
| 198 | A90 500h brn org | 55.00 | 10.00 |
| 199 | A90 1000h bister brown | 100.00 | 20.00 |
| | *Nos. 196-199 (4)* | 163.60 | 33.80 |
| | Set, never hinged | 325.00 | |

See Nos. 203C, 203D, 238-239, 248A, 250-251, 259, 261-262, 269-270, 279, 281-282.

Dok Do (Dok Island) — A91

Design: 10h, Dok Do, lateral view.

**1954, Sept. 15**

| | | | |
|---|---|---|---|
| 200 | A91 2h claret | 2.25 | *2.40* |
| 201 | A91 5h blue | 4.75 | *2.40* |
| 202 | A91 10h blue green | 8.50 | *2.40* |
| | *Nos. 200-202 (3)* | 15.50 | 7.20 |
| | Set, never hinged | 28.00 | |

Moth and Flag — A92

Pagoda Park, Seoul — A92a

**1954, Apr. 16 Wmk. 257 *Perf. 12½***

| | | | |
|---|---|---|---|
| 202A | A92 10h brown | 8.50 | 3.00 |
| 203 | A92a 30h dark blue | 1.00 | 1.40 |
| | Set, never hinged | 18.50 | |

See Nos. 203E, 260, 280.

**Types of 1952-54**

**1955-56 Unwmk. *Perf. 12½***

**Laid Paper**

| | | | |
|---|---|---|---|
| 203A | A87 1h aqua ('56) | .30 | *.50* |
| 203B | A85 2h aqua ('56) | .30 | *.50* |
| 203C | A88a 5h brt grn ('56) | .40 | *.50* |
| 203D | A89 100h brn car | 42.50 | 7.00 |
| 203E | A92a 200h violet | 10.00 | 2.40 |
| | *Nos. 203A-203E (5)* | 53.50 | 10.90 |
| | Set, never hinged | 125.00 | |

On No. 203C the right hand character is redrawn as in illustration above No. 212D.

Nos. 203A and 203C are found on horizontally and vertically laid paper.

Erosion Control on Mountainside — A93

**1954, Dec. 12 Wmk. 257**

| | | | |
|---|---|---|---|
| 204 | A93 10h dk grn & yel grn | 3.00 | 1.25 |
| 205 | A93 19h dk grn & yel grn | 3.50 | *1.75* |
| | Set, never hinged | 11.00 | |

Issued to publicize the 1954 forestation campaign.

Presidents Rhee and Eisenhower Shaking Hands — A94

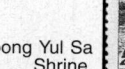

**1954, Dec. 25** ***Perf. 13½***

**206** A94 10h violet blue 1.90 *1.60*
**207** A94 19h brown 2.10 *2.00*
**208** A94 71h dull green 4.75 3.50
*Nos. 206-208 (3)* 8.75 7.10
Set, never hinged 15.50

Adoption of the US-Korea mutual defense treaty.

"Reconstruction" A95

**Wmk. 257**

**1955, Feb. 10** **Litho.** ***Perf. 12½***

**209** A95 10h brown 3.00 2.60
**210** A95 15h violet 3.00 2.60
**211** A95 20h blue 650.00 18.50
Never hinged 1,350.
**212** A95 50h plum 7.00 3.00
*Nos. 209-210,212 (3)* 13.00
*Nos. 209-212 (4)* 26.70
Set, #209-210, 212, never hinged 25.00

Korea's industrial reconstruction.

**1955, Oct. 19** **Unwmk.** ***Perf. 12½***
**Laid Paper**

**212A** A95 15h violet 2.75 2.25
**212B** A95 20h blue 2.75 2.00
**212C** A95 50h plum 4.75 1.00
*Nos. 212A-212C (3)* 10.25 5.25
Set, never hinged 18.50

No. 212B is found on horizontally and vertically laid paper.

**Same with Right Character at Top Redrawn**

Original

Redrawn

**1956, June 5** **Unwmk.** ***Perf. 12½***
**Laid Paper**

**212D** A95 10h brown 2.75 *2.40*
**212E** A95 15h violet 2.75 *2.40*
**212F** A95 20h blue 2.75 1.10
*a.* Booklet pane of 6 175.00
*Nos. 212D-212F (3)* 8.25 5.90
Set, never hinged 16.00

Nos. 212D-212F are found on horizontally and vertically laid paper. See Nos. 248B, 256, 272, 276.

Rotary Emblem — A96

**1955, Feb. 23** **Wmk. 257** ***Perf. 13½***

**213** A96 20h violet 5.00 3.50
**214** A96 25h dull green 1.75 1.50
**215** A96 71h magenta 1.75 1.50
*Nos. 213-215 (3)* 8.50 6.50
Set, never hinged 15.00

Rotary International, 50th anniversary.

Syngman Rhee, 80th Birthday, Apr. 26 — A98

**1955, Mar. 26**

**217** A98 20h deep blue 13.50 6.75
Never hinged 26.00

Flag and Arch of Independence A99

**1955, Aug. 15** **Litho.** ***Perf. 13½***

**218** A99 40h Prus green 6.00 1.60
**219** A99 100h lake 6.00 2.10
Set, never hinged 20.00

Tenth anniversary of independence.

UN Emblem in Circle of Clasped Hands — A100

**1955, Oct. 24**

**221** A100 20h bluish green 2.50 2.00
**222** A100 55h aqua 2.50 2.00
Set, never hinged 9.50

United Nations, 10th anniversary.

Olympic Torch and Runners — A101

**1955, Oct. 23**

**223** A101 20h claret 3.50 2.00
**224** A101 55h dark green 3.50 2.00
Set, never hinged 13.00

36th National Athletic Meet.

Adm. Li Sun-sin, Navy Flag and Tortoise Ship A102

***Perf. 13x13½***

**1955, Nov. 11** **Unwmk.**
**Laid Paper**

**225** A102 20h violet blue 5.00 2.60
Never hinged 9.50

Korean Navy, 10th anniversary.

Rhee Monument near Seoul — A103

**1956, Mar. 26** ***Perf. 13½x13***

**226** A103 20h dull green 3.25 2.60
Never hinged 7.00

81st birthday of Pres. Syngman Rhee.
No. 226 is found on horizontally and vertically laid paper.

Third Inauguration of Pres. Syngman Rhee — A104

**1956, Aug. 15** ***Perf. 13x13½***

**227** A104 20h brown 72.50 30.00
**228** A104 55h violet blue 27.00 12.00
Set, never hinged 170.00

Olympic Rings and Torch — A105

**1956, Nov. 1** **Litho.** ***Perf. 12½***
**Laid Paper**

**229** A105 20h red orange 2.75 *2.40*
**230** A105 55h brt green 2.75 *2.40*
Set, never hinged 10.50

16th Olympic Games in Melbourne, 11/22-12/8.

Central Post Office, Seoul A107

Stamp of 1884 — A108

Mail Delivered by Donkey A109

**1956, Dec. 4** **Laid Paper** **Unwmk.**

**232** A107 20h lt blue green 6.50 2.50
**233** A108 50h lt carmine 11.50 6.00
**234** A109 55h green 5.00 2.00
*Nos. 232-234 (3)* 23.00 10.50
Set, never hinged 42.50

Issued to commemorate Postal Day.

**Types of 1954 Redrawn and**

Hibiscus — A110

King Sejong — A111

Kyongju Observatory A112

**No Hwan Symbol; Redrawn Character**

**1956, Dec. 4** **Unwmk.** ***Perf. 12½***
**Laid Paper**

**235** A110 10h lilac rose 1.00 .75
**236** A111 20h lilac 1.75 1.00
**237** A112 50h violet 3.00 1.00
**238** A89 100h brn car 12.50 4.00
**239** A90 500h brn org 37.50 4.75
*Nos. 235-239 (5)* 55.75 11.50
Set, never hinged 100.00

On Nos. 238-239, the character after numeral has been omitted and the last character of the inscription has been redrawn as illustrated above No. 212D.

Nos. 235-236 are found on horizontally and vertically laid paper.

See Nos. 240-242, 253, 255, 258, 273, 275, 278, 291Bd, 291Bf, B3-B4.

**Types of 1956**

**1957, Jan. 21** **Wmk. 312** ***Perf. 12½***

**240** A110 10h lilac rose 1.00 .65
**241** A111 20h red lilac 2.25 1.05
**242** A112 50h violet 3.50 .65
*Nos. 240-242 (3)* 6.75 2.35
Set, never hinged 14.00

Telecommunication Symbols — A117

**1957, Jan. 31** ***Perf. 13½***

**243** A117 40h lt ultra 1.50 1.20
**244** A117 55h brt green 1.50 1.20
Set, never hinged 5.00

5th anniv. of Korea's joining the ITU.

Boy Scout and Emblem A118

**1957, Feb. 27** **Wmk. 312**

**245** A118 40h pale purple 1.40 *1.35*
**246** A118 55h lt magenta 1.40 *1.35*
Set, never hinged 5.25

50th anniversary of Boy Scout movement.

**Types of 1953-56**
**Top Right Character Redrawn; Hwan Symbol Retained**

**1957** **Wmk. 312** ***Perf. 12½***

**247** A87 1h aqua .65 *.55*
**248** A85 2h aqua .65 *.55*
**248A** A88a 5h brt green .65 *.55*
**248B** A95 15h violet 3.25 2.00
*Nos. 247-248B (4)* 5.20 3.65
Set, never hinged 11.50

**Redrawn Types of 1954, 1956 and**

Planting Trees — A119

South Gate, Seoul — A120

Tiger A121

Diamond Mountains A122

### No Hwan Symbol; Redrawn Character

**1957 Wmk. 312 Litho. *Perf. 12½***

| | | | | |
|---|---|---|---|---|
| **249** A119 | 2h aqua | .30 | *.40* |
| **250** A88a | 4h aqua | .45 | .40 |
| **251** A88a | 5h emerald | .45 | .40 |
| **252** A120 | 10h green | .50 | .75 |
| **253** A110 | 20h lilac rose | .65 | .40 |
| **254** A121 | 30h pale lilac | .65 | .40 |
| **255** A111 | 40h red lilac | .75 | .35 |
| *a.* | Booklet pane of 6 | 80.00 | |
| **256** A95 | 50h lake | 4.00 | 2.00 |
| **257** A122 | 55h violet brn | 1.50 | 1.50 |
| **258** A112 | 100h violet | 1.75 | 1.00 |
| **259** A89 | 200h brown car | 2.00 | 1.00 |
| **260** A92a | 400h brt violet | 32.50 | 4.75 |
| **261** A90 | 500h ocher | 32.50 | 5.75 |
| **262** A90 | 1000h dk ol bis | 80.00 | 10.50 |
| | *Nos. 249-262 (14)* | 158.00 | 29.60 |
| | Set, never hinged | 290.00 | |

The "redrawn character" is illustrated above No. 212D.

See Nos. 268, 271, 274, 277, 291c, 291e.

Mercury and Flags of Korea and US A123

**1957, Nov. 7 Wmk. 312 *Perf. 13½***

| | | | |
|---|---|---|---|
| **263** A123 40h dp orange | 1.00 | *1.00* |
| **264** A123 205h emerald | 1.90 | *2.00* |
| *a.* Souv. sheet of 2, #263-264, imperf. | 850.00 | |
| Never hinged | 1,500. | |
| Set, never hinged | 6.25 | |

Treaty of friendship, commerce and navigation between Korea and the US.

Star of Bethlehem and Pine Cone — A124

Designs: 25h, Christmas tree and tassel. 30h, Christmas tree, window and dog.

**1957, Dec. 11 Litho. *Perf. 12½***

| | | |
|---|---|---|
| **265** A124 15h org, brn & grn | 6.50 | *2.00* |
| *a.* Souv. sheet of 1, imperf. | 650.00 | |
| Never hinged | 1,100. | |
| **266** A124 25h lt grn, yel & red | 4.75 | *2.00* |
| *a.* Souv. sheet of 1, imperf. | 650.00 | |
| Never hinged | 1,100. | |
| **267** A124 30h bl, lt grn & yel | 14.50 | 3.00 |
| *a.* Souv. sheet of 1, imperf. | 650.00 | |
| Never hinged | 1,100. | |
| *Nos. 265-267 (3)* | 25.75 | 7.00 |
| Set, never hinged | 40.00 | |

Issued for Christmas and the New Year.

### Redrawn Types of 1954-57

**Wmk. 317**

**1957-59 Litho. *Perf. 12½***

| | | | |
|---|---|---|---|
| **268** A119 | 2h aqua | .35 | *.45* |
| **269** A88a | 4h aqua | .45 | .45 |
| **270** A88a | 5h emerald ('58) | .45 | .45 |
| **271** A120 | 10h green | .75 | .45 |
| **272** A95 | 15h violet ('58) | 2.50 | 2.25 |
| **273** A110 | 20h lilac rose | .90 | .35 |
| **274** A121 | 30h pale lil ('58) | 1.00 | .35 |
| **275** A111 | 40h red lilac | 1.00 | .35 |
| **276** A95 | 50h lake ('58) | 5.00 | .80 |
| **277** A122 | 55h vio brn ('59) | 1.90 | .85 |
| **278** A112 | 100h violet | 1.75 | .75 |
| **279** A89 | 200h brn car ('59) | 2.25 | .75 |
| **280** A92a | 400h brt vio ('59) | 57.50 | 6.00 |
| **281** A90 | 500h ocher ('58) | 37.50 | 6.00 |
| **282** A90 | 1000h dk ol bis ('58) | 80.00 | 10.00 |
| | *Nos. 268-282 (15)* | 193.30 | 30.25 |
| | Set, never hinged | 425.00 | |

Nos. 268-282 have no hwan symbol, and final character of inscription is the redrawn one illustrated above No. 212D.

See No. 291B.

**Catalogue values for unused stamps in this section, from this point to the end of the section, are for Never Hinged items.**

Winged Envelope — A125

**1958, May 20 Wmk. 317**

| | | |
|---|---|---|
| **283** A125 40h dk blue & red | 2.10 | .80 |
| *a.* Souv. sheet of 1, imperf. | *1,950.* | |

Issued for the Second Postal Week.

Children Looking at Industrial Growth A126

Design: 40h, Hibiscus forming "10".

**1958, Aug. 15 *Perf. 13½***

| | | |
|---|---|---|
| **284** A126 20h gray | 1.90 | .55 |
| **285** A126 40h dk carmine | 2.25 | .80 |
| *a.* Souv. sheet of 2, # 284-285, imperf. | 450.00 | |

10th anniversary of Republic of Korea.

UNESCO Building, Paris A127

**1958, Nov. 3 Wmk. 317**

| | | |
|---|---|---|
| **286** A127 40h orange & green | 1.45 | .60 |
| *a.* Souv. sheet of 1, imperf. | 170.00 | |

Opening of UNESCO. headquarters in Paris, Nov. 3.

Children Flying Kites — A128

Christmas Tree and Fortune Screen — A129

Children in Costume — A130

**1958, Dec. 11 Litho. *Perf. 12½***

| | | |
|---|---|---|
| **287** A128 15h yellow green | 2.10 | .70 |
| *a.* Souv. sheet of 1, imperf. | 67.50 | |
| **288** A129 25h blue, red & yel | 2.10 | .70 |
| *a.* Souv. sheet of 1, imperf. | 67.50 | |
| **289** A130 30h yell, ultra & red | 3.00 | 1.05 |
| *a.* Souv. sheet of 1, imperf. | 67.50 | |
| *Nos. 287-289 (3)* | 7.20 | 2.45 |
| *Nos. 287a-289a (3)* | 202.50 | |

Issued for Christmas and the New Year.

Flag and Pagoda Park A131

**1959, Mar. 1 *Perf. 13½***

| | | |
|---|---|---|
| **290** A131 40h rose lilac & brn | 1.60 | .60 |
| *a.* Souv. sheet of 1, imperf. | 115.00 | 115.00 |

40th anniv. of Independence Movement Day.

Korean Marines Landing A132

**1959, Apr. 15**

| | | |
|---|---|---|
| **291** A132 40h olive grn | 1.60 | .65 |
| *a.* Souv. sheet of 1, imperf. | 13.00 | 13.00 |

Korean Marine Corps, 10th anniversary.

### Types of 1956-57 Souvenir Sheet

**Wmk. 317**

**1959, May 20 Litho. *Imperf.***

| | | |
|---|---|---|
| **291B** Sheet of 4 | 9.75 | *9.25* |
| *c.* A120 10h green | 1.40 | .60 |
| *d.* A110 20h lilac rose | 1.40 | .60 |
| *e.* A121 30h pale lilac | 1.40 | .60 |
| *f.* A111 40h red lilac | 1.40 | .60 |

3rd Postal Week, May 20-26.

WHO Emblem and Family A133

**1959, Aug. 17 Wmk. 317 *Perf. 13½***

| | | |
|---|---|---|
| **292** A133 40h pink & rose vio | 1.45 | .65 |
| *a.* Souv. sheet of 1, imperf. | 10.50 | 10.50 |

10th anniv. of Korea's joining the WHO.

Diesel Train A134

**1959, Sept. 18 Litho.**

| | | |
|---|---|---|
| **293** A134 40h brown & bister | 2.25 | .90 |
| *a.* Souv. sheet of 1, imperf. | 23.00 | 23.00 |

60th anniversary of Korean railroads.

Relay Race and Emblem A135

**1959, Oct. 3**

| | | |
|---|---|---|
| **294** A135 40h lt bl & red brn | 1.50 | .70 |
| *a.* Souv. sheet of 1, imperf. | 16.50 | 16.50 |

40th National Athletic Meet.

Red Cross and Korea Map A136

55h, Red Cross superimposed on globe.

**1959, Oct. 27 *Perf. 13½***

| | | |
|---|---|---|
| **295** A136 40h red & bl grn | 1.45 | .60 |
| **296** A136 55h pale lilac & red | 1.45 | .60 |
| *a.* Souv. sheet of 2, #295-296, imperf. | 37.50 | 37.50 |

Centenary of the Red Cross idea.

Old Postal Flag and New Communications Flag — A137

**1959, Dec. 4**

| | | |
|---|---|---|
| **297** A137 40h blue & red | 1.45 | .60 |
| *a.* Souv. sheet of 1, imperf. | 19.50 | 19.50 |

75th anniv. of the Korean postal system.

Mice and Chinese Happy New Year Character — A138

Designs: 25h, Children singing Christmas hymns. 30h, Red-crested crane.

**1959, Dec. 15 *Perf. 12½***

| | | |
|---|---|---|
| **298** A138 15h gray, vio bl & pink | 1.45 | .40 |
| *a.* Souv. sheet of 1, imperf. | 27.00 | 27.00 |
| **299** A138 25h blue, red & emer | 1.45 | .40 |
| *a.* Souv. sheet of 1, imperf. | 27.00 | 27.00 |
| **300** A138 30h lt lilac, blk & red | 2.75 | .55 |
| *a.* Souv. sheet of 1, imperf. | 27.00 | 27.00 |
| *Nos. 298-300 (3)* | 5.65 | 1.35 |
| *Nos. 298a-300a (3)* | 81.00 | |

Issued for Christmas and the New Year.

UPU Monument and Means of Transportation — A139

**Wmk. 317**

**1960, Jan. 1 Litho. *Perf. 13½***

| | | |
|---|---|---|
| **301** A139 40h grnsh bl & brn | 1.60 | .80 |
| *a.* Souv. sheet of 1, imperf. | 32.50 | 32.50 |

60th anniv. of Korean membership in the UPU.

Bee, Honeycomb and Clover — A140

Snail and Money Bag — A141

**1960, Apr. 1 Wmk. 317 *Perf. 12½***

| | | |
|---|---|---|
| **302** A140 10h emer, brn & org | 1.45 | 1.00 |
| **303** A141 20h pink, bl & brn | 1.60 | 1.00 |

Issued to encourage systematic saving by children. See No. 313, souvenir sheet.

See Nos. 377-380.

Uprooted Oak Emblem and Yin Yang — A142

**1960, Apr. 7 Wmk. 312** ***Perf. 13½***

**304** A142 40h emer, car & ultra 1.45 .60
*a.* Souv. sheet of 1, imperf. 45.00 45.00

Issued to publicize World Refugee Year, July 1, 1959-June 30, 1960.

Dwight D. Eisenhower A143

**1960, June 19 Litho. Wmk. 317**

**305** A143 40h bl, red & bluish grn 4.00 1.60
*a.* Souv. sheet of 1, imperf. 30.00 30.00

Pres. Eisenhower's visit to Korea, June 19.

Children in School and Ancient Home Teaching A144

**1960, Aug. 3 Wmk. 317** ***Perf. 13½***

**306** A144 40h multicolored 1.45 .50
*a.* Souv. sheet of 1, imperf. 8.25 8.25

75th anniv. of the modern educational system.

Hibiscus and House of Councilors A145

**1960, Aug. 8**

**307** A145 40h blue 1.45 .50
*a.* Souv. sheet of 1, imperf. 8.25 8.25

Inaugural session, House of Councilors.

Woman Holding Torch and Man with Flag — A146

**1960, Aug. 15**

**308** A146 40h bis, lt bl & brn 1.75 .60
*a.* Souv. sheet of 1, imperf. 8.25 8.25

15th anniversary of liberation.

Weight Lifter A147

40h, South Gate, Seoul, & Olympic emblem.

**1960, Aug. 25 Litho.**

**309** A147 20h brn, lt bl & sal 1.50 .70
**310** A147 40h brn, lt bl & dk bl 1.50 .70
*a.* Souv. sheet of 2, #309-310, imperf. 26.00 26.00

17th Olympic Games, Rome, 8/25-9/11.

Swallow and Telegraph Pole — A148

**1960, Sept. 28** ***Perf. 13½***

**311** A148 40h lt bl, lil & gray 1.60 .70
*a.* Souv. sheet of 1, imperf. 7.50 7.50

Establishment of telegraph service, 75th anniv.

Students and Sprout A149

**1960, Oct. 1 Wmk. 317**

**312** A149 40h bl, sal pink & emer 1.60 .60
*a.* Souv. sheet of 1, imperf. 7.00 7.00

Rebirth of the Republic.

**Savings Types of 1960**
Souvenir Sheet

**1960, Oct. 7** ***Imperf.***

**313** Sheet of two 5.00 5.00
*a.* A140 10h emer, brn & org 2.10 1.90
*b.* A141 20h pink, blue & brown 2.10 1.90

4th Postal Week, Oct. 7-13, and Intl. Letter Writing Week, Oct. 3-9.

Torch — A150

**1960, Oct. 15** ***Perf. 13½***

**314** A150 40h dk bl, lt bl & yel 1.45 .50
*a.* Souv. sheet of 1, imperf. 6.75 6.75

Cultural Month (October).

UN Flag, Globe and Laurel — A151

**1960, Oct. 24 Litho.**

**315** A151 40h rose lil, bl & grn 1.45 .50
*a.* Souv. sheet of 1, imperf. 6.50 6.50

15th anniversary of United Nations.

UN Emblem and Grave Markers — A152

**1960, Nov. 1 Wmk. 317**

**316** A152 40h salmon & brn 1.45 .50
*a.* Souv. sheet of 1, imperf. 6.50 6.50

Establishment of the UN Memorial Cemetery, Tanggok, Pusan, Korea.

"Housing, Agriculture, Population" — A153

**1960, Nov. 15** ***Perf. 13½***

**317** A153 40h multicolored 1.45 .50
*a.* Souv. sheet of 1, imperf. 6.75 6.75

Issued to publicize the 1960 census.

Boy and Head of Ox — A154

Star of Bethlehem and Korean Sock — A155

Girl Giving New Year's Greeting — A156

**1960, Dec. 15 Litho.** ***Perf. 12½***

**318** A154 15h gray, brn & org yel 2.00 .40
*a.* Souv. sheet of 1, imperf. 9.00 9.00
**319** A155 25h vio bl, red & grn 2.60 .40
*a.* Souv. sheet of 1, imperf. 9.00 9.00
**320** A156 30h red, vio bl & yel 3.50 .60
*a.* Souv. sheet of 1, imperf. 9.75 9.75
*Nos. 318-320 (3)* 8.10 1.40
*Nos. 318a-320a (3)* 27.75

Issued for Christmas and the New Year.

UN Emblem, Windsock and Ancient Rain Gauge A157

**1961, Mar. 23** ***Perf. 13½***

**321** A157 40h lt blue & ultra 1.50 .50
*a.* Souv. sheet of 1, imperf. 4.00 4.00

1st World Meteorological Day.

Children, Globe and UN Emblem A158

**1961, Apr. 7 Wmk. 317**

**322** A158 40h salmon & brown 1.60 .50
*a.* Souv. sheet of 1, imperf. 4.00 4.00

10th World Health Day.

Students Demonstrating — A159

**1961, Apr. 19 Litho.**

**323** A159 40h red, grn & ultra 1.90 .75
*a.* Souv. sheet of 1, imperf. 10.00 10.00

1st anniv. of the Korean April revolution.

Workers — A160

**1961, May 6**

**324** A160 40h brt green 1.45 .60
*a.* Souv. sheet of 1, imperf. 6.00 6.00

International Conference on Community Development, Seoul.

Girl Scout A161

**1961, May 10**

**325** A161 40h brt green 1.90 .60
*a.* Souv. sheet of 1, imperf. 13.00 13.00

15th anniversary of Korea's Girl Scouts.

Soldier's Grave — A162

**Wmk. 317**

**1961, June 6 Litho.** ***Perf. 13½***

**326** A162 40h blk & ol gray 2.75 1.20
*a.* Souv. sheet of 1, imperf. 10.00 10.00

6th National Mourning Day.

Soldier with Torch — A163

**1961, June 16**

**327** A163 40h brown & yellow 2.75 1.20
*a.* Souv. sheet of 1, imperf. 9.50 9.50

Military Revolution of May 16, 1961.

Map of Korea, Torch and Broken Chain — A164

**1961, Aug. 15 Wmk. 317** ***Perf. 13½***

**328** A164 40h dk bl, ver & aqua 2.75 1.20
*a.* Souv. sheet of 1, imperf. 5.75 5.75

16th anniv. of liberation.

Flag and Servicemen — A165

**1961, Oct. 1** **Litho.**

**329** A165 40h vio bl, red & brn 3.00 1.25
*a.* Souv. sheet of 1, imperf. 5.25 5.25

Issued for Armed Forces Day.

Kyongbok Palace Art Museum — A166

**1961, Nov. 1** **Wmk. 317** ***Perf. 13½***

**330** A166 40h beige & dk brn 1.90 .60
*a.* Souv. sheet of 1, imperf. 4.25 4.25

10th Natl. Exhibition of Fine Arts.

"UNESCO," Candle and Laurel — A167

**1961, Nov. 4**

**331** A167 40h lt grn & dk bl 1.90 .60
*a.* Souv. sheet of 1, imperf. 4.00 4.00

15th anniv. of UNESCO.

Mobile X-Ray Unit A168

**1961, Nov. 16**

**332** A168 40h rose beige & red brn 1.50 .60
*a.* Souv. sheet of 1, imperf. 4.00 4.00

Tuberculosis Prevention Week.

Ginseng — A169

King Sejong and Hangul Alphabet — A170

Tristram's Woodpecker A171

Rice Farmer A172

Ancient Drums — A173

**1961-62** **Unwmk.** **Litho.** ***Perf. 12½***

**338** A169 20h rose brn ('62) 2.00 1.20
**339** A170 30h pale purple 5.25 1.00
**340** A171 40h dk blue & red 5.00 1.00
**341** A172 40h dk green ('62) 8.50 1.60
**342** A173 100h red brown 11.00 2.00
*Nos. 338-342 (5)* 31.75 6.80

See Nos. 363-366, 368, 388-392, 517-519, B5-B7.

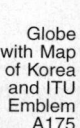

Globe with Map of Korea and ITU Emblem A175

**1962, Jan. 31** **Unwmk.** ***Perf. 13½***

**348** A175 40h ver & dk blue 1.90 .90
*a.* Souv. sheet of 1, imperf. 11.50 11.50

10th anniv. of Korea's joining the ITU.

Atomic Reactor and Atom Symbol A176

**1962, Mar. 30** **Litho.** ***Perf. 13½***

**349** A176 40h lt bl, sl grn & ol gray 2.10 .50

Inauguration of the Triga Mark II atomic reactor.

Malaria Eradication Emblem and Mosquito — A177

**1962, Apr. 7** **Unwmk.**

**350** A177 40h green & red org 1.50 .70
*a.* Souv. sheet of 1, imperf. 3.75 3.75

WHO drive to eradicate malaria.

YWCA Emblem and Girl A178

**1962, Apr. 20** ***Perf. 13½***

**351** A178 40h pink & dk blue 3.00 .60

40th anniv. of the Korean Young Women's Christian Association.

South Gate and FPA Emblem A179

**1962, May 12** **Wmk. 317**

**352** A179 40h lt bl, dk vio & red 3.00 .75

Meeting of the Federation of Motion Picture Producers in Asia, May 12-16.

Men Pushing Cogwheel A180

Soldiers on Hang Kang Bridge — A181

Yin Yang and Factory A182

**Wmk. 317**

**1962, May 16** **Litho.** ***Perf. 13½***

**353** A180 30h brn & pale olive 2.75 .85
*a.* Souv. sheet of 1, Korean text 15.00 15.00
*b.* Souv. sheet of 1, English text 25.00 20.00
**354** A181 40h brn, lt bl & citron 2.75 .85
*a.* Souv. sheet of 1, Korean text 15.00 15.00
*b.* Souv. sheet of 1, English text 25.00 20.00
**355** A182 200h ultra, yel & red 32.50 7.75
*a.* Souv. sheet of 1, Korean text 50.00 50.00
*b.* Souv. sheet of 1, English text 110.00 100.00
*Nos. 353-355 (3)* 38.00 9.45

1st anniv. of the May 16th Revolution.
The souvenir sheets are imperf.
The sheets with English text also exist with "E" in "POSTAGE" omitted. The English-text sheets are not watermarked except those with "E" omitted. Value, $200 for set.

Tortoise Warship, 16th Century A183

Design: 4w, Tortoise ship, heading right.

**1962, Aug. 14** **Unwmk.** ***Perf. 13½***

**356** A183 2w dk bl & pale bl 15.00 1.50
**357** A183 4w blk, bluish grn & lil 25.00 3.00

370th anniv. of Korea's victory in the naval battle with the Japanese off Hansan Island.

Flag, Scout Emblem and Tents — A184

**Wmk. 312**

**1962, Oct. 5** **Litho.** ***Perf. 13½***

**358** A184 4w brown, bl & red 1.90 .75
*a.* Souv. sheet of 1, imperf., unwmkd. 7.75 7.75

**Wmk. 317**

**359** A184 4w green, bl & red 1.90 .75
*a.* Souv. sheet of 1, imperf., unwmkd. 7.75 7.75

40th anniv. of Korean Boy Scouts.

**Types of 1961-62 and**

Hanabusaya Asiatica — A185

Folk Dancers — A185a

Miruk Bosal — A186

Long-horned Beetle — A186a

Symbols of Thrift and Development A186b

Meesun Blossoms and Fruit A186c

Library of Early Buddhist Scriptures A186d

Sika Deer A186e

King Songdok Bell, 8th Cent. — A186f

Bodhisattva in Cavern Temple, Silla Dynasty — A187

Tile of Silla Dynasty — A187a

Designs: 20ch, Jin-Do dog. 1.50w, Miruk Bosal. 2w, Ginseng. 3w, King Sejong. 4w, Rice farmer. 5w, Dragon waterpot. 10w, Ancient drums. 500w, Blue dragon fresco, Koguryo dynasty.

**1962-63** **Unwmk.** **Litho.** ***Perf. 12½***
**Ordinary Paper**
**Size: 22x25mm, 25x22mm**

**360** A186 20ch gldn brown 1.40 .40
**361** A185 40ch blue 1.40 .40
**362** A186 50ch claret brn 1.40 .40
**363** A185a 1w brt blue ('63) 3.25 .40
**364** A169 2w red brown 4.75 .40
**365** A170 3w violet brown 5.25 .40
**366** A172 4w green 5.50 .40
**367** A186 5w grnsh blue 6.25 1.00
**368** A173 10w red brown 67.50 4.00
**369** A186c 20w lil rose ('63) 14.00 1.60
**370** A186d 40w dl pur ('63) 100.00 4.75
*Nos. 360-370 (11)* 210.70 14.15

**1964-66** **Granite Paper**

*360a* A186 20ch org brn .90 .25
*361a* A185 40ch blue .95 .25
*362a* A186 50ch claret brn .95 .25
**362B** A186a 60ch blk ('66) .95 .30
*363a* A185a 1w bright blue 3.50 .25
**363B** A186 1.50w dk sl grn ('66) .70 .30
*364a* A169 2w red brown 5.50 .40
*365a* A170 3w vio brown 15.00 .30
*366a* A172 4w green 6.75 .30
*367a* A186 5w grnsh blue 32.50 1.50
**367B** A186b 7w lil rose ('66) 3.25 .75
*368a* A173 10w red brown 5.00 .40
*369a* A186c 20w lilac rose 5.00 .40
*370a* A186d 40w vio brown 50.00 2.25
**371** A186e 50w red brn 62.50 1.50
**372** A186f 100w slate grn 100.00 3.00
**373** A187 200w dk & lt grn ('65) 27.50 3.00
**374** A187a 300w sl grn & buff ('65) 55.00 4.00
**374A** A187a 500w dk & lt bl ('65) 27.50 4.00
*Nos. 360a-374A (19)* 403.45 23.40

The paper of Nos. 360a to 374A contains a few colored fibers; the paper of Nos. 385-396 contains many fibers.

Postal counterfeits exist of Nos. 369a, 370a, 371 and 372.

See Nos. 385-396, 516, 521-522, 582-584, 1076-1079, B8.

Map, Mackerel and Trawler
A188

**1962, Oct. 10** ***Perf. 13½***
**375** A188 4w dk bl & grnsh bl 5.00 1.00

10th anniv. of the Pacific Fishery Council.

ICAO Emblem and Plane
A189

**1962, Dec. 11** ***Perf. 13½***
**376** A189 4w blue & brown 2.40 .75
*a.* Souv. sheet of 1, imperf. 9.25 9.25

10th anniv. of Korea's joining the ICAO.

**Savings Types of 1960**

**1962-64** **Unwmk.** ***Perf. 12½***
**377** A140 1w emer, brn & org ('63) 7.25 1.25
*a.* Granite paper 16.00 12.50
**378** A141 2w pink, bl & brn 12.00 1.50
*a.* Granite paper 14.00 2.50

**Wmk. 317**

**379** A140 1w emer, brn & org ('64) 95.00 10.00
**380** A141 2w pink, bl & brn ('64) 14.00 1.75
*Nos. 377-380 (4)* 128.25 14.50

Wheat Emblem
A190

**Wmk. 317**

**1963, Mar. 21** **Litho.** ***Perf. 13½***
**381** A190 4w emer, dk bl & ocher 1.50 .70
*a.* Souv. sheet of 1, imperf. 4.50 4.50

FAO "Freedom from Hunger" campaign.

Globe and Letters
A191

**1963, Apr. 1**
**382** A191 4w rose lil, ol & dk bl 2.25 .60
*a.* Souv. sheet of 1, imperf. 4.50 4.50

1st anniv. of the formation of the Asian-Oceanic Postal Union, AOPU.

Centenary Emblem and World Map
A192

**1963, May 8** **Litho.**
**383** A192 4w org, red & gray 1.50 1.00
**384** A192 4w lt bl, red & gray 1.50 1.00
*a.* Souv. sheet of 2, #383-384, imperf. 12.50 12.50

Cent. of the Intl. Red Cross.

**Types of 1961-63**

Designs as before.

**1963-64** **Wmk. 317** ***Perf. 12½***
**Granite Paper**
**Size: 22x25mm, 25x22mm**

**385** A186 20ch gldn brn ('64) 1.25 .25
**386** A185 40ch blue 1.25 .25
**387** A186 50ch cl brn ('64) 1.25 .25
**388** A185a 1w brt blue 3.25 .35
**389** A169 2w red brown 6.25 .40
**390** A170 3w vio brown 12.00 .35
**391** A172 4w green 6.50 .60
**392** A173 10w red brown 6.25 .60
**393** A186c 20w lil rose ('64) 11.00 1.40
**394** A186d 40w dull purple 52.50 2.00
**395** A186e 50w brown 70.00 2.00
**396** A186f 100w slate grn 105.00 3.75
*Nos. 385-396 (12)* 276.50 12.20

Hibiscus and "15"
A193

**1963, Aug. 15** **Wmk. 317** ***Perf. 13½***
**398** A193 4w vio bl, pale bl & red 3.00 1.20

15th anniversary of the Republic.

Army Nurse and Corps Emblem
A194

**1963, Aug. 26** **Litho.**
**399** A194 4w citron, grn & blk 2.25 .85

Army Nurses Corps, 15th anniversary.

**First Five-Year Plan Issue**

Transformer and Power Transmission Tower
A195

Irrigated Rice Fields
A196

No. 402, Cement factory. No. 403, Coal Miner. No. 404, Oil refinery. No. 405, Fishing industry (ships). No. 406, Cargo ship and cargo. No. 407, Fertilizer plant and grain. No. 408, Radar and telephone. No. 409, Transportation (plane, train, ship and map).

**1962-66** **Unwmk.** ***Perf. 12½***
**400** A195 4w org & dk vio 27.50 3.00
**401** A196 4w lt bl & vio bl 27.50 3.00

**Wmk. 317**

**402** A195 4w dk bl & gray 13.00 1.60
**403** A196 4w buff & brn 13.00 1.60
**404** A195 4w yel & ultra 5.50 1.15
**405** A196 4w lt bl & blk 5.50 1.15

**Unwmk.**

**406** A195 4w pale pink & vio bl 1.90 .95
**407** A196 4w bis brn & blk 1.90 .95
**408** A195 7w yel bis & blk 3.25 1.00
**409** A196 7w vio bl & lt bl 3.25 1.00
*Nos. 400-409 (10)* 102.30 15.40

Economic Development Five-Year Plan.

Issued: Nos. 400-401, 12/28/62; Nos. 402-403, 9/1/63; Nos. 404-405, 6/15/64; Nos. 406-407, 6/1/65; Nos. 408-409, 6/1/66.

Ramses Temple, Abu Simbel — A197

**Wmk. 317**

**1963, Oct. 1** **Litho.** ***Perf. 13½***
**410** 3w gray & ol gray 5.50 1.75
**411** 4w gray & ol gray 5.50 1.75
*a.* Souv. sheet of 2, #410-411, imperf. 9.50 9.50
*b.* A197 Pair, #410-411 11.50 4.25

UNESCO world campaign to save historic monuments in Nubia.

Rugby and Torch Bearer
A199

**1963, Oct. 4** **Wmk. 317** ***Perf. 13½***
**412** A199 4w pale bl, red brn & dk grn 3.75 1.30

44th National Athletic Games.

Nurse & Mobile X-Ray Unit — A200

**1963, Nov. 6** ***Perf. 13½***
**413** A200 4w org & bluish blk 1.90 .75

10h anniv. of the Korean Natl. Tuberculosis Association.

Eleanor Roosevelt
A201

Design: 4w, Hands holding torch and globe.

**1963, Dec. 10** **Litho.** **Wmk. 317**
**414** A201 3w lt red brn & dk bl 1.60 1.00
**415** A201 4w dl org, ol & dk bl 1.60 1.00
*a.* Souv. sheet of 2, 414-415, imperf. 5.75 5.75

Eleanor Roosevelt; 15th anniv. of the Universal Declaration of Human Rights.

Korean Flag and UN Headquarters
A202

**1963, Dec. 12** **Wmk. 317** ***Perf. 13½***
**416** A202 4w grnsh bl, ol & blk 1.60 .50
*a.* Souv. sheet of 1, imperf. 4.75 4.75

15th anniv. of Korea's recognition by the UN.

Tang-piri (Recorder)
A203

Musical Instruments: No. 418, Pyen-kyeng (chimes). No. 419, Chang-ko (drums). No. 420, Tai-keum (large flute). No. 421, Taipyeng-so (Chinese oboe). No. 422, Na-bal (brass trumpet). No. 423, Hyang-pipa (Chinese short lute). No. 424, Wul-keum (banjo). No. 425, Kaya-ko (zither), horiz. No. 426, Wa-kong-hu (harp), horiz.

**1963, Dec. 17** **Unwmk.**
**417** A203 4w pink, blk & car 5.75 1.30
**418** A203 4w bl, bl grn & blk 5.75 1.30
**419** A203 4w rose, vio bl & brn 5.75 1.30
**420** A203 4w tan, dk grn & brn 5.75 1.30
**421** A203 4w yel, vio bl & brn 5.75 1.30
**422** A203 4w gray, brn & vio 5.75 1.30
**423** A203 4w pink, vio bl & red brn 5.75 1.30
**424** A203 4w grnsh bl, blk & bl 5.75 1.30
**425** A203 4w rose, red brn & blk 5.75 1.30
**426** A203 4w lil, blk & bl 5.75 1.30
*Nos. 417-426 (10)* 57.50 13.00

Pres. Park and Capitol
A204

**1963, Dec. 17** **Wmk. 317**
**427** A204 4w black & brt grn 65.00 16.00

Inauguration of Pres. Park Chung Hee.

Symbols of Metric System
A205

**1964, Jan. 1** **Litho.**
**428** A205 4w multicolored 1.60 .75
*a.* Imperf., pair 75.00

Introduction of the metric system.

UNESCO Emblem and Yin Yang — A206

**1964, Jan. 30 Wmk. 317 *Perf. 13½***

**429** A206 4w red, lt bl & ultra 1.90 .75

Korean Natl. Commission for UNESCO, 10th anniv.

Industrial Census A207

**1964, Mar. 23 Wmk. 317 *Perf. 13½***

**430** A207 4w gray, blk & red brn 1.90 .75

National Mining and Industrial Census.

YMCA Emblem and Head A208

**1964, Apr. 12 Litho.**

**431** A208 4w app grn, dk bl & red 1.50 .60

50th anniv. of the Korean YMCA.

Unisphere, Ginseng and Cargo Ship — A209

Design: 100w, Korean pavilion and globe.

**1964, Apr. 22 Wmk. 317 *Perf. 13½***

**432** A209 40w buff, red brn & grn 5.00 1.30

**433** A209 100w bl red brn & ultra 45.00 8.00

*a.* Souv. sheet of 2, imperf. 97.50 70.00

New York World's Fair, 1964-65.

Secret Garden, Changdok Palace, Seoul A210

Views: 2w, Whahong Gate, Suwon. 3w, Uisang Pavilion, Yangyang-gun. 4w, Maitreya Buddha, Bopju Temple at Mt. Songni. 5w, Paekma River and Rock of Falling Flowers. 6w, Anab Pond, Kyongju. 7w, Choksok Pavilion, Chinju. 8w, Kwanghan Pavilion. 9w, Whaom Temple, Mt. Chiri. 10w, Chonjeyon Falls, Soguipo.

**1964, May 25 Wmk. 317 *Perf. 13½***

**Light Blue Background**

**434** A210 1w green 1.40 .50

**435** A210 2w gray 1.40 .50

**436** A210 3w dk green 1.40 .50

**437** A210 4w emerald 2.60 .85

**438** A210 5w violet 5.25 1.35

**439** A210 6w vio blue 7.00 1.60

*a.* Souv. sheet of 2 (5w, 6w) 16.50 16.50

**440** A210 7w dk brown 11.50 2.50

*a.* Souv. sheet of 2 (4w, 7w) 16.50 16.50

**441** A210 8w brown 11.50 2.25

*a.* Souv. sheet of 2 (3w, 8w) 16.50 16.50

**442** A210 9w lt violet 13.50 2.40

*a.* Souv. sheet of 2 (2w, 9w) 16.50 16.50

**443** A210 10w slate grn 17.50 3.25

*a.* Souv. sheet of 2 (1w, 10w) 16.50 16.50

*Nos. 434-443 (10)* 73.05 15.70

*Nos. 439a-443a (5)* 82.50 82.50

The five souvenir sheets are imperf.

Globe and Wheel A211

**1964, July 1 Litho. *Perf. 13½***

**444** A211 4w lt ol grn, dl brn & ocher 1.50 .60

*a.* Souv. sheet of 1, imperf. 4.75 4.75

Colombo Plan for co-operative economic development of south and southeast Asia.

Hands and World Health Organization Emblem — A212

**1964, Aug. 17 Wmk. 317 *Perf. 13½***

**445** A212 4w brt yel grn, yel grn & blk 1.50 .60

*a.* Souv. sheet of 1, imperf. 4.75 4.75

15th anniv. of Korea's joining the UN.

Runner A213

**1964, Sept. 3**

**446** A213 4w red lil, grn & pink 3.75 1.20

45th Natl. Athletic Meet, Inchon, Sept. 3-8.

UPU Monument, Bern — A214

**1964, Sept. 15**

**447** A214 4w pink, red brn & bl 1.60 .60

*a.* Souv. sheet of 1, imperf. 5.25 5.25

1st Intl. Cong. for establishing the UPU, 90th anniv.

Crane Hook and Emblem — A215

**1964, Sept. 29 Wmk. 317 *Perf. 13½***

**448** A215 4w red brn & dull grn 1.60 .60

5th Convention of the Intl. Federation of Asian and Western Pacific Contractors' Assoc. (IFAWPCA), Seoul, Sept. 29-Oct. 7.

Marathon Runners A216

No. 453, "V," Olympic rings, laurel & track, vert.

**1964, Oct. 10 Litho.**

**449** A216 4w shown 3.00 1.00

**450** A216 4w Equestrian 3.00 1.00

**451** A216 4w Gymnast 3.00 1.00

**452** A216 4w Rowing 3.00 1.00

**453** A216 4w multicolored 3.00 1.00

*Nos. 449-453 (5)* 15.00 5.00

18th Olympic Games, Tokyo, Oct. 10-25.

**Souvenir Sheets of 1, Imperf., Unwmk.**

*449a* A216 4w 4.25 4.25

*450a* A216 4w 4.25 4.25

*451a* A216 4w 4.25 4.25

*452a* A216 4w 4.25 4.25

*453a* A216 4w 4.25 4.25

*Nos. 449a-453a (5)* 21.25 21.25

Stamp of 1885 — A217

Yong Sik Hong — A218

**1964, Dec. 4 Unwmk. *Perf. 13½***

**454** A217 3w lilac, vio & dl bl grn 3.75 .95

**455** A218 4w gray, vio bl & blk 5.25 1.20

80th anniv. of the Korean postal system. Hong Yong-Sik (1855-84) was Korea's 1st general postmaster.

Pine Branch and Cones — A219

No. 457, Plum Blossoms. No. 458, Forsythia. No. 459, Azalea. No. 460, Lilac. No. 461, Sweetbrier. No. 462, Garden balsam. No. 463, Hibiscus. No. 464, Crape myrtle. No. 465, Chrysanthemum lucidum. No. 466, Paulownia coreana. No. 467, Bamboo.

**1965 Litho. *Perf. 13½***

**456** A219 4w pale grn, dp grn & brn 2.25 .70

**457** A219 4w gray, blk, rose & yel 2.25 .70

**458** A219 4w lt bl, yel & brn 2.25 .70

**459** A219 4w brt grn, lil rose & sal 2.25 .70

**460** A219 4w red lil & brt grn 2.25 .70

**461** A219 4w yel grn, grn, car & brn 2.25 .70

**462** A219 4w bl, grn & red 2.25 .70

**463** A219 4w bluish gray, rose red & grn 2.25 .70

**464** A219 4w multicolored 2.25 .70

**465** A219 4w pale grn, dk brn, grn & car rose 2.25 .70

**466** A219 4w buff, ol grn & brn 2.25 .70

**467** A219 4w ultra & emer 2.25 .70

*Nos. 456-467 (12)* 27.00 8.40

**Souvenir Sheets of 1, Imperf.**

*456a* A219 4w 3.00 3.00

*457a* A219 4w 3.00 3.00

*458a* A219 4w 3.00 3.00

*459a* A219 4w 3.00 3.00

*460a* A219 4w 3.00 3.00

*461a* A219 4w 3.00 3.00

*462a* A219 4w 3.00 3.00

*463a* A219 4w 3.00 3.00

*464a* A219 4w 3.00 3.00

*465a* A219 4w 3.00 3.00

*466a* A219 4w 3.00 3.00

*467a* A219 4w 3.00 3.00

*Nos. 456a-467a (12)* 36.00 36.00

Dancing Women, PATA Emblem and Tabo Tower A220

**1965, Mar. 26**

**468** A220 4w lt bl grn, dk brn & dk vio bl 1.35 .50

*a.* Souv. sheet of 1, imperf. 3.50 3.50

14th conf. of the Pacific Travel Association, Seoul, Mar. 26-Apr. 2.

Map of Viet Nam and Flag of Korean Assistance Group — A221

**1965, Apr. 20 *Perf. 13½***

**469** A221 4w blk, lt yel grn & grnsh bl 1.25 .50

*a.* Souv. sheet of 1, imperf. 3.75 3.75

Issued to honor the Korean military assistance group in Viet Nam.

Symbols of 7-Year Plan — A222

**1965, May 1 Litho.**

**470** A222 4w emer, dk grn & dk brn 1.25 .50

Issued to publicize the 7-year plan for increased food production.

Scales with Families and Homes A223

**1965, May 8**

**471** A223 4w lt & dk grn & gray 1.25 .50

*a.* Souv. sheet of 1, imperf. 3.25 3.25

May as Month of Family Planning.

ITU Emblem, Old and New Communication Equipment — A224

**1965, May 17**

**472** A224 4w lt bl, car & blk 1.25 .50

*a.* Souv. sheet of 1, imperf. 3.25 3.25

Cent. of the ITU.

UN Emblem and Flags of Australia, Belgium, Great Britain, Canada and Colombia
A225

Gen. Douglas MacArthur and Flags of Korea, UN and US
A226

UN Emblem and Flags: No. 474, Denmark, Ethiopia, France, Greece and India. No. 475, Italy, Luxembourg, Netherlands, New Zealand and Norway. No. 476, Philippines, Sweden, Thailand, Turkey and South Africa.

**1965, June 25**

**Flags in Original Colors**

| | | | | | |
|---|---|---|---|---|---|
| **473** | A225 | 4w | gray & vio bl | 1.50 | .75 |
| **474** | A225 | 4w | grnsh bl & vio bl | 1.50 | .75 |
| **475** | A225 | 4w | grnsh bl & vio bl | 1.50 | .75 |
| **476** | A225 | 4w | grnsh bl & vio bl | 1.50 | .75 |
| **477** | A226 | 10w | lt bl, blk, vio bl & red | 5.00 | 1.50 |
| | | | *Nos. 473-477 (5)* | 11.00 | 4.50 |

15th anniv. of the participation of UN Forces in the Korean war.

**Souvenir Sheets of 1, Imperf.**

| | | | | |
|---|---|---|---|---|
| *473a* | A225 | 4w | 2.00 | 2.00 |
| *474a* | A225 | 4w | 2.00 | 2.00 |
| *475a* | A225 | 4w | 2.00 | 2.00 |
| *476a* | A225 | 4w | 2.00 | 2.00 |
| *477a* | A226 | 10w | 3.25 | 3.25 |
| | *Nos. 473a-477a (5)* | | 11.25 | 11.25 |

Flag, Factories and "20" — A227

South Gate, Seoul, Fireworks and Yin Yang — A228

**1965, Aug. 15** **Litho.**

| | | | | | |
|---|---|---|---|---|---|
| **478** | A227 | 4w | lt bl, vio bl & red | 2.75 | .60 |
| **479** | A228 | 10w | vio bl, lt bl & red | 3.75 | .80 |

20th anniv. of liberation from the Japanese.

Factory, Leaf and Ants — A229

**1965, Sept. 20** ***Perf. 13½***

| | | | | | |
|---|---|---|---|---|---|
| **480** | A229 | 4w | brt yel grn, brn & bister | 1.25 | .50 |

Issued to publicize the importance of saving.

Parabolic Antenna, Telephone Dial and Punched Tape
A230

Telegraph Operator, 1885
A231

**1965, Sept. 28**

| | | | | | |
|---|---|---|---|---|---|
| **481** | A230 | 3w | lt bl, blk & ol | 1.75 | .65 |
| **482** | A231 | 10w | citron, Prus bl & blk | 4.25 | .85 |

80th anniv. of telegraph service between Seoul and Inchon.

Korean Flag and Capitol, Seoul — A232

**1965, Sept. 28**

| | | | | | |
|---|---|---|---|---|---|
| **483** | A232 | 3w | org, slate grn & bl grn | 3.00 | 1.05 |

15th anniversary of recapture of Seoul.

Pole Vault
A233

**1965, Oct. 5**

| | | | | | |
|---|---|---|---|---|---|
| **484** | A233 | 3w | black, lil & sal | 2.25 | .90 |

46th Natl. Athletic Meet, Kwangju, Oct. 5-10.

ICY Emblem
A234

UN Flag and Headquarters, NY — A235

**1965, Oct. 24** **Litho.**

| | | | | | |
|---|---|---|---|---|---|
| **485** | A234 | 3w | lt & dk grn & org brn | 1.20 | .55 |
| *a.* | | | Souv. sheet of 1, imperf. | 3.75 | 3.75 |
| **486** | A235 | 10w | lt bl, vio bl & grn | 2.10 | .75 |
| *a.* | | | Souv. sheet of 1, imperf. | 3.75 | 3.75 |

ICY, 1965, and 20th anniv. of the UN.

Child Posting Letter
A236

Design: 10w, Airmail envelope, telephone.

**1965, Dec. 4** ***Perf. 13½***

| | | | | | |
|---|---|---|---|---|---|
| **487** | A236 | 3w | bl grn, blk, grn & red | 2.75 | .95 |
| **488** | A236 | 10w | ol, dk bl & red | 6.00 | 1.60 |

Tenth Communications Day.

Children with Sled — A237

Children and South Gate — A238

**1965, Dec. 11** **Litho.** ***Perf. 12½***

| | | | | | |
|---|---|---|---|---|---|
| **489** | A237 | 3w | pale grn, vio bl & red | 2.00 | .65 |
| **490** | A238 | 4w | lt bl, grn, vio bl & red | 3.50 | 1.10 |
| *a.* | | | Souv. sheet of 2, #489-490, imperf. | 4.25 | 4.25 |

Issued for Christmas and the New Year.

Freedom House
A239

**1966, Feb. 15** **Unwmk.** ***Perf. 12½***

| | | | | | |
|---|---|---|---|---|---|
| **491** | A239 | 7w | brt grn, blk & cit | 2.00 | .70 |
| **492** | A239 | 39w | lil, blk & pale grn | 13.00 | 3.25 |
| *a.* | | | Souv. sheet of 2, #491-492, imperf. | 22.50 | 17.50 |

Opening of "Freedom House" at Panmunjom.

**Wildlife Issue**

Mandarin Ducks
A240

Birds: 5w, Japanese cranes. 7w, Ring-necked pheasants.

**1966, Mar. 15** **Litho.** ***Perf. 12½***

| | | | | | |
|---|---|---|---|---|---|
| **493** | A240 | 3w | multicolored | 2.40 | 1.25 |
| **494** | A240 | 5w | multicolored | 2.40 | 1.25 |
| **495** | A240 | 7w | multicolored | 3.75 | 1.30 |

Alaska Pollack
A241

Fish: 5w, Manchurian trout. 7w, Yellow corvina.

**1966, June 15**

| | | | | | |
|---|---|---|---|---|---|
| **496** | A241 | 3w | bl, dk brn & yel | 3.00 | .90 |
| **497** | A241 | 5w | grnsh bl, blk & mag | 3.50 | .90 |
| **498** | A241 | 7w | brt grnsh bl, blk & yel | 4.50 | 1.00 |

Firefly
A242

Insects: 5w, Grasshopper. 7w, Silk butterfly (sericinus telamon).

**1966, Sept. 15**

| | | | | | |
|---|---|---|---|---|---|
| **499** | A242 | 3w | multicolored | 2.25 | .90 |
| **500** | A242 | 5w | dp yellow & multi | 2.75 | .90 |
| **501** | A242 | 7w | lt blue & multi | 3.00 | 1.00 |

Badger
A243

Animals: 5w, Asiatic black bear. 7w, Tiger.

**1966, Dec. 15**

| | | | | | |
|---|---|---|---|---|---|
| **502** | A243 | 3w | multicolored | 3.00 | .95 |
| **503** | A243 | 5w | multicolored | 3.00 | .95 |
| **504** | A243 | 7w | multicolored | 3.50 | .95 |
| | | | *Nos. 493-504 (12)* | 37.05 | 12.25 |

**Souvenir Sheets of 1, Imperf.**

| | | | | |
|---|---|---|---|---|
| *493a* | A240 | 3w | 3.75 | 3.75 |
| *494a* | A240 | 5w | 3.75 | 3.75 |
| *495a* | A240 | 7w | 5.75 | 5.75 |
| *496a* | A241 | 3w | 3.25 | 3.25 |
| *497a* | A241 | 5w | 3.75 | 3.75 |
| *498a* | A241 | 7w | 4.25 | 4.25 |
| *499a* | A242 | 3w | 3.25 | 3.25 |
| *500a* | A242 | 5w | 3.25 | 3.25 |
| *501a* | A242 | 7w | 3.75 | 3.75 |
| *502a* | A243 | 3w | 4.50 | 4.50 |
| *503a* | A243 | 5w | 4.50 | 4.50 |
| *504a* | A243 | 7w | 5.00 | 5.00 |
| | *Nos. 493a-504a (12)* | | 48.75 | 48.75 |

Hwansung-gun and Kwangnung Forests — A244

**1966, Apr. 5** **Unwmk.** ***Perf. 12½***

| | | | | | |
|---|---|---|---|---|---|
| **505** | A244 | 7w | green & brown | 1.50 | .60 |

Forestation Movement.

Symbolic Newspaper Printing and Pen — A245

**1966, Apr. 7** **Litho.**

| | | | | | |
|---|---|---|---|---|---|
| **506** | A245 | 7w | lt bl, vio brn & yel | 1.35 | .60 |

Tenth Newspaper Day.

Proper Guidance of Young People — A246

**1966, May 1** **Unwmk.** ***Perf. 12½***

| | | | | | |
|---|---|---|---|---|---|
| **507** | A246 | 7w | Children & bell | 1.35 | .60 |

Opening of WHO Headquarters, Geneva — A247

**1966, May 3** **Litho.**

**508** A247 7w lt bl, blk & yel 1.50 .60
*a.* Souv. sheet of 1, imperf. 4.25 4.25
**509** A247 39w bluish gray, yel & red 11.00 3.00

Girl Scout and Flag — A248

**1966, May 10**

**510** A248 7w yel, emer & dk bl 2.10 .80

Girl Scouts of Korea, 20th anniversary.

Pres. Park and Flags of Korea, Malaysia, Thailand and Republic of China A249

**1966, May 10**

**511** A249 7w multicolored 7.50 2.10

State visits of President Chung Hee Park.

Women's Ewha University, Seoul, and Student A250

**1966, May 31**

**512** A250 7w lt bl, vio bl & dp org 1.35 .50

80th anniv. of modern education for women.

### Types of 1961-66 Inscribed "Republic of Korea," and

Porcelain Incense Burner, 11th-12th Centuries — A253

Celadon Vessel, 12th Century — A254

Unjin Miruk Buddha, Kwanchok Temple — A255

60ch, Long-horned beetle. 1w, Folk dancers. 2w, Ginseng. 3w, King Sejong. 5w, Dragon waterpot. 7w, Symbols of thrift & development.

***Perf. 12½***

**1966, Aug. 20** **Unwmk.** **Litho.**

**Size: 22x19mm, 19x22mm**

**Granite Paper**

| | | | | |
|---|---|---|---|---|
| **516** | A186a | 60ch gray green | .70 | .25 |
| **517** | A185a | 1w green | 3.75 | .35 |
| **518** | A169 | 2w blue green | 1.00 | .25 |
| **519** | A170 | 3w dull red brn | .50 | .25 |
| **521** | A186 | 5w gray green | 5.00 | .70 |
| **522** | A186b | 7w grnsh blue | 4.75 | .50 |

**Size: 22x25mm**

| | | | | |
|---|---|---|---|---|
| **523** | A253 | 13w vio blue | 5.00 | 1.00 |
| **524** | A254 | 60w green | 27.50 | 1.35 |
| **525** | A255 | 80w slate grn | 7.25 | 1.35 |
| | | *Nos. 516-525 (9)* | 55.45 | 6.00 |

Souvenir Sheet

Carrier Pigeons — A258

**1966, July 13** **Wmk. 317** ***Imperf.***

**Red Brown Surcharge**

**534** A258 7w on 40h emer & dk grn 3.50 3.50

6th Intl. Letter Writing Week, June 13-19. No. 534 was not issued without surcharge.

Children and World Map Projection A259

**1966, July 28** **Unwmk.** ***Perf. 12½***

**535** A259 7w lt & dk vio bl & gray 2.00 .45
*a.* Souv. sheet of 1, imperf. 3.50 3.50

15th annual assembly of WCOTP (World Conf. of Teaching Profession), Seoul, July 28-Aug. 9.

Factory, Money Bag and Honeycomb A260

**1966, Sept. 1** **Unwmk.** ***Perf. 12½***

**536** A260 7w multicolored 1.35 .50

Issued to publicize systematic saving.

Map of Korea, and People A261

**1966, Sept. 1** **Litho.**

**537** A261 7w multicolored 1.35 .50

Ninth national census.

CISM Emblem and Round-Table Conference A262

**1966, Sept. 29** **Unwmk.** ***Perf. 12½***

**538** A262 7w multicolored 1.35 .50
*a.* Souv. sheet of 1, imperf. 3.50 3.50

21st General Assembly of the Intl. Military Sports Council (CISM), Seoul, 9/29-10/9.

Flags of Korea and Viet Nam and Korean Soldiers A263

**1966, Oct. 1**

**539** A263 7w multicolored 9.00 2.10

1st anniv. of Korean combat troops in Viet Nam.

Wrestlers A264

**1966, Oct. 10**

**540** A264 7w red brn, buff & blk 2.40 1.00

47th Natl. Athletic Meet, Seoul, Oct. 10-15.

Lions Emblem and Map of Southeast Asia — A265

**1966, Oct. 15**

**541** A265 7w multicolored 1.50 .90
*a.* Souv. sheet of 1, imperf. 3.75 3.75

5th East and Southeast Asia Lions Convention, Seoul, Oct. 15-17.

Seoul University Emblem A266

**1966, Oct. 15** **Litho.**

**542** A266 7w multicolored 1.50 1.00

20th anniversary of Seoul University.

Anticommunist League Emblem — A267

**1966, Oct. 31** **Unwmk.** ***Perf. 12½***

**543** A267 7w multicolored 1.50 .50
*a.* Souv. sheet of 1, imperf. 3.25 3.25

12th Conf. of the Asian Anticommunist League, Seoul, Oct. 31-Nov. 7.

Presidents Park and Johnson, Flags of US and Korea A268

**1966, Oct. 31** **Litho.** ***Perf. 12½***

**544** A268 7w multicolored 2.00 .75
**545** A268 83w multicolored 13.00 3.50
*a.* Souv. sheet of 2, #544-545, imperf. 14.50 14.50

Visit of Pres. Lyndon B. Johnson to Korea.

UNESCO Emblem and Symbols of Learning — A269

**1966, Nov. 4**

**546** A269 7w multicolored 1.50 .60
*a.* Souvenir sheets 3.50 3.50

20th anniv. of UNESCO.

Good Luck Bag and "Joy" A270

Ram and "Completion" A271

**1966, Dec. 10** ***Perf. 12½x13, 13x12½***

**547** A270 5w multicolored 2.10 .60
*a.* Souv. sheet of 1, imperf. 3.75 3.75
**548** A271 7w multicolored 3.75 .80
*a.* Souv. sheet of 1, imperf. 3.75 3.75

Issued for Christmas and the New Year.

Syncom Satellite over Globe — A272

**1967, Jan. 31** **Litho.** ***Perf. 12½***

**549** A272 7w dk blue & multi 1.60 .60
*a.* Souv. sheet of 1, imperf. 4.00 4.00

15th anniv. of Korea's membership in the ITU.

Presidents Park and Lübke A273

***Perf. 12½***

**1967, Mar. 2** **Litho.** **Unwmk.**

**550** A273 7w multicolored 2.40 1.15
*a.* Souv. sheet of 1, imperf. 4.25 4.25

Visit of Pres. Heinrich Lübke of Germany, Mar. 2-6.

Hand Holding Coin, Industrial and Private Buildings A274

**1967, Mar. 3**

**551** A274 7w lt green & blk brn 1.50 .60

1st anniv. of the Natl. Taxation Office.

### Folklore Series

Okwangdae Clown — A275

5w, Sandi mask & dance, horiz. 7w, Hafoe mask.

**1967, Mar. 15 Litho. *Perf. 12½***

| | | | |
|---|---|---|---|
| **552** A275 4w gray, blk & yel | 2.10 | .90 |
| **553** A275 5w multicolored | 2.10 | .90 |
| **554** A275 7w multicolored | 3.00 | 1.00 |

Perfect Peace Dance — A276

Designs: 4w, Sword dance, horiz. 7w, Buddhist Monk dance.

**1967, June 15**

| | | |
|---|---|---|
| **555** A276 4w multicolored | 3.25 | .90 |
| **556** A276 5w multicolored | 3.75 | .90 |
| **557** A276 7w multicolored | 4.50 | 1.10 |

Girls on Seesaw — A277

Designs: 4w, Girls on swing, horiz. 7w, Girls dancing in the moonlight.

**1967, Sept. 15**

| | | |
|---|---|---|
| **558** A277 4w multicolored | 3.75 | .90 |
| **559** A277 5w multicolored | 3.75 | 1.00 |
| **560** A277 7w multicolored | 6.00 | 1.20 |

Korean Shuttlecock — A278

Designs: 5w, Girls celebrating full moon, horiz. 7w, Archery.

**1967, Dec. 15**

| | | |
|---|---|---|
| **561** A278 4w multicolored | 3.00 | .90 |
| **562** A278 5w multicolored | 3.25 | 1.05 |
| **563** A278 7w multicolored | 3.00 | 1.00 |
| *Nos. 552-563 (12)* | 41.45 | 11.75 |

**Souvenir Sheets of 1, Imperf.**

| | | | | |
|---|---|---|---|---|
| *552a* | A275 | 4w | 3.25 | 3.25 |
| *553a* | A275 | 5w | 3.25 | 3.25 |
| *554a* | A275 | 7w | 4.25 | 4.25 |
| *555a* | A276 | 4w | 5.50 | 3.25 |
| *556a* | A276 | 5w | 5.50 | 3.25 |
| *557a* | A276 | 7w | 6.50 | 4.25 |
| *558a* | A277 | 4w | 5.75 | 5.75 |
| *559a* | A277 | 5w | 5.75 | 5.75 |
| *560a* | A277 | 7w | 6.75 | 6.75 |
| *561a* | A278 | 4w | 3.75 | 3.75 |
| *562a* | A278 | 5w | 3.75 | 3.75 |
| *563a* | A278 | 7w | 4.25 | 4.25 |
| *Nos. 552a-563a (12)* | | | 58.25 | 51.50 |

JCI Emblem and Kyunghoe Pavilion A279

**1967, Apr. 13 Litho. *Perf. 12½***

| | | |
|---|---|---|
| **564** A279 7w dk brn, brt grn, bl & red | 1.35 | .60 |
| *a.* Souv. sheet of 1, imperf. | 3.50 | 3.50 |

Intl. Junior Chamber of Commerce Conf., Seoul, Apr. 13-16.

Emblem, Map of Far East — A280

**1967, Apr. 24 Unwmk. *Perf. 12½***

| | | |
|---|---|---|
| **565** A280 7w vio bl & multi | 1.35 | .60 |
| *a.* Souv. sheet of 1, imperf. | 3.50 | 3.50 |

Issued to publicize the 5th Asian Pacific Dental Congress, Seoul, Apr. 24-28.

EXPO '67 Korean Pavilion A281

**1967, Apr. 28**

| | | |
|---|---|---|
| **566** A281 7w yel, blk & red | 3.25 | .75 |
| **567** A281 83w lt bl, blk & red | 22.50 | 4.50 |
| *a.* Souv. sheet of 2, #566-567, imperf. | 18.00 | 18.00 |

EXPO '67, Intl. Exhibition, Montreal, Apr. 28-Oct. 27, 1967.

Worker, Soldier, Emblem and Buildings — A282

**1967, May 1**

| | | |
|---|---|---|
| **568** A282 7w multicolored | 1.50 | .60 |

Veterans' Day, May 1.

**Second Five-Year Plan Issue**

Nut and Arrows A283

No. 570, Iron wheel and rail. No. 571, Express highway. No. 572, Cloverleaf intersection. No. 573, Rising income for fishermen and farmers (oysters, silk worm, mushrooms and bull's head). No. 574, Machine industry (cogwheels, automobile, wrench and motor). No. 575, Harbor. No. 576, Housing projects plans. No. 577, Atomic power plant. No. 578, Four Great River Valley development.

**1967-71 Litho. *Perf. 12½***

| | | |
|---|---|---|
| **569** A283 7w blk, red brn & dl org | 6.50 | 1.20 |
| **570** A283 7w dl org, yel & blk | 6.50 | 1.20 |
| **571** A283 7w grn, bl & ol | 12.00 | 2.00 |
| **572** A283 7w dk brn, yel & grn | 7.00 | 2.00 |
| ***Perf. 13x12½*** | | |
| **573** A283 7w brn, grn, yel & org | 1.50 | .40 |
| **574** A283 7w dk bl, lil rose & buff | 1.50 | .40 |
| **575** A283 10w dk bl, bl, yel & grn | 1.50 | .40 |
| **576** A283 10w lt bl, bl, grn & red | 1.50 | .40 |
| **Photo. *Perf. 13*** | | |
| **577** A283 10w blk, car & bl | 1.50 | .40 |
| **578** A283 10w blk, grn & brn | 1.50 | .40 |
| *Nos. 569-578 (10)* | 41.00 | 8.80 |

Second Economic Development Five-Year Plan.

Issued: Nos. 569-570, 6/1/67; Nos. 571-572, 12/5/68; Nos. 573-574, 12/5/69; Nos. 575-576, 12/5/70; Nos. 577-578, 12/5/71.

President Park and Phoenix A284

**1967, July 1 Unwmk. *Perf. 12½***

| | | |
|---|---|---|
| **579** A284 7w multicolored | 23.00 | 6.00 |
| *a.* Souv. sheet of 1, imperf. | 62.50 | 62.50 |

Inauguration of President Park Chung Hee for a 2nd term, July 1, 1967.

Korean Boy Scout, Emblem and Tents — A285

20w, Korean Boy Scout emblem, bridge & tents.

**1967, Aug. 10 Litho. *Perf. 12½***

| | | |
|---|---|---|
| **580** A285 7w multicolored | 1.50 | .60 |
| *a.* Souv. sheet of 1, imperf. | 4.75 | 4.75 |
| **581** A285 20w multicolored | 5.00 | 2.25 |
| *a.* Souv. sheet of 1, imperf. | 4.75 | 4.75 |

3rd Korean Boy Scout Jamboree, Hwarangdae, Seoul, Aug. 10-15.

**Types of 1962-66 Redrawn (Inscribed "Republic of Korea")**

Designs: 20w, Meesun blossoms and fruit. 40w, Library of early Buddhist scriptures. 50w, Deer.

**1967, Aug. 25 Granite Paper**

| | | |
|---|---|---|
| **582** A186c 20w green & lt bl grn | 77.50 | 2.00 |
| **583** A186d 40w dk grn & lt ol | 45.00 | 2.00 |
| **584** A186e 50w dk brn & bister | 8.50 | 1.50 |
| *Nos. 582-584 (3)* | 131.00 | 5.50 |

The printing of redrawn designs of the regular issue of 1962-66 became necessary upon discovery of large quantities of counterfeits, made to defraud the post. The position of the denominations was changed and elaborate fine background tracings were added.

Freedom Center and Emblem A286

Hand Breaking Chain — A287

**1967, Sept. 25 Litho. *Perf. 12½***

| | | |
|---|---|---|
| **586** A286 5w multicolored | 1.45 | .65 |
| *a.* Souv. sheet of 1, imperf. | 4.75 | 4.75 |
| **587** A287 7w multicolored | 1.60 | .65 |
| *a.* Souv. sheet of 1, imperf. | 4.75 | 4.75 |

1st Conf. of the World Anti-Communist League, WACL, Taipei, China, Sept. 25-29.

Boxing — A288

Design: 7w, Women's basketball.

**1967, Oct. 5**

| | | |
|---|---|---|
| **588** A288 5w tan & multi | 2.25 | .70 |
| **589** A288 7w pale rose & multi | 3.25 | .70 |

48th Natl. Athletic Meet, Seoul, Oct. 5-10.

Students' Memorial, Kwangjoo — A289

**1967, Nov. 3 Litho. *Perf. 12½***

| | | |
|---|---|---|
| **590** A289 7w lt green & multi | 1.50 | .50 |

Issued for Student Day commemorating 1929 students' uprising against Japan.

Symbolic Water Cycle — A290

**1967, Nov. 20**

| | | |
|---|---|---|
| **591** A290 7w multicolored | 1.50 | .60 |

Hydrological Decade (UNESCO), 1965-74.

Children Spinning Top — A291

Monkey and Oriental Zodiac — A292

**1967, Dec. 10**

| | | |
|---|---|---|
| **592** A291 5w sal, org & vio bl | 3.00 | .75 |
| *a.* Souv. sheet of 1, imperf. | 3.75 | 3.75 |
| **593** A292 7w yel bis, brn & vio bl | 3.75 | .75 |
| *a.* Souv. sheet of 1, imperf. | 3.75 | 3.75 |

Issued for Christmas and New Year.

Parabolic Antenna and Electric Waves — A293

**1967, Dec. 21**

| | | |
|---|---|---|
| **594** A293 7w lt bl, blk & yel | 1.50 | .70 |
| *a.* Souv. sheet of 1, imperf. | 3.75 | 3.75 |

Opening of the natl. microwave communications network, Dec. 21.

Carving from King Songdok Bell — A294

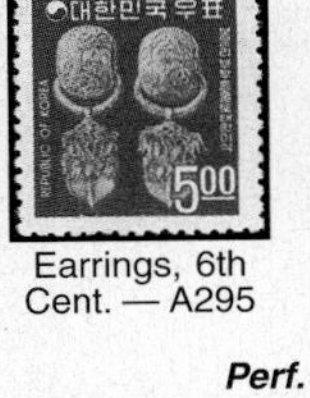

Earrings, 6th Cent. — A295

Flag — A296

***Perf. 13x12½***

**1968, Feb. 1 Litho. Unwmk.**

**Granite Paper**

| | | |
|---|---|---|
| **595** A294 1w yellow & brown | .80 | .25 |
| **596** A295 5w dk green & yellow | 3.25 | .55 |
| **597** A296 7w dark blue & red | 1.50 | .55 |
| *Nos. 595-597 (3)* | 5.55 | 1.35 |

WHO, 20th Anniv. — A297

**1968, Apr. 7 Unwmk. *Perf. 12½***

**598** A297 7w multicolored 1.50 .60
*a.* Souv. sheet of 1, imperf. 3.75 3.75

EATA Emblem and Korean Buildings — A298

**1968, Apr. 9 Litho.**

**599** A298 7w multicolored 1.50 .60
*a.* Souv. sheet of 1, imperf. 4.25 4.25

2nd General Meeting of the East Asia Travel Association (EATA), Seoul, Apr. 9-13.

Door Knocker, Factories and Emblem A299

**1968, May 6 Unwmk. *Perf. 12½***

**600** A299 7w multicolored 1.50 .60
*a.* Souv. sheet of 1, imperf. 4.00 4.00

2nd Conf. of the Confederation of Asian Chambers of Commerce and Industry, Seoul.

Pres. Park and Emperor Haile Selassie A300

**1968, May 18 Litho.**

**601** A300 7w multicolored 3.75 1.40
*a.* Souv. sheet of 1, imperf. 7.25 7.25

Visit of Haile Selassie I, May 18-20.

Mailman's Pouch A301

Mailman A302

**1968, May 31 Unwmk. *Perf. 12½***

**602** A301 5w multicolored 1.50 .70
**603** A302 7w multicolored 1.50 .70

First Postman's Day, May 31, 1968.

Atom Diagram and Symbols of Development A303

**1968, June 1 Litho.**

**604** A303 7w dk bl, citron & ver 1.50 .60

Issued to promote science and technology.

Kyung Hee University and Conference Emblem A304

**1968, June 18 Unwmk.**

**605** A304 7w bl, pink & blk 1.50 .50
*a.* Souv. sheet of 1, imperf. 5.00 5.00

2nd Conf. of the Intl. Association of University Presidents.

Liberated People A305

**1968, July 1 Litho. *Perf. 12½***

**606** A305 7w multicolored 1.50 .60

Issued to publicize the movement to liberate people under communist rule.

Peacock and Industrial Plant — A306

**1968, Aug. 15 Unwmk. *Perf. 12½***

**607** A306 7w multicolored 1.50 .60

Republic of Korea, 20th anniversary.

Fair Entrance A307

**1968, Sept. 9 Unwmk. *Perf. 12½***

**608** A307 7w lilac & multi 1.50 .60

Issued to publicize the first Korean Trade Fair, Seoul, Sept. 9-Oct. 18.

Assembly Emblem and Pills — A308

**1968, Sept. 16 Litho.**

**609** A308 7w multicolored 1.50 .60

3rd General Assembly of the Federation of Asian Pharmaceutical Associations, Seoul, Sept. 16-21.

Soldier, Insigne and Battle Scene — A309

No. 611, Sailor, insigne & ship's guns. No. 612, Servicemen & flags. No. 613, Aviator, insigne & planes. No. 614, Marine, insigne & landing group.

**1968, Oct. 1**

**610** A309 7w green & org 7.50 2.00
**611** A309 7w lt & dk blue 7.50 2.00
**612** A309 7w dk blue & org 7.50 2.00
**613** A309 7w dk & lt blue 7.50 2.00
**614** A309 7w orange & grn 7.50 2.00
*a.* Vert. strip of 5, #610-614 42.50 14.00

20th anniv. of the Korean armed forces.

Colombo Plan Emblem and Globe — A310

**1968, Oct. 8 Litho. *Perf. 12½***

**615** A310 7w dk brn, pale sal & grn 1.50 .60

19th meeting of the Consultative Committee of the Colombo Plan, Seoul, Oct. 8-28.

Bicycling (Type I) — A311

Type II — (2nd line flush left)

No. 617, Bicycling, Type II. No. 618-619, Wrestling. No. 620-621, Boxing. No. 622-623, Olympic flame, "68" & symbols of various sports events.

**1968, Oct. 12 Unwmk. *Perf. 12½***

**616** A311 7w pink & multi (I) 14.00 4.25
**617** A311 7w pink & multi (II) 14.00 4.25
*a.* Souv. sheet of 2, #616-617, imperf. 10.50 10.50
*b.* Pair, #616-617 35.00 35.00
**618** A311 7w olive & multi (I) 14.00 12.00
**619** A311 7w olive & multi (II) 14.00 12.00
*a.* Souv. sheet of 2, #618-619, imperf. 10.50 10.50
*b.* Pair, #618-619 35.00 35.00
**620** A311 7w orange & multi (I) 14.00 12.00
**621** A311 7w orange & multi (II) 14.00 12.00
*a.* Souv. sheet of 2, #620-621, imperf. 10.50 10.50
*b.* Pair, #620-621 35.00 35.00
**622** A311 7w bluish grn & multi (I) 14.00 12.00
**623** A311 7w bluish grn & multi (II) 14.00 12.00
*a.* Souv. sheet of 2, #622-623, imperf. 10.50 10.50
*b.* Pair, #622-623 35.00 35.00
*Nos. 616-623 (8)* 112.00 80.50

19th Olympic Games, Mexico City, 10/12-27.
The position of the "7" is reversed on Nos. 619, 621, 623 as are the designs of Nos. 619, 621.

"Search for Knowledge" and School Girls — A312

**1968, Oct. 15**

**624** A312 7w multicolored 1.50 .60

60th anniv. of public secondary education for women.

Coin and Statistics A313

**1968, Nov. 1**

**625** A313 7w multicolored 1.50 .50

National Wealth Survey.

Memorial to Students' Uprising — A314

**1968, Nov. 23**

**626** A314 7w gray & multi 1.90 .65

Issued to commemorate the anti-communist students' uprising, Nov. 23, 1945.

Men With Banners Declaring Human Rights A315

**1968, Dec. 10**

**627** A315 7w multicolored 1.50 .60

Declaration of Human Rights, 20th anniv.

Christmas Decorations A316

Cock and Good Luck Characters A317

**1968, Dec. 11**

**628** A316 5w salmon & multi 8.75 1.00
*a.* Souv. sheet of 1, imperf. 7.25 7.25
**629** A317 7w multicolored 9.50 1.00
*a.* Souv. sheet of 1, imperf. 7.25 7.25

Issued for Christmas and the New Year.

UN Emblems and Korean House A318

**1968, Dec. 12**

**630** A318 7w lt blue & multi 1.50 .60

20th anniv. of the recognition of the Republic of Korea by the UN.

Regional Boy Scout Conf. — A319

Design: Boy Scout Emblem.

**1968, Sept. 30** **Litho.** ***Perf. 12½***
**631** A319 7w black & multi 2.10 .75

Sam-il Movement, 50th Anniv. — A320

Design: Torch, map and students Demonstrating against Japan, 1919.

**1969, Mar. 1** **Unwmk.** ***Perf. 12½***
**632** A320 7w multicolored 1.50 .60

Hyun Choong Sa Shrine and Tortoise Ships A321

**1969, Apr. 28** **Unwmk.** ***Perf. 12½***
**633** A321 7w deep bl, grn & brn 1.50 .60

Completion of the Hyun Choong Sa Shrine at Onyang, dedicated to the memory of Adm. Li Sun-sin.

Pres. Park and Tuanku Nasiruddin of Malaysia A322

**1969, Apr. 29** **Litho.**
**634** A322 7w yellow & multi 3.50 1.20
*a.* Souv. sheet of 1, imperf. *57.50* *57.50*

Visit of Tuanku Ismail Nasiruddin, ruler of Malaysia, Apr. 29, 1969.

Hanabusaya Asiatica — A323

Old Man's Mask — A323a

Stone Lamp, 8th Cent. — A323b

Chipmunk — A323c

Flag of Korea — A324

Flag of Korea — A324a

Ancient Drums — A325

Flag of Korea — A325a

Red-crested Cranes — A326

Tiger Lily — A326a

Highway and Farm — A327

Pitcher (12-13th Centuries) A328

Ceramic Duck (Water Jar) A329

Bee — A329a

Library of Early Buddhist Scriptures A330

Vase, Yi dynasty (17th-18th Centuries) A331

Miruk Bosal A332

Gold Crown, Silla Dynasty A333

**Granite Paper (Lithographed); Ordinary Paper (Photogravure)**

***Perf. 13x12, 12x13 (Litho.); 13½x12½, 12½x13½ (Photo.)***

**Litho. (40ch, Nos. 641, 650); Photo.**

**1969-74** **Unwmk.**
**635** A323 40ch green 1.20 .35
**636** A323a 1w dk rose brn ('74) .40 .25
**637** A323b 5w brt plum 2.00 .25
**638** A323c 5w brn red ('74) .35 .25
**639** A324 7w blue ("7.00") 3.50 .50
**640** A324a 7w brt blue ("7") 2.00 .30
**641** A325 10w ultra 30.00 1.00
**642** A325a 10w dk blue ("10") ('70) 2.00 .25
**643** A326 10w bl & dk bl ('73) 1.15 .35
**644** A326a 10w grn & multi ('73) .90 .25
**645** A327 10w grn, red & gray ('73) .70 .25
**647** A328 20w green 1.75 .50
**648** A329 30w dull grn ('70) 6.75 .70
**649** A329a 30w yel & dk brn ('74) .65 .25
**650** A330 40w vio bl & pink 42.50 1.90
**651** A331 40w ultra & lilac 1.75 .70
**652** A332 100w dp claret & yel 75.00 1.90
**653** A333 100w brn & yel ('74) 37.50 2.40
*Nos. 635-653 (18)* 210.10 12.35

See No. 1090. For surcharge see No. B18. Counterfeits exist of No. 653.

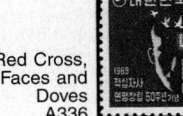

Red Cross, Faces and Doves A336

**1969, May 5** **Litho.** ***Perf. 12½***
**654** A336 7w multicolored 1.75 .45
*a.* Souv. sheet of 1, imperf. 5.00 5.00

50th anniv. of the League of Red Cross Societies.

Savings Bank, Factories and Highway — A337

**1969, May 20** **Unwmk.** ***Perf. 12½***
**655** A337 7w yellow grn & multi 1.50 .60

Second Economy Drive.

Pres. Park, Pres. Thieu and Flags of Korea and Viet Nam — A338

**1969, May 27** **Litho.**
**656** A338 7w pink & multi 3.00 1.15
*a.* Souv. sheet of 1, imperf. 7.75 7.75

Visit of Pres. Nguyen Van Thieu of Viet Nam, May 27.

"Reforestation and Parched Fields" — A339

Growing and Withering Plants — A340

**1969, June 10**
**657** A339 7w multicolored 1.50 .50
**658** A340 7w multicolored 1.50 .50

Issued to publicize the need for prevention of damages from floods and droughts.

Apollo 11, Separation of Second Stage A341

No. 660, Apollo 11, separation of 3rd Stage. No. 661, Orbits of command & landing modules around moon. No. 662, Astronauts gathering rock samples on moon. 40w, Spacecraft splashdown.

**1969, Aug. 15** **Unwmk.** ***Perf. 12½***
**659** A341 10w indigo, bl & red 3.50 1.30
**660** A341 10w indigo, bl & red 3.50 1.30
**661** A341 20w indigo, bl, red & lem 3.50 1.30
**662** A341 20w indigo, bl, red & lem 3.50 1.30
**663** A341 40w indigo, bl & red 3.50 1.30
*a.* Souv. sheet of 5, #659-663, imperf. 33.00 33.00
*b.* Strip of 5, #659-663 20.00 13.50

Man's 1st landing on the moon, July 20, 1969. US astronauts Neil A. Armstrong and Col. Edwin E. Aldrin, Jr., with Lieut. Col. Michael Collins piloting Apollo 11.

**Fable Issue**

Girl and Stepmother A342

Kongji and Patji (Cinderella): 7w, Sparrows help Kongji separate rice. 10w, Ox helps Kongji to weed a field. 20w, Kongji in a sedan chair on the way to the palace.

**1969, Sept. 1** **Litho.** ***Perf. 12½***
**664** A342 5w apple grn & multi 3.75 1.10
**665** A342 7w yellow & multi 3.75 1.10
**666** A342 10w lt violet & multi 6.25 1.20
**667** A342 20w lt green & multi 6.25 1.20

The Sick Princess A343

"The Hare's Liver": 7w, Hare riding to the palace on back of turtle. 10w, Hare telling a lie to the King to save his life. 20w, Hare mocking the turtle.

**1969, Nov. 1** ***Perf. 13x12½***
**668** A343 5w yellow & multi 2.00 .85
**669** A343 7w lt vio & multi 2.00 .85
**670** A343 10w lt grnsh bl & multi 2.00 .95
**671** A343 20w lt yel grn & multi 3.75 .95

Mother Meeting Tiger — A344

"The Sun and the Moon": 7w, Tiger disguised as mother at children's house. 10w, Tiger, and children on tree. 20w, Children safe on cloud, and tiger falling to his death.

**1970, Jan. 5**
**672** A344 5w orange & multi 2.00 .65
**673** A344 7w gray grn & multi 2.00 .65
**674** A344 10w lt green & multi 2.00 .80
**675** A344 20w gray & multi 4.00 .80

Woodcutter Stealing Fairy's Clothes A345

Designs: No. 677, Woodcutter with wife and children. No. 678, Wife taking children to heaven. No. 679, Husband joining family in heaven.

**1970, Mar. 5**
**676** A345 10w dull bl grn & multi 2.40 .95
**677** A345 10w buff & multi 2.40 .95
**678** A345 10w lt grnsh bl & multi 2.40 .95
**679** A345 10w pink & multi 2.40 1.10

Heungbu and Wife Release Healed Swallow
A346

Designs: No. 681, Heungbu and wife finding gold treasure in gourd. No. 682, Nolbu and wife with large gourd. No. 683, Demon emerging from gourd punishing evil Nolbu and wife.

**1970, May 5** ***Perf. 12½***

| | | | | | |
|---|---|---|---|---|---|
| **680** | A346 | 10w | lt grnsh bl & multi | 6.50 | 1.20 |
| **681** | A346 | 10w | org & multi | 6.50 | 1.20 |
| **682** | A346 | 10w | app grn & multi | 6.50 | 1.20 |
| **683** | A346 | 10w | tan & multi | 6.50 | 1.20 |
| | | | *Nos. 664-683 (20)* | 75.35 | 19.85 |

**Souvenir Sheets of 1, Imperf.**

| | | | | |
|---|---|---|---|---|
| 664a | A342 | 5w | 14.50 | 14.50 |
| 665a | A342 | 7w | 14.50 | 14.50 |
| 666a | A342 | 10w | 14.50 | 14.50 |
| 667a | A342 | 20w | 14.50 | 14.50 |
| 668a | A343 | 5w | 4.50 | 4.50 |
| 669a | A343 | 7w | 4.50 | 4.50 |
| 670a | A343 | 10w | 4.50 | 4.50 |
| 671a | A343 | 20w | 4.50 | 4.50 |
| 672a | A344 | 5w | 4.25 | 4.25 |
| 673a | A344 | 7w | 4.25 | 4.25 |
| 674a | A344 | 10w | 4.25 | 4.25 |
| 675a | A344 | 20w | 4.25 | 4.25 |
| 676a | A345 | 10w | 4.25 | 4.25 |
| 677a | A345 | 10w | 4.25 | 4.25 |
| 678a | A345 | 10w | 4.25 | 4.25 |
| 679a | A345 | 10w | 4.25 | 4.25 |
| 680a | A346 | 10w | 13.50 | 13.50 |
| 681a | A346 | 10w | 13.50 | 13.50 |
| 682a | A346 | 10w | 13.50 | 13.50 |
| 683a | A346 | 10w | 13.50 | 13.50 |
| | *Nos. 664a-683a (20)* | | 164.00 | 164.00 |

1869 Locomotive and Diesel Train — A347

Design: No. 685, Early locomotive.

***Perf. 12½***

**1969, Sept. 18 Litho. Unwmk.**

| | | | | | |
|---|---|---|---|---|---|
| **684** | A347 | 7w | yellow & multi | 1.90 | .65 |
| **685** | A347 | 7w | green & multi | 1.90 | .65 |

70th anniversary of Korean Railroads.

Formation of F-5A Planes
A348

Design: No. 687, F-4D Phantom.

**1969, Oct. 1 Photo.** ***Perf. 13½x13***

**686** A348 10w blue, blk & car 4.75 .70

**Litho.** ***Perf. 13x12½***

**687** A348 10w multicolored 6.75 .70

20th anniversary of Korean Air Force.

Cha-jun Game
A349

**1969, Oct. 3**

**688** A349 7w ap grn, dk bl & blk 1.20 .40

10th National Festival of Traditional Skills.

Institute of Science and Technology
A350

**1969, Oct. 23**

**689** A350 7w bister, grn & choc 1.20 .40

Completion of the Korean Institute of Science and Technology, Hongnung, Seoul.

Pres. Park and Diori Hamani
A351

**1969, Oct. 27**

| | | | | | |
|---|---|---|---|---|---|
| **690** | A351 | 7w | yel grn & multi | 2.10 | .90 |
| *a.* | | | Souv. sheet of 1, imperf. | 12.00 | 12.00 |

Visit of Diori Hamani, Pres. of Niger, Oct. 27.

Korean Wrestling
A352

No. 692, Fencing. No. 693, Korean karate (taekwondo). No. 694, Volleyball, vert. No. 695, Soccer, vert.

**1969, Oct. 28** ***Perf. 13x12½, 12½x13***

| | | | | | |
|---|---|---|---|---|---|
| **691** | A352 | 10w | yel grn & multi | 2.75 | .85 |
| **692** | A352 | 10w | blue & multi | 2.75 | .85 |
| **693** | A352 | 10w | green & multi | 2.75 | .85 |
| **694** | A352 | 10w | olive & multi | 2.75 | .85 |
| **695** | A352 | 10w | ultra & multi | 2.75 | .85 |
| | | | *Nos. 691-695 (5)* | 13.75 | 4.25 |

50th Natl. Athletic Meet, Seoul, Oct. 28-Nov. 2.

Allegory of National Education Charter — A353

**1969, Dec. 5 Litho.** ***Perf. 12½x13***

**696** A353 7w dull yel & multi 1.20 .35

1st anniv. of the proclamation of the Natl. Education Charter.

Toy Dogs and Lattice Pattern
A354

Candle, Lattice Door and Fence
A355

**1969, Dec. 11 Photo.** ***Perf. 13½***

| | | | | | |
|---|---|---|---|---|---|
| **697** | A354 | 5w | green & multi | 1.40 | .50 |
| **698** | A355 | 7w | blue & multi | 1.40 | .75 |

Issued for New Year 1970.

UPU Monument, Bern, and Korean Woman — A356

**1970, Jan. 1 Photo.** ***Perf. 13x13½***

**699** A356 10w multicolored 10.50 3.50

70th anniv. of Korea's admission to the UPU.

Education Year Emblem and Book — A357

**1970, Mar. 10 Litho.** ***Perf. 12½x13***

**700** A357 10w pink & multi 6.00 2.25

International Education Year 1970.

EXPO '70 Emblem, Seated Buddha, Korean Pavilion
A358

**1970, Mar. 15** ***Perf. 13x12½***

**701** A358 10w multicolored 6.00 1.45

Issued to publicize EXPO '70 International Exhibition, Osaka, Japan, March 15-Sept. 13.

Korean Youths and 4-H Club Emblem — A359

**1970, Mar. 28** ***Perf. 12½x13***

**702** A359 10w yellow & multi 2.75 .75

Issued to publicize the 15th Korean 4-H Club Central Contest, Suwon, March 28.

Money and Bank Emblem
A360

**1970, Apr. 9 Litho.** ***Perf. 13x12½***

**703** A360 10w yellow & multi 1.90 .75

3rd annual Board of Governors' meeting of the Asian Development Bank, Seoul, 4/9-11.

Royal Palanquin — A361

1899 Streetcar
A362

Historic Means of Transportation: No. 706, Emperor Sunjong's Cadillac, 1903. No. 707, Nieuport biplane, 1922.

***Perf. 13x13½, 13½x13***

**1970, May 20 Photo.**

| | | | | | |
|---|---|---|---|---|---|
| **704** | A361 | 10w | citron & multi | 2.50 | .85 |
| **705** | A362 | 10w | yellow & multi | 2.50 | .85 |
| **706** | A362 | 10w | ocher & multi | 2.50 | .85 |
| **707** | A362 | 10w | aqua & multi | 2.50 | .85 |
| | | | *Nos. 704-707 (4)* | 10.00 | 3.40 |

UPU Headquarters
A363

**1970, May 30** ***Perf. 13½x13***

**708** A363 10w multicolored 1.25 .35

New UPU Headquarters in Bern, Switzerland.

Map, Radar and Satellite — A364

**1970, June 2** ***Perf. 13x13½***

**709** A364 10w sky bl, vio bl & blk 1.90 .75

Issued to commemorate the completion of the Kum San Earth Station of the International Satellite Consortium (INTELSAT).

"PEN" and Manuscript Paper — A365

**1970, June 28 Photo.** ***Perf. 13x13½***

**710** A365 10w bl grn, bl & car 1.25 .35

37th Intl. P.E.N. Cong. (Poets, Playwrights, Editors, Essayists and Novelists), Seoul, June 28-July 4.

Seoul-Pusan Expressway — A366

**1970, June 30**

**711** A366 10w multicolored 1.90 .75

Opening of Seoul-Pusan Expressway.

Postal Code Symbol and Number — A367

**1970, July 1**

**712** A367 10w multicolored 1.25 .40

Issued to publicize the introduction of postal zone numbers, July 1, 1970.

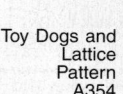

Mail Sorting Machine — A368

**1970, July 2**

**713** A368 10w lt vio & multi 1.25 .40
*a.* Souv. sheet, 2 each #712-713 92.50 92.50

Mechanization of Korean postal system.

Boy and Children's Hall — A369

**1970, July 25**

**714** A369 10w pink & multi 1.25 .40

### Paintings Issue

Jongyangsa Temple and Mt. Kumgang, by Chong Son (1676-1759) — A370

The Fierce Tiger, by Shim Sa-yung (1707-1769) A371

Paintings: No. 716, Mountains and Rivers, by Yi In-moon (1745-1821). No. 717, Mountains and Rivers in Moonlight, by Kim Doo-ryang (1696-1763).

***Perf. 13x13½, 13½x13***

**1970, Aug. 31** **Photo.**

**715** A370 10w blue & multi 2.25 .75
**716** A370 10w buff & multi 2.25 .75
**717** A371 10w multicolored 2.25 .75

**1970, Oct. 30**

Paintings: No. 719, Cats and Sparrows, by Pyun Sang-byuk (18th century). No. 720, Dog with puppies, by Yi Am (1499-?).

**718** A371 30w multicolored 8.75 1.60
**719** A371 30w multicolored 8.75 1.60
**720** A371 30w multicolored 8.75 1.60

Nos. 718-720 exist imperf. Value, set $50.

**1970, Dec. 30**

Paintings: No. 721, Cliff and Boat, by Kim Hong-do (1745-?). No. 722, Cock, Hens and Chick, by Pyun Sang-byuk (early 18th century). No. 723, Woman Playing Flute, by Shin Yun-bok (late 18th century).

**721** A371 10w yel brn, blk & red 2.25 .75
**722** A371 10w pale rose, blk & grn 2.25 .75
**723** A371 10w multicolored 2.25 .75
*Nos. 715-723 (9)* 39.75 9.30

### Souvenir Sheets of 2

*715a* A370 10w 5.00 5.00
*716a* A370 10w 5.00 5.00
*717a* A371 10w 5.00 5.00
*718a* A371 30w Imperf 31.00 31.00
*719a* A371 30w Imperf 31.00 31.00
*720a* A371 30w Imperf 31.00 31.00
*721a* A371 10w 8.00 8.00
*722a* A371 10w 8.00 8.00
*723a* A371 10w 8.00 8.00
*Nos. 715a-723a (9)* 132.00 132.00

Nos. 715a-717a have simulated perforations. Background color of stamps on No. 717a is yellow instead of greenish gray as on No. 717.

Nos. 718a-720a exist perf, twice the imperf values.

Nos. 721a-723a exist imperf. Value, each $3.50.

P.T.T.I. Emblem and Map of Far East — A372

**1970, Sept. 6** **Litho.** ***Perf. 13x12½***

**724** A372 10w lt yel grn, bl & dk bl 1.60 .50

Opening of the Councillors' Meeting of the Asian Chapter of the Postal, Telegraph and Telephone Intl. Org., Sept. 6-12.

Korean WAC and Emblem — A373

**1970, Sept. 6** **Photo.** ***Perf. 13x13½***

**725** A373 10w blue & multi 1.60 .50

20th anniv. of the founding of the Korean Women's Army Corps.

Pres. Park, Korean Flag and Means of Transportation — A374

Pres. Park, Highways, Factories A375

**1970** ***Perf. 13x13½, 13½x13***

**726** A374 10w vio bl, blk & car 8.25 3.00
**727** A375 10w dk bl, grnsh bl & blk 13.50 3.00

Presidents Park and Hernandez, Flags of Korea, Salvador A376

**1970, Sept. 28** **Litho.** ***Perf. 13x12½***

**728** A376 10w dk bl, red & blk 3.00 1.45
*a.* Souv. sheet of 1, imperf. 82.50 82.50

Visit of Gen. Fidel Sanchez Hernandez, President of El Salvador.

The first printing of 30,000 of No. 728a spelled "Salvadol." Second printing, also 30,000, corrected the error. Value is for first printing. Value, 2nd printing $7.50, unused or used.

People and Houses A377

**1970, Oct. 1** **Litho.** ***Perf. 13x12½***

**729** A377 10w lilac & multi 1.35 1.15

Natl. census of population & housing, Oct. 1.

Diver A378

**1970, Oct. 6** **Photo.** ***Perf. 12½x13½***

**730** A378 10w shown 4.25 .95
*a.* Souv. sheet of 2, imperf. 9.25 9.25
**731** A378 10w Field hockey 4.25 .95
*a.* Souv. sheet of 2, imperf. 9.25 9.25
**732** A378 10w Baseball 4.25 .95
*a.* Souv. sheet of 2, imperf. 9.25 9.25
*Nos. 730-732 (3)* 12.75 2.85
*Nos. 730a-732a (3)* 27.75

51st Natl. Athletic Games, Seoul, Oct. 6-11.

Police Emblem and Activities A379

**1970, Oct. 21** **Litho.** ***Perf. 12½***

**733** A379 10w ultra & multi 1.50 .55

The 25th Policemen's Day.

Freedom Bell, UN Emblem over Globe — A380

**1970, Oct. 24** **Photo.** ***Perf. 13x13½***

**734** A380 10w blue & multi 1.60 .55

25th anniversary of United Nations.

Kite and Holly — A380a

Boar — A381

**1970, Dec. 1** **Litho.** ***Perf. 13***

**735** A380a 10w lt blue & multi 1.45 .60
*a.* Souvenir sheet of 3 7.00 7.00
**736** A381 10w green & multi 1.45 .60
*a.* Souvenir sheet of 3 7.00 7.00

New Year 1971.

Pres. Park Quotation, Globe and Telecommunications Emblems — A382

**1970, Dec. 4** **Photo.**

**737** A382 10w multicolored 1.60 .55

For the 15th Communications Day.

Power Dam — A383

Crate Wrapped in World Map, & Ships — A383a

Irrigation Project & Farm — A383b

Coal Mining A384

Cement Factory — A384a

Fertilizer Factory — A384b

Increased National Income (Scales) — A384c

Increased Savings (factories, bee & coins) — A384d

Highway Intersection — A385

**1971** ***Perf. 13x13½, 13½x13***

| | | | | | |
|---|---|---|---|---|---|
| **738** | A383 | 10w | blue & multi | 2.25 | .55 |
| **739** | A383a | 10w | pale lil & multi | 2.25 | .55 |
| **740** | A383b | 10w | green & multi | 2.25 | .55 |
| **741** | A384 | 10w | bl grn, lt bl & blk | 1.25 | .45 |
| **742** | A384a | 10w | lt bl, vio & brt mag | 1.25 | .45 |
| **743** | A384b | 10w | vio, grn & bis | 1.25 | .45 |
| **744** | A384c | 10w | pink & multi | 1.40 | .65 |
| **745** | A384d | 10w | lt bl grn & multi | 1.40 | .65 |
| **746** | A385 | 10w | violet & multi | 1.40 | .65 |
| | | | *Nos. 738-746 (9)* | 14.70 | 4.95 |

Economic Development.

**Souvenir Sheets of 1, Imperf.**

| | | | | |
|---|---|---|---|---|
| *738a* | A383 | 10w | 6.50 | 6.50 |
| *739a* | A383a | 10w | 6.50 | 6.50 |
| *740a* | A383b | 10w | 6.50 | 6.50 |

**Souvenir Sheets of 2, Imperf.**

| | | | | |
|---|---|---|---|---|
| *741a* | A384 | 10w | 6.50 | 6.50 |
| *742a* | A384a | 10w | 6.50 | 6.50 |
| *743a* | A384b | 10w | 6.50 | 6.50 |
| *744a* | A384c | 10w | 4.75 | 4.75 |
| *745a* | A384d | 10w | 4.75 | 4.75 |
| *746a* | A385 | 10w | 4.75 | 4.75 |
| | *Nos. 738a-746a (9)* | | 53.25 | 53.25 |

No. 739a exists without date. Value $40.

Torch, Globe and Spider — A386

**1971, Mar. 1 Litho.** ***Perf. 12½x13***

| | | | | | |
|---|---|---|---|---|---|
| **747** | A386 | 10w | gray & multi | 1.60 | .45 |

March, the month for anti-espionage and victory over communism.

Reservist, Reserve Forces Emblem A387

**1971, Apr. 3 Photo.** ***Perf. 13½x13***

| | | | | | |
|---|---|---|---|---|---|
| **748** | A387 | 10w | lt ultra & multi | 1.60 | .45 |

Home Reserve Forces Day, Apr. 3.

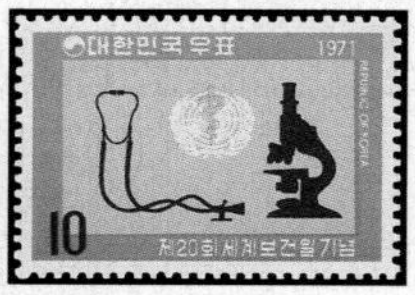

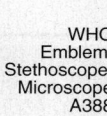

WHO Emblem, Stethoscope, Microscope A388

**1971, Apr. 7**

| | | | | | |
|---|---|---|---|---|---|
| **749** | A388 | 10w | lt bl, pur & yel | 1.60 | .50 |

20th World Health Day, Apr. 7.

Subway Tunnel and Train — A389

**1971, Apr. 12 Litho.** ***Perf. 12½x13***

| | | | | | |
|---|---|---|---|---|---|
| **750** | A389 | 10w | multicolored | 1.60 | .45 |

Seoul subway construction start.

First Asian Soccer Games, Seoul, May 2-13 — A390

**1971, May 2**

| | | | | | |
|---|---|---|---|---|---|
| **751** | A390 | 10w | grn, dk brn & blk | 1.90 | .60 |

Veterans Flag and Veterans — A391

**1971, May 8 Photo.** ***Perf. 13x13½***

| | | | | | |
|---|---|---|---|---|---|
| **752** | A391 | 10w | ultra & multi | 1.45 | .45 |

20th Korean Veterans Day.

Girl Scouts and Emblem — A392

**1971, May 10**

| | | | | | |
|---|---|---|---|---|---|
| **753** | A392 | 10w | lilac & multi | 1.50 | .45 |

25th anniversary of the Korean Federation of Girl Scouts.

Torch and Development A393

**1971, May 16**

| | | | | | |
|---|---|---|---|---|---|
| **754** | A393 | 10w | lt blue & multi | 1.45 | .45 |

10th anniversary of May 16th revolution.

"Telecommunication" A394

**1971, May 17**

| | | | | | |
|---|---|---|---|---|---|
| **755** | A394 | 10w | blue & multi | 1.45 | .45 |

3rd World Telecommunications Day.

UN Organizations A395

Korean Flag — A396

No. 756, ILO. No. 757, FAO. No. 758, General Assembly (UN Headquarters). No. 759, UNESCO. No. 760, WHO. No. 761, World Bank. No. 762, Intl. Development Association (IDA). No. 763, Security Council. No. 764, Intl. Finance Corp. (IFC). No. 765, Intl. Monetary Fund. No. 766, ICAO. No. 767, Economic and Social Council. No. 768, Korean Flag. No. 769, Trusteeship Council. No. 770, UPU. No. 771, ITU. No. 772, World Meteorological Org. (WMO). No. 773, Intl. Court of Justice. No. 774, Intl. Maritime Consultative Org. No. 775, UNICEF. No. 776, Intl. Atomic Energy Agency. No. 777, UN Industrial Development Org. No. 778, UN Commission for the Unification and Rehabilitation of Korea. No. 779, UN Development Program. No. 780, UN Conf. on Trade and Development.

**1971, May 30** ***Perf. 13½x13***

| | | | | | |
|---|---|---|---|---|---|
| **756** | A395 | 10w | grn, blk & pink | 3.75 | 1.15 |
| **757** | A395 | 10w | pink, blk & bl | 3.75 | 1.15 |
| **758** | A395 | 10w | bl, blk, grn & pink | 3.75 | 1.15 |
| **759** | A395 | 10w | pink, blk & bl | 3.75 | 1.15 |
| **760** | A395 | 10w | grn, blk & pink | 3.75 | 1.15 |
| **761** | A395 | 10w | pink, blk & bl | 3.75 | 1.15 |
| **762** | A395 | 10w | blue, blk & pink | 3.75 | 1.15 |
| **763** | A395 | 10w | grn, blk & pink | 3.75 | 1.15 |
| **764** | A395 | 10w | blue, blk & pink | 3.75 | 1.15 |
| **765** | A395 | 10w | pink, blk & bl | 3.75 | 1.15 |
| **766** | A395 | 10w | blue, blk & pink | 3.75 | 1.15 |
| **767** | A395 | 10w | grn, blk & pink | 3.75 | 1.15 |
| **768** | A396 | 10w | blue, blk & pink | 3.75 | 1.15 |
| **769** | A395 | 10w | grn, blk & pink | 3.75 | 1.15 |
| **770** | A395 | 10w | blue, blk & pink | 3.75 | 1.15 |
| **771** | A395 | 10w | pink, blk & bl | 3.75 | 1.15 |
| **772** | A395 | 10w | blue, blk & pink | 3.75 | 1.15 |
| **773** | A395 | 10w | grn, blk & pink | 3.75 | 1.15 |
| **774** | A395 | 10w | blue, blk & pink | 3.75 | 1.15 |
| **775** | A395 | 10w | pink, blk & bl | 3.75 | 1.15 |
| **776** | A395 | 10w | grn, blk & pink | 3.75 | 1.15 |
| **777** | A395 | 10w | pink, blk & bl | 3.75 | 1.15 |
| **778** | A395 | 10w | blue, blk & pink | 3.75 | 1.15 |
| **779** | A395 | 10w | pink, blk & bl | 3.75 | 1.15 |
| **780** | A395 | 10w | grn, blk & pink | 3.75 | 1.15 |
| | | | *Nos. 756-780 (25)* | 93.75 | 28.75 |

Sheet of 50 incorporates 2 each of Nos. 756-780.

Boat Ride, by Shin Yun-bok — A397

Man and Boy under Pine Tree — A398

Paintings by Shin Yun-bok: No. 782, Greeting travelers. No. 783, Sword dance. No. 784, Lady traveling with servants. No. 785, Man and woman on the road.

***Perf. 13x13½, 13½x13***

**1971, June 20** **Photo.**

| | | | | | |
|---|---|---|---|---|---|
| **781** | A397 | 10w | multicolored | 6.25 | 1.90 |
| **782** | A397 | 10w | multicolored | 6.25 | 1.90 |
| **783** | A397 | 10w | multicolored | 6.25 | 1.90 |
| **784** | A397 | 10w | multicolored | 6.25 | 1.90 |
| **785** | A397 | 10w | multicolored | 6.25 | 1.90 |
| *b.* | | | Vert. strip of 5, #781-785 | 40.00 | 40.00 |
| **786** | A398 | 10w | multicolored | 6.00 | 1.90 |
| | | | *Nos. 781-786 (6)* | 37.25 | 11.40 |

**Souvenir Sheets of 2**

| | | | | |
|---|---|---|---|---|
| *781a* | A397 | 10w | 11.50 | 11.50 |
| *782a* | A397 | 10w | 11.50 | 11.50 |
| *783a* | A397 | 10w | 11.50 | 11.50 |
| *784a* | A397 | 10w | 11.50 | 11.50 |
| *785a* | A397 | 10w | 11.50 | 11.50 |
| *786a* | A398 | 10w | 11.50 | 11.50 |
| | *Nos. 781a-786a (6)* | | 69.00 | 69.00 |

**Types A397-A398 with Inscription at Left**

Paintings: No. 787, Farmyard scene, by Kim Deuk-shin. No. 788, Family living in valley, by Lee Chae-kwan. No. 789, Man reading book under pine tree, by Lee Chae-kwan.

**1971, July 20**

| | | | | | |
|---|---|---|---|---|---|
| **787** | A397 | 10w | pale grn & multi | 3.25 | 1.60 |
| **788** | A398 | 10w | pale grn & multi | 3.25 | 1.60 |
| **789** | A398 | 10w | lt yel grn & multi | 3.25 | 1.60 |
| | | | *Nos. 787-789 (3)* | 9.75 | 4.80 |

**Souvenir Sheets of 2**

| | | | | |
|---|---|---|---|---|
| *787a* | A397 | 10w | 8.75 | 8.75 |
| *788a* | A398 | 10w | 8.75 | 8.75 |
| *789a* | A398 | 10w | 8.75 | 8.75 |
| | *Nos. 787a-789a (3)* | | 26.25 | 26.25 |

Teacher and Students, by Kim Hong-do A399

Paintings by Kim Hong-do (Yi Dynasty): No. 791, Wrestlers. No. 792, Dancer and musicians. No. 793, Weavers. No. 794, At the Well.

**1971, Aug. 20** ***Perf. 13½x13***

| | | | | | |
|---|---|---|---|---|---|
| **790** | A399 | 10w | blk, lt grn & rose | 5.50 | 2.75 |
| **791** | A399 | 10w | blk, lt grn & rose | 5.50 | 2.75 |
| **792** | A399 | 10w | blk, lt grn & rose | 5.50 | 2.75 |
| **793** | A399 | 10w | blk, lt grn & rose | 5.50 | 2.75 |
| **794** | A399 | 10w | blk, lt grn & rose | 5.50 | 2.75 |
| *b.* | | | Horiz. strip of 5, #790-794 | 33.00 | 33.00 |

**Souvenir Sheets of 2**

| | | | | |
|---|---|---|---|---|
| *790a* | A399 | 10w | 11.50 | 11.50 |
| *791a* | A399 | 10w | 11.50 | 11.50 |
| *792a* | A399 | 10w | 11.50 | 11.50 |
| *793a* | A399 | 10w | 11.50 | 11.50 |
| *794a* | A399 | 10w | 11.50 | 11.50 |
| | *Nos. 790a-794a (5)* | | 57.50 | 57.50 |

Pres. Park, Highway and Phoenix A400

**1971, July 1** ***Perf. 13½x13***

| | | | | | |
|---|---|---|---|---|---|
| **795** | A400 | 10w | grn, blk & org | 20.00 | 3.00 |
| *a.* | | | Souvenir sheet of 2 | 70.00 | 70.00 |

Inauguration of President Park Chung Hee for a third term, July 1.

Campfire and Tents — A401

**1971, Aug. 2 Photo.** ***Perf. 13x13½***

| | | | | | |
|---|---|---|---|---|---|
| **796** | A401 | 10w | blue grn & multi | 1.60 | .35 |

13th Boy Scout World Jamboree, Asagiri Plain, Japan, Aug. 2-10.

Symbol of Conference A402

**1971, Sept. 27** ***Perf. 13***

| | | | |
|---|---|---|---|
| **797** A402 10w multicolored | | 1.25 | .45 |
| *a.* | Souvenir sheet of 2 | 45.00 | 45.00 |

Asian Labor Ministers' Conference, Seoul, Sept. 27-30.

Archers — A403

**1971, Oct. 8 Photo.** ***Perf. 13x13½***

| | | | |
|---|---|---|---|
| **798** A403 10w shown | | 2.00 | .70 |
| *a.* | Souvenir sheet of 3 | *32.00* | 32.00 |
| **799** A403 10w Judo | | 2.00 | .70 |
| *a.* | Souvenir sheet of 3 | *32.00* | 32.00 |

52nd National Athletic Meet.

Taeguk on Palette A404

**1971, Oct. 11** ***Perf. 13½x13***

| | | |
|---|---|---|
| **800** A404 10w yellow & multi | 1.25 | .50 |

20th National Fine Arts Exhibition.

Physician, Globe and Emblem A405

**1971, Oct. 13**

| | | |
|---|---|---|
| **801** A405 10w multicolored | 1.25 | .50 |

7th Congress of the Confederation of Medical Associations in Asia and Oceania.

Symbols of Contest Events — A406

**1971, Oct. 20 Photo.** ***Perf. 13x13½***

| | | | |
|---|---|---|---|
| **802** A406 10w multicolored | | 1.25 | .50 |
| *a.* | Souvenir sheet of 2 | 37.50 | 37.50 |

2nd National Skill Contest for High School Students.

Slide Caliper and KS Emblem A407

**1971, Nov. 11** ***Perf. 13x13½***

| | | |
|---|---|---|
| **803** A407 10w multicolored | 1.25 | .50 |

10th anniversary of industrial standardization in Korea.

Rats — A408

Japanese Crane — A409

**1971, Dec. 1**

| | | | |
|---|---|---|---|
| **804** A408 10w multicolored | | 1.60 | .35 |
| *a.* | Souvenir sheet of 3 | 23.00 | 23.00 |
| **805** A409 10w multicolored | | 1.60 | .35 |
| *a.* | Souvenir sheet of 3 | 23.00 | 23.00 |

New Year 1972.

Emblem of Hangul Hakhoe and Hangul Letters — A410

**1971, Dec. 3** **Photo.**

| | | |
|---|---|---|
| **806** A410 10w dk blue & multi | 1.25 | .30 |

50th anniversary of Korean Language Research Society (Hangul Hakhoe).

Red Cross Headquarters and Map of Korea A411

**1971, Dec. 31** ***Perf. 13½x13***

| | | | |
|---|---|---|---|
| **807** A411 10w multicolored | | 1.75 | .55 |
| *a.* | Souvenir sheet of 2 | 11.50 | 11.50 |

First South and North Korean Red Cross Conference, Panmunjom, Aug. 20, 1971.

Globe and Book — A412

**1972, Jan. 5** ***Perf. 13x13½***

| | | | |
|---|---|---|---|
| **808** A412 10w multicolored | | 1.10 | .35 |
| *a.* | Souvenir sheet of 2 | 11.50 | 11.50 |

International Book Year 1972.

Intelsat 4 Sending Signals to Korea A413

**1972, Jan. 31** ***Perf. 13½x13***

| | | |
|---|---|---|
| **809** A413 10w dk blue & multi | 1.10 | .35 |

Korea's entry into ITU, 20th anniv.

Figure Skating, Sapporo '72 Emblem — A414

Design: No. 811, Speed skating.

**1972, Feb. 3** ***Perf. 13x13½***

| | | | |
|---|---|---|---|
| **810** A414 10w lt & dk bl & car | | 1.60 | .55 |
| **811** A414 10w lt & dk bl & car | | 1.60 | .55 |
| *a.* | Souvenir sheet of 2, #810-811 | 11.50 | 11.50 |

11th Winter Olympic Games, Sapporo, Japan, Feb. 3-13.

Map of Korea with Forest Sites — A415

**1972, Mar. 10 Photo.** ***Perf. 13x13***

| | | |
|---|---|---|
| **812** A415 10w buff, bl grn & red | 1.20 | .35 |

Publicity for forests planted to mark hope for re-unification of Korea.

Junior Chamber of Commerce Emblem and Beetles A416

**1972, Mar. 19** ***Perf. 13½x13***

| | | |
|---|---|---|
| **813** A416 10w pink & multi | 1.20 | .35 |

Junior Chamber of Commerce, 20th anniversary.

UN Emblem, Agriculture and Industry — A417

**1972, Mar. 28** ***Perf. 13x13½***

| | | |
|---|---|---|
| **814** A417 10w violet, grn & car | 1.20 | .35 |

Economic Commission for Asia and the Far East (ECAFE), 25th anniversary.

Flags — A418

**1972, Apr. 1** ***Perf. 13½x13***

| | | |
|---|---|---|
| **815** A418 10w blue & multi | 1.20 | .35 |

Asian-Oceanic Postal Union, 10th anniv.

Homeland Reserve Forces Flag — A419

**1972, Apr. 1 Photo.** ***Perf. 13x13½***

| | | |
|---|---|---|
| **816** A419 10w yellow & multi | 1.45 | .40 |

Homeland Reserve Forces Day, Apr. 1.

YWCA Emblem, Butterflies — A420

**1972, Apr. 20**

| | | |
|---|---|---|
| **817** A420 10w violet & multi | 1.50 | .40 |

50th anniv. of the YWCA of Korea.

Community Projects — A421

**1972, May 1** ***Perf. 13x13½***

| | | |
|---|---|---|
| **818** A421 10w pink & multi | 1.20 | .40 |

Rural rehabilitation and construction movement.

Korean Flag & Inscription — A422

**1972, May 1**

| | | |
|---|---|---|
| **819** A422 10w green & multi | 1.20 | .40 |

Anti-espionage and victory over communism month.

Children with Balloons A423

**1972, May 5** ***Perf. 13½x13***

| | | |
|---|---|---|
| **820** A423 10w yellow & multi | 1.20 | .40 |

Children's Day, May 5.

King Munyong's Gold Earrings A424

Design: No. 822, Gold ornament from King's crown, vert.

**1972, May 10** ***Perf. 13½x13, 13x13½***

| | | |
|---|---|---|
| **821** A424 10w green & multi | 1.30 | .40 |
| **822** A424 10w green & multi | 1.30 | .40 |

National treasures from tomb of King Munyong of Paekche, who reigned 501-523.

Kojo Island — A425

National parks: No. 823, Crater Lake.

**1972, May 30** ***Perf. 13½x13***

| | | |
|---|---|---|
| **823** A425 10w blue grn & multi | 3.25 | .40 |
| **824** A425 10w green & multi | 3.25 | .40 |

UN Conference on Human Environment, Stockholm, June 5-16 — A426

10w, Daisy, environment emblem.

**1972, May 30 Litho.** ***Perf. 13x13½***

**825** A426 10w multicolored 1.20 .35
*a.* Souvenir sheet of 2 7.75 7.75

7th Meeting of Asian-Pacific Council (ASPAC) — A427

10w, Gwanghwa Gate, flags of participants.

**1972, June 14**

**826** A427 10w multicolored 1.20 .35

**Third Five-Year Plan Issue**

Farm and Fish Hatchery A428

No. 828, Steel industry and products. No. 829, Globe and cargo.

**1972, July 1 Photo.** ***Perf. 13½x13***

**827** A428 10w shown 1.90 .50
**828** A428 10w multicolored 1.90 .50
**829** A428 10w multicolored 1.90 .50
*Nos. 827-829 (3)* 5.70 1.50

3rd Economic Development Five-Year Plan.

Weight Lifting — A429

**1972, Aug. 26 Photo.** ***Perf. 13x13½***

**830** A429 20w shown 1.20 .45
**831** A429 20w Judo 1.20 .45
*a.* Souvenir sheet of 2, #830-831 5.75 5.75
*b.* Pair, #830-831 5.00 2.50
**832** A429 20w Boxing 1.20 .45
**833** A429 20w Wrestling 1.20 .45
*a.* Souvenir sheet of 2, #832-833 6.00 6.00
*b.* Pair, #832-833 5.00 2.50
*Nos. 830-833 (4)* 4.80 1.80

20th Olympic Games, Munich, Aug. 26-Sept. 11. Nos. 831b, 833b each printed checkerwise.

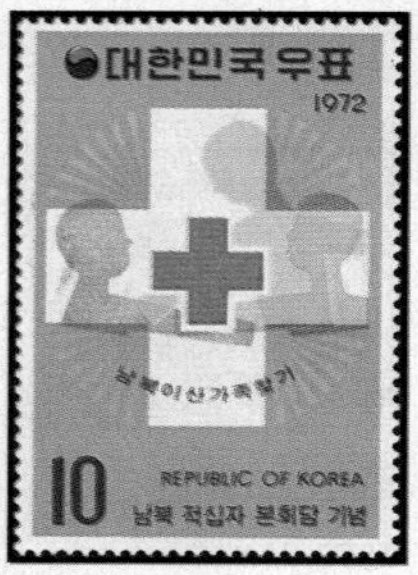

Families Reunited by Red Cross A430

**1972, Aug. 30 Photo.** ***Perf. 13½x13***

**834** A430 10w lt blue & multi 1.90 .60
*a.* Souvenir sheet of 2 24.00 24.00

Plenary meeting of the South-North Red Cross Conference, Pyongyang, Aug. 30, 1972.

Bulkuk-sa Temple, Kyongju Park — A431

Bopju-sa Temple, Mt. Sokri Park — A432

**1972, Sept. 20 Photo.** ***Perf. 13½x13***

**835** A431 10w brown & multi 1.35 .45
**836** A432 10w blue & multi 1.35 .45

National parks.

"5" and Conference Emblem — A433

**1972, Sept. 25** ***Perf. 13x13½***

**837** A433 10w vio blue & multi 1.15 .35

Fifth Asian Judicial Conf., Seoul, 9/25-29.

Lions Emblem, Taeguk Fan — A434

**1972, Sept. 28** ***Perf. 13½x13***

**838** A434 10w multicolored 1.30 .35

11th Orient and Southeast Asian Lions Convention, Seoul, Sept. 28-30.

Scout Taking Oath, Korean Flag and Scout Emblem A435

**1972, Oct. 5**

**839** A435 10w yellow & multi 1.90 .45

Boy Scouts of Korea, 50th anniversary.

Children and Ox — A436

Children in Balloon — A437

**1972, Dec. 1 Photo.** ***Perf. 13x13½***

**840** A436 10w green & multi 1.30 .40
*a.* Souvenir sheet of 2 4.50 4.50
**841** A437 10w blue & multi 1.30 .40
*a.* Souvenir sheet of 2 4.50 4.50

New Year 1973.

Mt. Naejang Park and Temple — A438

Mt. Sorang and Madeungryong Pass — A439

**1972, Dec. 10** ***Perf. 13x13½, 13½x13***

**842** A438 10w multicolored 1.35 .40
**843** A439 10w multicolored 1.35 .40

National parks.

Pres. Park, Korean Flag and Modern Landscape — A440

**1972, Dec. 27** ***Perf. 13x13½***

**844** A440 10w multicolored 8.50 2.00
*a.* Souvenir sheet of 2 65.00 65.00

Inauguration of Park Chung Hee for a 4th term as president of Korea.

**Tourism Issue**

Kyongbok Palace (National Museum) A441

Mt. Sorak and Kejo-am Temple A442

**1973, Feb. 20 Photo.** ***Perf. 13½x13***

**845** A441 10w multicolored 1.25 .40
**846** A442 10w multicolored 1.25 .40

Palmi Island and Beach — A443

Sain-am Rock, Mt. Dokjol — A444

**1973, Apr. 20** ***Perf. 13x13½***

**847** A443 10w multicolored 1.45 .40
**848** A444 10w multicolored 1.50 .40

Shrine for Adm. Li Sun-sin — A445

Limestone Cavern, Kusan-ni — A446

**1973, June 20**

**849** A445 10w multicolored 1.50 .40
**850** A446 10w multicolored 1.45 .40

Namhae Bridge A447

Hongdo Island — A448

**1973, Aug. 20** ***Perf. 13½x13***

**851** A447 10w multicolored 1.45 .35
**852** A448 10w multicolored 1.45 .35

Mt. Mai — A449

Tangerine Orchard, Cheju Island A450

**1973, Oct. 20**

**853** A449 10w multicolored .90 .25
**854** A450 10w multicolored .90 .25
*Nos. 845-854 (10)* 13.10 3.60

Praying Family — A451

**1973, Mar. 1** ***Perf. 13x13½***

**855** A451 10w yellow & multi 1.20 .50

Prayer for national unification.

Flags of Korea and South Viet Nam, Victory Sign — A452

**1973, Mar. 1**

**856** A452 10w violet & multi 1.20 .30

Return of Korean Expeditionary Force from South Viet Nam.

Workers, Factory, Cogwheel — A453

**1973, Mar. 10** **Unwmk.**

**857** A453 10w blue & multi 1.00 .30

10th Labor Day.

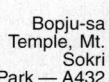

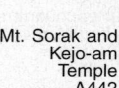

Satellite, WMO Emblem — A454

**1973, Mar. 23**

**858** A454 10w blue & multi 1.00 .30
*a.* Souvenir sheet of 2 5.00 5.00

Cent. of Intl. Meteorological Cooperation.

King's Ceremonial Robe — A455

Traditional Korean Costumes (Yi dynasty): No. 860, Queen's ceremonial dress. No. 861, King's robe. No. 862, Queen's robe. No. 863, Crown Prince. No. 864, Princess. No. 865, Courtier. No. 866, Royal bridal gown. No. 867, Official's wife. No. 868, Military official.

**1973 Photo.** ***Perf. 13½x13***

**859** A455 10w ocher & multi 3.25 .70
**860** A455 10w salmon & multi 3.25 .70
**861** A455 10w rose lil & multi 3.00 .90
**862** A455 10w apple grn & multi 3.00 .90
**863** A455 10w lt blue & multi 2.75 .90
**864** A455 10w lil rose & multi 2.75 .90
**865** A455 10w yellow & multi 1.35 .50
**866** A455 10w lt blue & multi 1.50 .90
**867** A455 10w ocher & multi 1.50 .90
**868** A455 10w lil rose & multi 1.50 .90
*Nos. 859-868 (10)* 23.85 8.20

Issued: Nos. 859-860, 3/30; Nos. 861-862, 5/30; Nos. 863-864, 7/30; Nos. 865-866, 9/30; Nos. 867-868, 11/30.

**Souvenir Sheets of 2**

| | | | | | |
|---|---|---|---|---|---|
| *859a* | A455 | 10w | (#1) | 7.00 | 7.00 |
| *860a* | A455 | 10w | (#2) | 7.00 | 7.00 |
| *861a* | A455 | 10w | (#3) | 7.50 | 7.50 |
| *862a* | A455 | 10w | (#4) | 7.50 | 7.50 |
| *863a* | A455 | 10w | (#5) | 7.00 | 7.00 |
| *864a* | A455 | 10w | (#6) | 7.00 | 7.00 |
| *865a* | A455 | 10w | (#7) | 4.25 | 4.25 |
| *866a* | A455 | 10w | (#8) | 4.25 | 4.25 |
| *867a* | A455 | 10w | (#9) | 4.25 | 4.25 |
| *868a* | A455 | 10w | (#10) | 4.25 | 4.25 |
| | *Nos. 859a-868a (10)* | | | 60.00 | 60.00 |

Parenthetical numbers after souvenir sheet listings appear in top marginal inscriptions.

Nurse Holding Lamp — A456

**1973, Apr. 1** ***Perf. 13½x13***

**869** A456 10w rose & multi 1.15 .30

50th anniv. of Korean Nurses Association.

Homeland Reservists and Flag — A457

**1973, Apr. 7** ***Perf. 13x13½***

**870** A457 10w yellow & multi 1.35 .30

Homeland Reserve Forces Day on 5th anniversary of their establishment.

Table Tennis Player, and Globe — A458

**1973, May 23** ***Perf. 13x13½***

**871** A458 10w pink & multi 2.25 .65

Victory of Korean women's table tennis team, 32nd Intl. Table Tennis Championships, Sarajevo, Yugoslavia, Apr. 5-15.

World Vision Children's Choir — A459

**1973, June 25** ***Perf. 13x13½***

**872** A459 10w multicolored 1.30 .30

20th anniversary of World Vision International, a Christian service organization.

Converter, Pohang Steel Works — A460

**1973, July 3** ***Perf. 13x13½***

**873** A460 10w blue & multi .95 .45

Inauguration of Pohang iron and steel plant.

INTERPOL Emblem A461

**1973, Sept. 3** ***Perf. 13½x13***

**874** A461 10w lt violet & multi 1.10 .25

50th anniversary of the International Criminal Police Organization (INTERPOL).

Children with Stamp Albums A462

**1973, Oct. 12** ***Perf. 13½x13***

**875** A462 10w dp grn & multi .85 .30
*a.* Souvenir sheet of 2 14.50 14.50

Philatelic Week, Oct. 12-18.

Woman Hurdler — A463

**1973, Oct. 12** ***Perf. 12½x13½***

**876** A463 10w shown 1.10 .30
**877** A463 10w Tennis player 1.10 .30

54th Natl. Athletic Meet, Pusan, Oct. 12-17.

Soyang River Dam, Map Showing Location A464

**1973, Oct. 15** ***Perf. 13½x13***

**878** A464 10w blue & multi .50 .25

Inauguration of Soyang River Dam and hydroelectric plant.

Fire from Match and Cigarette — A465

**1973, Nov. 1** ***Perf. 13x13½***

**879** A465 10w multicolored .65 .25

10th Fire Prevention Day.

Tiger and Candles — A466

Toys — A467

**1973, Dec. 1 Photo.** ***Perf. 13x13½***

**880** A466 10w emerald & multi .95 .30
*a.* Souvenir sheet of 2 4.50 4.50
**881** A467 10w blue & multi .95 .30
*a.* Souvenir sheet of 2 4.50 4.50

New Year 1974.

Human Rights Flame, and Head — A468

**1973, Dec. 10** ***Perf. 13½x13***

**882** A468 10w orange & multi .70 .25

25th anniversary of Universal Declaration of Human Rights.

**Musical Instruments Issue**

Komunko, Six-stringed Zither — A469

Design: 30w, Nagak, shell trumpet.

**1974, Feb. 20 Photo.** ***Perf. 13x13½***

**883** A469 10w lt bl, blk & brn 1.00 .30
**884** A469 30w orange & multi 2.75 .50

**1974, Apr. 20**

Designs: 10w, Tchouk; wooden hammer in slanted box, used to start orchestra. 30w, Eu; crouching tiger, used to stop orchestra.

**885** A469 10w brt blue & multi 1.10 .25
**886** A469 30w lt green & multi 2.25 .35

**1974, June 20**

Designs: 10w, A-chaing, 7-stringed instrument. 30w, Kyobang-ko, drum.

**887** A469 10w dull yel & multi 1.30 .25
**888** A469 30w salmon pink & multi 2.25 .35

**1974, Aug. 20**

Designs: 10w, So, 16-pipe ritual instrument. 30w, Kaikeum, 2-stringed fiddle.

**889** A469 10w lt blue & multi .80 .30
**890** A469 30w brt pink & multi 1.60 .40

**1974, Oct. 20**

10w, Pak (clappers). 30w, Pyenchong (bell chimes).

**891** A469 10w lt lilac & multi .95 .30
**892** A469 30w lemon & multi 1.90 .40
*Nos. 883-892 (10)* 15.90 3.40

**Souvenir Sheets of 2**

| | | | | | |
|---|---|---|---|---|---|
| *883a* | A469 | 10w | (#1) | 4.25 | 4.25 |
| *884a* | A469 | 30w | (#2) | 7.25 | 7.25 |
| *885a* | A469 | 10w | (#3) | 3.50 | 3.50 |
| *886a* | A469 | 30w | (#4) | 5.50 | 5.50 |
| *887a* | A469 | 10w | (#5) | 3.50 | 3.50 |
| *888a* | A469 | 30w | (#6) | 5.50 | 5.50 |
| *889a* | A469 | 10w | (#7) | 2.25 | 2.25 |
| *890a* | A469 | 30w | (#8) | 3.75 | 3.75 |
| *891a* | A469 | 10w | (#9) | 2.75 | 2.75 |
| *892a* | A469 | 30w | (#10) | 5.00 | 5.00 |
| | *Nos. 883a-892a (10)* | | | 43.25 | 43.25 |

**Fruit Issue**

Apricots — A470

**1974, Mar. 30 Photo.** ***Perf. 13x13½***

**893** A470 10w shown .90 .30
**894** A470 30w Strawberries 2.10 .40

**1974, May 30**

**895** A470 10w Peaches .90 .30
**896** A470 30w Grapes 2.10 .45

**1974, July 30**

**897** A470 10w Pears .60 .30
**898** A470 30w Apples 2.00 .45

**1974, Sept. 30**

**899** A470 10w Cherries .75 .30
**900** A470 30w Persimmons 1.90 .45

**1974, Nov. 30**

**901** A470 10w Tangerines .60 .30
**902** A470 30w Chestnuts 1.25 .35
*Nos. 893-902 (10)* 13.10 3.60

**Souvenir Sheets of 2**

| | | | | | |
|---|---|---|---|---|---|
| *893a* | A470 | 10w | (#1) | 3.25 | 3.25 |
| *894a* | A470 | 30w | (#2) | 6.75 | 6.75 |
| *895a* | A470 | 10w | (#3) | 3.25 | 3.25 |
| *896a* | A470 | 30w | (#4) | 6.00 | 6.00 |
| *897a* | A470 | 10w | (#5) | 2.75 | 2.75 |
| *898a* | A470 | 30w | (#6) | 6.50 | 6.50 |
| *899a* | A470 | 10w | (#7) | 2.10 | 2.10 |
| *900a* | A470 | 30w | (#8) | 4.25 | 4.25 |
| *901a* | A470 | 10w | (#9) | 2.40 | 2.40 |
| *902a* | A470 | 30w | (#10) | 3.00 | 3.00 |
| | *Nos. 893a-902a (10)* | | | 40.25 | 40.25 |

Reservist and Factory A471

**1974, Apr. 6 Photo.** ***Perf. 13½x13***

**903** A471 10w yellow & multi .70 .25

Homeland Reserve Forces Day.

WPY Emblem and Scales — A472

**1974, Apr. 10** ***Perf. 13x13½***

**904** A472 10w salmon & multi .55 .25
*a.* Souvenir sheet of 2 4.25 4.25

World Population Year 1974.

Train and Communications Emblem — A473

**1974, Apr. 22** *Perf. 13½x13*
**905** A473 10w multicolored .65 .25

19th Communications Day.

Emblem and Stylized Globe — A474

**1974, May 6** **Photo.** *Perf. 13*
**906** A474 10w red lilac & multi .55 .25

22nd Session of Intl. Chamber of Commerce (Eastern Division), Seoul, May 6-8.

New Dock at Inchon A475

**1974, May 10**
**907** A475 10w yellow & multi .65 .25

Dedication of dock, Inchon.

UNESCO Emblem, "20" and Yin Yang — A476

**1974, June 14** **Photo.** *Perf. 13*
**908** A476 10w org yel & multi .55 .25

20th anniversary of the Korean National Commission for UNESCO.

EXPLO '74 Emblems — A477

Design: No. 910, EXPLO emblem rising from map of Korea.

**1974, Aug. 13** **Photo.** *Perf. 13*
**909** A477 10w orange & multi .50 .25
**910** A477 10w blue & multi .50 .25

EXPLO '74, International Christian Congress, Yoido Islet, Seoul, Aug. 13-18.

Subway, Bus and Plane — A478

**1974, Aug. 15**
**911** A478 10w green & multi .80 .25

Inauguration of Seoul subway (first in Korea), Aug. 15, 1974.

Target Shooting — A479

**1974, Oct. 8** **Photo.** *Perf. 13x13½*
**912** A479 10w shown .55 .25
**913** A479 30w Rowing 1.75 .40

55th National Athletic Meet.

UPU Emblem A480

**1974, Oct. 9** *Perf. 13*
**914** A480 10w yellow & multi .45 .25
*a.* Souvenir sheet of 2 4.50 4.50

Cent. of UPU. See No. C43.

International Landmarks — A481

**1974, Oct. 11**
**915** A481 10w multicolored .55 .25

Intl. People to People Conf., Seoul, 10/11-14.

Korea Nos. 1-2 — A482

**1974, Oct. 17**
**916** A482 10w lilac & multi .70 .25
*a.* Souvenir sheet of 2 7.25 7.25

Philatelic Week, Oct. 17-23 and 90th anniversary of first Korean postage stamps.

Taekwondo and Kukkiwon Center A483

**1974, Oct. 18**
**917** A483 10w yellow grn & multi .55 .25

First Asian Taekwondo (self-defense) Games, Seoul, Oct. 18-20.

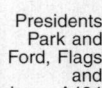

Presidents Park and Ford, Flags and Globe — A484

**1974, Nov. 22** **Photo.** *Perf. 13*
**918** A484 10y multicolored .95 .30
*a.* Souvenir sheet of 2 7.50 7.50

Visit of Pres. Gerald R. Ford to South Korea.

Yook Young Soo — A485

**1974, Nov. 29**
**919** A485 10w green .95 .30
**920** A485 10w orange .95 .30
**921** A485 10w lilac .95 .30
**922** A485 10w blue .95 .30
*a.* Souvenir sheet of 4, #919-922 32.00 32.00
*b.* Block of 4, #919-922 3.75 3.00

Yook Young Soo (1925-1974), wife of Pres. Park.

Rabbits — A486

Good-luck Purse — A487

**1974, Dec. 1** **Litho.** *Perf. 12½x13*
**923** A486 10w multicolored .70 .25
*a.* Souvenir sheet of 2 4.00 4.00
**924** A487 10w multicolored .70 .25
*a.* Souvenir sheet of 2 4.00 4.00

New Year 1975.

Good-luck Key and Pigeon A488

**1975, Jan. 1** **Photo.** *Perf. 13*
**925** A488 10w lt blue & multi .55 .25

Introduction of Natl. Welfare Insurance System.

UPU Emblem and "75" — A489

UPU Emblem and Paper Plane — A490

**1975, Jan. 1**
**926** A489 10w yellow & multi .55 .25
**927** A490 10w lt blue & multi .55 .25

75th anniv. of Korea's membership in UPU.

Dr. Albert Schweitzer, Map of Africa, Hypodermic Needle A491

**1975, Jan. 14**
**928** A491 10w olive .95 .35
**929** A491 10w brt rose .95 .35
**930** A491 10w orange .95 .35
**931** A491 10w brt green .95 .35
*a.* Block of 4, #928-931 4.75 3.00

### Folk Dance Issue

Dancer — A492

No. 933, Dancer with fan.

**1975, Feb. 20** **Photo.** *Perf. 13*
**932** A492 10w emerald & multi .70 .25
**933** A492 10w brt blue & multi .70 .25

No. 934, Woman with butterfly sleeves. No. 935, Group of Women.

**1975, Apr. 20**
**934** A492 10w yel grn & multi .70 .25
**935** A492 10w yellow & multi .70 .25

No. 936, Pongsan mask dance. No. 937, Pusan mask dance.

**1975, June 20**
**936** A492 10w pink & multi .70 .25
**937** A492 10w blue & multi .70 .25

No. 938, Buddhist drum dance. No. 939, Bara (cymbals) dance.

**1975, Aug. 20**
**938** A492 20w yellow & multi 1.25 .40
**939** A492 20w salmon & multi 1.25 .40

Bupo Nori — A492a

No. 940, Sogo dance.

**1975, Oct. 20**
**940** A492 20w blue & multi 1.35 .40
**941** A492a 20w yellow & multi 1.35 .40
*Nos. 932-941 (10)* 9.40 3.10

### Souvenir Sheets of 2

| | | | | | |
|---|---|---|---|---|---|
| *932a* | A492 | 10w | (#1) | 1.75 | 1.75 |
| *933a* | A492 | 10w | (#2) | 1.75 | 1.75 |
| *934a* | A492 | 10w | (#3) | 1.60 | 1.60 |
| *935a* | A492 | 10w | (#4) | 1.60 | 1.60 |
| *936a* | A492 | 10w | (#5) | 1.60 | 1.60 |
| *937a* | A492 | 10w | (#6) | 1.60 | 1.60 |
| *938a* | A492 | 20w | (#7) | 2.50 | 2.50 |
| *939a* | A492 | 20w | (#8) | 2.50 | 2.50 |
| *940a* | A492 | 20w | (#9) | 2.50 | 2.50 |
| *941a* | A492 | 20w | (#10) | 2.50 | 2.50 |
| | *Nos. 932a-941a (10)* | | | 19.90 | 19.90 |

Globe and Rotary Emblem A493

**1975, Feb. 23**
**942** A493 10w multicolored .60 .25

Rotary International, 70th anniversary.

Women and IWY Emblem A494

**1975, Mar. 8**
**943** A494 10w multicolored .60 .25

International Women's Year 1975.

## Flower Issue

Violets
A495

Anemones
A496

**1975, Mar. 15**

| | | | |
|---|---|---|---|
| **944** A495 10w orange & multi | .65 | .25 |
| **945** A496 10w yellow & multi | .65 | .25 |

Clematis
Patens — A496a

No. 946, Rhododendron.

**1975, May 15**

| | | |
|---|---|---|
| **946** A495 10w dk grn & multi | .75 | .25 |
| **947** A496a 10w yel grn & multi | .75 | .25 |

No. 948, Thistle. No. 949, Iris.

**1975, July 15**

| | | |
|---|---|---|
| **948** A495 10w emerald & multi | .75 | .25 |
| **949** A495 10w blue & multi | .75 | .25 |

Broad-bell
Flowers — A496b

No. 951, Bush clover.

**1975, Sept. 15**

| | | |
|---|---|---|
| **950** A496b 20w yellow & multi | 1.30 | .30 |
| **951** A495 20w blue grn & multi | 1.25 | .30 |

No. 952, Camellia. No. 953, Gentian.

**1975, Nov. 15**

| | | |
|---|---|---|
| **952** A495 20w yellow & multi | 1.90 | 1.45 |
| **953** A496 20w salmon & multi | 1.75 | .45 |
| *Nos. 944-953 (10)* | 10.50 | 4.00 |

Forest and Water Resources — A497

**1975, Mar. 20**

| | | |
|---|---|---|
| **954** A497 Strip of 4 | 4.50 | 3.00 |
| *a.* 10w Saemaeul forest | .70 | .30 |
| *b.* 10w Dam and reservoir | .70 | .30 |
| *c.* 10w Green forest | .70 | .30 |
| *d.* 10w Timber industry | .70 | .30 |

Natl. Tree Planting Month, Mar. 21-Apr. 20.

Map of Korea, HRF
Emblem — A498

**1975, Apr. 12 Photo. *Perf. 13***

| | | |
|---|---|---|
| **955** A498 10w blue & multi | .65 | .25 |

Homeland Reserve Forces Day.

Lily — A499

Ceramic
Jar — A500

Ceramic Vase
A501

Adm. Li Sun-sin
A502

**1975 Photo. *Perf. 13½x13***

| | | |
|---|---|---|
| **963** A499 6w green & bl grn | .55 | .25 |
| **964** A500 50w gray grn & brn | .75 | .25 |
| **965** A501 60w brown & yellow | .95 | .25 |
| **966** A502 100w carmine | 2.25 | .50 |
| *Nos. 963-966 (4)* | 4.50 | 1.25 |

Issued: Nos. 964-965, 3/15/75; Nos. 963, 966, 10/10/75.

Metric
System
Symbols
A507

**1975, May 20 *Perf. 13***

| | | |
|---|---|---|
| **975** A507 10w salmon & multi | .60 | .25 |

Centenary of International Meter Convention, Paris, 1875.

Praying
Soldier,
Incense
Burner
A508

**1975, June 6 Photo. *Perf. 13***

| | | |
|---|---|---|
| **976** A508 10w multicolored | .55 | .25 |

20th Memorial Day.

Flags of
Korea, UN
and
US — A509

Designs (Flags of): No. 978, Ethiopia, France, Greece, Canada, South Africa. No. 979, Luxembourg, Australia, Great Britain, Colombia, Turkey. No. 980, Netherlands, Belgium, Philippines, New Zealand, Thailand.

**1975, June 25 Photo. *Perf. 13***

| | | |
|---|---|---|
| **977** A509 10w dk blue & multi | .70 | .30 |
| **978** A509 10w dk blue & multi | .70 | .30 |
| **979** A509 10w dk blue & multi | .70 | .30 |
| **980** A509 10w dk blue & multi | .70 | .30 |
| *a.* Strip of 4, #977-980 | 4.00 | 2.75 |

25th anniv. of beginning of Korean War.

Presidents
Park and
Bongo, Flags
of Korea and
Gabon
A510

**1975, July 5**

| | | |
|---|---|---|
| **981** A510 10w blue & multi | .60 | .25 |
| *a.* Souvenir sheet of 2 | 2.75 | 2.75 |

Visit of Pres. Albert Bongo of Gabon, 7/5-8.

Scout Emblem,
Tents and
Neckerchief — A511

**1975, July 29 Photo. *Perf. 13***

| | | |
|---|---|---|
| **982** A511 10w shown | .80 | .30 |
| **983** A511 10w Pick and oath | .80 | .30 |
| **984** A511 10w Tents | .80 | .30 |
| **985** A511 10w Ax, rope and tree | .80 | .30 |
| **986** A511 10w Campfire | .80 | .30 |
| *a.* Strip of 5, #982-986 | 4.75 | 3.50 |

Nordjamb 75, 14th Boy Scout Jamboree, Lillehammer, Norway, July 29-Aug. 7.

Flame and
Broken Chain
A512

Balloons with
Symbols of
Development
over
Map — A513

**1975, Aug. 15 *Perf. 13½x13***

| | | |
|---|---|---|
| **987** A512 20w gold & multi | .75 | .25 |
| **988** A513 20w silver & multi | .75 | .25 |

30th anniversary of liberation.

Taekwondo — A514

**1975, Aug. 26 *Perf. 13***

| | | |
|---|---|---|
| **989** A514 20w multicolored | .60 | .25 |

2nd World Taekwondo Championships, Seoul, Aug. 25-Sept. 1.

National
Assembly and
Emblem
A515

**1975, Sept. 1 Photo. *Perf. 13½x13***

| | | |
|---|---|---|
| **990** A515 20w multicolored | .60 | .25 |

Completion of National Assembly Building.

Convention
Emblem and
Dump
Truck — A516

**1975, Sept. 7 Photo. *Perf. 13½x13***

| | | |
|---|---|---|
| **991** A516 20w ultra & multi | .60 | .25 |

14th Convention of the Intl. Fed. of Asian and Western Pacific Contractors.

Cassegrainian
Telescope
and Morse
Key — A517

**1975, Sept. 28**

| | | |
|---|---|---|
| **992** A517 20w red lil, org & blk | .60 | .25 |

90th anniversary of Korean telecommunications system.

Stalactite
Cave,
Yeongweol
A518

View of Mt.
Sorak
A519

**1975, Sept. 28**

| | | |
|---|---|---|
| **993** A518 20w multicolored | .65 | .25 |
| **994** A519 20w multicolored | .65 | .25 |

International Tourism Day.

Armed Forces Flag
and
Missiles — A519a

**1975, Oct. 1 Photo. *Perf. 13***

| | | |
|---|---|---|
| **994A** A519a 20w multicolored | .60 | .25 |

Armed Forces Day.

Gymnastics
A520

Handball
A521

**1975, Oct. 7 Photo. *Perf. 13***

| | | |
|---|---|---|
| **995** A520 20w yellow & multi | .50 | .25 |
| **996** A521 20w multicolored | .50 | .25 |

56th Natl. Athletic Meet, Taegu, Oct. 7-12.

Stamp Collecting Kangaroo — A522

**1975, Oct. 8**
**997** A522 20w multicolored .60 .25

Philatelic Week, Oct. 8-14.

Hands and UN Emblem — A523

**1975, Oct. 24**
**998** A523 20w multicolored .60 .25

United Nations, 30th anniversary.

Red Cross and Activities — A524

**1975, Oct. 30**
**999** A524 20w orange, red & brn .60 .25

Korean Red Cross, 70th anniversary.

Emblem and Dove — A525

**1975, Nov. 30 Photo. *Perf. 13***
**1000** A525 20w multicolored .60 .25

Asian Parliamentary Union, 10th anniv.

Children Playing — A526

Dragon — A527

**1975, Dec. 1**
**1001** A526 20w multicolored .65 .25
*a.* Souvenir sheet of 2 1.90 1.90
**1002** A527 20w multicolored .65 .25
*a.* Souvenir sheet of 2 1.90 1.90

New Year 1976.

Inchong-Bukpyong Railroad — A528

**1975, Dec. 5 Photo. *Perf. 13***
**1003** A528 20w multicolored .60 .25

Opening of electric cross-country railroad.

**Butterfly Issue**

Dilipa Fenestra A529

Butterflies: No. 1005, Luehdorfia puziloi.

**1976, Jan. 20 Photo. *Perf. 13***
**1004** A529 20w dp rose & multi 1.60 .30
**1005** A529 20w dp blue & multi 1.60 .30

Butterflies: No. 1006, Papilio xuthus linne. No. 1007, Parnassius bremeri.

**1976, Mar. 20**
**1006** A529 20w yellow & multi 1.60 .30
**1007** A529 20w yel grn & multi 1.60 .30

Byasa Alcinous Klug — A529a

Butterflies: No. 1008, Colias erate esper.

**1976, June 20**
**1008** A529 20w lt violet & multi 1.50 .30
**1009** A529a 20w citron & multi 1.50 .30

Graphium Sarpedon A529b

Butterflies: No. 1010, Hestina assimilis.

**1976, Aug. 20**
**1010** A529 20w tan & multi 2.00 .70
**1011** A529b 20w lt gray & multi 1.90 .70

Fabriciana Nerippe A529c

Nymphalis Xanthomelas A529d

**1976, Oct. 20**
**1012** A529c 20w lt grn & multi 2.60 .80
**1013** A529d 20w lilac & multi 2.60 .80
*Nos. 1004-1013 (10)* 18.50 4.80

Emblems of Science, Industry and KIST — A530

**1976, Feb. 10 Photo. *Perf. 13***
**1014** A530 20w multicolored .60 .25

Korean Institute of Science and Technology (KIST), 10th anniversary.

**Birds Issue**

A531

A532

No. 1015, Siberian Bustard. No. 1016, White-naped Crane.

**1976, Feb. 20 Photo. *Perf. 13x13½***
**1015** A531 20w multicolored 1.25 .35
**1016** A532 20w multicolored 1.25 .35

A532a

A532b

No. 1017, Blue-winged pitta. No. 1018, Tristam's woodpecker.

**1976, May 20**
**1017** A532a 20w multicolored 1.25 .35
**1018** A532b 20w multicolored 1.25 .35

A532c

A532d

No. 1019, Wood pigeon. No. 1020, Oyster catcher.

**1976, July 20**
**1019** A532c 20w multicolored 1.25 .35
**1020** A532d 20w multicolored 1.25 .35

A532e

A532f

No. 1021, Black-faced spoonbill. No. 1022, Black stork.

**1976, Sept. 20**
**1021** A532e 20w multicolored 1.25 .35
**1022** A532f 20w multicolored 1.25 .35

A532g

A532h

No. 1023, Whooper swan. No. 1024, Black vulture.

**1976, Nov. 20**
**1023** A532g 20w multicolored 3.25 1.15
**1024** A532h 20w multicolored 3.25 1.15
*Nos. 1015-1024 (10)* 16.50 5.10

1876 and 1976 Telephones, Globe — A533

**1976, Mar. 10**
**1025** A533 20w multicolored .60 .25

Centenary of first telephone call by Alexander Graham Bell, Mar. 10, 1876.

Homeland Reserves A534

**1976, Apr. 3 Photo. *Perf. 13½x13***
**1026** A534 20w multicolored .60 .25

8th Homeland Reserve Forces Day.

"People and Eye" — A535

**1976, Apr. 7 *Perf. 13x13½***
**1027** A535 20w multicolored .60 .25

World Health Day; "Foresight prevents blindness."

Pres. Park, New Village Movement Flag — A536

Intellectual Pursuits — A537

No. 1030, Village improvement. No. 1031, Agriculture. No. 1032, Income from production.

**1976, Apr. 22**
**1028** A536 20w shown 1.45 .45
**1029** A537 20w shown 1.45 .45
**1030** A537 20w multicolored 1.45 .45
**1031** A537 20w multicolored 1.45 .45
**1032** A537 20w multicolored 1.45 .45
*a.* Strip of 5, #1028-1032 10.00 6.00

6th anniv. of Pres. Park's New Village Movement for National Prosperity.

Mohenjo-Daro A538

**1976, May 1** *Perf. 13½x13*

**1033** A538 20w multicolored .60 .25

UNESCO campaign to save the Mohenjo-Daro excavations in Pakistan.

13-Star and 50-Star Flags — A539

American Bicentennial (Bicentennial Emblem and): No. 1035, Statue of Liberty. No. 1036, Map of US and Mt. Rushmore monument. No. 1037, Liberty Bell. No. 1038, First astronaut on moon.

**1976, May 8** *Perf. 13x13½*

**1034** A539 100w blk, dp bl & red 2.60 .85
*a.* Souvenir sheet of 1 5.50 5.50
**1035** A539 100w blk, dp bl & red 2.60 .85
**1036** A539 100w blk, dp bl & red 2.60 .85
**1037** A539 100w blk, dp bl & red 2.60 .85
**1038** A539 100w blk, dp bl & red 2.60 .85
*Nos. 1034-1038 (5)* 13.00 4.25

Girl Scouts, Campfire and Emblem — A540

**1976, May 10**

**1039** A540 20w orange & multi 1.00 .25

Korean Federation of Girl Scouts, 30th anniv.

Stupas, Buddha of Borobudur — A541

**1976, June 10**

**1040** A541 20w multicolored .60 .25

UNESCO campaign to save the Borobudur Temple, Java.

"Life Insurance" — A542

**1976, July 1 Photo.** *Perf. 13x13½*

**1041** A542 20w multicolored .60 .25

National Life Insurance policies: "Over 100 billion-won," Apr. 30, 1976.

Volleyball — A543

**1976, July 17**

**1042** A543 20w shown .50 .25
**1043** A543 20w Boxing .50 .25

21st Olympic Games, Montreal, Canada, July 17-Aug. 1.

Children and Books A544

**1976, Aug. 10** *Perf. 13½x13*

**1044** A544 20w brown & multi .60 .25

Books for children.

Civil Defense Corps, Flag and Members — A545

**1976, Sept. 15** *Perf. 13x13½*

**1045** A545 20w multicolored .60 .25

Civil Defense Corps, first anniversary.

Chamsungdan, Mani Mountain — A546

Front Gate, Tongdosa Temple A547

**1976, Sept. 28** *Perf. 13½x13*

**1046** A546 20w multicolored .70 .25
**1047** A547 20w multicolored .70 .25

International Tourism Day.

Cadets and Academy A548

**1976, Oct. 1**

**1048** A548 20w multicolored .60 .25

Korean Military Academy, 30th anniversary.

Leaves and Stones, by Cheong Ju — A549

**1976, Oct. 5** *Perf. 13x13½*

**1049** A549 20w blk, gray & red .60 .25
*a.* Souvenir sheet of 2 4.25 4.25

Philatelic Week, Oct. 5-11.

Snake-headed Figure, Bas-relief A550

Door-pull and Cranes A551

**1976, Dec. 1 Photo.** *Perf. 13x13½*

**1050** A550 20w multicolored .60 .25
*a.* Souvenir sheet of 2 2.25 2.25
**1051** A551 20w multicolored .60 .25
*a.* Souvenir sheet of 2 2.25 2.25

New Year 1977.

Arrows, Cogwheels, Worker at Lathe — A552

No. 1053, Arrows, Cogwheels, ship in dock.

**1977, Jan. 20 Photo.** *Perf. 13½x13*

**1052** A552 20w multicolored .60 .25
**1053** A552 20w multicolored .60 .25

4th Economic Development Five-Year Plan.

Satellite Antenna and Microwaves — A553

**1977, Jan. 31** *Perf. 13x13½*

**1054** A553 20w multicolored .60 .25

Membership in ITU, 25th anniv.

Korean Broadcasting Center A554

**1977, Feb. 16** *Perf. 13½x13*

**1055** A554 20w multicolored .60 .25

50th anniversary of broadcasting in Korea.

Parents and Two Children — A555

**1977, Apr. 1 Photo.** *Perf. 13½x13*

**1056** A555 20w brt grn & orange 2.10 .25

Family planning.

Reservist on Duty — A556

**1977, Apr. 2** *Perf. 13x13½*

**1057** A556 20w multicolored .60 .25

9th Homeland Reserve Forces Day.

Head with Symbols — A557

**1977, Apr. 21 Photo.** *Perf. 13x13½*

**1058** A557 20w dp lilac & multi .60 .25

10th anniversary of Science Day.

Book, Map, Syringe A558

**1977, Apr. 25**

**1059** A558 20w blue & multi .60 .25

35th Intl. Meeting on Military Medicine.

Boy with Flowers and Dog — A559

**1977, May 5**

**1060** A559 20w multicolored .60 .25

Proclamation of Children's Charter, 20th anniversary.

Veteran's Emblem and Flag — A560

**1977, May 8**

**1061** A560 20w multicolored .60 .25

25th anniversary of Korean Veterans' Day.

Buddha, 8th Century, Sokkulam Grotto — A561

**1977, May 25 Photo.** *Perf. 13x13½*

**1062** A561 20w sepia & olive .55 .25
*a.* Souvenir sheet of 2 4.50 4.50

"2600th" anniversary of birth of Buddha.

## Ceramic Issues

Jar with Grape Design, 17th Century — A562

Celadon Vase, Bamboo Design, 12th Century — A563

**1977, Mar. 15 Photo.** ***Perf. 13x13½***

| | | | | | |
|---|---|---|---|---|---|
| **1063** | A562 | 20w vio brn & multi | | 1.75 | .30 |
| **1064** | A563 | 20w gray, grn & bis | | 1.75 | .30 |

Celadon Jar with Peonies A564

Vase with Willow Reed Peony Pattern — A565

***Perf. 13x13½, 13½x13***

**1977, June 15** **Photo.**

| | | | | |
|---|---|---|---|---|
| **1065** | A564 | 20w multicolored | .95 | .30 |
| **1066** | A565 | 20w multicolored | .95 | .30 |

Celadon Manshaped Wine Jug — A566

Celadon Melon-shaped Vase — A567

**1977, July 15**

| | | | | |
|---|---|---|---|---|
| **1067** | A566 | 20w multicolored | .90 | .25 |
| **1068** | A567 | 20w multicolored | .90 | .25 |

**1977, Aug. 15**

Designs: No. 1069, White porcelain bowl with inlaid lotus vine design. No. 1070, Black Koryo ware vase with plum blossom vine.

| | | | | |
|---|---|---|---|---|
| **1069** | A564 | 20w multicolored | .90 | .25 |
| **1070** | A565 | 20w multicolored | .90 | .25 |

Punch'ong Jar — A568

Celadon Cylindrical Vase — A569

**1977, Nov. 15**

| | | | | |
|---|---|---|---|---|
| **1071** | A568 | 20w multicolored | .85 | .25 |
| **1072** | A569 | 20w multicolored | .85 | .25 |
| | | *Nos. 1063-1072 (10)* | 10.70 | 2.70 |

### Types of 1962-66 Designs as Before

**1976-77 Litho.** ***Perf. 12½***

**Granite Paper**

| | | | | |
|---|---|---|---|---|
| **1076** | A187 | 200w brn & lt grn | *25.00* | *7.00* |
| **1077** | A187a | 300w sl grn & sal ('76) | *50.00* | *8.00* |
| **1078** | A187a | 300w brn & sal | *50.00* | *8.00* |
| **1079** | A187a | 500w pur & lt grn | *100.00* | *10.00* |

Magpie A570

Nature Protection A571

"Family Planning" A572

Children on Swing A573

Ceramic Horseman A574

Muryangsu Hall, Busok Temple A575

Pagoda, Pobjusa Temple A576

Gold Crown, from Chonmachong Mound A577

Monster Mask Tile, 6th or 7th Century — A578

Flying Angels from Bronze Bell from Sangwon-sa, 725 A.D. — A579

***Perf. 12½x13½, 13½x12½***

**1977-79** **Photo.**

| | | | | |
|---|---|---|---|---|
| **1088** | A570 | 3w lt blue & blk | .60 | .25 |
| **1090** | A326 | 10w emer & blk | .55 | .25 |
| **1091** | A571 | 20w multicolored | .65 | .25 |
| **1092** | A572 | 20w emer & blk ('78) | 1.00 | .25 |
| **1093** | A573 | 20w grn & org ('79) | .45 | .25 |
| **1097** | A574 | 80w lt brn & sep | 1.60 | .35 |
| **1099** | A575 | 200w salmon & brn | 1.75 | .50 |
| **1100** | A576 | 300w brn purple | 2.25 | .60 |
| **1101** | A577 | 500w multicolored | 25.00 | 1.35 |

***Perf. 13½x13***

| | | | | |
|---|---|---|---|---|
| **1102** | A578 | 500w brown & pur | 13.50 | 1.00 |

***Perf. 13***

| | | | | |
|---|---|---|---|---|
| **1103** | A579 | 1000w slate grn ('78) | 7.75 | 1.20 |
| | | *Nos. 1088-1103 (11)* | 55.10 | 6.25 |

Ulleung Island — A580

Design: No. 1105, Haeundae Beach.

**1977, Sept. 28 Photo.** ***Perf. 13***

| | | | | |
|---|---|---|---|---|
| **1104** | A580 | 20w multicolored | .60 | .25 |
| **1105** | A580 | 20w multicolored | .60 | .25 |

World Tourism Day.

Armed Forces Day — A581

**1977, Oct. 1 Photo.** ***Perf. 13***

| | | | | |
|---|---|---|---|---|
| **1106** | A581 | 20w green & multi | .60 | .25 |

Mt. Inwang after the Rain, by Chung Seon (1676-1759) — A582

**1977, Oct. 4**

| | | | | |
|---|---|---|---|---|
| **1107** | | 20w mountain, clouds | .85 | .25 |
| **1108** | | 20w mountain, house | .85 | .25 |
| *a.* | | Souvenir sheet of 2 | 7.50 | 7.50 |
| *b.* | | A582 Pair, #1107-1108 | 2.00 | 1.50 |

Philatelic Week, Oct. 4-10.

Rotary Emblem on Bronze Bell, Koryo Dynasty — A584

**1977, Nov. 10 Photo.** ***Perf. 13***

| | | | | |
|---|---|---|---|---|
| **1109** | A584 | 20w multicolored | .55 | .25 |

Korean Rotary Club, 50th anniversary.

Korean Flag on Mt. Everest A585

**1977, Nov. 11**

| | | | | |
|---|---|---|---|---|
| **1110** | A585 | 20w multicolored | .85 | .25 |

Korean Mt. Everest Expedition, reached peak, Sept. 15, 1977.

Children and Kites A586

Horse-headed Figure, Bas-relief A587

**1977, Dec. 1 Photo.** ***Perf. 13***

| | | | | |
|---|---|---|---|---|
| **1111** | A586 | 20w multicolored | .40 | .25 |
| *a.* | | Souvenir sheet of 2 | 2.00 | 2.00 |
| **1112** | A587 | 20w multicolored | .40 | .25 |
| *a.* | | Souvenir sheet of 2 | 2.00 | 2.00 |

New Year 1978.

Clay Pigeon Shooting A588

Designs: No. 1114, Air pistol shooting. No. 1115, Air rifle shooting and target.

**1977, Dec. 3**

| | | | | |
|---|---|---|---|---|
| **1113** | A588 | 20w multicolored | .50 | .25 |
| *a.* | | Souvenir sheet of 2 ('78) | 4.00 | 4.00 |
| **1114** | A588 | 20w multicolored | .50 | .25 |
| *a.* | | Souvenir sheet of 2 ('78) | 4.00 | 4.00 |
| **1115** | A588 | 20w multicolored | .50 | .25 |
| *a.* | | Souvenir sheet of 2 ('78) | 4.00 | 4.00 |
| | | *Nos. 1113-1115 (3)* | 1.50 | .75 |
| | | *Nos. 1113a-1115a (3)* | 12.00 | |

42nd World Shooting Championships, Seoul, 1978.

Boeing 727 over Globe, ICAO Emblem A589

**1977, Dec. 11**

| | | | | |
|---|---|---|---|---|
| **1116** | A589 | 20w multicolored | .55 | .25 |

25th anniv. of Korea's membership in the ICAO.

Plane, Cargo, Freighter and Globe A590

**1977, Dec. 22 Photo.** ***Perf. 13***

| | | | | |
|---|---|---|---|---|
| **1117** | A590 | 20w multicolored | .55 | .25 |

Korean exports.

Ships and World Map — A591

**1978, Mar. 13 Photo.** ***Perf. 13***

| | | | | |
|---|---|---|---|---|
| **1118** | A591 | 20w multicolored | .55 | .25 |

Maritime Day.

### Stone Pagoda Issue

Four Lions Pagoda, Hwaom-sa — A592

Seven-storied Pagoda, T'appyongri — A592a

**1978, Mar. 20 Photo.** ***Perf. 13***

| | | | | |
|---|---|---|---|---|
| **1119** | A592 | 20w lt green & multi | 1.25 | .30 |
| **1120** | A592a | 20w ocher & multi | 1.25 | .30 |

Punhwang-sa Temple A593

Miruk-sa Temple — A593a

**1978, May 20**

**1121** A593 20w lt green & blk 1.25 .30
**1122** A593a 20w grn, brn & yel 1.25 .30

Tabo Pagoda, Pulguk-sa — A592b

Three-storied pagoda, Pulguk-sa — A592c

**1978, June 20**

**1123** A592b 20w gray, lt grn & blk .95 .25
**1124** A592c 20w lilac & black .95 .25

Kyongch'on sa Temple — A594

Octagonal Pagoda, Wolchong-sa Temple — A594a

**1978, July 20** ***Perf. 13½x12½***

**1125** A594 20w gray & brn 1.60 .30
**1126** A594a 20w lt green & blk 1.60 .30

13-storied Pagoda, Jeonghye-sa — A592d

Three-storied Pagoda, Jinjeon-sa — A592e

**1978, Nov. 20** ***Perf. 13x13½***

**1127** A592d 20w pale grn & multi .55 .25
**1128** A592e 20w lilac & multi .55 .25
*Nos. 1119-1128 (10)* 11.20 2.80

Ants and Coins — A595

**1978, Apr. 1**

**1129** A595 20w multicolored .55 .25

Importance of saving.

Reservist with Flag — A596

**1978, Apr. 1**

**1130** A596 20w multicolored .55 .25

10th Homeland Reserve Forces Day.

Seoul Cultural Center A597

**1978, Apr. 1**

**1131** A597 20w multicolored .75 .25

Opening of Seoul Cultural Center.

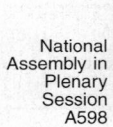

National Assembly in Plenary Session A598

**1978, May 31**

**1132** A598 20w multicolored .55 .25

30th anniversary of National Assembly.

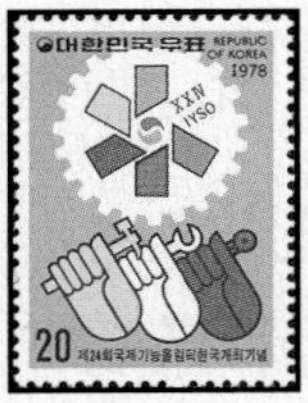

Hands Holding Tools, Competition Emblem — A599

**1978, Aug. 5** **Photo.** ***Perf. 13***

**1133** A599 20w multicolored .55 .25
*a.* Souvenir sheet of 2 3.25 3.25

24th World Youth Skill Olympics, Busan, Aug. 30-Sept. 15.

Bell of Joy and Crater Lake, Mt. Baegdu — A600

**1978, Aug. 15**

**1134** A600 20w multicolored .55 .25

Founding of republic, 30th anniversary.

Nurse, Badge and Flowers — A601

**1978, Aug. 26**

**1135** A601 20w multicolored .55 .25

Army Nurse Corps, 30th anniversary.

Sobaeksan Observatory A602

**1978, Sept. 13** **Photo.** ***Perf. 13***

**1136** A602 20w multicolored .55 .25

Opening of Sobaeksan Natl. Observatory.

Kyunghoeru Pavilion, Kyongbok Palace, Seoul A603

Design: No. 1138, Baeg Do (island).

**1978, Sept. 28**

**1137** A603 20w multicolored .45 .25
**1138** A603 20w multicolored .45 .25

Tourist publicity.

Customs Flag and Officers A604

**1978, Sept. 28**

**1139** A604 20w multicolored .45 .25

Cent. of 1st Korean Custom House, Busan.

Armed Forces A605

**1978, Oct. 1** **Photo.** ***Perf. 13***

**1140** A605 20w multicolored .45 .25

Armed Forces, 30th anniversary.

Clay Figurines, Silla Dynasty — A606

**1978, Oct. 1**

**1141** A606 20w lt green & blk .45 .25

Culture Month, October 1978.

Portrait of a Lady, by Shin Yoon-bok — A607

**1978, Oct. 24**

**1142** A607 20w multicolored .50 .25
*a.* Souvenir sheet of 2 3.50 3.50

Philatelic Week, Oct. 24-29.

Young Men, YMCA Emblem A608

**1978, Oct. 28**

**1143** A608 20w multicolored .45 .25

75th anniv. of founding of Korean YMCA.

Hand Protecting Against Fire — A609

**1978, Nov. 1** **Photo.** ***Perf. 13***

**1144** A609 20w multicolored .45 .25

Fire Prevention Day, Nov. 1.

Winter Landscape A610

Ram-headed Figure, Bas-relief A611

**1978, Dec. 1** **Photo.** ***Perf. 13x13½***

**1145** A610 20w multicolored .55 .25
*a.* Souvenir sheet of 2 1.75 1.75
**1146** A611 20w multicolored .55 .25
*a.* Souvenir sheet of 2 1.75 1.75

New Year 1979.

Hibiscus, Students, Globe — A612

**1978, Dec. 5**

**1147** A612 20w multicolored .45 .25

Proclamation of National Education Charter, 10th anniversary.

President Park — A613

**1978, Dec. 27**

**1148** A613 20w multicolored 1.00 .25
*a.* Souvenir sheet of 2 11.00 11.00

Inauguration of Park Chung Hee for fifth term as president.

### Nature Conservation Issue

Golden Mandarinfish A614

Lace-bark Pines A615

**1979, Feb. 20 Photo.** ***Perf. 13x13½***

**1149** A614 20w multicolored 1.60 .25
**1150** A615 20w multicolored 1.60 .25

Mandarin Ducks — A616

Neofinettia Orchid — A617

**1979, May 20**

**1151** A616 20w multicolored 1.60 .25
**1152** A617 20w multicolored 1.60 .25

Goral — A618

Lilies of the Valley — A619

**1979, June 20**

**1153** A618 20w multicolored 1.60 .25
**1154** A619 20w multicolored 1.60 .25

Rain Frog A620

Asian Polypody A621

**1979, Nov. 25**

**1155** A620 20w multicolored 1.60 .25
**1156** A621 20w multicolored 1.60 .25

Firefly — A622

Meesun Tree — A623

**1980, Jan. 20**

**1157** A622 30w multicolored 1.60 .25
**1158** A623 30w multicolored 1.60 .25
*Nos. 1149-1158 (10)* 16.00 2.50

Samil Monument — A624

**1979, Mar. 1 Photo.** ***Perf. 13x13½***

**1159** A624 20w multicolored .45 .25

Samil independence movement, 60th anniv.

Worker and Bulldozer A625

**1979, Mar. 10** ***Perf. 13½x13***

**1160** A625 20w multicolored .45 .25

Labor Day.

Hand Holding Tools, Gun and Grain — A626

**1979, Apr. 1** ***Perf. 13x13½***

**1161** A626 20w multicolored .45 .25

Strengthening national security.

Tabo Pagoda, Pulguk-sa Temple — A627

Women, Silk Screen — A628

Art Treasures: No. 1163, Statue. No. 1164, Crown. No. 1165, Celadon Vase.

**1979, Apr. 1**

**1162** A627 20w gray bl & multi .55 .25
**1163** A627 20w bister & multi .55 .25
**1164** A627 20w violet & multi .55 .25
**1165** A627 20w brt grn & multi .55 .25
**1166** A628 60w multicolored .90 .30
*a.* Souvenir sheet of 2 3.75 3.75
*Nos. 1162-1166 (5)* 3.10 1.30

5000 years of Korean art.
See Nos. 1175-1179, 1190.

Pulguk-sa Temple and PATA Emblem A629

**1979, Apr. 16** ***Perf. 13½x13***

**1167** A629 20w multicolored .45 .25

28th Pacific Area Travel Association (PATA) Conf., Seoul, Apr. 16-18, and Gyeongju, Apr. 20-21.

Presidents Park and Senghor A630

**1979, Apr. 22** ***Perf. 13½x13***

**1168** A630 20w multicolored .45 .25
*a.* Souvenir sheet of 2 1.75 1.75

Visit of Pres. Leopold Sedar Senghor of Senegal.

Basketball — A631

**1979, Apr. 29** ***Perf. 13x13½***

**1169** A631 20w multicolored .45 .25

8th World Women's Basketball Championship, Seoul, Apr. 29-May 13.

Children and IYC Emblem A632

**1979, May 5 Photo.** ***Perf. 13½x13***

**1170** A632 20w multicolored .45 .25
*a.* Souvenir sheet of 2 1.75 1.75

International Year of the Child.

Traffic Pollution — A633

**1979, June 5 Photo.** ***Perf. 13x13½***

**1171** A633 20w green & dk brn .75 .25

Pollution control.

Flags, Presidents Park and Carter A634

**1979, June 29** ***Perf. 13½x13***

**1172** A634 20w multicolored .45 .25
*a.* Souvenir sheet of 2 1.75 1.75

Visit of Pres. Jimmy Carter.

Korean Exhibition Center A635

**1979, July 3**

**1173** A635 20w multicolored .45 .25

Opening of Korean Exhibition Center.

Jet, Globe, South Gate — A636

**1979, Aug. 1 Photo.** ***Perf. 13½x13***

**1174** A636 20w multicolored .45 .25

10th anniversary of Korean airlines.

### Art Treasure Types

Designs: No. 1175, Porcelain jar, 17th century. No. 1176, Man on horseback, ceremonial pitcher, horiz. No. 1177, Sword Dance, by Shin Yun-bok. No. 1178, Golden Amitabha with halo, 8th century. No. 1179, Hahoe ritual mask.

**1979 Photo.** ***Perf. 13x13½, 13½x13***

**1175** A627 20w lilac & multi .60 .25
**1176** A627 20w multicolored .60 .25
**1177** A628 60w multicolored 1.00 .30
*a.* Souvenir sheet of 2 4.75 4.75
*Nos. 1175-1177 (3)* 2.20 .80

Issued: No. 1177, 9/1; Nos. 1175-1176, 10/15.

**1979, Nov. 15**

**1178** A627 20w dp green & multi .50 .25
**1179** A627 20w multicolored .50 .25

Yongdu Rock — A637

**1979, Sept. 28**

**1180** A637 20w shown .50 .25
**1181** A637 20w Mt. Mai, vert. .50 .25

World Tourism Day.

People, Blood and Heart — A637a

**1979, Oct. 1** ***Perf. 13½x13***

**1182** A637a 20w multicolored .70 .25

Blood Banks, 4th anniversary.

"My Life in the Year 2000" — A638

**1979, Oct. 30** ***Perf. 13½x13***

**1183** A638 20w multicolored .45 .25
*a.* Souvenir sheet of 2 1.60 1.60

Philatelic Week, Oct. 30-Nov. 4.

Monkey-headed Figure, Bas-relief A639

Children Playing Yut A640

**1979, Dec. 1**

**1184** A639 20w multicolored .45 .25
*a.* Souvenir sheet of 2 1.35 1.35
**1185** A640 20w multicolored .45 .25
*a.* Souvenir sheet of 2 1.35 1.35

New Year 1980.

Inauguration of Pres. Choi Kyu-hah A641

**1979, Dec. 21**

**1186** A641 20w multicolored .50 .25
*a.* Souvenir sheet of 2 4.75 4.75

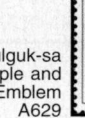

President Park — A642

**1980, Feb. 2 Photo.** ***Perf. 13x13½***

**1187** A642 30w orange brn .80 .25
**1188** A642 30w dull purple .80 .25
*a.* Souvenir sheet of 2 3.50 3.50
*b.* Pair, #1187-1188 2.00 2.00

President Park Chung Hee (1917-1979) memorial.

**Art Treasure Type of 1979 and**

Dragon-shaped Kettle — A643

Design: 60w, Landscape, by Kim Hong-do.

***Perf. 13½x13, 13x13½***

**1980, Feb. 20** **Photo.**

**1189** A643 30w multicolored .80 .25
**1190** A628 60w multicolored .90 .30
*a.* Souvenir sheet of 2 3.75 3.75

**Art Treasure Issue**

Heavenly Horse, Saddle A644

Dragon Head, Banner Staff A645

Tiger, Granite Sculpture A647

Mounted Nobleman Mural — A646

Human Face, Roof Tile — A648

Deva King Sculpture — A650

White Tiger Mural — A649

Earthenware Ducks — A651

Tiger, Folk Painting — A653

***Perf. 13½x13, 13x13½***

**1980-83** **Photo.**

**1191** A644 30w multicolored .70 .25
**1192** A645 30w multicolored .70 .25
**1193** A646 30w multicolored .70 .25
**1194** A647 30w multicolored .70 .25
**1195** A648 30w multicolored .70 .25
**1196** A649 30w multicolored .70 .25

**Engr.** ***Perf. 12½x13***

**1197** A650 30w black .90 .25
**1198** A650 30w red .90 .25

**1983** **Litho.** ***Perf. 13***

**1199** 1000w bis brn & red brn 5.25 .80
**1200** 1000w bis brn & red brn 5.25 .80
*a.* A651 Pair, #1199-1200 10.50 5.00
**1201** A653 5000w multicolored 23.00 5.00
*a.* Souvenir sheet, perf. 13½x13 30.00
*Nos. 1191-1201 (11)* 39.50 8.60

Issued: Nos. 1191-1192, 4/20; Nos. 1193-1194, 5/20; Nos. 1195-1196, 8/20; Nos. 1197-1198, 11/20. Nos. 1199-1200, 11/25/83. No. 1201, 12/1/83.

No. 1201a for PHILAKOREA '84. No. 1201a exists imperf. Value $150.

Lotus Blossoms and Ducks — A656

Tiger and Magpie A657

**1980, Mar. 10** ***Perf. 13x13½, 13½x13***

**1203** A656 30w multicolored .60 .25
**1204** A657 60w multicolored 1.40 .45

Red Phoenix (in Form of Rooster) — A658

Moon Over Mt. Konryun — A659

No. 1207, Sun over Mt. Konryun. No. 1207a has continuous design.

**1980, May 10** ***Perf. 13x13½***

**1205** A658 30w multicolored .55 .25
**1206** A659 60w multicolored 1.60 .45
**1207** A659 60w multicolored 1.60 .45
*a.* Souvenir sheet of 2, #1206-1207 4.75 4.75
*b.* Pair, #1206-1207 4.25 3.50
*Nos. 1205-1207 (3)* 3.75 1.15

Rabbits Pounding Grain in a Mortar — A660

Dragon in the Clouds — A661

**1980, July 10 Photo.** ***Perf. 13x13½***

**1208** A660 30w multicolored .65 .25
**1209** A661 30w multicolored .65 .25

Pine Tree, Pavilion, Mountain A662

Flowers and Birds, Bridal Room Screen A663

**1980, Aug. 9 Photo.** ***Perf. 13x13½***

**1210** A662 30w multicolored .60 .25
**1211** A663 30w multicolored .95 .30

Tortoises and Cranes — A664

Symbols of longevity: a, cranes, tortoises. b, buck. c, doe. d, waterfall.

**1980, Nov. 10 Photo.** ***Perf. 13½x13***

**1212** A664 Strip of 4 6.75 4.50
*a.-d.* 30w any single 1.35 .25

New Community Movement, 10th Anniv. — A668

**1980, Apr. 22** ***Perf. 13x13½***

**1216** A668 30w multicolored .45 .25

Freighters at Sea — A669

**1980, Mar. 13**

**1217** A669 30w multicolored .45 .25

Increase of Korea's shipping tonnage to 5 million tons.

Soccer — A670

**1980, Aug. 23** ***Perf. 13x13½***

**1218** A670 30w multicolored .45 .25

10th President's Cup Soccer Tournament, Aug. 23-Sept. 5.

Mt. Sorak — A671

Paikryung Island — A672

***Perf. 12½x13½***

**1980, Apr. 10** **Photo.**

**1219** A671 15w multicolored .35 .25
**1220** A672 90w multicolored 1.00 .25

Flag — A673

**1980, Sept. 10** ***Perf. 13½x13***

**1221** A673 30w multicolored .40 .25

**Coil Stamp**

***Perf. Vert.***

**1221A** A673 30w multicolored 1.10 .25

No. 1221A issued 2/1/87.

UN Intervention, 30th Anniv. — A674

**1980, June 25** ***Perf. 13x13½***

**1222** A674 30w multicolored .50 .25

Election of Miss World in Seoul — A675

**1980, July 8**

**1223** A675 30w multicolored .50 .25

Women's Army Corps, 30th Anniversary A676

**1980, Sept. 6** *Perf. 13½x13*
**1224** A676 30w multicolored .50 .25

Baegma River — A677

Three Peaks of Dodam A678

**1980, Sept. 28**
**1225** A677 30w multicolored .35 .25
**1226** A678 30w multicolored .35 .25

Inauguration of Pres. Chun Doo-hwan A679

**1980, Sept. 1**
**1227** A679 30w multicolored .60 .25
*a.* Souvenir sheet of 2 3.25 3.25

Ear of Corn — A680

**1980, Oct. 20** *Perf. 13x13½*
**1228** A680 30w multicolored .50 .25

12th population and housing census.

Symbolic Tree — A681

**1980, Oct. 27**
**1229** A681 30w multicolored .50 .25

National Red Cross, 75th anniversary.

"Mail-Delivering Angels" — A682

**1980, Nov. 6** *Perf. 13½x13*
**1230** A682 30w multicolored .50 .25
*a.* Souvenir sheet of 2 1.60 1.60

Philatelic Week, Nov. 6-11.

Korea-Japan Submarine Cable System Inauguration A683

**1980, Nov. 28** *Perf. 13x13½*
**1231** A683 30w multicolored .50 .25

Rooster — A684

Cranes — A685

**1980, Dec. 1**
**1232** A684 30w multicolored .50 .25
*a.* Souvenir sheet of 2 1.60 1.60
**1233** A685 30w multicolored .50 .25
*a.* Souvenir sheet of 2 1.60 1.60

New Year 1981.

Second Inauguration of Pres. Chun Doo-hwan A686

**1981, Mar. 3 Photo.** *Perf. 13½x13*
**1234** A686 30w multicolored .55 .25
*a.* Souvenir sheet of 2 1.60 1.60

### Ship Issue

Oil Tanker A687

Cargo Ship — A688

**1981, Mar. 13** *Perf. 13½x13, 13x13½*
**1235** A687 30w multicolored .45 .25
**1236** A688 90w multicolored .80 .25

5th Maritime Day.

Oil Tanker A689

Cargo Ship — A690

**1981, May 10 Photo.** *Perf. 13½x13*
**1237** A689 30w multicolored .45 .25
**1238** A690 90w multicolored .85 .30

Tug Boat — A691

Stern Trawler A692

**1981, July 10** *Perf. 13½x13*
**1239** A691 40w multicolored .65 .25
**1240** A692 100w multicolored 1.05 .30

Log Carrier A693

Auto Carrier A694

**1981, Aug. 10**
**1241** A693 40w multicolored .65 .25
**1242** A694 100w multicolored 1.05 .30

Chemical Carrier A695

Passenger Boat A696

**1981, Nov. 10 Engr.** *Perf. 13x12½*
**1243** A695 40w black .65 .25
**1244** A696 100w dk blue 1.10 .30
*Nos. 1235-1244 (10)* 7.70 2.70

11th Natl. Assembly Opening Session A697

**1981, Apr. 17 Photo.** *Perf. 13½x13*
**1245** A697 30w gold & dk brn .45 .25

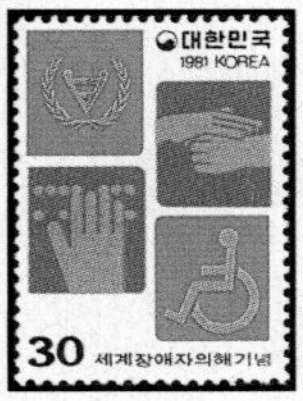

Hand Reading Braille, Helping Hands — A698

90w, Man in wheelchair.

**1981, Apr. 20 Photo.** *Perf. 13x13½*
**1246** A698 30w shown .35 .25
**1247** A698 90w multicolored .70 .25

International Year of the Disabled.

Ribbon and Council Emblem — A699

**1981, June 5 Photo.** *Perf. 13x13½*
**1248** A699 40w multicolored .45 .25

Advisory Council on Peaceful Unification Policy (North and South Korea) anniv.

Clena River and Mountains — A700

**1981, June 5**
**1249** A700 30w shown .35 .25
**1250** A700 90w Seagulls .75 .25

10th World Environment Day.

Pres. Chun and Pres. Suharto of Indonesia A701

Pres. Chun Visit to Asia: b, King of Malaysia. c, Korean, Singapore flags. d, King Bhumibol Adulyadej of Thailand. e, Pres. Marcos of Philippines.

**1981, June 25** *Perf. 13½x13*
**1251** Strip of 5 4.00 3.00
*a.-e.* A701 40w, any single .55 .25
*f.* Souvenir sheet of 5, imperf. 2.50 2.50

**Size: 49x33mm**

***Perf. 13x13½***

**1252** A701 40w multicolored .55 .25
*a.* Souvenir sheet of 2, imperf. 2.40 2.40

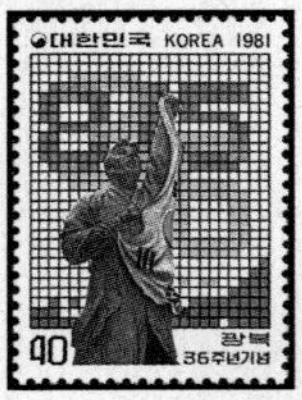

36th Anniv. of Liberation — A702

**1981, Aug. 15 Photo.** *Perf. 13x13½*
**1253** A702 40w multicolored .45 .25

Tolharubang, "Stone Grandfather" A704

Rose of Sharon A705

Porcelain Jar, 17th Cent. — A706

Chomsongdae Observatory, 7th Cent. — A707

Mounted Warrior, Earthenware Jug, 5th Cent. A708

Family Planning A709

Walking Stick A710

Ryu Kwan-soon (1904-20), Martyr A711

"Tasan" Chung Yak-yong, Lee Dynasty Scholar A712

Ahn Joong-geun (1879-1910), Martyr A713

Ahn Chang-ho (1878-1938), Independence Fighter A714

Koryo Celadon Incense Burner A715

Kim Ku (1876-1949), Statesman A716

Mountain Landscape Brick Bas-relief A717

Mandarin Duck, Celadon Incense Burner — A718

***Perf. 13½x12½ (Nos. 1256, 1257, 1266), 13, 13½x13, 13x13½***

**1981-89 Photo., Engr.**

| | | | | | |
|---|---|---|---|---|---|
| **1255** | A704 | 20w | multi ('86) | .45 | .25 |
| **1256** | A705 | 40w | multi | .55 | .25 |
| **1257** | A706 | 60w | multi | .55 | .25 |
| **1258** | A707 | 70w | multi | .65 | .25 |
| **1259** | A708 | 80w | multi ('83) | .70 | .25 |
| **1260** | A709 | 80w | multi ('86) | .90 | .25 |
| **1261** | A710 | 80w | multi ('89) | 2.25 | .25 |
| **1262** | A711 | 100w | mauve | .95 | .25 |
| **1263** | A712 | 100w | gray blk ('86) | 3.00 | .25 |
| **1264** | A713 | 200w | lt ol grn & ol | 1.30 | .25 |
| **1265** | A714 | 300w | dl lil ('83) | 1.90 | .25 |
| **1266** | A715 | 400w | multi | 5.75 | .45 |
| **1267** | A715 | 400w | pale grn & multi ('83) | 3.50 | .35 |
| **1268** | A716 | 450w | dk vio brn ('86) | 2.40 | .35 |
| **1269** | A717 | 500w | multi | 3.50 | .60 |
| **1270** | A718 | 700w | multi ('83) | 4.25 | .65 |
| | | | *Nos. 1255-1270 (16)* | 32.60 | 5.15 |

Inscription and denomination of No. 1266, colorless, No. 1267, dark brown.

See Nos. 1449, 1449C, 1594F.

**Coil Stamp**

**Photo. *Perf. 13 Horiz.***

**1271** A707 70w multicolored 2.00 .50

Girl Flying Model Plane — A721

Air Force Chief of Staff Cup, 3rd Aeronautic Competition: Various model planes.

**1981, Sept. 20 *Perf. 13½x13***

| | | | | |
|---|---|---|---|---|
| **1272** | Strip of 5 | | 4.00 | 3.50 |
| *a.* | A721 10w multi | | .50 | .25 |
| *b.* | A721 20w multi | | .50 | .25 |
| *c.* | A721 40w multi | | .50 | .25 |
| *d.* | A721 50w multi | | .65 | .30 |
| *e.* | A721 80w multi | | .80 | .35 |

WHO Emblem, Citizens — A722

**1981, Sept. 22 *Perf. 13x13½***

**1273** A722 40w multicolored .45 .25

WHO, 32nd Western Pacific Regional Committee Meeting, Seoul, Sept. 22-28.

World Tourism Day — A723

**1981, Sept. 28**

**1274** A723 40w Seoul Tower .45 .25
**1275** A723 40w Ulreung Isld. .45 .25

Bicycle Racing A724

**1981, Oct. 10 *Perf. 13½x13***

**1276** A724 40w shown .40 .25
**1277** A724 40w Swimming .40 .25

62nd Natl. Sports Festival, Seoul, 10/10-15.

Flags, Presidents Chun and Carazo A725

**1981, Oct. 12 *Perf. 13½x13***

**1278** A725 40w multicolored .45 .25

Visit of Pres. Rodrigo Carazo Odio of Costa Rica, Oct. 12-14.

World Food Day — A726

**1981, Oct. 16 *Perf. 13x13½***

**1279** A726 40w multicolored .45 .25

First Natl. Aviation Day — A727

**1981, Oct. 30 *Perf. 13½x13***

**1280** A727 40w multicolored .45 .25

1988 Olympic Games, Seoul — A728

**1981, Oct. 30 *Perf. 13x13½***

**1281** A728 40w multicolored .55 .25

9th Philatelic Week, Nov. 18-24 — A729

**1981, Nov. 18 *Perf. 13½x13***

**1282** A729 40w multicolored .45 .25
*a.* Souvenir sheet of 2 1.75 1.75

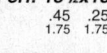

Camellia and Dog — A730

Children Flying Kite — A731

**1981, Dec. 1 *Perf. 13x13½***

| | | | |
|---|---|---|---|
| **1283** | A730 40w multicolored | .55 | .25 |
| *a.* | Souvenir sheet of 2 | 1.75 | 1.75 |
| **1284** | A731 40w multicolored | .55 | .25 |
| *a.* | Souvenir sheet of 2 | 1.75 | 1.75 |

New Year 1982 (Year of the Dog).

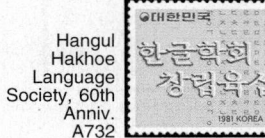

Hangul Hakhoe Language Society, 60th Anniv. A732

**1981, Dec. 3 *Perf. 13½x13***

**1285** A732 40w multicolored .45 .25

Telecommunications Authority Inauguration A733

**1982, Jan. 4 Photo. *Perf. 13x13½***

**1286** A733 60w multicolored .45 .25

Scouting Year — A734

**1982, Feb. 22**

**1287** A734 60w multicolored .45 .25

60th Anniv. of YWCA in Korea — A735

**1982, Apr. 20 Photo. *Perf. 13x13½***

**1288** A735 60w multicolored .45 .25

Intl. Polar Year Centenary A736

**1982, Apr. 21 *Perf. 13½x13***

**1289** A736 60w multicolored .55 .25

60th Children's Day — A737

**1982, May 5 *Perf. 13½x13***

**1290** A737 60w multicolored .45 .25

Visit of Liberian Pres. Samuel K. Doe, May 9-13 A738

**1982, May 9 Litho. *Perf. 13x12½***

**1291** A738 60w multicolored .55 .25
*a.* Souvenir sheet of 2, imperf. 1.75 1.75

Centenary of US-Korea Treaty of Amity — A739

No. 1292, Statue of Liberty, pagoda. No. 1293, Emblem.

**1982, May 18 Photo. *Perf. 13½x13***

| | | | |
|---|---|---|---|
| **1292** | A739 60w multicolored | .70 | .25 |
| **1293** | A739 60w multicolored | .70 | .25 |
| *a.* | Souvenir sheet of 2 | 3.00 | 3.00 |
| *b.* | Pair, #1292-1293 | 1.50 | 1.50 |

Visit of Zaire Pres. Mobutu Sese Seko, June 7-10 A740

**1982, June 7 Litho. *Perf. 13x12½***

**1294** A740 60w multicolored .45 .25
*a.* Souvenir sheet of 2, imperf. 1.75 1.75

### Historical Painting Issue

Gen. Kwon Yul's Victory at Haengju, by Oh Seung-woo — A747

Designs: No. 1295, Territorial Expansion by Kwanggaeto the Great, by Lee Chong-sang, 1975. No. 1296, Gen. Euljimunduck's Victory at Salsoo, by Park Kak-soon, 1975. No. 1297, Shilla's Repulse of Tang's Army, by Oh Seung-woo. No. 1298, Gen. Kang Kam-chan's Victory at Kyiju, by Lee Yong-hwan. No. 1299, Admiral Yi Sun-sin's Victory at Hansan, 1592, by Kim Hyung-ku. No. 1300, Gen. Kim Chwa-jin's Battle at Chungsanri, by Sohn Soo-kwang. No. 1302, Kim Chong-suh's Exploitation of Yukjin, 1434, by Kim Tae.

**1982 Photo. *Perf. 13x13½***

| | | | | | |
|---|---|---|---|---|---|
| **1295** | A747 | 60w | multicolored | .75 | .35 |
| **1296** | A747 | 60w | multicolored | 1.25 | .50 |
| **1297** | A747 | 60w | multicolored | .90 | .30 |
| **1298** | A747 | 60w | multicolored | .90 | .30 |
| **1299** | A747 | 60w | multicolored | 1.00 | .40 |
| **1300** | A747 | 60w | multicolored | 1.00 | .40 |
| **1301** | A747 | 60w | shown | 1.30 | .40 |
| **1302** | A747 | 60w | multicolored | 1.30 | .40 |
| | *Nos. 1295-1302 (8)* | | | 8.40 | 3.05 |

Issued: Nos. 1295-1296, 6/15; Nos. 1297-1298, 7/15; Nos. 1299-1300, 10/15; Nos. 1301-1302, 12/15.

55th Intl. YMCA Convention, Seoul, July 20-23 — A749

**1982, July 20**

**1303** A749 60w multicolored .45 .25

Flags, Presidents Chun and Arap Moi — A750

Pres. Chun's Visit to Africa & Canada: No. 1304, Kenya (Pres. Daniel T. Arap Moi), Aug. 17-19. No. 1305, Nigeria (Pres. Alhaji Shehe Shagari), Aug. 19-22. No. 1306, Gabon (Pres. El Hadj Omar Bongo), Aug. 22-24. No. 1307, Senegal (Pres. Abdou Diouf), Aug. 24-26. No. 1308, Canada, Aug. 28-31.

**1982, Aug. 17 *Perf. 13½x13***

| | | | | | |
|---|---|---|---|---|---|
| **1304** | A750 | 60w | multicolored | .45 | .25 |
| **1305** | A750 | 60w | multicolored | .45 | .25 |
| **1306** | A750 | 60w | multicolored | .45 | .25 |
| **1307** | A750 | 60w | multicolored | .45 | .25 |
| **1308** | A750 | 60w | multicolored | .45 | .25 |
| | *Nos. 1304-1308 (5)* | | | 2.25 | 1.25 |

#### Souvenir Sheets of 2

| | | | | |
|---|---|---|---|---|
| *1304a* | A750 | 60w | 2.10 | 2.10 |
| *1305a* | A750 | 60w | 2.10 | 2.10 |
| *1306a* | A750 | 60w | 2.10 | 2.10 |
| *1307a* | A750 | 60w | 2.10 | 2.10 |
| *1308a* | A750 | 60w | 2.10 | 2.10 |
| *Nos. 1304a-1308a (5)* | | | 10.50 | 10.50 |

Natl. Flag Centenary A751

**1982, Aug. 22**

**1309** A751 60w multicolored .45 .25
*a.* Souvenir sheet of 2 2.40 2.40

2nd Seoul Open Intl. Table Tennis Championship, Aug. 25-31 — A752

**1982, Aug. 25**

**1310** A752 60w multicolored .50 .25

27th World Amateur Baseball Championship Series, Seoul, Sept. 4-18 — A753

**1982, Sept. 4 Engr. *Perf. 13***

**1311** A753 60w red brown .75 .25

Seoul Intl. Trade Fair (SITRA '82), Sept. 24-Oct. 18 — A754

**1982, Sept. 17 Photo. *Perf. 13½x13***

**1312** A754 60w multicolored .45 .25

Philatelic Week, Oct. 15-21 — A755

Design: Miners reading consolatory letters.

**1982, Oct. 15**

**1313** A755 60w multicolored .45 .25
*a.* Souvenir sheet of 2 1.60 1.60

Visit of Indonesian Pres. Suharto, Oct. 16-19 — A756

**1982, Oct. 16 Litho. *Perf. 13x12½***

**1314** A756 60w multicolored .45 .25
*a.* Souvenir sheet of 2, imperf. 1.50 1.50

A757

**1982, Nov. 3 *Perf. 13½x13***

**1315** A757 60w multicolored .45 .25

37th Jaycee (Intl. Junior Chamber of Commerce) World Congress, Seoul, Nov. 3-18.

2nd UN Conference on Peaceful Uses of Outer Space, Vienna, Aug. 9-21 — A758

**1982, Nov. 20 *Perf. 13x13½***

**1316** A758 60w multicolored .40 .25

New Year 1983 (Year of the Boar) — A759

No. 1317, Magpies, money bag. No. 1318, Boar, bas-relief.

**1982, Dec. 1**

**1317** A759 60w multicolored .45 .25
*a.* Souvenir sheet of 2 2.10 2.10
**1318** A759 60w multicolored .45 .25
*a.* Souvenir sheet of 2 2.10 2.10

Flags of Korea and Turkey — A760

**1982, Dec. 20 *Perf. 13***

**1319** A760 60w multicolored .45 .25
*a.* Souvenir sheet of 2, imperf. 1.75 1.75

Visit of Pres. Kenan Evren of Turkey, Dec. 20-23.

Letter Writing Campaign — A761

**1982, Dec. 31 Photo. *Perf. 13x13½***

**1320** A761 60w multicolored .45 .25

First Intl. Customs Day — A762

**1983, Jan. 26 *Perf. 13½x13***

**1321** A762 60w multicolored .50 .25

#### Korean-made Vehicle Issue

Hyundai Pony-2 A764

Daewoo Maepsy A765

Super Titan Truck — A768

Flat-bed Truck — A770

**1983 Photo. *Perf. 13½x13***

| | | | | | |
|---|---|---|---|---|---|
| **1322** | A764 | 60w | Keohwa Jeep | .80 | .25 |
| **1323** | A764 | 60w | shown | .80 | .25 |
| *a.* | Pair, #1322-1323 | | | 2.10 | 2.10 |
| **1324** | A765 | 60w | shown | .75 | .25 |
| **1325** | A764 | 60w | Kia minibus | .75 | .25 |
| *a.* | Pair, #1324-1325 | | | 2.00 | 2.00 |
| **1326** | A764 | 60w | Highway bus | .85 | .25 |
| **1327** | A768 | 60w | shown | .85 | .25 |
| **1328** | A764 | 70w | Dump truck | 1.15 | .25 |
| **1329** | A770 | 70w | shown | 1.15 | .25 |
| **1330** | A764 | 70w | Cement mixer | 1.10 | .25 |
| **1331** | A764 | 70w | Oil truck | 1.05 | .25 |
| | *Nos. 1322-1331 (10)* | | | 9.25 | 2.50 |

Issued: Nos. 1322-1323, 2/25; Nos. 1324-1325, 3/25; Nos. 1326-1327, 5/25; Nos. 1328-1329, 7/25; Nos. 1330-1331, 8/25.

Visit of Malaysian Seri Paduka Baginda, Mar. 22-26 — A773

**1983, Mar. 22**

**1332** A773 60w multicolored .45 .25
*a.* Souvenir sheet of 2 1.25 1.25

#### Postal Service Issue

General Bureau of Postal Administration Building A774

Mailman, 1884 — A776

Ancient Mail Carrier A778

Nos. 1-2 — A780

Pre-modern Period Postal Symbol, Mailbox A782

Designs: No. 1334, Seoul Central PO. No. 1336, Mailman on motorcycle, 1983. No. 1338, Modern mail transport. No. 1340, No. 1201. No. 1342, Current postal symbol, mailbox.

**1983-84 Photo. *Perf. 13½x13***

**1333** A774 60w multicolored .65 .25
**1334** A774 60w multicolored .65 .25
**1335** A776 70w multicolored .80 .25
**1336** A776 70w multicolored .80 .25
**1337** A778 70w multicolored .80 .25
**1338** A778 70w multicolored .80 .25
**1339** A780 70w multicolored .65 .25
**1340** A780 70w multicolored .65 .25
**1341** A782 70w multicolored .65 .25
**1342** A782 70w multicolored .65 .25
*Nos. 1333-1342 (10)* 7.10 2.50

PHILAKOREA '84, Seoul, Oct. 22-31, 1984.
Issued: Nos. 1333-1334, 4/22; Nos. 1335-1336, 6/10; Nos. 1337-1338, 8/10; Nos. 1339-1340, 2/10/84; Nos. 1341-1342, 3/10/84.

Teachers' Day — A784

60w, Village schoolhouse, score.

**1983, May 15 Photo. *Perf. 13x13½***

**1343** A784 60w multicolored .50 .25
*a.* Souvenir sheet of 2 1.75 2.00

World Communications Year — A785

**1983, June 20**

**1344** A785 70w multicolored .55 .25
*a.* Souvenir sheet of 2 1.50 1.50

Communications Life Insurance Inauguration — A786

**1983, July 1 Photo. *Perf. 13½x13***

**1345** A786 70w multicolored .60 .25

Science and Technology Symposium, Seoul, July 4-8 — A787

**1983, July 4**

**1346** A787 70w multicolored .50 .25

Visit of Jordan's King Hussein, Sept. 10-13 A788

70w, Pres. Hwan, King Hussein, flags.

**1983, Sept. 10 Litho. *Perf. 13x12½***

**1347** A788 70w multicolored .50 .25
*a.* Souvenir sheet of 2, imperf. 1.60 1.60

ASTA, 53rd World Travel Congress, Seoul — A789

**1983, Sept. 25 Photo. *Perf. 13***

**1348** A789 70w multicolored .55 .25

A790

**1983, Oct. 4 Photo. *Perf. 13***

**1349** A790 70w multicolored .55 .25
*a.* Souvenir sheet of 2 1.60 1.60

70th Inter-Parliamentary Union Conference.

A791

**1983, Oct. 6 Photo. *Perf. 13***

**1350** A791 70w Gymnastics .55 .25
**1351** A791 70w Soccer .55 .25

64th National Sports Festival.

Pres. Chun and Pres. U San Yu of Burma A791a

Pres. Chun's Curtailed Visit to Southwest Asia: No. 1351B, India. No. 1351C, Pres. Junius R. Jayawardene, Sri Lanka. No. 1351D, Australia, flag. No. 1351E, New Zealand, flag. Withdrawn after one day due to political assassination.

**1983, Oct. 8 Photo. *Perf. 13½x13***

**1351A** A791a 70w multicolored 1.30 .60
**1351B** A791a 70w multicolored 1.30 .60
**1351C** A791a 70w multicolored 1.30 .60
**1351D** A791a 70w multicolored 1.30 .60
**1351E** A791a 70w multicolored 1.30 .60
*Nos. 1351A-1351E (5)* 6.50 3.00

**Souvenir Sheets of 2**

*1351f* A791a 70w 4.25 4.25
*1351g* A791a 70w 4.25 4.25
*1351h* A791a 70w 4.25 4.25
*1351i* A791a 70w 4.25 4.25
*1351j* A791a 70w 4.25 4.25
*Nos. 1351f-1351j (5)* 21.25 21.25

Water Resource Development A792

**1983, Oct. 15 Litho. *Perf. 13***

**1352** A792 70w multicolored .55 .25

Newspaper Publication Cent. — A793

**1983, Oct. 31 Litho. *Perf. 13***

**1353** A793 70w multicolored .55 .25

Natl. Tuberculosis Assoc., 30th Anniv. — A794

**1983, Nov. 6 Photo. *Perf. 13***

**1354** A794 70w multicolored .55 .25

Presidents Chun and Reagan, Natl. Flags — A795

**1983, Nov. 12 Photo. *Perf. 13***

**1355** A795 70w multicolored .65 .25
*a.* Souvenir sheet of 2 2.50 2.50

Visit of Pres. Ronald Reagan, Nov. 12-14.

11th Philatelic Week — A796

**1983, Nov. 18 Photo. *Perf. 13***

**1356** A796 70w multicolored .55 .25
*a.* Souvenir sheet of 2 2.40 2.40

New Year 1984
A797 A798

No. 1357, Mouse, stone wall relief. No. 1358, Cranes, pine tree.

**1983, Dec. 1 Photo. *Perf. 13***

**1357** A797 70w multicolored .70 .25
*a.* Souvenir sheet of 2 2.50 2.50
**1358** A798 70w multicolored .70 .25
*a.* Souvenir sheet of 2 2.50 2.50

Bicentenary of Catholic Church in Korea — A799

**1984, Jan. 4 Photo. *Perf. 13x13½***

**1359** A799 70w Cross .60 .25
*a.* Souvenir sheet of 2 3.00 3.00

Visit of Brunei's Sultan Bolkiah-Apr. 7-9 — A800

**1984, Apr. 7 Litho. *Perf. 13x12½***

**1360** A800 70w multicolored .55 .25
*a.* Souvenir sheet of 2, imperf. 1.75 1.75

Visit of Qatar's Sheik Khalifa, Apr. 20-22 A801

**1984, Apr. 20**

**1361** A801 70w multicolored .55 .25
*a.* Souvenir sheet of 2, imperf. 1.60 1.60

Girl Mailing Letter — A802

Mailman in City — A803

**1984, Apr. 22 Photo. *Perf. 13½x13***

**1362** A802 70w multicolored .55 .25
*a.* Souvenir sheet of 2 1.60 1.60
**1363** A803 70w multicolored .55 .25
*a.* Souvenir sheet of 2 1.60 1.60

Korean postal service.

Visit of Pope John Paul II, May 3-7 — A808

**1984, May 3 Engr. *Perf. 12½***

**1368** A808 70w dk brn .65 .25

**Photogravure & Engraved**

**1369** A808 70w multicolored .65 .25
*a.* Souvenir sheet of 2, #1368-1369, perf. 13½ 2.40 2.40

Tools, Brushes, Flower — A809

**1984, May 11 Photo.** ***Perf. 13x13½***

**1370** A809 70w multicolored .55 .25

Workers' Cultural Festival.

Jet, Ship, Asia Map — A810

**1984, May 21 Photo.** ***Perf. 13x13½***

**1371** A810 70w multicolored .55 .25

Customs Cooperation Council 63rd-64th Sessions, Seoul, May 21-25.

Visit of Sri Lanka's Pres. Jayewardene, May 27-30 — A811

70w, Asia map, flags, flowers.

**1984, May 27** ***Perf. 13½x13***

**1372** A811 70w multicolored .55 .25

*a.* Souvenir sheet of 2 1.50 1.50

Advertising Congress Emblem — A812

**1984, June 18 Photo.** ***Perf. 13x13½***

**1373** A812 70w multicolored .55 .25

14th Asian Advertising Cong., Seoul, June 18-21.

'88 Olympic Expressway Opening — A813

**1984, June 22**

**1374** A813 70w multicolored .60 .25

Intl. Olympic Committee, 90th Anniv. — A814

**1984, June 23**

**1375** A814 70w multicolored .55 .25

Asia-Pacific Broadcasting Union, 20th Anniv. A815

70w, Emblem, microphone.

**1984, June 30** ***Perf. 13½x13***

**1376** A815 70w multicolored .55 .25

Visit of Senegal's Pres. Diouf, July 9-12 A816

70w, Flags of Korea & Senegal.

**1984, July 9 Litho.** ***Perf. 13x12½***

**1377** A816 70w multicolored .55 .25

*a.* Souvenir sheet of 2, imperf. 1.75 1.75

1984 Summer Olympics A817

**Lithographed and Engraved**

**1984, July 28** ***Perf. 12½***

**1378** A817 70w Archery .70 .25

**1379** A817 440w Fencing 2.60 .65

Korean Protestant Church Cent. — A818

Stained glass windows.

**1984, Aug. 16** ***Perf. 13***

**1380** A818 70w Crucifixion .70 .25

**1381** A818 70w Cross, dove .70 .25

*a.* Souvenir sheet of 2 5.25 5.25

*b.* Pair, #1380-1381 1.75 1.75

Groom on Horseback — A819

Wedding Procession: a, Lantern carrier. b, Groom. c, Musician. d, Bride in sedan chair (52x33mm).

**1984, Sept. 1 Photo.** ***Perf. 13x13½***

**1382** Strip of 4 3.75 1.50

*a.-d.* A819 70w any single .70 .25

*e.* Souvenir sheet 2.10 2.10

No. 1382e contains No. 1382d.

Pres. Chun's Visit to Japan, Sept. 6-8 A820

70w, Chun, flag, Mt. Fuji.

**1984, Sept. 6 Litho.** ***Perf. 13x12½***

**1383** A820 70w multicolored .55 .25

*a.* Souvenir sheet of 2, imperf. 1.75 1.75

Visit of Gambia's Pres. Jawara, Sept. 12-17 A821

70w, Flags of Korea & Gambia.

**1984, Sept. 12**

**1384** A821 70w multicolored .55 .25

*a.* Souvenir sheet of 2, imperf. 1.75 1.75

Visit of Gabon's Pres. Bongo, Sept. 21-23 — A822

70w, Flags of Korea & Gabon.

**1984, Sept. 21** ***Perf. 13***

**1385** A822 70w multicolored .55 .25

*a.* Souvenir sheet of 2, imperf. 1.75 1.75

Seoul Intl. Trade Fair — A823

**1984, Sept. 18 Photo.** ***Perf. 13x13½***

**1386** A823 70w Products .55 .25

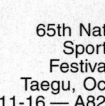

65th Natl. Sports Festival, Taegu, Oct. 11-16 — A824

**1984, Oct. 11 Photo.** ***Perf. 13½x13***

**1387** A824 70w Badminton .60 .25

**1388** A824 70w Wrestling .60 .25

Philakorea '84 Stamp Show, Seoul, Oct. 22-31 A825

No. 1389, South Gate, stamps. No. 1390, Emblem under magnifier, vert.

**1984, Oct. 22** ***Perf. 13½x13, 13x13½***

**1389** A825 70w multicolored .55 .25

*a.* Souvenir sheet of 4 3.25 3.25

**1390** A825 70w multicolored .55 .25

*a.* Souvenir sheet of 4 3.25 3.25

Visit of Maldives Pres. Maumoon Abdul Gayoom, Oct. 29-Nov. 1 A826

**1984, Oct. 29 Litho.** ***Perf. 13x12½***

**1392** A826 70w multicolored .55 .25

*a.* Souvenir sheet of 2, imperf. 1.90 1.90

Chamber of Commerce and Industry Cent. — A827

**1984, Oct. 31 Photo.** ***Perf. 13x13½***

**1393** A827 70w "100" .55 .25

Children Playing Jaegi-chagi — A828

New Year 1985 (Year of the ox).

**1984, Dec. 1 Photo.** ***Perf. 13x13½***

**1394** A828 70w Ox, bas-relief .55 .25

*a.* Souvenir sheet of 2 1.60 1.60

**1395** A828 70w shown .55 .25

*a.* Souvenir sheet of 2 1.60 1.60

Intl. Youth Year — A829

**1985, Jan. 25 Photo.** ***Perf. 13½x13***

**1396** A829 70w IYY emblem .55 .25

**Korean Folkways Series**

A830

No. 1397, Pounding rice. No. 1398, Welcoming full moon. No. 1399, Wrestling. No. 1400, Janggi, Korean chess.

**1985 Photo.** ***Perf. 13x13½***

**1397** A830 70w multicolored .70 .25

**1398** A830 70w multicolored .70 .25

**1399** A830 70w multicolored .85 .25

**1400** A830 70w multicolored .85 .25

Issued: Nos. 1397-1398, 2/19; Nos. 1399-1400, 8/20.

**Modern Art Series**

Rocky Mountain in the Early Spring, 1915, by Shimjoen, (Ahn Jung-shik) A831

Still-life with a Doll, 1927, by Suhlcho, (Lee Chong-woo) A832

Spring Day on a Farm, 1961, by Eijai, (Huh Paik-ryun, 1903-1977) A833

The Exorcist, 1941, by Chulma, (Kim Chung-hyun, 1901-1953) — A834

Chunhyang-do, by Kim Un-ho — A835

Flowers, by Lee Sang-bum A836

Image of A Friend, by Ku Bon-wung A837

Woman in a Ski Suit, by Son Ung-seng A838

Valley of the Peach Blossoms, 1964, by Pyen Kwan-Sik (1899-1976) A839

Rural Landscape, 1940, by Lee Yong-Wu (1904-1952) A840

Male, 1932, by Lee Ma-Dong A841

Woman with a Water Jar on Her Head, 1944, by Yun Hyo-Chung (1917-1967) A842

**Photo.; Litho. & Engr. (#1411-1412)**

**1985-87** ***Perf. 13½x13, 13x13½***

| | | | | | |
|---|---|---|---|---|---|
| **1401** | A831 | 70w | multicolored | .75 | .25 |
| **1402** | A832 | 70w | multicolored | .75 | .25 |
| **1403** | A833 | 70w | multicolored | .75 | .25 |
| **1404** | A834 | 70w | multicolored | .75 | .25 |
| **1405** | A835 | 80w | multi ('86) | 1.15 | .40 |
| **1406** | A836 | 80w | multi ('86) | 1.15 | .40 |
| **1407** | A837 | 80w | multi ('86) | 1.15 | .40 |
| **1408** | A838 | 80w | multi ('86) | 1.15 | .40 |
| **1409** | A839 | 80w | multi ('87) | *3.00* | .85 |
| **1410** | A840 | 80w | multi ('87) | *3.00* | .85 |
| **1411** | A841 | 80w | multi ('87) | *3.00* | .85 |
| **1412** | A842 | 80w | multi ('87) | *3.00* | .85 |
| | | | *Nos. 1401-1412 (12)* | *19.60* | 6.00 |

Issued: Nos. 1401-1402, 4/10; Nos. 1403-1404, 7/5; Nos. 1405-1408, 12/1; Nos. 1409-1412, 6/12.

State Visit of Pres. Chun to the US — A843

**Photo. & Engr.**

**1985, Apr. 24** ***Perf. 13***

| | | | | | |
|---|---|---|---|---|---|
| **1413** | A843 | 70w | multicolored | .60 | .25 |
| *a.* | | | Souvenir sheet of 2 | 1.75 | 1.75 |

**Coastal and Inland Fish Series**

Gak-si- Bung-eo (silver carp) — A844

Dot-sac-chi (sword fish) — A845

Eoreumchi A846

Sweetfish A847

Sardine A848

Hammerhead Shark A849

Cham-jung-go-ji — A850

Swi-ri — A851

Oar Fish — A852

Devil-ray A853

**1985-87** **Photo.** ***Perf. 13½x13***

| | | | | | |
|---|---|---|---|---|---|
| **1414** | A844 | 70w | multicolored | .70 | .25 |
| **1415** | A845 | 70w | multicolored | .70 | .25 |
| **1416** | A846 | 70w | multi ('86) | 1.60 | .55 |
| **1417** | A847 | 70w | multi ('86) | 1.60 | .55 |
| **1418** | A848 | 70w | multi ('86) | 1.60 | .55 |
| **1419** | A849 | 70w | multi ('86) | 1.60 | .55 |
| **1420** | A850 | 80w | multi ('87) | 2.50 | 1.00 |
| **1421** | A851 | 80w | multi ('87) | 2.50 | 1.00 |
| **1422** | A852 | 80w | multi ('87) | 2.50 | 1.00 |
| **1423** | A853 | 80w | multi ('87) | 2.50 | 1.00 |
| | | | *Nos. 1414-1423 (10)* | 17.80 | 6.70 |

Issued: Nos. 1414-1415, 5/30; Nos. 1416-1423, 7/25.

Yonsei University and Medical School, Cent. A854

**Photogravure and Engraved**

**1985, May 6** ***Perf. 13***

| | | | | | |
|---|---|---|---|---|---|
| **1424** | A854 | 70w | Underwood Hall | .55 | .25 |

State Visit of Pres. Mohammad Zia-Ul-Haq of Pakistan, May 6-10 — A855

**1985, May 6** **Photo.** ***Perf. 13x13½***

| | | | | | |
|---|---|---|---|---|---|
| **1425** | A855 | 70w | multicolored | .55 | .25 |
| *a.* | | | Souvenir sheet of 2 | 1.60 | 1.60 |

State Visit of Pres. Luis Alberto Monge of Costa Rica, May 19-23 — A856

**1985, May 18** ***Perf. 13½x13***

| | | | | | |
|---|---|---|---|---|---|
| **1426** | A856 | 70w | multicolored | .55 | .25 |
| *a.* | | | Souvenir sheet of 2 | 1.60 | 1.60 |

State Visit of Pres. Hussain Muhammad Ershad of Bangladesh, June 15-19 A857

**1985, June 15**

| | | | | | |
|---|---|---|---|---|---|
| **1427** | A857 | 70w | multicolored | .55 | .25 |
| *a.* | | | Souvenir sheet of 2, imperf. | 1.60 | 1.60 |

State Visit of Pres. Joao Bernardo Vieira of Guinea-Bissau, June 25-28 — A858

**1985, June 25**

| | | | | | |
|---|---|---|---|---|---|
| **1428** | A858 | 70w | multicolored | .55 | .25 |
| *a.* | | | Souvenir sheet of 2, imperf. | 1.60 | 1.60 |

Liberation from Japanese Occupation Forces, 40th Anniv. — A859

Heavenly Lake, Mt. Paektu, natl. flower.

**1985, Aug. 14 Litho. *Perf. 13x12½***
**1429** A859 70w multicolored .55 .25

### Music Series

The Spring of My Home, Music by Hong Nan-pa and Lyrics by Lee Won-su A860

A Leaf Boat, Music by Yun Yong-ha and Lyrics by Park Hong-Keun A861

Half Moon, 1924, by Yun Keuk-Young A862

Let's Go and Pick the Moon, by Yun Seok-Jung and Park Tae Hyun A863

**1985-86 Photo. *Perf. 13x13½***
**1430** A860 70w multicolored .80 .25
**1431** A861 70w multicolored .80 .25
**1432** A862 70w multicolored 1.00 .30
**1433** A863 70w multicolored 1.60 .50

Issued: Nos. 1430-1431, 9/10; Nos. 1432-1433, 6/25/86.

### Korean Folkways Series

Korean Farm Music A864

No. 1434 — Musicians with: a, Flag, hand gong. b, Drum flute. c, Drum, hand gong. d, Taborets, ribbons. e, Taboret, sun, woman, child. Has continuous design.

**1986, Aug. 26 Photo. *Perf. 13½x13***
**1434** Strip of 5 6.75 6.75
*a.-e.* A864 70w, any single 1.10 .25

### Music Series

Barley Field, by Park Wha-mok and Yun Yong-ha — A865

Magnolia, by Cho Young-Shik and Kim Dong-jin — A866

**1987, Mar. 25 Photo. *Perf. 13x13½***
**1435** A865 80w multicolored 2.50 1.00
**1436** A866 80w multicolored 2.50 1.00

### Korean Folkways Series

Chusok, Harvest Moon Festival — A867

No. 1437 — Harvest moon dance: a, Eight dancers, harvest moon. b, Four dancers, festival wheels, balloons. c, Three dancers, children on see-saw. d, Four dancers, women preparing meal.

**1987, Sept. 10 Photo. *Perf. 13x13½***
**1437** A867 Strip of 4 16.00 16.00
*a.-d.* 80w any single 3.25 .85

### Folkways and Music Series

*Tano,* Spring Harvest Festival — A868

No. 1438: a, Woman on shore, riding a swing. b, Sweet flag coiffures. c, Boy picking flowers, girl on swing. d, Boys wrestling.

**1988, Aug. 25 Photo. *Perf. 13x13½***
**1438** A868 Strip of 4 5.50 5.50
*a.-d.* 80w multicolored 1.10 .40

*Sick for Home,* by Lee Eun-sang and Kim Kong-jin A869

*Pioneer,* by Yoon Hae-young and Cho Doo-nam A870

**1988, Nov. 15**
**1439** A869 80w multicolored .70 .25
**1440** A870 80w multicolored .70 .25

Mask Dance (Talchum) — A871

No. 1441: a, Two mask dancers with scarves. b, Dancers with fans. c, Dancers with scarf and laurel or fan. d, Three dancers, first as an animal and two more carrying fan and bells or torch.

**1989, Feb. 25**
**1441** A871 Strip of 4 5.00 5.00
*a.-d.* 80w any single 1.10 .40

Korean Telecommunications, Cent. — A872

70w, Satellite, emblem, dish receiver.

**1985, Sept. 28 *Perf. 13½x13***
**1442** A872 70w multicolored .55 .25

World Bank Conference, Seoul, Oct. 8-11 — A873

**1985, Oct. 8 *Perf. 13x13½***
**1443** A873 70w Emblem .55 .25

Intl. Bank for Reconstruction & Development, 40th Anniv.

UN, 40th Anniv. A874

**1985, Oct. 24 *Perf. 13½x13***
**1444** A874 70w Emblem, doves .55 .25

Natl. Red Cross, 80th Anniv. A875

**1985, Oct. 26**
**1445** A875 70w red, blk & bl .55 .25

Segment of Canceled Cover — A876

**1985, Nov. 18 Photo. *Perf. 13½x13***
**1446** A876 70w multicolored .55 .25

12th Philatelic Week, Nov. 18-23.

New Year 1986 — A877

### Lithographed and Engraved

**1985, Dec. 2 *Perf. 13x13½***
**1447** A877 70w multicolored .55 .25

Mt. Fuji, Korean Airlines Jet — A878

**1985, Dec. 18 Photo.**
**1448** A878 70w brt bl, blk & red .65 .30

Normalization of diplomatic relations between Korea and Japan, 20th anniv.
See No. C44.

### Statesman Type of 1986 and Types of 1981-86

**Engr., Photo. (40w)**

**1986-87 *Perf. 13***
**1449** A716 550w indigo 2.75 .40

### Coil Stamps

***Perf. 13 Vert.***

**1449A** A704 20w multicolored .65 .35
**1449B** A705 40w multicolored .75 .30
**1449C** A708 80w multicolored 1.25 .55
*Nos. 1449A-1449C (3)* 2.65 1.20

Issue dates: 550w, Dec. 10; others, 1987.

Intl. Peace Year — A879

**1986, Jan. 15 Photo. *Perf. 13x13½***
**1450** A879 70w multicolored .60 .25

See No. C45.

State Visits of Pres. Chun — A880

Portrait, natl. flags and: No. 1452, Parliament, Brussels. No. 1453, Eiffel Tower, Paris. No. 1454, Cathedral, Cologne. No. 1455, Big Ben, London.

**1986, Apr. 4 Litho. *Perf. 12½x13***
**1452** A880 70w multicolored .65 .30
**1453** A880 70w multicolored .65 .30
**1454** A880 70w multicolored .65 .30
**1455** A880 70w multicolored .65 .30
*Nos. 1452-1455 (4)* 2.60 1.20

### Souvenir Sheets of 2

***Perf. 13½***

*1452a* A880 70w 3.00 3.00
*1453a* A880 70w 3.00 3.00
*1454a* A880 70w 3.00 3.00
*1455a* A880 70w 3.00 3.00
*Nos. 1452a-1455a (4)* 12.00 12.00

### Science Series

Observatories — A881

Designs: No. 1456, Chomsongdae Observatory, Satellites. No. 1457, Kwanchondae Observatory, Halley's Comet.

**1986, Apr. 21 *Perf. 13½x13***
**1456** 70w multicolored 2.60 .80
**1457** 70w multicolored 2.60 .80
*a.* A881 Pair, #1456-1457 6.50 2.40

Weather — A883

Designs: No. 1458, Wind observatory stone foundation, Chosun Dynasty. No. 1459, Rain gauge, Sejong Period to Chosun Dynasty.

**1987, Apr. 21 Photo. *Perf. 13½***

**1458** 80w multicolored 2.75 .90
**1459** 80w multicolored 2.75 .90
*a.* A883 Pair, #1458-1459 7.00 3.25

Clocks — A885

Designs: No. 1460, *Chagyokru*, water clock invented by Chang Yongshil and Kim Bin in 1434. No. 1461, *Angbuilgu*, sundial completed during King Sejong's reign (1418-1450).

**1988, Apr. 21 Photo. *Perf. 13½x13***

**1460** 80w multicolored .70 .30
**1461** 80w multicolored .70 .30
*a.* A885 Pair, #1460-1461 1.90 1.90

Early Printing Methods — A887

Designs: No. 1462, Sutra manuscript (detail) printed from wood type, Shila Dynasty, c.704-751. No. 1463, Two characters from a manuscript printed from metal type, Koryo, c.1237.

**1989, Apr. 21**

**1462** 80w buff & sepia 1.45 .35
**1463** 80w buff & sepia 1.45 .35
*a.* A887 Pair, #1462-1463 3.00 2.25

A889

Designs: No. 1464, 7th century gilt bronze Buddha. No. 1465, Bronze Age dagger, spear molds.

**1990, Apr. 21**

**1464** 100w multicolored .55 .25
**1465** 100w multicolored .55 .25
*a.* A889 Pair, #1464-1465 1.35 1.35
Complete bklt., 2 each #1464-1465 2.50
*Nos. 1456-1465 (10)* 16.10 5.20

Pairs have continuous designs.

---

**Souvenir Booklets**

Booklets containing the stamps listed below have a stamp, pair or strip of stamps, tied to the booklet cover with a first day cancel.

1464-1465, 1523-1524, 1529-1532, 1535-1536, 1539-1540, 1553, 1559-1566, 1572-1576, 1583-1584, 1595-1608, 1613-1621, 1622-1623B, 1624, 1635-1650, 1655-1656, 1657-1668, 1669-1676, 1678-1690, 1693-1699, 1700-1702, 1713-1714, 1745-1748, 1751-1758, 1763-1764, 1767-1768, 1770-1773, 1776-1787, 1797, 1799-1802, 1803-1806, 1810-1811.

---

Assoc. of Natl. Olympic Committees, 5th General Assembly, Seoul, Apr. 21-25 — A891

**1986, Apr. 21 *Perf. 13x13½***

**1466** A891 70w multicolored .55 .25

Souvenir Sheet

Butterflies — A892

**1986, May 22 Litho. *Perf. 13½***

**1467** A892 Sheet of 6 24.00 24.00
*a.* 70w multicolored 2.75 1.35
*b.* 370w multicolored 2.75 1.35
*c.* 400w multicolored 2.75 1.35
*d.* 440w multicolored 2.75 1.35
*e.* 450w multicolored 2.75 1.35
*f.* 470w multicolored 2.75 1.35

AMERIPEX '86, Chicago, May 22-June 1. No. 1467 contains stamps of different sizes (370w, 42x41mm; 400w, 42x33mm; 440w, 39x45mm; 450w, 32x42mm; 470w, 33x44mm); margin continues the designs.

Women's Education, Cent. A893

**1986, May 31 *Perf. 13x12½***

**1468** A893 70w multicolored .55 .25

State Visit of Pres. Andre Kolingba, Central Africa A894

**1986, June 10 *Perf. 13***

**1469** A894 70w multicolored .55 .25
*a.* Souvenir sheet of 2, imperf. 1.50 1.50

Completion of Han River Development Project — A895

**1986, Sept. 10 Litho. *Perf. 13***

**1470** Strip of 3 4.00 4.00
*a.* A895 30w Bridge 1.05 .30
*b.* A895 60w Buildings 1.05 .30
*c.* A895 80w Seoul Tower, buildings 1.05 .30

Printed in a continuous design.

Fireworks, Seoul Tower — A896

Games Emblem — A897

**1986, Sept. 20 Photo. *Perf. 13x13½***

**1471** A896 80w multicolored .65 .30
*a.* Souvenir sheet of 2 6.25 6.25
**1472** A897 80w multicolored .65 .30
*a.* Souvenir sheet of 2 6.25 6.25

Souvenir Sheet

10th Asian Games, Seoul, Sept. 20-Oct. 5 — A898

**1986, Oct. 31**

**1473** A898 550w multicolored 19.00 19.00

Juan Antonio Samaranch, Korean IOC Delegation, 1981 — A899

**1986, Sept. 30**

**1474** A899 80w multicolored .95 .40

Intl. Olympic Committee decision to hold 24th Olympic Games in Seoul, 5th anniv.

Philatelic Week — A900

**1986, Nov. 18 Photo. *Perf. 13½x13***

**1475** A900 80w Boy fishing for stamp .65 .25

New Year 1987 (Year of the Hare) — A901

**1986, Dec. 1 Photo. *Perf. 13x13½***

**1476** A901 80w multicolored .85 .30

Birds — A902

**1986, Dec. 20 *Perf. 13x14***

**1477** A902 80w Waxwing 1.25 .35
**1478** A902 80w Oriole 1.25 .35
**1479** A902 80w Kingfisher 1.25 .35
**1480** A902 80w Hoopoe 1.25 .35
**1481** A902 80w Roller 1.25 .35
*a.* Strip of 5, #1477-1481 6.75 6.75

**Coil Stamps**
***Perf. 14 Horiz.***

**1481B** A902 80w like No. 1479 2.40 .60
**1481C** A902 80w like No. 1480 2.40 .60
**1481D** A902 80w like No. 1481 2.40 .60
**1481E** A902 80w like No. 1477 2.40 .60
**1481F** A902 80w like No. 1478 2.40 .60
*g.* Strip of 5, #1481B-1481F 21.00 21.00

Wildlife Conservation A903

Endangered species: No. 1482, Panthera tigris altaica. No. 1483, Felis bengalensis. No. 1484, Vulpes vulpes. No. 1485, Sus scrofa.

**1987, Feb. 25 Photo. *Perf. 13½x13***

**1482** A903 80w multicolored 2.00 .60
**1483** A903 80w multicolored 2.00 .60
**1484** A903 80w multicolored 2.00 .60
**1485** A903 80w multicolored 2.00 .60
*a.* Strip of 4, #1482-1485 9.50 9.50

Flowers — A904

No. 1486, Dicentra spectabilis. No. 1487, Hanabusaya asiatica. No. 1488, Erythronium japonicum. No. 1489, Dianthus chinensis. No. 1490, Chrysanthemum zawadskii coreanum.

**1987, Mar. 20 Photo. *Perf. 14x13***

**1486** A904 550w multicolored 2.25 .50
**1487** A904 550w multicolored 2.25 .50
**1488** A904 550w multicolored 2.25 .50
**1489** A904 550w multicolored 2.25 .50
**1490** A904 550w multicolored 2.25 .50
*a.* Strip of 5, #1486-1490 13.50 13.50

**Coil Stamps**
***Perf. 13 Vert.***

**1490B** A904 550w like No. 1486 2.40 .75
**1490C** A904 550w like No. 1487 2.40 .75
**1490D** A904 550w like No. 1488 2.40 .75
**1490E** A904 550w like No. 1489 2.40 .75
**1490F** A904 550w like No. 1490 2.40 .75
*g.* Strip of 5, #1490B-1490F 16.00 16.00

State Visit of Pres. Ahmed Abdallah Abderemane of the Comoro Isls., Apr. 6-9 — A905

**1987, Apr. 6 Litho. *Perf. 13½x13***

| | | | |
|---|---|---|---|
| **1491** A905 80w multicolored | .55 | .25 |
| *a.* Souvenir sheet of 2 | 2.10 | 2.10 |

Electrification of Korea, Cent. — A906

**1987, Apr. 10 Photo.**

| | | |
|---|---|---|
| **1492** A906 80w multicolored | .55 | .25 |

Int'l. Assoc. of Ports and Harbors, 15th General Session, Seoul — A907

**1987, Apr. 25 Photo. *Perf. 13½x13***

| | | |
|---|---|---|
| **1493** A907 80w multicolored | .55 | .25 |

State Visit of Pres. U San Yu of Burma A908

**1987, June 8 Litho. *Perf. 13½x13***

| | | |
|---|---|---|
| **1494** A908 80w multicolored | .55 | .25 |
| *a.* Souvenir sheet of 2 | 1.90 | 1.90 |

Year of The Communications for Information Society — A909

No. 1495, Map, digital telephone. No. 1496, Emblem.

**1987, June 30 *Perf. 13x13½***

| | | |
|---|---|---|
| **1495** A909 80w multicolored | .60 | .25 |
| **1496** A909 80w multicolored | .60 | .25 |

Introduction of automatic switching telephone system.

Independence Hall, Monument to the Nation — A910

Statue of Indomitable Koreans, Nat'l. Flag — A911

**1987, Aug. 14 Photo. *Perf. 13½x13***

| | | |
|---|---|---|
| **1497** A910 80w multicolored | .95 | .30 |
| *a.* Souvenir sheet of 2 | 11.00 | 11.00 |
| **1498** A911 80w multicolored | .95 | .30 |
| *a.* Souvenir sheet of 2 | 11.00 | 11.00 |

Opening of Independence Hall, Aug. 15.

16th Pacific Science Congress, Seoul, Aug. 20-30 — A912

**1987, Aug. 20 *Perf. 13x13½***

| | | |
|---|---|---|
| **1499** A912 80w multicolored | .65 | .25 |
| *a.* Souvenir sheet of 2 | 3.00 | 3.00 |

State Visit of Pres. Virgilio Barco of Colombia A913

**1987, Sept. 8 Litho. *Perf. 13½x13***

| | | |
|---|---|---|
| **1500** A913 80w multicolored | .55 | .25 |
| *a.* Souvenir sheet of 2 | 2.10 | 2.10 |

Installation of 10-millionth Telephone A914

**1987, Sept. 28 *Perf. 13½x13***

| | | |
|---|---|---|
| **1501** A914 80w multicolored | .55 | .25 |

Armed Forces, 39th Anniv. — A915

Armed Forces Day: Servicemen, flags of three military services.

**1987, Sept. 30 Litho. *Perf. 13***

| | | |
|---|---|---|
| **1502** A915 80w multicolored | .75 | .25 |

14th Philatelic Week, Nov. 18-24 — A916

80w, Boy playing the nalrali.

**1987, Nov. 18 Photo. *Perf. 13½***

| | | |
|---|---|---|
| **1503** A916 80w multicolored | .65 | .25 |

A917

**1987, Nov. 28 Litho.**

| | | |
|---|---|---|
| **1504** A917 80w multicolored | .90 | .35 |

Signing of the Antarctic Treaty by Korea, 1st anniv.

A918

**1987, Dec. 1 Photo.**

| | | |
|---|---|---|
| **1505** A918 80w multicolored | 1.15 | .30 |

New Year 1988 (Year of the Dragon).

Natl. Social Security Program A919

**1988, Jan. 4 Litho. *Perf. 13½x13***

| | | |
|---|---|---|
| **1506** A919 80w multicolored | .65 | .25 |

Completion of the Korean Antarctic Base — A919a

**1988, Feb. 16 Photo. *Perf. 13x13½***

| | | |
|---|---|---|
| **1506A** A919a 80w multicolored | 1.00 | .30 |

Inauguration of Roh Tae-Woo, 13th President A920

**1988, Feb. 24 Photo. *Perf. 13½x13***

| | | |
|---|---|---|
| **1507** A920 80w multicolored | 2.50 | .40 |
| *a.* Souvenir sheet of 2 | 20.00 | 20.00 |

World Wildlife Fund — A921

White-naped crane *(Grus vipio)* displaying various behaviors: a, Calling (1). b, Running (2). c, Spreading wings (3). d, Flying (4).

**1988, Apr. 1 *Perf. 13x13½***

| | | |
|---|---|---|
| **1508** Strip of 4 | 7.00 | 7.00 |
| *a.-d.* A921 80w any single | 1.20 | .65 |

Intl. Red Cross & Red Crescent Organizations, 125th Annivs. — A922

**1988, May 7 Photo. *Perf. 13x13½***

| | | |
|---|---|---|
| **1509** A922 80w multicolored | .65 | .25 |

Telepress Medium, 1st Anniv. — A923

**1988, June 1 Litho.**

| | | |
|---|---|---|
| **1510** A923 80w multicolored | .55 | .25 |

Pierre de Coubertin, Olympic Flag — A924

Olympic Temple A925

View of Seoul — A926

Folk Dancers — A927

**Litho. & Engr.**

**1988, Sept. 16 *Perf. 13½x13***

| | | |
|---|---|---|
| **1511** A924 80w multicolored | .85 | .30 |
| **1512** A925 80w multicolored | .85 | .30 |

**Photo.**

***Perf. 13x13½***

| | | |
|---|---|---|
| **1513** A926 80w multicolored | .85 | .30 |
| **1514** A927 80w multicolored | .85 | .30 |
| *Nos. 1511-1514 (4)* | 3.40 | 1.20 |

1988 Summer Olympics, Seoul.

**Souvenir Sheets of 2**

| | | | |
|---|---|---|---|
| *1511a* A924 | 80w | 1.75 | 1.75 |
| *1512a* A925 | 80w | 1.75 | 1.75 |
| *1513a* A926 | 80w | 1.75 | 1.75 |
| *1514a* A927 | 80w | 1.75 | 1.75 |
| *Nos. 1511a-1514a (4)* | | 7.00 | 7.00 |

Margin inscriptions on Nos. 1511a-1512a are photo.

OLYMPHILEX '88, Sept. 19-28, Seoul — A928

**1988, Sept. 19 Photo. *Perf. 13x13½***

| | | |
|---|---|---|
| **1515** A928 80w multicolored | .55 | .25 |
| *a.* Souvenir sheet of 2 | 1.75 | 1.75 |

22nd Congress of the Intl. Iron and Steel Institute, Seoul A929

**1988, Oct. 8** ***Perf. 13½x13***

**1516** A929 80w multicolored .55 .25

A930

No. 1518, Archer seated in wheelchair.

**1988, Oct. 15** ***Perf. 13x13½***

**1517** A930 80w shown .90 .55
**1518** A930 80w multicolored .65 .30

1988 Natl. Special Olympics (Paralympics), Seoul.

A931

**1988, Dec. 1 Photo.** ***Perf. 13x13½***

**1519** A931 80w multicolored .95 .25

New Year 1989 (Year of the Snake).

Souvenir Sheet

Successful Completion of the 1988 Summer Olympics, Seoul — A932

**1988, Dec. 20 Litho.** ***Perf. 13x12½***

**1520** A932 550w Opening ceremony 13.50 13.50

### Music Series

Arirang — A933

Doraji — A934

Pakyon Falls A935

Chonan-Samkori A936

Natl. ballads.

**1989-90 Photo.** ***Perf. 13x13½***

**1521** A933 80w multicolored .65 .25
**1522** A934 80w multicolored .65 .25

**Litho.**

**1523** A935 80w multicolored .65 .25
Complete booklet, 4 #1523 5.50
**1524** A936 80w multicolored .65 .25
Complete booklet, 4 #1524 5.50

Issued: Nos. 1521-1522, 3/27; Nos. 1523-1524, 2/26/90.

### Korean Folkways Series

Willowing Bow — A937

Spinning Wheel A938

Treating Threads A939

Weaving Fabric A940

**Litho. & Engr.**

**1990, Sept. 25** ***Perf. 13½x13***

**1525** A937 100w multicolored .95 .30
**1526** A938 100w multicolored .95 .30
**1527** A939 100w multicolored .95 .30
**1528** A940 100w multicolored .95 .30
*a.* Strip of 4, #1525-1528 4.25 4.25

### Music Series

Orchard Avenue — A941

In Flower Garden — A942

A Swing A943

Longing for Mt. Keumkang A944

**1991-92 Litho.** ***Perf. 13x13½***

**1529** A941 100w multicolored .80 .30
Complete booklet, 4 #1529 7.00
**1530** A942 100w multicolored .80 .30
Complete booklet, 4 #1530 7.00
**1531** A943 100w multicolored .65 .25
Complete booklet, 4 #1531 7.00
**1532** A944 100w multicolored .65 .25
Complete booklet, 4 #1532 7.00

Issued: Nos. 1529-1530, 3/27; Nos. 1531-1532, 7/13/92.

14th Asian-Pacific Dental Congress — A945

**1989, Apr. 26 Photo.** ***Perf. 13x13½***

**1533** A945 80w multicolored .55 .25

Rotary Intl. Convention, Seoul, May 21-25 — A946

**1989, May 20 Photo.** ***Perf. 13x13½***

**1534** A946 80w multicolored .65 .25

19th Cong. of the Intl. Council of Nurses, Seoul, May 28-June 2 — A947

**1989, May 27**

**1535** A947 80w multicolored .65 .25
Complete booklet, 4 #1535 4.50

Information Industry Month — A948

**1989, June 1**

**1536** A948 80w multicolored .65 .25
Complete booklet, 4 #1536 4.50

World Environment Day — A949

**1989, June 5**

**1537** A949 80w multicolored .65 .25

Asia-Pacific Telecommunity, 10th Anniv. — A950

**1989, July 1 Photo.** ***Perf. 13x13½***

**1538** A950 80w multicolored .65 .25

French Revolution, Bicent. A951

**1989, July 14 Litho.** ***Perf. 13½x13***

**1539** A951 80w multicolored .55 .25
Complete booklet, 4 #1539 4.50

Federation of Asian and Oceanian Biochemists 5th Congress A952

**1989, Aug. 12** **Photo.**

**1540** A952 80w multicolored .55 .25
Complete booklet, 4 #1540 4.50

### Modern Art Series

*A White Ox,* by Lee Joong-Sub — A953

*A Street Stall,* by Park Lae-hyun A954

*A Little Girl,* by Lee Bong-Sang A955

*An Autumn Scene,* by Oh Ji-ho — A956

**Litho. & Engr.; Photo. (#1542, 1544)**

**1989, Sept. 4** ***Perf. 13x13½, 13½x13***

**1541** A953 80w multicolored .70 .30
**1542** A954 80w multicolored .70 .30
**1543** A955 80w multicolored .70 .30
**1544** A956 80w multicolored .70 .30
*Nos. 1541-1544 (4)* 2.80 1.20

Allegory: The Valiant Spirit of Koreans A965

**1989, Sept. 12 Litho.** ***Perf. 13½x13***

**1553** A965 80w multicolored .55 .25
Complete booklet, 4 #1553 4.50

1988 Seoul Olympics and the World Korean Sports Festival.

Personification of Justice and Ancient Codex — A966

**1989, Sept. 18**

**1554** A966 80w multicolored .65 .25

Constitutional Court, 1st anniv.

### Fish

A967

A968

A969

A970

No. 1555, Oplegnathus fasciatus. No. 1556, Cobitis multifasciata. No. 1557, Liobagrus mediadiposalis. No. 1558, Monocentris japonicus.

**1989, Sept. 30 Photo. *Perf. 13½x13***

**1555** A967 80w multicolored .75 .30
**1556** A968 80w multicolored .75 .30
**1557** A969 80w multicolored .75 .30
**1558** A970 80w multicolored .75 .30

A971

A972

A973

A974

No. 1559, Hapalogenys mucronatus. No. 1560, Fugu niphobles. No. 1561, Oncorhynchus masou. No. 1562, Rhodeus ocellatus.

**1990, July 2**

**1559** A971 100w multicolored .80 .30
Complete booklet, 4 #1559 8.75
**1560** A972 100w multicolored .80 .30
Complete booklet, 4 #1560 8.75
**1561** A973 100w multicolored .80 .30
Complete booklet, 4 #1561 8.75
**1562** A974 100w multicolored .80 .30
Complete booklet, 4 #1562 8.75

A975

A976

A977

A978

No. 1563, Microphyso- gobio longidorsalis. No. 1564, Gnathopogon majimae. No. 1565, Therapon oxyrhnchus. No. 1566, Psettina ijimae.

**1991, June 8**

**1563** A975 100w multicolored .85 .25
Complete booklet, 4 #1563 8.75
**1564** A976 100w multicolored .85 .25
Complete booklet, 4 #1564 8.75
**1565** A977 100w multicolored .85 .25
Complete booklet, 4 #1565 8.75
**1566** A978 100w multicolored .85 .25
Complete booklet, 4 #1566 8.75
*Nos. 1555-1566 (12)* 9.60 3.40

Light of Peace Illuminating the World — A979

**1989, Oct. 4**

**1567** A979 80w multicolored .55 .25

44th Intl. Eucharistic Cong., Seoul, Oct. 4-8.

29th World Congress of the Intl. Civil Airports Assoc., Seoul, Oct. 17-19 — A980

**1989, Oct. 17**

**1568** A980 80w multicolored .55 .25

Philatelic Week — A981

**1989, Nov. 18 Photo. *Perf. 13x13½***

**1569** A981 80w Lantern .55 .25
*a.* Souvenir sheet of 2 1.90 1.90

Two Cranes — A982

Folk Festival Customs A983

**1989, Dec. 1 *Perf. 13x13½, 13½x13***

**1570** A982 80w multicolored .70 .25
*a.* Souvenir sheet of 2 1.75 1.75
**1571** A983 80w multicolored .70 .25
*a.* Souvenir sheet of 2 1.75 1.75

New Year 1990.

World Meteorological Day — A984

**1990, Mar. 23 *Perf. 13½x13***

**1572** A984 80w multicolored .55 .25
Complete booklet, 4 #1572 6.25

UNICEF in Korea, 40th Anniv. — A985

**1990, Mar. 24 *Perf. 13x13½***

**1573** A985 80w multicolored .55 .25
Complete booklet, 4 #1573 6.25

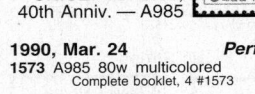

Cheju-Kohung Fiber Optic Submarine Cable A986

**1990, Apr. 21 *Perf. 13½x13***

**1574** A986 80w multicolored .55 .25
Complete booklet, 4 #1574 6.25

Saemaul Movement, 20th Anniv. A987

**1990, Apr. 21**

**1575** A987 100w multicolored .55 .25
Complete booklet, 4 #1575 6.25

Youth Month A988

**1990, May 1**

**1576** A988 100w multicolored .65 .25
Complete booklet, 4 #1576 6.25

**Type of 1981 and**

Korean Flag — A989

Korean Stork — A990

White Magnolia A991

Korean White Pine A991a

Cart-shaped Earthenware A992

Fire Safety A993

Environmental Protection A994

Traffic Safety A995

Waiting One's Turn A996

Saving Energy A997

Child Protection A997a

Purification of Language Movement A997b

Rose of Sharon A997c

Give Life to Water A997d

Ginger Jar — A998

Chong-IP'um-Song, Pine Tree Natl. Monument — A999

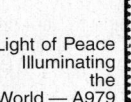

Drum, Drum Dance A1001

Mask, Wrestlers A1002

Hong Yong-Sik A1003

King Sejong, Korean Alphabet A1004

Dragon Head, Banner Staff — A1005

Gilt-bronze Buddha Triad with Inscription of Keymi — A1006

**Photo., Litho. (#1582), Litho. & Engr. (#1594)**

**1990-96** *Perf. 13½x13, 13x13½*

| | | | | | |
|---|---|---|---|---|---|
| **1577** | A989 | 10w multi | .40 | .25 |
| **1578** | A990 | 20w multi | .40 | .25 |
| **1579** | A991 | 30w multi | .45 | .25 |
| **1580** | A991a | 40w multi | .40 | .25 |
| **1581** | A992 | 50w multi | .55 | .25 |
| **1582** | A993 | 80w multi | 3.00 | .30 |
| **1583** | A994 | 100w multi | 8.00 | .35 |
| | | Complete booklet, 10 #1583 | 85.00 | |
| **1584** | A995 | 100w multi | 2.00 | .35 |
| | | Complete booklet, 10 #1584 | 20.00 | |
| **1585** | A996 | 100w multi | 1.90 | .25 |
| **1586** | A997 | 100w multi | 1.10 | .25 |
| **1587** | A997a | 100w multi | 1.10 | .25 |
| **1588** | A997b | 100w multi | 1.25 | .25 |
| **1589** | A997c | 110w multi | .90 | .25 |
| **1590** | A997d | 110w multi | 1.00 | .25 |
| **1591** | A998 | 150w multi | 1.30 | .25 |
| *a.* | | Booklet pane, 20 #1591 | 16.50 | |
| | | Complete booklet, #1591a | 19.00 | |
| **1592** | A999 | 160w multi | 1.30 | .25 |
| **1593** | A1001 | 370w multi | 2.50 | .45 |
| **1594** | A1002 | 440w multi | 3.25 | .50 |
| **1594A** | A1003 | 600w multi | 4.00 | .65 |
| **1594B** | A1004 | 710w multi | 4.75 | .80 |
| **1594C** | A1005 | 800w multi | 5.00 | .80 |
| **1594D** | A1006 | 900w multi | 5.75 | .70 |
| | | *Nos. 1577-1594D (22)* | 50.30 | 8.15 |

Issued: No. 1583, 6/5; 600w, 6/25; 150w, 7/2; 800w, 7/10; No. 1584, 7/25; 50w, 9/28; 80w, 11/1; No. 1585, 6/26/91; No. 1586, 11/1/91; No. 1587, 4/5/92; No. 1588, 11/2/92; 370w, 440w, 3/22/93; 10w, No. 1589, 3/30/93; 160w, 710w, 4/30/93; 20w, 30w, 40w, 5/24/93; No. 1590, 7/1/93; 900w, 9/20/93; #1591a, 3/20/96.

See Nos. 1715-1738, 1846, 1851-1852, 1860, 1862.

### Coil Stamps

**1990** **Litho.** *Perf. 13 Horiz.*

| | | | | |
|---|---|---|---|---|
| **1594E** | A992 50w multicolored | .90 | .30 |

*Perf. 13 Vert.*

| | | | |
|---|---|---|---|
| **1594F** | A706 60w multicolored | .70 | .25 |
| **1594G** | A994 100w multicolored | 1.50 | .60 |
| **1594H** | A997c 110w multicolored | 1.10 | .25 |
| | *Nos. 1594E-1594H (4)* | 4.20 | 1.40 |

Seoul Mail Center A1007

**1990, July 4** **Litho.** *Perf. 13½x13*

| | | | |
|---|---|---|---|
| **1595** | A1007 100w multicolored | .65 | .25 |
| *a.* | Souvenir sheet of 2 | 2.00 | 2.00 |
| | Complete booklet, 4 #1595 | 4.50 | |

8th Korean Boy Scout Jamboree — A1008

**1990, Aug. 8** *Perf. 13x13½*

| | | | |
|---|---|---|---|
| **1596** | A1008 100w multicolored | .65 | .25 |
| | Complete booklet, 4 #1596 | 5.00 | |

### Wild Flowers

Lilium — A1009

Aster — A1010

Adonis A1011

Scabiosa A1012

**1990, Aug. 25** **Photo.**

| | | | |
|---|---|---|---|
| **1597** | A1009 370w multicolored | 1.60 | .70 |
| | Complete booklet, 4 #1597 | 15.00 | |
| **1598** | A1010 400w multicolored | 2.00 | .90 |
| | Complete booklet, 4 #1598 | 19.50 | |
| **1599** | A1011 440w multicolored | 1.90 | .80 |
| | Complete booklet, 4 #1599 | 18.00 | |
| **1600** | A1012 470w multicolored | 2.25 | .80 |
| | Complete booklet, 4 #1600 | 21.00 | |

A1013

No. 1601, Aerides japonicum. No. 1602, Heloniopsis orientalis. No. 1603, Aquilegia buergeriana. No. 1604, Gentiana zollingeri.

**1991, July 26**

| | | | |
|---|---|---|---|
| **1601** | A1013 100w multicolored | .60 | .25 |
| | Complete booklet, 4 #1601 | 4.75 | |
| **1602** | A1013 100w multicolored | .60 | .25 |
| | Complete booklet, 4 #1602 | 4.75 | |
| **1603** | A1013 370w multicolored | 1.75 | .55 |
| | Complete booklet, 4 #1603 | 13.50 | |
| **1604** | A1013 440w multicolored | 2.00 | .60 |
| | Complete booklet, 4 #1604 | 16.00 | |

**1992, June 22** **Photo.** *Perf. 13x13½*

No. 1605, Lychnis wilfordii. No. 1606, Lycoris radiata. No. 1607, Commelina communis. No. 1608, Calanthe striata.

| | | | |
|---|---|---|---|
| **1605** | A1013 100w multicolored | .60 | .30 |
| | Complete booklet, 4 #1605 | 5.00 | |
| **1606** | A1013 100w multicolored | .60 | .30 |
| | Complete booklet, 4 #1606 | 5.00 | |
| **1607** | A1013 370w multicolored | 1.60 | .55 |
| | Complete booklet, 4 #1607 | 13.00 | |
| **1608** | A1013 440w multicolored | 1.90 | .60 |
| | Complete booklet, 4 #1608 | 15.00 | |
| | *Nos. 1597-1608 (12)* | 17.40 | 6.60 |

See Nos. 1751-1762, 1869-1872, 1907-1910.

Anglican Church of Korea, Cent. — A1021

**1990, Sept. 29** **Litho.** *Perf. 13x13½*

| | | | |
|---|---|---|---|
| **1609** | A1021 100w | .65 | .25 |

Opening of Seoul Tower, 10th Anniv. — A1022

**1990, Oct. 15**

| | | | |
|---|---|---|---|
| **1610** | A1022 100w blk, red & bl | .65 | .25 |

National Census — A1023

**1990, Oct. 20** *Perf. 13x13½*

| | | | |
|---|---|---|---|
| **1611** | A1023 100w multicolored | .55 | .25 |

UN Development Program, 40th Anniv. A1024

**1990, Oct. 24**

| | | | |
|---|---|---|---|
| **1612** | A1024 100w multicolored | .55 | .25 |

Philatelic Week — A1025

**Litho. & Engr.**

**1990, Nov. 16** *Perf. 13x13½*

| | | | |
|---|---|---|---|
| **1613** | A1025 100w multicolored | .65 | .25 |
| *a.* | Souvenir sheet of 2 | 4.00 | 4.00 |
| | Complete booklet, 4 #1613 | 5.00 | |

New Year 1991 (Year of the Sheep) — A1026

Two Cranes — A1027

**1990, Dec. 1** **Litho.** *Perf. 13x13½*

| | | | |
|---|---|---|---|
| **1614** | A1026 100w multicolored | .60 | .25 |
| | Complete booklet, 4 #1614 | 4.50 | |
| **1615** | A1027 100w multicolored | .60 | .25 |
| | Complete booklet, 4 #1615 | 4.50 | |
| *a.* | Souv. sheet of 2, #1614-1615 | 5.25 | 5.25 |

### Taejon Expo '93

A1028

A1029

**1990, Dec. 12**

| | | | |
|---|---|---|---|
| **1616** | A1028 100w multicolored | .75 | .30 |
| *a.* | Souvenir sheet of 2 | 1.60 | 1.60 |
| | Complete booklet, 4 #1616 | 6.25 | |
| **1617** | A1029 440w multicolored | 1.90 | .75 |
| *a.* | Souvenir sheet of 2 | 5.25 | 5.25 |
| | Complete booklet, 4 #1617 | 22.50 | |

A1030

A1031

**1991, Mar. 23**

| | | | |
|---|---|---|---|
| **1618** | A1030 100w multicolored | .70 | .30 |
| *a.* | Souvenir sheet of 2 | 1.60 | 1.60 |
| | Complete booklet, 4 #1618 | 5.75 | |
| **1619** | A1031 100w multicolored | .70 | .30 |
| *a.* | Souvenir sheet of 2 | 1.60 | 1.60 |
| | Complete booklet, 4 #1619 | 5.75 | |

A1032

A1033

**1992, Aug. 7** **Photo.** *Perf. 13½x13*

| | | | |
|---|---|---|---|
| **1620** | A1032 100w multicolored | .65 | .25 |
| *a.* | Souvenir sheet of 2 | 1.35 | 1.35 |
| | Complete booklet, 4 #1620 | 3.75 | |
| **1621** | A1033 100w multicolored | .65 | .25 |
| *a.* | Souvenir sheet of 2 | 1.35 | 1.35 |
| | Complete booklet, 4 #1621 | 3.75 | |

Government Pavilion A1034

Intl. Pavilion A1035

Recycling Art Pavilion A1035a

Telcom Pavilion A1035b

**1993, Aug. 7**

| | | | | |
|---|---|---|---|---|
| **1622** | A1034 110w multi | .70 | .25 |
| *a.* | Souvenir sheet of 2 | 1.25 | 1.25 |
| | Complete booklet, 4 #1622 | 5.00 | |
| **1623** | A1035 110w multi | .70 | .25 |
| *c.* | Souvenir sheet of 2 | 1.25 | 1.25 |
| | Complete booklet, 4 #1623 | 5.00 | |
| **1623A** | A1035a 110w multi | .70 | .25 |
| *d.* | Souvenir sheet of 2 | 1.25 | 1.25 |
| | Complete booklet, 4 #1623A | 5.00 | |
| **1623B** | A1035b 110w multi | .70 | .25 |
| *e.* | Souvenir sheet of 2 | 1.25 | 1.25 |
| | Complete booklet, 4 #1623B | 5.00 | |
| | *Nos. 1616-1623B (10)* | 8.15 | 3.15 |

Saemaul Minilibrary, 30th Anniv. A1036

**1991, Feb. 1 Litho. *Perf. 13½x13***

**1624** A1036 100w multicolored .60 .25
Complete booklet, 4 #1624 4.25

Moth A1037

Beetle A1038

Butterfly A1039

Beetle A1040

Cicada — A1041

**1991, Apr. 8 Photo. *Perf. 13½x13***

| | | | |
|---|---|---|---|
| **1625** | A1037 100w shown | .85 | .25 |
| **1626** | A1038 100w shown | .85 | .25 |
| **1627** | A1039 100w shown | .85 | .25 |
| **1628** | A1040 100w shown | .85 | .25 |
| **1629** | A1041 100w shown | .85 | .25 |
| **1630** | A1040 100w Water beetle | .85 | .25 |
| **1631** | A1040 100w Bee | .85 | .25 |
| **1632** | A1040 100w Lady bug | .85 | .25 |
| **1633** | A1037 100w Dragonfly | .85 | .25 |
| **1634** | A1037 100w Grasshopper | .85 | .25 |
| *a.* | Strip of 10, #1625-1634 | 11.00 | 12.00 |

Printed in sheets of 100 with each row shifted one design.

Traditional Performing Arts Center, 40th Anniv. — A1042

**1991, Apr. 10 *Perf. 13x13½***

**1635** A1042 100w multicolored .65 .25
Complete booklet, 4 #1635 4.50

Provisional Government, 72nd Anniv. A1043

**1991, Apr. 13 *Perf. 13½x13***

**1636** A1043 100w multicolored .65 .25
Complete booklet, 4 #1636 4.50

Hire the Handicapped A1044

**1991, Apr. 20**

**1637** A1044 100w multicolored .65 .25
Complete booklet, 4 #1637 5.00

Teachers' Day, 10th Anniv. A1045

**1991, May 15 Litho. *Perf. 13½x13***

**1638** A1045 100w multicolored .65 .25
Complete booklet, 4 #1638 4.50

A1046

**1991, Aug. 8 Litho. *Perf. 13x13½***

**1639** A1046 100w multicolored .65 .25
*a.* Souvenir sheet of 2 1.60 1.60
Complete booklet, 4 #1639 7.25

17th World Scouting Jamboree.

YMCA World Assembly — A1047

**1991, Aug. 22 Litho. *Perf. 13x13½***

**1640** A1047 100w multicolored .65 .25
Complete booklet, 4 #1640 7.25

Natl. Desire for Reunification A1048

**1991, Sept. 11 Litho. *Perf. 13x13½***

**1641** A1048 100w multicolored .65 .25
Complete booklet, 4 #1641 6.50

Admission to UN — A1049

**1991, Sept. 18 *Perf. 13½x13***

**1642** A1049 100w multicolored .65 .25
Complete booklet, 4 #1642 5.25

### Musical Instruments

Deerskin Drum (Galgo) A1050

Mouth Organ (Saenghwang) A1051

Seated Drum — A1052

Small Gong — A1053

Designs: No. 1645, Brass chimes (Unra). No. 1646, Large gong (Jing). No. 1649, Dragon drum. No. 1650, Single bell chime.

**1991-92 Photo. *Perf. 13x13½***

**Background color**

| | | | |
|---|---|---|---|
| **1643** | A1050 100w gray | .75 | .30 |
| | Complete booklet, 4 #1643 | 5.00 | |
| **1644** | A1051 100w tan | .75 | .30 |
| | Complete booklet, 4 #1644 | 5.00 | |
| **1645** | A1050 100w lt violet | .75 | .30 |
| | Complete booklet, 4 #1645 | 5.00 | |
| **1646** | A1050 100w pale green | .75 | .30 |
| | Complete booklet, 4 #1646 | 5.00 | |
| **1647** | A1052 100w gray | .80 | .30 |
| | Complete booklet, 4 #1647 | 5.00 | |
| **1648** | A1053 100w tan | .80 | .30 |
| | Complete booklet, 4 #1648 | 5.00 | |
| **1649** | A1052 100w pale violet | .80 | .30 |
| | Complete booklet, 4 #1649 | 5.00 | |
| **1650** | A1053 100w pale green | .80 | .30 |
| | Complete booklet, 4 #1650 | 5.00 | |
| | *Nos. 1643-1650 (8)* | 6.20 | 2.40 |

Issued: Nos. 1643-1646, 9/26; others, 2/24/92.

Month of Culture — A1056

**1991, Oct. 1 Litho. *Perf. 13x13½***

**1655** A1056 100w multicolored .65 .25
Complete booklet, 4 #1655 4.50

Telecom '91 — A1057

**1991, Oct. 7 Photo.**

**1656** A1057 100w multicolored .65 .25
Complete booklet, 4 #1656 5.00

Sixth World Telecommunication Exhibition & Forum, Geneva, Switzerland.

### Beauty Series

A1058

A1059

Kottam Architectural Patterns
A1060 A1061

**1991, Oct. 26**

| | | | |
|---|---|---|---|
| **1657** | A1058 100w multicolored | .85 | .30 |
| **1658** | A1059 100w multicolored | .85 | .30 |
| **1659** | A1060 100w multicolored | .85 | .30 |
| **1660** | A1061 100w multicolored | .85 | .30 |
| *a.* | Block or strip of 4, #1657-1660 | 4.25 | 4.25 |
| | Complete booklet, 2 #1660a | — | |

A1062

A1063

Norigae
A1064 A1065

**1992, Sept. 21 Photo. & Engr.**

| | | | |
|---|---|---|---|
| **1661** | A1062 100w multicolored | .70 | .30 |
| **1662** | A1063 100w multicolored | .70 | .30 |
| **1663** | A1064 100w multicolored | .70 | .30 |
| **1664** | A1065 100w multicolored | .70 | .30 |
| *a.* | Block or strip of 4, #1661-1664 | 3.75 | 3.75 |
| | Complete booklet, 2 #1664a | — | |

A1066

A1067

Tapestries
A1068 A1069

**1993, Oct. 11 Photo. *Perf. 13x13½***

| | | | |
|---|---|---|---|
| **1665** | A1066 110w multicolored | .60 | .30 |
| **1666** | A1067 110w multicolored | .60 | .30 |
| **1667** | A1068 110w multicolored | .60 | .30 |
| **1668** | A1069 110w multicolored | .60 | .30 |
| *a.* | Block or strip of 4, #1665-1668 | 3.00 | 3.00 |
| | Complete booklet, 2 #1668a | — | |

Philatelic Week — A1070

**1991, Dec. 5 Photo.** ***Perf. 13x13½***
**1669** A1070 100w multicolored .65 .25
*a.* Souvenir sheet of 2 1.50 1.50
Complete booklet, 4 #1669 4.50

New Year 1992, Year of the Monkey
A1071 A1072

**1991, Dec. 2** **Photo. & Engr.**
**1670** A1071 100w multicolored .70 .25
*a.* Souvenir sheet of 2 1.90 1.90
Complete booklet, 4 #1670 5.00
**1671** A1072 100w multicolored .70 .25
*a.* Souvenir sheet of 2 1.90 1.90
Complete booklet, 4 #1671 5.00

Hibiscus Syriacus, Natl. Flower — A1073

**1992, Mar. 9 Photo.** ***Perf. 13x13½***
**Background color**
**1672** A1073 100w lt green 1.10 .40
**1673** A1073 100w lt blue 1.10 .40

Im-Jin War, 400th Anniv. A1074

**1992, May 23 Photo.** ***Perf. 13½x13***
**1674** A1074 100w multicolored .55 .25
Complete booklet, 4 #1674 4.50

Science Day, 25th Anniv. A1075

**1992, Apr. 21 Photo.** ***Perf. 13½x13***
**1675** A1075 100w multicolored .55 .25
Complete booklet, 4 #1675 4.50

Pong-Gil Yoon, Assassin of Japanese Occupation Leaders, 60th Anniv. of Execution — A1076

**Photo. & Engr.**
**1992, Apr. 29** ***Perf. 13x13½***
**1676** A1076 100w multicolored .55 .25
Complete booklet, 4 #1676 4.50

60th Intl. Fertilizer Assoc. Conf. — A1077

**Photo & Engr.**
**1992, May 25** ***Perf. 13x13½***
**1678** A1077 100w multicolored .55 .25
Complete booklet, 4 #1678 4.50

1992 Summer Olympics, Barcelona — A1078

No. 1679, Pole vault. No. 1680, Rhythmic gymnastics.

**1992, July 25 Photo.** ***Perf. 13x13½***
**1679** A1078 100w multi .65 .25
Complete booklet, 4 #1679 4.50
**1680** A1078 100w multi .65 .25
Complete booklet, 4 #1680 4.50

21st Universal Postal Congress, Seoul, 1994 A1079

Designs: No. 1681, Korean Exhibition Center, Namdae-mun Gate. No. 1682, Stone statue of Tolharubang, Songsan Ilchulbong Peak.

**1992, Aug. 22 Photo.** ***Perf. 13½x13***
**1681** A1079 100w red vio & multi .60 .25
*a.* Souvenir sheet of 2 1.50 1.50
Complete booklet, 4 #1681 4.50
**1682** A1079 100w brown & multi .60 .25
*a.* Souvenir sheet of 2 1.50 1.50
Complete booklet, 4 #1682 4.50

A1086

**Litho. & Engr.**
**1992, Oct. 10** ***Perf. 13x13½***
**1683** A1086 100w sal & red brn .55 .25
Complete booklet, 4 #1683 4.50

Pong-Chang Yi (1900-1932), would-be assassin of Japanese Emperor Hirohito.

A1087

Design: No. 1684, Hwang Young-Jo, 1992 Olympic marathon winner. No. 1685, Shon Kee-Chung, 1936 Olympic Marathon Winner.

**1992, Oct. 10** **Litho.**
**1684** A1087 100w multicolored .70 .25
**1685** A1087 100w grn & multi .70 .25
*a.* Pair, #1684-1685 1.90 1.90
*b.* Souv. sheet of 2, #1684-1685 4.00 4.00
Complete booklet, 2 #1685a 9.00

Discovery of America, 500th Anniv. — A1088

**1992, Oct. 12** **Photo.**
**1686** A1088 100w multicolored .70 .25
Complete booklet, 4 #1686 8.00

Philatelic Week A1089

**1992, Nov. 14 Photo.** ***Perf. 13½x13***
**1687** A1089 100w multicolored .55 .25
*a.* Souvenir sheet of 2 1.60 1.60
Complete booklet, 4 #1687 4.50

New Year 1993 (Year of the Rooster)
A1090 A1091

**1992, Dec. 1 Photo.** ***Perf. 13x13½***
**1688** A1090 100w multicolored .70 .25
*a.* Souvenir sheet of 2 1.90 1.90
Complete booklet, 4 #1688 5.00
**1689** A1091 100w multicolored .70 .25
*a.* Souvenir sheet of 2 1.90 1.90
Complete booklet, 4 #1689 5.00

Intl. Conference on Nutrition, Rome A1092

**1992, Dec. 5** ***Perf. 13½x13***
**1690** A1092 100w multicolored .55 .25
Complete booklet, 4 #1690 4.50

Seoul Art Center, Grand Opening A1093

**1993, Feb. 15 Photo.** ***Perf. 13½x13***
**1691** A1093 110w multicolored .55 .25
Complete booklet, 4 #1691 4.50

Inauguration of Kim Young Sam, 14th President A1094

**1993, Feb. 24**
**1692** A1094 110w multicolored 1.00 .30
*a.* Souvenir sheet of 2 5.75 5.75

Student Inventions Exhibition — A1095

**1993, May 27 Photo.** ***Perf. 13x13½***
**1693** A1095 110w lilac & silver .55 .25
Complete booklet, 4 #1693 5.25

A1096

**1993, June 14 Photo.** ***Perf. 13x13½***
**1694** A1096 110w multicolored .55 .25
Complete booklet, 4 #1694 5.25

UN Conference on Human Rights, Vienna.

Mushrooms A1098

No. 1696, Ganoderma lucidum. No. 1697, Pleurotus ostreatus. No. 1698, Lentinula edodes. No. 1699, Tricholoma matsutake.

**1993, July 26 Photo.** ***Perf. 13x13½***
**1696** A1098 110w multicolored .50 .25
Complete booklet, 4 #1696 5.00
**1697** A1098 110w multicolored .50 .25
Complete booklet, 4 #1697 5.00
**1698** A1098 110w multicolored .50 .25
Complete booklet, 4 #1698 5.00
**1699** A1098 110w multicolored .50 .25
Complete booklet, 4 #1699 5.00
*Nos. 1696-1699 (4)* 2.00 1.00

See Nos. 1770-1773, 1803-1806, 1883-1886, 1912-1915, 1935.

A1099

**1993, Aug. 28 Photo.** ***Perf. 13x13½***
**1700** A1099 110w multicolored .65 .25
Complete booklet, 4 #1700 3.75

19th World Congress of Intl. Society of Orthopedic Surgery and Trauma Study.

O-Dol-Odo-Gi A1100
Ong-He-Ya A1101

**1993, Sept. 13**
**1701** A1100 110w multicolored .65 .25
Complete booklet, 4 #1701 3.75
**1702** A1101 110w multicolored .65 .25
Complete booklet, 4 #1702 3.75

Visit Korea Year '94
A1112 A1113

**1993, Sept. 27 Photo.** ***Perf. 13x13½***
**1713** A1112 110w multicolored .55 .25
Complete booklet, 4 #1713 3.75
**1714** A1113 110w multicolored .55 .25
Complete booklet, 4 #1714 3.75

**Type of 1993 and**

Squirrel A1114
Physalis Alkekengi A1115

Scops Owl
A1116

Reduce
Garbage
A1117

Narcissus
A1118

Little Tern
A1119

Sea Turtle — A1120

Airplane
A1122

Passenger
Airplane
A1123

Porcelain
Chicken Water
Dropper
A1124

Celadon
Water
Dropper
A1125

Gilt Bronze
Bongnae-san
Incense
Burner — A1127

Celadon
Pitcher — A1128

Designs: 300w, Van. 540w, Train. 1190w, Passenger ship.

***Perf. 13½x13, 13x13½ (210w, 1050w, #1728, 1732, 1734), 13½x12½ (60w, 90w), 12½x13½ (180w, 200w)***

**Photo., Litho. (#1726), Photo. & Engr. (#1734)**

**1993-95**

**1715** A1114 60w multi .50 .30
**1716** A1115 70w multi .45 .25
**1717** A1116 90w multi .65 .30
**1718** A1117 110w multi .85 .25
**1719** A997c 120w multi .85 .25
**1720** A1118 130w multi .85 .30
*a.* Booklet pane of 20 16.50
Complete booklet, #1720a 16.50
**1721** A1119 180w multi 1.25 .30
**1722** A1120 200w multi 1.60 .30
**1723** A1119 210w multi 1.40 .25
**1724** A1123 300w multi 1.90 .40
**1725** A1122 330w multi 2.75 .25
**1726** A1123 390w multi 2.50 .45
*a.* Booklet pane of 10 29.00
Complete booklet, #1726a 29.00
**1727** A1122 400w multi 2.00 .35
*a.* Booklet pane, 10 #1727 23.00
Complete booklet, #1727a 23.00
**1728** A1124 400w multi 2.00 .35
**1729** A1125 500w multi 2.25 .55
**1730** A1123 540w multi 3.00 .65
**1731** A1122 560w multi 3.25 .50
**1732** A1127 700w multi 3.50 .75
**1733** A1004 910w like #1594B 5.25 1.00
**1734** A1128 930w blue & multi 5.25 .85
**1735** A1128 930w tan & multi 5.25 1.00
*a.* Booklet pane of 10 67.50
Complete booklet, #1735a 67.50
**1736** A1128 1050w multi 5.50 .80
**1737** A1123 1190w multi 6.00 1.10
**1738** A1122 1300w multi 7.25 .95
*Nos. 1715-1738 (24)* 66.05 12.45

Issued: No. 1718, 11/1/93; 910w, 2/15/94; 90w, 4/22/94; 130w, 8/20/94; 80w, 9/12/94; 390w, No. 1734, 1190w, 10/1/94; 540w, 11/1/94; 300w, 11/18/94; 60w, 200w, 12/19/94;
No. 1720a, 2/28/95; 70w, 3/15/95; No. 1737, 3/11/95; No. 1735a, 3/20/95; 700w, 6/15/95; No. 1728, 8/28/95; No. 1727, 10/16/95; 1050w, 1300w, 10/25/95; 210w, 560w, 11/1/95; 500w, 11/6/95;
120w, 330w, 11/11/95; No. 1727a, 3/27/96.
Five versions of booklets with No. 1720a exist with blocks of different colors at the top of the booklet cover. The blocks of color match color bars printed in the selvage of the attached booklet pane.
See Nos. 1847-1848, 1857.

### Coil Stamp

**1990 Litho. *Perf. 13 Vert.***
**1739** A1118 130w multicolored 4.50 .40

Philatelic
Week — A1144

**1993, Nov. 13 Photo. *Perf. 13x13½***
**1745** A1144 110w multicolored .65 .25
*a.* Souvenir sheet of 2 1.35 1.35
Complete booklet, 4 #1745 8.00

21st UPU
Congress,
Seoul — A1145

No. 1746, Dancer, muscians. No. 1747, Weavers, horiz.

***Perf. 13x13½, 13½x13***
**1993, Nov. 18**
**1746** A1145 110w multicolored .55 .25
*a.* Souvenir sheet of 2 1.40 1.40
Complete booklet, 4 #1746 4.75
**1747** A1145 110w multicolored .55 .25
*a.* Souvenir sheet of 2 1.40 1.40
Complete booklet, 4 #1747 4.75

Trade Day,
30th Anniv.
A1146

**1993, Nov. 30 *Perf. 13½x13***
**1748** A1146 110w multicolored .55 .25
Complete booklet, 4 #1748 4.50

New Year
1994 (Year of
the Dog)
A1147

**1993, Dec. 1 *Perf. 13½x13, 13x13½***
**1749** A1147 110w shown .90 .25
*a.* Souvenir sheet of 2 1.60 1.60
**1750** A1147 110w Stuffed toy dog, vert. .90 .25
*a.* Souvenir sheet of 2 1.60 1.60

### Flower Type of 1991

No. 1751, Weigela bortensis. No. 1752, Caltha palustris. No. 1753, Iris ruthenica. No. 1754, Aceriphyllum rosii. No. 1755, Leontopodium japonicum. No. 1756, Geranium eriostemon. No. 1757, Lycoris aurea. No. 1758, Gentiana jamesii. No. 1759, Halenia corniculata. No. 1760, Erthyronium japonicum. No. 1761, Iris odaesanensis. No. 1762, Leontice microrrhyncha.

**1993-95 Photo. *Perf. 13x13½***
**1751** A1013 110w multicolored .70 .25
Complete booklet, 4 #1751 3.50
**1752** A1013 110w multicolored .70 .25
Complete booklet, 4 #1752 3.50
**1753** A1013 110w multicolored .70 .25
Complete booklet, 4 #1753 3.50
**1754** A1013 110w multicolored .70 .25
Complete booklet, 4 #1754 3.50
**1755** A1013 130w multicolored .95 .25
Complete booklet, 4 #1755 5.00
**1756** A1013 130w multicolored .95 .25
Complete booklet, 4 #1756 5.00
**1757** A1013 130w multicolored .95 .25
Complete booklet, 4 #1757 5.00
**1758** A1013 130w multicolored .95 .25
Complete booklet, 4 #1758 5.00
**1759** A1013 130w multicolored .95 .25
Complete booklet, 6 #1759 5.00
**1760** A1013 130w multicolored .95 .25
Complete booklet, 6 #1760 5.00
**1761** A1013 130w multicolored .95 .25
Complete booklet, 6 #1761 5.00
**1762** A1013 130w multicolored .95 .25
Complete booklet, 6 #1762 5.00
*Nos. 1751-1762 (12)* 10.40 3.00

Issued: Nos. 1751-1754, 12/20/93; Nos. 1755-1758, 10/4/94; Nos. 1759-1762, 7/24/95.

Visit Korea Year
A1148 A1149

No. 1763, Masked dancer. No. 1764, Piper, clouds.

**1994, Jan. 11 Photo. *Perf. 13x13½***
**1763** A1148 110w multicolored .60 .25
Complete booklet, 4 #1763 2.75
**1764** A1149 110w multicolored .60 .25
Complete booklet, 4 #1764 2.75

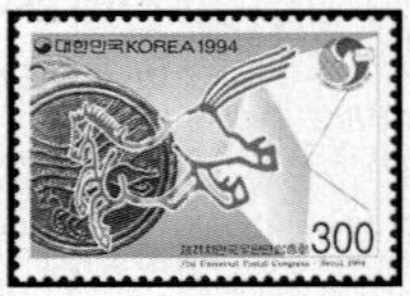
21st UPU
Congress,
Seoul
A1150

**1994, Jan. 24 *Perf. 13½x13***
**1765** A1150 300w multicolored 1.30 .45
*a.* Souvenir sheet of 2 3.25 3.25
*b.* Booklet pane of 10 27.00
Complete booklet, #1765b 27.00

Samil Independence
Movement, 75th
Anniv. — A1151

**1994, Feb. 28 Photo. *Perf. 13x13½***
**1766** A1151 110w multicolored .50 .25

Wildlife
Protection
A1152

No. 1767, Sasakia charonda. No. 1768, Allomyrina dichotoma.

**1994, Mar. 7 Photo. *Perf. 13½x13***
**1767** A1152 110w multicolored .70 .25
*a.* Souvenir sheet of 2 1.75 1.75
Complete booklet, 4 #1767 3.75
**1768** A1152 110w multicolored .70 .25
*a.* Souvenir sheet of 2 1.75 1.75
Complete booklet, 4 #1768 3.75

Intl. Year of
the Family
A1153

**1994, May 14 Photo. *Perf. 13***
**1769** A1153 110w multicolored .55 .25

### Mushroom Type of 1993

No. 1770, Oudemansiella platyphylla. No. 1771, Morchella esculenta. No. 1772, Cortinarius purpurascens. No. 1773, Gomphus floccosus.

**1994, May 30 Photo. *Perf. 13x13½***
**1770** A1098 110w multicolored .50 .25
*a.* Souvenir sheet of 2 1.35 1.35
Complete booklet, 4 #1770 2.50
**1771** A1098 110w multicolored .50 .25
*a.* Souvenir sheet of 2 1.35 1.35
Complete booklet, 4 #1771 2.50
**1772** A1098 110w multicolored .50 .25
*a.* Souvenir sheet of 2 1.35 1.35
Complete booklet, 4 #1772 2.50
**1773** A1098 110w multicolored .50 .25
*a.* Souvenir sheet of 2 1.35 1.35
Complete booklet, 4 #1773 2.50
*Nos. 1770-1773 (4)* 2.00 1.00
*Nos. 1770a-1773a (4)* 5.40 5.40

Opening of
War Memorial
Center
A1154

**1994, June 10 Photo. *Perf. 13***
**1774** A1154 110w multicolored .55 .25

PHILAKOREA
'94, Seoul
A1155

**1994, June 13 *Perf. 13***
**1775** A1155 910w multicolored 3.75 1.25
*a.* Souvenir sheet of 1 4.00 4.00
*b.* Booklet pane of 10 37.50
Complete booklet, #1775b 37.50

Stamps from No. 1775b have a straight edge at either top or bottom.

### Beauty Series

Fans — A1156

**1994, July 18 Photo. *Perf. 13x13½***
**1776** 110w Taeguk .60 .25
**1777** 110w Crane .60 .25
**1778** 110w Pearl .60 .25
**1779** 110w Wheel .60 .25
*a.* A1156 Strip of 4, #1776-1779 3.00 3.00
Complete booklet, 2 #1779a 13.50

Gates — A1160

No. 1780, Lofty Gate, traditional Yungban residence. No. 1781, Pomosa Temple. No. 1782, Osumun (Fish Water) Gate, Changdukkung Palace. No. 1783, Pullomun Gate, Changdukkung Palace.

**1995, May 22 Photo. *Perf. 13x13½***
**1780** 130w multicolored .60 .25
**1781** 130w multicolored .60 .25
**1782** 130w multicolored .60 .25
**1783** 130w multicolored .60 .25
*a.* A1160 Strip of 4, #1780-1783 3.00 3.00
Complete booklet, 2 #1783a *13.50*

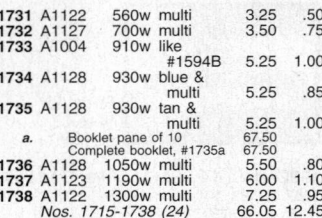

Pouches — A1164

**1996, Nov. 1 Photo. *Perf. 13x13½***

**1784** 150w multicolored .60 .25
**1785** 150w multicolored .60 .25
**1786** 150w multicolored .60 .25
**1787** 150w multicolored .60 .25
*a.* A1164 Strip of 4, #1784-1787 3.00 3.00
Complete booklet, 2 #1787a 13.50
*Nos. 1776-1787 (12)* 7.20 3.00

A1168

PHILAKOREA '94 — A1169

No. 1788, Winter scene. No. 1789, Grape vines. No. 1790, Cranes.

**1994, Aug. 16 Photo. *Perf. 13***

**1788** A1168 130w multi 1.00 .25
*a.* Souvenir sheet of 2 1.40 1.40
*b.* Booklet pane of 10 10.50
Complete booklet, #1788b 10.50
**1789** A1168 130w multi 1.00 .25
*a.* Souvenir sheet of 2 1.40 1.40
*b.* Booklet pane of 10 10.50
Complete booklet, #1789b 12.50
**1790** A1168 130w multi 1.00 .25
*a.* Souvenir sheet of 2 1.40 1.40
*b.* Booklet pane of 10 10.50
Complete booklet, #1790b 10.50
*Nos. 1788-1790 (3)* 3.00 .75

**Souvenir Sheet**

**Litho. & Engr.**

**1791** Sheet of 7 9.75 9.00
*a.* A1169 130w Crane, mountains .40 .25
*b.* A1169 300w Two cranes, sun .95 .40
*c.* A1169 370w Two cranes in trees 1.20 .50
*d.* A1169 400w Two deer 1.30 .55
*e.* A1169 440w Turtle, rapids 1.50 .60
*f.* A1169 470w River 1.50 .60
*g.* A1169 930w Trees 3.00 1.10

21st UPU Congress, Seoul — A1170

No. 1792, Pens, glasses, stamps. No. 1793, Sword dance. No. 1794, Dove holding envelope. No. 1795, Hong Yong-sik, Heinrich Von Stephan, horiz.

**1994, Aug. 22 Photo. *Perf. 13***

**1792** A1170 130w multicolored .55 .25
*a.* Souvenir sheet of 2 1.50 1.50
*b.* Booklet pane of 10 6.50
Complete booklet, #1792b 6.50
**1793** A1170 130w multicolored .55 .25
*a.* Souvenir sheet of 2 1.50 1.50
*b.* Booklet pane of 10 6.50
Complete booklet, #1793b 6.50
**1794** A1170 130w multicolored .55 .25
*a.* Souvenir sheet of 2 1.50 1.50
*b.* Booklet pane of 10 6.50
Complete booklet, #1794b 6.50
**1795** A1170 370w multicolored 1.50 .60
*a.* Souvenir sheet of 2 3.25 3.25
*b.* Souvenir sheet of 4, #1792-1795 7.00 7.00
*c.* Booklet pane of 10 45.00
Complete booklet, #1795b 45.00
*Nos. 1792-1795 (4)* 3.15 1.35

A1171

**1994, Sept. 27**

**1796** A1171 130w multicolored .60 .25

Seoul, Capital of Korea, 600th anniv.

A1172

**1994, Nov. 19 Photo. *Perf. 13x13½***

**1797** A1172 130w multicolored .60 .25
*a.* Souvenir sheet of 2 1.50 1.50
Complete booklet, 4 #1797 5.25

Philatelic Week. Complete booklet has one No. 1797 tied to cover with first day cancel.

A1173

**1994, Nov. 29**

**1798** A1173 130w multicolored .60 .25

Seoul becomes Korea's capital, 600th anniv.

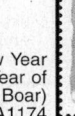

New Year 1995 (Year of the Boar) A1174

**1994, Dec. 1 *Perf. 13½x13***

**1799** A1174 130w shown .60 .25
*a.* Souvenir sheet of 2 1.50 1.50
Complete booklet, 4 #1799 6.00
**1800** A1174 130w Family outing .60 .25
*a.* Souvenir sheet of 2 1.50 1.50
Complete booklet, 4 #1800 6.00

Wildlife Protection A1175

**1995, Jan. 23 Photo. *Perf. 13½x13***

**1801** A1175 130w Rana plancyi .70 .30
*a.* Souv. sheet of 2, imperf. 1.75 1.75
Complete booklet, 4 #1801 5.50
**1802** A1175 130w Bufo bufo .70 .30
*a.* Souv. sheet of 2, imperf. 1.75 1.75
Complete booklet, 4 #1802 5.50

**Mushroom Type of 1993**

Designs: No. 1803, Russula virescens. No. 1804, Lentinus lepideus. No. 1805, Coprinus comalus. No. 1806, Laetiporus sulphureus.

**1995, Mar. 31 Photo. *Perf. 13x13½***

**1803** A1098 130w multicolored .70 .30
*a.* Souvenir sheet of 2 1.40 1.40
Complete booklet, 4 #1803 5.50
**1804** A1098 130w multicolored .70 .30
*a.* Souvenir sheet of 2 1.40 1.40
Complete booklet, 4 #1804 5.50
**1805** A1098 130w multicolored .70 .30
*a.* Souvenir sheet of 2 1.40 1.40
Complete booklet, 4 #1805 5.50
**1806** A1098 130w multicolored .70 .30
*a.* Souvenir sheet of 2 1.40 1.40
Complete booklet, 4 #1806 5.50
*Nos. 1803-1806 (4)* 2.80 1.20

Completion of HANARO Research Reactor A1176

**1995, Apr. 7 *Perf. 13½x13***

**1807** A1176 130w multicolored .70 .35
Complete booklet, 4 #1807 5.00

Modern Judicial System, Cent. — A1177

**1995, Apr. 25 Litho. *Perf. 13x13½***

**1808** A1177 130w multicolored .60 .25

Modern Legal Education, Cent. A1178

**1995, Apr. 25 *Perf. 13½x13***

**1809** A1178 130w multicolored .60 .25

Cartoons A1179

130w, "Dooly, the Little Dinosaur," baby, porpoise. 440w, "Kochuboo," riding in airplane.

**1995, May 4**

**1810** A1179 130w multicolored .65 .35
*a.* Souvenir sheet of 1 1.45 1.45
Complete booklet, 4 #1810 5.00
**1811** A1179 440w multicolored 1.60 .55
*a.* Souvenir sheet of 1 3.00 3.00
Complete booklet, 4 #1811 11.00

78th Lions Clubs Intl. Convention A1180

**1995, July 4 Photo. *Perf. 13½x13***

**1812** A1180 130w multicolored .70 .25

Liberation Day, 50th Anniv. A1181

Design: 440w, Mountain, yin/yang symbol.

**1995, Aug. 14 Photo. *Perf. 13½x13***

**1813** A1181 130w multicolored .60 .25
*a.* Booklet pane of 10 11.50
Complete booklet, #1813a 11.50
*b.* Souvenir sheet of 2 1.45 1.45

**Size: 97x19mm**

***Perf. 13x13½***

**1814** A1181 440w multicolored 1.60 .55
*a.* Souvenir sheet of 1 2.40 2.40

Opening of Bohyunsan Optical Astronomical Observatory A1183

**1995, Sept. 13 Litho. *Perf. 13x13½***

**1816** A1183 130w multicolored .70 .25
Complete booklet, 6 #1816 7.00

**Literature Series**

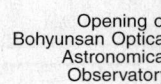

Kuji-ga Song (The Turtle's Back Song) — A1184

Chongeop-sa Song A1185

A1186

A1187

Record of Travel to Five Indian Kingdoms — A1188

A Poem to the Sui General Yu Zhong Wen — A1189

A1190

A1191

A1192

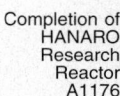

A1193

A1194

A1195

*Perf. 13x13½, 13½x13*

**1995-99** **Photo.**

**1817** A1184 130w multi .65 .25
  *a.* Souvenir sheet of 2 1.40 1.40
  Complete booklet, 6 #1817 5.75
**1818** A1185 130w multi .65 .25
  *a.* Souvenir sheet of 2 1.40 1.40
  Complete booklet, 6 #1818 5.75
**1819** A1186 150w multi .60 .25
  *a.* Souvenir sheet of 2 1.45 1.45
  Complete booklet, 10 #1819 *11.50*
**1820** A1187 150w multi .60 .25
  *a.* Souvenir sheet of 2 1.45 1.45
  Complete booklet, 10 #1820 *11.50*
**1821** A1188 170w multi .65 .25
  *a.* Souvenir sheet of 2 1.35 1.35
  Complete booklet, 10 #1821 9.00
**1822** A1189 170w multi .65 .25
  *a.* Sheet of 2 1.35 1.35
  Complete booklet, 10 #1822 9.00

**Photo. & Engr.**

**1823** A1190 170w multi .60 .25
  Complete booklet, 10 #1823 9.00
  *a.* Souvenir sheet of 1 1.10 1.10
**1824** A1191 170w multi .60 .25
  Complete booklet, 10 #1824 9.00
  *a.* Souvenir sheet of 1 1.10 1.10
**1825** A1192 170w multi .60 .30
  Complete booklet, 10 #1825 9.00
**1826** A1193 170w multi .60 .30
  Complete booklet, 10 #1826 9.00
**1827** A1194 170w multi .60 .30
  Complete booklet, 10 #1827 9.00
**1828** A1195 170w multi .60 .30
  Complete booklet, 10 #1828 9.00
  *Nos. 1817-1828 (12)* 7.40 3.20

**Souvenir Sheets**

**1828A** A1192 340w multi 1.60 1.60
**1828B** A1193 340w multi 1.60 1.60
**1828C** A1194 340w multi 1.60 1.60
**1828D** A1195 340w multi 1.60 1.60

Issued: Nos. 1817-1818, 9/25/95; Nos. 1819-1820, 9/16/96; Nos. 1821-1822, 12/12/97; Nos. 1823-1824, 9/14/98; Nos. 1825-1828D, 10/20/99

FAO, 50th Anniv. A1196

**Litho. & Engr.**

**1995, Oct. 16** *Perf. 13*

**1829** A1196 150w dp vio & blk .70 .25
  Complete booklet, 10 #1829 *8.75*

Korean Bible Society, Cent. A1197

**1995, Oct. 18** **Litho.**

**1830** A1197 150w multicolored .60 .25
  Complete booklet, 10 #1830 *8.75*

Population and Housing Census — A1198

**1995, Oct. 20**

**1831** A1198 150w multicolored .60 .25
  Complete booklet, 10 #1831 *8.75*

UN, 50th Anniv. A1199

**1995, Oct. 24** **Photo.**

**1832** A1199 150w multicolored .70 .25
  Complete booklet, 10 #1832 *8.75*

Wilhelm Röntgen (1845-1923), Discovery of the X-Ray, Cent. A1200

**1995, Nov. 8** *Perf. 13½x13*

**1833** A1200 150w multicolored 1.20 .25
  Complete booklet, 10 #1833 16.00

Philatelic Week — A1201

**1995, Nov. 18** **Photo.** *Perf. 13x13½*

**1834** A1201 150w multicolored .70 .25
  *a.* Souvenir sheet of 2 1.45 1.45
  Complete booklet, 10 #1834 *8.75*

A1202

New Year 1996 (Year of the Rat) — A1203

**1995, Dec. 1** *Perf. 13x13½, 13½x13*

**1835** A1202 150w multicolored .75 .25
  *a.* Souvenir sheet of 2 1.90 1.90
  Complete booklet, 10 #1835 *10.00*
**1836** A1203 150w multicolored .75 .25
  *a.* Souvenir sheet of 2 1.90 1.90
  Complete booklet, 10 #1836 *10.00*

Normalization of Korea-Japan Relations, 30th Anniv. — A1204

**1995, Dec. 18** **Litho.** *Perf. 13x13½*

**1837** A1204 420w multicolored 1.75 .60
  Complete booklet, 4 #1837 *8.75*

**Types of 1993-97 and**

Gallicrex Cinerea A1206

Zosterops Japonica A1208

Luffa Cylindrica A1209

Numenius Madagascariensis A1210

Cambaroides Similis — A1211

747 Airplane A1215

Mare and Colt — A1221

Soksu Stone Carving A1223

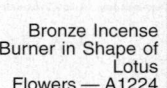

Bronze Incense Burner in Shape of Lotus Flowers — A1224

**Photo., Photo. & Embossed (#1844)**

**1996-98** *Perf. 13x13½, 13½x13*

**1839** A1206 50w multi .60 .25
**1840** A1208 80w multi .65 .25
**1841** A1209 100w multi 1.00 .25
**1842** A1118 140w multi 1.20 .25

*Perf. 13*

**1843** A1210 170w multi 2.00 .25
**1844** A1210 170w like #1843, braille inscription 1.90 .40

*Perf. 13x13½, 13½x13*

**1845** A1211 170w multi 1.60 .30
**1846** A997c 190w multi 1.60 .30
**1847** A1119 260w multi 2.00 .35

*Perf. 13x14*

**1848** A1119 300w Alauda arvensis 1.75 .35

*Perf. 13½x13, 13x13½, 13 (#1855)*

**1849** A1215 340w grn bl & multi 2.10 .40
**1850** A1215 380w lt lilac & multi 2.50 .45
**1851** A1001 420w like #1593 3.00 .40
**1852** A1002 480w like #1594 3.25 .45
**1854** A1221 800w multi 3.50 .50
**1855** A1223 1000w multi 5.00 .95
**1856** A1224 1170w multi 5.75 1.45
**1857** A1128 1190w multi 6.75 1.45
**1858** A1215 1340w brt grn & multi 8.00 1.20
**1859** A1215 1380w pink & multi 8.00 1.40
  *Nos. 1839-1859 (20)* 62.15 11.60

**Coil Stamps**

*Perf. 13 Horiz., 13 Vert. (#1860, 1862)*

**1996-97** **Photo.**

**1860** A998 150w like #1591 1.20 .60
**1861** A1211 170w like No. 1845 1.30 .30
**1862** A997c 190w like No. 1846 1.35 .30
  *Nos. 1860-1862 (3)* 3.85 1.20

Issued: 300w, 1/22/96; No. 1860, 2/1/96; 420w, 480w, 3/20/96; 1000w, 12/16/96; 100w, 3/5/97; 80w, 7/1/97; Nos. 1845-1846, 9/1/97; 340w, 380w, 1340w, 1380w, 9/12/97; Nos. 1842, 1847, 1856, 1857, 11/1/97; Nos. 1861, 1862, 11/18/97; No. 1843, 12/15/97; 50w, 2/19/98; 800w, 4/4/98; No. 1844, 10/15/98.

Opening of China-Korea Submarine Fiber Optic Cable System A1229

**1996, Feb. 8** **Litho.** *Perf. 13½x13*

**1863** A1229 420w multicolored 1.75 .45
  Complete booklet, 4 #1863 *9.25*

See People's Republic of China No. 2647.

Korea Institute of Science and Technology, 30th Anniv. A1230

**1996, Feb. 10** **Photo.** *Perf. 13½x13*

**1864** A1230 150w multicolored .70 .25
  Complete booklet, 10 #1864 *8.75*

Protection of Nature A1231

No. 1865, Geoclemys reevesii. No. 1866, Scincella laterale.

**1996, Mar. 5** **Photo.** *Perf. 13½x13*

**1865** A1231 150w multicolored .70 .25
  *a.* Souvenir sheet of 2 1.75 1.75
  Complete booklet, 10 #1865 *17.50*
**1866** A1231 150w multicolored .70 .25
  *a.* Souvenir sheet of 2 1.75 1.75
  Complete booklet, 10 #1866 *17.50*

Successful Launches of Mugunghwa Satellites A1232

**1996, Mar. 18** **Photo.** *Perf. 13*

**1867** A1232 150w multicolored .70 .25
  Complete booklet, 10 #1867 *8.75*

Tongnip Shinmum, First Privately Published Newspaper, Cent. A1233

So Chae-p'il, lead article of first issue.

**Litho. & Engr.**

**1996, Apr. 6** *Perf. 13*

**1868** A1233 150w multicolored .70 .25
  Complete booklet, 10 #1868 *10.00*

**Wildflower Type of 1992**

No. 1869, Cypripedium macranthum. No. 1870, Trillium tschonoskii. No. 1871, Viola variegata. No. 1872, Hypericum ascyron.

**1996, Apr. 22** **Photo.** *Perf. 13*

**1869** A1013 150w multicolored .95 .25
  Complete booklet, 10 #1869 *11.50*
**1870** A1013 150w multicolored .95 .25
  Complete booklet, 10 #1870 *11.50*
**1871** A1013 150w multicolored .95 .25
  Complete booklet, 10 #1871 *11.50*

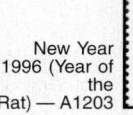

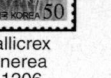

**1872** A1013 150w multicolored .95 .25
Complete booklet, 10 #1872 *11.50*
*Nos. 1869-1872 (4)* 3.80 1.00

Korea Military Academy, 50th Anniv. A1234

**1996, May 1 Litho. *Perf. 13½x13***
**1873** A1234 150w multicolored .70 .25
Complete booklet, 10 #1873 *9.00*

Cartoons A1235

No. 1874, Gobau running. No. 1875, Kkach'i in swordfight.

**1996, May 4 Photo.**
**1874** A1235 150w multicolored .70 .25
*a.* Souvenir sheet of 1 1.45 1.45
Complete booklet, 10 #1874 *9.00*
**1875** A1235 150w multicolored .70 .25
*a.* Souvenir sheet of 1 1.45 1.45
Complete booklet, 10 #1875 *9.00*

Girl Scouts of Korea, 50th Anniv. A1236

**1996, May 10 Litho.**
**1876** A1236 150w multicolored .70 .25
Complete booklet, 10 #1876 *10.00*

35th IAA World Advertising Congress — A1237

**1996, June 8 Litho. *Perf. 13***
**1877** A1237 150w multicolored .70 .25
Complete booklet, 10 #1877 *8.25*

Campaign Against Illegal Drugs A1238

**1996, June 26 Photo. *Perf. 13½x13***
**1878** A1238 150w multicolored .70 .25
Complete booklet, 10 #1878 *10.00*

Winter Universiade '97, Muju-Chonju A1239

No. 1880, Emblem, vert.

**1996, July 1 *Perf. 13½x13, 13x13½***
**1879** A1239 150w shown .70 .25
Complete booklet, 10 #1879 *8.75*
**1880** A1239 150w multicolored .70 .25
Complete booklet, 10 #1880 *8.75*

1996 Summer Olympic Games, Atlanta
A1240 A1241

**1996, July 20 *Perf. 13x13½***
**1881** A1240 150w multicolored .70 .25
Complete booklet, 10 #1881 *12.50*
**1882** A1241 150w multicolored .70 .25
Complete booklet, 10 #1882 *12.50*

**Mushroom Type of 1993**

Designs: No. 1883, Paxillus atrotomentosus. No. 1884, Sarcodon imbricatum. No. 1885, Rhodophyllus crassipes. No. 1886, Amanita inaurata.

**1996, Aug. 19 Photo. *Perf. 13x13½***
**1883** A1098 150w multicolored .70 .25
*a.* Souvenir sheet of 2 1.40 1.40
Complete booklet, 10 #1883 *12.50*
**1884** A1098 150w multicolored .70 .25
*a.* Souvenir sheet of 2 1.40 1.40
Complete booklet, 10 #1884 *12.50*
**1885** A1098 150w multicolored .70 .25
*a.* Souvenir sheet o 2 1.40 1.40
Complete booklet, 10 #1885 *12.50*
**1886** A1098 150w multicolored .70 .25
*a.* Souvenir sheet of 2 1.40 1.40
Complete booklet, 10 #1886 *12.50*
*Nos. 1883-1886 (4)* 2.80 1.00

Souvenir Sheets

2002 World Cup Soccer Championships, Korea — A1242

No. 1887, Players, Korean flag. No. 1888, 2 players.

**1996, Aug. 1 Photo. *Perf. 13½***
**1887** A1242 400w Sheet of 4 6.75 6.75
**1888** A1242 400w Sheet of 4 6.75 6.75

Korean Alphabet, 550th Anniv. — A1243

**Litho. & Engr.**
**1996, Oct. 9 *Perf. 13x13½***
**1889** A1243 150w multicolored .70 .25
*a.* Souvenir sheet of 2 1.35 1.35
Complete booklet, 10 #1889 *10.50*

Suwon Castle, Bicent. A1244

**Photo. & Engr.**
**1996, Oct. 10 *Perf. 13½x13***
**1890** A1244 400w multicolored 1.90 .55

Seoul Natl. University, 50th Anniv. A1245

**1996, Oct. 15 Photo. *Perf. 13½x13***
**1891** A1245 150w multicolored .70 .25
Complete booklet, 10 #1891 *9.50*

Philatelic Week — A1246

Painting: Poppy and a Lizard, by Shin Saimdang.

**1996, Nov. 18 Photo. *Perf. 13x13½***
**1892** A1246 150w multicolored .70 .25
*a.* Souvenir sheet of 2 1.40 1.40
Complete booklet, 10 #1892 *11.00*

A1247

New Year 1997 (Year of the Ox) — A1248

**1996, Dec. 2 *Perf. 13***
**1893** A1247 150w multicolored .85 .25
*a.* Souvenir sheet of 2 1.50 1.50
Complete booklet, 10 #1893 *13.00*
**1894** A1248 150w multicolored .85 .25
*a.* Souvenir sheet of 2 1.50 1.50
Complete booklet, 10 #1894 *13.00*

Winter Universiade '97, Muju-Chonju A1249

**1997, Jan. 24 Photo. *Perf. 13***
**1895** A1249 150w Skier .65 .25
Complete booklet, 10 #1895 *11.50*
*a.* Souvenir sheet of 2 1.25 1.25
**1896** A1249 150w Ice skater .65 .25
Complete booklet, 10 #1896 *11.50*
*a.* Souvenir sheet of 2 1.25 1.25

Modern Banking System in Korea, Cent. A1250

**1997, Feb. 19 Litho. *Perf. 13½x13***
**1897** A1250 150w multicolored .70 .25
Complete booklet, 10 #1897 *11.50*

A1251

**1997, Apr. 10 *Perf. 13x13½***
**1898** A1251 150w multicolored .60 .25
Complete booklet, 10 #1898 *10.00*

97th Inter-Parliamentary Conference, 160th Inter-Parliamentary Council.

World Book & Copyright Day — A1252

**1997, Apr. 23 Litho.**
**1899** A1252 150w multicolored .70 .25
Complete booklet, 10 #1899 *10.00*

Cartoons A1253

No. 1900, Mother holding child from "A Long, Long Journey in Search of Mommy." No. 1901, Girl in air holding medal from "Run, Run, Hannie."

**1997, May 3 Photo. *Perf. 13½x13***
**1900** A1253 150w multicolored .60 .25
*a.* Souvenir sheet of 1 1.05 1.05
Complete booklet, 10 #1900 *13.50*
**1901** A1253 150w multicolored .60 .25
*a.* Souvenir sheet of 1 1.05 1.05
Complete booklet, 10 #1901 *13.50*

Nos. 1900a, 1901a are continuous designs.

2nd Pusan East Asian Games — A1254

**1997, May 10 Litho. *Perf. 13x13½***
**1902** A1254 150w multicolored .70 .25
Complete booklet, 10 #1900 *10.00*

2002 World Cup Soccer, Korea/Japan
A1255 A1256

No. 1903, Jules Rimet, founder of World Cup. No. 1904, Painting of Ch'ukkuk match.

**1997, May 31 Photo. *Perf. 13x13½***
**1903** A1255 150w multicolored .75 .25
*a.* Souvenir sheet of 2 1.90 1.90
Complete booklet, 10 #1903 *11.50*
**1904** A1256 150w multicolored .75 .25
*a.* Souvenir sheet of 3 2.00 2.00
Complete booklet, 10 #1904 *11.50*

Wildlife Protection A1257

Fish: No. 1905, Pungitius sinensis. No. 1906, Coreoperca kawamebari.

**1997, June 5 *Perf. 13***
**1905** A1257 150w multicolored .70 .25
*a.* Souvenir sheet of 2 1.25 1.25
Complete booklet, 10 #1905 *11.50*
**1906** A1257 150w multicolored .70 .25
*a.* Souvenir sheet of 2 1.25 1.25
Complete booklet, 10 #1906 *11.50*

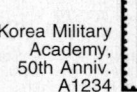

### Wildflower Type of 1992

No. 1907, Belamcanda chinensis. No. 1908, Hylomecon ernale. No. 1909, Campanula takesimana. No. 1910, Magnolia sieboldii.

**1997, June 19 Photo. *Perf. 13***

**1907** A1013 150w multicolored .70 .25
Complete booklet, 10 #1907 *12.50*
**1908** A1013 150w multicolored .70 .25
Complete booklet, 10 #1908 *12.50*
**1909** A1013 150w multicolored .70 .25
Complete booklet, 10 #1909 *12.50*
**1910** A1013 150w multicolored .70 .25
Complete booklet, 10 #1910 *12.50*
*Nos. 1907-1910 (4)* 2.80 1.00

1997 Kwangju Biennale — A1258

**1997, July 1**

**1911** A1258 150w multicolored .60 .25
Complete booklet, 10 #1911 *9.50*

### Mushroom Type of 1993

Designs: No. 1912, Inocybe fastigiata. No. 1913, Panaeolus papilionaceus. No. 1914, Ramaria flava. No. 1915, Amanita muscaria.

**1997, July 21 Photo. *Perf. 13x13½***

**1912** A1098 150w multicolored .70 .25
*a.* Souvenir sheet of 2 1.30 1.30
**1913** A1098 150w multicolored .70 .25
*a.* Souvenir sheet of 2 1.30 1.30
**1914** A1098 150w multicolored .70 .25
*a.* Souvenir sheet of 2 1.30 1.30
**1915** A1098 150w multicolored .70 .25
*a.* Souvenir sheet of 2 1.30 1.30
*Nos. 1912-1915 (4)* 2.80 1.00

85th World Dental Congress, Seoul A1259

**1997, Sept. 5 Photo. *Perf. 13½x13***

**1916** A1259 170w multicolored .65 .25

Opening of Port of Mokpo, Cent. A1260

**Litho. & Engr.**

**1997, Oct. 1 *Perf. 13½x13***

**1917** A1260 170w multicolored .65 .25

Soongsil Academy, Cent. A1261

**1997, Oct. 10 Photo. & Engr.**

**1918** A1261 170w multicolored .65 .25

### Beauty Series

Wrapping Cloths — A1262

**1997, Nov. 3 Photo. *Perf. 13x13½***

**1919** 170w multicolored .85 .25
**1920** 170w multicolored .85 .25
**1921** 170w multicolored .85 .25
**1922** 170w multicolored .85 .25
*a.* A1262 Strip of 4, #1919-1922 4.00 4.00

Philatelic Week — A1266

**1997, Nov. 18**

**1923** A1266 170w multicolored .75 .25
*a.* Souvenir sheet of 2 1.25 1.25

New Year 1998 (Year of the Tiger)
A1267 A1268

**1997, Dec. 1 Photo. *Perf. 13x13½***

**1924** A1267 170w multicolored .90 .25
*a.* Souvenir sheet of 2 1.60 1.60
**1925** A1268 170w multicolored .90 .25
*a.* Souvenir sheet of 2 1.60 1.60

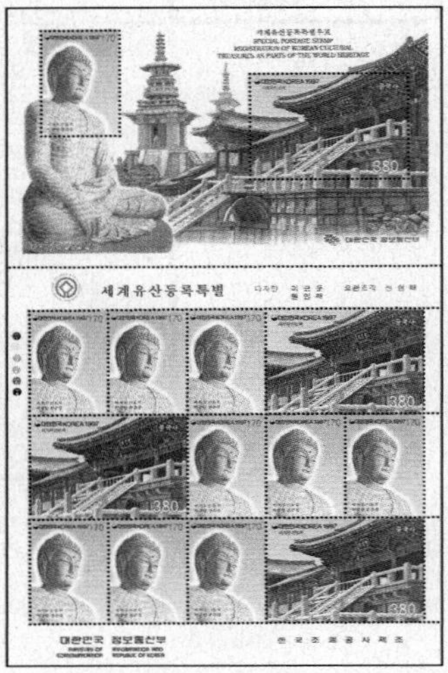

Pulguksa Temple — A1269

**Litho. & Engr.**

**1997, Dec. 9 *Perf. 13x13½***

**1926** A1269 Sheet of 14 35.00 35.00
*a.* 170w Buddha, Sokkuram Grotto 1.00 1.00
*b.* 380w Temple 4.00 4.00

Top part of No. 1926 contains one each Nos. 1926a-1926b and is separated from the bottom portion of the sheet by a row of perforations. The lower part of No. 1926 contains 9 No. 1926a and 3 No, 1926b.

Electric Power in Korea, Cent. A1271

**1998, Jan. 26 Photo. *Perf. 13½x13***

**1927** A1271 170w multicolored .70 .25

Inauguration of the 15th President, Kim Dae-jung A1272

**1998, Feb. 25 Litho. *Perf. 13½x13***

**1928** A1272 170w multicolored .90 .35
*a.* Souvenir sheet of 1 *5.75 5.75*

Protection of Wild Animals and Plants — A1273

Designs: a, Panthera pardus orientalis. b, Selenarctos thibetanus ussuricus. c, Lutra lutra. d, Moschus moschiferus.

**1998, Mar. 21 *Perf. 13x13½***

**1929** Sheet of 12 24.00 24.00
*a.-d.* A1273 340w Any single 1.50 .30

Top part of No. 1929 contains one each No. 1929a-1929d and is separated from the bottom portion of the sheet by a row of perforations. The lower part of No. 1929 contains 2 each Nos. 1929a-1929d.

Cartoons A1274

Designs: 170w, Boy daydreaming while holding flower, from "Aktong-i," by Lee Hi-jae. 340w, Mother on motorcycle, son making fists from "Challenger," by Park Ki-jong.

**1998, May 4 Photo. *Perf. 13½x13***

**1930** A1274 170w multicolored .75 .25
*a.* Souvenir sheet of 1 .75 .75
*b.* Booklet pane of 10 19.00
Complete booklet, #1930b 19.00

**Photo. & Engr.**

**1931** A1274 340w multicolored 1.45 1.25
*a.* Souvenir sheet of 1 1.50 1.50
*b.* Booklet pane of 10 24.00
Complete booklet, #1931b 24.00

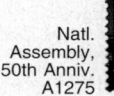

Natl. Assembly, 50th Anniv. A1275

**1998, May 30 Litho. *Perf. 13½x13***

**1932** A1275 170w multicolored .70 .25

2002 World Cup Soccer Championships, Korea/Japan — A1276

Designs: a, Player. b, Two players. c, Player heading ball. d, Player performing bicycle kick.

**1998, May 30 *Perf. 13x13½***

**1933** A1276 Strip of 4, #a.-d. 4.00 4.00
*a.-d.* 170w any single .70 .25
*e.* Souvenir sheet, #1933 3.25 3.25

Information Culture Special A1277

Communication through the ages: a, Rock drawings. b, Horseback messenger, beacon fire. c, Telephone, mailbox. d, Computers.

**1998, June 1 Litho. *Perf. 13½x13***

**1934** Strip of 4 4.00 4.00
*a.-c.* A1277 170w any single .60 .25
*d.* A1277 340w multicolored 1.25 .45

No. 1934d is 68x70mm.

### Mushroom Type of 1993

Designs: a, Pseudocolus schellenbergiae. b, Cyptotrama asprata. c, Laccaria vinaceoavellanea. d, Phallus rugulosus.

**1998, July 4**

**1935** Sheet of 16 17.00 17.00
*a.-d.* A1098 170w Any single .75 .30

Left part of No. 1935 contains 3 each Nos. 1935a-1935d, with each strip in a different order. This is separated from the right portion of the sheet by a row of perforations. The right part of No. 1935 contains 1 each Nos. 1935a-1935d.

Republic of Korea, 50th Anniv. A1278

**1998, Aug. 14 Photo. *Perf. 13½x13***

**1937** A1278 170w multicolored .70 .25

Philatelic Week — A1279

**1998, Aug. 19 *Perf. 13x13½***

**1938** A1279 170w multicolored .70 .25
*a.* Souvenir sheet of 2 1.20 1.20

A1280

**1998, Sept. 24 Photo. *Perf. 13x13½***

**1939** A1280 170w multicolored .70 .25
Complete booklet, 10 #1939 10.00

1998 Pusan Intl. Film Festival.

Founding of Songkyunkwan, 600th Anniv. — A1281

**Photo. & Engr.**

**1998, Sept. 25 *Perf. 13***

**1940** A1281 170w multicolored .70 .25
Complete booklet, 5 #1940 4.50

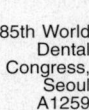

A1282

**1998, Oct. 1**

| | | | | |
|---|---|---|---|---|
| **1941** | A1282 170w multicolored | | .70 | .25 |
| | Complete booklet, 10 #1941 | | 7.25 | |

Korean Armed Forces, 50th anniv.

World Stamp Day — A1283

**1998, Oct. 9**

| | | | |
|---|---|---|---|
| **1942** | A1283 170w multicolored | .75 | .25 |
| | Complete booklet, 10 #1942 | 6.50 | |

### Beauty Series

Ceramics — A1284

No. 1944, Box with cranes on lid. No. 1945, Fish. No. 1946, Red, white blossom with blue leaf. No. 1947, Frog. No. 1948, Dragon. No. 1949, Monkeys. No. 1950, Pagoda.

**1998, Nov. 20 Photo. *Perf. 13***

| | | | |
|---|---|---|---|
| **1943** | A1284 170w multicolored | .80 | .35 |
| **1944** | A1284 170w multicolored | .80 | .35 |
| **1945** | A1284 170w multicolored | .80 | .35 |
| **1946** | A1284 170w multicolored | .80 | .35 |
| **1947** | A1284 170w multicolored | .80 | .35 |
| **1948** | A1284 170w multicolored | .80 | .35 |
| **1949** | A1284 170w multicolored | .80 | .35 |
| **1950** | A1284 170w multicolored | .80 | .35 |
| *a.* | Block of 8, #1243-1250 | 8.50 | 7.50 |

New Year 1999 (Year of the Rabbit) — A1286

**1998, Dec. 1 *Perf. 13x13½***

| | | | |
|---|---|---|---|
| **1952** | A1286 170w multicolored | .75 | .25 |
| | Complete booklet, 10 #1952 | 8.75 | |

Woodblock of Buddhist Tripitaka Koreana, Haeinsa Temple A1287

Haeinsa Temple Changgyong P'anjon Complex — A1288

**Litho. & Engr.**

**1998, Dec. 9 *Perf. 13½***

| | | | |
|---|---|---|---|
| **1953** | Sheet of 12 | 28.00 | 28.00 |
| *a.* | A1287 170w multicolored | .95 | .50 |
| *b.* | A1288 380w multicolored | 2.75 | 1.60 |

Top part of No. 1953 contains one each Nos. 1953a-1953b and is separated from the bottom portion of the sheet by a row of perforations. The lower part of No. 1953 contains 6 No. 1953a and 4 No. 1953b.

Opening of Kunsan Port, Cent. A1289

**1999, May 1 Litho. *Perf. 13¼***

| | | | |
|---|---|---|---|
| **1954** | A1289 170w multicolored | .65 | .25 |

Opening of Masan Port, Cent. — A1290

**1999, May 1**

| | | | |
|---|---|---|---|
| **1955** | A1290 170w multicolored | .85 | .25 |

Cartoons A1291

No. 1956, Boy and dog, "Tokgo T'ak," by Lee Sang-mu. No. 1957, Choson Dynasty robber, "Im Kkuk-jung," by Lee Du-ho. No. 1958, Fighter against alien invaders, "Rai-Fi," by Kim San-ho, vert.

**1999, May 3 Photo. *Perf. 13½***

| | | | |
|---|---|---|---|
| **1956** | A1291 170w multicolored | .65 | .30 |
| **1957** | A1291 170w multicolored | .65 | .30 |
| **1958** | A1291 170w multicolored | .65 | .30 |
| | *Nos. 1956-1958 (3)* | 1.95 | .90 |

### Souvenir Sheets

| | | | |
|---|---|---|---|
| **1959** | A1291 340w like #1956 | 1.45 | 1.25 |
| **1960** | A1291 340w like #1957 | 1.45 | 1.25 |
| **1961** | A1291 340w like #1958 | 1.45 | 1.25 |
| | *Nos. 1959-1961 (3)* | 4.35 | 3.75 |

Nos. 1959-1961 are continuous designs.

A1292

Raptors: a, Falco peregrinus. b, Accipiter soloensis. c, Bubo bubo. d, Haliaeetus pelagicus.

**1999, June 5 Litho. *Perf. 13x13¼***

| | | | |
|---|---|---|---|
| **1962** | Sheet of 12 | 27.00 | 27.00 |
| *a.-b.* | A1292 170w each | 1.00 | .30 |
| *c.-d.* | A1292 340w each | 1.90 | .50 |

Top part of No. 1962 contains one each Nos. 1962a-1962d and is separated from the bottom portion of the sheet by a row of perforations. The lower part of No. 1962 contains 2 blocks of Nos. 1962a-1962d.

A1293

**1999, June 12 Photo. *Perf. 13x13¼***

| | | | |
|---|---|---|---|
| **1963** | A1293 170w multicolored | .65 | .25 |
| | Complete booklet, 10 #1963 | 12.50 | |

1999 Intl. Olympic Committee Congress, Seoul.

Johann Wolfgang von Goethe, German Poet (1749-1832) A1294

**Litho. & Engr.**

**1999, Aug. 12 *Perf. 13x13½***

| | | | |
|---|---|---|---|
| **1964** | A1294 170w multicolored | .85 | .30 |

### Souvenir Sheet

| | | | |
|---|---|---|---|
| **1965** | A1294 480w multicolored | 2.40 | 2.40 |

See Germany No. 2052.

Kumgang Mountain by Kyomjae (1676-1759) — A1295

**1999, Aug. 13 Litho.**

| | | | |
|---|---|---|---|
| **1966** | A1295 170w multicolored | .75 | .30 |

### Souvenir Sheet

| | | | |
|---|---|---|---|
| **1967** | A1295 340w multicolored | 1.25 | 1.25 |

Korean National Railroad, Cent. — A1296

**Litho. & Engr.**

**1999, Sept. 18 *Perf. 13x13¼***

| | | | |
|---|---|---|---|
| **1968** | A1296 170w multicolored | .75 | .30 |
| | Complete booklet, 10 #1968 | 10.00 | |

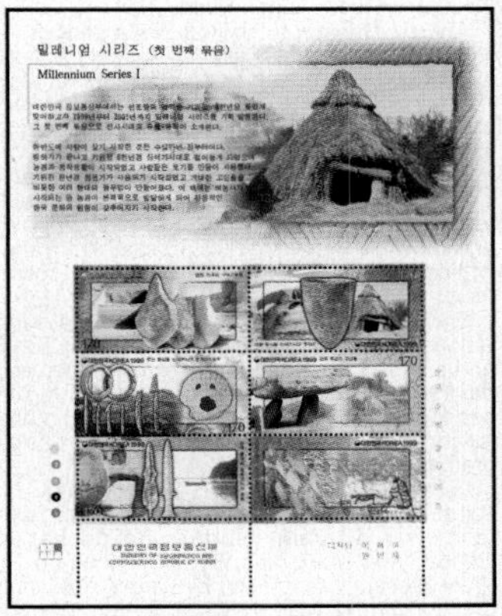

Millennium — A1297

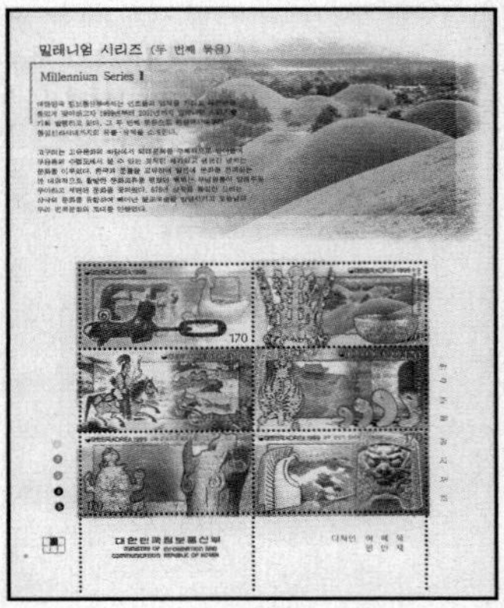

A1297a

A1297b

A1297c

A1297d

A1297e

A1297f

A1297g

A1297h

A1297i

A1297j

Prehistoric sites and artifacts — No. 1969: a, Paleolithic ruins, Chungok-ri (black denomination at LL). b, Neolithic sites, Amsa-dong (white denomination at UR). c, Neolithic shell mound ruins, Tongsam-dong (black denomination at LR). d, Dolmen, Pukon-ri (black denomination at UR). e, Bronze Age artifacts and ruins, Songguk-ri. f, Rock carvings, Ulsan.

Three Countries Era artifacts — No. 1970: a, Tiger-shpaed belt buckle from tomb of Sarari, duck-shaped earthenware container, Kyongsang. b, Gold crown, silver cup from Hwangnamdae tomb. c, Wall painting of hunting scene from Tomb of the Dancers, Chibanri. d, Gold diadem ornaments, curved jade pieces from tomb of King Muryong. e, Gold crown from Koryong, armor from Kimhae. f, Decorative tiles, Anapji Pond.

Ancient Choson to Unified Shilla periods — No. 1971: a, Writing, site of Asadal, ancient capital of Choson. b, Korean wrestlers. c, King Kwanggaet'o, stone stele, and circular artifact with writing. d, Archers on horseback. e, Admiral Chang Po-go, ship.

Koryo dynasty — No. 1972: a, Writing and buildings (civil service examinations). b, Monk and Tripitaka Koreana wood blocks. c, Jade and movable metal type. d, Scholar An-hyang, writing and buildings. e, Mun Ik-jom, cotton plants and spinning wheel.

Early Choson dynasty — No. 1973: a, King Sejong and Korean alphabet. b, Korean script and Lady Shin Saimdang, calligrapher and painter. c, Yi Hwang and Yi I and Confucian academy building. d, Admiral Yi Sun-shin and turtle boat. e, Sandae-nori mask dance dramas.

Late Choson Dynasty — No. 1974: a, Tongui Pogam, medical treatises by Huh Joon (anatomic diagram, mortar and pestle) b, Dancer and Musicians, by Kim Hong-do. c, Plum Blossoms and Bird, by Chong Yak-yong and building. d, Map of Korea, by Kim Chongho and compass. e, Carved stone monument at Tongchak Peasant Uprsing Memorial Hall.

Historic relics of Koryo and Choson Dynasties — No. 1975: a, Container, pitcher, Kangjin kiln site. b, Fenced-off monument and Nirvana Hall, Pongjungsa Temple (yellow building). c, Hahoe and Pyongsan wooden masks. d, Kunjong Hall, Kyongbok Palace. e, Dream Journey to the Peach Blossom land, by An Kyon. f, Water clock of King Sejong.

Joseon Dynasty — No. 1976: a, Spring Outing, by Sin Yun-bok. b, Chusa-style calligraphy, birthplace of Kim Jeong-hui. c, Beacon Lighthouse, book of technical drawings. d, Myeongdong Cathedral. e, Wongaksa Theater, performers. f, KITSAT-1 satellite.

Vision of the Future — No. 1977: a, Bicycle with wheels represening the two Koreas. b, Rainbow (environmental protection). c, Human genome project. d, IMT 2000 and satellites. e, Children's drawing of space travel. f, Solar-powered vehicle, windmills.

Pre-independence historic events and personalities — No. 1978: a, Kim Ku. b, March 1 Independence Movement, Declaration of Independence. c, Establishment of Korean interim government. d, Ahn Ik-tae, composer of national anthem. e, Yun Dong-ju, poet.

Historic events since independence — No. 1979: a, Liberation after World War II (People with flag). b, Korean War (soldiers, barbed wire). c, Construction of Seoul-Busan Expressway. d, Saemaul Undong movement (workers and flag). e, 1988 Summer Olympics, Seoul.

**1999-2001 Litho. *Perf. 13x13½***

| | | | | |
|---|---|---|---|---|
| 1969 | A1297 | Sheet of 6 | 5.50 | 5.50 |
| *a.-f.* | | 170w any single | .70 | .30 |
| 1970 | A1297a | Sheet of 6 | 5.50 | 5.50 |
| *a.-f.* | | 170w any single | .70 | .30 |

***Perf. 13½***

| | | | | |
|---|---|---|---|---|
| 1971 | A1297b | Sheet of 5 + label | 5.75 | 5.75 |
| *a.-e.* | | 170w any single | .70 | .30 |

**Photo.**

| | | | | |
|---|---|---|---|---|
| 1972 | A1297c | Sheet of 5 + label | 5.75 | 5.75 |
| *a.-e.* | | 170w any single | .70 | .30 |
| 1973 | A1297d | Sheet of 5 + label | 5.75 | 5.75 |
| *a.-e.* | | 170w any single | .70 | .30 |
| 1974 | A1297e | Sheet of 5 + label | 7.25 | 7.25 |
| *a.-e.* | | 170w Any single | .70 | .30 |

***Perf. 13***

| | | | | |
|---|---|---|---|---|
| 1975 | A1297f | Sheet of 6 | 7.50 | 7.50 |
| *a.-f.* | | 170w Any single | .90 | .30 |
| 1976 | A1297g | Sheet of 6 | 6.25 | 6.25 |
| *a.-f.* | | 170w Any single | .70 | .30 |
| 1977 | A1297h | Sheet of 6 | 5.75 | 5.75 |
| *a.-f.* | | 170w Any single | .70 | .30 |

***Perf. 13½***

| | | | | |
|---|---|---|---|---|
| 1978 | A1297i | Sheet of 5 + label | 7.50 | 7.50 |
| *a.-e.* | | 170w Any single | .90 | .30 |
| 1979 | A1297j | Sheet of 5 + label | 5.50 | 5.50 |
| *a.-e.* | | 170w Any single | .70 | .30 |
| | | *Nos. 1969-1979 (11)* | 68.00 | 68.00 |

Issued: No. 1969, 10/2; No. 1970, 11/16; No. 1971, 1/3/00; No. 1972, 3/2/00; No. 1973, 5/1/00; No. 1974, 7/1/00; No. 1975, 9/1/00; No. 1976, 11/1/00; No. 1977, 1/2/01; No. 1978, 4/2/01; No. 1979, 7/2/01.

UPU, 125th Anniv. — A1298

**1999, Oct. 9 Litho. *Perf. 13x13½***

| | | | | |
|---|---|---|---|---|
| 1980 | A1298 | 170w multi | .75 | .25 |

**Beauty Series**

A1299

a, Purple panel, 4 orange flowers in purple and blue vase, rabbit, duck. b, Blue green panel, red jar, rooster. c, Orange panel, 4 orange flowers in yellow vase. d, Purple panel, fish, purple vase with flower decoration. e, Blue green panel, fish in net. f, Red panel, crab. g, Purple panel, birds, red flowers. h, Orange panel, deer, 3 orange flowers.

**1999, Nov. 3 Litho. *Perf. 13x13¼***

| | | | | |
|---|---|---|---|---|
| 1981 | A1299 | Sheet of 8, #a.-h. | 13.50 | 13.50 |
| *a.-h.* | | 340w any single | 1.60 | .50 |

New Year 2000 (Year of the Dragon) — A1300

**1999, Dec. 1 Photo.**

| | | | | |
|---|---|---|---|---|
| 1982 | A1300 | 170w multi | .75 | .30 |
| *a.* | | Souvenir sheet of 2 | 1.50 | 1.50 |

A1301

Registration of Korean Sites on World Heritage List — A1302

**Litho. & Engr.**

**1999, Dec. 9 *Perf. 13x13¼***

| | | | |
|---|---|---|---|
| 1983 | Sheet of 10 | 17.50 | 17.50 |
| *a.* | A1301 170w multicolored | 1.00 | .30 |
| *b.* | A1302 340w multicolored | 2.60 | .55 |

Top part of No. 1983 contains one each Nos. 1983a-1983b. The lower part of No. 1983 contains 4 each Nos. 1983a-1983b.

Flag
A1303

Nycticorax Nycticorax
A1304

Vitis Amurensis
A1305

Purpuricenus Lituratus
A1306

Eophona Migratoria
A1307

Limenitis Populi
A1310

Plow
A1311

Sseore
A1311a

Sowing Basket, Namtae A1311b

Hoes A1311c

Namu-janngun, Jaetbak A1311d

Yongdurei A1311e

Winnower, Thresher A1311f

Meongseok, Wicker Tray A1311g

Mortar, Pestle, Grindstone A1311h

Carrier, Rice Chest A1311i

Hibiscus Syriacus A1312

Chionectes Opilio A1313

Falco Tinnunculus — A1314

Hibiscus Syriacus A1314a

Hibiscus Syriacus A1314b

Ficedula Zanthopygia — A1315

Hibiscus Syriacus A1315a

Celadon Pitcher A1316

Porcelain Container A1316a

Hong Yong-Sik, 1st General Postmaster A1317

Koryo Jade Ornament — A1319

Kylin Roof-End Tile — A1320

Ridge-End Tile — A1321

Porcelain Vase With Bamboo Design — A1322

Crown From Tombs of Shinch'on-ni A1323

Malus Asiatica A1326

Aquilegia Flabeliata — A1327

***Perf. 13¼x13 (#2000, 2002, 2004, 2005), 13x13¼ (#2001, 2003, 2006, 2007), 12¾x13¾ (#1984-1990, 1996), 13¾x12¾ (#1986, 1991, 1993, 1994, 1995, 1997, 1998)***

**1999-2003** **Photo.**

| | | | | | |
|---|---|---|---|---|---|
| **1984** | A1303 | 10w | multi | .35 | .25 |
| **1985** | A1304 | 20w | multi | .45 | .30 |
| **1986** | A1305 | 30w | multi | .45 | .35 |
| **1987** | A1306 | 40w | multi | .45 | .30 |
| **1988** | A1307 | 60w | multi | .45 | .35 |
| **1989** | A1310 | 160w | multi | .65 | .30 |
| **1990** | Horiz. strip of 10 | | | 15.50 | 10.00 |
| *a.* | A1311 170w multi | | | 1.00 | .30 |
| *b.* | A1311a 170w multi | | | 1.00 | .30 |
| *c.* | A1311b 170w multi | | | 1.00 | .30 |
| *d.* | A1311c 170w multi | | | 1.00 | .30 |
| *e.* | A1311d 170w multi | | | 1.00 | .30 |
| *f.* | A1311e 170w multi | | | 1.00 | .30 |
| *g.* | A1311f 170w multi | | | 1.00 | .30 |
| *h.* | A1311g 170w multi | | | 1.00 | .30 |
| *i.* | A1311h 170w multi | | | 1.00 | .30 |
| *j.* | A1311i 170w multi | | | 1.00 | .30 |
| **1991** | A1312 | 190w | multi | 1.00 | .30 |
| **1992** | A1313 | 200w | multi | 1.05 | .35 |
| **1993** | A1314 | 210w | multi | .90 | .30 |
| **1994** | A1314a | 220w | multi | 1.00 | .30 |
| **1995** | A1314b | 240w | multi | 1.45 | .40 |
| **1996** | A1315 | 280w | multi | 1.10 | .40 |
| **1997** | A1315a | 310w | multi | 1.30 | .60 |
| **1998** | A1316 | 400w | multi | 1.45 | .80 |
| **1999** | A1316a | 500w | multi | 1.90 | .85 |
| **2000** | A1317 | 600w | multi | 2.60 | .85 |
| **2001** | A1319 | 700w | multi | 3.25 | .85 |
| **2002** | A1320 | 1290w | multi | 5.75 | 1.90 |
| **2003** | A1321 | 1310w | multi | 6.00 | 1.90 |
| **2004** | A1320 | 1490w | buff & multi | 6.25 | 2.60 |
| **2005** | A1321 | 1510w | brn & multi | 6.25 | 2.60 |
| **2006** | A1322 | 1520w | multi | 5.50 | 2.50 |
| **2007** | A1323 | 2000w | multi | 7.25 | 1.20 |

**Booklet Stamps**

**Self-Adhesive**

***Serpentine Die Cut 11¼x11½, 11½x11¼***

| | | | | | |
|---|---|---|---|---|---|
| **2008** | A1326 | 190w | multi | 1.45 | .75 |
| *a.* | Booklet pane of 20 | | | 25.00 | |
| **2008A** | A1327 | 190w | multi | 1.45 | .75 |
| *a.* | Booklet pane of 20 | | | 25.00 | |
| | *Nos. 1984-2008A (26)* | | | 75.20 | 32.05 |

Issued: 600w, 11/15; 2000w, 11/1; 20w, 700w, 1/17/00; 40w, 6/10/00; No. 1990, 1/20/01; 200w, 3/5/01. 160w, 210w, 280w, 1290w, 1310w, 1/15/02; 10w, 3/6/03; 30w, 9/10/01; 60w, 3/15/02; 400w, 4/11/03; 1490w, 1510w, 1/1/03; Nos. 2008-2008A, 7/1/03; 500w, 7/11/03; No. 1991, 220w, 240w, 310w, 1520w, 11/1/04.

2002 World Cup Soccer Championships, Korea & Japan — A1328

Various players in action.

**1999, Dec. 31** **Photo.** ***Perf. 13x13½***

**Denomination Color**

| | | | | |
|---|---|---|---|---|
| **2009** | 170w orange | | .70 | .35 |
| **2010** | 170w green | | .70 | .35 |
| **2011** | 170w red | | .70 | .35 |
| **2012** | 170w blue | | .70 | .35 |
| *a.* | A1328 Strip of 4, #2009-2012 | | 3.25 | 3.25 |
| *b.* | Souvenir sheet, #2009-2012 | | 3.50 | 3.50 |

Korea's Entry into UPU, Cent. A1329

**2000, Jan. 3** **Photo.** ***Perf. 13¼x13***

| | | | |
|---|---|---|---|
| **2013** | A1329 170w multi | .75 | .30 |
| | Booklet, 10 #2013 | 12.50 | |

Steam Locomotives — A1330

Designs: No. 2014, Pashi. No. 2015, Teho. No. 2016, Mika. No. 2017, Hyouki.

**2000, Feb. 1** **Photo.** ***Perf. 13¾x12¾***

| | | | |
|---|---|---|---|
| **2014** | A1330 170w tan, blk & vio | .70 | .30 |
| **2015** | A1330 170w pink, blk & vio | .70 | .30 |
| **2016** | A1330 170w gray, blk & vio | .70 | .30 |
| **2017** | A1330 170w cit, blk & vio | .70 | .30 |
| *a.* | Block of 4, #2014-2017 | 3.75 | 3.75 |
| | Booklet, 2 #2017a | — | |

Endangered Flowers — A1331

a, Lilium cernuum. b, Hibiscus hamabo. c, Sedirea japonica. d, Cypripedium japonicum.

**2000, Feb. 25** ***Perf. 13x13¼***

| | | | |
|---|---|---|---|
| **2018** | Sheet of 12 | 17.50 | 17.50 |
| *a.-d.* | A1331 170w any single | 1.10 | .30 |

Top part of No. 2018 contains one each of Nos. 2018a-2018d and the lower part contains two each. No. 2018 is impregnated with floral scent.

World Water Day — A1332

**2000, Mar. 22** **Photo.** ***Perf. 13¼x13***

| | | | |
|---|---|---|---|
| **2019** | A1332 170w multi | .65 | .30 |
| | Booklet, 10 #2019 | 10.00 | |

World Meteorological Organization, 50th Anniv. — A1333

**2000, Mar. 23** ***Perf. 13x13¼***

| | | | |
|---|---|---|---|
| **2020** | A1333 170w multi | .75 | .30 |
| | Booklet, 10 #2020 | 10.00 | |

Love A1334

**2000, Apr. 20** **Photo.** ***Perf. 13¼***

| | | | |
|---|---|---|---|
| **2021** | A1334 170w multi | 1.10 | .30 |

No. 2021 has floral scent.
Value is for stamp with surrounding selvage.

Cyber Korea 21 Technology Plan — A1335

**2000, Apr. 22** **Litho.** ***Perf. 13¼x13***

| | | | |
|---|---|---|---|
| **2022** | A1335 170w multi | .80 | .30 |
| | Booklet, 10 #2022 | 10.50 | |

Cartoons — A1336

Designs: No. 2023: Goindol, by Park Soo-dong (cavemen). No. 2024, Youngsim-i, by Bae Gum-taek (girl with lipstick).

**2000, May 4** **Photo.** ***Perf. 13x13¼***

| | | | |
|---|---|---|---|
| **2023** | A1336 170w multi | .70 | .35 |
| *a.* | Souvenir sheet of 1 | .95 | .95 |
| | Booklet, 10 #2023 | 10.50 | |
| **2024** | A1336 170w multi | .70 | .35 |
| *a.* | Souvenir sheet of 1 | .95 | .95 |
| | Booklet, 10 #2024 | 10.50 | |

Summit Meeting Between North and South Korea A1337

**2000, June 12** **Photo.** ***Perf. 13¼x13***

| | | | |
|---|---|---|---|
| **2025** | A1337 170w multi | .65 | .45 |

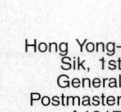

41st Intl. Mathematical Olympiad — A1338

**2000, July 13 Photo.** ***Perf. 13x13¼***

2026 A1338 170w multi .85 .35
Booklet, 10 #2026 10.50

### Literature Series

The Nine Cloud Dream, by Kim Man-jung A1339

From the Sea to a Child, by Chun Nam-seon A1340

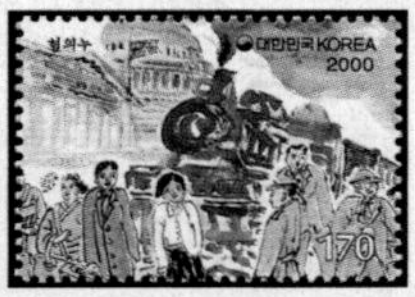

Tears of Blood, by Yi In-jik A1341

Yolha Diary, by Park Ji-won A1342

The Fisherman's Calendar, by Yun Seon-do A1343

**2000, Aug. 1** ***Perf. 13¼x13, 13x13¼***

2027 A1339 170w multi .85 .35
*a.* Souvenir sheet of 1 1.00 1.00
2028 A1340 170w multi .85 .35
*a.* Souvenir sheet of 1 1.00 1.00
2029 A1341 170w multi .85 .35
*a.* Souvenir sheet of 1 1.00 1.00
2030 A1342 170w multi .85 .35
*a.* Souvenir sheet of 1 1.00 1.00
2031 A1343 170w multi .85 .35
*a.* Souvenir sheet of 1 1.00 1.00
*Nos. 2027-2031 (5)* 4.25 1.75

The Puljongdae Cliff of Mt. Kumgang, by Chong Son — A1344

**2000, Aug. 2 Litho.** ***Perf. 13¼x13***

2032 A1344 340w multi 1.45 .65
*a.* Souvenir sheet of 1 1.60 1.45

Philately Week.

2000 Summer Olympics, Sydney — A1345

**2000, Sept. 15 Photo.** ***Perf. 13x13¼***

2033 A1345 170w multi .75 .40

Public Secondary Schools, Cent. — A1346

**2000, Oct. 2 Litho. & Engr.** ***Perf. 13***

2034 A1346 170w multi .70 .40

Third Asia-Europe Summit Meeting, Seoul A1347

**2000, Oct. 20 Photo.** ***Perf. 13¼x13***

2035 A1347 170w multi .70 .35

Intl. Council of Graphic Design Associations Millennium Congress — A1348

**2000, Oct. 25** ***Perf. 13x13¼***

2036 A1348 170w org & blk .70 .35

Cartoon Character Gobau. 50th Anniv. — A1349

**2000, Nov. 1 Litho.** ***Perf. 13¼***

2037 A1349 170w multi .70 .35

### Beauty Series

Tortoise-shell Comb A1350

Woman's Ceremonial Headdress A1351

Butterfly-shaped Hair Pin — A1352

Dragon and Phoenix Hair Pins — A1353

**2000, Nov. 16 Photo.** ***Perf. 13¼x13***

2038 Horiz. strip of 4 4.25 4.25
*a.* A1350 170w multi .70 .40
*b.* A1351 170w multi .70 .40
*c.* A1352 170w multi .70 .40
*d.* A1353 170w multi .70 .40

Seoul World Cup Stadium A1354

Busan Sports Complex Main Stadium A1355

Daegu Sports Complex Stadium A1356

Incheon Munhak Stadium A1357

Gwangju World Cup Stadium A1358

Daejeon World Cup Stadium A1359

Ulsan Munsu Soccer Stadium A1360

Suwon World Cup Stadium A1361

Jeonju World Cup Stadium A1362

Jeju World Cup Stadium A1363

**2000, Nov. 24 Photo.** ***Perf. 13¼x13***

2039 Block of 10 13.50 10.00
*a.* A1354 170w multi 1.15 .35
*b.* A1355 170w multi 1.15 .35
*c.* A1356 170w multi 1.15 .35
*d.* A1357 170w multi 1.15 .35
*e.* A1358 170w multi 1.15 .35
*f.* A1359 170w multi 1.15 .35
*g.* A1360 170w multi 1.15 .35
*h.* A1361 170w multi 1.15 .35
*i.* A1362 170w multi 1.15 .35
*j.* A1363 170w multi 1.15 .35
*k.* Souvenir sheet, #2039a-2039b 2.75 2.75
*l.* Souvenir sheet, #2039c-2039d 2.75 2.75
*m.* Souvenir sheet, #2039e-2039f 2.75 2.75
*n.* Souvenir sheet, #2039g-2039h 2.75 2.75
*o.* Souvenir sheet, #2039i-2039j 2.75 2.75

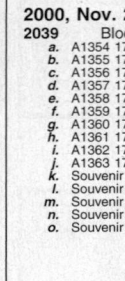

New Year 2001 (Year of the Snake) A1364

**2000 Photo.** ***Perf. 13¼***

2040 A1364 170w multi .95 .35
*a.* Souvenir sheet of 2 1.75 1.75

**Self-Adhesive**

***Serpentine Die Cut 10¼***

2041 A1364 170w multi 1.25 .35

Issued: No. 2040, 12/1; No. 241, 12/22. No. 2041 issued in sheets of 10.

King Sejong and Hunmin Chongun Manuscript — A1365

Annals of the Choson Dynasty and Repository — A1365a

**Litho. & Engr.**

**2000, Dec. 9** ***Perf. 13x13¼***

2042 Sheet of 8 15.50 15.50
*a.* A1365 340w multi 1.50 .90
*b.* A1365a 340w multi 1.50 .90

Addition of Hunmin Chongun manuscript and Annals of the Choson Dynasty to UNESCO Memory of the World Register. Top part of No. 2042 contains one each Nos. 2042a-2042b the lower part contains three each Nos. 2042a-2042b.

Awarding of Nobel Peace Prize to Pres. Kim Dae-jung A1366

**2000, Dec. 9 Photo.**

2043 A1366 170w multi .85 .35
*a.* Souvenir sheet of 1 2.25 2.25

Oksun Peaks, by Kim Hong-do A1367

**2001, Jan. 10 Photo. *Perf. 13¼***
**2044** A1367 170w multi .80 .35

Visit Korea Year.

A1368

A1369

A1370

Diesel and Electric Trains A1371

**2001, Feb. 1 Photo. *Perf. 13¾x12¾***

| | | | |
|---|---|---|---|
| **2045** | Block of 4 | 3.75 | 3.75 |
| *a.* | A1368 170w multi | .85 | .40 |
| *b.* | A1369 170w multi | .85 | .40 |
| *c.* | A1370 170w multi | .85 | .40 |
| *d.* | A1371 170w multi | .85 | .40 |

Endangered Flowers — A1372

Designs: a, Diapensia lapponica. b, Rhododendron aureum. c, Jeffersonia dubia. d, Sedum orbiculatum.

**2001, Feb. 26 *Perf. 13x13¼***

| | | | |
|---|---|---|---|
| **2046** | Sheet of 12 | 14.50 | 14.50 |
| *a.-d.* | A1372 170w Any single | .80 | .45 |

Top part of No. 2046 contains one each Nos. 2046a-2046d, the lower part contains two each Nos. 2046a-2046d.

Opening of Inchon Intl. Airport A1373

**2001, Mar. 29**
**2047** A1373 170w multi .75 .40

Intl. Olympic Fair, Seoul A1374

**2001, Apr. 27 *Perf. 13¼x13***

| | | | |
|---|---|---|---|
| **2048** | A1374 170w multi | .75 | .40 |
| *a.* | Souvenir sheet of 2 | 1.90 | 1.90 |

Personalized Greetings — A1375

Designs: No. 2049, 170w, Hugging bears. No. 2050, 170w, Carnation. No. 2051, 170w, Congratulations. No. 2052, 170w, Birthday cake.

**2001 Photo. *Perf. 13¼***
**Stamps + Labels**

**2049-2052** A1375 Set of 4 7.25 3.75

Issued: Nos. 2049-2050, 4/30; No. 2051, 6/1; No. 2052, 7/2. Each stamp was issued in sheets of 20+20 labels that could be personalized. Each sheet sold for 700w.

Cartoons — A1376

Designs: No. 2053, Iljimae, by Ko Woo-young (shown). No. 2054, Kkeobeongi, by Kil Chang-duk (student at desk).

**2001, May 4 Photo. *Perf. 13x13¼***

| | | | |
|---|---|---|---|
| **2053** | A1376 170w multi | .70 | .35 |
| *a.* | Souvenir sheet of 1 | 1.60 | 1.60 |
| **2054** | A1376 170w multi | .70 | .35 |
| *a.* | Souvenir sheet of 1 | 1.60 | 1.60 |

2002 World Cup Soccer Championships, Japan and Korea — A1377

Years of previous championships, soccer players, flags and scenes from host countries: a, 1954, Switzerland, mountains. b, 1986, Mexico, Chichen Itza. c, 1990, Italy, Colosseum. d, 1994, US, World Trade Center and Statue of Liberty. e, 1998, France, Eiffel Tower.

**2001, May 31 *Perf. 13¼x13***

| | | | |
|---|---|---|---|
| **2055** | A1377 Horiz. strip of 5 | 4.75 | 4.25 |
| *a.-e.* | 170w Any single | .80 | .35 |
| *f.* | Souvenir sheet, 2 #2055a | 1.60 | 1.60 |
| *g.* | Souvenir sheet, 2 #2055b | 1.60 | 1.60 |
| *h.* | Souvenir sheet, 2 #2055c | 1.60 | 1.60 |
| *i.* | Souvenir sheet, 2 #2055d | 1.60 | 1.60 |
| *j.* | Souvenir sheet, 2 #2055e | 1.60 | 1.60 |

Kkakdugi A1378

Bossam Kimchi A1379

Dongchimi A1380

Baechu Kimchi A1381

**2001, June 15 *Perf. 13x13¼***

| | | | |
|---|---|---|---|
| **2056** | Vert. strip of 4 | 3.50 | 3.50 |
| *a.* | A1378 170w multi | .65 | .35 |
| *b.* | A1379 170w multi | .65 | .35 |
| *c.* | A1380 170w multi | .65 | .35 |
| *d.* | A1381 170w multi | .65 | .35 |

Roses A1382

**2001, July 18 Photo. *Perf. 13¼***

| | | | |
|---|---|---|---|
| **2057** | A1382 170w Red Queen | .75 | .35 |
| *a.* | Souvenir sheet of 2 | 1.90 | 1.90 |
| **2058** | A1382 170w Pink Lady | .75 | .35 |
| *a.* | Souvenir sheet of 2 | 1.90 | 1.90 |

Phila Korea 2002, (Nos. 2057a, 2058a).

Love — A1383

**2001, Aug. 2**

| | | | |
|---|---|---|---|
| **2059** | A1383 170w multi | .70 | .40 |
| *a.* | Souvenir sheet of 2 | 1.75 | 1.75 |

World Ceramics Exhibition — A1384

**2001, Aug. 10 *Perf. 13x13¼***
**2060** A1384 170w multi .70 .35

53rd Session of the Intl. Statistical Institute A1385

**2001, Aug. 22 Litho. *Perf. 13¼x13***
**2061** A1385 170w multi .70 .35

Korea Minting and Security Printing Corp., 50th Anniv. A1386

**Litho. & Engr.**

**2001, Sept. 28 *Perf. 13¼***
**2062** A1386 170w multi .70 .40

Intl. Council of Industrial Design Societies Congress, Seoul — A1387

**2001, Oct. 8 Photo. *Perf. 13x13¼***
**2063** A1387 170w multi .70 .35

Year of Dialogue Among Civilizations A1388

**2001, Oct. 9 Litho.**
**2064** A1388 170w multi .70 .35

Intl. Organization of Supreme Audit Institutions, 17th Congress A1389

**2001, Oct. 19 *Perf. 13¼x13***
**2065** A1389 170w blue & red .70 .35

Orchids — A1390

No. 2066: a, Habenaria radiata. b, Orchis cyclochila. c, Dendrobium moniliforme. d, Gymnadenia camschatica.

**2001, Nov. 12 Photo. *Perf. 13¼x13***

| | | | |
|---|---|---|---|
| **2066** | A1390 Horiz. strip of 4 | 4.50 | 4.50 |
| *a.-d.* | 170w Any single | .75 | .40 |

No. 2066 is impregnated with orchid scent.

New Year 2002 (Year of the Horse) — A1391

**2001, Dec. 3 *Perf. 13x13¼***

| | | | |
|---|---|---|---|
| **2067** | A1391 170w multi | .75 | .40 |
| *a.* | Souvenir sheet of 2 | 1.90 | 1.90 |

Seonjeongjeon Hall, Changdeok Palace — A1392

Injeongjeon Hall, Changdeok Palace — A1393

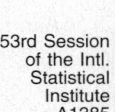

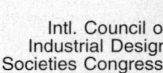

**Litho. & Engr.**

**2001, Dec. 10** *Perf. 13x13¼*

| | | | | |
|---|---|---|---|---|
| **2068** | Sheet of 10 | | 17.50 | 14.00 |
| *a.* | A1392 170w multi | | .85 | .35 |
| *b.* | A1393 340w multi | | 1.60 | .70 |

Top part of No. 2068 contains one each Nos. 2068a-2068b. The lower part of No. 2068 contains 4 each Nos. 2068a-2068b.

Priority Mail — A1394

**2002, Jan. 15 Photo.** *Perf. 13¼x13*

**Background Color**

| | | | | |
|---|---|---|---|---|
| **2069** | A1394 | 280w orange | 1.45 | .45 |
| **2070** | A1394 | 310w blue | 1.60 | .50 |
| **2071** | A1394 | 1380w green | 4.50 | 2.40 |
| **2072** | A1394 | 1410w red | 4.50 | 2.40 |
| | *Nos. 2069-2072 (4)* | | 12.05 | 5.75 |

See Nos. 2113-2114, 2127.

Lily — A1395

Roses — A1395a

Fish — A1396

Chick — A1396a

**2002, Jan. 15 Photo.** *Perf. 13¼*

**Stamp + Label**

| | | | | |
|---|---|---|---|---|
| **2073** | A1395 | 190w multi | 2.00 | 1.00 |
| **2073A** | A1395a | 190w multi | 2.00 | 1.00 |
| **2074** | A1396 | 190w multi | 2.00 | 1.00 |
| **2074A** | A1396a | 190w multi | 2.00 | 1.00 |
| | *Nos. 2073-2074A (4)* | | 8.00 | 4.00 |

Nos. 2073, 2073A and 2074 are impregnated with scents of items depicted. Labels could be personalized.

Korea's Entrance in Intl. Telecommunications Union, 50th Anniv. — A1397

**2002, Jan. 31 Photo.** *Perf. 13x13¼*

| | | | | |
|---|---|---|---|---|
| **2075** | A1397 | 190w multi | .70 | .35 |

Trains — A1398

No. 2076: a, Blue and white locomotive. b, Green, yellow and white locomotive. c, Green, yellow and white locomotive pulling cars. d, Red, yellow and white locomotive pulling cars.

**2002, Feb. 4 Photo.** *Perf. 13¾x12¾*

| | | | | |
|---|---|---|---|---|
| **2076** | A1398 | 190w Block of 4, #a-d | 4.25 | 4.25 |

Dye Plants — A1399

No. 2077: a, Carthamus tinctorius. b, Lithospermum erythrorhizon. c, Fraxinus rhynchophylla. d, Persicaria tinctoria.

**2002, Feb. 25 Photo.** *Perf. 13¼x13*

| | | | | |
|---|---|---|---|---|
| **2077** | A1399 | 190w Block of 4, #a-d | 4.25 | 3.50 |

See No. 2117, 2140, 2170.

Intl. Flower Exhibition, Anmyeon Island A1400

**2002, Apr. 26** *Perf. 13¼*

| | | | | |
|---|---|---|---|---|
| **2078** | A1400 | 190w multi | .85 | .35 |

Cartoons A1401

Designs: No. 2079, Girl from "Wogdoggle Dugdoggle," by Mi-Na Hwang. No. 2080, Schoolmaster and children from "Mengkkong-i Seodang Village School," by Seung-woon Yoon.

**2002, May 4** *Perf. 13¼x13*

| | | | | |
|---|---|---|---|---|
| **2079** | A1401 | 190w multi | .85 | .35 |
| *a.* | Souvenir sheet of 1 | | 1.05 | 1.05 |
| **2080** | A1401 | 190w multi | .85 | .35 |
| *a.* | Souvenir sheet of 1 | | 1.05 | 1.05 |

64th Rally of Intl. Federation of Camping and Caravanning, Donghae A1402

**2002, May 16**

| | | | | |
|---|---|---|---|---|
| **2081** | A1402 | 190w multi | *1.60* | .40 |

2002 World Cup Soccer Championships, Japan and Korea — A1403

No. 2082: a, Player with pink feet, part of map of Europe. b, Player with blue green feet, part of map of North and Central America. c, Player with blue violet feet, part of map of southeast Asia. d, Player with purple feet, part of map of southern Africa. e, Player with brown orange feet, part of map of South America.

**2002, May 31** *Perf.*

| | | | | |
|---|---|---|---|---|
| **2082** | A1403 | 190w Sheet, 2 each #a-e, + label | 10.00 | 10.00 |
| *f.* | Souvenir sheet, 2 #2082a | | 1.00 | .40 |
| *g.* | Souvenir sheet, 2 #2082b | | 1.00 | .40 |
| *h.* | Souvenir sheet, 2 #2082c | | 1.00 | .40 |
| *i.* | Souvenir sheet, 2 #2082d | | 1.00 | .40 |
| *j.* | Souvenir sheet, 2 #2082e | | 1.00 | .40 |

Korean Cuisine — A1404

No. 2083: a, Jeolpyeon (blue background). b, Shirutteok (red background). c, Injeolmi (tan background). d, Songpyeon (green background).

**2002, June 15** *Perf. 13x13¼*

| | | | | |
|---|---|---|---|---|
| **2083** | A1404 | 190w Block of 4, #a-d | 3.75 | 3.75 |

Women's Week — A1405

**2002, July 1 Litho.** *Perf. 13x13¼*

| | | | | |
|---|---|---|---|---|
| **2084** | A1405 | 190w multi | .70 | .35 |

Philakorea 2002 World Stamp Exhibition, Seoul A1406

Designs: No. 2085, Children, globe. No. 2086, Child, stamps showing flags of the world.

**2002, July 1 Photo.** *Perf. 13¼*

| | | | | |
|---|---|---|---|---|
| **2085** | A1406 | 190w multi | .75 | .35 |
| *a.* | Souvenir sheet of 2 | | 1.75 | 1.75 |
| **2086** | A1406 | 190w multi | .75 | .35 |
| *a.* | Souvenir sheet of 2 | | 1.75 | 1.75 |

**Regions of Korea**

Busan — A1407

Chungbuk — A1408

Chungnam — A1409

Daegu — A1410

Daejeon — A1411

Gangwon — A1412

Gwangju — A1413

Gyeongbuk — A1414

Gyeonggi — A1415

Gyeongnam — A1416

Incheon — A1417

Jeju — A1418

Jeonbuk — A1419

Jeonnam — A1420

Seoul — A1421

Ulsan — A1422

No. 2087: a, Dongnaeyaryu Festival. b, Cliffs.
No. 2088: a, Martial arts. b, Beopju Temple.
No. 2089: a, Weaver. b, Men in sailboat.
No. 2090: a, Forest and river. b, Gwanbong Seokjoyeorae statue.
No. 2091: a, Daeok Science Town, scientist at work. b, Expo Science Park.
No. 2092: a, Gangneung mask drama. b, Ulsanbawi Rock.
No. 2093: a, Men playing tug-of-war game. b, Statues and tower at May 18th Cemetery.
No. 2094: a, Men playing game with tied logs. b, Dokdo Island.
No. 2095: a, Yangjubyeol Sandaenori mask dance. b, Panmunjom Freedom House.
No. 2096: a, Goseong Ogwangdae clowns performing. b, Rock formations in Hallyeo Haesang Natl. Maritime Park.
No. 2097: a, Chamseongdam dancers. b, Cliffs.
No. 2098: a, Traditional house and gate. b, Mt. Halla.
No. 2099: a, Iri folk band. b, Mt. Mai.
No. 2100: a, Ganggang Sullae circle dance. b, Odong Island.
No. 2101: a, Songpa Sandaenori mask dance. b, Heung-injimun Fortress.
No. 2102: a, Cheoyongmu mask dance. b, Cheonjeonnigakseok prehistoric inscriptions.

**2002, Aug. 1** ***Perf. 13x13¼***

| | | |
|---|---|---|
| **2087** A1407 190w Horiz. pair, #a-b | 1.60 | .70 |
| **2088** A1408 190w Horiz. pair, #a-b | 1.60 | .70 |
| **2089** A1409 190w Horiz. pair, #a-b | 1.60 | .70 |
| **2090** A1410 190w Horiz. pair, #a-b | 1.60 | .70 |
| **2091** A1411 190w Horiz. pair, #a-b | 1.60 | .70 |
| **2092** A1412 190w Horiz. pair, #a-b | 1.60 | .70 |
| **2093** A1413 190w Horiz. pair, #a-b | 1.60 | .70 |
| **2094** A1414 190w Horiz. pair, #a-b | 1.60 | .70 |
| **2095** A1415 190w Horiz. pair, #a-b | 1.60 | .70 |
| **2096** A1416 190w Horiz. pair, #a-b | 1.60 | .70 |
| **2097** A1417 190w Horiz. pair, #a-b | 1.60 | .70 |
| **2098** A1418 190w Horiz. pair, #a-b | 1.60 | .70 |
| **2099** A1419 190w Horiz. pair, #a-b | 1.60 | .70 |
| **2100** A1420 190w Horiz. pair, #a-b | 1.60 | .70 |
| **2101** A1421 190w Horiz. pair, #a-b | 1.60 | .70 |
| **2102** A1422 190w Horiz. pair, #a-b | 1.60 | .70 |
| *Nos. 2087-2102 (16)* | 25.60 | 11.20 |

Philakorea 2002 World Stamp Exhibition, Seoul A1423

**2002, Aug. 2** ***Perf. 13¼x13***

| | | |
|---|---|---|
| **2103** A1423 190w multi | .70 | .35 |
| *a.* Sheet of 2, imperf. | 2.00 | 2.00 |

Philately Week A1424

**2002, Aug. 2** ***Perf. 13¼***

| | | |
|---|---|---|
| **2104** A1424 190w multi | .70 | .35 |
| *a.* Souvenir sheet of 2 | 1.90 | 1.90 |

South Korean Soccer Team's Fourth Place Finish at World Cup Championships — A1425

No. 2105: a, Coach Guus Hiddink. b, Goalie (jersey #1). c, Player with red shirt with white accents. d, Player with red shirt with white accents, with white sock. e, Player with white shirt with red accents, ball near shoulder. f, Player (jersey #5). g, Player (jersey #6). h, Player (jersey #7). i, Player (jersey #8.) j, Player (jersey #9). k, Player (jersey #10). l, Player with ball hiding part of head. m, Goalie with red hair, white gloves with dark trim. n, Player (jersey #13). o, Player (jersey #14). p, Player (jersey #15). q, Player with white shirt with red accents, with white sock. r, Player (jersey #17). s, Player (jersey #18). t, Player (jersey #19). u, Player (jersey #20). v, Player (jersey #21). w, Player (jersey #22). x, Goalie with brown hair, black gloves with red trim.

**2002, Aug. 7** ***Perf. 13¼x13***

| | | |
|---|---|---|
| **2105** A1425 190w Sheet of 24, #a-x | 18.50 | 18.50 |

14th Asian Games, Busan — A1426

**2002, Sept. 28** **Litho.** ***Perf. 13***

| | | |
|---|---|---|
| **2106** A1426 190w multi | .80 | .40 |
| *a.* Souvenir sheet of 2 | 2.00 | 2.00 |

8th Far East and South Pacific Games for the Disabled, Busan — A1427

**2002, Oct. 26** **Photo.** ***Perf. 13x13¼***

| | | |
|---|---|---|
| **2107** A1427 190w multi | .75 | .35 |

Orchids — A1428

No. 2108: a, Cymbidium kanran. b, Gastrodia elata. c, Pogonia japonica. d, Cephalanthera falcata.

**2002, Nov. 12** ***Perf. 13¼x13***

| | | |
|---|---|---|
| **2108** A1428 190w Block of 4, #a-d | 4.00 | 4.00 |

No. 2108 is impregnated with orchid scent.

Martial Arts — A1429

No. 2109: a, Taekwondo (white clothes). b, Kung Fu (red clothes).

**2002, Nov. 20** ***Perf. 13x13¼***

| | | |
|---|---|---|
| **2109** A1429 190w Horiz. pair, #a-b | 1.75 | 1.75 |

See People's Republic of China No. 3248.

New Year 2003 (Year of the Ram) — A1430

**2002, Dec. 2**

| | | |
|---|---|---|
| **2110** A1430 190w multi | .85 | .40 |
| *a.* Souvenir sheet of 2 | 1.90 | 1.90 |

Gongsimdon Observation Tower, Hwaseong Fortress — A1431

Banghwasuryu Pavilion, Hwaseong Fortress — A1432

**2002, Dec. 9** **Litho. & Engr.**

| | | |
|---|---|---|
| **2111** Sheet of 10 | 15.00 | 15.00 |
| *a.* A1431 190w multi | .80 | .40 |
| *b.* A1432 280w multi | 1.25 | .65 |

Top part of No. 2111 contains one each of Nos. 2111a-2111b. The lower part contains 4 each Nos. 2111a-2111b.

South Korea — Viet Nam Diplomatic Relations, 10th Anniv. — A1433

No. 2112: a, Dabo Pagoda, Gyeongju (denomination at right). b, Mot Cot Pagoda, Hanoi, Viet Nam (denomination at left).

**2002, Dec. 21** **Photo.** ***Perf. 13¼x13***

| | | |
|---|---|---|
| **2112** A1433 190w Horiz. pair, #a-b | 2.00 | 1.50 |

See Viet Nam Nos. 3167-3168.

**Priority Mail Type of 2002**

**2003, Jan. 1** **Photo.** ***Perf. 13¼x13***

**Background Color**

| | | |
|---|---|---|
| **2113** A1394 1580w lilac | 5.25 | 4.75 |
| **2114** A1394 1610w brown | 5.25 | 4.75 |

Korean Immigration to the US, Cent. — A1434

**2003, Jan. 13** **Photo.** ***Perf. 13¼x13***

| | | |
|---|---|---|
| **2115** A1434 190w multi | .80 | .40 |

Gondola Car A1435

Box Car A1436

Tanker Car A1437

Hopper Car A1438

**2003, Feb. 4** ***Perf. 13¾x13***

| | | |
|---|---|---|
| **2116** Block of 4 | 4.00 | 3.25 |
| *a.* A1435 190w multi | .70 | .35 |
| *b.* A1436 190w multi | .70 | .35 |
| *c.* A1437 190w multi | .70 | .35 |
| *d.* A1438 190w multi | .70 | .35 |

### Dye Plants Type of 2002

No. 2117: a, Rubia akane. b, Rhus javanica. c, Sophora japonica. d, Isatis tinctoria.

**2003, Feb. 22 Photo.** ***Perf. 13¼x13***
**2117** A1399 190w Horiz. strip of 4, #a-d 3.50 2.50

Inauguration of Pres. Roh Moo-hyun A1439

**2003, Feb. 25** ***Perf. 13x13¼***
**2118** A1439 190w multi 1.35 .65
*a.* Souvenir sheet of 1 2.00 2.00

### Traditional Culture

Footwear — A1440

Sedan Chairs — A1441

Lighting Implements — A1442

Tables — A1443

No. 2119: a, Unhye (denomination at LL, date at LR). b, Mokhwa (denomination at UR, date at L). c, Jipsin (denomination at UL, date at LR). d, Namaksin (denomination at LR, date at LL).

No. 2120: a, Eoyeon (no handles). b, Choheon (wheeled). c, Saingyo (with handles and roof). d, Nanyeo (with handles only).

No. 2121: a, Jojokdeung (round lantern). b, Deungjan (lamp oil container). c, Juchilmokje Yukgakjedeung (hexagonal lantern). d, Brass candlestick holder with butterfly design.

No. 2122: a, Gujok-ban (round table with legs connected at base. b, Punghyeol-ban (12-sided table, denomination at top). c, Ilju-ban (12-sided table, denomination at top). d, Haeju-ban (octagonal table).

**2003 Engr.** ***Perf. 12½***
**2119** A1440 190w Horiz. strip of 4, #a-d 4.00 2.50
**2120** A1441 190w Horiz. strip of 4, #a-d 4.00 2.50
**2121** A1442 190w Horiz. strip of 4, #a-d 4.00 2.50
**2122** A1443 190w Horiz. strip of 4, #a-d 4.00 2.50
*Nos. 2119-2122 (4)* 16.00 10.00

Issued: No. 2119, 3/19; No. 2120, 5/19; No. 2121, 7/25; No. 2122, 9/25.

Cartoons — A1444

Designs: No. 2123, The Goblin's Cap, by Shin Moon-soo (shown). No. 2124, The Sword of Fire, by Kim Hye-rin (woman with sword).

**2003, May 2 Photo.** ***Perf. 13x13¼***
**2123** A1444 190w multi .75 .35
*a.* Souvenir sheet of 1 1.05 1.05
**2124** A1444 190w multi .75 .35
*a.* Souvenir sheet of 1 1.05 1.05

Lighthouse Construction in Korea, Cent. — A1445

**2003, May 30** ***Perf. 13¼x13***
**2125** A1445 190w multi .75 .35

Dasik A1446

Yeot Gangjeong A1447

Yakgwa A1448

Yugwa A1449

**2003, June 13** ***Perf. 13x13¼***
**2126** Block or strip of 4 2.60 2.10
*a.* A1446 190w multi .55 .35
*b.* A1447 190w multi .55 .35
*c.* A1448 190w multi .55 .35
*d.* A1449 190w multi .55 .35

Nos. 2126a-2126d were printed in sheets of 20 that yield four No. 2126 and one vertical strip of four of Nos. 2126a-2126d.

### Priority Mail Type of 2002

**2003, July 1 Photo.** ***Perf. 13¼x13***
**Background Color**
**2127** A1394 420w blue green 4.50 1.00

Philately Week A1450

**2003, Aug. 1** ***Perf. 13¼***
**2128** A1450 190w multi .75 .35
*a.* Souvenir sheet of 2, imperf. 1.90 1.90

2003 Summer Universiade, Daegu — A1451

**2003, Aug. 21** ***Perf. 13x13¼***
**2129** A1451 190w multi .75 .35
*a.* Souvenir sheet of 2 1.90 1.90

YMCA in Korea, Cent. — A1452

**2003, Oct. 28 Photo.** ***Perf. 13¼x13***
**2130** A1452 190w multi .75 .35

Soong Eui School, Cent. — A1453

**2003, Oct. 31** ***Perf. 13x13¼***
**2131** A1453 190w multi .75 .35

Natl. Tuberculosis Association, 50th Anniv. — A1454

**2003, Nov. 6** ***Litho.***
**2132** A1454 190w black & red .75 .35

Orchids — A1455

No. 2133: a, Cremastra appendiculata. b, Cymbidium lancifolium. c, Orchis graminifolia. d, Bulbophyllum drymoglossum.

**2003, Nov. 12 Photo.** ***Perf. 13¼x13***
**2133** A1455 190w Block of 4, #a-d 3.75 3.75

No. 2133 is impregnated with a floral scent.

New Year 2004 (Year of the Monkey) — A1456

**2003, Dec. 1** ***Perf. 13x13¼***
**2134** A1456 190w multi .75 .35
*a.* Souvenir sheet of 2 1.90 1.90

A1457

Dolmens — A1458

**Litho. & Engr.**

**2003, Dec. 9** ***Perf. 13x13¼***
**2135** Sheet of 10 13.50 13.50
*a.* A1457 190w multi .90 .40
*b.* A1458 280w multi 1.25 .65

Top part of No. 2135 contains one each of Nos. 2135a-2135b. The lower part contains 4 each Nos. 2135a-2135b.

South Korea — India Diplomatic Relations, 30th Anniv. — A1459

No. 2136: a, Cheomsongdae Astronomical Observatory, Gyeongju, South Korea. b, Jantar Mantar, Jaipur, India.

**2003, Dec. 10 Photo.** ***Perf. 13¼x13***
**2136** A1459 190w Horiz. pair, #a-b 2.25 2.00

Dokdo Island Flora and Fauna — A1460

No. 2137: a, Calystegia soldanella. b, Aster spathulifolius, butterfly. c, Calonectris laucomelas. d, Larus crassirostris.

**2004, Jan. 16** ***Perf. 13x13¼***
**2137** A1460 Horiz. strip of 4 *15.50* —
*a.-d.* 190w Any single *3.75 3.75*

Korean National Commission for UNESCO, 50th Anniv. — A1461

**2004, Jan. 30**
**2138** A1461 190w multi .75 .30

Multiple Tie Tamper A1462

Ballast Regulator A1463

Track Inspection Car — A1464

Ballast Cleaner A1465

**2004, Feb. 4** *Perf. 13¾x12¾*

**2139** Block of 4 3.50 3.50
- *a.* A1462 190w brown & multi .70 .40
- *b.* A1463 190w lilac & multi .70 .40
- *c.* A1464 190w blue green & multi .70 .40
- *d.* A1465 190w blue & multi .70 .40

### Dye Plants Type of 2002

No. 2140: a, Juglans regia. b, Acer ginnala. c, Pinus densiflora. d, Punica granatum.

**2004, Feb. 25** *Perf. 13¼x13*

**2140** A1399 190w Block of 4, #a-d 3.00 3.00

12th World Water Day — A1466

**2004, Mar. 22 Litho.** *Perf. 13x13¼*

**2141** A1466 190w multi .75 .40

A1467

**2004, Mar. 25 Photo.**

**2142** A1467 190w multi .80 .40

Korean Meteorological Service, cent.

Inauguration of High Speed Railroads A1468

**2004, Apr. 1** *Perf. 13¼x13*

**2143** A1468 190w multi .80 .40

A1469

Winners of Future of Science Stamp Design Contest — A1470

*Perf. 13¼x13, 13x13¼*

**2004, Apr. 21 Photo.**

**2144** A1469 190w multi .80 .40
**2145** A1470 190w multi .80 .40

A1471

Cartoons: No. 2146, Wicked Boy Simsultong, by Lee Jeong-moon (shown). No. 2147, Nation of Winds, by Kim Jin.

**2004, May 4 Photo.** *Perf. 13x13¼*

**2146** A1471 190w multi .80 .40
- *a.* Souvenir sheet of 1 1.10 1.10

**2147** A1471 190w multi .80 .40
- *a.* Souvenir sheet of 1 1.10 1.10

A1472

**2004, May 21**

**2148** A1472 190w multi .55 .35

FIFA (Fédération Internationale de Football Association), cent.

Korean Cuisine — A1473

No. 2149: a, Sinseollo (blue background). b, Hwayangjeok (green background). c, Bibimbap (pink background). d, Gujeolpan (orange background).

**2004, June 15**

**2149** A1473 190w Block of 4, #a-d 3.25 3.25

### Traditional Culture

Needlework Equipment — A1474

Head Coverings — A1475

No. 2150: a, Octagonal storage basket. b, Thimbles with flower decorations. c, Cylindrical bobbin, bobbin and thread. d, Needle cases.

No. 2151: a, Gold crown with tassels. b, Bamboo hat with untied neck band. c, Gauze hat. d, Horsehair hat with tied neck band.

**2004 Engr.** *Perf. 12½*

**2150** A1474 190w Horiz. strip of 4, #a-d 3.50 3.50
**2151** A1475 190w Horiz. strip of 4, #a-d 3.50 3.50

Issued: No. 2150, 6/24; No. 2151, 8/20.

National Academies, 50th Anniv. — A1476

No. 2152: a, National Academy of Science. b, National Academy of Arts.

**2004, July 16 Litho.** *Perf. 13x13¼*

**2152** A1476 190w Horiz. pair, #a-b 1.60 1.60

Congratulations — A1477

**2004, July 22 Photo.** *Perf. 13¼*

**2153** A1477 190w multi .80 .40
- *a.* Souvenir sheet of 2 1.75 1.75

2004 Summer Olympics, Athens — A1478

**2004, Aug. 13** *Perf. 13x13¼*

**2154** A1478 190w multi .80 .40

Bridges — A1479

No. 2155: a, Geumcheongyo Bridge (two arches). b, Jeongotgyo Bridge (pillars and flat slabs). c, Jincheon Nongdari Bridge (loose rocks). d, Seungseongyo Bridge (single arch).

*Perf. 13¼ Syncopated*

**2004, Sept. 24**

**2155** A1479 190w Block of 4, #a-d 3.50 3.50

Intl. Council of Museums, 20th General Conference, Seoul — A1480

**2004, Oct. 1** *Perf. 13x13¼*

**2156** A1480 190w multi .80 .40

Obaegnahan — A1481

Seonjakjiwat — A1482

Baengnokdam — A1483

Oreum A1484

**2004, Oct. 18**

**2157** Block of 4 3.50 3.50
- *a.* A1481 190w multi .70 .35
- *b.* A1482 190w multi .70 .35
- *c.* A1483 190w multi .70 .35
- *d.* A1484 190w multi .70 .35

Flag — A1485

Flowers — A1486

Flower and Bee — A1487

Lamb, Church and Bible — A1488

Children and Lotus Flower — A1489

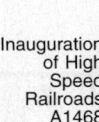

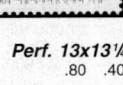

Stylized Animals — A1490

Teddy Bear — A1491

Dinosaur — A1492

Flower and Envelope — A1493

**2004, Nov. 1 Photo. *Perf. 13¼***

| | | | |
|---|---|---|---|
| **2158** | A1485 220w multi + label | 2.10 | 1.35 |
| **2159** | A1486 220w multi + label | 2.10 | 1.35 |
| **2160** | A1487 220w multi + label | 2.10 | 1.35 |
| **2161** | A1488 220w multi + label | 2.10 | 1.35 |
| **2162** | A1489 220w multi + label | 2.10 | 1.35 |
| **2163** | Strip of 4 + 4 alternating labels | 8.75 | 8.75 |
| *a.* | A1490 220w multi + label | 2.10 | 2.00 |
| *b.* | A1491 220w multi + label | 2.10 | 2.00 |
| *c.* | A1492 220w multi + label | 2.10 | 2.00 |
| *d.* | A1493 220w multi + label | 2.10 | 2.00 |
| | *Nos. 2158-2163 (6)* | 19.25 | 15.50 |

Labels attached to Nos. 2158-2163 could be personalized.

Orchids — A1494

No. 2164: a, Goodyera maximowicziana. b, Sarcanthus scolopendrifolius. c, Calanthe sieboldii. d, Bletilla striata.

**2004, Nov. 12 *Perf. 13¼x13***

| | | | |
|---|---|---|---|
| **2164** | A1494 220w Block of 4, #a-d | 3.50 | 3.50 |

No. 2164 is impregnated with orchid scent.

New Year 2005 (Year of the Chicken) — A1495

**2004, Dec. 1 *Perf. 13x13¼***

| | | | |
|---|---|---|---|
| **2165** | A1495 220w multi | .90 | .45 |
| *a.* | Souvenir sheet of 2 | 1.90 | 1.90 |

Daenungwon Tumuli Park, Seosuhyeong Ceramics, Royal Crown of Geumgwanchong — A1496

Anapji Pond, Scissors, Buddha, Lion Incense Burner — A1497

**2004, Dec. 9 Litho. & Engr.**

| | | | |
|---|---|---|---|
| **2166** | Sheet of 10 | 14.00 | 14.00 |
| *a.* | A1496 310w multi | 1.00 | .55 |
| *b.* | A1497 310w multi | 1.00 | .55 |

Top part of No. 2166 contains one each of Nos. 2166a-2166b. The lower part contains 4 each of Nos. 2166a-2166b.

Fish of Marado Island A1498

No. 2167: a, Girella punctata. b, Epinephelus septemfasciatus. c, Chromis notata. d, Sebastiscus marmoratus.

**2005, Jan. 18 Photo.**

| | | | |
|---|---|---|---|
| **2167** | Horiz. strip of 4 | 5.75 | 5.75 |
| *a.-d.* | A1498 220w Any single | 1.20 | .50 |

Cloning of Human Embryonic Stem Cells, 1st Anniv. — A1499

**2005, Feb. 12 *Perf. 12¾x13½***

| | | | |
|---|---|---|---|
| **2168** | A1499 220w multi | 2.75 | 1.00 |

Rotary International, Cent. A1500

**2005, Feb. 23 *Perf. 13¼x13***

| | | | |
|---|---|---|---|
| **2169** | A1500 220w multi | .80 | .40 |

**Dye Plants Type of 2002**

No. 2170: a, Taxus cuspidata. b, Smilax china. c, Clerodendron trichotomum. d, Gardenia jasminoides.

**2005, Feb. 25**

| | | | |
|---|---|---|---|
| **2170** | A1399 220w Block of 4, #a-d | 3.75 | 3.75 |

Gyeonggi Province Tourism — A1501

**2005, Mar. 10 Litho. *Perf. 13x13¼***

| | | | |
|---|---|---|---|
| **2171** | A1501 220w multi | .75 | .40 |

A1502

Information and Communication of the Future — A1503

**2005, Apr. 22 Photo. *Perf. 13¼x13***

| | | | |
|---|---|---|---|
| **2172** | A1502 220w multi | .75 | .40 |

***Perf. 13x13¼***

| | | | |
|---|---|---|---|
| **2173** | A1503 220w multi | .75 | .40 |

Korea University, Cent. A1504

**2005, May 4 Litho. *Perf. 13x13¼***

| | | | |
|---|---|---|---|
| **2174** | A1504 220w multi | .85 | .40 |

57th Intl. Whaling Commission Meeting, Ulsan A1505

**2005, May 27 Photo. *Perf. 13¼x13***

| | | | |
|---|---|---|---|
| **2175** | A1505 220w multi | .95 | .40 |

Neobani (Broiled Beef) A1506

Bindaetteok (Fried Ground Mung Beans) A1507

Jeongol (Stew) A1508

Hwajeon (Fried Rice Cakes and Flower Petals) A1509

**2005, June 15 *Perf. 13x13¼***

| | | | |
|---|---|---|---|
| **2176** | Block of 4 | 3.75 | 3.75 |
| *a.* | A1506 220w multi | .85 | .40 |
| *b.* | A1507 220w multi | .85 | .40 |
| *c.* | A1508 220w multi | .85 | .40 |
| *d.* | A1509 220w multi | .85 | .40 |

Goguryeo Kingdom — A1510

No. 2177: a, Sword, armored soldier on horse. b, Armored soldiers on horses, Onyeo Fortress, Baek-am Castle.

***Perf. 13x13¼ Syncopated***

**2005, July 1**

| | | | |
|---|---|---|---|
| **2177** | A1510 310w Vert. pair, #a-b | 3.00 | 3.00 |

Strix Aluco A1513

Arctous Ruber A1514

Parus Major A1516

Crinum Asiaticum A1517

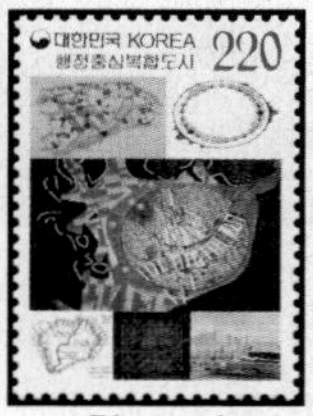
Planned City — A1521

Brown Hawk Owl — A1522

Rose of Sharon — A1523

Sungnyemun Gate — A1524

Suwon Hwaseong Fortress — A1524a

Haeundae Dongbaek Island — A1524b

Dodamsambong Peaks — A1524c

Hongdo Island — A1524d

Cheomseongdae Observatory — A1524e

Gwanghallu Pavilion — A1524f

Gyeongpodae Pavilion — A1524g

Baengnokdam Lake — A1524h

Whistling Swans A1525

Charonia Sauliae A1526

Pitta Nympha — A1526b

Celadon Incense Burner — A1527

Buncheong Jar — A1529

Buncheong Jar — A1530

Jar With Clay Figurines — A1530a

Gold Earrings — A1530c

Gilt Bronze Pagoda — A1531

Vessel With Dragon's Head — A1531a

Lofty Scholar Contemplating Water, Painting by Kang Hui An — A1531b

National Seal — A1531c

Euryale Ferox — A1532

Flag — A1533

**2005-14 Photo. *Perf. 13¾x12¾***

2178 A1513 50w multi .75 .25
2179 A1514 70w multi .45 .25

***Perf. 12¾x13¾***

2180 A1516 90w multi .65 .25

***Perf. 13¾x12¾***

2181 A1517 100w multi .65 .25

***Perf. 13x13¼***

2182 A1521 220w multi .95 .25
2183 A1522 250w multi 1.05 .35

***Perf. 13½***

2184 A1523 250w multi + label 2.00 .35

***Perf. 13x13¾***

2185 Horiz. strip of 9 8.75 8.75
*a.* A1524 300w multi .55 .25
*b.* A1524a 300w multi .55 .25
*c.* A1524b 300w multi .55 .25
*d.* A1524c 300w multi .55 .25
*e.* A1524d 300w multi .55 .25
*f.* A1524e 300w multi .55 .25
*g.* A1524f 300w multi .55 .25
*h.* A1524g 300w multi .55 .25
*i.* A1524h 300w multi .55 .25

***Perf. 13¾x13***

2186 A1525 340w multi 1.00 .40

***Perf. 12¾x13¾***

2187 A1526 360w multi .65 .30

***Perf. 13x13¾***

2188 A1526 390w multi 1.00 .25

***Perf. 13x13¼***

2189 A1526b 400w multi .90 .35
2190 A1527 1000w multi 3.00 1.00
2191 A1529 1720w multi 4.50 1.75

***Perf. 13x13½***

2192 A1530 1750w multi 5.50 1.90

***Perf. 13x13¼***

2193 A1530a 1770w multi 4.00 1.50

***Perf. 13x13½***

2194 A1530a 1930w multi 4.00 .90

***Perf. 13¾x13½***

2195 A1530c 1930w multi 4.00 2.00

***Perf. 13x13½***

2196 A1531 2000w multi 6.00 1.60

***Perf. 13¾x13½***

2197 A1531a 2000w multi 4.00 1.90
2198 A1531b 3000w multi 5.75 2.75
2199 A1531c 3550w multi 7.00 3.25
*Nos. 2180-2199 (20)* 65.35 30.05

**Self-Adhesive**

***Serpentine Die Cut 11¾x11½***

2200 A1532 250w multi 1.30 .25

***Serpentine Die Cut 11½x11¼***

2201 A1533 270w multi .60 .25

Issued: 50w, 9/1; 1720w, 8/1; 90w, 6/5/06; 100w, 3/2/06; 220w, 12/27/05. Nos. 2183, 2184, 2186, 2192, 11/1/06. 70w, 7/10/07. No. 2200, 6/30/08. No. 2190, 11/17/09; No. 2196, 5/25/09. Nos. 2187, 2193, 2201, 10/1/11. Nos. 2185, 2188, 2194, 11/11/13. Nos. 2189, 2197, 11/20/14. Nos. 2195, 2198, 8/7/14; No. 2199, 10/28/14.

No. 2190 was printed in sheets of 20 stamps and 20 labels that could be personalized.

Nos. 2197C, 2198A, 2198B and 2198C each have a die cut hole in the shape of the Korean Peninsula in the lower right corner of the stamp.

Happy Birthday A1536

**2005, Aug. 3 Photo. *Perf. 13¼***

2203 A1536 220w multi .85 .35
*a.* Souvenir sheet of 2 1.90 1.90

Philately Week. Portions of the design were printed with a thermochromic ink that changes color when warmed.

Liberation of Korea, 60th Anniv. A1537

No. 2204: a, Charter and headquarters of provisional government. b, Proclamation of Korean Independence. c, Soldiers taking oath. d, Emblem of 60th anniv. of Korean liberation.

**2005, Aug. 12 *Perf. 13¼x13***

2204 Horiz. strip of 4 7.75 7.75
*a.* A1537 480w multi 1.25 .75
*b.* A1537 520w multi 1.25 1.00
*c.* A1537 580w multi 1.50 1.10
*d.* A1537 600w multi 1.50 1.25

Fusion of Eastern and Western Cultures — A1538

**2005, Aug. 18 Litho. *Perf. 13x13¼***

2205 A1538 220w multi .85 .45

Hangang Bridge — A1539

Expogyo — A1540

Banghwa Bridge — A1541

Tongyeong Bridge — A1542

***Perf. 13¼ Syncopated***

**2005, Sept. 23 Photo.**

2206 Block of 4 3.75 3.75
*a.* A1539 220w multi .70 .40
*b.* A1540 220w multi .70 .40
*c.* A1541 220w multi .70 .40
*d.* A1542 220w multi .70 .40

Ikki Falls A1543

Piagol Valley A1544

Cheonwangbong Peak — A1545

Baraebong Peak A1546

**2005, Oct. 18 *Perf. 13x13¼***

2207 Horiz. strip of 4 5.00 5.00
*a.* A1543 220w multi .90 .40
*b.* A1544 220w multi .90 .40
*c.* A1545 220w multi .90 .40
*d.* A1546 220w multi .90 .40

Korean Red Cross, Cent. — A1547

**2005, Oct. 27**

2208 A1547 220w multi .85 .50

Relocation and Reopening of National Museum
A1548

**2005, Oct. 28** ***Perf. 13¼x13***
**2209** A1548 220w multi .85 .50

Orchids — A1549

No. 2210: a, Epipactis thunbergii. b, Cymbidium goeringii. c, Cephalanthera erecta. d, Spiranthes sinensis.

**2005, Nov. 11**
**2210** A1549 220w Block of 4, #a-d 3.75 3.75

2005 Asian-Pacific Economic Cooperation Economic Leaders' Meeting, Busan — A1550

No. 2211: a, The Sun, the Moon and Five Peaks. b, Murimaru APEC House, Dongbaek Island.

**2005, Nov. 18 Photo.** ***Perf. 13x13¼***
**2211** A1550 220w Horiz. pair, #a-b 1.60 1.60

New Year 2006 (Year of the Dog) — A1551

**2005, Dec. 1**
**2212** A1551 220w multi .85 .50
*a.* Souvenir sheet of 2 1.90 1.90

Jikjisimcheyojeol, Book Produced in 1377 by Movable Type — A1552

Seungjeongwon Ilgi, Diaries of the Joseon Dynasty — A1553

**2005, Dec. 9** **Litho. & Engr.**
**2213** Sheet of 10 15.00 15.00
*a.* A1552 310w multi 1.25 .60
*b.* A1553 310w multi 1.25 .60

Top part of No. 2213 contains one each of Nos. 2213a-2213b. The lower part contains 4 each of Nos, 2213a-2213b.

Wildlife of Baengnyeongdo — A1554

Designs: No. 2214, Phoca vitulina largha. No. 2215, Phalacrocorax pelagicus. No. 2216, Orithyia sinica. No. 2217, Ammodytes personatus.

**2006, Jan. 18** **Photo.**
**2214** A1554 220w multi .95 .50
**2215** A1554 220w multi .95 .50
**2216** A1554 220w multi .95 .50
**2217** A1554 220w multi .95 .50
*a.* Horiz. strip of 4, #2214-2217 4.00 4.00
*b.* Sheet, 1 each #2214-2217, 3 #2217a + 2 labels 18.50
*Nos. 2214-2217 (4)* 3.80 2.00

Designation of Cheju Island as Island of World Peace — A1555

**2006, Jan. 27** ***Perf. 13¾x12¾***
**2218** A1555 220w multi .85 .50

**Exports**

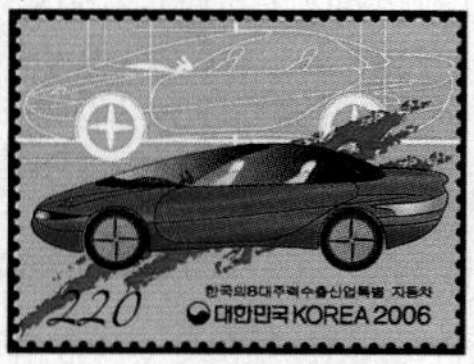

Automobiles — A1556

Semiconductors — A1557

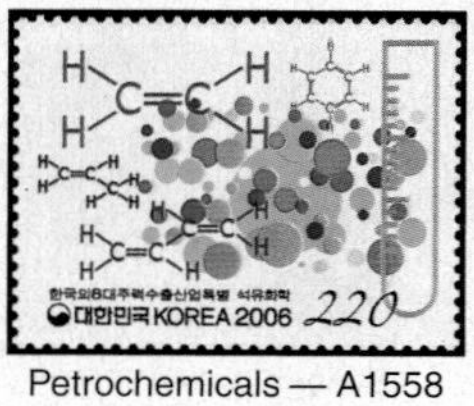

Petrochemicals — A1558

Electronics — A1559

Machinery A1560

Ships A1561

Steel A1562

Textiles A1563

**2006, Mar. 15** ***Perf. 13x13¼***
**2219** Block of 8 6.50 6.50
*a.* A1556 220w multi .75 .50
*b.* A1557 220w multi .75 .50
*c.* A1558 220w multi .75 .50
*d.* A1559 220w multi .75 .50
*e.* A1560 220w multi .75 .50
*f.* A1561 220w multi .75 .50
*g.* A1562 220w black .75 .50
*h.* A1563 220w multi .75 .50

Gyeongnam Goseong Dinosaur World Expo — A1564

***Serpentine Die Cut 11¼x11***
**2006, Apr. 14**
**2220** A1564 Horiz. pair 1.90 1.35
*a.* 220w Iguanodon .80 .50
*b.* 220w Megaraptor .80 .50

A1565

Children's Drawings on Automated World A1566

**2006, Apr. 21** ***Perf. 13x13¼, 13¼x13***
**2221** A1565 220w multi .85 .50
**2222** A1566 220w multi .85 .50

Dongguk University, Cent. — A1567

**2006, May 8 Litho.** ***Perf. 13x13¼***
**2223** A1567 220w multi, *cream* .85 .40

Sookmyung Women's University, Cent. — A1568

***Perf. 12¾x13¾***
**2006, May 22** **Photo.**
**2224** A1568 220w multi .85 .40

2006 World Cup Soccer Championships, Germany — A1569

**2006, June 2 Photo.** ***Perf. 13¼***
**2225** A1569 220w multi + label 4.00 —

No. 2225 was printed in sheets of 14 stamps + 14 labels picturing members of South Korean World Cup soccer team + one large label picturing entire team. Sheets sold for 6000w.

A1570

2006 World Cup Soccer Championships, Germany — A1571

***Perf. 12¾x13¾***
**2006, June 9** **Photo.**
**2226** Pair 1.75 1.35
*a.* A1570 220w multi .75 .45
*b.* A1571 220w multi .75 .45

Goguryeo Kingdom A1572

No. 2227: a, Janggun Tomb and Sanseongha Tombs. b, Sun and Moon Gods from Ohoebun Tomb No. 4.

*Perf. 13x13¼ Syncopated*

**2006, July 3** **Photo.**

**2227** A1572 480w Vert. pair, #a-b 3.75 3.75

No. 2227 was printed in sheets containing seven of each stamp.

Philately Week A1573

No. 2228: a, Denomination below heart. b, Denomination above heart.

**2006, Aug. 3** **Photo.** ***Perf. 13¼***

**2228** A1573 220w Pair, #a-b 1.45 1.45
*c.* Souvenir sheet, #2228a-2228b 1.90 1.90

Skateboarding — A1574

No. 2229: a, Tail stole. b, Drop in. c, Backside spin. d, Backside grab.

***Serpentine Die Cut 11¾x11¼***

**2006, Sept. 5** **Self-Adhesive**

**2229** A1574 220w Block of 4, #a-d 3.50 3.50

World Ginseng Expo, Geumsan — A1575

**2006, Sept. 22** ***Perf. 13x13¼***

**2230** A1575 220w multi .85 .40

Jindo Bridge — A1576

Changseon-Samcheonpo Bridge — A1577

Olympic Bridge — A1578

Seohae Bridge — A1579

***Perf. 13¼ Syncopated***

**2006, Sept. 26**

**2231** Block of 4 3.50 3.50
*a.* A1576 220w multi .70 .40
*b.* A1577 220w multi .70 .40
*c.* A1578 220w multi .70 .40
*d.* A1579 220w multi .70 .40

Hangeul Day — A1580

**2006, Oct. 9** ***Perf. 13x13¼***

**2232** A1580 (220w) multi .85 .40

Use of Hangeul as official Korean writing system, 560th anniv.

Sahmyook University, Cent. — A1581

**2006, Oct. 10**

**2233** A1581 220w multi .85 .40

Lineage — A1582

Maple Story — A1583

Ragnarok A1584

Gersang A1585

Legend of Mir III — A1586

Kartrider A1587

Mu — A1588

Pangya — A1589

Fortress 2 Forever Blue — A1590

Mabinogi A1591

***Serpentine Die Cut 11¾***

**2006, Nov. 9**

**2234** Block of 10 10.00 10.00
*a.* A1582 250w multi .90 .60
*b.* A1583 250w multi .90 .60
*c.* A1584 250w multi .90 .60
*d.* A1585 250w multi .90 .60
*e.* A1586 250w multi .90 .60
*f.* A1587 250w multi .90 .60
*g.* A1588 250w multi .90 .60
*h.* A1589 250w multi .90 .60
*i.* A1590 250w multi .90 .60
*j.* A1591 250w multi .90 .60

Internet games.

Janggunbong Peak — A1592

Ulsanbawi Rock A1593

Daecheongbong Peak — A1594

Sibiseonnyeotang Valley — A1595

**2006, Nov. 16** ***Perf. 13x13¼***

**2235** Block of 4 3.75 3.25
*a.* A1592 250w multi .80 .55
*b.* A1593 250w multi .80 .55
*c.* A1594 250w multi .80 .55
*d.* A1595 250w multi .80 .55

New Year 2007 (Year of the Pig) — A1596

**2006, Dec. 1** **Photo.** ***Perf. 13x13¼***

**2236** A1596 250w multi .85 .40
*a.* Souvenir sheet of 2 1.75 1.75

Text of Heungboga and Pansori Singer — A1597

Mo Heung-gap, Pansori Singer — A1598

**Litho. & Engr.**

**2006, Dec. 8** ***Perf. 13x13¼***

**2237** Sheet of 10 22.00 22.00
*a.* A1597 480w multi 2.10 1.75
*b.* A1598 480w multi 2.10 1.75

Top part of No. 2237 contains one each of Nos. 2237a-2237b. The lower part contains 4 each of Nos. 2237a-2237b.

A1599

Sharing and Caring A1600

**2006, Dec. 14 Photo.** ***Perf. 13x13¼***

| | | | |
|---|---|---|---|
| **2238** | A1599 250w multi | .85 | .25 |

***Perf. 13¼x13***

| | | | |
|---|---|---|---|
| **2239** | A1600 250w multi | .85 | .25 |

No. 2238 is impregnated with a pine scent; No. 2239 with a chocolate scent.

Nakdong River in Autumn — A1601

Nakdong River in Winter — A1602

Nakdong River in Spring — A1603

Nakdong River in Summer — A1604

***Perf. 13¼ Syncopated***

**2007, Jan. 18 Photo.**

| | | | |
|---|---|---|---|
| **2240** | Block of 4 | 3.25 | 3.00 |
| *a.* | A1601 250w multi | .70 | .25 |
| *b.* | A1602 250w multi | .70 | .25 |
| *c.* | A1603 250w multi | .70 | .25 |
| *d.* | A1604 250w multi | .70 | .25 |

Megatron/Matrix — A1605

TV Buddha A1606

The More the Better A1607

Oh-Mah (Mother) A1608

**2007, Jan. 29** ***Perf. 13¼***

| | | | |
|---|---|---|---|
| **2241** | Sheet of 12, 3 each #a-d | 12.00 | 12.00 |
| *a.* | A1605 250w multi | .75 | .25 |
| *b.* | A1606 250w multi | .75 | .25 |
| *c.* | A1607 250w multi | .75 | .25 |
| *d.* | A1608 250w multi | .75 | .25 |

Art by Nam June Paik (1932-2006).

National Debt Repayment Movement, Cent. — A1609

**2007, Feb. 21 Photo.** ***Perf. 13x13¼***

| | | | |
|---|---|---|---|
| **2242** | A1609 250w multi | .85 | .25 |

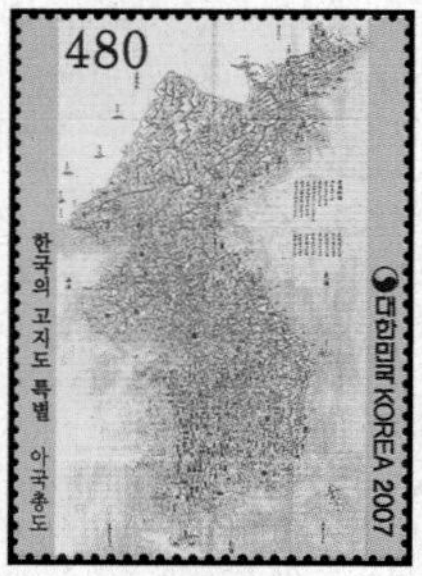

Maps of Korea A1610

No. 2243: a, Map from Atlas of Korea, 1780. b, Complete Territorial Map of the Great East, 19th cent. c, Map of the Eight Provinces, 1531. d, Comprehensive Map of the World and Nation's Successive Capitals, 1402.

**2007, Feb. 28 Photo.** ***Perf. 13½x13***

| | | | |
|---|---|---|---|
| **2243** | Sheet of 8, 2 each #a-d | 17.50 | 17.50 |
| *a.* | A1610 480w multi | 1.20 | 1.20 |
| *b.* | A1610 520w multi | 1.50 | 1.50 |
| *c.* | A1610 580w multi | 1.75 | 1.75 |
| *d.* | A1610 600w multi | 1.75 | 1.75 |

Daehan Hospital, Seoul, Cent. — A1611

**2007, Mar. 15 Litho.** ***Perf. 13x13¼***

| | | | |
|---|---|---|---|
| **2244** | A1611 250w multi | .85 | .25 |

Ninth Asia Pacific Orchid Conference, Goyang — A1612

**2007, Mar. 16 Photo.**

| | | | |
|---|---|---|---|
| **2245** | A1612 250w multi | .85 | .25 |

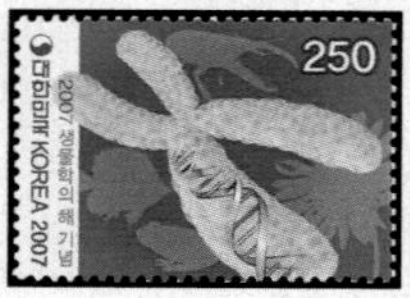

Biology Year — A1613

**2007, Mar. 19** ***Perf. 13¼x13***

| | | | |
|---|---|---|---|
| **2246** | A1613 250w multi | .85 | .25 |
| *a.* | Souvenir sheet of 2 | 2.25 | 2.25 |

Sunflower — A1614

**2007, Mar. 21 Litho.** ***Perf. 13¼***

| | | | |
|---|---|---|---|
| **2247** | A1614 250w multi + label | 2.50 | 2.50 |

Printed in sheets of 20 stamps + 20 labels and 14 stamps + 14 labels that sold for 7500w. Labels could be personalized.

Clover — A1615

Pig — A1616

**2007, Mar. 21 Photo.** ***Perf. 13¼***

| | | | |
|---|---|---|---|
| **2248** | A1615 250w multi + label | 2.75 | 2.75 |
| **2249** | A1616 250w multi + label | 2.75 | 2.75 |

Nos. 2248-2249 were each printed in sheets of 9 stamps + 9 labels. Each sheet sold for 4300w. Labels could be personalized.

Chinese Bride and Groom — A1617

Indian Bride and Groom — A1618

Malaysian Bride and Groom — A1619

Eurasian Bride and Groom — A1620

No. 2250 — Korean brides and grooms with: e, Mountains in background. f, Flowers on orange background. g, Flowers and foliage in background. h, Ducks in background.

**2007, Mar. 30** ***Perf. 13¼x13***

| | | | |
|---|---|---|---|
| **2250** | Block of 8 | 9.00 | 9.00 |
| *a.* | A1617 250w multi | .60 | .40 |
| *b.* | A1618 250w multi | .60 | .40 |
| *c.* | A1619 250w multi | .60 | .40 |
| *d.* | A1620 250w multi | .60 | .40 |
| *e.* | A1620 480w multi | 1.25 | 1.00 |
| *f.* | A1620 520w multi | 1.40 | 1.25 |
| *g.* | A1620 580w multi | 1.75 | 1.50 |
| *h.* | A1620 600w multi | 1.90 | 1.50 |

See Singapore No. 1241.

Opening of Fortress Wall in Mt. Bugaksan — A1621

**2007, Apr. 5 Photo.** ***Perf. 13¾x12¾***

| | | | |
|---|---|---|---|
| **2251** | A1621 250w multi | .85 | .30 |

A1622

Internet Culture A1623

**2007, Apr. 20 Litho.** ***Perf. 13¼x13***

| | | | |
|---|---|---|---|
| **2252** | A1622 250w multi | .85 | .30 |

**Photo.**

| | | | |
|---|---|---|---|
| **2253** | A1623 250w multi | .85 | .30 |

Children's Charter, 50th Anniv. — A1624

***Serpentine Die Cut***

**2007, May 4 Photo.**

**Self-Adhesive**

| | | | |
|---|---|---|---|
| **2254** | A1624 250w multi | .85 | .30 |

No. 2254 is impregnated with a strawberry scent.

Dispatch of Special Envoys to Second Hague Peace Conference, Cent. — A1625

**Litho. & Engr.**

**2007, June 27** ***Perf. 13x13¼***

| | | | |
|---|---|---|---|
| **2255** | A1625 250w multi | .85 | .30 |

A1626

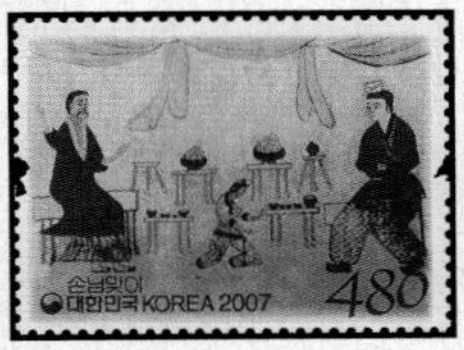
Goguryeo Kingdom A1627

No. 2256: a, Cooks preparing food. b, Host welcoming guest.

***Perf. 13 Syncopated***

**2007, July 2 Photo.**

| | | | |
|---|---|---|---|
| 2256 | Sheet of 14, 7 each #a-b | 20.00 | 20.00 |
| a. | A1626 480w multi | 1.25 | .60 |
| b. | A1627 480w multi | 1.25 | .60 |

Philately Week — A1628

No. 2257: a, Korea #1. b, Korea #2.

**2007, Aug. 1 Photo. *Perf. 13x13¼***

| | | | |
|---|---|---|---|
| 2257 | Horiz. pair | 2.00 | 2.00 |
| a.-b. | A1628 250w Either single | .75 | .30 |
| c. | Souvenir sheet, #2257 | 2.25 | 2.25 |

Rollerblading — A1629

No. 2258: a, Drop-in. b, Flip. c, Spin. d, Grind.

***Serpentine Die Cut 11¾x11¼***

**2007, Sept. 5 Photo.**

**Self-Adhesive**

| | | | |
|---|---|---|---|
| 2258 | A1629 250w Block of 4, #a-d | 4.00 | 4.00 |

Korean Bar Association, Cent. — A1630

**2007, Sept. 21 Litho. *Perf. 13x13¼***

| | | | |
|---|---|---|---|
| 2259 | A1630 250w multi | .85 | .30 |

Gwangan Bridge — A1631

Seongsu Bridge — A1632

Seongsan Bridge — A1633

Yeongjong Bridge — A1634

***Perf. 13¼x13½ Syncopated***

**2007, Sept. 28 Photo.**

| | | | |
|---|---|---|---|
| 2260 | Block of 4 | 3.50 | 3.50 |
| a. | A1631 250w multi | .75 | .30 |
| b. | A1632 250w multi | .75 | .30 |
| c. | A1633 250w multi | .75 | .30 |
| d. | A1634 250w multi | .75 | .30 |

Inter-Korean Summit, Pyongyang, North Korea — A1635

**2007, Oct. 2 *Perf. 13¼x13***

| | | | |
|---|---|---|---|
| 2261 | A1635 250w multi | .85 | .30 |

Hyeongje Falls A1636

Rimyeongsu Falls — A1637

Lake Samjiyeon A1638

Lake Chonji A1639

**2007, Oct. 18 Photo. *Perf. 13x13½***

| | | | |
|---|---|---|---|
| 2262 | Block of 4 | 3.50 | 3.50 |
| a. | A1636 250w multi | .75 | .30 |
| b. | A1637 250w multi | .75 | .30 |
| c. | A1638 250w multi | .75 | .30 |
| d. | A1639 250w multi | .75 | .30 |

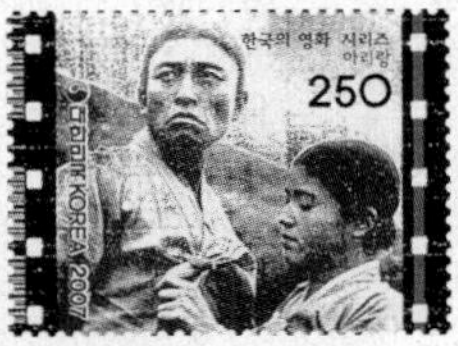
A1640

A1641

A1642

Korean Films A1643

No. 2263: a, Arirang, 1926. b, The Ownerless Ferryboat, 1932. c, Looking for Love, 1928. d, Chunhyangjeon, 1935.

**2007, Oct. 26 *Perf. 13x13¼***

| | | | |
|---|---|---|---|
| 2263 | Sheet of 16, 4 each #a-d | 16.00 | 16.00 |
| a. | A1640 250w multi | .75 | .30 |
| b. | A1641 250w multi | .75 | .30 |
| c. | A1642 250w multi | .75 | .30 |
| d. | A1643 250w multi | .75 | .30 |

A1644

Protection of Children's Rights A1645

**2007, Nov. 20 Photo. *Perf. 13x13¼***

| | | | |
|---|---|---|---|
| 2264 | A1644 250w multi | .85 | .30 |

**Litho.**

***Perf. 13¼x13***

| | | | |
|---|---|---|---|
| 2265 | A1645 250w multi | .85 | .30 |

Opening of New Central Post Office, Seoul — A1646

No. 2266: a, Hanseong Post Office, 1915, and new building. b, New building.

**2007, Nov. 22 Photo. *Perf. 13x13¼***

| | | | |
|---|---|---|---|
| 2266 | A1646 250w Horiz. pair, #a-b | 2.00 | 2.00 |

No. 2266 printed in sheet containing 7 pairs.

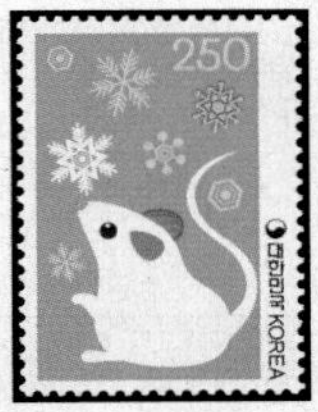
New Year 2008 (Year of the Rat) — A1647

**2007, Nov. 30**

| | | | |
|---|---|---|---|
| 2267 | A1647 250w multi | .85 | .30 |
| a. | Souvenir sheet of 2 | 1.50 | 1.50 |

Tapdeunggut Exorcism, Dano Festival, Gangneung — A1648

Gwanno Mask Drama, Dano Festival — A1649

**2007, Dec. 7 Litho. & Engr.**

| | | | |
|---|---|---|---|
| 2268 | Sheet of 10, 5 each #a-b | 18.00 | 18.00 |
| a. | A1648 480w multi | 1.50 | .75 |
| b. | A1649 480w multi | 1.50 | .75 |

Top part of No. 2268 contains one each of Nos. 2268a-2268b. The lower part contains 4 each of Nos. 2268a-2268b.

Seomjin River in Autumn — A1650

Seomjin River in Winter — A1651

Seomjin River in Spring — A1652

Seomjin River in Summer — A1653

***Perf. 13½x13¼ Syncopated***

**2008, Jan. 18** **Photo.**

| | | | |
|---|---|---|---|
| **2269** | Block of 4 | 3.25 | 3.25 |
| *a.* | A1650 250w multi | .75 | .30 |
| *b.* | A1651 250w multi | .75 | .30 |
| *c.* | A1652 250w multi | .75 | .30 |
| *d.* | A1653 250w multi | .75 | .30 |

Miniature Sheet

King Sejong Antarctic Station — A1654

No. 2270 — Penguins and: a, Scientists on snowmobiles. b, Station.

**2008, Feb. 15** **Photo.** ***Perf. 13¼***

**2270** A1654 250w Sheet of 10, 5 each #a-b 12.50 12.50

Inauguration of Pres. Lee Myung-Bak — A1655

**2008, Feb. 25** **Photo.** ***Perf. 13x13¼***

| | | | |
|---|---|---|---|
| **2271** | A1655 250w multi | .85 | .30 |
| *a.* | Souvenir sheet of 1 | 2.00 | 2.00 |

African Savanna — A1656

No. 2272: a, African child and mask. b, Leopard. c, Elephant. d, Zebra.

***Die Cut Perf. (outer edge) x Serpentine Die Cut 11 (radial sides) x Die Cut (inner edge)***

**2008, Mar. 26** **Self-Adhesive**

**2272** A1656 250w Block of 4, #a-d, + central label 4.00 4.00

Philakorea 2009 Intl. Stamp Exhibition, Seoul — A1657

No. 2273 — Dancers: a, Buchaechum (orange background). b, Salpurichum (pink background). c, Seungmu (blue background). d, Taepyeongmu (green background).

**2008, Apr. 10** ***Perf. 13¼x13***

| | | | |
|---|---|---|---|
| **2273** | Horiz. strip or block of 4 | 3.25 | 3.25 |
| *a.-d.* | A1657 250w Any single | .75 | .30 |
| *e.* | Souvenir sheet, #2273a-2273d, + label | 3.00 | 3.00 |

A1658

Winning Designs in "Mailboxes of the Future" Children's Stamp Design Contest — A1659

**2008, Apr. 22** **Photo.** ***Perf. 13¼x13***

**2274** A1658 250w multi .85 .30

**Litho.**

***Perf. 13x13¼***

**2275** A1659 250w multi .85 .30

Nurturing of Children

A1660 A1661

**Litho., Engr. & Embossed**

**2008, May 8** ***Perf. 13x13¼***

**2276** A1660 250w multi .85 .30

**Litho.**

**2277** A1661 250w multi .85 .30

Sun and Moon — A1662

Hands Making Heart — A1663

Tree-lined Path — A1664

Roses — A1665

**2008, May 19** **Photo.** ***Perf. 13¼***

| | | | |
|---|---|---|---|
| **2278** | A1662 250w multi + label | 1.50 | 1.50 |
| **2279** | A1663 250w multi + label | 1.50 | 1.50 |
| **2280** | A1664 250w multi + label | 1.50 | 1.50 |
| **2281** | A1665 250w multi + label | 1.50 | 1.50 |
| | *Nos. 2278-2281 (4)* | 6.00 | 6.00 |

Nos. 2278-2279 each were printed in sheets of 3 stamps + 3 labels, No. 2280 was printed in sheets of 14 stamps + 15 labels, and No. 2281 was printed in sheets of 20 stamps + 20 labels. Labels could be personalized.

Organization for Economic Cooperation and Development Ministerial Meeting, Seoul — A1666

**2008, June 17** ***Perf. 13¼***

**2282** A1666 250w multi .85 .30

Yun Bong-Gil (1908-32), Assassin of Japanese Colonial Generals A1667

**2008, June 20**

**2283** A1667 250w multi .85 .30

Miniature Sheet

Dangun Wanggeom — A1668

No. 2284: a, Hwanung descending from heavens at Taebaek Mountain. b, Bear and tiger who prayed to become human. c, Birth of Dangun Wanggeom. d, Dangun Wanggeom as adult.

**2008, July 10** **Photo.** ***Perf. 13¼x13***

**2284** A1668 250w Sheet of 12, 3 each #a-d 6.00 6.00

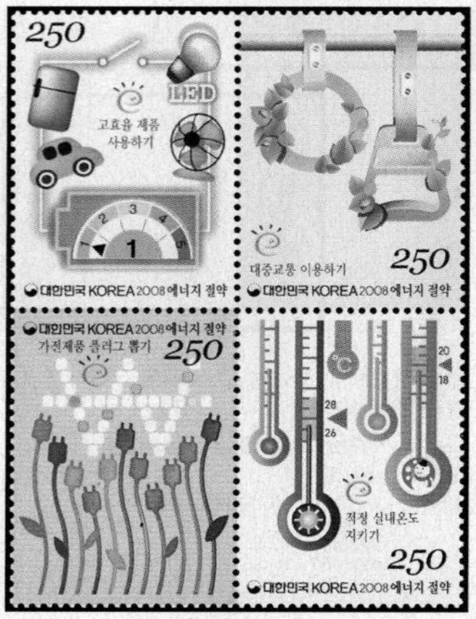

Energy Conservation — A1669

No. 2285: a, Open electrical circuit, car, refrigerator, light bulb, fan, meter. b, Hand-straps for public transportation. c, Electrical plugs on flower stems. d, Thermometers.

**2008, Aug. 1** **Photo.** ***Perf. 13¼x13***

**2285** A1669 250w Block or horiz. strip of 4, #a-d 3.00 3.00

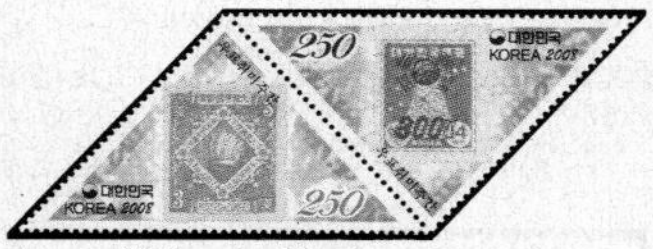

Philately Week — A1670

No. 2286: a, South Korea #34. b, South Korea #176.

**2008, Aug. 7** **Photo.** ***Perf. 13¼x13***

| | | | |
|---|---|---|---|
| **2286** | A1670 250w Pair, #a-b | 1.50 | 1.50 |
| *c.* | Souvenir sheet, #2286a-2286b | 2.00 | 2.00 |

2008 Summer Olympics, Beijing A1671

**2008, Aug. 8** **Photo.** ***Perf. 13¼x13***

**2287** A1671 250w multi .85 .30

Republic of Korea, 60th Anniv. — A1672

**2008, Aug. 14**

**2288** A1672 250w multi .85 .30

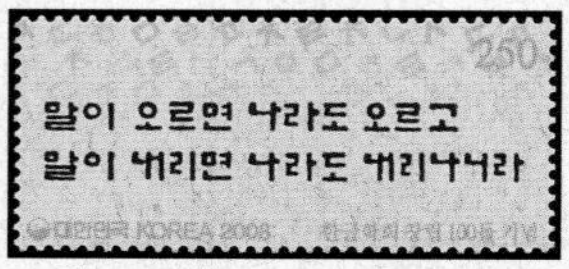

Korean Language Society, Cent. — A1673

**2008, Aug. 29** ***Perf. 12¾x13½***

**2289** A1673 250w multi .85 .30

Seoul Water Works, Cent. — A1674

**2008, Sept. 1 Litho. *Perf. 13x13¼***
**2290** A1674 250w multi .85 .30

Amateur Radio Direction Finding Championships, Hwaseong A1675

**2008, Sept. 2**
**2291** A1675 250w multi .85 .30

Snowboarding — A1676

No. 2292: a, Carving turn. b, Indy grab. c, Nose grab. d, Air.

***Serpentine Die Cut 11¾x11¼***
**2008, Sept. 5 Photo.**
**Self-Adhesive**
**2292** A1676 250w Block of 4, #a-d 3.50 3.50

Salvation Army in Korea, Cent. — A1677

**2008, Oct. 1 Photo. *Perf. 13x13¼***
**2293** A1677 250w multi .85 .30

Republic of Korea Armed Forces, 60th Anniv. A1678

**2008, Oct. 1**
**2294** A1678 250w multi .85 .30

Diplomatic Relations Between South Korea and Thailand, 50th Anniv. — A1679

No. 2295: a, Chakri Mahaprasat Hall, Thailand (denomination at left). b, Juhamnu Pavilion, South Korea (denomination at right).

**2008, Oct. 1 Litho. *Perf. 13¼***
**2295** A1679 250w Pair, #a-b 2.50 2.50

See Thailand No. 2383.

Manmulsang — A1680

Gwimyeonam Rock — A1681

Outer Geumgangsan — A1682

Sangpaldam Pools — A1683

**2008, Oct. 17 Photo. *Perf. 13x13½***
**2296** Block of 4 3.25 3.25
*a.* A1680 250w multi .75 .30
*b.* A1681 250w multi .75 .30
*c.* A1682 250w multi .75 .30
*d.* A1683 250w multi .75 .30

Korean Films — A1684

No. 2297: a, A Coachman, 1961 (blue background). b, Wedding Day, 1956 (dull lilac background). c, The Seashore Village, 1965 (dull green background). d, Mother and a Guest, 1961 (gray olive background).

**2008, Oct. 27 Litho. *Perf. 13x13½***
**2297** A1684 250w Block of 4, #a-d 3.25 3.25

Upo Wetlands — A1685

**2008, Oct. 28 Photo. *Perf. 13¼***
**2298** A1685 250w multi .85 .30

Tenth Ramsar Convention Meeting, Changwon.

Masks — A1686

No. 2299: a, Chwibari Mask, Korea (denomination at LL). b, Big head Buddha mask, Hong Kong (denomination at LR).

**2008, Nov. 6 *Perf. 13¼x13***
**2299** A1686 250w Horiz. pair, #a-b 2.00 2.00

See Hong Kong Nos. 1337-1338.

New Year 2009 (Year of the Ox) — A1687

**2008, Dec. 1 *Perf. 13x13¼***
**2300** A1687 250w multi 1.00 .30
*a.* Souvenir sheet of 2 2.00 2.00

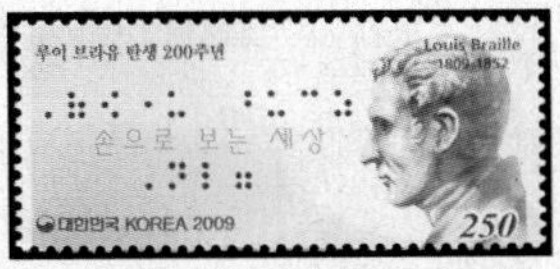

Louis Braille (1809-52), Educator of the Blind — A1688

**2009, Jan. 2 *Perf. 12¾x13½***
**2301** A1688 250w multi .85 .30

Intl. Year of Astronomy — A1689

No. 2302: a, Whirlpool Galaxy M51. b, Planetary Nebula NGC 3132.

**2009, Jan. 15 Photo. *Perf. 13x13¼***
**2302** A1689 250w Horiz. pair, #a-b 1.50 1.50

Geum River in Autumn — A1690

Geum River in Winter — A1691

Geum River in Spring — A1692

Geum River in Summer — A1693

***Perf. 13¼ Syncopated***
**2009, Feb. 10**
**2303** Block or horiz. strip of 4 3.25 3.25
*a.* A1690 250w multi .70 .30
*b.* A1691 250w multi .70 .30
*c.* A1692 250w multi .70 .30
*d.* A1693 250w multi .70 .30

Diplomatic Relations Between South Korea and the Philippines, 60th Anniv. A1694

Designs: No. 2304, 250w, Panagbenga Flower Festival, Baguio, Philippines. No. 2305, 250w, Cow Play, Hangawi, South Korea.

**2009, Mar. 3 Photo. *Perf. 13x13¼***
**2304-2305** A1694 Set of 2 1.50 1.50

Historic Trees — A1695

No. 2306: a, Fir tree (Natural Monument No. 495) (22x50mm). b, Zelkova tree (Natural Monument No. 478), horiz. (44x25mm). c, Ginkgo tree (Natural Monument No. 30) (22x50mm). d, Seosongnyeong tree (Natural Monument No. 294), horiz. (44x25mm).

**2009, Apr. 3 Litho. *Perf. 12¾***
**2306** A1695 250w Block of 4, #a-d 3.25 3.25

Republic of Korea Marine Corps, 60th Anniv. A1696

**2009, Apr. 15 *Perf. 12½***
**2307** A1696 250w multi .85 .30

A1697

Asia Becoming One — A1698

**2009, Apr. 22 Photo. *Perf. 13¼x13***
**2308** A1697 250w multi .85 .30

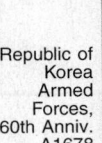

**Litho.**

***Perf. 13x13¼***

**2309** A1698 250w multi .85 .30

A1699

Love For the Earth — A1700

**2009, Apr. 22 Litho. *Perf. 13¼x13***

**2310** A1699 250w multi .85 .30

**Photo.**

***Perf. 13x13¼***

**2311** A1700 250w multi .85 .30

Cartooning in Korea, Cent. A1701

**2009, June 2 Litho. *Perf. 13x13¼***

**2312** A1701 250w multi .85 .30

Earrings From Korea, 5th-6th Cent. A1702

Earrings From Mongolia, 18th-19th Cent. A1703

Earrings From Kazakhstan, 2nd-1st Cent. B.C. — A1704

**2009, June 12 Photo. *Perf. 13x13¼***

**2313** Strip of 3 2.50 2.50
- *a.* A1702 250w multi .65 .30
- *b.* A1703 250w multi .65 .30
- *c.* A1704 250w multi .65 .30

See Kazakhstan No. 595, Mongolia No. 2674.

Cave Lake and Lava Tubes — A1705

Lava Tubes, Stalactites and Stalagmite — A1706

**Litho. & Engr.**

**2009, June 26 *Perf. 13x13¼***

**2314** Sheet of 10, 5 each #a-b 7.00 7.00
- *a.* A1705 250w multi .75 .30
- *b.* A1706 250w multi .75 .30

Jeju Volcanic Island and Lava Tubes UNESCO World Heritage Site.

Philately Week — A1707

No. 2315: a, Korea #19. b, South Korea #639.

**2009, July 30 Photo. *Perf. 13¼x13***

**2315** Pair 1.50 1.50
- *a.-b.* A1707 250w Either single .70 .30
- *c.* Souvenir sheet, #2315 .70 .30

A1708

A1709

A1710

A1711

A1712

A1713

A1714

Bird Drawings A1715

**2009, July 30 Litho. *Perf. 13¼x13***

**2316** Block of 8 4.50 4.50
- *a.* A1708 250w multi .50 .30
- *b.* A1709 250w multi .50 .30
- *c.* A1710 250w multi .50 .30
- *d.* A1711 250w multi .50 .30
- *e.* A1712 250w multi .50 .30
- *f.* A1713 250w multi .50 .30
- *g.* A1714 250w multi .50 .30
- *h.* A1715 250w multi .50 .30
- *i.* Souvenir sheet of 2, #2316a, 2316e 2.00 2.00
- *j.* Souvenir sheet of 2, #2316b, 2316f 2.00 2.00
- *k.* Souvenir sheet of 2, #2316c, 2316g 2.00 2.00
- *l.* Souvenir sheet of 2, #2316d, 2316h 2.00 2.00

Philakorea 2009, Seoul.

Command From God To Move Country's Capital A1716

Establishment of East Buyeo — A1717

Birth of King Geumwawang — A1718

King Geumwawang on Throne — A1719

**2009, Aug. 18 Photo. *Perf. 13x13¼***

**2317** Sheet of 12, 3 each #a-d 7.00 7.00
- *a.* A1716 250w multi .50 .30
- *b.* A1717 250w multi .50 .30
- *c.* A1718 250w multi .50 .30
- *d.* A1719 250w multi .50 .30

Legend of King Geumwawang of the Buyeo Kingdom.

Green Energy — A1720

No. 2318: a, House with solar panels, bicycle. b, Automobile with solar panels. c, Wind turbines. d, Dam.

**2009, Aug. 21 Photo. *Perf. 13¼***

**2318** A1720 250w Block of 4, #a-d 2.00 2.00

Groundbreaking for Taekwondo Park, Muju-gun — A1721

**2009, Sept. 4 *Perf. 13¾x12¾***

**2319** A1721 250w multi .85 .30

BMX Bicycling — A1722

No. 2320: a, X-up. b, No hand jump. c, One foot can can. d, Superman seat grab.

***Serpentine Die Cut 11¾x11¼***

**2009, Sept. 8 Photo.**

**2320** A1722 250w Block of 4, #a-d 2.00 2.00

Rice — A1723

No. 2321: a, Rice flowers and plants. b, Red, black and white rice grains.

**2009, Sept. 25 Litho. *Perf. 13¼***

| | | | |
|---|---|---|---|
| **2321** | Pair | 1.00 | 1.00 |
| *a.-b.* | A1723 250w Either single | .50 | .30 |

Third Organization for Economic Cooperation and Development World Forum, Busan — A1724

**2009, Oct. 27 Litho. *Perf. 13¼***

| | | | |
|---|---|---|---|
| **2322** | A1724 250w multi | .75 | .30 |

A1725

A1726

A1727

Korean Films A1728

No. 2323: a, Chilsu and Mansu, 1988. b, Never, Never Forget Me, 1976. c, A Road to Sampo, 1975. d, Yalkae, A Joker in High School, 1976.

**2009, Oct. 27 *Perf. 13x13¼***

| | | | |
|---|---|---|---|
| **2323** | Block or strip of 4 | 2.50 | 2.50 |
| *a.* | A1725 250w multi | .50 | .30 |
| *b.* | A1726 250w multi | .50 | .30 |
| *c.* | A1727 250w multi | .50 | .30 |
| *d.* | A1728 250w multi | .50 | .30 |

Diplomatic Relations Between South Korea and Brazil, 50th Anniv. — A1729

No. 2324: a, Octavio Frias de Oliveira Bridge, Brazil (denomination at UL). b, Incheon Bridge, South Korea (denomination at UR).

**2009, Oct. 30 *Perf. 13¼***

| | | | |
|---|---|---|---|
| **2324** | A1729 250w Pair, #a-b | 1.25 | 1.25 |

See Brazil No. 3113.

New Year 2010 (Year of the Tiger) — A1730

**2009, Dec. 1 Photo. *Perf. 13x13¼***

| | | | |
|---|---|---|---|
| **2325** | A1730 250w multi | .75 | .30 |
| *a.* | Souvenir sheet of 2 | 1.25 | 1.25 |

Visit Korea Year — A1731

No. 2326: a, Stylized face, denomination in blue. b, People as Korean flag, denomination in white.

**2010, Jan. 4 Photo. *Perf. 13¼x13***

| | | | |
|---|---|---|---|
| **2326** | A1731 250w Pair, #a-b | 1.00 | 1.00 |

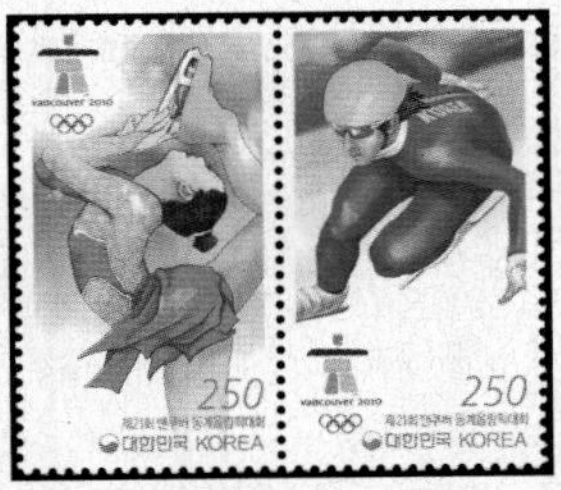

2010 Winter Olympics, Vancouver — A1732

No. 2327: a, Figure skater. b, Speed skater.

**2010, Feb. 12 *Perf. 12¾x13½***

| | | | |
|---|---|---|---|
| **2327** | A1732 250w Pair, #a-b | 1.00 | 1.00 |

Diplomatic Relations Between South Korea and Malaysia, 50th Anniv. — A1733

No. 2328: a, Panthera tigris altaica. b, Panthera tigris jacksoni.

**2010, Feb. 23 Litho. *Perf. 13¼***

| | | | |
|---|---|---|---|
| **2328** | A1733 250w Pair, #a-b | 1.00 | 1.00 |

Ahn Jung-geun (1879-1910), Assassin of Ito Hirobumi, Japanese Resident-General of Korea — A1734

No. 2329 — Ahn Jung-geun and: a, Handprint. b, Characters written on Korean flag with blood from his severed finger.

**Litho. & Engr.**

**2010, Mar. 26 *Perf. 13¼***

| | | | |
|---|---|---|---|
| **2329** | A1734 250w Pair, #a-b | 1.00 | 1.00 |

Seoul National University of Technology, Cent. — A1735

Jinju National University, Cent. — A1736

**2010, Apr. 1 Photo. *Perf. 12¾x13½***

| | | | |
|---|---|---|---|
| **2330** | A1735 250w multi | .50 | .30 |
| **2331** | A1736 250w multi | .50 | .30 |

Historic Trees — A1737

No. 2332: a, Old Buddha's plum tree (Natural Monument No. 486) (22x50mm). b, Pine tree (Natural Monument No. 290), horiz (44x25mm). c, Entwined Chinese junipers (Natural Monument No. 88) (22x50mm). d, Three Thunbergii camphor trees (Natural Monument No. 481), horiz. (44x25mm).

**2010, Apr. 5 Litho. *Perf. 12¾***

| | | | |
|---|---|---|---|
| **2332** | A1737 250w Block of 4, #a-d | 2.00 | 2.00 |

Mo Tae Bum A1738

Le Sang Hwa A1739

Lee Seung Hoon A1740

Kim Yu Na A1741

Kwak Yoon Gy A1742

Kim Seoung Il A1743

Park Seung Hi A1744

Sung Si Bak A1745

Lee Eun Byul A1746

Lee Jung Su A1747

Lee Ho Suk A1748

**2010, May 6 Photo. *Perf. 13½x12¾***

| | | | |
|---|---|---|---|
| **2333** | Sheet of 11 + label | 7.00 | 7.00 |
| *a.* | A1738 250w multi | .60 | .30 |
| *b.* | A1739 250w multi | .60 | .30 |
| *c.* | A1740 250w multi | .60 | .30 |
| *d.* | A1741 250w multi | .60 | .30 |
| *e.* | A1742 250w multi | .60 | .30 |
| *f.* | A1743 250w multi | .60 | .30 |
| *g.* | A1744 250w multi | .60 | .30 |

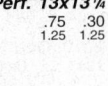

*h.* A1745 250w multi .60 .30
*i.* A1746 250w multi .60 .30
*j.* A1747 250w multi .60 .30
*k.* A1748 250w multi .60 .30

Medalists at 2010 Winter Olympics, Vancouver.

Han River in Spring — A1749

Han River in Summer — A1750

Han River in Autumn — A1751

Han River in Winter — A1752

**2010, May 11** ***Perf. 13½ Syncopated***
**2334** Block or strip of 4 2.00 2.00
*a.* A1749 250w multi .50 .30
*b.* A1750 250w multi .50 .30
*c.* A1751 250w multi .50 .30
*d.* A1752 250w multi .50 .30

2010 World Cup Soccer Championships, South Africa — A1753

***Perf. 13¼x13½***
**2010, June 11** **Photo.**
**2335** A1753 250w multi .75 .30

World Refugee Day, 10th Anniv. — A1754

**2010, June 18** ***Perf. 13¼***
**2336** A1754 250w multi .60 .30

Diplomatic Relations Between South Korea and United Arab Emirates, 30th Anniv. — A1755

No. 2337: a, Flag of United Arab Emirates and air-conditioning tower. b, Flag of South Korea and Mt. Amisan Chimney, Gyeongbokgung Palace.

**2010, June 18 Photo.** ***Perf. 13x13¼***
**2337** A1755 250w Pair, #a-b 1.00 1.00

See United Arab Emirates No. 990.

Start of Korean War, 60th Anniv. A1756

**2010, June 25** ***Perf. 13½x13***
**2338** A1756 250w multi .60 .30

Philately Week — A1757

No. 2339: a, South Korea #1197. b, South Korea #1198.

**2010, July 29** ***Perf. 13¼x13¼x13***
**2339** Pair, #a-b 1.00 1.00
*a.-b.* A1757 250w Either single .50 .30
*c.* Souvenir sheet, #2339a-2339b 1.25 1.25

Dinosaurs — A1758

No. 2340: a, Herrerasaurus. b, Coelophysis. c, Plateosaurus. d, Riojasaurus.

***Perf. 13¼ Syncopated***
**2010, Aug. 5** **Litho. & Engr.**
**2340** Sheet of 12, 3 each #2340a-2340d 7.50 7.50
*a.-b.* A1758 250w Either single .50 .30
*c.-d.* A1758 340w Either single .50 .30

23rd Intl. Union of Forest Research Organizations World Congress, Seoul A1759

**Litho. & Embossed**
**2010, Aug. 23** ***Perf. 12½***
**2341** A1759 340w multi .75 .30

Legend of Goguryeo Jumong — A1760

No. 2342: a, King Geumwa and soldiers meet woman. b, Baby Jumong, birds and animals. c, Jumong and others fleeing King Geumwa on horseback. d, Jumong on horse and followers at Jolboncheon.

**2010, Sept. 14 Photo.** ***Perf. 13x13½***
**2342** A1760 250w Block of 4, #a-d 2.00 2.00

A1761

A1762

A1763

Korean Films A1764

No. 2343: a, Seopyeonje, 1993. b, Shiri, 1999. c, Tae Guk Gi: The Brotherhood of War, 2004. d, Take Off, 2009.

**2010, Oct. 27 Litho.** ***Perf. 13x13¼***
**2343** Block of 4 2.00 2.00
*a.* A1761 250w multi .50 .30
*b.* A1762 250w multi .50 .30
*c.* A1763 250w multi .50 .30
*d.* A1764 250w multi .50 .30

Recycling A1765

No. 2344: a, Flowers in pot. b, Recycling robot.

**2010, Nov. 11 Photo.** ***Perf. 13¼x13***
**2344** A1765 250w Pair, #a-b 1.00 1.00

Miniature Sheet

G20 Summit, Seoul — A1766

No. 2345 — Summit emblem and: a, World map. b, Gate.

**2010, Nov. 11** ***Perf. 13x13¼***
**2345** A1766 Sheet of 14, 7 each #a-b 10.00 10.00
*a.-b.* 250w Either single .60 .35

New Year 2011 (Year of the Rabbit) — A1767

**2010, Dec. 1** ***Perf. 13x13¼***
**2346** A1767 250w multi .50 .30
*a.* Souvenir sheet of 2 1.00 1.00

A1768

Personalized Stamps A1769

**2010, Dec. 1 Photo.** ***Perf. 13x13¼***
**Denomination Color**
**2347** A1768 250w green *2.00 2.00*
**2348** A1768 250w blue *2.00 2.00*
**2349** A1768 250w red brown *2.00 2.00*
***Perf. 13¼x13½***
**2350** A1769 250w green *2.25 2.25*
**2351** A1769 250w blue *2.25 2.25*
**2352** A1769 250w red brown *2.25 2.25*
*Nos. 2347-2352 (6)* *12.75 12.75*

Nos. 2347-2349 each were available in sheets of 6 that sold for 5500w and sheets of 20 that sold for 9500w. Nos. 2350-2352 each were sold in sheets of 14 that sold for 8000y. images could be personalized.

Miniature Sheet

Characters in Pororo, the Little Penguin — A1770

No. 2353: a, Eddy, the Fox. b, Crong, the Baby Dinosaur on balloon. c, Pororo wearing helmet. d, Petty, the girl Penguin. e, Pipi and Popo, the Aliens. f, Poby, the Polar Bear. g, Harry, the Hummingbird on ball. h, Loopy, the Beaver with basket. i, Tong Tong, the Dragon. j, Rody, the Robot.

**2011, Feb. 22 Photo.** ***Die Cut***
**Self-Adhesive**
**2353** A1770 Sheet of 10 5.50 5.50
*a.-j.* 250w Any single .50 .30

Historic Trees — A1771

No. 2354: a, Japanese black pine trees at Sancheondan (Natural Monument No. 160)

(22x50mm). b, Ginkgo tree at Yogwang-ri (Natural Monument No. 84), horiz. (44x25mm). c, Pine tree at Chukji-ri (Natural Monument No. 491) (22x50mm). d, Zelkova tree at Haksaru (Natural Monument No. 407), horiz. (44x25mm).

**2011, Apr. 5 Litho. *Perf. 12¾***
**2354** A1771 250w Block of 4, #a-d 2.25 2.25

Diplomatic Relations Between South Korea and Portugal, 50th Anniv. A1772

No. 2355: a, Korean turtle ship, denomination at UL. b, Portuguese nau, denomination at UR.

**2011, Apr. 15 Photo. *Perf. 13x13¼***
**2355** Sheet of 14, 7 each #2355a-2355b 12.00 12.00
*a.-b.* A1772 250w Either single .75 .30

See Portugal Nos. 3305-3306.

Family — A1773

No. 2356: a, Stick-figure family and house. b, Heads in bunch of grapes.

**2011, May 13 Photo. *Perf. 13x13¼***
**2356** A1773 250w Pair, #a-b 1.25 1.25

Bamboo Grove, Damyang — A1774

Tea Field, Boesong — A1775

Upo Swamp, Changnyeong — A1776

Jusanji Pond, Cheongsong — A1777

**2011, May 27 *Perf. 13¼***
**2357** Block of 4 2.50 2.50
*a.* A1774 250w multi .55 .30
*b.* A1775 250w multi .55 .30
*c.* A1776 250w multi .55 .30
*d.* A1777 250w multi .55 .30

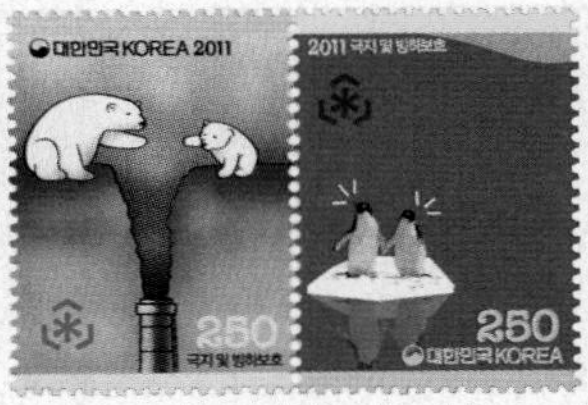

Preservation of Polar Regions and Glaciers — A1778

No. 2358: a, Polar bears. b, Penguins.

**2011, June 3 Litho. *Perf. 13x13¼***
**2358** A1778 250w Pair, #a-b 1.25 1.25

Shinheung Military Academy, Chugaga, Cent. A1779

**2011, June 10 Photo.**
**2359** A1779 250w multi .75 .30

Tomb of King Taejo — A1780

Tomb of King Sejong — A1781

**Litho. & Engr.**
**2011, June 30 *Perf. 13x13¼***
**2360** Sheet of 10, 5 each #2360a-2360b 6.50 6.50
*a.* A1780 250w multi .60 .30
*b.* A1781 250w multi .60 .30

Royal Tombs of the Joeson Dynasty UNESCO World Heritage Site.

Korea Disaster Relief Association, 50th Anniv. — A1782

**2011, July 13 Photo. *Perf. 13x13¼***
**2361** A1782 250w multi .75 .30

Philately Week — A1783

No. 2362 — Paintings: a, Sansu (mountain and houses), by Jo Seok-jin (denomination in green). b, Jangsongnakil (rider on horse), by Ji Woon-young (denomination in bister brown). c, Unnangjasang (portrait), by Chae Yong-sin (denomination in red brown). d, Gunmado (horses), by Kim Ki-chang (denomination in gold).

**2011, July 28 *Perf. 13***
**2362** A1783 250w Block of 4, #a-d 2.50 2.50
*e.* Souvenir sheet of 4, #2362a-2362d 3.00 3.00

Selection of Pyeongchang as Host of 2018 Winter Olympics — A1784

**2011, Aug. 3 *Perf. 13x13¼***
**2363** A1784 250w multi .75 .30

Dinosaurs — A1785

No. 2364: a, Scelidosaurus. b, Stegosaurus. c, Allosaurus. d, Dilophosaurus.

***Perf. 13¼ Syncopated***
**2011, Aug. 11 Litho. & Engr.**
**2364** Sheet of 12, 3 each #2364a-2364d *12.00 12.00*
*a.-d.* A1785 340w Any single .65 .30

Intl. Association of Athletics Federations World Championships, Daegu — A1786

No. 2365: a, Runners. b, Pole vault.

**2011, Aug. 26 Litho. *Perf. 13¼***
**2365** A1786 250w Pair, #a-b 1.50 1.50

Tripitaka Koreana, 1000th Anniv. A1787

**2011, Sept. 23 Photo. *Perf. 13x13¼***
**2366** A1787 250w multi .75 .30

Personalized Stamp — A1788

**2011, Oct. 1 Photo. *Perf. 13x13¼***
**2367** A1788 270w multi — —

Vignette portion could be personalized. Three additional stamps were issued in this set. The editors would like to examine any examples.

Tenth Session of the Conference of the Parties to the United Nations Convention to Combat Desertification, Changwon — A1792

**2011, Oct. 10 Photo. *Perf. 13¼x13***
**2371** A1792 270w multi .75 .30

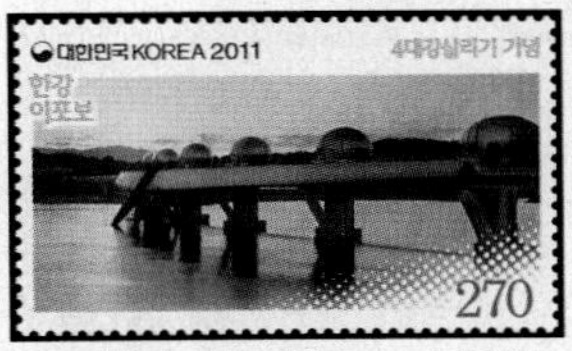

Ipo Weir, Han River — A1793

Gongju Weir, Geum River — A1794

Seungchon Weir, Yeongsan River — A1795

Gangjeong-Goryeong Weir, Nakdong River — A1796

**2011, Oct. 21 *Perf. 13¼***
**2372** Block of 4 2.25 2.25
*a.* A1793 270w multi .55 .30
*b.* A1794 270w multi .55 .30
*c.* A1795 270w multi .55 .30
*d.* A1796 270w multi .55 .30

Diplomatic Relations Between South Korea and Australia, 50th Anniv. — A1797

No. 2373: a, Korean woman playing haegeum. b, Australian aborigine playing didgeridoo.

**2011, Oct. 28 Photo. *Perf. 13¼x13***
**2373** A1797 270w Horiz. pair, #a-b 1.25 1.25

See Australia Nos. 3587-3588.

A1798

A1799

A1800

Daejoyong of the Balhae Kingdom
A1801

**2011, Nov. 17** ***Perf. 13x13¼***

**2374** Sheet of 12, 3 each #a-d, + label 6.00 6.00
*a.* A1798 270w multi .50 .25
*b.* A1799 270w multi .50 .25
*c.* A1800 270w multi .50 .25
*d.* A1801 270w multi .50 .25

New Year 2012 (Year of the Dragon) — A1802

**2011, Dec. 1**

**2375** A1802 270w multi .75 .30
*a.* Souvenir sheet of 2 1.25 1.25

South Korean Achievement of One Trillion Dollars in Trade — A1803

No. 2376: a, Automobile, computer chip, smart phone, container ship. b, Flag of South Korea, skyscraper.

**2011, Dec. 7**

**2376** A1803 270w Horiz. pair, #a-b 1.25 1.25

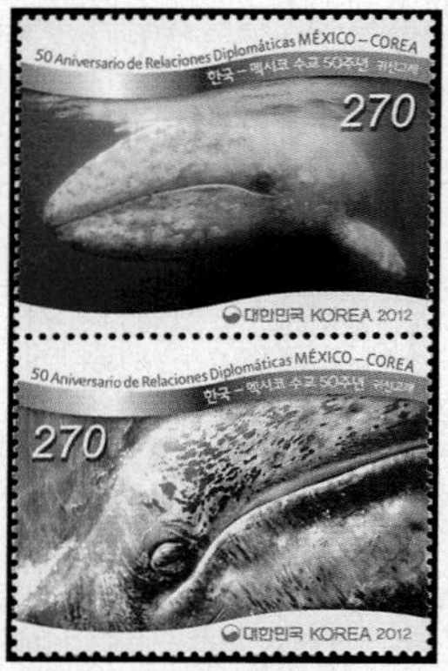
Diplomatic Relations Between South Korea and Mexico, 50th Anniv. — A1804

No. 2377: a, Juvenile gray whale, denomination at right. b, Adult gray whale, denomination at left.

**2012, Jan. 26** **Litho.** ***Perf. 13¼***

**2377** A1804 270w Vert. pair, #a-b 1.25 1.25

See Mexico Nos. 2771-2772.

Miniature Sheet

Characters in Pucca Animated Television Series — A1805

No. 2378: a, Ssoso, with stick and birds (blue green, light blue and gray background). b, Abyo, with frog (green andd light green background). c, Pucca, with heart (yellow and orange background). d, Garu, with cat (orange and light orange background. e, Ching, with mirror (pink and light pink background). f, Bruce, with guns (purple and gray background). g, Ho-Oh, with flame (purple and pink background). h, Santa (bright blue and light blue background). i, Nini, with earrings (gray blue background). j, Woo-Wuh, with rolling pins and dishes (dark blue and purple background).

***Serpentine Die Cut 10¼ Vert.***

**2012, Feb. 22** **Photo.**

**Self-Adhesive**

**2378** A1805 Sheet of 10 6.00 6.00
*a.-j.* 270w Any single .55 .30

Diplomatic Relations Between South Korea and Colombia, 50th Anniv.
A1806

No. 2379: a, Coffee beans and bush. b, Ginseng flowers and root.

**2012, Mar. 9** ***Perf. 13x13¼***

**2379** A1806 270w Pair, #a-b 1.25 1.25

See Colombia No. 1374.

2012 Nuclear Security Summit, Seoul — A1807

No. 2380 — Ribbon and: a, World map. b, Dove, flag of South Korea.

**2012, Mar. 26** ***Perf. 13¼x13***

**2380** A1807 270w Horiz. pair, #a-b 1.25 1.25

Historic Trees — A1808

No. 2381: a, Zelkova tree at Segan-ri (Natural Monument No. 493) (22x50mm). b, Trifoliate orange tree at Gapgot-ri (Natural Monument No. 78), horiz. (44x25mm). c, Spring cherry tree at Hwaeomsa Temple (Natural Monument No. 38) (22x50mm). d, Asian fringe trees at Gwangyang-eup (Natural Monument No. 235), horiz. (44x25mm).

**2012, Apr. 5** **Litho.** ***Perf. 12¾***

**2381** A1808 270w Block of 4, #a-d 1.90 .95

Winning Art in Stamp Design Contest — A1809

No. 2382: a, Hearts in ski cap, by Yeonju Chung. b, Children carrying rainbow, by Glen M. Isaac.

**2012, Apr. 25** **Photo.** ***Perf. 13¼x13***

**2382** A1809 270w Horiz. pair, #a-b .95 .50

Expo 2012, Yeosu — A1810

Nos. 2383 and 2384 — Expo 2012 emblem and mascot, fish and: a, Korea Pavilion. b, Theme Pavilion. c, Big-O. d, Sky Tower.

**2012, May 11**

**2383** Horiz. strip of 4 1.90 .95
*a.-d.* A1810 270w Any single .45 .25

***Perf. 13x13¼***

**2384** Horiz. strip of 4 1.90 .95
*a.-d.* A1810 270w Any single, 26x36mm .45 .25

No. 2383 was printed in sheets containing five strips. No. 2384 was printed in sheets of 10 containing two strips and two additional examples of No. 2384d.

Korea Trade Investment Promotion Agency (KOTRA), 50th Anniv. — A1811

No. 2385: a, 50th anniversary emblem, world map. b, Agency headquarters.

**2012, June 14** ***Perf. 13¼x13***

**2385** A1811 270w Horiz. pair, #a-b .95 .50

Gungnamji Pond, Buyeo — A1812

Daegwallyeong Sheep Ranch — A1813

Cheonjiyeon Waterfalls, Jeju Island — A1814

Dinosaur Ridge, Mt. Seoraksan — A1815

**2012, June 20** ***Perf. 13¼***

**2386** Block of 4 1.90 .95
*a.* A1812 270w multi .45 .25
*b.* A1813 270w multi .45 .25
*c.* A1814 270w multi .45 .25
*d.* A1815 270w multi .45 .25

2012 Summer Olympics, London — A1816

No. 2387: a, Swimming, Tower Bridge. b, Archery, Big Ben.

**2012, July 27** ***Perf. 13x13¼***

**2387** A1816 270w Vert. pair, #a-b .95 .50

Mask and Ogyeon Hall, Hahoe Village — A1817

Hyangdan, Yangdong Village — A1818

**2012, July 12 Litho. *Perf. 13x13¼***

| | | | |
|---|---|---|---|
| 2388 | Sheet of 10, 5 each #2388a-2388b | 4.75 | 4.75 |
| a. | A1817 270w multi | .45 | .45 |
| b. | A1818 270w multi | .45 | .45 |

Historic Villages of Korea UNESCO World Heritage Site.

Dinosaurs — A1819

No. 2384: a, Pachycephalosaurus. b, Tyrannosaurus. c, Oviraptor. d, Protoceratops.

***Perf. 13¼ Syncopated***

**2012, Aug. 8 Litho.**

| | | | |
|---|---|---|---|
| 2389 | Sheet of 12, 3 each # 2389a-2389d | 12.00 | 12.00 |
| a.-d. | A1819 360w Any single | 1.00 | 1.00 |

Philately Week — A1820

No. 2390 — Paintings: a, The Back Alley, by Dong Jin Seo (yellow green panel). b, Namhyangjip (A House Facing South), by Ji Ho Oh (blue panel). c, Tugye (Cockfighting), by Joong Seop Lee (pink panel). d, Chodong (Early Winter), by Sang Beom Lee (dull orange panel).

**2012, Aug. 9 Photo. *Perf. 13***

| | | | |
|---|---|---|---|
| 2390 | A1820 270w Block of 4, #a-d | 1.90 | .95 |
| e. | Souvenir sheet of 4, #2390a-2390d | 1.90 | .95 |

World Conservation Congress, Jeju Island — A1821

**2012, Sept. 6 *Perf. 13¼***

| | | | |
|---|---|---|---|
| 2391 | A1821 270w multi | .50 | .25 |

A1822

A1823

A1824

A1825

Park Hyeokgeose (69 B.C.-4 A.D.), Silla Kingdom Monarch — A1826

**2012, Nov. 21 *Perf. 13x13¼***

| | | | |
|---|---|---|---|
| 2392 | Horiz. strip of 5 | 2.50 | 1.25 |
| a. | A1822 270w multi | .50 | .25 |
| b. | A1823 270w multi | .50 | .25 |
| c. | A1824 270w multi | .50 | .25 |
| d. | A1825 270w multi | .50 | .25 |
| e. | A1826 270w multi | .50 | .25 |

New Year 2013 (Year of the Snake)

A1827 A1828

**2012, Dec. 3 *Perf. 13x13¼***

| | | | |
|---|---|---|---|
| 2393 | A1827 270w multi | .50 | .25 |
| 2394 | A1828 270w multi | .50 | .25 |
| a. | Souvenir sheet of 2, #2393-2394 | 1.00 | .50 |

Inauguration of 18th President, Park Geun-hye A1830

**2013, Feb. 25 Photo. *Perf. 13¼***

| | | | |
|---|---|---|---|
| 2396 | A1830 270w multi | .50 | .25 |

Miniature Sheet

Characters in Robocar Poli — A1831

No. 2397: a, Roy the Fire Truck. b, Amber the Ambulance. c, Poli the Police Car. d, Helly the Helicopter. e, Dumpoo the Dump Truck. f, Cap the Taxi. g, Posty the Postal Van. h, Spooky the Tow Truck. i, School B the School Bus. j, Cleany the Street Sweeper.

***Serpentine Die Cut 11½x9***

**2013, Mar. 12 Self-Adhesive**

| | | | |
|---|---|---|---|
| 2397 | A1831 Sheet of 10 | 5.00 | |
| a.-j. | 270w Any single | .50 | .25 |

Korean Baseball Players — A1832

No. 2398: a, Jang Hyo-Jo (1956-2011) at bat. b, Choi Dong-Won (1958-2011) pitching.

**2013, Mar. 29 Photo. *Perf. 13¼x13***

| | | | |
|---|---|---|---|
| 2398 | A1832 (270w) Pair, #a-b | — | — |

Diplomatic Relations Between Peru and South Korea, 50th Anniv. — A1833

No. 2399: a, Seongsan Ilchulbong, South Korea, South Korean and Peruvian flags at LR. b, Machu Picchu, Peru, South Korean and Peruvian flags at LL.

**2013, Apr. 1 Photo. *Perf. 13x13¼***

| | | | |
|---|---|---|---|
| 2399 | A1833 270w Horiz. pair, #a-b | .95 | .50 |

See Peru No. 1810.

Suncheon Bay Garden Expo 2013 — A1834

**2013, Apr. 19 Photo. *Perf. 13¾x13***

| | | | |
|---|---|---|---|
| 2400 | A1834 270w multi | .50 | .25 |

Information and Communication Day — A1835

No. 2401: a, Boy and girl holding envelope with heart, satellite, smartphone (blue background). b, Mailbox with letter in slot, robot, girl with parcels (orange yellow background). c, Boy on satellite dish, girl on television with legs (yellow background). d, Girl and robot in rocket circling Earth (purple background).

**2013, Apr. 22 Photo. *Perf. 13¼x13***

| | | | |
|---|---|---|---|
| 2401 | Horiz. strip of 4 | 2.00 | 1.00 |
| a.-d. | A1835 270w Any single | .50 | .25 |

Law Day A1836

**2013, Apr. 25 Photo. *Perf. 13x13¼***

| | | | |
|---|---|---|---|
| 2402 | A1836 270w multi | .50 | .25 |

Restoration of Sungnyemun Gate A1837

**2013, May 10 Litho. *Perf. 13¼x13***

| | | | |
|---|---|---|---|
| 2403 | A1837 270w multi | .50 | .25 |

Ahn Chang-ho (1878-1938), Founder of Young Korean Academy — A1838

**2013, May 13 Photo. *Perf. 13x13¼***

| | | | |
|---|---|---|---|
| 2404 | A1838 270w multi | .50 | .25 |

Diplomatic Relations Between Slovakia and South Korea, 20th Anniv. — A1839

No. 2405: a, Pansori performers, South Korea (woman and drummer). b, Lúcnica Art Ensemble dancers, Slovakia.

**2013, May 31 Photo. *Perf. 13x13¼***

| | | | |
|---|---|---|---|
| 2405 | A1839 270w Pair, #a-b | 1.00 | .50 |

See Slovakia Nos. 663-664.

Diplomatic Relations Between Germany and Korea, 130th Anniv. — A1840

No. 2406: a, Gyeongbokgung Palace, Seoul. b, Temple of the Sun, Bayreuth, Germany.

**2013, June 5 Litho. *Perf. 12¾x13***

| | | | |
|---|---|---|---|
| 2406 | A1840 270w Horiz. pair, #a-b | 1.00 | .50 |

See Germany Nos. 2739-2740.

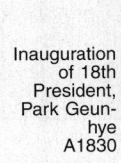

Energy Conservation — A1841

No. 2407: a, Leaves and smokestacks. b, Coin entering slot in piggy bank with electric cord as tail. c, Air conditioner and fans on balance with melting iceberg. d, Boy on stylized bicycle.

**2013, June 26 Photo. *Perf. 13¼***

**2407** A1841 270w Block or horiz. strip of 4, #a-d 2.00 1.00

Philately Week A1846

No. 2412: a, Girl writing letter. b, Girl placing letter in mailbox. c, Boy with magnifying glass examining stamp. d, Boy looking at stamp album.

600w, Combined design elements of Nos. 2412a-2412d (108x26mm).

**2013, Aug. 8 Photo. *Perf. 13¼x13***

| | | | |
|---|---|---|---|
| **2412** | Block or horiz. strip of 4 | 2.25 | 1.25 |
| ***a.-d.*** | A1846 300w Any single | .55 | .30 |

**Souvenir Sheet**

| | | | |
|---|---|---|---|
| **2413** | Sheet of 2 #2413a | 2.25 | 1.25 |
| ***a.*** | A1846 600w Single stamp | 1.10 | .60 |

Philakorea 2014 World Stamp Exhibition, Seoul.

Korean Coast Guard, 60th Anniv. A1847

**2013, Sept. 10 Photo. *Perf. 13x13¼***

**2414** A1847 300w multi .55 .30

Diplomatic Relations Between Indonesia and South Korea, 40th Anniv. — A1848

No. 2415: a, Small lion figure from Korean folk play, large bull figure from Indonesian folk play (denomination at left). b, Large lion figure, small bull figure (denomination at UR).

**2013, Sept. 17 Photo. *Perf. 13x13¼***

**2415** A1848 300w Pair, #a-b 1.10 .55

See Indonesia No. 2363.

Conference on Cyberspace, Seoul — A1849

**2013, Oct. 17 Litho. *Perf. 13x13¼***

**2416** A1849 300w multi .55 .30

A1850

A1851

A1852

A1853

Onjo of the Baekje Kingdom A1854

**2413, Nov. 20 Photo. *Perf. 13x13¼***

| | | | |
|---|---|---|---|
| **2417** | Horiz. strip of 5 | 3.00 | 1.50 |
| ***a.*** | A1850 300w multi | .60 | .30 |
| ***b.*** | A1851 300w multi | .60 | .30 |
| ***c.*** | A1852 300w multi | .60 | .30 |
| ***d.*** | A1853 300w multi | .60 | .30 |
| ***e.*** | A1854 300w multi | .60 | .30 |

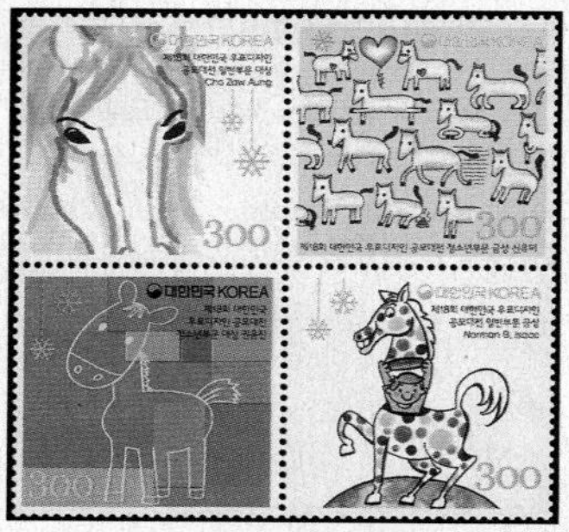


New Year 2014 (Year of the Horse) — A1855

No. 2418 — Snowflakes and: a, Close-up of horse's head. b, Horses and heart (yellow background). c, Line drawing of horse with multicolored squares and rectangles in background. d, Boy inside of horse raising horse's head.

No. 2419 — Combined designs of No. 2418 with cropped design of: a, No. 2418a at left. b, No. 2418b at left. c, No. 2418c at left. d, No. 2418d at left.

**2013, Dec. 2 Photo. *Perf. 13¼***

**2418** A1855 300w Block of 4, #a-d 2.40 1.25

**Souvenir Sheet**

**2419** A1855 630w Sheet of 4, #a-d 5.00 2.50

No. 2419 contains four 108x36mm stamps.

**Miniature Sheet**

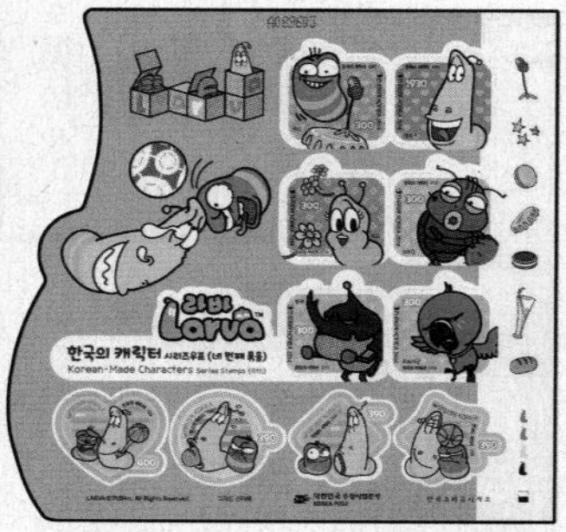


Characters from *Larva* Animated Television Series — A1856

No. 2420: a, Red at microphone. b, Pink and flowers. c, Brown and dung ball. d, Black with boxing gloves. e, Prussian (bird). f, Yellow eating roll and sweating, Red. g, Red, Yellow with open mouth. h, Yellow and Red with basketball. i, Red, Yellow holding lollipop. j, Yellow with open mouth.

***Serpentine Die Cut 10***

**2014, Feb. 28 Photo.**

| | | | |
|---|---|---|---|
| **2420** | A1856 Sheet of 10 | 9.50 | |
| ***a.-e.*** | 300w Any single | .55 | .25 |
| ***f.-h.*** | 390w Any single | .75 | .35 |
| ***i.*** | 400w multi | .75 | .40 |
| ***j.*** | 1930w multi | 3.75 | 1.90 |

Cadastral Resurveying A1857

No. 2421: a, 300w, Map of South Korea, surveying equipment. b, 390w, Smart phone.

**2014, Mar. 20 Photo. *Perf. 13¼x13***

**2421** A1857 Pair, #a-b 1.40 .70

Poets — A1858

No. 2422: a, Han Yongun (1879-1944), pink background. b, Lee Yuksa (1904-44), green background. c, Yun Dongju (1917-45), blue background.

**2014, Apr. 9 Photo. *Perf. 13x13¼***

**2422** A1858 (300w) Horiz. strip of 3, #a-c 1.75 .85

Philakorea 2014 World Stamp Exhibition, Seoul — A1859

No. 2423: a, 300w, Minhwa painting of birds and flowers. b, 300w, Hahoe wooden mask. c, 300w, Four Onggi pots. d, 300w, Neck of gayageum (stringed instrument). e, 300w, Baekja porcelain moon jar. f, 300w, Building roofs. g, 540w, Hanbok (traditional clothing). h, 540w, Hangeul (Korean text).

**2014, May 16 Litho. *Perf. 13¼x13***

**2423** A1859 Block of 8, #a-h 5.75 3.00

2014 World Cup Soccer Championships, Brazil — A1860

No. 2424 — Emblem and: a, 300w, Player and ball running toward goal. b, 540w, Players and ball.

**2014, June 3 Photo. *Perf. 13x13¼***

**2424** A1860 Pair, #a-b 1.75 .85

2014 Intl. Congress of Mathematics, Seoul A1861

No. 2425 — Person and: a, Pythagorean theorem. b, Leonhard Euler's trail (Seven Bridges of Königsburg problem). c, Blaise Pascal's triangle of binomial coefficients.

**2014, July 15 Photo. *Perf. 13¼***

| | | | |
|---|---|---|---|
| **2425** | Vert. strip of 3 | 2.25 | 1.10 |
| ***a.-b.*** | A1861 300w Either single | .60 | .30 |
| ***c.*** | A1861 540w multi | 1.00 | .50 |

Printed in sheets containing 5 strips + 3 labels.

17th Asian Games, Incheon A1862

No. 2426: a, Cricket. b, Wrestling. c, Squash. d, Bowling. e, Gymnastics. f, Mascots.

**2014, July 31 Photo. *Perf. 13¼x13***

| | | | |
|---|---|---|---|
| **2426** | Horiz. strip of 6 | 4.50 | 2.25 |
| ***a.-d.*** | A1862 300w Any single | .60 | .30 |
| ***e.-f.*** | A1862 540w Either single | 1.00 | .50 |

Printed in sheet containing 3 strips + 6 labels.

Arirang Dancer A1863

No. 2427: a, Feet of Arirang dancer. b, Head and arms of Arirang dancer.

**2014, Aug. 7 Litho. *Perf. 12¾***

**Thick Paper**

| | | | |
|---|---|---|---|
| **2427** | A1863 Vert. pair | 4.50 | 2.25 |
| ***a.*** | 300w multi | .60 | .30 |
| ***b.*** | 1930w multi | 3.75 | 1.90 |

Philately Week — A1864

No. 2428: a, 300w, Bird with letter in tree. b, 300w, Family holding large stamps. c, 540w, Children making person out of stamps. d, 540w, Stamp train.

**2014, Aug. 8 Photo. *Perf. 13¼***

**2428** A1864 Block or horiz. strip of 4, #a-d 3.50 1.75

Visit of Pope Francis to South Korea — A1865

No. 2429 — Pope Francis and: a, 300w, Coat of arms. b, 540w, Dove.

**2014, Aug. 8 Photo. *Perf. 13¼x13***

**2429** A1865 Pair, #a-b 1.75 .85

60th Baekje Cultural Festival — A1866

No. 2430: a, 300w, Gold earrings, top of incense burner. b, 540w, Base of incense burner and pagoda.

**2014, Aug. 21 Photo. *Perf. 13x13¼***

**2430** A1866 Vert. pair, #a-b 1.75 .85

Conference of the Parties to the Convention on Biological Diversity, Pyeongchang A1867

**2014, Sept. 16 Photo. *Perf. 13¼x13***

**2431** A1867 300w multi .60 .30

Gwanggan Bridge A1868

Log Fence Near House, Jeju Island A1869

Beacon Towers A1870

Emblem of 2014 International Telecommunication Union Plenipotentiary Conference, Busan — A1871

**2014, Oct. 1 Photo. *Perf. 13x13¼***

**2432** Horiz. strip of 4 3.00 1.50
- *a.* A1868 300w multi .60 .30
- *b.* A1869 300w multi .60 .30
- *c.* A1870 300w multi .60 .30
- *d.* A1871 540w multi 1.10 .55

Diplomatic Relations Between South Korea and Uruguay, 50th Anniv. A1872

Designs: No. 2433, Korean Nong-ak dancers and musicians. No. 2434, Uruguayan Candombe dancers and musicians.

**2014, Oct. 7 Photo. *Perf. 13x13¼***

**2433** A1872 300w multi .55 .30
**2434** A1872 540w multi 1.00 .50
- *a.* Horiz. pair, #2433-2434 1.60 .80

Nos. 2433-2434 were printed in sheets of 18 containing nine of each stamp. See Uruguay No. 2484.

Korean Day — A1873

**2014, Oct. 7 Litho. *Perf. 13¼x13***

**2435** A1873 300w multi .55 .30

Period of Nine Leaders A1874

Turtle Song A1875

Six Golden Eggs A1876

Birth of King Suro A1877

Wedding of King Suro A1878

**2014, Nov. 20 Photo. *Perf. 13x13¼***

**2436** Horiz. strip of 5 3.75 1.75
- *a.* A1874 300w multi .55 .25
- *b.* A1875 300w multi .55 .25
- *c.* A1876 300w multi .55 .25
- *d.* A1877 540w multi 1.00 .50
- *e.* A1878 540w multi 1.00 .50

Legend of King Suro of the Gaya Kingdom.

A1879

A1880

A1881

New Year 2015 (Year of the Sheep) — A1882

**2014, Dec. 1 Litho. *Perf. 14¼***

**2437** Block or horiz. strip of 4 2.25 1.00
- *a.* A1879 300w multi .55 .25
- *b.* A1880 300w multi .55 .25
- *c.* A1881 300w multi .55 .25
- *d.* A1882 300w multi .55 .25
- *e.* Souvenir sheet of 4, #2437a-2437d 2.25 1.00

Miniature Sheet

Constellations — A1883

No. 2438: a, Gemini (twins). b, Taurus (bull). c, Aries (ram). d, Pisces (fish). e, Aquarius (watere bearer). f, Capricorn (goat). g, Sagittarius (archer). h, Scorpio (scorpion). i, Libra (scales). j, Virgo (virgin). k, Leo (lion). l, Cancer (crab). m, Canis Major (dog). n, Cassiopeia (queen). o, Cygnus (swan). p, Boötes (herdsman with club).

Nos. 2438a-2438l (outer ring) are 31mm radially; Nos. 2438m-2438p are 26mm radially.

***Serpentine Die Cut 6¼ on 2 Sides***

**2015, Feb. 27 Litho.**

**Self-Adhesive**

**2438** A1883 Sheet of 16 + 5 labels 9.00
- *a.-p.* 300w Any single .55 .25

Happy School Life — A1884

No. 2439 — Winning designs in stamp design contest: a, Children at desks. b, School roof, clock, faces of children. c, Children holding letter. d, Faces of children as puzzle pieces.

**2015, Mar. 3 Litho. *Perf. 13¼***

**2439** A1884 300w Block of 4, #a-d 2.25 1.10

Seventh World Water Forum, Daegu and Gyeongbuk A1885

**2015, Mar. 12 Litho. *Die Cut***

**Self-Adhesive**

**2440** A1885 300w multi .55 .30

Endangered Wildlife — A1886

No. 2441: a, Female wolf and pups. b, Male wolf.

**Litho. With Foil Application**

**2015, Mar. 26 *Perf. 14¼***

**2441** A1886 300w Horiz. pair, #a-b 1.10 .55
- *c.* Souvenir sheet of 2, #2441a-2441b 1.10 .55

Scientists — A1887

No. 2442: a, Benjamin W. Lee (1935-77), theoretical physicist (purple panel). b, Seok Ju Myeong (1908-50), entomologist (pink panel). c, Han Man Choon (1921-84), electrical engineer (green panel).

**Litho. With Foil Application**

**2015, Apr. 10** *Perf. 14*

| | | | |
|---|---|---|---|
| **2442** | Horiz. strip of 3 | 1.75 | .90 |
| *a.-c.* | A1887 (300w) Any single | .55 | .30 |

Diplomatic Relations Between South Korea and Bolivia, 50th Anniv. A1888

No. 2443: a, Phibalura flavirostris. b, Mergus squamatus.

**2015, Apr. 24 Litho.** *Perf. 14x13½*

**2443** A1888 (300w) Pair, #a-b 1.10 .55

See Bolivia No. 1616.

Mangiyeoga Seal — A1889

Ssangri Seal — A1890

Ucheonhasa Seal — A1891

Hyangcheonsimjeongseohwajigi Seal — A1892

**2015, May 15 Litho.** *Perf. 14¼*

| | | | |
|---|---|---|---|
| **2444** | Horiz. strip of 4 | 2.25 | 1.10 |
| *a.* | A1889 (300w) pur & multi | .55 | .25 |
| *b.* | A1890 (300w) yel grn & multi | .55 | .25 |
| *c.* | A1891 (300w) pink & multi | .55 | .25 |
| *d.* | A1892 (300w) turq grn & multi | .55 | .25 |
| *e.* | Souvenir sheet of 4, #2444a-2444d | 2.25 | 1.10 |

Seals of the Joseon Dynasty.

Major Sim Il — A1893

Captain Kim Gyo-su — A1894

Vice Admiral Son Won-il (1909-80) A1895

Brigadier General Lee Geun-seok A1896

Police Inspector General Cha Il-hyeok A1897

General James Alward Van Fleet (1892-1992) A1898

Lieutenant Colonel James Power Carne (1906-86) A1899

First Lieutenant Jin Du-tae A1900

Lieutenant Colonel Ralph Monclar (1892-1964) A1901

Captain William Hamilton Shaw (1922-50) A1902

***Serpentine Die Cut 6½ Vert.***

**2015, June 1 Photo.**

**Self-Adhesive**

| | | | |
|---|---|---|---|
| **2445** | Block of 10 | 5.50 | |
| *a.* | A1893 (300w) multi | .55 | .25 |
| *b.* | A1894 (300w) multi | .55 | .25 |
| *c.* | A1895 (300w) multi | .55 | .25 |
| *d.* | A1896 (300w) multi | .55 | .25 |
| *e.* | A1897 (300w) multi | .55 | .25 |
| *f.* | A1898 (300w) multi | .55 | .25 |
| *g.* | A1899 (300w) multi | .55 | .25 |
| *h.* | A1900 (300w) multi | .55 | .25 |
| *i.* | A1901 (300w) multi | .55 | .25 |
| *j.* | A1902 (300w) multi | .55 | .25 |

Heroes of the Korean War.

Tourist Destinations — A1903

No. 2446: a, Aerial view of Yeongwol Donggang River. b, Aerial view of Chungju Chungjuho Lake. c, Confluence of Namhangang and Bukhangang Rivers. d, Rocks of Goesan Hwayang Gugok.

**2015, June 3 Litho.** *Perf. 14x13½*

**2446** A1903 (300w) Block or horiz. strip of 4, #a-d 2.25 1.10

2015 Universiade, Gwangju — A1904

No. 2447: a, Mascot. b, Soccer and stadium. c, Rhythmic gymnastics, Asian Culture Complex. c, Taekwondo, Ipseokdae Rock.

**2015, June 23 Litho.** *Perf. 13½x14*

| | | | |
|---|---|---|---|
| **2447** | Horiz. strip of 4 | 2.25 | 1.00 |
| *a.-d.* | A1904 (300w) Any single | .55 | .25 |
| *e.* | Souvenir sheet of 4, #2447a-2447d | 2.25 | 1.00 |

Silk Road Cultural Festival, Gyeongju — A1905

**2015, July 10 Litho.** *Perf. 14x13½*

**2448** A1905 (300w) multi .55 .25

Emblem — A1906

President Kim Koo (1876-1949) — A1907

***Serpentine Die Cut 10½ on 2 Sides***

**2015, Aug. 4 Litho.**

**Self-Adhesive**

| | | | |
|---|---|---|---|
| **2449** | A1906 (300w) multi | .50 | .25 |
| **2450** | A1907 (300w) multi | .50 | .25 |
| *a.* | Horiz. pair, #2449-2450 | 1.00 | |
| *b.* | Souvenir sheet of 2, #2449-2450 | 1.00 | |

Bamboo Forest in Snow A1908

Bamboo Stem A1909

Bamboo Forest A1910

Bamboo Shoots A1911

**2015, Aug. 13 Litho.** *Perf. 14*

| | | | |
|---|---|---|---|
| **2451** | Block of 4 | 2.00 | 1.00 |
| *a.* | A1908 (300w) multi | .50 | .25 |
| *b.* | A1909 (300w) multi | .50 | .25 |
| *c.* | A1910 (300w) multi | .50 | .25 |
| *d.* | A1911 (300w) multi | .50 | .25 |

Nos. 2451a-2451d are impregnated with a bamboo scent.

Lee Byung-chul (1910-87), Founder of Samsung Group A1912

Chung Ju-yung (1915-2001), Founder of Hyundai Groups — A1913

**Litho. & Embossed**

**2015, Aug. 26** *Perf. 14x13½*

| | | | |
|---|---|---|---|
| **2452** | Horiz. pair | 1.00 | .50 |
| *a.* | A1912 (300w) multi | .50 | .25 |
| *b.* | A1913 (300w) multi | .50 | .25 |

World Military Games, Mungyeong — A1914

No. 2453: a, Skydivers. b, Shooting. c, Mascots. d, Pentathlon competitors scaling wall.

**2015, Sept. 16 Litho.** *Perf. 13x13¼*

**2453** A1914 (300w) Block or horiz. strip of 4, #a-d 2.10 1.10

Namhansanseong UNESCO World Heritage Site — A1917

No. 2456 — Aerial view of buildings and: a, Courtyard (49x33mm). b, Gate (49x21mm).

***Perf. 13¾x13¼***

**2015, Oct. 29 Litho. & Engr.**

**2456** A1917 (300w) Vert. pair, #a-b 1.10 .55

Post Culture Week — A1918

No. 2457 — Winning art in stamp design contest: a, Open envelope, musical notes, posthorn. b, People and envelope on snail. c, Children following mailman on bicycle. d, Children and large mailbox.

**2015, Nov. 18 Litho.** *Perf. 13x13¼*

**2457** A1918 (300w) Block of 4, #a-d 2.10 1.10

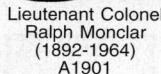

Souvenir Sheet

New Year 2016 (Year of the Monkey) — A1919

Designs: Nos. 2458a, 2459a, Monkey in tree. Nos. 2458b, 2459b, Six monkeys, gifts and flowers.

**2015, Dec. 1 Litho. *Perf. 14½x14¾***

2458 A1919 (300w) Sheet of 2, #a-b 1.10 .55

**Self-Adhesive**

***Serpentine Die Cut 9x9¼***

2459 A1919 Horiz. pair 1.10
*a.-b.* (300w) Either single .55 .25

Korea Institute of Science and Technology, 50th Anniv. — A1920

No. 2460: a, Technician and machinery. b, Building and monument.

**2016, Feb. 4 Litho. *Perf. 13x13¼***

2460 A1920 300w Pair, #a-b 1.00 .50

Lutra Lutra — A1921

No. 2461: a, Adult and juveniles. b, Head of animal.

**Litho. With Foil Application**

**2016, Mar. 15 *Perf. 14¼x14***

2461 A1921 390w Horiz. pair, #a-b 1.40 .70
*c.* Souvenir sheet of 2, #2461a-2461b 1.40 .70

A1922

Winning Art in International Stamp Design Contest — A1923

No. 2462: a, People painting peace dove on wall. b, Peace dove over rainbow. c, Children, trees, peace sign. d, Peace dove as balloon.

No. 2463: a, Man wearing seat belt. b, Woman and child in rain. c, Earth as person's head. d, People in floating hard hat.

**2016, Mar. 24 Litho. *Perf. 13x13¼***

2462 A1922 300w Block of 4, #a-d 2.10 1.10
2463 A1923 300w Block of 4, #a-d 2.10 1.10

Scientists — A1924

No. 2464: a, Jang Yeong-sil (1390-1443), mechanical engineer. b, Heo Jun (1538-1615), physician. c, Ree Taikyue (1902-92), chemist.

**Litho. With Foil Application**

**2016, Apr. 21 *Perf. 14¼x14***

2464 A1924 300w Horiz. strip of 3, #a-c 1.60 .80

Won Buddhism, Cent. A1925

**Litho. & Embossed With Foil Application**

**2016, Apr. 28 *Perf. 13x13¼***

2465 A1925 300w multi .55 .30

2016 Rotary International Convention, Goyang — A1926

**2016, May 2 Litho. *Perf. 13¼x13***

2466 A1926 300w multi .55 .30

Sorokdo National Hospital, Cent. — A1927

No. 2467 — Building and: a, Statue. b, Joined hands.

**2016, May 17 Litho. *Perf. 13¾***

2467 A1927 300w Pair, #a-b 1.00 .50

Nam Ja-hyeon (1872-1933), Female Military Leader A1928

Ju Si-gyeong (1876-1914), Independence Activist — A1929

***Serpentine Die Cut 12 Vert.***

**2016, June 1 Litho.**

**Self-Adhesive**

2468 Horiz. pair 1.00
*a.* A1928 300w multi .50 .25
*b.* A1929 300w multi .50 .25

Diplomatic Relations Betwen France and Korea, 130th Anniv. — A1930

No. 2469: a, Korean Celadon incense burner, 12th cent. b, French reliquary.

**2016, June 3 Litho. *Perf. 13¼x14***

2469 A1930 300w Horiz. pair, #a-b 1.10 .55

See France Nos. 5043-5044.

Stephen Kim Su-hwan (1922-2009), Cardinal A1931

Master Seongcheol (1912-93), Buddhist Monk A1932

***Perf. 13½x12¾***

**2016, June 27 Litho.**

2470 A1931 300w multi .55 .30
2471 A1932 300w multi .55 .30

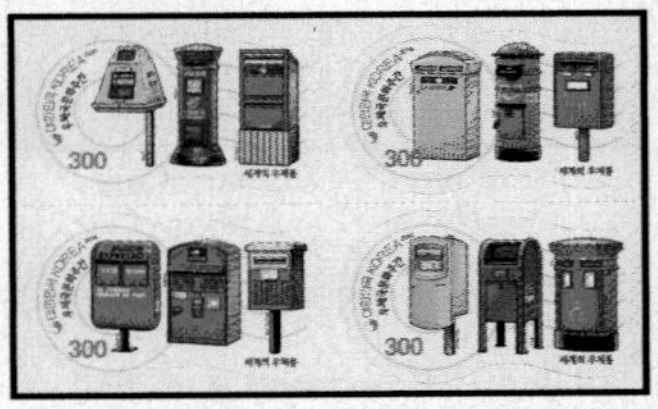

Mailboxes of the World — A1933

No. 2472 — Mailboxes from: a, Brazil, People's Republic of China, and Canada. b, France, India, and Japan. c, Mexico, Malaysia, and New Zealand. d, Switzerland, United States, and United Kingdom.

***Serpentine Die Cut 8¾ at Right***

**2016, July 19 Litho.**

**Self-Adhesive**

2472 A1933 Block of 4, #a-d 2.25
*a.-d.* 300w Any single .55 .30

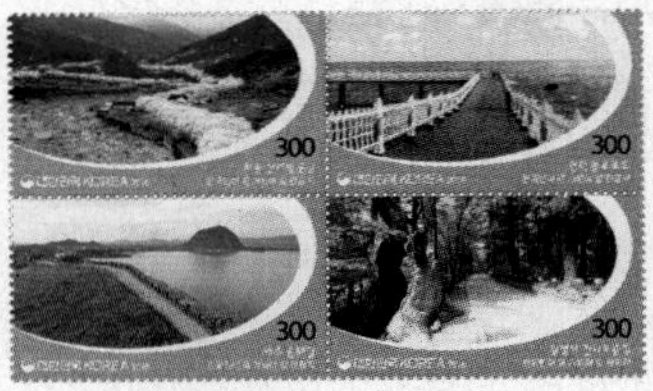

Tourism — A1934

No. 2473: a, Hadong Simri Cherry Blossom Road. b, Yeongdeok Blue Road. c, Jeju Olle Trail. d, Woljeongsan Jeonnamu Forest Trail.

**2016, Aug. 12 Litho. *Perf. 13¼***

2473 A1934 300w Block or horiz. strip of 4, #a-d 2.25 1.10

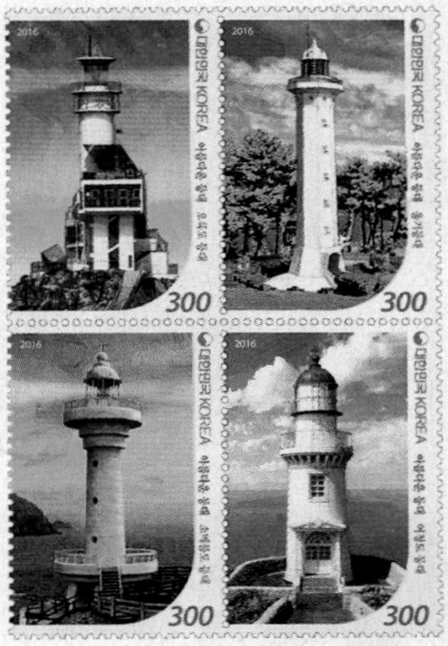

Lighthouses — A1935

No. 2474: a, Oryukdo Lighthouse. b, Ulgi Lighthouse. c, Somaemuldo Lighthouse. d, Eocheongdo Lighthouse.

**Litho. With Foil Application**

**2016, Aug. 25 *Perf. 13½***

2474 A1935 300w Block or horiz. strip of 4, #a-d 2.25 1.10

Painting by Lee Jung-Seop (1916-56) A1936

**Litho. With Foil Application**

**2016, Sept. 1 *Perf. 14x13¼***

2475 A1936 300w multi .55 .30

Gold Crowns — A1937

No. 2476 — Background color: a, Purple. b, Green. c, Red. d, Blue.

**Litho. & Embossed With Foil Application**

**2016, Sept. 21 *Perf. 14x13¼***

2476 A1937 300w Block or horiz. strip of 4, #a-d 2.25 1.10

Kia Tigers Cap and Mascot A1938

Nexen Heroes Cap and Mascot A1939

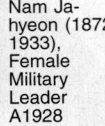

Doosan Bears Cap and Mascot A1940

Lotte Giants Cap and Mascot A1941

Samsung Lions Cap and Mascot A1942

NC Dinos Cap and Mascot A1943

SK Wyverns Cap and Mascot A1944

LG Twins Cap and Mascot A1945

KT Wiz Cap and Mascot A1946

Hanhwa Eagles Cap and Mascot A1947

**Litho. & Embossed With Foil Application**

***Serpentine Die Cut 12 At Bottom***

**2016, Oct. 7** **Self-Adhesive**

**2477** Sheet of 10 5.50
*a.* A1938 300w multi .55 .30
*b.* A1939 300w multi .55 .30
*c.* A1940 300w multi .55 .30
*d.* A1941 300w multi .55 .30
*e.* A1942 300w multi .55 .30
*f.* A1943 300w multi .55 .30
*g.* A1944 300w multi .55 .30
*h.* A1945 300w multi .55 .30
*i.* A1946 300w multi .55 .30
*j.* A1947 300w multi .55 .30

Korean Baseball Organization League teams.

A1950

A1951

A1952

Joseon Dynasty Seals — A1953

**2016, Nov. 10** **Litho.** ***Perf. 14¼***

**2479** Horiz. strip of 4 2.20 1.20
*a.* A1950 300w multi .55 .30
*b.* A1951 300w multi .55 .30
*c.* A1952 300w multi .55 .30
*d.* A1953 300w multi .55 .30
*e.* Souvenir sheet of 4, #2479a-2479d 2.20 1.20

Animals in the Demilitarized Zone — A1954

No. 2480: a, Great tit on barbed wire. b, Black-faced spoonbills.

**2016, Nov. 22** **Litho.** ***Perf. 14x13½***

**2480** A1954 300w Pair, #a-b 1.10 .55

New Year 2017 (Year of the Rooster) — A1955

No. 2481 — Rooster and: a, Snowflakes. b, Sun.

**Litho. & Embossed With Foil Application**

**2016, Dec. 1** ***Perf. 13¾***

**2481** A1955 300w Pair, #a-b 1.10 .55
*c.* Souvenir sheet of 4, 2 each #2481a-2481b 2.20 1.10

Kim Bong-ryong (1902-94), Inlayer of Mother-of-Pearl A1956

Kim Jeom-sun (1918-2008), Hemp Weaver — A1957

Lee Chi-ho (1910-2006), Ornament Painter — A1958

Cheong Sang-won (1926-2003), Furniture Maker — A1959

**Litho. With Foil Application**

**2017, Jan. 25** ***Perf. 14¼***

**2482** Block or horiz. strip of 4 2.20 1.20
*a.* A1956 300w multi .55 .30
*b.* A1957 300w multi .55 .30
*c.* A1958 300w multi .55 .30
*d.* A1959 300w multi .55 .30

Miniature Sheet

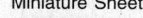

Webtoons — A1960

No. 2483: a, I Love You, by Kang Full (elderly couple on motorcycle, 39x36mm). b, With God, by Ju Homin (three people in traditional costumes, 35x40mm). c, Incomplete Life, by Yoon Taeho (man with briefcase, 36x37mm). d, The Sound of Your Heart, by Cho Seok (man, woman and dogs, 40x40mm).

***Serpentine Die Cut 9***

**2017, Feb. 10** **Litho.**

**Self-Adhesive**

**2483** A1960 Sheet of 4 2.20
*a.-d.* 300w Any single .55 .30

Nemorhaedus Caudatus — A1961

No. 2484: a, Adult and juvenile gorals. b, Head of goral.

**Litho. With Foil Application**

**2017, Feb. 20** ***Perf. 14¼***

**2484** A1961 300w Horiz. pair, #a-b 1.10 .55
*c.* Souvenir sheet of 2, #2484a-2484b 1.10 .55

Miniature Sheet

Astronomy — A1962

No. 2485: a, Aurora Borealis (41x31mm curved rectangle). b, Horsehead Nebula (denomination at left above star 37x35mm oval). c, Triangulanum Galaxy (denomination just above left end of inscription, 37x35mm oval). d, Messier 81 (spiral galaxy, denomination above middle of lower inscription, 37x37mm oval). e, Messier 82 (denomination above right end of inscription, 37x35mm oval). f, Orion Nebula (denomination above middle of lower inscription, 37x35mm oval). g, Observatory (51x25mm semicircle). h, Pleaides (36x36mm pentagon). i, Comet Lovejoy (36x36mm star). j, Rosette Nebula (37mm diameter).

***Serpentine Die Cut, Serpentine Die Cut 11½ Vert. (#2485a), Serpentine Die Cut 11 (#2485g), Serpentine Die Cut 11½ (#2485h, 2485i)***

**Litho. With Foil Application**

**2017, Mar. 21** **Self-Adhesive**

**2485** A1962 Sheet of 10 5.50
*a.-j.* 300w Any single .55 .30

Flag A1963

Hibiscus A1964

Buncheong Jar — A1965

**2017, Apr. 3** **Photo.** ***Perf. 12¾x13½***

**2486** A1963 330w multi .60 .30
**2487** A1964 420w multi .75 .40

***Perf. 13½***

**2488** A1965 1960w multi 3.50 1.75
*Nos. 2486-2488 (3)* 4.85 2.45

**Self-Adhesive**

***Serpentine Die Cut 11½***

**2489** A1963 330w multi .60 .30
**2490** A1964 420w multi .75 .40

A map of the Korean Peninsula is laser cut in the lower right corner of No. 2488.

Woodang (Lee Hoe-yeong, 1862-1932), Nationalist Leader A1966

**2017, Apr. 21** **Litho.** ***Perf. 13x12¾***

**2491** A1966 330w multi .60 .30

King Sejong (1397-1450) A1967

Choi Mu-seon (1325-95), Inventor and Military Commander A1968

Woo Jang-chan (1898-1959), Botanist — A1969

**2017, Apr. 27** **Litho.** ***Perf. 14***

**2492** Strip of 3 1.80 .90
*a.* A1967 330w multi .60 .30
*b.* A1968 330w multi .60 .30
*c.* A1969 330w multi .60 .30

Members of Korean Science and Technology Hall of Fame.

Winning Art in Postage Stamp Design Contest — A1970

No. 2493: a, Love of Hedgehogs, by Lee Su-jeong. b, My Home Filled With Love, by Jeong-Seo-han. c, A Family's Laughter, by Jang-Suk-yeong. d, The Happiness a Letter Brings, by Im Yu-ra.

**2017, May 2 Litho. *Perf. 13***

**2493** A1970 330w Block of 4, #a-d 2.40 1.25

Hearts are laser cut on Nos. 2493a-2493d.

Soswaewon Garden — A1971

Mungyeongsaejae Pass — A1972

Ullimsanbang Villa and Gardens — A1973

Jinjuseong Fortress — A1974

**2017, May 15 Litho. *Perf. 13¼***

| | | | |
|---|---|---|---|
| **2494** | Block of 4 | 2.40 | 1.20 |
| *a.* | A1971 330w multi | .60 | .30 |
| *b.* | A1972 330w multi | .60 | .30 |
| *c.* | A1973 330w multi | .60 | .30 |
| *d.* | A1974 330w multi | .60 | .30 |

Korean National Parks, 50th Anniv., and National Parks Service, 30th Anniv. — A1975

No. 2495 — Park ranger with: a, Magnifying glass and flowers. b, Binoculars, flowers and wildlife.

**Litho. With Foil Application**

**2017, May 29 *Perf. 13x13¼***

**2495** A1975 330w Horiz. pair, #a-b 1.20 .60

Wildlife in the Demilitarized Zone — A1976

No. 2496: a, Squirrel and army helmet. b, Kingfisher on barbed wire.

**2017, June 5 Litho. *Perf. 14x13½***

**2496** A1976 330w Pair, #a-b 1.20 .60

Iron powder particles are affixed to No. 2496a.

2017 World Taekwondo Championships, Muju — A1977

**2017, June 16 Litho. *Perf. 13x13½***

**2497** A1977 330w multi .60 .30

Kim Tong-ni (1913-95), Writer A1978

Pak Kyongni (1926-2008), Writer A1979

**2017, June 27 Litho. *Perf. 13¼***

**2498** A1978 330w multi .60 .30
**2499** A1979 330w multi .60 .30

Korean Independence Hall, 30th Anniv. — A1980

No. 2500: a, Independence Hall and "30." b, Statue of Indomitable Koreans.

**Litho. & Embossed**

**2017, Aug. 1 *Perf. 14***

**2500** A1980 330w Pair, #a-b 1.20 .60

A1981

Inauguration of Pres. Moon Jae-in — A1982

**2017, Aug. 17 Photo. *Perf. 13¼x13***

**2501** A1981 330w multi .60 .30

**Souvenir Sheet**

**2502** A1982 420w multi .75 .40

A1987

A1988

A1989

Highways — A1990

**Litho. With Foil Application**

**2017, Sept. 28 *Perf. 13½***

| | | | |
|---|---|---|---|
| **2504** | Block or horiz. strip of 4 | 2.40 | 1.20 |
| *a.* | A1987 330w multi | .60 | .30 |
| *b.* | A1988 330w multi | .60 | .30 |
| *c.* | A1989 330w multi | .60 | .30 |
| *d.* | A1990 330w multi | .60 | .30 |

Diplomatic Relations Between South Korea and Sri Lanka, 40th Anniv. — A1995

No. 2508: a, Korean dancer (green background). b, Sri Lankan dancer (blue background).

**2017, Nov. 14 Litho. *Perf. 13¼x13***

**2508** A1995 330w Pair, #a-b 1.20 .60

Snail Mailing Letter A1996

Chrysalis on Mailbox A1997

Chrysalis Under Mailbox A1998

Mailbox, Butterfly and Snail — A1999

**2017, Nov. 21 Litho. *Perf. 13¾***

| | | | |
|---|---|---|---|
| **2509** | Horiz. strip of 4 | 2.40 | 1.20 |
| *a.* | A1996 330w multi | .60 | .30 |
| *b.* | A1997 330w multi | .60 | .30 |
| *c.* | A1998 330w multi | .60 | .30 |
| *d.* | A1999 330w multi | .60 | .30 |

New Year 2018 (Year of the Dog) — A2000

No. 2510: a, Five dogs. b, Dog and snowflakes.

**Litho. With Holographic Foil**

**2017, Dec. 1 *Perf. 13x13¼***

| | | | |
|---|---|---|---|
| **2510** | A2000 330w Pair, #a-b | 1.20 | .60 |
| *c.* | Souvenir sheet of 4, 2 each #2510a-2510b | 2.40 | 1.20 |

## SEMI-POSTAL STAMPS

**Catalogue values for unused stamps in this section are for Never Hinged items.**

Field Hospital SP1

Nurses Supporting Patient — SP2

***Perf. 13½x14, 14x13½***

**1953, Aug. 1 Litho. Wmk. 257**

**Crosses in Red**

**B1** SP1 10h + 5h bl grn 14.00 2.25
**B2** SP2 10h + 5h blue 14.00 2.25

The surtax was for the Red Cross. Nos. B1-B2 exist imperf.

### Type of Regular Issue, 1956, with Added inscription at Upper Left

**1957, Sept. 1 Wmk. 312** ***Perf. 12½***

**Granite Paper**

**B3** A111 40h + 10h lt bl grn 8.25 2.75

**Wmk. 317**

**B4** A111 40h + 10h lt bl grn 8.25 2.75

The surtax was for flood relief.

### Rice Farmer Type of Regular Issue, 1961-62

**1963, July 10 Wmk. 317** ***Perf. 12½***

**B5** A172 4w + 1w dk bl 6.50 1.25

The surtax was for flood victims in southern Korea.

**1965, Oct. 1 Unwmk.** ***Perf. 12½***

**B6** A172 4w + 2w indigo 3.00 .75

The surtax was for flood relief.

**1965, Oct. 11**

**B7** A172 4w + 2w magenta 3.00 .75

The surtax was for a scholarship fund.

### Type of Regular Issue 1964-66

**1966, Nov. 10 Litho.** ***Perf. 12½***

**Granite Paper**

**B8** A186b 7w + 2w car rose 4.50 1.25

The surtax was to help the needy.

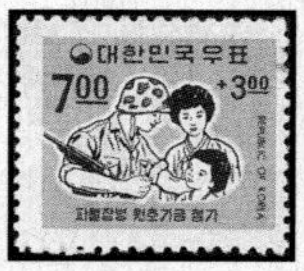

Soldier with Wife and Child — SP3

**1967, June 20** ***Perf. 12½x13***

**B9** SP3 7w + 3w rose lil & blk 4.50 .75

The surtax was for veterans of the war in Viet Nam and their families.

Reservist — SP4

**1968, Aug. 1 Litho.** ***Perf. 13x12½***

**B10** SP4 7w + 3w grn & blk 7.00 1.25

Issued for the fund-raising drive to arm reservists.

Flag — SP5

**1968, Nov. 1 Litho. Unwmk.**

**B11** SP5 7w + 3w dk bl & red 27.50 4.00

The surtax was for disaster relief.

**1969, Feb. 15**

**B12** SP5 7w + 3w lt grn, dk bl & red 7.50 1.00

Surtax for military helicopter fund.

### Flag Type of 1968 Redrawn Zeros Omitted

**1969, Nov. 1 Litho.** ***Perf. 13x12½***

**B13** SP5 7w + 3w dk bl & red 27.50 1.00

The surtax was for the searchlight fund.

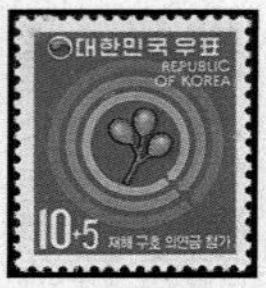

"Pin of Love" — SP6

**1972, Aug. 1 Photo.** ***Perf. 13½x12½***

**B14** SP6 10w + 5w blue & car 1.25 .75

Disaster relief.

"Pin of Love" — SP7

**1973, July 1 Photo.** ***Perf. 12½x13½***

**B15** SP7 10w + 5w multicolored .65 .50

Disaster relief.

Paddle and Ball — SP8

**1973, Aug. 1 Photo.** ***Perf. 13½x12½***

**B16** SP8 10w + 5w multicolored .65 .50

Surtax was for gymnasium to be built to commemorate the victory of the Korean women's table tennis team at the 32nd World Table Tennis Championships.

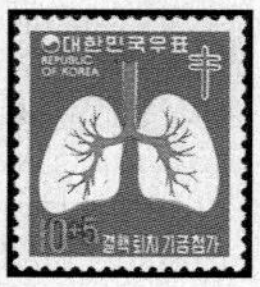

Lungs — SP9

**1974, Nov. 1** ***Perf. 13½x12½***

**B17** SP9 10w + 5w green & red .75 .25

Surtax was for tuberculosis control.

No. 647 Surcharged

***Perf. 13½x12½***

**1977, July 25 Photo.**

**B18** A328 20w + 10w green 12.50 12.50

Surtax was for flood relief.

### Seoul 1988 Olympic Games Series

'88 Seoul Games Emblem — SP10

Korean Tiger, Mascot — SP11

**1985, Mar. 20 Photo.** ***Perf. 13x13½***

**B19** SP10 70w + 30w blk & multi .45 .25

**B20** SP11 70w + 30w blk & multi .45 .25

*a.* Souvenir sheet of 2, #B19-20 1.10 1.10

Track and Field — SP12

**1985, June 10**

**B21** SP12 70w + 30w shown .45 .25

**B22** SP12 70w + 30w Rowing .45 .25

*a.* Souvenir sheet of 2, #B21-B22 1.10 1.10

**1985, Sept. 16**

**B23** SP12 70w + 30w Boxing .45 .25

**B24** SP12 70w + 30w Women's basketball .45 .25

*a.* Souvenir sheet of 2, #B23-B24 1.10 1.10

**1985, Nov. 1**

**B25** SP12 70w + 30w Canoeing .45 .30

**B26** SP12 70w + 30w Cycling .45 .30

*a.* Souvenir sheet of 2, #B25-B26 1.10 1.10

Surtax for the 24th Summer Olympic Games, Sept. 17-Oct. 2, 1988.

Equestrian — SP18

Designs: No. B28, Fencing. No. B29, Soccer. No. B30, Gymnastic rings.

**1986, Mar. 25 Photo.** ***Perf. 13x13½***

**B27** SP18 70w + 30w multi .45 .25

**B28** SP18 70w + 30w multi .45 .25

**B29** SP18 70w + 30w multi .45 .25

**B30** SP18 70w + 30w multi .45 .25

**Souvenir Sheets**

**B31** Sheet of 4 9.50 9.50

*a.* SP18 370w + 100w like #B27 2.25 2.25

**B32** Sheet of 4 9.50 9.50

*a.* SP18 400w + 100w like #B28 2.25 2.25

**B33** Sheet of 4 9.50 9.50

*a.* SP18 440w + 100w like #B29 2.25 2.25

**B34** Sheet of 4 9.50 9.50

*a.* SP18 470w + 100w like #B30 2.25 2.25

**1986 Photo.** ***Perf. 13x13½***

No. B35, Weight lifting. No. B36, Team handball. No. B37, Judo. No. B38, Field hockey.

**B35** SP18 80w +50w multi .55 .25

**B36** SP18 80w +50w multi .55 .25

**B37** SP18 80w +50w multi .55 .25

**B38** SP18 80w +50w multi .55 .25

**Souvenir Sheets**

**B39** Sheet of 4 8.25 8.25

*a.* SP18 370w + 100w like #B35 1.90 1.90

**B40** Sheet of 4 8.25 8.25

*a.* SP18 400w + 100w like #B36 1.90 1.90

**B41** Sheet of 4 9.00 9.00

*a.* SP18 440w + 100w like #B37 2.10 2.10

**B42** Sheet of 4 9.00 9.00

*a.* SP18 470w + 100w like #B38 2.10 2.10

Issue dates: Nos. B35-B36, B39-B40, Oct. 10; others, Nov. 1.

**1987, May 25 Photo.** ***Perf. 13x13½***

No. B43, Women's tennis. No. B44, Wrestling. No. B45, Show jumping. No. B46, Diving.

**B43** SP18 80w +50w multi .65 .40

**B44** SP18 80w +50w multi .65 .40

**B45** SP18 80w +50w multi .65 .40

**B46** SP18 80w +50w multi .65 .40

**1987, Oct. 10**

No. B47, Table Tennis. No. B48, Men's shooting. No. B49, Women's archery. No. B50, Women's volleyball.

**B47** SP18 80w +50w multi .65 .40

**B48** SP18 80w +50w multi .65 .40

**B49** SP18 80w +50w multi .65 .40

**B50** SP18 80w +50w multi .65 .40

**1988, Mar. 5 Photo.** ***Perf. 13x13½***

**B51** SP18 80w +20w Sailing .45 .25

**B52** SP18 80w +20w Taekwondo .45 .25

**1988, May 6 Photo.** ***Perf. 13½x13***

No. B53, Torch relay, horiz. No. B54, Olympic Stadium, horiz.

**B53** SP18 80w +20w multi .45 .25

**Litho. & Engr.**

**B54** SP18 80w +20w multi .45 .25

See Greece No. 1627.

**Souvenir Sheets of 2**

| | | | | |
|---|---|---|---|---|
| *B43a* | SP18 | 80w +50w | 3.00 | 3.00 |
| *B44a* | SP18 | 80w +50w | 3.00 | 3.00 |
| *B45a* | SP18 | 80w +50w | 3.00 | 3.00 |
| *B46a* | SP18 | 80w +50w | 3.00 | 3.00 |
| *B47a* | SP18 | 80w +50w | 3.00 | 3.00 |
| *B48a* | SP18 | 80w +50w | 3.00 | 3.00 |
| *B49a* | SP18 | 80w +50w | 3.00 | 3.00 |
| *B50a* | SP18 | 80w +50w | 3.00 | 3.00 |
| *B51a* | SP18 | 80w +20w | 3.00 | 3.00 |
| *B52a* | SP18 | 80w +20w | 3.00 | 3.00 |
| *B53a* | SP18 | 80w +20w | 3.00 | 3.00 |
| *B54a* | SP18 | 80w +20w | 3.00 | 3.00 |

## AIR POST STAMPS

Four-motor Plane and Globe — AP1

***Perf. 11½x11***

**1947-50 Litho. Wmk. 257**

**C1** AP1 50wn carmine rose 8.25 2.25

*a.* Horiz. pair, imperf. btwn. *165.00*

***Perf. 11***

**C2** AP1 150wn blue ('49) 1.25 1.25

*a.* "KORFA" 12.50 *.30*

**C3** AP1 150wn green ('50) 7.50 4.00

*Nos. C1-C3 (3)* 17.00

Set, never hinged 30.00

Nos. C2-C3 are redrawn and designs differ slightly from type AP1.

Issued: 50wn, 10/1.

For surcharge see No. C5.

Plane and Korea Map — AP2

**1950, Jan. 1**

**C4** AP2 60wn light blue 16.00 15.00

Never hinged 27.50

### No. C2 Surcharged with New Value and Wavy Lines in Black

**1951, Oct. 10**

**C5** AP1 500wn on 150wn bl 3.75 2.25

Never hinged 6.25

*a.* "KORFA" 20.00 *50.00*

Never hinged 30.00

*b.* Surcharge inverted 125.00

Douglas C-47 and Ship — AP3

***Perf. 13x12½***

**1952, Oct. 15 Litho. Wmk. 257**

**C6** AP3 1200wn red brown .90 .60

**C7** AP3 1800wn lt blue 1.50 .60

**C8** AP3 4200wn purple 1.90 1.25

*Nos. C6-C8 (3)* 4.30 2.45

Set, never hinged 7.25

Nos. C6-C8 exist imperf.

**1953, Apr. 5**

**C9** AP3 12h dp blue 1.00 .60

**C10** AP3 18h purple 1.50 .60

**C11** AP3 42h Prus green 2.10 1.25

*Nos. C9-C11 (3)* 4.60 2.45

Set, never hinged 7.75

Douglas DC-7 over East Gate, Seoul — AP4

**1954, June 15** *Perf. 12½*

**C12** AP4 25h brown 2.00 1.25
**C13** AP4 35h deep pink 2.75 1.00
**C14** AP4 38h dark green 2.75 1.50
**C15** AP4 58h ultra 2.75 1.75
**C16** AP4 71h deep blue 6.50 2.00
*Nos. C12-C16 (5)* 16.75 7.50
Set, never hinged 27.50

Nos. C12-C16 exist imperf.
Counterfeits exist of Nos. C12-C16.

### Type of 1954 Redrawn

**1956, July 20** **Unwmk.**

**Laid Paper**

**C17** AP4 70h brt bluish grn 5.00 3.00
**C18** AP4 110h brown 3.25 3.00
**C19** AP4 205h magenta 9.75 5.00
*Nos. C17-C19 (3)* 18.00 11.00
Set, never hinged 30.00

Nos. C18-C19 are found on horizontally and vertically laid paper.

**1957, July** **Wmk. 312** *Perf. 12½*

**Granite Paper**

**C20** AP4 70h brt bluish grn 4.75 3.00
**C21** AP4 110h brown 4.75 3.00
**C22** AP4 205h magenta 9.50 5.00
*Nos. C20-C22 (3)* 19.00 11.00
Set, never hinged 32.50

On the redrawn stamps, Nos. C17-C22, the lines of the entire design are lighter, and the colorless character at right end of bottom row has been redrawn as in illustration above No. 212D.

**Catalogue values for unused stamps in this section, from this point to the end of the section, are for Never Hinged items.**

Girl on Palace Balcony AP5

Designs: 100h, Suwon Castle. 200h, Songnyu Gate, Tuksu Palace. 400h, Kyunghoeru Pavilion.

*Perf. 12½*

**1961, Dec. 1** **Unwmk.** **Litho.**

**C23** AP5 50h lt blue & violet 12.50 5.00
**C24** AP5 100h pale grn & sepia 22.50 8.00
**C25** AP5 200h pale grn & brn 32.50 8.00
**C26** AP5 400h grn & pale bl 42.50 10.00
*Nos. C23-C26 (4)* 110.00 31.00

### Values in Won; Same Designs; Underlined Zeros Added

**1962-63**

**C27** AP5 5w lt bl & vio ('63) 67.50 20.00
**C28** AP5 10w pale grn & sepia 45.00 15.00
**C29** AP5 20w pale grn & brn ('63) 225.00 50.00
**C30** AP5 40w grn & pale bl ('63) 60.00 25.00
*Nos. C27-C30 (4)* 397.50 110.00

**1964, May 10** **Wmk. 317** *Perf. 12½*

**Granite Paper**

**C32** AP5 10w pale grn & sepia 12.50 4.00
**C33** AP5 20w pale grn & brn 42.50 12.00
**C34** AP5 40w pale bl & grn 25.00 8.00
*Nos. C32-C34 (3)* 80.00 24.00

**Granite Paper**

**1964, Oct.** **Unwmk.** *Perf. 12½*

Designs: 39w, Girl on palace balcony. 64w, Suwon Castle. 78w, Songnyu Gate, Tuksu Palace. 112w, Kyunghoeru Pavilion.

**C35** AP5 39w vio bl & gray olive 7.50 2.50
**C36** AP5 64w bl & grnsh gray 10.50 2.50
**C37** AP5 78w grnsh bl & ultra 19.00 5.00
**C38** AP5 112w blue & green 8.00 2.50
*Nos. C35-C38 (4)* 45.00 12.50

World Map and Plane — AP6

Designs: 135w, Plane over eastern hemisphere. 145w, Plane over world map. 180w, Plane over world map.

**1973, Dec. 30** **Photo.** *Perf. 13x12½*

**C39** AP6 110w pink & multi 6.75 4.00
**C40** AP6 135w yel grn & red 7.75 4.00
**C41** AP6 145w lt bl & rose 9.00 4.00
**C42** AP6 180w lilac & yellow 27.00 8.00
*Nos. C39-C42 (4)* 50.50 20.00

### UPU Type of 1974

**1974, Oct. 9** **Photo.** *Perf. 13*

**C43** A480 110w blue & multi 2.25 .75
*a.* Souvenir sheet of 2 11.50 11.50

### Mt. Fuji, Korean Airlines Jet Type

**1985, Dec. 18** **Photo.** *Perf. 13x13½*

**C44** A878 370w brt bl, blk & red 1.25 .75

### Int'l Year of Peace Type

**1986, Jan. 15** **Photo.** *Perf. 13x13½*

**C45** A879 400w multicolored 1.25 .75

Issued in sheets with two blocks of four.

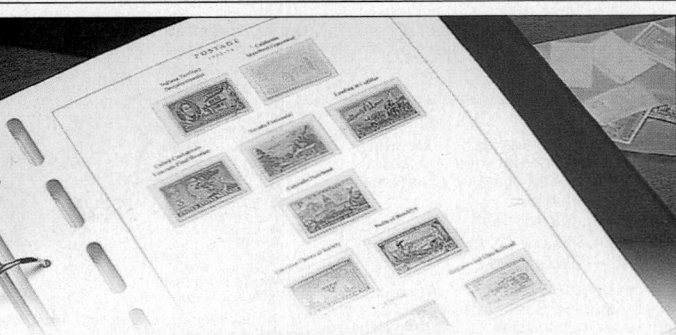

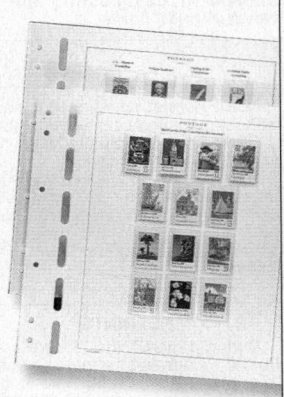

# KOREA, DEMOCRATIC PEOPLE'S REPUBLIC

kə-'rē-ə

LOCATION — Peninsula extending from Manchuria between the Yellow Sea and the Sea of Japan (East Sea)
GOVT. — Republic
AREA — 47,398 sq. mi.
POP. — 24,589,122 (2011 est.)
CAPITAL — Pyongyang

At the end of World War II, American forces occupied South Korea and Russian forces occupied North Korea, with the 38th parallel of latitude as the dividing line. North Korea was administered by a Provisional People's Committee after Feb. 9, 1946. Unoverprinted Japanese stamps continued to be used until the first North Korean issue of March 12, 1946. On Sept. 9, 1948, the Democratic People's Republic of Korea was established, and the last Soviet troops left Korea by the end of the year.

100 Chon = 1 Won (1962)

**Catalogue values for unused stamps in this country are for Never Hinged items.**

North Korean stamps were issued without gum, unless otherwise noted.
Early issues typically exist in a variety of color shades.
Used values are for cancelled-to-order stamps from 1957-on. Postally used stamps are worth more. Examples on non-philatelic covers are scarce, especially for 1946-1960 issues.

### REPRINTS

During 1955-57 the North Korean Postal Administration created "reprints," actually imitations, of most 1946-56 issues for sale to collectors. These reprints were postally valid, and in some cases may have served real postal needs, but most were created for and sold to overseas collectors.
The reprints are more finely printed than the original stamps and are normally printed on a higher quality white wove paper. They often differ from the original printings in both size and design details. Specific distinguishing characteristics are provided below, with the descriptions of each issue.
Value of reprints, $2-$5 each, unused or cto, unless otherwise noted.

### SOVIET OCCUPATION

Rose of Sharon — A1

Diamond Mountains (small "50") — A2

Diamond Mountains (large "50") — A3

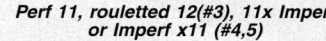

***Perf 11, rouletted 12(#3), 11x Imperf or Imperf x11 (#4,5)***

**1946, Mar. 12-1955 Litho.**

1 A1 20ch red 85.00 *300.00*
2 A2 50ch apple grn ('46) 55.00 *82.50*
a. 50ch yel green, *buff* 55.00 *82.50*
3 A2 50ch car rose 2,800. *2,300.*
4 A3 50ch rose red 165.00 125.00
a. Perf 12 ('48) 165.00 125.00
c. Perf 10 ('55) — —
5 A3 50ch violet 18.00 —
a. Perf 11 ('50) 300.00 —
b. Imperf ('50) 55.00 —
c. Perf 10 ('55) — —
d. ImperfxPerf 11, soft paper, vert. lines 20.00
e. Vert. pair, *tete-beche* 1,250.
*Nos. 1-5 (5)* 3,123. 2,808.

No. 4 has lines of colored dots along the horizontal rouletting.
Design sizes: No. 1, 18x21.5-22mm; No. 4, 17.5-18x22-23mm.
Reprints of No. 1 are in yellow green, perf 8½, 8½x9½, 10 or imperf, and measure 18-18.5x23mm. Denomination panel is 4mm high, rather than 3mm. Value $10.
Reprints of No. 4 are perf 10, 10x10½, 11 or imperf, on gummed paper, and measure 17.5-18x22-22.5mm. The double frame lines are clearly separated, and the figures of value are thin and well-formed. Value $10.

Gen. Kim Il Sung (1912-1994) — A4

**1946, Aug. 15 Litho. *Pin-Perf***
6 A4 50ch brown 700.00 700.00

First anniversary of liberation from Japan.
No. 6 has lines of colored dots along the horizontal pin perforations.
No. 6 is inscribed in Korean, Chinese and Russian.
No. 6 in deep violet brown and a 50ch red, similar in design, were printed for presentation to officials and privileged people. Value, $1,900 and $2,250, respectively.

Peasants — A5

***Pin-Perf 12, Imperf (#10)***

**1947, Apr. 22-1955 Litho.**
7 A5 1w turquoise 450.00 55.00
8 A5 1w violet ('49) 800.00 175.00
9 A5 1w dk bl, *buff* ('50) 110.00 55.00
10 A5 1w dark blue ('50) 60.00 60.00
a. Perf 11ximperf ('50) 6.00 *60.00*
b. Perf 10 ('55) — —

1st anniversary of agrarian reform.
Nos. 7-9 have lines of colored dots along the horizontal pin perforations.
Reprints of type A5 measure 21x24mm, versus the originals' 21-21.5x24-25mm, are finely printed in light blue and are perf 9, 10½, 11 or imperf. Value $10.

Worker and Factory — A6

**1948, June 5 Litho. *Perf. 11***
11 A6 50ch dark blue 3,200. 1,000.

Second anniversary of the Labor Law.
Design size: 20-20.5x31mm.
Reprints measure 20x30-30.5mm and are perf 9, 10½, 11 or imperf. Value, $10 perf, $10 imperf.

Workers and Flag — A7

**1948, Aug. 15**
12 A7 50ch red brown *4,000.* 1,500.

Third anniversary of liberation from Japan.

Flag and Map — A8

**1948, Aug. 20**
13 A8 50ch indigo & red *2,500.* 450.00

Adoption of the Constitution of the Democratic People's Republic of Korea, July 10, 1948.

### DEMOCRATIC PEOPLE'S REPUBLIC

North Korean Flag — A9

**1948, Sept. 19 *Rouletted 12***
14 A9 25ch reddish violet 15.00 *100.00*
15 A9 50ch gray blue 20.00 *50.00*
a. Perf 10½ 40.00 *75.00*

Establishment of the People's Republic, 9/9/48.
Design size: 23x30mm.
Reprints of No. 14 are in blue, on gummed paper, perf 9, 10½ or imperf. Size 20.5x28mm. Value, $10.
No. 15a is perforated over rouletting.

North Korean Flag — A10

**1949, Feb. 9**
16 A10 6w red & blue 4.00 *12.00*
a. Perf 10¼ 35.00 *35.00*

No. 16 exists on both brownish wove and white wove papers.
Design size: 24x32.5-33mm.
Reprints are perf 10¼, 11 or imperf. Size 19x26.5mm. On the originals, the top and bottom panels are blue, with the center field red. On the reprints, these colors are reversed. Value, $10.
For surcharge see No. 42. For overprint see No. 76.

A11

Kim Il Sung University, Pyongyang A12

**1949**
17 A11 1w violet 400.00 200.00
18 A12 1w blue 1,200. 125.00

Issue dates: No. 17, 8/9; No. 18, Sept.
Design size: 34x21mm.
Reprints of No. 17 are in slate lilac to reddish lilac, perf 8½, 9, 9x9½, 10 or imperf, on gummed paper. Size 31.5-32x20-20.5mm. Value, $10 perf, $10 imperf.

North Korean Flags
A13 A14

***Perf 11 or Rouletted 12 (#19)***

**1949, Aug. 15**

**With or Without Gum**

19 A13 1w red, grn & blue 1,000. 250.00
a. Imperfx11 1,000. 250.00
20 A14 1w red, grn & turq 1,200. *200.00*

4th anniversary of Liberation from Japan.
Design sizes: No. 19, 20.5x31mm; No. 20, 20x29.5mm

Order of the National Flag — A15

#21c Control overprint

***Rouletted 12, Imperf (#23)***

**1950, Apr. 4-1956 Litho.**
21 A15 1w pale sage green 7.00 *12.00*
a. 1w olive green 7.00 *12.00*
b. 1w yellow green 7.00 *12.00*
c. With control overprint ('51) — —
22 A15 1w red orange 20.00 *125.00*

**Typographed**

23 A15 1w brown orange *7,000.* *1,500.*
24 A15 1w dark green ('51) 60.00 *25.00*
a. Perf 10¼ ('56) 90.00 —
25 A15 1w light green 150.00 60.00

Design sizes: No. 21, 23-23.5x35mm; No. 22, 20x32mm; No. 23, 22.5-23x36-37mm; No. 24, 22x35.5mm; No. 25, 22.5x36mm.
No. 21c bears the seal of the DPRK MInistry of Posts and Telecommunications, which was applied to validate various stamps during the chaotic months following the landing of United Nations' forces at Inchon in mid-September, 1950, the retreat of North Korean forces to the far north by October, and their renewed advance, after the entry of the Chinese Volunteer Army into the war.
Reprints of type A15 are in dull blue green on white paper, perf 10¼ or imperf, size 22x35mm, or in red orange on white paper, perf 8½, 9, 10½, 10ximperf or imperf, size 20-20.5x32.5mm. Value (orange), $10 perf.

Flags, Liberation Monument A16

Flags, Soldier A17

Peasant and Worker — A18

Tractor — A19

**1950, June 20-1956**

**Lithographed, Thin Paper**

**Roul. 12xImperf, Roul. 12 (#28, 29)**

| | | | | | |
|---|---|---|---|---|---|
| 26 | A16 | 1w indigo, lt blue & red | 3.50 | *17.50* |
| a. | | Perf 10¼ ('55) | 12.00 | *24.50* |
| 27 | A16 | 1w brown orange | 9.00 | *60.00* |
| 28 | A17 | 2w red, stl bl & blk | 5.00 | *17.50* |
| a. | | Perf 10¼ ('55) | 12.00 | *24.00* |
| 29 | A18 | 6w green | 6.50 | — |
| 30 | A19 | 10w brown | 9.50 | — |

**Typographed, Thin Paper, Roul. 12**

| | | | | |
|---|---|---|---|---|
| 31 | A18 | 6w red | 3.50 | *17.50* |
| a. | | Perf 10¼ ('55) | 29.00 | *24.00* |
| b. | | Thick brownish paper, imperf x roul. 12 | 29.00 | *24.00* |
| 32 | A19 | 10w brown | 3.50 | — |
| a. | | Thick brownish paper, imperf x roul. 12 | 36.00 | *32.50* |
| | | *Nos. 26-32 (7)* | 40.50 | 112.50 |

Fifth anniversary of liberation from Japan.

Design sizes: No. 30, 20x27.5mm; No. 31, 22x33mm; No. 32, 22x30mm.

Reprints of No. 26 are on medium white paper, distinguishable by numerous design differences, among which are: characters in top inscription are 1½mm high, rather than 1mm, with 3 short lines at either side, rather than 2; top corner ornaments have a dark center, rather than white; 4 ray beams at left of monument, rather than 3; no dots on right face of spire, while originals have 3 small dots; value numerals within well-formed circles.

Reprints of Nos. 28 and 29 are on medium white paper, perf 10¼, 11 or imperf. No. 28 reprints are in light green, No. 29 in rose red, dull blue and black. Value, $10 each.

Reprints of type A19 are 22x31mm in size, on medium white paper and are perf 10¼ or imperf.

Capitol, Seoul — A20

**1950, July 10 Litho. *Roul. 12***

| | | | | |
|---|---|---|---|---|
| 33 | A20 | 1w bl grn, red & blue | 45.00 | *500.00* |

Capture of Seoul.

Order of Ri Sun Sin — A21

**1951, Apr. 5 Typo. *Imperf***

| | | | | |
|---|---|---|---|---|
| 34 | A21 | 6w orange | 15.00 | 15.00 |
| a. | | Perf 10¼ | 30.00 | — |

No. 34 also exists perf 9x10½.

No. 34 is on brownish laid paper. Design size: 21.5-22x29.5-30mm.

Reprints are on white paper, perf 10¼ or imperf. Size 21.5x30mm. On the reprints, the center of the lower left point of the star is open; on the originals, it is hatched. Value, $10 each.

For surcharge see No. 43.

Hero Kim Ki Ok — A22

**1951, Apr. 17**

| | | | | |
|---|---|---|---|---|
| 35 | A22 | 1w blue | 19.50 | 19.50 |
| a. | | Perf 10¼ | *180.00* | — |

No. 35 was printed on unbleached and off-white wood-pulp laid papers, with wood chips visible. The laid lines are often difficult or impossible to detect.

Design size: 23-23.5x35.5-36mm.

Reprints are on white wove paper, perf 10¼, 10½ or imperf. Size 22.5x33.5mm. Value, $10 each.

Soviet and North Korean Flags A23

Hero Kim Ki U A24

N. Korean, Chinese & Russian Soldiers — A25

**1951, Aug. 15-1955 Litho. *Roul. 12***

| | | | | |
|---|---|---|---|---|
| 36 | A23 | 1w dark blue | 105.00 | *105.00* |
| 37 | A23 | 1w red | 275.00 | *275.00* |
| 38 | A24 | 1w dark blue | 170.00 | *170.00* |
| 39 | A24 | 1w red | 170.00 | *170.00* |
| 40 | A25 | 2w dark blue | 65.00 | *65.00* |
| 41 | A25 | 2w red | 65.00 | *65.00* |
| | | *Nos. 36-41 (11)* | 1,720. | *1,720.* |

**Perf 10¼ Over Roulette (1955)**

| | | | | |
|---|---|---|---|---|
| *36a* | A23 | 1w dark blue) | 75.00 | *75.00* |
| *37a* | A23 | 1w red | 275.00 | *275.00* |
| *38a* | A24 | 1w dark blue | 275.00 | *275.00* |
| *39a* | A24 | 1w red | 170.00 | *170.00* |
| *40a* | A25 | 2w dark blue | 75.00 | *75.00* |
| *41a* | A25 | 2w red | 40.00 | *40.00* |
| | | *Nos. 36a-41a (11)* | 1,655. | *1,655.* |

Nos. 36-41 and 36a-41a exist on both coarse buff and white wove papers. Values are the same. Various perfs and roulettes and roulettes exists; not all combinations are known.

Design sizes: Nos. 36 and 37, 17x23.5mm; Nos. 38 and 39, 16x23mm; Nos. 40 and 41, 23x16.5mm.

Reprints of No. 36 are perf 9, 10½x10 or imperf. Size 15.5-16x22.5mm.

Reprints of No. 38 are perf 9, 10 or imperf. They have no lines of shading between the characters in the top inscription.

Reprints of No. 40 are perf 9, 10 or imperf. Size 22-22.5x16.5mm. The Korean "Won" character at lower right is in 4 parts, rather than 3.

Reprints are all light ultramarine. Value, $10 each.

**Nos. 16, 34 Surcharged**

On No. 16

On No. 34

**1951, Nov. 1 *Imperf***

| | | | | |
|---|---|---|---|---|
| 42 | A10 | 5w on 6w red & blue (#16) | 150.00 | 60.00 |
| 43 | A21 | 5w on 6w org (#34) | 1,000. | 725.00 |

Order of Soldier's Honor — A26

**1951, Nov. 15-1956**

| | | | | |
|---|---|---|---|---|
| 44 | A26 | 40w scarlet (16.5x25mm) | 22.50 | 4.50 |
| a. | | Perf 10¼ ('56) | 22.50 | 7.75 |
| 45 | A26 | 40w scarlet (17x24mm) | 12.00 | 4.50 |
| a. | | Perf 10¼ ('56) | 12.00 | 7.75 |

Victory Propaganda — A27

**1951, Nov. 15-1956**

| | | | | |
|---|---|---|---|---|
| 46 | A27 | 10w dark blue | 15.00 | 7.75 |
| 47 | A27 | 10w dark blue | 15.00 | 7.75 |
| a. | | Perf 10¼ ('56) | 22.50 | 22.50 |

No. 47 also exists perf 8½.

Design sizes: No. 46, 17x25.5mm; No. 47, 16.5-17x25mm.

Reprints are in light blue, perf 10¼, 11 or imperf. Size 16.5-17x25mm. Value and inscription at bottom are outlined and clear against cross-hatched background. Value, $10 each.

Ri Su Dok, Guerilla Hero — A28

**1952, Jan. 10-1955**

| | | | | |
|---|---|---|---|---|
| 48 | A28 | 70w brown | 15.00 | 3.50 |
| a. | | Perf 10¼ ('55) | 25.00 | 12.00 |
| b. | | 70w black brown | 120.00 | |
| c. | | As "b," perf 10¼ | 60.00 | |

Dove, Flag & Globe — A29

**1952, Jan. 20-1957**

| | | | | |
|---|---|---|---|---|
| 49 | A29 | 20w scar, dp bl & lt bl | 24.00 | 6.00 |
| a. | | Perf 10¼ ('55) | 24.00 | 12.00 |

Peace Propaganda.

No. 49 also exists perf 8½, 11 and rouletted 11½.

No. 49 was printed on off-white or buff paper, with broken lines between stamps. Design size: 22x31-31.5mm.

Reprints are perf 10¼ or imperf, in red, slate blue and pale turquoise blue on white paper. Size 22x31mm. They lack the broken lines between stamps. Value, each $50.

Gen. Pang Ho-san — A30

**1952, Apr.**

| | | | | |
|---|---|---|---|---|
| 50 | A30 | 10w dull purple | 60.00 | 24.00 |

Honoring North Korean General Bang Ho San.

No. 50 is also known with locally-applied rough perforation.

Labor Day — A31

**1952, Apr. 20-1955 *Imperf***

| | | | | |
|---|---|---|---|---|
| 51 | A31 | 10w rose red | 300.00 | *300.00* |
| a. | | Perf 10¼ ('55) | 300.00 | *300.00* |

Enforcement of the Labor Law, 6th Anniv. — A32

**1952, June 1-1955**

| | | | | |
|---|---|---|---|---|
| 52 | A32 | 10w light blue | 500.00 | *500.00* |
| a. | | Perf 10¼ ('55) | — | — |

Design size: 18x26mm. Broken lines between stamps.

Reprints are in dull or slate blue, on thick, gummed paper, with no broken lines between stamps. Size 17.5x25.5-26mm. Value, $10 each.

Day of Anti-U.S. Imperialist Struggle — A33

**1952, June 4-1956**

| | | | | |
|---|---|---|---|---|
| 53 | A33 | 10w rose red | 180.00 | 150.00 |
| a. | | Perf 10¼ ('56) | 180.00 | — |

Design size: 17.5x25.5-26mm. Broken lines between stamps.

Reprints are in bright rose red, perf 10, 10¼, 11 or imperf. on thick, gummed paper, with no broken lines between stamps. Size 17.5x26mm. Value, $10 each.

North Korean-Chinese Friendship — A34

**1952, July 25-1956**

| | | | | |
|---|---|---|---|---|
| 54 | A34 | 20w deep blue | 50.00 | 24.00 |
| a. | | Perf 10¼ ('56) | 50.00 | — |

Design size: 18x21.5mm. Printed on thin white wove paper, with clearly discernible mesh pattern.

Reprints are perf 10¼, 11 or imperf, on thick white wove paper, with no pattern visible. Size 18.5-19x21.5-22mm. Value, $10 each.

Flags & Monument A35

Soldier & Monument A36

**1952-55**

| | | | | |
|---|---|---|---|---|
| 55 | A35 | 10w carmine | 150.00 | 150.00 |
| a. | | Perf 10¼ ('55) | 200.00 | — |
| 56 | A36 | 10w scarlet | 275.00 | 275.00 |
| a. | | Perf 10¼ ('55) | 350.00 | 350.00 |

Seventh Anniversary of Liberation from Japan.

Issue dates: No. 55, 7/25/52; No. 56, 8/1/52.

Design sizes: No. 55, 20.5-21x27.5-28mm; No. 56, 29.5-30x18.5mm.

Reprints of No. 55 are in vermilion, on thick paper, perf 10½, 11 or imperf. Size 20.5x27-27.5mm. Value, $10 each.

Reprints of No. 56 are in rose red, perf 10, 10¼, 11 or imperf. Size 30.5-31x18.5-19mm. Value, $10 each.

Note: Original are typographed; reprints are lithographed on thin white paper.

International Youth Day — A37

**1952, Oct. 20-1955**
**57** A37 10w deep green 72.50 80.00
*a.* Perf 10¼ ('55) 72.50 —

No. 57 is on thick paper, with very thin gum. Design size: 20.5-21x28mm.
Reprints are on thin to medium paper, without gum, perf 10¼, 11 or imperf. Size 20x27mm. Value, $10 each.

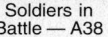

Soldiers in Battle — A38

Soldier and Flag — A39

**1953, Jan. 20-1955**
**58** A38 10w rose carmine 130.00 130.00
*a.* Perf 10¼ ('55) 130.00 —
**59** A39 40w red brown 60.00 60.00
*a.* Perf 10¼ ('55) 75.00 —

Fifth Anniversary of the Founding of the Korean People's Army.
Design sizes: No. 58, 21.5-22x26-26.5mm; No. 59, 21.5x27mm.
Reprints of No. 58 are on thick, gummed paper, perf 10¼, 11 or imperf. Size: 21.5-22x26.5mm. Value, $10 each.
Reprints of No. 59 are on thick, gummed paper, perf 10, 10½, 11 or imperf. Size: 21.5x26.5mm. Value, $10 each.

Woman with Flag — A40

Women and Globe — A41

**1953, Mar. 1-1955**
**60** A40 10w carmine 60.00 60.00
*a.* Perf 10¼ ('55) 60.00 —
**61** A41 40w yellow green 72.50 72.50
*a.* Perf 10¼ ('55) 72.50 —

International Women's Day.
Design sizes: No. 60, 20x29.5mm; No. 61, 21x29mm.
Reprints of No. 60 are in rose carmine, on thin paper, perf 10¼, 11 or imperf. Size 20.5x30mm.
Reprints of No. 61 may be distinguished from the originals by design differences: the dove's wing consists of many small feathers (3 large feathers on original), the women's mouths are all open (closed on original), and 3 thin connected lines on center woman's shirt (3 thick separate lines on original). Value, $10 each.

Worker — A42

Workers Marching — A43

**1953, Apr. 15-1955**
**62** A42 10w yellow green 60.00 60.00
*a.* Perf 10¼ ('55) 72.50 —
**63** A43 40w orange brown 60.00 60.00
*a.* Perf 10¼ ('55) 72.50 —

May Day
Reprints of No. 62 are in green or emerald green, perf 9½x8½, 10¼, 11 or imperf. Among many design differences, they have 4 horizontal lines between flag and frame line at upper left, many short hatching lines between frame line and top inscription, many horizontal lines between flag and flag pole at upper right, and won letter clear. On originals, there are one or no lines at upper left, no lines between frame line and top inscription, no lines between flag and flag pole, and the won character is not clearly defined. Value, $10 each.
Reprints of No. 63 are perf 10, 10¼ or imperf. On the reprints, the right flag pole touches the frame line, and the left center element of the won character resembles a "T." On the originals, the right flag pole does not touch the frame line, and the center element of the won character resembles an inverted "L." Value, $10 each.

Soldier — A44

Battle — A45

**1953, June 1-1955**
**64** A44 10w greenish blue 110.00 110.00
*a.* Perf 10¼ ('55) 110.00 —
**65** A45 40w scarlet 110.00 130.00
*a.* Perf 10¼ ('55) 110.00 —

Day of Anti-U.S. Imperialist Struggle.
Nos. 64 and 65 were issued with gum. Design sizes: 10w, 24x33mm; 40w, 24-24.5x33mm.
Reprints of No. 64 and 65 are on thick paper, perf 10¼, 11 or imperf. Design sizes: 10w, 23.5-24x32mm; 40w, 24x32-32.5mm. No. 64 is in turquoise blue, No. 65 in vermilion or orange vermilion. Value, $10 each.

4th World Festival of Youth & Students
A46 A47

**1953, June 10-1955** **With Gum**
**66** A46 10w dp dl bl & pale turq bl 72.50 72.50
*a.* Perf 10¼ ('55) 85.00 —
**67** A47 20w gray grn &pink 60.00 36.00
*a.* Perf 10¼ ('55) 72.50 —

Two types of reprints of No. 66 exist. On the reprints, the forelocks of the center and right heads have detailed hairlines, and the right head shows eye and eyebrow. On the originals, both features are solid. Value, $10 each.

Victory Issue — A48

**1953, June 1-1955** **With Gum**
**68** A48 10w brn & yel 360.00 400.00
*a.* Perf 10¼ ('55) 325.00 500.00

8th Anniversary of Liberation from Japan — A49

**1953, Aug. 5-1955**
**69** A49 10w red orange *4,000.* *4,000.*

Design size: 25x35.5mm.
Reprints are perf 10¼ or imperf. Size: 24.5-25x34.5-35mm. Left side of monument is shaded, and windows are fully drawn and shaded. On the originals, the monument is unshaded, and the windows are only partially drawn and half shaded. Value, $10 each.

5th Anniv. Founding of D.P.R.K. — A50

**1953, Aug. 25-1955**
**70** A50 10w dp blue & red 72.50 72.50
*a.* Perf 10¼ ('55) 95.00 —

Design size: 21.5-22x29.5-30mm. Inscribed "1948-1953."
Reprints are in blue and vermilion, perf 9x9½ or imperf and are inscribed "1948-1955." Size: 22.5x30mm. Value, each $100.

Liberation Monument — A51

**1953, Dec. 25-1955** **With Gum**
**71** A51 10w deep slate 72.50 47.50
*a.* Perf 10¼ ('55) 72.50 —

Design size: 20x31mm.
Reprints are in deep gray. Size: 19-19.5x30.5-31mm. Value, $10 each.

Worker & Crane — A52

**1954, Jan. 25-1955** **With Gum**
**72** A52 10w light blue 85.00 55.00
*a.* Perf 10¼ ('55) 110.00 —

Reconstruction and Economic Development.
Design size: 22x31.5mm.
Reprints are in greenish blue or dull blue, without gum. Size: 21.5x31mm. The horizontal lines defining the sky and clouds are clear and even, and the details of the crane are distinct. Value, $10 each.

Korean People's Army, 6th Anniv. — A53

**1954, Jan. 25-1955** **With Gum**
**73** A53 10w dp car red 500.00 —
*a.* Perf 10¼ ('55) 500.00 —
*b.* Rouletted 500.00

Design size: 23.5-24x38mm.
Reprints are in vermilion or orange vermilion. Size: 23-23.5x37.5-38mm. The design is much clearer than in the originals, with thin distinct characters in top inscription and complete unbroken frame line at right. Value, $10 each.

International Women's Day — A54

**1954, Feb. 25-1955** **With Gum**
**74** A54 10w carmine 250.00 250.00
*a.* Perf 10¼ ('55) 300.00 —

Design size: 19.5-20x29-29.5mm.
Reprints are in vermilion. Size: 20-20.5x29.5-30mm. The USSR and PRC flags at top right are legible, and the shading under the center and right women's chins is represented by several fine lines (solid on originals). Value, $10 each.

Labor Day — A55

**1954, Apr. 15-1955** **With Gum**
**75** A55 10w vermilion 72.50 72.50
*a.* Perf 10¼ ('55) 72.50 —

Design size: 20x27-27.5mm.
Reprints are in orange vermilion, perf 8½x9, 9, 10¼ or imperf. Size: 19-19.5x26-26.5. Value, $10 each.

No. 16 overprinted "Fee Collected" in Korean 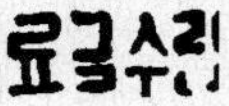

**1954, May (?)**
**76** A10 6w red & blue 1,500. 1,500.

Day of Anti-U.S. Imperialist Struggle — A56

**1954, June 10-1955** **With Gum**
**77** A56 10w red brown 210.00 *210.00*
*a.* Perf 10¼ ('55) 210.00 *210.00*

National Congress of Young Activists — A57

**1954, July 20-1955** **With Gum**
**78** A57 10w blue, red & slate 600.00 300.00
*a.* Perf 10¼ ('55) — —

Design size: 20x30mm.
Reprints are in blue, scarlet vermilion & deep slate. Size: 19.5-20x29-29.5mm. On the originals, the worker's hand is beneath the tassel of the flag and is less than 1mm from the frame line. On the reprints, hand is to the right of the tassel and 2mm from frame line. Value, $10 each.

Liberation from Japan, 9th Anniv. — A58

**1954, Aug. 1-1955** **With Gum**
**79** A58 10w chestnut 50.00 50.00
*a.* Perf 10¼ ('55) 50.00 —

Design size: 20-20.5x30mm.
Reprints of No. 79 are perf 10¼, 11 or imperf. Size: 20x29-29.5mm. Soldier's nose

line straight and strong, 3 lines of cooling holes in gun barrel (2 on originals). Value, $10 each.

North Korean Flag — A59

**1954, Aug. 25-1955 — With Gum**

80 A59 10w blue & dp red 100.00 *100.00*
 a. Perf 10¼ ('55) 120.00 —

Design size: 24x31.5-32mm.

Reprints are in dull blue and bright rose red. Size: 25-25.5x30.5-31mm. Value, $10 each.

Taedong Gate, Pyongyang A60

**1954, Sept. 1-1956 — With Gum**

81 A60 5w reddish brown 15.00 3.75
 a. Perf 10¼ ('56) 22.50 —
82 A60 5w lilac brown 15.00 3.75
 a. Perf 10¼ ('56) 22.50 —

Hwanghae Iron Works — A61

Hwanghae Iron Works & Workers — A61a

No. 84, Hwanghae Iron Works & workers, horiz.

**1954, Nov. 1-1956**

83 A61 10w light blue 22.50 3.00
 a. Perf 10¼ ('55) 45.00 —
84 A61a 10w chocolate 22.50 3.00
 a. Perf 10¼ ('55) 45.00 —
 b. Roul. 9x8½ ('56) 50.00 50.00

Korean People's Army, 7th Anniversary — A62

**1955, Jan. 25 — With Gum**

85 A62 10w rose red 36.00 36.00
 a. Perf 10¼ 36.00 —

International Women's Day — A63

**1955, Feb. 25 — With Gum**

86 A63 10w deep blue 36.00 36.00
 a. Perf 10¼ 45.00 —

Reprints are in blue, perf 10¼, imperf and imperf x 10¼. Corners of design are clearly and uniformly indented. Value, $10 each.

A63a

A63b

Labor Day

**1955, Apr. 16 — With Gum**

86A A63a 10w green 60.00 30.00
 a. Perf 10¼ — —
86B A63b 10w violet brown 60.00 30.00
 a. Perf 10¼ 60.00 —

Design sizes: No. 86A, 19.5-20x30mm. No. 86B, 19x30mm.

Reprints of 86B measure 19x29.5mm and are without gum. Value, $10 each.

Reprints of No. 86A measure 19.5x29mm.

Admiral Ri Sun-Sin — A64

**1955, May 14-1956**

87 A64 1w blue, *pale green* 15.00 15.00
 a. Perf 10¼ ('56) 18.00 —
88 A64 2w rose, *buff* 15.00 1.50
 a. Perf 10¼ ('56) 22.00 —
89 A64 2w rose red ('56) 30.00 2.75
 a. Perf 10¼ ('56) 30.00 —
 *Nos. 87-89 (3)* 60.00 19.25

No. 89 is redrawn, with a larger "2."

Design sizes: Nos. 87, 88, 20x29-30mm.

Reprints of No. 87 are in dull blue, on pale apple green, perf 10¼, 11½x10½, imperf, or roul. 8½. Size 19x28-28.5mm. Reprints of No. 88 are 19-19.5x28.-28.5mm in size. Value, $10 each.

Labor Law, 9th Anniv. — A65

**1955, May 30**

90 A65 10w rose 90.00 90.00
 a. Perf 10¼ — —

No. 90 was issued with a very thin yellow gum. Design size: 18.5-19x27.5-28mm.

Reprints exist perf 10¼, 11 or imperf. Size 18-18.5x27-27.5mm. Value unused, $10 each.

Korea-U.S.S.R. Friendship Month

A66 A67

**1955, July — *Perf. 10***

91 A66 10w rose red 30.00 —
 a. Imperf 30.00 21.00
92 A66 10w org red & vio blue 30.00 —
 a. Imperf 30.00 21.00
93 A67 20w red & lt blue 30.00 —
 a. Imperf 30.00 24.00
 b. Inscription below flag in two colors — —
 c. As "b," imperf — —
94 A67 20w ver & lt blue 24.00 —
 a. Imperf 24.00 21.00
 *Nos. 91-94 (4)* 114.00

Issue dates: Nos. 91, 93, 7/16; Nos. 92, 94, 7/20.

Design sizes: No. 91, 22x32.5mm; No. 92, 29.5x43mm; No. 93, 18.5x32mm; No. 94, 24.5-25x42.5x43mm.

Reprints of No. 94 are in light vermilion and light blue, perf 10¼, 11 or imperf, with a very thin gum. Size: 24-24.5x42-43mm. The two blue bands of the flag are solidly colored, with many white spots. On the originals, this area consists of fine lines with few or no white areas. Value, $10 each.

Liberation from Japan, 10th Anniv. — A68

**1955, July 20 — *Perf. 10¼***

95 A68 10w dull green 24.00 —
 a. Imperf 24.00 18.00
96 A68 10w ver, dull blue & chestnut 24.00 —
 a. Imperf 24.00 18.00

Design sizes: No. 95, 21.5-22x31.5-32mm; No. 96, 29-29.5-42-43mm.

Reprints of No. 95 are in dull blue green, perf 10¼, 11 or imperf, on gummed paper. Size: 21-21.5x31mm. Reprints of No. 96 are in rose red, dull to greenish blue and yellow brown, perf 10¼ or imperf. Size: 28-28.5x42.5-43mm. Value, $10 each.

Standing Rock in Sea-Kumgang Maritime Park — A69

**1956, Jan. 20**

97 A69 10w blue, *bluish* 20.00 —
 a. Imperf 25.00 25.00

People's Army, 8th Anniv. — A70

**1956, Jan. 20**

98 A70 10w lt brn, *pale yel grn* 100.00 *100.00*
 a. Imperf *90.00* *90.00*

Design size: 20x27-27.5mm.

Reprints are in chestnut on pale sage green paper, perf 10¼, 11 or imperf. Size: 19.5-20x27mm. Creases in the soldier's shirt are distinct, and nose and eyes are strongly shaded. Value, $10 each.

May Day — A71

**1956, Apr. 29**

99 A71 10w blue *100.00* *100.00*
 a. Imperf *100.00* *100.00*

Design size: 23.5-24x35-35.5mm.

Reprints are perf 10¼, 11 or imperf, on gummed paper. Size: 23.5x35mm. Clear hatching lines at right of top inscription; many feathers in dove's wing. Value, $10 each.

Ryongwang Pavilion and Taedong Gate, Pyongyang — A72

**1956, May 8**

100 A72 2w light blue *55.00* *55.00*
 a. Imperf *55.00* *55.00*
 b. Rouletted 85.00 —

Reprints of No. 100 are on thicker, gummed paper. The tail of the central left element in the "won" inscription at lower right extends beyond the left edge of the L-shaped character beneath it. Value, $10.

Moranbong Theater, Pyongyang A73

**1956, May 8**

101 A73 40w light green 30.00 12.00
 a. Imperf 85.00 72.50

Labor Law, 10th Anniv. — A74

**1956, June 7**

102 A74 10w dark brown 8.00 2.50
 a. Perf 9 *80.00* *60.00*
 b. Imperf 180.00 120.00

Korean Children's Union, 10th Anniv. A75

**1956, June 7**

103 A75 10w dk brown 15.00 6.50
 a. Imperf *160.00* *35.00*

Law on Equality of the Sexes, 10th Anniv. A76

**1956, July 10**

104 A76 10w dark brown 10.00 3.75
 a. Perf 9 *25.00* *15.00*
 b. Imperf 35.00 17.50

Nationalization of Major Industries, 10th Anniv. — A77

**1956, July 10**

105 A77 10w dark brown 90.00 —
 a. Imperf *210.00* —

Liberation from Japan, 11th Anniv. — A78

**1956, July 24**

**106** A78 10w rose red 14.00 3.25
*a.* Imperf *160.00 30.00*

Machinist
A79

**1956, July 28**

**107** A79 1w dark brown 3.75 2.00
*a.* Perf 9 *12.50 8.00*
*b.* Imperf 32.50 14.00

Kim Il Sung University, 10th Anniv. — A80

**1956, Sept. 30**

**108** A80 10w dark brown 10.00 9.00
*a.* Imperf *32.50 14.00*

4th Congress, Korean Democratic Youth League — A81

**1956, Nov. 3**

**109** A81 10w dark brown 14.00 3.25
*a.* Imperf 32.50 18.00

Model Peasant — A82

**1956, Nov. 14**

**110** A82 10w rose 7.50 2.25
*a.* Imperf 21.00 11.00
*b.* Rouletted — —

220th Anniv. Birth of Pak Ji Won (1737-1805)
A83

**1957, Mar. 4**

**111** A83 10w blue 5.00 1.25
*a.* Imperf 19.00 10.00

Tabo Pagoda in Pulguk Temple
A84

Ulmil Pavilion, Pyongyang
A85

**1957, Mar. 20**

**112** A84 5w light blue 6.00 2.50
*a.* Rouletted — —
*b.* Perf 11 (with gum) — —
*c.* Imperf 87.50 21.00
**113** A85 40w gray green 7.50 3.25
*a.* Perf 11 — —
*b.* Imperf 22.50 11.00

No. 113b was issued both with and without gum.

Productivity Campaign — A86

**1957, July 4 With or Without Gum**

**114** A86 10w ultramarine 6.75 4.50
*a.* Perf 11 — —
*b.* Imperf 32.50 15.00

Steelworker — A87

Voters Marching — A88

**1957, Aug.**

**115** A87 1w orange 3.50 .75
*a.* Imperf 9.50 4.25
**116** A87 2w brown 3.50 .75
*a.* Imperf 9.50 4.25
**117** A88 10w vermilion 17.50 3.25
*a.* Imperf 65.00 35.00
*Nos. 115-117 (3)* 24.50 4.75

Second General Election.

There are two types of the 1w. On type 1, the won character is approx. 2½mm in diameter and is distinct. On type 2, the character is approx. 1½mm in diameter and is virtually illegible.

Issued: 10w, 8/10; 1w, 2w, 8/13.

Founding of Pyongyang, 1530th Anniv. — A89

**1957, Sept. 28** ***Perf. 10***

**118** A89 10w blue green 3.00 .65
*a.* Imperf 30.00 9.00

Lenin — A90

Lenin & Flags — A91

Kim Il Sung at Pochonbo
A92

Pouring Steel
A93

**1957**

**119** A90 10w gray blue 2.00 .95
*a.* Imperf 30.00 9.00
**120** A91 10w blue green 2.00 .95
*a.* Imperf 30.00 9.00
*b.* Rouletted 13 — —
**121** A92 10w red 2.00 .95
*a.* Imperf 30.00 9.00
*b.* Rouletted 13 — —
**122** A93 10w red orange 4.50 .95
*a.* Imperf 120.00 13.00
*b.* Rouletted 13 — —
*Nos. 119-122 (4)* 10.50 3.80

40th Anniversary of the Russian October Revolution.

Issued: Nos. 119, 120, 9/30; No. 121, 10/3; 122, 10/16.

No. 120 exists with gum.

4th Congress World Federation of Trade Unions — A94

**1957, Oct. 3**

**123** A94 10w ultra & lt grn 2.50 1.10
*a.* Imperf 30.00 11.00

No. 123a exists with or without gum.

Russian Friendship Month — A95

**1957, Oct. 16**

**124** A95 10w green 4.50 1.10
*a.* Imperf *210.00 140.00*

Doctor Weighing Baby — A96

Bandaging Hand — A97

**1957, Nov. 1**

**125** A96 1w red 9.00 1.25
*a.* Imperf 65.00 12.00
**126** A96 2w red 9.00 1.25
*a.* Imperf 65.00 12.00
*b.* Rouletted — —
**127** A97 10w red 35.00 3.75
*a.* Imperf 130.00 35.00
*Nos. 125-127 (3)* 53.00 6.25

Red Cross.

No. 126 exists without or without gum. No. 126a was issued with gum.

Flying Dragon Kettle — A98

Flying Dragon Incense Burner — A99

**1958, Jan. 14**

**128** A98 10w blue 11.00 1.40
*a.* Imperf 87.50 18.00
**129** A99 10w gray green 11.00 1.40
*a.* Imperf 87.50 18.00

Nos. 128a and 129a exist with or without gum.

Woljong Temple Pagoda — A100

**1958, Feb. 21** ***10 (#130), 10½ (#131)***

**130** A100 5w lt green 1.75 .65
*a.* Imperf 24.50 11.50
*b.* Rouletted — —
**131** A100 10w lt blue 5.00 2.25
*a.* Imperf 30.00 16.00
*b.* Rouletted — —

No. 130 was issued with gum.

Soldier — A101

Soldier, Flag & Hwanghae Iron Works — A102

**Photo (#132), Litho (#133)**

**1958, Feb.** ***Perf. 10***

**132** A101 10w blue 7.25 1.00
*a.* Imperf 52.50 19.00
*b.* Rouletted — —
*c.* Perf 11 — —
**133** A102 10w rose 10.00 1.10
*a.* Imperf 52.50 19.00

10th Anniversary of the Korean People's Army.

No. 133 was issued with or without gum.

Rocket Launch, Sputnik — A103

Sputnik in Orbit — A104

Designs: 40w, Sputnik over observatory.

**1958, Mar. 26** **Photo.**

| | | | |
|---|---|---|---|
| 134 | A103 10w dull blue green | 7.75 | 4.50 |
| *a.* | Imperf | 65.00 | 19.00 |
| 135 | A104 20w dull blue green | 7.75 | 4.50 |
| *a.* | Imperf | 65.00 | 19.00 |
| *b.* | Rouletted | — | — |
| 136 | A104 40w dull blue green | 7.75 | 4.50 |
| *a.* | Imperf | 65.00 | 19.00 |
| 137 | A103 70w dull blue green | 9.00 | 8.00 |
| *a.* | Imperf | 100.00 | 30.00 |
| | *Nos. 134-137 (4)* | 32.25 | 21.50 |

International Geophysical Year.
Nos. 134-137 exist with or without gum.

Young Socialist Constructors Congress — A105

**1958, May 12** **Litho.**

| | | | |
|---|---|---|---|
| 138 | A105 10w blue | 4.00 | 1.10 |
| *a.* | Imperf | 27.00 | 10.00 |

Opening of Hwanghae Iron Works — A106

**1958, May 22**

| | | | |
|---|---|---|---|
| 139 | A106 10w lt blue | 7.75 | 1.10 |
| *a.* | Imperf | 37.50 | 12.50 |

Commemorative Badge — A107

**1958, May 27**

| | | | |
|---|---|---|---|
| 140 | A107 10w multicolored | 6.25 | 1.35 |
| *a.* | Imperf | 25.00 | 6.00 |
| *b.* | Perf 11 | — | — |
| *c.* | Rouletted | — | — |

Departure of Chinese People's Volunteers. See No. 150.

4th International Democratic Women's Congress — A108

**1958, June 5**

| | | | |
|---|---|---|---|
| 141 | A108 10w blue | 1.75 | .65 |
| *a.* | Imperf | 37.50 | 10.00 |

Congress Emblem A109

**1958, July 4**

| | | | |
|---|---|---|---|
| 142 | A109 10w grn & red brn | 3.25 | 2.25 |
| *a.* | Imperf | 27.00 | 6.00 |
| *b.* | Perf 11 | 11.00 | — |

First Congress of the Young Workers of the World Federation of Trade Unions.

Apartment House, East Pyongyang A110

**1958, July 24**

| | | | |
|---|---|---|---|
| 143 | A110 10w lt blue | 4.50 | 1.10 |
| *a.* | Imperf | 23.50 | 8.00 |
| *b.* | Perf 11 | — | — |

Workers' Apartment House, Pyongyang A111

**1958, Aug. 21**

| | | | |
|---|---|---|---|
| 144 | A111 10w blue green | 4.50 | 1.10 |
| *a.* | Imperf | 23.50 | 8.00 |

Hungnam Fertilizer Plant — A112

Pyongyang Railway Station A113

DPRK Arms — A114

Weaver — A115

Dam, Pyongyang A116

**1958** **Litho, Photo (#148, 149)**

| | | | |
|---|---|---|---|
| 145 | A112 10w blue green | 5.50 | .85 |
| *a.* | Imperf | *130.00* | *16.00* |
| *b.* | Perf 11 | — | — |
| 146 | A113 10w dp blue green | *20.00* | 3.00 |
| *a.* | Imperf | *150.00* | *37.50* |
| *b.* | Perf 11 | — | — |
| 147 | A114 10w red brn & yel grn | 4.00 | .85 |
| *a.* | Imperf | *325.00* | *110.00* |
| 148 | A115 10w sepia | 16.00 | 3.25 |
| *a.* | Imperf | *210.00* | *57.50* |
| 149 | A116 10w sepia | 27.00 | 11.00 |
| *a.* | Imperf | *150.00* | *32.50* |
| | *Nos. 145-149 (5)* | 72.50 | 18.95 |

10th Anniversary Korean People's Republic. Issued: Nos. 145, 146, 8/21; No. 147, 9/7; Nos. 148, 149, 9/10.

Soldier and Troop Train — A117

**1958, Sept. 10** **Photo.** ***Perf. 10***

| | | | |
|---|---|---|---|
| 150 | A117 10w sepia | 40.00 | 10.00 |
| *a.* | Imperf | *360.00* | *77.50* |

Departure of Chinese People's Volunteers.

Transplanting Rice Seedlings A118

**1958, Sept. 10** **Litho.**
**With or Without Gum**

| | | | |
|---|---|---|---|
| 151 | A118 10w sepia | 1.80 | .55 |
| *a.* | Imperf | 13.50 | 6.00 |

Winged Horse of Chollima — A119

**1958, Sept. 16**

| | | | |
|---|---|---|---|
| 152 | A119 10w brick red | 3.00 | .55 |
| *a.* | Imperf | 27.50 | 3.75 |

National Congress of the Innovators in Production.

North Korea-China Friendship Month — A120

**1958, Oct. 8** **With or Without Gum**

| | | | |
|---|---|---|---|
| 153 | A120 10w multicolored | 2.00 | .50 |
| *a.* | Imperf | 16.00 | 3.75 |
| *b.* | Rouletted | — | — |

National Congress of Agricultural Cooperatives A121

**1959, Jan. 5** **With or Without Gum**

| | | | |
|---|---|---|---|
| 154 | A121 10w dk grnish blue | 2.25 | .55 |
| *a.* | Imperf | 16.00 | 3.50 |

Gen. Ulchi Mundok — A122

**1959, Feb. 11** **With Gum**

| | | | |
|---|---|---|---|
| 155 | A122 10w lilac brn & yel | 5.00 | 1.00 |
| *a.* | Imperf | *27.50* | *12.50* |

See Nos. 157-159 and 209-212.

National Women's Workers Congress — A123

**1959, Mar. 29**
**With or Without Gum**

| | | | |
|---|---|---|---|
| 156 | A123 10ch brown & red | 3.25 | 1.10 |
| *a.* | Imperf | *52.50* | — |

Jeon Bong-jun A124

Kang Kam Chan A125

Ulchi Mundok — A126

**1959, Apr. 1**

| | | | |
|---|---|---|---|
| 157 | A124 2ch blue, *lt green* | 2.25 | .40 |
| *a.* | Imperf | *110.00* | — |
| 158 | A125 5ch lilac brn, *buff* | 2.50 | .45 |
| *a.* | Imperf | *150.00* | — |
| 159 | A126 10ch red brn, *cream* | 5.00 | .60 |
| *a.* | Imperf | *150.00* | — |
| | *Nos. 157-159 (3)* | 9.75 | 1.45 |

Nos. 157-159 were issued with gum. Nos. 157a-159a were issued with or without gum.

Soviet Luna 1 Moon Rocket Launch A127

**1959, May 4** ***Perf. 10, 10½***

| | | | |
|---|---|---|---|
| 160 | A127 2ch dk vio, *pale buff* | 11.00 | 5.75 |
| *a.* | Imperf | 260.00 | 57.50 |
| 161 | A127 10ch bl, *pale grn* | 22.50 | 8.50 |
| *a.* | Imperf | 260.00 | 57.50 |

Issued with gum (perf 10) or without gum (perf 10½). Nos. 160a and 161a were issued with gum.

Land Irrigation Program — A128

**1959, May 27** ***Perf. 10***

| | | | |
|---|---|---|---|
| 162 | A128 10ch multicolored | 9.00 | 2.50 |
| *a.* | Imperf | 37.50 | 10.00 |

Slogan-inscribed Tree, Chongbong Bivouac — A129

Statue of Kim Il Sung — A130

Mt. Paektu A131

**1959, June 4** ***10, 10¾ (#164)***

| | | | |
|---|---|---|---|
| 163 | A129 5ch multicolored | 3.00 | 1.10 |
| *a.* | Imperf | *87.50* | 16.00 |
| *b.* | Perf 10¾ | — | — |
| *c.* | Rouletted | — | — |
| 164 | A130 10ch blue & grnsh bl | 3.00 | 1.10 |
| *a.* | Imperf | *65.00* | 16.00 |
| 165 | A131 10ch violet blue | 4.50 | — |
| *a.* | Imperf | *65.00* | — |
| | *Nos. 163-165 (3)* | 10.50 | 2.20 |

22nd Anniversary of the Battle of Pochondo.
No. 163 also exists perf 10¾.
No. 164 was issued with gum.

Chollima Tractor A132

Jongihwa-58 Electric Locomotive — A133

Red Star-58 Bulldozer A134

Chollima Excavator A135

SU-50 Universal Lathe A136

Sungri-58 Truck A137

**With or without gum**

**1959, June 12** *Perf. 10¾*

| | | | |
|---|---|---|---|
| **166** A132 1ch multicolored | | 1.35 | .45 |
| *a.* Imperf | | *65.00* | 30.00 |
| *b.* Rouletted | | — | — |
| **167** A133 2ch multicolored | | 10.00 | 3.00 |
| *a.* Imperf | | *130.00* | 55.00 |
| *b.* Rouletted | | — | — |
| **168** A134 2ch multicolored | | 2.25 | .60 |
| *a.* Imperf | | *87.50* | 16.00 |
| *b.* Rouletted | | — | — |
| **169** A135 5ch multicolored | | 2.25 | 1.10 |
| *a.* Imperf | | *210.00* | — |
| *b.* Rouletted | | — | — |
| **170** A136 10ch multicolored | | 2.25 | .85 |
| *a.* Imperf | | *210.00* | — |
| *b.* Rouletted | | — | — |
| **171** A137 10ch multicolored | | 4.00 | .60 |
| *a.* Imperf | | *210.00* | — |
| *Nos. 166-171 (6)* | | 22.10 | 6.60 |

Machine-building Industry.

Armistice Building, Panmunjom — A138

Anti-U.S. Protester A139

Anti-South Korean Emigration Campaign A140

Peaceful Reunification of Korea — A141

**1959, June 25** **With Gum**

| | | |
|---|---|---|
| **172** A138 10ch dk blue & blue | 4.50 | .25 |
| *a.* Imperf | *175.00* | — |
| *b.* Perf 10¼ | — | — |
| **173** A139 20ch dk blue & lt blue | 1.35 | .45 |
| **174** A140 20ch sepia & brn | 6.25 | 1.75 |
| **175** A141 70ch dk brn & lt brn | 40.00 | 11.00 |
| *a.* Imperf | *175.00* | — |
| *b.* Perf 10¼xRoul | — | — |
| *Nos. 172-175 (4)* | 52.10 | 13.45 |

Day of Struggle for the withdrawal of U.S. troops from South Korea.

Metal Type A142

*Samil Wolgan* Monthly Breaking Chains — A143

Flag with Symbols of Peace and Literature A144

Korean Alphabet of 1443 — A145

**1959, Aug. 1**

| | | |
|---|---|---|
| **176** A142 5ch sepia | 22.50 | 8.50 |
| **177** A143 5ch green & red | 6.75 | 2.60 |
| **178** A144 10ch bright blue | 6.75 | 2.60 |
| **179** A145 10ch dp bl & pale bl | 10.00 | 4.25 |
| *a.* Souvenir sheet of 4, #176-179 imperf | 110.00 | 55.00 |
| *Nos. 176-179 (4)* | 46.00 | 17.95 |

International Book and Fine Arts Exhibition, Leipzig.

Nos. 176 and 178 were issued with gum. Nos. 177, 179 and 179a were issued without gum.

Milk Cow Farm A146

Pig Farm — A147

**1959, Sept. 20**

| | | |
|---|---|---|
| **180** A146 2ch multicolored | 3.50 | .85 |
| **181** A147 5ch multicolored | 5.00 | 1.10 |

No. 180 was issued without gum, No. 181 with gum.

**Economic Development**

Cement Making A148

Hydroelectrical Dam — A149

Salt Making — A150

Construction A151

Grain A152

Sugar A153

Steel-Making A154

Fishing A155

Iron-Making A156

Coal Mining A157

Textile Production A158

Fruit — A159

***Perf. 10½ (#182), 11***

**1959, Sept. 20-1960**

| | | |
|---|---|---|
| **182** A148 1ch multicolored | .65 | .50 |
| *a.* Imperf | *175.00* | — |
| **183** A149 2ch multicolored | 1.75 | .50 |
| *a.* Imperf | *175.00* | — |
| **184** A150 5ch multicolored | 2.75 | .60 |
| *a.* Imperf | *175.00* | — |
| **185** A151 10ch multicolored | 3.00 | .90 |
| *a.* Imperf | *175.00* | — |
| **186** A152 10ch multicolored | 1.35 | .50 |
| *a.* Imperf | *175.00* | — |
| **187** A153 10ch multicolored | 2.50 | .50 |
| *a.* Imperf | *175.00* | — |
| **188** A154 10ch multicolored | 2.25 | .50 |
| *a.* Imperf | *175.00* | — |
| **189** A155 10ch multicolored | 2.00 | .50 |
| *a.* Imperf | *175.00* | — |
| **190** A156 10ch multicolored | 1.35 | .50 |
| **191** A157 10ch multicolored | 2.25 | .50 |
| **192** A158 10ch multicolored | 1.35 | .50 |
| *a.* Imperf | *175.00* | — |
| **193** A159 10ch multicolored ('60) | 3.50 | .50 |
| *Nos. 182-193 (12)* | 24.70 | 6.50 |

No. 193 issued August 1960.

Nos. 183 and 185 were issued with gum, the other values without gum.

Musk Deer
A160

Sable
A161

Marten
A162

Otter
A163

Sika Deer — A164

Pheasant
A165

**1959-62** ***Perf. 11***

| | | | | | |
|---|---|---|---|---|---|
| **194** | A160 | 5ch | multicolored | 5.75 | .65 |
| **195** | A161 | 5ch | multicolored | 5.75 | .65 |
| **196** | A162 | 5ch | multicolored | 5.75 | .65 |
| **197** | A163 | 5ch | multicolored | 5.75 | .65 |
| **198** | A164 | 10ch | multicolored | 5.75 | .65 |
| **199** | A165 | 10ch | multicolored | 27.50 | 2.25 |
| | | | *Nos. 194-199 (6)* | 56.25 | 5.50 |

Game Preservation.

Issued: No. 198, 10/24/59; No. 199, 3/25/60; No. 194, 11/11/60; Nos. 195-197, 1/24/62.

Nos. 198 and 199 were issued with gum, Nos. 194-197 without gum.

3rd Korean Trade Unions Congress
A166

**1959, Nov. 4** **With Gum**

| | | | | | |
|---|---|---|---|---|---|
| **200** | A166 | 5ch | multicolored | 1.30 | .30 |

Electric Locomotive — A167

Freighter
A168

**1959, Nov. 5** **With Gum**

| | | | | | |
|---|---|---|---|---|---|
| **201** | A167 | 5ch | brnsh purple | 18.00 | 2.60 |
| **202** | A168 | 10ch | slate green | 7.50 | 2.25 |

Korean People's Army, 12th Anniv.
A169

**1960, Feb. 8** **With Gum**

| | | | | | |
|---|---|---|---|---|---|
| **203** | A169 | 5ch | blue | 225.00 | 125.00 |

Sword Dance — A170

Janggo Dance — A171

Peasant Dance — A172

**1960, Feb. 25**

| | | | | | |
|---|---|---|---|---|---|
| **204** | A170 | 5ch | multicolored | 4.50 | .40 |
| **205** | A171 | 5ch | multicolored | 4.50 | .40 |
| **206** | A172 | 10ch | multicolored | 4.50 | .40 |
| | | | *Nos. 204-206 (3)* | 13.50 | 1.20 |

Women of 3 Races, Dove — A173

Woman Worker — A174

**1960, Mar. 8** **With Gum**

| | | | | | |
|---|---|---|---|---|---|
| **207** | A173 | 5ch | grnish blue & red vio | 2.50 | .25 |
| **208** | A174 | 10ch | grn & org | 2.50 | .45 |

50th Anniv. of International Women's Day.

Kim Jong Ho, Geographer
A175

Kim Hong Do, Painter
A176

Pak Yon, Musician
A177

Jong Ta San, Scholar
A178

**1960** **With Gum**

| | | | | | |
|---|---|---|---|---|---|
| **209** | A175 | 1ch | gray & pale grn | 2.50 | .25 |
| **210** | A176 | 2ch | dp blue & yel buff | 3.00 | .25 |
| **211** | A177 | 5ch | grnish blue & grnish yel | 11.00 | .25 |
| **212** | A178 | 10ch | brn & yel | 3.00 | .25 |
| | | | *Nos. 209-212 (4)* | 19.50 | 1.00 |

Issued: 1ch-5ch, 3/16/60; 10ch 6/60.

Grapes — A179

Wild fruits: No. 214, Fruit of Actinidia arguta planch. No. 215, Pine-cone. No. 216, Hawthorn berries. No. 217, Chestnuts.

**1960, Apr. 8** **With Gum**

| | | | | | |
|---|---|---|---|---|---|
| **213** | A179 | 5ch | multicolored | 3.00 | .90 |
| **214** | A179 | 5ch | multicolored | 3.00 | .90 |
| **215** | A179 | 5ch | multicolored | 3.00 | .90 |
| **216** | A179 | 10ch | multicolored | 3.25 | 1.10 |
| **217** | A179 | 10ch | multicolored | 3.25 | 1.10 |
| | | | *Nos. 213-217 (5)* | 15.50 | 4.90 |

Nos. 214-215 also exist imperf.

Lenin, 90th Birthday — A180

**1960, Apr. 22** **With Gum**

| | | | | | |
|---|---|---|---|---|---|
| **218** | A180 | 10ch | violet brown | 1.60 | .25 |

Koreans and Caricature of U.S. Soldier — A181

**1960, June 20** **With Gum**

| | | | | | |
|---|---|---|---|---|---|
| **219** | A181 | 10ch | dark blue | 7.00 | .65 |

Day of Struggle for Withdrawal of U.S. Troops from South Korea.

Mao Tse-Tung Plaza — A182

Taedong River Promenade
A183

Youth Street — A184

People's Army Street — A185

Stalin Street — A186

**1960, June 29** **With Gum**

| | | | | | |
|---|---|---|---|---|---|
| **220** | A182 | 10ch | gray green | 1.10 | .25 |
| **221** | A183 | 20ch | dk bl green | 2.25 | .30 |
| **222** | A184 | 40ch | blackish green | 3.50 | .65 |
| **223** | A185 | 70ch | emerald | 6.50 | 1.60 |
| **224** | A186 | 1w | blue | 9.00 | 2.50 |
| | | | *Nos. 220-224 (5)* | 22.35 | 5.30 |

Views of rebuilt Pyongyang.

Luna 3 — A187

Luna 2 — A188

**1960, July 15**

| | | | | | |
|---|---|---|---|---|---|
| **225** | A187 | 5ch | multicolored | 7.00 | 6.50 |
| **226** | A188 | 10ch | multicolored | 10.00 | 2.75 |

Soviet space flights.

The 5ch was issued with gum, the 10ch without gum.

Mirror Rock — A189

Devil-faced Rock — A190

Dancing Dragon Bridge
A191

Nine Dragon Falls — A192

Mt. Diamond on the Sea A193

**1960, July 15-1961**

| | | | | |
|---|---|---|---|---|
| 227 | A189 | 5ch multicolored | 1.50 | .25 |
| 228 | A190 | 5ch multicolored | 1.50 | .30 |
| 229 | A191 | 10ch multi ('61) | 5.50 | .30 |
| 230 | A192 | 10ch multicolored | 5.00 | .35 |
| 231 | A193 | 10ch multicolored | 1.75 | .25 |
| | | *Nos. 227-231 (5)* | 15.25 | 1.45 |

Diamond Mountains scenery.
No. 229 issued 2/8/61.
See Nos. 761-764.

Lily A194

Rhododendron A195

Hibiscus A196

Blue Campanula A197

Mauve Campanula A198

**1960, July 15-1961** **With Gum**

| | | | | |
|---|---|---|---|---|
| 232 | A194 | 5ch multicolored | 1.75 | .25 |
| 233 | A195 | 5ch multicolored | 1.75 | .25 |
| 234 | A196 | 10ch multicolored | 2.50 | .45 |
| 235 | A197 | 10ch multicolored | 2.50 | .45 |
| 236 | A198 | 10ch multi ('61) | 2.50 | .45 |
| | | *Nos. 232-236 (5)* | 11.00 | 1.85 |

No. 236 issued 6/1/61.
Nos. 232-234 and 236 also exist without gum.

"The Arduous March" A199

Crossing the Amnok River A200

Young Communist League Meeting — A201

Showing the Way at Pochonbo A202

Return to Pyongyang — A203

**1960, July 26**

| | | | | |
|---|---|---|---|---|
| 237 | A199 | 5ch carmine red | .60 | .25 |
| 238 | A200 | 10ch deep blue | 1.35 | .25 |
| 239 | A201 | 10ch deep blue | 1.35 | .25 |
| 240 | A202 | 10ch carmine red | 1.35 | .25 |
| 241 | A203 | 10ch carmine red | 1.35 | .25 |
| | | *Nos. 237-242 (5)* | 6.00 | 1.25 |

Revolutionary activities of Kim Il Sung.

15th Anniv. Liberation from Japan A204

**1960, Aug. 6**

| | | | | |
|---|---|---|---|---|
| 242 | A204 | 10ch multicolored | 5.00 | .25 |

North Korean-Soviet Friendship Month — A205

**1960, Aug. 6**

| | | | | |
|---|---|---|---|---|
| 243 | A205 | 10ch lake, *cream* | 1.25 | .25 |

Okryu Bridge A206

Grand Theater A207

Okryu Restaurant A208

**1960, Aug. 11**

| | | | | |
|---|---|---|---|---|
| 244 | A206 | 10ch gray blue | 3.50 | .35 |
| 245 | A207 | 10ch dull violet | 3.00 | .25 |
| 246 | A208 | 10ch turquoise | 1.25 | .25 |
| | | *Nos. 244-246 (3)* | 7.75 | .85 |

Pyongyang buildings.

Tokro River Dam — A209

**1960, Sept. 9** **With Gum**

| | | | | |
|---|---|---|---|---|
| 247 | A209 | 5ch slate blue | 2.25 | .25 |

Inauguration of Tokro River Hydroelectric Power Station.

World Federation of Trade Unions, 15th Anniv. — A210

**1960, Sept. 16**

| | | | | |
|---|---|---|---|---|
| 248 | A210 | 10ch blue & lt blue | 1.40 | .25 |

Repatriation of Korean Nationals from Japan — A211

**1960, Sept. 26**

| | | | | |
|---|---|---|---|---|
| 249 | A211 | 10ch brnish violet | 5.00 | .30 |

Korean-Soviet Friendship — A212

**1960, Oct. 5** **With Gum**

| | | | | |
|---|---|---|---|---|
| 250 | A212 | 10ch brn & org | 1.60 | .25 |

Liberation Day Sports Festival, Pyongyang A213

Designs: 5ch (No. 251), Runner. 5ch (No. 252), Weight-lifter. 5ch (No. 253), Cyclist. 5ch (No. 254), Gymnast. 5ch (No. 255), Soccer players, horiz. 10ch (No. 256), Swimmer, horiz. 10ch (No. 257), Moranbong Stadium, horiz.

**1960, Oct. 5**

| | | | | |
|---|---|---|---|---|
| 251-257 | A213 | Set of 7 | 12.00 | 2.25 |

Chinese & North Korean Soldiers A214

Friendship Monument — A215

**1960, Oct. 20** **With Gum**

| | | | | |
|---|---|---|---|---|
| 258 | A214 | 5ch rose | 1.25 | .25 |
| 259 | A215 | 10ch dp blue | 1.25 | .25 |

10th Anniversary of Chinese People's Volunteers' Entry into Korean War.

World Federation of Democratic Youth, 15th Anniv. — A216

**1960, Nov. 11**

| | | | | |
|---|---|---|---|---|
| 260 | A216 | 10ch multicolored | 1.25 | .25 |

Woodpecker A217

Mandarin Ducks A218

Scops Owl — A219

Oriole — A220

**1960-61**

| | | | | |
|---|---|---|---|---|
| 261 | A217 | 2ch yel grn & multi | 6.50 | .35 |
| 262 | A218 | 5ch blue & multi | 7.00 | .45 |
| 263 | A219 | 5ch lt blue & multi | 11.00 | .90 |
| 264 | A220 | 10ch lt bl grn & multi | 7.00 | .90 |
| | | *Nos. 261-264 (4)* | 31.50 | 2.60 |

Issued: No. 262, 12/15/60; No. 264, 3/15/61; No. 261, 4/22/61; No. 263, 6/1/61.

Wrestling A221

Swinging — A222

Archery A223

Seesaw — A224

**1960, Dec. 15-1961**

| | | | | | |
|---|---|---|---|---|---|
| **265** | A221 | 5ch dull grn & multi | .90 | .25 |
| **266** | A222 | 5ch yel & multi ('61) | .90 | .25 |
| **267** | A223 | 5ch yel gold & multi | 4.00 | .40 |
| **268** | A224 | 10ch lt bl grn & multi | .90 | .25 |
| | | *Nos. 265-268 (4)* | 6.70 | 1.15 |

No. 266 issued 1/6/61.

Agriculture A225

Light Industry A226

Korean Workers' Party Flag — A227

Power Station A228

Steel-Making — A229

**1960, Dec. 15-1961**

| | | | | |
|---|---|---|---|---|
| **269** | A225 | 5ch multicolored | 1.75 | .25 |
| **270** | A226 | 5ch multicolored | 3.00 | .25 |
| **271** | A227 | 10ch multicolored | .85 | .25 |
| **272** | A228 | 10ch multicolored | 1.75 | .25 |
| **273** | A229 | 10ch multicolored | 1.25 | .25 |
| | | *Nos. 269-273 (5)* | 8.60 | 1.25 |

Wild Ginseng — A230

Design: 10ch, cultivated ginseng

**1961**

| | | | | |
|---|---|---|---|---|
| **274** | A230 | 5ch multicolored | 4.50 | .25 |
| **275** | A230 | 10ch multicolored | 4.50 | .25 |

Issued: 10ch, 1/5; 5ch, 3/15.

A231

A232

A233

Factories A234

**1961, Feb. 8** **With Gum**

| | | | | |
|---|---|---|---|---|
| **276** | A231 | 5ch red & pale yel | 1.25 | .25 |
| **277** | A232 | 10ch bl grn & pale yel | 2.75 | .25 |
| **278** | A233 | 10ch dp vio blue & pale yel | 2.75 | .25 |
| **279** | A234 | 20ch vio & pale yel | 3.25 | .50 |
| | | *Nos. 276-279 (4)* | 10.00 | 1.25 |

Construction of Vinalon Factory.
See Nos. 350-353.

Pyongyang Students' and Children's Palace A235

**1961, Feb. 8** **With Gum**

| | | | | |
|---|---|---|---|---|
| **280** | A235 | 2ch red, *yellow* | .90 | .25 |

Korean Revolution Museum A236

**1961, Feb. 8** **With Gum**

| | | | | |
|---|---|---|---|---|
| **281** | A236 | 10ch red | .75 | .25 |

Soviet Venus Rocket A237

**1961, Feb. 8**

| | | | | |
|---|---|---|---|---|
| **282** | A237 | 10ch turq bl & multi | 5.75 | .25 |

Tractor-Plow A238

Disk-Harrow A239

Wheat Harvester A240

Corn Harvester A241

Tractors A242

**1961, Feb. 21** **With Gum**

| | | | | |
|---|---|---|---|---|
| **283** | A238 | 5ch violet | .85 | .25 |
| **284** | A239 | 5ch blue green | .85 | .25 |
| **285** | A240 | 5ch dp gray green | .85 | .25 |
| **286** | A241 | 10ch violet blue | 1.25 | .25 |
| **287** | A242 | 10ch purple | 1.25 | .25 |
| | | *Nos. 283-287 (5)* | 5.05 | 1.25 |

Opening of Industrial College — A243

**1961, Mar. 1** **With Gum**

| | | | | |
|---|---|---|---|---|
| **288** | A243 | 10ch red brn, *buff* | 2.75 | .25 |

Agrarian Reform Law, 15th Anniv. A244

**1961, Mar. 1** **With Gum**

| | | | | |
|---|---|---|---|---|
| **289** | A244 | 10ch dull green, *yel* | 1.90 | .25 |

20-Point Political Program, 20th Anniv. A245

**1961, Mar. 15** **With Gum**

| | | | | |
|---|---|---|---|---|
| **290** | A245 | 10ch dull vio, *pale yel* | .90 | .25 |

Mackerel A246

Dolphin A247

Whale A248

Tunny — A249

Walleye Pollack A250

**1961, Apr. 3**

| | | | | |
|---|---|---|---|---|
| **291** | A246 | 5ch yel grn & multi | 4.50 | .45 |
| **292** | A247 | 5ch lt blue & multi | 11.00 | 1.30 |
| **293** | A248 | 10ch lt grnish blue & multi | 12.00 | .45 |
| **294** | A249 | 10ch gray & multi | 12.00 | .45 |
| **295** | A250 | 10ch dk grn & multi | 12.00 | .45 |
| | | *Nos. 291-295 (5)* | 51.50 | 3.10 |

Crane-Mounted Tractor — A251

"Sungri-1010" Truck A252

Vertical Milling Machine A253

Victory April-15 Automobile A254

8-Meter Turning Lathe A255

Radial Boring Lathe — A256

Hydraulic Press — A257

750-Kg Air Hammer A258

200mm Boring Lathe A259

3,000-Ton Press A260

3-Ton Air Hammer A261

Ssangma-15 Excavator A262

Jangbaek Excavator A263

400-HP Diesel Engine — A264

Honing Lathe — A265

Trolley — A266

8-Meter Planer — A267

Boring Lathe — A268

Hobbing Lathe — A269

Tunnel Drill — A270

**1961-65**

| | | | | | |
|---|---|---|---|---|---|
| **296** | A251 | 1ch | red brown | 2.50 | .25 |
| **297** | A252 | 2ch | dk brown | 2.50 | .25 |
| **298** | A253 | 2ch | dk green | .90 | .25 |
| **299** | A253 | 2ch | grayish brn | 50.00 | 11.00 |
| **300** | A254 | 4ch | dk blue | 6.25 | .25 |
| **301** | A255 | 5ch | dk green | 3.50 | .25 |
| **302** | A256 | 5ch | dk bl gray | 1.90 | .25 |
| *a.* | | | 5ch dark gray green | 50.00 | 11.00 |
| **303** | A257 | 5ch | bl green | 1.90 | .25 |
| **304** | A258 | 5ch | red brown | 1.60 | .25 |
| **305** | A259 | 5ch | sl violet | 2.25 | .25 |
| **306** | A260 | 10ch | gray violet | 3.25 | .25 |
| *a.* | | | 10ch dark blue | 50.00 | .25 |
| **307** | A261 | 10ch | blue | 3.00 | .25 |
| **308** | A261 | 10ch | brown | *200.00* | *50.00* |
| **309** | A262 | 10ch | dk vio gray | 1.60 | .25 |
| **310** | A263 | 10ch | dk green | 3.25 | .25 |
| **311** | A264 | 10ch | dk sl blue | 3.25 | .25 |
| **312** | A265 | 10ch | dk blue | 3.00 | .25 |
| **313** | A266 | 40ch | dk blue | 12.00 | .25 |
| **314** | A267 | 90ch | dk bl green | 5.25 | .30 |
| **315** | A268 | 1w | dk vio brown | 16.00 | .45 |
| **316** | A269 | 5w | dk brown | 32.50 | 3.25 |
| **317** | A270 | 10w | vio brown | 50.00 | 6.75 |
| | *Nos. 296-317 (22)* | | | 406.40 | 75.75 |

Issued: 1ch, 4/22/61; 2ch, 4/27/61; Nos. 301, 306, 5/20/61; Nos. 307, 308, 3/13/62; Nos. 302, 317, 7/30/62; 5w, 9/5/62; No. 302a, 9/15/62; No. 308, 12/26/62; Nos. 297, 298, 2/11/63; No. 303, 4/9/63; 90ch, 5/15/63; 4ch, 6/15/63; 40ch, 9/13/63; 1w, 10/16/63; No. 310, 3/20/64; No. 305, 4/28/64; No. 311, 6/25/64; No. 312, 1/1/65.

Nos. 296, 297, 301, 303, 306 and 316 are perf 10¾. Other values are perf 12½.

Nos. 296-302, 304-307 and 309-315 were issued with gum. Nos. 303, 308, 316 and 317 were issued without gum.

Nos. 296-297, 301, 303, 306-308 and 316 are lithographed. Other values are engraved.

Reforestration Campaign — A271

**1961, Apr. 27** **With Gum**

**318** A271 10ch green 2.25 .30

Peaceful Reunification of Korea — A272

**1961, May 9**

**319** A272 10ch multicolored 27.00 2.25

Young Pioneers (Children's Union) of Korea, 15th Anniv. — A273

Designs: 5ch, Pioneers swimming. 10ch (No. 321), Pioneer bugler. 10ch (No. 322) Pioneer visiting battlefield.

**1961, June 1**

**320-322** A273 Set of 3 6.00 .90

Labor Law, 15th Anniv. A274

**1961, June 21** **With Gum**

**323** A274 10ch dp blue, *pale yel* 1.60 .25

Plums — A275

Peaches A276

Apples A277

Persimmons A278

Pears — A279

**1961, July 11**

| | | | | | |
|---|---|---|---|---|---|
| **324** | A275 | 5ch | multicolored | 1.40 | .25 |
| **325** | A276 | 5ch | multicolored | 1.40 | .25 |
| **326** | A277 | 5ch | multicolored | 1.40 | .25 |
| **327** | A278 | 10ch | multicolored | 1.40 | .25 |
| **328** | A279 | 10ch | multicolored | 1.40 | .25 |
| | *Nos. 324-328 (5)* | | | 7.00 | 1.25 |

Yuri Gagarin & Vostok I — A280

**1961, July 11**

| | | | | | |
|---|---|---|---|---|---|
| **329** | A280 | 10ch | dp bl & pale bl | 2.00 | .45 |
| **330** | A280 | 10ch | red vio & pale bl | 2.00 | .45 |

First manned space flight, April 12.

Nationalization of Industry, 15th Anniv. — A281

**1961, July 11** **With Gum**

**331** A281 10ch lt red brown 18.00 .80

Sex Equality Law, 15th Anniv. A282

**1961, July 27** **With Gum**

**332** A282 10ch brn red & rose 1.10 .25

Children Planting Tree — A283

Children: 5ch (No. 334), Reading book. 10ch (No. 335), Playing with ball. 10ch (No. 336), Building a toy house. 10ch (No. 337), Waving banner.

**1961, Aug. 29**

**333-337** A283 Set of 5 5.75 .80

Livestock Breeding — A284

Fishing Industry A285

Farming A286

Textile Industry — A287

**1961, Aug. 29**

| | | | | | |
|---|---|---|---|---|---|
| **338** | A284 | 5ch | multicolored | 2.00 | .25 |
| **339** | A285 | 10ch | multicolored | 1.75 | .25 |
| **340** | A286 | 10ch | multicolored | 3.00 | .25 |
| **341** | A287 | 10ch | multicolored | 2.75 | .30 |
| | *Nos. 338-341 (4)* | | | 9.50 | 1.05 |

Improvement of living standards.

Kim Il Sung Writing Under Tree A288

Kim Il Sung at Desk A289

Soldiers Studying A290

**1961, Sept. 8** **With Gum**

| | | | | | |
|---|---|---|---|---|---|
| **342** | A288 | 10ch | violet | .75 | .30 |
| **343** | A289 | 10ch | dull violet | .75 | .30 |
| **344** | A290 | 10ch | dp blue & yel | 1.40 | .30 |
| | *Nos. 342-344 (3)* | | | 2.90 | .90 |

15th Anniv. of Kim Il Sung's "Ten-Point Program of the Association for the Restoration of the Fatherland."

Kim Il Sung & Party Banner A291

Party Emblem, Workers — A292

Chollima Statue — A293

**1961, Sept. 8** **With Gum**

| | | | | |
|---|---|---|---|---|
| **345** | A291 | 10ch brown red | .60 | .30 |
| **346** | A292 | 10ch green | .60 | .30 |
| **347** | A293 | 10ch violet | .60 | .30 |
| | | *Nos. 345-347 (3)* | 1.80 | .90 |

4th Korean Workers' Party Congress.

Miners' Day — A294

**1961, Sept. 12** **With Gum**

| | | | | |
|---|---|---|---|---|
| **348** | A294 | 10ch brown | 11.50 | .65 |

Pak In Ro (1561-1642), Poet — A295

**1961, Sept. 12**

| | | | | |
|---|---|---|---|---|
| **349** | A295 | 10ch dk blue & gray blue | 3.25 | .25 |

Aldehyde Shop A296

Polymerization & Saponification Shops — A297

Glacial Acetic Acid Shops A298

Spinning Shop A299

**1961, Oct. 17** **With Gum**

| | | | | |
|---|---|---|---|---|
| **350** | A296 | 5ch red & pale yel | 1.25 | .25 |
| **351** | A297 | 10ch dp blue & pale yel | 1.90 | .25 |
| **352** | A298 | 10ch dk brn & pale yel | 1.90 | .25 |
| **353** | A299 | 20ch purple & pale yel | 3.00 | .35 |
| | | *Nos. 350-353 (4)* | 8.05 | 1.10 |

Completion of Vinalon Factory.

Korean & Soviet Flags — A300

Korean & ChineseFlags A301

**1961, Oct. 26**

| | | | | |
|---|---|---|---|---|
| **354** | A300 | 10ch multicolored | 1.25 | .30 |
| **355** | A301 | 10ch multicolored | 1.25 | .30 |

North Korean Friendship Treaties with the Soviet Union and China.

Day of Sports and Physical Culture — A302

Sports: 2ch, Table tennis. 5ch, Flying model glider. 10ch (No. 358), Basketball. 10ch (No. 359), Rowing. 10ch (No. 360), High jump. 20ch, Emblem.

**1961, Nov. 4** **With Gum**

| | | | | |
|---|---|---|---|---|
| **356-361** | A302 | Set of 6 | 9.00 | 1.60 |

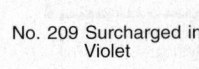

No. 209 Surcharged in Violet

**1961, Nov. 5**

| | | | |
|---|---|---|---|
| **362** | 5ch on 1ch gray & pale grn | 200.00 | 150.00 |

Centenary of publication of "Taedongyojido," map.

Janggun Rock — A303

Chonbul Peak A304

Mansa Peak — A305

Kiwajip Rock A306

Mujigae Rock A307

**1961, Nov. 29** **With Gum**

| | | | | |
|---|---|---|---|---|
| **363** | A303 | 5ch slate | 1.35 | .25 |
| **364** | A304 | 5ch brown | 1.35 | .25 |
| **365** | A305 | 10ch br lilac | 2.50 | .25 |
| **366** | A306 | 10ch sl blue | 2.50 | .25 |
| **367** | A307 | 10ch dk blue | 2.50 | .25 |
| | | *Nos. 363-367 (5)* | 10.20 | 1.25 |

Mt. Chilbo scenes.

Protection of State Property — A308

**1961, Nov. 29** **With Gum**

| | | | | |
|---|---|---|---|---|
| **368** | A308 | 10ch gray green | 1.25 | .25 |

WFTU Emblem — A309

**1961, Nov. 29** **With Gum**

| | | | | |
|---|---|---|---|---|
| **369** | A309 | 10ch multicolored | .75 | .25 |

5th Congress of World Federation of Trade Unions.

"Red Banner" Electric Locomotive A310

**1961, Nov. 29** **With Gum**

| | | | | |
|---|---|---|---|---|
| **370** | A310 | 10ch vio & buff | 17.00 | 1.60 |

Railway Electrification.

Winter Sports A311

Designs (all 10ch): No. 371, Figure skater. No. 372, Speed skater. No. 373, Ice hockey. No. 374, Skiier.

**Figures in Sepia**

**1961, Dec. 12** **With Gum**

| | | | | |
|---|---|---|---|---|
| **371-374** | A311 | Set of 4 | 10.00 | .80 |

**Six Objectives of Production**

Steel A312

Coal A313

Grain A314

Textiles A315

Sea-Foods A316

Apartments A317

**1962, Jan. 1** **With Gum**

| | | | | |
|---|---|---|---|---|
| **375** | A312 | 5ch multicolored | 1.10 | .25 |
| **376** | A313 | 5ch multicolored | 7.75 | .40 |
| **377** | A314 | 10ch multicolored | 1.10 | .25 |
| **378** | A315 | 10ch multicolored | 3.50 | .25 |
| **379** | A316 | 10ch multicolored | 3.25 | .25 |
| **380** | A317 | 10ch multicolored | 1.10 | .25 |
| | | *Nos. 375-380 (6)* | 17.80 | 1.65 |

See Nos. 442-447.

**Animals**

Korean Tiger — A318

Racoon Dog — A319

Badger A320

Bear — A321

**1962, Jan. 24**

| | | | | |
|---|---|---|---|---|
| **381** | A318 | 2ch multicolored | 4.75 | .25 |
| **382** | A319 | 2ch lt grn & brn | 3.25 | .25 |
| **383** | A320 | 5ch lt bl grn & lt red brn | 2.25 | .25 |
| **384** | A321 | 10ch grn & brn | 3.25 | .25 |
| | | *Nos. 381-384 (4)* | 13.50 | 1.00 |

**Traditional Musical Instruments**

Kayagum — A322

Jotae (Flute) — A323

Wolgum — A324

Haegum — A325

Wagonghu A326

**1962, Feb. 2**

| | | | | |
|---|---|---|---|---|
| **385** | A322 | 10ch multicolored | 3.25 | .25 |
| **386** | A323 | 10ch multicolored | 3.25 | .25 |
| **387** | A324 | 10ch multicolored | 3.25 | .25 |
| **388** | A325 | 10ch multicolored | 3.25 | .25 |
| **389** | A326 | 10ch multicolored | 3.25 | .25 |
| | | *Nos. 385-389 (5)* | 16.25 | 1.25 |

See Nos. 472-476.

**Butterflies**

Luehdorfia puziloi — A327

Sericinus telamon — A328

Parnassius nomion — A329

Inachusio A330

**1962, Mar. 13**

| | | | | |
|---|---|---|---|---|
| **390** | A327 | 5ch multicolored | 4.00 | .25 |
| **391** | A328 | 10ch multicolored | 4.00 | .25 |
| **392** | A329 | 10ch multicolored | 4.00 | .25 |
| **393** | A330 | 10ch multicolored | 4.00 | .25 |
| | | *Nos. 390-393 (4)* | 16.00 | 1.00 |

G. Titov & Vostok 2 A331

**1962, Mar. 13**

| | | | | |
|---|---|---|---|---|
| **394** | A331 | 10ch multicolored | 3.25 | .25 |

Second Soviet Manned Space Flight.

Kim Il Sung Commanding Troops — A332

Kim Il Sung Adressing Workers — A333

*Perf. 10¾ (#397), 12½*

**1962, Apr. 14 Engr. With Gum**

| | | | | |
|---|---|---|---|---|
| **395** | A332 | 10ch blue | 1.00 | .25 |
| **396** | A333 | 10ch green | 1.00 | .25 |
| **397** | A333 | 10ch rose red | 1.00 | .25 |
| | | *Nos. 395-397 (3)* | 3.00 | .75 |

Marshall Kim Il Sung's 50th Birthday.

Kim Chaek — A334

Kang Kon — A335

An Kil — A336

Ryu Kyong Su — A337

Kim Jong Suk — A338

Choe Chun Guk — A339

**1962, Apr. 23** *Perf. 12½*

**With Gum**

| | | | | |
|---|---|---|---|---|
| **398** | A334 | 10ch dark brown | 6.25 | .25 |
| **399** | A335 | 10ch dark blue | 6.25 | .25 |
| **400** | A336 | 10ch rose | 6.25 | .25 |
| **401** | A337 | 10ch dark brown | 6.25 | .25 |
| **402** | A338 | 10ch dark blue gray | 6.25 | .25 |
| **403** | A338 | 10ch dark blue green | 6.25 | .25 |
| **404** | A339 | 10ch violet brown | 6.25 | .25 |
| | | *Nos. 398-404 (7)* | 43.75 | 1.75 |

Anti-Japanese Revolutionary Fighters.
See Nos. 480-484.

National Mothers' Meeting, Pyongyang — A340

**1962, May 23 Litho.** *Perf. 10¾*

| | | | | |
|---|---|---|---|---|
| **405** | A340 | 10ch multicolored | .75 | .25 |

Black-faced Spoonbill — A341

Brown Hawk Owl — A342

Eastern Broad-billed Roller — A343

Black Paradise Flycatcher A344

Whistling Swan — A345

**1962, May 23** *Perf. 10¾*

| | | | | |
|---|---|---|---|---|
| **406** | A341 | 5ch multicolored | 3.00 | .35 |
| **407** | A342 | 5ch multicolored | 11.00 | .45 |
| **408** | A343 | 10ch multicolored | 6.25 | .45 |
| **409** | A344 | 10ch multicolored | 6.25 | .45 |
| **410** | A345 | 20ch multicolored | 7.75 | .50 |
| | | *Nos. 406-410 (5)* | 34.25 | 2.20 |

Beneficial birds.

Battle of Pochonbo, 25th Anniv. — A346

**1962, May 23**

| | | | | |
|---|---|---|---|---|
| **411** | A346 | 10ch multicolored | 1.75 | .25 |

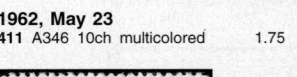

Croaker A347

Hairtail A348

Japanese Croaker A349

Japanese Sea Bass A350

Gizzard Shad A351

**1962, June 28**

**412** A347 5ch dp grn & multi 1.75 .25
**413** A348 5ch dp blue & multi 1.75 .25
**414** A349 10ch apple grn & multi 3.00 .25
**415** A350 10ch vio blue & multi 3.00 .25
**416** A351 10ch grn & multi 3.00 .25
*Nos. 412-416 (5)* 12.50 1.25

Sea Fish.

Brush Case — A352

Ink Container — A353

Ink Slab Case A354

Writing Brush Stand A355

Paperweight — A356

Ink Slab A357

Filing Cabinet A358

Kettle — A359

**1962, July 30** **Centers in Black**

**417** A352 4ch pale blue 1.25 .25
**418** A353 5ch ochre 1.25 .25
**419** A354 10ch pale green 1.75 .25
**420** A355 10ch salmon 1.75 .25
**421** A356 10ch violet 1.75 .25
**422** A357 10ch orange brown 1.75 .25
**423** A358 10ch pale yellow 1.75 .25
**424** A359 40ch gray 4.00 .45
*Nos. 417-424 (8)* 15.25 2.20

Antiques of the Koryo and Yi Dynasties.
Nos. 418 and 420 were issued with gum, the other values without gum.

Jong Ta San — A360

**1962, July 30** **Engr.** ***Perf. 12½***

**425** A360 10ch dp brnish violet 1.40 .25

200th Anniv. birth of Jong Ta San, philosopher.

National Assembly Elections
A361 A362

**1962, Oct. 3** **Litho.** ***Perf. 10¾***

**426** A361 10ch multicolored 1.40 .25
**427** A362 10ch multicolored 1.40 .25

Pyongyang, 1535th Anniv. — A363

**1962, Oct. 15** **With Gum**

**428** A363 10ch pale blue & blk 1.00 .25

Launch of Soviet Manned Rockets Vostok 3 & 4 — A364

**1962, Nov. 12**

**429** A364 10ch multicolored 3.25 .65

Spiraea — A365

Echinosophoora koreensis — A366

Codonopsis sylvestris — A367

Ginseng — A368

**1962, Nov. 30**

**430** A365 5ch multicolored 1.75 .25
**431** A366 10ch multicolored 1.75 .25
**432** A367 10ch multicolored 1.75 .25
**433** A368 10ch multicolored 1.75 .25
*Nos. 430-433 (4)* 7.00 1.00

Korean plants.

Uibangryuchui A369

**1962, Dec. 26**

**434** A369 10ch multicolored 5.00 .35

485th anniversary of publication of the medical encyclopedia *Uibangryuchui*, printed with moveable type.

Korean Academy of Sciences, 10th Anniv. A370

**1962, Dec. 26**

**435** A370 10ch dull ultra & pale turq grn 2.00 .25

Fishing — A371

**1962, Dec. 30**

**436** A371 10ch ultra 5.00 .25

European Mink A372

Korean Hare A373

Eurasian Red Squirrel — A374

Goral — A375

Siberian Chipmunk A376

**1962, Dec. 30-1963**

**437** A372 4ch app grn & red brn 1.40 .35
**438** A373 5ch lt grn & gray ('63) 1.40 .35
**439** A374 10ch yel & gray 2.25 .35
**440** A375 10ch pale grn & dk brn 2.25 .35
**441** A376 20ch lt gray blue & red brn 4.50 .35
*Nos. 437-441 (5)* 11.80 1.75

Fur-bearing animals.
No. 438 issued 12/30/63.

Coal A377

Grain A378

Textiles A379

Apartment Construction — A380

Steel A381

Seafood — A382

**1963, Jan. 1**

| | | | | | |
|---|---|---|---|---|---|
| **442** | A377 | 5ch | multicolored | 1.25 | .25 |
| **443** | A378 | 10ch | multicolored | 1.00 | .25 |
| **444** | A379 | 10ch | multicolored | 1.25 | .25 |
| **445** | A380 | 10ch | multicolored | 1.00 | .25 |
| **446** | A381 | 10ch | multicolored | 1.00 | .25 |
| **447** | A382 | 40ch | multicolored | 3.00 | .40 |
| | | | *Nos. 442-447 (6)* | 8.50 | 1.65 |

Consolidation of the Achievement of the 6 Objectives. For surcharge, see No. 4539.

Korean People's Army, 15th Anniv. — A383

Designs: 5ch, Airman. 10ch (No. 449), Soldier. 10ch (No. 450), Sailor.

**1963, Feb. 1 Engr. *Perf. 12½***
**With Gum**

| | | | | |
|---|---|---|---|---|
| **448-450** | A383 | Set of 3 | 5.75 | .60 |

Peony — A384

Rugosa Rose — A385

Rhododendron A386

Campion A387

Orchid — A388

**1963, Mar. 21 Litho. *Perf. 10¾***

| | | | | | |
|---|---|---|---|---|---|
| **451** | A384 | 5ch | gray & multi | 1.00 | .25 |
| **452** | A385 | 10ch | grnsh yel & multi | 1.40 | .25 |
| **453** | A386 | 10ch | lemon & multi | 1.40 | .25 |
| **454** | A387 | 10ch | br yel & multi | 1.40 | .25 |
| **455** | A388 | 40ch | green & multi | 4.50 | .40 |
| | | | *Nos. 451-455 (5)* | 9.70 | 1.40 |

Korean flowers.

Sword Dance — A389

Fan Dance — A390

**1963, Apr. 15**

| | | | | | |
|---|---|---|---|---|---|
| **456** | A389 | 10ch | multicolored | 7.00 | .25 |
| **457** | A390 | 10ch | multicolored | 7.00 | .25 |

International Music and Dance Competition, Pyongyang, April 16-May 17.

South Korea Uprising of April 19, 3rd Anniv. A391

**1963, Apr. 19**

| | | | | | |
|---|---|---|---|---|---|
| **458** | A391 | 10ch | multicolored | 1.40 | .25 |

Karl Marx — A392

**1963, Apr. 23 Engr. *Perf. 12½***
**With Gum**

| | | | | | |
|---|---|---|---|---|---|
| **459** | A392 | 10ch | ultra | 2.50 | .25 |

Youth Day — A393

Designs: 2ch, Children in chemistry class. 5ch, Children running. 10ch (No. 462), Girl chasing butterfly. 10ch (No. 463), Boy leading chorus.

**1963, June 15 Litho. *Perf. 10¾***

| | | | | |
|---|---|---|---|---|
| **460-463** | A393 | Set of 4 | 11.50 | 1.00 |

Armed Koreans & Caricature of American Soldier — A394

**1963, June 25**

| | | | | | |
|---|---|---|---|---|---|
| **464** | A394 | 10ch | multicolored | 1.70 | .25 |

Month of Struggle for the Withdrawal of U.S. Troops from South Korea.

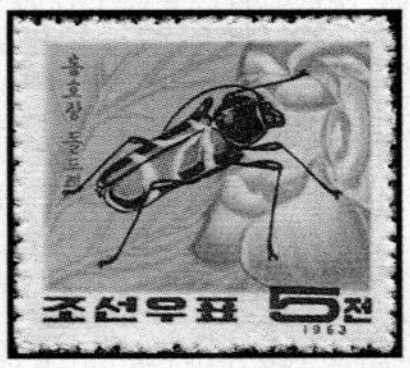
Cyrtoclytus caproides A395

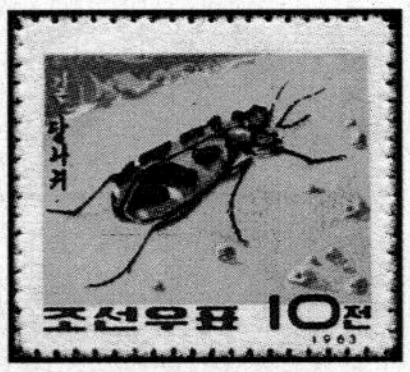
Cicindela chinensis A396

Purpuricenus lituratus A397

Agapanthia pilicornus A398

**1963, July 24**

| | | | | | |
|---|---|---|---|---|---|
| **465** | A395 | 5ch | multicolored | 2.25 | .25 |
| **466** | A396 | 10ch | multicolored | 3.00 | .25 |
| **467** | A397 | 10ch | multicolored | 3.00 | .25 |
| **468** | A398 | 10ch | multicolored | 3.00 | .25 |
| | | | *Nos. 465-468 (4)* | 11.25 | 1.00 |

Korean beetles.

Victory in Korean War, 10th Anniv. — A399

**1963, July 27**

| | | | | | |
|---|---|---|---|---|---|
| **469** | A399 | 10ch | multicolored | 1.50 | .25 |

National Emblem — A400

North Korean Flag — A401

**1963, Aug. 15**

| | | | | | |
|---|---|---|---|---|---|
| **470** | A400 | 10ch | multicolored | .55 | .25 |
| **471** | A401 | 10ch | multicolored | .55 | .25 |

No. 471 exists with background in blue. Not issued. Value $750.

Ajaeng (Zither) — A402

Phyongyong (Jade Chimes) — A403

Saenap (Flute) — A404

Rogo (Drums) — A405

Phiri (Pipe) — A406

**1963, Sept. 13**

| | | | | | |
|---|---|---|---|---|---|
| **472** | A402 | 5ch | multicolored | 1.40 | .25 |
| **473** | A403 | 5ch | multicolored | 1.40 | .25 |
| **474** | A404 | 10ch | multicolored | 2.25 | .25 |
| **475** | A405 | 10ch | multicolored | 2.25 | .25 |
| **476** | A406 | 10ch | multicolored | 2.25 | .25 |
| | | | *Nos. 472-476 (5)* | 9.55 | 1.25 |

Korean traditional musical instruments.

Nos. 472 and 475 were issued with gum, the other values without gum.

South Gate, Kaesong A407

Taedong Gate, Pyongyang A408

Pothong Gate, Pyongyang A409

**1963, Sept. 13 Engr. *Perf. 12½***

**With Gum**

| | | | | | |
|---|---|---|---|---|---|
| **477** | A407 | 5ch | black | .45 | .25 |
| **478** | A408 | 10ch | brown | 1.10 | .25 |
| **479** | A409 | 10ch | blue | 1.10 | .25 |
| | | | *Nos. 477-479 (3)* | 2.65 | .75 |

Korean historic buildings.

See Nos. 537-538.

Kwon Yong Byok — A410

Ma Tong Hui — A411

Pak Tal — A412

Ri Je Sun — A413

Kim Yong Bom — A414

**1963, Oct. 10 With Gum**

| | | | | | |
|---|---|---|---|---|---|
| **480** | A410 | 5ch | brown | 8.00 | — |
| **481** | A411 | 5ch | brown purple | 8.00 | — |
| **482** | A412 | 10ch | grnsh slate | 8.00 | — |
| **483** | A413 | 10ch | carmine rose | 8.00 | — |
| **484** | A414 | 10ch | black brown | 70.00 | 50.00 |

Anti-Japanese revolutionary fighters.

Nurse & Children at Playground A415

Teacher & Children at Fairground A416

**1963, Nov. 30 Litho. *Perf. 10¾***

| | | | | | |
|---|---|---|---|---|---|
| **485** | A415 | 10ch | multicolored | .75 | .25 |
| **486** | A416 | 10ch | multicolored | .75 | .25 |

Child welfare.

Hwajang Temple — A417

Hyangsan Stream A418

Kwanum Pavilion & Pagoda A419

Sangwon Temple — A420

**1963, Nov. 30**

| | | | | | |
|---|---|---|---|---|---|
| **487** | A417 | 5ch | multicolored | 1.00 | .25 |
| **488** | A418 | 10ch | multicolored | 5.25 | .25 |
| **489** | A419 | 10ch | multicolored | 2.50 | .25 |
| **490** | A420 | 10ch | multicolored | 2.50 | .25 |
| | | | *Nos. 487-490 (4)* | 11.25 | 1.00 |

Mount Myohyang.

Arming the People — A421

Technical Innovation A422

Mining Industry A423

Building Homes — A424

**1963, Dec. 5 Engr. *Perf. 12½***

**With Gum**

| | | | | | |
|---|---|---|---|---|---|
| **491** | A421 | 5ch | dp rose red | .50 | .25 |
| **492** | A422 | 10ch | red brown | 3.00 | .25 |
| **493** | A423 | 10ch | gray violet | 1.75 | .25 |
| **494** | A424 | 10ch | gray black | 3.25 | .25 |
| | | | *Nos. 491-494 (4)* | 8.50 | 1.00 |

Seven-Year Plan.

Sowing Gourd Seeds A425

Saving a Swallow A426

Swallow Carrying Gourd Seed A427

Sawing Gourd A428

Treasure Pouring from Gourd A429

**1963, Dec. 5 Litho. *Perf. 10¾***

| | | | | | |
|---|---|---|---|---|---|
| **495** | A425 | 5ch | multicolored | 1.10 | .25 |
| **496** | A426 | 10ch | multicolored | 2.25 | .25 |
| **497** | A427 | 10ch | multicolored | 2.25 | .25 |
| **498** | A428 | 10ch | multicolored | 1.75 | .25 |
| **499** | A429 | 10ch | multicolored | 1.75 | .25 |
| | | | *Nos. 495-499 (5)* | 9.10 | 1.25 |

Tale of Hung Bu.

Pistol Shooting A430

Small-Caliber Rifle Shooting — A431

Rifle Shooting A432

**1963, Dec. 15**

| | | | | | |
|---|---|---|---|---|---|
| **500** | A430 | 5ch | multicolored | .60 | .25 |
| **501** | A431 | 10ch | multicolored | 1.10 | .25 |
| **502** | A432 | 10ch | multicolored | 1.10 | .25 |
| | | | *Nos. 500-502 (3)* | 2.80 | .75 |

Marksmanship Competition.

Chongjin Mill — A433

Sinuiju Mill — A434

**1964, Jan. 10 Engr. *Perf. 12½***

**With Gum**

| | | | | | |
|---|---|---|---|---|---|
| **503** | A433 | 10ch | brn violet | 1.10 | .25 |
| **504** | A434 | 10ch | gray | 1.10 | .25 |

Chemical fiber industry.

Wonsan General Strike, 35th Anniv. A435

**1964, Jan. 14 With Gum**

| | | | | | |
|---|---|---|---|---|---|
| **505** | A435 | 10ch | brown | 1.25 | .25 |

Korean Alphabet, 520th Anniv. — A436

**1964, Jan. 15 Litho.** ***Perf. 10¾***

**506** A436 10ch multicolored 1.25 .25

Lenin's Death, 40th Anniv. — A437

**1964, Jan. 22 Engr.** ***Perf. 12½***
**With Gum**

**507** A437 10ch rose red 1.00 .25

Whaler A438

Trawler A439

Purse-Seine Boat — A440

Dragnet Boat A441

**1964, Feb. 10 Litho.** ***Perf. 10¾***

**508** A438 5ch multicolored 1.40 .25
**509** A439 5ch multicolored 1.40 .25
**510** A440 10ch multicolored 3.00 .25
**511** A441 10ch multicolored 3.00 .25
*Nos. 508-511 (4)* 8.80 1.00

Korean fishing industry.

March 1 Popular Uprising, 45th Anniv. A442

**1964, Feb. 10 Engr.** ***Perf. 12½***
**With Gum**

**512** A442 10ch dark violet 1.00 .25

Kabo Peasant War, 70th Anniv. — A443

**1964, Feb. 15 With Gum**

**513** A443 10ch violet black 1.00 .25

Students' and Children's Palace, Pyongyang A444

**1964, Mar. 3 With Gum**

**514** A444 10ch grnsh black .75 .25

5th Congress, Democratic Youth League of Korea — A445

**1964, May 12 Litho.** ***Perf. 10¾***

**515** A445 10ch multicolored 1.00 .25

Electric Train A446

**1964, May 21**

**516** A446 10ch multicolored 9.00 .35

Electrification of Railway between Pyongyang and Sinuiju.

Popular Movement in Chongsan-ri — A447

**1964, June 4 Engr.** ***Perf. 12½***
**With Gum**

**517** A447 5ch chestnut 275.00 125.00

Drum Dance — A448

Dance of Ecstasy — A449

Small Drum Dance — A450

**1964, June 15 Litho.** ***Perf. 10¾***

**518** A448 2ch multicolored 1.40 .45
**519** A449 5ch multicolored 2.25 .45
**520** A450 10ch multicolored 3.75 .45
*Nos. 518-520 (3)* 7.40 1.35

Korean folk dances.

*For the Sake of the Fatherland* A451

**1964, June 15 Engr.** ***Perf. 12½***
**With Gum**

**521** A451 5ch carmine red 1.75 .25

Li Su Bok, soldier.

Nampho Smelter A452

Hwanghae Iron Works A453

**1964 With Gum**

**522** A452 5ch bronze green 5.75 .25
**523** A453 10ch gray 4.00 .25

Issued: 5ch, 6/15. 10ch, 10/15.

Asian Economic Seminar, Pyongyang A454

Design: 10ch, Flags, industrial skyline and cogwheel.

**1964, June 15 Litho.** ***Perf. 10¾***

**524** A454 5ch multicolored .80 .25
**525** A454 10ch multicolored 1.25 .25

Koreans and Statue of Kang Ho Yong, War Hero A455

**1964, June 25**

**526** A455 10ch multicolored 1.40 .25

Korean Reunification

Domestic Poultry — A456

Designs: 2ch, Chickens. 4ch, White chickens. 5ch (No. 529), Black chickens. 5ch (No. 530), Varicolored chickens. 40ch, Helmet guineafowl.

**1964, Aug. 5**

**527-531** A456 Set of 5 7.00 2.00

9th Winter Olympic Games, Innsbruck A457

Designs: 5ch, Skier. 10ch (No. 533), Slalom skier. 10ch (No. 534), Speed skater.

**1964, Aug. 5**

**532-534** A457 Set of 3 4.00 .50

Flags & "Tobolsk," Repatriation Ship — A458

Welcoming Repatriates A459

**1964, Aug. 13**

**535** A458 10ch multicolored 2.25 .25
**536** A459 30ch multicolored 2.25 .25

5th anniversary of agreement for the repatriation of Korean nationals in Japan.

Thonggun Pavilion, Uiju — A460

Inphung Pavilion, Kanggye City — A461

**1964, Aug. 22 Engr.** ***Perf. 12½***
**With Gum**

**537** A460 5ch black violet .65 .25
**538** A461 10ch emerald .80 .25

Korean historic sites.

18th Olympic Games, Tokyo A462

Designs: 2ch, Rifleman. 5ch, Cyclists, vert. 10ch (No. 541), Runner. 10ch (No. 542), Wrestlers, vert.. 40ch, Volleyball, vert.

**Photo, Centers Litho**

**1964, Sept. 5** *Perf. 10¾*

| | | | | |
|---|---|---|---|---|
| **539-543** | A462 | Set of 5 | 5.00 | 1.00 |

Nos. 539-543 exist imperf. Value, $18 unused, $5 canceled.

Sinking of the *General Sherman,* 1866 A463

**1964, Sept. 28** **Engr.** *Perf. 12½*
**With Gum**

| | | | | |
|---|---|---|---|---|
| **544** | A463 | 30ch red brown | 5.50 | .50 |

Kim Il Sung & Guerrilla Fighters A464

Kim Il Sung Speaking to Peasants A465

Battle of Xiaowangqing — A466

**1964, Sept. 28** **Engr.** *Perf. 12½*
**With Gum**

| | | | | |
|---|---|---|---|---|
| **545** | A464 | 2ch brt violet | .50 | .25 |
| **546** | A465 | 5ch blue | .90 | .25 |
| **547** | A466 | 10ch grnsh black | 1.00 | .25 |
| | | *Nos. 545-547 (3)* | 2.40 | .75 |

Revolutionary paintings.

Kwangju Students' Uprising, 35th Anniv. A467

**1964, Oct. 15** **With Gum**

| | | | | |
|---|---|---|---|---|
| **548** | A467 | 10ch blue violet | 2.00 | .25 |

Weight Lifter — A468

Runner — A469

Boxers A470

Soccer Goalie A471

GANEFO Emblem A472

**1964, Oct. 15** **Litho.** *Perf. 10¾*

| | | | | |
|---|---|---|---|---|
| **549** | A468 | 2ch multicolored | .60 | .25 |
| **550** | A469 | 5ch multicolored | .60 | .25 |
| **551** | A470 | 5ch multicolored | .60 | .25 |
| **552** | A471 | 10ch multicolored | 1.25 | .25 |
| **553** | A472 | 10ch multicolored | 1.00 | .25 |
| | | *Nos. 549-553 (5)* | 4.05 | 1.25 |

1st Games of New Emerging Forces (GANEFO), Djakarta, Indonesia, 1963.

Nos. 549-553 exist imperf. Value, $12 unused, $5 canceled.

Wild Animals A473

Animals: 2ch, Lynx. 5ch, Leopard cat. 10ch (No. 556), Yellow-throated marten. 10ch (No. 559), Leopard.

**1964, Nov. 20** **Engr.** *Perf. 12½*
**With Gum**

| | | | | |
|---|---|---|---|---|
| **554-557** | A473 | Set of 4 | 13.00 | .90 |

Fighting South Vietnam A474

**1964, Dec. 20** **Litho.** *Perf. 10¾*

| | | | | |
|---|---|---|---|---|
| **558** | A474 | 10ch multicolored | 1.25 | .25 |

Support for North Vietnam.

Prof. Kim Bong Han A475

"Bonghan" Duct — A476

"Bonghan" Corpuscle A477

**1964, Dec. 20** **Photo.** *Perf. 10¾*

| | | | | |
|---|---|---|---|---|
| **559** | A475 | 2ch ol grn & brown | .90 | .25 |
| **560** | A476 | 5ch multicolored | 1.25 | .25 |
| **561** | A477 | 10ch multicolored | 1.75 | .25 |
| | | *Nos. 559-561 (3)* | 3.90 | .75 |

Kyongrak Biological System.

Technical Revolution — A478

Ideological Revolution — A479

Cultural Revolution — A480

**1964, Dec. 30** **Litho.**

| | | | | |
|---|---|---|---|---|
| **562** | A478 | 5ch multicolored | .25 | .25 |
| **563** | A479 | 10ch multicolored | .50 | .25 |
| **564** | A480 | 10ch multicolored | .50 | .25 |
| | | *Nos. 562-564 (3)* | 1.25 | .75 |

Ideological, Technical and Cultural Revolutions in the Countryside.

"For Arms" A481

**1964, Dec. 30** **Engr.** *Perf. 12½*
**With Gum**

| | | | | |
|---|---|---|---|---|
| **565** | A481 | 4ch brown | 1.00 | .25 |

Revolutionary painting.

Consumer Goods — A482

Livestock Breeding A483

"All for the Grand Chollima March" — A484

**1964, Dec. 30** **Litho.** *Perf. 10¾*

| | | | | |
|---|---|---|---|---|
| **566** | A482 | 5ch multicolored | 1.40 | .25 |
| **567** | A483 | 10ch multicolored | 1.40 | .25 |
| **568** | A484 | 10ch multicolored | 1.00 | .25 |
| | | *Nos. 566-568 (3)* | 3.80 | .75 |

Seven-Year Plan.

No. 566 was issued with gum, Nos. 567 and 568 without gum.

Nos. 566-568 also exist imperf. Value, unused $100.

Battle of Luozigou A485

Battle of Fusong County Seat A486

Battle of Hongqihe A487

**1965, Jan. 20** **Engr.** *Perf. 12½*
**With Gum**

| | | | | |
|---|---|---|---|---|
| **569** | A485 | 10ch dp slate green | 1.00 | .25 |
| **570** | A486 | 10ch deep violet | 1.00 | .25 |
| **571** | A487 | 10ch slate violet | 1.00 | .25 |
| | | *Nos. 569-571 (3)* | 3.00 | .75 |

Guerrilla warfare against Japan 1934-1940.

Tuman River A488

Taedong River — A489

Amnok River A490

**1965, Feb. 27** **Litho.** *Perf. 10¾*

| | | | | |
|---|---|---|---|---|
| **572** | A488 | 2ch multicolored | .75 | .25 |
| **573** | A489 | 5ch multicolored | 3.00 | .25 |
| **574** | A490 | 10ch multicolored | 1.25 | .25 |
| | | *Nos. 572-574 (3)* | 5.00 | .75 |

Korean rivers.

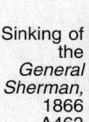

1st Congress of the Union of Agricultural Working People of Korea — A491

**1965, Mar. 25** **With Gum**

**575** A491 10ch multicolored 1.40 .25

Furnacemen, Workers — A492

**1965, Mar. 25** **With Gum**

**576** A492 10ch multicolored 1.00 .25

Ten Major Tasks of Seven-Year Plan.

Sinhung Colliery A493

Tanchou A494

**1965, Mar. 31** **Engr.** ***Perf. 12½***
**With Gum**

**577** A493 10ch olive black 1.75 .25
**578** A494 40ch violet 1.75 .25

35th anniversary of workers' uprisings.

Sunhwa River Works A495

**1965, Mar. 31** **Litho.** ***Perf. 10¾***
**With Gum**

**579** A495 10ch multicolored .75 .25

A496

South Korean Uprising of April 19, 5th Anniv. — A497

**1965, Apr. 10** **With Gum**

**580** A496 10ch multicolored .75 .25
**581** A497 40ch multicolored 1.25 .25

Nos. 580-581 exist imperf. Value, $5 unused.

Construction of Pyongyang Thermal Power Station A498

**1965, Apr. 10** **With Gum**

**582** A498 5ch dp brn & lt blue 1.90 .25

No. 582 exists imperf. Value, $5 unused.

1st Afro-Asian Conf., Bandung, 10th Anniv. — A499

**1965, Apr. 18** **With Gum**

**583** A499 10ch multicolored .85 .25

Crowd Rejoicing — A500

Japanese Koreans Demonstrating for Reunification — A501

**1965, Apr. 27** **Photo.** **With Gum**

**584** A500 10ch blue & red 1.00 .25
**585** A501 40ch multicolored 1.25 .25

10th Anniv. of the General Association of Koreans in Japan.

Nos. 584-585 exist imperf. Value, $25 unused.

Workers Demonstrating — A502

**1965, May 10** **Engr.** ***Perf. 12½***
**With Gum**

**586** A502 10ch brown 2.50 .25

35th Anniv. of General Strike at Pyongyang Rubber Goods Factory.

Workers in Battle — A503

Korean & African Soldiers A504

**1965, June 20** **Photo.** ***Perf. 10¾***
**With Gum**

**587** A503 10ch multicolored 1.60 .25
**588** A504 40ch multicolored 3.00 .25

2nd Asian-African Conference, Algiers (subsequently canceled).

Nos. 587-588 exist imperf. Value, $18 unused.

*Victory-64* 10-Ton Truck — A505

**1965, June 20** **Engr.** ***Perf. 12½***
**With Gum**

**589** A505 10ch grnsh blue 2.25 .25

Kim Chang Gol A506

Jo Kun Sil A507

An Hak Ryong A508

**1965, June 20** **With Gum**

**590** A506 10ch slate .75 .25
**591** A507 10ch red brown .75 .25
**592** A508 40ch violet 2.50 .25
*Nos. 590-592 (3)* 4.00 .75

War heroes.

See Nos. 775-777 and 827-830.

Postal Ministers' Conference, Peking A509

**1965, June 20** **Photo.** ***Perf. 10¾***
**With Gum**

**593** A509 10ch red, yel & blk 2.00 .25

Lake Samil A510

Jipson Peak A511

Kwanum Waterfalls A512

**1965, June 20** **Litho.** **With Gum**

**594** A510 2ch multicolored .85 .25
**595** A511 5ch multicolored 1.40 .25
**596** A512 10ch multicolored 4.00 .25
*Nos. 594-596 (3)* 6.25 .75

Diamond Mountain Scenery.

Nos. 594-596 exist imperf. Value, unused $100.

Kusimuldong — A513

Lake Samji A514

**1965, June 20** **Photo.** **With Gum**

**597** A513 5ch slate blue .75 .25
**598** A514 10ch grnsh blue 1.00 .25

Revolutionary battle sites.

Soccer Player — A515

Emblem & Stadium — A516

**1965, Aug. 1 Litho. With Gum**

| | | | | |
|---|---|---|---|---|
| **599** | A515 | 10ch multicolored | 1.40 | .25 |
| **600** | A516 | 10ch multicolored | 1.40 | .25 |

GANEFO Games, Pyongyang.

Nos. 599-600 exist imperf, with gum. Value, $20 unused.

Liberation from Japan, 20th Anniv. — A517

**1965, Aug. 15 With Gum**

| | | | | |
|---|---|---|---|---|
| **601** | A517 | 10ch multicolored | 1.00 | .25 |

Friedrich Engels, 145th Anniv. Birth — A518

**1965, Sept. 10 Engr. *Perf. 12½***
**With Gum**

| | | | | |
|---|---|---|---|---|
| **602** | A518 | 10ch brown | .50 | .25 |

Sports — A519

Designs: 2ch, Pole vault. 4ch, Javelin. 10ch (No. 605), Discus. 10ch (No. 606), High jump. 10ch (No. 607), Shot put.

**1965, Sept. 24 Litho. *Perf. 11***
**With Gum**

| | | | | |
|---|---|---|---|---|
| **603-607** | A519 | Set of 5 | 4.00 | .90 |

Nos. 603-607 exist imperf, without gum. Value. $18 unused.

Korean Workers' Party, 20th Anniv. — A520

Designs: No. 608a, 10ch, Korean fighters. No. 608b, 10ch, Party emblem. No. 608c, 10ch, Lenin & Marx. No. 608d, 10ch, Workers marching. No. 608e, 10ch, Soldiers & armed workers. No. 608f, 40ch, Workers.

**1965, Oct. 10 Photo. *Perf. 13X13½***
**With Gum**

| | | | | |
|---|---|---|---|---|
| **608** | A520 | Block of 6, #a.-f. | 55.00 | 22.50 |
| *608g* | | Souvenir sheet of 6, #608-613 | 600.00 | *400.00* |

Chongjin Steel Mill A521

Kim Chaek Iron Works A522

**1965, Nov. 25 Engr. *Perf. 12½***
**With Gum**

| | | | | |
|---|---|---|---|---|
| **614** | A521 | 10ch deep violet | 5.00 | .25 |
| **615** | A522 | 10ch sepia | 5.00 | .25 |

Rainbow Trout — A523

Dolly Trout — A524

Grass Carp — A525

Carp — A526

Manchurian Trout — A527

Crucian Carp — A528

**1965, Dec. 10 Photo. *Perf. 13½***
**With Gum**

| | | | | |
|---|---|---|---|---|
| **616** | A523 | 2ch multicolored | .75 | .25 |
| **617** | A524 | 4ch multicolored | .90 | .25 |
| **618** | A525 | 10ch multicolored | 2.00 | .25 |
| **619** | A526 | 10ch multicolored | 2.00 | .25 |
| **620** | A527 | 10ch multicolored | 2.00 | .25 |
| **621** | A528 | 40ch multicolored | 3.25 | .45 |
| | | *Nos. 616-621 (6)* | 10.90 | 1.70 |

Freshwater fishes.

Nos. 616-621 exist imperf, without gum. Value $20 unused.

House Building — A529

Hemp Weaving — A530

Blacksmith A531

Wrestling A532

School — A533

Dance — A534

**1965, Dec. 15 Engr. *Perf. 12½***
**With Gum**

| | | | | |
|---|---|---|---|---|
| **622** | A529 | 2ch green | .65 | .25 |
| **623** | A530 | 4ch maroon | 1.25 | .25 |
| **624** | A531 | 10ch violet | 1.60 | .25 |
| **625** | A532 | 10ch carmine red | 1.75 | .25 |
| **626** | A533 | 10ch blue | 1.10 | .25 |
| **627** | A534 | 10ch brown | 1.00 | .25 |
| | | *Nos. 622-627 (6)* | 7.35 | 1.50 |

Paintings by Kim Hong Do, 18th century Korean artist.

Students' Extracurricular Activities A535

Designs: 2ch, Children in workshop. 4ch, Boxing. 10ch (No. 630), Playing violin. 10ch (No. 631), Chemistry lab.

**1965, Dec. 15 Litho. *Perf. 13¼***
**With Gum**

| | | | | |
|---|---|---|---|---|
| **628-631** | A535 | Set of 4 | 2.75 | .50 |

Nos. 628-631 exist imperf. Value, unused $75.

Whaler A536

Service Vessel A537

**1965, Dec. 15 Engr. *Perf. 12½***
**With Gum**

| | | | | |
|---|---|---|---|---|
| **632** | A536 | 10ch deep blue | 1.75 | .25 |
| **633** | A537 | 10ch slate green | 1.75 | .25 |

Korean fishing boats.

Black-capped Kingfisher — A538

Korean Great Tit — A539

Blue Magpie A540

White-faced Wagtail A541

Migratory Korean Grosbeak A542

***Perf. 11, 13½ (#640)***
**1965, Dec. 30 Litho. With Gum**

| | | | | |
|---|---|---|---|---|
| **634** | A538 | 4ch pale yel & multi | 2.25 | .25 |
| **635** | A539 | 10ch pale sal & multi | 3.00 | .25 |
| **636** | A540 | 10ch pale grnsh blue & multi | 3.00 | .25 |
| **637** | A541 | 10ch yel & multi | 3.00 | .25 |
| **638** | A542 | 40ch pale yel grn & multi | 8.50 | .75 |
| | | *Nos. 634-638 (5)* | 19.75 | 1.75 |

Korean birds.

Nos. 634-638 exist imperf, without gum. Value $27.50 unused.

Korean sericulture — A543

Designs: 2ch, Silkworm moth & cocoon. No. 640, 10ch, Ailanthus silk moth. No. 641, 10ch, Chinese Oak silk moth.

**1965, Dec. 30 Engr. *Perf. 12½***
**With Gum**

| | | | | |
|---|---|---|---|---|
| **639-641** | A543 | Set of 3 | 100.00 | 2.75 |

Hooded Crane — A544

Japanese White-necked Crane — A545

Manchurian Crane — A546

Gray Heron — A547

**1965, Dec. 30** **With Gum**

| | | | | |
|---|---|---|---|---|
| **642** | A544 | 2ch olive brown | 3.00 | .25 |
| **643** | A545 | 10ch dp vio blue | 3.25 | .35 |
| **644** | A546 | 10ch slate purple | 3.25 | .35 |
| **645** | A547 | 40ch slate green | 5.75 | .65 |
| | | *Nos. 642-645 (4)* | 15.25 | 1.60 |

Wading birds. For surcharge, see No. 4540.

Mollusks A548

Designs: 5ch, Japanese common squid. 10ch, Giant Pacific octopus.

**1965, Dec. 31** **Litho.** ***Perf. 11***
**With Gum**

| | | | | |
|---|---|---|---|---|
| **646-647** | A548 | Set of 2 | .50 | .35 |

Nos. 646-647 exist imperf, without gum. Value $8 unused.

Korean Ducks — A549

Designs: 2ch, Spotbill. 4ch, Ruddy shelduck. 10ch, Mallard. 40ch, Baikal teal.

**1965, Dec. 31** **Litho.** ***Perf. 11***
**With Gum**

| | | | | |
|---|---|---|---|---|
| **648-651** | A549 | Set of 4 | 15.00 | 1.75 |

Nos. 648-651 exist imperf. Value $30 unused.

Circus, Pyongyang — A550

Trapeze Performers A551

Balancing Act — A552

Seesawing A553

Tightrope Walker — A554

**1965, Dec. 31** **Photo.**

| | | | | |
|---|---|---|---|---|
| **652** | A550 | 2ch multicolored | .75 | .25 |
| **653** | A551 | 10ch multicolored | 2.00 | .25 |
| **654** | A552 | 10ch multicolored | 2.00 | .25 |
| **655** | A553 | 10ch multicolored | 2.00 | .25 |
| **656** | A554 | 10ch multicolored | 2.00 | .25 |
| | | *Nos. 652-656 (5)* | 8.75 | 1.25 |

Korean acrobatics.

Nos. 652-655 were issued with gum, No. 656 without gum.

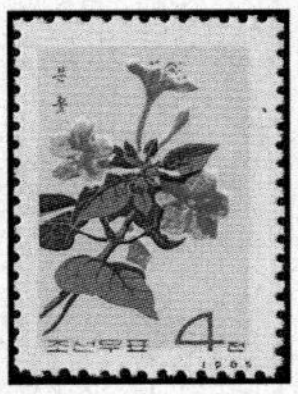
Korean Flowers — A555

Designs: No. 657, 4ch, Marvel-of-Peru. No. 658, 10ch, Peony (violet background). No. 659, 10ch, Moss rose (yellow background). No. 660, 10ch, Magnolia (light blue background).

**1965, Dec. 31** **Litho.**

| | | | | |
|---|---|---|---|---|
| **657-660** | A555 | Set of 4 | 11.50 | .90 |

No. 657 was issued without gum, Nos. 658-60 with gum.

Nos. 657-660 exist imperf, without gum. Value $20 unused.

Yachts — A556

Designs: No. 661, 2ch, Finn Class. No. 662, 10ch, Dragon Class (blue background). No. 663, 10ch, 5.5 Class (violet background). No. 664, 40ch, Star Class.

**1965, Dec. 31** **With Gum** ***Perf. 13½***

| | | | | |
|---|---|---|---|---|
| **661-664** | A556 | Set of 4 | 5.75 | 1.75 |

Nos. 661-664 exist imperf, without gum. Value $10 unused.

10ch depicting Netherlands class yacht, with blue background, not issued. Value $750.

1st Congress of the Org. of Solidarity of Peoples of Asia, Africa and Latin America — A557

**1966, Jan. 3** **With Gum** ***Perf. 11***

| | | | | |
|---|---|---|---|---|
| **665** | A557 | 10ch multicolored | .50 | .25 |

Hosta — A558

Dandelion — A559

Lily of the Valley — A560

Pink Convolvulus A561

Catalpa Blossom — A562

**1966, Jan. 15** **With Gum**

| | | | | |
|---|---|---|---|---|
| **666** | A558 | 2ch multicolored | 1.25 | .25 |
| **667** | A559 | 4ch multicolored | 1.25 | .25 |
| **668** | A560 | 10ch multicolored | 1.75 | .25 |
| **669** | A561 | 10ch multicolored | 1.75 | .25 |
| **670** | A562 | 40ch multicolored | 5.25 | .70 |
| | | *Nos. 666-670 (5)* | 11.25 | 1.70 |

Korean wildflowers.

Imperfs exist, without gum. Value, $25 unused.

Primrose — A563

Brillian Campion — A564

Amur Pheasant's Eye — A565

Orange Lily — A566

Rhododendron A567

**1966, Feb. 10** **With Gum**

| | | | | |
|---|---|---|---|---|
| **671** | A563 | 2ch multicolored | 1.00 | .25 |
| **672** | A564 | 4ch multicolored | 1.00 | .25 |
| **673** | A565 | 10ch multicolored | 1.40 | .25 |
| **674** | A566 | 10ch multicolored | 1.40 | .25 |
| **675** | A567 | 90ch multicolored | 7.00 | .90 |
| | | *Nos. 671-675 (5)* | 11.80 | 1.90 |

Korean wildflowers.

Land Reform Law, 20th Anniv. — A568

**1966, Mar. 5** **With Gum**

| | | | | |
|---|---|---|---|---|
| **676** | A568 | 10ch multicolored | .90 | .25 |

Battle of Jiansanfen A569

Battle of Taehongdan — A570

Battle of Dashahe A571

**1966, Mar. 25** **Engr.** ***Perf. 12½***

| | | | | |
|---|---|---|---|---|
| **677** | A569 | 10ch violet brown | .60 | .25 |
| **678** | A570 | 10ch dp blue green | .60 | .25 |
| **679** | A571 | 10ch brown carmine | .60 | .25 |
| | | *Nos. 677-679 (3)* | 1.80 | .75 |

Battles of the anti-Japanese revolution.

No. 678 was issued without gum, the other values with gum.

Art Treasures of the Silla Dynasty — A572

Designs: 2ch, Covered bowl. 5ch, Jar. 10ch, Censer.

**1966, Apr. 30 With Gum**
**680-682** A572 Set of 3 4.50 .55

Labor Day, 80th Anniv. — A573

**1966, May 1 Litho. *Perf. 11***
**With Gum**
**683** A573 10ch multicolored .75 .25

Assoc. for the Restoration of the Fatherland, 30th Anniv. — A574

**1966, May 5 Photo. With Gum**
**684** A574 10ch brn red & yel .75 .25

Farmer A575

Worker A576

**1966, May 30 Litho. With Gum**
**685** A575 5ch multicolored .50 .25
**686** A576 10ch multicolored .75 .25

Young Pioneers, 20th Anniv. A577

**1966, June 6 With Gum**
**687** A577 10ch multicolored .75 .25

Kangson Steel Works A578

Pongung Chemical Works A579

**1966, June 10 Engr. *Perf. 12½***
**With Gum**
**688** A578 10ch gray 5.00 .25
**689** A579 10ch deep red 5.00 .25

Korean Factories.

Fish — A580

Designs: 2ch, Saury. 5ch, Pacific cod. No. 692, Chum salmon. No. 693, Mackerel. 40ch, Pink salmon.

**1966, June 10 Photo. *Perf. 11***
**690-694** A580 Set of 5 15.00 4.50

Nos. 690-692 were issued with gum, Nos. 693-694 without gum.
Nos. 690-694 exist imperf, without gum. Value, $22, either unused or cancelled.

Prof. Kim Bong Han & Kyongrak Biological System — A581

**1966, June 30 Photo. With Gum**
**695** A581 Block of 8, #a.-h. 11.00 8.00
*695i* Souvenir sheet of 8, #695-702 125.00 100.00

Voshkod 2 A582

Luna 9 A583

Luna 10 A584

**1966, June 30**
**703** A582 5ch multicolored .30 .25
**704** A583 10ch multicolored 1.00 .25
**705** A584 40ch multicolored 1.75 .35
*Nos. 703-705 (3)* 3.05 .85

Space Flight Day.
Nos. 703-705 exist imperf. Value, $8 unused.

Jules Rimet Cup A585

Dribbling A586

Goal-keeper A587

**1966, July 11 Litho.**
**706** A585 10ch multicolored 1.75 .25
**707** A586 10ch multicolored 1.75 .25
**708** A587 10ch multicolored 1.75 .25
*Nos. 706-708 (3)* 5.25 .75

World Cup Championship.
Nos. 706-708 exist imperf. Value, $20 unused.

Battle of Naphalsan A588

Battle of Seoul A589

Battle of Height 1211 A590

**1966, July 27 Engr. *Perf. 12½***
**With Gum**
**709** A588 10ch red violet .75 .25
**710** A589 10ch deep green .75 .25
**711** A590 10ch violet .75 .25
*Nos. 709-711 (3)* 2.25 .75

Korean War of 1950-53.

Sex Equality Law, 20th Anniv. A591

**1966, July 30 Litho. *Perf. 11***
**With Gum**
**712** A591 10ch multicolored .75 .25

Nationalization of Industry, 20th Anniv. — A592

**1966, Aug. 10 With Gum**
**713** A592 10ch multicolored 1.00 .25

Water Jar Dance — A593

Bell Dance — A594

Dancer in Mural Painting — A595

Sword Dance — A596

Golden Cymbal Dance — A597

**1966, Aug. 10**
**714** A593 5ch multicolored 1.40 .25
**715** A594 10ch multicolored 2.50 .25
**716** A595 10ch multicolored 2.50 .25
**717** A596 15ch multicolored 2.50 .25
**718** A597 40ch multicolored 4.50 .30
*Nos. 714-718 (5)* 13.40 1.30

Korean Folk Dances.
5ch and 10ch issued with or without gum. Other values issued without gum.
Nos. 714-718 exist imperf, without gum. Value, $20 unused.

Attacking U.S. Soldier — A598

Worker with Child — A599

Industrialization A600

**1966, Aug. 15 Engr. *Perf. 12½***
**With Gum**
**719** A598 10ch deep green 1.25 .25
**720** A599 10ch red violet 1.25 .25
**721** A600 10ch violet 5.75 .40
*Nos. 719-721 (3)* 8.25 .90

Korean Reunification Campaign.

Crop-spraying — A601

Observing Forest Fire — A602

Geological Survey — A603

Fish Shoal Detection A604

**1966, Sept. 30 Photo. *Perf. 11***

| | | | | |
|---|---|---|---|---|
| **722** | A601 | 2ch multicolored | .50 | .25 |
| **723** | A602 | 5ch multicolored | 7.00 | .25 |
| **724** | A603 | 10ch multicolored | 1.75 | .25 |
| **725** | A604 | 40ch multicolored | 1.75 | .25 |
| | | *Nos. 722-725 (4)* | 11.00 | 1.00 |

Industrial uses of aircraft.

2ch, 5ch issued without gum. 10ch, 40ch issued with gum.

Nos. 722-725 exist imperf, without gum. Value, $20 unused.

---

A three-value set honoring revolutionary fighters, with designs similar to types A334-A339, was prepared but not issued. Value $3,500.

---

Kim Il Sung University, 20th Anniv. — A605

**1966, Oct. 1 Engr. *Perf. 12½***
**With Gum**

| | | | | |
|---|---|---|---|---|
| **726** | A605 | 10ch slate violet | .80 | .25 |

> **Imperforate Stamps**
> Imperforate varieties are without gum, unless otherwise noted.

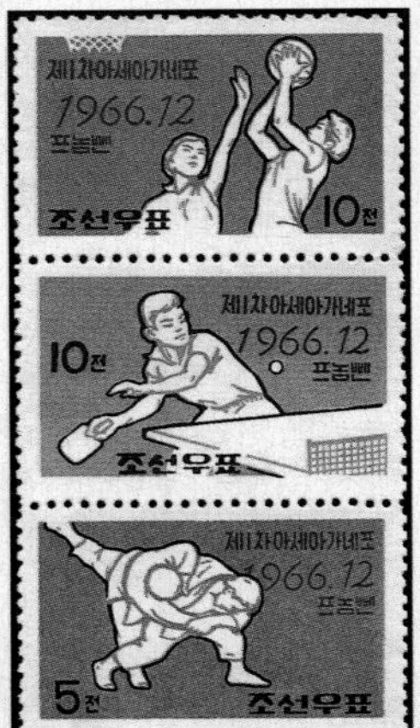

1st Asian GANEFO Games A606

Designs: a, 5ch, Judo. b, 10ch, Basketball. c, 10ch, Table tennis.

**1966, Oct. 30 Litho. *Perf. 11***

| | | | | |
|---|---|---|---|---|
| **727** | A606 | Strip of 3, #a-c | 2.00 | .55 |
| | | Strip of 3, #a-c imperf | 50.00 | — |

Scarlet Finch — A607

Hoopoe — A608

Korean Crested Lark — A609

Brown Thrush A610

White-bellied Black Woodpecker A611

**1966, Oct. 30**

| | | | | |
|---|---|---|---|---|
| **730** | A607 | 2ch multicolored | 2.25 | .25 |
| **731** | A608 | 5ch multicolored | 2.50 | .25 |
| **732** | A609 | 10ch multicolored | 2.75 | .30 |
| **733** | A610 | 10ch multicolored | 2.75 | .30 |
| **734** | A611 | 40ch multicolored | 5.75 | .80 |
| | | *Nos. 730-734 (5)* | 16.00 | 1.90 |
| | | Set of 5, imperf | 30.00 | — |

Korean birds. For surcharge, see No. 4513.

Construction — A612

Machine-Tool Production — A613

Worker & Graph A614

Miners A615

**1966, Nov. 20**

| | | | | |
|---|---|---|---|---|
| **735** | A612 | 5ch multicolored | .30 | .25 |
| **736** | A613 | 10ch multicolored | .55 | .25 |
| **737** | A614 | 10ch multicolored | .55 | .25 |
| **738** | A615 | 40ch multicolored | 1.75 | .35 |
| | | *Nos. 735-738 (4)* | 3.15 | 1.10 |

Propaganda for increased production.

Nos. 735-737 issued with gum. No. 738 issued without gum.

Parachuting — A616

Show Jumping A617

Motorcycling — A618

Telegraphists' Competition — A619

**1966, Nov. 30 Engr. *Perf. 12½***
**With Gum**

| | | | | |
|---|---|---|---|---|
| **739** | A616 | 2ch dark brown | .85 | .25 |
| **740** | A617 | 5ch org vermilion | .60 | .25 |
| **741** | A618 | 10ch dp violet blue | 3.00 | .30 |
| **742** | A619 | 40ch deep green | 2.00 | .25 |
| | | *Nos. 739-742 (4)* | 6.45 | 1.05 |

National Defense sports.

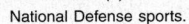

Samil Wolgan Magazine, 30th Anniv. — A620

**1966, Dec. 1 Photo. *Perf. 11***

| | | | | |
|---|---|---|---|---|
| **743** | A620 | 10ch multicolored | — | — |

Korean Deer — A621

Designs: 2ch, Red deer. 5ch, Sika deer. No. 746, 10ch, Reindeer (grazing). No. 747, 10ch, Japanese sambar (erect). 70ch, Fallow deer.

**1966, Dec. 20 Litho.**

| | | | | |
|---|---|---|---|---|
| **744-748** | A621 | Set of 5 | 18.00 | 4.50 |
| | | Imperf, #744-748 | — | — |

No. 747 was issued with gum. Other values issued without gum. For surcharge, see No. 4560.

Wild Fruit — A622

Designs: 2ch, Blueberries. 5ch, Pears. 10ch (No. 751), Plums. 10ch (No. 752), Schizandra. 10ch (No. 753), Raspberries. 40ch, Jujube.

**1966, Dec. 30**

| | | | | |
|---|---|---|---|---|
| **749-754** | A622 | Set of 6 | 5.75 | .90 |
| | | Imperf, #749-754 | 12.50 | — |

Samson Rocks — A623

Ryonju Pond — A624

Jinju Pond — A625

The Ten Thousand Rocks, Manmulsang A626

**1966, Dec. 30** **Litho.** ***Perf. 11***

| | | | | |
|---|---|---|---|---|
| **755** | A623 | 2ch multicolored | 1.00 | .25 |
| **756** | A624 | 4ch multicolored | 4.00 | .25 |
| **757** | A625 | 10ch multicolored | 1.00 | .25 |
| **758** | A626 | 10ch multicolored | 4.00 | .25 |
| | | *Nos. 755-758 (4)* | 10.00 | 1.00 |

Diamond Mountains scenery.

Nos. 755-758 are inscribed "1964" but were actually issued in 1966.

2ch and 4ch issued without gum. 10ch values issued with gum.

Onpo A627

Myohyang — A628

Songdowon — A629

Hongwon A630

**1966, Dec. 30** **Engr.** ***Perf. 12½***
**With Gum**

| | | | | |
|---|---|---|---|---|
| **759** | A627 | 2ch blue violet | .45 | .25 |
| **760** | A628 | 4ch turquoise green | .50 | .25 |
| **761** | A629 | 10ch dp blue green | .80 | .25 |
| **762** | A630 | 40ch black | 1.40 | .30 |
| | | *Nos. 759-762 (4)* | 3.15 | 1.05 |

Korean rest homes.

Korean People's Army, 19th Anniv. A631

**1967, Feb. 8** **Photo.** ***Perf. 11***
**763** A631 10ch multicolored .75 .25

Livestock Farming A632

Designs: 5ch, Sow. 10ch, Goat. 40ch, Bull.

**1967, Feb. 28** **Litho.**
**764-766** A632 Set of 3 6.75 1.50
Imperf, #764-766 55.00 —

5ch, 10ch issued without gum. 40ch issued both with and without gum.

Battle of Pochonbo, 30th Anniv. — A633

**1967, Feb. 28** **Photo.** **With Gum**
**767** A633 10ch multicolored .75 .25

Universal Compulsory Technical Education A634

**1967, Apr. 1**
**768** A634 10ch multicolored .75 .25

29th World Table Tennis Championships, Pyongyang — A635

10ch, 40ch designs similar to 5ch.

**1967, Apr. 11** **Litho.**
**769-771** A635 Set of 3 3.00 .55
Imperf, #769-771 100.00 —

5ch issued with or without gum. 10ch, 40ch issued without gum. For surcharge, see No. 4514.

People Helping Guerrillas, Wangyugou — A636

Blowing Up Railway Bridge A637

Shooting Down Japanese Plane A638

**1967, Apr. 25** **Engr.** **With Gum**

| | | | | |
|---|---|---|---|---|
| **772** | A636 | 10ch deep violet | .50 | .25 |
| **773** | A637 | 10ch dk vio brown | 4.00 | .25 |
| **774** | A638 | 10ch slate | .50 | .25 |
| | | *Nos. 772-774 (3)* | 5.00 | .75 |

Paintings of the guerrilla war against Japan.

Ri Tae Hun A639

Choe Jong Un A640

Kim Hwa Ryong A641

**1967, Apr. 25** **With Gum**

| | | | | |
|---|---|---|---|---|
| **775** | A639 | 10ch slate | 1.00 | .25 |
| **776** | A640 | 10ch reddish violet | 3.00 | .25 |
| **777** | A641 | 10ch ultramarine | 1.00 | .25 |
| | | *Nos. 775-777 (3)* | 5.00 | .75 |

Heroes of the Republic.

Labor Day A642

**1967, May 1** **Litho.**
**778** A642 10ch multicolored .70 .25

Pre-School Education — A643

Designs of children: 5ch, Learning to count. 10ch, Making model tractor. 40ch, Playing with ball.

**1967, June 1**
**779-781** A643 Set of 3 3.50 .55

Victory Monument, Battle of Pochonbo — A644

**1967, June 4**
**782** A644 10ch multicolored 1.00 .25

Military Sculpture A645

Designs: 2ch, Soldier attacking tank. 5ch, Soldiers with musical instruments. 10ch, Soldier in heroic pose. 40ch, Soldier and child.

**1967, June 25** **Photo.**
**783-786** A645 Set of 4 3.00 .75

2ch issued with or without gum. Other values issued without gum.

Medicinal Plants — A646

Designs: 2ch, Polygonatum japonicum. 5ch, Abelmoschus manihat. 10ch (No. 789), Rehmannia glutinosa (olive yellow). 10ch (No. 790), Scutellaria baicalensis (turquoise blue background). 10ch (No. 791), Pulsatilla koreana (violet blue). 40ch, Tanacetum boreale.

**1967, July 20** **Photo.**
**787-792** A646 Set of 6 11.00 1.00

Nos. 787-789, 791 issued with or without gum. Nos. 790, 792 issued without gum.

Korean People's Army — A647

Designs: 5ch, Aviator, sailor, soldier. 10ch (No. 794), Officer decorating soldier. 10ch (No. 795), Soldier and farmer.

**1967, July 25**
**793-795** A647 Set of 3 1.40 .45

5ch issued with or without gum. 10ch values issued without gum.

Freighter "Chollima" A648

**1967, July 30** **Engr.** **With Gum**
**796** A648 10ch deep green 1.75 .25

Drilling Rock — A649

Felling Trees — A650

Reclaiming Tideland — A651

**1967, Aug. 5**

| | | | | |
|---|---|---|---|---|
| **797** | A649 | 5ch black brown | .60 | .25 |
| **798** | A650 | 10ch blue green | .80 | .25 |
| **799** | A651 | 10ch slate | 1.10 | .25 |
| | | *Nos. 797-799 (3)* | 2.50 | .75 |

Revolutionary paintings.
5ch issued without gum. 10ch values issued with gum.

Crabs A652

Designs: 2ch, Erimaculus isenbeckii. 5ch, Neptunus trituberculatus. 10ch, Paralithodes camtschatica. 40ch, Chionoecetes opilio.

**1967, Aug. 10** **Photo.**
**800-803** A652 Set of 4 8.00 .90

Reunification of Korea Propaganda — A653

**1967, Aug. 15** **Litho.**
**804** A653 10ch multicolored 3.50 .35

A five-value set, featuring details from famous Korean paintings of the 15th-16th centuries, was prepared for release in August, 1967, but was not issued. Value $2,500.

A 10ch stamp celebrating the 10th anniversary of the launch of the first USSR space satellite was prepared for release on Sept. 10 but was not issued. Value $1,500.

Waterfalls A654

Designs: 2ch, Tongrim waterfalls 10ch, Sanju waterfall, Mt. Myohyang. 40ch, Sambang waterfall, Mt. Chonak.

**1967, Oct. 10**
**805-807** A654 Set of 3 11.50 .75

2ch issued with or without gum. 10ch, 40ch issued without gum.

"For Fresh Great Revolutionary Upsurge" — A655

Designs: 5ch, Ship, train and truck. 10ch (No. 809), Machine industry. 10ch (No. 810), Truck, bulldozer, tractor and farmers. 10ch (No. 811), Construction machinery, buildings. 10ch (No. 812), Chollima flying horse and banners.

**1967, Nov. 1** **Engr.**
**808-812** A655 Set of 5 10.00 .90

Russian Revolution, 50th Anniv. — A656

**1967, Nov. 7** **Photo.**
**813** A656 10ch multicolored 1.00 .25

Korean Elections — A657

Designs: 10ch (No. 814), Voters and flags. 10ch (No. 815), Woman casting ballot (vert.)

**1967, Nov. 23** **Litho.**
**814-815** A657 Set of 2 1.25 .35

Raptors A658

Designs: 2ch, Black vulture. 10ch, Rough-legged buzzard. 40ch, White-tailed eagle.

**1967, Dec. 1** **Photo.**
**816-818** A658 Set of 3 14.00 1.75

2ch issued with or without gum. 10ch, 40ch issued without gum. For surcharge, see No. 4512.

Chongjin — A659

Hamhung — A660

Sinuiju A661

**1967, Dec. 20** **Engr.** **With Gum**

| | | | | |
|---|---|---|---|---|
| **819** | A659 | 5ch bronze green | 1.00 | .25 |
| **820** | A660 | 10ch violet | 1.00 | .25 |
| **821** | A661 | 10ch red violet | 1.00 | .25 |
| | | *Nos. 819-821 (3)* | 3.00 | .75 |

Korean cities.

Whaler Firing Harpoon A662

**With or Without Gum**

**1967, Dec. 30**
**822** A662 10ch ultramarine 2.25 .25

Soldier with Red Book A663

Soldier Mounting Bayonet — A664

Worker and Bayoneted Rifle — A665

**Litho or Photo (#829)**

**1967, Dec. 30**

| | | | | |
|---|---|---|---|---|
| **823** | A663 | 10ch multicolored | .50 | .25 |
| **824** | A664 | 10ch multicolored | .50 | .25 |
| **825** | A665 | 10ch multicolored | .50 | .25 |
| | | *Nos. 823-825 (3)* | 1.50 | .75 |

Korean People's Army, 20th Anniv. — A666

Designs: a, Airman, soldier and sailor. b, Soldier, battle in background. c, Soldier & KDPR arms. d, Soldier & flag. e, Soldier with Red Book. f, Three soldiers, North Korean flag. g, Soldier & worker. h, Soldier saluting. i, Soldier attacking. j, Soldier, sailor & airman beneath flag.

**1968, Feb. 3** **Litho.**

| | | | | |
|---|---|---|---|---|
| **826** | A666 | Sheet of 10 | 80.00 | *30.00* |
| *a.-j.* | | 10ch, any single | .45 | .25 |

Ri Su Bok (1934-51) — A667

Han Kye Ryol (1926-51) — A668

**1968, Feb. 10** **Engr.** **With Gum**

| | | | | |
|---|---|---|---|---|
| **827** | A667 | 10ch dark rose | *550.00* | |
| **828** | A667 | 10ch light violet | .50 | .25 |
| **829** | A668 | 10ch dark green | 550.00 | |
| **830** | A668 | 10ch lt blue violet | .50 | .25 |
| | | *Nos. 827-830 (4)* | 1,101. | .50 |

War heroes.
Nos. 827 and 829 were prepared but not issued.

Apartment Building, Pyongyang — A669

**1968, Mar. 5** **Litho.** **With Gum**
**831** A669 10ch bright blue .75 .25

Kim Il Sung, 56th Birthday A670

**1968, Apr. 15** **With Gum**
**832** A670 40ch multicolored 1.00 .35

Printed in sheets of four stamps.
Exists in a miniature sheet of one, which is rare (2 examples reported),

Kim Il Sung's Family Home in Mangyongdae — A671

Leaving Home at Age 13 — A672

Mangyong Hill — A673

Kim Il Sung with Father — A674

Kim Il Sung with Mother — A675

**1968, Apr. 15**

| | | | | |
|---|---|---|---|---|
| **833** A671 | 10ch multicolored | | .60 | .25 |
| **834** A672 | 10ch multicolored | | .60 | .25 |
| **835** A673 | 10ch multicolored | | .60 | .25 |
| **836** A674 | 10ch multicolored | | .60 | .25 |
| **837** A675 | 10ch multicolored | | .60 | .25 |
| | *Nos. 833-837 (5)* | | 3.00 | 1.25 |

Childhood of Kim Il Sung.
See Nos. 883-887, 927-930.

Dredger *2 September* A676

**1968, June 5**

| | | | |
|---|---|---|---|
| **838** A676 | 5ch green | 1.40 | .25 |
| **839** A676 | 5ch blue | *850.00* | *600.00* |

Matsutake Mushroom A677

Shiitake Mushroom — A678

Meadow Mushroom A679

**1968, Aug. 10 Photo. With Gum**

| | | | |
|---|---|---|---|
| **840** A677 | 5ch multicolored | 20.00 | .55 |
| **841** A678 | 10ch multicolored | 40.00 | .90 |
| **842** A679 | 10ch multicolored | 40.00 | .90 |
| | *Nos. 840-842 (3)* | 100.00 | 2.35 |

Founding of the Korean Democratic People's Republic, 20th Anniv. — A680

Designs: a, Statue of national arms. b, North Korean flag. c, Worker, peasant & flag. d, Soldier & flag. e, Flying Horse of Chollima. f, Soldiers & tanks. g, Battle scene. h, Workers, banner & monument.

**1968, Sept. 2 Litho. With Gum**

| | | | |
|---|---|---|---|
| **843** A680 | Block of 8, #a.-h. | 40.00 | *35.00* |
| ***a.-h.*** | 10ch, any single | 1.25 | .25 |

Kaesong Students' and Children's Palace A681

**1968, Oct. 5 With Gum**

**844** A681 10ch greenish blue .50 .25

Domestic Goods — A682

Designs: 2ch, Shopper with domestic items. 5ch, Textile manufacturing. 10ch, Cannery.

**1968, Nov. 5 Photo. With Gum**

**845-847** A682 Set of 3 2.50 .55

Kim Il Sung's 10-Point Program A683

Design: 10ch, Two soldiers, Red Book, horiz.

**1968, Dec. 5 Litho.**

**848-849** A683 Set of 2 1.00 .25

Increasing Agricultural Production — A684

Designs: 5ch, Woman carrying eggs. 10ch (No. 851), Woman harvesting wheat. 10ch (No. 852), Woman holding basket of fruit.

**1968, Dec. 10 Photo. With Gum**

**850-852** A684 Set of 3 1.25 .45

Shellfish A685

Designs: 5ch (No. 853), Scallop. 5ch (No. 854), Clam. 10ch, Mussel.

**1968, Dec. 20 With Gum**

**853-855** A685 Set of 3 5.75 .45

Details of Battle of Pochonbo Victory Monument — A686

Designs (all 10ch): No. 856, Kim Il Sung at head of columns, vert. No. 857, shown. No. 858, Figures marching to right, green sky at right (42.75x28mm). No. 859, Figures marching to left (55.5x28mm). No. 860, Figures marching to right (55.5x28mm). No. 861, Figures marching to left, sky at right (42.75x28mm). No. 862, Figures marching to left, sky at left (42.75x28mm).

**1968, Dec. 30**

**856-862** A686 Set of 7 3.25 1.25

Grand Theater, Pyongyang — A687

**1968, Dec. 30**

**863** A687 10ch dark brown 1.00 .25

Revolutionary Museum, Pochonbo — A688

**1968, Dec. 30**

**864** A688 2ch dark green .50 .25

Rural Technical Development — A689

Designs: 2ch, Irrigation. 5ch, Mechanization of agriculture. 10ch, Electrification. 40ch, Mechanical fertilization and spraying.

**1969, Feb. 25**

**865-868** A689 Set of 4 2.25 .70

Rabbits A690

Designs: 2ch, Gray rabbits. 10ch (No. 870), White rabbits. 10ch (No. 871), Black rabbits. 10ch (No. 872), Brown rabbits. 40ch, White rabbits.

**1969, Mar. 10**

**869-873** A690 Set of 5 10.00 1.10

Nos. 869-873 were issued both with and without gum.

Public Health A691

Designs: 2ch, Old man & girl. 10ch, Nurse with syringe. 40ch, Doctor with woman & child.

**1969, Apr. 1**

**874-876** A691 Set of 3 4.00 .55

Farm Machines — A692

Designs: 10ch (No. 877), Rice sower. 10ch (No. 878), Rice harvester. 10ch (No. 879), Herbicide sprayer. 10ch (No. 880), Wheat & barley thresher.

**1969, Apr. 10 Engr.**

**877-880** A692 Set of 4 3.00 .70

Mangyongdae — A693

Ponghwa — A694

**1969, Apr. 15 Litho.**

| | | | |
|---|---|---|---|
| **881** A693 | 10ch multicolored | 1.75 | .25 |
| **882** A694 | 10ch multicolored | 1.75 | .25 |

Revolutionary historical sites.

Early Revolutionary Years of Kim Il Sung — A695

Designs (all 10ch): No. 883, Kim crossing into Manchuria 1926, aged 13. No. 884, Kim talking to four students around table (blue green frame). No. 885, Kim speaking outdoors to Young Communist League meeting (apple green frame). No. 886, Kim speaking to Young Communist League meeting indoors (lilac frame). No. 887, Kim leading demonstration against teachers (peach frame).

**1969, Apr. 15**
**883-887** A695 Set of 5 3.25 1.00

No. 884 was issued with gum. The other values were issued without gum.

Kang Pan Sok (1892-1932), Mother of Kim Il Sung — A696

Designs (all 10ch): No. 888, Birthplace at Chilgol. No. 889, Resisting Japanese police in home. No. 890, Meeting with women's revolutionary association.

**1969, Apr. 21** **Photo.**
**888-890** A696 Set of 3 4.50 .60

Bivouac Sites in War against Japan — A697

Designs: 5ch, Pegaebong. 10ch (No. 892), Mupho, horiz. 10ch (No. 893), Chongbong. 40ch, Konchang, horiz.

**1969, Apr. 21**
**891-894** A697 Set of 4 3.00 .80

Chollima Statue — A698

**1969, May 1**
**895** A698 10ch blue .85 .25

Poultry A699

Designs: 10ch (No. 896), Mangyong chickens. 10ch (No. 897), Kwangpho ducks.

**1969, June 1** **Engr.**
**896-897** A699 Set of 2 5.75 .50

Socialist Education System — A700

Designs: 2ch, Kim Il Sung & children. 10ch, Student & worker with books. 40ch, Male & female students, figure "9."

**1969, June 1** **Photo.**
**898-900** A700 Set of 3 2.25 .60

Pochonbo Battlefield Memorials — A701

Designs: 5ch, Machine gun platform on mountainside. 10ch (No. 902), Statue of Kim Il Sung, vert. 10ch (No. 903), Aspen Tree monument (stele & enclosed tree trunk). 10ch (No. 904), Konjang Hill monument (within forest).

**1969, June 4**
**901-904** A701 Set of 4 2.25 .80

Kim Hyong Jik (1894-1926), Father of Kim Il Sung — A702

Designs: 10ch (No. 905), Teaching at Myongsin School. 10ch (No. 906), Outdoor meeting with five other members of Korean National Association.

**1969, July 10**
**905-906** A702 Set of 2 1.90 .40

---

A 10ch stamp honoring the Juvenile Chess Game of Socialist Countries was prepared for release Aug. 5, 1969, but was not issued. Value $1,000.

---

Sports Day, 20th Anniv. — A703

**1969, Sept. 10**
**907** A703 10ch multicolored 1.10 .25

Korean Revolution Museum, Pyongyang A704

**1969, Sept. 10** **Litho.**
**908** A704 10ch dk blue green .85 .25

Pres. Nixon Attacked by Pens — A705

**1969, Sept. 18** **Litho.**
**909** A705 10ch multi 3.25 .25

Anti-U.S. Imperialism Journalists' Conference, Pyongyang.

Implementation of the 10-Point Program — A706

Designs: 5ch, Soldiers, battle. 10ch (No. 911), Globe, bayonets attacking dismembered U.S. soldier. 10ch (No. 912), Workers holding Red Books & slogan, vert.

**1969, Oct. 1** **Photo.**
**910-912** A706 Set of 3 3.25 .60

Reunification of Korea — A707

Designs: 10ch (No. 913), Kim Il Sung, marching workers. 10ch (No. 914), Worker & soldier bayoneting U.S. soldier. 50ch, Armed workers in battle, horiz.

**1969, Oct. 1** **Litho.**
**913-915** A707 Set of 3 1.60 .60

Refrigerator-Transport Ship "Taesongsan" — A708

**1969, Dec. 20** **Engr.**
**916** A708 10ch slate purple 1.40 .25

Korean Fish A709

Designs: 5ch, Yellowtail. 10ch, Dace. 40ch, Mullet.

**1969, Dec. 20** **Photo.**
**917-919** A709 Set of 3 6.00 .60

Guerrilla Conference Sites A710

Designs: 2ch, Dahuangwai, 1935. 5ch, Yaoyinggou, 1935 (log cabin). 10ch, Xiaohaerbaling, 1940 (tent).

**1970, Feb. 10**
**920-922** A710 Set of 3 1.40 .45

Mt. Paektu, Birthplace of the Revolution — A711

Views of Mt. Paektu (all 10ch): No. 923, Lake Chon (dull green, tan, black). No. 924, Janggun Peak (pale peach, dull blue, black). No. 925, Piryu Peak (dull yellow, blue green, black). No. 926, Pyongsa Peak (brown orange, blue, red violet).

**1970, Mar. 10**
**923-926** A711 Set of 4 2.75 .60

See Nos. 959-961.

Support for North Vietnam — A712

**1970, Mar. 10**
**927** A712 10ch multicolored .65 .25

Revolutionary Activities of Kim Il Sung — A713

Designs (all 10ch): No. 928, Receiving his father's pistols from his mother. No. 929, Receiving smuggled pistols from his mother (other young revolutionaries present). No. 930, Kim speaking with four farmers in field. No. 931, Kim speaking at Kalun meeting.

**1970, Apr. 15** **Litho.**
**928-931** A713 Set of 4 5.50 .90

Lenin Birth Centenary A714

Design: 10ch (No. 933), Lenin with cap, in three-quarter profile.

**1970, Apr. 22** **Photo.**
**932-933** A714 Set of 2 1.60 .40

Assoc. of Koreans in Japan, 15th Anniv. — A715

Designs (both 10ch): No. 934, Red. No. 935, Maroon.

**1970, Apr. 27** **Engr.**
**934-935** A715 Set of 2 1.40 .40

Worker-Peasant Red Guard — A716

Design: 10ch (No. 936), Factory worker in uniform, vert.

**1970, May 5** **Photo.**

**936-937** A716 Set of 2 1.10 .40

Peasant Education — A717

Designs: 2ch, Students & newspapers. 5ch, Peasant reading book. 10ch, Students in class.

**1970, June 25**

**938-940** A717 Set of 3 1.60 .45

Army Electrical Engineer A718

**1970, June 25**

**941** A718 10ch purple brown .85 .25

Month of the Campaign for Withdrawal of U.S. Troops from South Korea — A719

Design: 10ch, Soldier & partisan.

**1970, June 25**

**942-943** A719 Set of 2 1.50 .25

Anti-U.S., South Korea Propaganda — A720

**1970, June 25** **Engr.**

**944** A720 10ch deep violet .65 .25

Campaign for Increased Productivity A721

Designs (all 10ch): No. 945, Quarryman. No. 946, Steelworker. No. 947, Machinist. No. 948, Worker with bag. No. 949, Construction worker. No. 950, Railway flagman.

**1970, Sept. 10** **Photo.**

**945-950** A721 Set of 6 4.50 1.20

Workers' Party Program A722

Designs: 5ch, Peasant, farm scene. 10ch, Steelworker. 40ch, Soldiers.

**1970, Oct. 5** **Engr.**

**951-953** A722 Set of 3 4.00 .50

Korean Workers' Party, 25th Anniv. — A723

**1970, Oct. 10** **Photo.**

**954** A723 10ch multicolored .85 .25

5th Korean Workers' Party Congress — A724

Issued in miniature sheet of 10, with one 40ch value (No. 955j) and nine 10ch values. Designs: a, Kim Il Sung, marchers. b, Family & apartment buildings. c, Soldier with Red Book. d, Soldier with binoculars, various weapons. e, Steelworker. f, Workers killing U.S. soldier. g, Farmers. h, Students. i, Schoolgirl with Red Book, atomic energy symbol. j, Cooperation with South Korean guerillas.

**1970, Nov. 2** **Litho.**

**955** Sheet of 10, #a.-j. 900.00

*a.-i.* A724 10ch Any single 1.40 .50

*j.* A724 40ch multi 600.00

Soon after release, a design error was discovered on No. 955j, and this stamp was removed from souvenir sheets remaining in stock, usually with the bottom selvage. This is the form in which this set is commonly offered. Value, $25. The full sheet of 10 is scarce.

League of Socialist Working Youth of Korea, 25th Anniv. — A725

**1971, Jan. 17** **Photo.**

**956** A725 10ch multicolored .55 .25

Nanhutou Conference, 35th Anniv. — A726

**1971, Feb. 28**

**957** A726 10ch multicolored .55 .25

Land Reform Law, 25th Anniv. A727

**1971, Mar. 5**

**958** A727 2ch multicolored .55 .25

Mt. Paektu, Second Issue — A728

Designs: 2ch, Mountainscape. 5ch, Paektu Waterfalls, vert. 10ch, Western Peak.

**1971, Mar. 10**

**959-961** A728 Set of 3 5.00 .60

Revolutionary Museums — A729

Designs (all 10ch): No. 962, Mangyongdae (red orange & ultramarine). No. 963, Phophyong (yellow & brown). No. 964, Junggang (salmon & green).

**1971, Apr. 1**

**962-964** A729 Set of 3 1.60 .60

Coal Production 6-Year Plan — A730

**1971, Apr. 1**

**965** A730 10ch multicolored .85 .25

Revolutionary Activities of Kim Il Sung — A731

Designs (all 10ch): No. 966, Portrait, vert. No. 967, Kim addressing crowd at guerrilla base camp. No. 968, Kim speaking with children on hillside. No. 969, Kim reviewing Anti-Japanese Guerrilla Army 1932.

**1971, Apr. 15** **Litho.**

**966-969** A731 Set of 4 3.25 .80

May Day — A732

**1971, May 1** **Photo.**

**970** A732 1w multicolored 3.75 .40

Association for the Restoration of the Fatherland, 35th Anniv. — A733

**1971, May 5**

**971** A733 10ch multicolored .85 .25

Battles in the Musan Area Command (1939) — A734

Designs: 5ch, Sinsadong Monument. 10ch, Taehongdan Monument, with encased machine guns, horiz. 40ch, Musan headquarters (log cabins in forest), horiz.

**1971, May 23**

**972-974** A734 Set of 3 2.25 .60

Koreans in Japan A735

**1971, May 25**

**975** A735 10ch chocolate .65 .25

A 10ch stamp commemorating the Asia-Africa Invitational Table Tennis Game for Friendship was prepared for release on May 27, 1971, but was not issued. Value $750.

Korean Children's Union, 25th Anniv. — A736

**1971, June 6**

**976** A736 10ch multicolored .55 .25

6th Congress, League of Socialist Working Youth of Korea — A737

Designs: 5ch, Marchers & banners. 10ch, Marchers, banners & globe with map of Korea.

**1971, June 21**

**977-978** A737 Set of 2 1.10 .25

Labor Law, 25th Anniv. A738

**1971, June 24**
**979** A738 5ch multicolored .60 .25

Sex Equality Law, 25th Anniv. A739

**1971, July 30**
**980** A739 5ch multicolored .60 .25

Universal Compulsory Primary Education, 15th Anniv. — A740

**1971, Aug. 1**
**981** A740 10ch multicolored .70 .25

South Korean Revolutionaries — A741

Designs: 5ch, Choe Yong Do (1923-69). 10ch (No. 983), Kim Jong Thae (1926-69), portrait with rioters killing U.S. soldier. 10ch (No. 984), Guerrilla fighter with machine gun & Red Book, battle scene.

**1971, Aug. 1**
**982-984** A741 Set of 3 1.40 .45

Nationalization of Industry, 25th Anniv. — A742

**1971, Aug. 10**
**985** A742 5ch multicolored 2.75 .25

Anti-Imperialist, Anti-U.S. Struggle — A743

Designs: 10ch (No. 986), N. Korean soldier, U.S. prisoners. 10ch (No. 987), S. Korean guerrilla fighter. 10ch (No. 988), N. Vietnamese soldiers, map. 10ch (No. 989), Cuban soldier, map. 10ch (No. 990), African guerrilla fighters, map. 40ch, six soldiers of various nationalities bayoneting dismembered U.S. soldier.

**1971, Aug. 12**
**986-991** A743 Set of 6 5.00 1.00

Kim Il Sung University, 25th Anniv. A744

**1971, Oct. 1**
**992** A744 10ch multicolored .55 .25

Large Machines — A745

Designs: 2ch, 6,000-ton press. 5ch, Refrigerated cargo ship "Ponghwasan." 10ch (No. 995), Sungrisan heavy truck. 10ch (No. 996), Bulldozer.

**1971, Nov. 2** **Litho.**
**993-996** A745 Set of 4 6.50 .50

Tasks of the 6-Year Plan — A746

Designs (all 10ch): No. 997, Workers & text on red field. No. 998, Mining. No. 999, Consumer goods. No. 1000, Lathe. No. 1001, Construction equipment. No. 1002, Consumer electronic products. No. 1003, Grains, farming. No. 1004, Railway track, transportation. No. 1005, Freighter. No. 1006, Hand with wrench, manufacturing scenes. No. 1007, Crate & export goods on dock.

**1971, Nov. 2** **Photo.**
**997-1007** A746 Set of 11 14.50 1.75

Cultural Revolution — A747

Designs: 2ch, Technical students, university. 5ch, Mechanic. 10ch (No. 1010), Chemist. 10ch (No. 1011), Composer at piano. 10ch (No. 1012), Schoolchildren.

**1971, Nov. 2**
**1008-1012** A747 Set of 5 4.50 .40

Ideological Revolution — A748

Designs (all 10ch): No. 1013, Workers with Red Books, banners. No. 1014, Worker with hydraulic drill. No. 1015, Two workers reading Red Book. No. 1016, Workers' lecture.

**1971, Nov. 2**
**1013-1016** A748 Set of 4 2.50 .40

Improvement in Living Standards — A749

**1971, Nov. 2**
**1017** A749 10ch multicolored .60 .25

Solidarity with International Revolutionary Forces — A750

Designs (all 10ch): No. 1018, Revolutionary placards being driven into U.S. soldier. No. 1019, Japanese militarists being hammered by mallet. No. 1020, Bayoneted rifles held aloft. No. 1021, Armed international revolutionaries advancing, horiz.

**1971, Nov. 2**
**1018-1021** A750 Set of 4 3.25 .50

6-Year Plan — A751

**1971, Nov. 2**
**1022** A751 10ch multicolored 1.75 .25

Three sets were prepared for release on Nov. 2, 1971, but were not issued: Butterflies (3 stamps), value $2,500; Korean Reunification (2 10ch stamps), value $750; Cultural Revolution/Improvement of the People's Living Standards (7 10ch stamps), value $5,000.

*Samil Wolgan* Monthly, 35th Anniv. — A752

**1971, Dec. 1**
**1023** A752 10ch multicolored 1.10 .25

### Domestic Printings

Sometime in the early 1970s, the DPRK post office begin to produce separate printings of some issues for domestic use. These stamps were generally printed on poorer quality white or brownish unsurfaced papers and demonstrated poorer overall production values. Serious students of the period are now working to identify just which stamps exist in this form and how to easily distinguish them from the higher-quality printings intended for sale to foreign collectors. At this time, these domestic-use printings are generally sold for $5-$20 per stamp.

Poultry Breeding — A753

Designs: 5ch, Chicks. 10ch, Chickens & automated henhouse. 40ch, Eggs, canned chicken, dead chickens hanging on hooks.

**1972, Feb. 1**
**1024-1026** A753 Set of 3 2.25 .60

War Films A754

Designs (all 10ch): No. 1027, Man & woman, from *Vintage Shrine.* No. 1028, Guerrilla bayoneting soldier in back, from *The Fate of a Self-Defense Corps Member.* No. 1029, Young woman with a pistol, from *Sea of Blood.*

**1972, Apr. 1**
**1027-1029** A754 Set of 3 3.75 .30

A 10ch value picturing *The Flower Girl* was prepared but not issued. Value $2,000.

Kim Il Sung A755

Kim at Military Conference — A756

Kim by Lake Chon — A757

Various portraits of Kim Il Sung: No. 1030, shown. No. 1031, In heroic pose. No. 1032, shown. No. 1033, In wheatfield. No. 1034, In factory. No. 1035, With foundry workers. No. 1036, Aboard whaling ship. No. 1037, Visiting hospital. No. 1038, Visiting fruit farm. No. 1039, With railroad surveyors. No. 1040, With women workers. No. 1041, Sitting with villagers. No. 1042, Touring chicken plant. No. 1043, On park bench with children. No. 1044, Portrait with marchers.

**1972, Apr. 15** **Litho.**
**1030** A755 5ch multicolored .25 .25
*a.* Strip of 3, #1030-1031, 1044 2.25

| | | | | | |
|---|---|---|---|---|---|
| **1031** | A755 | 5ch | multicolored | .25 | .25 |
| **1032** | A756 | 5ch | multicolored | .25 | .25 |
| *a.* | | Pair, #1032, 1043 | | 1.10 | |
| **1033** | A756 | 10ch | multicolored | .50 | .25 |
| *a.* | | Block of 10, #1033-1042 | | 10.00 | |
| **1034** | A756 | 10ch | multicolored | 2.25 | .40 |
| **1035** | A756 | 10ch | multicolored | .25 | .25 |
| **1036** | A756 | 10ch | multicolored | .65 | .25 |
| **1037** | A756 | 10ch | multicolored | 1.00 | .25 |
| **1038** | A756 | 10ch | multicolored | .25 | .25 |
| **1039** | A756 | 10ch | multicolored | 2.25 | .25 |
| **1040** | A756 | 10ch | multicolored | 1.40 | .25 |
| **1041** | A756 | 10ch | multicolored | .25 | .25 |
| **1042** | A756 | 10ch | multicolored | .45 | .25 |
| **1043** | A755 | 40ch | multicolored | .60 | .25 |
| **1044** | A756 | 1wn | multicolored | .90 | .40 |
| | | *Nos. 1030-1044 (15)* | | 11.50 | 4.05 |

**Souvenir Sheet**

| | | | | | |
|---|---|---|---|---|---|
| **1045** | A757 | 3wn | multicolored | 10.00 | 6.00 |

60th birthday of Kim Il Sung.

Nos. 1030-1031 and 1044, 1032 and 1043, and 1033-1042, respectively, were printed setenant within their sheets.

A 4-stamp set (2ch, 5ch, 10ch and 15ch values) honoring the 20th Olympic Games were prepared but not issued. Value $3,000.

Guerrilla Army, 40th Anniv. — A758

**1972, Apr. 25** **Photo.**

**1046** A758 10ch multicolored .95 .25

Revolutionary Sites — A759

Designs: 2ch, Ryongpho. 5ch, Onjong. 10ch, Kosanjin. 40ch, Jonsung.

**1972, July 27** **Litho.**

**1047-1050** A759 Set of 4 2.25 .50

Olympic Games, Munich A760

Designs: 2ch, Volleyball. 5ch, Boxing, horiz. 10ch (No. 1053), Judo. 10ch (No. 1054), Wrestling, horiz. 40ch, Rifle-shooting.

**1972, Oct. 1**

**1051-1055** A760 Set of 5 3.75 1.00

Chollima Street, Pyongyang — A761

Designs (street scenes): 5ch, salmon & black. 10ch (No. 1057), dull yellow & black. 10ch (No. 1058), green & black.

**1972, Nov. 1**

**1056-1058** A761 Set of 3 5.50 .85

Resource Management — A762

Designs: 5ch, Dredging river. 10ch, Forest conservation. 40ch, Tideland reclamation.

**1972, Nov. 1** **Photo.**

**1059-1061** A762 Set of 3 2.75 .35

6-Year Plan - Metallurgical — A763

Designs (all 10ch): No. 1062, Sheet metal, ingots, smelters. No. 1063, Pipes, foundry.

**1972, Nov. 1**

**1062-1063** A763 Set of 2 3.75 .35

6-Year Plan — Mining Industry — A764

Designs (all 10ch): No. 1064, Iron ore. No. 1065, Coal.

**1972, Nov. 1** **Litho.**

**1064-1065** A764 Set of 2 4.50 .45

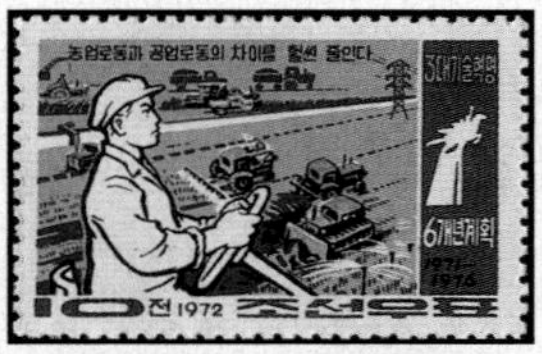

Three Major Goals of the Technical Revolution — A765

Designs (all 10ch): No. 1066, Agricultural mechanization. No. 1067, Industrial automation. No. 1068, Lightening of women's household chores.

**1972, Nov. 2** **Photo.**

**1066-1068** A765 Set of 3 3.25 .45

6-Year Plan - Machine-Building — A766

Designs (all 10ch): No. 1069, Machine tools. No. 1070, Electronics & automation tools. No. 1071, Single-purpose machines.

**1972, Nov. 2** **Photo.**

**1069-1071** A766 Set of 3 2.75 .45

6-Year Plan — Chemical Industry — A767

Designs (all 10ch): No. 1072, Chemical fertilizers, herbicides, insecticides. No. 1073, Tire, tubing, various chemical products.

**1972, Nov. 2**

**1072-1073** A767 Set of 2 2.25 .35

6-Year Plan — Light Industry — A768

Designs (all 10ch): No. 1074, Clothing, textiles. No. 1075, Clothing, kitchenware. No. 1076, Household Goods.

**1972, Nov. 2**

**1074-1076** A768 Set of 3 2.75 .45

6-Year Plan - Rural Economy — A769

Designs (all 10ch): No. 1077, Irrigating field. No. 1078, Bulldozers levelling field. No. 1079, Applying chemical fertilizer.

**1972, Nov. 2** **Litho.**

**1077-1079** A769 Set of 3 2.50 .45

6-Year Plan - Transportation — A770

Designs (all 10ch): No. 1080, Electric train. No. 1081, New railway construction. No. 1082, Coastal & river transport.

**1972, Nov. 2**

**1080-1082** A770 Set of 3 6.50 .45

6-Year Plan - Military — A771

Designs (all 10ch): No. 1083, Soldier with artillery shell. No. 1084, Navy gunner. No. 1085, Air Force pilot in cockpit.

**1972, Nov. 2**

**1083-1085** A771 Set of 3 4.50 .45

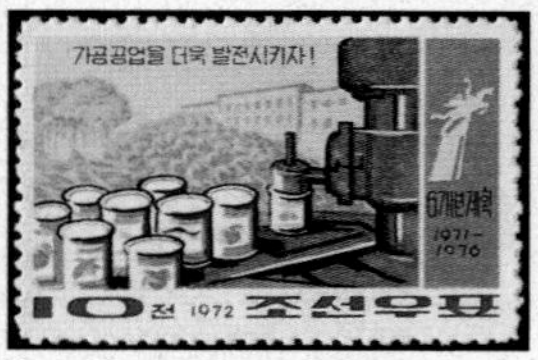

6-Year Plan - Food Storage — A772

Designs (all 10ch): No. 1086, Food Processing. No. 1087, Packing foodstuffs. No. 1088, Food storage (radishes, fruit, fish).

**1972, Nov. 2** **Photo.**

**1086-1088** A772 Set of 3 8.25 .45

Struggle for Reunification of Korea — A773

Designs (all 10ch): No. 1089, South Koreans with banners praising Kim Il Sung. No. 1090, S. Korean guerrillas killing U.S. & S. Korean soldiers. No. 1091, March of armed S. Korean workers. No. 1092, S. Koreans rioting, rioters on top of U.S. tank. No. 1093, N. Koreans demonstrating in support of S. Korean revolutionaries. No. 1094, International revolutionaries condemning U.S. soldier. No. 1095, S. Korean marchers carrying banner & Red Book.

**1972, Nov. 2**

**1089-1095** A773 Set of 7 11.00 1.00

A 10ch anti-United States propaganda stamp was prepared for release Nov. 2, 1972, but not issued. Value $750.

Machine Tools A774

Designs: 5ch, Single-axis automatic lathe. 10ch, *Kusong-3* lathe. 40ch, 2,000-ton crank press.

**1972, Dec. 1** **Litho.**

**1096-1098** A774 Set of 3 2.75 .45

National Elections A775

Designs (both 10ch): No. 1099, Voter with registration card. No. 1100, Voter casting ballot.

**1972, Dec. 12** **Photo.**

**1099-1100** A775 Set of 2 1.90 .30

Korean People's Army, 25th Anniv. — A776

Designs: 5ch, Soldier. 10ch, Sailor. 40ch, Pilot.

**1973, Feb. 8**
**1101-1103** A776 Set of 3 3.75 .75

Mangyongdae Historic Sites — A777

Scenes from Kim Il Sung's childhood: 2ch, Wrestling site. 5ch, "Warship" rock. 10ch (No. 1106), Swinging tree, vert. 10ch (No. 1107), Sliding rock. 40ch, Fishing spot on riverside.

**1973, Apr. 15**
**1104-1108** A777 Set of 5 4.50 1.00

Mansu Hill Monument A778

Designs: 10ch (No. 1109), Anti-Japanese revolutionary monument. 10ch (No. 1110), Socialist Revolution & Construction monument. 40ch, Statue of Kim Il Sung. 3w, Korean Revolution Museum, hrz.

**1973, Apr. 15** **Litho.**
**1109-1112** A778 Set of 4 13.00 2.25

Secret Revolutionary Camps in the 1932 Guerrilla War — A780

Designs: 10ch (No. 1113), Karajibong Camp. 10ch (No. 1114), Soksaegoi Camp.

**1973, Apr. 26**
**1113-1114** A780 Set of 2 1.40 .25

Anti-Japanese Propaganda — A781

**1973, June 1**
**1115** A781 10ch multicolored .55 .25

Reunification of Korea — A782

Designs: 2ch, Finger pointing down at destroyed U.S. tanks. 5ch, Electric train, crane lifting tractor. 10ch (No. 1118), Hand holding declaration, map of Korea. 10ch (No. 1119), Leaflets falling on happy crowd. 40ch, Flag & globe.

**1973, June 23**
**1116-1120** A782 Set of 5 6.50 .75

Trucks & Tractors A783

Designs: 10ch (No. 1121), Trucks. 10ch (No. 1122), Bulldozer, tractors.

**1973, July 1** **Photo.**
**1121-1122** A783 Set of 2 1.60 .30

Socialist Countries' Junior Women's Volleyball Games — A784

**1973, July 27** **Litho.**
**1123** A784 10ch multicolored 1.10 .25

North Korean Victory in the Korean War A785

Designs: 10ch (No. 1124), Triumphant N. Koreans & battlefield scene. 10ch (No. 1125), N. Koreans & symbols of military & industrial power.

**1973, July 27** **Photo.**
**1124-1125** A785 Set of 2 3.25 .30

Mansudae Art Troupe — A786

Dances: 10ch, *Snow Falls,* dancers with red streamers. 25ch, *Bumper Harvest of Apples.* 40ch, *Azalea of the Fatherland.*

**1973, Aug. 1** **Litho.**
**1126-1128** A786 Set of 3 4.50 .75

Compulsory Secondary Education, 10th Anniv. A787

**1973, Sept. 1**
**1129** A787 10ch multicolored .85 .25

Writings of Kim Il Sung — A788

Designs (all 10ch): No. 1130, *On Juche in Our Revolution* (claret scene). No. 1131, *Kim Il Sung Selected Works,* crowd holding glowing book aloft. No. 1132, *Let Us Further Strengthen Our Socialist System,* four figures holding open book aloft.

**1973, Sept. 1**
**1130-1132** A788 Set of 3 1.90 .30

See Nos. 1180-1181.

DPRK, 25th Anniv. A789

Designs: 5ch, Foundation of the republic ("1948-1973"). 10ch, Korean War ("1950-1953"). 40ch, Farmer, worker & soldier with scenes of economic development in background ("1948-1973").

**1973, Sept. 9**
**1133-1135** A789 Set of 3 2.75 .60

Mt. Myohyang Scenes — A790

Designs: 2ch, Popwang Peak. 5ch, Inhodae Rock. 10ch, Taeha Falls, vert. 40ch, Ryongyon Falls, vert.

**1973, Oct. 1** **Photo.**
**1136-1139** A790 Set of 4 8.25 .75

Party Founding Museum — A791

**1973, Oct. 10**
**1140** A791 1w multicolored 2.25 .45

People's Athletic Meeting A792

Designs: 2ch, Soccer player, basketball players. 5ch, High jumper, women sprinters. 10ch (No. 1143), Wrestlers, skier. 10ch (No. 1144), Speed skaters, skier. 40ch, Parachutist, motorcyclists.

**1973, Nov. 1** **Litho.**
**1141-1145** A792 Set of 5 6.50 .75

Socialist Countries' Junior Weightlifting Competition A793

**1973, Nov. 21**
**1146** A793 10ch multicolored 1.40 .25

Moran Hill Scenery — A794

Designs: 2ch, Chongryu Cliff. 5ch, Moran Waterfalls. 10ch, Pubyok Pavilion. 40ch, Ulmil Pavilion.

**1973, Nov. 1**
**1147-1150** A794 Set of 4 9.25 1.00

Mt. Kumgang Scenery A795

Designs: 2ch, Mujigae (Rainbow) Bridge. 5ch, Suspension bridge, Okryu Valley, horiz. 10ch (No. 1153), Chonnyo Peak. 10ch (No. 1154), Chilchung Rock & Sonji Peak, horiz. 40ch, Sujong & Pari Peaks, horiz.

**1973, Nov. 1**
**1151-1155** A795 Set of 5 8.25 1.00

Magnolia A796

**1973, Nov. 1**
**1156** A796 10ch multicolored 2.25 .40

South Korean Revolutionary Struggle — A797

Designs (both 10ch): No. 1157, Mob beating U.S. soldier. No. 1158, Armed demonstrators killing U.S. soldier.

**1973, Nov. 2** **Photo.**
**1157-1158** A797 Set of 2 5.25 .30

Scenes from *Butterflies and Cock* Fairy Tale — A798

Designs: 2ch, Cock appearing in the village of butterflies. 5ch, Butterflies discussing how to repel cock. No. 1161, 10ch, Cock chasing butterflies with basket. No. 1162, 10ch, Butterflies luring cock up cliff. 40ch, Cock chasing butterflies off cliff edge. 90ch, Cock drowning.

**1973, Dec. 1** **Litho.**
**1159-1164** A798 Set of 6 17.50 1.20

For surcharge, see No. 4556.

Revolutionary Sites — A799

Designs: 2ch, Buildings, Yonphung. 5ch, Buildings, iron-rail fence, Hyangha. 10ch, Three buildings surrounding courtyard, Changgol. 40ch, Monuments in park-like setting, Paeksong.

**1973, Dec. 1**
**1165-1168** A799 Set of 4 3.25 .60

Modern Buildings in Pyongyang — A800

Designs: 2ch, Science Library, Kim Il Sung University. 5ch, Building No. 2, Kim Il Sung University, vert. 10ch, War Museum. 40ch, People's Palace of Culture. 90ch, Pyongyang Indoor Stadium.

**1973, Dec. 1** **Photo.**
**1169-1173** A800 Set of 5 4.00 1.00

Nos. 1171-1172 are 60x24mm.

Socialist Constitution of North Korea — A801

Designs (all 10ch): No. 1174, Socialist Constitution, national scenes. No. 1175, Marchers with Red Book & national arms. No. 1176, Marchers with Red Books, national flag, banners.

**1973, Dec. 27** **Litho.**
**1174-1176** A801 Set of 3 1.60 .60

Korean Songbirds A802

Designs: 5ch, Great reed warbler. 10ch (No. 1178), Gray starling (green background). 10ch (No. 1179), Daurian starling (pink background).

**1973, Dec. 28** **Photo.**
**1177-1179** A802 Set of 3 14.50 2.00

Writings of Kim Il Sung A803

Designs: No. 1180, 10ch, *Let Us Intensify the Anti-Imperialist, Anti-U.S. Struggle,* bayonets threatening U.S. soldier. No. 1181, 10ch, *On the Chollima Movement and the Great Upsurge of Socialist Construction,* Chollima statue.

**1974, Jan. 10** **Litho.**
**1180-1181** A803 Set of 2 1.60 .30

Opening of Pyongyang Metro — A804

Designs (all 10ch): No. 1182, Train at platform. No. 1183, Escalators. No. 1184, Underground station hall.

**1974, Jan. 20**
**1182-1184** A804 Set of 3 2.75 .45

Socialist Construction — A805

Designs (all 10ch): No. 1185, Capital construction. No. 1186, Industry (foundry), vert. No. 1187, Agriculture. No. 1188, Transport. No. 1189, Fishing industry.

**1974, Feb. 20**
**1185-1189** A805 Set of 5 6.50 1.00

*Theses on the Socialist Rural Question in Our Country,* 10th Anniv. of Publication — A806

**1974, Feb. 25**
**1190** A806 10ch Strip of 3, #a-c 2.75 .50

Farm Machines A807

Designs: 2ch, Compost sprayer. 5ch, *Jonjin* tractor. 10ch, *Taedoksan* tractor (with flat bed).

**1974, Feb. 25** **Photo.**
**1193-1195** A807 Set of 3 3.25 .45

N. Korean Victories at 1973 Sports Contests A808

Designs: 2ch, Archery (Grenoble). 5ch, Gymnastics (Varna). 10ch, Boxing (Bucharest). 20ch, Volleyball (Pyongyang). 30ch, Rifle-shooting (Sofia). 40ch, Judo (Tbilisi). 60ch, Model aircraft flying (Vienna), horiz. 1.50w, Table tennis (Beijing), horiz.

***Perf. 11, 12 (#1196, 1202-1203)***
**1974, Mar. 10** **Litho.**
**1196-1203** A808 Set of 8 11.00 2.00

For surcharges, see Nos. 4562, 4564, 4600.

D.P.R.K.: World's First Tax-Free Country — A809

**1974, Apr. 1** ***Perf. 11***
**1204** A809 10ch multicolored 1.10 .25

Revolutionary Activities of Kim Il Sung — A810

Designs (all 10ch): No. 1205, Kim at Nanhutou Meeting (in log room). No. 1206, Kim writing the 10-Point Program in forest. No. 1207, Kim instructing revolutionary (sitting on bench, outdoor winter scene). No. 1208, Kim at Battle of Laoheishan.

**1974, Apr. 15** ***Perf. 12***
**1205-1208** A810 Set of 4 3.00 .60

Scenes from the Revolutionary Opera *The Flower Girl* — A811

Designs: 2ch, Kkot Pun's blind younger sister. 5ch, Death of Kkot Pun's mother. 10ch, Kkot Pun resists landlord. 40ch, Kkot Pun setting out on the road of revolution.

**1974, Apr. 30**
**1209-1212** A811 Set of 4 12.00 .60

**Souvenir Sheet**

**1213** A811 50ch multicolored 16.50 1.50

No. 1213 contains one larger 50ch value, depicting Kroi Pun (The Flower Girl) and the flowers of Revolution, imperf.

Pyongyang Zoo, 15th Anniv. — A812

A813

Designs: 2ch, Wildcat. 5ch, Lynx. No. 1216, 10ch, Fox. No. 1217, 10ch. Wild boar. 20ch, Wolf. 40ch, Bear. 60ch, Leopard. 70ch, Korean tiger. 90ch, Lion.

No. 1223: a, 10ch, Wildcat. b, 30ch, Lynx. c, 50ch, Leopard. d, 60ch, Tiger.

**1974, May 10** ***Perf. 11***
**1214-1222** A812 Set of 9 14.50 2.50

**Souvenir Sheet**

**1223** A813 Sheet of 4, imperf 60.00 —

For surcharges, see Nos. 4541, 4579.

Wild Roses — A814

Designs: 2ch, Prickly wild rose. 5ch, Yellow sweet briar. 10ch (No. 1226), Pink aromatic rose. 10ch (No. 1227), Aronia sweet briar (yellow centers). 40ch, Rosa rugosa.

**1974, May 20**
**1224-1228** A814 Set of 5 8.25 1.00

Souvenir Sheet

Kim Il Sung with Children — A815

**1974, June 1** ***Imperf***
**1229** A815 1.20w multicolored 8.25 7.50

Wild Flowering Plants — A816

Designs: 2ch, Chinese trumpet vine. 5ch, Day lily. 10ch, Shooting star lily. 20ch, Tiger lily. 40ch, Azalea. 60ch, Yellow day lily.

**1974, May 20** ***Perf. 11***
**1230-1235** A816 Set of 6 8.25 1.00

Universal Postal Union, Cent. — A817

U.P.U. emblem and: 10ch, Letter carrier and construction site. 25ch, Chollima statue. 40ch, World map & airplanes.

**1974, June 30** ***Perf. 12***
**1236-1238** A817 Set of 3 6.00 .50

A 60ch souvenir sheet was prepared but not issued. Value $750. For surcharge, see No. 4567.

Amphibians — A818

Designs: 2ch, Black spotted frog. 5ch, Oriental fire belly toad. 10ch, North American bull frog. 40ch, Common toad.

**1974, July 10** ***Perf. 11***
**1239-1242** A818 Set of 4 15.50 1.50

For surcharge, see No. 4542.

Soviet Space Flights — A819

Designs: 10ch, Electron 1 & 2. 20ch, Proton 1. 30ch, Venera 3. 40ch, Venera 5 & 6. 50ch, Launch of Chinese satellite Chicomsat 1. 1w, Space flight of dogs "Bjelka" and "Strjelka."

**1974, July 10**
**1243-1246** A819 Set of 4 3.75 .60

**Souvenir Sheets**
**Imperf**

**1247** A819 50ch multicolored 8.25 1.00
**1248** A819 1w multicolored 18.50 3.00

Nos. 1247-1248 each contain one 47x72mm stamp.

Korean Paintings — A820

Designs: 2ch, Woman in Namgang Village. 5ch, Old Man on the Raktong River (60x49mm). 10ch, Inner Kumgang in the Morning. 20ch, Mt. Kumgang (60x49mm). 1.50w, Evening Glow Over Kangson.

**1974, July 10**
**1249-1252** A820 Set of 4 5.75 .75

**Souvenir Sheet**
**Imperf**

**1253** A820 1.50w multicolored 11.00 10.00

For surcharge, see No. 4592.

Korean Civil Aviation A821

Designs: 2ch, Antonov AN-2. 5ch, Lisunov LI-2. 10ch, Ilyushin IL-14P. 40ch, Antonov AN-24. 60ch, Ilyushin IL-18. 90ch, Antonov AN-24.

**1974, Aug. 1**
**1254-1258** A821 Set of 5 9.25 1.75

**Souvenir Sheet**
**Imperf**

**1259** A821 90ch multicolored 13.00 6.50

No. 1264 contains one 49x30mm stamp.

Alpine Plants — A822

Designs: 2ch, Rhododendron. 5ch, White mountain-avens. 10ch, Shrubby cinquefoil. 20ch, Poppies. 40ch, Purple mountain heather. 60ch, Oxytropis anertii.

**1974, Aug. 10** ***Perf. 12***
**1260-1265** A822 Set of 6 7.00 1.75

Korean Paintings — A823

Designs: 10ch, Sobaek Stream in the Morning. 20ch, Combatants of Mt. Laohei (60x40mm).. 30ch, Spring on the Terraced Field. 40ch, Night of Tideland. 60ch, Daughter.

**1974, Aug. 15** ***Perf. 11***
**1266-1270** A823 Set of 5 12.00 2.00

For surcharge, see No. 4563.

Italian Communist Newspaper L'Unita, 50th Anniv. — A824

**1974, Sept. 1** ***Imperf***
**1271** A824 1.50w multicolored 24.50 5.00

Revolutionary Sites — A825

Designs: 5ch, Munmyong. 10ch, Unha (log cabin).

**1974, Sept. 9** ***Perf. 11***
**1272-1273** A825 Set of 2 1.40 .25

Oil-producing Crops — A826

Designs: 2ch, Sesame. 5ch, Perilla-oil plant. 10ch, Sunflower. 40ch, Castor bean.

**1974, Sept. 30**
**1274-1277** A826 Set of 4 5.50 1.00

For surcharge, see No. 4543.

Revolutionary Activities of Kim Il Sung — A827

Designs (all 10ch): No. 1278, Portrait in guerrilla uniform, vert. No. 1279, On horseback. No. 1280, Helping a farm family. No. 1281, Negotiating anti-Japanese united front with Chinese commander.

**1974, Oct. 10** ***Perf. 12***
**1278-1281** A827 Set of 4 3.25 .60

No. 1278 is 42x65mm. Nos. 1279-1281 are 52x34.5mm.

Grand Monument on Mansu Hill — A828

Designs (all 10ch): No. 1282, Soldiers marching right, lead figure holding rifle aloft. No. 1283, Soldiers marching left, lead figure holding rifle aloft. No. 1284, Workers marching right, lead figure holding torch aloft. No. 1285, Workers marching left, lead figure holding torch aloft.

**1974, Oct. 10** ***Perf. 11***
**1282-1285** A828 Set of 4 2.75 .60

Deep-Sea Fishing — A829

Designs: a, 2ch, Factory ship *Chilbosan.* b, 5ch, Factory ship *Paektusan.* c, 10ch, Cargo ship *Moranbong.* d, 20ch, All-purpose ship. e, 30ch, Trawler. f, 40ch, Stern trawler.

**1974, Nov. 20**
**1286** A829 Block of 6 7.75 2.00
*a.-f.* Any single 1.25 .30

A830

Kim Il Sung's Crossing of the Amnok River, 50th Anniv.

**1975, Feb. 3** ***Perf. 12***
**1287** A830 10ch multicolored .65 .25

Pak Yong Sun — A831

33rd World Table Tennis Championships — A832

**1975, Feb. 16** ***Perf. 11x12***
**1288** A831 10ch multicolored 1.90 .25

**Souvenir Sheet**
***Imperf***

**1289** A832 80ch multicolored 3.25 1.50

Honoring Pak Yong Sun, winner of the 33rd World Table Tennis Championship, Calcutta.

Pyongyang Zoo — A833

Designs: 10ch (No. 1290), Zebra. 10ch (No. 1291), African buffalo. 20ch, Giant panda, horiz. 25ch, Bactrian camel. 30ch, Indian elephant, horiz.

***Perf. 12¼, 10¾ (#1291, 1294)***

**1975, Feb. 20**

**1290-1294** A833 Set of 5 6.25 1.00

Koguryo Period Tomb Paintings, 7th Century — A834

Designs: 10ch, Blue dragon. 15ch, White tiger. 25ch, Red phoenix, vert. 40ch, Turtle and snake.

**1975, Mar. 20** ***Perf. 12***

**1295-1298** A834 Set of 4 6.50 1.00

*The Guerrilla Base in Spring* (1968) — A835

*Guerrilla Army Landing at Unggi* (1969) — A836

*The Sewing Team Members* (1961) — A837

*North Manchuria of China in Spring* (1969) — A838

*Comrade Kim Jong Suk Giving Guidance to the Children's Corps Members* (1970) — A839

**1975, Mar. 30**

| | | | | | |
|---|---|---|---|---|---|
| **1299** | A835 | 10ch | multicolored | .55 | .25 |
| **1300** | A836 | 10ch | multicolored | .55 | .25 |
| **1301** | A837 | 15ch | multicolored | .85 | .25 |
| **1302** | A838 | 20ch | multicolored | 1.75 | .25 |
| **1303** | A839 | 30ch | multicolored | 1.40 | .25 |
| | *Nos. 1299-1303 (5)* | | | 5.10 | 1.25 |

Korean Paintings, Anti-Japanese Struggle. Compare with Nos. 1325-1329, 1330-1335.

Cosmonauts' Day — A840

Designs: 10ch, Cosmonaut. 30ch, Lunokhod-2 on Moon, horiz. 40ch, Soyuz and Saiyut coupling, horiz.

**1975, Apr. 12** ***Perf. 11¾***

**1304-1306** A840 Set of 3 3.25 .50

Revolutionary Activities of Kim Il Sung — A841

Multicolor portraits of Kim Il Sung: 10ch (No. 1307), Speaking with troops in tent (aqua frame). 10ch (No. 1308), Greeting peasants bringing supplies (tan frame). 10ch (No. 1309), Speaking to crowd, arm upraised (light blue frame). 10ch (No. 1310), With soldiers around winter campfire (pale tan frame). 10ch (No. 1311), Lecturing to troops (pink frame). 15ch, At head of troop column in forest. 25ch, Standing by lake. 30ch, Speaking with peasants, child in lap. 40ch, Presiding over staff meeting, in tent.

**1975, Apr. 15** ***Perf. 12***

**1307-1315** A841 Set of 9 8.25 2.00

Souvenir Sheet

Victory Monument — A842

**1975, Apr. 15** ***Imperf***

**1316** A842 1w multicolored 16.50 4.00

Battle of Pochonbo, 38th Anniversary.

Flower Basket & Kim Il Sung's Birthplace A843

Kim Il Sung's Birthplace, Mangyongdae — A844

**1975, Apr. 15** ***Perf. 12***

| | | | | | |
|---|---|---|---|---|---|
| **1317** | A843 | 10ch | multicolored | .35 | .25 |
| **1318** | A844 | 40ch | multicolored | 1.60 | .25 |

63rd Birthday of Kim Il Sung.

April 19 South Korean Popular Uprising, 15th Anniv. — A845

**1975, Apr. 19** ***Perf. 11***

**1319** A845 10ch multicolored .65 .25

Ri Dynasty Paintings A846

Designs: 5ch, *Kingfisher at Lotus Pond*. 10ch, *Crabs*. 15ch, *Rose of Sharon*. 25ch, *Lotus and Water Bird*. 30ch, *Tree Peony and Cock and Hen*.

**1975, May 10**

**1320-1324** A846 Set of 5 13.00 1.25

*On the Road of Advance Southward* (1966) A847

*The Assigned Post* (1968) A848

*For the Sake of the Fatherland* (1965) — A849

*Retaliation* (1970) — A850

*The Awaited Ranks* (1970) — A851

**1975, May 10**

| | | | | | |
|---|---|---|---|---|---|
| **1325** | A847 | 5ch | multicolored | 2.25 | .25 |
| **1326** | A848 | 10ch | multicolored | 1.25 | .25 |
| **1327** | A849 | 15ch | multicolored | 1.90 | .25 |
| **1328** | A850 | 25ch | multicolored | 2.75 | .25 |
| **1329** | A851 | 30ch | multicolored | 4.50 | .25 |
| | *Nos. 1325-1329 (5)* | | | 12.65 | 1.25 |

Korean Paintings, Anti-Japanese Struggle. For surcharge, see No. 4606.

*Blue Signal Lamp* (1960) A852

*Pine Tree* (1966) A853

*Night with Snowfall* (1963) — A854

*Smelters* (1968) — A855

*Reclamation of Tideland* (1961) — A856

*Mt. Paekgum* (1966) — A857

**1975, May 20**

| | | | | |
|---|---|---|---|---|
| **1330** | A852 | 10ch multicolored | 1.10 | .25 |
| **1331** | A853 | 10ch multicolored | 3.75 | .25 |
| **1332** | A854 | 15ch multicolored | 1.10 | .25 |
| **1333** | A855 | 20ch multicolored | 1.25 | .25 |
| **1334** | A856 | 25ch multicolored | 1.25 | .25 |
| **1335** | A857 | 30ch multicolored | 1.25 | .25 |
| | | *Nos. 1330-1335 (6)* | 9.70 | 1.50 |

Korean Paintings. For surcharge, see No. 4596.

Chongryon Assoc. of Koreans in Japan, 20th Anniv. — A858

**1975, May 25** ***Perf. 11¾***

| | | | | |
|---|---|---|---|---|
| **1336** | A858 | 10ch multicolored | 1.10 | — |
| **1337** | A858 | 3w multicolored | 40.00 | — |

Marathon Race of Socialist Countries — A859

**1975, June 8** ***Imperf***

**1338** A859 1w multicolored 22.50 4.00

Diving — A860

Divers: 10ch, Man entering water feet-first. 25ch, Man performing somersalt pike. 40ch, Woman entering water head-first.

**1975, June 20** ***Perf. 10¾***

**1339-1341** A860 Set of 3 3.25 .75

Month of Anti-U.S. Joint Struggle — A861

**1975, June 25** ***Perf. 12¼***

**1342** A861 10ch multicolored 1.40 .25

Fresh-Water Fish — A862

Fish: 10ch (No. 1343), Memorial fish, swimming to left. 10ch (No. 1344), White fish, swimming to right. 15ch, Notch-jowl. 25ch, Amur catfish. 30ch (No. 1347), Catfish, swimming to right. 30ch (No. 1348), Snakehead, swimming to left.

**1975, June 25** ***Perf. 10¾***

**1343-1348** A862 Set of 6 9.25 1.25

A863

10th International Socialist Countries' Junior Friendship Soccer Tournament — A864

Soccer players, with diff. stadiums in background: 5ch, Green border. 10ch, Tan border. 15ch, Lilac border. 20ch, Pale violet border. 50ch, Dull gold border.

***Perf. 10¾, Imperf (#1354)***

**1975, July 10**

**1349-1353** A863 Set of 5 4.50 1.00

**Souvenir Sheet**

**1354** A864 1w multicolored 9.25 3.50

Parrots — A865

Parrots: 10ch, Blue & yellow macaw. 15ch, Sulphur-crested cockatoo. 20ch, Blyth's parakeet. 25ch, Rainbow lory. 30ch, Budgerigar.

**1975, July 10** ***Perf. 12***

**1355-1359** A865 Set of 5 19.50 1.50

For surcharge, see No. 4581.

Saesallim Street A866

Apartment House — A867

Pothonggang Hotel — A868

**1975, July 20** ***Perf. 11, 12 (#1360)***

| | | | | |
|---|---|---|---|---|
| **1360** | A866 | 90ch multicolored | 20.00 | 20.00 |
| **1361** | A867 | 1w multicolored | 25.00 | 25.00 |
| **1362** | A868 | 2w multicolored | 35.00 | 35.00 |
| | | *Nos. 1360-1362 (3)* | 80.00 | 80.00 |

New street, buildings in Pyongyang.

Blossoms A869

Blossoms of Flowering Trees: 10ch, White peach. 15ch, Red peach. 20ch, Red plum. 25ch, Apricot. 30ch, Cherry.

**1975, Aug. 20** ***Perf. 10¾***

**1363-1367** A869 Set of 5 7.75 1.50

Diamond Mts. Landscapes A870

Designs: 5ch, Sejon Peak. 10ch, Chonson Rock. 15ch, Pisa Gate. 25ch, Manmulsang. 30ch, Chaeha Peak.

**1975, Aug. 20** ***Perf. 11¾***

**1368-1372** A870 Set of 5 7.75 1.00

Flowers A871

Designs: 5ch, Azalea. 10ch, White azalea. 15ch, Mountain rhododendron. 20ch, White rhododendron. 25ch, Rhododendron. 30ch, Yellow rhododendron.

**1975, Aug. 30** ***Perf. 10¾***

**1373-1378** A871 Set of 6 6.50 1.50

A872

Aerial Sports for National Defence — A873

Designs: 5ch (No. 1379), Gliders. 5ch (No. 1380), Remote-controlled model airplane. 10ch (No. 1381), Parachutist in free fall, vert.

10ch (No. 1382), Parachutists landing, vert. 20ch, Parachutist with bouquet of flowers. 50ch, Formation skydiving.

***Perf. 12x11¾, Imperf (#1384)***

**1975, Sept. 9**

**1379-1383** A872 Set of 5 5.00 .75

**Souvenir Sheet**

**1384** A873 50ch multicolored 6.00 .50

Flowers — A874

Fruit tree blossoms: 10ch, Wild apple. 15ch, Wild pear. 20ch, Hawthorn. 25ch, Chinese quince. 30ch, Flowering quince.

**1975, Sept. 30** ***Perf. 12¼x12***

**1385-1389** A874 Set of 5 5.00 1.25

Korean Workers' Party, 30th Anniv. A875

Designs: 2ch (No. 1390), Symbolic creation of the Juche Idea. 2ch (No. 1391), Korean soldiers above American graves. 5ch (No. 1392), Hand holding torch with Juche inscription. 5ch (No. 1393), Monument of Chollima, idealized city. 10ch (No. 1394), Chollima winged horse and rider with banner. 10ch (No. 1395), Worker with Red Book. 25ch, South Koreans rioting. 70ch, Map of Korea, Red Book, flowers.

90ch (No. 1398), Kim Il Sung addressing workers, horiz. stamp, vert. souvenir sheet. 90ch (No. 1399), Kim with crowd of workers, city skyline in background, horiz. stamp, horiz. souvenir sheet.

***Perf. 12, Imperf (#1398-1399)***

**1975, Oct. 10**

**1390-1397** A875 Set of 8 4.50 1.00
**1398-1399** A875 Set of 2 sheets 8.25 4.00

Return of Kim Il Sung to Pyongyang, 30th Anniv. — A876

**1975, Oct. 14** ***Perf. 12***

**1400** A876 20ch multicolored 1.00 .25

*Redong Sinmun*, 30th Anniv. — A877

**1975, Nov. 1** ***Perf. 11***

**1401** A877 10ch multicolored .85 .25
*a.* 1w, souvenir sheet, imperf 5.50 5.00

Hyonmu Gate A878

Taedong Gate A879

Pothong Gate A880

Jongum Gate A881

Chilsong Gate — A882

***Perf. 12x12¼, 12¼x12 (#1406)***

**1975, Nov. 20**

**1402** A878 10ch multicolored 1.40 .25
**1403** A879 10ch multicolored 1.40 .25
**1404** A880 15ch multicolored 1.90 .25
**1405** A881 20ch multicolored 3.50 .25
**1406** A882 30ch multicolored 5.00 .40
*Nos. 1402-1406 (5)* 13.20 1.40

Ancient gates of Pyongyang.

Mt. Chilbo Views — A883

Designs: No. 1407, 10ch, Mae Rock (pale green border). No. 1408, 10ch, Jangsu Peak (pale yellow border). 15ch, Suri Peak. 20ch, Jangsu Peak, diff. 30ch, Rojok Peak.

**1975, Nov. 30** ***Perf. 12x11¾***

**1407-1411** A883 Set of 5 10.00 1.25

Wangjaesan Monument — A884

Designs: 10ch, Workers marching. 15ch, Soldiers marching. 25ch, Monument beacon tower, vert. 30ch, Base of tower, statues of Kim Il Sung, workers and soldiers.

***Perf. 11¾, 10¾ (#1413)***

**1975, Dec. 20**

**1412-1415** A884 Set of 4 2.75 .75

Banners, Slogan — A885

Banners, Workers — A886

**1976, Jan. 17** ***Perf. 12***

**1416** A885 2ch multicolored .30 .25
**1417** A886 70ch multicolored 1.60 .75

League of Socialist Working Youth, 30th Anniv.

Ducks & Geese A887

Designs: 10ch, Geese. 20ch, Domesticated ducks. 40ch, Kwangpo ducks.

***Perf. 12, 12x12¼ (#1418)***

**1976, Feb. 5**

**1418-1420** A887 Set of 3 8.25 .50

For surcharge, see No. 4519.

Korean People's Army, Sculpture A888

Designs: 5ch, *Oath.* 10ch (No. 1422), *Unity Between Men and Officers*, horiz. 10ch (No. 1423), *This Flag to the Height.*

***Perf. 12, 12¼x12 (#1421)***

**1976, Feb. 8**

**1421-1423** A888 Set of 3 2.75 .50

*Rural Road at Evening* (1965) A889

*Passing-on Technique* (1970) — A890

*Mother* (1965) A891

*Medical Examination in Kindergarten* (1970) — A892

*Doctress of the Village* (1970) — A893

**1976, Feb. 10** ***Perf. 12***

**1424** A889 10ch multicolored .65 .25
**1425** A890 15ch multicolored .70 .25
**1426** A891 25ch multicolored 1.10 .25
**1427** A892 30ch multicolored 1.90 .25
**1428** A893 40ch multicolored 2.25 .35
*Nos. 1424-1428 (5)* 6.60 1.35

Modern Korean paintings.

Agrarian Reform Law, 30th Anniv. — A894

**1976, Mar. 5** ***Perf. 12***

**1429** A894 10ch multicolored .65 .25

Telephone Communication Centenary — A895

Designs: 2ch, Telephones and communication satellite. 5ch, Satellite and antenna. 10ch, Satellite and telecommunications systems. 15ch, Telephone and lineman. 25ch, Satellite and map of receiving stations. 40ch, Satellite and cable-laying barge.
50ch, Satellite and antique telephone.

**Surface Coated Paper**

**1976, Mar. 12** ***Perf. 13¼***
**1430-1435** A895 Set of 6 8.75 1.00
*1435a* Sheet of 8, as #1430-1436 + label, ordinary paper 10.00 —

**Souvenir Sheet**

***Imperf, Without Gum***

**1436** A895 50ch multicolored 3.25 .50

Flowers A896

Designs: 5ch, Cosmos. 10ch, Dahlia. 20ch, Zinnia. 40ch, China aster.

**1976, Mar. 20** ***Perf. 12***
**1437-1440** A896 Set of 4 3.00 1.00

Pukchong Conference, 15th Anniv. — A897

Designs: 5ch, Fruit processing industry. 10ch, Fruit and orchards.

**1976, Apr. 7** ***Perf. 11½x12***
**1441-1442** A897 Set of 2 2.25 .25

Locomotives — A898

Designs: 5ch, Pulgungi electric train. 10ch, Jaju underground electric train. 15ch, Saeppyol diesel locomotive.

**1976, Apr. 10** ***Perf. 11¾***
**1443-1445** A898 Set of 3 3.25 .50

For surcharges, see Nos. 4594, 4603.

Many North Korean issues from 1976 on were also issued imperforate. These imperfs were issued for sale for hard currency, mostly to overseas collectors, and were not valid for postage.

Limited quantities of many sets from Scott No. 1446 on were issued without gum.

Day of Space Flight — A899

Designs: 2ch, Satellite. 5ch, Space station. 10ch, Communications satellite. 15ch, Future space station. 25ch, Satellite. 40ch, Communications satellite.
50ch, Lunar surface vehicle.

**1976, Apr. 12** ***Perf. 13¼***
**1446-1451** A899 Set of 6 3.25 1.00

**Souvenir Sheet**

***Imperf***

**1452** A899 50ch multicolored 1.60 .50

A900

Kim Il Sung, 64th Birthday — A901

**1976, Apr. 15** ***Perf. 12***
**1453** A900 10ch multicolored .85 .25

**Souvenir Sheet**

***Imperf***

**1454** A901 40ch multicolored 5.00 .75

A902

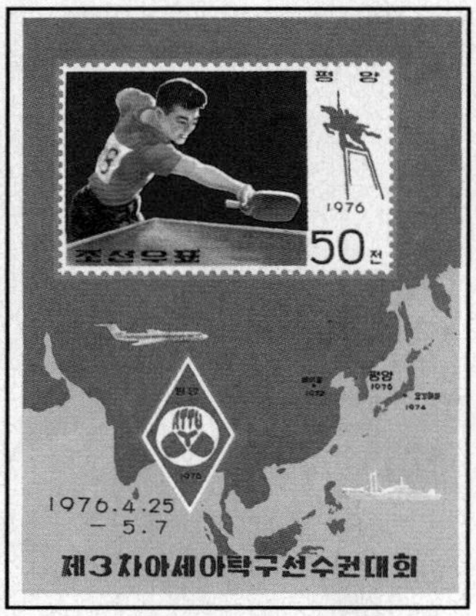

3rd Asian Table Tennis Championships — A903

Designs: 5ch, Paddle and ribbon. 10ch, Three female players with bouquet. 20ch, Female player. 25ch, Male player.

**Without Gum**

**1976, Apr. 25** ***Perf. 12***
**1455-1458** A902 Set of 4 2.50 1.00

**Souvenir Sheet**

***Imperf***

**1459** A903 50ch multicolored 2.50 .75

For surcharges, see Nos. 4582, 4593, 4607.

Association for the Restoration of the Fatherland, 40th Anniv. — A904

**1976, May 5** ***Perf. 12***
**1460** A904 10ch multicolored .50 .25

Pheasants — A905

Designs: 2ch, Golden pheasant. 5ch, Lady Amherst's pheasant. 10ch, Silver pheasant. 15ch, Reeves' pheasant. 25ch, Copper pheasant. 40ch, Albino ring-necked pheasant.
50ch, Ring-necked pheasant.

**Surface Coated Paper**

**1976, May 5** ***Perf. 11¾***
**1461-1466** A905 Set of 6 5.00 1.50
*1466a* Sheet of 8, as #1461-1467 + label, perf 12, ordinary paper 7.50 7.50

**Souvenir Sheet**

***Imperf***

**1467** A905 50ch multicolored 3.50 1.50

Potong River Monument A906

**1976, May 21** ***Perf. 11½***
**1468** A906 10ch multicolored 75.00 —

21st Olympic Games, Montreal — A907

Stadium, Olympic rings, and: 2ch, Runners. 5ch, Diver. 10ch, Judo. 15ch, Gymnast. 25ch, Gymnast. 40ch, Fencers.
50ch, Runner with Olympic Torch.

**Surface Coated Paper**

**1976, July 17** ***Perf. 13¾***
**1469-1474** A907 Set of 6 5.00 1.00
*1474a* Sheet of 8, as #1469-1475 + label, perf 12, ordinary paper 9.00 —

**Souvenir Sheet**

***Imperf***

**1475** A907 50ch multicolored 3.50 1.50

For overprints and surcharges, see Nos. 1632-1638, 4568.

Winners, 21st Olympic Games, Montreal A908

Designs: 2ch, Bronze Medal, Hockey — Pakistan. 5ch, Bronze Medal, Free Pistol — Rudolf Dollinger (Austria). 10ch, Silver Medal, Boxing — Li Byong Uk (DPRK). 15ch, Silver Medal, Cycling — Daniel Morelon (France). 25ch, Gold Medal, Marathon — Waldemar Cierpinski (DDR). 40ch, Gold Medal, Boxing — Ku Yong Jo (DPRK).
50ch, Gold, Silver, Bronze Medals.

**Multicolored, with Winners' Inscriptions in Silver**

**Surface Coated Paper**

**1976, Aug. 2** ***Perf. 13¼***
**1476-1481** A908 Set of 6 6.00 1.00
*1481a* Sheet of 8, as #1476-1482 + label 9.00 —

**Souvenir Sheet**

***Imperf***

**1482** A908 50ch multicolored 4.00 2.00

**Same, with Different Winners' Names**

Designs: 2ch, Swimming — David Wilkie (UK). 5ch, Running — Lasse Viren (Finland). 10ch, Weight Lifting — Vasili Alexeev (USSR). 15ch Swimming — Kornelia Ender (DDR). 25ch, Platform Diving — Klaus Dibiasi (Italy). 40ch, Boxing — Ku Yong Jo (DPRK). No. 1489, 50ch, Gymnastics — Nadia Comaneci (Romania).
No. 1490, 50ch, Kornelia Ender.

**Ordinary Paper**

**1976, Aug. 2** ***Perf. 13¼***
**1483-1489** A908 Sheet of 7 + label 10.00 4.00

**Souvenir Sheet**

***Imperf***

**1490** A908 50ch multi 4.00 2.00

For overprints, see Nos. 1639-1645.

Winners, 21st Olympic Games, Montreal A909

Designs: 2ch, Boxing — Ku Yong Jo (DPRK). 5ch, Gymnastics — Nadie Comaneci (Romania). 10ch, Pole Vault — Tadeusz Slusarski (Poland). 15ch, Hurdling — Guy Drut (France). 25ch, Cycling — Bernt Johansson (Sweden). 40ch, Soccer (DDR).
50ch, Boxing — Ko Yong Do (DPRK).

**Surface Coated Paper**

**1976, Aug. 2** ***Perf. 13¼***

**1491-1496** A909 Set of 6 4.50 1.00
*1496a* Sheet of 12, as #1491-1497, + 5 labels, ordinary paper 8.00 —

**Souvenir Sheet**

***Imperf***

**1497** A909 50ch multicolored 3.00 .50

International Activities — A910

Designs: 2ch, UPU Headquarters, Bern. 5ch, World Cup. 10ch, Montreal Olympics Stadium. 15ch, Runner with Olympic Torch. 25ch, Satellite, junk. 40ch, Satellites.
50ch, World map.

**Surface Coated Paper**

**1976, Aug. 5** ***Perf. 13¼***

**1506-1511** A910 Set of 6 5.00 1.50
*1511a* Sheet of 8, as #1505-1512 + label, ordinary paper 7.00 —

**Souvenir Sheet**

***Imperf***

**1512** A910 50ch multicolored 2.50 2.50

For overprints, see Nos. 1646-1652.

Embroidery — A911

Designs: 2ch, Marsh Magpies. 5ch, Golden Bird. 10ch, Deer. 15ch, Golden Bird. 25ch, Fairy. 40ch, Tiger.
50ch, Tiger.

**Surface Coated Paper**

**1976, Aug. 8** ***Perf. 12***

**1513-1518** A911 Set of 6 7.50 1.50
*1518a* Sheet of 8, as #1513-1519 + label, perf 13¾, ordinary paper 18.00 —

**Souvenir Sheet**

***Imperf***

**1519** A911 50ch multicolored 4.00 .50

For surcharges, see Nos. 4598, 4599, 4604.

Model Airplane Championships (1975) — A912

Designs: 5ch, Trophy, certificate and medal. 10ch, Trophy and medals. 20ch, Model airplane and emblem. 40ch, Model glider and medals.

**Without Gum**

**1976, Aug. 15** ***Perf. 12***

**1520-1523** A912 Set of 4 4.75 1.00

5th Summit Conference of Non-Aligned States — A913

**1976, Aug. 16** **Without Gum**

**1524** A913 10ch multicolored .50 .25

Locomotives — A914

Designs: 2ch, "Pulgungi" diesel locomotive. 5ch, "Saeppyol" diesel locomotive. 10ch, "Saeppyol" diesel locomotive (diff.). 15ch, Electric train. 25ch, "Kumsong" diesel locomotive. 40ch, "Pulgungi" electric locomotive.
50ch, "Kumsong" diesel locomotive.

**Surface Coated Paper**

**1976, Sept. 14** ***Perf. 12x11¾***

**1525-1530** A914 Set of 6 5.50 1.00
*1530a* Sheet of 8, as #1525-1531 + label, perf 10½ 15.00 —

**Souvenir Sheet**

***Imperf***

**1531** A914 50ch multicolored 6.00 3.50

House of Culture A915

**Without Gum**

**1976, Oct. 7** ***Perf. 12***

**1532** A915 10ch black & brown 75.00 —

Revolutionary Activities of Kim Il Sung — A916

Kim Il Sung: 2ch, Visiting the Tosongrang. 5ch, With peasants on hillside. 10ch, With boy and man at seashore. 15ch, Giving house to farm-hand. 25ch, On muddy road at front, with driver and girl. 40ch, Walking in rain with umbrella.
50ch, Watching boy draw picture by roadside.

**1976, Oct. 10** ***Perf. 13¼***

**1533-1538** A916 Set of 6 3.00 .75

**Souvenir Sheet**

***Imperf***

**1539** A916 50ch multicolored 2.00 1.50

Down-With-Imperialism Union, 50th Anniv. — A917

**Without Gum**

**1976, Oct. 17** ***Perf. 12***

**1540** A917 20ch multicolored 1.00 .25

21st Olympic Games, Montreal A918

Olympic Rings, stadium and: 5ch, Fencer. 10ch, Weightlifter. 15ch, Horse racer. 20ch, Runner. 25ch, Shot putter. 40ch, Basketball player.
60ch, Yacht race.

**Simulated 3-D Printing Using Plastic Overlays**

**1976, Dec. 21** ***Imperf.***

**1541-1546** A918 Set of 6 25.00 25.00

**Souvenir Sheet**

**1547** A918 60ch multicolored 45.00 45.00

**No. 1547 Overprinted with Gold Medal Winners' Names, Events**

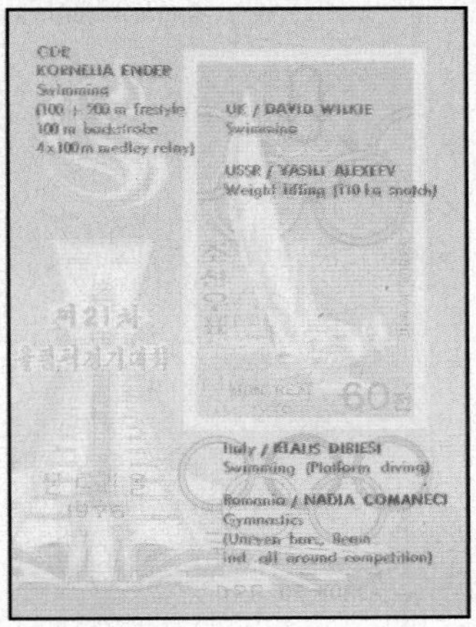

**1548** A918 60ch multicolored — —

New Year — A919

**Without Gum**

**1977, Jan. 1** ***Perf. 12¼x12***

**1549** A919 20ch multicolored .50 .25

21st Olympic Games, Montreal (1976) — A920

Designs: 5ch, Reverse of Bronze Medal, Montreal skyline. 10ch, Obverse of Bronze Medal, diff. Montreal skyline. 15ch, Obverse of Silver Medal, stadium. 20ch, Reverse of Silver Medal, stadium. 25ch, Reverse of Gold Medal, Olympic Flame. 40ch, Obverse of Gold Medal, Olympic Flame.
60ch, Gold, Silver and Bronze Medals.

**Simulated 3-D Printing Using Plastic Overlays**

**1977, Jan. 23** ***Imperf.***

**1550-1555** A920 Set of 6 25.00 25.00

**Souvenir Sheet**

**1556** A920 60ch multicolored 55.00 55.00

**No. 1556 Overprinted with Gold Medal Winners' Names, Events**

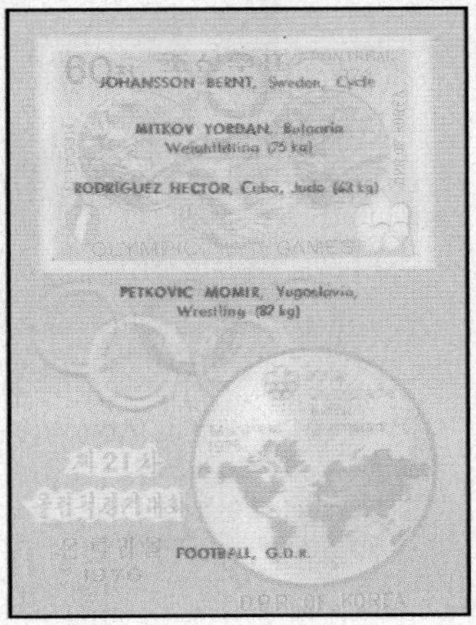

**1557** A920 60ch multicolored — —

National Costumes of Li Dynasty A921

Seasonal costumes: 10ch, Spring. 15ch, Summer. 20ch, Autumn. 40ch, Winter.

**1977, Feb. 10** ***Perf. 11¾x12***

**1558-1561** A921 Set of 4 3.50 .75
*1561a* Sheet of 4, #1558-1561 5.00 —

No. 1561 is airmail.

Korean Cultural Relics (5th-12th Centuries)
A922

Designs: 2ch, Two Deva kings, Koguryo Dynasty. 5ch, Gold-copper ornament, Koguryo Dynasty. 10ch, Bronze Buddha, Koguryo Dynasty. 15ch, Gold-copper Buddha, Paekje Dynasty. 25ch, Gold crown, Koguryo Dynasty, horiz. 40ch, Gold-copper ornament, Koguryo Dynasty, horiz. 50ch, Gold crown, Silla Dynasty.

**1977, Feb. 26** ***Perf. 13¼***

**1562-1568** A922 Set of 7 5.00 1.50
*1568a* Sheet of 8, #1562-1568 + label 6.00 —

No. 1568 is airmail.

Five-Point Program for Land Development — A923

**Without Gum**

**1977, Mar. 5** ***Perf. 12***

**1569** A923 10ch multicolored .50 .25

21st Olympic Games, Montreal (1976)
A924

Events, winner's name, nationality, and: 5ch, Cycling. 10ch, Weightlifting. 15ch, Judo. 20ch, Wrestling. 25ch, Football (soccer). 40ch, Boxing.
60ch, Boxing.

**Simulated 3-D Printing Using Plastic Overlays**

**1977, Mar.8** ***Imperf.***

**1570-1575** A924 Set of 6 45.00 45.00

**Souvenir Sheet**

**1576** A924 60ch multicolored — —

Korean National Association, 60th Anniv. — A925

**Without Gum**

**1977, Mar. 23** ***Perf. 11¾***

**1577** A925 10ch multicolored .65 .25

34th World Table-Tennis Championships — A926

Designs: 10ch, Emblem and trophy. 15ch, Pak Yong Sun. 20ch, Pak Yong Sun with trophy. 40ch, Pak Yong Ok and Yang Ying with trophy.

**1977, Apr. 5** ***Perf. 12***

**1578-1581** A926 Set of 4 3.25 .75

No. 1581 is airmail. For surcharge, see No. 4518.

Kim Il Sung, 65th Birthday — A927

Painting of Kim Il Sung: 2ch, Leading Mingyuehkou Meeting. 5ch, Commanding encirclement operation. 10ch, Visiting workers in Kangson. 15ch, Before battle. 25ch, Visiting school. 40ch, Looking over grain fields.
50ch, Kim Il Sung among the artists.

**1977, Apr. 15** ***Perf. 12***

**1582-1587** A927 Set of 6 2.25 .50

**Souvenir Sheet**

**1588** A927 50ch multicolored 1.50 .90

Trolley Buses
A928

Designs: 5ch, "Chollima 72." 10ch, "Chollima 74."

**Without Gum**

**1977, Apr. 20** ***Perf. 12***

**1589-1590** A928 Set of 2 3.00 .25

Korean People's Revolutionary Army, 45th Anniv. — A929

**Without Gum**

**1977, Apr. 25** ***Perf. 12***

**1591** A929 40ch multicolored 1.50 .25

Battle of Pochonbo, 40th Anniv. — A930

**Without Gum**

**1977, June 4** ***Perf. 13¼***

**1592** A930 10ch multicolored .50 .25

Porcelain
A931

Designs: 10ch, White ceramic teapot, Koryo dynasty. 15ch, White ceramic vase, Ri dynasty. 20ch, Celadon vase, Koryo dynasty. 40ch, Celadon vase, Koryo dynasty, diff.

**1977, June 10** ***Perf. 13¼***

**1593-1596** A931 Set of 4 3.50 .75
*1596a* Sheet of 4, #1593-1596 7.00 .95

No. 1596 is airmail.

Postal Service
A932

Designs: 2ch, Railway, ship and trucks. 10ch, Postwoman delivering mail. 30ch, Mil Mi-8 helicopter. 40ch, Airliner and world map.

**Without Gum**

**1977, June 28** ***Perf. 13¼***

**1597-1600** A932 Set of 4 4.00 1.00

For surcharges, see Nos. 4515, 4561.

---

A 3-stamp set and souvenir sheet commemorating the Second Conference of Third World Youth was prepared for release July 1, 1977, but was not issued. Value $3,500.

---

Butterflies — A933

Designs: 2ch, Rapala arata. 5ch, Colias aurora. 10ch, Limenitis populi. 15ch, Anax partherope julius. 25ch, Sympetrum pademontanum elatum.
50ch, Papilio maackii.

**1977, July 25** ***Perf. 12x12¼***

**1601-1606** A933 Set of 6 7.00 1.00
*1606a* Sheet of 6, #1601-1606 15.00 —

No. 1606 is airmail.

**Cats and Dogs**

A934

A935

Cats: 2ch, Gray cat. 10ch, Black and white cat. 25ch, Ginger cat.
Dogs: 5ch, Brindled dog. 15ch, Chow. 50ch, Pungsang.

**1977, Aug. 10** ***Perf. 11¾x12***

**1607-1609** A934 Set of 3 6.00 .50
*1609a* Sheet of 3, #1607-1609 8.00 —
**1610-1612** A935 Set of 3 4.00 .50
*1612a* Sheet of 3, #1610-1612 6.00 —

No. 1612 is airmail.

Visit of Pres. Tito of Yugoslavia
A936

Color of Frame: 10ch, blue green; 15ch, dk gray; 20ch, pale orange; 40ch, light gray.

**1977, Aug. 25** ***Perf. 12***

**1613-1616** A936 Set of 4 40.00 8.00

11-Year Compulsory Education, 5th Anniv. — A937

**Without Gum**

**1977, Sept. 1** ***Perf. 13¼x13½***

**1617** A937 10ch multicolored .50 .25

Shell-Fish and Fish — A938

Designs: 2ch, Mactra sulcataria. 5ch, Natica fortunel. 10ch, Arca inflata. 25ch, Rapana thomasiana. 50ch, Sphoeroides porphyreus.

**1977, Sept. 5** ***Perf. 11¾x12***

**1618-1622** A938 Set of 5 5.00 1.00
*1622a* Sheet of 6, #1618-1622 + label 9.00 —

No. 1622 is airmail. For surcharges, see Nos. 4565, 4578.

Publication of Kim Il Sung's *Theses on Socialist Education* A939

Designs: 10ch, Students, banners and *Theses*. 20ch, Students, crowd and *Theses*.

**1977, Sept. 5**

**1623-1624** A939 Set of 2 1.00 .25

Int'l Seminar on the Juche Idea — A940

Designs: 2ch, Juche Torch. 5ch, Interracial crowd holding copies of Kim's Red Book. 10ch, Chollima statue, flags. 15ch, Joined hands of different races, banner and globe. 25ch, Map of Korea. 40ch, Crowd and slogan.
50ch, Seminar emblem.

**1977, Sept. 14** ***Perf. 11¾x12***

**1625-1630** A940 Set of 6 3.50 .60

**Souvenir Sheet**

***Imperf***

**1631** A940 50ch multicolored 3.00 1.00

**Stamps of 1976 Overprinted**

**On Montreal Olympics, #1469-1474**

***Methods & Perfs as Before***

**1977, Nov. 8**

**1632-1637** A907 Set of 6 9.00 —
*1637a* On #1474a, sheet of 8 10.00 —

**Souvenir Sheet**

***Imperf***

**1638** A907 50ch multicolored 5.00 —

On Montreal Olympics Medal Winners, #1476-1482

**1639-1644** A908 Set of 6 13.00 —
*1644a* On #1481a, sheet of 8 15.00 —

**Souvenir Sheet**

***Imperf***

**1645** A908 50ch multicolored 5.00 —

**On International Activities, #1506-1512**

**1646-1651** A910 Set of 6 10.00 —
*1651a* On #1511a, sheet of 8 15.00 —

**Souvenir Sheet**

***Imperf***

**1652** A910 50ch multicolored 5.00 —

Amphilex '77 International Stamp Exhibition, Amsterdam.

Election of Deputies, Supreme People's Assembly A941

**1977, Nov. 11** ***Perf. 12¼x12***

**1653** A941 10ch multicolored .50 .25

Argentina '78, World Soccer Championship — A942

Designs: 10ch, Defense. 15ch, Attack. 40ch, Tackle.
50ch, Shot.

**1977, Dec. 10** ***Perf. 13½***

**1654-1656** A942 Set of 3 3.50 .75
*1656a* Sheet of 4, as #1654-1657 10.00 —

**Souvenir Sheet**

***Imperf***

**1657** A942 50ch multicolored 2.50 —

Reelection of Kim Il Sung — A943

**1977, Dec. 15** ***Perf. 12***

**1658** A943 10ch multicolored .60 .25

Org. for Communication Cooperation of Socialist Countries, 20th Anniv. — A944

**Without Gum**

**1977, Dec. 16** ***Perf. 11¾x12***

**1659** A944 10ch multicolored .50 .25

New Year — A945

**1978, Jan. 1** ***Perf. 13¼***

**1660** A945 10ch multicolored .60 .25

Winter Olympic Games, Sapporo-Innsbruck — A946

Designs: 2ch, 19th century skater. 5ch, Skier. 10ch, Ice ballet. 15ch, Hunter on skis. 20ch, 18th century woman skiier. 25ch, Medieval Scandinavian hunter. 40ch, Skiier.
50ch, Landscape. 60ch, Speed skater.

**1978, Feb. 18** ***Perf. 13¼***

**1661-1667** A946 Set of 7 6.00 1.00
*1667a* Sheet of 10, as #1661-1669 + label 9.00 —

**Souvenir Sheets**

**1668** A946 50ch multicolored 5.00 .50
**1669** A946 60ch multicolored 4.00 .50

No. 1667 is airmail.
For overprints, see Nos. 1821-1829.

Postal History A947

Designs: 2ch, Post rider and horse token. 5ch, Postman on motorcycle. 10ch, Electric train and postal van. 15ch, Mail steamer and Mi-8 helicopter. 25ch, Tupolev Tu-154 jetliner and satellite. 40ch, Dove and UPU headquarters.
50ch, Dove and UPU emblem. 60ch, Dove and UPU headquarters.

**1978, Mar. 2** ***Perf. 13¼***

**1670-1675** A947 Set of 6 6.00 1.00
*1675a* Sheet of 8, as #1670-1677 8.00 —

**Souvenir Sheets**

**1676-1677** A947 Set of 2 6.00 —

No. 1675 is airmail.

Rubens, 400th Anniv. Birth — A948

2ch, 5ch, 40ch, 50ch, Self-portrait, same design.

**1978, Mar. 20**

**1678-1680** A948 Set of 3 2.50 .50
*1680a* Sheet of 4, as #1678-1681 6.00 —

**Souvenir Sheet**

**1681** A948 50ch multicolored 3.00 1.50

Farm Machines A949

Designs: 10ch (No. 1682), *Chungsong* tractor. 10ch (No. 1683), Sprayer.

**1978, Apr. 1** ***Perf. 11¾x12***

**1682-1683** A949 Set of 2 2.50 .25

Pre-Olympics, Moscow 1980 — A950

Equestrian events: 2ch, Show jumping. 5ch, Jumping bar. 10ch, Cross Country. 15ch, Dressage. 25ch, Water splash. 40ch, Dressage (diff.).
50ch, 3-Step bar jump.

**1978, Apr. 1** ***Perf. 13¼***

**1684-1689** A950 Set of 6 3.50 1.50
*1689a* Sheet of 8, as #1684-1690 + label 7.00 —

**Souvenir Sheet**

**1690** A950 50ch multicolored 2.50 —

Korean People's Army Day — A951

Designs: 5ch, Soldier, battle scene. 10ch, Pilot, soldier, sailor saluting.

**1978, Apr. 1** ***Perf. 11¾x12***

**1691-1692** A951 Set of 2 1.00 .25

Meeting of Kim Il Sung and Hua Guo Feng of the People's Republic of China — A951a

Denominations: 15ch, 20ch

**1978, May** *Perf. 12*

**1692B-1692C** A951a Set of 2

This set includes a third stamp and a souvenir sheet, which the editors would like to examine.

Released prior to the meeting between Kim Il Sung and Hua Guo Feng and withdrawn when the meeting was canceled.

Ships — A952

Korean ships: 2ch, Cargo ship *Mangyongbong*. 5ch, Freighter *Hyoksin*. 10ch, Freighter *Chongchongang*. 30ch, Tanker *Sonbang*. 50ch, Freighter *Taedonggang*.

**1978, May 5** *Perf. 13¼*

**1693-1697** A952 Set of 5 6.00 1.25
*1697a* Sheet of 6, as #1693-1697+ label 8.00 —

No. 1697 is airmail.

History of the World Cup — A953

World Cup Winners (all 20ch, except Nos. 1709, 1710): No. 1698, Uruguay 1930. No. 1699, Italy 1934. No. 1700, France 1938. No. 1701, Brazil 1950. No. 1702, Switzerland 1954. No. 1703, Sweden 1958. No. 1704, Chile 1962. No. 1705, England 1966. No. 1706, Mexico 1970. No. 1707, West Germany 1974. No. 1708, Argentina 1978. 50ch (No. 1709), Soccer players and emblem, horiz.
50ch (No. 1710), World Cup and championship emblem.

**1978, June 1**

**1698-1709** A953 Set of 12 10.00 3.00
*1709a* Sheet of 12, as #1698-1708, 1710 12.00 —

**Souvenir Sheet**

**1710** A953 50ch multicolored 6.00 .60

No. 1709 is airmail.
For overprints, see Nos. 2051-2063.

World Cup Winners — A954

Designs: 5ch, Uruguay, 1930, 1950. 10ch, Italy, 1934, 1938. 15ch, West Germany, 1954, 1974. 25ch, Brazil, 1958, 1962, 1970. 40ch, England, 1966. 50ch, World Cup, vert.
50ch, World Cup.

**1978, June 1**

**1711-1716** A954 Set of 6 5.00 1.25
*1716a* Sheet of 6, as #1711-15, 1717 6.00 —

**Souvenir Sheet**

**1717** A954 50ch multicolored 4.00 .75

No. 1716 is airmail.

Art of the Revolution — A955

Designs: 10ch, Opera, *Sea of Love*. 15ch, Embroidered kerchief with floral design in the form of map of Korea. 20ch, *Tansimjul* dance.
40ch, *Song of Korea*.

**1978, June 2**

**1718-1720** A955 Set of 3 2.50 .50

**Souvenir Sheet**

**1721** A955 40ch multicolored 2.50 .50

**Domestic Printings**

Beginning in the 1970s, a number of North Korean stamps have been reprinted for sale and use within the country. Typically, these printings were on unsurfaced paper, with poorer production qualities, and without gum.

Second Seven-Year Plan — A956

Designs: 5ch, Electricity and Coal. 10ch, Steel and nonferrous metals. 15ch, Machine products and chemical fertilizers. 30ch, Cement and fishing. 50ch, Grain and tideland reclamation.

**1978, June 15** *Perf. 11½x12*

**1722-1726** A956 Set of 5 3.25 .90
*1722a* 5ch Unsurfaced white paper, without gum 8.00 —
*1723a* 10ch Unsurfaced white paper, without gum 8.00 —
*1724a* 15ch Unsurfaced white paper, without gum 8.00 —
*1725a* 30ch Unsurfaced white paper, without gum 5.00 —

History of Olympic Games & Winners — A957

Games emblems / medal winners (all 20ch): No. 1727, Athens 1896 / Alfred Flatow. No. 1728, Paris 1900 / Michel Theato. No. 1729, London 1908 / Wyndham Halswelle. No. 1730, Stockholm 1912 / William Kinnear. No. 1731, Antwerp 1920 / Paul Anspach. No. 1732, Paris 1924 / Ugo Frigerio. No. 1733, Amsterdam 1928 / Ahmed El Quafi. No. 1734, Berlin 1936 / Robert Charpentier. No. 1735, London 1948 / Josef Stalder. No. 1736, Helsinki 1952 / Laszlo Papp. No. 1737, Melbourne 1956 / Ronald Delany. No. 1738, Rome 1960 / Jolanda Balas. No. 1739, Tokyo 1964 / Valery Brumel. No. 1740, Mexico 1968 / Vera Caslavska. No. 1741, Munich 1972 / Li Ho Jun.
50ch, Montreal 1976 / Ku Yong Jo.

**1978, June 16** *Perf. 13¼*

**1727-1741** A957 Set of 15 12.00 4.50
*1741a* Sheet of 16, as #1727-1741 14.00 —

**Souvenir Sheet**

**1742** A957 50ch multicolored 2.00 .75

Passenger Aircraft — A958

Designs: 2ch, Douglas DC-8-63 jetliner and Comte AC-4 Gentleman. 10ch, Ilyushin Il-62M jetliner and Avia BH-25. 15ch, Douglas DC-8-63 jetliner and Savola Marchetti S-71. 20ch, Tupolev Tu-144 jetliner and Kalinin K-5. 25ch, Tupolev Tu-154 jetliner and Antonov An-2 biplane. 30ch, Ilyushin Il-18 airliner and '30s-era airplane. 40ch, Concorde supersonic jetliner and Wibault 283 trimotor.
50ch, Airbus.

**1978, July 25**

**1743-1749** A958 Set of 7 7.00 1.20
*1749a* Sheet of 8, as #1743-1750 10.00 —

**Souvenir Sheet**

**1750** A958 50ch multicolored 2.50 .50

For surcharge, see No. 4586.

White-Bellied Black Woodpecker Preservation A959

Designs: 5ch, Dryocopus richardsi, map of habitat, inset map of Korea. 10ch, Woodpecker and eggs. 15ch, Woodpecker feeding young. 25ch, Woodpecker feeding young, diff. 50ch, Woodpecker on tree trunk.

**1978, Aug. 5** *Perf. 11¾x12*

**1751-1755** A959 Set of 5 7.50 2.00
*1755a* Sheet of 6, #1751-1755 + label 9.00 —

For surcharge, see No. 4583.

Democratic People's Republic of Korea, 30th Anniv. A960

Designs (all 10ch): No. 1756, Building and flag. No. 1757, Flag with silhouetttes of workers and peasants. No. 1758, Flag with aviator and two soldiers. No. 1759, Chollima statue and city. No. 1760, Workers demonstrating, map of Korea in background. No. 1761, Asian, European and African clasping hands, with torch and "Solidarity" in background.

**Without Gum**

**1978, Sep. 9** *Perf. 13½x13¼*

**1756-1761** A960 Set of 6 2.75 .50
*1758a* 10ch Unsurfaced toned paper 10.00 —
*1759a* 10ch Unsurfaced toned paper 15.00 —
*1760a* 10ch Unsurfaced toned paper 15.00 —

Paintings by Ri Am (16th Century) A961

Designs: 10ch, *Cat and Pup*. 15ch, *Cat on a Tree*. 40ch, *A Pair of Wild Geese*.

**1978, Oct. 16** *Perf. 13¼*

**1762-1764** A961 Set of 3 7.50 1.10
*1764a* Sheet of 4, #1762-1764 + label 11.00 —

World Cup Winners, Argentina '78 — A962

Soccer players: 10ch, Argentina, Champion. 15ch, Holland, Sub-Champion. 25ch, Brazil, Third Place.
50ch, Argentina, Champion.

**1978, Dec. 15**

**1765-1767** A962 Set of 3 3.00 .50
*1767a* Sheet of 4, as #1765-1768 12.00 —

**Souvenir Sheet**

**1768** A962 50ch multicolored 2.50 1.50

New Year — A963

**Without Gum**

**1979, Jan. 1** *Perf. 12*

**1769** A963 10ch multicolored .50 .25

A964

International Year of the Child — A965

Kim Il Sung and children: 5ch, With Children's Corps members in Maanshan. 10ch, Children's Corps members in classroom. 15ch, "The New Year Gathering." 20ch, by roadside, with snowman, kite. 30ch, Looking at children's school work.

Children: 10ch, Tug of war. 15ch, Ballerinas. 20ch, Children of different races holding hands in circle around globe. 25ch, Singing at piano. 30ch, Playing on toy airplane ride.

No. 1780, Kim visiting a kindergarten. No. 1781, as No. 1777.

**1979, Jan. 1** ***Perf. 13¼x13½***

**1770-1774** A964 Set of 5 4.00 1.00
**1775-1779** A965 Set of 5 3.00 1.00

**Souvenir Sheets**

***Imperf***

**1780** A964 50ch multicolored 2.50 1.75
**1781** A965 50ch multicolored 2.50 1.75

Nos. 1770-1779 were issued with setenant labels. Nos. 1780-1781 exist perf. 13¼x13½.

---

A set of four stamps depicting roses, similar to Type A970, was prepared for release on Jan. 5, 1979, but was not issued.

---

*Story of Two Generals* A966

Designs: 5ch, Two warriors on horseback. 10ch (No. 1783), Man blowing feather. 10ch (No. 1784), Two generals fighting Japanese invaders. 10ch (No. 1785), Two generals on horseback.

**Without Gum**

**1979, Jan. 10** ***Perf. 11¾x12***

**1782-1785** A966 Set of 4 3.00 .50

Worker-Peasant Red Guards, 20th Anniv. — A967

**Without Gum**

**1979, Jan. 14** ***Perf. 12x11¾***

**1786** A967 10ch multicolored .50 .25

Airships — A968

Designs: 10ch, Clement-Bayard Airship *Fleurus*. 20ch, NI *Norge*.
50ch, *Graf Zeppelin*.

**1979, Feb. 27** ***Perf. 13¼***

**1787-1788** A968 Set of 2 2.00 .40
*1788a* Sheet of 3, as #1787-1789 5.00 —

**Souvenir Sheet**

**1789** A968 50ch multicolored 3.00 1.75

March 1 Popular Uprising, 60th Anniv. A969

**Without Gum**

**1979, Mar. 1** ***Perf. 11¾x12***

**1790** A969 10ch multicolored .60 .25

Roses A970

Designs: 5ch, Rose. 10ch, Red star rose. 15ch, Flamerose. 20ch, Yellow rose. 30ch, White rose. 50ch, Deep pink rose.

**1979, Apr. 18** ***Perf. 13¼***

**1791-1796** A970 Set of 6 3.50 1.00
*1796a* Sheet of 6, #1791-1796 4.00 —

No. 1796 is airmail.

35th World Table Tennis Championships, Pyongyang — A971

Designs: 5ch, Championship Cup. 10ch, Female doubles. 15ch, Female singles. 20ch, Male doubles. 30ch, Male singles.
50ch, Chollima statue. "Welcome."

**1979, Apr. 25**

**1797-1801** A971 Set of 5 3.00 .75
*1801a* Sheet of 6, as #1797-1802 4.00 —

**Souvenir Sheet**

**1802** A971 50ch multicolored 3.00 .45

For surcharges, see Nos. 4516, 4531.

"Let Us Step Up Socialist Construction Under the Banner of the Juche Idea" — A972

Designs: 5ch, Marchers, banner. 10ch (No. 1804), Map of Korea. 10ch (No. 1805), Hand holding torch.

**Without Gum**

**1979, Apr. 28** ***Perf. 12***

**1803-1805** A972 Set of 3 3.00 .25
*1803a* 5ch Unsurfaced dull white paper 15.00 —
*1804a* 10ch Unsurfaced dull white paper 15.00 —
*1805a* 10ch Unsurfaced dull white paper 15.00 —

Order of Honor of the Three Revolutions — A973

**1979, May 2** **Without Gum**

**1806** A973 10ch dp blue & lt blue 1.50 .25
*a.* Unsurfaced dull white paper 15.00 —

World Telecommunications Day — A974

**1979, May 17** **Without Gum**

**1807** A974 10ch multicolored 1.00 .25

Battle in Musan Area, 40th Anniv. A975

**1979, May 23** **Without Gum**

**1808** A975 10ch multicolored .60 .25

Int'l Friendship Exhibition A976

**1979, May 29** **Without Gum**

**1809** A976 10ch multicolored .60 .25

Albrecht Dürer, 450th Anniv. Death A977

Details from Dürer paintings: 15ch, Peonies. 20ch, Akeley. 25ch, A Big Tuft of Grass. 30ch, Wing of a Bird.
50ch, Like 30ch.

**1979, June 8** ***Perf. 13¼***

**1810-1813** A977 Set of 4 5.50 .75
*1813a* Souvenir sheet of 4, #1810-1813 9.00 —

**Souvenir Sheet**

**1814** A977 50ch multicolored 3.50 .60

For surcharge, see No. 4584.

Olympic Games, Moscow 1980 — A978

Olympic Torch, Moscow 1980 emblem and: 5ch, Fencers. 10ch, Gymnast. 20ch, Yacht race. 30ch, Runner. 40ch, Weightlifter.
50ch, Horse jump.

**1979, July 1**

**1815-1819** A978 Set of 5 3.50 1.25
*1819a* Sheet of 6, as #1815-1820 5.00 —

**Souvenir Sheet**

**1820** A978 50ch multicolored 3.00 1.50

Nos. 1661-1669 Overprinted

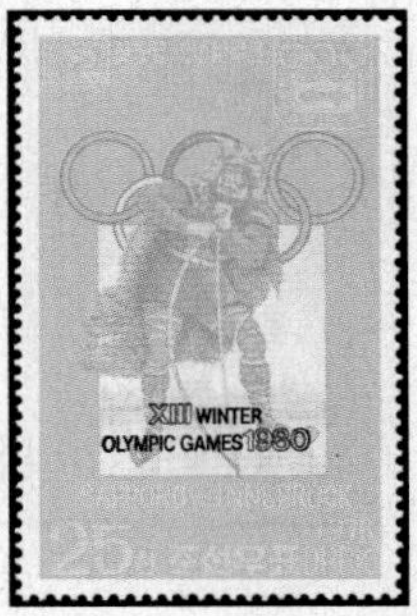


**1979, July 17**

**1821-1827** A946 Set of 7 10.00 3.50
*1827a* Sheet of 10, as #1821-1829 + label 18.00 —

**Souvenir Sheets**

**1828** A946 50ch multicolored 4.25 1.50
**1829** A946 60ch multicolored 8.50 —

No. 1827 is airmail.

Koguryo Dynasty Horsemen — A979

Designs: 5ch, Hunting. 10ch, Archery contest. 15ch, Drummer. 20ch, Rider blowing horn. 30ch, Horse and rider in chain mail. 50ch, Hawk hunting.

**1979, Aug. 1**

**1830-1835** A979 Set of 6 6.00 .75
*1835a* Sheet of 6, as #1830-1835 9.00 —

Olympic Games, Moscow 1980 — A980

Designs: 5ch, Judo. 10ch, Volleyball. 15ch, Cycling. 20ch, Basketball. 25ch, One-oared boat. 30ch, Boxing. 40ch, Shooting. 50ch, Gymnastics.

**1979, Aug. 5** ***Perf. 11¾x12***

**1836-1842** A980 Set of 7 5.00 1.25
*1842a* Sheet of 8, as #1836-1843 + label 9.00 —

**Souvenir Sheet**

**1843** A980 50ch multicolored 3.00 1.00

Ri Dynasty Knights' Costumes A981

Designs: 5ch, Knight in armor. 10ch, Knight in ceremonial dress. 15ch, Knight in armor (diff.) 20ch, Soldier in uniform. 30ch, Knight in armor (diff.) 50ch, Knight in armor (diff.)

**1979, Aug. 6** ***Perf. 11¾***

| | | | | |
|---|---|---|---|---|
| **1844-1849** | A981 | Set of 6 | 3.75 | .75 |
| *1849a* | | Sheet of 6, #1844-1849 | 6.00 | — |

No. 1849 is airmail.

1980 Summer Olympics, Moscow A982

Designs: 10ch, Judo. 15ch, Handball. 20ch, Archery. 25ch, Field hockey. 30ch, Boat race. 40ch, Soccer.
50ch, Horse race.

**1979, Sept. 5** ***Perf. 11¾x11½***

| | | | | |
|---|---|---|---|---|
| **1850-1855** | A982 | Set of 6 | 5.25 | 1.25 |
| *1855a* | | Sheet of 8, #1850-1856 + label | 8.00 | — |

**Souvenir Sheet**

| | | | | |
|---|---|---|---|---|
| **1856** | A982 | 50ch multi | 3.00 | 1.25 |

For surcharges, see Nos. 4585, 4595.

Chongbong Monument A983

**Without Gum**

**1979, Sep. 10** ***Perf. 12***

| | | | | |
|---|---|---|---|---|
| **1857** | A983 | 10ch multicolored | .60 | .25 |

Sika Deer A984

Designs: 5ch, Breeder feeding fawn from bottle. 10ch, Doe and suckling fawn. 15ch, Deer drinking from stream. 20ch, Buck walking. 30ch, Deer running.
50ch, Antlers.

**1979, Oct. 5** ***Perf. 13½***

| | | | | |
|---|---|---|---|---|
| **1858-1863** | A984 | Set of 6 | 4.00 | 1.25 |
| *1863a* | | Sheet of 6, #1858-1863 | 6.00 | — |

Central Zoo, Pyongyang A985

Designs: 5ch, Moscovy ducks. 10ch, Ostrich. 15ch, Turkey. 20ch, Pelican. 30ch, Guinea fowl. 50ch, Mandarin ducks.

**1979, Oct. 9** ***Perf. 12***

| | | | | |
|---|---|---|---|---|
| **1864-1869** | A985 | Set of 6 | 5.00 | 1.50 |
| *1869a* | | Sheet of 6, #1864-1869 | 6.00 | — |

No. 1869 is airmail. For surcharge, see No. 4569.

Int'l Year of the Child — A986

Designs: 20ch (No. 1870), Girl with toy sail boat. 20ch (No. 1871), Boy with toy train. 20ch (No. 1872), Boy with model biplane. 20ch (No. 1873), Boy with model spaceman. 30ch (No. 1874), Boy with toy motor boat. 30ch (No. 1875), Boy sitting on toy train. 30ch (No. 1876), Boy with model airplane. 30ch (No. 1877), Boy with model spaceman.

Souvenir Sheets (all 80ch): No. 1878, Boy and model ocean liner. No. 1879, Boy and girl with model train. No. 1880, Boy and Concorde. No. 1881, Girl and satellite.

Miniature sheets of 4: No. 1882, Nos. 1870, 1874, 1878 + label. No. 1883, Nos. 1871, 1875, 1879 + label. No. 1884, Nos. 1872, 1876, 1880 + label. No. 1885, Nos. 1873, 1877, 1881 + label.

**1979, Oct. 13** ***Perf. 12x11¾***

| | | | | |
|---|---|---|---|---|
| **1870-1877** | A986 | Set of 8 | 12.00 | 2.50 |

**Souvenir Sheets**

| | | | | |
|---|---|---|---|---|
| **1878-1881** | A986 | Set of 4 | 25.00 | 2.50 |

**Miniature Sheets**

| | | | | |
|---|---|---|---|---|
| **1882-1885** | A986 | Set of 4 | 25.00 | 2.50 |

For surcharges, see Nos. 4520, 4532.

Int'l Year of the Child — A987

Children playing soccer: 20ch, Kicking. 30ch, Dribbling.
80ch, Tackling.

**1979, Nov. 15** ***Perf. 12x11¾***

| | | | | |
|---|---|---|---|---|
| **1886-1887** | A987 | Set of 2 | 5.00 | .75 |
| *1887a* | | Sheet of 3, as #1886-1888 | 10.00 | — |

**Souvenir Sheet**

| | | | | |
|---|---|---|---|---|
| **1888** | A987 | 80ch multicolored | 5.00 | .75 |

Marine Life — A988

Designs: 20ch, Devil stinger fish (*Inimicas japonicus*). 30ch, Black rockfish (*Sebastes schlegeli*). 50ch, Northern sea lion (*Eumetopias jubatus*).

| | | | | |
|---|---|---|---|---|
| **1889-1891** | A988 | Set of 3 | 3.50 | .75 |
| *1891a* | | Sheet of 3, #1889-1891 | 5.00 | — |

Winter Olympics Games, Lake Placid — A989

Designs: 10ch, Figure skating (Irina Rodnina and Aleksandr Zaitsev). 20ch, Ice hockey (Soviet team). 30ch, Ladies' ski relay team. 40ch, Cross-country skiing (Sergei Saveliev, USSR), vert. 50ch, Ladies' speed skating (Tatiana Averina), vert.

60ch, Ice dancing (Ludmila Pakhomova and Aleksandr Gorshkov), stamp vert.

**1979, Dec. 9**

| | | | | |
|---|---|---|---|---|
| **1892-1896** | A989 | Set of 5 | 6.00 | 1.50 |
| *1892a* | | Sheet of 3, #1892-1894 | 5.00 | — |
| *1895a* | | Sheet of 3, as #1895-1897 | 10.00 | — |

**Souvenir Sheet**

| | | | | |
|---|---|---|---|---|
| **1897** | A989 | 60ch multicolored | 5.50 | 4.50 |

Honey Bees — A990

Designs: 20ch, Bee gathering nectar. 30ch, Bee and blossoms. 50ch, Bee over flower.

**1979, Dec. 22**

| | | | | |
|---|---|---|---|---|
| **1898-1900** | A990 | Set of 3 | 6.00 | .60 |
| *1900a* | | Sheet of 3, #1898-1900 | 7.50 | — |

Kim Il Sung's Birthplace, Hoeryang A991

Sinpha Revolutionary Museum — A992

**1979, Dec. 24**

| | | | | |
|---|---|---|---|---|
| **1901** | A991 | 10ch multicolored | .75 | .25 |
| **1902** | A992 | 10ch multicolored | .75 | .25 |

Revolutionary historical sites.

New Year A993

**1980, Jan. 1**

| | | | | |
|---|---|---|---|---|
| **1903** | A993 | 10ch multicolored | 1.00 | .25 |

Studying — A994

**1980, Jan. 10** ***Perf. 12x11¾***

| | | | | |
|---|---|---|---|---|
| **1904** | A994 | 10ch multicolored | .50 | .25 |

Unryul Mine Conveyor Belt — A995

**1980, Jan. 20** ***Perf. 11¾x12***

| | | | | |
|---|---|---|---|---|
| **1905** | A995 | 10ch multicolored | 1.00 | .25 |

Kim Il Sung, Soldiers and Children — A996

Children Playing — A997

Kim Visiting Kindergarten — A998

**International Day of the Child**

Type A997 (all 10ch): No. 1907, Black, Asian and White children with "6" and "1." No. 1908, Children playing accordion. No. 1909, Children on airplane ride. No. 1910, Children on rocket ride. No. 1911, Children riding tricycles. No. 1912, Children playing with model train.

**1980, Jan. 28** ***Perf. 12x11¾***

| | | | | |
|---|---|---|---|---|
| **1906** | A996 | 10ch multicolored | .35 | .25 |
| **1907** | A997 | 10ch multicolored | 1.50 | .35 |
| **1908** | A997 | 10ch multicolored | .35 | .25 |
| **1909** | A997 | 10ch multicolored | .60 | .25 |
| **1910** | A997 | 10ch multicolored | 2.25 | .50 |
| **1911** | A997 | 10ch multicolored | .50 | .25 |
| **1912** | A997 | 10ch multicolored | .35 | .25 |
| | | *Nos. 1906-1912 (7)* | 5.90 | 2.10 |

**Souvenir Sheet**

***Perf. 13¼***

| | | | | |
|---|---|---|---|---|
| **1913** | A998 | 50ch multicolored | 3.00 | 1.25 |

Chongsan-ri Monument — A999

Chongsan-ri Party Headquarters — A1000

**1980, Feb. 5** ***Perf. 11¾x12***

| | | | | |
|---|---|---|---|---|
| **1914** | A999 | 10ch multicolored | .50 | .25 |
| **1915** | A1000 | 10ch multicolored | .50 | .25 |

Monument in Honor of Kim Jong Suk's Return A1001

**1980, Feb. 16**

**1916** A1001 10ch multicolored .50 .25

Explorers A1002

Designs: 10ch, Vasco Nunez be Balboa (Spain). 20ch, Francisco de Orellana (Spain). 30ch, Haroun Tazieff (France). 40ch, Sir Edmund Hillary (New Zealand) and Shri Tenzing (Nepal).

70ch, Ibn Battuta (Morocco).

**1980, Feb. 18** ***Perf. 13¼***

**1917-1920** A1002 Set of 4 4.50 1.00

*1920a* Sheet of 6, as #1917-1921 + label 10.00 —

**Souvenir Sheet**

**1921** A1002 70ch multicolored 4.50 1.50

Ryongpo Revolutionary Museum — A1003

**1980, Feb. 23** ***Perf. 11¾***

**1922** A1003 10ch lt blue & black .50 .25

Rowland Hill (1795-1879), Centenary of Death — A1004

Rowland Hill and stamps of: 30ch, Germany, Great Britain (#1), Russia, Switzerland, DPRK and Wurttemberg. 50ch, Great Britain (#1, pair), France, Roman States, Canada, Two Sicilies and India.

**1980, Mar. 1**

**1923-1924** A1004 Set of 2 7.00 1.00

*1924a* Sheet of 2, #1923-1924 10.00 —

World Red Cross Day — A1005

Designs: No. 1925, 10ch, Emblem of DPRK Red Cross. No. 1926, 10ch, Jean-Henri Dunant. No. 1927, 10ch, Nurse and infant. No. 1928, 10ch, Red Cross ship. No. 1929, 10ch, Red Cross helicopter. No. 1930, 10ch, Nurse with child and doll. No. 1931, 10ch, Map, Red Cross, transports.

50ch, Nurse with syringe.

**1980, Apr. 17** ***Perf. 11¾x11½***

**1925-1931** A1005 Set of 7 8.00 1.50

*1931a* Sheet of 8, as #1925-1932 15.00 —

**Souvenir Sheet**

**1932** A1005 50ch multicolored 5.50 1.75

For overprints and surcharges, see Nos. 2043-2050, 4517, 4570.

Conquerors of the Sea A1006

Designs: 10ch, Fernando Magellan (Portugal). 20ch, Fridtjof Nansen (Norway). 30ch, Auguste and Jacques Piccard (Sweden). 40ch, Jacques Cousteau (France).

70ch, Capt. James Cook (UK).

**1980, Apr. 30** ***Perf. 13¼***

**1933-1936** A1006 Set of 4 8.00 1.50

*1936a* Sheet of 6, as #1933-1937 + label 15.00 —

**Souvenir Sheet**

**1937** A1006 70ch multicolored 6.50 1.50

London 1980 Int'l Philatelic Exhibition — A1007

Designs: 10ch, Great Britain #1 and Korean stamps. No. 1939, 20ch, British Guiana One-Cent Magenta and Korean cover. No. 1940, 30ch, Korea #1 (in blue) and modern Korean First Day Cover. 40ch, DPRK Nos. 1 (in green) and 1494. No. 1942, 50ch, DPRK Nos. 470-471.

No. 1943: a, 20ch, Like 10ch. b, 30ch, Like No. 1939. c, 50ch, Like 40ch.

**1980, May 6**

**1938-1942** A1007 Set of 5 10.00 1.50

**Souvenir Sheet**

**1943** A1007 Sheet of 3, #a-c 15.00 1.50

Nos. 1941, 1943c are airmail.

Conquerors of Sky and Space A1008

Designs: 10ch, Wright Brothers (USA). 20ch, Louis Bleriot (France). 30ch, Anthony Fokker (USA). 40ch, Secondo Campini (Italy) and Sir Frank Whittle (UK).

70ch, Count Ferdinand von Zeppelin (Germany).

**1980, May 10**

**1944-1947** A1008 Set of 4 6.00 1.25

*1947a* Sheet of 6, as #1944-1948 + label 13.00 —

**Souvenir Sheet**

**1948** A1008 70ch multicolored 5.00 1.25

Conquerors of the Universe A1009

Designs: 10ch, Spaceships. 20ch, Spaceship landing on another planet. 30ch, Spaceships landing on another planet, greeted by dinosaurs. 40ch, Spaceship, dinosaurs.

70ch, Spaceman and dragons.

**1980, May 20** ***Perf. 11¾x12***

**1949-1952** A1009 Set of 4 3.50 1.25

*1952a* Sheet of 6, as #1949-1953 + label 12.00 —

**Souvenir Sheet**

**1953** A1009 70ch multicolored 3.50 1.25

Chongryon, 25th Anniv. — A1010

**1980, May 25** ***Perf. 12¼x12***

**1954** A1010 10ch multicolored .50 .25

Chongryon is the General Association of Korean Residents in Japan.

Pyongyang Maternity Hospital — A1011

**1980, May 30** ***Perf. 12***

**1955** A1011 10ch multicolored 1.10 .25

Changgwang Health Complex — A1012

**1980, June 2** ***Perf. 11¾x12***

**1956** A1012 2ch black & lt blue .60 .25

Korean Revolutionary Army, 50th Anniv. — A1013

**1980, July 6** ***Perf. 12***

**1957** A1013 10ch multicolored .60 .25

Regular Issue — A1014

Designs (all 10ch): No. 1958, Workers' hostel, Samjiyon. No. 1959, *Chongsanri* rice harvester. No. 1960, *Taedonggang* rice transplanter. No. 1961, corn harvester. No. 1962, Samhwa Democratic Propaganda Hall. No. 1963, Songmun-ri revolutionary historic building (with trees). No. 1964, Sundial. No. 1965, Turtle ship. No. 1966, Phungsan dog. No. 1967, Quail.

***Perf. 11¾, 11½ (#1960, 1965), 12x11¾ (#1964)***

**1980**

**1958-1967** A1014 Set of 10 25.00 3.00

Issued: Nos. 1958-1961, 7/25. Nos. 1962-1967, 8/1.

6th Congress, Workers' Party of Korea A1015

"Leading the van in the Arduous March" — A1016

"The great leader inspires and encourages colliers on the spot." — A1017

Designs (all 10ch): No. 1968, Party emblem, fireworks. No. 1969, Students, Red Book. No. 1970, Workers, banner, Red Book. No. 1971, Young workers, one with accordion. No. 1972, Worker holding wrench aloft. No. 1973, Four young workers, one with streamer, building in background. No. 1974, Map, propaganda slogans. No. 1975, Workers marching with three banners, smoke stacks in background.

**1980, July 30** ***Perf. 12¼x12***

**1968-1975** A1015 Set of 8 6.00 1.25

**Souvenir Sheets**

**1976** A1016 50ch multicolored 3.00 .75

**1977** A1017 50ch multicolored 2.00 .75

World Cup Soccer Championship 1978-1982 A1018

Designs: 20ch, Two soccer players dribbling ball. 30ch, Tackling.

40ch, Tackling (diff.). 60ch, Moving in to tackle.

**1980, Aug. 5** ***Perf. 12***

**1978-1979** A1018 Set of 2 7.50 2.00

*1979a* Sheet of 4, as #1978-1980 — —

**Souvenir Sheet**

**1980** A1018 Sheet of 2 + label 16.00 2.00

*a.* 40ch multicolored 3.00 1.00

*b.* 60ch multicolored 4.00 1.00

Winter Olympic Games 1980, Gold Medal Winners — A1019

Designs: 20ch, Irina Rodnina and Aleksandr Zaitsev.
1w, Natalia Linitschnuk and Gennadi Karponosov.

**1980, Aug. 10** ***Perf. 13¼***

**1981** A1019 20ch multicolored 6.00 1.50
*a.* Sheet of 2, as #1981-1982 15.00 —

**Souvenir Sheet**

**1982** A1019 1w multicolored 6.50 2.00

Albrecht Dürer, 450th Anniv. Death — A1020

Designs: 20ch, *Soldier with Horse.*
1w, *Horse and Rider.*

**1980, Aug. 18** ***Perf. 11¾x12***

**1983** A1020 20ch multicolored 6.00 1.50
*a.* Sheet of 2 as #1983-1984 20.00 —

**Souvenir Sheet**

**1984** A1020 1w multicolored 9.00 2.50

Johannes Kepler, 350th Anniv. Death — A1021

Designs: 20ch, Kepler, astrolabe and satellites.
1w, Kepler, astrolabe and satellites (diff.).

**1980, Aug. 25**

**1985** A1021 20ch multicolored 2.75 1.25
*a.* Sheet of 2, as #1985-1986 12.00 —

**Souvenir Sheet**

**1986** A1021 1w multicolored 6.00 2.00

3rd Int'l Stamp Fair Essen 1980 — A1022

Designs, Stamps from German and Russian Zeppelin sets, respectively: 10ch, 1m and 30k. 20ch, 2m and 35k. 30ch, 4m and 1r.
50ch, Russian 2r Polar Flight stamp and DPRK No. 1780 stamp.

**1980, Sep. 25** ***Perf. 13¼***

**1987-1989** A1022 Set of 3 6.50 1.25
*1989a* Sheet of 4, as #1987-1990 30.00 —

**Souvenir Sheet**

**1990** A1022 50ch multicolored 9.00 2.50

A1023

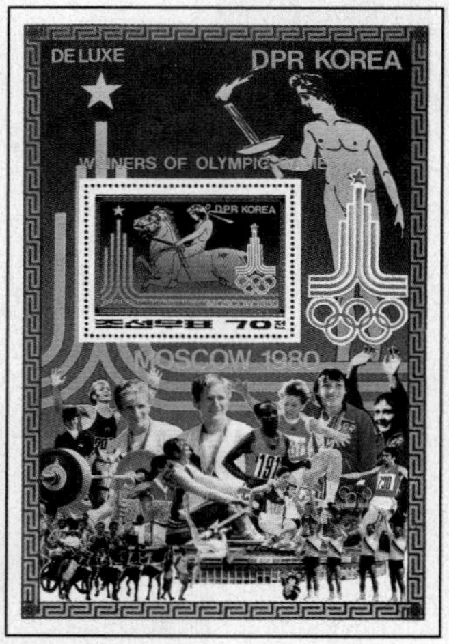


Moscow Olympic Games Winners — A1024

Designs: 10ch, Free pistol shooting — Aleksandr Melentiev (USSR). 20ch, 4000m Individual pursuit bicycle race — Robert Dill-Bundi (Switzerland). 25ch, Gymnastics — Stoyan Deltchev (Bulgaria). 30ch, Free style wrestling — K). 35ch, Weight-lifting — Ho Bong Choi (DPRK). 40ch, Running — Marita Koch (DDR). 50ch, Modern pentathlon — Anatoly Starostin (USSR).
No. 1998, Boxing — Teofilo Stevenson (Cuba). No. 1999, Ancient Greek rider on horse.

**1980, Oct. 20** ***Perf. 12x11¾***

**1991-1997** A1023 Set of 7 7.00 2.25
*1997a* Sheet of 8, as #1991-1998 12.00 —

**Souvenir Sheet**

**1998** A1023 70ch multicolored 2.75 2.00
**1999** A1024 70ch multicolored 4.50 2.00

Josip Broz Tito (1892-1980) A1025

**1980, Dec. 4** ***Perf. 12¼x12***

**2000** A1025 20ch multicolored 1.00 .25

First Post-WWII Lufthansa Flight, 25th Anniv. A1026

Designs: 20ch, Convair CV 340 airliner.
1w, Airbus A 300.

**1980, Dec. 10** ***Perf. 13¼***

**2001** A1026 20ch multicolored 5.50 2.00
*a.* Sheet of 2, as #2001-2002 15.00 —

**Souvenir Sheet**

**2002** A1026 1w multicolored 7.00 3.00

Liverpool-Manchester Railway, 150th Anniv. — A1027

Designs: 20ch, *The Rocket.*
1w, Locomotive pulling passenger car and horse car.

**1980, Dec. 16** ***Perf. 11¾***

**2003** A1027 20ch multicolored 6.00 3.00
*a.* Sheet of 2, as #2003-2004 15.00 —

**Souvenir Sheet**

**2004** A1027 1w multicolored 6.00 2.50

Electric Train Centenary — A1028

Designs: 20ch, First E-type electric and steam locomotives.
1w, Electric locomotive exhibited in Berlin, 1879.

**1980, Dec. 24** ***Perf. 13¼***

**2005** A1028 20ch multicolored 6.00 2.00
*a.* Sheet of 2, as #2005-2006 20.00 —

**Souvenir Sheet**

**2006** A1028 1w multicolored 12.00 2.50

Dag Hammarskjold (1905-61), 75th Anniv. of Birth — A1029

Designs: 20ch, Hammarskjold and UN Building.
1w, Hammarskjold (diff.).

**1980, Dec. 26** ***Perf. 11¾***

**2007** A1029 20ch multicolored 3.25 2.25
*a.* Sheet of 2, as #2007-2008 10.00 —

**Souvenir Sheet**

**2008** A1029 1w multicolored 4.50 2.75

World Chess Championship, Merano — A1030

Designs: 20ch, Bobby Fischer-Boris Spassky chess match.
1w, Viktor Korchnoi-Anatoly Karpov chess match.

**1980, Dec. 28** ***Perf. 13¼***

**2009** A1030 20ch multicolored 7.00 2.00
*a.* Sheet of 2, as #2009-2010 17.00 —

**Souvenir Sheet**

**2010** A1030 1w multicolored 9.00 2.00

Robert Stolz (1880-1975), Composer, Birth Cent. — A1031

Designs: 20ch, Stoltz with music from *At the Flower Bed.*
1w, Stoltz working with stamp collection.

**1980, Dec. 30**

**2011** A1031 20ch multicolored 3.00 1.00
*a.* Sheet of 2, as #2011-2012 12.00 —

**Souvenir Sheet**

**2012** A1031 1w multicolored 5.00 1.00

New Year — A1032

**1981, Jan. 1** ***Perf. 12***

**2013** A1032 10ch multicolored .90 .25

Fairy Tales A1033

Designs (all 10ch): No. 2014 Russian fairy tale. No. 2015 Icelandic. No. 2016, Swedish. No. 2017, Irish. No. 2018, Italian. No. 2019, Japanese. No. 2020, German.
70ch (No. 2021): Korean fairy tale, *A Gold Nugget and Maize Cake.*

**1981, Jan. 30** ***Perf. 13¼***

**2014-2020** A1033 Set of 7 10.00 3.50
*2020a* Sheet of 8, as #2014-2021 15.00 —

**Souvenir Sheet**

**2021** A1033 70ch multicolored 5.75 3.00

International Year of the Child, 1979.

Changgwang Street, Pyongyang — A1034

**1981, Feb. 16** ***Perf. 11¾x12***

**2022** A1034 10ch multicolored .70 .25

World Soccer Cup Championship ESPAÑA '82 — A1035

Designs: 10ch, Tackling. 20ch, Kicking. 30ch, Feinting.
70ch, Three players.

**1981, Feb. 20** ***Perf. 13¼***

| | | | | |
|---|---|---|---|---|
| 2023-2025 | A1035 | Set of 3 | 9.00 | 2.75 |
| *2025a* | | Sheet of 4, as #2023-2026 | 17.00 | — |

**Souvenir Sheet**

| | | | | |
|---|---|---|---|---|
| 2026 | A1035 | 70ch multicolored | 8.00 | 3.25 |

For overprints, see Nos. 2216.

World Soccer Cup Championship ESPAÑA '82 (2nd issue) — A1036

Designs: 10ch, Emblem, map and cup. 15ch, Dribbling. 20ch, Heading ball. 25ch, Tackling. 30ch, Pass.
70ch, Sliding tackle.

**1981, Feb. 28**

| | | | | |
|---|---|---|---|---|
| 2027-2031 | A1036 | Set of 5 | 9.00 | 3.75 |
| *2031a* | | Sheet of 6, as #2027-2032 | 18.00 | — |

**Souvenir Sheet**

| | | | | |
|---|---|---|---|---|
| 2032 | A1036 | 70ch multicolored | 9.00 | 3.00 |

Implementations of Decisions of 6th Korean Workers' Party Congress A1037

Designs: 2ch, Marchers with book, banners. 10ch (No. 2034), Worker with book. 10ch (No. 2035), Workers and factory. 10ch (No. 2036), Electricity generation (horiz.). 10ch (No. 2037), Factory, construction scene (horiz.). 10ch (No. 2038), Cement factory, fertilizer (horiz.). 30ch, Fishing, fabrics (horiz.). 40ch, Grain, port facilities (horiz.). 70ch, Clasped hands, map of Korea. 1w, Hand holding torch, "peace" and "solidarity" slogans.

**1981, Mar. 15** ***Perf. 12¼***

| | | | | |
|---|---|---|---|---|
| 2033-2042 | A1037 | Set of 10 | 6.00 | 2.50 |
| *2033a* | 2ch | Unsurfaced white paper, without gum | 10.00 | — |
| *2034a* | 10ch | Unsurfaced white paper, without gum | 10.00 | — |
| *2035a* | 10ch | Unsurfaced white paper, without gum | 10.00 | — |
| *2039a* | 30ch | Unsurfaced white paper, without gum | 10.00 | — |
| *2040a* | 40ch | Unsurfaced white paper, without gum | 10.00 | — |
| *2041a* | 70ch | Unsurfaced white paper, without gum | 10.00 | — |
| *2042a* | 1w | Unsurfaced white paper, without gum | 10.00 | — |

**Nos. 1925-1932 Overprinted For Nobel Prize Winners in Medicine**

**1981, Mar. 20** ***Perf. 11¾x11½***

| | | | | |
|---|---|---|---|---|
| 2043-2049 | A1005 | Set of 7 | 9.00 | 3.00 |
| *2049a* | | Sheet of 8, as #2043-2050 | 12.00 | — |

**Souvenir Sheet**

| | | | | |
|---|---|---|---|---|
| 2050 | A1005 | 50ch multicolored | 9.00 | — |

**Nos. 1698-1710 Overprinted History of the World Cup**

**1981, Mar. 20** ***Perf. 13¼***

| | | | | |
|---|---|---|---|---|
| 2051-2062 | A953 | Set of 12 | 24.00 | — |
| *2062a* | | Sheet of 12, #2051-2062 | 25.00 | — |

**Souvenir Sheet**

| | | | | |
|---|---|---|---|---|
| 2063 | A953 | 50ch multicolored | 12.00 | — |

Copa de Oro Mini-World Cup Championships — A1038

Designs: 20ch, Uruguayan and Brazilian soccer players.
1w, Goalkeeper blocking ball.

**1981, Mar. 27**

| | | | | |
|---|---|---|---|---|
| 2064 | A1038 | 20ch multicolored | 4.00 | 1.25 |

**Souvenir Sheet**

| | | | | |
|---|---|---|---|---|
| 2065 | A1038 | 1w multicolored | 8.00 | 1.00 |

España '82 — A1039

Nos. 2066-2068 depict different designs incorporating bleachers and crowds, with images of soccer players and trophy that appear or disappear, depending upon the angle from which the stamps are viewed. This effect is created by printing on multiple layers of thin plastic, with gummed paper backing.

**1981, Apr. 10** ***Imperf.***

| | | | | |
|---|---|---|---|---|
| 2066-2067 | A1039 | Set of 2, 20ch, 30ch | 25.00 | 9.00 |

**Souvenir Sheet**

| | | | | |
|---|---|---|---|---|
| 2068 | A1039 | 1w multicolored | 25.00 | 25.00 |

Nos. 2066-2068 are airmail.

Naposta '81 Int'l Stamp Exhibition, Stuttgart — A1040

Designs: 10ch, Dornier Do-X flying boat. 20ch, Count von Zeppelin and airship LZ-120. 30ch, Goetz von Berlichingen (1480-1562), German knight and subject of poem by Johann von Goethe (1749-1832), also pictured.
70ch, Mercedes-Benz W 196, 1954 automobile.

**1981, Apr. 28** ***Perf. 12x11¾***

| | | | | |
|---|---|---|---|---|
| 2069-2071 | A1040 | Set of 3 | 8.00 | 1.60 |

**Souvenir Sheet**

***Perf. 11½x11¾***

| | | | | |
|---|---|---|---|---|
| 2072 | A1040 | 70ch multicolored | 5.50 | 2.75 |

World Telecommunications Day — A1041

**1981, May 17** ***Perf. 11¾x11½***

| | | | | |
|---|---|---|---|---|
| 2073 | A1041 | 10ch multicolored | 2.75 | .25 |

Flowers — A1042

Designs: 10ch, Iris pseudodacorus. 20ch, Iris pallasii. 30ch, Gladiolus gandavensis.

**1981, May 20** ***Perf. 12x11¾***

| | | | | |
|---|---|---|---|---|
| 2074-2076 | A1042 | Set of 3 | 3.50 | 1.60 |
| *2076a* | | Sheet of 3, #2074-2076 | 3.75 | — |

WIPA 1981 Stamp Exhibition, Vienna — A1043

Designs: 20ch, Austrian WIPA 1981 and Rudolf Kirchschlager stamps. 30ch, Austrian Maria Theresa and Franz Josef stamps.
50ch, Kim Il Sung and Korean Children's Union choir, vert.

**1981, May 22** ***Perf. 13¼***

| | | | | |
|---|---|---|---|---|
| 2077-2078 | A1043 | Set of 2 | 6.00 | 1.60 |

**Souvenir Sheet**

***Perf. 11½***

| | | | | |
|---|---|---|---|---|
| 2079 | A1043 | 50ch multicolored | 6.00 | 2.75 |

International Gymnastc Federation, Centen. A1044

Gymnastic events: 10ch, Rings. 15ch, Pommel horse. 20ch, Long horse. 25ch, Floor. 30ch, Hoop.
70ch, Ribbon, horiz.

**1981, May 25** ***Perf. 11¾x12***

| | | | | |
|---|---|---|---|---|
| 2080-2084 | A1044 | Set of 5 | 3.75 | 1.40 |
| *2084a* | | Sheet of 6, as #2080-2085 | 15.00 | — |

**Souvenir Sheet**

***Perf. 11½x11¾***

| | | | | |
|---|---|---|---|---|
| 2085 | A1044 | 70ch multicolored | 3.00 | 1.00 |

For overprints, see Nos. 2270-2275.

Mingyuehgou Meeting, 50th Anniv. — A1045

**1981, June 15** ***Perf. 12¼x12***

| | | | | |
|---|---|---|---|---|
| 2086 | A1045 | 10ch multicolored | .50 | .25 |

Taen Work System, 20th Anniv. A1046

**1981, June 25** ***Perf. 12x12¼***

| | | | | |
|---|---|---|---|---|
| 2087 | A1046 | 10ch multicolored | .50 | .25 |

New System of Agricultural Guidance, 20th Anniv. — A1047

**1981, June 25**

| | | | | |
|---|---|---|---|---|
| 2088 | A1047 | 10ch multicolored | .50 | .25 |

Anti-Japanese Women's Assoc., 55th Anniv. — A1048

**1981, July 5** ***Perf. 12¼***

| | | | | |
|---|---|---|---|---|
| 2089 | A1048 | 5w multicolored | 12.00 | 1.00 |

Opera *Sea of Blood,* 10th Anniv. A1049

**1981, July 17** ***Perf. 12***

| | | | | |
|---|---|---|---|---|
| 2090 | A1049 | 10w multicolored | 30.00 | 10.00 |

Joan of Arc, 550th Anniv. Death A1050

Designs: 10ch (No. 2091), Joan of Arc. 10ch (No. 2092a), Archangel Michael. 70ch, Joan of Arc in armor.
No. 2094, as No. 2092b.

**1981, July 20**

2091 A1050 multicolored 3.50 .75
2092 Sheet of 2, #2092a-2092b 9.00 —
a. 10ch multicolored — —
b. 70ch multicolored — —

**Souvenir Sheet**

***Perf. 11½***

2094 A1050 70ch multicolored 7.00 1.90

Down-with-Imperialism Union, 55th Anniv. — A1051

**1981, July 25** ***Perf. 12¼***

2095 A1051 1w multicolored 6.00 2.00

Rembrandt, 375th Birth Anniv. A1052

Designs: 10ch, *Young Girl by the Window.* 20ch, *Rembrandt's Mother.* 30ch, *Saskia van Uylenburgh.* 40ch, *Pallas Athenae.*
70ch, *Self-portrait.*

**1981, July 25** ***Perf. 13¼***

2096-2099 A1052 Set of 4 7.00 2.75

**Souvenir Sheet**

2100 A1052 70ch multicolored 5.50 3.00

Symposium of the Non-Aligned Countries on Increasing Agricultural Production — A1053

Designs: 10ch, Emblem, banners over Pyongyang. 50ch, Harvesting grain. 90ch, Marchers with banners, tractors, fields, factories.

**1981, Aug. 26** ***Perf. 12***

2101-2103 A1053 Set of 3 2.00 1.00

Royal Wedding A1054

Designs: 10ch, St. Paul's Cathedral. 20ch, Prince Charles on Great Britain #599. 30ch, Princess Diana. 40ch, Prince Charles in military uniform.
70ch, Prince Charles and Princess Diana.

**1981, Sept. 18** ***Perf. 13¼***

2104-2107 A1054 Set of 4 10.00 3.00

**Souvenir Sheet**

2108 A1054 70ch multicolored 15.00 5.00

For overprints, see Nos. 2205-2209.

Reubens Paintings — A1055

Designs: 10ch, *The Four Philosophers.* 15ch, *Portrait of Helena Fourment.* 20ch, *Portrait of Isabella Brandt.* 25ch, *The Education of Maria de Medici.* 30ch, *Helena Fourment and Her Child.* 40ch, *Helena Fourment in Her Wedding Dress.*
70ch, *Portrait of Nikolaas Rubens.*

**1981, Sept. 20** ***Perf. 11¾x12***

2109-2114 A1055 Set of 6 9.00 2.75

**Souvenir Sheet**

**Perf 11½**

2115 A1055 70ch multicolored 5.50 2.75

Royal Wedding — A1056

Designs: a, 10ch, Prince Charles and Princess Diana wedding portrait. b, 20ch, Charles and Diana with Flower Girl. c, 30ch, Charles and Diana leaving St. Paul's Cathedral. d, 40ch, Wedding portrait (diff.)
70ch, Charles and Diana with Queen Elizabeth on balcony.

**1981, Sept. 29** ***Perf. 13¼***

2116 A1056 Sheet of 4, #a.-d. 20.00 4.50

**Souvenir Sheet**

2120 A1056 70ch multicolored 25.00 6.00

No. 2120 exist imperf.

Philatokyo '81 International Stamp Exhibition, Tokyo — A1057

Design: 10ch, Rowland Hill and first stamps of Great Britain, Japan and DPRK. 20ch, DPRK World Fairy Tale stamps. 30ch, Three Japanese stamps.
70ch, Exhibition Hall.

**1981, Oct. 9** ***Perf. 11¾x11x½***

2121-2123 A1057 Set of 3 9.00 2.50
*2123a* Sheet of 4, as #2121-2124, perf 12x11½ 27.50 —

**Souvenir Sheet**

2124 A1057 70ch multicolored 7.00 2.00

Philatokyo '81 — A1058

Designs (both 10ch): No. 2125, Two DPRK stamps. No. 2126, DPRK stamp featuring Juche torch.

**1981, Oct. 9** ***Perf. 12x12¼***

2125-2126 A1058 Set of 2 4.00 1.40

League of Socialist Working Youth of Korea, 7th Congress — A1059

**1981, Oct. 20** ***Perf. 12x11¾***

2127 A1059 10ch multicolored .25 .25
2128 A1059 80ch multicolored 1.00 .35

Bulgarian State, 1300th Anniv. A1060

**1981, Oct. 20** ***Perf. 12x12¼***

2129 A1060 10ch multicolored .50 .25

Georgi Dimitrov (1882-1949), Birth Centenary A1061

**1981, Nov. 5** ***Perf. 12***

2130 A1061 10ch multicolored .50 .25

Philatelia '81 Int'l Stamp Fair, Frankfurt-am-Main — A1062

**1981, Nov. 14** ***Perf. 13¼***

2131 A1062 20ch multicolored 3.00 .45

A1063

Philexfrance '82 International Stamp Exhibition, Paris A1064

Designs: 10ch, Count Ferdinand von Zeppelin, *Graf Zeppelin,* Concorde. 20ch, Aircraft — Santos-Dumont 1905, Brequet 1930, Brequet Provence 1950, Concorde 1970. 30ch, Mona Lisa, six French stamps.
No. 2135: 10ch, Hotel des Invalides, Paris. 20ch, Pres. Mitterand of France. 30ch, International Friendship Building. 70ch, Kim Il Sung.
No. 2136: 60ch, Two French stamps picturing Rembrandt portrait and Picasso painting.

**1981, Dec. 1** ***Perf. 13¼***

2132-2134 A1063 Set of 3 10.00 2.00
2135 Sheet of 4, #a.-d. 7.50 2.50
a. A1064 10ch multicolored 1.25 .50
b. A1064 20ch multicolored 1.25 .50
c. A1064 30ch multicolored 1.25 .50
d. A1064 70ch multicolored 1.25 .50

**Souvenir Sheet**

2136 A1063 60ch multicolored 7.50 2.25

New Year — A1065

**1982, Jan. 1** ***Perf. 12***

2137 A1065 10ch multicolored .90 .25

"Korea Prospering Under the Wise Leadership of the Party" — A1066

Party emblem and: 2ch, banners. 10ch (No. 2139), Iron industry. 10ch (No. 2140), Produce, city, countryside. 10ch (No. 2141), Film industry. 10ch (No. 2142), Mining. 10ch (No. 2143), Lighthouse, helicopter. 40ch, Idealized cityscape.

**1982, Feb. 1**

2138-2144 A1066 Set of 7 7.00 1.50

A1067

Pablo Picasso (1881-1973), Painter, Birth Centenary — A1068

Designs (Nos. 2145-2148): 10ch, *La Coiffure.* 20ch, *Woman Leaning on Arm.* 25ch, *Child with Pigeon.* 35ch, *Portrait of Gertrude Stein.*

No. 2149: 10ch, *Paulo on a Donkey.* 20ch, *Harlequin.* 25ch, *Reading a Letter.* 35ch, *Harlequin* (diff.) 80ch, *Minotaur.* 90ch, *Mother and Child.*

Nos. 2150-2151: 80ch, *Minotaur.* 90ch, *Mother and Child.*

**1982, Mar. 30** ***Perf. 11¾***

| | | | |
|---|---|---|---|
| **2145-2148** | A1067 Set of 4 | 6.00 | 1.50 |
| **2149** | Sheet of 6, #a.-f. | 14.00 | 2.75 |
| *a.* | A1067 10ch multicolored | 2.25 | .45 |
| *b.* | A1067 20ch multicolored | 2.25 | .45 |
| *c.* | A1067 25ch multicolored | 2.25 | .45 |
| *d.* | A1067 35ch multicolored | 2.25 | .45 |
| *e.* | A1067 80ch multicolored | 2.25 | .45 |
| *f.* | A1067 90ch multicolored | 2.25 | .45 |

**Souvenir Sheets**

| | | | |
|---|---|---|---|
| **2150-2151** | A1068 Set of 2 | 8.00 | 4.00 |

A1069

A1070

Kim Il Sung, 70th Birthday — A1071

Type A1069 (both 10ch): No. 2152, Kim Il Sung's Birthplace. No. 2153, Fireworks over Pyongyang.

Type A1070 (10ch), paintings of Kim Il Sung: No. 2154, "The Day Will Dawn." No. 2155, Signaling the start of the Pochonbo battle. No. 2156, Groundbreaking of Potong River Project. No. 2157, Embracing bereaved children. No. 2158, Directing operations at front. No. 2159, "On the Road of Advance." No. 2160, Speaking with workers at Kangson Steel Plant. No. 2161, Talking with peasants. No. 2162, Choosing site for reservoir.

Type A1070 (20ch): No. 2163, Visiting Komdok Valley. No. 2164, With Red Flag Company. No. 2165, With farmers. No. 2166, Opening metallurgical plant. No. 2167, Talking with smelters. No. 2168, At chemical plant. No. 2169, With fishermen.

No. 2170, Kim surrounded by adoring Koreans. No. 2171, Kim as a boy.

***Perf. 11¾x12 (#2151-2152), 12x11¾***

**1982, Apr. 15**

| | | | |
|---|---|---|---|
| **2152-2169** | Set of 18 | 8.00 | 2.25 |

**Souvenir Sheets**

***Perf. 13¼***

| | | | |
|---|---|---|---|
| **2170-2171** | A1071 60ch Set of 2 | 5.00 | 1.75 |

All type A1070 stamps were issued with setenant labels bearing inscriptions relating to theme of stamp. Values are for stamps with labels attached.

Korean People's Army, 50th Anniv. A1072

**1982, Apr. 25** ***Perf. 12***

| | | | |
|---|---|---|---|
| **2172** | A1072 10ch multicolored | .50 | .25 |

ESSEN '82 Int'l Stamp Fair — A1073

**1982, Apr. 28** ***Perf. 11¾x12***

| | | | |
|---|---|---|---|
| **2173** | A1073 30ch multicolored | 4.50 | .50 |

Four Nature-Remaking Tasks — A1074

**1982, Apr. 30** ***Perf. 12***

| | | | |
|---|---|---|---|
| **2174** | A1074 10ch multicolored | .60 | .25 |

Issued to publicize the program for nature transformation contained in the Second Seven-Year Plan, which included irrigation, land reclamation, terracing, afforestation and water conservation, and reclamation of tidal lands.

Princess Diana, 21st Birthday A1075

Princess Diana (Nos. 2175-2177): 10ch, As a baby. 20ch, As little girl on swing. 30ch, As little girl wearing red parka.

No. 2178: 50ch, As girl, wearing blue turtleneck sweater. 60ch, With long hair, wearing gray hat. 70ch, Wearing white hat. 80ch, Wearing white blouse and sweater.

Nos. 2179-2180: 40ch, Diana pushing her brother on swing. 80ch, As No. 2178d.

**1982, May 1** ***Perf. 13¼***

| | | | |
|---|---|---|---|
| **2175-2177** | A1075 Set of 3 | 4.00 | 1.00 |
| **2178** | Sheet of 4, #a.-d. | 18.00 | 5.50 |
| *a.* | A1075 50ch multicolored | 3.50 | 1.25 |
| *b.* | A1075 60ch multicolored | 3.50 | 1.25 |
| *c.* | A1075 70ch multicolored | 3.50 | 1.25 |
| *d.* | A1075 80ch multicolored | 3.50 | 1.25 |

**Souvenir Sheets**

| | | | |
|---|---|---|---|
| **2179-2180** | A1075 Set of 2 | 10.00 | 5.00 |

For overprints, see Nos. 2210-2215.

Tower of the Juche Idea — A1076

**1982, May 21** ***Perf. 12***

| | | | |
|---|---|---|---|
| **2182** | A1076 2w multicolored | 7.50 | 2.00 |

Arch of Triumph — A1077

**1982, May 22**

| | | | |
|---|---|---|---|
| **2183** | A1077 3w multicolored | 8.50 | 2.00 |

Tigers A1078

Nos. 2184-2185: 20ch, Tiger cubs. 30ch, Tiger cubs (diff.)

No. 2186 (designs horizontal): 30ch, Tiger cub with mother. 40ch, Two cubs playing. 80ch, Two cubs playing, diff.

Nos. 2187: 80ch, Two cubs, horiz.

***Perf. 11¾x12 (#2185-2186), 12x11¾***

**1982, May 30**

| | | | |
|---|---|---|---|
| **2184-2185** | A1078 Set of 2 | 7.00 | 1.00 |
| **2186** | Sheet of 3, #a.-c. | 16.00 | 3.00 |
| *a.* | A1078 30ch multicolored | 3.00 | .50 |
| *b.* | A1078 40ch multicolored | 3.00 | .50 |
| *c.* | A1078 80ch multicolored | 3.00 | .50 |

**Souvenir Sheet**

| | | | |
|---|---|---|---|
| **2187** | A1078 80ch Multicolored | 6.00 | 1.50 |

ESPANA '82 World Cup Championship — A1079

Flags and players of: 10ch, Group 1 countries — Italy, Peru, Poland, Cameroun. 20ch, Group 2 countries — Germany, Chile, Algeria, Austria. 30ch, Group 3 countries — Argentina, Hungary, Belgium, El Salvador. 40ch, Group 4 countries — Great Britain, Czechoslovakia, France, Kuwait. 50ch, Group 5 countries — Spain, Yugoslavia, Honduras, Northern Ireland. 60ch, Group 6 countries — Brazil, Scotland, USSR, New Zealand.

1w, Soccer players, flags, trophy and ESPANA '82 emblem.

**1982, June 12** ***Perf. 13¼***

| | | | |
|---|---|---|---|
| **2188-2193** | A1079 Set of 6 | 13.00 | 4.00 |

**Souvenir Sheet**

| | | | |
|---|---|---|---|
| **2194** | A1079 1w multicolored | 11.00 | 4.00 |

For overprints, see Nos. 2217-2223.

Space Exploration A1080

Designs: 10ch, Rocket launch. 20ch, Spaceship over planet.

No. 2197a, Spaceship between planets.

No. 2198, Spaceship exploring desert area of other planet.

**1982, June 20** ***Perf. 11¾x11½***

| | | | |
|---|---|---|---|
| **2195-2196** | A1080 Set of 2 | 3.50 | 1.50 |
| **2197** | Sheet of 3, #2195-2196, 2197a + label | 6.00 | 2.50 |
| *a.* | A1080 80ch multicolored | 2.00 | .75 |

**Souvenir Sheet**

| | | | |
|---|---|---|---|
| **2198** | A1080 80ch multicolored | 3.75 | 1.50 |

Johann von Goethe (1749-1832), Writer, 150th Death Anniv. A1081

Silhouettes: 10ch, Charlotte von Stein, 20ch, Goethe's sister. 25ch, Charlotte Buff. 35ch, Lili Schönemann.

No. 2203: 10ch, Goethe's mother. 20ch, Angelika Kauffman. 25ch, Anna Amalia. 35ch, Charlotte von Lengefeld. 80ch, Goethe.

No. 2204: 80ch, Goethe.

**1982, July 25** *Perf. 11¾x12*

**2199-2202** A1081 Set of 4 3.75 1.50
**2203** Sheet of 5, #a.-e. + label 9.00 2.00
*a.* A1081 10ch multicolored 1.75 .50
*b.* A1081 20ch multicolored 1.75 .50
*c.* A1081 25ch multicolored 1.75 .50
*d.* A1081 35ch multicolored 1.75 .50
*e.* A1081 80ch multicolored 1.75 .50

**Souvenir Sheet**

**2204** A1081 80ch multicolored 4.00 1.75

Nos. 2104-2108 Overprinted in Blue

**1982, Aug. 20**

**2205-2208** A1054 Set of 4 15.00 —

**Souvenir Sheet**

**2209** A1054 70ch multicolored 15.00 —

Nos. 2175-2180 Overprinted in Blue

**1982, Aug. 20**

**2210-2212** A1075 Set of 3 15.00 —
**2213** Sheet of 4, #a-d 30.00 —

**Souvenir Sheets**

**2214-2215** A1075 Set of 2 25.00 —

**Nos. 2025a, 2188-2194 Overprinted in Blue**

**1982, Aug. 25**

**2216** A1035 Sheet of 4, #a.-d. 14.00 —
*a.* 10ch multicolored 1.00 —
*b.* 20ch multicolored 2.00 —
*c.* 30ch multicolored 3.00 —
*d.* 70ch multicolored 6.00 —
**2217-2222** A1079 Set of 6 15.00 —

**Souvenir Sheet**

**2223** A1079 1w multicolored 12.50 —

ESPANA '82 World Soccer Cup Winners — A1082

Designs: 20ch, Player holding World Cup aloft. 30ch, Three players with World Cup.

No. 2226: 30ch, as No. 2222. 40ch, As No. 2223. 80ch, King Juan Carlos of Spain and two players with World Cup.

No. 2227: 80ch, as No. 2226c.

**1982, Aug. 30** *Perf. 13¼*

**2224-2225** A1082 Set of 2 4.00 1.00
**2226** Sheet of 3, #a.-c. + label 8.00 —
*a.* A1082 30ch multicolored — —
*b.* A1082 40ch multicolored — —
*c.* A1082 80ch multicolored — —

**Souvenir Sheet**

**2227** A1082 80ch multicolored 9.00 2.00

A1083

1st Wedding Anniv. of Prince and Princess of Wales — A1084

**1982, Sept. 21**

**2228** A1083 30ch multicolored 10.00 4.00

**Souvenir Sheet**

**2229** A1084 80ch multicolored 15.00 5.00

No. 2228 was issued in sheets of four stamps and two labels.

Birth of Prince William of Wales A1085

Designs: 10ch, Charles and Diana with Prince William (Charles in suit, Diana in pink hat and dress). 20ch, Couple with William. 30ch, Couple with William (diff.). 40ch, Diana with William. 50ch, Diana with William (diff.).

No. 2235: 10ch, Diana holding bouquet. 20ch, Charles carrying William, with Diana. 30ch, Charles carrying William, with Diana (diff.). 80ch, Couple with William (diff.).

No. 2236 (horiz.): 40ch, Charles and Diana. 50ch, Charles and Diana in evening dress. 80ch, Charles holding William, with Diana.

Nos. 2237-2238 (both 80ch): Diana holding William, with Royal Family; Diana holding William, with godparents.

**1982, Sept. 29**

**2230-2234** A1085 Set of 5 16.00 5.00
**2235** Sheet of 4, #a.-d. 15.00 6.00
*a.* A1085 10ch multicolored 3.25 1.25
*b.* A1085 20ch multicolored 3.25 1.25
*c.* A1085 30ch multicolored 3.25 1.25
*d.* A1085 80ch multicolored 3.25 1.25
**2236** Sheet of 3, #a.-c. 15.00 6.00
*a.* A1085 40ch multicolored 4.00 1.75
*b.* A1085 50ch multicolored 4.00 1.75
*c.* A1085 80ch multicolored 4.00 1.75

**Souvenir Sheets**

**2237-2238** A1085 Set of 2 20.00 8.00

A1086

Birth of Prince William of Wales — A1087

Nos. 2239-2244 are composed of layered plastic, on gummed paper, which creates two different images on each stamp, depending on the angle at which it is viewed.

30ch: No. 2239, Charles, Diana and William/Diana holding William. No. 2240, Charles, Diana and William (diff.)/Couple with William (Charles in suit, Diana in pink hat and dress). No. 2241, Diana and William/Charles and Diana with William (Charles in suit, Diana in blue dress).

80ch: No. 2242, Diana and William, Portrait of Diana/Charles. No. 2243, Diana and William, St. Paul's Church/Wedding portrait of Royal Couple. No. 2244, Charles and Diana with William/Diana holding bouquet.

**1982, Oct. 1** *Imperf.*

**2239-2241** A1086 Set of 3 35.00 —

**Souvenir Sheets**

**2242-2244** A1087 Set of 3 60.00 —

Nos. 2242-2244 have simulated rouletting.

Bicentenary of Manned Flight — A1088

Designs: 10ch, Baldwin's airship *Nulli Secundus II*, 1908. 20ch, Tissandier Brothers' airship, 1883. 30ch, Parseval *PL VIII*, 1912. 40ch, Count Lennox's balloon *Eagle*, 1834.

No. 2249: 10ch, Pauley and Durs Egg's airship, *The Dolphin*, 1818. 20ch, Guyton de Morveau's balloon, 1784. 30ch, Sir George Cayley's airship, 1837. 40ch, Camille Vert's balloon *Poisson Volant*, 1859. 80ch, Dupuy de Lôme's airship, 1872.

No. 2250: Masse's oar-powered balloon, 1784, vert.

**1982, Nov. 21** *Perf. 13¼*

**2245-2248** A1088 Set of 4 7.00 2.00
**2249** Sheet of 5, #a.-e. + label 13.00 6.00
*a.* A1088 10ch multicolored 2.25 1.00
*b.* A1088 20ch multicolored 2.25 1.00
*c.* A1088 30ch multicolored 2.25 1.00
*d.* A1088 40ch multicolored 2.25 1.00
*e.* A1088 80ch multicolored 2.25 1.00

**Souvenir Sheet**

**2250** A1088 80ch multicolored 4.50 2.00

Bicentenary of Manned Flight A1089

Designs: 10ch, Balthasar Antoine Dunker's *Utopic Balloon Post*, 1784-90. 20ch, "and they fly into heaven and have no wings." 30ch, Pierre Testu-Brissy's balloon flight with horse, 1796. 40ch, Test flight of Gaston Tissandier's balloon *Zenith*, 1875.

No. 2255: 10ch, Montgolfier balloon at Versailles, 1783. 20ch, Montgolfier Brothers' balloon, 1783. 30ch, Charles' hydrogen balloon landing at Nesle. 40ch, Blanchard and Jeffries' flight over the English Channel, 1785. 80ch, Henri Giffard's balloon *Le Grand Ballon Captif* at World's Fair, 1878.

No. 2256: "Ballons Monte" balloon mail service from besieged Paris, 1870-1871.

**1982, Dec. 10**

**2251-2254** A1089 Set of 4 11.00 4.00
**2255** Sheet of 5, #a.-e. + label 25.00 6.50
*a.* A1089 10ch multicolored 4.50 1.25
*b.* A1089 20ch multicolored 4.50 1.25
*c.* A1089 30ch multicolored 4.50 1.25
*d.* A1089 40ch multicolored 4.50 1.25
*e.* A1089 80ch multicolored 4.50 1.25

**Souvenir Sheet**

**2256** A1089 80ch multicolored 5.00 2.00

Tale of the Hare — A1090

Designs: 10ch, Turtle searching for hare. 20ch, Turtle and hare going to Dragon King Palace. 30ch, Hare swindling Dragon King, demanding her liver. 40ch, Hare cheating turtle.

**1982, Dec. 25** *Perf. 12*

**2257-2260** A1090 Set of 4 8.00 1.25

Socialist Constitution, 10th Anniv. — A1091

**1982, Dec. 27**

**2261** A1091 10ch multicolored .50 .25

New Year — A1092

**1983, Jan. 1** ***Perf. 12¼x12***
**2262** A1092 10ch multicolored .50 .25

*Saenal* Newspaper, 55th Anniv. — A1093

**1983, Jan. 15** ***Perf. 11½x11¾***
**2263** A1093 10ch multicolored .90 .25

Rembrandt Paintings A1094

Designs: 10ch, *Man in Oriental Costume.* 20ch, *The Noble Slav.* 30ch, *Dr. Tulp's Anatomy Lesson* (detail). 40ch, *Two Scholars Disputing.*
No. 2268: 10ch, *Child with Dead Peacocks.* 20ch, *Old Man in Fur Hat.* 30ch, *Portrait of a Fashionable Couple.* 40ch, *Woman with Child.* 80ch, *Woman Holding an Ostrich Feather Fan.*
No. 2269: 80ch, *Self-Portrait.*

**1983, Jan. 25** ***Perf. 11¾x11½***
**2264-2267** A1094 Set of 4 7.50 1.50
**2268** Sheet of 5, #a.-e. + label 15.00 7.50
*a.* A1094 10ch multicolored 2.00 1.00
*b.* A1094 20ch multicolored 2.00 1.00
*c.* A1094 30ch multicolored 2.00 1.00
*d.* A1094 40ch multicolored 2.00 1.00
*e.* A1094 80ch multicolored 2.00 1.00

**Souvenir Sheet**
***Perf. 11¾x12***

**2269** A1094 80ch multicolored 4.00 1.25

**Nos. 2080-2085 Overprinted "XXIII Summer Olympic Games 1984" and Olympic Rings**

**1983, Feb. 10**
**2270-2274** A1044 Set of 5 *20.00* —
*2274a* Sheet of 6, as #2270-2275 *75.00* —

**Souvenir Sheet**

**2275** A1044 70ch multicolored *25.00* —

Luposta Int'l Air Mail Exhib., Köln — A1095

**1983, Jan. 25** ***Perf. 11¾x11½***
**2276** 30ch multicolored 3.00 1.00
**2277** 40ch multicolored 3.00 1.00
*a.* A1095 Pair, #2276-2277 7.00 3.00

*Virgin and Child*, by Stephan Lochner — A1096

**Souvenir Sheet**
***Perf. 13¼***

**2278** A1096 80ch multicolored 3.50 1.75

Wangjaesen Meeting, 50th Anniv. A1097

**1983, Mar. 11** ***Perf. 11½x11¾***
**2279** A1097 10ch multicolored .50 .25

Karl Marx, Centenary of Death — A1098

**1983, Mar. 14** ***Perf. 11¾x12***
**2280** A1098 10ch multicolored 2.25 .25

Thousand-ri Journey for Learning, 60th Anniv. — A1099

**1983, Mar. 16** ***Perf. 12***
**2281** A1099 10ch multicolored 1.00 .25

A1100

Raphael (1483-1520), 500th Birth Anniv. — A1101

Designs: 10ch, *Madonna of the Goldfinch.* 30ch, *Madonna of the Grand Duke.* 50ch (No. 2284), *Madonna of the Chair.*
No. 2285: 20ch, *The School of Athens* (detail). 50ch (No. 2285b), *Madonna of the Lamb.* 80ch, *The Beautiful Gardener.*
No. 2286: 80ch, *Madonna of St. Sixte.*

**1983, Mar. 20** ***Perf. 13½***
**2282-2284** A1100 Set of 3 6.00 1.00
**2285** Sheet of 3, #a.-c. + label 15.00 3.50
*a.* A1100 20ch multicolored 4.00 .75
*b.* A1100 50ch multicolored 4.00 .75
*c.* A1100 80ch multicolored 4.00 .75

**Souvenir Sheet**

**2286** A1101 80ch multicolored 4.50 1.25

Pyongyang Buildings — A1102

Designs: 2ch, Chongryu Restaurant. 10ch (No. 2288), Munsu Street. 10ch (No. 2289), Ice Rink. 40ch, Department Store No. 1. 70ch, Grand People's Study House.

**1983, Apr. 7** ***Perf. 12¼***
**2287-2291** A1102 Set of 5 6.00 .75
*2287a* 2ch Unsurfaced white paper, without gum 10.00 —
*2288a* 10ch Unsurfaced white paper, without gum 10.00 —
*2289a* 10ch Unsurfaced white paper, without gum 10.00 —
*2290a* 40ch Unsurfaced white paper, without gum 10.00 —
*2291a* 40ch Unsurfaced white paper, without gum 10.00 —

Int'l Institute of the Juche Idea, 5th Anniv. — A1103

**1983, Apr. 9** ***Perf. 12¼x12***
**2292** A1103 10ch multicolored .50 .25

Pre-Olympic Games, Los Angeles '84 — A1104

Designs (values in gold): 20ch (No. 2293), Judo. 30ch (No. 2294), Judo (diff.). 40ch (No. 2295), Boxing. 50ch (No. 2296), Weightlifting.
No. 2297 (values in black): 20ch, Wrestling. 30ch, Judo (diff.). 40ch, Shooting. 50ch, Wrestling. (diff.) 80ch, Boxing (diff.).
No. 2298: 80ch, Judo (diff.)

**1983, Apr. 20** ***Perf. 11¼***
**2293-2296** A1104 Set of 4 13.00 1.50
**2297** Sheet of 5, #a.-e. + label 25.00 1.00
*a.* A1104 20ch multicolored 4.00 .25
*b.* A1104 30ch multicolored 4.00 .25
*c.* A1104 40ch multicolored 4.00 .25
*d.* A1104 50ch multicolored 4.00 .25
*e.* A1104 80ch multicolored 4.00 .25

**Souvenir Sheet**
***Perf. 13½***

**2298** A1104 80ch multicolored 10.00 1.00

World Communications Year — A1105

**1983, Apr. 30** ***Perf. 11¾x12***
**2299** A1105 10ch multicolored 2.00 .25

TEMBAL '83 Int'l Topical Stamp Exhib., Basel — A1106

Designs: 20ch, Emblem, giant panda and stamp. 30ch, Emblem, DPRK flag and "Basel Dove" stamp (Switzerland No. 3L1).

**1983, May 21** ***Perf. 12***
**2300-2301** A1106 Set of 2 7.50 .75

Old Ships — A1107

Designs: 20ch, *Colourful Cow* (Hamburg, 1402). 35ch, *Great Harry* (England, 1555). 50ch, *Eagle of Lübeck* (Lübeck, 1567).
No. 2305: 20ch, Turtle Boat (Korea, 1592). 35ch, Admiral Li Sun Sin (1545-98), inventor of the Turtle Boat. 50ch, *Merkur* (Prussia, 1847). 80ch, *Duchess Elisabeth* (West Germany).
No. 2306: 80ch, *Christoforo Colombo* (Italy).

**1983, May 30** ***Perf. 11x11¼***
**2302-2304** A1107 Set of 3 5.00 1.50
**2305** Sheet of 4, #a.-d. + 2 labels 12.00 2.50
*a.* A1107 20ch multicolored 3.00 .50
*b.* A1107 35ch multicolored 3.00 .50
*c.* A1107 50ch multicolored 3.00 .50
*d.* A1107 80ch multicolored 3.00 .50

**Souvenir Sheet**
***Perf. 13½x13¼***

**2306** A1107 80ch multicolored 6.00 3.00

Steam Locomotives — A1108

Designs: 20ch, *Locomotion* (Great Britain, 1825). 35ch, *De Adler* (Germany, 1835). 50ch, *Austria* (1837).

No. 2310: 20ch, *Drache* (Germany, 1848. 35ch, Korean Train. 50ch, Bristal and Exeter Railway locomotive (Great Britain, 1853). 80ch, Caledonian Railway locomotive (Great Britain, 1859).

No. 2311: 80ch, *Ilmarinen* (Finland, 1860).

**1983, June 20** ***Perf. 12x11¾***

| | | | | |
|---|---|---|---|---|
| **2307-2309** | A1108 Set of 3 | | 13.00 | 2.50 |
| **2310** | Sheet of 4, #a.-d. + 2 labels | | 40.00 | 3.50 |
| *a.* | A1108 20ch multicolored | | 3.00 | .75 |
| *b.* | A1108 35ch multicolored | | 3.00 | .75 |
| *c.* | A1108 50ch multicolored | | 3.00 | .75 |
| *d.* | A1108 80ch multicolored | | 3.00 | .75 |

**Souvenir Sheet**

***Perf. 12***

**2311** A1108 80ch multicolored 30.00 1.50

Publication of the Five-Point Policy for Korean Reunification, 10th Anniv. — A1109

**1983, June 23** ***Perf. 12¼***

**2312** A1109 10ch multicolored 1.40 .25

World Conference of Journalists Against Imperialism and for Friendship and Peace — A1110

Designs: 10ch, Emblem, Tower of Juche Idea, fireworks, "Welcome." 40ch, Emblem, clasped hands, rainbow, "Friendship." Emblem, map, hand with raised forefinger, "Korea Is One."

**1983, July 2** ***Perf. 12x11¾***

**2313-2315** A1110 Set of 3 1.75 .30

"Let's Create the Speed of the 80s" A1111

**1983, July 10** ***Perf. 12x12¼***

**2316** A1111 10ch multicolored .50 .25

Korean War, 30th Anniv. A1112

**1983, July 27**

**2317** A1112 10ch multicolored .50 .25

Bangkok 1983 Int'l Stamp Exhib. — A1113

Designs: 40ch, *Gorch Foch* and DPRK #1693. 80ch, Bangkok temple, Great Britain #1 and DPRK IYC stamp.

**1983, Aug. 4** ***Perf. 12x11¾***

**2318** A1113 40ch multicolored 3.50 1.00

**Souvenir Sheet**

***Perf. 11½x11¾***

**2319** A1113 80ch multicolored 7.00 3.50

A1114

Winter Olympic Games, Sarajevo 1984 — A1115

Designs: 10ch, Skiier. 30ch, Figure skaters. 50ch, Ski jumper.

No. 2323 (all vert.): 20ch, Woman figure skater. 50ch, Hockey player. 80ch, Speed skater.

No. 2324, 80ch, Skier shooting rifle (biathlon).

**1983, Aug. 20**

| | | | | |
|---|---|---|---|---|
| **2320-2322** | A1114 Set of 3 | | 8.00 | 1.50 |
| **2323** | Sheet of 3, #a.-c., perf 11¾x12 | | 17.00 | 2.75 |
| *a.* | A1114 20ch multicolored | | 4.00 | .75 |
| *b.* | A1114 50ch multicolored | | 4.00 | .75 |
| *c.* | A1114 80ch multicolored | | 4.00 | .75 |

**Souvenir Sheet**

**2324** A1115 80ch multicolored 7.50 1.25

Democratic People's Republic of Korea, 35th Anniv. — A1116

**1983, Sept. 9** ***Perf. 13¼x13½***

**2325** A1116 10ch multicolored .65 .25

Folk Games — A1117

Designs: 10ch (No. 2326), Archery. 40ch (No. 2327), Seesaw. No. 2328: 10ch, Flying kites. 40ch, Swinging.

**1983, Sept. 20** ***Perf. 11¾x12***

| | | | | |
|---|---|---|---|---|
| **2326-2327** | A1117 Set of 2 | | 5.00 | .50 |
| **2328** | Sheet of 2, #a.-b. | | 2.50 | .40 |
| *a.* | A1117 10ch multicolored | | .75 | .25 |
| *b.* | A1117 40ch multicolored | | .75 | .25 |

Korean-Chinese Friendship A1118

**1983, Oct. 25** ***Perf. 12***

**2329** A1118 10ch multicolored .75 .25

A1119

World Communications Year — A1120

Designs: 30ch (No. 2330), *Redong Sinmun* and magazine. 40ch (No. 2331), Letters and forms of postal transport.

No. 2332: 30ch, Communications satellite, satellite dish. 40ch, TV camera and relay tower. 80ch, Telephone and satellite dishes.

No. 2333, 80ch, Emblem, communications satellite.

**1983, Oct. 30** ***Perf. 13½***

| | | | | |
|---|---|---|---|---|
| **2330-2331** | A1119 Set of 2 | | 9.00 | 1.75 |
| **2332** | Sheet of 3, #a.-c. | | 5.50 | 1.00 |
| *a.* | A1119 30ch multicolored | | 1.00 | .25 |
| *b.* | A1119 40ch multicolored | | 1.00 | .25 |
| *c.* | A1119 80ch multicolored | | 1.00 | .25 |

**Souvenir Sheet**

**2333** A1120 80ch multicolored 6.00 1.25

A1121

Paintings by Peter Paul Rubens — A1122

No. 2334, *Portrait of Helene Fourmet.*

No. 2335 (both horiz.): a., Detail from *Portrait of a Young Lady.* b., *Diana Returning from Hunt.*

No. 2336: *The Bear Hunt.*

**1983, Nov. 10**

| | | | | |
|---|---|---|---|---|
| **2334** | A1121 40ch multicolored | | 1.75 | .45 |
| **2335** | Sheet of 2, #a.-b. | | 4.50 | 1.25 |
| *a.* | A1121 40ch multicolored | | 1.75 | .45 |
| *b.* | A1121 80ch multicolored | | 1.75 | .45 |

**Souvenir Sheet**

**2336** A1122 80ch multicolored 3.25 .75

Olympic Games, Los Angeles 1984 A1123

Designs: 10ch, Sprinter. 30ch, Cyclists. 50ch, Volleyball.

No. 2340: 20ch, Show jumping. 50ch, Fencing. 80ch, Gymnastics.

No. 2341: 80ch, Judo.

**1983, Nov. 30** ***Perf. 11½***

| | | | | |
|---|---|---|---|---|
| **2337-2339** | A1123 Set of 3 | | 10.50 | 1.25 |
| **2340** | Sheet of 3, #a.-c. | | 30.00 | 2.00 |
| *a.* | A1123 20ch multicolored | | 7.00 | .50 |
| *b.* | A1123 50ch multicolored | | 7.00 | .50 |
| *c.* | A1123 80ch multicolored | | 7.00 | .50 |

**Souvenir Sheet**

**2341** A1123 80ch multicolored 3.50 1.00

Six deluxe souvenir sheets of one, each denominated 1w, exist. Value, set of 6 sheets, $100.

A1124

Antonio Correggio (1489-1534), 450th Death Anniv. — A1125

Designs: 20ch, *St. Catherine.* 35ch, *Madonna.* 50ch, *Madonna with St. John.*
No. 2345: a., *Morning* (detail). b., *Morning* (diff. detail). c., *St. Catherine* (diff.). d., *Madonna and Child.*
No. 2346: *Madonna and Child with Music-Making Angels.*

**1983, Dec. 12** — ***Perf. 13¼***

**2342-2344** A1124 Set of 3 — 5.00 1.25
**2345** Sheet of 4, #a.-d. — 12.00 3.50
*a.* A1124 20ch multicolored — 2.50 .75
*b.* A1124 35ch multicolored — 2.50 .75
*c.* A1124 50ch multicolored — 2.50 .75
*d.* A1124 80ch multicolored — 2.50 .75

**Souvenir Sheet**

**2346** A1125 80ch multicolored — 4.50 1.25

Cats A1126

Domestic cats, each different, denominated 10ch. Frame color: No. 2347, green. No. 2348, gray. No. 2349, gold. No. 2350, red. No. 2351, blue.

**1983, Dec. 20**

**2347-2351** A1126 Set of 5 — 12.00 .50

> Six souvenir sheets inscribed Sarajevo '84, each containing one 1w stamp, were issued on Dec. 31, 1983. Value $80.

New Year — A1127

**1984, Jan. 1** — ***Perf. 12***

**2352** A1127 10ch multicolored — 1.00 .25

Korean Workers Party A1128

Designs (both 10ch): No. 2353, Komdok General Mining Enterprise, Ore-dressing Plant No. 3, and Party flag. No. 2354, Worker holding books, and Party flag.

**1984, Feb. 16**

**2353-2354** A1128 Set of 2 — 1.00 .25
*2353a* 10ch Unsurfaced white paper, without gum — 20.00 —
*2354a* 10ch Unsurfaced white paper, without gum — 20.00 —

Farm Worker, Grain A1129

**1984, Feb. 25**

**2355** A1129 10ch multicolored — .60 .25

Publication of the *Theses on the Socialist Rural Question in Our Country,* 20th anniv.

Changdok School, Chilgol A1130

Kim's Birthplace, Rejoicing Crowd A1131

**1984, Apr. 15**

**2356** A1130 5ch multicolored — .50 .25
*a.* Unsurfaced white paper, without gum — 15.00 —
**2357** A1131 10ch multicolored — .50 .25
*a.* Unsurfaced white paper, without gum — 20.00 —

Kim Il Sung, 72nd birthday.

A1132

España '84 Int'l Stamp Exhib. — A1133

Designs: 10ch, *Spanish Riding School of Vienna,* by Julius von Blaas. 20ch, *Ferdinand of Austria,* by Rubens.
No. 2360: 80ch, *Spanish Riding School,* by von Blaas.

**1984, Apr. 27** — ***Perf. 13½***

**2358-2359** A1132 Set of 2 — 3.50 .75

**Souvenir Sheet**

**2360** A1133 80ch multicolored — 6.50 1.25

Kiyang Irrigation System, 25th Anniv. — A1134

**1984, Apr. 30**

**2361** A1134 10ch multicolored — .65 .25

Raphael, 500th Anniv. of Birth (in 1983) — A1135

Designs: 10ch, *Portrait of Angolo Doni.* 20ch, *Portrait of La Donna Velata.* 30ch, *Portrait of Jeanne d'Aragon.*
80ch, *St. Sebastian.*

**1984, Apr. 30** — ***Perf. 11¾x12***

**2362-2364** A1135 Set of 3 — 4.00 1.00

**Souvenir Sheet**

***Perf. 11¾x11½***

**2365** A1135 80ch multicolored — 3.50 1.25

Socialist Construction A1136

**1984, May 20** — ***Perf. 12***

**2366** A1136 10ch multicolored — .65 .25

1984 Winter Olympics Games Medal Winners — A1137

Designs: 20ch (No. 2367), Speed skating (Karin Enke, DDR). 30ch (No. 2368), Bobsledding (DDR).
No. 2369: 10ch, Ski jumping (Matti Nykaenen, Finland). 20ch (No. 2369b), Slalom (Max Julen, Switzerland). 30ch (No. 2369c), Downhill skiing (Maria Walliser, Switzerland).
No. 2370 (both vert.): 40ch, Cross-country skiing (Thomas Wassberg, Sweden). 80ch, Cross-country skiing (Maria Liisa Hamalainen).
No. 2371 (vert.): 80ch, Biathlon (Peter Angerer, West Germany).

**1984, May 20** — ***Perf. 13½***

**2367-2368** A1137 Set of 2 — 3.00 .75
**2369** Sheet of 3, #a.-c. — 25.00 1.25
*a.* A1137 10ch multicolored — 6.00 .35
*b.* A1137 20ch multicolored — 6.00 .35
*c.* A1137 30ch multicolored — 6.00 .35
**2370** Sheet of 2, #a.-b. — 5.00 1.00
*a.* A1137 40ch multicolored — 2.00 .40
*b.* A1137 80ch multicolored — 2.00 .40

**Souvenir Sheet**

**2371** A1137 80ch multicolored — 3.50 1.00

Essen '84 Int'l Stamp Exhib. — A1138

Designs: 20ch, Type "202" express locomotive (1939). 30ch, Type "E" freight locomotive (1919).
No. 2374: 80ch, Type "D" locomotive in Germany.

**1984, May 26** — ***Perf. 12x11¾***

**2372-2373** A1138 Set of 2 — 10.00 1.00

**Souvenir Sheet**

**2374** A1138 80ch multicolored — 9.00 1.25

Edgar Degas, 150th Birth Anniv. — A1139

Designs: 10ch, *Mlle. Fiocre in the Ballet 'La Source.'* 20ch, *The Dance Foyer at the Rue le Peletier Opera.* 30ch, *Race Meeting.*
No. 2378: 80ch, *Dancers at the Bars.*

**1984, June 10** — ***Perf. 12***

**2375-2377** A1139 Set of 3 — 8.00 1.25

**Souvenir Sheet**

***Perf. 11½***

**2378** A1139 80ch multicolored — 4.50 1.25

Irrigation Experts Meeting — A1140

**1984, June 16** — ***Perf. 11¾x12***

**2379** A1140 2ch multicolored — .80 .25

UPU Congress/Hamburg 1984 Stamp Exhib. — A1141

No. 2381: 80ch, *Gorch Fock,* DPRK stamp depicting Turtle Boat.

**1984, June 19**

**2380** A1141 20ch multicolored — 3.50 .35

**Souvenir Sheet**

***Perf. 11¾x11½***

**2381** A1141 80ch multicolored — 6.00 2.00

Tripartite Talks Proposal — A1142

**1984, June 25** ***Perf. 12¼***
**2382** A1142 10ch multicolored .65 .25

Alfred Bernhard Nobel, 150th Birth Anniv. (in 1983) A1143

Designs: 20ch, Nobel in laboratory. 30ch, Nobel portrait.
No. 2385: 80ch, Nobel portrait, diff.

**1984, June 30** ***Perf. 13½***
**2383-2384** A1143 Set of 2 8.00 .75

**Souvenir Sheet**

**2385** A1143 80ch multicolored 7.00 2.00

Nos. 2383 and 2384 were issued se-tenant with labels depicting Nobel's laboratory and home, respectively.

Improvement of Korean Living Standards — A1144

**1984, July 10** ***Perf. 11¾x12***
**2386** A1144 10ch multicolored .70 .25

Kuandian Conf., 65th Anniv. A1145

**1984, Aug. 17** ***Perf. 12x12¼***
**2387** A1145 10ch multicolored 1.25 .25

Sunhwa School, Mangyongdae — A1146

**1984, Aug. 17** ***Perf. 12***
**2388** A1146 10ch multicolored 1.10 .25

School of Kim Il Sung's father, Kim Hyong Jik.

A1147

A1148

Flowers: 10ch, *Cattleya loddigesii.* 20ch, *Thunia bracteata.* 30ch, *Phalaenopsis amabilis.*
No. 2392: 80ch, *Kimilsungia.*

**1984, Aug. 20**
**2389-2391** A1147 Set of 3 4.00 .60

**Souvenir Sheet**

**2392** A1148 80ch multicolored 5.00 1.00

Fishing Industry A1149

Designs: 5ch, Swordfish and trawler. 10ch, Marlin and trawler. 40ch, *Histiophorus orientalis.*

**1984, Aug. 25**
**2393-2395** A1149 Set of 3 4.50 1.00

Revolutionary Museum, Chilgol — A1150

**1984, Aug. 29**
**2396** A1150 10ch multicolored .90 .25

"Let's All Become the Kim Hyoks and Cha Gwang Sus of the '80s!" — A1151

**1984, Aug. 31**
**2397** A1151 10ch multicolored .90 .25

Orient Express, Centenary — A1152

Designs: 10ch, Inauguration of a French railway line in 1860. 20ch, Opening of a British railway line in 1821. 30ch, Inauguration of Paris-Rouen line, 1843.
No. 2401: 80ch, Interior views of passenger cars, 1905.

**1984, Sept. 7** ***Perf. 13½x13¼***
**2398-2400** A1152 Set of 3 8.00 1.25

**Souvenir Sheet**

**2401** A1152 80ch multicolored 7.00 1.75

Greenwich Meridian Time, Centenary A1153

Designs: 10ch, Clockface, astronomical observatory.
No. 2403: 80ch, Clock face, buildings, Chollima statue.

**1984, Sept. 15** ***Perf. 12***
**2402** A1153 10ch multicolored 4.00 —

**Souvenir Sheet**

***Perf. 11¾x11½***

**2403** A1153 80ch multicolored 6.00 1.25

Hamhung Grand Theater A1154

**1984, Sept. 21**
**2404** A1154 10ch multicolored .90 .25

Automation of Industry — A1155

**1984, Sept. 25** ***Perf. 12¼***
**2405** A1155 10ch multicolored .90 .25
*a.* Unsurfaced white paper, without gum 8.00 —

A1156

18th Century Korean Paintings — A1157

Designs: 10ch, *Dragon Angler.* 20ch, *Ox Driver,* horiz. 30ch, *Bamboo,* horiz.
80ch, *Autumn Night.*

**1984, Sept. 30** ***Perf. 12 (#2406), 13¼***
**2406-2408** A1156 Set of 3 4.00 .60

**Souvenir Sheet**

***Perf. 13¼***

**2409** A1157 80ch multicolored 3.50 1.25

K.E. Tsiolkovski (1857-1935), Russian Space Scientist A1158

Designs: 20ch, Portrait. 30ch, Earth, sputnik.
No. 2412: 80ch, Rocket launch.

**1984, Oct. 5** ***Perf. 11¾***
**2410-2411** A1158 Set of 2 2.00 .45

**Souvenir Sheet**

***Perf. 11¾x11½***

**2412** A1158 80ch multicolored 4.00 .75

Container Ships — A1159

Designs: 10ch, *Pongdaesan.* 20ch, *Ryongnamsan.* 30ch, *Rungrado.*
No. 2416: 80ch, *Kumgangsan*

**1984, Oct. 6** ***Perf. 12x11¾***
**2413-2415** A1158 Set of 3 3.50 .75

**Souvenir Sheet**

***Perf. 12***

**2416** A1159 80ch multicolored 5.00 1.25

A1160

A1161

Wild Animals: 10ch, Spotted hyenas. 20ch, Caracal. 30ch, Black-backed jackals. 40ch, Foxes.
80ch, Falcon.

**1984, Oct. 13** ***Perf. 13¼***
**2417-2420** A1160 Set of 4 4.50 1.00

**Souvenir Sheet**

**2421** A1161 80ch multicolored 6.50 1.25

Marie Curie (1867-1934), Physicist, 50th Death Anniv. A1162

No. 2423: 80ch, Portrait of Mme. Curie.

**1984, Oct. 21** ***Perf. 12***
2422 A1162 10ch multicolored 4.00 .25

**Souvenir Sheet**
***Perf. 11¾x11½***
2423 A1162 80ch multicolored 6.00 1.25

A1163

Birds: 10ch, Hoopoe. 20ch, South African crowned cranes. 30ch, Saddle-bill stork. 40ch, Chestnut-eared Aracari.
No. 2428: 80ch, Black kite.

**1984, Nov. 5** ***Perf. 11½***
2424-2427 A1163 Set of 4 8.50 1.25

**Souvenir Sheet**
2428 A1163 80ch multicolored 8.50 1.25

Space Exploration — A1164

Designs: 10ch, Cosmonaut. 20ch, Cosmonaut on space-walk. 30ch, Cosmonaut (diff.)
No. 2432: 80ch, Moon vehicle.

**1984, Nov. 15** ***Perf. 12***
2429-2431 A1164 Set of 3 2.50 .50

**Souvenir Sheet**
2432 A1164 80ch multicolored 4.00 1.00

Russian Icebreakers — A1165

Designs: 20ch, *Arktika*. 30ch, *Ermak*.
No. 2435: 80ch, *Lenin*.

**1984, Nov. 26** ***Perf. 13¼***
2433-2434 A1165 Set of 2 3.25 .60

**Souvenir Sheet**
2435 A1165 80ch multicolored 5.00 1.25

A1166

Dmitri Mendeleev (1834-1907), Chemist, 150th Birth Anniv. — A1167

**1984, Dec. 1** ***Perf. 13¼***
2436 A1166 10ch multicolored 1.75 .25

**Souvenir Sheet**
2437 A1167 80ch multicolored 4.00 1.25

Historic European Royalty, Scenes — A1168

British Monarchs — A1169

Queen Elizabeth II — A1170

Type A1168: No. 2438 (all 10ch): a, Konrad III, 1149 (Germany). b, Henry VIII (England). c, Henry VI (England). d, King John (England). e, Fleet of Elizabeth I (England). f, Philip II Augustus (France). g, Thames and London Bridge, 1616. h, Elizabeth I (England). i, Charles VII, parade (England).

No. 2439 (all 10ch): a, Prince Eugene, 1706 (Savoy). b, Kaiser Wilhelm II (Germany). c, Philip V (Spain). d, Ludwig II (Bavaria). e, Alfonso XIII (Spain). f, Mary Stuart (Scotland). g, Charles Edward Stuart, 1745 (Scotland). h, Marie-Louise (Austria). i, Charles V, 1547 (Spain).

No. 2440 (Horiz., all 10ch): a, Maria Theresa (Austria). b, Francis I, 1814 (Austria). c, Leopold II, 1844 (Austria). d, Louis XVIII (France). e, Versailles, 1688. f, Louis XIV (France). g, Prince Wilhelm (Germany). h, Franz Joseph I (Austria). i, Ludwig II (Bavaria).

No. 2441 (Horiz., all 10ch): a, Napoleon III (France. b, Rudolph of Habsburg, Basel 1273. c, Henry IV (France). d, Louis XII (France). e, Maximilian I (Holy Roman Empire). f, Peter the Great, Amsterdam Harbor (Russia). g, Louis VIII (France). h, Don Juan/Battle of Lepanto, 1571. i, Neuschwaustein Castle.

Type A1169: No. 2442 (all 10ch): a, William I. b, Richard II. c, Henry V. d, Henry VI. e, Richard III. f, Edward IV. g, Henry VII. h, Henry VIII, full length portrait. i, Henry VIII, ¾-face portrait, as young man.

No. 2443 (all 10ch): a, Henry VIII, ¾-face portrait, as middle-aged man. b, Mary I. c, Elizabeth I, facing left. d, Edward VI. e, Elizabeth I, facing right. f, Lady Jane Grey. g, Mary, Queen of Scots. h, James I. i, Charles I.

No. 2444 (all 10ch): a, Charles I. b, Henrietta Marie. c, Charles II. d, James II. e, George I, seated. f, William IV. g, Queen Anne, full-length portrait. h, George I, in profile. i. Queen Mary II.

No. 2445 (all 10ch): a, Queen Anne, with her son, William, Duke of Gloucester. b, George II, facing forward. c, George II, in profile. d, George IV. e, George III. f, William III. g, William IV. h, Queen Victoria. i, Prince Albert.

No. 2446 (all 10ch): a, Edward VII. b, Queen Alexandra. c, George V and Royal Family. d, George VI. e, George VI and Royal Family. f, Queen Elizabeth II. g, Prince Charles. h, Prince William of Wales, with Prince Charles and Princess Diana. i, Princess Diana.

**Sheets of 9, #a.-i.**

**1984, Dec. 20** ***Perf. 12¼x12***
**Types A1168-A1169**
2438-2446 Set of 9 125.00 —

**Souvenir Sheet**
***Perf. 11½***
2447 A1170 80ch multicolored 20.00 12.00

Kim Il Sung's Visits to Eastern Europe — A1171

No. 2448 (all 10ch): a, USSR. b, Poland. c, DDR. d, Czechoslovakia.
No. 2249 (all 10ch): a, Hungary. b, Bulgaria. c, Romania.
No. 2450: 10ch, China.

**1984, Dec. 30** ***Perf. 12***
2448 A1171 Sheet of 4, #a.-d. 4.50 1.25
2449 A1171 Sheet of 3, #a.-c. 3.50 1.00

**Souvenir Sheet**
***Perf. 11½***
2450 A1171 10ch multicolored 2.75 1.00

New Year — A1172

**1985, Jan. 1** ***Perf. 12***
2451 A1172 10ch multicolored 1.90 .25

Kim Il Sung's 1,000-ri Journey, 60th Anniv. — A1173

**1985, Jan. 22** ***Perf. 12¼***
2452 A1173 Pair, #a.-b. 2.25 .25
*a.* 5ch multicolored .75 .25
*b.* 10ch multicolored .75 .25

A1174

History of the Motorcar — A1175

Designs: 10ch, Gugnot's Steam Car, 1769. 15ch, Goldsworthy Steam Omnibus, 1825. 20ch, Gottlieb Daimler diesel car, 1885. 25ch, Benx three-wheeled diesel car, 1886. 30ch, Peugot diesel car, 1891.
80ch, Wind-power car.

**1985, Jan. 25** ***Perf. 11½***
2453-2457 A1174 Set of 5 7.00 .85

**Souvenir Sheet**
2458 A1175 80ch multicolored 4.50 1.25

Secret Camp, Mt. Paektu — A1176

**1985, Feb. 16** ***Perf. 12***
2459 A1176 10ch multicolored .65 .25

Korean Revolution Headquarters

Lighthouses — A1177

10ch, Taechodo. 20ch, Sodo. 30ch, Pido. 40ch, Suundo.

**1985, Feb. 23** *Perf. 12¼x11¾*
**2460-2463** A1177 Set of 4 9.00 1.25

For surcharges, see Nos. 4533-4534.

*The Hedgehog Defeats the Tiger*, Fairy Tale
A1178

Designs: 10ch, Tiger bragging about his strength. 20ch, Tiger going to stamp on rolled-up hedgehog. 30ch, Hedgehog clinging to tiger's nose. 35ch, Fleeing tiger. 40ch, Tiger crawling before hedgehog.

**1985, Mar. 6** *Perf. 11½*
**2464-2468** A1178 Set of 5 6.50 1.25

A1179

Mushrooms: 10ch, Pieurotus cornucopiae. 20ch, Pluerotus ostreatus. 30ch, Catathelasma ventricosum.

**1985, Mar. 16**
**2469-2471** A1179 Set of 3 6.00 .65

For surcharge, see No. 4521.

A1180

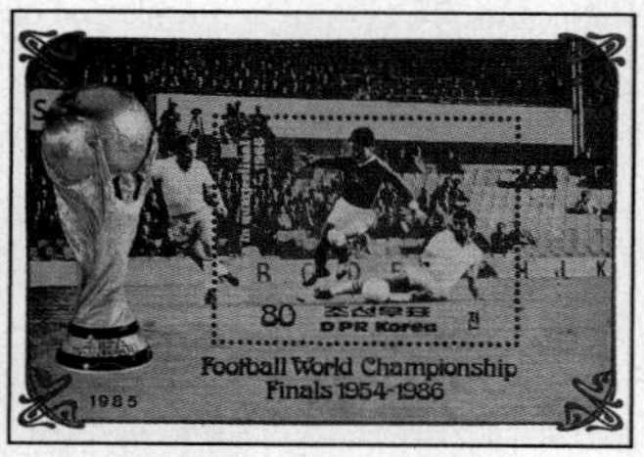

World Cup Soccer 1954-1966 — A1181

Designs: 10ch, W. Germany vs. Hungary, 1954. 20ch, Brazil vs. Sweden, 1958. 30ch, Brazil vs. Czechoslovakia, 1962. 40ch, England vs. W. Germany, 1966.
80ch, DPRK team in quarter final, 1966.

**1985, Mar. 20** *Perf. 13¼*
**2472-2475** A1180 Set of 4 4.50 1.00

**Souvenir Sheet**

**2476** A1181 80ch multicolored 4.00 1.25

A1182

World Cup Soccer 1970-1986 — A1183

Designs: 10ch, Brazil vs. Italy, 1970. 20ch, W. Germany vs. Netherlands, 1974. 30ch, Argentina vs. Netherlands, 1978. 40ch, Italy vs. W. Germany, 1982.
80ch, Aztec Stadium, Mexico City.

**1985, Mar. 20** *Perf. 13¼*
**2477-2480** A1182 Set of 4 4.00 1.00

**Souvenir Sheet**

**2481** A1183 80ch multicolored 4.00 1.25

Kim Il Sung, 73rd Birthday
A1184

**1985, April 15** *Perf. 12*
**2482** A1184 10ch multicolored .65 .25

4th Century Musical Instruments
A1185

Designs: 10ch, Horn player. 20ch So (panpipes) player.

**1985, May 7** *Perf. 11½*
**2483-2484** A1185 Set of 2 3.50 .25

Chongryon Hall, Tokyo — A1186

**1985, May 25**
**2485** A1186 10ch deep brown .65 .25

30th anniv. of Chongryon, the General Association of Korean Residents in Japan.

A1187

Mammals: 5ch, Common marmoset (callithrix jacchus). 10ch, Ring-tailed lemur (Lemur catta).

**1985, June 7**
**2486-2487** A1187 Set of 2 2.50 .25

National Emblem — A1188

**1985, June 20**
**2488** A1188 80ch multicolored 3.00 .70

A1189

Argentina '85 Int'l Stamp Exhib. — A1190

Designs: 10ch, Buenos Aires and Argentina stamp. 20ch, Iguaçu Falls and Argentine, DPRK stamps, horiz.
80ch, Gaucho.

**1985, July 5** *Perf. 11¾*
**2489-2490** A1189 Set of 2 3.50 .25

**Souvenir Sheet**

**2491** A1190 80ch multicolored 4.00 4.00

12th World Youth and Students' Festival, Moscow — A1191

Designs: 10ch, Korean dancer with streamer, gymnast. 20ch, Spassky Tower, Festival emblem. 30ch, Youths of different races.

**1985, July 27** *Perf. 12¼*
**2492-2494** A1191 Set of 3 3.50 .75

Pyongyang Buildings — A1192

Designs: 2ch, Phyonghwa Pavilion. 40ch, Skyscraper apartments, Chollima Street.

**1985, Aug. 1** *Perf. 12*
**2495-2496** A1192 Set of 2 .90 .25

| | | | |
|---|---|---|---|
| *2495a* | 2ch Thick toned unsurfaced paper, without gum | 10.00 | — |
| *2496a* | 40ch Thick toned unsurfaced paper, without gum | 5.00 | — |

A1193

Liberation, 40th Anniv. — A1194

Designs: 5ch, Soldiers, battle scene. 10ch (No. 2498), Korean and Russian soldier with raised arms. 10ch (No. 2499), Japanese soldiers surrendering. 10ch (No. 2500), Crowd with banners, Flame of Juche. 10ch (No. 2501), Student marchers with banners. 10ch (No. 2502), Liberation monument, vert. 40ch, Students bearing banners.
80ch, Monument.

**1985, Aug. 15** *Perf. 11½*
**2497-2503** A1193 Set of 7 2.50 1.00

| | | | |
|---|---|---|---|
| *2497a* | 5ch Toned unsurfaced paper, without gum | 8.00 | — |
| *2498a* | 10ch Toned unsurfaced paper, without gum | 8.00 | — |
| *2499a* | 10ch Toned unsurfaced paper, without gum | 8.00 | — |
| *2500a* | 10ch Toned unsurfaced paper, without gum | 8.00 | — |
| *2501a* | 10ch Toned unsurfaced paper, without gum | 8.00 | — |
| *2502a* | 10ch Toned unsurfaced paper, without gum | 8.00 | — |
| *2503a* | 40ch Toned unsurfaced paper, without gum | 8.00 | — |

**Souvenir Sheet**

**2504** A1194 80ch multicolored 2.00 2.00

A1195

Halley's Comet — A1196

Designs: 10ch, Halley and Comet. 20ch, Comet, diagram of course, space probe.
80ch, Comet's trajectory.

**1985, Aug. 25** *Perf. 13½*
**2505-2506** A1195 Set of 2 2.00 .25

**Souvenir Sheet**

**2507** A1196 80ch multicolored 4.00 1.25

Flowers — A1197

Designs: 10ch, Hippeastrum hybridum. 20ch, Camellia japonica. 30ch, Cyclamen persicum.

**1985, Sept. 10** *Perf. 12*
**2508-2510** A1197 Set of 3 7.00 .65

A1198

Koguryo Culture, 4th-6th Centuries A.D. — A1199

Designs: 10ch, Hero. 15ch, Heroine. 20ch, Flying fairy. 25ch, Hunting.
50ch, Pine tree.

**1985, Sep. 30** *Perf. 13¼*
**2511-2514** A1198 Set of 4 3.50 .65
*2514a* Sheet of 4, #2511-2514 4.00 1.00

**Souvenir Sheet**
*Perf. 12*

**2515** A1199 50ch multicolored 3.00 .75

Nos. 2511-2514 were issued both in separate sheets and in setenant sheets of four stamps (No. 2514a).

Korean Worker's Party, 40th Anniv. — A1200

Designs: 5ch, Party Founding Museum. 10ch (No. 2517), Soldier, workers. 10ch (No. 2518), Miner, workers. 40ch, Worker, peasant, professional worker holding up Party emblem.
No. 2520: 90ch, People holding bouquets of flowers.

**1985, Oct. 10** *Perf. 11½*
**2516-2519** A1200 Set of 4 1.40 .75
*2516a* 5ch Thick toned unsurfaced paper, without gum 5.00 —
*2517a* 10ch Thick toned unsurfaced paper, without gum 10.00 —
*2518a* 10ch Thick toned unsurfaced paper, without gum 5.00 —
*2519a* 40ch Thick toned unsurfaced paper, without gum 10.00 —

**Souvenir Sheet**

**2520** A1200 90ch multicolored 1.60 .50

Kim Il Sung's Return, 40th Anniv. — A1201

**1985, Oct. 14** *Perf. 12*
**2521** A1201 10ch red brn & lt grn 1.00 .25
*a.* Dull white unsurfaced paper, without gum 8.00 —

Italia '85, Int'l Stamp Exhib., Rome A1202

Designs: 10ch, Colosseum, Rome, and DPRK stamp. 20ch, *The Holy Family*, by Raphael. 30ch. Head of Michelangelo's *David*, vert.
No. 2525: 80ch, Pantheon, Rome.

**1985, Oct. 25** *Perf. 11½*
**2522-2524** A1202 Set of 3 2.75 .65

**Souvenir Sheet**

**2525** A1202 80ch multicolored 4.00 1.25

South-West German Stamp Bourse, Sindelfingen — A1203

Designs, Mercedes Benz: 10ch, Type 300, 1960. 15ch, Type 770. 20ch, Type W150, 1937. 30ch, Type 600, 1966.
No. 2530: 80ch, Mercedes Benz, Type W31, 1938.

**1985, Oct. 25**
**2526-2529** A1203 Set of 4 6.50 .65

**Souvenir Sheet**
*Perf. 11¾*

**2530** A1203 80ch multicolored 5.25 .75

A1204

13th World Cup Championship, Mexico City — A1205

Designs: 20ch, Dribbling and sliding tackle. 30ch, Jumping kick.
80ch, Goalkeeper and Mexican monuments.

**1985, Nov. 1** *Perf. 13¼*
**2531-2532** A1204 Set of 2 3.25 .50

**Souvenir Sheet**

**2533** A1205 80ch multicolored 4.50 1.10

Int'l Youth Year A1206

Designs: 10ch, Traditional dance. 20ch, Sculpture depicting gymnasts. 30ch, Scientific research.
No. 2537: 80ch, Young people of different races.

**1985, Nov. 9** *Perf. 11½*
**2534-2536** A1206 Set of 3 3.50 .50

**Souvenir Sheet**

**2537** A1206 80ch multicolored 4.50 1.10

A1207

13th World Cup Championship, Mexico City — A1208

Designs: 20ch, Dribbling. 30ch, Tackling.
80ch, Goalkeeper, bullfighter.

**1985, Nov. 20** *Perf. 12*
**2538-2539** A1207 Set of 2 3.50 .50

**Souvenir Sheet**

**2540** A1208 80ch multicolored 5.00 1.10

Juche Torch — A1209

New Year

**1986, Jan. 1** *Perf. 12x12¼*
**2541** A1209 10ch multicolored 1.25 .25

History of the Motor Car A1210

Designs: 10ch, Amédée Bollée and Limousine, 1901. 20ch, Stewart Rolls, Henry Royce and Silver Ghost, 1906. 25ch, Giovanni Agnelli and Fiat car, 1912. 30ch, Ettore Bugatti and Royal coupe, 1928. 40ch, Louis Renault and fiacre, 1906.
No. 2547: 80ch, Gottlieb Daimler, Karl Benz and Mercedes S, 1927.

**1986, Jan. 20** *Perf. 11½*
**2542-2546** A1210 Set of 5 9.50 1.25

**Souvenir Sheet**

**2547** A1210 80ch multicolored 7.50 .75

World Chess Championship, Moscow A1211

Designs: 20ch, Gary Kasparov.
No. 2549: 80ch, Kasparov-Karpov chess match.

**1986, Feb. 5** *Perf. 11¾x12*
**2548** A1211 20ch multicolored 2.25 .25

**Souvenir Sheet**
*Perf. 12*

**2549** A1211 80ch multicolored 5.00 1.25

For surcharges, see Nos. 4522-4523.

Revolutionary Martyrs' Cemetery, Pyongyang — A1212

Designs: 5ch, Cemetery Gate. 10ch, Bronze sculpture of draped flag, soldier, workers (detail).

**1986, Feb. 10** *Perf. 12*
**2550-2551** A1212 Set of 2 1.50 .25

Songgan Revolutionary Site, 37th Anniv. of Kim Il Sung's Visit — A1213

**1986, Feb. 16**
**2552** A1213 10ch multicolored .90 .25

Mt. Myohyang Historic Buildings — A1214

Designs: 10ch, Buddhist Scriptures Museum. 20ch, Taeung Hall of the Pohyon Temple.

**1986, Feb. 20** *Perf. 12¼*
**2553-2554** A1214 Set of 2 2.00 .25

Tropical Fish A1215

Designs: 10ch, Heniochus acuminatus. 20ch, Amphiprion frenatus.

**1986, Mar. 12** *Perf. 11½*
**2555-2556** A1215 Set of 2 2.50 .30

World Cup Championship, Mexico City — A1216

Designs, soccer players and flags of: 10ch, Italy, Bulgaria, Argentina. 20ch, Mexico, Belgium, Paraguay, Iraq. 25ch, France, Canada, USSR, Hungary. 30ch, Brazil, Spain, Algeria, Northern Ireland. 35ch, W. Germany, Uruguay, Scotland, Denmark. 40ch, Poland, Portugal, Morocco, England.

No. 2563: 80ch, Soccer players, World Cup, gold soccer ball, boots.

**1986, Mar. 21** ***Perf. 12***

**2557-2562** A1216 Set of 6 10.00 1.60

**Souvenir Sheet**

**2563** A1216 80ch multicolored 6.50 .65

For overprints see Nos. 2599-2605.

4th Spring Friendship Art Festival, Pyongyang — A1217

**1986, Apr. 5**

**2564** A1217 1w multicolored 3.00 .65

Mercedes-Benz, 60th Anniv. — A1218

Designs: 10ch (No. 2565), Daimler No. 1 ("Motorwagen"), 1886. 10ch (No. 2566), Benz-Velo, 1894. 20ch (No. 2567), Mercedes, 1901. 20ch (No. 2568), Benz limousine, 1909. 30ch (No. 2569), Mercedes Tourenwagen, 1914. 30ch (No. 2570), Mercedes Benz 170/6 cylinder, 1931. 40ch (No. 2571), Mercedes Benz 380, 1933. 40ch (No. 2572), Mercedes Benz 540K, 1936.

No. 2573: 80ch, Mercedes-Simplex Phaeton, 1904.

**1986, Apr. 8** ***Perf. 11½***

**2565-2572** A1218 Set of 8 9.00 2.00

**Souvenir Sheet**

**2573** A1218 80ch multicolored 5.00 1.25

Kim Il Sung, 74th Birthday — A1219

**1986, Apr. 15** ***Perf. 12***

**2574** A1219 10ch multicolored .65 .25

Association for the Restoration of the Fatherland, 50th Anniv. — A1220

**1986, May 5** ***Perf. 11¾x12***

**2575** A1220 10ch multicolored .65 .25

Intl. Year of Peace A1221

Designs: 10ch, Dove carrying letter. 20ch, Dove, UN Headquarters. 30ch, Dove, globe, broken missiles.

No. 2579: 80ch, Sculpture of children and dove.

**1986, June 18** ***Perf. 11¾x12***

**2576-2578** A1221 Set of 3 4.00 1.25

**Souvenir Sheet**

***Perf. 11¾x11½***

**2579** A1221 80ch multicolored 5.00 .75

*Mona Lisa*, by da Vinci — A1222

**1986, July 9** ***Perf. 13½x13¼***

**2580** A1222 20ch multicolored 3.00 .25

Irises — A1223

Designs: 20ch, Pink iris. 30ch, Violet iris.

No. 2583: 80ch, Magenta iris.

**1986, July 20** ***Perf. 11½***

**2581-2582** A1223 Set of 2 5.00 .50

**Souvenir Sheet**

**2583** A1223 80ch multicolored 6.50 1.10

Tennis Players — A1224

Designs: 10ch, Kim Un Suk. 20ch, Ivan Lendi. 30ch, Steffi Craf. 50ch, Boris Becker.

**1986, July 30** ***Perf. 13½***

**2584** A1224 Block of 4, #a.-d. 7.00 1.00
- *a.* 10ch multicolored 1.50 .25
- *b.* 20ch multicolored 1.50 .25
- *c.* 30ch multicolored 1.50 .25
- *d.* 50ch multicolored 1.50 .25
- *e.* 10ch Toned unsurfaced paper, without gum 10.00 —

No. 2584 was printed in sheets containing two setenant blocks.

No. 2584d is airmail.

Stampex '86 Stamp Exhib., Adelaide A1225

Designs: 10ch, Cockatoo; 80ch, Kangaroo, map of Australia, emblems.

**1986, Aug. 4** ***Perf. 11½***

**2585** A1225 10ch multicolored 5.50 .25

**Souvenir Sheet**

**2586** A1225 80ch multicolored 5.50 1.10

*L'Unita* Festival, Milan A1227

Designs: 10ch, First issue of *L'Unita*. 20ch, Milan Cathedral. 30ch, Michelangelo's *Pieta*, vert.

No. 2590: 80ch, Enrico Berlinguer, Italian Communist Party leader.

**1986, Aug. 26**

**2587-2589** A1227 Set of 3 5.50 2.50

**Souvenir Sheet**

**2590** A1227 80ch multicolored 4.50 .75

National Festival of *L'Unita*, the Italian Communist Party newspaper.

A1228

Stockholmia '86 Int'l Stamp Exhib., Stockholm — A1229

Design: 10ch, Icebreaker *Express II* and Swedish stamp.

80ch, UPU emblem, mail coach and Swedish stamps.

**1986, Aug. 28**

**2591** A1228 10ch multicolored 2.00 .25

**Souvenir Sheet**

**2592** A1229 80ch multicolored 7.00 1.50

DPRK Postage Stamps, 40th Anniv. — A1230

Designs: 10ch, Perf green reprint of Scott No. 1. 15ch, Imperf green reprint of Scott No. 1. 50ch, Scott No. 5.

**1986, Sep. 12** ***Perf. 12¼x12***

**2593-2595** A1230 Set of 3 6.00 1.50

No. 2595 is airmail.

DPRK Postage Stamps, 40th Anniv. — A1231

Designs: 10ch, Postal emblems, DPRK #387, 2505. 15ch, Postal emblems, General Post Office, Pyongyang, DPRK #1529, 1749. 50ch, Postal emblems, Kim Il Jung. DPRK #1, #1 reprint in green, vert.

**1986, Oct. 5** ***Perf. 12***

**2596-2598** A1231 Set of 3 8.00 1.00

No. 2598 is airmail. For surcharge, see No. 4580.

**Nos. 2557-2563 Overprinted with World Cup Soccer Championship Results**

**1986, Oct. 14**

**2599-2604** A1216 Set of 6 16.00 2.50

**Souvenir Sheet**

**2605** A1216 80ch multicolored 10.00 1.40

Down-with-Imperialism Union, 60th Anniv. — A1232

**1986, Oct. 17** ***Perf. 11½***

**2606** A1232 10ch multicolored .70 .25

Gift Animals House, 1st Anniv. — A1233

**1986, Oct. 18** ***Perf. 12x11¾***

**2607** A1233 2w multicolored 8.50 .90
- *a.* On toned unsurfaced paper, without gum 10.00 —

United Nations Educational, Scientific and Cultural Organization (UNESCO), 40th anniv. — A1234

Designs: 10ch, Schoolchildren. 50ch, UNESCO emblem, Grand People's Study

House, televion, communications satellite and dish, horiz.

**1986, Nov. 4** *Perf. 12*
**2608-2609** A1234 Set of 2 4.50 1.25

Inter-Sputnik, 15th Anniv. — A1235

**1986, Nov. 15**
**2610** A1235 5w multicolored 10.00 2.25
*a.* On toned unsurfaced paper, without gum 10.00 —

West Sea Barrage — A1236

Designs: 10ch, Oil tanker, lock. 40ch, Aerial view of dam. 1.20w, Aerial view of dam (diff.)

**1986, Nov. 20** *Perf. 12x11¾*
**2611-2613** A1236 Set of 3 8.50 1.00
*2611a* 10ch Toned unsurfaced paper, without gum 5.00 —
*2612a* 40ch Toned unsurfaced paper, without gum 8.00 —
*2613a* 1.20w Toned unsurfaced paper, without gum 8.00 —

Mushrooms and Minerals — A1237

Designs: a, 10ch Lengenbachite. b, 10ch Clitocybe infundibuliformis. c, 15ch Rhodocrosite. d, 15ch Morchella esculenta. e, 50ch Annabergite. f, 50ch Russula.

**1986, Nov. 23** *Perf. 13¼*
**2614** A1237 Block of 6, #a.-f. 16.50 1.25
*a.* 10ch multicolored 2.50 .25
*b.* 10ch multicolored 2.50 .25
*c.* 15ch multicolored 2.50 .25
*d.* 15ch multicolored 2.50 .25
*e.* 50ch multicolored 2.50 .25
*f.* 50ch multicolored 2.50 .25

Printed in setenant blocks within the sheet.
Nos. 2614e and 2614f are airmail.

A1238

Exhib. of North Korean 3-D Photos and Stamps, Lima — A1239

Design: 10ch, Machu Picchu and DPRK #1402.
80ch, Korean and Peruvian children.

**1986, Nov. 25** *Perf. 13¼x13½*
**2615** A1238 10ch multicolored 2.00 .25

**Souvenir Sheet**

**2616** A1239 80ch multicolored 9.00 2.00

New Year — A1240

Designs: 10ch, Sun, pine tree. 40ch, Hare.

**1987, Jan. 1** *Perf. 12*
**2617-2618** A1240 Set of 2 3.50 .50

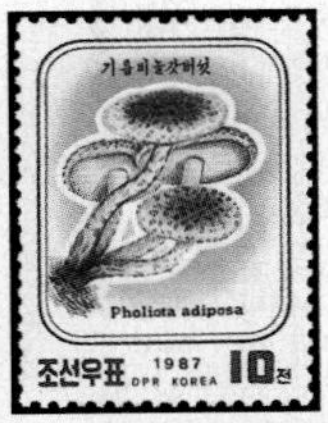


A1241

Fungi — A1242

Designs: 10ch, *Pholiota adiposa*. 20ch, *Cantharellus cibarius*. 30ch, *Boletus impolitus*. 80ch, *Gomphidius rutilus*.

**1987, Jan. 5** *Perf. 11½*
**2619-2621** A1241 Set of 3 5.75 .75

**Souvenir Sheet**

**2622** A1242 80ch multicolored 7.00 1.50

For surcharge, see No. 4535.

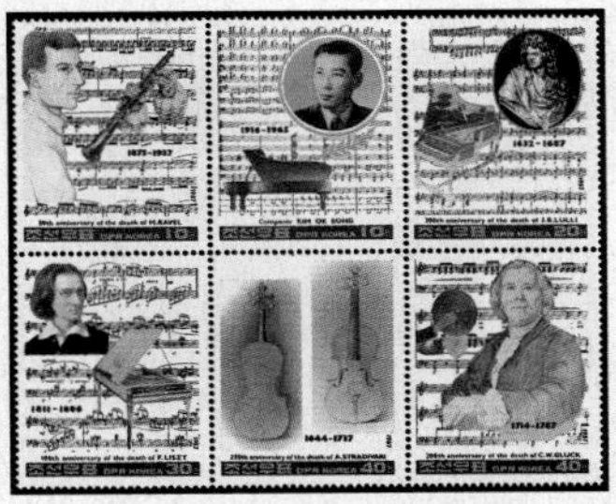

Famous Composers, Death Anniv. — A1243

Designs: 10ch (No. 2623a), Maurice Ravel (1875-1937). 10ch (No. 2623b), Kim Ok Song (1916-65). 20ch, Giovanni Lully (1632-67). 30ch, Franz Liszt (1811-86). 40ch (No.2623e), Stradivarius violins (Antonio Stradivari, 1644-1737). 40ch (No. 2623f), Christoph Gluck (1714-87).

**1987, Jan. 29** *Perf. 13¼*
**2623** A1243 Block of 6, #a.-f. 12.00 1.10
*a.* 10ch multicolored 1.50 .25
*b.* 10ch multicolored 1.50 .25
*c.* 20ch multicolored 1.50 .25
*d.* 30ch multicolored 1.50 .25
*e.* 40ch multicolored 1.50 .25
*f.* 40ch multicolored 1.50 .25

No. 2623 was printed in se-tenant blocks of six within the sheet.

Kim Jong Il, 45th Birthday — A1244

**1987, Feb. 16**
**2624** A1244 80ch multicolored 2.50 .40

Buildings — A1245

Designs: 5ch, East Pyongyang Grand Theater. 10ch, Pyongyang Koryo Hotel (vert.). 3w, Rungnado Stadium.

**1987, Feb. 23** *Perf. 12*
**2625-2627** A1245 Set of 3 7.50 1.20
*2625a* 5ch Stiff paper, without gum 10.00 —
*2626a* 10ch Stiff paper, without gum 5.00 —
*2627a* 3w Stiff paper, without gum 5.00 —

Sailing Ships — A1246

Designs: 20ch, *Gorch Fock*. 30ch, *Tovarisch*, vert.. 50ch (No. 2630), *Belle Poule*, vert. 50ch (No. 2631), *Sagres II*, vert. 1w (No. 2632), Merchantman, Koryo Period (918-1392). 1w (No. 2633), *Dar Mlodziezy*, vert..

**1987, Feb. 25** *Perf. 13¼*
**2628-2633** A1246 Set of 6 11.50 2.75

Nos. 2630-2633 are airmail.

Fire Engines — A1247

Designs: 10ch, German fire engine. 20ch, Benz fire engine. 30ch, Chemical fire engine. 50ch, Soviet fire engine.

**1987, Feb. 27** *Perf. 12*
**2634-2637** A1247 Set of 4 10.00 1.20

No. 2637 is airmail.

Road Safety — A1248

Designs (multiple traffic signs): 10ch (No. 2638), Blue sign lower center. 10ch (No. 2639), Red sign lower center. 20ch, Various signs. 50ch, Various signs (diff.)

**1987, Feb. 27**
**2638-2641** A1248 Set of 4 7.50 .90

Nos. 2641 is airmail.

Butterflies and Flowers — A1249

Designs: No. 2642, Apatura ilia and spiraea. No. 2643, Ypthinia argus and fuchsia. No. 2644, Neptis philyra and aguilegia. No. 2645, Papilio protenor and chrysanthemum. No. 2646, Parantica sita and celosia. No. 2847, Vanessa indica and hibiscus.

**1987, Mar. 12**
**2642-2647** A1249 Set of 6 11.00 1.50

For surcharge, see No. 4524.

Korean National Assoc., 70th Anniv. — A1250

Design: 10ch, Association Monument, Pyongyang.

**1987, Mar. 23** *Perf. 11½*
**2648** A1250 10ch multicolored .60 .25

5th Spring Friendship Art Festival — A1251

**1987, Apr. 6**

| | | | | |
|---|---|---|---|---|
| **2649** | A1251 | 10ch multicolored | .70 | .25 |

A1252

Kim Il Sung, 75th Birthday — A1253

Designs: No. 2650, Mangyong Hill. No. 2651, Kim Il Sung's birthplace, Mangyongdae, horiz. No 2652, Painting, *Profound Affection for the Working Class.* No. 2653, Painting, *A Bumper Crop of Pumpkins.*

**1987, Apr. 15** ***Perf. 12***

| | | | | |
|---|---|---|---|---|
| **2650** | A1252 | 10ch multicolored | .50 | .25 |
| **2651** | A1252 | 10ch multicolored | .50 | .25 |
| **2652** | A1253 | 10ch multicolored | .50 | .25 |
| **2653** | A1253 | 10ch multicolored | .50 | .25 |
| | | *Nos. 2650-2653 (4)* | 2.00 | 1.00 |

Horses — A1254

Designs: No. 2654a, Bay. No. 2654b, Bay, diff. No. 2654c, Gray, rearing. No. 2654d, White horse on beach.

**1987, Apr. 20** ***Perf. 13¼***

| | | | | |
|---|---|---|---|---|
| **2654** | A1254 | Block of 4, #a.-d. | 7.00 | 2.10 |
| *a.* | | 10ch multicolored | .50 | .25 |
| *b.* | | 10ch multicolored | .50 | .25 |
| *c.* | | 40ch multicolored | 2.50 | .70 |
| *d.* | | 40ch multicolored | 2.50 | .70 |

No. 2654 was printed in se-tenant blocks of four within the sheet.

Transport — A1255

Designs: No. 2655, Electric train *Juche.* No. 2656, Electric train *Mangyongdae.* No. 2657, *Sputnik I,* vert. No. 2658, Laika, first animal in space, vert. No. 2659, Tupolev Tu-144 jetliner. No. 2660, Concorde jetliner. No. 2661, Count Ferdinand von Zeppelin and LZ-4. No. 2662, Zeppelin and diagrams of airships.

**1987, Apr. 30**

| | | | | |
|---|---|---|---|---|
| **2655** | A1255 | 10ch multicolored | .60 | .25 |
| **2656** | A1255 | 10ch multicolored | .60 | .25 |
| *a.* | | Pair, #2655-2656 | .75 | .40 |
| **2657** | A1255 | 10ch multicolored | .60 | .25 |
| **2658** | A1255 | 20ch multicolored | 1.10 | .25 |
| *a.* | | Pair, #2657-2658 | 2.00 | .40 |
| **2659** | A1255 | 20ch multicolored | 1.10 | .25 |
| **2660** | A1255 | 20ch multicolored | 1.10 | .25 |
| *a.* | | Pair, #2659-2660 | 2.50 | .40 |
| **2661** | A1255 | 30ch multicolored | 1.50 | .25 |
| **2662** | A1255 | 80ch multicolored | 4.50 | 1.00 |
| *a.* | | Pair, #2661-2662 | 7.00 | 1.25 |
| | | *Nos. 2655-2662 (8)* | 11.10 | 2.75 |

Nos. 2655/2656, 2657/2658, 2659/2660, 2661/2662 were printed se-tenant within their sheets.

No. 2662 is airmail.

CAPEX '87 Int'l Stamp Exhibition, Toronto — A1256

Designs: 10ch, Musk ox. 40ch, Jacques Cartier, *Grand Hermine* and modern ice-breaker, horiz. 60ch, Ice hockey, Calgary '88, horiz.

**1987, May 30** ***Perf. 11***

| | | | | |
|---|---|---|---|---|
| **2663-2665** | A1256 | Set of 3 | 6.00 | 1.25 |

Int'l Circus Festival, Monaco — A1257

Designs: No. 2666, Trapeze artists. No. 2667, "Brave Sailors" (N. Korean acrobatic troupe), vert. No. 2668, Korean performers receiving prize. No. 2669, Clown and elephant, vert. 40ch, Performing cat, horses. 50ch, Prince Rainier and family applauding.

**1987, May 31** ***Perf. 12***

| | | | | |
|---|---|---|---|---|
| **2666-2671** | A1257 | Set of 6 | 9.50 | 1.50 |

No. 2871 is airmail.

Battle of Pochonbo, 50th Anniv. — A1258

**1987, June 4** ***Perf. 11½***

| | | | | |
|---|---|---|---|---|
| **2672** | A1258 | 10ch multicolored | .75 | .25 |

Chongchun Street Sports Complex — A1259

Designs: 5ch, Various sports. 10ch, Indoor swimming pool. 40ch, Weightlifting gymnasium. 70ch, Table-tennis gymnasium. 1w, Angol football stadium. 1.20w, Handball gymnasium.

**1987, June 18** ***Perf. 12***

| | | | | |
|---|---|---|---|---|
| **2673-2678** | A1259 | Set of 6 | 10.00 | 2.25 |
| *2675a* | 40ch | Toned unsurfaced paper, without gum | 8.00 | — |
| *2676a* | 70ch | Toned unsurfaced paper, without gum | 8.00 | — |
| *2677a* | 1w | Toned unsurfaced paper, without gum | 8.00 | — |
| *2678a* | 1.20w | Toned unsurfaced paper, without gum | 8.00 | — |

Worldwide Fund for Nature (WWF) — A1260

Aix galericulata: No. 2679, On branch. No. 2680, On shore. No. 2681, In water and on shore. No. 2682, In water.

**1987, Aug. 4** ***Perf. 13¼***

| | | | | |
|---|---|---|---|---|
| **2679-2682** | A1260 | Set of 4 | 11.50 | 2.00 |

For surcharge, see No. 4605.

A1261

OLYMPHILEX '87 Stamp Exhibition, Rome — A1262

**1987, Aug. 29** ***Perf. 13¼***

| | | | | |
|---|---|---|---|---|
| **2683** | A1261 | 10ch multicolored | 1.50 | .25 |

**Souvenir Sheet**

| | | | | |
|---|---|---|---|---|
| **2684** | A1262 | 80ch multicolored | 7.00 | 1.25 |

Railway Uniforms — A1263

No. 2685, Electric train and Metro dispatcher. No. 2686, Underground station and conductress. No. 2687, Train and conductress. No. 2688, Train and railway dispatcher. No. 2689, Orient Express and conductor. No. 2690, Express train and ticket inspector.

**1987, Sep. 23**

| | | | | |
|---|---|---|---|---|
| **2685-2690** | A1263 | Set of 6 | 7.50 | 1.25 |

HAFNIA '87 Int'l Stamp Exhibition, Copenhagen — A1264

Designs: 40ch, White stork. 60ch, The Little Mermaid and sailing ship *Danmark.*

**1987, Sep. 26**

| | | | | |
|---|---|---|---|---|
| **2691-2692** | A1264 | Set of 2 | 5.25 | .70 |

A1265

Winter Olympic Games, Calgary — A1266

40ch: No. 2693, Figure skating. No. 2694, Ski jump. No. 2695, Downhill skiing. No. 2696, Cross-country skiing.

**1987, Oct. 16**

| | | | | |
|---|---|---|---|---|
| **2693-2696** | A1265 | Set of 4 | 8.00 | 1.00 |

**Souvenir Sheet**

| | | | | |
|---|---|---|---|---|
| **2697** | A1266 | 80ch multicolored | 5.25 | 1.00 |

PHILATELIA '87 (Koln) and 750th Anniv. Berlin — A1267

Designs: 10ch, Victory Column. 20ch, Reichstag, horiz. 30ch, Pfaueninsel Castle. 40ch, Charlottenburg Castle, horiz.
80ch, Olympic Stadium.

**1987, Nov. 5** ***Perf. 12***
**2698-2701** A1267 Set of 4 150.00

**Souvenir Sheet**
***Perf. 11½x12***

**2702** A1267 80ch multicolored 100.00

Roland Garros Birth Centenary and Tennis as an Olympic Sport — A1268

Designs: 20ch (No. 2703), Roland Garros (1888-1918), aviator; 20ch (No. 2704), Ivan Lendl and trophy; 40ch, Steffi Graf.
No. 2706: 80ch, Steffi Graf and trophy.

**1987, Nov. 10** ***Perf. 13¼***
**2703-2705** A1268 Set of 3 7.50 .75

**Souvenir Sheet**
***Perf. 11½x12***

**2706** A1268 80ch multicolored 10.00 3.00

Kim Jong Suk (1917-49), Revolutionary Hero — A1269

**1987, Dec. 24**
**2707** A1269 80ch multicolored 2.50 .50

Pyongyang Buildings — A1270

Dragon — A1271

**1988, Jan. 1** ***Perf. 12***
**2708** A1270 10ch multicolored .60 .25
**2709** A1271 40ch multicolored 1.50 .25

New Year.

*Saenal* Newspaper, 60th Anniv. A1272

**1988, Jan. 15** ***Perf. 11½***
**2710** A1272 10ch multicolored .90 .25

A1273

Kim Jong Il, 46th Birthday — A1274

Designs: 10ch, Kim Jong Il's birthplace, Mt. Paektu. 80ch, Kim Jong Il.

**1988, Feb. 16** ***Perf. 12x11¾***
**2711** A1273 10ch multicolored .50 .25

**Souvenir Sheet**

**2712** A1274 80ch multicolored 2.50 .50

Int'l Red Cross, 125th Anniv. — A1275

Designs: a, Henry Dunant. b, N. Korean Red Cross emblem, map. c, International Committee Headquarters, Geneva; d, Doctor examining child, Pyongyang Maternity Hospital.
80ch, Red Cross and Red Crescent, flags, globe.

**1988, Feb. 17** ***Perf. 12***
**2713** A1275 Sheet of 4 7.00 .90
*a.* 10ch multicolored 1.75 .20
*b.* 20ch multicolored 1.75 .20
*c.* 20ch multicolored 1.75 .20
*d.* 40ch multicolored 1.75 .20

**Souvenir Sheet**

**2714** A1275 80ch multicolored 4.50 .75

A1276

Columbus' Discovery of America, 500th Anniv. — A1277

10ch, *Santa Maria.* 20ch, *Pinta.* 30ch, *Nina.*
80ch, Columbus.

**1988, Mar. 10** ***Perf. 13¼***
**2718** A1276 Strip of 3 5.25 .75
*a.* 10ch multicolored 1.25 .25
*b.* 20ch multicolored 1.25 .25
*c.* 30ch multicolored 1.25 .25

**Souvenir Sheet**

**2719** A1277 80ch multicolored 5.25 .75

Nos. 2718a-2718c were printed together in the sheet in se-tenant strips of three.

JUVALUX '88 — A1278

Designs: 40ch, Hot air balloons. 60ch, Steam engine, railroad map of Luxembourg 1900.

**1988, Mar. 29**
**2720-2721** A1278 Set of 2 5.25 .75

JUVALUX '88 International Youth Stamp Exhibition, Luxembourg.

6th Spring Friendship Art Festival — A1279

Designs: 10ch, Singer. 1.20w, Dancers.

**1988, Apr. 7** ***Perf. 12***
**2722-2723** A1279 Set of 2 4.25 1.25
*2722a* 10ch, on toned unsurfaced paper, without gum 8.00 —

Int'l Institute of the Juche Idea, 10th Anniv. — A1280

**1988, Apr. 9**
**2724** A1280 10ch multicolored .50 .25

A1281

Kim Il Sung, 76th Birthday — A1282

Designs: 10ch, Kim Il Sung's Birthplace, Mangyongdae.
80ch, Kim Il Sung and schoolchildren.

**1988, Apr. 15**
**2725** A1281 10ch multicolored .50 .25

**Souvenir Sheet**

**2726** A1282 80ch multicolored 2.50 .40

FINLANDIA '88 Int'l Stamp Exhibition, Helsinki — A1283

Designs: 40ch, *Urho* ice-breaker. 60ch, Matti Nykänen, Finnish Olympic ski-jumping gold and silver medallist.

**1988, May 2** ***Perf. 13¼***
**2727-2728** A1283 Set of 2 5.00 .60

ITALIA '90, 14th World Soccer Championships — A1284

Designs: 10ch, Soccer match. 20ch, Post-card for 1934 Championship. 30ch, Player tackling, horiz.
80ch, Italian team, 1982 winners, horiz.

**1988, May 19**
**2729-2731** A1284 Set of 3 5.25 .50

**Souvenir Sheet**

**2732** A1284 80ch multicolored 4.50 .60

13th World Festival of Youth and Students — A1285

Designs: No. 2734, Festival emblem. No. 2735, Woman dancer. No. 2736, Woman, gymnast, Angol Sports Village. No. 2737, Map of Korea, globe and doves. No. 2738, Finger pointing at broken rockets ("Let's build a new world without nuclear weapons"). No. 2739, Three hands of different races releasing dove.

**1988, May 27** ***Perf. 12***
**2734-2739** A1285 Set of 6 7.50 1.25
*2734a* 10ch Thick toned unsurfaced paper, without gum 8.00 —
*2735a* 10ch Thick toned unsurfaced paper, without gum 8.00 —
*2736a* 10ch Thick toned unsurfaced paper, without gum 8.00 —
*2739a* 1.20w Thick toned unsurfaced paper, without gum 8.00 —

Eight Fairies of Mt. Kumgang, Folk-Tale — A1286

Designs: 10ch, Fairy playing the *haegum.* 15ch, Fairies with rainbow. 20ch, Fairy and herdsman husband. 25ch, Couple with infant. 30ch, Couple with son and daughter. 35ch, Family on rainbow, returning to Mt. Kumgang.

**1988, June 20**
**2740-2745** A1286 Set of 6 5.00 1.10

PRAGA '88 Int'l Stamp Exhibition, Prague — A1287

Designs: 20ch, Mallard ducks. 40ch, Vladimir Remek, Czechoslovak cosmonaut.

**1988, June 26** ***Perf. 13¼***
**2746-2747** A1287 Set of 2 4.00 .45

Birds — A1288

Designs: 10ch, Red crossbill (*Loxia curvirostra japonica*). 15ch, Stonechat (*Saxicola torquata stejnegeri*). 20ch, European nuthatch (*Sitta eoropaea hondoensis*). 25ch, Great spotted woodpecker (*Dendrocopos major japonicus*). 30ch, Common kingfisher (*Alcedo atthis bengalensis*). 35ch, Bohemian waxwing (*Bombycilla garrula centralasiae*).

**1988, July 9** ***Perf. 12***
**2748-2753** A1288 Set of 6 10.00 1.75

For surcharge, see No. 4530.

A1289

RICCIONE '88 Int'l Stamp Fair — A1290

**1988, July 25**
**2754** A1289 20ch multicolored .90 .25

**Souvenir Sheet**

**2755** A1290 80ch multicolored 3.75 .50

A1291

Australia Bicentenary — A1292

Designs: 10ch, Emu. 15ch, Statin bower birds. 25ch, Kookaberra, vert.
80ch, H.M.S. *Resolution.*

**1988, July 30** ***Perf. 13¼***
**2756-2758** A1291 Set of 3 4.00 .60

**Souvenir Sheet**

**2759** A1292 80ch multicolored 5.00 .65

Ships — A1293

Designs: 10ch, Floating crane *5-28.* 20ch, Cargo ship *Hwanggumsan.* 30ch, Cargo ship *Jangjasan Chongnyon-ho.* 40ch, Passenger ship *Samjiyon.*

**1988, Aug. 12** ***Perf. 12***
**2760-2763** A1293 Set of 4 5.50 .85

A1294

Count Ferdinand von Zeppelin, 150th Birth Anniv. — A1295

Designs: 10ch, LZ 13 *Hansa.* 20ch, LZ 10 *Schwaben.* 30ch, LZ 11 *Viktoria Luise.* 40ch, LZ 3.
1w, Count von Zeppelin.

**1988, Aug. 21** ***Perf. 11¼***
**2764-2767** A1294 Set of 4 5.50 .85

**Souvenir Sheet**

***Perf. 13¼***

**2768** A1295 1w multicolored 5.00 1.00

Kim Il Sung and Jambyn Batmunkh — A1296

**1988, Aug. 30** ***Perf. 12***
**2769** A1296 10ch multicolored .75 .25

Kim Il Sung's visit to Mongolia.

National Heroes Congress — A1297

**1988, Sep. 1** ***Perf. 11¾***
**2770** A1297 10ch multicolored 4.50 .25

A1298

Independence, 40th Anniversary — A1299

Designs: 5ch, Tower of Juche Idea. 10ch (No. 2772), Worker, factory. 10ch (No. 2773), Soldier and Mt. Paektu. 10ch (No. 2774), Map, broken U.S. missile. 10ch (No. 2775), Hand holding sign, peace march, globe, doves.
1.20w, Kim Il Sung presiding over design of DPRK flag and emblem.

**1988, Sept. 9** ***Perf. 12***
**2771-2775** A1298 Set of 5 1.75 .55
*2771a* 5ch Toned unsurfaced paper, without gum 20.00 —

**Souvenir Sheet**

***Perf. 11½***

**2776** A1299 1.20w multicolored 2.50 .75

FILACEPT '88 Philatelic Exhib., The Hague A1300

Designs: 40ch, *Sunflowers,* by Vincent Van Gogh. 60ch, *The Chess Game,* by Lucas van Leyden.

**1988, Sept. 18** ***Perf. 13½***
**2777-2778** A1300 Set of 2 7.50 1.40

Emblem — A1301

**1988, Sep. 23** ***Perf. 11½***
**2779** A1301 10ch multicolored .60 .25

16th Conference of the Ministers of Communications of Socialist Countries.

Dump Trucks A1302

Designs: 20ch, *Jaju 82* 10-ton truck. 40ch, *Kumsusan* 40-ton truck.

**1988, Sept. 18** ***Perf. 13½***
**2780-2781** A1302 Set of 2 2.00 .75

Paintings by O Un Byol — A1303

Designs: 10ch, *Owl.* 15ch, *Dawn.* 20ch, *The Beautiful Rose Received by the Respected Marshall.* 25ch, *The Sun and Bamboo.* 30ch, *Autumn.*

**1988, Oct. 5** ***Perf. 11½***
**2782-2786** A1303 Set of 5 6.00 .90

Historic Locomotives — A1304

Designs: 10ch, *Junggi No. 35.* 20ch, *Junggi No. 22.* 30ch, *Jongihwa No. 3.* 40ch, *Junggi No. 307.*

**1988, Oct. 28** ***Perf. 12***
**2787-2790** A1304 Set of 4 5.00 .75

A1305

Calgary '88 Winter Olympic Games Winners — A1306

Designs: 10ch, Pirmin Zurbriggen (Switzerland). 20ch, Yvonne Van Gennip (Netherlands). 30ch, Marjo Matikainen (Finland). 40ch, USSR hockey team.
80ch, Katarina Witt (DDR).

**1988, Nov. 1** ***Perf. 13¼***
**2791-2794** A1305 Set of 4 3.50 1.25

**Souvenir Sheet**

**2795** A1306 80ch multicolored 2.50 .50
*a.* Overprinted with names of winners in selvage 2.50 .50

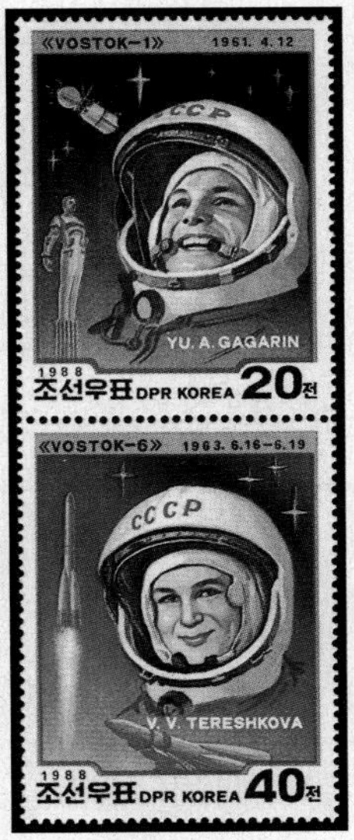


First Man and Woman in Space — A1307

Designs: 20ch, Yuri Gagarin. 40ch, Valentina Tereshkova.

**1988, Nov. 12** ***Perf. 13¼***
**2796** A1307 Pair, #a.-b. 1.75 .60
*a.* 20ch multicolored .40 .25
*b.* 40ch multicolored 1.10 .45

A1308

INDIA '89 Int'l Philatelic Exhib., New Delhi — A1309

Design: 20ch, Jawaharlal Nehru (1889-1964), 100th anniversary of birth.
60ch, *Fan Dance*, Korean Folk Dance.

**1988, Dec. 15** ***Perf. 11¾x12***
**2797** A1308 20ch multicolored 1.20 .25

**Souvenir Sheet**

***Perf. 11¾x11½***

**2798** A1309 60ch multicolored 3.50 .40

New Year — A1310

Designs: 10ch, Chollima Statue. 20ch, Painting, *Dragon Angler.* 40ch, *Tortoise Serpent*, Kangso tomb mural painting, horiz.

**1989, Jan. 1** ***Perf. 13¼***
**2799-2801** A1310 Set of 3 3.50 .50

Archery — A1311

Designs: 10ch, Archery. 15ch, Rifle shooting. 20ch, Pistol shooting. 25ch, Parachuting. 30ch, Launching model glider.

**1989, Jan. 10** ***Perf. 12***
**2802-2806** A1311 Set of 5 4.50 .75

National defense training.

A1312

Pets Presented to Kim Il Sung — A1313

Designs: 10ch, Dobermann pinscher. 20ch, Labrador. 25ch, German shepherd. 30ch, Border collies, horiz. 35ch, Serval, horiz.
80ch, *Felix libica.*

**1989, Jan. 23** ***Perf. 13½***
**2807-2811** A1312 Set of 5 5.00 .90

**Souvenir Sheet**

**2812** A1313 80ch multicolored 4.00 .60

Kim Jong Il, 47th Birthday — A1314

**1989, Feb. 16** ***Perf. 11¾x12***
**2813** A1314 80ch multicolored 2.00 .45

Agriculture A1315

**1989, Feb. 25** ***Perf. 12***
**2814** A1315 10ch multicolored .70 .25
*a.* Toned unsurfaced paper, without gun 5.00 —

25th anniversary of publication of Kim Il Sung's *Theses on the Socialist Rural Question in Our Country.*

Mushrooms and Wild Fruits — A1316

Designs: 10ch, Rozites caperata and Vitisamurensis. 20ch, Amanita caesarea and Schizandra chinensis. 25ch, Lactarius hygrophoides and Eleagnus crispa. 30ch, Agaricus placomyces and Actinidia arguta. 35ch, Agaricus arvensis and Lycium chinense. 40ch, Suillus grevillei and Juglans cordiformis.
1w, Gomphidius roseus and Diospyros lotus.

**1989, Feb. 27** ***Perf. 12***
**2815-2820** A1316 Set of 6 8.00 1.25

**Souvenir Sheet**

***Perf. 11½x11¾***

**2821** A1316 1w multicolored 4.50 .90

13th World Youth and Students' Festival — A1317

Designs: 10ch, Girl. 20ch, Children of different races. 30ch, Fairy, rainbow. 40ch, Young people and Tower of Juche Idea.

**1989, Mar. 18** ***Perf. 12¼***
**2822-2825** A1317 Set of 4 2.75 1.00
*2822a* 10ch Soft toned unsurfaced paper, without gum 15.00 —
*2823a* 20ch Soft toned unsurfaced paper, without gum 8.00 —
*2824a* 30ch Soft toned unsurfaced paper, without gum 8.00 —
*2825a* 40ch Soft toned unsurfaced paper, without gum 8.00 —
*2825b* 40ch Stiff dull white unsurfaced paper, without gum 8.00 —

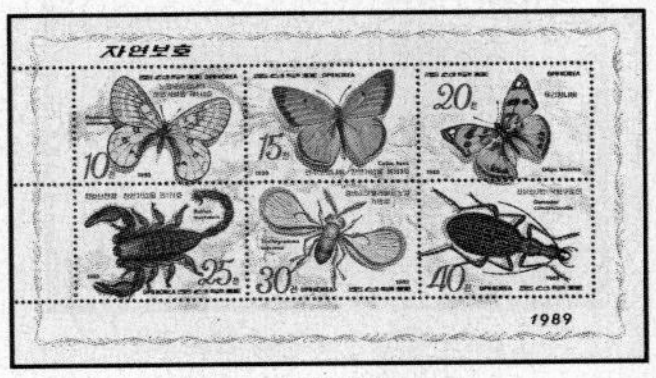

A1318

Butterflies and Insects — A1319

Designs: 10ch, Parnassius eversmanni. 15ch, Colias heos. 20ch, Dilipa fenestra. 25ch, Buthus martensis. 30ch, Trichogramma ostriniae. 40ch, Damaster constricticollis.
80ch, Parnassius nomion.

**1989, Mar. 23** ***Perf. 12***
**2826** A1318 Sheet of 6, #a.-f. 6.00 1.00

**Souvenir Sheet**

**2827** A1319 80ch multicolored 3.75 .75

Spring Friendship Art Festival — A1320

**1989, Apr. 6**
**2828** A1320 10ch multicolored .80 .25

Kim Il Sung, 77th Birthday — A1321

**1989, Apr. 15** ***Perf. 11½***
**2829** A1321 10ch multicolored .50 .25
*a.* Toned unsurfaced paper, without gum 10.00 —

Battle of the Musan Area, 50th Anniv. A1322

**1989, May 19** ***Perf. 12***
**2830** A1322 10ch multicolored 1.10 .25

Jamo System of Dance Notation — A1323

Designs: 10ch, Mexican dance. 20ch, Ballet duet in *Don Quixote.* 25ch, Dance of Guinea. 30ch, Cambodian folk dance.
80ch, Korean folk dance.

**1989, May 30**
**2831-2834** A1323 Set of 4 3.75 .65

**Souvenir Sheet**

**2835** A1323 80ch multicolored 3.25 .50

13th World Festival of Youth and Students

A1324 A1325

**1989, June 8** ***Perf. 11½***
**2836** A1324 5ch deep blue .25 .25
*a.* Soft toned unsurfaced paper, without gum 15.00 —
**2837** A1325 10ch red brown .30 .25

Cartoon, *Badger Measures the Height* — A1326

Designs: 10ch, Badger racing cat and bear to flag pole. 40ch, Cat and bear climbing pole, while badger measures shadow. 50ch, Badger winning the prize.

**1989, June 21**
**2838-2840** A1326 Set of 3 4.00 .65

Astronomy A1327

20ch, Chomosongdae Observatory.
80ch, Saturn (horiz.)

**1989, June 29** ***Perf. 12***
**2841** A1327 20ch multicolored 1.40 .25

**Souvenir Sheet**

**2842** A1327 80ch multicolored 3.00 .50

Eugène Delacroix's *Liberty Guiding the People* — A1328

**1989, July 7** ***Perf. 12x11½***
**2843** A1328 70ch multicolored 3.00 2.00

PHILEXFRANCE '89, Int'l Philatelic Exhib., Paris.

BRASILIANA '89, Int'l Philatelic Exhib., Rio de Janeiro — A1329

**1989, July 28** ***Perf. 12***
**2844** A1329 40ch Pele, #1714 1.40 .30

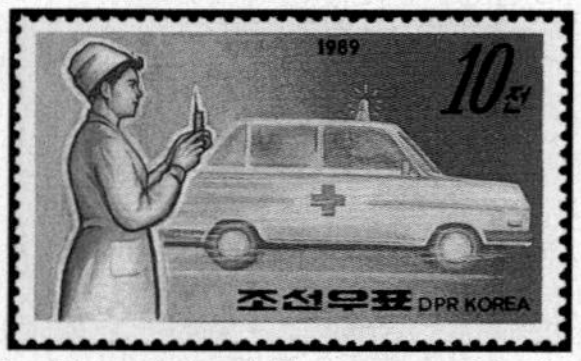

Fire Brigade and Emergency Medical Services — A1330

Designs: 10ch, Nurse and ambulance. 20ch, Surgeon and ambulance. 30ch, Fireman and fire engine. 40ch, Fireman and fire engine (diff.)

**1989, Aug. 12**
**2845-2848** A1330 Set of 4 6.00 .65

Plants Presented as Gifts to Kim Il Sung — A1331

Designs: 10ch, Kafir lily (Clivia miniata). 15ch, Tulips (Tulipa gesneriana). 20ch, Flamingo lily (Anthurium andreanum). 25ch, Rhododendron obtusum. 30ch, Daffodils (Narcissus pseudonarcissus).
80ch, (Gerbera hybrida).

**1989, Aug. 19**
**2849-2853** A1331 Set of 5 5.50 1.00

**Souvenir Sheet**

**2854** A1331 80ch multicolored 4.50 .50

150th Anniv. of Postage Stamps / STAMP WORLD LONDON '90 Int'l Philatelic Exhib. — A1332

Designs: 5ch, Letter, ship, plane, map. 10ch, Letters and mail box. 20ch, Stamps, magnifying glass, tongs. 30ch, Fiirst stamps pf DPRK. 40ch, UPU emblem, headquarters, Berne. 50ch, Sir Rowland Hill and Penny Black.

**1989, Aug. 27**
**2855-2860** A1332 Set of 6 7.50 1.25

A1333

Alpine Flowers — A1334

Designs: 10ch, Iris setosa. 15ch, Aquilegia japonica. 20ch, Bistorta incana. 25ch, Rhodiola elongata. 30ch, Sanguisorba sitchensis.
80ch, Trollius japonicus.

**1989, Sept. 8** ***Perf. 11½***
**2861-2865** A1333 Set of 5 5.25 1.00

**Souvenir Sheet**

**2866** A1334 80ch multicolored 3.50 .55

Trees bearing Anti-Japanese Patriotic Slogans — A1335

Designs: 10ch, "20 million compatriots, an anti-Japanese heroine of Korea rose on Mt. Paektu," inscribed on tree, Mt. Paektu. 3w, "The future of Korea is bright with the Luminous Star of Mt. Paektu," inscribed on tree, Qun-dong, Pyongyang. 5w, "The General Star of Mt. Paektu shines three thousand-ri expanse of land," inscribed on tree, Mt. Kanbaek.

**1989, Sept. 21** ***Perf. 12¼***
**2867-2869** A1335 Set of 3 18.00 11.00

Compare with No. 2885.

Children's Games — A1336

Designs: 10ch, Girl skipping rope. 20ch, Boy with whirligig. 30ch, Boy flying kite. 40ch, Girl spinning top.

**1989, Sept. 30** ***Perf. 12***
**2870** A1336 Block of 4, #a.-d. 4.00 .80
*a.* 10ch multicolored .25 .25
*b.* 20ch multicolored 1.75 .25
*c.* 30ch multicolored .50 .25
*d.* 40ch multicolored .60 .25

Int'l March for Peace and Reunification of Korea — A1337

**1989, Oct. 1** ***Perf. 11½x12***
**2871** A1337 80ch multicolored 3.00 1.75

Locomotives — A1338

Designs: 10ch, Electric train entering station yard. 20ch, Electric train crossing bridge. 25ch, Diesel locomotive. 30ch, Diesel locomotive (diff.). 40ch, Steam locomotive. 50ch, Steam locomotive (diff.).

**1989, Oct. 19** *Perf. 11¾x12¼*
**2872-2877** A1338 Set of 6 6.00 1.25

14th World Soccer Championship, *Italia '90* — A1339

Designs: 10ch, Players and map of Italy. 20ch, Free kick. 30ch, Goal scrimmage. 40ch, Goalkeeper blocking ball.

**1989, Oct. 28** *Perf. 12x11¾*
**2878-2881** A1339 Set of 4 4.00 .60

Magellan
A1340

**1989, Nov. 25** *Perf. 12*
**2882** A1340 30ch multicolored 1.25 .25

*Descobrex '89* International Philatelic Exhibition, Portugal.

A1341

A1342

10ch, Mangyong Hill and snow-covered pine branches. 20ch, Koguryo warriors.

*Perf. 11½ (#2883), 12 (#2884)*

**1990, Jan. 1**
**2883** A1341 10ch multicolored .25 .25
*a.* Toned unsurfaced paper, without gum 15.00 —
**2884** A1342 20ch multicolored 1.20 .25
*a.* Toned unsurfaced paper, without gum 5.00 —

New Year.

Tree, Mt. Paektu, Bearing Anti-Japanese Patriotic Slogan — A1343

**1990, Jan. 12** *Perf. 11½*
**2885** A1343 5ch multicolored .50 .25
*a.* Toned unsurfaced paper, without gum 5.00 —

Dogs — A1344

Designs: 20ch, Ryukwoli. 30ch, Phalryuki. 40ch, Komdungi. 50ch, Olruki.

**1990, Jan. 17**
**2886** A1344 Sheet of 4 5.50 1.50
*a.* 20ch multicolored .90 .25
*b.* 30ch multicolored .90 .25
*c.* 40ch multicolored .90 .25
*d.* 50ch multicolored .90 .25

Birthplace, Mt. Paektu — A1345

**1990, Feb. 16**
**2887** A1345 10ch dp red brn .50 .25
*a.* Toned unsurfaced paper, without gum 5.00 —

Kim Jong Il's 48th birthday.

Stone Age Man
A1346

Designs: 10ch, Primitive man, stone tools. 20ch, Paleolithic and Neolithic men, camp scene.

**1990, Feb. 21**
**2888-2889** A1346 Set of 2 3.00 .30

Bridges — A1347

Designs: 10ch, Rungra Bridge, Pyongyang. 20ch, Pothong Bridge, Pyongyang. 30ch, Suspension bridge between Sinuiju-Ryucho Island. 40ch, Chungsongui Bridge, Pyongyang.

**1990, Feb. 27** *Perf. 11½*
**2890-2893** A1347 Set of 4 4.50 .60
*2890a* 10ch Thin, coarse brownish paper, without gum 5.00 —

Traditional Warriors' Costumes
A1348

Designs: 20ch, Infantryman (3rd century BC-7th century AD). 30ch, Archer. 50ch, Commander in armor (3rd century BC-7th century AD). 70ch, Koguryo Period officer (10th-14th centuries).

**1990, Mar. 18**
**2894-2897** A1348 Set of 4 6.25 2.00
*2897a* 70ch Dull white unsurfaced paper, without gum 5.00 —

Crabs
A1349

Designs: 20ch, Atergatis subdentatus. 30ch, Platylambrus validus. 50ch, Uca arcuata.

**1990, Mar. 25**
**2898-2900** A1349 Set of 3 3.00 .60

Dancers — A1350

**1990, Apr. 7**
**2901** A1350 10ch multicolored .50 .25

Spring Friendship Art Festival, Pyongyang.

A1351

Kim Il Sung's 78th Birthday
A1352

Designs: 10ch, 'Fork in the Road' Monument, Mangyongdae Revolutionary Site.
80ch, Kim Il Sung.

**1990, Apr. 15** *Perf. 11½x11¾*
**2902** A1351 10ch multicolored .50 .25

**Souvenir Sheet**

**2903** A1352 80ch multicolored 2.50 .50

Cacti — A1353

Designs: 10ch, Gynmocalycium sp. 30ch, Phyllocactus hybridus. 50ch, Epiphyllum truncatum.

**1990, Apr. 21** *Perf. 12¼*
**2904-2906** A1353 Set of 3 4.00 .60

A1354

Stamp World London '90 — A1355

Designs: 20ch, Exhibition emblem.
70ch, Sir Rowland Hill.

**1990, May 3** *Perf. 11½*
**2907** A1354 20ch multicolored .90 .25

**Souvenir Sheet**

**2908** A1355 70ch multicolored 2.75 1.20

A1356

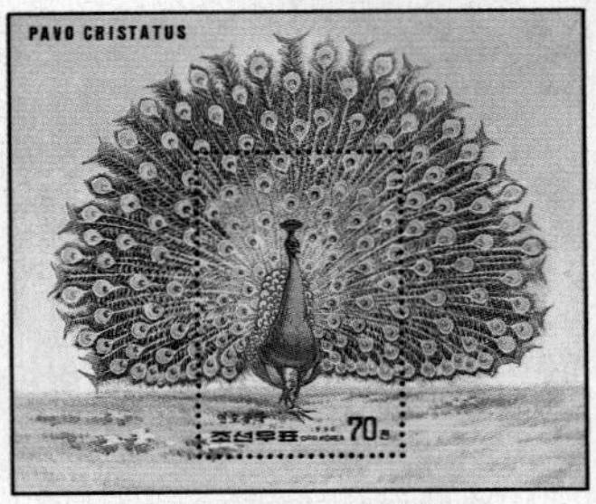


Peafowl — A1357

Designs: 10ch, Congo peafowl (Afropavo congensis). 20ch, Common peafowl (Pavo cristatus).
70ch, Common peafowl with tail displayed.

**1990, May 10** *Perf. 11¾x12*
**2909-2910** A1356 Set of 2 3.00 .60

**Souvenir Sheet**

**2911** A1357 70ch multicolored 3.00 .60

Bio-engineering — A1358

Designs: 10ch, Dolphin and submarine. 20ch, Bat and sonar dish, satellite. 30ch, Eagle and airplanes. 40ch, Squid and jets.

**1990, May 24**

**2912** A1358 Sheet of 4, #a.-d. 7.00 1.25
*a.* 10ch multicolored 1.25 .25
*b.* 20ch multicolored 1.25 .25
*c.* 30ch multicolored 1.25 .25
*d.* 40ch multicolored 1.25 .25

BELGICA '90 Int'l Philatelic Exhib., Brussels A1359

Designs: 10ch, Rembrandt, *Self Portrait.* 20ch, Raphael, *Self Portrait.* 30ch, Rubens, *Self Portrait.*

**1990, June 2** ***Perf. 12¼x12***

**2913-2915** A1359 Set of 3 2.25 .40

Düsseldorf '90, 10th Int'l Youth Philatelic Exhib. — A1360

Designs: 20ch, Steffi Graf, tennis player, with bouquet. 30ch, Exhibition emblem. 70ch, K.H. Rummenigge, German soccer player.

**1990, June 20**

**2916-2918** A1360 Set of 3 7.00 .75

A1361

Designs: 10ch, Games mascot, Workers' Stadium, Beijing. 30ch, Chollina Statue and Korean athletes. 40ch, Games emblem, athletes.

**1990, July 14**

**2919-2921** A1361 Set of 3 2.00 .60

11th Asian Games, Beijing (Nos. 2919-2920). Third Asian Winter Games, Samjiyon (No. 2921).

14th World Cup Soccer Championship — A1362

Designs: 15ch, Emblem of F.I.F.A. (Federation of Football Associations). 20ch, Jules Rimet. 25ch, Soccer ball. 30ch, Olympic Stadium, Rome. 35ch, Goalkeeper. 40ch, Emblem of the German Football Association. 80ch, Emblem of German Football Association and trophy.

**1990, Aug. 8** ***Perf. 13½***

**2922-2927** A1362 Set of 6 6.00 1.00

**Souvenir Sheet**

**2928** A1362 80ch multicolored 3.00 1.50

New Zealand '90 Int'l Philatelic Exhib., Auckland A1363

**1990, Aug. 24** ***Perf. 12***

**2929** A1363 30ch multicolored 1.75 .40

*Summer at Chipson Peak* — A1364

**1990, Aug. 24** ***Perf. 11½***

**2930** A1364 80ch multicolored 3.00 .50

Europa '90 International Stamp Fair, Riccione.

Koguryo Wedding Procession — A1365

Designs: 10ch, Man on horse blowing bugle. 30ch, Bridegroom on horse. 50ch, Bride in carriage. 1w, Man on horse beating drum.

**1990, Sept. 3** ***Perf. 12***

**2931** Strip of 4, #a.-d. 6.00 .80
*a.* A1365 10ch multicolored 1.25 .25
*b.* A1365 30ch multicolored 1.25 .25
*c.* A1365 50ch multicolored 1.25 .25
*d.* A1365 1w multicolored 1.25 .25

Printed in setenant strips of four within the sheet.

A1366

Pan-National Rally for Peace and Reunification of Korea — A1367

Designs: 10ch, Rally emblem, crowd descending Mt. Paektu.
1w, Crowd watching dancers.

**1990, Sept. 15**

**2932** A1366 10ch multicolored .50 .25

**Souvenir Sheet**

**2933** A1367 1w multicolored 2.75 .55

Insects A1368

Designs: 20ch, Praying mantis (Mantis religiosa). 30ch, Lady bug (Coccinella septempunctata). 40ch, Pheropsophus jussoensis. 70ch, Phyllium siccifolium.

**1990, Sept. 20**

**2934-2936A** A1368 Set of 4 6.00 1.10

Soccer Players — A1369

No. 2938, North and South Korean players entering May Day Stadium.

**1990, Oct. 11**

**2937** A1369 Pair, #a.-b. 2.75 .40
*a.* 10ch multicolored 1.25 .25
*b.* 20ch multicolored 1.25 .25

**Souvenir Sheet**

**2938** A1369 1w multicolored 4.50 .75

North-South Reunification Soccer Games, Pyongyang.

National Reunification Concert — A1370

**1990, Oct. 17**

**2939** A1370 10ch multicolored .50 .25

Farm Animals — A1371

Designs: 10ch, Ox. 20ch, Pig. 30ch, Goat. 40ch, Sheep. 50ch, Horse.

**1990, Oct. 18**

**2940-2944** A1371 Set of 5 5.75 .85
*2944a* Sheet of 10, 2 ea #2940-2944 13.00 1.75

A1372

A1373

Chinese Entry Into Korean War, 40th Anniv. — A1374

Designs: 10ch, N. Korean and Communist Chinese soldiers. 20ch, Korean civilians welcoming Chinese soldiers. 30ch, Battle scene, victorious soldiers. 40ch, Postwar reconstruction.
80ch, Friendship Monument.

**1990, Oct. 23**

**2945** A1372 10ch multicolored .25 .25
**2946** A1373 20ch multicolored .75 .25
**2947** A1373 30ch multicolored 1.00 .25
**2948** A1373 40ch multicolored 1.50 .25
*Nos. 2945-2948 (4)* 3.50 1.00

**Souvenir Sheet**

***Perf. 11¾x11½***

**2949** A1374 80ch multicolored 3.00 .50

For overprint see No. 3282.

UN Development Program, 40th Anniv. A1375

**1990, Oct. 24** ***Perf. 13¼***

**2950** A1375 1w multicolored 4.00 1.20

Fish — A1376

Designs: 10ch, Sturgeon (Acipenser mikadoi). 20ch, Sea bream (Sparus macrocephalus). 30ch, Flying fish (Cypsilurus agoö). 40ch, Fat greenling (Heragrammos otakii). 50ch, Ray (Myliobatus tobeijei).

**1990, Nov. 20** ***Perf. 12***

**2951-2955** A1376 Set of 5 5.75 2.00
*2955a* Sheet of 10, 2 ea #2951-2955 12.00 4.00

New Year — A1377

**1990, Dec. 1**
**2956** A1377 40ch multicolored 1.75 .25

Birds — A1378

Designs: 10ch, Moorhen (Gallinula chloropus). 20ch, Jay (Garrulus glandarius). 30ch, Three-toed woodpecker (Picodes tridactylus). 40ch, Whimbrel (Numenius phaeopus). 50ch, Water rail (Rallus aquaticus)

**1990, Dec. 18** ***Perf. 12***
**2957-2961** A1378 Set of 5 6.50 2.00
*2961a* Sheet of 10, 2 ea #2957-2961 13.00 5.00

A1379

Pandas — A1380

Designs: 10ch, Giant panda. 20ch, Two giant pandas feeding. 30ch, Giant panda on limb. 40ch, Giant panda on rock. 50ch, Pair of giant pandas. 60ch, Giant panda in tree.

**1991, Jan. 10** ***Perf. 11¾x12***
**2962-2967** A1379 Set of 6 7.00 1.75
*2967a* Sheet of 6, #2962-2967 7.00 1.75

**Souvenir Sheet**

***Perf. 11½***

**2968** A1380 1w multicolored 3.25 .60

For surcharges, see No. 4536-4537.

A1381

Revolutionary Sites — A1382

**1991, Jan. 10** ***Perf. 12***
**2969** A1381 5ch Changsan .25 .25
**2970** A1382 10ch Oun .30 .25

Endangered Birds — A1383

Designs: 10ch, Black-faced spoonbills (Platalea minor). 20ch, Gray herons (Ardea cinerea). 30ch, Great egrets (Egretta alba). 40ch, Manchurian cranes (Grus japonensis). 50ch, Japanese white-necked cranes (Grus vipio). 70ch, White storks (Ciconia boyciana).

**1991, Feb. 5**
**2971-2976** A1383 Set of 6 6.00 1.40
*2976a* Sheet of 6, #2971-2976 7.50 1.75

Alpine Butterflies — A1384

Designs: 10ch, Clossiana angarensis. 20ch, Erebia embla. 30ch, Nymphalis antiopa. 40ch, Polygonia c-album). 50ch, Colias erate. 60ch, Thecla betulae.

**1991, Feb. 20** ***Perf. 13¼***
**2977-2982** A1384 Set of 6 7.50 2.50
*2982a* Sheet of 6, #2977-2982 7.50 2.50

Fungi — A1385

Designs: 10ch, Hydnum repandum. 20ch, Phylloporus rhodoxanthus. 30ch, Calvatia craniformis. 40ch, Ramaria botrytis. 50ch, Russula integra.

**1991, Feb. 26** ***Perf. 12x12¼***
**2983-2987** A1385 Set of 5 5.00 1.25
*2987a* Sheet of 10, 2 ea #2983-2987 10.00 2.50

For surcharge, see No. 4546.

A1386

Revolutionary Sites — A1387

**1991, Mar. 15** ***Perf. 12***
**2988** A1386 10ch Kumchon .30 .25
**2989** A1387 40ch Samdung 1.20 .30

A1388

Silkworm Research A1389

Designs: 10ch, Dr. Kye Ung (1893-1967), silkworm researcher. 20ch, Chinese oak silk moth, Antheraea pernyi. 30ch, Attacus ricini. 40ch, Antheraea yamamai. 50ch, Bombyx mori. 60ch, Aetias artemis.

**1991, Mar. 27**
**2990** A1388 10ch multicolored .25 .25
**2991** A1389 20ch multicolored .60 .30
**2992** A1389 30ch multicolored .80 .40
**2993** A1389 40ch multicolored 1.20 .50
**2994** A1389 50ch multicolored 1.60 .75
**2995** A1389 60ch multicolored 2.00 .80
*a.* Sheet of 6, #2990-2995 6.50 3.50
*Nos. 2990-2995 (6)* 6.45 3.00

9th Spring Friendship Art Festival, Pyongyang A1390

**1991, Apr. 3**
**2996** A1390 10ch multicolored .50 .25

Antarctic Exploration A1391

Designs: 10ch, Penguins. 20ch, Research station. 30ch, Elephant seals. 40ch, Research ship. 50ch, Black-backed gulls.
80ch, DPRK flag and map of Antarctica.

**1991, Apr. 20** ***Perf. 11¾x12***
**2997-3001** A1391 Set of 5 6.00 1.25
*3001a* Sheet of 6, #2997-3002 9.00 1.80

**Souvenir Sheet**

***Perf. 11¾***

**3002** A1391 80ch multicolored 3.00 .55

A single stamp like that in No. 3002 is included in No. 3001a.

85th Interparliamentary Union Conference, Pyongyang — A1392

Designs: 10ch, Peoples Palace of Culture. 1.50w, Conference emblem and azalea.

**1991, Apr. 29** ***Perf. 12***
**3003-3004** A1392 Set of 2 5.00 1.40

Map and Kim Jong Ho — A1393

**1991, May 8** ***Perf. 11¾x12***
**3005** A1393 90ch multicolored 2.50 .80

Dinosaurs — A1394

Designs: a, 10ch, Cynognathus. b, 20ch, Brontosaurus. c, 30ch, Stegosaurus and allosaurus. d, 40ch, Pterosauria. e, 50ch, Ichthyosaurus.

**1991, May 21** ***Perf. 12x11¾***
**3006** A1394 Strip of 5 + label 7.50 1.75
*3006f* Sheet of 5 + label 17.00 2.00

Barcelona '92 Olympic Games — A1395

Designs: No. 3011, 10ch, 100-Meter dash. No. 3012, 10ch, Hurdle race. No. 3013 20ch, Broad jump. No. 3014, 20ch, Throwing discus. No. 3015, 30ch, Shot-put. No. 3016, 30ch, Pole vault. No. 3017, 40ch, High jump. No. 3018, 40ch, Javelin throw.
No. 3019, 80ch, 400-meter race. No. 3020, 80ch, 1500-meter race.

**1991, June 18**
**3011-3018** A1395 Set of 8 4.00 1.40
*3018a* Sheet of 10, #3011-3020 12.50 2.75

**Souvenir Sheets**

***Perf. 11½x11¾***

**3019-3020** A1395 Set of 2 3.50 1.25

No. 3018a contains single stamps from Nos. 3019-3020 in addition to Nos. 3011-3018.

Cats — A1396

Designs: 10ch, Cats and birds. 20ch, Cat and rat. 30ch, Cat and butterfly. 40ch, Cats and ball. 50ch, Cat and frog.

**1991, July 21** ***Perf. 13¼***
**3021-3025** A1396 Set of 5 5.25 2.25

For surcharges, see Nos. 4538, 4547.

Riccione '91 Int'l Stamp Fair — A1397

**1991, Aug. 27** ***Perf. 11¾x12***

**3026** A1397 80ch multicolored 2.75 .60

Horses A1398

Designs: 10ch, Equus caballus. 20ch, Equus asinus and Equus caballus. 30ch, Equus przewalskii. 40ch, Equus asinus. 50ch, Equus caballus, diff.

**1991, Sept. 2** ***Perf. 13½***

**3027-3031** A1398 Set of 5 5.00 1.25
*3031a* Sheet of 5, #3027-3031 5.00 1.40

A1399

Phila Nippon '91 International Stamp Exhibition — A1400

Fish: 10ch, Pennant coral fish (Heniochus acuminatus). 20ch, Big-spotted trigger fish (Balistoides conspicillum). 30ch, Anemone fish (Amphiprion frenatus). 40ch, Blue surgeon fish (Paracanthurus hepatus). 50ch, Angel fish (Pterophyllum eimekei).
80ch, Tetras (Hyphessobrycon innesi).

**1991, Sept. 20** ***Perf. 12x12¼***

**3032-3036** A1399 Set of 5 5.00 1.25
*3036a* Sheet of 5, #3032-3036 5.00 1.25

**Souvenir Sheet**

***Perf. 11¾***

**3037** A1400 80ch multicolored 5.00 .60

No. 3036 is airmail.

Flowers A1401

Designs: 10ch, Begonia. 20ch, Gerbera. 30ch, Rhododendrons. 40ch, Phalaenopsis. 50ch, Impatiens sultani. 60ch, Streptocarpus.

**1991, Oct. 16** ***Perf. 12¼x12***

**3038-3043** A1401 Set of 6 6.50 1.75
*3043a* Sheet of 6, #3038-3043 6.50 2.00

Nos. 3041-3043 commemorate Canada '92 International Youth Stamp Exhibition, Montreal, and include the exhibition emblem.

Panmunjon — A1402

**1991, Oct. 12** ***Perf. 12***

**3044** A1402 10ch multicolored .60 .25

Magnolia — A1403

**1991, Nov. 1** ***Perf. 11½***

**3045** A1403 10ch multicolored .60 .25

DPRK National Flower.

Women's World Soccer Championship, China — A1404

Designs: 10ch, Dribbling. 20ch, Dribbling, diff. 30ch, Heading the ball. 40ch, Overhead kick. 50ch, Tackling. 60ch, Goalkeeper.

**1991, Nov. 3** ***Perf. 12***

**3046-3051** A1404 Set of 6 6.50 1.75
*3051a* Sheet of 6, #3046-3051 6.50 2.00

A1405

Monkeys — A1406

Designs: 10ch, Squirrel monkeys (Samiri sciureus). 20ch, Pygmy marmosets (Cebuella pygmaea). 30ch, Red-handed tamarins (Saquinas midas).
80ch, Monkey leaping.

**1992, Jan. 1**

**3052-3054** A1405 Set of 3 2.25 .70
*3054a* Sheet of 3, #3052-3054 2.50 .80

**Souvenir Sheet**

***Perf. 11¾x11½***

**3055** A1406 80ch multicolored 2.50 1.00

A1407

Birds of Prey — A1408

Designs: 10ch, Bubo bubo. 20ch, Buteo buteo. 30ch, Haliaeetus vocifer. 40ch, Haliaeetus pelagicus. 50ch, Aquila chrysaetos.
80ch, Falco tinnunculus.

**1992, Jan. 5** ***Perf. 13¼***

**3056-3060** A1407 Set of 5 4.75 1.75
*3060a* Sheet of 12, 2 #3056-3060 + 2 labels 10.00 3.50

**Souvenir Sheet**

***Perf. 11½***

**3061** A1408 80ch multicolored 2.50 .60

No. 3060a, Granada '92 International Stamp Exhibition. For surcharge, see No. 4609.

A1409

50th Birthday of Kim Jong Il — A1410

Designs: 10ch, Birthplace, Mt. Paektu. 20ch, Mt. Paektu. 30ch, Lake Chon on top of Mt. Paektu. 40ch, Lake Samji.
80ch, *Snowstorm in Mt. Paektu.*

**1992, Feb. 16** ***Perf. 12x11¾***

**3062-3065** A1409 Set of 4 3.25 .75

**Souvenir Sheet**

***Perf. 11¾x11½***

**3066** A1410 80ch multicolored 3.00 .60

Transport A1411

Designs: 10ch, Bus, "Jipsam 88." 20ch, Bus, "Pyongyang 86." 30ch, Trolley bus, "Chollima 84." 40ch, Bus, "Kwangbok Sonyon." 50ch, Tram. 60ch, July 17 Tram.

**1992, Feb. 20** ***Perf. 12¼***

**3067-3072** A1411 Set of 6 6.50 1.75
*3072a* Sheet of 6, #3067-3072 6.50 1.90

No. 3072a, Essen '92 International Stamp Fair.

Spring Fellowship Art Festival, Pyongyang A1412

**1992, Apr. 7**

**3073** A1412 10ch multicolored .50 .25

A1413

80th Birthday of Kim Il Sung — A1414

Revolutionary Sites: 10ch (No. 3074), Birthplace, Mangyongdao. 10ch (No. 3075), Party emblem, Turubong. 10ch (No. 3076), Map, Ssuksom. 10ch (No. 3077), Statue of soldier, Tongchang. 40ch (No. 3078), Chollima Statue, Kangson. 40ch (No. 3079), Cogwheels, Taean. 1.20w, Monument, West Sea Barrage.
80ch, Kim Il Sung among participants in the April Spring Friendship Art Festival.

**1992, Apr. 15**

**3074-3080** A1413 Set of 7 7.50 2.25

**Souvenir Sheet**

***Perf. 11½***

**3081** A1414 80ch multicolored 3.00 .60

No. 2080 is airmail.

Kang Ban Sok, Mother of Kim Il Sung, Birth Centenary — A1415

**1992, Apr. 21** ***Perf. 13¼***

**3082** A1415 80ch multicolored 2.25 .60

Korean People's Army, 60th Anniv. A1416

Designs (all 10ch): No. 3083, Soldier, troops on parade. No. 3084, Pilot, soldiers. No. 3085, Soldier with two civilian women.

**1992, Apr. 25** *Perf. 12¼*

**3083-3085** A1416 Set of 3 1.10 .25
*3085a* Sheet of 9, 4 #3085, 2 ea. #3083-3084 + label 3.00 1.00

25th Olympic Games, Barcelona '92 — A1417

Women's events: 10ch, Hurdle race. 20ch, High jump. 30ch, Shot-put. 40ch, 200-meter race. 50ch, Broad jump. 60ch, Javelin throw.
80ch, 800-meter race.

**1992, May 10** *Perf. 12x11¾*

**3086-3091** A1417 Set of 6 6.50 1.75
*3091a* Sheet of 8, #3086-3092 + label 9.50 2.50

**Souvenir Sheet**

**3092** A1417 80ch multicolored 2.75 .60

Prehistoric Man — A1418

Designs: 10ch, Planting crops. 20ch, Family in shelter, with cooking pot. 30ch, Plowing. 40ch, Indoor life. 50ch, Laying a dolmen.

**1992, June 1** *Perf. 12x11¾*

**3093-3097** A1418 Set of 5 5.00 1.25
*3097a* Sheet of 5, #3093-3097 + label 6.00 1.40

Birds — A1419

Designs: 10ch, Dryocopus javensis. 20ch, Phasianis colchicus. 30ch, Ciconia boyciana. 40ch, Pitta brachyura. 50ch, Syrrhaptes paradoxus. 60ch, Lyrurus tetrix.
80ch, Sturnus sturnus.

**1992, June 28** *Perf. 11½*

**3098-3103** A1419 Set of 6 7.00 1.75
*3103a* Sheet of 7, #3098-3104 + label 15.00 —

**Souvenir Sheet**

**3104** A1419 80ch multicolored 3.50 1.40

No. 3103a contains a single stamp from No. 3104 in addtion to Nos. 3098-3103.

North-South Joint Statement, 20th Anniv. — A1420

**1992, July 4**

**3105** A1420 1.50w multicolored 4.50 1.40

**Souvenir Sheet**

**3106** A1420 3w multicolored 9.00 2.75

No. 3106 contains two copies of No. 3105 and label.

Flowers — A1421

Designs: 10ch, Bougainvillea spectabilis. 20ch, Ixora chinensis. 30ch, Dendrobium taysuwie. 40ch, Columnea gloriosa. 50ch, Crinum. 60ch, Ranunculus asiaticus.

**1992, July 15** *Perf. 12¼*

**3107-3112** A1421 Set of 6 6.50 1.75
*3112a* Sheet of 8, #3107-3112 + 2 labels 7.00 2.00

No. 3112a, Genova '92 International Stamp Exhibition.

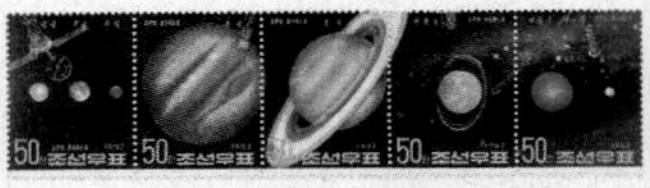

The Solar System — A1422

No. 3113: a, Satellite, Venus, Earth, Mars. b, Jupiter. c, Saturn. d, Uranus. e, Neptune, Pluto.
80ch, Earth.

**1992, Aug. 10** *Perf. 11½*

**3113** A1422 50ch Strip of 5, #a-e 8.00 2.50
*3113f* Sheet of 5, #3113, + 5 labels 9.00 2.75

**Souvenir Sheet**

**3114** A1422 80ch multicolored 2.50 1.50

Riccione '92 Int'l Stamp Fair — A1423

Designs: 10ch, C-class yacht. 20ch, Sailboard. 30ch, Rager-class yacht. 40ch, Pin-class yacht. 50ch, 470-class yacht. 60ch, Fair emblem.

**1992, Aug. 27** *Perf. 12¼*

**3119-3124** A1423 Set of 6 6.50 2.25
*3119a* Sheet of 6 stamps, 2 ea. #3119, 3121, 3123 6.50 2.50
*3120a* Sheet of 6 stamps, 2 ea. #3120, 3122, 3124 6.50 2.50

A1424

U.C. Sampdoria, Italian Soccer Champion 1991 — A1425

Designs: a, 20ch, Moreno Mannini, defender. b, 30ch, Gianluca Vialli, forward. c, 40ch, Pietro Vierchowod, back. d, 50ch, Fausto Pari, center-half. e, 60ch, Roberto Mancini, forward. f, 1w, club president.
1w, Vialli and Riccardo Garrone, president of club sponsor, ERG.

**1992, Aug. 31** *Perf. 12*

**3125** A1424 Sheet of 6, #a.-f. 9.00 3.00

**Souvenir Sheet**

*Perf. 11½x12*

**3131** A1425 1w multicolored 3.00 1.50

A1426

8th World Taekwondo Championship, Pyongyang — A1427

Designs: 10ch, Team pattern. 30ch, Side kick. 50ch, Flying high kick. 70ch, Flying twisting kick. 90ch, Black-belt breaking tiles with fist.
1.20w, Flying twin foot side kick; Choe Hong Hin, president of International Taekwon-Do Federation, in margin.

**1992, Sept. 1** *Perf. 12*

**3132-3136** A1426 Set of 5 8.00 2.50
*3136a* Sheet of 5, #3132-3136 + label 8.00 2.50

**Souvenir Sheet**

**3137** A1427 1.20w multicolored 4.00 1.75

No. 3137 is airmail.

Frogs and Toads A1428

Designs: No. 3138, 40ch, Rana chosenica. No. 3139, 40ch, Rana arvalis. No. 3140, 40ch, Bufo bufo. No. 3141, 70ch, Rana nigromaculata. No. 3142, 70ch , Hyla japonica. No. 3143, 70ch Rana coreana.

**1992, Sept. 10** *Perf. 12¼*

**3138-3143** A1428 Set of 6 10.00 3.00
*3139a* Sheet of 8, 4 #3139, 2 ea. #3138, #3140 + label 15.00 5.00
*3142a* Sheet of 8, 4 #3142, 2 ea. #3141, #3143 + label 15.00 5.00

No. 3143 is airmail.

World Environment Day — A1429

Designs: 10ch, Rhododendron mucronulatum. 30ch, Hirundo rustica. 40ch, Stewartia koreana. 50ch, Dictoptera aurora. 70ch, Metasequoia glyptostroboides. 90ch, Hynobius leechi. 1.20w, Gingko biloba. 1.40w, Cottus poecilopus.

**1992, Oct. 20** *Perf. 12*

**3144-3151** A1429 Set of 8 19.00 4.75
*3151a* Sheet of 8 stamps, #3144-3151 20.00 5.25

Nos. 3150 and 3151 are airmail.

Whales and Dolphins A1430

Designs: No. 3152, 50ch, Balaenoptera physalus. No. 3153, 50ch, Delphinus delphis. No. 3154, 50ch, Orcinus orca. No. 3155, 50ch, Megaptera nodosa. No. 3156, 50ch, Berardius bairdii. No. 3157, 50ch, Physeter catadon.

**1992, Oct. 20**

**3152-3157** A1430 Set of 6 12.00 2.75
*3152a* Sheet of 3, #3152-3154 5.50 1.25
*3155a* Sheet of 3, #3155-3157 5.50 1.25

No. 3157 is airmail. For surcharges, see No. 4548, 4588.

New Year (Year of the Rooster) A1431

Chickens in various cartoon forms: 10ch, Hen and chicks. 20ch, Young hen. 30ch, Strong cock. 40ch, Prince cock. 50ch, Princess hen. 60ch, King cock.
1.20w, Cock.

**1992, Dec. 7** *Perf. 11½*

**3158-3163** A1431 Set of 6 6.50 1.75
*3163a* Sheet of 4, #3158-3160, 3163c 4.00 1.50
*3163b* Sheet of 4, #3161-3163, 3163c 5.00 2.00

**Souvenir Sheet**

**3163C** A1431 1.20w multicolored 5.00 1.00

A single stamp like that in No. 3163C is included in Nos. 3163a and 3163b. For surcharges, see Nos. 4525-4526.

N. Korean Gold Medal Winners at Barcelona Olympics A1432

Designs: 10ch, Choe Chol Su (boxing). 20ch, Pae Kil Su (gymnastics). 50ch, Ri Hak Son (Wrestling). 60ch, Kim Il (wrestling).
No. 3168: a, 30ch, Archer, flame, gold medal, flags of DPRK and Spain. b, 40ch, Emblem, game mascot and Church of the Holy Family, Barcelona.

**1992, Dec. 20** *Perf. 12*

**3164-3167** A1432 Set of 4 4.50 1.20

**Sheet of 6**

**3168** #3164-3167, 3168a-3168b 7.00 .60
*a.* A1432 30ch multicolored .35 .25
*b.* A1432 40ch multicolored .50 .30

Fungi — A1433

Designs: 10ch, Golden mushroom (Flammulina velutipes). 20ch, Shaggy caps (Coprinus comatus). 30ch, Ganoderma lucidum. 40ch, Brown mushroom (Lentinus edodes). 50ch, (Volvaria bombycina). 60ch, (Sarcodon aspratus).
1w, Scarlet caterpillar (Cordyceps militaris).

**1993, Jan. 10** ***Perf. 11½***

**3169-3174** A1433 Set of 6 7.50 2.50
*3169a* Sheet of 4, #3169, 3172, 3174, 3175 7.00 2.25
*3170a* Sheet of 4, #3170, 3171, 3173, 3175 7.00 2.25

**Souvenir Sheet**

**3175** A1433 1w multicolored 4.50 .80

A single stamp like that in No. 3175 is included in Nos. 3169a and 3170a.

A1434

Korean Plants — A1435

Designs: 10ch, Keumkangsania asiatica. 20ch, Echinosophora koreensis. 30ch, Abies koreana. 40ch, Benzoin angustifolium. 50ch, Abeliophyllum distichum. 60ch, (Abelia mosanensis).
1w, Pentactina rupicola.

**1993, Jan. 20** ***Perf. 12¼***

**3176-3181** A1434 Set of 6 7.00 2.00
*3181a* Sheet of 6, #3176-3181 7.00 2.25

**Souvenir Sheet**
***Perf. 11½***

**3182** A1435 1w multicolored 3.50 2.00

8th Congress of the League of Socialist Working Youth of Korea — A1436

Designs: 10ch, Youths, banner. 20ch, Flame, emblem, motto.

**1993, Jan. 25** ***Perf. 12¼***

**3183-3184** A1436 Set of 2 1.50 .40

Phophyong Revolutionary Site Tower & March Corps Emblem — A1437

**1993, Jan. 29** ***Perf. 12x12¼***

**3185** A1437 10ch multicolored .50 .25

70th anniv. of the 250-mile Journey for Learning.

Tower of the Juche Idea, Grand Monument, Mt. Wangjae A1438

**1993, Feb. 11**

**3186** A1438 60ch multicolored .50 .25

60th anniv. of the Wangjaesan Meeting.

A1439

Kim Jong Il, 51st Birthday — A1440

Designs: 10ch, Kimjongilia (Begonia).
1w, Kim Il Sung writing poem praising Kim Jong Il. Illustration of stamp only. Sheet measures 170mmx95mm, with marginal inscriptions that include reproductions of Kim Il Sung's poem.

**1993, Feb. 16** ***Perf. 12***

**3187** A1439 10ch multicolored 1.00 .25

**Souvenir Sheet**
***Perf. 13¼***

**3188** A1440 1w multicolored 3.50 .75

Sea Fish A1441

Designs: 10ch, Pilot fish (Naucrates ductor). 20ch, Japanese stingray (Dasyatis akajei). 30ch, Moonfish (Lampris guttatus). 40ch, Coelacanth (Latimeria chalumnae). 50ch, Grouper (Epinephelus moara).
1.20w, Mako shark (Isurus oxyrhynchus).

**1993, Feb. 25** ***Perf. 11½***

**3189-3193** A1441 Set of 5 5.00 1.25
*3189a* Sheet of 2, #3189, #3194 3.25 .45
*3190a* Sheet of 2, #3190, #3193 3.25 .45
*3191a* Sheet of 2, #3191, #3192 3.25 .45

**Souvenir Sheet**

**3194** A1441 1.20w multicolored 4.50 .80

A single stamp like that in No. 3194 is included in No. 3189a.
No. 3194, Naposta '93.

*Spring on the Hill*, 18th century Korean Painting — A1442

**1993, Mar. 20** ***Perf. 12x11½***

**3195** A1442 Sheet of 5 6.50 1.75
*a.-e.* 40ch, any single 1.00 .30

Spring Friendship Art Festival — A1443

**1993, Apr. 5** ***Perf. 12x12¼***

**3196** A1443 10ch multicolored .75 .25

For surcharge, see No. 4602.

A1444

Kim Il Sung, 80th Birthday, and Publication of *With the Century* — A1445

Designs: 10ch, *With the Century*, Kim Il Sung's Memoir.
1w, Kim Il Sung writing *With the Century.*

**1993, Apr. 15**

**3197** A1444 10ch multicolored .50 .25

**Souvenir Sheet**
***Perf. 11½***

**3198** A1445 1w multicolored 3.50 .75

A1446

Pyongyang Scenes — A1447

Designs: 10ch, Kwangbok Street. 20ch, Chollima Street. 30ch, Munsu Street. 40ch, Moranbong Street. 50ch, Thongil Street.
1w, Changgwang Street.

**1993, Apr. 20** ***Perf. 12x11¾***

**3199-3203** A1446 Set of 5 4.50 1.25

**Souvenir Sheet**
***Perf. 11½***

**3204** A1447 1w multicolored 3.50 .75

Insects A1448

Designs: 10ch, Fly (Trichogramma dendrolimi). 20ch, Fly (Brachymeria obscurata). 30ch, Cricket (Metrioptera brachyptera). 50ch, Cricket (Gryllus campestris). 70ch, Beetle (Geocoris pallidipennis). 90ch, Wasp (Cyphononyx dorsalis).

**1993, May 10** ***Perf. 12x12¼***

**3205-3210** A1448 Set of 6 10.00 2.25
*3205a* Sheet of 3, #3205, 3207, 3210 5.00 1.25
*3206a* Sheet of 3, #3206, 3208, 3209 5.00 1.25

Nos. 3205-3210 were issued both in separate sheets and in sheets of 3.

A1449

A1450

**1993, May 19** ***Perf. 11½***

**3211** A1449 10ch multicolored .50 .25

**Souvenir Sheet**
***Perf. 13¼***

**3212** A1450 1.20w multicolored 4.00 .80

Release of Ri In Mo, North Korean war correspondent, from South Korean prison.

World Cup Soccer Championship, U.S.A. — A1451

World Cup and soccer players: 10ch, Tackling. 20ch, Kicking. 30ch, Kicking (diff.). 50ch, Tackling (diff.). 70ch, Blocking. 90ch, Feinting.

**1993, May 25** ***Perf. 11½***

**3213-3218** A1451 Set of 6 8.50 2.25
*3213a* Sheet of 3, #3213, 3215, 3218 4.25 1.25
*3214a* Sheet of 3, #3214, 3216, 3217 4.25 1.25

Birds — A1452

Designs: 10ch, Gray-headed green woodpecker (Picus canus). 20ch, King of paradise (Cicinnurus regius. 30ch, Lesser bird of paradise (Paradisea minor). 40ch, Paradise whydah (Steganura paradisea). 50ch, Magnificent bird of paradise (Diphyllodes magnificus). 60ch, Greater bird of paradise (Paradisea apoda).

**1993, May 29** ***Perf. 12***

**3219-3224** A1452 Set of 6 7.00 1.75
*3219a* Sheet of 4, 2 ea. #3219, 3224 4.00 1.10
*3220a* Sheet of 4, 2 ea. #3220, 3223 4.00 1.10
*3221a* Sheet of 2, #3221, #3222 4.00 1.10

Nos. 3221, 3221a, 3222, Indopex '93 International Stamp Exhibition, Surabaya, Indonesia.

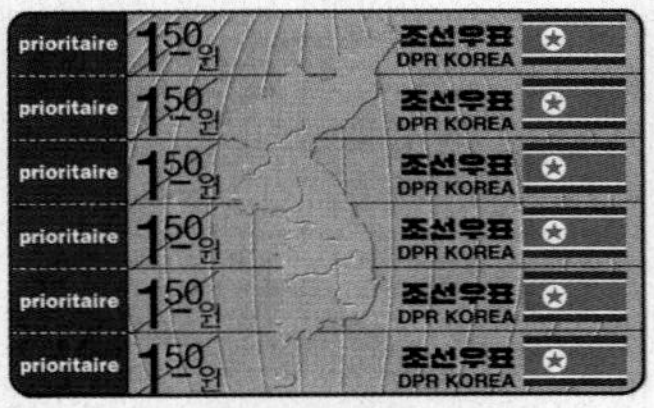


Stampcard — A1453

Map of Korean peninsula.

**1993, May 29** ***Rouletted***

**Self-adhesive**

**3225** A1453 Card of 6 stamps 20.00 20.00
***a.-f.*** 1.50w, any single 3.00 3.00

For surcharges, see No. 3441.

Korean World Champions — A1454

Designs: 10ch, Kim Myong Nam (weight-lifting, 1990). 20ch, Kim Kwang Suk (gymnastics, 1991). 30ch, Pak Yong Sun (table tennis, 1975, 1977). 50ch, Kim Yong Ok (radio direction-finding, 1990). 70ch, Han Yun Ok (taekwondo, 1987, 1988, 1990). 90ch, Kim Yong Sik (free-style wrestling, 1986, 1989).

**1993, June 15** ***Perf. 12x11¾***

**3226-3231** A1454 Set of 6 9.00 2.25
*3226a* Sheet of 6, 2 ea. #3226, 3228, 3231 9.00 2.50
*3227a* Sheet of 6, 2 ea. #3227, 3229, 3230 9.00 2.50

For surcharge, see No. 4573.

Fruits and Vegetables A1455

Designs: 10ch, Cabbage and chili peppers. 20ch, Squirrel and horse chestnuts. 30ch, Peach and grapes. 40ch, Birds and persimmons. 50ch, Tomatoes, eggplant and cherries. 60ch, Onion, radishes, garlic bulbs.

**1993, June 25** ***Perf. 11¾x12***

**3232-3237** A1455 Set of 6 6.50 1.75
*3232a* Sheet of 3, #3232, 3235, 3237 2.50 .90
*3232b* As "a.," ovptd. "Polska '93" 5.00 1.25
*3233c* Sheet of 3, #3233, 3234, 3236 2.50 .90

National Emblem — A1456

**1993, July 5** ***Perf. 12***

**3238** A1456 10ch vermilion .60 .25

Korean War, 40th Anniv. A1457

A1458

A1459

A1460

Kim Leading Soldiers on the Front — A1461

Kim Surveying Battlefield — A1462

Kim Making 1953 Victory Speech — A1463

Designs: No. 3239, 10ch, Soldiers and civilian women. No. 3240, 10ch, Officer and enlisted man. No. 3241, 10ch, Anti-aircraft missiles on military trucks. No. 3242, 10ch, Guided missiles on carriers. No. 3243, 10ch, Self-propelled missile launchers.

No. 3244, 1w, Kim Il Jong taking salute of paraders.

No. 3245, 10ch, Victory statue (soldier with flag). No. 3246, 10ch, Machine-gunners and refugees. 40ch, Soldiers and flag.

No. 3248a, 10ch, Kim Il Sung conducting planning meeting. b, 20ch, Kim inspecting artillery unit. No. 3249a, 10ch, Kim directing battle for Height 1211. b, 20ch, Kim encouraging machine gun crew. No. 3250a, 10ch, Kim at munitions factory. b, 20ch, Kim directing units of the Second Front. No. 3251a, 10ch, Kim with tank commanders. b, 20ch, Kim directing airmen. No. 3252a, 10ch, Kim with victorious soldiers. b, 20ch, Musicians.

**1993, July 27**

**3239-3243** A1457 Set of 5 2.50 .75

**Souvenir Sheet**

***Perf. 13¼***

**3244** A1458 1w multicolored 4.00 .55

***Perf. 11¾x12***

**3245-3247** A1459 Set of 3 2.25 .50
*3247a* Sheet of 3, #3245-3247 2.50 .60

**Souvenir Sheets of 2, #a-b**

***Perf. 11½***

**3248-3252** A1460 Set of 5 5.00 1.40

**Souvenir Sheets**

***Perf. 13¼***

**3253** A1461 80ch multicolored 4.50 .60
**3254** A1462 80ch multicolored 4.50 .60
**3255** A1463 1w multicolored 6.00 .60

National Reunification Prize Winners — A1464

Designs: 10ch, Choe Yong Do (1923-69). 20ch, Kim Gu (1875-1949). 30ch, Hong Myong Hui (1888-1968). 40ch, Ryo Un Hyong (1886-1947). 50ch, Kim Jong Thae (1926-69). 60ch, Kim Chaek (1903-51).

**1993, Aug. 1** ***Perf. 12***

**3256-3261** A1464 Set of 6 6.50 1.75

A1465

Taipei '93 Int'l Philatelic Exhib. — A1466

Designs: 20ch, *Robina sp.* 30ch, *Hippeastrum cv.*
1w, Deer.

**1993, Aug. 14**

**3262-3263** A1465 Set of 2 1.50 .45

**Souvenir Sheet**

**3264** A1466 1w multicolored 3.50 1.50

350th Anniv. Birth of Sir Isaac Newton, Mathematician and Scientist A1467

Designs: 10ch, Portrait of Newton. 20ch, Apple tree and formula for Law of Gravitation. 30ch, Reflecting telescope invented by Newton. 50ch, Formula of Binomial Theorem. 70ch, Newton's works, statue.

**1993, Sept. 1** ***Perf. 12¼x12***

**3265-3269** A1467 Set of 5 7.50 1.50
*3265a* Sheet of 3, #3265, 3266, 3269 3.75 3.75
*3265b* Sheet of 3, #3265, 3267, 3268 3.75 3.75

For surcharge, see No. 4597.

A1468

Restoration of the Tomb of King Tongmyong, Founder of Koguryo — A1469

Designs: 10ch, King Tongmyong shooting arrow. 20ch, King Tongmyong. 30ch, Restoration monument. 40ch, Jongrung Temple of the Tomb of King Tongmyong. 50ch, Tomb. 80ch, Kim Il Sung visiting restored tomb.

**1993, Sept. 10**
**3270-3274** A1468 Set of 5 4.50 1.25

### Souvenir Sheet

***Perf. 11½***

**3275** A1469 80ch multicolored 2.50 1.50

Bangkok '93 Int'l Philatelic Exhib. — A1470

First stamps of North Korea and Thailand.

**1993, Oct. 1**
**3276** A1470 1.20w multicolored 5.00 2.00

Orchids — A1471

Designs: 10ch, Cyrtopodium andresoni. 20ch, Cattleya. 30ch, Cattleya intermedia "Oculata." 40ch, Potinaria "Maysedo godonsia." 50ch, "Kimilsungia."

**1993, Oct. 15** ***Perf. 12***
**3277-3281** A1471 Set of 5 6.00 1.25
*3281a* Strip of 5, #3277-3281 6.00 6.00
*3277b-3281b* Set of 5 complete booklets, each containing 5 stamps 30.00

Nos. 3277b-3281b each contain horizontal strips of 5 of one value, taken from sheets. For surcharge, see No. 4549.

### No. 2949 Overprinted

**1993, Nov. 16**
**3282** A1373 80ch multicolored 2.50 1.50

Mao Zedong, Birth Centennial.

A1472

A1473

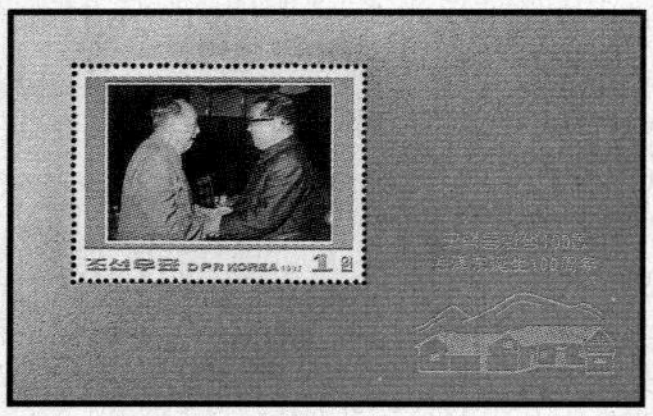

Mao Zedong, Birth Centennial — A1474

Designs: 10ch, Mao in Yannan (1940). 20ch, Mao in Beijing (1960). 30ch, Mao voting (1953). 40ch, Mao with middle-school students (1959).

No. 3287: Nos. 3283-3286 and: a, Mao proclaiming People's Republic of China (1949). b, Mao and his son, Mao Anying, in Xiangshan, Beijing (1949). c, Mao and Kim Il Sung (1975).

No. 3288: As No. 3287c.

**1993, Dec. 26** ***Perf. 11½***
**3283-3286** A1472 Set of 4 3.25 .90

### Souvenir Sheets

**3287** A1473 Sheet of 7 6.00 6.00
*a.* 25ch multicolored .50 .30
*b.* 25ch multicolored .50 .30
*c.* 1w multicolored 2.00 .90
**3288** A1474 1w multicolored 2.00 2.00

A1475

A1476

New Year, Year of the Dog — A1477

Designs: 10ch, Phungsan. 20ch, Yorkshire terriers. 30ch, Gordon setter. 40ch, Pomeranian. 50ch, Spaniel with pups.

No. 3294, Pointer.

No. 3295, 2 #3289, 1 #3294a; No. 3296, 2 #3290, 1 #3294a; No. 3297, 2 #3291, 1 #3294a; No. 3298, 2 #3292, 1 #3294a; No. 3299, 2 #3293, 1 #3294a.

**1994, Jan. 1** ***Perf. 12***
**3289-3293** A1475 Set of 5 5.00 1.00
*3289a-3293a* Set of 5 complete booklets, each containing 5 stamps 25.00

### Souvenir Sheet

**3294** A1476 1w multicolored 4.50 1.25

### Sheets of 3, #a.-c.

***Perf. 12***

**3295-3299** A1477 Set of 5 30.00 30.00

Nos. 3289a-3293a each contain horizontal strips of 5 of one value, taken from sheets.

A1478

Kim Jong Il, 52nd Birthday — A1479

Designs: 10ch, Purple hyosong flower (Prinula polyantha). 40ch, Yellow hyosong flower (Prinula polyantha).

No. 3302, Kim Il Sung and Kim Jong Il, from embroidery *The Sun of Juche.*

**1994, Feb. 16** ***Perf. 13¼***
**3300-3301** A1478 Set of 2 1.50 .45
*a.* Pair, #3300-3301 1.75 1.75

### Souvenir Sheet

**3302** A1479 1w multicolored 3.50 1.25

Nos. 3300-3301 exist in a miniature sheet containing 4 of each value, with central label depicting Jong Il Peak and *Kimjongilia.*

Goldfish — A1480

Designs: 10ch, Red and black dragon-eye. 30ch, Red and white bubble-eye. 50ch, Red and white long-finned wenyu. 70ch, Red and white fringetail.

**1994, Feb. 18** ***Perf. 12***
**3303** A1480 Sheet of 4 6.50 1.25
*a.* 10ch multicolored 1.60 .25
*b.* 30ch multicolored 1.60 .25
*c.* 50ch multicolored 1.60 .25
*d.* 70ch multicolored 1.60 .25

A1481

Publication of the *Program of Modeling the Whole Society on the Juche Idea,* 20th Anniv. — A1482

Kim Il Sung proclaiming the *Program,* 1974.

**1994, Feb. 19**
**3307** A1481 20ch multicolored .50 .25

### Souvenir Sheet

***Perf. 11½***

**3308** A1482 1.20w multicolored 4.25 1.25

A1483

A1484

Publication of Kim Il Sung's *Theses on the Socialist Rural Question in Our Country,* 30th Anniv. — A1485

Designs: 10ch (No. 3309), Woman propagandist, sound truck. 10ch (No. 3310), Electrical generator, pylon. 10ch (No. 3311), Farm, farm equipment, piles of grain. 40ch (No. 3312), Lab technician with microscope. 40ch (No. 3313), Dancers celebrating bounty harvest.

No. 3314, Kim Il Sung in field. No. 3315, Kim Jong Il walking through field with peasants.

**1994, Feb. 25** ***Perf. 12***
**3309-3313** A1483 Set of 5 3.50 .90

### Souvenir Sheets

***Perf. 11½***

**3314** A1484 1w multicolored 2.50 1.25
**3315** A1485 1w multicolored 2.50 1.25

Ships A1486

Designs: 20ch, Passenger ship, *Mangyongbong-92.* 30ch, Cargo ship, *Osandok.*

40ch, Processing stern trawler, *Ryongaksan*. 50ch, Stern trawler.
80ch, Passenger ship, *Maekjon No. 1*.

**1994, Mar. 25** ***Perf. 12***

**3316-3319** A1486 Set of 4 4.50 1.25
**3320** Sheet of 6, #3316-3319 + 2 #3320a 10.00 2.50
*a.* A1486 80ch multicolored 2.50 .75

DPRK Flag — A1487

**1994, Mar. 30** ***Perf. 13¼***

**3321** A1487 10ch car & dp blue .50 .25

For surcharge, see No. 4571.

A1488

Kim Il Sung, 82nd Birthday — A1489

Designs: 10ch, Magnolia and Kim's home. 40ch, Kimilsungia and Kim's home.

No. 3324, Five 40ch stamps, together forming design of Lake Chon (crater lake of Mt. Paektu), with *Song of General Kim Il Sung* music within design, lyrics in sheet margin.

**1994, Apr. 15** ***Perf. 12***

**3322-3323** A1488 Set of 2 1.50 .50
*3323a* 10ch Sheet of 8 7.00 2.25
*3323b* 40ch Sheet of 8 7.00 2.25

**Souvenir Sheet**

**3324** A1489 2w Sheet of 5 7.00 7.00
*a.-e.* 40ch any single 1.25 1.25

Alpine Plants of the Mt. Paektu Area — A1490

Designs: 10ch, Chrysoplenium sphaerospermum. 20ch, Campanula cephalotes. 40ch, Trollius macropetafus. 50ch, Sedum kamtschaticum.
1w, Dianthus repens.

**1994, Apr. 25** ***Perf. 13¼***

**3325-3329** A1490 Set of 5 4.50 1.25
*3325a* Sheet of 3, #3325, 3327, #3330 4.25 1.75
*3326a* Sheet of 3, #3326, 3328, 3329 4.25 1.75

**Souvenir Sheet**

**3330** A1490 1w multicolored 3.50 1.50

A single stamp like that in No. 3330 is included in No. 3325a.

A1491

Int'l Olympic Committee Centenary — A1492

Designs: 10ch, Olympic rings, DPRK flag. 20ch, Pierre de Coubertin, founder. 30ch, Olympic flag, flame. 50ch, IOC Centenary Congress emblem.

No. 3335, Runner with Olympic Torch. No. 3336, Juan Antonio Samaranch, IOC President and new IOC headquarters.

**1994, May 2** ***Perf. 12***

**3331-3334** A1491 Set of 4 4.00 1.00

**Souvenir Sheets**

***Perf. 13¼***

**3335-3336** A1492 Set of 2 6.50 2.00

International Federation of Red Cross and Red Crescent Societies, 75th Anniv. — A1493

Designs: a, 10ch, Train, pedestrians crossing on overpass ("Prevention of traffic accident"). b, 20ch, Medical personnel in Red Cross boat ("Relief on the Sea"). c, 30ch, Man and girl planting tree ("Protection of the environment"). d, 40ch, Dam, sailboat on lake ("Protection of drought damage").

**1994, May 5**

**3337** A1493 Strip of 4, #a.-d. 3.50 2.50

**No. 3225 Surcharged**

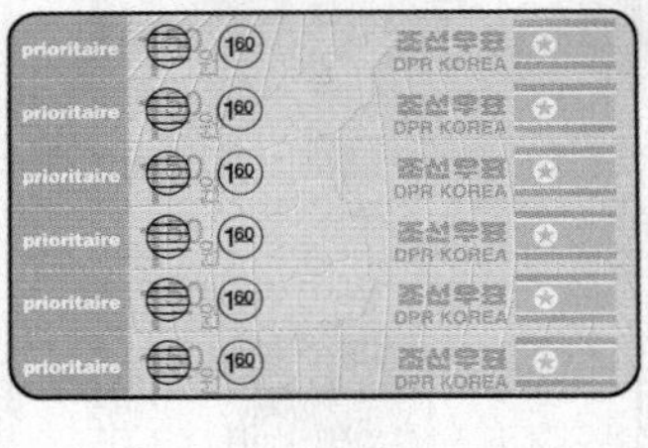

**1994, May 29** **Self-adhesive** ***Imperf***

**3341** A1452 1.60w on 1.50w Card of 6 28.00 28.00
*a.-f.* 1.60w on 1.50w, any single 7.00 7.00

A1494

Seals — A1495

Designs: 10ch, Northern fur seal (Callorhinus ursinus). 40ch, Southern elephant seal (Mirounga leonina). 60ch, Southern sea lion (Otaria byronia).

No. 3345: 20ch, California sea lion (Zalophus californianus). 30ch, Ringed seal (Phoca hispida). 50ch, Walrus (Odobenus rosmarus).

No. 3346, Harp seal (Pagophilus groenlandicus).

**1994, June 10** ***Perf. 11½***

**3342-3344** A1494 Set of 3 4.00 .90
**3345** A1494 Sheet of 3 4.50 1.00
*a.* 20ch multicolored .75 .25
*b.* 30ch multicolored 1.25 .25
*c.* 50ch multicolored 2.25 .50

**Souvenir Sheet**

**3346** A1495 1w multicolored 3.50 1.00

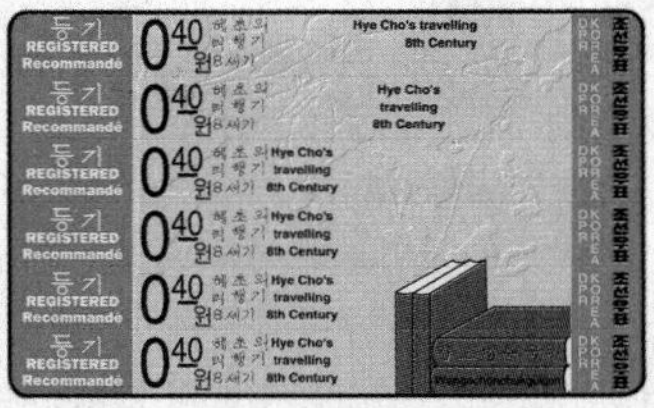

Stampcard — A1496

Map of Asia, books.

**1994, June 17** ***Rouletted***

**Self-adhesive**

**3347** A1496 Card of 6 stamps 10.00 10.00
*a.-f.* 40ch, any single 1.65 1.65

Hye Cho's 8th century travels in Central Asia and India.

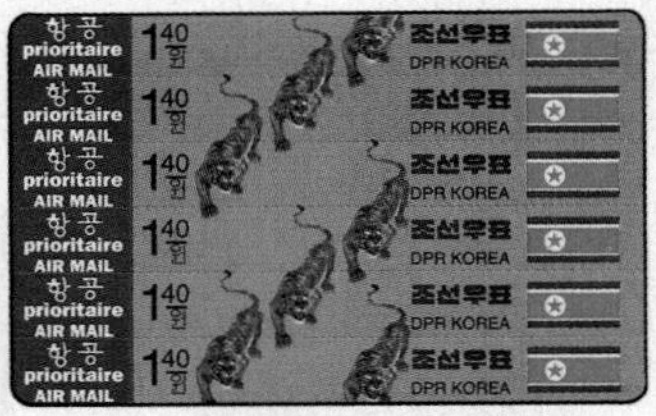

Stampcard — A1497

Korean Tigers.

**1994, June 18** ***Rouletted***

**Self-adhesive**

**3348** A1497 Card of 6 stamps 30.00 30.00
*a.-f.* 1.40w, any single 5.00 5.00

A1498

Kim Il Sung's Leadership of the Korean Workers' Party, 30th Anniv. — A1499

Designs (all 40ch): a, Kim and supporters on cliff ledge, overlooking lake. b, Kim on mountain top, pointing across lake to Mt. Paektu. c, Kim on film set. d, Kim visiting restaurant. e, Kim reviewing tank corps. f, Kim at conference, shaking hands onstage as audience applauds.

**1994, June 19** ***Perf. 12***

**3349** A1498 Sheet of 6 8.00 2.50
*3349g* Booklet pane of 6, 3 ea. #3349a-3349b 8.00 —
Complete booklet, #3349g 8.50
*3349h* Booklet pane of 6, 3 ea. #3349c, 3349e 8.00 —
Complete booklet, #3349h 8.50
*3349i* Booklet pane of 6, 3 ea. #3349d, 3349f 8.00 —
Complete booklet, #3349i 8.50

**Souvenir Sheet**

***Perf. 11½***

**3350** A1499 1w multicolored 3.00 1.00

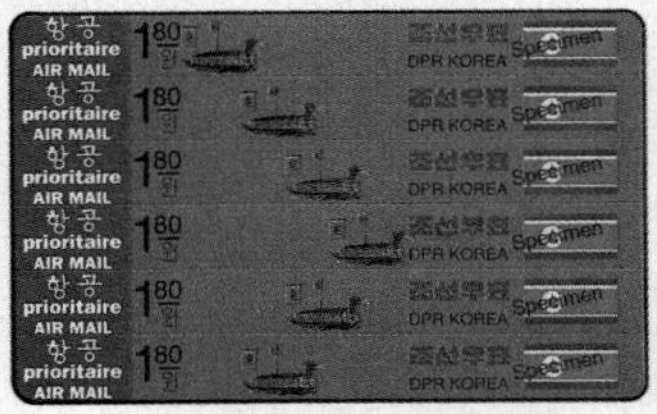

Stampcard — A1500

Turtle ship.

**1994, June 20** ***Rouletted***

**Self-adhesive**

**3356** A1500 Card of 6 stamps 33.00 33.00
*a.-f.* 1.80w, any single 5.50 5.50



A1501

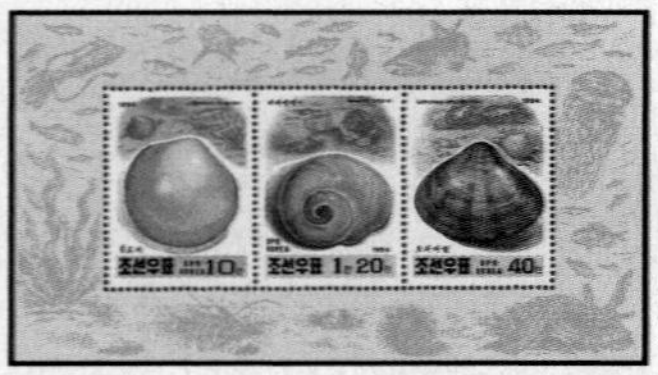

A1502

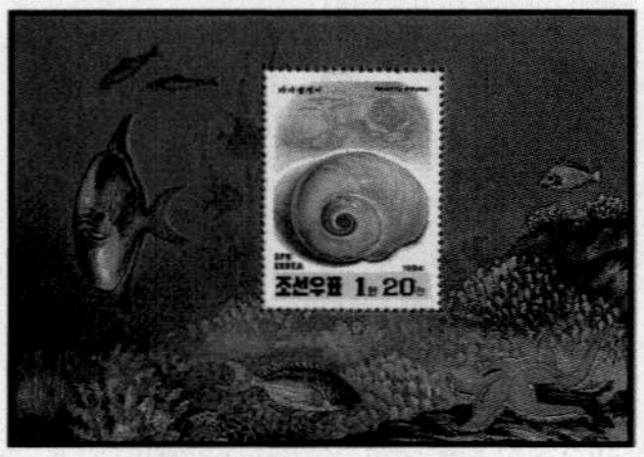

Mollusks — A1503

Designs: 30ch, Phalium strigatum. 40ch, Gomphina veneriformis.

No. 3359: a, 10ch, Cardium muticum, No. 3358 and the stamp found in No. 3361.

No. 3360: a, 20ch, Buccinum bayani, No. 3357 and the stamp found in No. 3361.

No. 3361: Neverita didyma

**1994, June 25** ***Perf. 12***

**3357-3358** A1501 Set of 2 2.50 .60

**Sheets of 3, #a.-c.**

***Perf. 13¼***

**3359-3360** A1502 Set of 2 14.00 10.00

**Souvenir Sheet**

**3361** A1503 1.20w multicolored 5.00 1.40

For surcharge, see No. 4608.

Circus Acrobats — A1504

Designs: a, 10ch, Flying trapeze. b, 20ch, Rope dance. c, 30ch, Seesaw. d, 40ch, Unicycle show.

**1994, July 7** ***Perf. 11½***

**3362** A1504 Sheet of 4, #a.-d. 4.00 1.25

A1505

Centenary of Birth of Kim Hyong Jik (1894-1926), Father of Kim Il Sung — A1506

**1994, July 10** ***Perf. 13¼***

**3363** A1505 10ch multicolored .50 .25

**Souvenir Sheet**

***Perf. 11¾x11½***

**3364** A1506 1w multicolored 3.50 1.25

Jeon Bong-jun & Battle Scene — A1507

**1994, July 15** ***Perf. 12***

**3365** A1507 10ch multicolored .60 .25

Centenary of Kabo Peasant War.

Inoue Shuhachi — A1508

**1994, July 30** ***Perf. 13¼***

**3366** A1508 1.20w multicolored 4.00 1.25

Award of the First International Kim Il Sung Prize to Inoue Shuhachi, Director General of the International Institute of the Juche Idea (Japan).

Workers Marching A1509

**1994, Aug. 1** ***Perf. 11½***

**3367** A1509 10ch multicolored .50 .25

Workers' Party Economic Strategy.

Fossils A1510

Designs: 40ch (No. 3368), Onsong fish. 40ch (No. 3369), Metasequoia. 40ch (No. 3370), Mammoth teeth. 80ch, Archaeopteryx.

No. 3372 contains 2 each Nos. 3368, 3371. No. 3373 contains 2 each Nos.3369, 3371. No. 3374 contains 2 each Nos. 3370-3371.

**1994, Aug. 10** ***Perf. 12***

**3368-3371** A1510 Set of 4 13.00 1.75
Complete booklet, 7 #3368 16.00
Complete booklet, 7 #3369 16.00
Complete booklet, 7 #3370 16.00
Complete booklet, 7 #3371 32.00

**Souvenir Sheets**

**3372-3374** A1510 Set of 3 sheets 26.00 20.00

Medicinal Plants — A1511

Designs: 20ch, Acorus calamus. 30ch, Arctium lappa.

No. 3377 (133x86mm): a, 80ch, Lilium lancifolium. b, 80ch, Codonopsis lanceolata.

No. 3378 (56x83mm): 1w, Ginseng (Panax schinseng), vert.

**1994, Aug. 25**

**3375-3376** A1511 Set of 2 1.75 .50
Complete booklet, 10 #3375 7.00
Complete booklet, 10 #3376 10.50

**Souvenir Sheets**

***Perf. 13¼***

**3377-3378** A1511 Set of 2 sheets 8.00 2.00

Calisthenics — A1512

Gymnastic routines: a, 10ch, Ribbon twirling. b, 20ch, Ball. c, 30ch, Hoop. d, 40ch, Ribbon twirling (diff.). e, 50ch, Clubs.

**1994, Sept. 7** ***Perf. 12***

**3379** A1512 Strip of 5 + label 5.50 1.50

No. 3379 was printed in sheets of 18, containing three No. 3379 in horizontal rows, with a different label in each row.

A1513

A1514

Zhou Enlai (1898-1976), Birth Centenary — A1515

Portraits of Zhou Enlai: 10ch, As student revolutionary (1919). 20ch, Arrival in Northern Shansi after Long March (1936). 30ch, At Conference of Asian and African Countries, Bandung, Indonesia (1955). 40ch, Speaking with children.

No. 3384: 80ch, Zhou Enlai and Kim Il Sung (1970).

No. 3385: 10ch, as #3380. a, 20ch, Zhou leading Nanchang Uprising (1927). 40ch, as #3383. 80ch, as #3384.

No. 3386: 20ch, as #3381. a, 20ch, Zhou and Mao Tzedong at airport, horiz. 30ch, as #3383. 80ch, as #3385b.

**1994, Oct. 1** ***Perf. 11½***

**3380-3383** A1513 Set of 4 3.25 1.00

**Souvenir Sheets**

***Perf. 13¼***

**3384** A1514 80ch multicolored 2.75 1.00

***Perf 11½ (Vert. stamps), 11¾x12¼ (Horiz. stamps)***

**3385-3386** A1515 Set of 2 9.50 4.00

Nos. 3380-3383 were issued in sheets of 30 (6x5), with a label beneath each stamp.

World Environment Day — A1516

Each sheetlet contains two 50ch stamps with designs reflecting environmental issues. Themes: No. 3387, Prevention of air pollution. No. 3388, Preventation of water pollution. No. 3389, Protection of animal resources. No. 3390, Protection of forest resources.

**1994, Oct. 5** ***Perf. 12***

**Sheets of 2**

**3387-3390** A1516 Set of 4 12.50 12.50

A1517

A1518

Kim Il Sung (1912-94) — A1519

Photos of Kim Il Sung (all 40ch).

No. 3391: a, As young man (1927). b, With Kim Jong Suk, his first wife and mother of Kim Jong Il. c, As captain in Soviet army (1944).

No. 3392: Speaking at lectern upon return to Pyongyang (1945). b, Sitting at desk in office of People's Committee of North Korea. c, Speaking at microphone.

**1994, Oct. 8**

| | | | | |
|---|---|---|---|---|
| **3391** | A1517 | Sheet of 3, #a.-c. | 4.00 | 2.00 |
| **3392** | A1518 | Sheet of 3, #a.-c. | 4.00 | 2.00 |

**Souvenir Sheet**

***Perf. 12¼x11¾***

| | | | | |
|---|---|---|---|---|
| **3393** | A1519 | 1w multicolored | 3.75 | 1.25 |

Compare with Nos. 3401-3403.

A1520

World Cup '94, 15th World Soccer Championship — A1521

Soccer Players Dribbling: 10ch, Player No. 4. 20ch, Player No. 5. 30ch, Player No. 6. 40ch, Player No. 7. 1w, Player No. 8. 1.50w, Player No. 9.

**1994, Oct. 13** ***Perf. 13½***

| | | | | |
|---|---|---|---|---|
| **3394-3399** | A1520 | Set of 6 | 12.00 | 6.00 |
| *3399a* | | Sheet of 6, #3394-3399 | 18.00 | 10.00 |

**Souvenir Sheet**

| | | | | |
|---|---|---|---|---|
| **3400** | A1521 | 2.50w multicolored | 7.50 | 4.00 |

Nos. 3394-3400 were also issued imperf. Value: set, $24; souvenir sheet, $15.

Nos. 3394-3399 exist in sheetlets on one, perf and imperf. Value: perf, $24; imperf, $47.50.

A1522

Kim Il Sung (1912-94) — A1523

Photos of Kim Il Sung (all 40ch).

No. 3401: a, Making radio broadcast (1950). b, With soldiers (1951). c, Clapping hands, crowd of soldiers in background (1953).

No. 3402: a, Talking with workers at Chongjin Steel Plant (1959). b, Standing in field, Onchon Plain. c, Talking on telephone.

No. 3403, Kim Il Sung and Kim Jong Il.

**1994, Oct. 15** ***Perf. 12***

**Sheets of 3**

| | | | | |
|---|---|---|---|---|
| **3401-3402** | A1522 | Set of 2 | 8.00 | 4.00 |

***Perf. 12¼x11¾***

| | | | | |
|---|---|---|---|---|
| **3403** | A1523 | 1w multicolored | 3.50 | 1.50 |

Compare with Nos. 3391-3393.

A1524

North Korean-Chinese Friendship — A1525

1w, Kim Il Sung with Mao Zedong.

**1994, Oct. 25** ***Perf. 11½***

| | | | | |
|---|---|---|---|---|
| **3404** | A1524 | 40ch multicolored | 1.50 | .50 |

**Souvenir Sheet**

***Perf. 13¼***

| | | | | |
|---|---|---|---|---|
| **3405** | A1525 | 1.20w multicolored | 4.25 | 2.00 |

Composers A1526

Designs: No. 3406, Ri Myon Sang (1908-89), score from *It Snows.* No. 3407, Pak Han Gyu (1919-92), score from *Nobody Knows.* No. 3408, Ludwig van Beethoven (1770-1827), score of *Piano Sonata No. 14.* No. 3409, Wolfgang Mozart (1756-91), score of *Symphony No. 39.*

**1994, Nov. 25** ***Perf. 11½***

| | | | | |
|---|---|---|---|---|
| **3406-3409** | A1526 | 50ch Set of 4 | 6.50 | 2.25 |

For surcharge, see No. 4550.

National Emblem — A1527

**1994, Dec. 10** ***Perf. 12***

| | | | | |
|---|---|---|---|---|
| **3410** | A1527 | 1w dp bl green | 4.00 | 1.00 |
| **3411** | A1527 | 3w deep brown | 8.00 | 2.50 |

For surcharge, see No. 4575.

A1528

A1529

Gold Medal Winners, Winter Olympic Games, Lillehammer — A1530

Designs: 10ch, Pernilla Wiberg (Sweden), Alpine combined skiing. 20ch, Deborah Compagnoni (Italy), Slalom. 30ch, Oksana Baiul (Ukraine), Figure skating. 40ch, Dan Jansen (USA), Speed skating. 1w (No. 3416), Yubow Jegorowa (Russia), Cross-country skiing. 1w (No. 3417), Bonnie Blair (USA), Speed skating.

No. 3418, Bjorn Dåehlie and Norwegian skiing team, Alpine combined skiing. No. 3419, Jekaterina Gordejewa and Serge Grinkow (Russia), Pairs figure skating. No. 3420, Vreni Schneider (Switzerland), Alpine combined skiing. No. 3421, Georg Hackl (Germany), Luge. No. 3422, Jens Weissflog (Germany), Ski jumping. No. 3423, Masashi Abe, Takanori Kono, Kenji Ogiwara (Japan), Cross-country skiing.

No. 3424, Tommy Moe (USA), Downhill skiing.

**1994, Dec. 20** ***Perf. 13¼***

| | | | | |
|---|---|---|---|---|
| **3412-3417** | A1528 | Set of 6 | 11.00 | 3.00 |
| *3417a* | | Sheet of 6, #3412-3417 | 12.00 | 5.00 |

**Souvenir Sheets**

| | | | | |
|---|---|---|---|---|
| **3418-3423** | A1529 | 1w Set of 6 | 18.00 | 6.00 |
| **3424** | A1530 | 2.50w multicolored | 8.00 | 1.50 |

New Year — Year of the Pig A1531

Designs: 20ch, Pigs relaxing. 40ch, Pigs going to work.

Each 1w: No. 3427, Pigs carrying pumpkin. No. 3428, Piglets bowing to adult pig.

**1995, Jan. 1** ***Perf. 11½***

| | | | | |
|---|---|---|---|---|
| **3425-3426** | A1531 | Set of 2 | 1.10 | .65 |
| *3426a* | | Sheet of 4, 2 ea #3425-3426 | 3.50 | 3.50 |

**Souvenir Sheets**

| | | | | |
|---|---|---|---|---|
| **3427-3428** | A1531 | Set of 2 | 6.00 | 5.00 |

No. 3426a inscribed in margins for Singapore '95 Intl. Stamp Exhibition. Issued, 9/1.

World Tourism Org., 20th Anniv. — A1532

Designs, each 30ch: a, Tower of the Juche Idea, Pyongyang. b, Pison Falls on Mt. Myohyang. c, Myogilsang (relief carving of Buddha), Mt. Kumgang.

**1995, Jan. 2** ***Perf. 12¼***

| | | | | |
|---|---|---|---|---|
| **3429** | A1532 | Sheet of 3, #a.-c. + label | 3.50 | .90 |

Mangyondae, Badasgou, Emblem — A1533

**1995, Jan. 22** ***Perf. 11½***
**3430** A1533 40ch multicolored 1.50 .90

70th anniversary of 250-Mile Journey for the Restoration of the Fatherland.

A1534

A1535

A1536

Kim Jong Il, 53rd Birthday — A1537

Designs: 10ch, Jong Il Peak (Mt. Paekdu) and 50th Birthday Ode Monument.
No. 3432 (horiz.): a, 20ch Kim Il Sung and Kim Jong Il; b, 80ch Kim Jong Il inspecting the West Sea Barrage. No. 3433 (vert.): a, 40ch Kim Jong Il in business suit; b, Kim Jong Il in uniform in Taesongsan Martyrs' Cemetary. No. 3434: 1w, Kim Jong Il inspecting the Ryongsong Machine Complex.

**1995, Feb. 16** ***Perf. 12¼***
**3431** A1534 10ch multicolored .25 .25

**Souvenir Sheets**

**3432** A1535 Sheet of 2, #a.-b. 2.00 1.50
**3433** A1536 Sheet of 2, #a.-b. 1.75 1.25
**3434** A1537 1w multicolored 2.00 2.00

Mausoleum of King Tangun — A1537a

King Tangun and Mausoleum — A1537b

Designs: 10ch, Monument. 30ch, Straight bronze dagger tower. 50ch, Monument inscribed with King Tangun's exploits. 70ch, Gate of mausoleum.
50ch, King Tangun and Mausoleum.

**1995, Feb. 25** ***Perf. 12¼***
**3434A-3434D** A1537a Set of 4 3.00 3.00

**Souvenir Sheet**
***Perf. 11½***

**3434E** A1537b 1.40w multi 3.00 3.00

Lighthouses A1538

Designs: 20ch, Tamaedo Lighthouse. 1.20w, Phido Lighthouse, West Sea Barrage.

**1995, Mar. 10** ***Perf. 13½***
**3435-3436** A1538 Set of 2 5.00 1.75

Mushrooms A1539

Designs: 20ch, Russula virescens. 30ch, Russula atropurpurea.
1w, Caesar's Mushroom (Amanita caesarea.

**1995, Mar. 25**

| | | | | |
|---|---|---|---|---|
| **3437-3438** | A1539 Set of 2 | | 2.00 | .60 |
| *3437a* | Booklet pane of 10 #3437 | | 3.50 | — |
| | Complete booklet, #3437a | | 4.00 | |
| *3438a* | Booklet pane of 10 #3438 | | 17.00 | — |
| | Complete booklet, #3438a | | 17.50 | |

**Souvenir Sheet**

**3439** A1539 1w multicolored 4.50 2.50

For surcharges, see Nos. 4527-4528.

Tree Planting Day — A1540

**1995, Apr. 6** ***Perf. 11½***
**3440** A1540 10ch multicolored .60 .25
*a.* Sheet of 6 3.50 3.50

**No. 3225 Surcharged with New Values**

**1995, Apr. 8** ***Rouletted***
**3441** Card of 6 stamps 8.00 8.00
*a.-f.* 30ch on 1.50w, any single 1.30 1.30

Finlandia '95.

Mangyongdae, Birthplace of Kim Il Sung — A1541

Tower of Juche Idea and Kimilsungia A1542

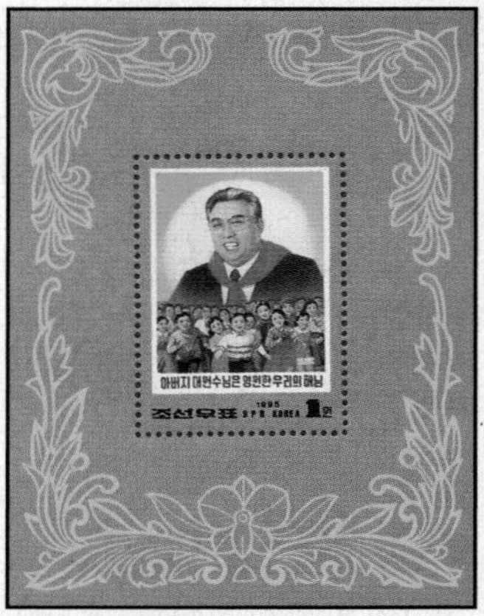

Kim Il Sung and Children — A1543

**1995, Apr. 15** ***Perf. 11½***

| | | | |
|---|---|---|---|
| **3442** | A1541 10ch multicolored | .25 | .25 |
| *a.* | Sheet of 6 | 1.50 | 1.50 |
| *b.* | Booklet pane of 5 | — | — |
| | Complete booklet, #3442b | — | |
| **3443** | A1542 40ch multicolored | 1.25 | 1.00 |
| *a.* | Sheet of 6 | 7.50 | 7.50 |
| *b.* | Booklet pane of 5 | — | — |
| | Complete booklet, #3443b | — | |

**Souvenir Sheet**
***Perf. 13½***

**3444** A1543 1w multicolored 3.50 3.50

Kim Il Sung, 82nd birthday. For surcharge, see No. 4610.

A1544

Kim Il Sung's Visit to China, 20th Anniv. — A1545

Designs: 10ch, Deng Xiaoping waving. 20ch, Deng sitting in armchair, vert.
50ch, Kim and Deng sitting in armchairs.

**1995, Apr. 17** ***Perf. 13½***
**3445-3446** A1544 Set of 2 1.25 1.25

**Souvenir Sheet**
***Perf. 11½***

**3447** A1545 50ch multicolored 2.00 2.00

A1546

A1547

Asian-African Conf., Bandung, 40th Anniv. — A1548

Designs: 10ch, Site of Bendung Conference. 50ch, Kim Il Sung receiving honorary doctorate from Indonesia University.
1w, Kim Il Sung and Kim Jong Il at Conference 40th Anniversary ceremony.

**1995, Apr. 18** ***Perf. 11½***
**3448** A1546 10ch multicolored .25 .25
**3449** A1547 50ch multicolored 1.75 .70

**Souvenir Sheet**

**3450** A1548 1w multicolored 3.50 3.50

A1549

Int'l Sports and Cultural Festival for Peace, Pyongyang — A1550

Designs: 20ch, Emblem. 40ch (No. 3452), Dancer. 40ch (No. 3453), Inoki Kanji, leader of Sports Peace Party of Japan.
1w, Nikidozan, wrestling champion.

**1995, Apr. 28**

**3451-3453** A1549 Set of 3 3.00 2.00
*3451a* Sheet of 3, 1 #3451 + 2 #3452 3.00 2.00
*3453a* Sheet of 3, 2 #3453 + 1 as #3454 7.00 4.00

**Souvenir Sheet**

**3454** A1550 1w multicolored 3.50 3.50

Amethyst — A1551

**1995, May 2**

**3455** A1551 20ch multicolored 1.00 .40
*a.* Sheet of 6 7.50 7.50
*b.* Booklet pane of 10 10.00 —
Complete booklet, #3455b 11.00

Finlandia '95. No. 3455a marginal selvage contains a mountain valley scene and is inscribed "Finlandia 95." No. 3455b has selvage around the block of 10 stamps.

White Animals — A1552

Each 40ch: No. 3456, Tree sparrow (*Passer montanus*). No. 3457, Sea slug (*Stichopus japonicus*).

**1995, May 12** ***Perf. 13½***

**3456-3457** A1552 Set of 2 2.50 1.50
*3457a* Sheet of 6, 3 #3456 + 3 #3457 9.00

Fossils — A1553

Designs: a, 50ch, Ostrea. b, 1w, Cladophiebis (fern).

**1995, May 15** ***Perf. 12***

**3458** A1553 Pair, #a.-b. 4.00 1.75
*c.* Booklet pane of 7, 4 #3458a, 3 #3458b — —
Complete booklet, #3458c —

Traditional Games A1554

Designs: 30ch, Chess. 60ch, Taekwondo. 70ch, Yut.

**1995, May 20** ***Perf. 11½***

**3459-3461** A1554 Set of 3 5.25 2.00
*3459a* Sheet of 2 #3459 + label 1.75 1.75
*3460a* Sheet of 2 #3460 + label 4.00 4.00
*3461a* Sheet of 2 #3461 + label 6.00 6.00
*3461b* Booklet pane of 6, 2 ea. #3459-3461 10.50 —
Complete booklet. #3461b 11.00

General Assoc. of Koreans in Japan, 40th Anniv. — A1555

**1995, May 25**

**3462** A1555 1w multicolored 3.50 .90

Atlanta '96 — A1556

Designs, each 50ch: No. 3463, Weight lifter. No. 3464, Boxing.
1w, Marksman shooting clay pigeon.

**1995, June 2**

**3463-3464** A1556 Set of 2 3.25 1.25
*3464a* Sheet of 2 #3463 + 2 #3464 7.50 7.50

**Souvenir Sheet**

**3465** A1556 1w multicolored 5.00 5.00

Fungi — A1557

Designs: 40ch, Russula citrina. 60ch, Craterellus cornucopioides. 80ch, Coprinus comatus.

**1995, July 1** ***Perf. 13¼***

**3466-3468** A1557 Set of 3 6.50 2.00
*3466a* Booklet pane of 10 #3466 14.00 —
Complete booklet, #3466a 14.50
*3467a* Booklet pane of 10 #3467 21.00 —
Complete booklet, #3467a 22.00
*3468a* Booklet pane of 10 #3468 29.00 —
Complete booklet, #3468a 30.00

For surcharge, see No. 4553.

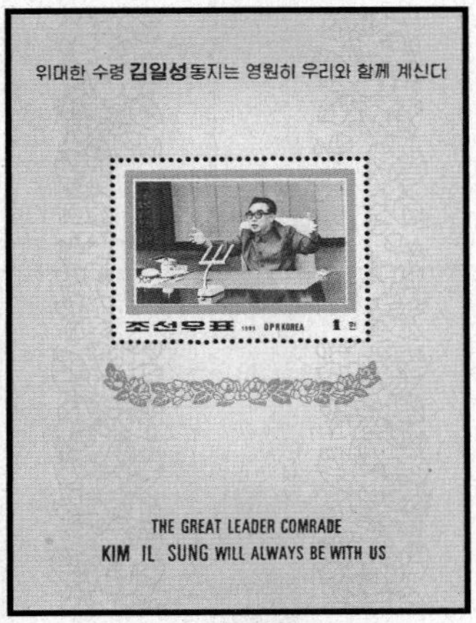


A1558

A1559

A1560

Kim Il Sung, 1st Death Anniv. — A1561

No. 3469, 1w, Kim addressing conference for development of agriculture in African countries, 1981.
No. 3470: a, 10ch, Kim greeting Robert Mugabe, President of Zimbabwe. b, 70ch, Kim with King Norodom Sihanouk of Cambodia.
No. 3471: a, 20ch, Kim receiving honorary doctorate, Algeria University, 1975. b, 50ch, Kim with Fidel Castro, 1986.
No. 3472: a, 30ch, Kim talking with Ho Chi Minh, 1958. b, 40ch, Kim greeting Che Guevara, 1960.

**1995, July 8**

**3469** A1558 1w multicolored 2.75 2.75
**3470** A1559 Sheet of 2, #a.-b. 2.25 2.25
**3471** A1560 Sheet of 2, #a.-b. 2.50 2.50
**3472** A1561 Sheet of 2, #a.-b. 2.00 2.00

Liberation, 50th Anniv. — A1562

Designs: 10ch, Korean army officer. 30ch, Map of Korea, family. 60ch, Hero of the DPRK medal.
No. 3476, a, 20ch revolutionary soldier, #3414, 2 each.
No. 3477, a, 40ch demonstrators, #3474, 2 each.

**1995, Aug. 15** ***Perf. 11½***

**3473-3475** A1562 Set of 3 2.75 1.25
*3475a* Booklet pane of 5, #3473-3475, 3476a, 3477a 4.50 —
Complete booklet, #3475a 5.00

**Souvenir Sheets**

**3476** Sheet of 4 2.50 2.50
*a.* A1562 20ch multicolored .50 .25
**3477** Sheet of 4 4.50 4.50
*a.* A1562 40ch multicolored 1.00 .45

1st Military World Games — A1564

**1995, Sept. 4**

**3479** A1564 40ch multicolored 1.00 .45

A1565

A1566

Korea-China Friendship — A1567

Designs: No. 3480, 80ch, Kim Il Sung and Mao Zedong. No. 3481, 80ch, Kim and Zhou Enlai.
No. 3482: a, 50ch, Kim and Zhou Enlai. b, 50ch, Kim receiving gift from Deng Ying-Chao, Premier of the State Council of the People's Republic of China.

**1995, Oct. 1** ***Perf. 12¼***

**3480** A1565 80ch multicolored 1.50 1.50
**3481** A1566 80ch multicolored 1.50 1.50
**3482** A1567 Sheet of 2, #a.-b. 2.25 2.25

A1568

Korean Workers' Party, 50th Anniv. — A1569

Designs: 10ch, Korean Workers' Party Emblem and Banner. 20ch, Statue of three workers holding party symbols. 40ch, Monument to founding of Party.
No. 3486, Kim Il Sung.

**1995, Oct. 10** — ***Perf. 11½***

| | | | |
|---|---|---|---|
| **3483-3485** A1568 Set of 3 | 1.60 | .75 |

**Souvenir Sheet**

***Perf. 13½***

| | | |
|---|---|---|
| **3486** A1569 1w multicolored | 2.75 | 2.75 |

Kim Il Sung's Return to Korea, 50th Anniv. A1570

Design: 50ch, Arch of Triumph, Pyongyang.

**1995, Oct. 14** — ***Perf. 11½***

| | | |
|---|---|---|
| **3487** A1570 10ch multicolored | .60 | .25 |

Great Tunny — A1571

**Fish**

No. 3488, Great tunny. No. 3489, Pennant coralfish. No. 3490, Needlefish. No. 3491, Bullrout. No. 3492, Imperial butterfly fish.

**1995** — ***Perf. 13¼***

| | | |
|---|---|---|
| **3488** 40ch choc & black | 1.25 | .35 |
| **3489** 50ch choc & black | 1.50 | .40 |
| **3490** 50ch choc & black | 1.50 | .40 |
| **3491** 60ch choc & black | 1.75 | .45 |
| **3492** 5w choc & black | 15.00 | 3.50 |
| *a.* Horiz. strip of 5, #3488-3492 | 22.50 | 5.00 |

**Machines**

10ch, 40-ton truck *Kumsusan.* 20ch, Large bulldozer. 30ch, Hydraulic excavator. 40ch, Wheel loader, vert. 10w, Tractor *Chollima-80*, vert.

| | | |
|---|---|---|
| **3493** 10ch choc & black | .35 | .25 |
| **3494** 20ch choc & black | .75 | .25 |
| **3495** 30ch choc & black | 1.00 | .25 |
| **3496** 40ch choc & black | 1.60 | .30 |
| **3497** 10w choc & black | 27.50 | 7.50 |
| *a.* Horiz. strip of 5, #3493-3497 | 32.50 | 10.00 |

**Animals**

30ch, Giraffe, vert. 40ch, Ostrich, vert. 60ch, Bluebuck, vert. 70ch, Bactrian camel. 3w, Indian rhinoceros.

| | | |
|---|---|---|
| **3498** 30ch choc & black | .85 | .25 |
| **3499** 40ch choc & black | 1.10 | .35 |
| **3500** 60ch choc & black | 1.60 | .50 |
| **3501** 70ch choc & black | 2.00 | .55 |
| **3502** 3w choc & black | 8.00 | 2.25 |
| *a.* Horiz. strip of 5, #3498-3502 | 16.00 | 4.00 |

**Sculptures of Children**

30ch, Boy and pigeon, vert. 40ch, Boy and goose, vert. 60ch, Girl and geese vert. 70ch, Boy and girl comparing heights, vert. 2w, Boy and girl with soccer ball, vert.

| | | |
|---|---|---|
| **3503** 30ch choc & black | .85 | .25 |
| **3504** 40ch choc & black | 1.10 | .35 |
| **3505** 60ch choc & black | 1.60 | .50 |
| **3506** 70ch choc & black | 2.00 | .50 |
| **3507** 2w choc & black | 5.75 | 1.60 |
| *a.* Vert. strip of 5, #3503-3507 | 13.00 | 4.00 |

**Buildings**

60ch, Pyongyang Circus. 70ch, Country apartment building. 80ch, Pyongyang Hotel. 90ch, Urban apt. towers. 1w, Sosan Hotel.

| | | |
|---|---|---|
| **3508** 60ch choc & black | 1.75 | .50 |
| **3509** 70ch choc & black | 2.00 | .55 |
| **3510** 80ch choc & black | 2.25 | .65 |
| **3511** 90ch choc & black | 2.50 | .75 |
| **3512** 1w choc & black | 2.75 | .85 |
| *a.* Horiz. strip of 5, #3508-3512 | 13.00 | 4.00 |

Issued: Nos. 3488-3492, 10/20; Nos. 3493-3497, 11/2; Nos. 3498-3502, 11/20; Nos. 3503-3507, 12/5; Nos. 3508-3512, 12/15.

Nos. 3488-3492, 3493-3497, 3498-3502, 3503-3507, and 3508-3512 were printed in vertical (Nos. 3503-3507) or horizontal se-tenant strips within their sheets.

No. 3512B

No. 3512D

**1995, Oct. 20** — ***Rouletted x Imperf***

**Stampcards**

**Self-Adhesive**

| | | |
|---|---|---|
| **3512B** black, *gold*, card of 8 | 6.00 | 6.00 |
| *a.* 20ch single stamp | .75 | .75 |
| **3512D** card of 2 | 50.00 | 50.00 |
| *e.* 20ch red, *gold* | — | — |
| *f.* 17.80w On 20ch, red, *gold* | — | — |

50th anniversary of the first North Korean stamps.

Kim Hyong Gwon, Kim Il Sung's Uncle, 90th Birth Anniv. — A1572

**1995, Nov. 4** — ***Perf. 12½x12***

| | | |
|---|---|---|
| **3513** A1572 1w multicolored | 2.75 | 1.50 |

New Year — A1573

Rodents: a, 20ch, Guinea pig. b, 20ch, Squirrel. 30ch, White mouse.

**1996, Jan. 1** — ***Perf. 11½***

| | | |
|---|---|---|
| **3514** A1573 Strip of 3, #a.-c. | 3.00 | .75 |

No. 3514 was issued in sheetlets of eight stamps, two each Nos. 3514a-3514b and four No. 3514c, plus one center label picturing an idyllic landscape, inscribed "1996."

League of Socialist Working Youth, 50th Anniv. — A1574

**1996, Jan. 17**

| | | |
|---|---|---|
| **3517** A1574 10ch multicolored | .50 | .25 |

Reconstruction of Tomb of King Wanggon of Koryo — A1575

Designs: 30ch, Restoration monument, horiz. 40ch, Entrance gate to royal cemetery. 50ch, King Wanggon's tomb, horiz.

**1996, Jan. 30**

| | | |
|---|---|---|
| **3518-3520** A1575 Set of 3 | 3.50 | 1.00 |

Teng Li-Chuang (Chinese Singer) — A1576

**1996, Feb. 1** — ***Perf. 13¼***

| | | |
|---|---|---|
| **3521** A1576 40ch multicolored | 1.50 | .50 |

3rd Asian Winter Games, Harbin, China — A1577

Designs, each 30ch: a, Kim Song Sun, Korean speed skater. b, Ye Qiaobo, Chinese sprint skater.

**1996, Feb 4** — ***Perf. 11½***

| | | |
|---|---|---|
| **3522** A1577 Sheet of 2, #a.-b. | 3.50 | .50 |

See No. 3556.

A1578

Kim Jong Il, 54th Birthday — A1579

10ch, Jong Il Peak and *Kimjongilia.*
80ch, Kim Jong Il and soldiers.

**1996, Feb. 16**

| | | |
|---|---|---|
| **3523** A1578 10ch multicolored | .50 | .25 |

**Souvenir Sheet**

***Perf. 13¼***

| | | |
|---|---|---|
| **3524** A1579 80ch multicolored | 2.75 | .75 |

5th Paektusan Prize International Figure Skating Championship. A1580

Various pairs figure skaters: 10ch, 20ch, 30ch.
50ch, Women's individual skating.

**1996, Feb. 17** — ***Perf. 11½***

| | | |
|---|---|---|
| **3525-3527** A1580 Set of 3 | 2.00 | .60 |
| *3527a* Booklet pane of 4, #3525-3527, 3528a | 5.50 | — |
| Complete booklet, #3527a | 6.00 | |

**Souvenir Sheet**

| | | |
|---|---|---|
| **3528** Sheet of 4 | 3.50 | 1.00 |
| *a.* A1580 50ch multi | 3.25 | |

Folk Tales — A1581

Screen painting by Ryu Suk: 8 stamps in continuous design, within 206mmx84mm skeetlet.

**1996, Mar. 2**

| | | |
|---|---|---|
| **3529** Sheet of 8 | 5.00 | 2.25 |
| *a.-h.* A1581 any single | .60 | .25 |

Agrarian Reform Law, 50th Anniv. A1582

**1996, Mar. 5**

| | | |
|---|---|---|
| **3530** A1582 10ch multicolored | .50 | .25 |

No. 3530 was issued in sheetlets of six, containing 5 No. 3530 and a label depicting a music score, *Song of Plowing.*

First North Korean Stamps, 50th Anniv. — A1583

**1996, Mar. 12**

| | | |
|---|---|---|
| **3531** A1583 1w multicolored | 3.25 | .85 |

Yangzhou, China — A1584

Taihou Lake, China — A1585

**1996, Mar. 20**

**3532** A1584 50ch multicolored 1.75 .50
**3533** A1585 50ch multicolored 1.75 .50

Chinese Imperial Post, Centennial.

A1586

Kim Il Sung, 83rd Birthday — A1587

Designs: 10ch, Birthplace, Mangyondae. 1w, Portrait of Kim Il Sung.

**1996, Apr. 15**

**3534** A1586 10ch multicolored .50 .25

**Souvenir Sheet**

**3535** A1587 1w multicolored 3.25 .85

China '96 Int'l Stamp Exhib., Beijing — A1588

Designs: No. 3536, Seacoast gateway. No. 3537, Haiyin Pool.
60ch. Pantuo Stone.

**1996, Apr. 22** ***Perf. 13½***

**3536-3537** A1588 10ch Set of 2 .50 .25

**Souvenir Sheet**

***Perf. 11½***

**3538** A1588 60ch multicolored 1.60 .60

Folk Games A1589

Designs: 20ch, Kicking stone handmill. 40ch, Shuttlecock. 50ch, Sledding.

**1996, May 2**

**3539-3541** A1589 Set of 3 3.50 1.00
*3539a-3541a* Set of 3 sheets of 2 + label 7.00 7.00

Assoc. for the Restoration of the Fatherland, 60th Anniv. — A1590

**1996, May 5**

**3542** A1590 10ch multicolored .50 .25
*a.* Sheet of 5 #3542 + label 2.50 1.50

Ri Po Ik — A1591

**1996, May 31** ***Perf. 13½***

**3543** A1591 1w multicolored 3.00 .80

Ri Po Ik, Kim Il Sung's grandmother, 125th birth anniv.

Polar Animals — A1592

Designs, 50ch: No. 3544a, Arctic fox. No. 3544b, Polar bear. No. 3545a, Emperor penguins. No. 3546b, Leopard seals.

**1996, June 2** ***Perf. 11½***

**3544-3545** A1592 Set of 2 sheets 6.50 4.00

A1593

Korea Children's Union, 50th Anniv. — A1594

Designs: 10ch, Boy saluting.
1w, Painting of Kim Il Sung with Children's Union members, *There's Nothing to Envy in the World.*

**1996, June 6**

**3546** A1593 10ch multicolored .50 .25

**Souvenir Sheet**

***Perf. 11½x12***

**3547** A1594 1w multicolored 3.00 .85

Locomotives A1595

Designs, all 50ch: No. 3548, Steam locomotive, facing left. No. 3549, Electric locomotive, facing right. No. 3550, Steam locomotive, facing right. No. 3551, Electric locomotive, facing left.

**1996, June 6** ***Perf. 11½***

**3548-3551** A1595 Set of 4 3.50 1.25

Capex '96 World Philatelic Exhibition. For surcharge, see No. 4551.

Kim Chol Ju, Kim Il Sung's Brother, 80th Birth Anniv. — A1596

**1996, June 12** ***Perf. 13¼***

**3552** A1596 1.50w multicolored 4.25 2.00

Open Book — A1597

**1996, June 15** ***Perf. 13½***

**3553** A1597 40ch multicolored 1.10 .50

760th anniversary of publication of the *Complete Collection of Buddhist Scriptures Printed from 80,000 Wooden Blocks.*

Labor Law, 50th Anniv. A1598

**1996, June 24** ***Perf. 11½***

**3554** A1598 50ch multicolored .50 .40

Seasonal Birds — A1599

Designs: 10ch, Broad-billed roller. 40ch, Tricolor flycatcher. 50ch, Cuckoo.

**1996, July 5**

**3555** A1599 Sheet of 3, #a.-c. 4.00 2.00

See No. 3569.

3rd Asian Winter Games, Harbin, China (2nd issue) — A1600

Design same as No. 3522, but with a new 30ch value picturing Ye Qiaobo replacing No, 3522b

**1996, July 5**

**3556** A1600 Sheet of 2 1.75 1.00
*a.* 30ch multi .85 .40

Kumsusan Memorial Palace — A1601

Outdoor Crowd, Statue of Kim Il Sung — A1602

Hymn, *The Leader will be with us forever* — A1603

Statue of Kim Il Sung in hall of the Kumsusan Memorial Palace — A1604

**1996, July 8** ***Perf. 12***
**3557** A1601 10ch multicolored .25 .25

**Souvenir Sheets**

***Perf. 13¼, 12 (#3558)***

**3558** A1602 1w multicolored 3.00 1.00
**3559** A1603 1w multicolored 3.00 1.00
**3560** A1604 1w multicolored 3.00 1.00

Kim Il Sung, 2nd Death Anniv.

A1605

Designs, both 10ch: No. 3561, Kim Il Sung meeting Mao Zedong of China, 1954. No. 3562, Kim Il Sung meeting Jiang Zemin of China, 1991.
80ch, Kim shaking hands with Deng Xiaoping of China, horiz.

**1996, July 11** ***Perf. 11½***
**3561-3562** A1605 Set of 2 .50 .25

**Souvenir Sheet**

**3563** A1605 80ch multicolored 2.25 1.00

26th Olympic Games, Atlanta — A1606

Designs, each 50ch: No. 3564, Soccer. No. 3565, Tennis. No. 3566, Hammer throw. No. 3567, Baseball.

**1996, July 19** ***Perf. 12¼***
**3564-3567** A1606 Set of 4 5.50 2.00

Sexual Equality Law, 50th Anniv. — A1607

**1996, July 30** ***Perf. 11½***
**3568** A1607 10ch multicolored .25 .25

**Seasonal Bird Type**

Designs: 10ch, Crested shelduck. 40ch, Demoiselle crane. 50ch, White swan.

**1996, Aug. 5**
**3569** A1600 Sheet of 3, #a.-c. 2.75 1.25

Industrial Nationalization, 50th Anniv. — A1608

**1996, Aug. 10** ***Perf. 11½***
**3570** A1608 50ch multicolored .90 .40

UNICEF, 50th Anniv. — A1609

Designs: 10ch, Boy with ball, net. 20ch, Boy playing with building blocks. 50ch, Boy eating meal, holding watermelon slice. 60ch, Girl playing accordion.

**1996, Aug. 20**
**3571-3574** A1609 Set of 4 2.75 1.10

Nos. 3571-3574 were issued in sheets of four, one containing 2 No. 3571, 1 No. 3574 and a label, the other containing 2 No. 3572, 1 No. 3573 and a different label.

1st Asian Gymnastics Championship, Changsha, China — A1610

No. 3575: a, Pae Kil Su (N. Korea), men's pommel. b, Chen Cui Ting (China), rings. c, Li Jing (China). d, Kim Kwang Suk (N. Korea), asymmetrical bars.

**1996, Sept. 24**
**3575** A1610 15ch Sheet of 4, #a-d, + 2 labels 1.50 .60

Kim Il Sung University, 50th Anniv. A1611

**1996, Oct. 1**
**3579** A1611 10ch multicolored .50 .25

Tiger — A1612

Designs, 50ch: No. 3580, Tiger. No. 3581, Royal spoonbill.
80ch: Stylized dove/hand nurturing sapling, growing out of planet Earth.

**1996, Oct. 13**
**3580-3581** A1612 Set of 2 3.00 .70

**Souvenir Sheet**

**3582** A1612 80ch multicolored 6.50 1.50

Nos. 3580-3581 were each printed in sheets of four, containing three stamps and a label.

Down-with-Imperialism Union, 70th Anniv. — A1613

**1996, Oct. 17**
**3583** A1613 10ch multicolored .25 .25

A1614

Designs: a, 30ch Huang Ji Gwang. b, 10ch, Score of theme song of film *Red Mountain Ridge*. c, 30ch Huang Ji Gwang heroically dying in battle.

**1996, Oct. 25**
**3584** A1614 Sheet of 3, #a.-c. 2.00 1.00

Hwang Ji Gwang, Chinese Volunteer, hero of Korean War, 44th death anniiv.

History of the Earth — A1615

Each 50ch: a, Earth 7.5 billion years ago. b, 4.5-5 billion years ago. c, 450 million-4.5 billion years ago. d, 100-450 million years ago. e, 100 million years ago to the present.

**1996, Nov. 1** ***Perf. 13½***
**3585** A1615 Sheet of 5, #a.-e. 8.00 4.00

Freshwater Fish A1616

Designs, 20ch: No. 3586, Japanese eel. No. 3587, Menada gray mullet.
80ch, Silver carp.

**1996, Nov. 20** ***Perf. 11½***
**3586-3587** A1616 Set of 2 1.50 .35

**Souvenir Sheet**

**3588** A1616 80ch multicolored 3.00 .75

Kim Jong Il' Appointment as Supreme Commander of the People's Army, 5th Anniv. — A1617

**1996, Dec. 24** ***Perf. 12***
**3589** A1617 20ch multicolored .60 .25

New Year — Year of the Ox — A1618

Designs, 70ch: No. 3590, *Ox Driver*, by Kim Tu Ryang. No. 3591, Bronze ritual plate decorated with a tiger and two bulls. No. 3592, Cowboy and bull. No. 3593, Cowboy playing flute, sitting on bull.
80ch, *Kosong People's Support to the Front.*

**1997, Jan. 1** ***Perf. 11¾***
**3590-3593** A1618 Set of 4 8.00 2.00
*3591a, 3593a* Set of 2 sheets 8.00 2.00

**Souvenir Sheet**

**3594** A1618 80ch multicolored 3.00 .75

No. 3591a contains Nos. 3590 and 3591, with a central label depicting a bull's head surrounded by zodiacal signs. No. 3593a contains Nos. 3592 and 3593, with the same label.

*Flowers and Butterflies*, by Nam Kye-u (1811-88) — A1619

Designs, each 50ch: a, Three butterflies, flower. b, One small butterfly, flower. c, Large butterfly, leaves.

**1997, Jan. 5** ***Perf. 12¼x11¾***
**3595** A1619 Sheetlet of 3, #a.-c. 4.50 1.00
*d.* Booklet pane of 6, 2 each #3595a-3595b 9.00 —
Complete booklet, #3595d 9.00

Paintings of Cats and Dogs — A1620

Designs, 50ch: No. 3598, Puppy in basket, touching noses with kitten. No. 3599, Two dogs in basket, kitten.
No. 3600: a, Cat in basket, with dog and skein of yarn alongside. b, Kitten in basket with fruit and flowers, puppy alongside.

**1997, Jan. 25** ***Perf. 11¾x12¼***
**3598-3599** A1620 Set of 2 3.25 1.00

**Sheets of 4**

**3600** Sheet of 4, #3598, 3600b, 2 #3600a 3.50 1.50
*a.* A1620 50ch multicolored 1.50
*b.* A1620 50ch multicolored 1.50
**3601** Sheet of 4, #3599, #3600a, 2 #3600b 3.50 1.50

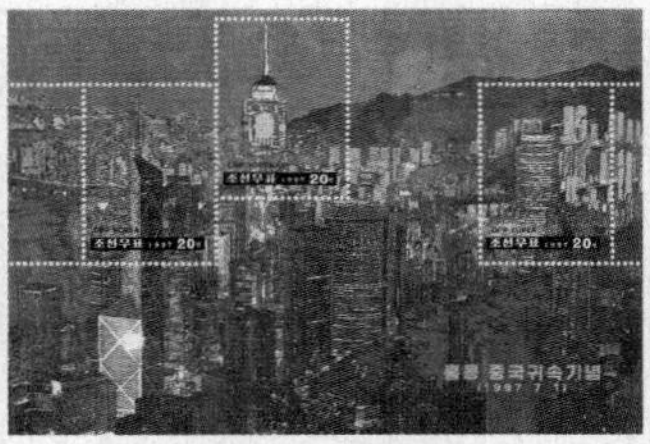

Return of Hong Kong to China — A1621

Hong Kong nightscape, each 20ch: a, Skyscraper with double antennae. b, Skyscraper with single spire. c, Round skyscraper, high-rise apartment buildings.

**1997, Feb. 1** ***Perf. 13½***

**3602** A1621 Sheet of 3, #a.-c. 2.50 .65

A1622

Kim Jong Il, 55th Birthday — A1623

Designs: 10ch, Birthplace, Mt. Paekdu.

No. 3604, Kim Il Sung and Kim Jong Il with farm machine. No. 3605, Kim Jong Il inspecting a Korean People's Army unit.

**1997, Feb. 16** ***Perf. 12***

**3603** A1622 10ch multicolored .50 .25

**Souvenir Sheets**

**3604-3605** A1623 1w Set of 2 5.50 1.75

6th Paektusan Prize Int'l Figure Skating Championships, Pyongyang — A1624

Pairs skating, different routines, 50ch: No. 3606, pale reddish brown. No. 3607, blue. No. 3608, green.

**1997, Feb. 17** ***Perf. 11½***

| | | | |
|---|---|---|---|
| **3606-3608** | A1624 Set of 3 | 4.00 | 1.00 |
| *3607a* | Sheet of 4, 2 ea #3606, 3607 | 5.50 | 1.50 |
| *3608a* | Booklet pane of 6, 2 ea. #3606-3608 | 8.00 | — |
| | Complete booklet, #3608a | 8.50 | |
| *3608b* | Sheet of 4, 2 ea #3607, 3608 | 5.50 | 1.50 |

Kye Sun Hui, Women's Judo Gold Medalist, 1996 Summer Olympic Games, Atlanta — A1625

**1997, Feb. 20**

| | | | |
|---|---|---|---|
| **3611** | A1625 80ch multicolored | 2.50 | .60 |
| *3611a* | Booklet pane of 5 #3611 | — | — |
| | Complete booklet, #3611a | — | |

Choe Un A — A1626

**1997, Feb. 25**

| | | | |
|---|---|---|---|
| **3612** | A1626 80ch multicolored | 3.00 | .60 |
| *a.* | Booklet pane of 5 | | |
| | Complete booklet, #3612a | | |

Issued to honor Choe Un A, a seven-year-old entrant in the World Go Championships.

Apricots — A1627

Various types of apricots, 50ch: No. 3613, Prunus ansu. No. 3614, Prunus mandshurica. No. 3615, Prunus armeniaca. No. 3616, Prunus sibirica.

**1997, Mar. 4** ***Perf. 11¼***

| | | | |
|---|---|---|---|
| **3613-3616** | A1627 Set of 4 | 6.00 | 1.50 |
| *3613a* | Sheet of 8, 2 ea#3613-3614 | 12.00 | 3.00 |

Foundation of Korean National Assoc., 80th Anniv. — A1628

**1997, Mar. 23** ***Perf. 12¼***

| | | | |
|---|---|---|---|
| **3617** | A1628 10ch lt brn & dk grn | .50 | .25 |
| *a.* | Sheet of 8 | 4.00 | 1.00 |

A1629

Reforestation Day, 50th Anniv. — A1630

Designs: 10ch, Pine sapling.

No. 3619, Kim Il Sung planting sapling on Munsu Hill.

**1997, Apr. 6** ***Perf. 11½***

| | | | |
|---|---|---|---|
| **3618** | A1629 10ch multicolored | .50 | .25 |
| | Complete booklet, 8 #3618 | | |

**Souvenir Sheet**

***Perf. 13¼***

**3619** A1630 1w multicolored 3.00 .90

A1631

A1632

Kim Il Sung, 85th Birth Anniv. — A1633

Designs: 10ch, Kim's birthplace, Mangyongdae. 20ch, Sliding rock, horiz. 40ch, Warship Rock, horiz.

Each 1w: No. 3623, Painting of Kim among crowd symbolic of the Korean people. No. 3624, Kim in business suit, surrounded by flowers.

**1997, Apr. 15** ***Perf. 12¼***

**3620-3622** A1631 Set of 3 2.00 .55

**Souvenir Sheets**

***Perf. 13¼ (#3623), 11¾x12¼ (#3624)***

| | | | |
|---|---|---|---|
| **3623** | A1632 1w multicolored | 2.75 | .90 |
| **3624** | A1633 1w multicolored | 2.75 | .90 |

A1634

Korean People's Army, 65th Anniv. — A1635

Designs: 10ch, KPA cap badge, rockets and jet fighters.

1w, Kim Il Sung and Kim Jong Il at military review.

**1997, Apr. 25** ***Perf. 11½***

**3625** A1634 10ch multicolored .50 .25

**Souvenir Sheet**

***Perf. 12¼x11¾***

**3626** A1635 1w multicolored 3.00 .90

A1636

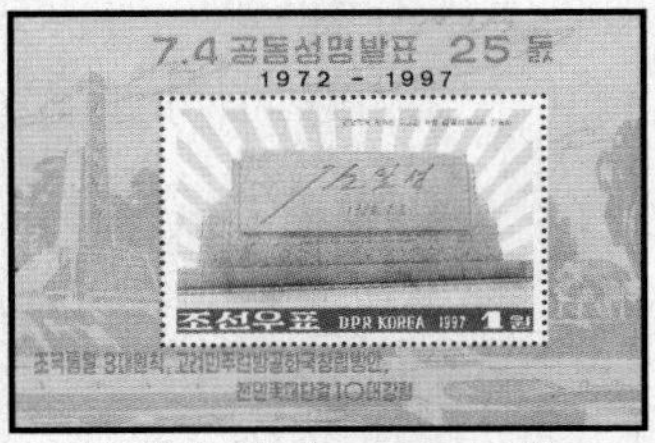

North-South Agreement, 25th Anniv. — A1637

Designs: 10ch, Map of Korea.

1w, Monument to Kim Il Sung's Autograph, Phanmunjom.

**1997, May 4** ***Perf. 11½***

**3627** A1636 10ch multicolored 1.00 .25

**Souvenir Sheet**

***Perf. 12x11½***

**3628** A1637 1w multicolored 4.00 .90

A1638

Each 10ch: No. 3629, Tower of Juche Idea, flag. No. 3630, Man with flag. No. 3631, Soldier, miner, farmer, scientist.

**1997, May 25** ***Perf. 12¼x12***
**3629-3631** A1638 Set of 3 .90 .40

Int'l Friendship Exhib., Myohyang Mountains — A1639

Each 70ch: No. 3632, Exhibition Center. No. 3633, Statue of Kim Il Sung in exhibition entrance hall. No. 3634, Ivory sculpture *Native House in Mangyongdae.* No. 3635, Stuffed crocodile holding wooden cups, with ashtray.

**1997, May 30** ***Perf. 11¾***
**3632-3635** A1639 Set of 4 sheets 7.50 5.00

Battle of Poconbo, 60th Anniv. — A1640

**1997, June 4** ***Perf. 11½***
**3636** A1640 40ch multicolored 1.25 .35
*a.* Sheet of 6 7.50 7.50
*b.* Booklet pane of 6 #3636 7.50 —
Complete booklet, #3636b 8.00

No. 3636b contains six stamps in a horizontal strip, within decorative selvage.

Rice Transplantation, Mirin Plain, 50th Anniv. — A1641

Each 1w: No. 3637, Kim Il Sung transplanting rice. No. 3638, Kim Il Sung inspecting a rice-transplanting machine.

**1997, June 7** ***Perf. 13¼***
**3637-3638** A1641 Set of 2 sheets 5.75 1.75

A1642

Return of Hong Kong to China — A1643

No. 3639, each 20ch: a, Signing the Nanjing Treaty, 1842. b, Signing the China-Britain Joint Statement, 1984. c, Deng Xiaoping and Margaret Thatcher. d, Jiang Zenin and Tong Jianhua.
97ch, Deng Xiaoping.

**1997, July 1** ***Perf. 11¾***
**3639** A1642 Sheet of 4, #a.-d. 3.00 .75

**Souvenir Sheet**
***Perf. 13¼***
**3640** A1643 97ch multicolored 3.00 1.00

Fossils — A1644

Designs: 50ch, Redlichia chinensis. 1w, Ptychoparia coreanica.

**1997, July 5** ***Perf. 11½***
**3641** A1644 Pair, #a.-b. 5.00 1.25
*c.* Booklet pane, 5 #3641a 8.75 —
Complete booklet #3641c 9.00
*d.* Booklet pane, 5 #3641b 17.50 —
Complete booklet #3641d 18.00

Nos. 3641c-3641d each contain horizontal strips of five stamps.

Kim Il Sung, 3rd Death Anniv. A1645

Each 50ch, Portrait of Kim Il Sung and: No. 3643, Kim speaking at party conference, 1985. No. 3644, Kim inspecting Kim Chaek Ironworks, 1985. No. 3645, Kim at Songsin Cooperative Farm, Sadong District, 1993. No. 3646, Kim being cheered by performing artists, 1986. No. 3647, Kim visiting Jonchon Factory, Jagang Province, 1991. No. 3648, Kim receiving bouquet from soldiers.

**1997, July 8** ***Perf. 11¾x12***
**3643-3648** A1645 Set of 6 9.00 2.25
*3645a* Sheet of 3, #3643-3645 4.50 2.00
*3648a* Sheet of 3, #3646-3648 4.50 2.00

Folk Games A1646

Designs: 30ch, Blindman's Bluff. 60ch, Jackstones. 70ch, Arm wrestling.

**1997, July 26** ***Perf. 11½***
**3649-3651** A1646 Set of 3 4.50 1.25
*3649a-3651a* Set of 3 sheets 9.00 4.00
*3651b* Booklet pane of 6, 2 ea. #3649-3651 9.00 —
Complete booklet, #3651b 9.50

Nos. 3649a-3651a each contain 2 stamps + a central label.
No. 3281b contains two each of Nos. 3649-3651, printed in a se-tenant block (3x2), with decorative selvage.

Traditional Korean Women's Clothing — A1647

Designs: 10ch, Spring costume. 40ch, Summer. 50ch, Autumn. 60ch, Winter.

**1997, Aug. 10**
**3652-3655** A1647 Set of 4 4.50 2.00
*3652a-3654a* Set of 3 sheets 18.00 12.00

No. 3652a contains 2 each Nos. 3652-3653; No. 3653a contains 2 each Nos. 3653-3654; No. 3654a contains 2 each Nos. 3654-3655.

Chongryu Bridge A1648

Both 50ch: No. 3656, Night view of Chongryu Bridge. No. 3657, Panoramic view.

**1997, Aug. 25**
**3656-3657** A1648 Set of 2 3.00 1.00
*3657a* Sheet of 2, #3656-3657 3.50 1.50
*3657b* Booklet pane of 6, 3 ea. #3656-3657 9.00 —
Complete booklet, #3657b 9.50

A1649

Juche Era and Sun Day, 85th Anniv. — A1650

10ch, Sun, magnolias, banner, balloons.
Each 1w: No. 3659, Kim Il Sung, slogan, doves. No. 3660, Kim, birthplace Mongyangdae. No. 3661, Kim, Lake Chon, Mt. Paekdu. No. 3662, Kim, Kumsusan Memorial Palace.

**1997, Sept. 3** ***Perf. 13¼***
**3658** A1649 10ch multicolored .50 .25

**Souvenir Sheets**
**3659-3662** A1650 Set of 4 sheets 11.00 6.00

*Theses on Socialist Education, 20th Anniv. of Publication* A1651

**1997, Sept. 5** ***Perf. 11½***
**3663** A1651 10ch multicolored .50 .25

No. 3663 was issued in sheetlets of 6.

Air Koryo — A1652

Sheets of 2 stamps and central label: 20ch, TU-134. 30ch, TU-154. 50ch, IL-62.

**1997, Sept. 14** ***Perf. 13¼***
**3664-3666** A1652 Set of 3 sheets 5.00 1.50
*3665a* Complete booklet, pane of 8, 4 ea. #3664, 3666 7.00
*3666a* Complete booklet, pane of 8, 4 ea. #3665, 3666 8.00

Korean Membership in World Tourism Org., 10th Anniv. — A1653

Views of Mt. Chilbo, each 50ch: No. 3667, Kim Chol Ung. No. 3668, Rojok Beach. No. 3669, Chonbul Peak.

**1997, Sept. 22** ***Perf. 12***
**3667-3669** A1653 Set of 3 4.50 1.25
*3669a* Sheet, #3667-3669 + label 5.00 1.40

Kumgang Mountains A1654

Each 50ch: No. 3670, Kumgang Gate. No. 3671, Podok Hermitage.

**1997, Oct. 2**

**3670-3671** A1654 Set of 2 3.00 .75
*3670a* Booklet pane of 5 #3670 7.50 —
Complete booklet, #3670a 8.00
*3671a* Sheet of 6, 3 each #3670-3671 10.00 4.00
*3671b* Booklet pane of 5 #3671 7.50 —
Complete booklet, #3671b 8.00

Mangyongdae Revolutionary School, 50th Anniv. — A1655

**1997, Oct. 12** ***Perf. 11½***

**3672** A1655 40ch multicolored 1.25 .30
*a.* Booklet pane of 6 7.50 —
Complete booklet, #3672a 8.00

Gift Animals A1656

Animals presented to Kim Il Sung as gifts from foreign governments: 20ch, Lion (from Ethiopia, 1987). 30ch, Jaguar (Japan, 1992). 50ch, Barbary sheep (Czechoslovakia, 1992). 80ch, Scarlet macaw (Austria, 1979).

**1997, Oct. 15**

**3673-3676** A1656 Set of 4 5.50 1.25
*3673a* Sheet of 8, 2 each #3673-3676 11.00 5.00
*3673b* Booklet pane of 8, 2ea. #3673-3676 11.00 —
Complete booklet, #3673b 12.00

For surcharges, see No. 4554-4555.

Qu Shao Yun, Chinese Volunteer Hero — A1657

Designs: a, 30ch, Bust of Qu Shao Yun. b, 10ch, Monument to Qu Shao Yun. c, 30ch, Qu Shao Yun burning to death in battle.

**1997, Oct. 18**

**3677** A1657 Sheet of 3, #a.-c. 2.25 .75

Sports — A1658

Designs: No. 3678, 50ch, Bowling. No. 3679, 50ch, Fencing. No. 3680, 50chGolf.

**1997, Nov. 10** ***Perf. 13¼***

**3678-3680** A1658 Set of 3 5.25 1.25
*3680a* Sheet, 2 each #3678-3680 + 2 labels 11.00 5.00

For surcharge, see No. 4574.

Snails — A1659

Each 50ch: a, Two snails copulating. b, Snail laying eggs. c, Snail.

**1997, Nov. 15** ***Perf. 12¼***

**3681** A1659 Strip of 3, #a.-c. 4.75 2.00
*d.* Sheet of 6, 2 each #3681a-3681c 9.50 4.00
*e.* Booklet pane of 6, 2 ea. #3681a-3681c 9.50 —
Complete booklet, #3681e 10.00

Shanghai Int'l Stamp & Coin Exhib. — A1660

**1997, Nov. 19** ***Perf. 11½***

**3684** A1660 Sheet of 2, #a.-b. 2.50 1.00
*a.* 30ch multicolored 1.00 .30
*b.* 50ch multicolored 1.50 .60

New Year — Year of the Tiger
A1661 A1662

Designs: 10ch, "Juche 87," pine boughs, temple. 50ch (No. 3686), Tiger in rocket. 50ch (No. 3687), Tiger in ship. 80ch, Tiger in train.

***Perf. 13¼, 11½ (#3686-3687)***

**1997, Dec. 15**

**3685** A1661 10ch multicolored .25 .25
**3686** A1662 50ch multicolored .90 .25
**3687** A1662 50ch multicolored .90 .25
*a.* Sheet of 4, 1 ea #3686-#3687, 2 #3688a 4.50 2.00
*Nos. 3685-3687 (3)* 2.05 .75

**Souvenir Sheet**

**3688** A1662 80ch multicolored 2.00 .75
*a.* Perf. 11½ — —
*b.* Booklet pane of 8, 2 each #3686-3687, 4 #3688a — —
Complete booklet, #3688b —

Complete booklet sold for 5.40w.

Birthplace, Hoeryong A1663

Kim Jong Suk, 80th Birth Anniv. — A1664

**1997, Dec. 24** ***Perf. 13¼***

**3689** A1663 10ch multicolored .50 .25

**Souvenir Sheet**

**3690** A1664 1w multicolored 3.00 .75

Winter Olympic Games, Nagano, Japan — A1665

Designs: 20ch, Skiing. 40ch, Speed skating.

**1998, Feb. 7** ***Perf. 11½***

**3691-3692** A1665 Set of 2 1.25 .65
*3692a* Sheet of 4, 2 ea #3691-#3692 2.50 1.25
*3692b* Booklet pane of 8, 4 ea. #3691-3692 5.00 —
Complete booklet, #3692b 5.50

A1666

Kim Jong Il, 56th Birthday — A1667

Designs: 10ch, Birth date ("2.16"). 3w, Birthplace, log cabin on Mt. Paekdu.

**1998, Feb. 16**

**3693** A1666 10ch multicolored .50 .25

**Souvenir Sheet**

**3694** A1667 3w multicolored 4.50 2.00

A1668

Paintings of Mt. Paekdu Wildlife — A1669

Designs, 50ch: No. 3695, Korean tigers. No. 3696, White crane.

No. 3697, 50ch: a, Bears. b, Racoons.

**1998, Mar. 6** ***Perf. 11¾x12***

**3695-3696** A1668 Set of 2 2.00 1.00
*3696a* Booklet pane of 8, 2 ea. #3695-3696, 3697a-3697b 8.00 —
Complete booklet, #3696a 8.50

**Souvenir Sheet**

**3697** A1669 Sheet of 4, #3695-3696, 3697a-3697b 4.00 2.00
*a.* A1668 50ch multicolored 1.00 .50
*b.* A1668 50ch multicolored 1.00 .50

Kim Il Sung's 1000-ri Journey, 75th Anniv. A1670

**1998, Mar. 16** ***Perf. 11½***

**3698** A1670 10ch multicolored .50 .25
*a.* Sheet of 10 5.00 1.50

Appt. of Kim Jong Il as Chairman of the Nat'l Defense Commission, 5th Anniv. A1671

**1998, Apr. 9**

**3699** A1671 10ch multicolored .50 .25

A1672

Kim Il Sung, 86th Birth Anniv. — A1673

Designs: 10ch, Birthplace, flags, flowers.

Circular stamps, each 80ch, within 84x155mm sheetlets, depicting portraits of Kim Il Sung at different stages in his life: #3701, As child. #3702, As middle school student. #3703, As young revolutionary. #3704, In suit and tie, ca. 1946. #3705, In military uniform during Korean War. #3706, As middle-aged man, in uniform. #3707, As middle-aged man, in suit and tie. #3708, As old man in suit and tie.

**1998, Apr. 15**

**3700** A1672 10ch multicolored .50 .25

**Souvenir Sheets**

**3701-3708** A1673 Set of 8 9.00 4.00

North-South Joint Conference, 50th Anniv. — A1674

**1998, Apr. 21** ***Perf. 13¼***

**3709** A1674 10ch multicolored .50 .25

16th World Cup Soccer Championship, France — A1675

Designs: 30ch, Dribbling. 50ch, Kicking.

**1998, May 5** ***Perf. 11½***

**3710-3711** A1675 Set of 2 1.60 .80

*3711a* Sheet of 6, 2 ea #3710-#3711, #3712 6.00 3.00

*3711b* Booklet pane of 10, 5 ea. #3710-3711 8.00 —

Complete booklet, #3711b 8.50

**Souvenir Sheet**

**3712** A1675 80ch multicolored 1.60 .80

A single stamp like that in No. 3712 is included in No. 3711a.

A1676

Int'l Friendship Art Exhib., Mt. Myohyang — A1677

Designs, 1w: No. 3713, *Diagram of Automatic Space Station* (USSR). No. 3714, Ceramic flower vase (Egypt). No. 3715, *Crane* (USA).

1w, Kim Il Sung receiving a gift from Deng Xiaoping.

**1998, May 20** ***Perf. 11¾***

**3713-3715** A1676 Set of 3 4.50 2.25

*3714a* Sheet of 2, #3713 & #3714 2.75 1.40

*3715a* Sheet of 2, #3713 & #3715 2.75 1.40

**Souvenir Sheet**

***Perf. 13¼***

**3716** A1677 1w multicolored 2.00 1.00

A1678

Korean Art Gallery — A1679

Designs: 60ch, *A Countryside in May.* 1.40w, *Dance.*

3w, *Heart-to-heart Talk with a Peasant.*

**1998, May 20**

**3717-3718** A1678 Set of 2 3.00 1.50

**Souvenir Sheet**

**3719** A1679 3w multicolored 4.50 2.25

Vegetables — A1680

Designs: 10ch, Cabbage. 40ch, Radish. 50ch, Green onion. 60ch, Cucumber. 70ch, Pumpkin. 80ch, Carrot. 90ch, Garlic. 1w, Red pepper.

**1998, May 20** ***Perf. 13¼***

**3720** A1680 Sheet of 8, #a.-h. 9.00 4.50

A1681

Int'l Year of the Ocean — A1682

Designs: 10ch, Hydro-Meteorological Headquarters building, ship, oceanographic floating balloons, dolphins, emblem. 80ch, Woman holding child, yachts, emblem.

5w, Vasco da Gama (1460-1524), Portuguese explorer.

**1998, May 22**

**3730-3731** A1681 Set of 2 2.00 .90

*3731a* Sheet of 4, 2 ea. #3730-3731 2.00 .90

**Souvenir Sheet**

**3732** A1682 5w multicolored 7.50 3.75

A1683

Korean Central History Museum, Pyongyang — A1684

Designs: 10ch, Stone Age tool. 2.50w, Fossil monkey skull.

4w, Kim Il Sung visiting the museum.

**1998, June 15**

**3733-3734** A1683 Set of 2 4.00 2.00

**Souvenir Sheet**

**3735** A1684 4w multicolored 6.00 3.00

A1685

Dr. Ri Sung Gi (1905-96), Inventor of Vinalon — A1686

Designs: 40ch, Dr. Ri Sung Gi and diagram of vinalon nuclear structure.

80ch, Gi working in laboratory.

**1998, June 15** ***Perf. 11½***

**3736** A1685 40ch multicolored .60 .25

*a.* Booklet pane of 10

Complete booklet, #3736a

**Souvenir Sheet**

**3737** A1686 80ch multicolored 1.60 1.00

*Squirrels and Hedgehogs* Cartoon — A1687

Designs: 20ch, Squirrel and Commander of Hedgehog Unit. 30ch, Commander of Hedgehog Unit receiving invitation to banquet celebrating bumper crop. 60ch, Weasel Commander and mouse. 1.20w, Bear falling dead-drunk. 2w, Weasel Commander and mice invading the flower village. 2.50w, Hedgehog scout saving the squirrel.

**1998, June 15**

**3738-3743** A1687 Set of 6 12.00 6.00

*3743a* Sheet of 6, #3737-3743 12.00 6.00

A1688

Return of Hong Kong to China, 1st Anniv. — A1689

Designs, 10w: No. 3744, Deng Xiaoping (1904-97), Chinese Prime Minister. No. 3745, Mao Zedong. No. 3746, Kim Il Sung.

No. 3747, Deng Xiaoping, Mao Zedong and Kim Il Sung, horiz.

**1998, July 1**

**Embossed with gold foil application**

**3744-3746** A1688 Set of 3 30.00 10.00

**Souvenir Sheet**

**3747** A1689 10w Gold & multi 10.00 10.00

Young Wild Mammals A1690

Designs: 10ch, Tiger cub. 50ch, Donkey foal. 1.60w, Elephant. 2w, Lion cubs.

**1998, July 10** ***Perf. 11½***

**3748-3751** A1690 Set of 4 3.00 1.50
*3751a* Booklet pane of 8, 2 each #3748-3751 — —
Complete booklet, #3751a —

Complete booklet sold for 8.60w.

A1691

A1692

Korean War "Victory," 45th Anniv. — A1693

Designs: 45ch, War monument, flag.
No. 3753, Kim Il Sung inspecting the front. No. 3754, Gaz-67 jeep and map of Korea, showing Kim's inspection route.

**1998, July 27** ***Perf. 13¼***

**3752** A1691 45ch multicolored .25 .25

**Souvenir Sheets**

**3753** A1692 2w multicolored 2.00 1.00
**3754** A1693 2w multicolored 2.00 1.00

Embroidery A1694

Designs: 10ch, *White Herons in Forest.* 40ch, *Carp.* 1.20w, *Hollyhock.* 1.50w, *Cockscomb.*
4w, *Pine and Cranes.*

**1998, Aug. 10** ***Perf. 11¾x12***

**3755-3758** A1694 Set of 4 2.50 1.25
*3758a* Booklet pane of 6, #3757, 3758, 2 each #3755-3756 — —
Complete booklet, #3758a —

Complete booklet sold for 3.90w.

***Perf. 12x12¼***

**3759** Sheet of 5, #a.-e. + label 5.75 3.00
*a.* A1694 10ch multicolored .25 .25
*b.* A1694 40ch multicolored .40 .25
*c.* A1694 1.20w multicolored 1.00 .50
*d.* A1694 1.50w multicolored 1.00 .50
*e.* A1694 4w multicolored 2.50 1.25

**Souvenir Sheet**

***Perf. 11¾x12***

**3760** A1694 4w multicolored 3.00 1.50

Traditional Costumes A1695

Designs: 10ch, Pouch. 50ch, Playthings (dress ornaments). 1.50w, Hairpin. 1.90w, Ornamental silver sword.

**1998, Aug. 20** ***Perf. 11½***

**3761-3764** A1695 Set of 4 3.00 1.50
*3763a* Sheet of 20, 10 se-tenant pairs #3761 and #3763 15.00 7.50
*3764a* Sheet of 20, 10 se-tenant pairs #3762 and #3764 15.00 7.50
*3764b* Booklet pane of 8, 2 each #3761-3764 — —
Complete booklet, #3764b —

Complete booklet sold for 8.20w.

Launch of *Kwangmyongsong I*, DPRK's First Earth Satellite — A1696

Designs: 40ch, Rocket, satellite, world map and flag.
1.50w, Rocket, earth and satellite orbit.

**1998, Aug. 31** ***Perf. 13¼***

**3765** A1696 40ch multicolored .35 .25

**Souvenir Sheet**

**3766** A1696 1.50w multicolored 1.25 .65

A1697

Acclamation of Kim Jong Il as Chairman of the DPRK National Defense Commission — A1698

Designs: 10ch, Proclamation, *Kimjongilia.* 1w, Kim Jong Il.

**1998, Sept. 5** ***Perf. 11½***

**3767** A1697 10ch multicolored .25 .25

**Souvenir Sheet**

***Perf. 13¼***

**3768** A1698 1w multicolored .75 .40

A1699

Korean DPR, 50th Anniversary — A1700

Designs: 10ch, State Arms, Flag, Tower of Juche Idea.
No. 3770: a, Kim Il Sung saluting crowd from balcony. b, Kim raising cap to crowd in street. c, Kim in suit and white hat, with fruit, stylized and idealized Korean peninsula in background.

**1998, Sept. 9** ***Perf. 13¼***

**3769** A1699 10ch multicolored .25 .25
**3770** A1700 1w Sheet of 6, 2 each a-c 4.50 2.25

Poster: "Let Us Push Ahead with the Forced March for Final Victory" A1701

**1998, Sept. 15** ***Perf. 11½***

**3773** A1701 10ch multicolored .25 .25

A1702

Korean DPR, 50th Anniversary (2nd Issue) — A1703

**1998, Sept. 20** ***Perf. 13¼***

**3774** A1702 40ch multicolored .35 .25

***Perf. 11½***

**3775** A1703 1w multicolored 1.00 .50

Summer Olympic Games, Sydney — A1704

Designs: 20ch, Cyclist. 50ch, Soccer. 80ch, Show jumping. 1.50w, Javelin throwing. 2.50w, Basketball.

**1998, Sept. 25**

**3776-3779** A1704 Set of 4 2.50 1.25
*3778a* Sheet of 3, #3777, 3778, as #3780 3.00 1.50
*3779a* Sheet of 3, #3776, 3779, as #3780 3.00 1.50

**Souvenir Sheet**

**3780** A1704 2.50w multi 2.00 1.00

For surcharge, see No. 4529.

Plants Presented as Gifts to Kim Jong Il — A1705

Designs: 20ch, Cyclamen persicum. 2w, Dianthus chinensis.

**1998, Sept. 28** ***Perf. 11½***

**3781-3782** A1705 Set of 2 1.60 .80

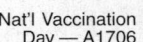

Nat'l Vaccination Day — A1706

**1998, Oct. 20** ***Perf. 13¼***

**3783** A1706 40ch multicolored .35 .25
*a.* Sheet of 6 2.10 1.00

Worldwide Fund for Nature (WWF) A1707

Panthera pardus orientalis: No. 3784, 1w, Climbing branch. No. 3785, 1w, Walking in snow. No. 3786, 1w, Looking to left. No. 3787, 1w, Head, full-face.

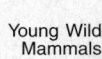

**1998, Oct. 21**
**3784-3787** A1707 Set of 4 4.00 2.00
*3787a* Sheet of 16, 4 se-tenant blocks of #3784-3787 16.00 8.00

For surcharges, see Nos. 4589-4590.

A1708

Land and Environment Conservation Day — A1709

Designs: 10ch, Canal, countryside. 40ch, Modern highway exchange, apartment towers.
1w, Kim Il Sung breaking ground for construction of Pothong River project.

**1998, Oct. 23** *Perf. 11½*
**3788-3789** A1708 Set of 2 .45 .25

**Souvenir Sheet**
*Perf. 12x12¼*

**3790** A1709 1w multicolored .75 .40

Italia '98 Int'l stamp Exhib., Milan — A1710

**1998, Oct. 23** *Perf. 12¼x12*
**3791** A1710 2w multicolored 1.50 .75

A1711

Designs: a, 20ch, Peng Dehuai and Kim Il Sung. b, 20ch, Peng Dehuai, Zhou Enlai, Mao Zedong. c, 30ch, Marshal Peng Dehuai. d, 30ch, Painting, *On the Front.*

**1998, Oct. 24** *Perf. 11½*
**3792** A1711 Sheet of 4, #a-d .75 .40

Birth centenary of Peng Dehuai, Commander of the Chinese People's Volunterrs in the Korean War.

Liu Shaoqi
A1712

Designs: 10ch, Liu Shaoqi. 20ch, Liu sitting with Mao Zedong (1965). 30ch, Liu and his daughter, Xiao Xiao (1964). 40ch, Liu sitting with his wife, Wang Guangmei (1961).

**1998, Nov 24** *Perf. 13¼*
**3796-3799** A1712 Set of 4 .75 .40

**Souvenir Sheet**
*Perf. 11¾x12¼*

**3800** A1712 1w multicolored .75 .40

A1713

Victory in Korean-Japanese War, 400th Anniv. — A1714

Designs: 10ch, Victory monument, Yonsang area, Yonan fortress, banners. 30ch, Naval victory monument, Myongryang area, Gen. Ri Sun Sin, turtleship. 1.60w, Monument to Buddhist priest Hyujong, Sosan-Chonghodang, Hyujong, sword, helmet.
No. 3804, *Sea Battle Off Hansan Islet in 1592.*

**1998, Nov 24** *Perf. 11½*
**3801-3803** A1713 Set of 3 1.50 .75
*3803a* Sheet of 15, 5 se-tenant strips of #3801-3803 7.50 3.75

**Souvenir Sheet**

**3804** A1714 10w multicolored 7.50 3.00

DPRK Entry into INTERSPUTNIK, 15th Anniv. — A1715

**1998, Nov. 25** *Perf. 13¼*
**3805** A1715 1w dp grn & lt grn .75 .40

Korean Goats — A1716

Goat with background color of: 10c, Green. 1w, Purple.

**1998, Nov. 26**
**3806-3807** A1716 Set of 2 .80 .40

For surcharge, see No. 4576.

Sculpture, *A Floral Carriage of Happiness*
A1717

Quotation from Kim Il Sung — A1718

Designs: 10ch, Sculpture, panoramic view of Mangyongdae Schoolchildren's Palace.
1w, Kim Il Sung quotation, "Children are the treasure of our country. Korea of the future is theirs."

**1998, Nov. 26** *Perf. 11½*
**3808** A1717 40ch multicolored .35 .25
*a.* Sheet of 4 2.00 1.00

**Souvenir Sheet**

**3809** A1718 1w multicolored .75 .40

Univeral Declaration of Human Rights, 50th Anniv. — A1719

**1998, Dec. 10**
**3810** A1719 20ch multicolored .25 .25

Reptiles — A1720

Designs: a, 10ch, Reeves turtle. b, 40ch, Skink. c, 60ch, Loggerhead turtle. d, 1.20w, Leatherback turtle.

**1998, Dec. 15** *Perf. 13¼*
**3811** A1720 Block of 4, #a-d 1.75 .90
*e.* Sheet of 16, 4 #3811 17.00 3.50
*f.* Complete booklet, 3 ea. #3811 13.00

Mt. Chilbo — A1721

Designs: 30ch, Thajong Rock. 50ch, Peasant Rock. 1.70w, Couple Rock.

**1998, Dec. 15** *Perf. 11½*
**3815-3817** A1721 Set of 3 1.75 .90

Tale of Chung Hyang — A1722

Designs: 40ch, Marriage of Ri Mong Ryong and Song Chun Hyang. 1.60w, Pyon Hak Do watching Chun Hyang. 2.50w, Ri Mong Ryong and Chun Hyang.
50ch, Chun Hyang in wedding veil.

**1998, Dec. 20**
**3818-3820** A1722 Set of 3 3.50 1.75
**3821** Sheet of 4, #3818-3820, 3821a 5.00 2.50
*a.* A1722 multicolored 1.00 .50

Chollima Statue
A1723

Arch of Triumph
A1724

Tower of Juche Idea — A1725

**1998, Dec. 22** *Perf. 13¼*

| | | | | | |
|---|---|---|---|---|---|
| **3822** | A1723 | 10ch | red | .25 | .25 |
| **3823** | A1724 | 10ch | red | .25 | .25 |
| **3824** | A1725 | 10ch | red | .25 | .25 |
| **3825** | A1725 | 20ch | red org | .25 | .25 |
| **3826** | A1723 | 30ch | red org | .35 | .25 |
| **3827** | A1724 | 40ch | yel brown | .40 | .25 |
| **3828** | A1725 | 40ch | yel brown | .40 | .25 |
| **3829** | A1723 | 70ch | yel grn | .65 | .35 |
| **3830** | A1724 | 70ch | yel grn | .65 | .35 |
| **3831** | A1724 | 1.20w | green | 1.10 | .55 |
| **3832** | A1723 | 1.50w | blue green | 1.50 | .75 |
| **3833** | A1725 | 2w | blue | 2.00 | 1.00 |
| **3834** | A1724 | 3w | blue | 2.75 | 1.40 |
| **3835** | A1723 | 5w | dk blue | 5.00 | 2.50 |
| **3836** | A1725 | 10w | violet | 9.75 | 5.00 |
| | *Nos. 3822-3836 (15)* | | | 25.55 | 13.65 |

For surcharges, see Nos. 4577, 4591, 4611.

New Year — Year of the Rabbit — A1726

Designs: 10ch, Rabbit meeting Lion on the road. 1w, Rabbit using mirror to lure lion into pit. 1.50w, Rabbit laughing at Lion in trap.
2.50w, Rabbit.

**1999, Jan. 1** *Perf. 11½*
**3837-3839** A1726 Set of 3 2.00 1.00
**3840** Sheet of 4, #3837-3839, 3840a 4.00 2.00
*a.* A1726 2.50w multicolored 2.00 1.00
*b.* Booklet pane of 8, 2 each #3837-3839, 3840a — —
Complete booklet, #3840b —

Complete booklet sold for 10.40w.

Worker-Peasant Red Guards, 40th Anniv. — A1727

**1999, Jan. 14** ***Perf. 13¼***
**3841** A1727 10ch multicolored .25 .25

Kim Jong Il, 57th Birthday A1728

40ch, Log cabin (birthplace) on Mt. Paekdu.

**1999, Feb. 16** ***Perf. 11½***
**3842** A1728 40ch multicolored .35 .25

Publication of Kim Il Sung's *Theses on the Socialist Rural Question in Our Country* — A1729

**1999, Feb. 25** ***Perf. 13¼***
**3843** A1729 10ch multicolored .25 .25

March 1 Popular Uprising, 80th Anniv. — A1730

**1999, Feb. 25**
**3844** A1730 10ch olive brn & black .25 .25

Turtle Ship — A1731

**1999, Mar. 19**
**3845** A1731 2w multicolored 1.60 .80
*a.* Booklet pane of 5 #3845 —
Complete booklet, #3845a —

Australia '99 World Stamp Expo, Melbourne. Complete booklet sold for 10.20w.

A1732

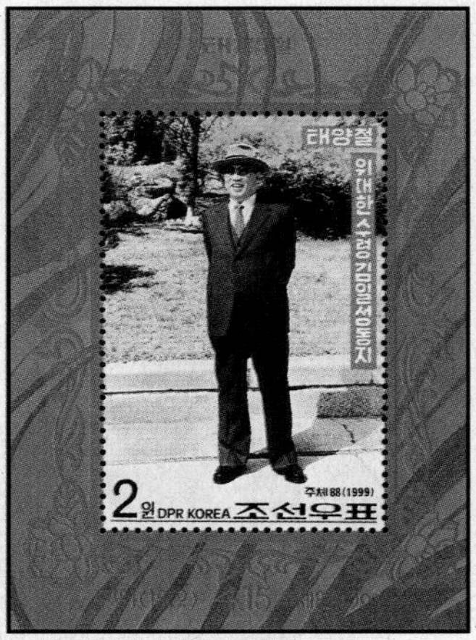

Kim Il Sung, 87th Birth Anniv. — A1733

Designs: 10ch, Childhood Home, Mangyongdae. No. 3847, Kim Il Sung.

**1999, Apr. 15** ***Perf. 11½***
**3846** A1732 10ch multicolored .25 .25

**Souvenir Sheet**

***Perf. 11½x12***

**3847** A1733 2w multicolored 1.60 .80

45th World Table Tennis Championships, Belgrade — A1734

**1999, Apr. 26** ***Perf. 11½***
**3848** A1734 1.50w multicolored 1.20 .60

For surcharge, see No. 4559.

Ibra '99 Int'l Stamp Exhib., Nuremberg A1735

**1999, Apr. 27**
**3849** A1735 1w multicolored .85 .40

For surcharge, see No. 4557.

Central Zoo, Pyongyang, 40th Anniv. — A1736

Designs: 50ch, Chimpanzee, rhinoceros. 60ch, Manchurian crane, deer. 70ch, Zebra, kangaroo.
2w, Tiger.

**1999, Apr. 30** ***Perf. 13¼***
**3850-3852** A1736 Set of 3 1.60 .80
*3852a* Booklet pane of 6, 2 each #3850-3852 — —
Complete booklet, #3852a —

**Souvenir Sheet**

**3853** A1736 2w multicolored 1.75 .90

For surcharge, see No. 4552.
Complete bookletof No. 3852a sold for 3.80w.

Central Botanical Garden, Pyongyang, 40th Anniv. — A1737

Designs: 10ch, *Benzoin obtusilobum.* 30ch, *Styrax obassia.* 70ch, *Petunia hybrida.* 90ch, *Impatiens hybrida.*
2w, *Kimsungilia* and *Kimjongilia.*

**1999, Apr. 30** ***Perf. 11½***
**3854-3857** A1737 Set of 4 1.60 .80
*3857a* Sheet of 4, #3854-3857 1.75 .90
*3857b* Booklet pane of 12, 3 each #3854-3857 — —
Complete booklet, #3857b —

Complete booklet sold for 6.20w.

**Souvenir Sheet**

**3858** A1737 2w multicolored 1.75 .90

Three Revolution Exhibit A1738

Designs: 60ch, Light Industry Hall. 80ch, Heavy Industry Hall

**1999, May 2**
**3859-3860** A1738 Set of 2 1.20 .60

Three Revolution (ideological, technical, cultural) Exhibition, Ryonmotdong, Sosong District, Pyongyang.

Asia-Pacific Telecommunications Union, 20th Anniv. — A1739

**1999, May 8** ***Perf. 13¼***
**3861** A1739 1w multicolored .80 .40

Battle of Musan Area, 60th Anniv. A1740

**1999, May 19** ***Perf. 11½***
**3862** A1740 10ch multicolored .25 .25

A1741

Charles Darwin, 190th Birth Anniv. — A1742

No. 3863: a, 30ch, Seagulls. b, 50ch, Bats. c, 1w, Dolphins. d, 1.20w, Rider on horseback. e, 1.50w, Korean dancer in traditional dress.

**1999, May 20** **Sheet of 5 + labels**
**3863** A1741 #a-e 3.00 1.50

**Souvenir Sheet**

***Perf. 13¼x12***

**3864** A1742 2w multicolored 4.00 2.00

Diego Velazquez (1599-1660), Artist, 400th Birth Anniv. A1743

Designs: No. 3869, 50ch, *Princess Margarita in a White Dress.* No. 3866, 50ch, *Men Drawing Water from a Well.*
3.50w, *Self-portrait.*

**1999, May 30** ***Perf. 11¾***
**3869-3870** A1743 Set of 2 1.00 .50

**Souvenir Sheet**

**3871** A1743 3.50w multicolored 3.00 1.50
*a.* Sheet of 3, #3869-3871 4.00 2.00
*b.* Booklet pane of 6, 2 each #3869-3871 — —
Complete booklet, #3871b —

Complete booklet sold for 9.20w.

Medium and Small Hydroelectric Power Stations — A1744

Designs: 50ch, Rimyongsu Power Station. 1w, Janggasan Power Station.

**1999, May 30** ***Perf. 11½***
**3872-3873** A1744 Set of 2 1.20 .60

3rd Women's World Soccer Championship, USA — A1745

Designs: a, 1w, Dribbling. b, 1.50w, Tackling. c, 1.50w, Goal shot. d, 2w, Knee kick.

**1999, June 8** *Perf. 13¼*
**3874** A1745 Sheet of 4, #a-d 5.00 2.50
*e.* Booklet pane of 4, #3874a-3874d — —
Complete booklet, #3874e —

Complete booklet sold for 6.20w.

Mars Exploration — A1746

Designs, each 2w: a, Vostock Rocket. b, Satellite over Martian crater. c, Mars probe landing, Martian moons.

**1999, June 10** *Perf. 11½*
**3878** A1746 Sheet of 3, #a.-c. 4.75 2.50

Movie, *The Nation and Destiny* — A1747

Scenes from film: a, Man holding candlestick. b, Man in white coat, woman with pistol. c, Old man in prison cell. d, Man in protective suit, with goggles on hat.

**1999, June 10**
**3879** A1747 1w Sheet of 4, #a-d 3.20 1.60
*e.* Booklet pane of 8, 2 each #3879a-3879d — —
Complete booklet, #3879e —

Complete booklet sold for 8.20w.

Tourism — Mt. Kumgang — A1748

Designs: 20ch, Samil Lagoon. 40ch, Samson Rocks, vert. 60ch, Standing Rock. 80ch, Kuryong Waterfall. 1w, Kwimyon Rock.

**1999, June 15** *Perf. 12*
**3883-3887** A1748 Set of 5 2.50 1.25

UPU, 125th Anniv. — A1749

**1999, June 20** *Perf. 11½*
**3888** A1749 2w multicolored 1.40 .70

PHILEXFANCE '99 — A1750

2.50w, First stamps of France (1870) and DPRK (1946).

**1999, July 2** *Perf. 12*
**3889** A1750 2.50w multicolored 2.00 1.00

Kim Il Sung, 5th Death Anniv. — A1751

Designs: a, Kim Il Sung's Mercedes. b, Kim's railway car.

**1999, July 8** *Perf. 11½*
**3890** A1751 1w Sheet of 2, #a-b 1.60 .80

Kim Hyong Jik (1894-1926), Revolutionary, 105th Anniv. Birth — A1752

10ch, Chinese characters for "Jiwon" ("Aim High"), Kim Hyong Jik's motto, and Mangyong Hill.

**1999, July 10**
**3892** A1752 10ch multicolored .25 .25

History of Ceramics A1753

Designs: 70ch, Engraved-patterned vessel (5000 B.C.). 80ch, Wit and beauty jar (3rd-4th Centuries). 1w, Flowered jar. 1.50w, Lotus decoration celadon kettle (10th-14th Centuries). 2.50w, White china pot with blue flower (15th Century).

**1999, July 15** *Perf. 13¼*
**3893-3897** A1753 Set of 5 5.00 2.50

Fish Breeding A1754

Designs: 50ch, Silver carp. 1w, Common carp. 1.50w, Spotted silver carp.

**1999, July 20**
**3898-3900** A1754 Set of 3 2.40 1.20
*3900a* Booklet pane of 6, 2 each #3898-3900 — —
Complete booklet, #3900a —

Complete booklet sold for 6.20w.

Year of Nat'l Independence and Great Solidarity — A1755

**1999, Aug. 5**
**3901** A1755 40ch multicolored .35 .25

Repatriation of Korean Nationals in Japan, 40th Anniv. A1756

**1999, Aug. 16** *Perf. 11½*
**3902** A1756 1.50w multicolored 1.25 .60

Year For a Turning Point in Building a Powerful Nation A1757

**1999, Aug. 17**
**3903** A1757 40ch multicolored .35 .25

7th World Athletic Championships, Seville — A1758

Designs: 30ch, 100-Meter Race. 40ch, Hurdles. 80ch, Discus.

**1999, Aug. 18**
**3904-3906** A1758 Set of 3 1.20 .60

Gift Plants — A1759

No. 3907: a, Acalypha hispida Burm f. b, Allamanda neriifolia Hook. c, Begonia x hiemalis Fotsch. d, Fatsia japonica Decne. e, Streptocarpus hydrida hort. f, Streptocarpus rexii Lindl.

**1999, Aug. 20**
**3907** A1759 40ch Sheet of 6, #a-f 2.00 1.00

22nd UPU Congress & China '99 World Philatelic Exhib. — A1760

Paintings by Qiu Ying: a, *Play a Flute to Call Phoenix.* b, *Six Friends in a Pine Forest.* c, *Relics Kept in the Bamboo Field.* d, *Ladies Morning Dressing.*

**1999, Aug. 21**
**3913** A1760 40ch Sheet of 4, #a-d 1.50 .75

Mushrooms A1761

Designs: 40ch, Grifola frondosa. 60ch Lactarius volemus. 1w, Cariolus versicolor.

**1999, Aug. 25**
**3917-3919** A1761 Set of 3 2.00 1.00

For surcharge, see No. 4558.

Cacti — A1762

Designs: 40ch, *Aporocactus flagelliformis.* 50ch *Astrophytum ornatum.* 60ch, *Gymnocalycium michanorichii.*

**1999, Sept. 1**
**3920-3922** A1762 Set of 3 1.25 .60

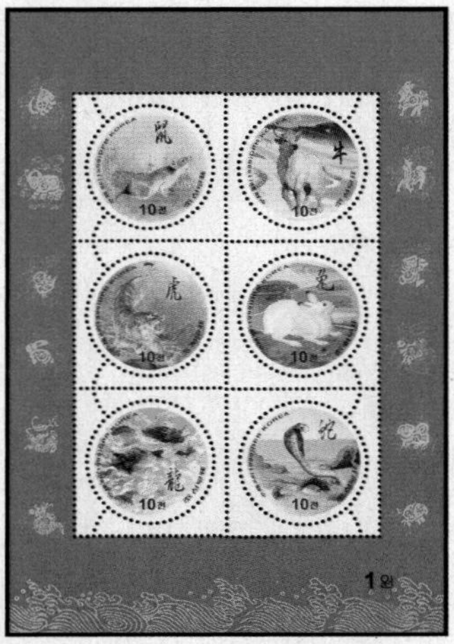

Animals of the Zodiac — A1763

No. 3923: a, Rat. b, Ox. c, Tiger. d, Rabbit. e, Dragon. f, Snake.
No. 3924: a, Horse. b, Sheep. c, Monkey. d, Rooster. e, Dog. f, Pig.

**1999, Sept. 10** *Perf. 12½*
**Sheets of 6, #a-f**
**3923-3924** A1763 10ch Set of 2 2.00 1.00

Crustaceans A1764

Designs: 50ch, Pendalus hypsinotus 70ch, Penaeus orientalis. 80ch, Homarus vulgarus.

**1999, Sept. 10** *Perf. 11½*
**3935-3937** A1764 Set of 3 2.00 1.00
*3937a* Booklet pane of 6, 2 each #3935-3937 — —
Complete booklet, #3937a —

Complete booklet sold for 4.20w.

A1765

Jong Song Ok, Marathon Runner — A1766

**1999, Sept. 20** *Perf. 13¼*
**3938** A1765 40ch multicolored .35 .25
*a.* Booklet pane of 6 #3938 — —
Complete booklet, #3938a —

Complete booklet sold for 2.60w.

**Souvenir Sheet**

**3939** A1766 2w multicolored 1.60 .80

Victory of Jong Song Ok, Women's Marathon winner at 7th IAAF World Championships, Seville.

DPRK-China Diplomatic Relations, 50th Anniv. — A1767

Designs: 40ch, Mt. Kumgang, Korea. 60ch, Mt. Lushan, China.

**1999, Oct. 5** *Perf. 12¼x11¼*
**3940-3941** A1767 Set of 2 1.00 .50
*3941a* Sheet of 4, #3940-3941 + 2 labels 3.00 1.50

Nos. 3940-3941 were printed both in sheetlets of 6, containg three vertical se-tenant pairs of the two stamps, and in sheetlets of 4, containing a horizontal se-tenant pair and two labels.

A1768

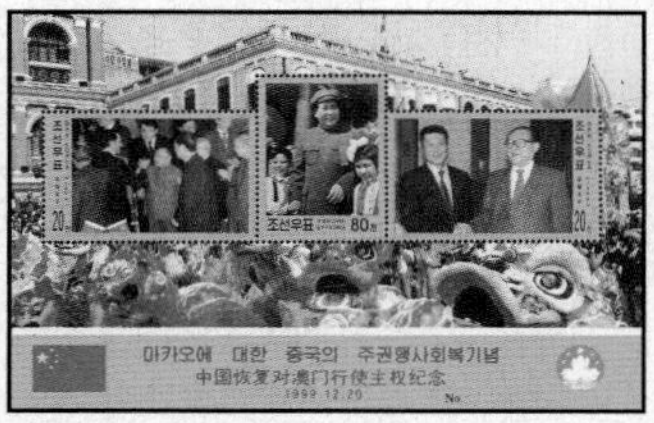

Return of Macao to China — A1769

Type A1768, 1w, Portrait of Pres. Jiang Zemin of China: No. 3942, Gold frame. No. 3943, Green frame.

Type A1769: 20ch (a), Deng Xiaoping sharing toast with Portuguese Prime Minister. 20ch (b), Jiang Zemin shaking hands with He Houhua, newly-appointed mayor of Macao special administrative region. 80ch (c), Mao Zedong at National Day Celebration, Tiananmen Square, 1951. Nos. 3944a-3944c, gold background. Nos. 3945a-3945c, green background.

**1999, Nov. 10** *Perf. 13¼*
**3942-3943** A1768 Set of 2 sheets 2.00 1.00
**3944-3945** A1769 Set of 2 sheets, #a-c 2.50 1.25

New Year — April 19 Uprising, 40th Anniv. — A1770

**2000, Jan. 1** *Perf. 11½*
**3946** A1770 10ch multicolored .25 .25

A1771

Koguryo Era (2nd Century B.C.-7th Century A.D.) — A1772

Designs: 70ch, Yellow dragon. 1.60w, Blue dragon.

**2000, Jan. 1**
**3947** A1771 70ch multicolored .70 .35
Complete booklet, 8 #3947 —

**Souvenir Sheet**

***Perf. 11½x11¾***

**3948** A1772 1.60w multicolored 1.60 .80

Complete booklet sold for 5.80w.

Painting, *Rural Life* (18th Century) — A1773

No. 3949: a, Peasants weeding. b, Weaving hemp cloth. c, Peasants threshing grain. d, Riverside market.

**2000, Jan. 25** *Perf. 13¼*
**3949** A1773 40ch Sheet of 4, #a-d 1.60 .80

Mt. Paekdu Rock Formations — A1774

Designs, 20ch: No. 3953, Dinosaur-shaped rock. No. 3954, Eagle-shaped rock. No. 3955, Owl-shaped rock.

**2000, Jan. 30**
**3953-3955** A1774 Set of 3 .70 .35

Pongsan Mask Dance — A1775

Folk dances: a, 50ch, Chuibari mask dance. b, 80ch, Ryangban mask dance. c, 1w, Malttugi mask dance.

**2000, Feb. 3** *Perf. 11½*
**3956** A1775 Sheet of 3, #a-c 2.25 1.10

Cats — A1776

DesignsNo. 3959, 50ch, Cat on windowsill. No. 3960, 50ch, Kittens playing. No. 3961, 50ch, Mother cat and kittens in basket.

**2000, Feb. 3** *Perf. 13¼*
**3959-3961** A1776 Set of 3 1.75 .85
*3961a* Booklet pane of 8, 2 #3959, 3 each #3960-3961 — —
Complete booklet, #3961a —

Complete booklet sold for 4.20w.

Fauna — A1777

No. 3962: Cats: a, Singapura. b, Blue Abyssinian. c, Oriental. d, Scottish fold tabby.

No. 3963: Dogs: a, Shiba inu. b, Yorkshire terrier. c, Japanese chin. d, Afghan hound.

No. 3964: Horses: a, Przewalski's horse. b, Gray cob. c, White horse. d, Donkeys.

No. 3965: Pandas: a, In tree. b, Eating. c, Leaning against tree. d, Mother and cub.

No. 3966: Bears: a, Two polar bears. b, Mother and cub. c, Bear standing. d, Bear reclining.

No. 3967: Snakes: a, Mexican lance-headed rattlesnake (Crotalus polystictus). b, Scarlet king snake (Lampropeltis triangulum elapsoides). c, Green tree python (Chondropython viridis). d, Blood python (Python curtus).

No. 3968: Dinosaurs: a, Corythosaurus. b, Psittacosaurus. c, Megalosaurus. d, Muttaburrasaurus.

No. 3969: Marine Mammals: a, Burmeister's porpoise (Phocoena spinipinnis). b, Finless porpoise (Neophocaena phocaenoides). c, Bottle-nosed dolphin (Tursiops truncatus).d, Curvier's beaked whale (Ziphius cavirostris).

No. 3970: Sharks: a, Port Jackson shark (Heterodontus portusjacksoni). b, Great hammerhead shark (Sphyrna mokarran). c, Zebra shark (Stegostoma fasciatum). d, Ornate Wobbegong carpet shark (Orectolobus cavirostris).

No. 3971: Ducks: a, Ruddy shelduck (Tadorna ferruginea). b, European widgeon (Anas penelope). c, Mandarin drake (Aix galericulata). d, Hottentot teal (Anas hottentota).

No. 3972: Owls: a, Little owl (Athene noctua). b, Ural owl (Strix uralensis). c, Great horned owl (Bubo virginianus). d, Snowy owl (Nyctea scandiaca).

No. 3973: Parrots: a, Slaty-headed parakeet (Psittacula himalayana). b, Male eclectus parrot (Eclectus roratus). c, Major Mitchell's cockatoo (Cacatua leadbeateri). d, Female eclectus parrot (Eclectus roratus).

No. 3974: Butterflies: a, Indian leaf butterfly (Kallima paralekta). b, Spanish festoon (Zerynthia rumina). c, Male and female emerald swallowtails (Papillo palinurus). d, Bhutanitis lidderdalii.

No. 3975: Bees: a, Bumble bee. b, Bumble bee on flower. c, Honey bee (Apis mellifera). d, Honey bee fighting spider.

No. 3976: Spiders: a, Micrommata virescens. b, Araneus quadratus. c, Dolomedes fimbriatus. d, Aculepeira ceropegia.

**2000, Feb. 10** **Sheets of 4, #a-d**
**3962-3976** A1777 2w Set of 15 150.00 150.00

Kim Jong Il, 59th Birthday A1778

Design: Birthplace, Mt. Paekdu.

**2000, Feb. 16** *Perf. 11½*
**4022** A1778 40ch multicolored .40 .25

Dinosaurs — A1779

Designs: a, Triceratops. b, Saltasaurus. c, Tyrannosaurus.

**2000, Mar. 5** *Perf. 13¼*
**4023** A1779 1w Sheet of 3, #a-c 3.50 1.75
*d.* Sheet of 3, ovptd. with show emblem in margin 3.50 1.75

No. 4023d, Espana 2000 International Stamp Exhibition, Madrid. Issued, 10/6/06.

A1780

Monkeys — A1781

Designs: No. 4026, 50ch, Western tarsier (Tarsius spectrum). No. 4027, 50ch, Patas monkey (Erythrocebus patas).
2w, Mona monkey (Cercopithecus mona).

**2000, Mar. 25** ***Perf. 11½***

| | | | |
|---|---|---|---|
| **4026-4027** A1780 Set of 2 | | 1.00 | .50 |
| *4027a* | Sheet of 4, 2 each #4026-4027 | 2.25 | 1.10 |
| *4027b* | Booklet pane of 8, 4 each #4026-4027 | — | — |
| | Complete booklet, #4027b | — | |

Complete booklet sold for 4.20w.

**Souvenir Sheet**

**4028** A1781 2w multicolored 1.80 .90

Nos. 4026-4027 were issued both separately in panes of 10 and together in sheets of 4.

Butterflies — A1782

No. 4029: a, 40ch Peacock (Inachus io). b, 60ch, Swallowtail (Papilio machaon). c, 80ch, Mimic (Hypolimnas misippus Linnaeus). d, 1.20w, (Papilio bianor cramer).

**2000, Mar. 25**

| | | | |
|---|---|---|---|
| **4029** A1782 Sheet of 4, #a-d | | 3.50 | 1.75 |
| *e.* | Booklet pane of 8, 2 each #4029a-4029d | — | — |
| | Complete booklet, #4029e | — | |

Complete booklet sold for 6.20w.

Grand Chollima March — A1783

**2000, Mar. 28**

**4033** A1783 10ch multicolored .25 .25

55th anniversary of the Korean Workers' Party.

April 19 Popular Uprising, 40th Anniv. A1784

**2000, April 1**

**4034** A1784 10ch multicolored .25 .25

Sun's Day A1785

**2000, April 15**

**4035** A1785 40ch multicolored .40 .25

88th anniversary of birth of Kim Il Sung. For surcharge, see No. 4587.

Mun Ik Hwan — A1786

**2000, April 25** ***Perf. 13¼***

**4036** A1786 50ch multicolored .60 .25

Issued in honor of Mun Ik Hwan (1918-94), South Korean political activist, winner of 1990 National Reunification Prize.

Millennium; Korean Workers' Party, 55th Anniv. — A1787

Designs: 40ch, Chollima statue, flag, symbols of national power. 1.20w, Dove with letter, map, "2000."

**2000, May 5**

**4037-4038** A1787 Set of 2 1.75 .85

A1788

Orchids — A1789

Designs: 20ch, Cattleya intermedia. 50ch, Dendrobium moschatum. 70ch, Brassolaeliocattleya.
2w, Laeliocattleya.

**2000, May 15**

| | | | |
|---|---|---|---|
| **4039-4041** A1788 Set of 3 | | 1.60 | .80 |
| *4041a* | Booklet pane of 8, 2 each #4039-4040, 4 #4041 | — | — |
| | Complete booklet, #4041a | — | |

Complete booklet sold for 4.40w, and exists imperforate.

**Souvenir Sheet**

**4042** A1789 2w multicolored 2.00 1.00

Bridges A1790

Designs: 20ch, Okryn Bridge. 30ch, Ansan Bridge. 1w, Rungna Bridge.

**2000, May 21**

| | | | |
|---|---|---|---|
| **4043-4045** A1790 Set of 3 | | 2.25 | 1.10 |
| *4045a* | Booklet pane of 8, 2 #4043, 3 each #4044-4045 | — | — |
| | Complete booklet, #4045a | — | |

Complete booklet sold for 4.50w.

WIPA 2000 Int'l Stamp Exhib., Vienna — A1791

Traditional Korean musical instruments and folk dances: a, 1w, Okryugum and Jaenggang dance. b, 1.50w, Bungum and Full Moon Viewing dance. c, 1.50w, Janggo drum and "Trio" dance.

**2000, May 30**

**4046** A1791 Sheet of 3, #a-c 4.00 2.00

Nos. 4046b-4046c are airmail stamps.

Children's Songs A1792

Designs: 40ch, Song "Halfmoon," two children in boat. 60ch, Song "Kangram Nostalgia," boy and girl.
1.50w, Song "Spring in Home Village," boy and girl with flowers.

**2000, June 1** ***Perf. 11¾x12¼***

**4049-4050** A1792 Set of 2 1.00 .50

**Souvenir Sheet**

**4051** A1792 1.50w multicolored 1.75 .85

Cephalopods A1793

Designs: 40ch, Nautilus pompilius. 60ch, Octopus vularis.
1.50w, Ommastrephes sloanei pacificus.

**2000, June 15** ***Perf. 11½***

**4052-4053** A1793 Set of 2 1.25 .60

**Souvenir Sheet**

| | | | |
|---|---|---|---|
| **4054** A1793 1.50w multicolored | | 1.75 | .85 |
| *a.* | Booklet pane of 8, 4#4052, 2 each #4053-4054 | — | — |
| | Complete booklet, #4054a | — | |

No. 4054a exists imperforate. Complete booklet sold for 6w.
For surcharges, see Nos. 4544-4545.

Mandarin Ducks A1794

Designs: No. 4055, 50ch, Pair of ducks, couple on bridge. No. 4056, 50ch, Pair of ducks, couple in row boat.
1w, Pair of ducks, ducklings.

**2000, June 16** ***Perf. 11¾x12¼***

| | | | |
|---|---|---|---|
| **4055-4056** A1794 Set of 2 | | 1.00 | .50 |
| *4056a* | Booklet pane of 7, 3 #4055, 4 #4056 | 3.75 | 1.75 |
| | Complete booklet, #4056a | 3.75 | |

**Souvenir Sheet**

**4057** A1794 1w multicolored 1.00 .50

Nos. 4055-4056 were issued both in separate sheets of 9 (3x3) and in booklet panes of 7, containing 3 No. 4055 and 4 No. 4056, in an alternating arrangement. Complete booklet sold for 3.70w.
For overprints, see Nos. 4071-4073.

Sports A1795

Designs: 80ch, Table tennis. 1w, Basketball. 1.20w, Baseball.

**2000, July 7** ***Perf. 13¼***

| | | | |
|---|---|---|---|
| **4058-4060** A1795 Set of 3 | | 3.50 | 1.75 |
| *4060a* | Booklet pane of 7, 2 each #4058-4059, 3 #4060 | — | — |
| | Complete booklet, #4060a | — | |

Complete booklet sold for 7.40w.

Trucks A1796

Designs: 40ch, *Sungri-61 NA.* 70ch, Flatbed truck. 1.50w, *Konsol* 25-50n dump truck.

**2000, July 24** ***Perf. 12***

**4061-4063** A1796 Set of 3 2.75 1.50

Korean People's Army A1797

Portraits of KPA commanders and weapons: 60ch, Ri Tae Hun and 76mm field gun, 80ch, Ko hyon Bink and T-34 tank. 1w, Paek Ki Rah and Yak-9P pursuit plane.

**2000, July 27**

**4064-4066** A1797 Set of 3 2.25 1.10

Minerals A1798

Designs: 30ch, Fluorite. 60ch, Graphite. 1.60w, Magnesite.

**2000, Aug. 15** ***Perf. 13¼***

**4067-4069** A1798 Set of 3 1.10 .60

*4069a* Booklet pane of 8, 3 each #4067-4068, 2 #4069 — —

Complete booklet, #4069a —

Complete booklet sold for 6.10w.

**Souvenir Sheet**

**4070** A1798 1.60w multicolored 1.60 .80

Nos. 4055-4057 Overprinted

**2000, Aug. 15** ***Perf. 13¼***

**4071** A1794 50ch On #4055 .50 .25

**4072** A1794 50ch On #4056 .50 .25

*a.* Booklet pane of 7, 3 #4071, 4 #4072 — —

Complete booklet, #4072a —

Complete booklet sold for 7.20w.

**Souvenir Sheet**

**4073** 1w On #4057 1.00 .50

International Stamp Exhibition, Jakarta.

Sydney 2000, Summer Olympic Games — A1799

Designs: a, 80ch, Swimmer. b, 1.20, Cyclist. c, 2w, Runner.

**2000, Sept. 15** ***Perf. 13½***

**4074** A1799 Sheet of 3, #a-c 4.25 2.25

Myohyang Mountain A1800

Designs: 40ch (No. 4077), Sanju Falls, wild pig and piglet. 40ch (No. 4078), Inho Rock, Fallow deer, pair. 1.20w, stag and fawn.

**2000, Sept. 27** ***Perf. 13¼***

**4077-4079** A1800 Set of 3 2.00 1.00

A1801

Korean Workers' Party, 55th Anniv. — A1802

Designs: 40ch, Party emblem, Party Museum.

No. 4082: a, Kim Il Sung. b, Kim Jong Il. c, Kim Jong Suk.

**2000, Oct. 10** ***Perf. 13¼***

**4081** A1801 40ch multicolored .25 .25

**Souvenir Sheet**

**4082** A1802 50ch Sheet of 3, #a-c 1.50 .70

Land Rezoning Project A1803

10ch, Flags, bulldozer and trucks, urban scene and rice fields.

**2000, Oct. 15**

**4083** A1803 10ch multicolored .25 .25

A1804

Tae Hongdae Potato Farms — A1805

Designs: 40ch, Potatoes, pigs, scientist, collective farm.

2w, painting, *The Great Leader President Kim Il Sung Brought a Bumper Crop of Potato in the Paektu Pleateau.*

**2000, Oct. 20** ***Perf. 11½***

**4084** A1804 40ch multicolored .40 .25

**Souvenir Sheet**

**4085** A1805 2w multicolored 1.75 .90

Kim Jong Il & Pres. Jiang Zemin — A1806

**2000, Oct. 21** ***Perf. 11¾x12¼***

**4086** A1806 1.20w multicolored 1.75 .85

Visit of Kim Jong Il to China.

Kim Jong Il & Pres. Kim Dae Jung — A1807

**2000, Oct. 23** ***Perf. 11½x12***

**4087** A1807 2w multicolored 2.75 1.50

North-South Korean Summit Talks, Pyongyang.

Kim Jong Il & Pres. Putin — A1808

**2000, Oct. 24** ***Perf. 11¾x11½***

**4088** A1808 1.50w multicolored 2.25 1.10

Visit of Kim Jong Il to Russia.

Chinese & Korean Soldiers — A1809

Chinese People's Volunteers' Entry Into Korean War, 50th Anniv. — A1810

No. 4090: a, 10ch, Soldiers crossing the Amnok River. b, 10ch, Battle scene. c, 50ch, Kim Il Sung and Chinese officers. d, 50ch, Mao Zedong presiding over meeting to decide upon entry into Korean War. e, 80ch, Chinese soldiers observing battle.

**2000, Oct. 25** ***Perf. 13¼***

**4089** A1809 30ch multicolored .65 .35

**4090** A1810 Sheet of 5, #a-e 2.25 1.10

Alpine Flowers — A1811

Designs: 30ch, Aquilegia oxysepala. 50ch, Brilliant campion (Lychnis fulgens). 70ch, Self-heal (Prunela vulgaris).

**2000, Nov. 5** ***Perf. 13½***

**4095-4097** A1811 Set of 3 1.50 .60

Nos. 4095-4097 were printed in sheets containing a decorative label.

A1812

Repatriation of Long-Term Prisoners of War — A1813

Designs: 80ch, Returning prisoners receiving bouquets of flowers from women in Pyongyang. 1.20w, Prisoners welcomed by crowd, in front of statue of Kim Il Sung.

**2000, Dec. 20**

**4098-4099** Set of 2 sheets 2.25 1.10

New Year — A1814

10ch, Flag, trees, factory, missiles, ship, jet planes.

**2001, Jan. 1** ***Perf. 11½***

**4100** A1814 10ch multicolored .25 .25

New Year (2nd Issue) — A1815

Tale of the White Snake: 10ch, White Snake meeting Xu Xian. 40ch, Stealing the Immortal Greass. 50ch, White and Green Snakes and Xu Xian. 80ch, Flooding of Jinshan Hill.
1.20w, White Snake and Green Snake.

**2001, Jan. 1** ***Perf. 12½x12***

**4101-4104** A1815 Set of 4 3.75 1.75
*4104a* Sheet of 4, #4101-4104 3.75 1.75

**Souvenir Sheet**

**4105** A1815 1.20w multicolored 2.50 1.10

Nos. 4101-4104 were each issued singly in larger sheets and in combination in sheets of 4 (No. 4104a).

A1816

World Chess Champions — A1817

Designs: 10ch, E. Lasker (1868-1941) and J.R. Capablanca (1888-1942). 20ch, A. Alekhine (1892-1946) and E. Euwe (1901-80). 30ch, M. Botvinnik (1911-95) and V. Smylov (b. 1921). 40ch, T. Petrosian (1929-84) and M. Tal (1936-93). 50ch, B. Spassky (b. 1937) and R. Fisher (b. 1943). 1w, A. Karpov (b. 1954) and G. Kasparov (b. 1963).
2.50w, Wilhelm Steinmetz (1836-1900).

**2001, Jan. 5** ***Perf. 13½***

**4106-4111** A1816 Set of 6 5.00 2.50
*4111a* Sheet of 6, #4106-4111 5.00 2.50
*4111b* Booklet pane of 6, #4106-4111 5.25 —
Complete booklet, #4111b 5.75

**Souvenir Sheet**

**4112** A1817 2.50w multicolored 5.00 2.50

No. 4111b contains Nos. 4106-4111 in a se-tenant vertical strip of six, with narrow decorative selvage.
For overprints, see Nos. 4129-4135.

Ri-Dynasty Men's Costumes A1818

Designs: 10ch, Trousers and jacket. 40ch, Vest. 50ch, Magoja. 70ch, Turumagi
1.50w, Wedding attire.

**2001, Jan. 19** ***Perf. 12x12½***

**4113-4116** A1818 Set of 4 3.50 1.75
*4116a* Sheet of 5, #4113-4116, 4117a 7.00 3.50
*4116b* Booklet pane of 6, #4113-4114, 4116, 4117a, 2 #4115 7.75 —
Complete booklet, #4116b 8.00

**Souvenir Sheet**

**4117** A1818 1.50w multicolored 3.50 1.75

Nos. 4113-4116 were each issued both in large sheets and within sheets of 5, in combination with the 1.50w (No. 4117a) value contained in the souvenir sheet, No. 4117.
No. 4116b contains the six stamps in a se-tenant horizontal strip with narrow distinctive selvage.

Fire Engines — A1819

Fire-fighting vehicles and logos warning against specific fire hazards: 20ch, Small 2-door vehicle (small appliances). 30ch, Large ladder truck (oil can). 40ch, 2-door truck with closed back (match). 60ch, Small truck with ladder and external hose port (gas can).
2w, Old-fashioned fire truck with ladder (cigarette).

**2001, Jan. 20** ***Perf. 12½x12***

**4118-4121** A1819 Set of 4 3.50 1.75
*4121a* Booklet pane of 12, 3 ea. #4118-4121 10.00 —
Complete booklet, #4121a 10.50
*4121b* Sheet of 5, #4118-4121, type of #4122 + label 11.00

**Souvenir Sheet**

**4122** A1819 2w multicolored 4.50 2.25

No. 4121a contains three attached se-tenant blocks of Nos. 4118-4121, arranged horizontally, with inscribed selvage on left and right sides.

Hong Kong 2001 Stamp Exhibition — A1820

1.40w, Black-naped oriole (Oriolus chinensis).

**2001, Feb. 1** ***Perf. 11½***

**4123** A1820 1.40w multicolored 2.75 1.50

Kim Jong Il, 59th Birthday — A1821

10ch, Jong Il Peak in Paekdu Range, *Kimjongilia.*

**2001, Feb. 10** ***Perf. 13½***

**4124** A1821 10ch multicolored .35 .25

New Millenium, Joint Editorial *Rodong Sinmun, Josoninmingun* and *Chongnyonjonwi* Newspapers — A1822

10ch, Flag, symbols of Industry, Agriculture, Transportation

**2001, Mar. 5**

**4125** A1822 10ch multicolored .35 .25

Log Cabin at Revolutionary Headquarters on Mt. Paekdu — A1823

**2001, Mar. 7** ***Perf. 11½***

**4126** A1823 40ch multicolored .70 .30

Kim Il Sung's Birthplace at Mangyongdae — A1824

Portraits of Kim Il Sung — A1825

No. 1428 (each 80ch): a, As child. b, As Jilin-Yuwen Middle School student. c, As anti-Japanese revolutionary. d, As leader in early DPRK period. e, As supreme commander of the Korean People's Army. f, As leader during post-Korean War period. g, Portrait in middle age. h, Portrait in old age.

**2001, Apr. 10** ***Perf. 13½***

**4127** A1824 10ch multicolored .45 .25

**Sheet of 8**

**4128** A1825 Sheet of 8, #a.-#g 11.00 5.75

Day of the Sun.

**Nos. 4106-4112 Overprinted in Gold with Biographical Information**

**2001, Apr. 20**

**4129-4134** A1816 Set of 6 5.75 3.00

**Souvenir Sheet**

**4135** A1817 2.50w multicolored 5.75 3.00

Kim Jong Il — A1826

**2001, Apr. 25** ***Perf. 12***

**4136** A1826 1w multicolored 1.75 .85

Propaganda issue, with the theme "Long Live the Great Victory of Songun Politics!"

Highways — A1827

Designs: 40ch, Pyongyang-Kaesong motorway. 70ch, Pyongyang-Hyangsan tourist expressway. 1.20w, Youth Hero motorway. 1.50w, Pyongyang-Wonsan tourist expressway.

**2001, May 7** ***Perf. 12½x12***

**4137-4140** A1827 Set of 4 6.25 3.00

Historical Pavilions A1828

Designs: 40ch, Ryongwang Pavilion in Pyongyang. 80ch, Inphung Pavilion in Kanggye. 1.50w, Paeksang Pavilion in Anju. 2w, Thonggun Pavilion in Uiju.

**2001, May 15** ***Perf. 13¼***

**4141-4144** A1828 Set of 4 8.00 4.00
*4144a* Booklet pane of 4, #4141-4144 8.00 —
Complete booklet, #4144a 8.50

No. 4144a contains Nos. 4141-4144 in a se-tenant block of four, within decorative selvage.

Education in Class Consciousness — A1829

**2001, June 5**

**4145** A1829 10ch multicolored .35 .25

Korean Birds — A1830

Designs: 10ch, Luscinia svecica. 40ch, Anser anser. 80ch, Diomedea albatrus. 1w, Charadrius dubius. 1.20w, Uria aalge. 1.50w, Delichon urbica.

**2001, June 9** ***Perf. 11½***

**4146** A1830 Sheet of 6, #a.-f. 10.00 5.00
*g.* Booklet pane of 8, #4146c-4146f, 2 ea. #4146a-4146b 11.50 —
Complete booklet, #4146g 12.50

BELGICA 2001 Philatelic Exhibition.
No. 4146g contains the eight stamps in a se-tenant horizontal (4x2) block with inscribed selvage on left and right sides.

Chinese Communist Party, 80th Anniv. — A1831

Designs, each 80ch: No. 4147, Mao Zedong. No. 4148, Deng Xiaoping. No. 4149, Jiang Zemin.

**2001, June 15**

**4147-4149** A1831 Set of 3 4.25 2.00

Compare with Nos. 4226-4228.

Mt. Kumol — A1832

Designs: 10ch, Woljong Temple. 40ch, Revolutionary site. 70ch, Potnamu Pavilion. 1.30w, Rock of Tak Peak. 1.50w, Ryongyon Falls.

**2001, July 9** ***Perf. 12x12¼***

**4150** A1832 Sheet of 5, #a.-e. + label 6.75 3.50

*f.* Booklet pane of 5, #4150a-4150e + label 7.00 —

Complete booklet, #4150f 7.50

No. 4150f contains the stamps and labels of No. 4150 in the same format, but top and bottom marginal selvage is blank, with side selvage containing maple leaf on left and inscriptions on left and right.

Protected Plants A1833

Designs: 10ch, Rheum Coreanum. 40ch, Forsythia densiflora. 1w, Rhododendron yedoense. 2w, Iris setosa.

**2001, July 20** ***Perf. 13½***

**4151-4154** A1833 Set of 4 6.25 3.00

*4154a* Booklet pane of 6, #4152, 4154, 2 ea. #4151, 4153 8.00 —

Complete booklet, #4154a 9.00

No. 4154a contains the six stamps in a se-tenant vertical strip of 6, with inscribed selvage on top and bottom margins.

Orchids — A1834

Designs: 10ch, Eria pannea. 40ch, Cymbidium. 90ch, Sophrolaeliocattleya. 1.60w, Cattleya trianae.

No. 4159: 2w, Cypripedium macranthum.

**2001, Aug. 1**

**4155-4158** A1834 Set of 4 6.75 3.50

*4158a* Booklet pane of 6, #4155-4156, 4158, #4159a, 2 #4157 13.00 —

Complete booklet, #4158a 14.00

### Souvenir Sheet

**4159** A1834 2w multicolored 4.50 2.25

No. 4158a contains the six stamps in a se-tenant horizontal strip of 6, with decorative selvage on left and right sides.

Lighthouses — A1835

Designs: 40ch, Pibaldo Lighthouse. 70ch, Soho Lighthouse. 90ch, Komalsan Lighthouse.

No. 4163: 1.50w, Alsom Lighthouse.

**2001, Aug. 18**

**4160-4162** A1835 Set of 3 4.50 2.25

*4162a* Booklet pane of 6, #4160-4161, 2 #4162, 2 #4163a 14.00 —

Complete booklet, #4162a 14.50

*4162b* Sheet of 4, #4160-4162, 4163a 8.00 4.00

### Souvenir Sheet

**4163** A1835 1.50w multicolored 3.50 1.75

Nos. 4160-4162 were issued both separately in large sheets and together, with the 1.50w value from No. 4163, in a sheet of 5 (No.4162b). No. 4162a contains the six stamps in a horizontal strip of 6, with thin plain selvage.

Kim Po Hyon (1871-1955), Grandfather of Kim Il Sung — A1836

**2001, Aug. 19**

**4164** A1836 1w multicolored 1.75 .85

Protected Animals — A1837

Designs: 10ch, Ciconia nigra. 40ch, Aegypius monachus. 70ch, Hydropotes inermis. 90ch, Nemorhaedus goral.

1.30w, Bubo bubo.

**2001, Sept. 2**

**4165-4168** A1837 Set of 4 4.50 2.25

*4168a* Sheet of 5, #4165-4168, 4169a 8.00 —

*4168b* Booklet pane of 6, #4165-1467, 1469a, 2 x 1468 9.00 —

Complete booklet, #4168b 9.50

### Souvenir Sheet

**4169** A1837 1.30w multicolored 2.75 1.50

Nos. 4165-4168 were issued both separately in large sheets and together, with the 1.30w value from No. No. 4169, in a sheet of 5 (No. 4168a).

No. 4168b contains the six stamps in a se-tenant vertical strip, within narrow decorated selvage.

For surcharge, see No. 4572.

Olympic Games 2008, Beijing — A1838

Designs, each 56ch: a, Deng Ya Ping, Gold medalist ('96), Women's Singles, Table Tennis. b, Jiang Zemin, PRC president. c, Wang Jun Xia, Chinese athlete. d, Li Ning, Chinese gymnast. e, Fu Ming Xia, Chinese diver.

**2001, Sept. 10** ***Perf. 12½***

**4170** A1838 Sheet of 5, #a.-e. 5.75 2.75

Cycle Sports — A1839

Designs: 10ch, Cycle soccer. 40ch, Road racing. 1.50w, Mountainbike racing. 2w, Indoor race.

**2001, Sept. 20** ***Perf. 12***

**4171** A1839 Sheet of 4, #a.-d. 8.00 4.00

Space Exploration — A1840

Designs: 10ch, Yuri Gagarin (1934-68), Soviet Cosmonaut. 40ch, Apollo 11 Moon Landing. 1.50w, *Kwangmyongsong*, North Korean satellite (1998). 2w, Edmund Hailey (1656-1742), Halley's Comet and *Giotto* satellite.

**2001, Sept. 25**

**4172** A1840 Sheet of 4, #a.-d. 7.50 3.50

*e.* Booklet pane of 5, #4172a-4172c, 2 #1472d 12.00 —

Complete booklet, #4172e 13.00

No. 4172e contains five stamps in a se-tenant horizontal strip.

Vladimir Putin and Kim Jong Il — A1841

**2001, Oct. 12** ***Perf. 12½x12***

**4173** A1841 1.50w multicolored 2.50 1.25

Visit of Kim Jong Il to Russia.

Kim Jong Il and Jiang Zemin — A1842

**2001, Oct. 25** ***Perf. 11½x12***

**4174** A1842 1.50w multicolored 2.50 1.25

Meeting between Kim Jong Il and Jiang Zemin, president of the People's Republic of China.

Kim Jong Suk in Battle — A1843

**2001, Nov. 24** ***Perf. 12½x12***

**4175** A1843 1.60w multicolored 3.50 1.75

Kim Jong Suk, anti-Japanese revolutionary hero, 84th birth anniv.

Kim Jong Il Inspecting Troops — A1844

**2001, Dec. 1** ***Perf. 13½***

**4176** A1844 1w multicolored 1.75 .85

10th anniv. of appointment of Kim Jong Il as Supreme Commander of the Korean People's Army.

Chollima Statue — A1845

**2002, Jan. 1**

**4177** A1845 10ch multicolored .35 .25

New Year.

A1846

A1847

Horses from painting *Ten Horses*, by Wang Zhi Cheng (1702-68): 10ch, White horse. 40ch, Bay. 60ch, Pinto. 1.30w, Piebald.

1.60w, Black stallion, from painting *Horse Master Jiu Fang Gao*, by Xu Bei Hong (1895-1953).

**2002, Jan. 1**

| | | | |
|---|---|---|---|
| **4178-4181** | A1846 Set of 4 | 4.25 | 2.00 |
| *4181a* | Sheet of 5, #4178-4181, 4182a | 7.25 | 3.50 |
| *4181b* | Booklet pane of 6, #4178, 4181, 2 each #4179-4180 | 10.00 | — |
| | Complete booklet, #4181b | 10.00 | |

**Souvenir Sheet**

**4182** A1847 1.60w multicolored 2.75 1.50

Traditional New Year — Year of the Horse.

Nos. 4178-4181 were issued both separately in large sheets and together, with the 1.60w value from No. 4182, in a sheet of 5 (No. 4181a).

Complete booklet sold for 3.60w.

Flower Basket — A1848

Kim Jong Il with Soldiers — A1849

Kim Jong Il — A1850

Kim Il Sung, Kim Jong Il, Kim Jong Suk — A1851

**2002, Feb. 1** ***Perf. 13½***

**4183** A1848 10ch multicolored .35 .25

**Souvenir Sheets**

**4184** A1849 1.50w multicolored 2.75 1.50

***Perf. 11½x12***

**4185** A1850 2w multicolored 3.50 1.75

***Perf. 12x12½***

**4186** A1851 Sheet of 3, #a.-c. 6.75 3.50

Kim Jong Il, 60th Birthday.

No. 4185 bears a metallic gold application.

Centenary of First Zeppelin Flight — A1852

Designs: 40ch, LZ-1. 80ch, LZ-120. 1.20w, Zeppelin NT.

2.40w, Zeppelin NT (different view).

**2002, Feb. 5** ***Perf. 12***

| | | | |
|---|---|---|---|
| **4187-4189** | A1852 Set of 3 | 4.25 | 2.00 |
| *4189a* | Sheet of 4, #4187-4189, 4190a | 8.50 | 4.25 |

**Souvenir Sheet**

| | | | |
|---|---|---|---|
| **4190** | A1852 2.40w multicolored | 4.25 | 2.00 |
| *a.* | Booklet pane of 4, #4187-4190 | *16.00* | — |
| | Complete booklet, #4190a | *16.00* | |

Nos. 4187-4187 were issued both separately in large sheets and together, with the 2.40w value from No. 4190, in a sheet of 4 (No. 4189a). Complete booklet sold for 4.90w.

Banner, Torch, Soldiers — A1853

**2002, Feb. 25** ***Perf. 13½***

**4191** A1853 10ch multicolored .35 .25

Annual joint editorial of the three state newspapers, *Rodong Sinmun, Josoninmingum* and *Chongnyonjonwi.*

Mushrooms — A1854

Designs: a, 10ch, Collybia confluons. b, 40ch, Sparassis laminosa. c, 80ch, Amanita vaginata. d, 1.20w, Russia integra. e, 1.50w, Pholiota squarrosa.

**2002, Feb. 25** ***Perf. 13½***

| | | | |
|---|---|---|---|
| **4192** | A1854 Block of 5, #a-e + label | 7.50 | 3.75 |
| *f.* | Booklet pane of 5, #4192a-4192e, + label | *19.00* | — |
| | Complete booklet, #4192f | *19.00* | |

Complete booklet sold for 4.20w.

A1855

A1856

Kim Il Sung (1912-1994) — A1857

Designs: 10ch, Kim Il Sung's birthplace, *Kimsungilia.*

Nos. 4198-4200 (each 1.50w): No, 4198, Kim Il Sung with Kim Jong Suk (1941). No. 4199, Kim Il Sung as student, with black cap (1927). No. 4200, Kim Il Sung and Kim Chaek, political commissar.

No. 4201: 2w, Portrait of Kim Il Sung.

**2002, Mar. 15** ***Perf. 13½***

**4197** A1855 10ch multicolored .35 .25

**Souvenir Sheets**

**4198-4200** A1856 1.50w Set of 3 6.75 3.50

**With Gold Metallic Application**

***Perf. 11½x12***

**4201** A1857 2w multicolored 3.50 1.75

Kang Pan Suk — A1858

**2002, Mar. 21** ***Perf. 11½x11¾***

**4202** A1858 1w multicolored 1.75 .85

Kang Pan Sok, mother of Kim Il Sung, 110th birth anniv.

20th April Spring Friendship Art Festival — A1859

**2002, Mar. 25** ***Perf. 13¼***

**4203** A1859 10ch multicolored .60 .25

Locomotives A1860

Designs: 10ch, Kanghaenggun 1.5-01 electric train. 40ch, Samjiyon 1001 electric train. 1.50w, Steam locomotive. 2w, Steam locomotive, diff.

No. 4208, 2w, Pulgungi 5112 diesel locomotive.

**2002, Apr. 10** ***Perf. 11½***

**4204-4207** A1860 Set of 4 6.75 3.50

**Souvenir Sheet**

**4208** A1860 2w multicolored 3.50 1.75

*a.* Booklet pane of 5, #4204-4208 27.50 —

Complete booklet, #4208a *27.50*

For surcharge, see No. 4566. Complete booklet sold for 6.20w.

He Baozhen, 100th Anniv. Birth — A1861

Designs: a, 1w, He Baozhen and Liu Shaoqi in 1923. b, 40ch, He Baozhen's family. c, 30ch, Family home in Dao xian County, Henan Province. d, 10ch, Letter in Chinese, from Liu Ying, a wife of Zhang Wentian, Chinese Communist Party official. e, 20ch, Monument at He Baozhen's birthplace.

**2002, Apr. 20** ***Perf. 13¼***

**4209** A1861 Sheet of 5, #a.-e. 3.50 1.75

He Baozhen, first wife of Liu Shaoqi, Chairman of the People's Republic of China 1959-68.

Shells A1862

Designs: 10ch, Cristaria plicata. 40ch, Lanceolaria cospidata kuroda. 1w, Schistodesmus lampreyanus. 1.50w, Lamprotula coreana.

**2002, Apr. 21**

**4210-4213** A1862 Set of 4 5.75 2.75

*4213a* Booklet pane of 6, #4212-4213. 2 each #4210-4211 15.00 —

Complete booklet, #4213a *15.00*

For surcharge, see No. 4601. Complete booklet sold for 3.70w.

A1863

Korean People's Army, 70th Anniv. — A1864

Designs: 10ch, Soldier, sailor, pilot, symbolizing the three branches of the armed forces.

1.60w, Kim Il Sung and Kim Jong Il walking with army officers and political functionaries.

**2002, Apr. 25** ***Perf. 12¼x11¾***

**4214** A1863 10ch multicolored .35 .25

**Souvenir Sheet**

**4215** A1864 1.60w multicolored 2.75 1.50

Legend 'Arirang' — A1865

Designs: a, 10ch, Ri Rang and Song Bu as children. b, 40ch, As young adults. c, 50ch, Ri Rang killing the landlord. d, 1.50w, Song Bu.

**2002, Apr. 28** ***Perf. 13¼***

**4216** A1865 Sheet of 4, #a.-d. 4.25 2.00

A1866

Mass Gymnastics and Artistic Performance of 'Arirang' — A1867

Designs: 10ch, Actors. 20ch, Cartoon characters. 30ch, Dancer holding fan. 40ch, Dancer, gymnasts with hoops.

1w, Dancer with tambourine.

**2002, Apr. 28** ***Perf. 12¼***

**4217-4220** A1866 Set of 4 1.75 .85

**Souvenir Sheet**

**4221** A1867 1w multicolored 2.00 1.00

Nos. 4217-4220 were each issued in sheets of 6, with pictorial margins and Arirang logo.

Symbols of Modern Science & Industry A1868

**2002, May 2** ***Perf. 13¼***

**4222** A1868 10ch multicolored .35 .25

Science and Technology promotion: "Science and Technology are the Driving Force of Building a Great Prosperous Powerful Nation."

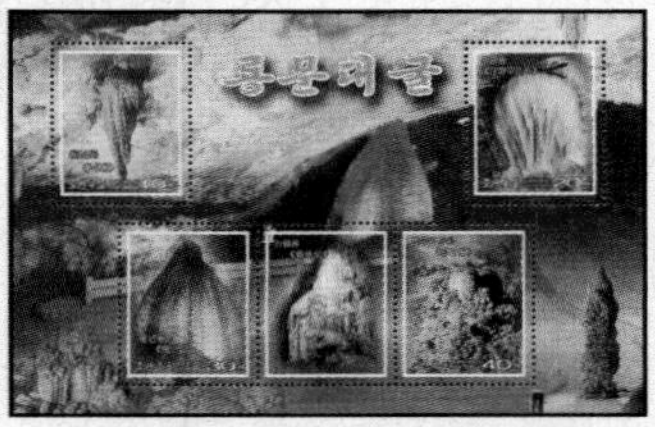

Ryongmun Cavern — A1869

Designs: a, 10ch, Pink stalactite. b, 20ch, Green stalactite. c, 30ch, Golden stalagmite. d, 40ch, Rough-surfaced orange stalagmite.

**2002, May 25** ***Perf. 11½***

**4223** A1869 Sheet of 4, #a.-d. 2.75 1.50

Monument — A1870

**2002, May 2** ***Perf. 13¼***

**4224** A1870 10ch multicolored .35 .25

30th Anniv. of the Elucidation of the Three Principles for National Reunification.

Butterflies — A1871

Designs: a, 10ch, Stauropus fagi. b, 40ch, Agrias claudina. c, 1.50w, Catocala nupta. d, 2w, Morpho rhetenor.

**2002, June 30** ***Perf. 11¾***

**4225** A1871 Block of 4, #a.-d. 8.50 4.25

*e.* Booklet pane of 5, #4225a, 4225c-4225d, 2 #4225b *17.50* —

Complete booklet, #4225e *17.50*

Complete booklet sold for 4.60w.

**Nos. 4147-4149 with Added Flags in Margins**

A1872

**2002, June 30** ***Perf. 11½***

**4226-4228** A1872 Set of 3 sheets 4.75 2.25

16th National Congress of the Communist Party of China, Beijing, Nov. 8-14.

Compare with Nos. 4147-4149.

Elderly Man, Child, Hospital A1873

**2002, July 5** ***Perf. 12¼***

**4229** A1873 10ch multicolored .35 .25

50th Anniv. of Universal Free Medical System.

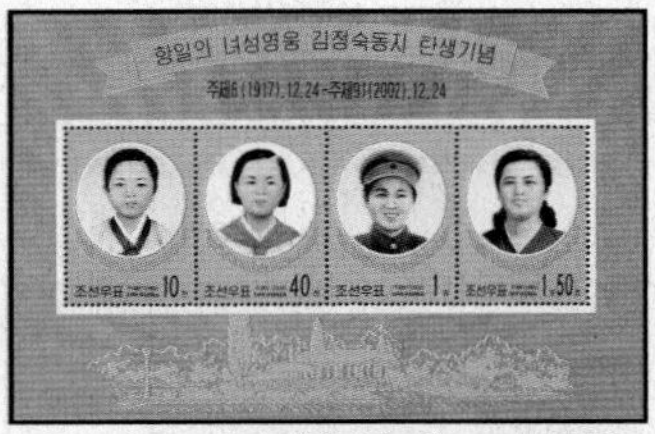

Kim Jong Suk (1917-49) — A1874

Designs: a, 10ch, As child. b, 40ch, As young woman in Children's Corps. c, 1w, In army uniform. d, 1.50w, With long hair, in civilian clothing.

**2002, July 20** ***Perf. 13¼***

**4230** A1874 Sheet of 4, #a.-d. 2.50 1.25

Kim Jong Suk, first wife of Kim Il Sung and mother of Kim Jong Il.

Soldier, Worker, Farmer — A1875

**2002, July 29** ***Perf. 11½***

**4231** A1875 10ch multicolored .35 .25

30th anniv. of the DPRK Constitution.

A1876

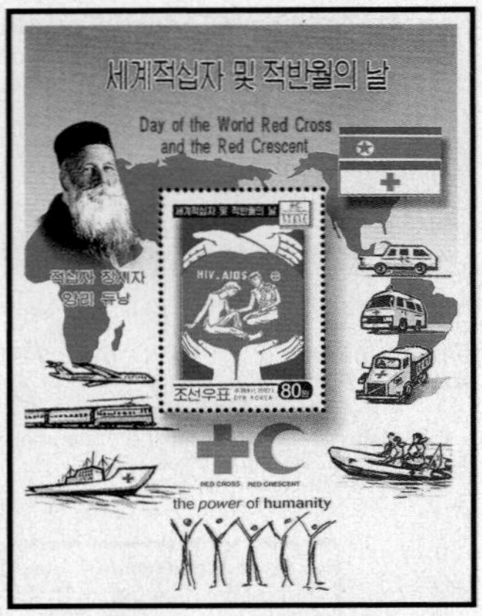


World Red Cross & Red Crescent Day — A1877

No. 4232: a, 3w, Korean returnees. b, 12w, Red Cross medics administering first aid. c, 150w, North Korean truck delivering aid to South Korean flood victims.
No. 4233: 80w, AIDS victim, family.

**2002, Sept. 20** ***Perf. 13¼***

**Sheet of 6**

| | | | | |
|---|---|---|---|---|
| **4232** | A1876 | Sheet, 2 each #a.-c. | 5.75 | 2.50 |

**Souvenir Sheet**

| | | | | |
|---|---|---|---|---|
| **4233** | A1877 80w multicolored | | 1.75 | .85 |
| *a.* | Booklet pane of 5, #4232c, 4233, 2 each #4232a, 4232b | | *11.00* | — |
| | Complete booklet, #4233a | | *11.00* | |

Complete booklet sold for 2.75w.

Hong Chang Su, 2000 World Super-Flyweight Boxing Champion — A1878

**2002, Sept. 25** ***Perf. 11½***

| | | | | |
|---|---|---|---|---|
| **4234** | A1878 | 75w multicolored | 1.75 | .85 |

Kim Jong Il with Pres. Putin — A1879

Kim Jong Il Shaking Hands with Pres. Putin — A1880

No. 4235 measures 85x70mm, No. 4236 120x100mm.

**2002, Oct. 15** ***Perf. 13¼***

**Souvenir Sheets**

| | | | | |
|---|---|---|---|---|
| **4235** | A1879 | 70w multicolored | 1.75 | .85 |
| **4236** | A1880 | 120w multicolored | 2.25 | 1.10 |

Kim Jong Il's Visit to Russia

Siamese Cat — A1881

Cavalier King Charles Spaniel — A1882

Designs: 12w, Phungsan dog. 100w, White shorthair cat. 150w, Black and white shorthair cat.

**2002, Oct. 20** ***Perf. 12***

| | | | | |
|---|---|---|---|---|
| **4237-4240** | A1881 | Set of 4 | 5.75 | 2.75 |
| *4240a* | | Booklet pane of 6, #4239-4240, 2 each #4237-4238 | *16.00* | — |
| | | Complete booklet, #4240a | *16.00* | |

**Souvenir Sheet**

| | | | | |
|---|---|---|---|---|
| **4241** | A1882 | 150w multicolored | 3.50 | 1.75 |
| *a.* | | Inscr. "World Philatelic Exhibition Bangkok 2003" and emblem in margin | 3.50 | 1.75 |

No. 4241a issued 10/4/2003. Complete booklet sold for 295w. No. 4240a exists imperforate.

Minerals — A1883

Designs: a, 3w, Pyrite. b, 12w, Magnetite. c, 130w, Calcite. d, 150w, Galena.

**2002, Oct. 25** ***Perf. 13¼***

| | | | | |
|---|---|---|---|---|
| **4242** | A1883 | Block of 4, #a-d | 6.25 | 3.50 |
| *e.* | | Booklet pane of 5, #4242am 4242cm 4242d, 2 each #4242b | *15.00* | — |
| | | Complete booklet, #4242e | *15.00* | — |

Complete booklet sold for 322w.

Kim Jong Il and PM Junichiro Signing Declaration — A1884

Kim Jong Il with Japanese Prime Minister Koizumi Junichiro — A1885

Japan-Korea Bilateral Declaration
No. 4246 measures 90x80mm, No. 4247 75x65mm.

**2002, Oct. 25** **Souvenir Sheets**

| | | | | |
|---|---|---|---|---|
| **4246** | A1884 | 120w multicolored | 2.25 | 1.10 |
| **4247** | A1885 | 150w multicolored | 3.50 | 1.75 |

Kim Il Sung's Birthplace, Mangyongdae — A1886

Kim Jong Il's Birthplace, Mt. Paektu — A1887

Kim Jong Suk's Birthplace, Hoeryong A1888

*Kimilsungia* A1889

Torch, Tower of Juche Idea A1890

DPRK Flag A1891

*Kimjongilia* A1892

Magnolia Blossom A1893

DPRK Coat of Arms A1894

Chollima Statue A1895

Victory Monument A1896

Party Founding Monument — A1897

***Perf. 11½, 13¼x13½ (#4252-4253, 4256-4259)***

**2002, Nov. 20**

| | | | | |
|---|---|---|---|---|
| **4248** | A1886 | 1w violet brn | .25 | .25 |
| **4249** | A1887 | 3w blue green | .25 | .25 |
| **4250** | A1888 | 5w olive brn | .25 | .25 |
| **4251** | A1889 | 10w dk lilac rose | .25 | .25 |
| **4252** | A1890 | 12w dk reddish brn | .25 | .25 |
| **4253** | A1891 | 20w dp blue & red | .40 | .25 |
| **4254** | A1892 | 30w brnsh red | .60 | .25 |
| **4255** | A1893 | 40w dp grnsh blue | .75 | .40 |
| **4256** | A1894 | 50w dk brown | .85 | .50 |
| **4257** | A1895 | 70w dk olive grn | 1.10 | .60 |
| **4258** | A1896 | 100w brown | 1.75 | .85 |
| **4259** | A1897 | 200w dk lilac rose | 3.50 | 1.75 |
| | | *Nos. 4248-4259 (12)* | 10.20 | 5.85 |

See No. 4877. For surcharges, see Nos. 4877A, 4877F.

New Year — A1898

**2003, Jan. 1** ***Perf. 13¼***

| | | | | |
|---|---|---|---|---|
| **4260** | A1898 | 3w multicolored | .35 | .25 |

A1899

Animated Film, *Antelopes Defeat Bald Eagles* — A1900

Designs: 3w, Mother antelope pleading with bald eagle stealing her baby. 50w, Antelopes uniting to defeat bald eagle. 70w, Bald eagle eating fish poisoned by antelopes. 100w, Mother antelope reunited with her child.
150w, Antelopes carrying litter full of fruit.

**2003, Jan. 1**

**4261-4264** A1899 Set of 4 3.00 1.50
*4264a* Booklet pane of 8, 2 each #4261-4264 *25.00* —
Complete booklet, #4264a *25.00*

**Souvenir Sheet**

**4265** A1900 150w multicolored 1.75 .85

Complete booklet sold for 461w.

Folk Festivals A1901

Designs: 3w, Mother and children greeting Full Moon (Lunar New Year, Jan. 15). 12w, Dancers with Full Moon (Lunar New Year). 40w, Two girls on swing (Spring Festival). 70w, Mother and daughter laying flowers on anti-Japanese martyrs' monument (Hangawi - Harvest Moon Festival). 140w, Peasant dance (Hangawi - Harvest Moon Festival).
112w, Wresting (Spring Festival).

**2003, Jan. 20** ***Perf. 11¾***

**4266-4270** A1901 Set of 5 3.25 1.50

**Souvenir Sheet**

**4271** A1901 112w multicolored 1.75 .75

Soldier A1902

**2003, Feb. 14** ***Perf. 13¼***

**4272** A1902 12w multicolored .50 .25

Annual joint editorial of the three state newspapers, *Rodong Sinmun, Josoninmingum* and *Chongnyonjonwi.*

Weapons, Proclamation A1903

**2003, Feb. 15**

**4273** A1903 30w multicolored .60 .25

North Korean withdrawal from the Nuclear Non-Proliferation Treaty.

Ode Monument — A1904

Sunrise at Mt. Paektu — A1905

**2003, Feb. 16** ***Perf. 12¼x11¼***

**4274** A1904 3w multicolored .35 .25

**Souvenir Sheet**

**4275** A1905 75w multicolored 1.10 .60

Kim Jong Il, 61st Birthday.

A1906

Ships — A1907

Designs: 15w, Cargo ship *Paekmagang.* 50w, Dredger *Konsol.* 70w, Passenger ship *Undok No. 2.* 112w, Cargo ship *Piryugang.*
150w, Excursion ship *Pyongyang No. 1.*

**2003, Feb. 18** ***Perf. 13½***

**4276-4279** A1906 Set of 4 3.50 1.75
*4279a* Booklet pane of 6, #4276-4277, 2 each #4278-4279 *20.00* —
Complete booklet, #4279a *20.00*

**Souvenir Sheet**

**4280** A1907 150w multicolored 2.00 1.00

Complete booklet sold for 444w.

A1908

Cars Used by Kim Il Sung — A1909

Designs: 3w, *Zis.* 14w, *Gaz.* 70w, *Pobeda.* 90w, *Mercedes Benz.*
150w, Painting by Kim San Gon *Delaying His Urgent Journey.*

**2003, Feb. 20** ***Perf. 11¾***

**4281-4284** A1908 Set of 4 2.50 1.25
*4284a* Booklet pane of 6, #4281-4282, 2 each #4283-4284 *18.50* —
Complete booklet, #4284a *18.50*

**Souvenir Sheet**

**4285** A1909 150w multicolored 2.25 1.10

Complete booklet sold for 352w.

Book — A1910

**2003, Mar. 15** **Souvenir Sheet**

**4286** A1910 120w multicolored 2.00 .90

*On the Art of Cinema,* by Kim Jong Il, 30th anniv. of publication.

Army Trumpeter, Map, Soldiers Marching — A1911

**2003, Mar. 16**

**4287** A1911 15w multicolored .35 .25

80th anniv. of Kim Il Sung's "250-mile Journey for Learning."

Soldier & Workers — A1912

**2003, Mar. 29**

**4288** A1912 3w multicolored .25 .25

Propaganda issue: "Let us meet the requirements of Songun in ideological viewpoint, fighting spirit and way of life!"

A1913

Election of Kim Jong Il as Chairman of the DPRK National Defense Commission, 10th Anniv. — A1914

Designs: 3w, Flags, "10."
No. 4290: a, 12w, Kim Jong Il with computer. b, 70w, Kim with military officers, pointing. c, 112w, Kim, with military officers, hand raised.

**2003, Apr. 9**

**4289** A1913 3w multicolored .25 .25

**Souvenir Sheet**

**4290** A1914 Sheet of 3, #a.-c. 4.00 2.00

Kim Il Sung's Birthplace, Mangyongdae, *Kimsungilia* — A1915

**2003, Apr. 15**

**4291** A1915 3w multicolored .25 .25

Day of the Sun—Kim Il Sung, 91st birth anniv.

A1916

Medals and Orders Presented to Kim Il Sung — A1917

Designs: 12w, Order of Suhbaatar (Mongolia, 1953). 35w, National Order of Grand Cross (Madagascar, 1985). 70w, Order of Lenin (USSR, 1987). 140w, Order of Playa Giron (Cuba, 1987).
120w, Kim Il Sung being presented with medal by Fidel Castro (1986).

**2003, Apr. 15** ***Perf. 13¼***

**4292-4295** A1916 Set of 4 4.00 2.00

**Souvenir Sheet**

***Perf. 13¼***

**4296** A1917 120w multicolored 1.75 .75

Insects — A1918

Designs: a, 15w, *Pantala flavescens.* b, 70w, *Tibicen japonicus.* c, 220w, Xylotrupes dichotomus. d, 300w, *Lycaena dispar.*

**2003, Apr. 20** ***Perf. 13¼***

**4297** A1918 Sheet of 4, #a.-d. 10.00
*e.* Booklet pane of 6, #4297c, 4297d, 2 each #4297a-4297b *20.00* —
Complete booklet, #4297e *20.00*

Complete booklet sold for 705w.

Korean National Dishes — A1919

Designs: 3w, Glutinous rice cake. 30w, Thongkimchi. 70w, Sinsollo.
120w, Pyongyang cold noodles.

**2003, May 1** ***Perf. 11¾***

**4298-4300** A1919 Set of 3 1.75 .85

**Souvenir Sheet**

**4301** A1919 120w multicolored 1.75 .85

Victory Monument, Battle in Musan Area — A1920

**2003, May 19** ***Perf. 12¾***

**4302** A1920 90w multicolored 1.50 .75

Ryangchon Temple — A1921

Designs: 3w, Manse Pavilion. 12w, Buddhist statues. 40w, Painting of Buddha with two saints. 50w, Painting of Buddha with four saints.
120w, Taeung Hall, main shrine of temple.

**2003, May 30** ***Perf. 13¼***

**4303-4306** A1921 Set of 4 2.00 1.00

**Souvenir Sheet**

**4307** A1921 120w multicolored 2.00 1.00

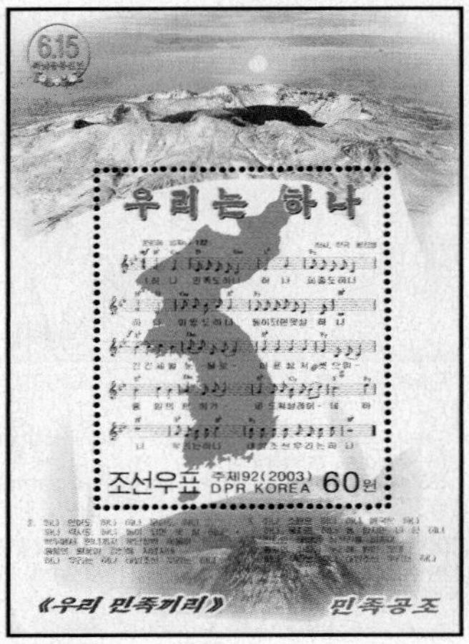

Map, Song "We Are One" — A1922

**2003, June 1**

**4308** A1922 60w multicolored 1.10 .50

Wild Animals — A1923

Designs: a, 3w, Tigers. b, 70w, Bears. c, 150w, Wild boars. d, 230w, Roe deer.

**2003, June 10**

**4309** A1923 Sheet of 4, #a.-d. 2.50
*e.* Booklet pane of 4, #4309a-4309d 30.00 —
Complete booklet, #4309e 30.00

Complete booklet sold for 460w.

Public Bonds of 1950, 2003 A1924

**2003, July 25** ***Perf. 13½***

**4310** A1924 140w multicolored 2.50 1.25

Campaign to promote purchase of public bonds.

A1925

A1926

DPRK "Victory" in Korean War, 50th Anniv. — A1927

Designs: 3w, Distinguished Service Medal.
No. 4312: Kim Il Sung in commander's uniform.
No. 4313: a, 12w, Kim delivering radio address. 35w, Kim talking to soldiers. c, 70w, Kim ratifying armistace agreement. d, 140w, Kim in uniform.
No. 4314: a, 12w, Kim smiling, surrounded by soldiers. 35w, Kim inspecting soldier. c, 70w, Kim Il Sung, Kim Jong Il inspecting army training. d, 140w, Middle-aged Kim Il Sung in suit and tie.
No. 4315: a, 12w, Kim Jong Il receiving bouquet from female soldier. 35w, Kim Jong Il being applauded by soldiers. c, 70w, Kim Jong Il on military inspection. d, 140w, Smiling Kim Jong Il.

**2003, July 27** ***Perf. 13¼***

**4311** A1925 3w multicolored .25 .25

**Souvenir Sheet**

**4312** A1926 120w multicolored 2.00 1.00

**Sheets of 4**

***Perf. 11½***

**4313-4315** A1927 Set of 3 13.50 6.50

Orchids — A1928

Designs: a, 3w, Minicattleya coerulea. b, 100w, Phalanopsis aphrodite. c, 150w, Calanthe discolor. d, 200w, Dendrobium snowflake.

**2003, July 29** ***Perf. 13¼***

**4316** A1928 Sheet of 4, #a.-d. 8.25 4.00
*e.* Booklet pane of 4, #4316a-4316d 8.25 —
Complete booklet, #4316e 8.75

No. 4316e contains Nos. 4316a-4316d in a horizontal strip of four, with selvage similar to that of No. 4316.

A1929

Birds — A1930

Designs: 12w, Grus vipio. 70w, Nycticorax nycticorax. 100w, Columba livia var doestricus. 120w, Nymphicus hollandicus. 150w, Strix aluco.
225w, Pseudogyps africanus.

**2003, Aug. 4** ***Perf. 13¼***

**4317-4321** A1929 Set of 5 7.00 3.50
*4321a* Booklet pane of 6, #4317-4318, 4320-4321, 2 #4319 *19.50* —
Complete booklet, #4321a *19.50*

**Souvenir Sheet**

***Perf. 11¾***

**4322** A1930 225w multicolored 3.50 2.10

Complete booklet sold for 567w.

Arctic & Antarctic Animals — A1931

Designs: a, 15w, Adelie penguins (Pygoscelis adeliae). b, 70w, Walrus (Odobenus rosmarus). c, 140w, Polar bear and cubs (Thalarctos maritimus). d, 150w, Bowhead whale (Balaena mysticetus). e, 220w, Spotted seals (Phoca largha).

**2003, Aug. 20** ***Perf. 11½***

**4323** A1931 Sheet of 5, #a.-e. + label 11.00 5.25
*a.* Booklet pane of 5 + label —
Complete booklet 15.00

No. 4323a contains one pane, with stamps and label in same arrangement as in No. 4323, surrounded by selvage containing a distinctive arrangement of Polar animals on a primarily yellowish background.

Mushrooms — A1932

Designs: a, 3w, Pholiota flammans. b, 12w, Geastrum fimbriatum. c, 70w, Coprinus atramentarius. d, 130w, Pleuotus cornucopiae. 250w, Elfvingia applanata.

**2003, Sept. 5** *Perf. 13¼*

**4324** A1932 Block of 4, #a-d 4.00 2.10

**Souvenir Sheet**

**4328** A1932 250w multicolored 4.75 2.40
- *a.* Booklet pane of 5, #4324a-4324d, 4328 *23.00* —
- Complete booklet, #4328a *23.00*

Complete booklet sold for 480w. No. 4328a exists imperforate.

Korean Stamp Exhibition Hall — A1933

Korean Stamps, Interior of Hall — A1934

**2003, Sept. 5**

**4329** A1933 3w multicolored .30 .30
**4330** A1934 60w multicolored 1.25 .50

Korean Stamp Exhibition celebrating the 55th anniversary of the DPRK and the inauguration of the Korean Stamp Exhibition Hall.

A1935

A1936

55th Anniv. Founding of DPRK — A1937

Designs: 3w, DPRK Arms, Flag.
No. 4332: Kim Il Sung.
Sheets of 2 with central label: No. 4333: a, 60w, "The Birth of a New Korea" (Kim saluting marchers carrying DPRK flag). b, 60w, "In the Period of Building a New Korea" (Kim Jong Suk and factory workers). No. 4334: a, 60w, "Braving Through a Rain of Bullets Personally" (Kim in jeep in war zone). b, 60w, "Comrade Kim Il Sung, Ever-Victorious Iron-Willed Commander, Personally Commanding the Battle at Height 1211" (Kim on bluff, pointing to battlefield.) No. 4335: a, 60w, "We Trust and Follow Only You, the Leader" (Kim being greeted by villagers). b, 60w, "The Great Leader Kim Il Sung Giving On-the-Spot Guidance to the Pukchang Thermal Power Station" (Kim and factory workers). No. 4336: a, 60w, "The Victory of Korean Revolution Will Be Ensured by the Arms in Our Hand" (Kim speaking to soldiers, Kim Jong Il standing behind). b, 60w, "Keeping Up Songun Politics as All-Powerful Means" (Smiling Kim walking with soldiers symbolizing modern arms).

**2003, Sept. 9** *Perf. 11½*

**4331** A1935 3w multicolored .30 .30

**Souvenir Sheet**

***Perf. 13¼***

**4332** A1936 120w multicolored 2.40 1.25

**Sheets of 2, #a.-b. + label**

***Perf. 12¼x12***

**4333-4336** A1937 Set of 4 7.00 3.50

Mao Zedong, 110th Birth Anniv. — A1938

No. 4337: a, 20w, Young Mao speaking at political meeting; b, 30w, Mao walking on shore with woman carrying manuscript. No. 4338: a, 30w, Mao addressing Red partisans; b, 30w, Mao (wearing trenchcoat) leading partisans in field. No. 4339: a, 20w, Mao talking with workers, soldiers; b, 30w, Mao in casual setting, leading discussion with soldiers. No. 4340: a, 30w, Mao addressing crowd in Beijing; b, 30w, Mao with people of various races and nationalities.

No. 4341: Sheet containing Nos. 4337-4338, with attached large label depicting 110 stamps picturing Mao and denominated 140w, the price for which the sheet was sold. No. 4342: Same, but containing Nos. 4339-4340.

**2003, Dec. 26** *Perf. 13¼*

**Se-Tenant Pairs with Label Between**

**4337-4340** A1938 Set of 4 4.00 2.10

**Souvenir Sheets**

**4341-4342** A1938 Set of 2 4.75 2.40

New Year — A1939

Design: 2w, Soldier, workers, tower.

**2004, Jan. 1** *Perf. 11½*

**4343** A1939 3w multicolored .30 .30

For surcharge, see No. 4877B.

A1940

Monkeys — A1941

Designs: 3w, *Cebus apella*. 60w, *Papio doguera*. 70w, *Cercopithecus aethiops*. 100w, *Saguinus oedipus*. 155w, *Macaca mulatta*.

**2004, Jan. 1**

**4344-4347** A1940 Set of 4 4.75 2.40

**Souvenir Sheet**

**4348** A1941 155w multicolored 3.00 2.40
- *a.* Booklet pane of 5, #4344-4348 23.00 —
- Complete booklet, #4348a 23.00

Complete booklet sold for 403w. See Nos. 4351-4355.

Lunar New Year's Day — A1942

**2004, Jan. 1**

**4349** A1942 3w multicolored .30 .30

**Souvenir Sheet**

First Chinese Manned Space Flight — A1943

Designs: a, 91w, Yang Liwei, first Chinese cosmonaut (46mm diameter). b, 98w, Landing capsule, parachute, helicopter (54x45mm).

***Perf. 13¼, Perf. (#4350a)***

**2004, Jan. 30**

**4350** A1943 Sheet of 2, #a.-b. 3.00 1.50
- *c.* Booklet pane, 2 each #4350a-4350b — —
- Complete booklet, #4350c —
- *d.* #4350 with Hong Kong 2004 emblem opvt. in sheet margin 3.00 1.50

Booklets containing No. 4350c were issued with and without the Hong Kong 2004 emblem on the cover.

**Nos. 4344-4348 with Hong Kong 2004 Emblem**

**2004, Jan. 30**

**4351-4354** A1940 Set of 4 4.75 2.40

**Souvenir Sheet**

**4355** A1941 155w multicolored 3.00 1.50

Joint Editorial *Rodong Sinmun, Josoninmingun* and *Chongnyonjonwi* Newspapers — A1944

**2004, Feb. 15** *Perf. 13¼*

**4357** A1944 3w multicolored .30 .30

A1945

Kim Jong Il, 62nd Birthday — A1946

No. 4358: 3w, Kim Jong Il's birthplace, Mt. Paektu.

No. 4359 (each 30w): a, "The Thaw of Sobaek Stream" (Spring). b, "The Thunderclap of Jong Il Peak" (Summer). c, "The Secret Camp in Autumn" (Autumn). d, "Hoarfrost in February" (Winter).

**2004, Feb. 16** *Perf. 11½*

**4358** A1945 3w multicolored .30 .30

**Souvenir Sheet**

***Perf. 13¼***

**4359** A1946 Sheet of 4, #a.-d. 2.40 1.25

Kim Jong Il — A1947

**2004, Feb. 19** ***Perf. 13¼***

**4360** A1947 120w multicolored 2.40 1.25

30th anniv. of publication of the *Program of Modelling the Whole Society on the Juche Idea.*

Rural Village A1948

Kim Il Sung and Farmers — A1949

**2004, Feb. 25** ***Perf. 11½***

**4361** A1948 3w multicolored .30 .30

**Souvenir Sheet**

***Perf. 12½ x11¾***

**4362** A1949 120w multicolored 2.10 2.10

40th anniv. of publication of the "Theses on the Socialist Rural Question in Our Country."

Lighthouses — A1950

Designs: a, 3w, Sokgundo Lighthouse. b, 12w, Yubundo Lighthouse. c, 100w, Jangdokdo Lighthouse. d, 195w, Amryongdan Lighthouse.

**2004, Mar. 20** ***Perf. 11¾x12½***

**4363** A1950 Sheet of 4, #a.-d. 6.00 3.00
*e.* Booklet pane of 4, #4363a-4363d 6.00 —
Complete booklet, #4363e 6.50

No. 4363e contains Nos. 4363a-4363d in a horizontal strip of 4, surrounded by a seashore selvage.

A1951

Board Games — A1952

Designs: a, 3w, Korean Chess. b, 12w, Goe. c, 90w, Yut. d, 120w, Kknoni (Chinese Checkers).

98w, Playing Korean Chess.

**2004, Mar. 20** ***Perf. 13¼***

**4364** A1951 Sheet of 4, #a.-d. 4.75 2.40
*e.* Booklet pane of 5, #4364a-4364b. 4364d, 2 x 4364c 6.00 —
Complete booklet, #4363e 6.50

**Souvenir Sheet**

**4365** A1952 98w multicolored 2.40 1.25

No. 4364e contains Nos. 4364a-4364d in a horizontal strip of 5, which includes a second copy of the 90w value, with a distinctive printed selvage.

Kim Il Sung's Birthplace, Mangyongdae — A1953

Kim Il Sung — A1954

**2004, Apr. 15** ***Perf. 13¼***

**4366** A1953 3w multicolored .30 .30

**Souvenir Sheet**

***Perf. 11¾***

**4367** A1954 120w multicolored 2.10 1.10

Kim Il Sung, 92nd birth anniv.

A1955

Tok Islands — A1956

No. 4368: a, 3w, 19th century map of Korea. b, 12w, Western island. c, 106w, Eastern island.

No. 4369: 116w, Both islands, sea gulls.

**2004, Apr. 20** ***Perf. 11½***

**4368** A1955 Sheet, #a.-c. + label 3.00 1.50

**Souvenir Sheet**

***Perf.***

**4369** A1956 116w multicolored 2.40 1.25
*a.* Booklet pane of 4, #4368a-4368c, 4369 — —
Complete booklet, #4369a —

Fossils — A1957

No. 4370: a, 3w, Calcinoplax antiqua. b, 12w, Podozamites lanceolatus. c, 70w, Comptonia naumannii. d, 140w, Clinocardium asagaiense.

No. 4371: 120w, Tingia carbonica.

**2004, May 20** ***Perf. 13¼***

**4370** A1957 Sheet of 4, #a.-d. 4.75 2.40
*e.* Booklet pane of 5, #4370a-4370d, #4371a 6.00 —
Complete booklet, #4370e 6.50 —

**Souvenir Sheet**

***Perf. 12½***

**4371** A1957 120w multicolored 2.40 1.25
*a.* single stamp 2.40 1.25

Cacti — A1958

No. 4372: a, 70w, *Notocactus leninghausii.* b, 90w, *Echinocactus grusonii.* c, 100w, *Gymnocalycium baldianum.* d, 140w, *Mammillaria insularis.*

**2004, June 2** ***Perf. 11¾x12¼***

**4372** A1958 Sheet of 4, #a.-d. 6.00 3.00
*e.* Ovptd. "World Stamp Championship 2004" and Singapore 2004 emblem in margin 6.00 3.00
*f.* Booklet pane of 4, #4372a-4372d *16.00* —
Complete booklet, #4372f *16.00*

Complete booklet sold for 416w. No. 4372e was issued 8/28.

A1959

Unofficial Visit of Kim Jong Il to China — A1960

No. 4373: a, 74w, Kim Jong Il with Hu Jintao, President of the People's Republic of China.

No. 4374: a, 3w, Kim shaking hands with Hu Jintao. b, 12w, Kim with Jiang Zemin, President of China 1997-2003. c, 40w, Kim with Wu Bangguo, Chinese Communist Party leader. d, 60w, Kim clapping hands at outdoor reception.

No. 4375: a, 3w, Kim with Wen Jiabao, Premier of the State Council of the PRC. b, 12w, Kim with Jia Qinglin, Chinese Communist Party leader. c, 40w, Kim with Zeng Qinghong, Vice-President of the PRC. d, 60w, Kim visiting Tianjin.

**2004, June 18** ***Perf. 13¼***

**Souvenir Sheet**

**4373** A1959 74w multicolored 1.50 .70
*a.* As No. 4373, diff. (horiz.) selvage 1.50 .70

**Sheets of 4, #a-d**

**4374-4375** A1960 Set of 2 4.00 2.10
*4375e* Booklet pane of 9, #4373a, 4374a-d, 4375a-d 6.00 —
Complete booklet, #4375e 6.50

No. 4373a is from the booklet No. 4375e.

WPK Flag A1961

A1962

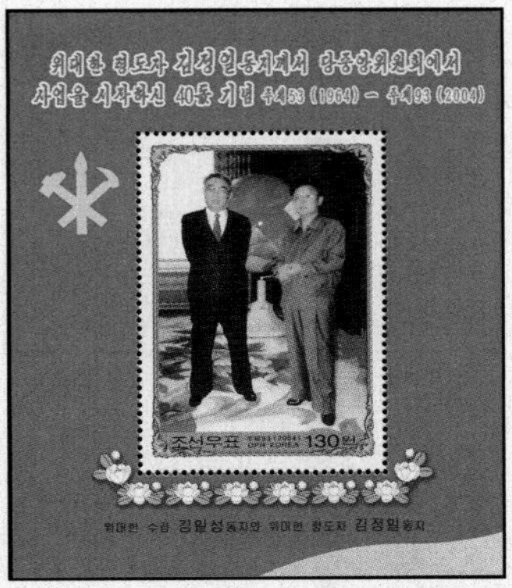

Kim Jong Il's Appointment to the Central Committe of the Workers' Party of Korea, 40th Anniv. — A1963

No. 4377: a, 12w, Kim reading at desk. b, 100w, Kim standing in front of renderings of proposed Samjiyon Battle Site memorial.
No. 4378: a, 12w, Kim inspecting power station in Jagang Province. b, 100w, Kim with army officers.
No. 4379: a, 12w, Kim visiting the Komdok mine. b, 100w, Kim, outdoor photo portrait.
No. 4380: 130w, Kim Jong Il and Kim Il Sung.

**2004, June 19**

**4376** A1961 3w multicolored .30 .30

**Sheets of 2**

**4377-4379** A1962 Set of 3 6.00 3.00

**Souvenir Sheet**

**4380** A1963 130w multicolored 1.50 .70

A1964

A1965

Kim Il Sung, 10th Death Anniv. — A1966

No. 4381: 3w, *Kimilsungia*, monument to Kim Il Sung.
No. 4382: a, 12w, Kim Il Sung and Kim Jong Il visiting State Academy of Sciences. b, 116w, Kim Il Sung and Kim Jong Il on Mt. Paektu.
No. 4383: a, 12w, Kim iil Sung with workers b, 116w, Kim directing farmers at Chongan co-operative farm.
No. 4384: a, 12w, Kim with soldiers. b, 116w, Kim with children.
No. 4385: a, 12w, Kim embracing Rev. Mun Ik Hwan. 116w, Kim talking on telephone.
No. 4386: 112w, Kim waving.

**2004, July 8** *Perf. 11¾*

**4381** A1964 3w multicolored .30 .30

**Sheets of 4, #a-d**

**4382-4385** A1965 Set of 4 8.25 4.00

**Souvenir Sheet**

**4386** A1966 112w multicolored 1.90 .85

Monument — A1967

**2004, July 10** *Perf. 11¾*

**4387** A1967 112w multicolored 1.90 .85

Kim Hyong Jik, father of Kim Il Sung, 110th birth anniv.

A1968

A1969

Deng Xiaoping, Birth Centennial — A1970

No. 4388: a, 3w, Deng Xiaoping as a student in France. b, 12w, Deng hiking on the Huangshan. c, 35w, Deng saluting at military review. d. 50w, Deng addressing rally celebrating the 35th anniversary of the People's Republic of China.
No. 4389a: Kim Il Sung being greeted by Deng, Chinese crowd during visit to China.
No. 4390: 80w, Deng at seashore.

**2004, July 15** *Perf. 13¼*

**4388** A1968 Strip of 4, #4a-d + label 1.90 .85

**Sheet of 5**

**4389** A1969 Sheet, #4388, 4389a, label 3.00 1.50
*a.* 70w multicolored .85 .50

**Souvenir Sheet**

**4390** A1970 80w multicolored 1.50 .70

Fresh Water Fish — A1971

Designs: a, 3w, Carassius auratus. b, 12w, Tlilapia nilotica. c, 140w, Ophiocephalus argus. d, 165w, Clarias gariepinus.

**2004, Aug. 10**

**4391** A1971 Sheet of 4, #a.-d. 5.50 2.75

28th Olympic Games, Athens — A1972

Designs: a, 3w, Boxing. b, 12w, Soccer. c, 85w, Track and field events. d, 140w, Gymnastics.

**2004, Aug. 10**

**4392** A1972 Block or strip of 4, #a.-d. 4.00 2.25
*e.* Booklet pane of 4, #a.-d. 4.00 —
Complete booklet, #4392e 4.75

No. 4392 was printed in panes of 8 stamps, 2 sets of Nos. 4392a-4392d, with decorative margin depicting athletes, Olympic emblems and Korean inscription. No. 4392e contains Nos. 4392a-4392d in a horizontal strip, with plain marginal selvage.
For overprints, see No. 4409.

Fire Engines — A1973

Designs: a, 3w, Mercedes Benz ladder truck. b, 12w, Fire truck. c, 40w, Jelcz pumper truck. d, 105w, Mercedes Benz fire truck.
97w, ladder truck, diff.

**2004, Aug. 15**

**4393** A1973 Sheet of 4, #a.-d. 3.00 1.50
*e.* Booklet pane of 4, #a.-d. 3.00 —
Complete booklet, #4393e 3.50
*f.* A1973 97w Souvenir sheet 1.90 .85

No. 4393e contains Nos. 4393a-4393d in a vertical strip, with marginal selvage similar to that of the sheet.

Airplanes — A1974

Designs: a, 3w, Airbus A340-600. b, 97w, Concorde. c, 104w, Graf Zeppelin DO-X. d, 116w, Junkers JU 52/3m.

**2004, Aug. 20** *Perf. 12*

**4394** A1974 Sheet of 4, #a.-d. 6.25 3.25
*e.* Booklet pane of 4, #a.-d. 6.25 —
Complete booklet, #4394e 6.75

No. 4394e contains Nos. 4394a-4394d in a horizontal strip, with pale yellow marginal selvage, with simple ruled lines and inscription.

Visit of Japanese Prime Minister Koizumi Zunichiro — A1975

**2004, Aug. 25** *Perf. 11¾*

**4395** A1975 220w multicolored 3.75 1.90

A1976

**2004, Sept. 21**

**4396** A1976 112w multicolored 1.90 .85

An Jung Gun (1879-1910), assassin of Japanese Prime Minister Ito Hirdoumi in 1909, 125th birth anniv.

A1977

Kim Jong Suk (1917-49), Mother of Kim Jong Il. — A1978

Designs: 3w, Kim Jong Suk's pistol. 97w, Kim Jong Suk.

**2004, Sept. 22** ***Perf. 13¼***

| | | | | |
|---|---|---|---|---|
| **4397** | A1977 | 3w multicolored | .30 | .30 |

**Souvenir Sheet**

***Perf. 12***

| | | | | |
|---|---|---|---|---|
| **4398** | A1978 | 97w multicolored | 1.90 | .85 |

World Wildlife Fund A1979

Swans: 3w, Swan in profile, looking left. 97w, Swan, ¾ profile, head turned to left. 104w, Two swans, one with outstretched wings. 120w, Two swans in water.

**2004, Sept. 30** ***Perf. 11½***

| | | | | |
|---|---|---|---|---|
| **4399-4402** | A1979 Set of 4 | | 5.75 | 3.00 |
| *4402a* | Booklet pane of 4, #4399-4102 | | 5.75 | — |
| | Complete booklet, #4402a | | 6.25 | |

Nos. 4399-4402 were each printed in sheets of 4, with decorative selvage. No. 4402a contains the four stamps in a horizontal se-tenant strip, surrounded by plain selvage.

A1980

Simwon Temple — A1981

Designs: 3w, View of Powkang Hall. 97w, Interior of Powkang Hall, with three golden Buddha statues.

**2004, Oct. 5** ***Perf. 11¾***

| | | | | |
|---|---|---|---|---|
| **4403** | A1980 | 3w multicolored | .30 | .30 |

**Souvenir Sheet**

***Perf. 13¼***

| | | | | |
|---|---|---|---|---|
| **4404** | A1981 | 97w multicolored | 2.10 | 1.10 |

Sidelfingen International Stamp Fair — A1982

Electric trains: a, 3w, Red and blue train. b, 40w, Yellow train. c, 75w, Green and white train. d, 150w, Red and green train. 120w, Vintage electric train.

**2004, Nov. 5** ***Perf. 11½***

| | | | | |
|---|---|---|---|---|
| **4405** | A1982 | Sheet of 4, #a.-d. | 4.50 | 2.25 |

**Souvenir Sheet**

| | | | | |
|---|---|---|---|---|
| **4406** | A1982 | 120w multicolored | 2.40 | 1.25 |
| *a.* | | 120w stamp from souvenir sheet | 2.40 | 1.25 |
| *b.* | | Booklet pane of 5, #4405a-4405d, #4606a | 7.50 | — |
| | | Complete booklet, #4406b | 8.25 | |

A1983

Repatriation of Korean Nationals in Japan, 45th Anniv. — A1984

Designs: 3w, Repatriation ship *Mangyongbong.* 80w, Kim Il Sung with repatriated Korean children.

**2004, Dec. 16** ***Perf. 11½***

| | | | | |
|---|---|---|---|---|
| **4407** | A1983 | 3w multicolored | .30 | .30 |

**Souvenir Sheet**

***Perf. 11¾***

| | | | | |
|---|---|---|---|---|
| **4408** | A1984 | 80w multicolored | 1.50 | .70 |

**No. 4392 Overprinted in Silver**

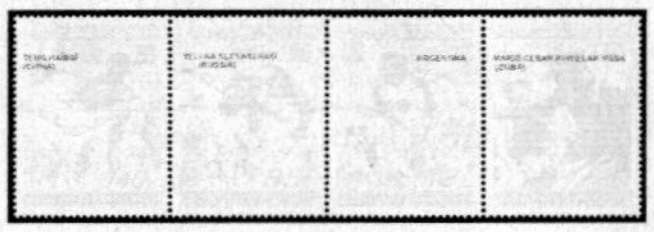

Overprints: a, 3w, Mario Cesar Kindelan Mesa (Boxing, Cuba). b, 12w, Argentine Soccer Team. c, 85w, Yelena Slesarenko (Women's High Jump, Russia). d, 140w, Teng Haibin (Women's Gymnastics, China).

**2004, Dec. 20** ***Perf. 13¼***

| | | | | |
|---|---|---|---|---|
| **4409** | A1972 | Block or strip of 4, #a.-d. | 4.25 | 2.25 |

New Year 2005 A1985

**2005, Jan. 1**

| | | | | |
|---|---|---|---|---|
| **4410** | A1985 | 3w multicolored | .30 | .30 |

A1986

New Year 2005 — Year of the Rooster — A1987

Domestic fowl, millet stalk figures: 3w, Rooster. 12w, Hen.

No. 4413: a, 3w, Chick. b, 70w, Rooster, chick. c, 100w, Rooster. d, 140w, Basket of eggs.

**2005, Jan. 1**

| | | | | |
|---|---|---|---|---|
| **4411** | A1986 | 3w multicolored | .30 | .30 |
| **4412** | A1986 | 12w multicolored | .70 | .35 |
| **4413** | A1987 | Sheet of 4, #a.-d. | 4.75 | .30 |
| *e.* | | Booklet pane of 6, #4411-4412, #4413a-d | 5.50 | — |
| | | Complete booklet, #4413e | 5.70 | |

No. 4413e contains all six values of the set, printed in a se-tenant strip of six, within a plain yellow and green border.

Hen, Classic Chinese Painting — A1988

**Souvenir Sheet**

**2005, Jan. 10** ***Perf. 11½***

| | | | | |
|---|---|---|---|---|
| **4414** | A1988 | 97w multicolored | 1.90 | .85 |

Kim Il Sung's 250-Mile Journey, 80th Anniv. — A1989

**Souvenir Sheet**

**2005, Jan. 22** ***Perf. 11¾***

| | | | | |
|---|---|---|---|---|
| **4415** | A1989 | 120w multicolored | 1.90 | .85 |

Statue of Kim Il Sung, Chongsan-ri — A1990

**Souvenir Sheet**

**2005, Feb. 8** ***Perf. 13¼***

| | | | | |
|---|---|---|---|---|
| **4416** | A1990 | 120w multicolored | 1.80 | .85 |

Creation of the Chongsan-ri Spirit and Chongsan-ri Method.

Songun Scenes — A1991

Designs: a, 3w, Sunrise at Mt. Paektu. b, 12w, Snowscape. c, 40w, Royal azaleas on Chol Pass. d, 50w, Jangja River. e, 60w, Ullim Falls. f, 70w, Handure Plain. g, 70w, Potato blossoms at Taehongdan. h, 100w, Poman-ri.

**2005, Feb. 10** ***Perf. 12¼***

| | | | | |
|---|---|---|---|---|
| **4417** | A1991 | Sheet of 8, #a.-h. | 6.00 | 3.00 |

A1992

A1993

Kim Jong Il, 63rd Birthday — A1994

Design: 3w, *Kimjongilia*, mountains.

No. 4419, *216 Peaks Around Lake Chon on Mt. Paektu*, summer scenes, each 50w: a, Mountains, lake on lower right. b, Mountains, lake across foreground. c, Mountains, lake in foreground, shore at lower right.

No. 4420, *216 Peaks Around Lake Chon on Mt. Paektu*, winter scenes, each 50w: a, Mountains, frozen lake in foreground. b, Mountains. lake in foreground, sun showing over peaks. c, Mountains, lake in left foreground.

**2005, Feb. 16** ***Perf. 13¼***

| | | | | |
|---|---|---|---|---|
| **4418** | A1992 | 3w multicolored | .30 | .30 |

**Sheets of 3, #a.-c.**

***Perf. 12***

| | | | | |
|---|---|---|---|---|
| **4419** | A1993 | multicolored | 2.40 | 1.25 |
| **4420** | A1994 | multicolored | 2.40 | 1.25 |

Joint Editorial *Rodong Sinmun, Josoninmingun* and *Chongnyonjonwi* Newspapers A1995

**2005, Feb. 16** ***Perf. 13¼***

**4421** A1995 3w multicolored .30 .30

A1996

Naming of the *Kimilsungia*, 40th Anniv. — A1997

Designs: 3w, *Kimilsungia* and Kimilsungia-Kimjongilia Exhibition Hall.

120w: Kim Il Sung receiving a *Kimilsungia* plant from Pres. Sukarno of Indonesia.

**2005, Apr. 13**

**4422** A1996 3w multicolored .30 .30

**Souvenir Sheet**

**4423** A1997 120w multicolored 1.90 .85

A1998

Kim Il Sung, 93rd Birth Anniv. — A1999

Designs: 3w, *Kimilsungia* and Mangyong Hill.

112w: Kim Il Sung standing in front of straw-thatched house at Mangyongdae.

**2005, Apr. 15**

**4424** A1998 3w multicolored .30 .30

**Souvenir Sheet**

***Perf. 11¾***

**4425** A1999 112w multicolored 1.90 .85

48th World Table Tennis Championships, Shanghai — A2000

Designs: 3w, Pak Young Sun, Korea. b, 5w, Mao Zedong playing table tennis at the Communist base in Yanan. c, 12w, Wang Liqin, China. d, 20w, J.O. Waldner, Sweden. e, Zhang Yining, China. f, 102w, Werner Schlager, Austria.

**2005, Apr. 23** ***Perf. 11½***

**4426** A2000 Sheet of 6, #a.-f. 3.75 1.90

*g.* Booklet pane of 6, #4426a-4426f 3.75 —

Complete booklet, #4426g 4.25

No. 4426g contains Nos. 4426a-4426f in a se-tenant horizontal strip of six, surrounded by blue selvage depicting the Shanghai 2005 emblem, stylized athletes and Korean inscription.

Pandas A2001

Designs: 15w, Panda on tree limb. 45w, Panda walking. 70w, Two pandas. 140w, Panda standing

120w, Panda with cub.

**2005, May 3** ***Perf. 13¼***

**4427-4430** A2001 Set of 4 4.75 .30

*4430a* Booklet pane of 5, #4427-4430, 4432a 4.75 —

Complete booklet, #4430a 5.25

**Sheet of 5**

**4431** A2001 Sheet, #4427-4430, 4432a 7.00 3.00

**Souvenir Sheet**

**4432** A2001 120w multicolored 3.50 —

*a.* Single stamp

Nos. 4427-4430 were each issued in separate large panes. No. 4430a contains Nos. 4427-30, 4432a in a se-tenant horizontal strip of 5, with plain white marginal selvage.

For overprints, see Nos. 4451-4455.

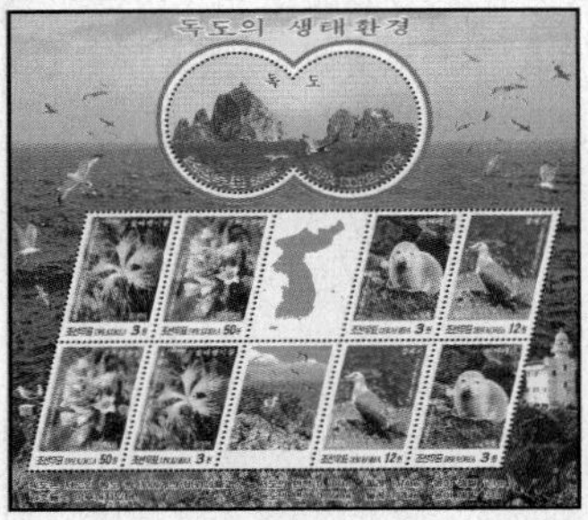

Ecosystem of Tok Island — A2002

Designs: a, 3w, *Dianthus superbus.* b, 3w, *Eumetopia jubata.* c, 12w, Seagull. d, 50w, *Lysimachia mauritania Lam.*

e, 97w: Eastern and Western islands, Tok Island.

***Perf. 11¼, Perf. (#4433e)***

**2005, May 5**

**4433** A2002 Sheet of 9, #4433e, 2 each #4433a-4433d + 2 labels 14.00 7.00

*f.* Booklet pane, #4433e — 

*g.* Booklet pane of 8, 2 each #4433a-4433d, perf. 11¼ on 3 sides — —

Complete booklet, # 4433f, 4433g —

A2003

General Association of Korean Residents in Japan, 50th Anniv. — A2004

Designs: 3w, Korean family waving flag.

130w: Kim Il Sung shaking hands with man in suit.

**2005, May 25** ***Perf. 13¼***

**4434** A2003 3w multicolored .30 .30

**Souvenir Sheet**

**4435** A2004 130w multicolored 1.60 .85

Fauna — A2005

Designs, each 40w: No. 4436, Korean Tiger. No. 4437, Sable.

**2005, June 1**

**4436** 40w multicolored .85 .50

**4437** 40w multicolored .85 .50

*a.* A2005 Pair, #4436-4437 with label between 2.40 1.25

*b.* Booklet pane, 2 #4437a 2.40 —

Complete booklet, #4437b 3.00

See Russia No. 6911.

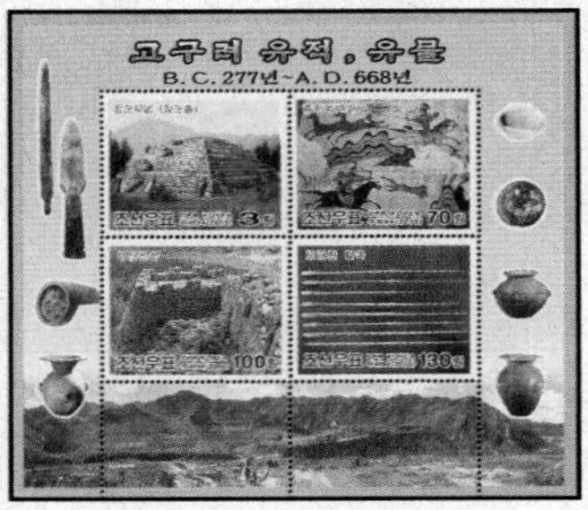

A2006

Koguryo Historic Site — A2007

Designs: a, Tomb of a general of Koguryo. b, 70w, Tomb mural depicting hunting scene. c, 100w, Mt. Songsan fortress. d, 130w, Gilded arrowheads.

97w: Monument at Mausoleum of King Kwanggaetho.

**2005, June 14**

**4438** A2006 Sheet of 4, #a.-d. 4.75 2.40

*e.* Booklet pane, #4438a-4438d, 4439a 7.00 —

Complete booklet, #4438e 6.50

**Souvenir Sheet**

**4439** A2007 97w multicolored 2.40 1.25

*a.* 97w Single from souvenir sheet 2.40 1.25

No. 4438a contains Nos. 4438a-4438d in a horizontal strip of 4, with No. 4439a placed separately, within a 69mmx279mm sheetlet with selvage depicting hunting scene, artifacts and inscription.

Kim Chol Ju (1919-35), Brother of Kim Il Sung. — A2008

**Souvenir Sheet**

**2005, June 14** ***Perf. 11½***

**4440** A2008 170w multicolored 1.90 .85

A2009

North-South Joint Declaration, 5th Anniv. — A2010

Designs, all 112w: a, Kim Jong Il and S. Korean President Kim Dae Jung shaking hands. b, Kim Jong Il and Kim Dae Jung standing side-by-side. c, Kim Il Jong and Kim Dae Jung sitting together at table with large flower arrangement. d, Kim Dae Jong and Kim Il Jong at conference table.

167w, Kim Dae Jung and Kim Jong Il smiling, shaking hands, with representatives in background.

**2005, June 15**

**4441** A2009 Sheet of 4, #a.-d. 7.00 3.50

**Souvenir Sheet**

**4442** A2010 167w multicolored 2.50 1.50

A2011

Amur Tiger — A2012

Designs: a, 3w, Tiger looking left. b, 12w, Tiger growling. c, 130w, Tiger looking forward. d, 200w, Tiger growling, turned to right.

150w: Tiger with cubs.

**2005, July 10** ***Perf. 11¾***

**4443** A2011 Sheet of 4, #a.-d. 4.75 2.40
*e.* Booklet pane, #4443a-4443d 4.75 —
Complete booklet, #4443e 5.25

**Souvenir Sheet**

***Perf. 11½***

**4444** A2012 150w multicolored 2.40 1.25

No. 4443e contains Nos. 4443a-4443d in a horizontal strip of 4, within selvage depicting forest skyline and inscription "Panthera tigris altaika."

Map of Korea — A2013

**Souvenir Sheet**

**2005, July 25** ***Perf. 11½***

**4445** A2013 130w multicolored 1.90 .90

"June 25-July 27 - Period of Joint Anti-US Struggle" A2014

Design: 3w, Korean soldier, U.S. POWs, military cemetary, military vehicles.

**2005, July 27** ***Perf. 12***

**4446** A2014 3w multicolored .30 .30

A2015

A2016

A2017

National Liberation, 60th Anniv. — A2018

Design: 3w, Arch of Triumph, magnolia.

No. 4448: a, 60w, Kim Il Sung receiving his father's pistol from his mother. b, 60w, Kim Il Sung founding the Juche-oriented revolutionary armed force. c, 60w, Kim Il Sung commanding the battle at Taehongdan. 60w, Kim Il Sung addressing staff on eve of final offensive against the Japanese. 102w, Kim Il Sung, WWII-era photo.

No. 4449: a, Kim Il Sung on ship en route to Wonsan Port landing. b, 60w, Kim Il Sung visiting Kangson Steel Works. c, 60w, Kim Il Sung delivering speech. d, 60w, Kim Il Sung meeting his grandparents, upon his return to Korea. e, 102w, Kim Il Sung with microphone.

No. 4450: 128w, Kim Il Sung.

**2005, Aug. 15** ***Perf. 13¼***

**4447** A2015 3w multicolored .30 .30

**Sheets of 5**

**4448** A2016 Sheet, #a.-e. 4.75 2.40
**4449** A2017 Sheet, #a.-e. 4.75 2.40

**Souvenir Sheet**

**4450** A2018 128w multicolored 1.90 .90

**Nos. 4427-4430, 4432 Overprinted "Taipei 2000" and Emblem in Red and Blue**

**2005, Aug. 19** ***Perf. 13¼***

**4451-4454** A2001 Set of 4 4.75 2.50

**Souvenir Sheet**

**4455** A2001 120w multicolored 2.50 1.25

18th Asian International Stamp Exhibition, Taipei.

A2019

National Costumes — A2020

Designs: a, 3w, Woman in red dress. b, 80w, Woman in blue dress. c, 100w, Woman in green dress. d, 120w, Woman in white dress with fur collar.

140w, Children.

**2005, Aug. 30** ***Perf. 11½***

**4456** A2019 Sheet of 4, #a.-d. 4.00 2.10
*4456e* Booklet pane of 4, #4456a-d 4.00 —
Complete booklet, #4456e 4.50

**Souvenir Sheet**

***Perf. 11¾***

**4457** A2020 140w multicolored 2.10 1.10

No. 4456e contains Nos. 4456a-d in a horizontal strip of 4, without the small decorative labels that are printed below the stamps in No. 4456. The stamps are surrounded by a narrow selvage similar to that of the sheet of 4.

Korean Workers' Party, 60th Anniv. — A2021

Design: 3w, Korean soldier and workers, banners, proclamation of Joint Slogan.

**2005, Sept. 8** ***Perf. 13¼***

**4458** A2021 3w multicolored .30 .30

A2022

A2023

A2024

A2025

Korean Workers' Party, 60th Anniv. — A2026

Design: 3w, Monument to founding of Party.

No. 4460: a, 12w, Kim Il Sung organizing Down-with-Imperialism Union. b, 30w, Kim Il Sung forming the first Juche-oriented Party organization. c, 60w, Kim Il Sung discussing a draft resolution to Communist Party leaders. d, 90w, Kim Il Sung addressing Central Committee of the Communist Party.

No. 4461: a, 12w, Kim Il Sung at bank of microphones, addressing 6th Congress of the WPK. b, 30w, Kim Il Sung and Kim Jong Il with military officers. c, 60w, Kim Jong Il inspecting Tabaksol Company, a camouflaged army unit. d, 90w, Kim Jong Il addressing crowd in stadium.

No. 4462: 120w, Kim Il Sung. No. 4463: 120w, Kim Jong Il.

**2005, Oct. 10** ***Perf. 13¼***

| | | | | |
|---|---|---|---|---|
| **4459** | A2022 | 3w multicolored | .25 | .25 |

**Sheets of 4**

***Perf. 11¾***

| | | | | |
|---|---|---|---|---|
| **4460** | A2023 | Sheet, #a.-d. | 2.40 | 1.25 |
| **4461** | A2024 | Sheet, #a.-d. | 2.40 | 1.25 |

**Souvenir Sheets**

***Perf. 13¼***

| | | | | |
|---|---|---|---|---|
| **4462** | A2025 | 120w multicolored | 1.50 | .70 |
| **4463** | A2026 | 120w multicolored | 1.50 | .70 |

Bees — A2027

Designs: a, 3w, Four bees surrounding queen. 12w, Two bees attending to larva. 128w, Bee filling comb cell with honey. 200w, Bee flying.

**2005, Oct. 20** ***Perf. 11½***

| | | | | |
|---|---|---|---|---|
| **4464** | A2027 | Sheet of 4, #a.-d. | 4.75 | 2.40 |
| *e.* | | Booklet pane, as #4464a-4464d | 4.75 | — |
| | | Complete booklet, #4443e | 5.25 | |

No. 4464e contains four stamps like Nos. 4464a-4464d, but with slightly less yellow in the comb background and a slightly paler blue on the blue design elements. It bears a marginal selvage, with Korean inscription at left and three bees at right.

United Nations, 60th Anniv. A2028

**2005, Oct. 24** ***Perf. 13¼***

| | | | | |
|---|---|---|---|---|
| **4465** | A2028 | 15w multicolored | .35 | .30 |

A2029

Kaesong Historic Site — A2030

No 4466: a, 35w, Pogwang Hall. b, 35w, Monument to Taegakguksa. c, 35w, Pojo Hall. d, 75w, Ryongthong Temple.

No. 4467: a, 35w, Taesong Shrine. b, 35w, Myongryun Hall. c, 35w, Metal type (round). d, 75w, Sam Gate.

**2005, Oct. 31** ***Perf. 12***

**Sheets of 4, #a.-d.**

| | | | | |
|---|---|---|---|---|
| **4466** | A2029 | multicolored | 2.40 | 1.25 |
| **4467** | A2030 | multicolored | 2.40 | 1.25 |

Nos. 4466-4467 each contain three nondenominated labels.

Kim Hyong Gwon Monument — A2031

**Souvenir Sheet**

**2005, Nov. 4** ***Perf. 11½***

| | | | | |
|---|---|---|---|---|
| **4468** | A2031 | 120w multicolored | 1.90 | .90 |

Kim Hyong Gwon (1905-36), uncle of Kim Il Sung.

Ulsa Treaty, Centennial A2032

**2005, Nov. 17** ***Perf. 11¾***

| | | | | |
|---|---|---|---|---|
| **4469** | A2032 | 12w multicolored | .35 | .30 |

Ulsa Treaty, under which Korea became a Japanese protectorate.

A2033

A2034

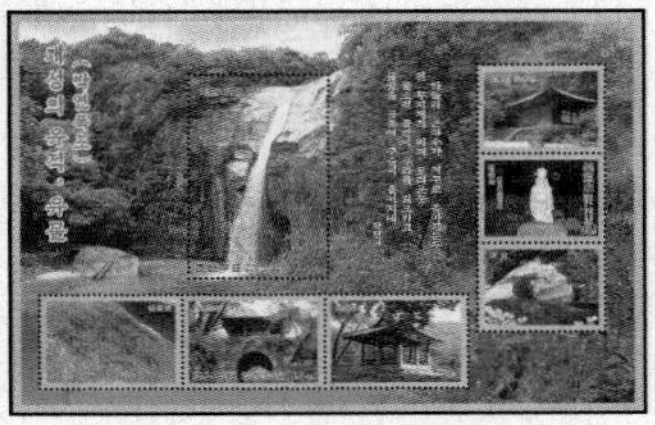

Kaesong Historic Site — A2035

No 4470: a, 35w, Kaesong Namdaemun. b, 35w, Mausoleum of King Kongmin. c, 35w, Sonjuk Bridge. d, 35w, Sungyang Private School. e, 35w, Anhwa Temple (Five Hundred Rahan). f, 35w, Tomb of Pak Ji Won (Yonam).

No. 4471: a, 35w, King Wanggon, founder of Kingdom of Koryo, 935 A.D., round. b, 35w, Front Gate at Mausoleum of King Wanggon. c, 75w, Mausoleum of King Wanggon.

No. 4472: a, 35w, Fortress on Mt. Taehung (North Gate). b, 35w, Marble statue of Kwanumbosal, Kwanum Temple. c, 75w, Pakyon Falls.

**Sheet of 6, #a.-f. + 6 labels**

**2005, Nov. 18** ***Perf. 11½***

| | | | | |
|---|---|---|---|---|
| **4470** | A2033 | multicolored | 1.90 | .90 |

**Sheet of 3, #a.-c. + 2 labels**

***Perf. 13¼***

| | | | | |
|---|---|---|---|---|
| **4471** | A2034 | multicolored | 1.90 | .90 |

**Sheet of 3, #a.-c. + 4 labels**

***Perf. 12¼ (a, b); 11½ (c)***

| | | | | |
|---|---|---|---|---|
| **4472** | A2035 | multicolored | 1.90 | .90 |

Visit to DPRK by Hu Jintao, President of the People's Republic of China — A2036

Design: a, 35w, Kim Jong Il meeting with Hu Jintao. b, 35w, Kim Jong Il and Hu Jintao visiting the Taean Friendship Glass Factory. c, 35w, Kim Jong Il and Hu Jintao at state banquet. d, 102w, Kim Jong Il shaking hands with Hu Jintao.

***Perf. 11½, 13¼ (#4473d)***

**2005, Dec. 15** **Sheet of 4, #a.-d.**

| | | | | |
|---|---|---|---|---|
| **4473** | A2036 | multicolored | 3.00 | 1.50 |

New Year 2006 — A2037

**2006, Jan. 1** **Litho.** ***Perf. 11½***

| | | | | |
|---|---|---|---|---|
| **4474** | A2037 | 3w multi | .30 | .30 |

New Year 2006 (Year of the Dog) — A2038

Various dogs: 3w, 70w.

No. 4477 — Various dogs: a, 15w. b, 100w. c, 130w.

**2006, Jan. 1** ***Perf. 13¼***

| | | | | |
|---|---|---|---|---|
| **4475-4476** | A2038 | Set of 2 | 1.90 | .65 |
| **4477** | A2038 | Sheet of 5, #4475-4476, 4477a-4477c | 5.25 | 2.75 |
| *d.* | | Souvenir sheet of 1 #4477c | 3.00 | 1.50 |
| | | Complete booklet, #4475-4476, 4477a-4477c | 7.00 | |

Complete booklet sold for 335w.

A2039

League of Socialist Working Youth, 60th Anniv. — A2040

No. 4478: a, 3w, Kim Il Sung and microphone. b, 111w, Kim Il Sung and crowd. c, 150w, Kim Jong Il receiving torch.

**2006, Jan. 17** ***Perf. 13¼***

**4478** A2039 Sheet of 3, #a-c 6.00 2.40

**Souvenir Sheet**

***Perf. 11½x12***

**4479** A2040 128w multi 3.00 1.50

A2041

New Year 2006 (Year of the Dog) — A2042

**Photo. & Engr.**

**2006, Jan. 29** ***Perf. 11x11¼***

**4480** A2041 12w multi .30 .30

**Souvenir Sheet**

***Perf. 11½x11¼***

**4481** A2042 70w multi 1.25 .60

Down With Imperialism Union, 80th Anniv. — A2043

**2006, Feb. 9** **Litho.** ***Perf. 13½***

**4482** A2043 3w multi .30 .30

Miniature Sheet

2006 Winter Olymics, Turin — A2044

No. 4483: a, 15w, Ice dancing. b, 85w, Ice hockey. c, 110w, Ski jumping. d, 135w, Speed skating.

**2006, Feb. 10** ***Perf. 13¼***

**4483** A2044 Sheet of 4, #a-d 5.75 3.00

*4483e* Booklet pane of 4, #4483a-4483d 6.00 —

Complete booklet, #4483e 6.00

Complete booklet sold for 362w.

A2045

Kim Jong Il, 64th Birthday — A2046

No. 4485: a, 12w, Polemonium racemosum. b, 45w, Day lily. c, 100w, Dandelion. d, 140w, Parnassia palustris.

**2006, Feb. 16** ***Perf. 13½***

**4484** A2045 3w multi .30 .30

**Souvenir Sheet**

**4485** A2046 Sheet of 4, #a-d 4.75 2.50

A2047

Visit of Kim Jong Il to People's Republic of China — A2048

No. 4486 — Kim Jong Il: a, 3w, At Crop Research Institute. b, 12w, At optical fiber factory. c, 35w, At Three Gorges Dam. d, 70w, At Guangzhou Intl. Conference and Exhibition Center. e, 100w, At air conditioner factory. f, 120w, At port of Yandian.

102w, Kim Jong Il and Hu Jintao.

**2006, Mar. 4** ***Perf. 12x12¼***

**4486** A2047 Sheet of 6, #a-f 5.50 3.00

**Souvenir Sheet**

***Perf. 11¾***

**4487** A2048 102w multi 1.90 .85

A2049

Agrarian Reform Law, 60th Anniv. — A2050

**2006, Mar. 5** ***Perf. 11½***

**4488** A2049 12w multi + label .30 .30

**Souvenir Sheet**

**4489** A2050 150w multi 1.40 1.25

Souvenir Sheet

First North Korean Postage Stamps, 60th Anniv. — A2051

**2006, Mar. 12** ***Perf. 11¾***

**4490** A2051 158w multi 2.60 1.40

Mt. Kumgang Scenery A2052

Designs: 3w, Pibong Falls. 12w, Podok Hermitage. 35w, Sokka Peak. 50w, Jipson Peak. 70w, Chongsok Rocks, horiz. 100w, Sejon Peak, horiz. 120w, Chonhwa Rock, horiz. 140w, Piro Peak, horiz.

**2006, Mar. 15** ***Perf. 11¾x12¼***

**4491-4498** A2052 Set of 8 8.75 4.50

Belgica 2006 World Youth Philatelic Exhibition, Brussels A2053

Designs: No. 4499, 140w, Jules Verne (1828-1905), writer. No. 4500, 140w, Tyto alba, Volvariella speciosa, Scouting emblem. No. 4501, 140w, Disa grandiflora, Nymphalidae. No. 4502, 140w, Australopithecus afarensis, rocks. No. 4503, 140w, Alaskan malamute, Birman cat, Scouting emblem. No. 4504, 140w, Sunflowers, by Vincent Van Gogh. No. 4505, 140w, Soccer ball, chess knight, table tennis paddle and ball. No. 4506, 140w, Tursiops truncatus, Scouting emblem. No. 4507, 140w, Maglev train, horiz. No. 4508, 140w, 1962 Ernst Grube Type S 4000-1 fire truck, horiz.

**2006, Apr. 13** ***Perf. 11¾***

**4499-4508** A2053 Set of 10 23.00 11.50

Kim Il Sung, 94th Anniv. of Birth — A2054

**2006, Apr. 15** ***Perf. 11½***

**4509** A2054 3w multi + label .30 .30

Association for the Restoration of the Fatherland, 70th Anniv. A2055

**2006, May 5** ***Perf. 13½***

**4510** A2055 3w multi .30 .30

Pothong River Improvement Project, 60th Anniv. — A2056

**2006, May 21** ***Perf. 12***

**4511** A2056 12w multi .30 .30

**Various Stamps of 1963-2002 Surcharged in Black and Red**

**Methods and Perfs. As Before**

**2006**

| | | | | |
|---|---|---|---|---|
| **4512** | A658 | 3w on 2ch #816 (R) | — | — |
| **4513** | A608 | 3w on 5ch #731 | — | — |
| **4514** | A635 | 3w on 10ch #770 | — | — |
| **4515** | A932 | 3w on 10ch #1598 | — | — |
| **4516** | A971 | 3w on 10ch #1798 | — | — |
| **4517** | A1005 | 3w on 10ch #1929 | — | — |
| **4518** | A926 | 3w on 15ch #1579 | — | — |
| **4519** | A887 | 3w on 20ch #1419 | — | — |
| **4520** | A986 | 3w on 20ch #1873 (R) | — | — |
| **4521** | A1179 | 3w on 20ch #2470 | — | — |
| **4522** | A1211 | 3w on 20ch #2548 | — | — |

| | | | | |
|---|---|---|---|---|
| **4523** | A1211 | 3w on 20ch #2548 (R) | — | — |
| **4524** | A1249 | 3w on 20ch #2645 | — | — |
| **4525** | A1431 | 3w on 20ch #3159 | — | — |
| **4526** | A1431 | 3w on 20ch #3159 (R) | — | — |
| **4527** | A1539 | 3w on 20ch #3437 | — | — |
| **4528** | A1539 | 3w on 20ch #3437 (R) | — | — |
| **4529** | A1704 | 3w on 20ch #3776 | — | — |
| **4530** | A1288 | 3w on 25ch #2751 | — | — |
| **4531** | A971 | 3w on 30ch #1801 | — | — |
| **4532** | A986 | 3w on 30ch #1875 | — | — |
| **4533** | A1177 | 3w on 30ch #2462 | — | — |
| **4534** | A1177 | 3w on 30ch #2462 (R) | — | — |
| **4535** | A1241 | 3w on 30ch #2621 | — | — |
| **4536** | A1379 | 3w on 30ch #2964 | — | — |
| **4537** | A1379 | 3w on 30ch #2964 (R) | — | — |
| **4538** | A1396 | 3w on 30ch #3023 | — | — |
| **4539** | A382 | 3w on 40ch #447 | — | — |
| **4540** | A547 | 3w on 40ch #645 (R) | — | — |
| **4541** | A812 | 3w on 40ch #1219 | — | — |
| **4542** | A818 | 3w on 40ch #1242 | — | — |
| **4543** | A826 | 3w on 40ch #1277 | — | — |
| **4544** | A1793 | 3w on 40ch #4052 | — | — |
| **4545** | A1793 | 3w on 40ch #4052 (R) | — | — |
| **4546** | A1385 | 3w on 50ch #2987 | — | — |
| **4547** | A1396 | 3w on 50ch #3025 | — | — |
| **4548** | A1430 | 3w on 50ch #3154 | — | — |
| *a.* | | Double surcharge | | |
| **4549** | A1471 | 3w on 50ch #3281 | — | — |
| **4550** | A1526 | 3w on 50ch #3408 (R) | — | — |
| **4551** | A1595 | 3w on 50ch #3548 (R) | — | — |
| **4552** | A1736 | 3w on 60ch #3851 | — | — |
| **4553** | A1557 | 3w on 80ch #3468 | — | — |
| **4554** | A1656 | 3w on 80ch #3676 | — | — |
| **4555** | A1651 | 3w on 80ch #3676 (R) | — | — |
| **4556** | A798 | 3w on 90ch #1164 | — | — |
| **4557** | A1735 | 3w on 1w #3849 | — | — |
| **4558** | A1761 | 3w on 1w #3919 | — | — |
| **4559** | A1734 | 3w on 1.50w #3848 | — | — |
| **4560** | A621 | 12w on 2ch #744 | — | — |
| **4561** | A932 | 12w on 2ch #1597 | — | — |
| **4562** | A808 | 12w on 20ch #1199 | — | — |
| **4563** | A823 | 12w on 30ch #1268 (R) | — | — |
| **4564** | A808 | 12w on 40ch #1201 | — | — |
| **4565** | A938 | 12w on 50ch #1622 | — | — |
| **4566** | A1860 | 12w on 2w #4207 | — | — |
| **4567** | A817 | 101w on 10ch #1236 | — | — |
| **4568** | A907 | 101w on 10ch #1471 | — | — |
| **4569** | A985 | 101w on 10ch #1865 | — | — |
| **4570** | A1005 | 101w on 10ch #1926 | — | — |
| **4571** | A1487 | 101w on 10ch #3321 | — | — |
| **4572** | A1837 | 101w on 10ch #4165 | — | — |
| **4573** | A1454 | 101w on 30ch #3228 | — | — |
| **4574** | A1658 | 101w on 50ch #3680 | — | — |
| **4575** | A1527 | 101w on 1w #3410 | — | — |
| **4576** | A1716 | 101w on 1w #3807 | — | — |
| **4577** | A1724 | 101w on 1.20w #3831 | — | — |
| **4578** | A938 | 128w on 5ch #1619 | — | — |
| **4579** | A812 | 128w on 10ch #1216 | — | — |
| **4580** | A1231 | 128w on 15ch #2597 | — | — |
| **4581** | A865 | 128w on 20ch #1357 | — | — |
| **4582** | A903 | 128w on 20ch #1457 | — | — |
| **4583** | A959 | 128w on 25ch #1754 | — | — |
| **4584** | A977 | 128w on 25ch #1812 | — | — |
| **4585** | A982 | 128w on 25ch #1853 | — | — |
| **4586** | A958 | 128w on 40ch #1749 | — | — |
| **4587** | A1785 | 128w on 40ch #4035 | — | — |
| **4588** | A1430 | 128w on 50ch #3157 | — | — |
| **4589** | A1707 | 128w on 1w #3785 | — | — |
| **4590** | A1707 | 128w on 1w #3785 (R) | — | — |
| **4591** | A1725 | 128w on 2w #3833 | — | — |
| **4592** | A820 | 134w on 5ch #1250 | — | — |
| **4593** | A903 | 134w on 5ch #1455 | — | — |
| **4594** | A898 | 134w on 10ch #1444 | — | — |
| **4595** | A982 | 134w on 10ch #1850 | — | — |
| **4596** | A855 | 134w on 20ch #1333 | — | — |
| **4597** | A1467 | 134w on 30ch #3267 | — | — |
| **4598** | A911 | 134w on 40ch #1518 | — | — |
| **4599** | A911 | 134w on 40ch #1518 (R) | — | — |
| **4600** | A806 | 134w on 1.50w #1203 | — | — |
| **4601** | A1862 | 134w on 1.50w #4213 | — | — |
| **4602** | A1443 | 158w on 10ch #3196 | — | — |
| **4603** | A898 | 158w on 15ch #1445 | — | — |
| **4604** | A911 | 158w on 15ch #1516 | — | — |
| **4605** | A1260 | 158w on 20ch #2680 | — | — |
| **4606** | A850 | 158w on 25ch #1328 | — | — |
| **4607** | A902 | 158w on 25ch #1458 | — | — |
| **4608** | A1501 | 158w on 30ch #3357 | — | — |
| **4609** | A1407 | 158w on 40ch #3059 | — | — |
| **4610** | A1542 | 158w on 40ch #3443 | — | — |
| **4611** | A1723 | 158w on 5w #3835 | — | — |

Nos. 4562-4564, 4581, 4588, 4598-4599, 4604-4605 are airmail.

Korean Children's Union, 60th Anniv. A2057

**2006, June 6 Litho. *Perf. 13½***
**4612** A2057 3w multi .30 .30

2006 World Cup Soccer Championships, Germany A2058

Various soccer players in action: 3w, 130w, 160w, 210w.

**2006, June 9 *Perf. 13½***
**4613-4616** A2058 Set of 4 8.25 4.00
*4616a* Souvenir sheet, #4616 + label 3.50 1.75
*4616b* Booklet pane of 4, #4613-4616 8.50 —
Complete booklet, #4616b 8.50

Issued: No. 4616a, 10/21/09. Italia 2009 Intl. Philatelic Exhibition (No. 4616a).
Complete booklet sold for 520w.

### Souvenir Sheet

Kim Chol Ju (1919-35) — A2059

**2006, June 12 *Perf. 11½x12***
**4617** A2059 170w multi 2.75 1.50

### Souvenir Sheet

Ri Su Bok (1933-51), War Hero and Poet — A2060

**2006, July 27 *Perf. 11¾***
**4618** A2060 120w multi 2.10 1.00

### Miniature Sheet

Circus Performers — A2061

Designs: a, 3w, Trapeze artists (42x35mm). b, 12w, Aerial acrobatic troupe (42x35mm). c, 130w, Seesaw jumper (42x35mm). d, 200w, Juggler (42x64mm).

***Perf. 11½, 11½x12 (200w)***
**2006, Aug. 10 Litho.**
**4619** A2061 Sheet of 4, #a-d 6.00 3.00

Korean Cuisine A2062

Designs: 3w, Kimchi. 12w, Umegi. 130w, Rice cake dumplings with bean paste. 200w, Sweet rice.

**2006, Aug. 12 *Perf. 13½***
**4620-4623** A2062 Set of 4 6.00 3.00
*4623a* Booklet pane of 4, #4620-4623 6.00 —
Complete booklet, #4623a 6.00

Sea Mammals — A2063

Designs: 3w, Megaptera nodosa. 70w, Balaenoptera musculus. 160w, Physeter catodon. 240w, Inia geoffrensis.

**2006, Aug. 20 *Perf. 11¾***
**4624-4627** A2063 Set of 4 7.75 3.75
*4627a* Booklet pane of 4, #4624-4627 7.75 —
Complete booklet, #4627a 7.75

Motorcycles A2064

Various motorcycles.

**2006, Sept. 1 *Perf. 11½***
**4628** Horiz. strip of 4 8.25 4.25
*a.* A2064 3w multi .25 .25
*b.* A2064 102w multi 1.60 .85
*c.* A2064 150w multi 2.40 1.25
*d.* A2064 240w multi 3.75 1.90
*e.* Booklet pane of 4, #4628a-4628d 8.25 —
Complete booklet, #4628e 8.25

Sinking of the General Sherman, 140th Anniv. A2065

**2006, Sept. 2 Litho. *Perf. 13¼***
**4629** A2065 130w multi 2.25 1.10

Owls A2066

Designs: 12w, Tyto alba. 111w, Strix uralensis. 130w, Strix aluco. 160w, Nyctea scandiaca.

**2006, Sept. 10 *Perf. 11¾***
**4630-4633** A2066 Set of 4 6.75 3.50
*4633a* Booklet pane of 4, #4630-4633 6.75 —
Complete booklet, #4633a 6.75

For overprints see Nos. 4648-4651.

### Souvenir Sheet

Kim Il Sung University, 60th Anniv. — A2067

**2006, Oct. 1 *Perf. 11½x12***
**4634** A2067 70w multi 1.25 .60

Famous Koreans A2068

Designs: 3w, Ulgi Mundok, general. 12w, So Hui (942-998), diplomat and general. 35w, Kim Ung So (1564-1624), general. 70w, Kang Kam Chan (948-1031), general. 102w, Yongae Somun, general. 130w, Ri Kyu Bo (1168-1241), poet. 160w, Mun Ik Jom (1329-98), civil official.

**2006, Oct. 2 *Perf. 13½***
**4635-4641** A2068 Set of 7 8.25 4.50

A2069

Down With Imperialism Union, 80th Anniv. — A2070

No. 4643: a, 70w, Kim Il Sung and followers (50x38mm). b, 102w, Kim Il Sung (46mm diameter). c, 120w, Kim Il Sung and followers on railroad track (50x38mm).

**2006, Oct. 17 Litho. *Perf. 13¼***
**4642** A2069 3w multi —

**Souvenir Sheet**

***Perf. 11¾ (#4643a, 4643c), Perf.***
**4643** A2070 Sheet of 3, #a-c 5.00 2.50

Red Cross Society of North Korea, 60th Anniv. — A2071

**2006, Oct. 18 Litho. *Perf. 13½***
**4644** A2071 30w multi .55 .30

**Souvenir Sheet**

Secondary Education for Koreans in Japan, 60th Anniv. — A2072

**2006, Oct. 21 *Perf. 13¼***
**4645** A2072 110w multi 1.90 .95

**Miniature Sheet**

Koguryo Tombs UNESCO World Heritage Site — A2073

No. 4646 — Murals: a, 3w, King (30x42mm). b, 70w, Queen (30x42mm). c, 130w, Subak (52x34mm). d, 135w, Procession (52x34mm). e, 160w, Kitchen (52x34mm).

***Perf. 13¼ (3w, 70w), 12¼x11¾***
**2006, Nov. 4 Litho.**
**4646** A2073 Sheet of 5, #a-e —

**Souvenir Sheet**

Joson University, 50th Anniv. — A2074

**2006, Nov. 4 *Perf. 11½***
**4647** A2074 110w multi + label 1.90 .95

Nos. 4630-4633 Overprinted in Gold

**Methods and Perfs As Before**
**2006, Nov. 16**
**4648** A2066 12w on #4630 .30 .30
**4649** A2066 111w on #4631 1.75 .90
**4650** A2066 130w on #4632 2.10 1.25
**4651** A2066 160w on #4633 2.60 1.40
*Nos. 4648-4651 (4)* 6.75 3.85

Belgica 2006 World Youth Stamp Exhibition. Location of the overprint varies.

**Souvenir Sheet**

Wooden Sculpture Presented by People's Army Soldiers to Kim Jong Il — A2075

**2006, Dec. 24 Litho. *Perf. 11½x12***
**4652** A2075 130w multi 2.25 1.10

New Year 2007 A2076

**2007, Jan. 1 Litho. *Perf. 13½***
**4653** A2076 3w multi .30 .30

New Year 2007 (Year of the Pig) A2077

Various pigs: 3w, 45w.
No. 4656 — Various pigs: a, 70w. b, 130w.

**2007, Jan. 1 *Perf. 11½***
**4654-4655** A2077 Set of 2 .85 .40
**4656** A2077 Sheet, #4654-4655, 4656a, 4656b 4.00 2.10
*c.* Booklet pane, #4654-4655, 4656a, 4656b 4.00 —
Complete booklet, #4656c 4.00
*d.* Souvenir sheet of 1 #4656a 1.20 .60

A2078

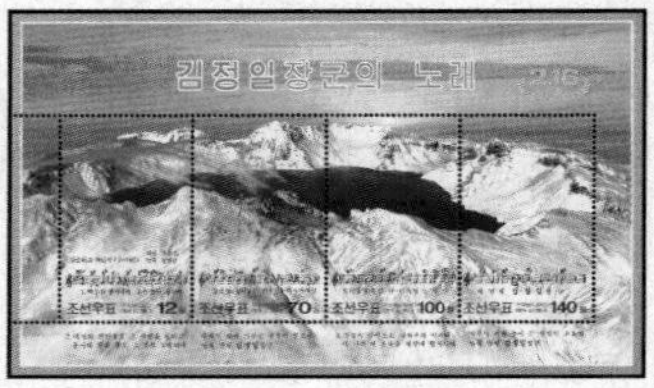

Kim Jong Il, 65th Birthday — A2079

Designs: 3w, Kimiljonghwa begonia and butterfly.
No. 4658 — Mountain, lake and musical score: a, 12w. b, 70w. c, 100w. d, 140w.

**2007, Feb. 16 *Perf. 13¼***
**4657** A2078 3w multi .30 .30
**4658** A2079 Sheet of 4, #a-d 5.25 2.60

Symbols of Progress A2080

**2007, Feb. 28 *Perf. 13¼***
**4659** A2080 3w multi .30 .30

Annual joint editorial of state newspapers.

Butterflies — A2081

Designs: 15w, Callicore selima. 85w, Morpho rhetenor. 110w, Atrophaneura alcinous. 160w, Parnassius bremeri.

**2007, Mar. 5**
**4660-4663** A2081 Set of 4 6.25 3.00
*4663a* Booklet pane of 4, #4660-4663 6.25 —
Complete booklet, #4663a 6.25

**Miniature Sheet**

Koguryo Tombs UNESCO World Heritage Site — A2082

No. 4664 — Anak Tomb No. 3 paintings: a, 3w, Stable (60x42mm). b, 70w, Well (60x42mm). c, 130w, Milling area (30x42mm). d, 160w, Man blowing horn (30x42mm).

**2007, Mar. 10**
**4664** A2082 Sheet of 4, #a-d 6.25 3.00
*e.* Booklet pane of 4, #4664a-4664d 6.25 —
Complete booklet, #4664e 6.25

Korean National Association, 90th Anniv. — A2083

**2007, Mar. 23**
**4665** A2083 12w multi .30 .30

Ludwig van Beethoven (1770-1827), Composer — A2084

**2007, Mar. 26**
**4666** A2084 80w multi 1.40 .65

Mangyongdae, Birthplace of Kim Il Sung — A2085

Paintings of Kim Il Sung — A2086

Kim Il Sung and Family — A2087

No. 4668: a, 45w, The Great Leader Kim Il Sung on the 250-Mile Journey for Learning. b, 70w, The Great Leader Kim Il Sung Who Braved Through the Arduous Road of the Anti-Japanese War. c, 100w, Ever Victorious Road. d, 160w, At the Field Predicting the Rich Harvest.

**2007, Apr. 15** ***Perf. 13¼***

| | | | | |
|---|---|---|---|---|
| **4667** | A2085 | 3w multi | .30 | .30 |

***Perf. 11¾***

| | | | | |
|---|---|---|---|---|
| **4668** | A2086 | Sheet of 4, #a-d | 6.25 | 3.00 |

**Souvenir Sheet**

***Perf. 11¾x11½***

| | | | | |
|---|---|---|---|---|
| **4669** | A2087 | 130w multi | 2.25 | 1.10 |

Kim Il Sung (1912-94).

Miniature Sheet

Rodents — A2088

No. 2088: a, 3w, Sciurus vulgaris. b, 12w, Muscardinus avellanarius. c, 20w, Hypogeomys antimena. d, 30w, Lemniscomys striatus. e, 40w, Pedetes capensis. f, 50w, Rattus norvegicus. g, 80w, Eliomys quercinus. h, 102w, Micromys minutus.

**2007, Apr. 20** ***Perf. 13x13x12¼***

| | | | | |
|---|---|---|---|---|
| **4670** | A2088 | Sheet of 8, #a-h, + 2 labels | 5.50 | 3.75 |

Korean People's Army Soldiers and Mt. Paektu A2089

Leaders Reviewing Troops — A2090

Kim Il Sung and Kim Jong Il Reviewing Troops — A2091

No. 4672: a, 80w, Kim Il Sung and Kim Jong Il reviewing troops. b, 100w, Kim Jong Il and soldiers.

**2007, Apr. 25** ***Perf. 13¼***

| | | | | |
|---|---|---|---|---|
| **4671** | A2089 | 12w multi | .30 | .30 |

***Perf. 11¾***

| | | | | |
|---|---|---|---|---|
| **4672** | A2090 | Sheet of 2, #a-b | 3.00 | 1.50 |

**Souvenir Sheet**

***Perf. 12x11½***

| | | | | |
|---|---|---|---|---|
| **4673** | A2091 | 120w multi | 2.00 | 1.00 |

Korean People's Army, 75th anniv.

Prevention of Bird Flu — A2092

**2007, May 10** ***Perf. 13¼***

| | | | | |
|---|---|---|---|---|
| **4674** | A2092 | 85w multi | 1.60 | .70 |

Miniature Sheet

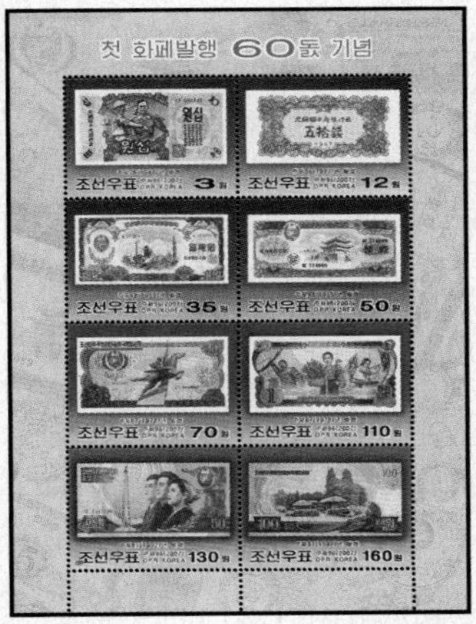


First North Korean Currency, 60th Anniv. — A2093

No. 4675 — Banknotes: a, 3w, 10-won note of 1947. b, 12w, 50-chon note of 1947. c, 35w, 100-won note of 1959. d, 50w, 10-won note of 1959. e, 70w, 10-won note of 1978. f, 110w, 1-won note of 1978. g, 130w, 50-won note of 1992. h, 160w, 100-won note of 1992.

**2007, May 20** **Litho.**

| | | | | |
|---|---|---|---|---|
| **4675** | A2093 | Sheet of 8, #a-h | 9.25 | 4.75 |

Souvenir Sheet

Battle of Pochonbo, 70th Anniv. — A2094

**2007, June 4** ***Perf. 11½x12***

| | | | | |
|---|---|---|---|---|
| **4676** | A2094 | 120w multi | 2.00 | 1.00 |

Fish A2095

Designs: 15w, Naso lituratus. 50w, Carassius auratus. 110w, A. citrinellus. 200w, Symphysodon discus.

**2007, July 1** ***Perf. 13¼***

| | | | | |
|---|---|---|---|---|
| **4677-4680** | A2095 | Set of 4 | 6.25 | 3.00 |
| *4680a* | | Booklet pane of 4, #4677-4680 | 6.25 | — |
| | | Complete booklet, #4680a | 6.25 | |

Self-disembowelment of Ri Jun at Hague Intl. Peace Conference, Cent. — A2096

**2007, July 14**

| | | | | |
|---|---|---|---|---|
| **4681** | A2096 | 110w brn & grn | 1.90 | .95 |

Fossils A2097

Designs: 15w, Tetracorallia. 70w, Neuropteridium. 130w, Yoldia. 200w, Rhinoceros mandible.

**2007, July 20**

| | | | | |
|---|---|---|---|---|
| **4682-4685** | A2097 | Set of 4 | 7.00 | 3.75 |
| *4685a* | | Booklet pane of 4, #4682-4685 | 7.00 | — |
| | | Complete booklet, #4685a | 7.00 | |

Miniature Sheet

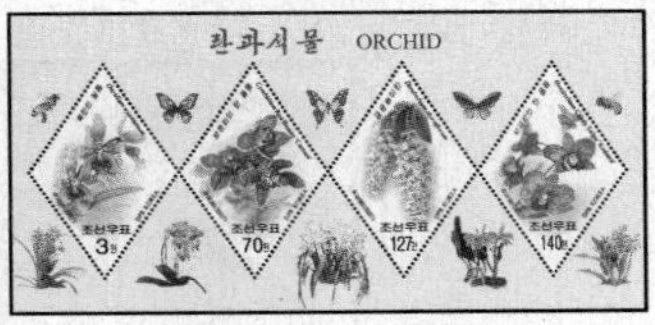


Orchids — A2098

No. 4686: a, 3w, Oncidium wyattianum. b, 70w, Cymbidium Red Beauty "Carmen." c, 127w, Dendrobium thyrsifolium. d, 140w, Dendrobium Candy Stripe "Kodama."

**2007, Aug. 3** ***Perf. 12¾***

| | | | | |
|---|---|---|---|---|
| **4686** | A2098 | Sheet of 4, #a-d | 5.50 | 2.75 |
| *e.* | | Booklet pane of 4, #4686a-4686d | 5.50 | — |
| | | Complete booklet, #4686e | 5.50 | |

Women's Soccer — A2099

No. 4687 — Various women soccer players making plays: a, 12w. b, 40w. c, 70w. d, 110w. e, 140w.

**2007, Sept. 10** ***Perf.***

| | | | | |
|---|---|---|---|---|
| **4687** | A2099 | Sheet of 5, #a-e | 6.00 | 3.00 |

**Souvenir Sheet**

| | | | | |
|---|---|---|---|---|
| **4688** | A2099 | 130w shown | 2.25 | 1.10 |

Miniature Sheet

Flowers — A2100

No. 4689: a, Gladiolus gandavensis. b, Iris ensata. c, Rosa hybrida. d, Nelumbo nucifera.

**2007, Sept. 26** ***Perf. 13¼***

| | | | | |
|---|---|---|---|---|
| **4689** | A2100 | 30w Sheet of 4, #a-d | 2.10 | 1.00 |
| *e.* | | Booklet pane of 4, #4689a-4689d | 2.10 | — |
| | | Complete booklet, #4689e | 2.10 | |

See Russia No. 7045.

Miniature Sheets

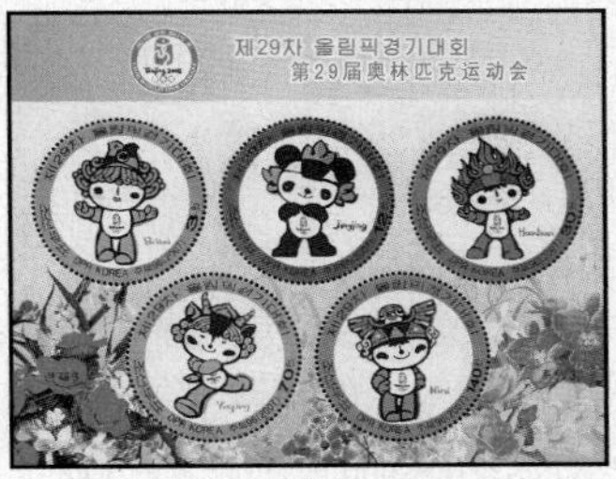


A2101

2008 Summer Olympics, Beijing — A2102

Nos. 4690 and 4691 — Mascots: a, 3w, Beibei. b, 12w, Jingjing. c, 30w, Huanhuan. d, 70w, Yingying. e, 140w, Nini.

2008 Olympics emblem and: 300w, Hurdler, shooter, group of athletes. 500w, Athletes holding flower bouquets.

**2007, Oct. 15** **Litho.** ***Perf.***

| | | | | |
|---|---|---|---|---|
| **4690** | A2101 | Sheet of 5, #a-e | — | — |

**Litho. With Three-Dimensional Plastic Affixed**

| | | | | |
|---|---|---|---|---|
| **4691** | A2101 | Sheet of 5, #a-e | — | — |

**Printed on Plastic DVD Without Gum**

| | | | | |
|---|---|---|---|---|
| **4692** | A2102 | 300w multi | *12.50* | *12.50* |
| **4693** | A2102 | 500w multi | *20.00* | *20.00* |

No. 4691 sold for 500w, and stamps have other three-dimensional images.

Furniture and Household Furnishings — A2103

Designs: 3w, Seal box. 12w, Ornamental chest. 40w, Collapsible dressing table. 70w, Wardrobe. 110w, Chest of drawers. 130w, Chest of drawers, diff.

**2007, Nov. 1 Litho. *Perf. 13¼***
**4694-4699** A2103 Set of 6 8.00 6.00
*4699a* Booklet pane of 6, #4694-4699 8.00 —
Complete booklet, #4699a 8.00

Food
A2104

Designs: 12w, Potato and rice cakes. 50w, Yongchae kimchi. 70w, Fermented flatfish. 110w, Potato cakes.

**2007, Nov. 5**
**4700-4703** A2104 Set of 4 5.25 3.75
*4703a* Booklet pane of 4, #4700-4703 5.25 —
Complete booklet, #4703a 5.25

Souvenir Sheet

Summit Meeting of Pres. Kim Jong Il and South Korean Pres. Roh Moo Hyun — A2105

**2007, Nov. 10 *Perf. 11½x12***
**4704** A2105 170w multi 3.75 3.00

Miniature Sheets

Scenes From Arirang Gymnastics Performance — A2106

No. 4705 — Various scenes: a, 12w. b, 50w.
No. 4706 — Various scenes: a, 120w. b, 155w.

**2007, Nov. 15 *Perf. 11½***
**Sheets of 2, #a-b, + Label**
**4705-4706** A2106 Set of 2 6.00 4.00

Paintings of Kim Dong Ho — A2107

Designs: 3w, Plowing. 12w, Weaving a Straw Mat. 70w, Thrashing. 130w, Archery.

**2007, Nov. 18 *Perf. 13¼***
**4707-4710** A2107 Set of 4 4.75 3.00
*4710a* Booklet pane of 4, #4707-4710 4.75 —
Complete booklet, #4710a 4.75

Souvenir Sheet

Visit of Viet Nam Communist Party Secretary General Nong Duc Manh — A2108

**2007, Dec. 16 *Perf. 12x11½***
**4711** A2108 120w multi 2.60 1.75

Home of Kim Jong Suk — A2109

Paintings Depicting Kim Jong Suk — A2110

No. 4713: a, 30w, Kim Jong Suk and Kim Il Sung (54x45mm). b, 70w, Kim Jong Suk (45mm diameter). c, 110w, Kim Jong Suk in battle (54x45mm).

**2007, Dec. 24 *Perf. 12x11½***
**4712** A2109 3w multi .35 .30

**Souvenir Sheet**
***Perf. 13¼, Perf. (#4713b)***
**4713** A2110 Sheet of 3, #a-c 4.75 3.50

New Year 2008 — A2111

**2008, Jan. 1 Litho. *Perf. 13¼***
**4714** A2111 3w multi .30 .30

Publication of Saenal Sinmun, 80th Anniv. — A2112

**2008, Jan. 15**
**4715** A2112 85w multi 1.50 .75

Joint Editorials of State Newspapers — A2113

Red flag in upper left corner and: No. 4716, 3w, Arms and flag of North Korea, tower. No. 4717, 3w, Soldiers. No. 4718, 12w, Soldier and flag. No. 4719, 12w, Soldiers, factories and electrical tower, horiz. 30w, Woman and food, horiz. 120w, Musicians, children playing soccer, building. 130w, Men and woman, doves, map of Korea.

**2008, Jan. 30 *Perf. 11¾***
**4716-4722** A2113 Set of 7 6.75 4.75

Parrots
A2114

Designs: 15w, Melopsittacus undulatus. 85w, Agapornis roseicollis. 155w, Agapornis personata, horiz. 170w, Two Melopsittacus undulatus, horiz.

**2008, Feb. 5 *Perf. 13¼***
**4723-4726** A2114 Set of 4 9.50 7.00
*4726a* Booklet pane of 4, #4723-4726 9.50 —
Complete booklet, #4726a 9.50

Souvenir Sheet

Naming of Kimjongilhwa Begonia, 20th Anniv. — A2115

**2008, Feb. 13 *Perf. 11½x12***
**4727** A2115 85w multi 2.10 1.50

A2116

Flowers — A2117

Designs: 3w, Pyrethrum hybridum.
No. 4729: a, 12w, Tulipa gesneriana (30x42mm). b, 70w, Adonis amurensis (30x42mm). c, 120w, Mathiola incana (30x42mm). d, 155w, Kimjongilhwa begonia (44mm diameter)

**2008, Feb. 16 *Perf. 13¼***
**4728** A2116 3w multi .50 .30
**4729** A2117 Sheet of 4, #a-d 7.50 5.25

Kim Jong Il, 66th birthday.

**Kim Il Sung Birthplace Type of 2002**
**2008, Mar. 15 Litho. *Perf. 11½***
**4730** A1886 3w red .50 .30

For surcharge, see No. 4877C.

Miniature Sheet

Publication of "On the Art of Cinema," by Kim Jong Il, 35th Anniv. — A2118

No. 4731 — Various actors and actresses: a, 3w, Musician. b, 85w, Man holding gun. c, 135w, Martial artist. d, 170w, Man, woman and children.

**2008, Mar. 15 *Perf. 13¼***
**4731** A2118 Sheet of 4, #a-d 6.50 3.25

250-Mile Journey for Learning, 85th Anniv. — A2119

**2008, Mar. 16 *Perf. 12***
**4732** A2119 15w multi .50 .30

2008 Summer Olympics, Beijing — A2120

No. 4733: a, 3w, Soccer. b, 12w, Basketball. c, 30w, Tennis. d, 70w, Table tennis.

**2008, Mar. 28** ***Perf. 13¼***

| | | | | |
|---|---|---|---|---|
| **4733** | A2120 | Block or horiz. strip of 4, #a-d | 2.60 | 1.25 |

Famous Men — A2121

Designs: 85w, Choe Yong (1316-88), military leader. 160w, Ho Jun (1546-1615), doctor.

**2008, Mar. 29** ***Perf. 12***

| | | | | |
|---|---|---|---|---|
| **4734-4735** | A2121 | Set of 2 | 4.00 | 2.10 |

Election of Kim Jong Il as Chairman of National Defense Commission, 15th Anniv. — A2122

**2008, Apr. 9** ***Perf. 13¼***

| | | | | |
|---|---|---|---|---|
| **4736** | A2122 | 12w multi | .50 | .30 |

Souvenir Sheet

Election of Kim Jong Il as Chairman of National Defense Commission, 15th Anniv. — A2123

**2008, Apr. 9** ***Perf. 11½x12***

| | | | | |
|---|---|---|---|---|
| **4737** | A2123 | 120w multi | — | — |

International Friendship Exhibition A2124

Gifts to Kim Il Sung: 3w, Pitcher and oil lamp. 85w, Painting of rooster. 155w, Throne. 135w, Vase with two handles.

**2008, Apr. 15** ***Perf. 11½***

| | | | | |
|---|---|---|---|---|
| **4738-4740** | A2124 | Set of 3 | 4.00 | 2.10 |

**Souvenir Sheet**

| | | | | |
|---|---|---|---|---|
| **4741** | A2124 | 135w multi | 3.50 | 1.50 |

North-South Joint Conference, 60th Anniv. — A2125

**2008, Apr. 21** ***Perf. 12***

| | | | | |
|---|---|---|---|---|
| **4742** | A2125 | 12w gray green | .50 | .30 |

Mushrooms A2126

Designs: 12w, Amanita muscaria. 50w, Armilliariella mellea. 135w, Macrolepota procera. 155w, Tricholoma terreum.

**2008, May 8** ***Perf. 11½***

| | | | | |
|---|---|---|---|---|
| **4743-4746** | A2126 | Set of 4 | 6.50 | 3.75 |
| *4746a* | | Booklet pane of 4, #4743-4746 | 6.50 | — |
| | | Complete booklet, #4746a | 6.50 | |

Buildings on Mt. Ryongak A2127

Designs: 35w, Two buildings. 155w, Building and wall.

**2008, May 25** ***Perf. 13¼***

| | | | | |
|---|---|---|---|---|
| **4747-4748** | A2127 | Set of 2 | 3.75 | 2.10 |

Musical Instruments — A2128

Designs: 15w, Hyangbipha (stringed instrument). 50w, Phiri (contrabassoon). 120w, Jangsaenap (oboe). 160w, Kayagum (zither), horiz.

**2008, June 1** ***Perf. 13¼***

| | | | | |
|---|---|---|---|---|
| **4749-4752** | A2128 | Set of 4 | 6.50 | 3.75 |
| *4752a* | | Booklet pane of 4, #4749-4752 | 6.50 | — |
| | | Complete booklet, #4752a | 6.50 | |

Opera Scenes and Scores — A2129

Designs: 3w, Sea of Blood. 12w, The Flower Girl. 85w, The True Daughter of the Party. 120w, Tell Oh Forest. 155w, The Song of Mt. Kumgang.

**2008, June 5** ***Perf. 12x11½***

| | | | | |
|---|---|---|---|---|
| **4753-4757** | A2129 | Set of 5 | 6.75 | 4.75 |

North Korea No. 1 and Romania No. 1 — A2130

**2008, June 20** ***Perf. 12¼x11¾***

| | | | | |
|---|---|---|---|---|
| **4758** | A2130 | 85w multi | 1.90 | .95 |

EFIRO 2008 Intl. Stamp Exhibition, Bucharest, Romania.

Capture of the USS Pueblo, 40th Anniv. — A2131

**2008, June 25** ***Perf. 12¼x11¾***

| | | | | |
|---|---|---|---|---|
| **4759** | A2131 | 12w multi | .50 | .30 |

Souvenir Sheet

Olympic Torch Relay in Pyongyang — A2132

**2008, June 26** ***Perf. 11¾x12¼***

| | | | | |
|---|---|---|---|---|
| **4760** | A2132 | 120w multi | 2.60 | 1.40 |

Minerals — A2133

Designs: 12w, Serpentine. 75w, Copper pyrite. 135w, Sphalerite. 155w, Molybdenite.

**2008, July 5** ***Perf. 12¼x11¾***

| | | | | |
|---|---|---|---|---|
| **4761-4764** | A2133 | Set of 4 | 7.00 | 4.00 |
| *4764a* | | Booklet pane of 4, #4761-4764 | 7.00 | — |
| | | Complete booklet, #4764a | 7.00 | |

Souvenir Sheets

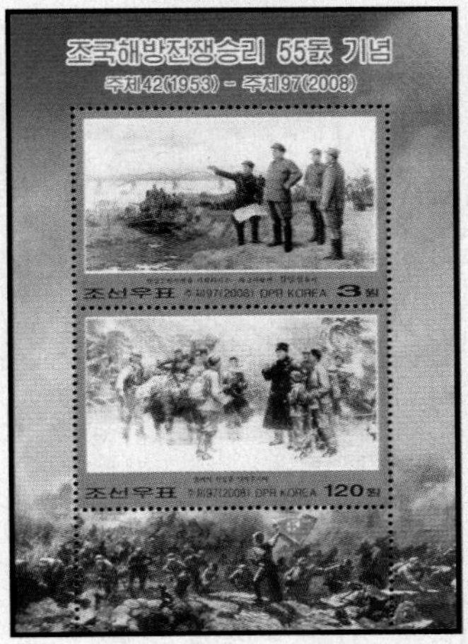


A2134

A2135

Korean War Ceasefire, 55th Anniv. — A2136

No. 4765: a, 3w, Kim Il Sung leading troop crossing of Han River. b, 120w, Kim Il Sung with troops.
No. 4766: a, 35w, Kim Il Sung and seated troops. b, 155w, Celebration.
85w, Kim Il Sung at battleground.

**2008, July 27** ***Perf. 12x11½***

**4765** A2134 Sheet of 2, #a-b 2.40 1.40
**4766** A2135 Sheet of 2, #a-b 3.50 2.10

***Perf. 11½***

**4767** A2136 85w multi 1.90 1.00

Souvenir Sheet

Jong Il Peak, 20th Anniv. of Renaming — A2137

**2008, Aug. 9** ***Perf. 13¼***

**4768** A2137 120w multi 2.60 1.50

Food A2138

Designs: 3w, Rice and wormwood cakes. 70w, Rice cakes. 135w, Pancakes. 155w, Garlic in soy sauce.

**2008, Aug. 20** **Litho.** ***Perf. 13¼***

**4769-4772** A2138 Set of 4 6.25 3.75
*4772a* Booklet pane of 4, #4769-4772 6.25 —
Complete booklet, #4772a 6.25

A2139

Songun Revolutionary Leadership — A2140

**2008, Aug. 25**

**4773** A2139 12w multi .30 .30

**Souvenir Sheet**

**4774** A2140 135w multi 2.75 1.50

Miniature Sheet

Koguryo Tombs UNESCO World Heritage Site — A2141

No. 4775 — Anak Tomb No. 3 paintings: a, 3w, Mask dance (60x42mm). b, 90w, Janghaedok, aide to King Kogukwon (30x42mm). c, 120w, Garage (60x42mm). d, 155w, Stable (60x42mm).

**2008, Sept. 2** **Litho.** ***Perf. 13¼***

**4775** A2141 Sheet of 4, #a-d, + label 6.25 3.75
*e.* Booklet pane of 4, #4775a-4775d 6.25 —
Complete booklet, #4775e 6.25

A2142

Flag A2143

**2008, Sept. 9** ***Perf. 11½***

**4776** A2142 3w multi .50 .30
**4777** A2143 155w multi 3.00 1.75

See No. 4876.

A2144

Creation of North Korea, 60th Anniv. — A2145

Designs: 3w, Chollima Statue, flag of North Korea, city and flowers. 12w, Torch, flag of the Supreme Commander, people. 70w, Soldiers. 120w, People on horses. 160w, Handshake.
155w, Creation of National Flag and Arms.

**2008, Sept. 9** ***Perf. 13¼***

**4778-4782** A2144 Set of 5 6.25 4.00

**Souvenir Sheet**

**4783** A2145 155w multi 3.00 1.50

Transportation — A2146

Designs: No. 4784, 680w, Niña, ship of Christopher Columbus. No. 4785, 680w, 1910 Russian steam engine. No. 4786, 680w, Hindenburg over Lake Constance. No. 4787, 680w, Siberian husky dog sled team. No. 4788, 680w, Ivan Basso, cyclist. No. 4789, 680w, Mercedes-Benz-Mets LF 16 fire truck. No. 4790, 680w, Two Ferrari Enzos. No. 4791, 680w, Eurostar train. No. 4792, 680w, Concorde. No. 4793, 680w, Laika the dog and Sputnik 2.

**2008, Sept. 15** ***Perf.***

**4784-4793** A2146 Set of 10 180.00 150.00

Nos. 4784-4793 each were printed in sheets of 2.

Souvenir Sheet

Salvelinus Malma — A2147

**2008, Oct. 2** **Litho.** ***Perf. 13¼***

**4794** A2147 135w multi 2.40 1.10

Miniature Sheet

Moran Hill, Pyongyang — A2148

No. 4795: a, 3w, Small shelter and bridge. b, 45w, Large shelter and walkway. c, 100w, Flora with small shelter, bridges and Pyongyang in distance. d, 135w, Building with steps.

**2008, Oct. 20**

**4795** A2148 Sheet of 4, #a-d 5.00 3.00

Introduction of Compulsory Secondary Education, 50th Anniv. — A2149

**2008, Nov. 1**

**4796** A2149 12w multi .50 .30

Soldier and Flag A2150

Woman in Bean Field A2151

**2008, Nov. 17**

**4797** A2150 12w multi .35 .30
**4798** A2151 85w multi 1.50 .70

Furniture A2152

Designs: 50w, Haeju table. 70w, Inkstone table. 120w, Dressing table with drawer. 170w, Jewel box.

**2008, Dec. 3**

**4799-4802** A2152 Set of 4 6.50 3.50
*4802a* Booklet pane of 4, #4799-4802 6.50 —
Complete booklet, #4802a 6.50

Souvenir Sheet

Ulmil Pavilion, Moran Hill, Pyongyang — A2153

**Litho. With Three-Dimensional Plastic Affixed**

**2008, Dec. 15** ***Perf. 13¼***

**Without Gum**

**4803** A2153 85w multi 2.40 1.25

New Year 2009 A2154

**2009, Jan. 1** **Litho.** ***Perf. 11½***

**4804** A2154 3w multi .50 .30

For surcharge, see No. 4877D.

A2155

Red Guards, 50th Anniv. — A2156

**2009, Jan. 14** *Perf. 11¾*
**4805** A2155 12w multi .50 .30

**Souvenir Sheet**

**4806** A2156 160w multi 3.00 2.00

Traditional Games — A2157

Designs: 3w, Tug-of-war. 120w, Knee fighting.

**2009, Jan. 25** *Perf. 13¼*
**4807-4808** A2157 Set of 2 2.40 1.50

Kim Jong Il, 67th Birthday A2158

Unnamed butterfly and flowers: 3w, Crinum bracteatum. 12w, Begonia. 120w, Callistemon phoeniceus. 160w, Plumeria rubra.

**2009, Feb. 16** *Perf. 11¾*
**4809-4812** A2158 Set of 4 5.25 3.00

**Souvenir Sheet**

Proclamation of Juche Model for Society, 50th Anniv. — A2159

**2009, Feb. 19** *Perf. 11½x12*
**4813** A2159 170w multi 3.25 1.90

**Souvenir Sheets**

A2160

A2161

A2162

Joint Editorials of State Newspapers — A2163

No. 4814: a, 3w, Torch, Chollima statue. b, 170w, Symbols of industry and transportation.
No. 4815: a, 12w, Food crops, canned foods, city. b, 150w, Musical instruments, sheet music, orchestra, soccer players.
No. 4816: a, 30w, Soldiers, flag, ships, airplanes and missiles. b, 120w, Soldiers, flags, city.
No. 4817: a, 80w, Map of Korea, text. b, 100w, Hands crushing bomb.

**2009, Feb. 22** *Perf. 11½*

| | | | | |
|---|---|---|---|---|
| **4814** | A2160 | Sheet of 2, #a-b, + 2 labels | 3.25 | 2.10 |
| **4815** | A2161 | Sheet of 2, #a-b, + 2 labels | 3.00 | 1.90 |
| **4816** | A2162 | Sheet of 2, #a-b, + 2 labels | 2.75 | 1.90 |
| **4817** | A2163 | Sheet of 2, #a-b, + 2 labels | 3.25 | 2.10 |
| | | *Nos. 4814-4817 (4)* | 12.25 | 8.00 |

For surcharge, see No. 4877E.

**Souvenir Sheets**

China 2009 World Stamp Exhibition, Luoyang — A2164

No. 4818: a, 3w, Flowers. b, 100w, Flowers, diff.

No. 4819: a, 12w, Statue of horse. b, 90w, Building, steps, sculpture.

**2009, Feb. 25** *Perf. 11¾*

**Sheets of 2, #a-b**

**4818-4819** A2164 Set of 2 5.25 2.40
*4819c* Booklet pane of 4, #4818a-4818b, 4819a-4819b 5.25 —
Complete booklet, #4819c 5.25

March 1 Uprising Against Japan, 90th Anniv. — A2165

**2009, Mar. 1** *Perf. 12¼x11¾*
**4820** A2165 90w multi 1.90 1.25

Intl. Women's Day, Cent. — A2166

**2009, Mar. 8** *Perf. 13¼*
**4821** A2166 35w multi .60 .35

Gifts to Kim Il Sung — A2167

Designs: 3w, Painting of horses. 12w, Fossil fish. 140w, Rifle. 150w, Bear skin.

**2009, Apr. 15** *Perf. 13¼*
**4822-4825** A2167 Set of 4 5.50 3.50
*4825a* Booklet pane of 4, #4822-4825 5.50 —
Complete booklet, #4825a 5.50

Complete booklet sold for 322w.

Central Zoo, Pyongyang, 50th Anniv. A2168

Birds: 12w, Anthropoides paradisea. 70w, Accipiter gentilis. 120w, Larus argentatus. 140w, Balearica pavonina.

**2009, Apr. 30** *Perf. 11¾x12¼*
**4826-4829** A2168 Set of 4 6.25 3.75
*4829a* Booklet pane of 4, #4826-4829 6.25 —
Complete booklet, #4829a 6.25

Central Botanical Garden, Pyongyang, 50th Anniv. A2169

Trees: 3w, Catalpa ovata. 50w, Betula platyphylla. 120w, Juglans cordiformis. 160w, Metasequoia glyptostroboides.

**2009, Apr. 30** *Perf. 13¼*
**4830-4833** A2169 Set of 4 6.25 3.75
*4833a* Booklet pane of 4, #4830-4833 6.25 —
Complete booklet, #4833a 6.25

Complete booklet sold for 350w.

Sports A2170

Designs: 12w, Baseball. 90w, Bowling. 160w, Fencing. 200w, Golf.

**2009, May 2**
**4834-4837** A2170 Set of 4 7.75 3.75
*4837a* Booklet pane of 4, #4834-4837 7.75 —
Complete booklet, #4837a 7.75

**No. 4189a Surcharged in Gold**

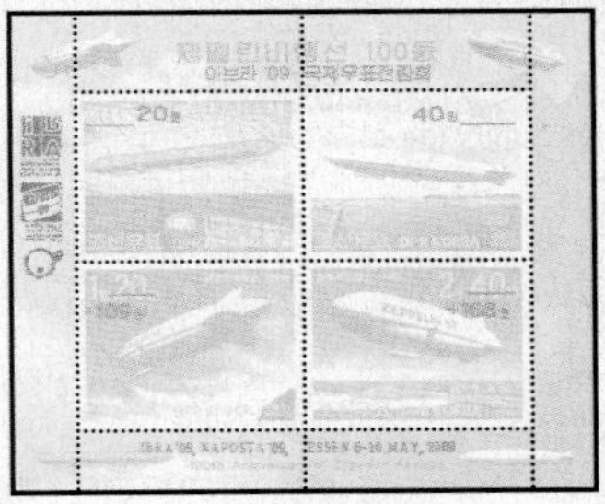

No. 4838: a, 20w on 40ch, LZ1. b, 40w on 80ch, LZ120. c, 1w+109w on 1.20w, Zeppelin NT. d, 2w+168w on 2.40w, Zeppelin NT, diff.

**Method and Perf As Before**

**2009, May 5**
**4838** A1852 Sheet of 4, #a-d 6.25 4.00

Naposta '09 and IBRA '09, Essen, Germany. On Nos. 4838c and 4838d, the obliterator covers the part of the original denomination expressed in chon.

Children's Union Camp A2171

Children: 3w, Mountaineering. 80w, Collecting butterflies. 120w, At campfire. 170w, At beach.

**2009** **Litho.** *Perf. 11½*
**4839-4842** A2171 Set of 4 6.25 3.75
*4842a* Booklet pane of 4, #4839-4842 6.25 —
Complete booklet, #4842a 6.25
*4842b* Souvenir sheet of 4, #4839-4842 6.25 3.75

Issued: Nos. 4839-4842, 4842a, 5/6; No. 4842b, 5/14. Hong Kong 2009 Intl. Stamp Exhibition (No. 4842b).

Souvenir Sheet

Battle of Musan, 70th Anniv. — A2172

**2009, May 22** ***Perf. 13¼***
**4843** A2172 120w multi 2.90 1.50

Miniature Sheet

Kim Jong Il as Member of Central Committee of Workers' Party, 45th Anniv. — A2173

No. 4844 — Kim Jong Il: a, 3w, At desk. b, 12w, At machine shop. c, 120w, Wearing white lab jacket. d, 170w, Looking inside cooking pot.

**2009, June 19** ***Perf. 11¾***
**4844** A2173 Sheet of 4, #a-d 5.75 3.50

Universal Postal Union, 135th Anniv. — A2174

**2009, June 20** ***Perf. 13¼***
**4845** A2174 50w multi 1.10 .60

Insects A2175

Designs: 50w, Vespa mandarinia, rose. 90w, Cicindela japonica, dandelion. 120w, Locusta migratoria, plant. 140w, Aphaenogaster famelica, mushroom.

**2009, July 1** ***Perf. 11½***
**4846-4849** A2175 Set of 4 7.00 4.75
*4849a* Booklet pane of 4, #4846-4849 7.00 —
Complete booklet, #4849a 7.00

Okryu Restaurant, Pyongyang — A2176

Renovated Pyongyang Buildings — A2177

No. 4851: a, 3w, Kim Chaek University Library (35x28mm). b, 70w, Taedongmun Theater (35x28mm). c, 90w, Chongryu Restaurant (70x28mm). d, 150w, Pyongyang Grand Theater (70x28mm).

**2009, July 2** ***Perf. 13¼***
**4850** A2176 12w multi .40 .35
***Perf. 11½***
**4851** A2177 Sheet of 4, #a-d 5.25 3.25

Miniature Sheet

Eternal Sun of Juche — A2178

No. 4852 — Paintings: a, 12w, The Great Leader Kim Il Sung Drawing the Brush Into Our Party's Emblem. b, 50w, First Military Flag. c, 70w, Birth. d, 140w, Every Field With Bumper Harvest.

**2009, July 8** ***Perf. 13¼***
**4852** A2178 Sheet of 4, #a-d 5.25 3.25

Nurse and Child A2179

Ambulance and Hospital — A2180

**2009, July 25**
**4853** A2179 12w multi .40 .30
**4854** A2180 150w multi 2.60 1.75

Souvenir Sheet

Launch of Kwangmyongsong 2 Rocket — A2181

**2009, July 27** ***Perf. 11½x12***
**4855** A2181 120w multi 2.75 1.50

Souvenir Sheet

Northern Area Victory Monument, Hamgyong Province — A2182

**2009, Aug. 3** ***Perf. 13¼***
**4856** A2182 120w multi 2.75 1.50

Musical Instruments A2183

Designs: 12w, Saenap. 80w, Drum. 140w, Sogoghu. 170w, Flute.

**2009, Aug. 5** **Litho.**
**4857-4860** A2183 Set of 4 6.50 3.50

150-Day Innovation Campaign — A2184

**2009, Aug. 10**
**4861** A2184 12w multi .40 .30

Fish A2185

Ships and: 15w, Theragra chalcogramma. 60w, Cyprinus carpio. 140w, Euthynnus pelamis. 160w, Mugil cephalus.

**2009, Sept. 1**
**4862-4865** A2185 Set of 4 6.25 3.75
*4865a* Booklet pane of 4, #4862-4865 6.25 —
Complete booklet, #4865a 6.25

Miniature Sheets

Intl. Year of Astronomy — A2186

No. 4866, 95w: a, Chollima Statue, solar eclipse. b, Galileo Galilei, telescope, planets, satellite.
No. 4867, 95w: a, Rabbits, solar eclipse. b, Planets, galaxy.
No. 4868, 95w: a, Dogs, total solar eclipse. b, Chomsongdae Observatory.

**2009, Aug. 29** **Litho.** ***Perf. 13½***
**Sheets of 2, #a-b, + 2 Labels**
**4866-4868** A2186 Set of 3 9.50 7.00
*4868c* Souvenir sheet of 1, #4868a 1.40 .95
*4868d* Booklet pane of 6, #4866a-4866b, 4867a-4867b, 4868a-4868b 9.50 —
Complete booklet, #4868d 9.50

Souvenir Sheets

A2187

Year of Friendship With People's Republic of China — A2188

No. 4869: a, #3287c, 3384, 3716. b, #3563, 4374b, 4473c.
No. 4870: a, Five stamps. b, Six stamps.

**2009, Sept. 2** ***Perf. 13½***
**4869** A2187 60w Sheet of 2, #a-b 2.40 1.25
**4870** A2188 60w Sheet of 2, #a-b 2.40 1.25

Miniature Sheet

Birdpex 2010, Antwerp, Belgium — A2189

No. 4871: a, 12w, Coturnicops exquisitus. b, 90w, Porzana pusilla. c, 170w, Porzana fusca.

**2009, Sept. 12** ***Perf. 11½***
**4871** A2189 Sheet of 5, #4871c, 2 each #4871a-4871b, + label 6.00 3.25
*d.* Booklet pane of 3, #4871a-4871c 4.50 —
Complete booklet, #4871d 4.50

Souvenir Sheet

Intl. Red Cross and Red Crescent Year — A2190

No. 4872 — Flags of Red Cross, North Korea and: a, 75w, Jean-Henri Dunant, founder of Red Cross. b, 95w, Disaster risk reduction. c, 95w, First aid.

**2009, Sept. 21** ***Perf. 13½***
**4872** A2190 Sheet of 3, #a-c 4.25 2.25

Souvenir Sheet

Kim Jong Suk (1917-49), Mother of Kim Jong Il — A2191

No. 4873: a, 90w, Portrait (33x45mm). b, 100w, Kim Jong Suk with troops, horiz. (57x36mm).

**2009, Sept. 22**
**4873** A2191 Sheet of 2, #a-b 3.25 1.60

Miniature Sheet

People's Republic of China, 60th Anniv. — A2192

No. 4874: a, 10w, Chinese President Hu Jintao. b, 67w, Chinese astronauts. c, 67w, National Stadium, Beijing. d, 84w, National Grand Theater, Beijing.

**2009, Oct. 1**
**4874** A2192 Sheet of 4, #a-d 4.00 2.40

Worldwide Fund for Nature (WWF) — A2193

No. 4875 — Platalea minor and: a, Snail. b, Fish. c, Crab. d, Shrimp.

**2009, Oct. 5** ***Perf. 13½***
**4875** Horiz. strip of 4 6.25 3.25
- *a.* A2193 3w multi .25 .25
- *b.* A2193 12w multi .25 .25
- *c.* A2193 99w multi 1.75 .80
- *d.* A2193 266w multi 4.25 2.25
- *e.* Sheet of 8, 2 each #4875a-4875d, + label 13.00 6.25

**Flag and Torch Types of 2002-08**

**2009, Oct. 15 Litho.** ***Perf. 11½***
**4876** A2142 10w multi .30 .30

***Perf. 13¼***
**4877** A1890 30w multi .50 .30

Nos. 4249, 4252, 4343, 4730, 4804 and 4814a Surcharged

**Methods and Perfs As Before**

**2009, Oct.**
**4877A** A1887 10w on 3w #4249 *1.10 1.10*
**4877B** A1939 10w on 3w #4343 *1.10 1.10*
**4877C** A1886 10w on 3w #4730 *1.10 1.10*
**4877D** A2154 10w on 3w #4804 *1.10 1.10*
**4877E** A2160 10w on 3w #4814a *1.10 1.10*
**4877F** A1890 30w on 12w #4252 *3.50 3.50*
*Nos. 4877A-4877F (6) 9.00 9.00*

Reptiles — A2194

Designs: 15w, Chamaeleo jacksonii. 50w, Naja naja. 110w, Caretta caretta, horiz. 160w, Crocodylus niloticus, horiz.

**2009, Oct. 20**
**4878-4881** A2194 Set of 4 5.50 2.75
*4881a* Booklet pane of 4, #4878-4881 5.75 —
Complete booklet, #4881a 5.75

Miniature Sheets

Lighthouses — A2195

No. 4882: a, Cape Palliser Lighthouse, New Zealand, and Sousa chinensis. b, Tater Du Lighthouse, United Kingdom, and Mary Rose. c, Hornby Lighthouse, Australia, and Passat, Germany. d, Rubjerg Knude Lighthouse, Denmark, and Wappen von Hamburg.

No. 4883: a, Bengtskär Lighthouse, Finland, and Phoebastria albatrus. b, Fanad Lighthouse, Ireland, and Bolma rugosa. c, Cordouan Lighthouse, France, and Sterna fuscata. d, Brandaris Lighthouse, Netherlands, and Pleurotomaria africana.

No. 4884: a, Cape St. Vincent Lighthouse, Portugal, and Sula bassana. b, Europa Point Lighthouse, Gibraltar, and Lambis scorpio. c, Vorontsov Lighthouse, Ukraine, and Grampus griseus. d, Gelendzhik Lighthouse, Russia, and Gibbula magus.

No. 4885: a, Hoy High Lighthouse, Scotland, and Delphinus delphis. b, Lindesnes Lighthouse, Norway, and Stenella coeruleoalba. c, Reykjanesviti Lighthouse, Iceland, and Chlamys varia. d, Seal Point Lighthouse, South Africa, and Chroicocephalus ridibundus.

**2009, Oct. 24 Litho.** ***Perf. 13x13½***
**4882** A2195 760w Sheet of 4, #a-d 50.00 50.00
- *e.* Souvenir sheet of 2 #4882a 24.00 24.00
- *f.* Souvenir sheet of 2 #4882b 24.00 24.00
- *g.* Souvenir sheet of 2 #4882c 24.00 24.00
- *h.* Souvenir sheet of 2 #4882d 24.00 24.00

**4883** A2195 760w Sheet of 4, #a-d 50.00 50.00
- *e.* Souvenir sheet of 2 #4883a 24.00 24.00
- *f.* Souvenir sheet of 2 #4883b 24.00 24.00
- *g.* Souvenir sheet of 2 #4883c 24.00 24.00
- *h.* Souvenir sheet of 2 #4883d 24.00 24.00

**4884** A2195 760w Sheet of 4, #a-d 50.00 50.00
- *e.* Souvenir sheet of 2 #4884a 24.00 24.00
- *f.* Souvenir sheet of 2 #4884b 24.00 24.00
- *g.* Souvenir sheet of 2 #4884c 24.00 24.00
- *h.* Souvenir sheet of 2 #4884d 24.00 24.00

**4885** A2195 760w Sheet of 4, #a-d 50.00 50.00
- *e.* Souvenir sheet of 2 #4885a 24.00 24.00
- *f.* Souvenir sheet of 2 #4885b 24.00 24.00
- *g.* Souvenir sheet of 2 #4885c 24.00 24.00
- *h.* Souvenir sheet of 2 #4885d 24.00 24.00

Souvenir Sheet

Repatriation of Korean Nationals in Japan, 50th Anniv. — A2196

**2009, Dec. 16 Litho.** ***Perf. 11½x12***
**4887** A2196 160w multi 2.60 1.25

Miniature Sheet

End of Juche 98 — A2197

No. 4888: a, 10w, Launch of Kwangmyongsong No. 2 satellite. b, 20w, CNC machine tool industry. c, 20w, Oxygen separator, finished steel products, train and vehicles. d, 30w, Construction vehicles. e, 50w, Namhung Gasification Project, crane with pipe. f, 50w, Apartment buildings on Mansudae Street, Pyongyang. g, 57w, Sturgeons, ostriches, chicken, pig. h, 70w, Apples, farm, Migok-ri model village.i, 80w, Audience, soccer players, singer.

**2009, Dec. 31 Litho.** ***Perf. 13½***
**4888** A2197 Sheet of 9, #a-i 6.25 3.25

Souvenir Sheet

Kim Jong Il and Workers — A2198

**2009, Dec. 31 Litho.** ***Perf. 13¼***
**4889** A2198 100w multi 1.60 .80

End of Juche 98.

New Year 2010 A2199

**2010, Jan. 1** ***Perf. 13¼***
**4890** A2199 10w multi .30 .30

Tigers A2200

Tiger and: 30w, Sun. 67w, Tree. 171w, Tiger and cubs, horiz.

**2010, Jan. 5 Litho.** ***Perf. 11¾x12¼***
**4891-4892** A2200 Set of 2 1.60 .80
*4892a* Booklet pane of 4, 2 each #4891-4892 3.50 —
Complete booklet, #4892a 3.50

**Souvenir Sheet**

**Litho. with Three-Dimensional Plastic Affixed**

***Perf. 13¼***

**Without Gum**

**4893** A2200 171w multi 2.75 1.50

Complete booklet sold for 213w. No. 4893 contains one 60x42mm stamp.

Wildlife A2201

Designs: 35w, Ailuropoda melanoleuca. 60w, Aix galericulata. 80w, Lagenorhynchus obliquidens. 110w, Panthera pardus.

**2010, Jan. 30 Litho.** ***Perf. 13¼***
**4894-4897** A2201 Set of 4 4.75 2.40
*4897a* Booklet pane of 4, #4894-4897 *11.00* —
Complete booklet, #4897a *11.00*

Complete booklet sold for 304w. No. 4897a exists imperforate.

Miniature Sheet

2010 Winter Olympics, Vancouver — A2202

No. 4898: a, 10w, Ice hockey. b, 40w, Figure skating. c, 50w, Speed skating. d, 70w, Skiing.

**2010, Feb. 1** ***Perf. 13***
**4898** A2202 Sheet of 8, 2 each #a-d 5.50 5.50

See No. 4919.

Kim Jong Il, 68th Birthday — A2203

No. 4899: a, 10w, Impatiens sultanii Royal Rose. b, 50w, Gazania hybrida. c, 70w, Paeonia suffructicosa. d, 110w, Bougainvillea glabra Sanderiana.

**2010, Feb. 16** *Perf. 11½*

**4899** A2203 Vert. strip or block of 4, #a-d, + 8 labels 4.25 2.10

*e.* Booklet pane of 4, #4899a-4899d, + 8 labels 4.50 —

Complete booklet, #4899e 4.50

Complete booklet sold for 259w.

Miniature Sheet

Joint Editorials of State Newspapers — A2204

No. 4900: a, 10w, People, soldier, Party Founding Monument, flowers. b, 20w, Woman, city, manufactured items. c, 30w, Woman carrying crops, vegetables. d, 57w, Worker, factory, train, dam. e, 67w, Soldiers. f, 95w, People holding flag showing mpa of unified Korea. g, 125w, Doves, map showing unified Korea.

**2010, Feb. 20** *Perf. 13¼*

**4900** A2204 Sheet of 7, #a-g, + 2 labels 6.50 3.50

A2205

Anti-Imperialism Posters A2206

**2010, Mar. 5**

**4901** A2205 76w multi 1.40 .65

**4902** A2206 95w multi 1.60 .75

Cats A2207

Designs: 10w, Cat, chicks. 70w, Cats, flower, butterfly. 133w, Cat, mouse. 170w, Cat, kittens, ball of yarn.

**2010, Mar. 25** *Perf. 11½*

**4903-4906** A2207 Set of 4 6.25 3.25

*4906a* Booklet pane of 4, #4903-4906 6.50 —

Complete booklet, #4906a 6.50

Complete booklet sold for 402w.

Souvenir Sheet

Birds — A2208

No. 4907: a, 30w, Brachyramphus perdix. b, 125w, Gallinago solitaria. c, 133w, Porzana paykullii.

**2010, Apr. 9**

**4907** A2208 Sheet of 3, #a-c, + 3 labels 4.75 2.40

*d.* Booklet pane of 3, #4907a-4907c 5.00 —

Complete booklet, #4907d 5.00

Antverpia 2010 International Philatelic Exhibition, Antwerp. Complete booklet sold for 307w.

Gifts to Kim Il Sung A2209

Designs: 10w, Eagle figurine. 30w, Crane figurine. 95w, Tiger painting. 152w, Sea turtle figurine, horiz.

**2010, Apr. 15** *Perf. 13¼*

**4908-4911** A2209 Set of 4 4.75 2.40

Orchids and Insects A2210

Designs: 30w, Sophronitella brevipenduncu-lata, bee. 80w, Epidendrum radiatum, dragonfly. 120w, Cymbidium Lillian Stewart "Red Carpet," bee. 152w Dendrobium hybrid, butterfly.

**2010, Apr. 20** *Perf. 11½*

**4912-4915** A2210 Set of 4 6.25 3.25

*4915a* Booklet pane of 4, #4912-4915 6.75 —

Complete booklet, #4915a 6.75

Nos. 4912-4915 each were printed in sheets of 5 + label. Complete booklet sold for 401w.

Souvenir Sheet

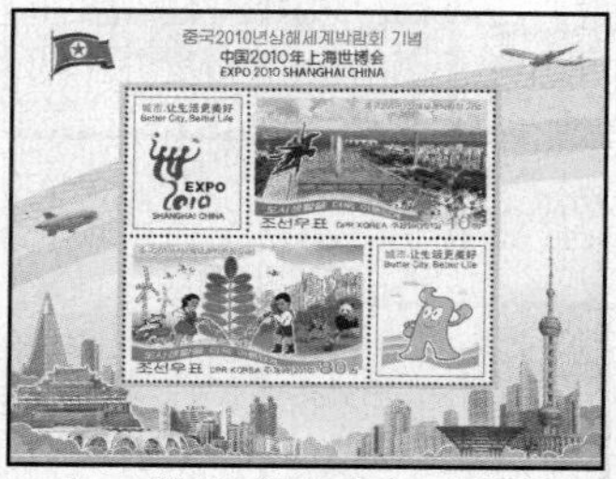

Expo 2010, Shanghai — A2211

No. 4916: a, 10w, Chollima statue, city, flowers. b, 80w, Children watering plant, wind turbines, wildlife.

**2010, May 1** **Litho.**

**4916** A2211 Sheet of 2, #a-b, + 2 labels 1.50 .75

Miniature Sheet

Table Tennis — A2212

No. 4917: a, 10w, Man with green shirt. b, 30w, Woman with red shirt. c, 95w, Woman with blue shirt. d, 152w, Man with pink shirt.

**2010, May 10** *Perf.*

**4917** A2212 Sheet of 4, #a-d 4.75 2.50

*e.* Booklet pane of 4, #4917a-4917d 5.00 —

Complete booklet, #4917e 5.00

Complete booklet sold for 306w.

Joint Slogans — A2213

**2010, May 12** *Perf. 11½*

**4918** A2213 10w multi .30 .30

**No. 4898 With Flags of Countries Winning Depicted Events Added at Left of Athlete**

Miniature Sheet

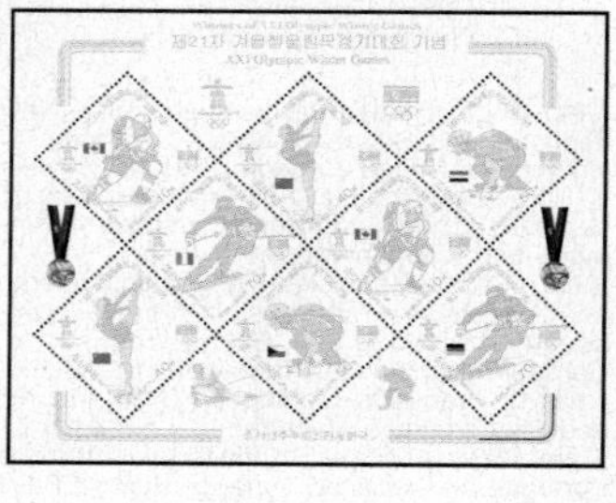

No. 4919: a, 10w, Ice hockey, flag of Canada. b, 40w, Figure skating, flag of People's Republic of China. c, 50w, Speed skating, flag of Netherlands. d, 50w, Speed skating, flag of Czech Republic. e, 70w, Skiing, flag of Italy. f, 70w, Skiing, flag of Germany.

**2010, May 25** *Perf. 13*

**4919** A2202 Sheet of 8, #4919c-4919f, 2 each #4919a-4919b 5.25 5.25

Souvenir Sheet

Dinosaurs — A2214

No. 4920: a, 10w, Brontosaurus. b, 125w, Allosaurus. c, 152w, Pterodactylus.

**2010, June 16** *Perf. 12¾*

**4920** A2214 Sheet of 3, #a-c, + label 4.75 2.40

*d.* Booklet pane of 3, #4920a-4920c 5.00 —

Complete booklet, #4920d 5.00

*e.* As #4920, with Euro-phila 2010 emblem in sheet margin 5.25 2.60

Complete booklet sold for 306w.

Issued: No. 4920e, 10/2.

2010 World Cup Soccer Championships, South Africa — A2215

No. 4921 — Shirt colors of soccer players: a, 20w, Green, yellow. b, 57w, Yellow, blue. c, 190w, Red, white.

114w, Yellow, white.

**2010, May 31** *Perf. 13¼*

**4921** A2215 Sheet of 3, #a-c, + 3 labels 4.25 2.25

**Souvenir Sheet**

**4922** A2215 114w multi 1.90 .95

*a.* Booklet pane of 4, #4921a-4921c, 4922 6.75 —

Complete booklet, #4922a 6.75

Complete booklet sold for 400w.

Souvenir Sheet

Intl. Children's Day, 60th Anniv. — A2216

**2010, June 1** *Perf. 11¾*

**4923** A2216 95w multi 1.60 .85

*a.* As #4923, with Bangkok 2010 emblem in sheet margin 1.60 .85

Issued: No. 4923a, 8/4.

Joint Declaration of June 15, 2000 on Reunification of Korea — A2217

**2010, June 15** *Perf. 13¼*

**4924** A2217 190w multi 3.25 1.60

A2218

A2219

A2220

Visit of Kim Jong Il to People's Republic of China — A2221

No. 4925 — Kim Jong Il: a, 20w, And Chinese man pointing. b, 40w Pointing. c, 67w, Walking.

No. 4926 — Kim Jong Il: a, 20w, Standing next to woman. b, 35w, With leg raised. c, 80w, Looking through window.

No. 4927 — Kim Jong Il: a, 30w, Standing next to Chinese Pres. Hu Jintao. b, 40w, Seated at table with Pres. Hu. c, 70w, Shaking hands with Pres. Hu.

60w, Kim Jong Il and Pres. Hu.

**2010, June 20** ***Perf. 13¼***

| | | | | |
|---|---|---|---|---|
| **4925** | A2218 | Sheet of 3, #a-c, + 6 labels | 2.10 | 1.10 |
| **4926** | A2219 | Sheet of 3, #a-c, + 6 labels | 2.25 | 1.15 |
| **4927** | A2220 | Sheet of 3, #a-c, + 3 labels | 2.40 | 1.25 |
| | | *Nos. 4925-4927 (3)* | 6.75 | 3.50 |

**Souvenir Sheet**

***Perf. 11½x12***

| | | | | |
|---|---|---|---|---|
| **4928** | A2221 | 60w multi | 1.00 | .45 |

Miniature Sheet

Children's Animated Films — A2222

No. 4929 — Scenes from children's animated films: a, 10w, Butterfly and Cock. b, 30w, A Clever Raccoon Dog. c, 95w, A Hedgehog Defeats a Tiger. d, 133w, Regret of Rabbit.

**2010, June 30** ***Perf. 13¼***

| | | | | |
|---|---|---|---|---|
| **4929** | A2222 | Sheet of 4, #a-d | 4.50 | 2.25 |

Souvenir Sheet

Azaleas — A2223

**2010, July 1** **Litho.**

| | | | | |
|---|---|---|---|---|
| **4930** | A2223 | 85w multi | 1.50 | .70 |

Souvenir Sheet

National Anthem — A2224

**2010, July 5** ***Perf. 13½***

| | | | | |
|---|---|---|---|---|
| **4931** | A2224 | 50w black | .80 | .40 |

A2225

Liberation of Korea, 65th Anniv. — A2226

No. 4932 — Paintings: a, 10w, The Great Leader Forming the Korean Revolutionary Army. b, 15w, Bloody and Long Anti-Japanese War. c, 20w, The Azalea in the Fatherland. d, 40w, Pyongyang in New Spring. e, 100w, Historical That Night.

60w, February Festival on the Eve of Korea's Liberation.

**2010, Aug. 15** ***Perf. 13¼***

| | | | | |
|---|---|---|---|---|
| **4932** | A2225 | Sheet of 5, #a-e, + label | 3.00 | 1.60 |

**Souvenir Sheet**

| | | | | |
|---|---|---|---|---|
| **4933** | A2226 | 60w multi | 1.00 | .45 |

A2227

A2228

Start of Songun Revolutionary Leadership, 50th Anniv. — A2229

No. 4935 — Paintings: a, 15w, General Kim Jong Il Instilling the Traditions of Mt. Paektu in the Soldiers (63x41mm). b, 30w, Military Song of Victory (50x38mm). c, 55w, General to the Frontline, Children to the Camp (50x38mm). d, 80w, Saying He Feels Happiest Among the Soldiers (50x38mm).

70w, Blizzard on Mt. Paektu.

**2010, Aug. 25** ***Perf. 11½***

| | | | | |
|---|---|---|---|---|
| **4934** | A2227 | 10w multi | .30 | .30 |

***Perf. 12x11½ (#4935a), 11¾***

| | | | | |
|---|---|---|---|---|
| **4935** | A2228 | Sheet of 4, #a-d | 3.00 | 1.50 |

**Souvenir Sheet**

***Perf. 11¾***

| | | | | |
|---|---|---|---|---|
| **4936** | A2229 | 70w multi | 1.25 | .60 |

Souvenir Sheet

Diplomatic Relations Between North Korea and Cuba, 50th Anniv. — A2230

**2010, Aug. 29** **Litho.** ***Perf. 11¾***

| | | | | |
|---|---|---|---|---|
| **4937** | A2230 | 85w multi | 1.75 | .80 |

Paintings A2231

Designs: 15w, Pine Tree and Hawk, by Sin Yun Bok. 35w, Waves of Ongchon, by Jong Son. 70w, Reeds and Wild Geese, by Jo Sok Jin. 100w, After Picking Medicinal Herbs, by Kim Hong Do.

**2010, Sept. 1** **Litho.** ***Perf. 13¼***

| | | | | |
|---|---|---|---|---|
| **4938-4941** | A2231 | Set of 4 | 3.75 | 1.90 |
| *4941a* | | Booklet pane of 4, #4938-4941 | 3.75 | — |
| | | Complete booklet, #4941a | 3.75 | |

A2232

A2233

A2234

A2235

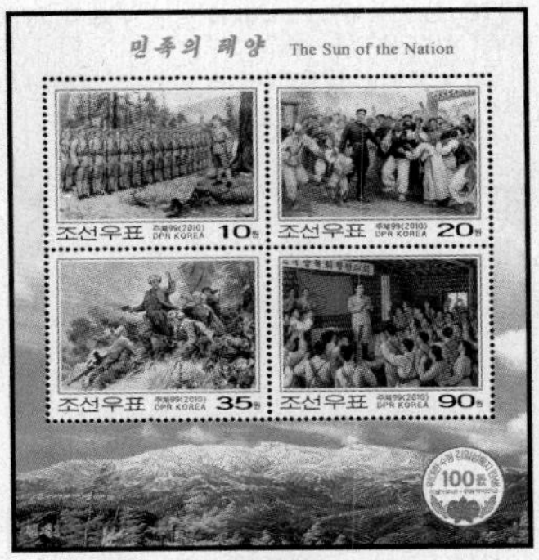

A2236

A2237

Pres. Kim Il Sung (1912-94) — A2238

No. 4942: a, 20w, Kim Il Sung being educated by father. b, 55w, Kim Il Sung being educated by mother.

No. 4943: a, 25w, Kim Jong Suk defending Kim Il Sung (64x42mm). b, 30w, Kim Il Sung at secret camp on Mt. Paektu in spring (45x35mm). c, 45w, Kim Il Sung on horseback leading other riders (454x35mm).

No. 4944: a, 10w, Kim Il Sung crossing Amnok River in winter. b, 30w, Kim Il Sung leading protest against Jilin-Hoeryong railway. c, 40w, Kim Il Sung reporting at Youth League meeting. d, 55w, Kang Pan Sok handing over pistols to Kim Il Sung.

No. 4945: a, 20w, Gunshot of Pochonbo. b, 30w, Kim Il Sung burning Minsaengdan documents. c, 40w, Kim Il Sung with members of children's corps. d, 45w, Kim Il Sung leading soldiers.

No. 4946: a, 10w, Kim Il Sung speaking to Anti-Japanese People's Guerilla Army. b, 20w, Kim Il Sung with people after establishing People's Revolutionary Government. c, 35w, Kim Il Sung leading soldiers, diff. d, 90w, Kim Il Sung founding Association for the Restoration of the Fatherland.

50w, Kim Il Sung at podium giving speech. 60w, Kim Il Sung leading solders, diff.

***Perf. 13¼, 12x11½ (#4943a)***

**2010, Sept. 5** **Litho.**

**4942** A2232 Sheet of 2, #a-b, + label 1.25 .60
**4943** A2233 Sheet of 3, #a-c, + label 1.60 .80
**4944** A2234 Sheet of 4, #a-d 2.10 1.10
**4945** A2235 Sheet of 4, #a-d 2.10 1.10
**4946** A2236 Sheet of 4, #a-d 2.40 1.25
*Nos. 4942-4946 (5)* 9.45 4.85

**Souvenir Sheets**

***Perf. 11¾***

**4947** A2237 50w multi .95 .45
**4948** A2238 60w multi 1.10 .50

Expo 2010, Shanghai A2239

**2010, Sept. 6** **Litho.** ***Perf. 11½***

**4949** A2239 25w multi .40 .30

No. 4949 was printed in sheets of 6 + 9 labels.

A2240

Entry of Chinese People's Volunteer Army Into Korean War, 60th Anniv. — A2241

Designs: 25w, Chinese soldier and Korean woman.

No. 4951: a, 10w, Meeting to decide on the entry of Chinese Volunteer Army into the Korean War, by Gao Quan. (60x42mm). b, 15w, North Korean and Chinese soldiers fighting together (30x42mm). c, For the Peace sculpture (60x42mm). d, Korean children with doves (30x42mm).

**2010, Sept. 10** **Litho.** ***Perf. 13¼***

**4950** A2240 25w multi .50 .30
**4951** A2241 Sheet of 4, #a-d, + 2 labels 1.25 .65

A2242

A2243

Worker's Party of Korea, 65th Anniv. — A2244

Designs: 10w, Flag of Worker's Party.

No. 4953 — Kim Il Sung: a, 20w, On naval vessel. b, 25w, At rail yard. c, 50w, With farmers. d, 50w, At technology display. e, 60w, With fabric vendor.

70w, Kim Il Sung with party flag.

**2010, Oct. 10** **Litho.** ***Perf. 11¾***

**4952** A2242 10w multi .30 .30
**4953** A2243 Sheet of 6, #4952, 4953a-4953e 3.75 1.75

**Souvenir Sheet**

***Perf. 13½***

**4954** A2244 70w multi 1.25 .60

A2245

Visit of Kim Jong Il to People's Republic of China — A2246

Designs: No. 4955, Kim Jong Il shaking hands with Chinese Pres. Hu Jintao.

No. 4956 — Kim Jong Il: a, 30w, Signing guestbook at Julin Middle School. b, 42w, Inspecting railway coach. c, 70w, Holding bottle at food processing plant.

**2010, Oct. 28** **Litho.** ***Perf. 11½x12***

**4955** A2245 70w multi 1.25 .65

***Perf. 11½***

**4956** A2246 Sheet of 3, #a-c, + 5 labels 2.75 1.25

Conference of Worker's Party of Korea, Pyongyang A2247

**2010, Oct. 30** ***Perf. 13¼***

**4957** A2247 30w multi .60 .30

New Year 2011 (Juche 100) A2248

**2011, Jan. 1** **Litho.**

**4958** A2248 10w multi .30 .30

**Souvenir Sheet**

Year of the Rabbit — A2249

Rabbits — No. 4959: a, 70w, Two rabbits. b, 140w, Two rabbits, diff.

**2011, Jan. 5** ***Perf. 11½***

**4959** A2249 Sheet of 2, #a-b 4.75 1.90
*c.* Booklet pane of 2, #4959a-4959b, + 2 labels 5.00 —
Complete booklet, #4959c 5.00
*d.* Like #4959, with inscriptions and emblems added in sheet margin 5.25 1.90

Complete booklet sold for 224w.

Issued: No. 4959d, 3/3/12. Added inscriptions on No. 4959d are for Frimung 2012 and Huddex 2012 Stamp Shows, Huddinge, Sweden.

**Souvenir Sheet**

Indipex 2011 World Philatelic Exhibition, New Delhi — A2250

**2011, Feb. 12** ***Perf. 13¼***

**4960** A2250 70w multi 1.75 .65

Zoo Animals Given to Kim Jong Il as Gifts — A2251

Designs: 30w, Capra hircus. 42w, Cercopithecus aethiops. 112w, Cebuella pygmaea. 125w, Hystrix indica, horiz.

**2011, Feb. 16** ***Perf. 11½***

**4961-4964** A2251 Set of 4 7.00 2.75
*4964a* Horiz. strip of 4, #4961-4964 7.25 2.75
*4964b* Booklet pane of 4, #4961-4964 7.25 —
Complete booklet, #4964b 7.50

Kim Jong Il, 69th birthday. Nos. 4961-4964 were printed in sheets of 8, containing 2 of each stamp, + 3 labels. Complete booklet sold for 323w.

Fourth International Martial Arts Games, Tallinn, Estonia — A2252

No. 4965: a, 42w, Emblem. b, 56w, Karate. c, 70w, Pankration. d, 112w, Muaythai.

No. 4966, 70w, Taekwondo.

**2011, Feb. 23** **Litho.**

**4965** A2252 Sheet of 4, #a-d, + 4 labels 5.25 2.60

**Souvenir Sheet**

**4966** A2252 70w multi + label 1.25 .65

Joint Editorials of State Newspapers — A2253

Red flag at upper left and: No. 4967, 10w, Two women, three men and pink ribbon. No. 4968, 10w, Man with arm extended, symbols of progress. 30w, Farmer holding sheaf of wheat, train, truck, tractor and food. 70w, Soldiers and flags. 112w, Two men and woman punching missile, map of Korea, vert.

**2011, Feb. 25** ***Perf. 13¼***

**4967-4971** A2253 Set of 5 5.75 2.10

Birds A2254

Designs: 30w, Paradisaea raggiana. 42w, Cygnus olor. 75w, Pulsatrix perspicillata. 133w, Goura victoria.

**2011, Mar. 2** ***Perf. 11½***

**4972-4975** A2254 Set of 4 2.00 2.75
*4975a* Booklet pane of 4, #4972-4975 7.25 —
Complete booklet, #4975a 7.25

Nos. 4972-4975 were printed in sheets of 8 containing 2 of each stamp + 4 labels. Complete booklet sold for 294w.

Flag of North Korea, Magnolia Flowers, North Korea No. 4 — A2255

**2011, Mar. 12** *Perf. 13¼*
**4976** A2255 30w multi .70 .30

First North Korean postage stamps, 65th anniv.

Miniature Sheets

A2256

Treaty on Friendship Between North Korea and People's Republic of China, 50th Anniv. — A2257

No. 4977: a, Mao Zedong at microphones proclaiming foundation of People's Republic of China, fireworks (30x42mm). b, Mao Zedong and Pres. Kim Il Sung shaking hands, 1975 (54x45mm). c, Mao Zedong at microphone holding Chinese coat of arms (30x42mm). d, Mao Zedong at microphone in front of crowd (56x38mm). e, Mao Zedong in front of Chinese flag (28x38mm). f, Mao Zedong and Deng Xiaoping shaking hands (56x38mm).

No. 4978: a, Mao Zedong and Pend Dehuai, wearing cap (45x33mm). b, Mao Zedong and Pres. Kim Il Sung shaking hands (36x45mm). c, Mao Zedong and Chen Yi at table with cup and saucer (45x33mm). d, Mao Zedong and Liu Shaoqi, pointing (56x38mm). e, Mao Zedong and Zhou Enlai, teapot and glasses on table (28x38mm). f, Mao Zedong and Zhu De clapping (56x38mm).

***Perf. 13¼ (#4977a-4977c, 4978a-4978c), 11½***

**2011, Mar. 15**
**4977** A2256 10w Sheet of 6, #a-f 1.50 .50
**4978** A2257 10w Sheet of 6, #a-f 1.50 .45

Souvenir Sheet

Intl. Year of Volunteers — A2258

No. 4979 — Red Cross and: a, 30w, Disaster risk reduction. b, 42w, Promotion activities. c, Emergency relief activities.

**2011, Mar. 31** **Litho.** *Perf. 13¼*
**4979** A2258 Sheet of 3, #a-c, + 2 labels 3.50 1.25

Apples on Branch A2259

Kim Il Sung at Fruit Orchard — A2260

**2011, Apr. 7** *Perf. 12*
**4980** A2259 30w multi .60 .30

**Souvenir Sheet**

***Perf. 11¾***

**4981** A2260 70w multi 1.90 .65

Pukchong Enlarged Meeting of the Presidium of the Central Committee of the Workers' Party of Korea, 50th anniv.

Flowers — A2261

No. 4982: a, 30w, Kimilsungia. b, 42w, Callistephus chinensis. c, 70w, Iris ensata var. hortensis. d, 98w, Rosa hybrida. e, 112w, Lilium hybridum cv. Enchantment.

**2011, Apr. 15** *Perf. 13*
**4982** A2261 Sheet of 5, #a-e 7.00 3.25
*f.* Booklet pane of 5, #4982a-4982e 7.25 —
Complete booklet, #4982f 7.25

Birthday of Pres. Kim Il Sung. No. 4982f sold for 366w.

Sites in Pyongyang — A2262

Designs: 30w, Yonggwang Metro Station. 42w, Mangyongdae School Children's Palace. 56w, May Day Stadium. 70w, People's Palace of Culture. 84w, Arch of Triumph. 98w, State Theater. 112w, Party Founding Museum. 140w, Birthpace of Pres. Kim Il Sung.

**2011, Apr. 20** *Perf. 12¼x11¾*
**4983-4990** A2262 Set of 8 12.50 5.50
*4990a* Booklet pane of 8, #4983-4990 12.50 —
Complete booklet, #4990a 12.50

No. 4990a sold for 646w.

Magnolia Seiboldii A2263

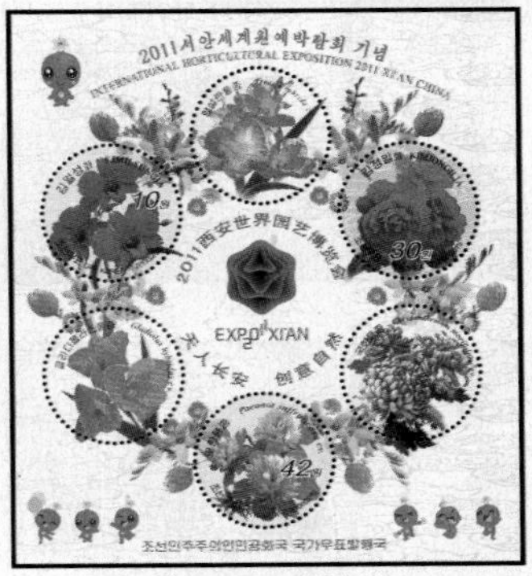

Flowers — A2264

No. 4992: a, 10w, Kimilsungia. b, 30w, Kimjongilia. c, 42w, Paeonia suffructicosa.

**2011, Apr. 28** *Perf. 13¼*
**4991** A2263 30w multi .60 .30

**Souvenir Sheet**

***Perf.***

**4992** A2264 Sheet of 3, #a-c, + 3 labels 1.40 .75
*d.* Booklet pane of 4, #4991, 4992a-4992c *2.40* —
Complete booklet, #4992d *2.40*

2011 Intl. Horticultural Exposition, Xi'an, People's Republic of China. Complete booklet sold for 126w.

Miniature Sheet

Circus Performers — A2265

No. 4993: a, 42w, Woman suspended by neck. b, 70w, Woman juggling while hanging from trapeze. c, 98w, Unicyclist, members of rope skipping act. d, 140w, Rope skipping act.

**2011, May 5** *Perf.*
**4993** A2265 Sheet of 4, #a-d 8.50 3.25

Souvenir Sheet

Chollima Statue, Pyongyang — A2266

**2011, May 20** *Perf. 11¾x12¼*
**4994** A2266 98w multi 2.40 .85

Souvenir Sheet

Apples, Taedonggang Combined Fruit Farm — A2267

**2011, June 5** *Perf. 12¼x11¾*
**4995** A2267 70w multi 1.75 .65

Orchids — A2268

No. 4996: a, 10w, Vanda hybrida. b, 30w, Laeliocattleya. c, 70w, Laelia gouldiana. d, 142w, Phalaenopsis.

**2011, June 20** *Perf. 13¼*
**4996** A2268 Block or horiz. strip of 4, #a-d 4.75 2.40
*e.* Booklet pane of 4, #4996a-4996d 5.25 —
Complete booklet, #4996e 5.50

No. 4996e sold for 266w.

A2269

A2270

A2271

A2272

A2273

A2274

A2275

A2276

A2277

A2278

A2279

A2280

A2281

A2282

A2283

A2284

A2285

A2286

A2287

A2288

A2289

A2290

A2291

A2292

A2293

A2294

Pres. Kim Il Sung (1912-94) — A2295

Various paintings depicting scenes in the life of Kim Il Sung.

No. 5020: a, 25w, October Morning (64x42mm). b, 30w, Kim Il Sung Drawing the Brush Into the Party's Emblem (45x36mm). c, 45w, Kim Il Sung Making Report at Inaugural Conference of the Central Organizational Committee of the Communist Party of North Korea (45x36mm).

**2011, July 5 Litho. *Perf. 13½***

| | | | | |
|---|---|---|---|---|
| **4997** | A2269 | 10w multi + label | .30 | .30 |
| **4998** | A2270 | 10w multi + label | .30 | .30 |
| **4999** | A2271 | 10w multi + label | .30 | .30 |
| **5000** | A2272 | 30w multi + label | .70 | .30 |
| **5001** | A2273 | 30w multi + label | .70 | .30 |
| **5002** | A2274 | 30w multi + label | .70 | .30 |
| **5003** | A2275 | 30w multi + label | .70 | .30 |
| **5004** | A2276 | 30w multi + label | .70 | .30 |
| **5005** | A2277 | 30w multi + label | .70 | .30 |
| **5006** | A2278 | 30w multi + label | .70 | .30 |
| **5007** | A2279 | 30w multi + label | .70 | .30 |
| **5008** | A2280 | 30w multi + label | .70 | .30 |
| **5009** | A2281 | 30w multi + label | .70 | .30 |
| **5010** | A2282 | 42w multi + label | 1.00 | .35 |
| **5011** | A2283 | 42w multi + label | 1.00 | .35 |
| **5012** | A2284 | 42w multi + label | 1.00 | .35 |
| **5013** | A2285 | 42w multi + label | 1.00 | .35 |
| **5014** | A2286 | 42w multi + label | 1.00 | .35 |
| **5015** | A2287 | 42w multi + label | 1.00 | .35 |
| **5016** | A2288 | 42w multi + label | 1.00 | .35 |
| **5017** | A2289 | 42w multi + label | 1.00 | .35 |
| **5018** | A2290 | 42w multi + label | 1.00 | .35 |
| **5019** | A2291 | 42w multi + label | 1.00 | .35 |
| | | *Nos. 4997-5019 (23)* | 17.90 | 7.40 |

**Miniature Sheet**

***Perf. 12x11½ (#5020a), 13½***

| | | | | |
|---|---|---|---|---|
| **5020** | A2292 | Sheet of 3, #a-c, + label | 1.75 | .85 |

**Souvenir Sheets**

***Perf. 13½***

| | | | | |
|---|---|---|---|---|
| **5021** | A2293 | 40w multi | .85 | .35 |

***Perf. 11¾***

| | | | | |
|---|---|---|---|---|
| **5022** | A2294 | 50w multi | 1.10 | .45 |
| **5023** | A2295 | 60w multi | 1.25 | .55 |
| | | *Nos. 5021-5023 (3)* | 3.20 | 1.35 |

Souvenir Sheets

A2296

A2297

Visit of Kim Jong Il to People's Republic of China — A2298

**2011, July 15 Litho. *Perf. 12¼x11¾***

| | | | | |
|---|---|---|---|---|
| **5024** | A2296 | 90w multi | 2.50 | .80 |
| **5025** | A2297 | 90w multi | 2.50 | .80 |

***Perf. 11¾***

| | | | | |
|---|---|---|---|---|
| **5026** | A2298 | 90w multi + label | 2.00 | .80 |
| | | *Nos. 5024-5026 (3)* | 7.00 | 2.40 |

Intl. Year of Chemistry A2299

**2011, July 29** *Perf. 13½x13¼*

**5027** A2299 50w multi 1.25 .55

Camellias and Birds — A2300

No. 5028: a, Denomination at LL. b, Denomination at UR.

**2011, July 30** *Perf. 11½*

**5028** A2300 20w Horiz. pair, #a-b 2.00 .35

Souvenir Sheet

Intl. Year of Forests — A2301

**2011, July 30** *Perf. 13¼*

**5029** A2301 100w multi 2.40 .90

Souvenir Sheet

Diplomatic Relations Between North Korea and the European Union, 10th Anniv. — A2302

**2011, Aug. 1** *Perf. 12x11½*

**5030** A2302 140w multi 3.50 1.75

Miniature Sheet

Cacti and Insects — A2303

No. 5031: a, 30w, Gymnocalycium schuetzianum and bee. b, 70w, Rebutia euanthema and butterfly. c, 98w, Rebutia xanthocarpa and grasshopper. d, 112w, Notocactus herteri and beetle.

**2011, Aug. 5** *Perf. 11½*

**5031** A2303 Sheet of 4, #a-d 7.25 2.75
*e.* Booklet pane of 4, #5031a-5031d 7.50 —
Complete booklet, #5031e 7.75

Complete booklet sold for 324w.

2018 World Cup Soccer Championships, Russia — A2304

Various soccer players with city names inscribed at side: No. 5032, 200w, Nizhniy Novgorod. No. 5033, 200w, Krasnodar. No. 5034, 200w, Kaliningrad. No. 5035, 200w, Moscow. No. 5036, 200w, Sochi. No. 5037, 200w, Rostov-na-Donu. No. 5038, 200w, St. Petersburg.

**2011, Aug. 31** **Stamps + Labels**

**5032-5038** A2304 Set of 7 35.00 11.50
*5038a* Sheet of 7, #5032-5038, + 2 labels 35.00 11.50
*5038b* Booklet pane of 7, #5032-5038, without labels 35.00 —
Complete booklet, #5038b 35.00

Complete booklet sold for 1414w.

Dinosaurs — A2305

No. 5039: a, Megalosaurus bucklandi. b, Staurikosaurus pricei. c, Chasmosaurus belli.

**2011, Sept. 5** *Perf. 12¼x11¾*

**5039** Horiz. strip of 3 5.25 2.60
*a.* A2305 42w multi .75 .35
*b.* A2305 98w multi 1.75 .85
*c.* A2305 140w multi 2.50 1.25
*d.* Booklet pane of 3, #5039a-5039c 5.50 —
Complete booklet, #5039d 5.50

Complete booklet sold for 294w.

World Leisure Expo 2011, Hangzhou, People's Republic of China — A2306

Emblems and: 10w, Samil Lagoon. 30w, Xihu.

**2011, Sept. 17** *Perf. 13¼*

**5040-5041** A2306 Set of 2 .90 .35

Fire Engines — A2307

No. 5042: a, 70w, Mercedes-Benz fire engine. b, 98w, ZIL ladder truck.
No. 5043: a, 30w, ZIL fire engine. b, 140w, Mercedes-Benz ladder truck.

**2011, Oct. 5** *Perf. 13¼*

**5042** A2307 Sheet of 2, #a-b, + 2 labels 4.00 1.40
**5043** A2307 Sheet of 2, #a-b, + 2 labels 4.00 1.40
*c.* Booklet pane of 4, #5042a-5042b, 5043a-5043b, + 2 labels 8.75 —
Complete booklet, #5043c 8.75

Complete booklet sold for 352w.

Famous People A2308

Designs: 10w, Pak Yon (1378-1458), musician. 30w, Sinsa Im Dang (1504-51), painter. 50w, Jong Yak Yong (1762-1836), philosopher. 70w, Ryu Rin Sok (1842-1915), military leader.

**2011, Oct. 15**

**5044-5047** A2308 Set of 4 3.50 1.40

Souvenir Sheet

Kim Jong Il and Chinese State Councilor Dai Bingguo — A2309

**2011, Oct. 18**

**5048** A2309 70w multi 1.75 1.25

Souvenir Sheets

A2310

A2311

Visit of Kim Jong Il to Russia — A2312

**2011, Oct. 18** **Litho.** *Perf. 11½x12*

**5049** A2310 70w multi — —

*Perf. 13¼*

**5050** A2311 70w multi — —
**5051** A2312 70w multi — —

A2313

A2314

A2315

A2316

Friendship Between North Korea and People's Republic of China — A2317

Design: No. 5052, 10w, Mao Zedong Going to Anyuan. No. 5053: a, 10w, Mao Zedong. b, 10w, Mao Zedong in army vehicle reviewing troops. c, 10w, Mao Zedong writing. d, 30w, Kim Il Sung in suit and tie. e, 30w, Kim Il Sung and Mao Zedong shaking hands. f, 30w, Kim Il Sung and Mao Zedong standing at military parade.

No. 5054: a, 10w, Deng Xiaoping. b, 10w, Deng Xiaoping in automobile reviewing troops. c, 10w, Deng Xiaoping saluting. d, 30w, Kim Il Sung in black shirt. e, 30w, Deng Xiaoping and Kim Il Sung embracing. f, Deng Xiaoping and Kim Il Sung standing.

No. 5055: a, 10w, Jiang Zemin. b, 10w, Jiang Zemin in automobile reviewing troops. c, 10w, Jiang Zemin at ceremony returning Hong Kong to China. d, 30w, Kim Jong Il wearing glasses. e, 30w, Kim Jong Il and Jiang Zemin shaking hands. f, 30w, Jiang Zemin and Kim Jong Il shaking hands, cameramen.

No. 5056: a, 10w, Hu Jintao. b, 10w, Hu Jintao in automobile reviewing troops. c, 10w, Hu Jintaou holding Olympic torch. d, 30w, Kim Jong Il without glasses. e, 30w, Hu Jintao walking with Kim Jong Il. f, 30w, Kim Jong Il and Hu Jintao shaking hands.

***Perf. 13¼ (#5052), 11¾x12¼***

**2011, Oct. 28 — Litho.**

| | | | | |
|---|---|---|---|---|
| **5052** | A2313 | 10w multi | .30 | .30 |

**Miniature Sheets**

| | | | | |
|---|---|---|---|---|
| **5053** | A2314 | Sheet of 6, #a-f | 3.00 | 2.25 |
| **5054** | A2315 | Sheet of 6, #a-f | 3.00 | 2.25 |
| **5055** | A2316 | Sheet of 6, #a-f | 3.00 | 2.25 |
| **5056** | A2317 | Sheet of 6, #a-f | 3.00 | 2.25 |
| | | *Nos. 5052-5056 (5)* | 12.30 | 9.30 |

Publication of Taedongyojido Map of Korea by Kim Jong Ho, 150th Anniv. A2318

**2011, Nov. 5 — *Perf. 13¼***

| | | | | |
|---|---|---|---|---|
| **5057** | A2318 | 98w multi | 2.40 | .90 |

Minerals — A2319

Designs: 30w, Limonite, crucible with molten metal. 42w, Kotoite, rocket. 58w, Wollastonite, ceramic vases. 98w, Stibnite, tractor and parts.

**2011, Dec. 5**

| | | | | |
|---|---|---|---|---|
| **5058-5061** | A2319 | Set of 4 | 5.75 | 2.10 |
| *5061a* | | Booklet pane of 4, #5057-5060 | 6.00 | — |
| | | Complete booklet, #5060a | 6.00 | |

Complete booklet sold for 242w.

A2320

Appointment of Kim Jong Il as Supreme Commander of Army, 20th Anniv. — A2321

No. 5062 — Kim Jong Il and: a, 10w, Pilots. b, 30w, Tank soldiers. c, 70w, Sailors. d, 98w, Soldiers carrying packs.

No. 5063, Kim Jong Il and military officer reviewing troops in military vehicle.

**2011, Dec. 24**

| | | | | |
|---|---|---|---|---|
| **5062** | A2320 | Sheet of 4, #a-d, + central label | 3.75 | 1.90 |

**Souvenir Sheet**

***Perf. 11¾***

| | | | | |
|---|---|---|---|---|
| **5063** | A2321 | 98w multi | 2.40 | 1.90 |

Souvenir Sheets

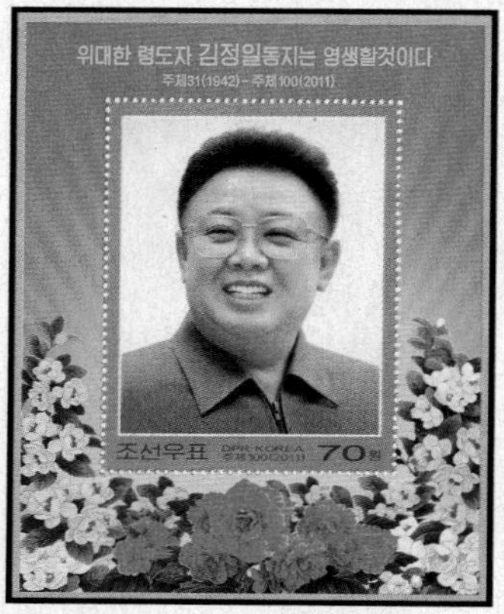


Kim Jong Il (1942-2011) — A2322

Kim Jong Il and Son, Kim Jong Un — A2323

**2011, Dec. 29 — *Perf. 12¼x11¾***

| | | | | |
|---|---|---|---|---|
| **5064** | A2322 | 70w multi | 1.50 | .70 |
| **5065** | A2323 | 70w multi | 1.50 | .70 |

New Year 2012 — A2324

**2012, Jan. 1 — *Perf. 13¼***

| | | | | |
|---|---|---|---|---|
| **5066** | A2324 | 10w multi | .30 | .30 |

Dragons — A2325

No. 5067 — Various dragons: a, 10w. b, 30w. c, 60w.

**2012, Jan. 5 — *Perf. 11½***

| | | | | |
|---|---|---|---|---|
| **5067** | A2325 | Horiz. strip of 3, #a-c | 2.40 | 1.00 |

No. 5067 was printed in sheets containing two strips of 3.

Mt. Paektu — A2326

Designs: 20w, Lake Samji and Mt. Paektu. 30w, Lake Chon on Mt. Paektu.

**2012, Jan. 17 — *Perf. 12¼x11¾***

| | | | | |
|---|---|---|---|---|
| **5068-5069** | A2326 | Set of 2 | 1.20 | .50 |

Butterflies — A2327

No. 5070: a, 30w, Pachliopta coon. b, 70w, Agrias pericles. c, 90w, Buthanitis lidderdalei. d, 120w, Cethosia biblis.

**2012, Jan. 25 — *Perf. 11½***

| | | | | |
|---|---|---|---|---|
| **5070** | A2327 | Block of 4, #a-d | 7.00 | 3.00 |
| *e.* | | Booklet pane of 4, #5070a-5070d, + 2 labels | 7.25 | — |
| | | Complete booklet, #5070e | 7.25 | |

Complete booklet sold for 324w.

Joint Editorials of State Newspapers A2328

Red flag at upper left and: No. 5071, 10w, Birthplace of Kim Il Sung, torch, soldier, workers. No. 5072, 10w, City buildings, packaged foods, crops and farm animals, horiz. No. 5073, 30w, Torch, symbols of industry, train and truck. No. 5074, 30w, Soldier holding rifle with bayonet, flags, missiles. 40w, Fist squashing people, U.S. Capitol. 50w, Dove, North Korea highlighted on map, rainbow.

**2012, Jan. 27 — *Perf. 13¼***

| | | | | |
|---|---|---|---|---|
| **5071-5076** | A2328 | Set of 6 | 3.50 | 1.40 |

Calls for Victory by Central Committee and Central Military Commission A2329

**2012, Jan. 30 — Litho.**

| | | | | |
|---|---|---|---|---|
| **5077** | A2329 | 10w multi | .30 | .30 |

Architecture — A2330

Designs: 60w, Kopernik House, Moscow, Mansudae Street Apartment Buildings, Pyongyang. 100w, Patriarch House, Moscow, East Pyongyang Grand Theater. No. 5080, 140w, Grand People's Study House, Pyongyang, Gnezdikovskiy Palace, Moscow. 190w, Apartement house, Pyongyang, Egg House, Moscow. 210w, Hyangsan Hotel, Pyongyang, Weber Villa, Moscow.

No. 5083, 140w, Patriarch House, Moscow and National Theater, Pyongyang at night.

**2012, Jan. 30 — *Perf. 12***

| | | | | |
|---|---|---|---|---|
| **5078-5082** | A2330 | Set of 5 | 16.00 | 6.25 |

**Souvenir Sheet**

***Perf. 12x11½***

| | | | | |
|---|---|---|---|---|
| **5083** | A2330 | 140w multi | 3.25 | 1.40 |
| *a.* | | Souvenir sheet of 6, #5078-5083, perf. 12x11½, + 3 labels | 16.50 | 6.75 |
| *b.* | | Booklet pane of 6, #5078-5083, perf. 12x11½ | 16.50 | — |
| | | Complete booklet, #5083b | 16.50 | |

Nos. 5078-5082 were each printed in sheets of 5 + label. Complete booklet sold for 854w.

A2331

A2332

Birthday of Kim Jong Il (1942-2011) — A2333

Designs: 10w, Kimjongilia flower.
No. 5085: a, 40w, Kim Jong Il, soldiers and artillery. 70w, Kim Jong Il, people with flags and sled.
No. 5085, 70w, Kimg Jong Il.

**2012, Feb. 16** ***Perf. 13¼***

**5084** A2331 10w multi .30 .30
**5085** A2332 Sheet of 2, #a-b, + 3 labels 2.75 1.00

**Souvenir Sheet**
***Perf. 11½x12***

**5086** A2333 70w multi 1.75 .70

Ceramics
A2334

Designs: 30w, Container with lotus flower pattern. 40w, Container with dragon and cloud design.
70w, Pitcher and bowl.

**2012, Mar. 10** ***Perf. 11½***

**Stamps + Labels**

**5087-5088** A2334 Set of 2 1.75 .70

**Souvenir Sheet**

**5089** A2334 70w multi + label 1.75 .70
*a.* Booklet pane of 3, #5087-5089, + 7 labels 5.25 —
Complete booklet, #5089a 5.25

Complete booklet sold for 154w.

Posthumous Granting of Title of Generalissimo to Kim Jong Il — A2335

**2012, Mar. 20** ***Perf. 13¼***

**5090** A2335 10w multi .30 .30

Birthplace of Kim Jong Il — A2336

**2012, Mar. 20**

**5091** A2336 10w multi .30 .30

Designation of Feb. 16 (birthday of Kim Jong Il) as Day of the Shining Star.

Floriade 2012 World Horticultural Expo, Venlo, Netherlands
A2337

**2012, Mar. 22** **Litho.**

**5092** A2337 30w multi .50 .30

Korean National Association, 95th Anniv. — A2338

**2012, Mar. 23** ***Perf. 13¼***

**5093** A2338 30w citron .85 .30

Opening of Korean Stamp Museum, Pyongyang
A2339

**2012, Apr. 15** ***Perf. 11½***

**5094** A2339 10w multi .30 .30

A2340

A2341

A2342

A2343

A2344

A2345

A2346

A2347

A2348

A2349

Pres. Kim Il Sung (1912-94) — A2350

No. 5102 — Kim Il Sung: a, With adults and children. b, Wearing hat, addressing men. c, Seated behind microphone. d, With workers at plant.
No. 5103 — Kim Il Sung: a, At trainyard. b, With workers at textile factory. c, Holding ear of corn, with farmers in field. d, Holding ear of corn, with agricultural scientists.
No. 5104 — Kim Il Sung: a, With pilots. b, Seated, talking to soldiers. c, With soldiers inspecting artillery. d, Wearing white jacket, walking with military.

**2012, Apr. 15** ***Perf. 11½***

**5095** A2340 30w multi + label .90 .30
**5096** A2341 30w multi + label .90 .30
**5097** A2342 30w multi + label .90 .30
**5098** A2343 30w multi + label .90 .30
**5099** A2344 30w multi + label .90 .30
**5100** A2345 30w multi + label .90 .30
**5101** A2346 30w multi + label .90 .30
*Nos. 5095-5101 (7)* 6.30 2.10

**Miniature Sheets**
***Perf. 13¼***

**5102** A2347 20w Sheet of 4, #a-d 2.10 .70
**5103** A2348 30w Sheet of 4, #a-d 3.00 1.10
**5104** A2349 40w Sheet of 4, #a-d 3.75 1.40
*Nos. 5102-5104 (3)* 8.85 3.20

**Souvenir Sheet**
***Perf. 11¾***

**5105** A2350 70w multi 1.75 1.00

A2351

A2352

Pres. Kim Il Sung (1912-94) — A2353

Designs: 10w, Birthplace of Kim Il Sung, flowers.
No. 5107: a, 70w, Kim Il Sung in field with children. b, 100w, Kim Il Sung seated, holding hand of girl.
No. 5108, 100w, Kim Il Sung at birthplace.

**2012, Apr. 15** ***Perf. 13¼***
**5106** A2351 10w multi .40 .30

**Miniature Sheet**
***Perf. 11¾***

**5107** A2352 Sheet of 2, #a-b 3.75 1.40

**Souvenir Sheet**
***Perf. 11½x12***

**5108** A2353 100w multi 2.40 1.00

Souvenir Sheet

Kang Pan Sok (1892-1932), Mother of Kim Il Sung — A2354

**2012, Apr. 21** ***Perf. 11¾***
**5109** A2354 70w multi 1.75 .70

Flags of Guerilla Army, North Korea and Supreme Commander A2355

Kim Il Sung in Military Uniform — A2356

**2012, Apr. 25** ***Perf. 13¼***
**5110** A2355 30w multi .90 .30

**Souvenir Sheet**
***Perf. 11½x12***

**5111** A2356 70w multi 1.75 .70
Korean People's Army, 80th anniv.

Roses A2357

Color of roses: 30w, Pink and white. 50w, Yellow. 70w, Red.

**2012, Apr. 30** ***Perf. 12½***
**5112-5114** A2357 Set of 3 3.50 1.50
*5114a* Booklet pane of 3, #5112-5114, + label 3.75 —
Complete booklet, #5114a 4.00

Values are for stamps with surrounding selvage. Complete booklet sold for 164w.

Principles for National Reunification, 40th Anniv. — A2358

**2012, May 3** ***Perf. 11½***
**5115** A2358 50w red & blue 1.10 .50

2012 Summer Olympics, London A2359

Designs: 10w, Track and field. 30w, Judo. 70w, Rhythmic gymnastics. 110w, Swimming and diving.

**2012, May 3** ***Perf. 13¼***
**5116-5119** A2359 Set of 4 5.00 2.10
*5119a* Booklet pane of 4, #5116-5119 5.25 —
Complete booklet, #5119a 5.50

Complete booklet sold for 234w.

Souvenir Sheet

Erection of Statues to Kim Il Sung and Kim Jong Il in Pyongyang — A2360

**2012, May 30**
**5120** A2360 50w multi 1.25 .50

Locomotives — A2361

Designs: 50w, Songun Pulgungi 1. 70w, Velaro D407. 90w, Renfe 112.

**2012, May 31**
**5121-5123** A2361 Set of 3 5.00 1.90
*5123a* Booklet pane of 3, #5121-5123 5.25 —
Complete booklet, #5123a 5.25

Complete booklet sold for 224w.

Battle of Pochonbo, 75th Anniv. — A2362

**2012, June 4**
**5124** A2362 30w multi .85 .30

Souvenir Sheet

2012 Planete Timbres Stamp Exhibition, Paris — A2363

**2012, June 9** ***Perf. 12¼x11¾***
**5125** A2363 70w multi 1.75 .70

2012 World Stamp Championships, Jakarta, Indonesia A2364

**2012, June 18** ***Perf. 11½***
**5126** A2364 30w multi .75 .30

Birds A2365

Designs: 50w, Fringilla montifringilla. 70w, Zosterops erythropleura. 90w, Uragus sibiricus.

**2012, June 30** **Litho.**
**5127-5129** A2365 Set of 3 4.75 1.75
*5129a* Booklet pane of 3, #5127-5129, + label 5.00 —
Complete booklet, #5129a 5.00

Complete booklet sold for 224w.

Free Universal Medical System, 60th Anniv. A2366

**2012, July 5** ***Perf. 13¼***
**5130** A2366 30w multi .90 .30

Souvenir Sheets

Mao Zedong (1893-1976) and Poetry — A2367

Kim Il Sung (1912-94) and Quotes — A2368

No. 5131: a, The Yellow Crane Pavilion, poem by Mao Zedong (character at UL a diagonal line) (34x52mm). b, Mao Zedong writing (54x42mm). c, Huichang, poem by Mao Zedong (complex character with vertical line at UL).
No. 5132: a, 7½ lines of text from reminiscences of Kim Il Sung, and signature (34x52mm). b, Kim Il Sung writing (54x42mm). c, 8 lines of text from reminiscences of Kim Il Sung, and signature (34x52mm).

***Perf. 11¾x12¼, 13¼ (#5131b, 5132b)***
**2012, July 15**
**5131** A2367 10w Sheet of 3, #a-c .60 .30
**5132** A2368 30w Sheet of 3, #a-c 1.60 .80

Souvenir Sheet

Fourth Conference of the Korean Workers' Party — A2369

No. 5133: a, Kim Jong Il wearing glasses (1941-2011). b, Kim Jong Un.

**2012, July 20** ***Perf. 11¾x12¼***
**5133** A2369 30w Sheet of 2, #a-b 1.50 .60

A2370

Korean Children's Union, 66th Anniv. — A2371

**2012, Aug. 10** *Perf. 13¼*

**5134** A2370 10w multi .30 .30

**Souvenir Sheet**

**5135** A2371 70w multi 1.60 .65

Mother's Day — A2372

**2012, Sept. 20** *Perf. 11½*

**5136** A2372 10w multi .30 .30

**Miniature Sheets**

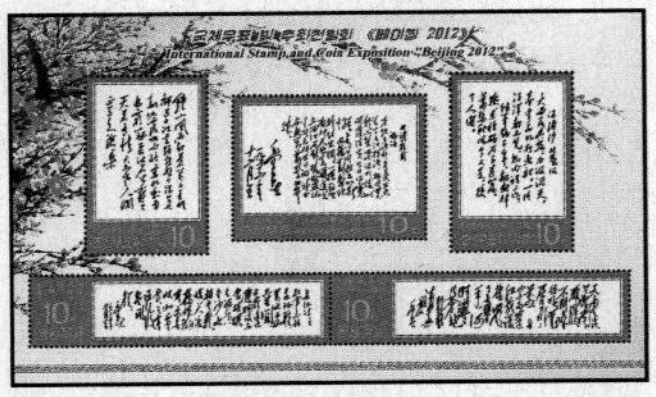

A2373

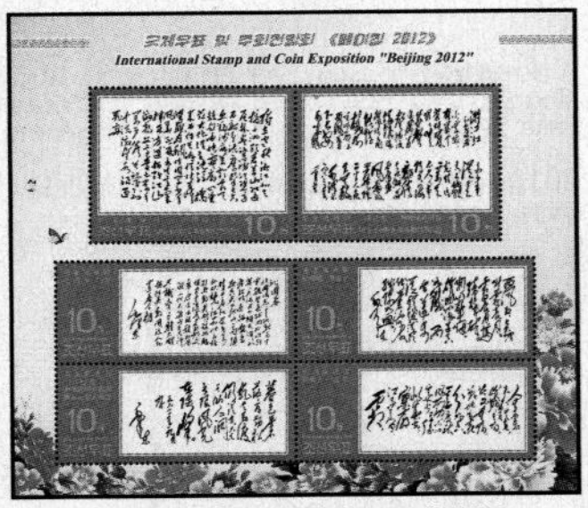

Poetry of Mao Zedong (1893-1976) — A2374

No. 5137: a, The People's Liberation Army Captures Nanjing (5½ lines) (34x52mm). b, Swimming (large white areas at UL and LR) (54x42mm). c, Beidaihe (6 full long lines of characters, 2 shorter lines at sides) (34x52mm). d, The Long March (3mm from line at right to frame) (84x21mm). e, Mt. Liupan (6mm from line at right to frame) (84x21mm).

No. 5138: a, Changsha (line at left with 2 characters) (54x42mm). b, Reply to Comrade Guo Moruo (white area in middle of poem (54x42mm). c, Snow (line at right three characters) (63x27mm). d, Loushan Pass (12 lines) (63x27mm). e, In Praise of the Photo Taken by Comrade Lijin of the Fairy Cave at Mt. Lushan (second line from left is single character) (63x27mm). f, The Double Ninth (13 lines with large whtie areas at top and bottom) (63x27mm).

***Perf. 11¾x12¼ (#5137a, 5137c), 13¼***

**2012, Sept. 25**

**5137** A2373 10w Sheet of 5, #a-e 1.10 .50

**5138** A2374 10w Sheet of 6, #a-f 2.00 .60

Beijing 2012 Intl. Stamp and Coin Exposition.

Giant Pandas — A2375

Designs: 70w, Panda on branch. 90w, Adult and juvenile panda.

120w, Two adult pandas, horiz.

**2012, Dec. 14 Litho.** *Perf. 11½*

**5139-5140** A2375 Set of 2 2.75 1.50

**Souvenir Sheet**

***Perf. 13½***

**5141** A2375 120w multi 2.25 1.10

No. 5141 contains one 90x42mm stamp.

Compulsory Education — A2376

**2012, Dec. 15 Litho.** *Perf. 13¼*

**5142** A2376 10w multi .30 .30

**Souvenir Sheets**

A2377

Kim Jong Il (1942-2011) — A2378

**2012, Dec. 17 Litho.** *Perf. 11½x12*

**5143** A2377 50w multi 1.10 .50

***Perf. 13¼***

**5144** A2378 50w multi 1.10 .50

**Souvenir Sheet**

Kim Jong Suk (1917-49) — A2379

**2012, Dec. 24** *Perf.*

**5145** A2379 70w multi 1.75 .65

Constitution, 40th Anniv. — A2380

**2012, Dec. 27** *Perf. 13¼*

**5146** A2380 30w multi .70 .30

**Souvenir Sheet**

Launch of Kwangmyongsong 3-2 Satellite — A2381

**2012, Dec. 30 Litho.** *Perf. 13¼*

**5147** A2381 50w multi 1.00 .45

New Year 2013 — A2382

**2013, Jan. 1 Litho.** *Perf. 11¾*

**5148** A2382 10w multi .25 .25

Stylized Snake A2383

**2013, Jan. 5 Litho.** *Perf. 11½*

**5149** A2383 10w multi .25 .25

No. 5149 was printed in sheets of 16 + 4 labels.

Sports — A2384

Designs: 30w, Tennis. 50w, Cricket. 70w, Cycling. 90w, Rugby.

**2013, Jan. 20 Litho.** *Perf. 13¼*

**5150-5153** A2384 Set of 4 3.75 1.90

*5153a* Booklet pane of 4, #5150-5153 4.00 —

Complete booklet, #5153a 4.00

Complete booklet sold of 254w.

A2386

A2387

Kim Jong Il (1942-2011) — A2388

**2013, Feb. 16 Litho.** *Perf. 11¾*

**5155** A2386 10w multi .25 .25

**Souvenir Sheets**

**5156** A2387 50w multi .80 .40

**5157** A2388 50w multi .80 .40

An additional stamp was issued in this set. The editors would like to examine any example of it.

New Year's Speech
A2389

Emblem and: No. 5158, 10w, Man with arm extended, rocket, sheaf of wheat, tower for electric lines, train, steel products. No. 5159, 10w, Woman, soldiers, flag, sculptures. No. 5160, 30w, Soccer player, city skyline, silhouettes of musicians and soldiers. No. 5161, 30w, Map of Korean Peninsula, doves.

**2013, Feb. 19 Litho. *Perf. 11½***

| | | | | |
|---|---|---|---|---|
| **5158-5161** | A2389 | Set of 4 | 1.25 | .60 |
| *5161a* | | Souvenir sheet of 4, #5158-5161 | 1.25 | .60 |

Souvenir Sheet

Kim Jong Un Making New Year's Speech — A2390

**2013, Feb. 19 Litho. *Perf. 11¾***

| | | | | |
|---|---|---|---|---|
| **5162** | A2390 | 50w multi | .80 | .40 |

A2391

A2392

A2393

Military Posters in Korean Art Gallery, Pyongyang — A2394

**2013, Feb. 25 Litho. *Perf. 11½***

| | | | | |
|---|---|---|---|---|
| **5163** | A2391 | 10w multi | .25 | .25 |
| **5164** | A2392 | 10w multi | .25 | .25 |
| **5165** | A2393 | 30w multi | .45 | .25 |
| **5166** | A2394 | 30w multi | .45 | .25 |
| | | *Nos. 5163-5166 (4)* | 1.40 | 1.00 |

International Red Cross, 150th Anniv. — A2395

**2013, Mar. 6 Litho. *Perf. 13¼***

| | | | | |
|---|---|---|---|---|
| **5167** | A2395 | 30w multi | .45 | .25 |

Miniature Sheet

Marine Life — A2396

No. 5168: a, 30w, Carcharodon carcharias (44mm diameter). b, 50w, Caretta caretta (38x28mm). c, 90w, Peprilus simillina (28x38mm). d, 110w, Hippocampus histrix (28x38mm).

**2013, Mar. 21 Litho. *Perf. 11½***

| | | | | |
|---|---|---|---|---|
| **5168** | A2396 | Sheet of 4, #a-d | 4.25 | 2.10 |
| *e.* | | Booklet pane of 4, #5168a-5168d | 4.50 | — |
| | | Complete booklet, #5168e | 4.50 | |

Complete booklet sold for 294w.

Election of Kim Jong Il as Chairman of National Defense Commission, 20th Anniv. — A2397

**2013, Apr. 9 Litho. *Perf. 13¼***

| | | | | |
|---|---|---|---|---|
| **5169** | A2397 | 30w multi | .45 | .25 |

Souvenir Sheet

Monkeys — A2398

No. 5170: a, 10w, Monkey. b, 20w, Adult and juvenile monkey.

**Litho. & Engr.**

**2013, Apr. 10 *Perf. 12***

| | | | | |
|---|---|---|---|---|
| **5170** | A2398 | Sheet of 2, #a-b | .45 | .25 |

Flowers — A2399

Designs: 30w, Zinnia elegans cv. Scarlet Flame. 50w, Celosia cristata. 70w, Dahlia x cultorum. 90w, Tropaeolum majus.

**2013, Apr. 15 Litho. *Perf. 13¼***

| | | | | |
|---|---|---|---|---|
| **5171-5174** | A2399 | Set of 4 | 3.75 | 1.90 |
| *5174a* | | Booklet pane of 4, #5171-5174 | 4.00 | — |
| | | Complete booklet, #5174a | 4.00 | |

Birthday of Kim Il Sung. Nos. 5171-5174 were printed in sheets of 4 + 2 labels. Complete booklet sold for 254w.

Passage of Kumsusan Palace of the Sun Preservation Law — A2401

**2013, Apr. 25 Litho. *Perf. 13¼***

| | | | | |
|---|---|---|---|---|
| **5176** | A2401 | 30w multi | .45 | .25 |

Values are for stamps with surrounding selvage.

Australia 2013 World Stamp Exhibition, Melbourne A2402

**2013, May 10 Litho. *Perf. 11½***

| | | | | |
|---|---|---|---|---|
| **5177** | A2402 | 30w multi | .45 | .25 |

Miniature Sheet

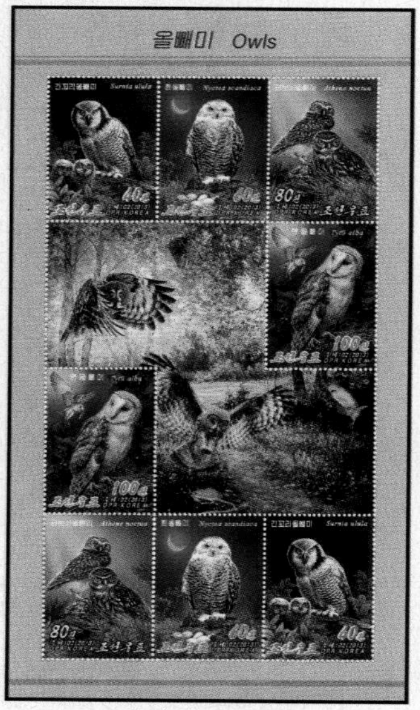


Owls — A2404

No. 5179: a, 40w, Surnia ulula. b, 60w, Nyctea scandiaca. c, 80w, Athene noctua. d, 100w, Tyto alba.

**2013, May 22 Litho. *Perf. 13¼***

| | | | | |
|---|---|---|---|---|
| **5179** | A2404 | Sheet of 8, 2 each #5179a-5179d, + 4 labels | 8.50 | 4.25 |
| *e.* | | Booklet pane of 4, #5179a-5179d, + 2 labels | 4.50 | — |
| | | Complete booklet, #5179e | 4.50 | |

Complete booklet sold for 294w.

Souvenir Sheet

Meeting of Kim Jong Il and Chinese Leaders — A2405

No. 5180 — Meeting with Kim Jong Il at: a, Left. b, Right.

**2013, June 10 Litho. *Perf. 12x11½***

| | | | | |
|---|---|---|---|---|
| **5180** | A2405 | 30w Sheet of 2, #a-b, + 4 labels | .95 | .45 |

Souvenir Sheet

Mt. Paektu — A2406

No. 5181: a, Sun over Hyangdo Peak. b, Mountains surrounding Lake Chon. c, Shore of Lake Chon. d, Mt. Paektu, trees in foreground.

**2013, June 10 Litho. *Perf. 12x11½***

| | | | | |
|---|---|---|---|---|
| **5181** | A2406 | 10w Sheet of 4, #a-d, + 2 labels | .60 | .30 |

Bees
A2407

Various bees and orchids: 30w, 70w, 110w.

**2013, June 12 Litho. *Perf. 13¼***

| | | | | |
|---|---|---|---|---|
| **5182-5184** | A2407 | Set of 3 | 3.25 | 1.60 |
| *5184a* | | Booklet pane of 3, #5182-5184, + label | 3.50 | — |
| | | Complete booklet, #5184a | 3.50 | |

Complete booklet sold for 224w.

A2408

Soldiers A2409

**2013, June 25 Litho. *Perf. 13¼***

**5185** A2408 10w multi .25 .25
**5186** A2409 150w multi 2.25 1.10

Arctic and Antarctic Animals — A2410

Designs: 30w, Aptenodytes excelsior. 50w, Rangifer tarandus.

**2013, July 7 Litho. *Perf.***

**5187-5188** A2410 Set of 2 — —
*5188a* Booklet pane of 2, #5187-5188, + 2 labels — —
Complete booklet, #5188a —

Nos. 5187-5188 were each printed in sheets of 3 + label.

**Souvenir Sheet**

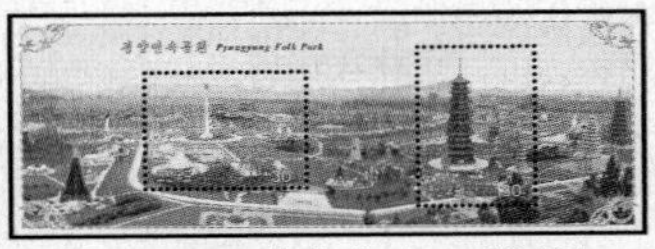

Pyongyang Folk Park — A2411

No. 5189: a, Tower of the Juche Idea, Arch of Triumph. b, Pagoda at Kumgang Temple, vert.

**2013, July 20 Litho. *Perf. 11½***

**5189** A2411 30w Sheet of 2, #a-b .95 .45

Victory Sculpture A2413

Ceasefire in Korean War, 60th Anniv. — A2514

Kim Il Sung Delivering Radio Address — A2415

Kim Il Sung at Rally — A2416

No. 5195: a, 50w, Kim Il Sung. b, 70w, Kim Il Sung and soldiers.

***Perf. 13¼, 11½x11¾ (#5195)***

**2013, July 27 Litho.**

**5194** A2413 10w multi .25 .25

**Souvenir Sheets**

**5195** A2514 Sheet of 2, #a-b, + 3 labels 1.90 .95
**5196** A2415 70w multi 1.10 .55
**5197** A2416 70w multi 1.10 .55

Thailand 2013 World Stamp Exhibition, Bangkok A2417

**2013, Aug. 2 Litho. *Perf. 13¼***

**5198** A2417 10w multi .25 .25

**Souvenir Sheet**

7th Congress of Korean Children's Union — A2419

**2013, Aug. 10 Litho. *Perf. 13¼***

**5200** A2419 70w multi 1.10 .55

Horses A2420

Designs: 30w, Shire horses. 50w, Orlov trotter.
70w, Thoroughbred horses, horiz.

**2013, Aug. 28 Litho. *Perf. 13¼***

**5201-5202** A2420 Set of 2 1.25 .60

**Souvenir Sheet**

**5203** A2420 70w multi 1.10 .55
*a.* Booklet pane of 3, #5301-5303 2.60 —
Complete booklet, #5203a 2.60

Complete booklet sold for 164w.

A2421

Founding of the Democratic People's Republic of Korea, 65th Anniv. — A2422

No. 5205: a, Kim Il Sung and flags. b, Kim Jong Il and mountain.

**2013, Sept. 9 Litho. *Perf. 11½***

**5204** A2421 30w multi .50 .25

**Souvenir Sheet**

***Perf. 13¼***

**5205** A2422 50w Sheet of 2, #a-b 1.60 .80

Mangyongdae in Spring — A2423

Rungna Island in Summer A2424

Moran Hill in Autumn A2425

Ryongwang Pavilion in Winter — A2426

**2013, Sept. 25 Litho. *Perf. 13¼***

**5206** A2423 30w multi .50 .25
**5207** A2424 50w multi .80 .40
**5208** A2425 70w multi 1.10 .55
**5209** A2426 110w multi 1.75 .85
*Nos. 5206-5209 (4)* 4.15 2.05

Ships A2427

Designs: 30w, Restaurant ship Taedong-gang. 50w, Cargo ship Kumrung No. 5. 90w, Refrigerator cargo ship Rimyongsu No. 7. 110w, Refrigerator cargo ship Turubong No. 3.

**2013, Oct. 15 Litho. *Perf. 11½***

**5210-5213** A2427 Set of 4 4.25 2.10
*5213a* Booklet pane of 4, #5210-5213 4.50 —
Complete booklet, #5213a 4.50

Complete booklet sold for 294w.

Soldier Commanding Speedier Construction, Skiers at Masik Pass Resort — A2428

**2013, Oct. 20 Litho. *Perf. 13¼x13½***

**5214** A2428 30w multi .45 .25

Fossils — A2430

Designs: 30w, Ditomopharangia. 70w, Dumangia. 110w, Hormotoma.

**2013, Nov. 10 Litho. *Perf. 13***

**5219-5221** A2430 Set of 3 3.25 1.60
*5221a* Booklet pane of 3, #5219-5221 + label 3.50 —
Complete booklet, #5221a 3.50

Complete booklet sold for 224w.

Souvenir Sheets

Kim Jong Il (1942-2011) and Soldiers — A2435

Kim Jong Il Inspecting Cotton — A2436

***Perf. 13½x13¼***

**2013, Dec. 17** **Litho.**

| | | | | |
|---|---|---|---|---|
| **5226** | A2435 | 50w multi | .80 | .40 |
| **5227** | A2436 | 70w multi | 1.10 | .55 |

Paintings A2437

Designs: No. 5228, 30w, Hawk, by Kim Tuk Sin. No. 5229, 30w, Tiger, by Kim Tuk Sin. No. 5230, 50w, Eagle, by Jang Sung Up. No. 5231, 50w, Carp, by Jo Sok Jin. 70w, Cats, by Pyon Sang Byok.

***Perf. 11¾x12¼***

**2013, Dec. 21** **Litho.**

| | | | | |
|---|---|---|---|---|
| **5228-5232** | A2437 | Set of 5 | 3.50 | 1.75 |

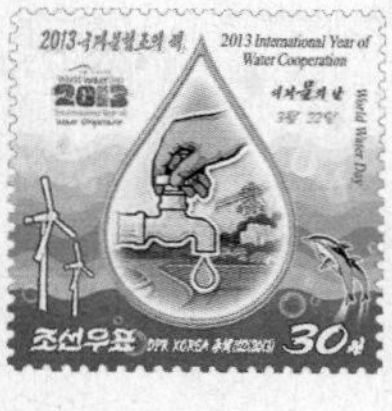

Intl. Year of Water Cooperation A2438

**2013, Dec. 26** **Litho.** ***Perf. 11½***

| | | | | |
|---|---|---|---|---|
| **5233** | A2438 | 30w multi | .45 | .25 |

Worker-Peasant Red Guards, 55th Anniv. — A2440

**2014, Jan. 14** **Litho.** ***Perf. 11½***

| | | | | |
|---|---|---|---|---|
| **5235** | A2440 | 30w multi + label | .50 | .25 |

Foods — A2441

Designs: 10w, Peaches and melons. 30w, Eggplants and grapes. 50w, Pumpkins and kiwis. 70w, Chestnuts and mushrooms. 90w, Chinese mustard and persimmons. 110w, Radish, Chinese cabbage, peppers, garlic and pears.

**2014, Jan. 20** **Litho.** ***Perf. 12¼x11½***

| | | | | |
|---|---|---|---|---|
| **5236-5241** | A2441 | Set of 6 | 5.50 | 2.25 |
| *5241a* | | Booklet pane of 6, #5236-5241 | 5.75 | — |
| | | Complete booklet, #5241a | 5.75 | |

Complete booklet sold for 374w.

Ceramics A2442

Designs: 30w, 12th century Celadon vase. 40w, 19th century porcelain jar.

**2014, Jan. 25** **Litho.** ***Perf. 11½***

**Stamp + label**

| | | | | |
|---|---|---|---|---|
| **5242-5243** | A2442 | Set of 2 | 1.10 | .55 |
| *5243a* | | Booklet pane of 2, #5242-5243, + 6 labels | 1.40 | — |
| | | Complete booklet, #5243a | 1.40 | |

Complete booklet sold for 84w.

A2443

A2444

A2445

A2446

A2447

New Year's Address of Kim Jong Un — A2448

***Perf. 13¼x13½, 13½x13¼***

**2014, Feb. 1** **Litho.**

| | | | | |
|---|---|---|---|---|
| **5244** | A2443 | 10w multi | .25 | .25 |
| **5245** | A2444 | 10w multi | .25 | .25 |
| **5246** | A2445 | 10w multi | .25 | .25 |
| **5247** | A2446 | 30w multi | .45 | .25 |
| **5248** | A2447 | 30w multi | .45 | .25 |
| **5249** | A2448 | 30w multi | .45 | .25 |
| | | *Nos. 5244-5249 (6)* | 2.10 | 1.50 |

2014 Winter Olympics, Sochi, Russia — A2449

Designs: 30w, Skiing. 50w, Speed skating. 70w, Ice hockey. 90w, Bobsledding.

**2014, Feb. 7** **Litho.** ***Perf. 13¼x13½***

| | | | | |
|---|---|---|---|---|
| **5250-5253** | A2449 | Set of 4 | 3.75 | 1.90 |
| *5253a* | | Booklet pane of 4, #5250-5253 | 4.00 | — |
| | | Complete booklet, #5253a | 4.00 | |

Complete booklet sold for 254w.

Souvenir Sheet

Kim Jong Il (1942-2011), 72nd Birthday — A2453

**2014, Feb. 16** **Litho.** ***Perf. 11½x12***

| | | | | |
|---|---|---|---|---|
| **5257** | A2453 | 50w multi | .80 | .40 |

Traditional Sports — A2458

Designs: 10w, Wrestling. 30w, Archery. 50w, Horse racing.

***Perf. 13½x13¼***

**2014, Mar. 10** **Litho.**

| | | | | |
|---|---|---|---|---|
| **5262-5264** | A2458 | Set of 3 | 1.40 | .70 |

Souvenir Sheet

International Years — A2459

No. 5265: a, Intl. Year of Family Farming. b, Intl. Year of Crystallography.

**2014, Mar. 21** **Litho.** ***Perf. 11½***

| | | | | |
|---|---|---|---|---|
| **5265** | A2459 | 50w Sheet of 2, #a-b, + 2 labels | 1.60 | .80 |

Souvenir Sheet

Munsu Water Park, Pyongyang — A2461

No. 5267: a, Water slide (32mm diameter). b, Swimming pools (64x30mm).

***Perf. 11¾x11½ (#5267b)***

**2014, Apr. 3** **Litho.**

**5267** A2461 30w Sheet of 2, #a-b .95 .45

Korean Alphabet, 570th Anniv. — A2462

**2014, Apr. 10** **Litho.** ***Perf. 13¼***

**5268** A2462 30w multi .50 .25

No. 5268 was printed in sheets of 8 + central label.

Plants Presented to Kim Il Sung — A2463

Designs: 30w, Zygopetalum mackayi. 60w, Oncidium splendidum. 90w, Paphiopedilum insigne. 120w, Bletilla striata.

**2014, Apr. 15** **Litho.** ***Perf. 13¼***

**5269-5272** A2463 Set of 4 4.75 2.40

*5272a* Booklet pane of 4, #4269-5272 5.00 —

Complete booklet, #5272a 5.00

Nos. 5269-5272 were each printed in sheets of 3 + label. Complete booklet sold for 314w.

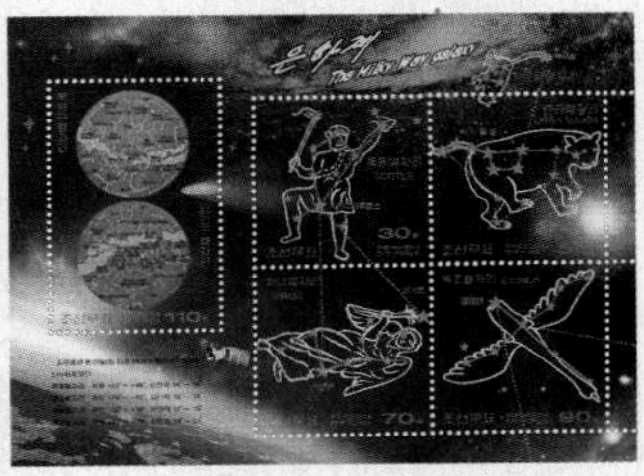

Astronomy — A2464

No. 5273: a, 30w, Boötes (35x35mm). b, 50w, Ursa Major (35x35mm). c, 70w, Virgo (35x35mm). d, 90w, Cygnus (35x35mm). e, Milky Way and maps of constellations (35x53mm).

***Perf. 11½, 11¾x12¼ (110w)***

**2014, Apr. 20** **Litho.**

**5273** A2464 Sheet of 5, #a-e 5.50 2.75

*f.* Booklet pane of 5, #5273a-5273e 5.75 —

Complete booklet, #5273f 5.75

Complete booklet sold for 364w.

2014 Intl. Horticultural Exposition, Qingdao, People's Republic of China — A2465

**2014, Apr. 25** **Litho.** ***Perf. 13¼***

**5274** A2465 30w multi .50 .25

Fish and Shellfish A2467

Designs: 50w, Rhodeus ocellatus ocellatus, Anodonta calypigos. 70w, Apogon semilineatus, Glycymeris albolineata. 90w, Diodon halacanthus, Atrina pectinata japonica. 110w, Cyclopterus lumpus, Pinctata margarittfera.

**2014, May 11** **Litho.** ***Perf. 13¼***

**5276-5279** A2467 Set of 4 5.00 2.50

*5279a* Booklet pane of 4, #5276-5279 5.25 —

Complete booklet, #5279a 5.25

Complete booklet sold for 334w.

Universal Postal Union, 140th Anniv. A2468

**2014, May 29** **Litho.** ***Perf. 11½***

**5280** A2468 30w multi .50 .25

Admission of North Korea into UPU, 40th anniv. Printed in sheets of 5 + label.

2014 World Cup Soccer Championships, Brazil — A2469

Player in red shirt: 40w, #12 Dribbling ball. 60w, Tackling opponent, horiz. 80w, #11 Dribbling ball.
100w, Player in yellow shirt.

**2014, June 12** **Litho.** ***Perf. 13¼***

**5281-5283** A2469 Set of 3 2.75 1.40

**Souvenir Sheet**

**5284** A2469 110w multi 1.75 .85

*a.* Booklet pane of 4, #5281-5284 4.75 —

Complete booklet, #5284a 4.75

Complete booklet sold for 304w.

International Olympic Committee, 120th Anniv. — A2470

**2014, June 16** **Litho.** ***Perf. 13¼***

**5285** A2470 30w multi .50 .25

A2471

Kim Jong Il's Leadership of Central Committee of Workers' Party, 50th Anniv. — A2472

No. 5286 — Paintings of Kim Jong Il: a, Visiting Mt. Taedok military post. b, With arms around office workers. c, In barley field. d, Surrounded by people.
50w, Kim Jong Il.

**2014, June 19** **Litho.** ***Perf. 11¾***

**5286** A2471 30w Sheet of 4, #a-d 1.90 .95

**Souvenir Sheet**

***Perf. 11¾x12¼***

**5287** A2472 50w multi .80 .40

Medicinal Plants — A2476

Designs: 30w, Aronia melanocarpa. 50w, Lycium chinense. 70w, Ginkgo biloba. 110w, Crataegus pinnatifida var. major.

**2014, July 17** **Litho.** ***Perf. 13¼***

**5291-5294** A2476 Set of 4 4.00 2.00

*5294a* Booklet pane of 4, #5291-5294 4.25 —

Complete booklet, #5294a 4.25

Complete booklet sold for 275w.

Sports — A2477

Designs: 30w, Table tennis. 50w, Running. 90w, Weight lifting. 110w, Judo.

**2014, July 25** **Litho.** ***Perf. 13***

**5295-5298** A2477 Set of 4 4.25 2.10

*5298a* Booklet pane of 4, #5295-5298 4.50 —

Complete booklet, #5298a 4.50

Complete booklet sold for 295w.

Worldwide Fund for Nature (WWF) A2478

No. 5299 — Grus japonensis: a, In flight. b, Adult and chick. c, Adults in water. d, Adults and chicks.

**2014, Aug. 5** **Litho.** ***Perf. 13¼***

**5299** Horiz. strip of 4 3.25 1.75

*a.* A2478 10w multi .25 .25

*b.* A2478 30w multi .45 .25

*c.* A2478 50w multi .75 .40

*d.* A2478 110w multi 1.75 .85

*e.* Booklet pane of 4, #5299a-5299d 3.50 —

Complete booklet, #5299e 3.50

Complete booklet sold for 215w.

## AIR POST STAMPS

Lisunov Li-2 Airliner over Pyongyang AP1

**1958, Feb. 4** **Photo.** ***Perf. 10***

**C1** AP1 20w blue 11.00 2.00

*a.* Imperf 22.50 10.00

*b.* Perf 11 12.00 2.50

*c.* Rouletted 15.00 10.00

Korean Civil Aviation.

# REPUBLIC OF KOSOVO

ˈko-sə-ˌvō

LOCATION — North of Albania and Macedonia
GOVT. — REPUBLIC
AREA — 4,212 sq. mi.
POP. — 2,100,000 (2007 est.)
CAPITAL — Pristina

From 1974 to 1990, Kosovo was an autonomous province of Serbia, a republic within Yugoslavia. In 1990, the autonomy of Kosovo was revoked. A Separatist faction declared Kosovo independence that year, but only Albania recognized it. In 1999, the United Nations Security Council placed Kosovo under a transitional United Nations Administration, and the institutions created by the independent Kosovo were replaced with the United Nations Interim Administration. Starting in 2000, postage stamps were issued by the United Nations Interim Administration, and these can be found as part of the listings for United Nations. The Kosovo Assembly declared independence on Feb. 17, 2008. Kosovo was recognized as independent by numerous countries soon thereafter, and the United Nations Interim Administration ceased issuing stamps. Serbia maintains its claim to the territory.

100 pfennigs = 1 mark
100 cents = (€)1 (2002)

**Catalogue values for all unused stamps in this country are for Never Hinged items.**

Peace in Kosovo — A1

Designs: 20pf, Mosaic depicting Orpheus, c. 5th-6th cent., Podujeve. 30pf, Dardinian idol, Museum of Kosovo. 50pf, Silver coin of Damastion from 4th cent. B.C. 1m, Statue of Mother Teresa, Prizren. 2m, Map of Kosovo.

***Perf. 13½x13, 13½x13¼ (30pf)***

**2000, Mar. 14 Litho. Unwmk.**

| | | | | | |
|---|---|---|---|---|---|
| 1 | A1 | 20pf multicolored | .50 | .50 |
| 2 | A1 | 30pf multicolored | 1.00 | 1.00 |
| 3 | A1 | 50pf multicolored | 1.40 | 1.40 |
| 4 | A1 | 1m multicolored | 1.80 | 1.60 |
| 5 | A1 | 2m multicolored | 3.50 | 3.25 |
| | | *Nos. 1-5 (5)* | 8.20 | 7.75 |

Beginning with No. 6, Kosovan stamps were not available to collectors through the United Nations Postal Administration.

Peace in Kosovo — A2

Designs: 20pf, Bird. 30pf, Street musician. 50pf, Butterfly and pear. 1m, Children and stars. 2m, Globe and handprints.

**2001, Nov. 12 Litho. *Perf. 14***

| | | | | |
|---|---|---|---|---|
| 6 | A2 | 20pf multicolored | 1.00 | 1.00 |
| 7 | A2 | 30pf multicolored | 1.25 | 1.25 |
| 8 | A2 | 50pf multicolored | 2.00 | 2.00 |
| 9 | A2 | 1m multicolored | 4.00 | 4.00 |
| 10 | A2 | 2m multicolored | 7.50 | 7.50 |
| | | *Nos. 6-10 (5)* | 15.75 | 15.75 |

**Peace in Kosovo Type of 2001 With Denominations in Euros Only**

**2002, May 2 Litho. *Perf. 14***

| | | | | |
|---|---|---|---|---|
| 11 | A2 | 10c Like #6 | .75 | .75 |
| 12 | A2 | 15c Like #7 | 1.00 | 1.00 |
| 13 | A2 | 26c Like #8 | 1.50 | 1.50 |
| 14 | A2 | 51c Like #9 | 4.50 | 4.50 |
| 15 | A2 | €1.02 Like #10 | 8.00 | 8.00 |
| | | *Nos. 11-15 (5)* | 15.75 | 15.75 |

Christmas — A3

Designs: 50c, Candles and garland. €1, Stylized men.

**2003, Dec. 20 Litho. *Perf. 14***

| | | | | |
|---|---|---|---|---|
| 16 | A3 | 50c multicolored | 7.50 | 7.50 |
| 17 | A3 | €1 multicolored | 14.50 | 14.50 |

Return of Refugees — A4

Five Years of Peace — A5

**2004, June 29 Litho. *Perf. 13¼x13***

| | | | | |
|---|---|---|---|---|
| 18 | A4 | €1 multicolored | 7.00 | 7.00 |
| 19 | A5 | €2 multicolored | 16.00 | 16.00 |

Musical Instruments — A6

**2004, Aug. 31 Litho. *Perf. 13¼x13***

| | | | | |
|---|---|---|---|---|
| 20 | A6 | 20c Flute | 5.00 | 5.00 |
| 21 | A6 | 30c Ocarina | 10.00 | 10.00 |

Aprons A7

Vests — A8

Designs: 20c, Apron from Prizren. 30c, Apron from Rugova. 50c, Three vests. €1, Two vests.

**2004, Oct. 28 Litho. *Perf. 13x13¼***

| | | | | |
|---|---|---|---|---|
| 22 | A7 | 20c multicolored | 5.50 | 5.50 |
| 23 | A7 | 30c multicolored | 8.50 | 8.50 |
| 24 | A8 | 50c multicolored | 12.00 | 12.00 |
| 25 | A8 | €1 multicolored | 26.00 | 26.00 |
| | | *Nos. 22-25 (4)* | 52.00 | 52.00 |

Mirusha Waterfall A9

**2004, Nov. 26 Litho. *Perf. 13x13¼***

| | | | | |
|---|---|---|---|---|
| 26 | A9 | €2 multicolored | 7.50 | 7.50 |

House A10

**2004, Dec. 14 Litho. *Perf. 13x13¼***

| | | | | |
|---|---|---|---|---|
| 27 | A10 | 50c multicolored | 4.50 | 4.50 |

Flowers — A11

**2005, June 29 Litho. *Perf. 13½***

| | | | | |
|---|---|---|---|---|
| 28 | A11 | 15c Peony | 2.25 | 2.25 |
| 29 | A11 | 20c Poppies | 3.25 | 3.25 |
| 30 | A11 | 30c Gentian | 5.00 | 5.00 |
| | | *Nos. 28-30 (3)* | 10.50 | 10.50 |

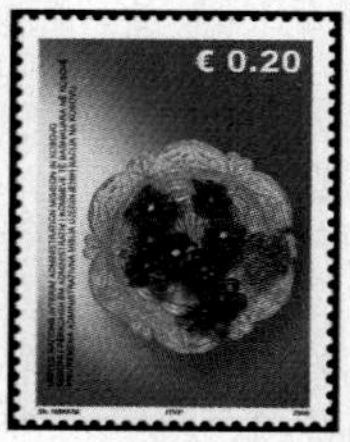


A12

Handicrafts A13

**2005, July 20 *Perf. 13¼x13***

| | | | | |
|---|---|---|---|---|
| 31 | A12 | 20c shown | 2.50 | 2.50 |
| 32 | A12 | 30c Cradle | 3.00 | 3.00 |
| 33 | A13 | 50c shown | 3.25 | 3.25 |
| 34 | A12 | €1 Necklace | 4.25 | 4.25 |
| | | *Nos. 31-34 (4)* | 13.00 | 13.00 |

Village A14

Town A15

City — A16

**2005, Sept. 15 *Perf. 13x13½***

| | | | | |
|---|---|---|---|---|
| 35 | A14 | 20c multicolored | 2.00 | 2.00 |
| 36 | A15 | 50c multicolored | 3.00 | 3.00 |
| 37 | A16 | €1 multicolored | 6.00 | 6.00 |
| | | *Nos. 35-37 (3)* | 11.00 | 11.00 |

Archaeological Artifacts — A17

**2005, Nov. 2 *Perf. 13½x13***

| | | | | |
|---|---|---|---|---|
| 38 | A17 | 20c shown | 1.25 | 1.25 |
| 39 | A17 | 30c Statue | 1.75 | 1.75 |
| 40 | A17 | 50c Sculpture | 2.50 | 2.50 |
| 41 | A17 | €1 Helmet | 7.50 | 7.50 |
| | | *Nos. 38-41 (4)* | 13.00 | 13.00 |

Minerals A18

**2005, Dec. 10 *Perf. 13x13½***

| | | | | |
|---|---|---|---|---|
| 42 | A18 | €2 multicolored | 10.00 | 10.00 |

A19

Europa — A20

**2006, July 20 *Perf. 13¼x13***

| | | | | |
|---|---|---|---|---|
| 43 | A19 | 50c multicolored | 2.25 | 2.25 |
| 44 | A20 | €1 multicolored | 4.25 | 4.25 |

Exists Imperf. Value set: 2 pairs $75.

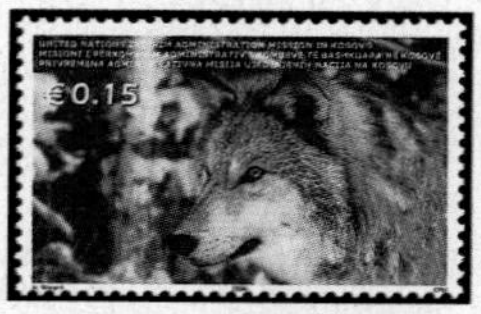


Fauna A21

**2006, May 23 Litho. *Perf. 13***

| | | | | |
|---|---|---|---|---|
| 45 | A21 | 15c Wolf | 1.00 | 1.00 |
| 46 | A21 | 20c Cow | 1.25 | 1.25 |
| 47 | A21 | 30c Pigeon | 1.40 | 1.40 |
| 48 | A21 | 50c Swan | 1.60 | 1.60 |
| 49 | A21 | €1 Dog | 2.75 | 2.75 |
| | *a.* | Souvenir sheet, #45-49, + label | 8.75 | 8.75 |
| | | *Nos. 45-49 (5)* | 8.00 | 8.00 |

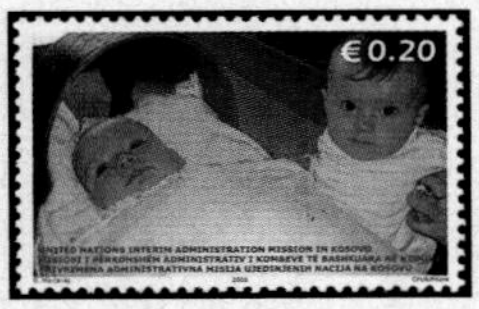


Children A22

Designs: 20c, Children in cradle. 30c, Children reading. 50c, Girls dancing. €1, Child in water.

**2006, June 30 Litho. *Perf. 13***

| | | | | |
|---|---|---|---|---|
| 50 | A22 | 20c multicolored | 1.00 | 1.00 |
| 51 | A22 | 30c multicolored | 1.25 | 1.25 |
| 52 | A22 | 50c multicolored | 1.75 | 1.75 |
| 53 | A22 | €1 multicolored | 3.50 | 3.50 |
| *a.* | | Souvenir sheet, #50-53 | 7.75 | 7.75 |
| | | *Nos. 50-53 (4)* | 7.50 | 7.50 |

A23

A24

A25

Tourist Attractions — A26

**2006, Sept. 1 Litho. *Perf. 13***

| | | | | |
|---|---|---|---|---|
| 54 | A23 | 20c multicolored | 1.00 | 1.00 |
| 55 | A24 | 30c multicolored | 1.25 | 1.25 |
| 56 | A25 | 50c multicolored | 1.75 | 1.75 |
| 57 | A26 | €1 multicolored | 3.25 | 3.25 |
| *a.* | | Souvenir sheet, #54-57 | 9.50 | 9.50 |
| | | *Nos. 54-57 (4)* | 7.25 | 7.25 |

Intl. Peace Day — A27

**2006, Sept. 21 Litho. *Perf. 13***

| | | | | |
|---|---|---|---|---|
| 58 | A27 | €2 multicolored | 7.00 | 7.00 |

Ancient Coins — A28

Various coins.

**2006, Nov. 1 Litho. *Perf. 13***

| | | | | |
|---|---|---|---|---|
| 59 | A28 | 20c multicolored | 1.00 | 1.00 |
| 60 | A28 | 30c multicolored | 1.50 | 1.50 |
| 61 | A28 | 50c multicolored | 1.75 | 1.75 |
| 62 | A28 | €1 multicolored | 3.25 | 3.25 |
| *a.* | | Souvenir sheet, #59-62 | 9.50 | 9.50 |
| | | *Nos. 59-62 (4)* | 7.50 | 7.50 |

Sculpture — A29

**2006, Dec. 1 Litho. *Perf. 13***

| | | | | |
|---|---|---|---|---|
| 63 | A29 | €2 multicolored | 8.00 | 8.00 |
| *a.* | | Miniature sheet, #45-57, 59-63, + 2 labels | 80.00 | 80.00 |

Convention on the Rights of Persons With Disabilities — A30

Emblems of handicaps and: 20c, Children and butterfly. 50c, Handicapped women. 70c, Map of Kosovo. €1, Stylized flower.

**2007, Apr. 23 Litho. *Perf. 14x14¼***

| | | | | |
|---|---|---|---|---|
| 64 | A30 | 20c multicolored | 1.25 | 1.25 |
| 65 | A30 | 50c multicolored | 2.50 | 2.50 |
| 66 | A30 | 70c multicolored | 3.00 | 3.00 |
| 67 | A30 | €1 multicolored | 3.75 | 3.75 |
| *a.* | | Souvenir sheet, #64-67 | 11.00 | 11.00 |
| | | *Nos. 64-67 (4)* | 10.50 | 10.50 |

Scouting, Cent. — A31

Europa — A32

**2007, May 12 Litho. *Perf. 13¼***

| | | | | |
|---|---|---|---|---|
| 68 | A31 | 70c multicolored | 4.25 | 4.25 |
| 69 | A32 | €1 multicolored | 6.25 | 6.25 |
| *a.* | | Souvenir sheet, #68-69 | 90.00 | 90.00 |

A33

A34

A35

International Children's Day — A36

**2007, June 1 Litho. *Perf. 13¼***

| | | | | |
|---|---|---|---|---|
| 70 | A33 | 20c multicolored | 1.25 | 1.25 |
| 71 | A34 | 30c multicolored | 1.50 | 1.50 |
| 72 | A35 | 70c multicolored | 2.50 | 2.50 |
| 73 | A36 | €1 multicolored | 4.00 | 4.00 |
| | | *Nos. 70-73 (4)* | 9.25 | 9.25 |

Nos. 70-73 exist imperf.

Native Costumes — A37

Designs: 20c, Serbian woman. 30c, Prizren Region woman. 50c, Sword dancer. 70c, Drenica Region woman. €1, Shepherd, Rugova.

**2007, July 6 Litho. *Perf. 13½x13¼***

| | | | | |
|---|---|---|---|---|
| 74 | A37 | 20c multicolored | 1.25 | 1.25 |
| 75 | A37 | 30c multicolored | 1.75 | 1.75 |
| 76 | A37 | 50c multicolored | 2.00 | 2.00 |
| 77 | A37 | 70c multicolored | 2.50 | 2.50 |
| 78 | A37 | €1 multicolored | 3.25 | 3.25 |
| *a.* | | Souvenir sheet, #74-78, + label | 12.50 | 12.50 |
| | | *Nos. 74-78 (5)* | 10.75 | 10.75 |

Masks — A38

Various masks.

***Perf. 13½x13¼***

**2007, Sept. 11 Litho.**

| | | | | |
|---|---|---|---|---|
| 79 | A38 | 15c multicolored | .75 | .75 |
| 80 | A38 | 30c multicolored | 1.00 | 1.00 |
| 81 | A38 | 50c multicolored | 2.00 | 2.00 |
| 82 | A38 | €1 multicolored | 3.00 | 3.00 |
| | | *Nos. 79-82 (4)* | 6.75 | 6.75 |

Sports — A39

Designs: 20c, Soccer ball, basketball, two people standing, person in wheelchair. 50c, Wrestlers. €1, Symbols of 24 sports.

**2007, Oct. 2 Litho. *Perf. 13¼x13½***

| | | | | |
|---|---|---|---|---|
| 83 | A39 | 20c multicolored | 1.00 | 1.00 |
| 84 | A39 | 50c multicolored | 2.25 | 2.25 |
| 85 | A39 | €1 multicolored | 4.00 | 4.00 |
| | | *Nos. 83-85 (3)* | 7.25 | 7.25 |

Nos. 83-85 exist imperf.

Architecture A40

Designs: 30c, Stone bridge, Vushtrri. 50c, Hamam, Prizren. 70c, Tower. €1, Tower, diff.

**2007, Nov. 6 Litho. *Perf. 13¼***

| | | | | |
|---|---|---|---|---|
| 86 | A40 | 30c multicolored | 1.50 | 1.50 |
| 87 | A40 | 50c multicolored | 2.00 | 2.00 |
| 88 | A40 | 70c multicolored | 2.50 | 2.50 |
| 89 | A40 | €1 multicolored | 3.50 | 3.50 |
| | | *Nos. 86-89 (4)* | 9.50 | 9.50 |

Nos. 86-89 exist imperf.

Locomotives A41

Designs: €1, Diesel locomotive. €2, Steam locomotive

**2007, Dec. 7 Litho. *Perf. 13¼***

| | | | | |
|---|---|---|---|---|
| 90 | A41 | €1 multicolored | 4.00 | 4.00 |
| 91 | A41 | €2 multicolored | 8.00 | 8.00 |

Nos. 90-91 exist imperf.

Skanderbeg (1405-68), Albanian National Hero — A42

**2008, Jan. 17 Litho. *Perf. 13¼***

| | | | | |
|---|---|---|---|---|
| 92 | A42 | €2 multicolored | 7.50 | 7.50 |

No. 92 exists imperf.

Kosovo declared its independence from Serbia on Feb. 17, 2008, ending the United Nations Interim Administration. Stamps issued after Feb. 17, 2008, by the Republic of Kosovo will be listed under Kosovo in the *Scott Standard Postage Stamp Catalogue.*

---

**Republic of Kosovo**

A42

Teacher's Day — A43

**2008, Mar. 7 Litho. *Perf. 13x13¼***

| | | | | |
|---|---|---|---|---|
| 93 | A42 | 70c multi | 2.25 | 2.25 |
| 94 | A43 | €1 multi | 3.25 | 3.25 |

Independence A44

**2008, Mar. 19 *Perf. 13¼x13***

**Stamps With White Frames**

| | | | | |
|---|---|---|---|---|
| 95 | | Vert. pair | 5.50 | 5.50 |
| *a.* | | A44 20c vio blue & multi | .75 | .50 |
| *b.* | | A44 70c red & multi | 3.00 | 2.00 |

**Souvenir Sheet**

**Stamp With Colored Border**

| | | | | |
|---|---|---|---|---|
| 96 | A44 | 70c red & multi | 7.00 | 7.00 |

Earth Day — A45

Designs: 30c, Globe, olive branch. 50c, Trees. 70c, Tree, parched land. €1, Man holding tree.

**2008, Apr. 22** ***Perf. 13x13¼***
**97-100** A45 Set of 4 8.00 8.00

Europa — A46

Designs: Nos. 101, 103a, 70c, Handwritten letter, pen. Nos. 102, 103b, €1, Letter folded into paper airplane.

**2008, May 9** **Litho.**

**Stamps With White Frames**

**101-102** A46 Set of 2 *7.50 7.50*

**Souvenir Sheet**

**Stamps With Colored Frames**

**103** A46 Sheet of 2, #a-b *20.00 20.00*

Filigree — A47

Designs: 10c, Chest. 15c, Earring. 20c, Figurine of woman. 50c, Necklace. €1, Necklace, diff.

**2008, June 12** ***Perf. 13¼x13***
**104-108** A47 Set of 5 6.75 6.75

A48

A49

A50

A51

Medicinal Herbs

**2008, Sept. 9** **Litho.** ***Perf. 13¼x13***

| | | | |
|---|---|---|---|
| **109** | Horiz. strip of 4 | 8.00 | 8.00 |
| *a.* | A48 30c multi | .75 | .75 |
| *b.* | A49 50c multi | 1.00 | 1.00 |
| *c.* | A50 70c multi | 2.00 | 2.00 |
| *d.* | A51 €1 multi | 2.75 | 2.75 |

Exists Imperf. Value, strip $135.

Breast Cancer Prevention — A52

**2008, Oct. 15** **Litho.** ***Perf. 13¼x13***
**110** A52 €1 multi 7.00 7.00

Albanian Alphabet, Cent. — A53

No. 111: a, 70c, Alphabet. b, €1, Notebook page for handwriting practice.

**2008, Nov. 14** ***Perf. 13x13¼***
**111** A53 Vert. pair, #a-b 4.50 4.50

Adem Jashari (1955-98), Independence Leader — A54

**2008, Nov. 28** ***Perf. 13¼x13***
**112** A54 €2 multi 6.00 6.00

A55

A56

A57

Visual Arts — A58

**2008, Dec. 2** **Litho.** ***Perf. 13¼***

| | | | |
|---|---|---|---|
| **113** | Horiz. strip of 4 | 8.00 | 8.00 |
| *a.* | A55 20c multi | .55 | .55 |
| *b.* | A56 50c multi | 1.10 | 1.10 |
| *c.* | A57 70c multi | 1.75 | 1.75 |
| *d.* | A58 €1 multi | 2.50 | 2.50 |

William G. Walker, Head of Kosovo Verification Mission — A59

Torn Page — A60

**2009, Jan. 15**
**114** A59 50c multi 1.25 1.25
**115** A60 70c multi 2.25 2.25

Reçak Massacre, 10th anniv.

Independence, 1st Anniv. — A61

No. 116: a, €1, Hand with pen, independence declaration. b, €2, Flag of Kosovo, date of independence.
Illustration reduced.

**2009, Feb. 16** **Litho.** ***Perf. 13¼***
**116** A61 Horiz. pair, #a-b 8.00 8.00

Edith Durham (1863-1944), Writer — A62

**2009, Mar. 21**
**117** A62 €1 multi 3.25 3.25

A63

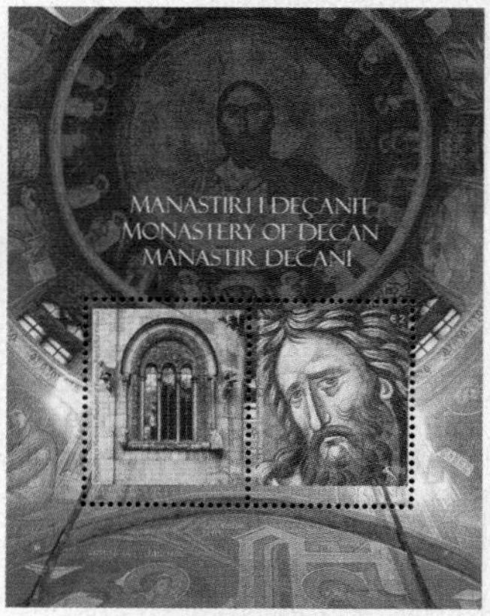

Decan Monastery — A64

Designs: No. 118, €1, Monastery. No. 119, €2, Monastery, diff.
No. 120: a, €1, Window. b, €2, Painting of Jesus.

**2009, Apr. 22**
**118-119** A63 Set of 2 7.00 7.00

**Souvenir Sheet**

**120** A64 Sheet of 2, #a-b 7.50 7.50

Europa — A65

Designs: €1, Map of Europe, ring of stars, man and girl at telescope. No. 122, €2, Boy and rocket on map of Europe (with white frame around stamp).
No. 123, Like #122, without white frame around stamp.

**2009, May 9**
**121-122** A65 Set of 2 9.50 9.50

**Souvenir Sheet**

**123** A65 €2 multi 10.00 10.00

Intl. Year of Astronomy.

A66

A67

A68

A69

Declaration of the Rights of the Child, 20th Anniv.

**2009, June 1**

| | | | |
|---|---|---|---|
| **124** | A66 20c multi | .75 | .75 |
| **125** | A67 50c multi | 1.75 | 1.75 |
| **126** | A68 70c multi | 2.50 | 2.50 |
| **127** | A69 €1 multi | 3.50 | 3.50 |
| | *Nos. 124-127 (4)* | 8.50 | 8.50 |

Kosovo's Friendship With United States — A70

**2009, Sept. 4**
**128** A70 €2 multi 7.00 7.00

Lorenc Antoni (1909-91), Composer — A71

**2009, Sept. 23**
**129** A71 €1 multi 4.50 4.50

Germany Weeks in Kosovo — A72

**2009, Oct. 3** **Litho.** ***Perf. 13¼***
**130** A72 €1 multi 3.50 3.50

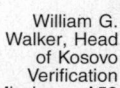

Pjeter Bogdani (c. 1630-89), Writer — A73

**2009, Nov. 22**
**131** A73 €1 multi 3.25 3.25

Art — A74

Works by: 30c, M. Mulliqi. 50c, I. Kodra. 70c, G. Gjokaj. €1, M. Mulliqi, diff.

**2009, Dec. 4**
**132-135** A74 Set of 4 7.00 7.00

A75

Film Personalities — A76

Designs: No. 136, 30c, Faruk Begolli (1944-2007), actor and director. No. 137, 70c, Melihate Qena (1939-2005), actress. €1, Abdurrahman Shala (1922-94), actor and producer.
No. 139: a, 30c, Unnamed person in yellow. b, 70c, Unnamed person in brown, diff.

**2010, Jan. 26**
**136-138** A75 Set of 3 5.50 5.50
**Souvenir Sheet**
**139** A76 Sheet of 2, #a-b 3.25 3.25

Emblems of Kosovo Police, Defense Forces and Security Forces — A77

Police and Emblem — A78

Security Forces — A79

**2010, Feb. 16** **Litho.**
**140** A77 30c multi .85 .85
**141** A78 50c multi 1.40 1.40
**142** A79 70c multi 1.90 1.90
*Nos. 140-142 (3)* 4.15 4.15

A80

Europa — A81

Designs: €1, Child reading book under tree. No. 144, €2, Child leaving open book.
No. 145, €2, Boy sitting on book.

**2010, May 5** ***Perf. 13¼***
**143-144** A80 Set of 2 8.00 8.00
**Souvenir Sheet**
***Perf. 14x14¼***
**145** A81 €2 multi 5.25 5.25

2010 World Cup Soccer Championships, South Africa — A82

Designs: €1, Map of Kosovo and emblem of Kosovo Soccer Federation, map of Africa with soccer field. €2, Map of Kosovo and emblem of Kosovo Soccer Federation, map of Africa on soccer ball.
No. 148: a, Soccer ball as pendant on multicolored ribbon. b, Flag of South Africa on soccer ball.

**2010, June 29** ***Perf. 13¼***
**146-147** A82 Set of 2 8.00 8.00
**Souvenir Sheet**
***Perf. 14¼x14***
**148** A82 50c Sheet of 2, #a-b 3.50 3.50

Azem (1889-1924) and Shota (1895-1927) Galica, Fighters for Albanian Independence A83

**2010, July 14** ***Perf. 13¼***
**149** A83 €2 multi 5.25 5.25

National Parks — A84

Scenery from: 20c, Mirusha National Park. 50c, Rugova National Park. 70c, Gjeravica National Park. €1, Sharri National Park.

**2010, Aug. 2** **Litho.**
**150-153** A84 Set of 4 6.25 6.25

Mother Teresa (1910-97), Humanitarian A85

**2010, Aug. 26** ***Perf. 13***
**154** A85 €1 multi 2.75 2.75

See Albania No. 2889, Macedonia No. 529.

A86

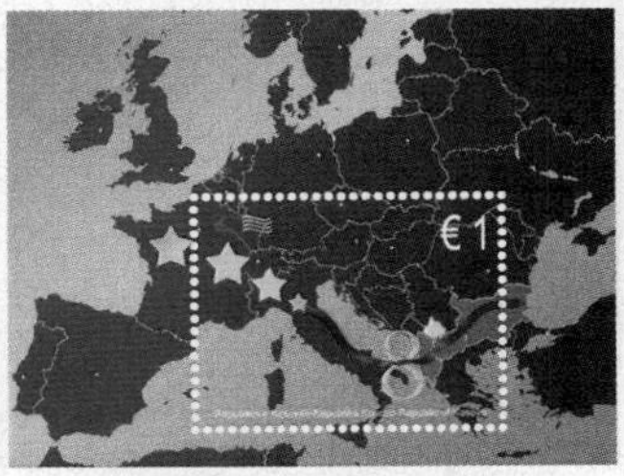

Traffic in the Pathways of Integration — A87

**2010, Sept. 9** **Litho.** ***Perf. 13¼***
**155** A86 70c multi 2.25 2.25
**Souvenir Sheet**
***Perf. 14¼x14***
**156** A87 €1 multi 3.50 3.50

A88

A89

A90

A91

Birds — A92

No. 161: a, 30c, Brown bird on branch. b, 30c, Blue and red bird on wire. c, 70c, Bird in flight. d, 70c, Blue and red bird on wire, bird in flight.

**2010, Sept. 23** ***Perf. 14x14¼***
**157** A88 30c multi .85 .85
**158** A89 50c multi 1.50 1.50
**159** A90 70c multi 2.00 2.00
**160** A91 €1 multi 3.00 3.00
*Nos. 157-160 (4)* 7.35 7.35
**Souvenir Sheet**
**161** A92 Sheet of 4, #a-d 7.50 7.50

Local Foods — A93

Designs: 70c, Beehive, honeycombs, jar of honey. €1, Plates of food.

**2010, Nov. 8** ***Perf. 14¼x14***
**162-163** A93 Set of 2 4.75 4.75

Campaign Against Violence Towards Women A94

**2010, Nov. 25**
**164** A94 €1 multi 3.00 3.00

Historical Photographs of Basare — A95

Various street scenes: 50c, 70c, €1.

**2010, Dec. 6**
**165-167** A95 Set of 3 6.50 6.50

A96

Independence, 3rd Anniv. — A97

**2011, Feb. 27** *Perf. 14¼x14*

**168** A96 €1 multi 2.50 2.50
**169** A97 €2 multi 5.50 5.50

Elena Gjika (Dore D'Istria, 1828-88), Writer — A98

**2011, Mar. 8** *Perf. 14x14¼*

**170** A98 €1 multi 2.75 2.75

Prizren — A99

Designs: 20c, Houses on hillside. 50c, House and benches. 70c, View of city.

**2011, Mar. 15**

**171-173** A99 Set of 3 4.00 4.00

A100

A101

Intl. Year of Forests — A102

**2011, May 9** *Perf. 14¼x14*

**174** A100 €1 multi 3.00 3.00
**175** A101 €2 multi 5.75 5.75

**Souvenir Sheet**

**176** A102 €2 multi 6.00 6.00

Archaeology A103

Designs: 10c, Building ruins. 15c, Building ruins, diff. €1, Bas-relief head.

**2011, June 7** *Perf. 14x14¼*

**177-179** A103 Set of 3 3.75 3.75

Compare No. 178 with Nos. 243A and 329.

A104

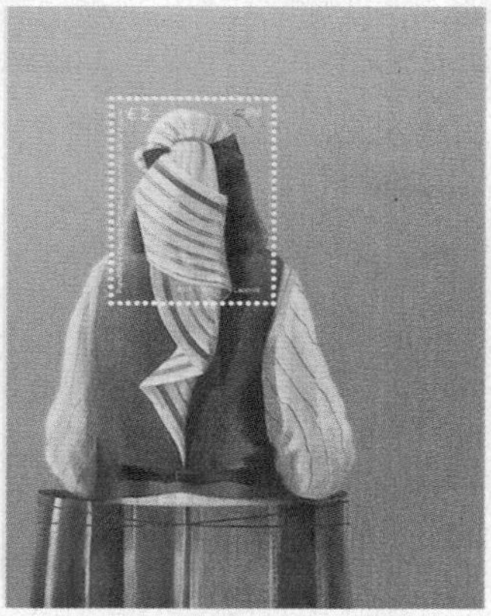

Traditional Costumes of Hasit Region — A105

Designs: 30c, Shoes. 50c, Women's dress. 70c, Pouch. €1, Vest.
€2, Kerchief.

**2011, Oct. 19**

**180-183** A104 Set of 4 6.75 6.75

**Souvenir Sheet**

**184** A105 €2 multi 5.50 5.50

A106

A107

A108

Mills — A109

**2011, Nov. 2**

**185** A106 50c multi 1.40 1.40
**186** A107 70c multi 2.00 2.00
**187** A108 €1 multi 2.75 2.75
*Nos. 185-187 (3)* 6.15 6.15

**Souvenir Sheet**

***Perf. 14¼x14***

**188** A109 €2 multi 5.50 5.50

A110

Caves A111

**2011, Nov. 15** *Perf. 14x14¼*

**189** A110 70c multi 1.90 1.90
**190** A111 €1 multi 2.75 2.75

Rooster A112

Rooster facing: 70c, Right. €1, Left.

**2011, Nov. 21**

**191-192** A112 Set of 2 4.75 4.75

Esat Mekuli (1916-93), Poet — A113

**2011, Dec. 17** *Perf. 14¼x14*

**193** A113 €1 multi 2.60 2.60

Enver Zymeri (1979-2011), Police Officer — A114

**2011, Dec. 26**

**194** A114 €1 multi 2.60 2.60

Mitrovica A115

Designs: €1, Monument, workers, street, aerial view of city. €2, Old and new street scenes.

**2012, Jan. 20** *Perf. 14¼x14*

**195-196** A115 Set of 2 8.00 8.00

A116

Freedom Fighters — A117

**2012, Jan. 27**

**197** A116 €1 multi 2.60 2.60
**198** A117 €1 multi 2.60 2.60

Rexho Mulliqi (1923-82), Composer A118

**2012, Feb. 23**

**199** A118 €1 multi 2.75 2.75

Butterflies A119

Various butterflies: 10c, 70c, €1.
€2, Butterflies and orchids.

**2012, Mar. 9** *Perf. 14x14¼*

**200-202** A119 Set of 3 4.75 4.75

**Souvenir Sheet**

**203** A119 €2 multi 6.00 6.00

A120

Europa — A121

Designs: €1, Cliff and valley. No. 205, €2, House.
No. 206, €2, Buildings and bridge.

**2012, Apr. 12** ***Perf. 14¼x14***
**204-205** A120 Set of 2 8.00 8.00

**Souvenir Sheet**

**206** A121 €2 multi 5.75 5.75

Lakes
A122

Designs: 20c, Badovac Lake. 50c, Gazivoda Lake. 70c, Lake Licenat.

**2012, May 3** ***Perf. 14x14¼***
**207-209** A122 Set of 3 3.75 3.75

Isa Boletini (1864-1916), Kosovar Freedom Fighter — A123

Hasan Prishtina (1873-1933), Prime Minister of Albania — A124

**2012, May 21** ***Perf. 14¼x14***
**210** A123 70c multi 1.75 1.75
**211** A124 €1 multi 2.50 2.50

Bride in Archway — A125

**2012, June 18**
**212** A125 €1 multi 2.50 2.50

Mejlinda Kelmendi, Kosovar Judoka Competing for Albania at 2012 Summer Olympics — A126

No. 213: a, 70c, Three images of Kelmendi. b, €1, Two images of Kelmendi.

**2012, July 25** ***Perf. 14x14¼***
**213** A126 Pair, #a-b 4.25 4.25

Printed in sheets containing two pairs.

A127

A128

Myths and Legends — A129

**2012, Sept. 5** ***Perf. 14¼x14***
**214** A127 70c multi 1.90 1.90
**215** A128 €1 multi 2.60 2.60

**Souvenir Sheet**

***Perf. 14x14¼***

**216** A129 €2 multi 5.25 5.25

Traditional Dances — A130

Various dancers: 50c, 70c, €1.

**2012, Oct. 25** ***Perf. 14¼x14***
**217-219** A130 Set of 3 5.75 5.75

Albanian Independence, Cent. — A131

**2012, Nov. 27**
**220** A131 €1 multi 2.60 2.60

Marin Barleti (c.1450-c. 1512), Historian
A132

**2012, Dec. 26**
**221** A132 €1 multi 2.75 2.75

Independence, 5th Anniv. — A133

**2013, Feb. 17** ***Perf. 14x14¼***
**222** A133 €2 multi 5.25 5.25

Pristina — A134

Designs: 50c, Old and modern photographs of Pristina. 70c, Drawing of Pristina buildings. €1, People near building, Pristina skyline.

**2013, Mar. 20** ***Perf. 14¼x14***
**223-225** A134 Set of 3 5.75 5.75

A135

A136

Museum Exhibits — A137

No. 228 — Table with window and small wall niche at: a, Left. b, Right.

**2013, Apr. 5** ***Perf. 14x14¼***
**226** A135 70c multi 1.90 1.90
**227** A136 €1 multi 2.60 2.60

**Souvenir Sheet**

***Perf. 14¼x14***

**228** A137 €1 Sheet of 2, #a-b 5.25 5.25

A138

A139

Postal Transportation — A140

No. 231: a, Horse-drawn wagon. b, Postman on scooter.

**2013, May 2** **Litho.** ***Perf. 14x14¼***
**229** A138 €1 multi 2.60 2.60
**230** A139 €2 multi 5.25 5.25

**Souvenir Sheet**

***Perf. 14¼x14***

**231** A140 €1 Sheet of 2, #a-b 5.25 5.25

Mountain Scenery — A141

Designs: 50c, Mt. Gjeravica. 70c Rugova Canyon (Gryka e Rugoves). €1, Mt. Gjeravica, diff.

**2013, June 14** **Litho.** ***Perf. 14¼x14***
**232-234** A141 Set of 3 6.00 6.00

Villages A142

Designs: 50c, Stublla e Eperme. 70c, Opoja. €1, Lluka e Eperme.

**2013, July 18 Litho. *Perf. 14x14¼***

**235-237** A142 Set of 3 6.00 6.00
*235a* Dated "2016" 1.10 1.10

Famous Women — A143

No. 238: a, 50c, Hyrije Hana (1929-2004), radio broadcaster. b, 70c, Xheve Lladrovici (1955-98), freedom fighter. c, €1, Katarina Josipi (1923-69), actress.

**2013, Aug. 15 Litho. *Perf. 14¼x14***

**238** A143 Horiz. strip of 3, #a-c 5.50 5.50

Bajram Curri (1862-1925), Albanian Politician — A144

**2013, Sept. 9 Litho. *Perf. 14x14¼***

**239** A144 €1 multi 2.75 2.75

Paintings by Adem Kastrati (1930-2000) — A145

Various paintings depicting: a, 70c, Buildings on hill. b, €1, Sheep and shepherds. c, €2, Musicians.

**2013, Sept. 26 Litho. *Perf. 14x14¼***

**240** A145 Vert. strip of 3, #a-c 10.00 10.00

Pristina University A146

**2014, Oct. 28 Litho. *Perf. 14x14¼***

**241** A146 €1 multi 2.75 2.75

Singers A147

No. 242: a, 20c, Qamili i Vogel (1923-91). b, 30c, Sali Krasniqi (1919-87). c, 50c, Dervish Shaqa (1912-85).

**2013, Nov. 15 Litho. *Perf. 14x14¼***

**242** A147 Vert. strip of 3, #a-c 2.75 2.75
*d.* As #242a, dated "2015" — —

Bekim Fehmiu (1936-2010), Actor — A148

**2013, Dec. 5 Litho. *Perf. 14¼x14***

**243** A148 €1 multi 2.75 2.75

Building Ruins — A148a

**2013 Litho. *Perf. 14¼x14***

**243A** A148a 15c multi — —

Compare No. 243A with Nos. 178 and 329.

Paintings by Muslim Mulliqi (1934-98) A149

Various paintings.

**2014, Jan. 13 Litho. *Perf. 14¼x14***

**244** Horiz. strip of 4 7.75 7.75
*a.* A149 30c multi .80 .80
*b.* A149 60c multi 1.60 1.60
*c.* A149 90c multi 2.50 2.50
*d.* A149 €1 multi 2.75 2.75

Mountain Climbers — A150

Mountaineering — A151

**2014, Feb. 7 Litho. *Perf. 14¼x14***

**245** A150 €1 multi 2.75 2.75

**Souvenir Sheet**

**246** A151 €2 multi 5.50 5.50

Pec A152

Buildings in Pec: €1, Color photograph. €2, Sepia-toned photograph.

**2014, Mar. 10 Litho. *Perf. 14x14¼***

**247-248** A152 Set of 2 8.25 8.25

World Shotokan Karate Championships, Pristina — A153

No. 249 — Two karateka and: a, 80c, Colored belts and "5." b, 90c, Map of Kosovo and world.
€2, Karateka and map of Kosovo and world.

**2014, Apr. 3 Litho. *Perf. 14x14¼***

**249** A153 Pair, #a-b 4.75 4.75

**Souvenir Sheet**

**250** A153 €2 multi 5.50 5.50

No. 249 was printed in sheets containing two pairs + label.

Ibrahim Rugova Highway — A154

No. 251: a, €1, Bridge and interchange. b, €2, Entrance and exit ramps.

**2014, Apr. 25 Litho. *Perf. 14x14¼***

**251** A154 Pair, #a-b 8.25 8.25

Europa — A155

Musical instruments: €1, Two instruments. No. 253, €2, Lakuta.
No. 254, €2, Four instruments, horiz.

**2014, May 8 Litho. *Perf. 14¼x14***

**252-253** A155 Set of 2 8.25 8.25

**Souvenir Sheet**

***Perf. 14x14¼***

**254** A155 €2 multi 5.50 5.50

Flowers — A156

Designs: 80c, Liliaceae. 90c, Gladiolus illyricus. €1, Tulipa kosovarica.
€2, Red flowers.

**2014, June 12 Litho. *Perf. 14¼x14***

**255-257** A156 Set of 3 7.50 7.50

**Souvenir Sheet**

**258** A156 €2 multi 5.50 5.50

Jeronim de Rada (1814-1903), Writer — A157

**2014, July 3 Litho. *Perf. 14¼x14***

**259** A157 €1 multi 2.75 2.75

Woven Items — A158

Various woven items.

**2014, Aug. 8 Litho. *Perf. 14¼x14***

**260** Horiz. strip or block of 4, #a-d 8.75 8.75
*a.* A158 60c multi 1.60 1.60
*b.* A158 80c multi 2.10 2.10
*c.* A158 90c multi 2.40 2.40
*d.* A158 €1 multi 2.60 2.60

Fehmi (1950-98) and Xheve (1955-98) Lladrovci, Freedom Fighters A159

**2014, Sept. 22 Litho. *Perf. 14x14¼***

**261** A159 €2 multi 5.00 5.00

Adrian Krasniqi (1972-97), Freedom Fighter — A160

**2014, Oct. 16 Litho.** ***Perf. 14¼x14***
**262** A160 €1 multi 2.50 2.50

Tringe Smajli (1880-1917), Freedom Fighter — A161

**2014, Nov. 2 Litho.** ***Perf. 14¼x14***
**263** A161 €1 multi 2.50 2.50

Intl. Year of Crystallography — A162

Various mineral crystals: €1, €2.

**2014, Nov. 20 Litho.** ***Perf. 14x14¼***
**264-265** A162 Set of 2 7.50 7.50

Granting of Intl. Olympic Committee Membership to Kosovo Olympic Committee A163

**2014, Dec. 5 Litho.** ***Perf. 14¼x14***
**266** A163 €2 multi 5.00 5.00

No. 266 was printed in sheets of 6 + 3 labels.

Gjakova — A164

Various street scenes: €1,€2.

**2015, Jan. 23 Litho.** ***Perf. 14¼x14***
**267-268** A164 Set of 2 7.00 7.00

Circular Labyrinth, Smira — A165

**2015, Feb. 12 Litho.** ***Perf. 14¼x14***
**269** A165 €1 multi 2.50 2.50

Lynx A166

Designs: 80c, Lynx in tree. 90c, Head of lynx. €1, Head of lynx, flag and map of Kosovo.

**2015, Mar. 19 Litho.** ***Perf. 14x14¼***
**270-272** A166 Set of 3 *6.00 6.00*

Hashim Hajdini (1949-99), Patriot — A167

**2015, Mar. 27 Litho.** ***Perf. 14¼x14***
**273** A167 €1 multi 2.50 2.50

Waterfall — A168

Designs: 60c, Bridge and rapids. 80c, Rock-strewn river. 90c, Tree near small waterfall.

**2015, Apr. 15 Litho.** ***Perf. 14¼x14***
**274** A168 30c multi .70 .70
**275** A168 60c multi 1.40 1.40
**276** A168 80c multi 1.90 1.90
**277** A168 90c multi 2.00 2.00

Ilaz Kodra (1966-99), Military Leader — A169

**2015, Apr. 30 Litho.** ***Perf. 14¼x14***
**278** A169 €2 multi 4.75 4.75

A170

A171

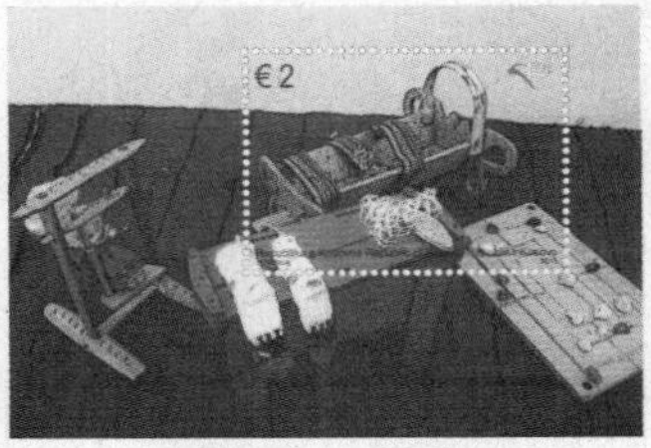


Europa — A172

**2015, May 4 Litho.** ***Perf. 14x14¼***
**279** A170 €1 multi 2.50 2.50
**280** A171 €2 multi 4.75 4.75

**Souvenir Sheet**

**281** A172 €2 multi 4.75 4.75

Ukshin Hoti (1943-99), Philosopher — A173

**2015, June 17**
**282** A173 €1 multi 2.50 2.50

Traditional Clothing — A174

Designs: 80c, Men's clothing. 90c, Women's clothing. €1, Decorated bag. €2, Vest.

**2015, July 1** ***Perf. 14¼x14***
**283-285** A174 Set of 3 6.00 6.00

**Souvenir Sheet**

**286** A174 €2 multi 4.75 4.75

Disapora A175

**2015, Aug. 2 Litho.** ***Perf. 14x14¼***
**287** A175 €2 multi 4.75 4.75

Mark (1926-98), Pren (1964-99), Kole (1967-99), and Meme (1973-99) Lleshi, Patriots — A176

**2015, Aug. 7 Litho.** ***Perf. 14¼x14***
**288** A176 €1 multi 4.75 4.75

Grapes and Wine Making — A177

Designs: 60c, Embroidered grape design. 80c, Grapes, wine bottle and glass. 90c, Vineyard.
€2, Woman harvesting grapes.

**2015, Sept. 18 Litho.** ***Perf. 14¼x14***
**289-291** A177 Set of 3 5.25 5.25

**Souvenir Sheet**

**292** A177 €2 multi 4.75 4.75

Anton Ceta (1920-95), Folklorist, Founder of Reconciliation Committee — A178

**2015, Nov. 3 Litho.** ***Perf. 14x14¼***
**293** A178 €1 multi 2.50 2.50

Archaeological Artifacts — A179

**2015, Dec. 15 Litho.** ***Perf. 14¼x14***
**294** A179 €2 multi 4.75 4.75

Street in Vucitrrn A180

Vojinovic Tower, Vucitrn A181

**2016, Jan. 18 Litho.** ***Perf. 14x14¼***
**295** A180 €1 multi 2.50 2.50
**296** A181 €2.10 multi 4.75 4.75

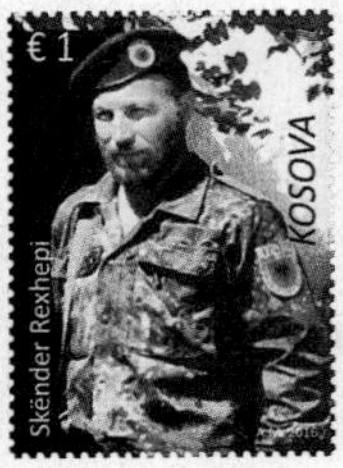


Skender Rexhepi (1965-99), Kosovo Liberation Army Hero — A182

Luan Haradinaj (1973-97), Kosovo Liberation Army Hero — A183

**2016, Feb. 17 Litho. *Perf. 14¼x14***

**297** A182 €1 multi 2.50 2.50
**298** A183 €1 multi 2.50 2.50

Art of Rexhep Ferri — A184

Various paintings.

**2016, Feb. 29 Litho. *Perf. 14¼x14***

**299** Horiz. strip of 3 4.75 4.75
*a.* A184 40c multi .90 .90
*b.* A184 80c multi 1.75 1.75
*c.* A184 90c multi 2.00 2.00

Souvenir Sheet

Mountain Tourism — A185

**2016, Mar. 28 Litho. *Perf. 14x14¼***

**300** A185 €2.10 multi + label 4.75 4.75

See Macedonia No. 704.

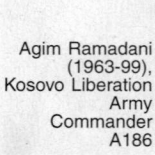

Agim Ramadani (1963-99), Kosovo Liberation Army Commander A186

Sali Cekaj (1956-99), Kosovo Liberation Army Commander A187

**2016, Apr. 9 Litho. *Perf. 14¼x14***

**301** A186 €1 multi 2.25 2.25
**302** A187 €1 multi 2.25 2.25

A188

A189

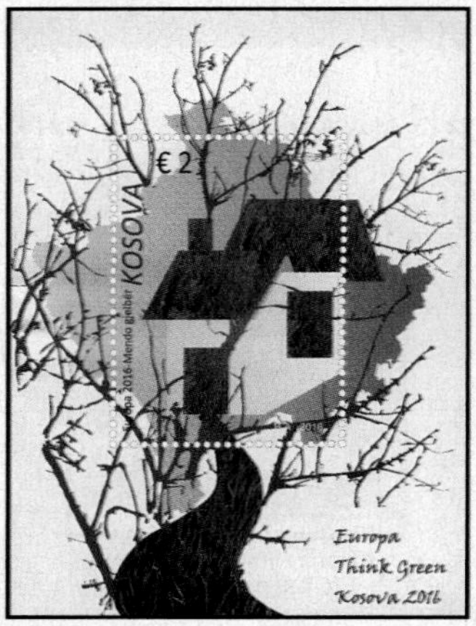


Europa — A190

**2016, May 9 Litho. *Perf. 14x14¼***

**303** A188 €1 multi 2.50 2.50
**304** A189 €2.10 multi 4.75 4.75

**Souvenir Sheet**

***Perf. 14¼x14***

**305** A190 €2 multi 4.75 4.75

Think Green Issue.

2016 European Individual Chess Championships, Gjakova — A191

**2016, May 23 Litho. *Perf. 14x14¼***

**306** A191 €1.80 multi 4.00 4.00

No. 306 was printed in sheets of 2.

Miniature Sheet

Mushrooms — A192

No. 307: a, 60c, Boletus edulis. b, 80c, Morchella vulgaris. c, 90c, Amanita muscaria. d, €1.30, Leccinum scabrum.

**2016, July 4 Litho. *Perf. 14¼x14***

**307** A192 Sheet of 4, #a-d 8.00 8.00

Nos. 307a-307c has incorrect inscriptions.

2016 Summer Olympics, Rio de Janeiro A193

Emblem of the Kosovo Olympic Committee and: €1, Flag of Kosovo. €2.10, Judoka. €2, Stylized sprinter.

**2016, July 29 Litho. *Perf. 14x14¼***

**308-309** A193 Set of 2 7.00 7.00

**Souvenir Sheet**

**310** A193 €2 multi 4.50 4.50

Canonization of St. Teresa of Calcutta — A194

**2016, Aug. 15 Litho. *Perf. 14x14¼***

**311** A194 €2.10 multi 4.75 4.75

Dervish Rozhaja (1934-96), Biologist A195

**2016, Aug. 23 Litho. *Perf. 14x14¼***

**312** A195 €1.30 multi 3.00 3.00

Kosovo's Affiliation With Soccer Organizations — A196

Inscriptions: €1.30, Kosovo in UEFA. €2.10, Kosovo in FIFA.

**2016, Sept. 2 Litho. *Perf. 14x14¼***

**313-314** A196 Set of 2 7.75 7.75

Fruits A197

Designs: 40c, Apples and apple pie. 60c, Pears, juice and cookie. 80c, Blackberries and blackberry jam.

**2016, Sept. 20 Litho. *Perf. 14x14¼***

**315-317** A197 Set of 3 4.00 4.00

Traditional Costumes A198

Designs: 80c, Women's blouse and vest. 90c, Woman wearing costume.
€2, Man and woman in costumes.

**2016, Oct. 15 Litho. *Perf. 14¼x14***

**318-319** A198 Set of 2 3.75 3.75

**Souvenir Sheet**

**320** A198 €2 multi 4.50 4.50

Tetrau Urogallus A199

Bird facing: 90c, Left. €1.30, Right.

**2016, Oct. 28 Litho. *Perf. 14x14¼***

**321-322** A199 Set of 2 5.00 5.00

Dodona Puppet Theater A200

Designs: 80c, Puppet of girl with basket. 90c, Puppets of men on horseback.

**2016, Nov. 12 Litho. *Perf. 14x14¼***

**323-324** A200 Set of 2 3.75 3.75

80th Birthday of Ismail Kadare, Writer A202

**2016, Dec. 20 Litho. *Perf. 14x14¼***

**328** A202 €1 multi 2.10 2.10

Building Ruins — A203

**2016 Litho. *Perf. 14¼x14***

**329** A203 15c multi .35 .35

Compare No. 329 with Nos. 178 and 243A.

Buildings in Ferizaj — A206

Designs: €1.30, Buildings at night. €2, Mosque and buildings in daylight.

**2017, Jan. 20 Litho.** ***Perf. 14¼x14***
**332-333** A206 Set of 2 7.25 7.25

Farm Animals A207

Designs: 20c, Bardoka ewes.
No. 335: a, Red goat. b, Syke ewe and lamb. c, Bardoka ram.

**2017, Feb. 4 Litho.** ***Perf. 14x14¼***
**334** A207 20c multi .45 .45
**335** Horiz. strip of 3 4.00 4.00
*a.* A207 40c multi .85 .85
*b.* A207 50c multi 1.10 1.10
*c.* A207 90c multi 1.90 1.90

Malush Ahmeti (1951-99), Kosovo Liberation Army Commander — A208

Nesimi Dervishdana (1964-81), Independence Demonstrator Shot by Yugoslavian Army — A209

**2017, Feb. 17 Litho.** ***Perf. 14x14¼***
**336** A208 €1.30 multi 2.75 2.75
**337** A209 €1.30 multi 2.75 2.75

Flowers — A210

Designs: 80c, Solenanthus krasniqi. 90c, Aster albanicus. €1, Tulipa luanica.

**2017, Mar. 3 Litho.** ***Perf. 14¼x14***
**338-340** A210 Set of 3 5.75 5.75

Xheladin Gashi (1946-2005), General — A211

**2017, Mar. 21 Litho.** ***Perf. 14x14¼***
**341** A211 €1.30 multi 2.75 2.75

Enver Hadri (1941-90), Assassinated Human Rights Activist — A212

**2017, Apr. 2 Litho.** ***Perf. 14x14¼***
**342** A212 €1.30 multi 3.00 3.00

Ulpiana Baptistry A213

**2017, Apr. 18 Litho.** ***Perf. 14x14¼***
**343** A213 €2 multi 4.50 4.50

Ulpiana Castle A214

Prizren Fortress A215

Novo Brdo Fortress — A216

**2017, May 9 Litho.** ***Perf. 14x14¼***
**344** A214 €1 multi 2.25 2.25
**345** A215 €2 multi 4.50 4.50

**Souvenir Sheet**

**346** A216 €2 multi 4.50 4.50

Europa.

A217

A218

A219

Paintings by Engjell Berisha (1926-2010) A220

**2017, June 6 Litho.** ***Perf. 14¼x14***
**347** Horiz. strip of 4 7.75 7.75
*a.* A217 60c multi 1.40 1.40
*b.* A218 80c multi 1.90 1.90
*c.* A219 90c multi 2.10 2.10
*d.* A220 €1 multi 2.25 2.25

Esat Stavileci (1942-2015), Law Professor — A221

**2017, July 11 Litho.** ***Perf. 14x14¼***
**348** A221 €1.30 multi 3.25 3.25

Diving From the Fshetje Bridge A222

Design: €1.80, Drawing of diver. €2, Photograph of diver, vert.

**2017, July 21 Litho.** ***Perf. 14x14¼***
**349** A222 €1.80 multi 4.25 4.25

**Souvenir Sheet**

***Perf. 14¼x14***

**350** A222 €2 multi 4.75 4.75

Traditional Clothing of Medvegja — A225

Designs: €1, Women's kerchief. No. 354, €2, Beaded vest.
No. 355, €2, Women's shoes.

**2017, Sept. 6 Litho.** ***Perf. 14¼x14***
**353-354** A225 Set of 2 7.00 7.00

**Souvenir Sheet**

**355** A225 €2 multi 4.75 4.75

Protestant Reformation, 500th Anniv. — A227

**2017, Oct. 21 Litho.** ***Perf. 14¼x14***
**357** A227 €1.80 multi 4.25 4.25

# KUWAIT

ku-'wāt

LOCATION — Northwestern coast of the Persian Gulf
GOVT. — Sheikdom
AREA — 7,000 sq. mi.
POP. — 1,991,115 (1999 est.)
CAPITAL — Kuwait

Kuwait was under British protection until June 19, 1961, when it became a fully independent state.

16 Annas = 1 Rupee
100 Naye Paise = 1 Rupee (1957)
1000 Fils = 1 Kuwaiti Dinar (1961)

**Catalogue values for unused stamps in this country are for Never Hinged items, beginning with Scott 72 in the regular postage section, Scott C5 in the air post section, and Scott J1 in the postage due section.**

There was a first or trial setting of the overprint with the word "Koweit." Twenty-four sets of regular and official stamps were printed with this spelling. Value for set, *$50,000.*

**Catalogue values for Nos. 1-71 used, are for postally used examples. Stamps with telegraph cancellations are worth less.**

### Iraqi Postal Administration

Stamps of India, 1911-23, Overprinted

a

b

**1923-24 Wmk. 39 *Perf. 14***

**1** A47(a) ½a green 4.75 *15.00*
*a.* Double overprint 400.00
*b.* Vertical pair, one without overprint *2,100.*
**2** A48(a) 1a dk brn 8.00 *5.50*
*a.* Double overprint 525.00
*b.* Vertical pair, one without overprint *2,100.*
**3** A58(a) 1½a choc 6.75 *13.50*
**4** A49(a) 2a violet 5.75 *9.50*
*a.* 2a reddish purple 14.50
**5** A57(a) 2a6p ultra 4.25 *8.75*
**6** A51(a) 3a brn org 5.00 *26.50*
**7** A51(a) 3a ultra ('24) 12.50 *4.50*
**8** A52(a) 4a ol green 11.50 *27.00*
**9** A53(a) 6a bister 13.00 *16.00*
**10** A54(a) 8a red vio 12.00 *57.50*
**11** A55(a) 12a claret 16.00 *62.50*
**12** A56(b) 1r grn & red brn 50.00 *55.00*
*a.* 1r dp turq grn & org brown 62.00 75.00
**13** A56(b) 2r brn & car rose 67.50 *120.00*
**14** A56(b) 5r vio & ultra 140.00 *275.00*
**15** A56(b) 10r car & grn 275.00 *575.00*
*Nos. 1-15 (15)* 632.00 *1,271.*

Overprint "a" on India No. 102 is generally considered unofficial.

Nos. 1-4, 6-7 exist with inverted overprint. None of these are believed to have been sold at the Kuwait post office.

For overprints see Nos. O1-O13.

### Stamps of India, 1926-35, Overprinted Type "a"

**1929-37 Wmk. 196**

**17** A47 ½a green 6.50 3.00
**18** A71 ½a green ('34) 11.00 2.00
**19** A48 1a dark brown 7.75 4.00
**20** A72 1a dk brown ('34) 16.50 1.25
**21** A60 2a dk violet 9.50 2.00
**22** A60 2a vermilion 27.50 *95.00*
**23** A49 2a ver ('34) 17.50 6.75
*a.* Small die 8.75 3.00
**24** A51 3a ultramarine 6.00 3.50
**25** A51 3a car rose ('34) 9.00 4.50
**26** A61 4a olive green 40.00 *100.00*
**27** A52 4a ol green ('34) 17.50 *14.50*
**28** A53 6a bister ('37) 27.50 *70.00*
**29** A54 8a red violet 10.00 15.00
**30** A55 12a claret 35.00 *50.00*

Overprinted — c

**31** A56 1r grn & brn 27.50 *50.00*
**32** A56 2r orange & carmine 25.00 *72.50*
**33** A56 5r dk vio & ultra ('37) 145.00 *325.00*
**34** A56 10r car & grn ('34) 325.00 *550.00*
**35** A56 15r ol grn & ultra ('37) 1,000. *1,300.*
*Nos. 17-35 (19)* 1,764. *2,669.*

For overprints see Nos. O15-O25.

### Stamps of India, 1937, Overprinted Type "a" (A80, A81) or "c" (A82)

**1939 Wmk. 196 *Perf. 13½x14***

**45** A80 ½a brown 4.25 *3.50*
**46** A80 1a carmine 4.25 *3.50*
**47** A81 2a scarlet 4.50 *5.00*
**48** A81 3a yel green 6.00 3.25
**49** A81 4a dark brown 25.00 *30.00*
**50** A81 6a peacock blue 16.00 *20.00*
**51** A81 8a blue violet 17.50 *35.00*
**52** A81 12a car lake 12.00 *85.00*
**53** A82 1r brown & slate 16.00 *8.75*
*a.* Elongated "T" 650.00 675.00
**54** A82 2r dk brn & dk vio 5.00 *27.50*
*a.* Elongated "T" 650.00 1,125.
**55** A82 5r dp ultra & dk green 12.00 *30.00*
*a.* Elongated "T" 950.00
**56** A82 10r rose car & dk violet 50.00 *100.00*
*a.* Double overprint 500.00 —
*b.* Elongated "T" 1,525.
**57** A82 15r dk grn & dk brn 75.00 *225.00*
*a.* Elongated "T" 3,250.
*Nos. 45-57 (13)* 247.50 *576.50*
Set, never hinged 400.00

The elongated "T" variety was corrected in later printings.

### Indian Postal Administration

From May 24, 1941, until August 1947, the Kuwaiti postal service was administered by India, and during 1941-45 unoverprinted Indian stamps were used in Kuwait.

Kuwait postal services were administered by Pakistan from August 1947 through March 1948. Control was transferred to Great Britain on April 1, 1948.

Stamps of India 1940-43, Overprinted in Black

**1945 Wmk. 196 *Perf. 13½x14***

**59** A83 3p slate 2.75 *10.00*
**60** A83 ½a rose violet 1.75 *5.50*
**61** A83 9p lt green 2.75 *18.50*
**62** A83 1a car rose 2.00 *2.50*
**63** A84 1½a dark purple 2.75 *11.00*
**64** A84 2a scarlet 3.00 *8.50*
**65** A84 3a violet 4.00 *16.00*
**66** A84 3½a ultramarine 3.75 *17.50*
**67** A85 4a chocolate 4.00 *4.75*
**68** A85 6a peacock blue 11.00 22.50
**69** A85 8a blue violet 5.75 15.00
**70** A85 12a car lake 6.00 9.00
**71** A81 14a rose violet 11.00 *24.00*
*Nos. 59-71 (13)* 60.50 *164.75*
Set, never hinged 110.00

**Catalogue values for unused stamps in this section, from this point to the end of the section, are for Never Hinged items.**

### British Postal Administration

See Oman (Muscat) for similar stamps with surcharge of new value only.

Great Britain Nos. 258 to 263, 243 and 248 Surcharged in Black

**1948-49 Wmk. 251 *Perf. 14½x14***

**72** A101 ½a on ½p grn 4.00 *4.25*
**73** A101 1a on 1p ver 4.00 2.50
**74** A101 1½a on 1½p lt red brown 4.50 2.50
**75** A101 2a on 2p lt org 4.00 2.50
**76** A101 2½a on 2½p ultra 4.25 1.25
**77** A101 3a on 3p violet 4.25 1.10
*a.* Pair, one without surcharge *20,000.* —
**78** A102 6a on 6p rose lil 4.25 1.00
**79** A103 1r on 1sh brn 9.00 2.50

Great Britain Nos. 249A, 250 and 251A Surcharged in Black

**Wmk. 259 *Perf. 14***

**80** A104 2r on 2sh6p yel grn 9.50 *9.00*
**81** A104 5r on 5sh dull red 12.50 9.00
**81A** A105 10r on 10sh ultra 62.50 11.50
*Nos. 72-81A (11)* 122.75 47.10

Issued: Nos. 72-81, 4/48; 10r, 7/4/49.
Bars of surcharge at bottom on No. 81A.

### Silver Wedding Issue

Great Britain Nos. 267 and 268 Surcharged in Black

***Perf. 14½x14, 14x14½***

**1948 Wmk. 251**

**82** A109 2½a on 2½p brt ultra 3.00 3.00
**83** A110 15r on £1 deep chalky blue 42.50 42.50

Three bars obliterate the original denomination on No. 83.

### Olympic Games Issue

Great Britain Nos. 271 to 274 Surcharged "KUWAIT" and New Value in Black

**1948 *Perf. 14½x14***

**84** A113 2½a on 2½p brt ultra 1.75 3.25
**85** A114 3a on 3p dp violet 2.00 3.50
**86** A115 6a on 6p red violet 2.10 4.00
**87** A116 1r on 1sh dk brown 2.50 4.50
*Nos. 84-87 (4)* 8.35 15.25

A square of dots obliterates the original denomination on No. 87.

### UPU Issue

Great Britain Nos. 276 to 279 Surcharged "KUWAIT", New Value and Square of Dots in Black

**1949, Oct. 10 Photo.**

**89** A117 2½a on 2½p brt ultra 1.25 *2.50*
**90** A118 3a on 3p brt vio 1.50 *3.00*
**91** A119 6a on 6p red vio 1.60 *3.00*
**92** A120 1r on 1sh brown 1.75 1.75
*Nos. 89-92 (4)* 6.10 10.25

### Great Britain Nos. 280-285 Surcharged Like Nos. 72-79 in Black

**1950-51 Wmk. 251 *Perf. 14½x14***

**93** A101 ½a on ½p lt org 2.75 1.50
**94** A101 1a on 1p ultra 2.75 1.60
**95** A101 1½a on 1½p green 2.75 *2.25*
**96** A101 2a on 2p lt red brown 2.75 1.50
**97** A101 2½a on 2½p ver 2.75 *2.75*
**98** A102 4a on 4p ultra ('50) 2.75 1.50

### Great Britain Nos. 286-288 Surcharged in Black

***Perf. 11x12***
**Wmk. 259**

**99** A121 2r on 2sh6p green 24.00 8.75
**100** A121 5r on 5sh dl red 30.00 10.00
**101** A122 10r on 10sh ultra 50.00 11.00
*Nos. 93-101 (9)* 120.50 40.85

Longer bars, at lower right, on No. 101.
Issued: 4a, 10/2/50; others, 5/3/51.

### Stamps of Great Britain, 1952-54 Surcharged "KUWAIT" and New Value in Black or Dark Blue

**1952-54 Wmk. 298 *Perf. 14½x14***

**102** A126 ½a on ½p red org ('53) .30 *1.25*
**103** A126 1a on 1p ultra ('53) .30 .25
**104** A126 1½a on 1½p green .25 *1.75*
**105** A126 2a on 2p red brn ('53) .35 .25
**106** A127 2½a on 2½p scarlet .40 *1.75*
**107** A127 3a on 3p dk pur (Dk Bl) ('54) .55 .25
**108** A128 4a on 4p ultra ('53) 1.60 1.00
**109** A129 6a on 6p lilac rose ('54) 2.25 .25
**111** A132 12a on 1sh3p dk green ('53) 6.00 2.50
**112** A131 1r on 1sh6p dk blue ('53) 4.75 .25
*Nos. 102-112 (10)* 16.75 9.50

### Coronation Issue

Great Britain Nos. 313-316 Surcharged "KUWAIT" and New Value in Black

**1953, June 3**

**113** A134 2½a on 2½p scarlet 3.75 2.00
**114** A135 4a on 4p brt ultra 3.25 2.00
**115** A136 12a on 1sh3p dk grn 5.00 3.50
**116** A137 1r on 1sh6p dk blue 4.00 1.00
*Nos. 113-116 (4)* 16.00 8.50

Squares of dots obliterate the original denominations on Nos. 115 and 116.

### Great Britain Stamps of 1955-56 Surcharged "KUWAIT" and New Value in Black

**1955 Wmk. 308 Engr. *Perf. 11x12***

**117** A133 2r on 2sh6p dk brown 10.00 3.00
**118** A133 5r on 5sh crimson 11.00 8.00
**119** A133 10r on 10sh dp ultra 12.00 6.00
*Nos. 117-119 (3)* 33.00 17.00

The surcharge on Nos. 117-119 exists in two types.

**1956 Photo. *Perf. 14½x14***

**120** A126 ½a on ½p red org .35 *1.75*
**121** A126 1a on 1p ultra .50 *3.25*
**122** A126 1½a on 1½p green .40 *.75*
**123** A126 2a on 2p red brn .40 *.50*
**124** A127 2½a on 2½p scar .85 *3.75*
**125** A128 4a on 4p ultra 4.75 3.50
**126** A129 6a on 6p lil rose 2.25 .40
**127** A132 12a on 1sh3p dk grn 10.00 8.00
**128** A131 1r on 1sh6p dk bl 12.00 .35
*Nos. 120-128 (9)* 31.50 *22.25*

### Great Britain Nos. 317-325, 328 and 332 Surcharged "KUWAIT" and New Value in Black

**1957-58 Wmk. 308 *Perf. 14½x14***

**129** A129 1np on 5p lt brown .35 *.70*
**130** A126 3np on ½p red org .75 *3.00*
**131** A126 6np on 1p ultra .75 *1.25*
**132** A126 9np on 1½p green .75 *3.25*
**133** A126 12np on 2p red brn .75 *4.25*
**134** A127 15np on 2½p scar, type I .75 *5.50*
*a.* Type II ('58) 50.00 *110.00*
**135** A127 20np on 3p dk pur .80 .45
**136** A128 25np on 4p ultra 2.75 3.25
**137** A129 40np on 6p lilac rose 1.00 .30
**138** A130 50np on 9p dp ol grn 5.75 4.00

| | | | | |
|---|---|---|---|---|
| **139** | A132 | 75np on 1sh3p dk grn | 6.50 | 5.00 |
| | | *Nos. 129-139 (11)* | 20.90 | *30.95* |

The arrangement of the surcharge varies on different values; there are three bars through value on No. 138.

Sheik Abdullah A1

Dhow A2

Oil Derrick A3

Designs: 50np, Pipe lines. 75np, Main square, Kuwait. 2r, Dhow, derrick and Sheik. 5r, Mosque and Sheik. 10r, Oil plant at Burgan and Sheik.

*Perf. 12½*

**1959, Feb. 1 Unwmk. Engr.**

| | | | | |
|---|---|---|---|---|
| **140** | A1 | 5np green | 1.00 | .25 |
| **141** | A1 | 10np rose brown | .70 | .25 |
| **142** | A1 | 15np yellow brown | .45 | .25 |
| **143** | A1 | 20np gray violet | .45 | .25 |
| **144** | A1 | 25np vermilion | .75 | .25 |
| **145** | A1 | 40np rose claret | 4.25 | 1.25 |

*Perf. 13½x13*

| | | | | |
|---|---|---|---|---|
| **146** | A2 | 40np dark blue | .80 | .25 |
| **147** | A2 | 50np carmine | .80 | .25 |
| **148** | A2 | 75np olive green | .85 | .45 |

*Perf. 14x13½*

| | | | | |
|---|---|---|---|---|
| **149** | A3 | 1r claret | 1.50 | .55 |
| **150** | A3 | 2r red brn & dp bl | 3.75 | 1.00 |
| **151** | A3 | 5r green | 7.50 | 2.75 |
| **152** | A3 | 10r purple | 25.00 | 6.50 |
| | | *Nos. 140-152 (13)* | 47.80 | 14.25 |

No. 140-141 and 145 were issued in 1958 for local use. They became valid for international mail on Feb. 1, 1959, but No. 145 was withdrawn after two weeks.

Sheik Abdullah and Flag — A4

**1960, Feb. 25 Engr.** *Perf. 14*

| | | | | |
|---|---|---|---|---|
| **153** | A4 | 40np olive grn & red | .65 | .25 |
| **154** | A4 | 60np blue & red | .95 | .30 |

10th anniv. of the accession of Sheik Sir Abdullah As-Salim As-Sabah.

**Types of 1959, Redrawn**

Designs: 20f, 3d, Mosque and Sheik. 25f, 100f, Vickers Viscount. 30f, 75f, Dhow, derrick and Sheik. 35f, 90f, Shuwaikh secondary school. 45f, 1d, Wara Hill, Burgan oil field.

**1961** *Perf. 12½*

| | | | | |
|---|---|---|---|---|
| **155** | A1 | 1f green | .45 | .25 |
| **156** | A1 | 2f rose brown | .45 | .25 |
| **157** | A1 | 4f yellow brown | .45 | .25 |
| **158** | A1 | 5f gray violet | .50 | .25 |
| **159** | A1 | 8f salmon pink | .50 | .25 |
| **160** | A1 | 15f rose claret | .50 | .25 |

*Perf. 14x13½, 13½ (40f, 250f)*

| | | | | |
|---|---|---|---|---|
| **161** | A3 | 20f green | .55 | .25 |
| **162** | A3 | 25f blue | .75 | .25 |
| **163** | A3 | 30f red brn & dp bl | 1.00 | .25 |
| **164** | A3 | 35f ver & black | 1.10 | .30 |
| **165** | A2 | 40f dark blue | 1.25 | .30 |
| **166** | A3 | 45f violet brown | 1.50 | .30 |
| **167** | A3 | 75f green & sepia | 2.25 | .75 |
| **168** | A3 | 90f ultra & brown | 2.00 | .65 |
| **169** | A3 | 100f rose red | 3.25 | .30 |
| **170** | A2 | 250f olive green | 12.50 | 1.50 |
| **171** | A3 | 1d orange | 22.50 | 5.00 |
| **172** | A3 | 3d brick red | 60.00 | 30.00 |
| | | *Nos. 155-172 (18)* | 111.50 | 41.35 |

Nos. 165 and 170 are 32x22mm.
Issued: 75f, 90f, 4/27; 35f, 5/8; others, 4/1.

Symbols of Telecommunications — A5

*Perf. 11½*

**1962, Jan. 11 Unwmk. Photo.**
**Granite Paper**

| | | | | |
|---|---|---|---|---|
| **173** | A5 | 8f blue & black | .45 | .25 |
| **174** | A5 | 20f rose & black | 1.00 | .55 |

4th Arab Telecommunications Union Conference.

Mubarakiya School and Sheiks Abdullah and Mubarak — A6

**1962, Apr. 15 Unwmk.** *Perf. 11½*

| | | | | |
|---|---|---|---|---|
| **175** | A6 | 8f gldn brn, blk, org & gold | .45 | .25 |
| **176** | A6 | 20f lt blue, blk, org & gold | .90 | .45 |

50th anniversary of Mubarakiya School.

Arab League Building, Cairo, and Emblem — A7

**1962, Apr. 23** *Perf. 13½x13*

| | | | | |
|---|---|---|---|---|
| **177** | A7 | 20f purple | .30 | .25 |
| **178** | A7 | 45f brown | 1.00 | .55 |

Arab Publicity Week, Mar. 22-28.

Flag of Kuwait — A8

**1962, June 19** *Perf. 11½*
**Flag in Green, Black & Red**

| | | | | |
|---|---|---|---|---|
| **179** | A8 | 8f black & tan | .30 | .25 |
| **180** | A8 | 20f black & yellow | .45 | .30 |
| **181** | A8 | 45f black & lt blue | .90 | .45 |
| **182** | A8 | 90f black & lilac | 1.40 | 1.00 |
| | | *Nos. 179-182 (4)* | 3.05 | 2.00 |

Issued for National Day, June 19.

Malaria Eradication Emblem — A9

**1962, Aug. 1** *Perf. 13½x13*

| | | | | |
|---|---|---|---|---|
| **183** | A9 | 4f slate green & yel grn | .30 | .25 |
| **184** | A9 | 25f green & gray | .60 | .30 |

WHO drive to eradicate malaria.

No. 184 has laurel leaves added and inscription rearranged.

Cogwheel, Oil Wells, Camels and Modern Building — A10

*Perf. 11x13*

**1962, Dec. 8 Unwmk. Litho.**

| | | | | |
|---|---|---|---|---|
| **185** | A10 | 8f multicolored | .35 | .25 |
| **186** | A10 | 20f multicolored | .60 | .25 |
| **187** | A10 | 45f multicolored | 1.00 | .50 |
| **188** | A10 | 75f multicolored | 1.75 | 1.00 |
| | | *Nos. 185-188 (4)* | 3.70 | 2.00 |

Bicentenary of the Sabah dynasty.

Mother and Child — A11

**1963, Mar. 21 Photo.** *Perf. 14½x14*

| | | | | |
|---|---|---|---|---|
| **189** | A11 | 8f yel, red, blk & green | .30 | .25 |
| **190** | A11 | 20f blue, red, blk & grn | .40 | .25 |
| **191** | A11 | 45f lt ol, red, blk & grn | .90 | .50 |
| **192** | A11 | 75f gray, red, blk & grn | 1.10 | .60 |
| | | *Nos. 189-192 (4)* | 2.70 | 1.60 |

Issued for Mother's Day, Mar. 21, 1963.

Wheat Emblem, Date Palm, Cow and Sheep — A12

**1963, Mar. 21** *Perf. 14x14½*

| | | | | |
|---|---|---|---|---|
| **193** | A12 | 4f red brn, lt blue & grn | .50 | .25 |
| **194** | A12 | 8f brown, yel & green | .60 | .25 |
| **195** | A12 | 20f red brn, pale vio & green | .90 | .60 |
| **196** | A12 | 45f red brn, rose & green | 1.75 | 1.25 |
| | | *Nos. 193-196 (4)* | 3.75 | 2.35 |

FAO "Freedom from Hunger" campaign.

Test Tube, Oil Drops and Ship — A13

**1963, Apr. 15 Photo.** *Perf. 14½x14*

| | | | | |
|---|---|---|---|---|
| **197** | A13 | 4f brown, yel & blue | .30 | .25 |
| **198** | A13 | 20f green, yel & blue | .45 | .25 |
| **199** | A13 | 45f brt mag, yel & blue | 1.00 | .50 |
| | | *Nos. 197-199 (3)* | 1.75 | 1.00 |

Issued for Education Day.

Sheik Abdullah, Flags and Map of Kuwait A14

**1963, June 19** *Perf. 14x13*
**Flags in Black, Bright Green & Red; Denominations in Black**

| | | | | |
|---|---|---|---|---|
| **200** | A14 | 4f ultramarine | 1.00 | .50 |
| **201** | A14 | 5f ocher | 1.25 | .80 |
| **202** | A14 | 20f bright lilac | 4.50 | 3.00 |
| **203** | A14 | 50f olive | 9.00 | 6.00 |
| | | *Nos. 200-203 (4)* | 15.75 | 10.30 |

Second anniversary of National Day.

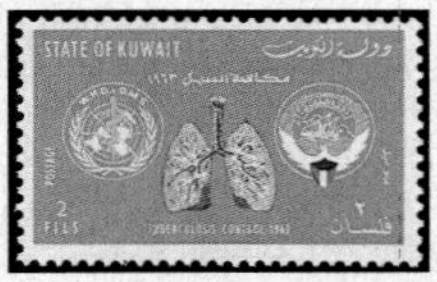


Lungs and Emblems of World Health Organization and Kuwait Tuberculosis Society A15

**1963, July 27** *Perf. 13x13½*
**Design in Yellow, Black, Emerald & Red**

| | | | | |
|---|---|---|---|---|
| **204** | A15 | 2f ocher | .30 | .25 |
| **205** | A15 | 4f dark green | .35 | .25 |
| **206** | A15 | 8f lt violet blue | .50 | .25 |
| **207** | A15 | 20f rose brown | 1.10 | .60 |
| | | *Nos. 204-207 (4)* | 2.25 | 1.35 |

Issued to publicize tuberculosis control.

Sheik Abdullah, Scroll and Scales of Justice — A16

**1963, Oct. 29 Photo.** *Perf. 11x13*
**Center in Gray**

| | | | | |
|---|---|---|---|---|
| **208** | A16 | 4f dp red & red brn | .35 | .25 |
| **209** | A16 | 8f dk green & red brn | .50 | .25 |
| **210** | A16 | 20f vio brn & red brn | .75 | .30 |
| **211** | A16 | 45f brn org & red brn | 1.25 | .65 |
| **212** | A16 | 75f purple & red brown | 1.90 | 1.25 |
| **213** | A16 | 90f ultra & red brown | 2.50 | 1.60 |
| | | *Nos. 208-213 (6)* | 7.25 | 4.30 |

Promulgation of the constitution.

Soccer — A17

Sports: 4f, Basketball. 5f, Swimming, horiz. 8f, Track. 15f, Javelin, horiz. 20f, Pole vault, horiz. 35f, Gymnast on rings, horiz. 45f, Gymnast on parallel bars.

**1963, Nov. 8 Unwmk.** *Perf. 14½x14*

| | | | | |
|---|---|---|---|---|
| **214** | A17 | 1f multicolored | .30 | .25 |
| **215** | A17 | 4f multicolored | .30 | .25 |
| **216** | A17 | 5f multicolored | .30 | .25 |
| **217** | A17 | 8f multicolored | .40 | .25 |
| **218** | A17 | 15f multicolored | .70 | .25 |
| **219** | A17 | 20f multicolored | 1.00 | .30 |
| **220** | A17 | 35f multicolored | 1.75 | .75 |
| **221** | A17 | 45f multicolored | 3.00 | 1.40 |
| | | *Nos. 214-221 (8)* | 7.75 | 3.70 |

Arab School Games of 1963.

UNESCO Emblem, Scales and Globe — A18

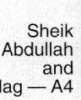

**1963, Dec. 10 Litho.** ***Perf. 13x12½***

| | | | | |
|---|---|---|---|---|
| **222** | A18 | 8f violet, blk & pale grn | .30 | .25 |
| **223** | A18 | 20f gray, black & yel | .60 | .45 |
| **224** | A18 | 25f blue, black & tan | 1.25 | .80 |
| | | *Nos. 222-224 (3)* | 2.15 | 1.50 |

15th anniv. of the Universal Declaration of Human Rights.

Sheik Abdullah — A19

***Perf. 12½x13***

**1964, Feb. 1 Unwmk. Photo.**

**Portrait in Natural Colors**

| | | | | |
|---|---|---|---|---|
| **225** | A19 | 1f gray & silver | .25 | .25 |
| *a.* | | Booklet pane of 6 ('66) | 2.25 | |
| **226** | A19 | 2f brt blue & silver | .25 | .25 |
| **227** | A19 | 4f ocher & silver | .30 | .25 |
| *a.* | | Booklet pane of 6 ('66) | 2.25 | |
| **228** | A19 | 5f fawn & silver | .30 | .25 |
| **229** | A19 | 8f dk brown & sil | .30 | .25 |
| **230** | A19 | 10f citron & sil | .40 | .25 |
| *a.* | | Booklet pane of 6 ('66) | 2.25 | |
| *b.* | | Silver (country name and denomination) omitted | 2,000. | |
| **231** | A19 | 15f brt green & sil | .75 | .25 |
| *a.* | | Booklet pane of 6 ('66) | 6.00 | |
| **232** | A19 | 20f blue gray & sil | .55 | .25 |
| *a.* | | Booklet pane of 6 ('66) | 3.75 | |
| *b.* | | Silver (country name and denomination) omitted | 2,250. | |
| **233** | A19 | 25f green & silver | .65 | .30 |
| **234** | A19 | 30f gray grn & sil | .75 | .30 |
| **235** | A19 | 40f brt vio & sil | 1.10 | .45 |
| **236** | A19 | 45f violet & silver | 1.20 | .55 |
| **237** | A19 | 50f olive & silver | 1.25 | .55 |
| **238** | A19 | 70f red lilac & sil | 1.50 | .65 |
| **239** | A19 | 75f rose red & sil | 2.00 | .75 |
| **240** | A19 | 90f ultra & silver | 3.00 | .75 |
| **241** | A19 | 100f pale lilac & sil | 3.50 | .65 |

***Perf. 14x14½***

**Size: 25x30mm**

| | | | | |
|---|---|---|---|---|
| **242** | A19 | 250f brown & sil | 10.00 | 2.75 |
| **243** | A19 | 1d brown vio & sil | 35.00 | 10.00 |
| | | *Nos. 225-243 (19)* | 63.05 | 19.70 |

Ramses II Battling the Hittites (from Abu Simbel) — A20

**Engr. & Litho.**

**1964, Mar. 8** ***Perf. 13x12½***

| | | | | |
|---|---|---|---|---|
| **244** | A20 | 8f buff, ind & maroon | .30 | .25 |
| **245** | A20 | 20f lt blue, indigo & vio | .75 | .55 |
| **246** | A20 | 30f bluish grn, ind & vio | 1.10 | .65 |
| | | *Nos. 244-246 (3)* | 2.15 | 1.45 |

UNESCO world campaign to save historic monuments in Nubia.

Mother and Child — A21

**1964, Mar. 21 Litho.** ***Perf. 14x13***

| | | | | |
|---|---|---|---|---|
| **247** | A21 | 8f green, gray & vio blk | .30 | .25 |
| **248** | A21 | 20f green, red & vio blk | .45 | .25 |
| **249** | A21 | 30f grn, ol bis & vio blk | .60 | .40 |
| **250** | A21 | 45f grn, saph & vio blk | .75 | .60 |
| | | *Nos. 247-250 (4)* | 2.10 | 1.50 |

Issued for Mother's Day, Mar. 21.

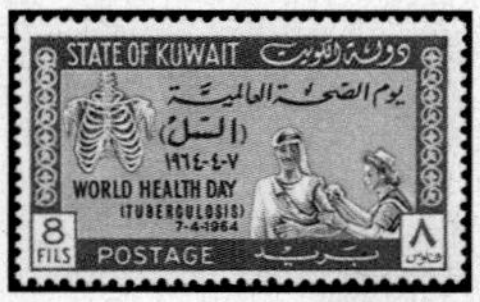


Nurse Giving TB Test, and Thorax A22

***Perf. 13x13½***

**1964, Apr. 7 Photo. Unwmk.**

| | | | | |
|---|---|---|---|---|
| **251** | A22 | 8f brown & green | .50 | .25 |
| **252** | A22 | 20f green & rose red | 1.40 | .35 |

Issued for World Health Day (fight against tuberculosis), Apr. 7, 1964.

Microscope and Dhow — A23

**1964, Apr. 15** ***Perf. 12½x13***

| | | | | |
|---|---|---|---|---|
| **253** | A23 | 8f multicolored | .25 | .25 |
| **254** | A23 | 15f multicolored | .30 | .25 |
| **255** | A23 | 20f multicolored | .50 | .30 |
| **256** | A23 | 30f multicolored | .75 | .60 |
| | | *Nos. 253-256 (4)* | 1.80 | 1.40 |

Issued for Education Day.

Doves and State Seal — A24

**1964, June 19 Litho.** ***Perf. 13½***

**Seal in Blue, Brown, Black, Red & Green**

| | | | | |
|---|---|---|---|---|
| **257** | A24 | 8f black & bister brn | .35 | .25 |
| **258** | A24 | 20f black & green | .55 | .30 |
| **259** | A24 | 30f black & gray | 1.10 | .50 |
| **260** | A24 | 45f black & blue | 1.25 | .75 |
| | | *Nos. 257-260 (4)* | 3.25 | 1.80 |

Third anniversary of National Day.

Arab Postal Union Emblem — A25

**1964, Nov. 21 Photo.** ***Perf. 11x11½***

| | | | | |
|---|---|---|---|---|
| **261** | A25 | 8f lt blue & brown | .35 | .25 |
| **262** | A25 | 20f yellow & ultra | .70 | .25 |
| **263** | A25 | 45f olive & brown | 1.25 | .70 |
| | | *Nos. 261-263 (3)* | 2.30 | 1.20 |

Permanent Office of the APU, 10th anniv.

Conference Emblem A26

**1965, Feb. 8 Litho.** ***Perf. 14***

| | | | | |
|---|---|---|---|---|
| **264** | A26 | 8f black, org brn & yel | .45 | .25 |
| **265** | A26 | 20f multicolored | .75 | .30 |

First Arab Journalists' Conference.

Oil Derrick, Dhow, Sun and Doves — A27

**1965, Feb. 25** ***Perf. 13½***

| | | | | |
|---|---|---|---|---|
| **266** | A27 | 10f lt green & multi | .35 | .25 |
| **267** | A27 | 15f pink & multi | .75 | .25 |
| **268** | A27 | 20f gray & multi | 1.10 | .45 |
| | | *Nos. 266-268 (3)* | 2.20 | .95 |

Fourth anniversary of National Day.

Mother and Children — A28

**1965, Mar. 21 Unwmk.** ***Perf. 13½***

| | | | | |
|---|---|---|---|---|
| **269** | A28 | 8f multicolored | .35 | .25 |
| **270** | A28 | 15f multicolored | .50 | .35 |
| **271** | A28 | 20f multicolored | .75 | .60 |
| | | *Nos. 269-271 (3)* | 1.60 | 1.20 |

Mother's Day, Mar. 21.

Weather Balloon A29

**1965, Mar. 23 Photo.** ***Perf. 11½x11***

| | | | | |
|---|---|---|---|---|
| **272** | A29 | 4f deep ultra & yellow | .55 | .25 |
| **273** | A29 | 5f blue & dp orange | .65 | .25 |
| **274** | A29 | 20f dk blue & emerald | 1.25 | 1.00 |
| | | *Nos. 272-274 (3)* | 2.45 | 1.50 |

Fifth World Meteorological Day.

Census Chart, Map and Family A30

**1965, Mar. 28 Litho.** ***Perf. 13½***

| | | | | |
|---|---|---|---|---|
| **275** | A30 | 8f multicolored | .30 | .25 |
| **276** | A30 | 20f multicolored | .75 | .25 |
| **277** | A30 | 50f multicolored | 1.90 | .85 |
| | | *Nos. 275-277 (3)* | 2.95 | 1.35 |

Issued to publicize the 1965 census.

ICY Emblem A31

**1965, Mar. 7 Engr.**

| | | | | |
|---|---|---|---|---|
| **278** | A31 | 8f red & black | .30 | .25 |
| **279** | A31 | 20f lt ultra & black | .65 | .30 |
| **280** | A31 | 30f emerald & black | 1.25 | .55 |
| | | *Nos. 278-280 (3)* | 2.20 | 1.10 |

International Cooperation Year.

Dagger in Map of Palestine — A31a

***Perf. 11x11½***

**1965, Apr. 9 Photo. Unwmk.**

| | | | | |
|---|---|---|---|---|
| **281** | A31a | 4f red & ultra | *2.25* | .35 |
| **282** | A31a | 45f red & emerald | *4.75* | 1.00 |

Deir Yassin massacre, Apr. 9, 1948. See Iraq Nos. 372-373 and Jordan No. 499.

Tower of Shuwaikh School and Atom Symbol A32

**1965, Apr. 15 Litho.** ***Perf. 14x13***

| | | | | |
|---|---|---|---|---|
| **283** | A32 | 4f multicolored | .30 | .25 |
| **284** | A32 | 20f multicolored | .65 | .40 |
| **285** | A32 | 45f multicolored | 1.25 | 1.00 |
| | | *Nos. 283-285 (3)* | 2.20 | 1.65 |

Issued for Education Day.

ITU Emblem, Old and New Communication Equipment — A33

**1965, May 17** ***Perf. 13½x14***

| | | | | |
|---|---|---|---|---|
| **286** | A33 | 8f dk blue, lt bl & red | .40 | .30 |
| **287** | A33 | 20f green, lt grn & red | 1.50 | .40 |
| **288** | A33 | 45f red, pink & blue | 2.75 | 1.25 |
| | | *Nos. 286-288 (3)* | 4.65 | 1.95 |

ITU, centenary.

Library Aflame and Lamp A33a

**1965, June 7 Photo.** ***Perf. 11***

| | | | | |
|---|---|---|---|---|
| **289** | A33a | 8f black, green & red | .70 | .25 |
| **290** | A33a | 15f black, red & green | 1.40 | .45 |

Burning of Library of Algiers, June 7, 1962.

Falcon — A34

**1965, Dec. 1 Engr.** ***Perf. 13***

**Center in Sepia**

| | | | | |
|---|---|---|---|---|
| **291** | A34 | 8f red lilac | 2.25 | .30 |
| **292** | A34 | 15f olive green | 2.00 | .30 |
| **293** | A34 | 20f dark blue | 3.00 | .55 |
| **294** | A34 | 25f orange | 3.25 | .70 |
| **295** | A34 | 30f emerald | 4.00 | .80 |
| **296** | A34 | 45f blue | 8.00 | 1.25 |
| **297** | A34 | 50f claret | 9.00 | 1.40 |
| **298** | A34 | 90f carmine | 16.00 | 2.75 |
| | | *Nos. 291-298 (8)* | 47.50 | 8.05 |

Book and Wreath Emblem — A35

**1966, Jan. 10 Photo.** ***Perf. 14x15***

| | | | | |
|---|---|---|---|---|
| **299** | A35 | 8f lt violet & multi | .35 | .25 |
| **300** | A35 | 20f brown red & multi | .70 | .40 |
| **301** | A35 | 30f blue & multi | 1.25 | .65 |
| | | *Nos. 299-301 (3)* | 2.30 | 1.30 |

Issued for Education Day.

Sheik Sabah as-Salim as-Sabah — A36

**1966, Feb. 1 Photo.** ***Perf. 14x13***

| | | | | |
|---|---|---|---|---|
| **302** | A36 | 4f lt blue & multi | .30 | .25 |
| **303** | A36 | 5f pale rose & multi | .30 | .25 |
| **304** | A36 | 20f multicolored | .50 | .25 |
| **305** | A36 | 30f lt violet & multi | .75 | .35 |

**306** A36 40f salmon & multi .90 .50
**307** A36 45f lt gray & multi 1.00 .60
**308** A36 70f yellow & multi 2.00 1.00
**309** A36 90f pale green & multi 3.00 1.50
*Nos. 302-309 (8)* 8.75 4.70

Wheat and Fish — A37

**1966, Feb. 15** ***Perf. 11x11½***
**310** A37 20f multicolored 2.25 .90
**311** A37 45f multicolored 3.50 1.60

"Freedom from Hunger" campaign.

Eagle, Banner, Scales and Emblems — A38

**1966, Feb. 25 Litho.** ***Perf. 12½x13***
**312** A38 20f tan & multi 1.25 .40
**313** A38 25f lt green & multi 1.25 .55
**314** A38 45f gray & multi 3.00 1.25
*Nos. 312-314 (3)* 5.50 2.20

Fifth anniversary of National Day.

Wheel of Industry and Map of Arab Countries A39

**1966, Mar. 1** ***Perf. 14x13½***
**315** A39 20f brt blue, brt grn & blk .75 .25
**316** A39 50f lt red brn, brt grn & black 1.25 .75

Issued to publicize the conference on industrial development in Arab countries.

Mother and Children — A40

**1966, Mar. 21** ***Perf. 11½x11***
**317** A40 20f pink & multi .75 .25
**318** A40 45f multicolored 1.60 .75

Mother's Day, Mar. 21.

Medical Conference Emblem — A41

**1966, Apr. 1 Photo.** ***Perf. 14½x14***
**319** A41 15f blue & red .60 .75
**320** A41 30f red & blue 1.20 .75

Fifth Arab Medical Conference, Kuwait.

Composite View of a City — A42

**1966, Apr. 7 Litho.** ***Perf. 12½x13***
**321** A42 8f multicolored .75 .25
**322** A42 10f multicolored 1.25 .30

Issued for World Health Day, Apr. 7.

Inauguration of WHO Headquarters, Geneva — A43

**1966, May 3 Litho.** ***Perf. 11x11½***
**323** A43 5f dull sal, ol grn & vio bl .70 .25
**324** A43 10f lt grn, ol grn & vio blue 1.40 .25

Traffic Signal at Night — A44

**1966, May 4**
**325** A44 10f green, red & black 1.00 .25
**326** A44 20f green, red & black 1.25 .40

Issued for Traffic Day.

"Blood Transfusion" — A45

**1966, May 5** ***Perf. 13½***
**327** A45 4f multicolored .70 .25
**328** A45 8f multicolored 1.10 .50

Blood Bank Day, May 5.

Sheik Ahmad and Ship Carrying First Crude Oil Shipment A46

**1966, June 30** ***Perf. 13½***
**329** A46 20f multicolored 1.25 .55
**330** A46 45f multicolored 2.50 1.10

20th anniv. of the first crude oil shipment, June 30, 1946.

Ministry of Guidance and Information — A47

**1966, July 25 Photo.** ***Perf. 11½x11***
**331** A47 4f rose & brown .25 .25
**332** A47 5f yel brn & brt grn .30 .25
**333** A47 8f brt green & purple .45 .25
**334** A47 20f salmon & ultra .85 .30
*Nos. 331-334 (4)* 1.85 1.05

Opening of Ministry of Guidance and Information Building.

Fishing Boat, Lobster, Fish, Crab and FAO Emblem A48

**1966, Oct. 10 Litho.** ***Perf. 13½***
**335** A48 4f buff & multi .80 .25
**336** A48 20f lt lilac & multi 2.10 .95

Fisheries' Conference of Near East Countries under the sponsorship of the FAO, Oct. 1966.

United Nations Flag — A49

**1966, Oct. 24** ***Perf. 13x14***
**337** A49 20f blue, dk blue & pink 1.00 .30
**338** A49 45f blue, dk bl & pale grn 2.25 1.25

Issued for United Nations Day.

UNESCO Emblem — A50

**1966, Nov. 4 Litho.** ***Perf. 12½x13***
**339** A50 20f multicolored 1.00 .30
**340** A50 45f multicolored 2.25 1.10

20th anniversary of UNESCO.

Kuwait University Emblem — A51

**1966, Nov. 27 Photo.** ***Perf. 14½***
**Emblem in Yellow, Bright Blue, Green and Gold**
**341** A51 8f lt ultra, vio & gold .35 .25
**342** A51 10f red, brown & gold .45 .25
**343** A51 20f lt yel grn, slate & gold 1.00 .30
**344** A51 45f buff, green & gold 2.00 1.25
*Nos. 341-344 (4)* 3.80 2.05

Opening of Kuwait University.

Jabir al-Ahmad al-Jabir and Sheik Sabah A52

**1966, Dec. 11** ***Perf. 14x13***
**345** A52 8f yel green & multi .40 .25
**346** A52 20f yellow & multi .80 .30
**347** A52 45f pink & multi 1.90 1.10
*Nos. 345-347 (3)* 3.10 1.65

Appointment of the heir apparent, Jabir al-Ahmad al-Jabir.

Scout Badge and Square Knot — A52a

**1966, Dec. 21 Litho.** ***Perf. 14x13***
**347A** A52a 4f lt ol green & fawn 1.40 .45
**347B** A52a 20f yel brn & blue grn 3.75 1.50

Kuwait Boy Scouts, 30th anniversary.

"Symbols of Science and Peace" — A53

**1967, Jan. 15 Litho.** ***Perf. 13x14***
**348** A53 10f multicolored .40 .25
**349** A53 45f multicolored 1.20 .55

Issued for Education Day.

Fertilizer Plant — A54

**1967, Feb. 19 Unwmk.** ***Perf. 13***
**350** A54 8f lt blue & multi .55 .25
**351** A54 20f cream & multi 1.40 .45

Opening of Chemical Fertilizer Plant.

Sun, Dove and Olive Branch — A55

**1967, Feb. 25 Litho.** ***Perf. 13***
**352** A55 8f salmon & multi .50 .25
**353** A55 20f yellow & multi 1.10 .45

Sixth anniversary of National Day.

Map of Arab States and Municipal Building A56

**1967, Mar. 11** ***Perf. 14½x13***
**354** A56 20f gray & multi 1.50 .55
**355** A56 30f lt brown & multi 2.75 1.40

1st conf. of the Arab Cities Org., Kuwait.

Family — A57

**1967, Mar. 21 Litho. *Perf. 13x13½***
**356** A57 20f pale rose & multi 1.50 .55
**357** A57 45f pale green & multi 2.75 1.40

Issued for Family Day, Mar. 21.

Arab League Emblem — A58

**1967, Mar. 27 *Perf. 13x14***
**358** A58 8f gray & dk blue .45 .25
**359** A58 10f bister & green .85 .25

Issued for Arab Publicity Week.

Sabah Hospital and Physicians at Work — A59

**1967, Apr. 7 *Perf. 14x13***
**360** A59 8f dull rose & multi 1.20 .25
**361** A59 20f gray & multi 1.60 .55

Issued for World Health Day.

Two Heads of Ramses II — A60

**1967, Apr. 17 *Perf. 13½***
**362** A60 15f citron, green & brn .90 .30
**363** A60 20f chalky blue, grn & pur 1.60 .55

Arab Week to Save the Nubian Monuments.

Traffic Policeman A61

**1967, May 4 Litho. *Perf. 14x13***
**364** A61 8f lt green & multi 1.00 .35
**365** A61 20f rose lilac & multi 2.25 .75

Issued for Traffic Day.

ITY Emblem — A62

**1967, June 4 Photo. *Perf. 13***
**366** A62 20f Prus blue, lt bl & blk 1.00 .30
**367** A62 45f rose lilac, lt bl & blk 2.00 1.10

International Tourist Year.

Arab League Emblem and Hands Reaching for Knowledge — A63

**1967, Sept. 8 Litho. *Perf. 13x14***
**368** A63 8f blue & multi 1.25 .25
**369** A63 20f dull rose & multi 2.25 .65

Issued to publicize the literacy campaign.

Map of Palestine and UN Emblem — A64

**1967, Oct. 24 Litho. *Perf. 13***
**370** A64 20f blue & pink 2.25 .30
**371** A64 45f orange & pink 3.25 1.00

Issued for United Nations Day.

Factory and Cogwheels — A65

**1967, Nov. 25 Photo. *Perf. 13***
**372** A65 20f crimson & yellow 1.00 .30
**373** A65 45f gray & yellow 2.00 1.25

3rd Conf. of Arab Labor Ministers, Kuwait.

Flag and Open Book — A66

**1968, Jan. 15 Litho. *Perf. 14***
**374** A66 20f brt blue & multi .65 .30
**375** A66 45f yel orange & multi 2.00 1.10

Issued for Education Day.

Map of Kuwait and Oil Derrick — A67

**1968, Feb. 23 Litho. *Perf. 12***
**376** A67 10f multicolored 1.00 .35
**377** A67 20f multicolored 2.25 1.10

30th anniv. of the discovery of oil in the Greater Burgan Field.

Sheik Sabah and Sun — A68

**1968, Feb. 25 Litho. *Perf. 14x15***
**378** A68 8f red lilac & multi .45 .25
**379** A68 10f lt blue & multi .50 .25
**380** A68 15f violet & multi .60 .25
**381** A68 20f vermilion & multi .80 .35
*Nos. 378-381 (4)* 2.35 1.10

Seventh anniversary of National Day.

Open Book and Emblem — A69

**1968, Mar. 2 *Perf. 14***
**382** A69 8f yellow & multi .40 .25
**383** A69 20f lilac rose & multi .90 .25
**384** A69 45f orange & multi 1.75 1.10
*Nos. 382-384 (3)* 3.05 1.60

Issued for Teachers' Day.

Family Picnic A70

**1968, Mar. 21 *Perf. 13½x13***
**385** A70 8f blue & multi .30 .25
**386** A70 10f red & multi .45 .25
**387** A70 15f lilac & multi .50 .25
**388** A70 20f dk brown & multi .90 .25
*Nos. 385-388 (4)* 2.15 1.00

Issued for Family Day.

Sheik Sabah, Arms of WHO and Kuwait — A71

**1968, Apr. 7 Photo. *Perf. 12***
**389** A71 20f brt lilac & multi .95 .55
**390** A71 45f multicolored 2.25 1.30

20th anniv. of WHO.

Dagger in Map of Palestine — A72

**1968, Apr. 9 Litho. *Perf. 14***
**391** A72 20f lt blue & vermilion 3.00 .60
**392** A72 45f lilac & vermilion 5.25 1.25

Deir Yassin massacre, 20th anniv.

Street Crossing A74

**1968, May 4 Photo. *Perf. 14x14½***
**395** A74 10f dk brown & multi 1.00 .50
**396** A74 15f brt violet & multi 1.50 .70
**397** A74 20f green & multi 2.60 .90
*Nos. 395-397 (3)* 5.10 2.10

Issued for Traffic Day.

Map of Palestine and Torch — A75

**1968, May 15 Litho. *Perf. 13½x12½***
**398** A75 10f lt ultra & multi 1.10 .45
**399** A75 20f yellow & multi 2.75 .55
**400** A75 45f aqua & multi 4.75 1.75
*Nos. 398-400 (3)* 8.60 2.75

Issued for Palestine Day.

Palestinian Refugees — A76

**1968, June 5 Litho. *Perf. 13x13½***
**401** A76 20f pink & multi .55 .25
**402** A76 30f ultra & multi .90 .45
**403** A76 45f green & multi 1.50 .55
**404** A76 90f lilac & multi 3.00 1.60
*Nos. 401-404 (4)* 5.95 2.85

International Human Rights Year.

Museum of Kuwait — A77

***Perf. 12½***
**1968, Aug. 25 Unwmk. Engr.**
**405** A77 1f dk brown & brt grn .30 .25
**406** A77 2f dp claret & grn .30 .25
**407** A77 5f black & orange .30 .25
**408** A77 8f dk brown & grn .30 .25
**409** A77 10f Prus blue & cl .45 .25
**410** A77 20f org brown & blue .75 .25
**411** A77 25f dk blue & orange .85 .25
**412** A77 30f Prus blue & yel grn 1.10 .30
**413** A77 45f plum & vio black 1.75 .60
**414** A77 50f green & carmine 2.00 1.00
*Nos. 405-414 (10)* 8.10 3.65

Man Reading Book, Arab League, UN and UNESCO Emblems A78

**1968, Sept. 8 Litho. *Perf. 12½x13***
**415** A78 15f blue gray & multi .40 .25
**416** A78 20f pink & multi 1.10 .30

Issued for International Literacy Day.

Map of Palestine on UN Building and Children with Tent — A79

**1968, Oct. 25 Litho. *Perf. 13***
**417** A79 20f multicolored .50 .25
**418** A79 30f gray & multi .75 .45
**419** A79 45f salmon pink & multi 1.10 .55
*Nos. 417-419 (3)* 2.35 1.25

Issued for United Nations Day.

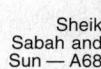

Kuwait Chamber of Commerce A80

**1968, Nov. 6 Litho.** ***Perf. 13½x12½***

| | | | | |
|---|---|---|---|---|
| **420** | A80 | 10f dp orange & dk brn | .40 | .25 |
| **421** | A80 | 15f rose claret & vio bl | .45 | .25 |
| **422** | A80 | 20f brown org & dk green | .65 | .45 |
| | | *Nos. 420-422 (3)* | 1.50 | .95 |

Opening of the Kuwait Chamber of Commerce Building.

Conference Emblem — A81

**1968, Nov. 10 Litho.** ***Perf. 13***

**Emblem in Ocher, Blue, Red and Black**

| | | | | |
|---|---|---|---|---|
| **423** | A81 | 10f dk brown & blue | .50 | .25 |
| **424** | A81 | 15f dk brown & orange | .60 | .25 |
| **425** | A81 | 20f dk brown & vio blue | .75 | .45 |
| **426** | A81 | 30f dk brown & org brn | 1.00 | .55 |
| | | *Nos. 423-426 (4)* | 2.85 | 1.50 |

14th Conference of the Arab Chambers of Commerce, Industry and Agriculture.

Shuaiba Refinery — A82

**1968, Nov. 18** ***Perf. 13½***

**Emblem in Red, Black and Blue**

| | | | | |
|---|---|---|---|---|
| **427** | A82 | 10f black & lt blue grn | .65 | .25 |
| **428** | A82 | 20f black & gray | 1.10 | .40 |
| **429** | A82 | 30f black & salmon | 1.25 | .60 |
| **430** | A82 | 45f black & emerald | 2.10 | 1.10 |
| | | *Nos. 427-430 (4)* | 5.10 | 2.35 |

Opening of Shuaiba Refinery.

Koran, Scales and People A83

**1968, Dec. 19 Photo.** ***Perf. 14x14½***

| | | | | |
|---|---|---|---|---|
| **431** | A83 | 8f multicolored | .45 | .25 |
| **432** | A83 | 20f multicolored | 1.00 | .60 |
| **433** | A83 | 30f multicolored | 1.60 | .85 |
| **434** | A83 | 45f multicolored | 1.90 | 1.25 |
| | | *Nos. 431-434 (4)* | 4.95 | 2.95 |

The 1400th anniversary of the Koran.

Boeing 707 — A84

**1969, Jan. 1 Litho.** ***Perf. 13½x14***

| | | | | |
|---|---|---|---|---|
| **435** | A84 | 10f brt yellow & multi | .75 | .25 |
| **436** | A84 | 20f green & multi | 1.00 | .50 |
| **437** | A84 | 25f multicolored | 1.50 | .75 |
| **438** | A84 | 45f lilac & multi | 2.75 | 1.00 |
| | | *Nos. 435-438 (4)* | 6.00 | 2.50 |

Introduction of Boeing 707 service by Kuwait Airways.

Globe, Retort and Triangle — A85

**1969, Jan. 15** ***Perf. 13***

| | | | | |
|---|---|---|---|---|
| **439** | A85 | 15f gray & multi | .80 | .30 |
| **440** | A85 | 20f multicolored | .90 | .60 |

Issued for Education Day.

Kuwait Hilton Hotel — A86

**1969, Feb. 15 Litho.** ***Perf. 14x12½***

| | | | | |
|---|---|---|---|---|
| **441** | A86 | 10f brt blue & multi | .45 | .25 |
| **442** | A86 | 20f pink & multi | .95 | .30 |

Opening of the Kuwait Hilton Hotel.

Teachers' Society Emblem, Father and Children — A87

**1969, Feb. 15** ***Perf. 13***

| | | | | |
|---|---|---|---|---|
| **443** | A87 | 10f violet & multi | .45 | .25 |
| **444** | A87 | 20f rose & multi | .95 | .40 |

Issued for Education week.

Wreath, Flags and Dove — A88

**1969, Feb. 25 Photo.** ***Perf. 14½x14***

| | | | | |
|---|---|---|---|---|
| **445** | A88 | 15f lilac & multi | .40 | .25 |
| **446** | A88 | 20f blue & multi | .60 | .30 |
| **447** | A88 | 30f ocher & multi | .90 | .55 |
| | | *Nos. 445-447 (3)* | 1.90 | 1.10 |

Eighth anniversary of National Day.

Emblem, Teacher and Students — A89

**1969, Mar. 8 Litho.** ***Perf. 13x12½***

| | | | | |
|---|---|---|---|---|
| **448** | A89 | 10f multicolored | .45 | .25 |
| **449** | A89 | 20f deep red & multi | .75 | .55 |

Issued for Teachers' Day.

Family A90

**1969, Mar. 21** ***Perf. 13½***

| | | | | |
|---|---|---|---|---|
| **450** | A90 | 10f dark blue & multi | .55 | .25 |
| **451** | A90 | 20f deep car & multi | 1.10 | .30 |

Issued for Family Day.

Avicenna, WHO Emblem, Patient and Microscope — A91

**1969, Apr. 7 Litho.** ***Perf. 13½***

| | | | | |
|---|---|---|---|---|
| **452** | A91 | 15f red brown & multi | 1.00 | .25 |
| **453** | A91 | 20f lt green & multi | 1.75 | .30 |

Issued for World Health Day, Apr. 7.

Motorized Traffic Police A92

**1969, May 4 Litho.** ***Perf. 12½x13***

| | | | | |
|---|---|---|---|---|
| **454** | A92 | 10f multicolored | 1.40 | .25 |
| **455** | A92 | 20f multicolored | 3.00 | .60 |

Issued for Traffic Day.

ILO Emblem A93

**1969, June 1** ***Perf. 11½***

| | | | | |
|---|---|---|---|---|
| **456** | A93 | 10f red, black & gold | .45 | .25 |
| **457** | A93 | 20f lt blue grn, blk & gold | .95 | .30 |

50th anniv. of the ILO.

S.S. Al Sabahiah A94

**1969, June 10 Litho.** ***Perf. 13½***

| | | | | |
|---|---|---|---|---|
| **458** | A94 | 20f multicolored | 1.10 | .55 |
| **459** | A94 | 45f multicolored | 2.75 | 1.50 |

4th anniversary of Kuwait Shipping Co.

UNESCO Emblem, Woman, Globe and Book — A95

**1969, Sept. 8 Litho.** ***Perf. 13½***

| | | | | |
|---|---|---|---|---|
| **460** | A95 | 10f blue & multi | .45 | .25 |
| **461** | A95 | 20f rose red & multi | .90 | .45 |

International Literacy Day, Sept. 8.

Sheik Sabah — A96

**1969-74 Litho.** ***Perf. 14***

| | | | | |
|---|---|---|---|---|
| **462** | A96 | 8f lt blue & multi | .40 | .25 |
| **463** | A96 | 10f pink & multi | .45 | .25 |
| **464** | A96 | 15f gray & multi | .50 | .25 |
| **465** | A96 | 20f yellow & multi | .55 | .25 |
| **466** | A96 | 25f violet & multi | .75 | .30 |
| **467** | A96 | 30f sal & multi | 1.00 | .35 |
| **468** | A96 | 45f tan & multi | 1.50 | .50 |
| **469** | A96 | 50f yel grn & multi | 1.60 | .50 |
| **470** | A96 | 70f multicolored | 1.90 | .75 |
| **471** | A96 | 75f ultra & multi | 2.50 | .90 |
| **472** | A96 | 90f pale rose & multi | 2.50 | 1.00 |
| *a.* | | 90f brownish rose & multi | 2.50 | 1.00 |
| **473** | A96 | 250f lilac & multi | 7.50 | 2.75 |
| **473A** | A96 | 500f gray green & multi | 17.50 | 10.00 |
| **473B** | A96 | 1d lilac rose & multi | 30.00 | 16.00 |
| | | *Nos. 462-473B (14)* | 68.65 | 34.05 |

Issued: Nos. 473A-473B, 1/12/74; others 10/5/69.

UN Emblem and Scroll — A97

**1969, Oct. 24 Litho.** ***Perf. 13***

| | | | | |
|---|---|---|---|---|
| **474** | A97 | 10f emer & multi | .50 | .25 |
| **475** | A97 | 20f bister & multi | 1.00 | .25 |
| **476** | A97 | 45f rose red & multi | 2.50 | .90 |
| | | *Nos. 474-476 (3)* | 4.00 | 1.40 |

Issued for United Nations Day.

Radar, Satellite Earth Station, Kuwait A98

Design: 45f, Globe and radar, vert.

**1969, Dec. 15 Photo.** ***Perf. 14½***

| | | | | |
|---|---|---|---|---|
| **477** | A98 | 20f silver & multi | 1.25 | .30 |
| **478** | A98 | 45f silver & multi | 2.75 | 1.10 |

Inauguration of the Kuwait Earth Station for Satellite Communications.

Globe with Science Symbols, and Education Year Emblem — A99

**1970, Jan. 15 Photo.** ***Perf. 13½x13***

| | | | | |
|---|---|---|---|---|
| **479** | A99 | 20f brt lilac & multi | .75 | .30 |
| **480** | A99 | 45f blue & multi | 1.50 | .95 |

International Education Year.

Shoue A100

Old Kuwaiti Vessels: 10f, Sambook. 15f, Baghla. 20f, Batteel. 25f, Boom. 45f, Bakkara. 50f, Shipbuilding.

**1970, Feb. 1** *Perf. 14½x14*
**481** A100 8f multicolored .55 .30
**482** A100 10f multicolored .60 .40
**483** A100 15f multicolored 1.00 .50
**484** A100 20f multicolored 1.50 .65
**485** A100 25f multicolored 1.75 .75
**486** A100 45f multicolored 2.75 1.40
**487** A100 50f multicolored 3.25 1.60
*Nos. 481-487 (7)* 11.40 5.60

Refugee Father and Children — A101

**1970** **Photo.** *Perf. 14x12½*
**488** A101 20f red brown & multi 2.00 .65
**489** A101 45f olive & multi 4.00 2.00

Issued for Universal Palestinian Refugees Week, Dec. 16-22, 1969.

Kuwait Flag, Emblem and Sheik Sabah — A102

**1970, Feb. 25** *Perf. 13½x13*
**490** A102 15f silver & multi .85 .25
**491** A102 20f gold & multi 1.10 .25

Ninth anniversary of National Day.

Dome of the Rock, Jerusalem, and Boy Commando — A103

Designs: 20f, Dome and man commando. 45f, Dome and woman commando.

**1970, Mar. 4** **Litho.** *Perf. 13*
**492** A103 10f pale violet & multi 1.40 .85
**493** A103 20f lt blue & multi 2.75 1.75
**494** A103 45f multicolored 5.75 3.75
*Nos. 492-494 (3)* 9.90 6.35

Honoring Palestinian commandos.

Parents and Children A104

**1970, Mar. 21** *Perf. 14*
**495** A104 20f multicolored .55 .25
**496** A104 30f pink & multi .95 .35

Issued for Family Day.

Map of Arab League Countries, Flag and Emblem A104a

**1970, Mar. 22** *Perf. 11½x11*
**497** A104a 20f lt blue, grn & lt brn .70 .25
**498** A104a 45f sal, grn & dk pur 1.25 .60

25th anniversary of the Arab League.

Census Graph and Kuwait Arms A105

**1970, Apr. 1** **Litho.** *Perf. 13½x13*
**499** A105 15f dull orange & multi .45 .25
**500** A105 20f yellow & multi .50 .35
**501** A105 30f pink & multi .75 .40
*Nos. 499-501 (3)* 1.70 1.00

Issued to publicize the 1970 census.

"Fight Cancer," Kuwait Arms, WHO Emblem — A106

**1970, Apr. 7** *Perf. 13½x13*
**502** A106 20f blue, vio bl & rose lil 1.10 .50
**503** A106 30f dl yel, vio bl & lil rose 1.40 .70

World Health Organization Day, Apr. 7, and to publicize the fight against cancer.

Traffic Signs A107

**1970, May 4** **Photo.** *Perf. 13½*
**504** A107 20f multicolored 1.50 .65
**505** A107 30f multicolored 2.10 1.10

Issued for Traffic Day.

Red Crescent A108

**1970, May 8** **Litho.** *Perf. 12½x13½*
**506** A108 10f yellow & multi .50 .25
**507** A108 15f emerald & multi 1.10 .45
**508** A108 30f tan & multi 2.25 .75
*Nos. 506-508 (3)* 3.85 1.45

Intl. Red Crescent and Red Cross Day.

Opening of UPU Headquarters, Bern — A109

**1970, May 25** **Photo.** *Perf. 12x11½*
**509** A109 20f multicolored .95 .30
**510** A109 30f multicolored 1.40 .75

Sheik Sabah A110

**1970, June 15** **Photo.** *Perf. 14*
**511** A110 20f silver & multi 1.50 .50
**512** A110 45f gold & multi 3.00 1.00
*a.* Miniature sheet of 2 8.50 5.00

Nos. 511-512 have circular perforation around vignette set within a white square of paper, perforated on 4 sides. No. 512a contains 2 imperf. stamps similar to Nos. 511-512.

UN Emblem, Symbols of Peace, Progress, Justice — A111

**1970, July 1** **Litho.** *Perf. 13½x12½*
**513** A111 20f lt green & multi .55 .25
**514** A111 45f multicolored 1.10 .50

25th anniversary of the United Nations.

Tanker Loading Crude Oil from Sea Island A112

**1970, Aug. 1** *Perf. 13½x13*
**515** A112 20f multicolored 1.75 .50
**516** A112 45f multicolored 3.25 1.10

Issued to publicize the artificial "Sea Island" loading facilities in Kuwait.

"Writing," Kuwait and UN Emblems A113

**1970, Sept. 8** **Photo.** *Perf. 13½*
**517** A113 10f brt blue & multi 1.10 .25
**518** A113 15f brt green & multi 1.30 .50

International Literacy Day, Sept. 8.

National Guard and Emblem A114

**1970, Oct. 20** **Photo.** *Perf. 13x13½*
**519** A114 10f gold & multi 1.00 .25
**520** A114 20f silver & multi 1.60 .50

First National Guard graduation.

Flag of Kuwait, Symbols of Development A115

**1971, Feb. 25** **Litho.** *Perf. 12*
**521** A115 20f gray & multi 1.10 .40
**522** A115 30f multicolored 1.60 .55

Tenth anniversary of National Day.

Charles H. Best, Frederick G. Banting A116

**1971, Apr. 7** **Litho.** *Perf. 14*
**523** A116 20f multicolored 1.40 .25
**524** A116 45f multicolored 3.00 .75

World Health Day; discoverers of insulin.

Globe with Map of Palestine A117

**1971, May 3** **Litho.** *Perf. 12½x13*
**525** A117 20f yel green & multi 2.00 1.10
**526** A117 45f lilac & multi 3.75 2.25

International Palestine Week.

ITU Emblem and Waves A118

**1971, May 17** **Photo.** *Perf. 13x13½*
**527** A118 20f silver, dk red & blk 1.10 .30
**528** A118 45f gold, dk red & blk 2.40 .85

3rd World Telecommunications Day.

Men of 3 Races — A119

**1971, June 5** **Litho.** *Perf. 11½x11*
**529** A119 15f red brown & multi .75 .30
**530** A119 30f ultra & multi 1.25 .60

Intl. Year against Racial Discrimination.

Arab Postal Union Emblem A120

**1971, Aug. 30** *Perf. 13x12½*
**531** A120 20f brown & multi .90 .30
**532** A120 45f blue & multi 1.60 .70

25th anniv. of the Conf. of Sofar, Lebanon, establishing the Arab Postal Union.

Symbols of Learning, UNESCO and Kuwait Emblems A121

**1971, Sept. 8** *Perf. 12*
**533** A121 25f dull yellow & multi .90 .25
**534** A121 60f lt blue & multi 2.10 1.00

International Literacy Day, Sept. 8.

Soccer A122

Design: 30f, Soccer, different.

**1971, Dec. 10** *Perf. 13*
**535** A122 20f green & multi 1.75 .55
**536** A122 30f ultra & multi 2.40 .95

Regional Sports Tournament, Kuwait, Dec.

UNICEF Emblem and Arms of Kuwait — A123

**Litho. & Engr.**

**1971, Dec. 11** *Perf. 11x11½*
**537** A123 25f gold & multi .60 .30
**538** A123 60f silver & multi 1.50 .75

25th anniv. of UNICEF.

Book Year Emblem A124

**1972, Jan. 2** **Litho.** *Perf. 14x13*
**539** A124 20f black & buff .70 .45
**540** A124 45f black & lt blue grn 1.60 .95

International Book Year.

Kuwait Emblem with 11 Rays, Olive Branch A125

**1972, Feb. 25** **Litho.** *Perf. 13x13½*
**541** A125 20f pink, gold & multi 1.10 .30
**542** A125 45f lt blue, gold & multi 1.90 1.00

11th anniversary of National Day.

Telecommunications Center — A126

**1972, Feb. 28** *Perf. 13½*
**543** A126 20f lt blue & multi 1.40 .50
**544** A126 45f multicolored 3.75 1.40

Opening of Kuwait Telecommunications Center.

"Your Heart is your Health" — A127

**1972, Apr. 7** **Photo.** *Perf. 14½x14*
**545** A127 20f red & multi 1.75 .60
**546** A127 45f red & multi 4.50 1.40

World Health Day.

Nurse and Child — A128

**1972, May 8** **Litho.** *Perf. 12½x13*
**547** A128 8f vio bl, red & emer 1.00 .30
**548** A128 40f pink & multi 4.00 1.25

Red Cross and Red Crescent Day.

Soccer, Olympic Emblems — A129

**1972, Sept. 2** **Litho.** *Perf. 14½*
**549** A129 2f shown .35 .25
**550** A129 4f Running .35 .25
**551** A129 5f Swimming .40 .25
**552** A129 8f Gymnastics .45 .25
**553** A129 10f Discus .70 .30
**554** A129 15f Equestrian 1.00 .35
**555** A129 20f Basketball 1.10 .40
**556** A129 25f Volleyball 1.25 .55
*Nos. 549-556 (8)* 5.60 2.60

20th Olympic Games, Munich, 8/26-9/11.

FAO Emblem, Vegetables, Fish and Ship — A130

**1972, Sept. 9** **Litho.** *Perf. 14x13½*
**557** A130 5f blue & multi .50 .40
**558** A130 10f emerald & multi 1.50 1.10
**559** A130 20f orange & multi 3.00 2.25
*Nos. 557-559 (3)* 5.00 3.75

11th FAO Regional Conference in the Near East, Kuwait, Sept.

National Bank Emblem A131

**1972, Nov. 15** **Photo.** *Perf. 13x14*
**560** A131 10f green & multi .50 .25
**561** A131 35f dull red & multi 1.75 .90

20th anniversary of Kuwait National Bank.

Capitals A132

Relics of Failaka: 5f, View of excavations. 10f, Acanthus leaf capital. 15f, Excavations.

**1972, Dec. 4** **Litho.** *Perf. 12*
**562** A132 2f lilac rose & multi .30 .25
**563** A132 5f bister & multi .40 .25
**564** A132 10f lt blue & multi 1.25 .30
**565** A132 15f green & multi 1.75 .40
*Nos. 562-565 (4)* 3.70 1.20

Flower and Kuwait Emblem — A133

**1973, Feb. 25** **Litho.** *Perf. 13½x13*
**566** A133 10f lt olive & multi .45 .25
**567** A133 20f multicolored .90 .40
**568** A133 30f yellow & multi 1.40 .85
*Nos. 566-568 (3)* 2.75 1.50

12th anniversary of National Day.

INTERPOL Emblem A134

**1973, June 3** **Litho.** *Perf. 12*
**569** A134 10f emerald & multi 1.00 .75
**570** A134 15f red orange & multi 1.75 1.00
**571** A134 20f blue & multi 2.75 1.25
*Nos. 569-571 (3)* 5.50 3.00

50th anniv. of Intl. Criminal Police Org. (INTERPOL).

I.C.M.S. Emblem and Flag of Kuwait — A135

**1973, June 24** *Perf. 13*
**572** A135 30f gray & multi 1.10 .55
**573** A135 40f brown & multi 1.75 .75

Intl. Council of Military Sports, 25th anniv.

Kuwait Airways Building — A136

**1973, July 1** **Litho.** *Perf. 12½x14*
**574** A136 10f lt green & multi .65 .25
**575** A136 15f lilac & multi .85 .30
**576** A136 20f lt ultra & multi 1.00 .50
*Nos. 574-576 (3)* 2.50 1.05

Opening of Kuwait Airways Corporation Building.

Weather Map of Suez Canal and Persian Gulf Region — A137

**1973, Sept. 4** **Photo.** *Perf. 14*
**577** A137 5f red & multi .65 .25
**578** A137 10f green & multi .90 .30
**579** A137 15f multicolored 1.25 .60
*Nos. 577-579 (3)* 2.80 1.15

Intl. meteorological cooperation, cent.

Sheiks Ahmad and Sabah — A138

**1973, Nov. 12** **Photo.** *Perf. 14*
**580** A138 10f lt green & multi .60 .25
**581** A138 20f yel orange & multi 1.25 .40
**582** A138 70f lt blue & multi 3.75 1.50
*Nos. 580-582 (3)* 5.60 2.15

Stamps overprinted "Kuwait," 50th anniv.

Mourning Dove, Eurasian Hoopoe, Rock Dove, Stone Curlew — A139

Designs: Birds and traps.

**1973, Dec. 1** **Litho.** *Perf. 14*

**Size (single stamp): 32x32mm**

**583** A139 Block of 4 5.50 5.50
*a.* 5f Mourning dove .70 .25
*b.* 5f Eurasian hoopoe .70 .25
*c.* 5f Rock dove .70 .25
*d.* 5f Stone curlew .70 .25
**584** A139 Block of 4 7.25 7.25
*a.* 8f Great gray shrike .90 .35
*b.* 8f Red-backed shrike .90 .35
*c.* 8f Rufous-backed shrike .90 .35
*d.* 8f Black-naped oriole .90 .35
**585** A139 Block of 4 8.00 8.00
*a.* 10f Willow warbler 1.00 .45
*b.* 10f Great reed warbler 1.00 .45
*c.* 10f Blackcap 1.00 .45
*d.* 10f Common (barn) swallow 1.00 .45
**586** A139 Block of 4 11.50 11.50
*a.* 15f Common rock thrush 1.50 1.50
*b.* 15f European redstart 1.50 1.50
*c.* 15f Wheatear 1.50 1.50
*d.* 15f Bluethroat 1.50 1.50
**587** A139 Block of 4 13.50 13.50
*a.* 20f Houbara bustard 1.60 1.60
*b.* 20f Pin-tailed sandgrouse 1.60 1.60
*c.* 20f Ypecaha wood rail 1.60 1.60
*d.* 20f Spotted crake 1.60 1.60

**Size (single stamp): 35x35mm**

**588** A139 Block of 4 17.50 17.50
*a.* 25f American sparrow hawk 2.00 2.00
*b.* 25f Great black-backed gull 2.00 2.00
*c.* 25f Purple heron 2.00 2.00
*d.* 25f Wryneck 2.00 2.00

**589** A139 Block of 4 25.00 25.00
*a.* 30f European bee-eater 3.00 3.00
*b.* 30f Goshawk 3.00 3.00
*c.* 30f Gray wagtail 3.00 3.00
*d.* 30f Pied wagtail 3.00 3.00
**590** A139 Block of 4 32.50 32.50
*a.* 45f Crossbows 4.25 4.25
*b.* 45f Tent-shaped net 4.25 4.25
*c.* 45f Hand net 4.25 4.25
*d.* 45f Rooftop trap 4.25 4.25
*Nos. 583-590 (8)* 120.75 120.75

Human Rights Flame — A141

**1973, Dec. 10 Litho. *Perf. 12***
**594** A141 10f red & multi .60 .25
**595** A141 40f lt green & multi 1.50 .55
**596** A141 75f lilac & multi 2.75 1.50
*Nos. 594-596 (3)* 4.85 2.30

25th anniv. of the Universal Declaration of Human Rights.

Promoting Animal Resources A142

**1974, Feb. 16 Litho. *Perf. 12½***
**597** A142 30f violet blue & multi .95 .40
**598** A142 40f rose & multi 1.20 .90

4th Congress of the Arab Veterinary Union, Kuwait.

Stylized Wheat and Kuwaiti Flag — A143

**1974, Feb. 25 *Perf. 13½x13***
**599** A143 20f lemon & multi .45 .25
**600** A143 30f bister brn & multi .85 .40
**601** A143 70f silver & multi 1.75 .90
*Nos. 599-601 (3)* 3.05 1.55

13th anniversary of National Day.

Conference Emblem and Sheik Sabah — A144

**1974, Mar. 8 *Perf. 12½***
**602** A144 30f multicolored 1.90 .55
**603** A144 40f yellow & multi 3.00 1.10

12th Conf. of the Arab Medical Union and 1st Conf. of the Kuwait Medical Soc.

Tournament Emblem — A145

**1974, Mar. 15**
**604** A145 25f multicolored 1.25 .50
**605** A145 45f multicolored 2.25 1.10

Third Soccer Tournament for the Arabian Gulf Trophy, Kuwait, Mar. 1974.

Scientific Research Institute — A146

**1974, Apr. 3 Photo. *Perf. 12½***
**606** A146 15f magenta & multi 1.50 .45
**607** A146 20f green & multi 2.00 .65

Opening of Kuwait Scientific Research Institute.

Arab Postal Union, Kuwait and UPU Emblems A147

**1974, May 1 *Perf. 13x14***
**608** A147 20f gold & multi .60 .25
**609** A147 30f gold & multi .75 .45
**610** A147 60f gold & multi 1.40 .80
*Nos. 608-610 (3)* 2.75 1.50

Centenary of Universal Postal Union.

Telephone Dial with Communications Symbols and Globe — A148

**1974, May 17 *Perf. 14x13½***
**611** A148 10f blue & multi .70 .25
**612** A148 30f multicolored 1.60 .60
**613** A148 40f black & multi 2.25 .80
*Nos. 611-613 (3)* 4.55 1.65

World Telecommunications Day, May 17.

Emblem of Unity Council and Flags of Member States — A149

**1974, June 25 Litho. *Perf. 13½***
**614** A149 20f red, black & green .85 .45
**615** A149 30f green, black & red .90 .65

17th anniversary of the signing of the Arab Economic Unity Agreement.

WPY Emblem, Embryo, "Growth" — A150

**1974, Aug. 19 Litho. *Perf. 14x14½***
**616** A150 30f black & multi 1.00 .40
**617** A150 70f violet blue & multi 2.25 1.50

World Population Year.

Development Building and Emblem — A151

**1974, Oct. 30 Litho. *Perf. 13x13½***
**618** A151 10f pink & multi .70 .25
**619** A151 20f ultra & multi 1.10 .45

Kuwait Fund for Arab Economic Development.

Emblem of Shuaiba Industrial Area — A152

**1974, Dec. 17 Litho. *Perf. 12½x12***
**620** A152 10f lt blue & multi .60 .25
**621** A152 20f salmon & multi 1.50 .45
**622** A152 30f lt green & multi 2.00 .95
*Nos. 620-622 (3)* 4.10 1.65

Shuaiba Industrial Area, 10th anniversary.

Arms of Kuwait and "14" — A153

**1975, Feb. 25 Litho. *Perf. 13x13½***
**623** A153 20f multicolored .50 .30
**624** A153 70f yel green & multi 1.50 .85
**625** A153 75f rose & multi 2.50 1.00
*Nos. 623-625 (3)* 4.50 2.15

14th anniversary of National Day.

Male and Female Symbols — A154

**1975, Apr. 14 Photo. *Perf. 11½x12***
**626** A154 8f lt green & multi .35 .25
**627** A154 20f rose & multi .40 .25
**628** A154 30f blue & multi .65 .45
**629** A154 70f yellow & multi 1.75 1.10
**630** A154 100f black & multi 3.00 1.40
*Nos. 626-630 (5)* 6.15 3.45

Kuwaiti census 1975.

IWY and Kuwaiti Women's Union Emblems — A155

**1975, June 10 Litho. *Perf. 14½***
**631** A155 15f brown org & multi .90 .25
**632** A155 20f olive & multi 1.10 .40
**633** A155 30f violet & multi 1.60 .65
*Nos. 631-633 (3)* 3.60 1.30

International Women's Year.

Classroom and UNESCO Emblem A156

**1975, Sept. 8 Litho. *Perf. 12½x12***
**634** A156 20f green & multi .80 .25
**635** A156 30f multicolored 1.40 .65

International Literacy Day.

Symbols of Measurements A157

**1975, Oct. 14 Photo. *Perf. 14x13***
**636** A157 10f green & multi .70 .25
**637** A157 20f purple & multi 1.00 .45

World Standards Day.

UN Flag, Rifle and Olive Branch — A158

**1975, Oct. 24 Litho. *Perf. 12x12½***
**638** A158 20f multicolored .60 .25
**639** A158 45f orange & multi 1.40 .75

United Nations, 30th anniversary.

Sheik Sabah — A159

**1975, Dec. 22 Litho. *Perf. 12½x12***
**640** A159 8f yellow & multi .95 .25
**641** A159 20f lilac & multi 1.25 .40
**642** A159 30f buff & multi 1.50 .50
**643** A159 50f salmon & multi 2.25 .75
**644** A159 90f lt blue & multi 4.00 1.25
**645** A159 100f multicolored 5.00 1.50
*Nos. 640-645 (6)* 14.95 4.65

"Progress" — A160

**1976, Feb. 25 Litho. *Perf. 12***

| | | | | |
|---|---|---|---|---|
| 646 | A160 10f multicolored | .70 | .25 |
| 647 | A160 20f multicolored | 1.25 | .30 |

15th anniversary of National Day.

Medical Equipment, Emblem and Surgery — A161

**1976, Mar. 1 Litho. *Perf. 14½***

| | | | |
|---|---|---|---|
| 648 | A161 5f dull green & multi | .40 | .25 |
| 649 | A161 10f blue & multi | 1.20 | .45 |
| 650 | A161 30f gray & multi | 3.00 | 1.50 |
| | *Nos. 648-650 (3)* | 4.60 | 2.20 |

Kuwait Medical Assoc., 2nd annual conference.

Telephones, 1876 and 1976 — A162

**1976, Mar. 10 Litho. *Perf. 12***

| | | | |
|---|---|---|---|
| 651 | A162 5f orange & black | .50 | .25 |
| 652 | A162 15f lt blue & black | 1.10 | .30 |

Centenary of first telephone call by Alexander Graham Bell, Mar. 10, 1876.

Human Eye — A163

**Photo. & Engr.**

**1976, Apr. 7 *Perf. 11½***

| | | | |
|---|---|---|---|
| 653 | A163 10f multicolored | .70 | .25 |
| 654 | A163 20f black & multi | 1.10 | .30 |
| 655 | A163 30f multicolored | 1.40 | .85 |
| | *Nos. 653-655 (3)* | 3.20 | 1.40 |

World Health Day: "Foresight prevents blindness."

Red Crescent Emblem A164

**1976, May 8 Litho. *Perf. 12x11½***

| | | | |
|---|---|---|---|
| 656 | A164 20f brt green, blk & red | .50 | .30 |
| 657 | A164 30f vio blue, blk & red | .90 | .55 |
| 658 | A164 45f yellow, blk & red | 1.50 | .85 |
| 659 | A164 75f lilac rose, blk & red | 3.25 | 2.00 |
| | *Nos. 656-659 (4)* | 6.15 | 3.70 |

Kuwait Red Crescent Society, 10th anniv.

Modern Suburb of Kuwait A165

**1976, June 1 Photo. *Perf. 13x13½***

| | | | |
|---|---|---|---|
| 660 | A165 10f light green & multi | .65 | .25 |
| 661 | A165 20f salmon & multi | 1.10 | .30 |

Habitat, UN Conference on Human Settlements, Vancouver, Canada, May 31-June 11.

Basketball, Kuwait Olympic Emblem — A166

Designs: 8f, Running. 10f, Judo. 15f, Fieldball. 20f, Gymnastics. 30f, Water polo. 45f, Soccer. 70f, Swimmers at start.

**1976, July 17 Litho. *Perf. 14½***

| | | | |
|---|---|---|---|
| 662 | A166 4f black & multi | .30 | .25 |
| 663 | A166 8f red & multi | .30 | .25 |
| 664 | A166 10f green & multi | .35 | .25 |
| 665 | A166 15f lemon & multi | .45 | .25 |
| 666 | A166 20f blue & multi | .55 | .30 |
| 667 | A166 30f lilac & multi | .90 | .55 |
| 668 | A166 45f multicolored | 1.25 | .75 |
| 669 | A166 70f brown & multi | 1.75 | 1.10 |
| | *Nos. 662-669 (8)* | 5.85 | 3.70 |

21st Olympic Games, Montreal, Canada, July 17-Aug. 1.

Various Races, Map of Sri Lanka — A167

**1976, Aug. 16 Photo. *Perf. 14***

| | | | |
|---|---|---|---|
| 670 | A167 20f dk blue & multi | .50 | .25 |
| 671 | A167 30f purple & multi | .70 | .45 |
| 672 | A167 45f green & multi | 1.10 | .65 |
| | *Nos. 670-672 (3)* | 2.30 | 1.35 |

5th Summit Conf. of Non-aligned Countries, Colombo, Sri Lanka, Aug. 9-19.

"UNESCO," Torch and Kuwait Arms — A168

**1976, Nov. 4 Litho. *Perf. 12x11½***

| | | | |
|---|---|---|---|
| 673 | A168 20f yel green & multi | .65 | .25 |
| 674 | A168 45f scarlet & multi | 1.50 | .60 |

30th anniversary of UNESCO.

Blindman's Buff A169

Popular games. 5f, 15f, 30f, vertical.

***Perf. 14½x14, 14x14½***

**1977, Jan. 10 Litho.**

| | | | |
|---|---|---|---|
| 675 | A169 5f Pot throwing | .35 | .25 |
| 676 | A169 5f Kite flying | .35 | .25 |
| 677 | A169 5f Balancing sticks | .35 | .25 |
| 678 | A169 5f Spinning tops | .35 | .25 |
| *a.* | Block of 4, #675-678 | 2.00 | 2.00 |
| 679 | A169 10f shown | .65 | .25 |
| 680 | A169 10f Rowing | .65 | .25 |
| 681 | A169 10f Hoops | .65 | .25 |
| 682 | A169 10f Ropes | .65 | .25 |
| *a.* | Block of 4, #679-682 | 3.00 | 3.00 |
| 683 | A169 15f Rope skipping | 1.10 | .35 |
| 684 | A169 15f Marbles | 1.10 | .35 |
| 685 | A169 15f Cart steering | 1.10 | .35 |
| 686 | A169 15f Teetotum | 1.10 | .25 |
| *a.* | Block of 4, #683-686 | 5.00 | 5.00 |
| 687 | A169 20f Halma | 1.25 | .55 |
| 688 | A169 20f Model boats | 1.25 | .55 |
| 689 | A169 20f Pot and candle | 1.25 | .55 |
| 690 | A169 20f Hide and seek | 1.25 | .55 |
| *a.* | Block of 4, #687-690 | 6.00 | 6.00 |
| 691 | A169 30f Throwing bones | 1.50 | .75 |
| 692 | A169 30f Mystery gifts | 1.50 | .75 |
| 693 | A169 30f Hopscotch | 1.50 | .75 |
| 694 | A169 30f Catch as catch can | 1.50 | .75 |
| *a.* | Block of 4, #691-694 | 7.00 | 7.00 |
| 695 | A169 40f Bowls | 2.75 | 1.00 |
| 696 | A169 40f Sword fighting | 2.75 | 1.00 |
| 697 | A169 40f Mother and child | 2.75 | 1.00 |
| 698 | A169 40f Fivestones | 2.75 | 1.00 |
| *a.* | Block of 4, #695-698 | 12.00 | 12.00 |
| 699 | A169 60f Hiding a cake | 3.50 | 1.75 |
| 700 | A169 60f Chess | 3.50 | 1.75 |
| 701 | A169 60f Dancing | 3.50 | 1.75 |
| 702 | A169 60f Treasure hunt | 3.50 | 1.75 |
| *a.* | Block of 4, #699-702 | 16.00 | 16.00 |
| 703 | A169 70f Hobby-horses | 4.25 | 1.90 |
| 704 | A169 70f Hide and seek | 4.25 | 1.90 |
| 705 | A169 70f Catch | 4.25 | 1.90 |
| 706 | A169 70f Storytelling | 4.25 | 1.90 |
| *a.* | Block of 4, #703-706 | 19.00 | 19.00 |
| | *Nos. 675-706 (32)* | 61.40 | 27.10 |

Diseased Knee — A170

**1977, Feb. 15 *Perf. 13x13½***

| | | | |
|---|---|---|---|
| 707 | A170 20f yellow & multi | .75 | .25 |
| 708 | A170 30f multicolored | 1.25 | .45 |
| 709 | A170 45f red & multi | 1.50 | .70 |
| 710 | A170 75f black & multi | 2.50 | 1.25 |
| | *Nos. 707-710 (4)* | 6.00 | 2.65 |

World Rheumatism Year.

Sheik Sabah A171

**1977, Feb. 25 Photo. *Perf. 13½x13***

| | | | |
|---|---|---|---|
| 711 | A171 10f multicolored | .50 | .25 |
| 712 | A171 15f multicolored | .65 | .30 |
| 713 | A171 30f multicolored | 1.25 | .55 |
| 714 | A171 80f multicolored | 1.50 | 1.10 |
| | *Nos. 711-714 (4)* | 3.90 | 2.20 |

16th National Day.

Kuwait Tower — A172

**1977, Feb. 26 *Perf. 14x13½***

| | | | |
|---|---|---|---|
| 715 | A172 30f multicolored | .85 | .25 |
| 716 | A172 80f multicolored | 2.25 | 1.10 |

Inauguration of Kuwait Tower.

APU Emblem — A173

**1977, Apr. 12 Litho. *Perf. 13½x14***

| | | | |
|---|---|---|---|
| 717 | A173 5f yellow & multi | .35 | .25 |
| 718 | A173 15f pink & multi | .40 | .25 |
| 719 | A173 30f lt blue & multi | .80 | .30 |
| 720 | A173 80f lilac & multi | 1.90 | .90 |
| | *Nos. 717-720 (4)* | 3.45 | 1.70 |

Arab Postal Union, 25th anniversary.

Electronic Tree — A174

**1977, May 17 Litho. *Perf. 12x12½***

| | | | |
|---|---|---|---|
| 721 | A174 30f brown & red | 1.00 | .40 |
| 722 | A174 80f green & red | 2.10 | 1.50 |

World Telecommunications Day.

Sheik Sabah — A175

**1977, June 1 Photo. *Perf. 11½x12***

| | | | |
|---|---|---|---|
| 723 | A175 15f blue & multi | 1.25 | 1.10 |
| 724 | A175 25f yellow & multi | 2.00 | 1.10 |
| 725 | A175 30f red & multi | 2.50 | 1.60 |
| 726 | A175 80f violet & multi | 6.75 | 2.75 |
| 727 | A175 100f dp org & multi | 8.00 | 3.50 |
| 728 | A175 150f ultra & multi | 12.00 | 6.00 |
| 729 | A175 200f olive & multi | 16.00 | 9.00 |
| | *Nos. 723-729 (7)* | 48.50 | 25.05 |

Games Emblem — A176

**1977, Oct. 1 Litho. *Perf. 12***

| | | | |
|---|---|---|---|
| 730 | A176 30f multicolored | .90 | .50 |
| 731 | A176 80f multicolored | 1.90 | 1.10 |

4th Asian Basketball Youth Championship, Oct. 1-15.

Dome of the Rock, Bishop Capucci, Fatima Bernawi, Sheik Abu Tair — A177

**1977, Nov. 1** *Perf. 14*

| | | | |
|---|---|---|---|
| **732** A177 30f multicolored | 2.50 | 1.25 |
| **733** A177 80f multicolored | 5.75 | 3.00 |

Struggle for the liberation of Palestine.

Children and Houses A178

Children's Paintings: No. 735, Women musicians. No. 736, Boats. No. 737, Women preparing food, vert. No. 738, Women and children, vert. No. 739, Seated woman, vert.

**1977, Nov. Photo.** *Perf. 13½x13*

| | | |
|---|---|---|
| **734** A178 15f lt green & multi | .40 | .30 |
| **735** A178 15f yellow & multi | .40 | .30 |
| **736** A178 30f brt yellow & multi | .85 | .60 |
| **737** A178 30f lt violet & multi | .85 | .60 |
| **738** A178 80f black & multi | 2.00 | 1.60 |
| **739** A178 80f rose & multi | 2.00 | 1.60 |
| *Nos. 734-739 (6)* | 6.50 | 5.00 |

Dentist Treating Patient A179

**1977, Dec. 3**

| | | |
|---|---|---|
| **740** A179 30f green & multi | 1.40 | .75 |
| **741** A179 80f violet & multi | 2.60 | 1.40 |

10th Arab Dental Union Congress, Kuwait, Dec. 3-6.

Ships Unloading Water A180

Kuwait water resources. 30f, 80f, 100f, vert.

*Perf. 14x13½, 13½x14*

**1978, Jan. 25** **Litho.**

| | | |
|---|---|---|
| **742** Block of 4 | 1.50 | 1.50 |
| *a.* 5f shown | .30 | .25 |
| *b.* 5f Home delivery by camel | .30 | .25 |
| *c.* 5f Man with water bags | .30 | .25 |
| *d.* 5f Man with wheelbarrow | .30 | .25 |
| **743** Block of 4 | 2.50 | 2.50 |
| *a.* 10f Well | .50 | .25 |
| *b.* 10f Trough | .50 | .25 |
| *c.* 10f Water hole | .50 | .25 |
| *d.* 10f Irrigation | .50 | .25 |
| **744** Block of 4 | 3.00 | 3.00 |
| *a.* 15f Sheep drinking | .60 | .25 |
| *b.* 15f Laundresses | .60 | .25 |
| *c.* 15f Sheep and camels drinking | .60 | .25 |
| *d.* 15f Water stored in skins | .60 | .25 |
| **745** Block of 4 | 3.50 | 3.50 |
| *a.* 20f Animals at well | .75 | .25 |
| *b.* 20f Water in home | .75 | .25 |
| *c.* 20f Water pot | .75 | .25 |
| *d.* 20f Communal fountain | .75 | .25 |
| **746** Block of 4 | 4.25 | 4.25 |
| *a.* 25f Distillation plant | .85 | .30 |
| *b.* 25f Motorized delivery | .85 | .30 |
| *c.* 25f Water trucks | .85 | .30 |
| *d.* 25f Water towers | .85 | .30 |
| **747** Block of 4 | 6.00 | 6.00 |
| *a.* 30f Shower bath | 1.25 | .30 |
| *b.* 30f Water tower | 1.25 | .30 |
| *c.* 30f Gathering rain water | 1.25 | .30 |
| *d.* 30f 2 water towers | 1.25 | .30 |
| **748** Block of 4 | 13.50 | 13.50 |
| *a.* 80f Donkey with water bags | 2.75 | .90 |
| *b.* 80f Woman with water can | 2.75 | .90 |
| *c.* 80f Woman with water skin | 2.75 | .90 |
| *d.* 80f Loading tank car | 2.75 | .90 |
| **749** Block of 4 | 17.50 | 17.50 |
| *a.* 100f Truck delivering water | 3.50 | 1.10 |
| *b.* 100f Barnyard water supply | 3.50 | 1.10 |
| *c.* 100f Children at water basin | 3.50 | 1.10 |
| *d.* 100f Well in courtyard | 3.50 | 1.10 |
| *Nos. 742-749 (8)* | 51.75 | 51.75 |

Radar, Torch, Minarets A181

**1978, Feb. 25 Litho.** *Perf. 14x14½*

| | | |
|---|---|---|
| **750** A181 30f multicolored | .60 | .25 |
| **751** A181 80f multicolored | 1.50 | .75 |

17th National Day.

Man with Smallpox, Target — A182

**1978, Apr. 17 Litho.** *Perf. 12½*

| | | |
|---|---|---|
| **752** A182 30f violet & multi | 1.00 | .50 |
| **753** A182 80f green & multi | 2.50 | 1.10 |

Global eradication of smallpox.

Antenna and ITU Emblem A183

**1978, May 17** *Perf. 14*

| | | |
|---|---|---|
| **754** A183 30f silver & multi | .50 | .30 |
| **755** A183 80f silver & multi | 1.50 | .85 |

10th World Telecommunications Day.

Sheik Sabah — A184

**1978, June 28 Litho.** *Perf. 13x14*

**Portrait in Brown**

**Size: 21½x27mm**

| | | |
|---|---|---|
| **756** A184 15f green & gold | .40 | .25 |
| **757** A184 30f orange & gold | .65 | .45 |
| **758** A184 80f rose lilac & gold | 1.50 | 1.10 |
| **759** A184 100f lt green & gold | 1.75 | 1.25 |
| **760** A184 130f lt brown & gold | 2.00 | 1.75 |
| **761** A184 180f violet & gold | 3.50 | 2.75 |

**Size: 23½x29mm**

| | | |
|---|---|---|
| **762** A184 1d red & gold | *15.00* | *12.50* |
| **763** A184 4d blue & gold | *67.50* | *57.50* |
| *Nos. 756-763 (8)* | 92.30 | 77.55 |

Mt. Arafat, Pilgrims, Holy Kaaba A185

**1978, Nov. 9 Photo.** *Perf. 11½*

| | | |
|---|---|---|
| **764** A185 30f multicolored | 1.00 | .50 |
| **765** A185 80f multicolored | 2.50 | 1.25 |

Pilgrimage to Mecca.

UN and Anti-Apartheid Emblems — A186

**1978, Nov. 27 Litho.** *Perf. 12*

| | | |
|---|---|---|
| **766** A186 30f multicolored | .50 | .30 |
| **767** A186 80f multicolored | 1.10 | 1.00 |
| **768** A186 180f multicolored | 2.50 | 2.00 |
| *Nos. 766-768 (3)* | 4.10 | 3.30 |

Anti-Apartheid Year.

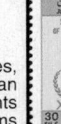

Refugees, Human Rights Emblems A187

**1978, Dec. 10 Photo.** *Perf. 13x13½*

| | | |
|---|---|---|
| **769** A187 30f multicolored | .65 | .35 |
| **770** A187 80f multicolored | 1.60 | .80 |
| **771** A187 100f multicolored | 2.25 | 1.50 |
| *Nos. 769-771 (3)* | 4.50 | 2.65 |

Declaration of Human Rights, 30th anniv.

Information Center — A188

**1978, Dec. 26 Photo.** *Perf. 13*

| | | |
|---|---|---|
| **772** A188 5f multicolored | .30 | .25 |
| **773** A188 15f multicolored | .40 | .25 |
| **774** A188 30f multicolored | .70 | .35 |
| **775** A188 80f multicolored | 1.60 | .95 |
| *Nos. 772-775 (4)* | 3.00 | 1.80 |

New Kuwait Information Center.

Kindergarten A189

**1979, Jan. 24 Photo.** *Perf. 13½x14*

| | | |
|---|---|---|
| **776** A189 30f multicolored | .75 | .50 |
| **777** A189 80f multicolored | 1.90 | 1.10 |

International Year of the Child.

Flag and Peace Doves — A190

**1979, Feb. 25** *Perf. 14½x14*

| | | |
|---|---|---|
| **778** A190 30f multicolored | .75 | .45 |
| **779** A190 80f multicolored | 1.50 | 1.10 |

18th National Day.

Modern Agriculture in Kuwait — A191

**1979, Mar. 13 Photo.** *Perf. 14*

| | | |
|---|---|---|
| **780** A191 30f multicolored | .60 | .45 |
| **781** A191 80f multicolored | 1.50 | 1.10 |

4th Congress of Arab Agriculture Ministers of the Gulf and Arabian Peninsula.

World Map, Book, Symbols of Learning A192

**1979, Mar. 22**

| | | |
|---|---|---|
| **782** A192 30f multicolored | .75 | .45 |
| **783** A192 80f multicolored | 1.75 | 1.10 |

Cultural achievements of the Arabs.

Children with Balloons — A193

Children's Paintings: No. 785, Boys flying kites. No. 786, Girl and doves. No. 787, Children and houses, horiz. No. 788, Four children, horiz. No. 789, Children sitting in circle, horiz.

**1979, Apr. 18 Photo.** *Perf. 14*

| | | |
|---|---|---|
| **784** A193 30f yellow & multi | .90 | .55 |
| **785** A193 30f buff & multi | .90 | .55 |
| **786** A193 30f pale yel & multi | .90 | .55 |
| **787** A193 80f lt blue & multi | 2.00 | 1.25 |
| **788** A193 80f yel green & multi | 2.00 | 1.25 |
| **789** A193 80f lilac & multi | 2.00 | 1.25 |
| *Nos. 784-789 (6)* | 8.70 | 5.40 |

Cables, ITU Emblem, People A194

**1979, May 17**

| | | |
|---|---|---|
| **790** A194 30f multicolored | .60 | .40 |
| **791** A194 80f multicolored | 1.60 | 1.10 |

World Telecommunications Day.

Military Sports Council Emblem — A195

**1979, June 1 Photo.** *Perf. 14*

| | | |
|---|---|---|
| **792** A195 30f multicolored | .60 | .40 |
| **793** A195 80f multicolored | 1.75 | 1.25 |

29th Intl. Military Soccer Championship.

Child, Industrial Landscape, Environmental Emblems — A196

**1979, June 5** *Perf. 12x11½*

| | | |
|---|---|---|
| **794** A196 30f multicolored | .85 | .60 |
| **795** A196 80f multicolored | 2.10 | 1.60 |

World Environment Day, June 5.

Children Holding Globe, UNESCO Emblem A197

**1979, July 25 Litho. *Perf. 11½x12***

| | | | | | |
|---|---|---|---|---|---|
| 796 | A197 | 30f | multicolored | .50 | .40 |
| 797 | A197 | 80f | multicolored | 1.25 | 1.00 |
| 798 | A197 | 130f | multicolored | 2.25 | 1.50 |
| | | | *Nos. 796-798 (3)* | 4.00 | 2.90 |

Intl. Bureau of Education, Geneva, 50th anniv.

Kuwait Kindergartens, 25th Anniversary A198

Children's Drawings: 80f, Children waving flags.

**1979, Sept. 15 Litho. *Perf. 12½***

| | | | | | |
|---|---|---|---|---|---|
| 799 | A198 | 30f | multicolored | .60 | .40 |
| 800 | A198 | 80f | multicolored | 1.60 | 1.00 |

Pilgrims at Holy Ka'aba, Mecca Mosque A199

**1979, Oct. 29 *Perf. 14x14½***

| | | | | | |
|---|---|---|---|---|---|
| 801 | A199 | 30f | multicolored | 1.00 | .50 |
| 802 | A199 | 80f | multicolored | 2.50 | 1.00 |

Hegira (Pilgrimage Year).

International Palestinian Solidarity Day — A200

**1979, Nov. 29 Photo. *Perf. 11½x12***

| | | | | | |
|---|---|---|---|---|---|
| 803 | A200 | 30f | multicolored | 2.00 | .95 |
| 804 | A200 | 80f | multicolored | 4.75 | 1.90 |

Kuwait Airways 25th Anniversary A201

**1979, Dec. 24 Photo. *Perf. 13x13½***

| | | | | | |
|---|---|---|---|---|---|
| 805 | A201 | 30f | multicolored | 1.10 | .60 |
| 806 | A201 | 80f | multicolored | 2.75 | 1.75 |

19th National Day A202

**1980, Feb. 25 Litho. *Perf. 14x14½***

| | | | | | |
|---|---|---|---|---|---|
| 807 | A202 | 30f | multicolored | .75 | .40 |
| 808 | A202 | 80f | multicolored | 1.75 | 1.00 |

1980 Population Census A203

**1980, Mar. 18 *Perf. 13½x14***

| | | | | | |
|---|---|---|---|---|---|
| 809 | A203 | 30f | multicolored | .70 | .35 |
| 810 | A203 | 80f | multicolored | 1.60 | .95 |

World Health Day A204

**1980, Apr. 7**

| | | | | | |
|---|---|---|---|---|---|
| 811 | A204 | 30f | multicolored | 1.25 | .35 |
| 812 | A204 | 80f | multicolored | 2.75 | 1.25 |

Kuwait Municipality, 50th Anniversary A205

**1980, May 1 Photo. *Perf. 14***

| | | | | | |
|---|---|---|---|---|---|
| 813 | A205 | 15f | multicolored | .40 | .25 |
| 814 | A205 | 30f | multicolored | .85 | .50 |
| 815 | A205 | 80f | multicolored | 2.00 | 1.25 |
| | | | *Nos. 813-815 (3)* | 3.25 | 2.00 |

Citizens of Kuwait A206

Future Kuwait (Children's Drawings): 80f, Super highway.

**1980, May 14 Litho. *Perf. 14x14½***

| | | | | | |
|---|---|---|---|---|---|
| 816 | A206 | 30f | multicolored | .85 | .50 |
| 817 | A206 | 80f | multicolored | 2.40 | 1.50 |

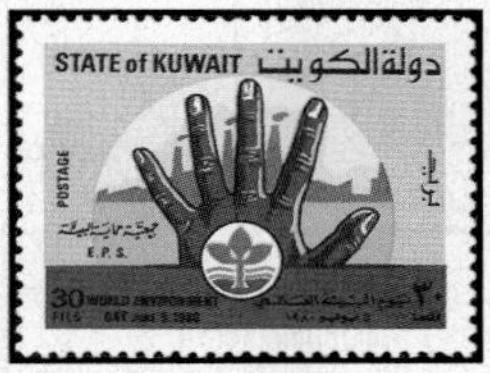


World Environment Day — A207

**1980, June 5 Litho. *Perf. 12x11½***

| | | | | | |
|---|---|---|---|---|---|
| 818 | A207 | 30f | multicolored | .85 | .45 |
| 819 | A207 | 80f | multicolored | 2.25 | 1.10 |

Swimming, Moscow '80 and Kuwait Olympic Committee Emblems — A208

**1980, July 19 Litho. *Perf. 12x12½***

| | | | | | |
|---|---|---|---|---|---|
| 820 | A208 | 15f | Volleyball | .40 | .25 |
| 821 | A208 | 15f | Tennis | .40 | .25 |
| *a.* | | | Vert. pair, #820-821 | 1.00 | 1.00 |
| 822 | A208 | 30f | shown | .60 | .30 |
| 823 | A208 | 30f | Weight lifting | .60 | .30 |
| 824 | A208 | 30f | Basketball | .60 | .30 |
| 825 | A208 | 30f | Judo | .60 | .30 |
| *a.* | | | Block of 4, #822-825 | 4.00 | 4.00 |
| 826 | A208 | 80f | Gymnast | 1.50 | .80 |
| 827 | A208 | 80f | Badminton | 1.50 | .80 |
| 828 | A208 | 80f | Fencing | 1.50 | .80 |
| 829 | A208 | 80f | Soccer | 1.50 | .80 |
| *a.* | | | Block of 4, #826-829 | 8.50 | 8.50 |
| | | | *Nos. 820-829 (10)* | 9.20 | 4.90 |

22nd Summer Olympic Games, Moscow, July 19-Aug. 3.

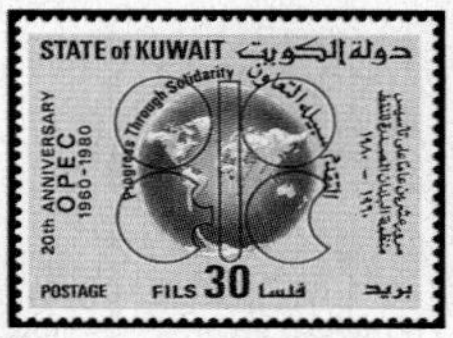


20th Anniversary of OPEC A209

**1980, Sept. 16 Litho. *Perf. 14x14½***

| | | | | | |
|---|---|---|---|---|---|
| 830 | A209 | 30f | multicolored | 1.00 | .50 |
| 831 | A209 | 80f | multicolored | 2.00 | 1.10 |

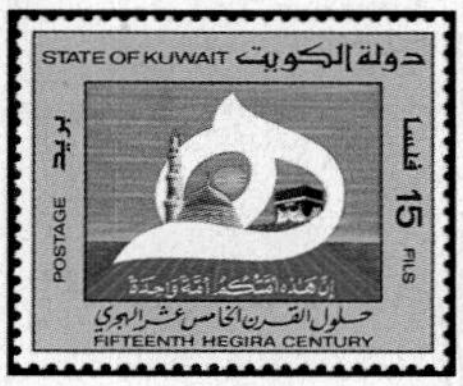


Hegira (Pilgrimage Year) A210

**1980, Nov. 9 Photo. *Perf. 12x11½***

| | | | | | |
|---|---|---|---|---|---|
| 832 | A210 | 15f | multicolored | .60 | .25 |
| 833 | A210 | 30f | multicolored | 1.00 | .45 |
| 834 | A210 | 80f | multicolored | 2.25 | 1.25 |
| | | | *Nos. 832-834 (3)* | 3.85 | 1.95 |

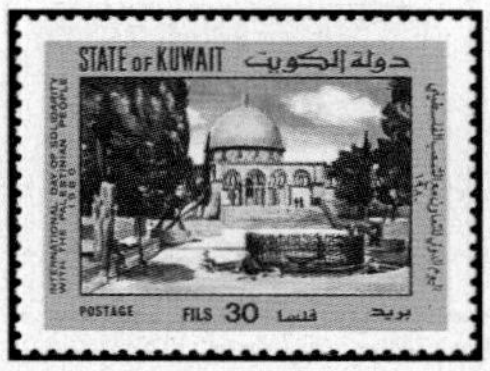


Dome of the Rock, Jerusalem — A211

**1980, Nov. 29 *Perf. 12x11½***

| | | | | | |
|---|---|---|---|---|---|
| 835 | A211 | 30f | multicolored | 1.75 | .85 |
| 836 | A211 | 80f | multicolored | 4.50 | 2.40 |

International Palestinian Solidarity Day.

Avicenna (980-1037), Philosopher and Physician A212

**1980, Dec. 7 *Perf. 12x12½***

| | | | | | |
|---|---|---|---|---|---|
| 837 | A212 | 30f | multicolored | 1.25 | .35 |
| 838 | A212 | 80f | multicolored | 2.50 | 1.20 |

Conference Emblem — A213

**1981, Jan. 12 Photo. *Perf. 13½x13***

| | | | | | |
|---|---|---|---|---|---|
| 839 | A213 | 30f | multicolored | .90 | .65 |
| 840 | A213 | 80f | multicolored | 2.50 | 1.60 |

First Islamic Medical Conference.

Girl in Wheelchair A214

International Year of the Disabled: 30f, Man in wheelchair playing billiards, vert.

***Perf. 13½x13, 13x13½***

**1981, Jan. 26 Photo.**

| | | | | | |
|---|---|---|---|---|---|
| 841 | A214 | 30f | multicolored | .90 | .40 |
| 842 | A214 | 80f | multicolored | 2.10 | 1.40 |

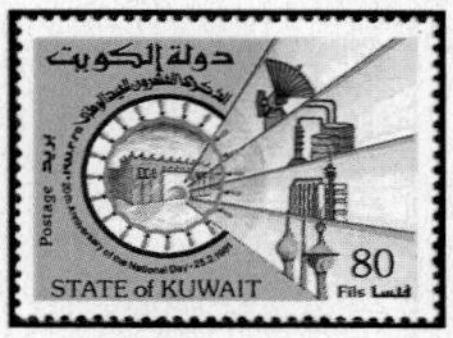


20th National Day A215

**1981, Feb. 25 Litho. *Perf. 13x13½***

| | | | | | |
|---|---|---|---|---|---|
| 843 | A215 | 30f | multicolored | .85 | .40 |
| 844 | A215 | 80f | multicolored | 2.00 | 1.40 |

First Kuwait Dental Association Conference A216

**1981, Mar. 14 *Perf. 11½x12***

| | | | | | |
|---|---|---|---|---|---|
| 845 | A216 | 30f | multicolored | 1.75 | 1.00 |
| 846 | A216 | 80f | multicolored | 4.75 | 2.25 |

A217

**1981, May 8 Photo. *Perf. 14***

| | | | | | |
|---|---|---|---|---|---|
| 847 | A217 | 30f | multicolored | 1.75 | 1.25 |
| 848 | A217 | 80f | multicolored | 4.75 | 3.50 |

Intl. Red Cross day.

A218

**1981, May 17 Litho. *Perf. 14½x14***

| | | | | | |
|---|---|---|---|---|---|
| 849 | A218 | 30f | multicolored | 1.50 | .75 |
| 850 | A218 | 80f | multicolored | 3.25 | 2.25 |

13th World Telecommunications day.

World Environment Day — A219

**1981, June 5 Photo. *Perf. 12***

| | | | | | |
|---|---|---|---|---|---|
| 851 | A219 | 30f | multicolored | 1.00 | .60 |
| 852 | A219 | 80f | multicolored | 2.75 | 1.75 |

Sief Palace A220

A221

**1981, Sept. 16 Litho. *Perf. 12***

| | | | | | |
|---|---|---|---|---|---|
| **853** | A220 | 5f | multicolored | .25 | .25 |
| **854** | A220 | 10f | multicolored | .25 | .25 |
| **855** | A220 | 15f | multicolored | .25 | .25 |
| **856** | A220 | 25f | multicolored | .25 | .25 |
| **857** | A220 | 30f | multicolored | .25 | .25 |
| **858** | A220 | 40f | multicolored | .40 | .25 |
| **859** | A220 | 60f | multicolored | .65 | .25 |
| **860** | A220 | 80f | multicolored | .85 | .45 |
| **861** | A220 | 100f | multicolored | 1.10 | .65 |
| **862** | A220 | 115f | multicolored | 1.25 | .80 |
| **863** | A220 | 130f | multicolored | 1.40 | 1.00 |
| **864** | A220 | 150f | multicolored | 1.75 | 1.00 |
| **865** | A220 | 180f | multicolored | 2.10 | 1.10 |
| **866** | A220 | 250f | multicolored | 3.00 | 1.25 |
| **867** | A220 | 500f | multicolored | 6.00 | 2.25 |
| **868** | A221 | 1d | multicolored | 12.50 | 3.75 |
| **869** | A221 | 2d | multicolored | 27.50 | 8.50 |
| **870** | A221 | 3d | multicolored | 40.00 | 14.00 |
| **871** | A221 | 4d | multicolored | 50.00 | 17.50 |
| | | | *Nos. 853-871 (19)* | 149.75 | 54.00 |

Islamic Pilgrimage A222

**1981, Oct. 7 Photo. *Perf. 13x13½***

| | | | | | |
|---|---|---|---|---|---|
| **872** | A222 | 30f | multicolored | .80 | .60 |
| **873** | A222 | 80f | multicolored | 2.75 | 1.50 |

World Food Day A223

**1981, Oct. 16 Litho. *Perf. 13***

| | | | | | |
|---|---|---|---|---|---|
| **874** | A223 | 30f | multicolored | .90 | .60 |
| **875** | A223 | 80f | multicolored | 2.50 | 1.50 |

A224

**1981, Dec. 30 Photo. *Perf. 14***

| | | | | | |
|---|---|---|---|---|---|
| **876** | A224 | 30f | multicolored | 1.00 | .50 |
| **877** | A224 | 80f | multicolored | 3.00 | 1.50 |

20th anniv. of national television.

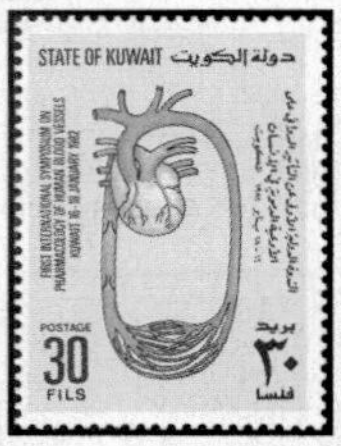

A225

**1982, Jan. 16 Photo. *Perf. 14***

| | | | | | |
|---|---|---|---|---|---|
| **878** | A225 | 30f | multicolored | 1.10 | 1.10 |
| **879** | A225 | 80f | multicolored | 3.50 | 1.75 |

First Intl. Pharmacology of Human Blood Vessels Symposium, Jan. 16-18.

21st Natl. Day — A226

**1982, Feb. 25 *Perf. 13½x13***

| | | | | | |
|---|---|---|---|---|---|
| **880** | A226 | 30f | multicolored | .65 | .45 |
| **881** | A226 | 80f | multicolored | 1.90 | 1.25 |

Scouting Year A227

**1982, Mar. 22 Photo. *Perf. 12x11½***

| | | | | | |
|---|---|---|---|---|---|
| **882** | A227 | 30f | multicolored | .80 | .60 |
| **883** | A227 | 80f | multicolored | 2.25 | 1.50 |

Arab Pharmacists' Day — A228

**1982, Apr. 2 Litho. *Perf. 12x11½***

| | | | | | |
|---|---|---|---|---|---|
| **884** | A228 | 30f | lt green & multi | 1.00 | .60 |
| **885** | A228 | 80f | pink & multi | 3.00 | 1.60 |

World Health Day — A229

**1982, Apr. 7 Litho. *Perf. 13½x13***

| | | | | | |
|---|---|---|---|---|---|
| **886** | A229 | 30f | multicolored | 1.25 | .90 |
| **887** | A229 | 80f | multicolored | 3.75 | 2.75 |

Arab Postal Union, 30th Anniv. — A230

**1982, Apr. 12 Photo. *Perf. 13½x13***

| | | | | | |
|---|---|---|---|---|---|
| **888** | A230 | 30f | multicolored | 1.00 | .50 |
| **889** | A230 | 80f | multicolored | 3.25 | 1.50 |

TB Bacillus Centenary A231

**1982, May 24 Litho. *Perf. 11½x12***

| | | | | | |
|---|---|---|---|---|---|
| **890** | A231 | 30f | multicolored | 2.00 | .90 |
| **891** | A231 | 80f | multicolored | 5.50 | 2.50 |

1982 World Cup A232

**1982, June 17 Photo. *Perf. 14***

| | | | | | |
|---|---|---|---|---|---|
| **892** | A232 | 30f | multicolored | 1.00 | .50 |
| **893** | A232 | 80f | multicolored | 3.50 | 1.50 |

10th Anniv. of Science and Natural History Museum A233

**1982, July 14 *Perf. 14***

| | | | | | |
|---|---|---|---|---|---|
| **894** | A233 | 30f | multicolored | 4.50 | 2.00 |
| **895** | A233 | 80f | multicolored | 11.00 | 5.00 |

6th Anniv. of United Arab Shipping Co. A234

Designs: Freighters.

**1982, Sept. 1 *Perf. 13***

| | | | | | |
|---|---|---|---|---|---|
| **896** | A234 | 30f | multicolored | 1.00 | .40 |
| **897** | A234 | 80f | multicolored | 2.75 | 1.25 |

Arab Day of the Palm Tree — A235

**1982, Sept. 15 *Perf. 14***

| | | | | | |
|---|---|---|---|---|---|
| **898** | A235 | 30f | multicolored | .75 | .45 |
| **899** | A235 | 80f | multicolored | 1.75 | 1.25 |

Islamic Pilgrimage A236

**1982, Sept. 26 Litho.**

| | | | | | |
|---|---|---|---|---|---|
| **900** | A236 | 15f | multicolored | .50 | .30 |
| **901** | A236 | 30f | multicolored | 1.10 | .50 |
| **902** | A236 | 80f | multicolored | 3.00 | 1.50 |
| | | | *Nos. 900-902 (3)* | 4.60 | 2.30 |

Desert Flowers & Plants — A237

Frame colors: No. 903a, green. b, violet. c, deep salmon. d, rose red. e, pale brown. f, deep green. g, pale orange. h, brown red. i, tan. j, violet blue.

No. 904: a, yellow green. b, pink. c, pale blue. d, dark blue. e, pale gray green. f, lake. g, pale orange. h, blue. i, red lilac. j, red orange.

No. 905: a, brown. b, pink. c, blue. d, olive green. e, orange red. f, dark blue. g, green. h, rose. i, bister. j, pale orange.

No. 906: a, yellow green. b, dark blue. c, pale orange. d, rose red. e, green. f, gray violet. g, gray blue. h, violet. i, yellow brown. j, orange red.

No. 907: a, lilac. b, blue green. c, pale orange. d, pale brown. e, violet blue. f, yellow. g, green blue. h, purple. i, pale brown. j, pale orange.

**1983, Jan. 25 Litho. *Perf. 12***

| | | | |
|---|---|---|---|
| **903** | Strip of 10 | 3.50 | 2.00 |
| ***a.-j.*** | A237 10f any single | .30 | .25 |
| **904** | Strip of 10 | 4.50 | 2.75 |
| ***a.-j.*** | A237 15f any single | .35 | .25 |
| **905** | Strip of 10 | 7.50 | 4.50 |
| ***a.-j.*** | A237 30f any single | .55 | .45 |
| **906** | Strip of 10 | 9.00 | 5.50 |
| ***a.-j.*** | A237 40f any single, horiz. | .70 | .55 |
| **907** | Strip of 10 | 20.00 | 12.00 |
| ***a.-j.*** | A237 80f any single, horiz. | 1.50 | .85 |
| | *Nos. 903-907 (5)* | 44.50 | 26.75 |

22nd Natl. Day A238

**1983, Feb. 25 Litho. *Perf. 12½***

| | | | | | |
|---|---|---|---|---|---|
| **908** | A238 | 30f | multicolored | .75 | .35 |
| **909** | A238 | 80f | multicolored | 2.00 | 1.25 |

25th Anniv. of Intl. Maritime Org. A239

**1983, Mar. 17 Photo. *Perf. 14***

| | | | | | |
|---|---|---|---|---|---|
| **910** | A239 | 30f | multicolored | .50 | .30 |
| **911** | A239 | 80f | multicolored | 1.40 | .85 |

Map of Middle East and Africa, Conference Emblem — A240

**1983, Mar. 19 *Perf. 13***

| | | | | | |
|---|---|---|---|---|---|
| **912** | A240 | 15f | multicolored | .40 | .25 |
| **913** | A240 | 30f | multicolored | .85 | .50 |
| **914** | A240 | 80f | multicolored | 2.50 | 1.50 |
| | | | *Nos. 912-914 (3)* | 3.75 | 2.25 |

3rd Intl. Conference on the Impact of Viral Diseases on the Development of the Middle East and Africa, Mar. 19-27.

World Health Day A241

**1983, Apr. 7 *Perf. 12x11½***

| | | | | | |
|---|---|---|---|---|---|
| **915** | A241 | 15f | multicolored | .45 | .30 |
| **916** | A241 | 30f | multicolored | .90 | .70 |
| **917** | A241 | 80f | multicolored | 2.50 | 1.90 |
| | | | *Nos. 915-917 (3)* | 3.85 | 2.90 |

World Communications Year — A242

**1983, May 17 Photo.** *Perf. 13x13½*

**918** A242 15f multicolored .50 .30
**919** A242 30f multicolored 1.00 .70
**920** A242 80f multicolored 2.75 1.90
*Nos. 918-920 (3)* 4.25 2.90

World Environment Day — A243

**1983, June 5 Litho.** *Perf. 12½*

**921** A243 15f multicolored .50 .30
**922** A243 30f multicolored 1.00 .70
**923** A243 80f multicolored 3.50 1.90
*Nos. 921-923 (3)* 5.00 2.90

Wall of Old Jerusalem A244

**1983, July 25 Litho.** *Perf. 12*

**924** A244 15f multicolored .70 .25
**925** A244 30f multicolored 1.50 .55
**926** A244 80f multicolored 3.50 1.60
*Nos. 924-926 (3)* 5.70 2.40

World Heritage Year.

Islamic Pilgrimage A245

**1983, Sept. 15 Photo.** *Perf. 11½*

**927** A245 15f multicolored .55 .25
**928** A245 30f multicolored 1.25 .55
**929** A245 80f multicolored 3.00 1.60
*Nos. 927-929 (3)* 4.80 2.40

Intl. Palestinian Solidarity Day — A246

**1983, Nov. 29 Photo.** *Perf. 14*

**930** A246 15f multicolored .50 .25
**931** A246 30f multicolored 1.25 .65
**932** A246 80f multicolored 3.50 1.75
*Nos. 930-932 (3)* 5.25 2.65

21st Pan Arab Medical Congress, Jan. 30-Feb. 2 — A247

**1984, Jan. 30 Litho.** *Perf. 14½x14*

**933** A247 15f purple & multi .50 .25
**934** A247 30f blue grn & multi 1.25 .65
**935** A247 80f pink & multi 3.25 1.75
*Nos. 933-935 (3)* 5.00 2.65

Key, Natl. Emblem, and Health Establishments Emblem A248

**1984, Feb. 20 Photo.** *Perf. 13x13½*

**936** A248 15f multicolored .55 .25
**937** A248 30f multicolored .95 .45
**938** A248 80f multicolored 3.00 1.50
*Nos. 936-938 (3)* 4.50 2.20

Inauguration of Amiri and Al-Razi Hospitals, Allergy Center and Medical Stores Center.

23rd National Day — A249

**1984, Feb. 25 Litho.** *Perf. 13½*

**939** A249 15f multicolored .40 .25
**940** A249 30f multicolored 1.00 .45
**941** A249 80f multicolored 2.75 1.50
*Nos. 939-941 (3)* 4.15 2.20

2nd Kuwait Intl. Medical Science Conf., Mar. 4-8 — A250

**1984, Mar. 4 Photo.** *Perf. 12*
**Granite Paper**

**942** A250 15f multicolored .50 .25
**943** A250 30f multicolored 1.10 .65
**944** A250 80f multicolored 2.75 1.70
*Nos. 942-944 (3)* 4.35 2.60

30th Anniv. of Kuwait Airways Corp. A251

**1984, Mar. 15** *Perf. 13½*

**946** A251 30f multicolored .80 .80
**947** A251 80f multicolored 2.25 1.75

Al-Arabi Magazine, 25th Anniv. — A252

**1984, Mar. 20** *Perf. 14½x14*

**948** A252 15f multicolored .40 .25
**949** A252 30f multicolored .85 .50
**950** A252 80f multicolored 2.25 1.40
*Nos. 948-950 (3)* 3.50 2.15

World Health Day — A253

**1984, Apr. 7** *Perf. 12*

**951** A253 15f multicolored .40 .25
**952** A253 30f multicolored .80 .45
**953** A253 80f multicolored 2.40 1.50
*Nos. 951-953 (3)* 3.60 2.20

Hanan Kuwaiti Orphan Village, Sudan A254

**1984, May 15 Litho.** *Perf. 12*

**954** A254 15f multicolored .50 .25
**955** A254 30f multicolored .90 .45
**956** A254 80f multicolored 2.60 1.50
*Nos. 954-956 (3)* 4.00 2.20

Intl. Civil Aviation Org., 40th Anniv. A255

**1984, June 12**

**957** A255 15f multicolored .55 .30
**958** A255 30f multicolored 1.00 .65
**959** A255 80f multicolored 2.75 1.75
*Nos. 957-959 (3)* 4.30 2.70

Arab Youth Day — A256

**1984, July 5** *Perf. 13½*

**960** A256 30f multicolored .75 .55
**961** A256 80f multicolored 2.25 1.60

1984 Summer Olympics A257

**1984, July 28** *Perf. 15x14*

**962** A257 30f Swimming .55 .55
**963** A257 30f Hurdles .55 .55
*a.* Pair, #962-963 1.40 1.40
**964** A257 80f Judo 1.60 1.60
**965** A257 80f Equestrian 1.60 1.60
*a.* Pair, #964-965 4.00 4.00
*Nos. 962-965 (4)* 4.30 4.30

10th Anniv. of the Science Club A258

**1984, Aug. 11 Photo.** *Perf. 13½x13*

**966** A258 15f multicolored .45 .30
**967** A258 30f multicolored 1.00 .65
**968** A258 80f multicolored 2.60 1.80
*Nos. 966-968 (3)* 4.05 2.75

Islamic Pilgrimage — A259

**1984, Sept. 4 Photo.** *Perf. 12x11½*

**969** A259 30f multicolored 1.25 .75
**970** A259 80f multicolored 3.25 2.00

INTELSAT '84, 20th Anniv. A260

**1984, Oct. 1 Litho.** *Perf. 13½x14*

**971** A260 30f multicolored 1.00 .70
**972** A260 80f multicolored 2.50 1.75

G.C.C. Supreme Council, 5th Session A261

**1984, Nov. 24 Litho.** *Perf. 15x14*

**973** A261 30f multicolored .75 .55
**974** A261 80f multicolored 2.25 1.60

Map of Israel, Fists, Shattered Star of David — A262

**1984, Nov. 29 Photo.** *Perf. 12*

**975** A262 30f multicolored 1.75 .75
**976** A262 80f multicolored 4.50 2.00

Intl. Palestinian Solidarity Day.

Globe, Emblem A263

**1984, Dec. 24** *Perf. 12x11½*
**Granite Paper**

**977** A263 30f multicolored 1.00 .50
**978** A263 80f multicolored 2.50 1.50

Kuwait Oil Co., 50th anniv.

Intl. Youth Year — A264

**1985, Jan. 15** *Perf. 13½*

**979** A264 30f multicolored .50 .25
**980** A264 80f multicolored 1.50 1.20

24th Natl. Day — A265

**1985, Feb. 25 Litho. *Perf. 14x15***

**981** A265 30f multicolored .65 .40
**982** A265 80f multicolored 2.50 1.25

Intl. Program for the Development of Communications — A266

**1985, Mar. 4 Photo. *Perf. 11½***
**Granite Paper**

**983** A266 30f multicolored .75 .45
**984** A266 80f multicolored 2.25 1.50

1st Arab Gulf Week for Social Work — A267

**1985, Mar. 13 Photo. *Perf. 13½x13***

**985** A267 30f multicolored 1.00 .45
**986** A267 80f multicolored 2.25 1.50

Kuwait Dental Assoc. 3rd Conference A268

**1985, Mar. 23 Litho. *Perf. 13½***

**987** A268 30f multicolored 1.00 .70
**988** A268 80f multicolored 2.25 1.75

1985 Census — A269

**1985, Apr. 1 *Perf. 14x13½***

**989** A269 30f multicolored 1.00 .45
**990** A269 80f multicolored 2.50 1.50

World Health Day — A270

**1985, Apr. 7 Photo. *Perf. 13½x13***

**991** A270 30f multicolored 1.10 .55
**992** A270 80f multicolored 2.50 1.60

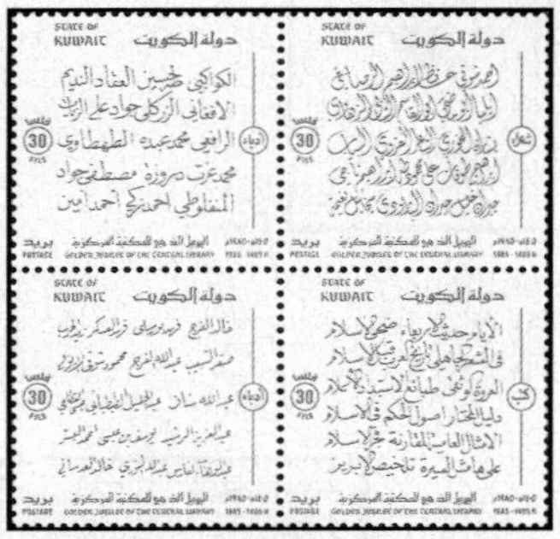

Names of Books, Authors and Poets in Arabic — A271

**1985, May 20 *Perf. 12***
**Granite Paper**

**993** A271 Block of 4 6.75 4.00
*a.-d.* 30f any single 1.40 .75
**994** A271 Block of 4 16.50 10.00
*a.-d.* 80f any single 3.50 1.40

Central Library, 50th anniv.

World Environment Day — A272

**1985, June 5 *Perf. 11½***

**995** A272 30f multicolored 1.40 .75
**996** A272 80f multicolored 3.25 2.00

Org. of Petroleum Exporting Countries, 25th Anniv. A273

**1985, Sept. 1 *Perf. 13x13½***

**997** A273 30f multicolored 1.10 .55
**998** A273 80f multicolored 2.75 1.60

Inauguration of Civil Information System — A274

**1985, Oct. 1 Photo. *Perf. 12x11½***

**999** A274 30f multicolored 1.00 .45
**1000** A274 80f multicolored 2.50 1.50

Intl. Day of Solidarity with Palestinian People A275

**1985, Nov. 29 Photo. *Perf. 12***

**1001** A275 15f multicolored 1.00 .45
**1002** A275 30f multicolored 1.75 .90
**1003** A275 80f multicolored 4.00 2.50
*Nos. 1001-1003 (3)* 6.75 3.85

25th Natl. Day A276

**1986, Feb. 25 Litho. *Perf. 15x14***

**1004** A276 15f multicolored .40 .25
**1005** A276 30f multicolored 1.10 .60
**1006** A276 80f multicolored 2.75 1.75
*Nos. 1004-1006 (3)* 4.25 2.60

Natl. Red Crescent Soc., 20th Anniv. A277

**1986, Mar. 26 Photo. *Perf. 13½***

**1007** A277 20f multicolored .75 .40
**1008** A277 25f multicolored 1.00 .60
**1009** A277 70f multicolored 2.75 1.75
*Nos. 1007-1009 (3)* 4.50 2.75

World Health Day — A278

**1986, Apr. 7 *Perf. 13½x13***

**1010** A278 20f multicolored .85 .65
**1011** A278 25f multicolored 1.25 .80
**1012** A278 70f multicolored 3.00 2.00
*Nos. 1010-1012 (3)* 5.10 3.45

Intl. Peace Year A279

**1986, June 5 Litho. *Perf. 13½***

**1013** A279 20f multicolored .75 .45
**1014** A279 25f multicolored 1.25 .70
**1015** A279 70f multicolored 2.75 1.60
*Nos. 1013-1015 (3)* 4.75 2.75

United Arab Shipping Co., 10th Anniv. A280

**1986, July 1 Photo. *Perf. 12x11½***

**1016** A280 20f Al Mirqab .75 .50
**1017** A280 70f Al Mubarakiah 3.50 2.00

Gulf Bank, 25th Anniv. A281

**1986, Oct. 1 Photo. *Perf. 12½***

**1018** A281 20f multicolored .65 .50
**1019** A281 25f multicolored 1.10 .60
**1020** A281 70f multicolored 3.25 1.75
*Nos. 1018-1020 (3)* 5.00 2.85

Sadu Art — A282

Various tapestry weavings.

**1986, Nov. 5 Photo. *Perf. 12x11½***
**Granite Paper**

**1021** A282 20f multicolored .75 .40
**1022** A282 70f multicolored 2.50 1.50
**1023** A282 200f multicolored 6.00 3.75
*Nos. 1021-1023 (3)* 9.25 5.65

Intl. Day of Solidarity with the Palestinian People — A283

**1986, Nov. 29 *Perf. 14***

**1024** A283 20f multicolored 1.50 .85
**1025** A283 25f multicolored 2.00 1.10
**1026** A283 70f multicolored 5.25 3.25
*Nos. 1024-1026 (3)* 8.75 5.20

5th Islamic Summit Conference — A284

**1987, Jan. 26 Litho. *Perf. 14½***

**1027** A284 25f multicolored .85 .45
**1028** A284 50f multicolored 1.60 .80
**1029** A284 150f multicolored 4.75 2.25
*Nos. 1027-1029 (3)* 7.20 3.50

26th Natl. Day A285

**1987, Feb. 25 *Perf. 13½x14***

**1030** A285 50f multicolored 1.40 .60
**1031** A285 150f multicolored 4.25 2.00

Natl. Health Sciences Center A286

**1987, Mar. 15 Photo. *Perf. 12x11½***
**Granite Paper**

**1032** A286 25f multicolored .75 .35
**1033** A286 150f multicolored 3.50 2.00

3rd Kuwait Intl. Medical Sciences Conference on Infectious Diseases in Developing Countries.

World Health Day — A287

**1987, Apr. 7 Photo. *Perf. 13x13½***

| | | | | | |
|---|---|---|---|---|---|
| **1034** | A287 | 25f multicolored | .75 | .40 |
| **1035** | A287 | 50f multicolored | 1.40 | .70 |
| **1036** | A287 | 150f multicolored | 4.75 | 2.00 |
| | | *Nos. 1034-1036 (3)* | 6.90 | 3.10 |

Day of Ghods (Jerusalem) — A288

**1987, June 7 Photo. *Perf. 12x11½***

| | | | | |
|---|---|---|---|---|
| **1037** | A288 | 25f multicolored | .75 | .30 |
| **1038** | A288 | 50f multicolored | 1.50 | .65 |
| **1039** | A288 | 150f multicolored | 4.25 | 2.25 |
| | | *Nos. 1037-1039 (3)* | 6.50 | 3.20 |

Islamic Pilgrimage to Miqat Wadi Mihrim — A289

**1987, Aug. Photo. *Perf. 13½x14½***

| | | | | |
|---|---|---|---|---|
| **1040** | A289 | 25f multicolored | .75 | .30 |
| **1041** | A289 | 50f multicolored | 1.50 | .80 |
| **1042** | A289 | 150f multicolored | 4.00 | 2.25 |
| | | *Nos. 1040-1042 (3)* | 6.25 | 3.35 |

Arab Telecommunications Day — A290

**1987, Sept. 9 Litho. *Perf. 14x13½***

| | | | | |
|---|---|---|---|---|
| **1043** | A290 | 25f multicolored | .60 | .30 |
| **1044** | A290 | 50f multicolored | 1.25 | .80 |
| **1045** | A290 | 150f multicolored | 3.50 | 1.25 |
| | | *Nos. 1043-1045 (3)* | 5.35 | 2.35 |

World Maritime Day A291

**1987, Sept. 24 *Perf. 12x11½***

**Granite Paper**

| | | | | |
|---|---|---|---|---|
| **1046** | A291 | 25f multicolored | .85 | .35 |
| **1047** | A291 | 50f multicolored | 1.75 | .75 |
| **1048** | A291 | 150f multicolored | 5.00 | 2.00 |
| | | *Nos. 1046-1048 (3)* | 7.60 | 3.10 |

Al Qurain Housing Project — A292

**1987, Oct. 5 *Perf. 13x13½***

| | | | | |
|---|---|---|---|---|
| **1049** | A292 | 25f multicolored | .60 | .35 |
| **1050** | A292 | 50f multicolored | 1.25 | .60 |
| **1051** | A292 | 150f multicolored | 3.50 | 1.75 |
| | | *Nos. 1049-1051 (3)* | 5.35 | 2.70 |

Port Authority, 10th Anniv. — A293

**1987, Nov. 16 Litho. *Perf. 14½***

| | | | | |
|---|---|---|---|---|
| **1052** | A293 | 25f multicolored | .75 | .25 |
| **1053** | A293 | 50f multicolored | 1.25 | .65 |
| **1054** | A293 | 150f multicolored | 4.00 | 2.00 |
| | | *Nos. 1052-1054 (3)* | 6.00 | 2.90 |

A294

**1987, Nov. 29 *Perf. 14x13½***

| | | | | |
|---|---|---|---|---|
| **1055** | A294 | 25f multicolored | .65 | .30 |
| **1056** | A294 | 50f multicolored | 1.25 | .60 |
| **1057** | A294 | 150f multicolored | 4.00 | 2.00 |
| | | *Nos. 1055-1057 (3)* | 5.90 | 2.90 |

Intl. Day of Solidarity with the Palestinian People

A295

**1988, Feb. 3 Photo. *Perf. 14***

| | | | | |
|---|---|---|---|---|
| **1058** | A295 | 25f multicolored | .55 | .30 |
| **1059** | A295 | 50f multicolored | 1.00 | .50 |
| **1060** | A295 | 150f multicolored | 2.75 | 1.25 |
| | | *Nos. 1058-1060 (3)* | 4.30 | 2.05 |

Women's Cultural and Social Soc., 25th anniv.

A296

**1988, Feb. 25**

| | | | | |
|---|---|---|---|---|
| **1061** | A296 | 25f multicolored | .55 | .25 |
| **1062** | A296 | 50f multicolored | .90 | .50 |
| **1063** | A296 | 150f multicolored | 2.50 | 1.10 |
| | | *Nos. 1061-1063 (3)* | 3.95 | 1.85 |

National Day, 27th anniv.

A297

**1988, Apr. 7 Litho. *Perf. 14x15***

| | | | | |
|---|---|---|---|---|
| **1064** | A297 | 25f multicolored | .75 | .30 |
| **1065** | A297 | 50f multicolored | 1.25 | .65 |
| **1066** | A297 | 150f multicolored | 3.75 | 1.25 |
| | | *Nos. 1064-1066 (3)* | 5.75 | 2.20 |

World Health Day, WHO 40th anniv.

A298

**1988, Apr. 24 Photo. *Perf. 12***

**Granite Paper**

| | | | | |
|---|---|---|---|---|
| **1067** | A298 | 35f multicolored | .80 | .35 |
| **1068** | A298 | 50f multicolored | 1.25 | .55 |
| **1069** | A298 | 150f multicolored | 4.25 | 1.75 |
| | | *Nos. 1067-1069 (3)* | 6.30 | 2.65 |

Regional Marine Environment Day. Kuwait Regional Convention on the Marine Environment, 10th anniv. See Iraq Nos. 1333-1336.

A299

**1988, July 10 Photo. *Perf. 14***

| | | | | |
|---|---|---|---|---|
| **1070** | A299 | 25f multicolored | .85 | .25 |
| **1071** | A299 | 50f multicolored | 1.25 | .60 |
| **1072** | A299 | 150f multicolored | 4.25 | 1.75 |
| | | *Nos. 1070-1072 (3)* | 6.35 | 2.60 |

Kuwait Teachers Soc., 25th anniv.

Pilgrimage to Mecca A300

**1988, Sept. 12 Litho. *Perf. 13½x14***

| | | | | |
|---|---|---|---|---|
| **1073** | A300 | 25f multicolored | .85 | .25 |
| **1074** | A300 | 50f multicolored | 1.50 | .55 |
| **1075** | A300 | 150f multicolored | 4.50 | 1.75 |
| | | *Nos. 1073-1075 (3)* | 6.85 | 2.55 |

Palestinian "Children of Stone" Fighting Israelis — A301

**1988, Sept. 15 Photo. *Perf. 13x13½***

| | | | | |
|---|---|---|---|---|
| **1076** | A301 | 50f multicolored | 2.00 | .70 |
| **1077** | A301 | 150f multicolored | 7.00 | 2.50 |

Palestinian Uprising. Dated 1987.

Arab Housing Day — A302

**1988, Oct. 3**

| | | | | |
|---|---|---|---|---|
| **1078** | A302 | 50f multicolored | 1.10 | .60 |
| **1079** | A302 | 100f multicolored | 2.25 | 1.25 |
| **1080** | A302 | 150f multicolored | 3.75 | 1.75 |
| | | *Nos. 1078-1080 (3)* | 7.10 | 3.60 |

Intl. Day for Solidarity with the Palestinian People A303

**1988, Nov. 29 Litho. *Perf. 14x13***

| | | | | |
|---|---|---|---|---|
| **1081** | A303 | 50f multicolored | 1.10 | .60 |
| **1082** | A303 | 100f multicolored | 2.25 | 1.25 |
| **1083** | A303 | 150f multicolored | 4.00 | 1.75 |
| | | *Nos. 1081-1083 (3)* | 7.35 | 3.60 |

A304

**1988, Dec. 5 *Perf. 13x14***

| | | | | |
|---|---|---|---|---|
| **1084** | A304 | 50f multicolored | .90 | .50 |
| **1085** | A304 | 100f multicolored | 2.00 | 1.00 |
| **1086** | A304 | 150f multicolored | 3.25 | 1.50 |
| | | *Nos. 1084-1086 (3)* | 6.15 | 3.00 |

Intl. Volunteers Day.

A305

**1989, Feb. 18 Litho. *Perf. 14x13½***

| | | | | |
|---|---|---|---|---|
| **1087** | A305 | 50f multicolored | 1.00 | .50 |
| **1088** | A305 | 100f multicolored | 2.00 | 1.00 |
| **1089** | A305 | 150f multicolored | 3.50 | 1.50 |
| | | *Nos. 1087-1089 (3)* | 6.50 | 3.00 |

18th Arab Engineering Conference.

28th Natl. Day A306

**1989, Feb. 25 *Perf. 13x13½***

| | | | | |
|---|---|---|---|---|
| **1090** | A306 | 50f multicolored | 1.00 | .50 |
| **1091** | A306 | 100f multicolored | 2.00 | 1.00 |
| **1092** | A306 | 150f multicolored | 3.50 | 1.50 |
| | | *Nos. 1090-1092 (3)* | 6.50 | 3.00 |

5th Natl. Dental Assoc. Conference A307

**1989, Mar. 30 Litho. *Perf. 13½x13***

| | | | | |
|---|---|---|---|---|
| **1093** | A307 | 50f multicolored | 1.00 | .50 |
| **1094** | A307 | 150f multicolored | 3.00 | 1.25 |
| **1095** | A307 | 250f multicolored | 4.50 | 2.00 |
| | | *Nos. 1093-1095 (3)* | 8.50 | 3.75 |

World Health Day A308

**1989, Apr. 7** *Perf. 13x13½*

| | | | | |
|---|---|---|---|---|
| **1096** | A308 50f multicolored | .80 | .40 |
| **1097** | A308 150f multicolored | 2.50 | 1.25 |
| **1098** | A308 250f multicolored | 4.25 | 2.00 |
| | *Nos. 1096-1098 (3)* | 7.55 | 3.65 |

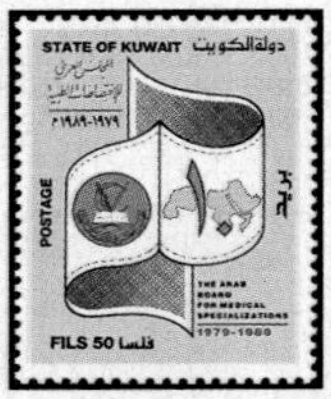


A309

**1989, May 10** *Perf. 13x14*

| | | | |
|---|---|---|---|
| **1099** | A309 50f multicolored | .80 | .40 |
| **1100** | A309 150f multicolored | 2.50 | 1.25 |
| **1101** | A309 250f multicolored | 4.25 | 2.00 |
| | *Nos. 1099-1101 (3)* | 7.55 | 3.65 |

Arab Board for Medical Specializations, 10th anniv.

A310

**1989, June 10 Litho.** *Perf. 14x15*

| | | | |
|---|---|---|---|
| **1102** | A310 50f multicolored | .90 | .50 |
| **1103** | A310 200f multicolored | 3.50 | 2.25 |
| **1104** | A310 250f multicolored | 4.50 | 2.75 |
| | *Nos. 1102-1104 (3)* | 8.90 | 5.50 |

Natl. Journalists Assoc., 25th anniv.

Al-Taneem Mosque — A311

**1989, July 9 Litho.** *Perf. 13½x14½*

| | | | |
|---|---|---|---|
| **1105** | A311 50f multicolored | 1.00 | .50 |
| **1106** | A311 150f multicolored | 3.00 | 1.50 |
| **1107** | A311 200f multicolored | 4.00 | 2.00 |
| | *Nos. 1105-1107 (3)* | 8.00 | 4.00 |

Pilgrimage to Mecca.

Arab Housing Day — A312

**1989, Oct. 2** *Perf. 13½*

| | | | |
|---|---|---|---|
| **1108** | A312 25f multicolored | .65 | .25 |
| **1109** | A312 50f multicolored | 1.50 | .50 |
| **1110** | A312 150f multicolored | 4.75 | 1.50 |
| | *Nos. 1108-1110 (3)* | 6.90 | 2.25 |

Annual Greenery Week Celebration A313

**1989, Oct. 15** *Perf. 13½x13*

| | | | |
|---|---|---|---|
| **1111** | A313 25f multicolored | .75 | .25 |
| **1112** | A313 50f multicolored | 1.75 | .50 |
| **1113** | A313 150f multicolored | 5.00 | 1.50 |
| | *Nos. 1111-1113 (3)* | 7.50 | 2.25 |

Dhow — A314

**Numbers in Black, Moon and Dhow in Gold**

**1989, Nov. 1** *Perf. 14x15*

**Coil Stamps**

| | | | |
|---|---|---|---|
| **1114** | A314 50f brt apple grn | *3.00* | *3.00* |
| **1115** | A314 100f brt blue | *5.50* | *5.50* |
| **1116** | A314 200f vermilion | *10.00* | *10.00* |
| | *Nos. 1114-1116 (3)* | *18.50* | *18.50* |

Nos. 1114-1116 available only at two post office locations, where they were dispensed from machines. Printed in rolls of 3000 consecutively numbered stamps. Stamps with overprinted asterisks but lacking printed numbers are from the ends of coil rolls.

Gulf Investment Corp., 5th Anniv. — A315

**1989, Nov. 4** *Perf. 15x14*

| | | | |
|---|---|---|---|
| **1117** | A315 25f multicolored | .80 | .25 |
| **1118** | A315 50f multicolored | 1.50 | .50 |
| **1119** | A315 150f multicolored | 4.50 | 1.50 |
| | *Nos. 1117-1119 (3)* | 6.80 | 2.25 |

Declaration of Palestinian State, 1st Anniv. — A316

**1989, Nov. 15 Litho.** *Perf. 14x15*

| | | | |
|---|---|---|---|
| **1120** | A316 50f multicolored | 1.00 | .50 |
| **1121** | A316 150f multicolored | 3.00 | 1.75 |
| **1122** | A316 200f multicolored | 4.25 | 2.25 |
| | *Nos. 1120-1122 (3)* | 8.25 | 4.50 |

Zakat House, Orphan Sponsorship Program — A317

**1989, Dec. 10** *Perf. 13½x13*

| | | | |
|---|---|---|---|
| **1123** | A317 25f multicolored | .50 | .30 |
| **1124** | A317 50f multicolored | 1.10 | .75 |
| **1125** | A317 150f multicolored | 3.50 | 2.00 |
| | *Nos. 1123-1125 (3)* | 5.10 | 3.05 |

Kuwait Police, 50th Anniv. — A318

**1989, Dec. 30 Litho.** *Perf. 15x14*

| | | | |
|---|---|---|---|
| **1126** | A318 25f gray & multi | .50 | .30 |
| **1127** | A318 50f lt ultra & multi | 1.10 | .75 |
| **1128** | A318 150f lt violet & multi | 3.50 | 2.00 |
| | *Nos. 1126-1128 (3)* | 5.10 | 3.05 |

National Day, 29th Anniv. — A319

**1990, Feb. 25** *Perf. 14x13½*

| | | | |
|---|---|---|---|
| **1129** | A319 25f multicolored | .55 | .30 |
| **1130** | A319 50f multicolored | 1.00 | .75 |
| **1131** | A319 150f multicolored | 3.25 | 1.75 |
| | *Nos. 1129-1131 (3)* | 4.80 | 2.80 |

World Meteorological Day — A320

**1990, Mar. 23 Litho.** *Perf. 13½x14*

| | | | |
|---|---|---|---|
| **1132** | A320 50f multicolored | 1.00 | .50 |
| **1133** | A320 100f multicolored | 2.25 | 1.25 |
| **1134** | A320 150f multicolored | 3.25 | 2.00 |
| | *Nos. 1132-1134 (3)* | 6.50 | 3.75 |

World Health Day — A321

**1990, Apr. 7** *Perf. 14x15*

| | | | |
|---|---|---|---|
| **1135** | A321 50f multicolored | 1.10 | .50 |
| **1136** | A321 100f multicolored | 2.25 | 1.25 |
| **1137** | A321 150f multicolored | 3.00 | 2.00 |
| | *Nos. 1135-1137 (3)* | 6.35 | 3.75 |

Hawk — A322

**1990, July 7 Litho.** *Perf. 14½*

| | | | |
|---|---|---|---|
| **1138** | A322 50f blue & gold | 6.00 | 6.00 |
| **1139** | A322 100f maroon & gold | 8.00 | 8.00 |
| **1140** | A322 150f green & gold | 11.00 | 11.00 |
| | *Nos. 1138-1140 (3)* | 25.00 | 25.00 |

Liberation of Kuwait — A323

**1991 Litho.** *Perf. 14½*

| | | | |
|---|---|---|---|
| **1141** | A323 25f multicolored | .75 | .40 |
| **1142** | A323 50f multicolored | 1.50 | .80 |
| **1143** | A323 150f multicolored | 4.00 | 2.50 |
| | *Nos. 1141-1143 (3)* | 6.25 | 3.70 |

Peace — A324

**1991, May** *Perf. 13½x14*

| | | | |
|---|---|---|---|
| **1144** | A324 50f multicolored | 1.25 | .75 |
| **1145** | A324 100f multicolored | 2.50 | 1.50 |
| **1146** | A324 150f multicolored | 4.00 | 2.25 |
| | *Nos. 1144-1146 (3)* | 7.75 | |

Reconstruction A325

**1991, May**

| | | | |
|---|---|---|---|
| **1147** | A325 50f multicolored | 1.25 | .85 |
| **1148** | A325 150f multicolored | 3.25 | 2.00 |
| **1149** | A325 200f multicolored | 4.00 | 2.75 |
| | *Nos. 1147-1149 (3)* | 8.50 | 5.60 |

Liberation of Kuwait — A326

Flags of forces joining international coalition for liberation of Kuwait: a, Sweden. b, USSR. c, U.S. d, Kuwait. e, Saudi Arabia. f, UN. g, Singapore. h, France. i, Italy. j, Egypt. k, Morocco. l, UK. m, Philippines. n, UAE. o, Syria. p, Poland. q, Australia. r, Japan. s, Hungary. t, Netherlands. u, Denmark. v, New Zealand. w, Czechoslovakia. x, Bahrain. y, Honduras. z, Turkey. aa, Greece. ab, Oman. ac, Qatar. ad, Belgium. ae, Sierra Leone. af, Argentina. ag, Norway. ah, Canada. ai, Germany. aj, South Korea. ak, Bangladesh. al, Bulgaria. am, Senegal. an, Spain. ao, Niger. ap, Pakistan.

No. 1151, Flags of all forces of coalition.

**1991, July 25 Litho.** *Perf. 14½*

| | | | |
|---|---|---|---|
| **1150** | 50f Sheet of 42 | *50.00* | *50.00* |
| *a.-ap.* | A326 Any single | 1.00 | 1.00 |

**Size: 87x134mm**

***Imperf***

| | | | |
|---|---|---|---|
| **1151** | A326 1d multicolored | *27.50* | *27.50* |

Invasion of Kuwait, 1st Anniv. — A327

50f, Human terror. 100f, Invasion of Kuwait. 150f, Environmental terrorism, horiz. 250f, Desert Storm.

**1991, Aug. 2** *Perf. 14½*

| | | | |
|---|---|---|---|
| **1152** | A327 50f multi | *1.50* | 1.00 |
| **1153** | A327 100f multi | *2.75* | 1.50 |
| **1154** | A327 150f multi | *4.25* | 2.50 |

**Size: 90x65mm**

***Imperf***

| | | | |
|---|---|---|---|
| **1155** | A327 250f multi | *10.00* | *10.00* |
| | *Nos. 1152-1155 (4)* | *18.50* | 15.00 |

12th Gulf Cooperation Council Summit
A328

Design: 150f, Tree of flags.

**1991, Dec. 23 Litho. *Perf. 14½***

| | | | | | |
|---|---|---|---|---|---|
| **1156** | A328 | 25f multicolored | | .75 | .55 |
| | *a.* | see footnote | | .80 | .55 |
| **1157** | A328 | 150f multicolored | | 4.25 | 3.25 |
| | *a.* | Sheet, 2 ea #1156-1157 | | *10.00* | *10.00* |
| | *b.* | Sheet, 2 ea #1156a, 1157 | | *10.00* | *10.00* |

No. 1156a has tree with inscriptions (country names in Arabic) in colors of flags shown on No. 1157.

Intl. Literacy Year — A329

**1992, Feb. 12 Litho. *Perf. 13½x13***

| | | | | |
|---|---|---|---|---|
| **1158** | A329 | 50f dark blue & buff | 1.00 | .75 |
| **1159** | A329 | 100f dark blue & cit | 2.00 | 1.50 |
| **1160** | A329 | 150f dk blue & pale lil | 3.00 | 2.00 |
| | | *Nos. 1158-1160 (3)* | 6.00 | 4.25 |

Dated 1990.

OPEC, 30th Anniv. (in 1990) — A330

**1992, Oct. 29 *Perf. 14½x13½***

| | | | | |
|---|---|---|---|---|
| **1161** | A330 | 25f red & multi | .75 | .50 |
| **1162** | A330 | 50f yellow & multi | 1.50 | 1.00 |
| **1163** | A330 | 150f green & multi | 4.00 | 3.00 |
| | | *Nos. 1161-1163 (3)* | 6.25 | 4.50 |

31st Natl. Day
A331

**1992 *Perf. 14½***

| | | | | |
|---|---|---|---|---|
| **1164** | A331 | 50f Flag, doves | .75 | .50 |
| **1165** | A331 | 150f Flags | 2.25 | 1.50 |
| | *a.* | Min. sheet, 2 ea #1164-1165 | 7.50 | 7.50 |

Liberation Day (No. 1165). Issue dates, 50f, Feb. 25; 150f, Feb. 26.

Don't Forget Our P.O.W.'s — A332

50f, Flag, chains. 150f, Cell bars, chains.

**1991, Nov. 16**

| | | | | |
|---|---|---|---|---|
| **1166** | A332 | 50f multicolored | 1.25 | .75 |
| **1167** | A332 | 150f multicolored | 4.00 | 2.25 |
| | *a.* | Min. sheet, 2 each #1166-1167 | *14.00* | *14.00* |

Dated 1991. Issued: 50f, 2/25; 150f, 2/26.

Camels
A333

**1991, Nov. 16 *Perf. 12½***

| | | | | |
|---|---|---|---|---|
| **1168** | A333 | 25f pink & multi | .60 | .60 |
| **1169** | A333 | 50f beige & multi | 1.00 | 1.00 |
| **1170** | A333 | 150f lt violet & multi | 2.50 | 2.50 |
| **1171** | A333 | 200f blue & multi | 3.00 | 3.00 |
| **1172** | A333 | 350f orange & multi | 6.00 | 6.00 |
| | | *Nos. 1168-1172 (5)* | 13.10 | 13.10 |

Environmental Terrorism, by Jafar Islah — A334

Designs: No. 1174, Snake, flag, map. No. 1175, Skull, dead fish. No. 1176, Dying camel.

**1992, June *Perf. 14½***

| | | | | | |
|---|---|---|---|---|---|
| **1173** | A334 | 150f multicolored | | 2.00 | 1.50 |
| **1174** | A334 | 150f multicolored | | 2.00 | 1.50 |
| **1175** | A334 | 150f multicolored | | 2.00 | 1.50 |
| **1176** | A334 | 150f multicolored | | 2.00 | 1.50 |
| | *a.* | Block of 4, #1173-1176 | | 13.00 | 10.00 |
| | *b.* | Minature sheet of 4, #1173-1176 | | 15.00 | 15.00 |

Earth Summit, Rio De Janeiro. No. 1176a printed in continuous design.

EXPO '92, Seville
A335

Designs: No. 1177, Kuwaiti Pavilion, La Giralda Tower, Seville. No. 1178, Dhows. No. 1179, Dhow. No. 1180, Pavilion, dhow.

Flags of Spain or Kuwait and: No. 1181, Pavilion. No. 1182, La Giralda Tower. No. 1183, La Giralda Tower, dhow. No. 1184, Pavilion, dhow.

**1992, June 19**

| | | | | |
|---|---|---|---|---|
| **1177** | A335 | 50f multicolored | .60 | .60 |
| **1178** | A335 | 50f multicolored | .60 | .60 |
| **1179** | A335 | 50f multicolored | .60 | .60 |
| **1180** | A335 | 50f multicolored | .60 | .60 |
| | *a.* | Block of 4, #1177-1180 | 2.75 | 2.75 |
| **1181** | A335 | 150f multicolored | 1.90 | 1.90 |
| **1182** | A335 | 150f multicolored | 1.90 | 1.90 |
| **1183** | A335 | 150f multicolored | 1.90 | 1.90 |
| **1184** | A335 | 150f multicolored | 1.90 | 1.90 |
| | *a.* | Block of 4, #1181-1184 | 9.00 | 9.00 |
| | *b.* | Miniature sheet of 8, #1177-1184 | 16.50 | 16.50 |
| | | *Nos. 1177-1184 (8)* | 10.00 | 10.00 |

Nos. 1180a, 1184a have continuous designs.

Palace of Justice
A336

**1992, July 4 *Perf. 12½***

| | | | | |
|---|---|---|---|---|
| **1185** | A336 | 25f lilac & multi | .40 | .30 |
| **1186** | A336 | 50f lil rose & multi | .80 | .50 |
| **1187** | A336 | 100f yel grn & multi | 1.25 | .90 |
| **1188** | A336 | 150f yel org & multi | 2.00 | 1.25 |
| **1189** | A336 | 250f blue grn & multi | 3.00 | 2.25 |
| | | *Nos. 1185-1189 (5)* | 7.45 | 5.20 |

1992 Summer Olympics, Barcelona — A337

Olympic flag, Fahed Al Ahmed Al Sabah, member of the Intl. Olympic committee and: 50f, Swimmer, soccer player. 100f, Runner, basketball player. 150f, Judo, equestrian.

**1992, July 25 *Perf. 14½***

| | | | | |
|---|---|---|---|---|
| **1190** | A337 | 50f multicolored | 1.00 | .65 |
| **1191** | A337 | 100f multicolored | 2.25 | 1.25 |
| **1192** | A337 | 150f multicolored | 3.25 | 2.00 |
| | | *Nos. 1190-1192 (3)* | 6.50 | 3.90 |

Invasion by Iraq, 2nd Anniv.
A338

Children's paintings: No. 1193, Tanks, people holding signs, two people being tortured. No. 1194, Truck, Iraqi soldiers looting. No. 1195, Iraqi soldiers killing civilians, tanks. No. 1196, Houses ablaze. No. 1197, Tanks, civilians, soldiers. No. 1198, Planes bombing in attack on fort. No. 1199, Tank, civilians holding flags, signs. No. 1200, Battlefield.

**1992, Aug. 2 Litho. *Perf. 14x14½***

| | | | | |
|---|---|---|---|---|
| **1193** | A338 | 50f multicolored | .60 | .60 |
| **1194** | A338 | 50f multicolored | .60 | .60 |
| **1195** | A338 | 50f multicolored | .60 | .60 |
| **1196** | A338 | 50f multicolored | .60 | .60 |
| | *a.* | Block of 4, #1193-1196 | 2.75 | 2.75 |
| **1197** | A338 | 150f multicolored | 1.90 | 1.90 |
| **1198** | A338 | 150f multicolored | 1.90 | 1.90 |
| **1199** | A338 | 150f multicolored | 1.90 | 1.90 |
| **1200** | A338 | 150f multicolored | 1.90 | 1.90 |
| | *a.* | Block of 4, #1197-1200 | 9.50 | 9.50 |
| | *b.* | Min. sheet of 8, #1193-1200 | 15.00 | 15.00 |
| | | *Nos. 1193-1200 (8)* | 10.00 | 10.00 |

Extinguishing of Oil Well Fires, 1st Anniv. — A339

Various scenes showing oil well fire being extinguished.

**1992 Litho. *Perf. 14½***

| | | | | |
|---|---|---|---|---|
| **1201** | A339 | 25f multi, vert. | .35 | .35 |
| **1202** | A339 | 50f multi, vert. | .70 | .70 |
| **1203** | A339 | 150f multi, vert. | 2.00 | 2.00 |
| **1204** | A339 | 250f multicolored | 3.50 | 3.50 |
| | | *Nos. 1201-1204 (4)* | 6.55 | 6.55 |

Kuwait Tower — A340

**1993, Jan. 16 Litho. *Perf. 14x15***

**Background Color**

| | | | | |
|---|---|---|---|---|
| **1205** | A340 | 25f lilac | .35 | .35 |
| **1206** | A340 | 100f blue | 1.25 | 1.25 |
| **1207** | A340 | 150f salmon | 2.00 | 1.75 |
| | | *Nos. 1205-1207 (3)* | 3.60 | 3.35 |

A341

**1993, Feb. 25 Litho. *Perf. 13½x14***

| | | | | |
|---|---|---|---|---|
| **1208** | A341 | 25f green & multi | .35 | .35 |
| **1209** | A341 | 50f blue & multi | .75 | .70 |
| **1210** | A341 | 150f pink & multi | 2.00 | 1.75 |
| | | *Nos. 1208-1210 (3)* | 3.10 | 2.80 |

National Day, 32nd anniv.

Liberation Day, 2nd Anniv. — A342

**1993, Feb. 26 *Perf. 15x14***

| | | | | |
|---|---|---|---|---|
| **1211** | A342 | 25f org yel & multi | .35 | .35 |
| **1212** | A342 | 50f green & multi | .75 | .75 |
| **1213** | A342 | 150f red lilac & multi | 2.00 | 1.75 |
| | | *Nos. 1211-1213 (3)* | 3.10 | 2.85 |

Remembering Prisoners of War — A343

Designs: 50f, Prisoner shackled in cell, vert. 150f, Shackled hand pointing to cell window, bird. 200f, Cell, prisoner's face, vert.

***Perf. 13½x14, 14x13½***

**1993, May 15 Litho.**

| | | | | |
|---|---|---|---|---|
| **1214** | A343 | 50f multicolored | .75 | .75 |
| **1215** | A343 | 150f multicolored | 2.00 | 2.00 |
| **1216** | A343 | 200f multicolored | 2.50 | 2.50 |
| | | *Nos. 1214-1216 (3)* | 5.25 | 5.25 |

18th Deaf Child Week — A344

**1993, Apr. 20 Litho. *Perf. 11½x12***

**Granite Paper**

| | | | | |
|---|---|---|---|---|
| **1217** | A344 | 25f gray & multi | .35 | .35 |
| **1218** | A344 | 50f green & multi | .75 | .75 |
| **1219** | A344 | 150f yellow & multi | 2.60 | 2.00 |
| **1220** | A344 | 350f blue & multi | 4.75 | 4.00 |
| | | *Nos. 1217-1220 (4)* | 8.45 | 7.10 |

A345

**1993, Aug. 2 Litho. *Perf. 13½x14***

| | | | | |
|---|---|---|---|---|
| **1221** | A345 | 50f green & multi | .60 | .60 |
| **1222** | A345 | 150f orange & multi | 2.00 | 1.75 |

Invasion by Iraq, 3rd anniv.

Kuwait Airforce, 40th Anniv. A346

**1993, Dec. 9 Litho. *Perf. 13x13½***

| | | | | |
|---|---|---|---|---|
| **1223** | A346 | 50f blue & multi | .60 | .60 |
| **1224** | A346 | 150f green & multi | 2.00 | 1.75 |

Natl. Day, 33rd Anniv. — A347

**1994, Feb. 25 Litho. *Perf. 13½x14***

| | | | | |
|---|---|---|---|---|
| **1225** | A347 | 25f salmon & multi | .40 | .40 |
| **1226** | A347 | 50f yellow & multi | .75 | .75 |
| **1227** | A347 | 150f green & multi | 2.00 | 1.75 |
| | | *Nos. 1225-1227 (3)* | 3.15 | 2.90 |

Liberation Day, 3rd Anniv. — A348

**1994, Feb. 26**

| | | | | |
|---|---|---|---|---|
| **1228** | A348 | 25f yellow & multi | .40 | .40 |
| **1229** | A348 | 50f blue & multi | .75 | .75 |
| **1230** | A348 | 150f gray green & multi | 2.10 | 1.90 |
| | | *Nos. 1228-1230 (3)* | 3.25 | 3.05 |

Central Bank of Kuwait, 25th Anniv. — A349

**1994, Apr. 20 Litho. *Perf. 13½x13***

| | | | | |
|---|---|---|---|---|
| **1231** | A349 | 25f salmon & multi | .40 | .40 |
| **1232** | A349 | 50f green & multi | .75 | .75 |
| **1233** | A349 | 150f blue violet & multi | 2.25 | 2.00 |
| | | *Nos. 1231-1233 (3)* | 3.40 | 3.15 |

A350

A351

Intl. Year of the Family A352

**1994, May 15 Litho. *Perf. 13***

| | | | | |
|---|---|---|---|---|
| **1234** | A350 | 50f multicolored | .75 | .75 |
| **1235** | A351 | 150f multicolored | 2.25 | 2.25 |
| **1236** | A352 | 200f multicolored | 3.25 | 3.00 |
| | | *Nos. 1234-1236 (3)* | 6.25 | 6.00 |

A353

**1994, June 5 Litho. *Perf. 14***

| | | | | |
|---|---|---|---|---|
| **1237** | A353 | 50f yellow & multi | .65 | .65 |
| **1238** | A353 | 100f blue & multi | 1.25 | 1.25 |
| **1239** | A353 | 150f green & multi | 2.00 | 1.75 |
| | | *Nos. 1237-1239 (3)* | 3.90 | 3.65 |

Industrial Bank of Kuwait, 20th anniv.

Martyr's Day — A354

**1994, June 15 Litho. *Perf. 13***

| | | | | |
|---|---|---|---|---|
| **1240** | A354 | 50f Whirlpool | .75 | .50 |
| **1241** | A354 | 100f Shifting sands | 1.50 | 1.00 |
| **1242** | A354 | 150f Finger print | 2.25 | 2.25 |
| **1243** | A354 | 250f Clouds | 2.75 | 2.50 |
| ***a.*** | | Min. sheet of 4, #1240-1243 | 9.00 | 9.00 |
| | | *Nos. 1240-1243 (4)* | 7.25 | 6.25 |

ILO, 75th Anniv. — A355

**1994, June 25 Litho. *Perf. 14***

| | | | | |
|---|---|---|---|---|
| **1244** | A355 | 50f vio & multi | .75 | .75 |
| **1245** | A355 | 150f pink & multi | 2.00 | 2.00 |
| **1246** | A355 | 350f blue & multi | 4.75 | 4.25 |
| | | *Nos. 1244-1246 (3)* | 7.50 | 7.00 |

A356

**1994, Aug. 2 Litho. *Perf. 12½x13½***

| | | | | |
|---|---|---|---|---|
| **1247** | A356 | 50f green blue & multi | .75 | .75 |
| **1248** | A356 | 150f blue & multi | 2.00 | 2.00 |
| **1249** | A356 | 350f lilac & multi | 4.75 | 4.25 |
| | | *Nos. 1247-1249 (3)* | 7.50 | 7.00 |

Invasion by Iraq, 4th anniv.

Port Authority — A357

**1994, Aug. 31 Litho. *Perf. 12½x14***

| | | | | |
|---|---|---|---|---|
| **1250** | A357 | 50f pink & multi | .75 | .75 |
| **1251** | A357 | 150f blue & multi | 2.00 | 2.00 |
| **1252** | A357 | 350f green & multi | 4.75 | 4.25 |
| | | *Nos. 1250-1252 (3)* | 7.50 | 7.00 |

Science Club, 20th Anniv. — A358

**1994, Sept. 11 *Perf. 14***

| | | | | |
|---|---|---|---|---|
| **1253** | A358 | 50f blue & multi | .75 | .75 |
| **1254** | A358 | 100f green & multi | 1.50 | 1.50 |
| **1255** | A358 | 150f red & multi | 2.00 | 1.75 |
| | | *Nos. 1253-1255 (3)* | 4.25 | 4.00 |

A359

Designs showing emblem and: 50f, Map of Arab countries, building. 100f, Windows, building. 150f, Doors below portico.

**1994, Nov. 12 *Perf. 11½***

| | | | | |
|---|---|---|---|---|
| **1256** | A359 | 50f multicolored | .75 | .75 |
| **1257** | A359 | 100f multicolored | 1.25 | 1.25 |
| **1258** | A359 | 150f multicolored | 2.50 | 2.25 |
| | | *Nos. 1256-1258 (3)* | 4.50 | 4.25 |

Arab Towns Organization, opening of headquarters.

ICAO, 50th Anniv. — A360

Designs: 100f, Emblems, sailing ship. 150f, Emblems, co-operation, co-ordination. 350f, Emblem, airplane in flight.

**1994, Dec. 7 *Perf. 14½***

| | | | | |
|---|---|---|---|---|
| **1259** | A360 | 100f silver, gold & multi | 1.50 | 1.50 |
| **1260** | A360 | 150f silver, gold & multi | 2.25 | 2.25 |
| **1261** | A360 | 350f gold & multi | 5.00 | 4.00 |
| | | *Nos. 1259-1261 (3)* | 8.75 | 7.75 |

Kuwait Airways, 40th Anniv. — A361

**1994, Dec. 20 *Perf. 13x14***

| | | | | |
|---|---|---|---|---|
| **1262** | A361 | 50f lake & multi | .75 | .75 |
| **1263** | A361 | 100f green & multi | 1.25 | 1.25 |
| **1264** | A361 | 150f slate & multi | 2.50 | 2.25 |
| | | *Nos. 1262-1264 (3)* | 4.50 | 4.25 |

1995 Census — A362

**1995, Feb. 6 Litho. *Perf. 14***

| | | | | |
|---|---|---|---|---|
| **1265** | A362 | 50f yellow & multi | .75 | .75 |
| **1266** | A362 | 100f green & multi | 1.25 | 1.25 |
| **1267** | A362 | 150f brown & multi | 2.50 | 2.25 |
| | | *Nos. 1265-1267 (3)* | 4.50 | 4.25 |

National Day, 34th Anniv. — A363

**1995, Feb. 25 *Perf. 13***

| | | | | |
|---|---|---|---|---|
| **1268** | A363 | 25f blue & multi | .40 | .40 |
| **1269** | A363 | 50f yellow & multi | .75 | .75 |
| **1270** | A363 | 150f lilac & multi | 2.25 | 1.75 |
| | | *Nos. 1268-1270 (3)* | 3.40 | 2.90 |

Liberation Day, 4th Anniv. — A364

**1995, Feb. 26**

| | | | | |
|---|---|---|---|---|
| **1271** | A364 | 25f blue & multi | .40 | .40 |
| **1272** | A364 | 50f green & multi | .75 | .75 |
| **1273** | A364 | 150f rose lilac & multi | 2.25 | 1.75 |
| | | *Nos. 1271-1273 (3)* | 3.40 | 2.90 |

Medical Research A365

50f, Medical building. 100f, Classroom instruction. 150f, Map of Kuwait.

**1995, Mar. 20 *Perf. 14***

| | | | | |
|---|---|---|---|---|
| **1274** | A365 | 50f multi | .75 | .75 |
| **1275** | A365 | 100f multi | 1.25 | 1.25 |
| **1276** | A365 | 150f multi | 2.25 | 2.00 |
| | | *Nos. 1274-1276 (3)* | 4.25 | 4.00 |

Arab League, 50th Anniv. A366

Designs: 50f, Kuwaiti, league flags over emblems, map, vert. 100f, Flags over "50," emblem. 150f, Flags as clasping hands, vert.

**1995, Mar. 22 *Perf. 13***

| | | | | |
|---|---|---|---|---|
| **1277** | A366 | 50f multicolored | .75 | .75 |
| **1278** | A366 | 100f multicolored | 1.25 | 1.25 |
| **1279** | A366 | 150f multicolored | 2.25 | 2.00 |
| | | *Nos. 1277-1279 (3)* | 4.25 | 4.00 |

World Health Day — A367

**1995, Apr. 7 Litho. *Perf. 13½x13***

| | | | | |
|---|---|---|---|---|
| **1280** | A367 | 50f blue & multi | .75 | .75 |
| **1281** | A367 | 150f pink & multi | 2.25 | 2.00 |
| **1282** | A367 | 200f yellow & multi | 2.75 | 2.50 |
| | | *Nos. 1280-1282 (3)* | 5.75 | 5.25 |

Volleyball, Cent. — A368

Designs: 50f, One gold ball. 100f, Gold "1," one gold ball. 150f, "1," both balls in gold.

**1995, June 5 Litho. *Perf. 14***

| | | | | |
|---|---|---|---|---|
| **1283** | A368 | 50f shown | .75 | .75 |
| **1284** | A368 | 100f multicolored | 1.25 | 1.25 |
| **1285** | A368 | 150f multicolored | 2.25 | 2.00 |
| | | *Nos. 1283-1285 (3)* | 4.25 | 4.00 |

Invasion by Iraq, 5th Anniv. — A369

**1995, Aug. 2 Litho. *Perf. 13***

| | | | | |
|---|---|---|---|---|
| **1286** | A369 | 50f purple & multi | .75 | .75 |
| **1287** | A369 | 100f red & multi | 1.25 | 1.25 |
| **1288** | A369 | 150f green & multi | 2.25 | 2.00 |
| | | *Nos. 1286-1288 (3)* | 4.25 | 4.00 |

UN, 50th Anniv. A370

**1995, Aug. 12 *Perf. 13x13½***

| | | | | |
|---|---|---|---|---|
| **1289** | A370 | 25f multi | .50 | .50 |
| **1290** | A370 | 50f orange & multi | 1.00 | 1.00 |
| **1291** | A370 | 150f bl grn & multi | 2.00 | 1.75 |
| | | *Nos. 1289-1291 (3)* | 3.50 | 3.25 |

FAO, 50th Anniv. — A371

People in traditional dress with: 50f, Cattle, camels, sheep. 100f, Fish, boat. 150f, Poultry, fruits, vegetables.

**1995, Sept. 21 *Perf. 13½x13***

| | | | | |
|---|---|---|---|---|
| **1292** | A371 | 50f multicolored | .75 | .75 |
| **1293** | A371 | 100f multicolored | 1.25 | 1.25 |
| **1294** | A371 | 150f multicolored | 2.25 | 2.00 |
| *a.* | | Min. sheet of 3, #1292-1294 | 5.00 | 5.00 |
| | | *Nos. 1292-1294 (3)* | 4.25 | 4.00 |

A372

World Standards Day — A373

**1995, Oct. 14 *Perf. 13***

| | | | | |
|---|---|---|---|---|
| **1295** | A372 | 50f multicolored | .75 | .75 |
| **1296** | A373 | 100f green & multi | 1.25 | 1.25 |
| **1297** | A373 | 150f violet & multi | 2.25 | 2.00 |
| | | *Nos. 1295-1297 (3)* | 4.25 | 4.00 |

Flowers — A374

Designs: 5f, Onobrychis ptolemaica. 15f, Convolvulus oxyphyllus. 25f, Papaver rhoeas. 50f, Moltkiopsis ciliata. 150f, Senecio desfontainei.

**1995, Nov. 15 Litho. *Perf. 14½***

| | | | | |
|---|---|---|---|---|
| **1298** | A374 | 5f multicolored | .30 | .30 |
| **1299** | A374 | 15f multicolored | .40 | .40 |
| **1300** | A374 | 25f multicolored | .75 | .75 |
| **1301** | A374 | 50f multicolored | 1.25 | 1.25 |
| **1302** | A374 | 150f multicolored | 2.50 | 2.00 |
| | | *Nos. 1298-1302 (5)* | 5.20 | 4.70 |

Natl. Day, 35th Anniv. — A375

**1996, Feb. 25 *Perf. 14***

| | | | | |
|---|---|---|---|---|
| **1303** | A375 | 25f lil rose & multi | .40 | .40 |
| **1304** | A375 | 50f blue green & multi | .75 | .75 |
| **1305** | A375 | 150f salmon & multi | 2.25 | 2.00 |
| | | *Nos. 1303-1305 (3)* | 3.40 | 3.15 |

Liberation Day, 5th Anniv. A376

**1996, Feb. 26**

| | | | | |
|---|---|---|---|---|
| **1306** | A376 | 25f violet & multi | .40 | .40 |
| **1307** | A376 | 50f brown & multi | .75 | .75 |
| **1308** | A376 | 150f blue green & multi | 2.25 | 2.00 |
| | | *Nos. 1306-1308 (3)* | 3.40 | 3.15 |

Arab City Day — A377

**1996, Mar. 1 *Perf. 13½***

| | | | | |
|---|---|---|---|---|
| **1309** | A377 | 50f yel grn & multi | .75 | .75 |
| **1310** | A377 | 100f pink & multi | 1.50 | 1.50 |
| **1311** | A377 | 150f blue green & multi | 2.25 | 2.00 |
| | | *Nos. 1309-1311 (3)* | 4.50 | 4.25 |

A378

**1996, Jan. 27 *Perf. 14***

| | | | | |
|---|---|---|---|---|
| **1312** | A378 | 50f blue & multi | .75 | .75 |
| **1313** | A378 | 100f gray & multi | 1.25 | 1.25 |
| **1314** | A378 | 150f rose lilac & multi | 2.25 | 2.00 |
| | | *Nos. 1312-1314 (3)* | 4.25 | 4.00 |

Scouting in Kuwait, 60th Anniv. — A379

50f, On top of watchtower. 100f, Drawing water from well. 150f, Planting seedling.

**1996, Jan. 14 *Perf. 13½***

| | | | | |
|---|---|---|---|---|
| **1315** | A379 | 50f yellow & multi | 1.00 | 1.00 |
| **1316** | A379 | 100f lilac & multi | 2.25 | 2.25 |
| **1317** | A379 | 150f blue green & multi | 3.50 | 3.00 |
| | | *Nos. 1315-1317 (3)* | 6.75 | 6.25 |

Kuwait Money Show — A380

**1996, Jan. 2 *Perf. 14***

| | | | | |
|---|---|---|---|---|
| **1318** | A380 | 25f gold & multi | .40 | .40 |
| **1319** | A380 | 100f blue & multi | 1.50 | 1.25 |
| **1320** | A380 | 150f dk gray & multi | 2.25 | 2.00 |
| | | *Nos. 1318-1320 (3)* | 4.15 | 3.65 |

7th Kuwait Dental Assoc. Conference — A381

**1996, Mar. 27 Litho. *Perf. 14x13½***

| | | | | |
|---|---|---|---|---|
| **1321** | A381 | 25f orange & multi | .40 | .40 |
| **1322** | A381 | 50f violet & multi | .75 | .75 |
| **1323** | A381 | 150f blue & multi | 2.25 | 2.00 |
| | | *Nos. 1321-1323 (3)* | 3.40 | 3.15 |

UNESCO, 50th Anniv. — A382

**1996, Apr. 10 *Perf. 13½x14***

| | | | | |
|---|---|---|---|---|
| **1324** | A382 | 25f violet & multi | .40 | .40 |
| **1325** | A382 | 100f green & multi | 1.25 | 1.25 |
| **1326** | A382 | 150f orange & multi | 2.25 | 2.00 |
| | | *Nos. 1324-1326 (3)* | 3.90 | 3.65 |

1st Oil Exports, 50th Anniv. — A383

**1996, June 30 Litho. *Perf. 13***

| | | | | |
|---|---|---|---|---|
| **1327** | A383 | 25f multicolored | .40 | .40 |
| **1328** | A383 | 100f gray & multi | 1.50 | 1.50 |
| **1329** | A383 | 150f bister & multi | 2.25 | 2.00 |
| | | *Nos. 1327-1329 (3)* | 4.15 | 3.90 |

Rule of Al-Sabah Family, Cent. — A384

**1996, Aug. 12**

| | | | | |
|---|---|---|---|---|
| **1330** | A384 | 25f shown | .40 | .40 |
| **1331** | A384 | 50f Shiek, flags | .75 | .75 |
| **1332** | A384 | 150f like #1330 | 2.25 | 2.00 |
| | | *Nos. 1330-1332 (3)* | 3.40 | 3.15 |

1996 Summer Olympic Games, Atlanta — A385

**1996, Oct. 5 *Perf. 13½***

| | | | | |
|---|---|---|---|---|
| **1333** | A385 | 25f Shooting | .50 | .40 |
| **1334** | A385 | 50f Running | 1.00 | .75 |
| **1335** | A385 | 100f Weight lifting | 2.00 | 1.25 |
| **1336** | A385 | 150f Fencing | 3.25 | 2.25 |
| | | *Nos. 1333-1336 (4)* | 6.75 | 4.65 |

A 750f souvenir sheet exists. Value $150.

Kuwait University, 30th Anniv. — A386

**1996, Nov. 27 Litho. *Perf. 13½x14***

| | | | | |
|---|---|---|---|---|
| **1337** | A386 | 25f green & multi | .40 | .40 |
| **1338** | A386 | 100f blue & multi | 1.50 | 1.50 |
| **1339** | A386 | 150f yellow & multi | 2.25 | 2.00 |
| | | *Nos. 1337-1339 (3)* | 4.15 | 3.90 |

1st Children's Cultural Festival — A387

**1996, Nov. 20 *Perf. 14x13½***

| | | | | |
|---|---|---|---|---|
| **1340** | A387 | 25f brn gray & multi | .40 | .40 |
| **1341** | A387 | 100f multicolored | 1.50 | 1.50 |
| **1342** | A387 | 150f yel grn & multi | 2.25 | 2.00 |
| | | *Nos. 1340-1342 (3)* | 4.15 | 3.90 |

3rd Al-Qurain Cultrual Festival — A388

**1996, Nov. 20 *Perf. 14***

| | | | | |
|---|---|---|---|---|
| **1343** | A388 | 50f orange & multi | .75 | .75 |
| **1344** | A388 | 100f blue & multi | 1.50 | 1.50 |
| **1345** | A388 | 150f green & multi | 2.25 | 2.00 |
| | | *Nos. 1343-1345 (3)* | 4.50 | 4.25 |

Liberation Tower — A389

**1996, Dec. 10** *Perf. 13x13½*

1346 A389 5f red & multi .25 .25
1347 A389 10f yel bis & multi .25 .25
1348 A389 15f brt rose & multi .40 .30
1349 A389 25f pale pink & multi .50 .45
*a.* Booklet pane of 4 —
Complete booklet, #1349a —
1350 A389 50f violet & multi 1.10 .90
*a.* Booklet pane of 4 —
Complete booklet, #1350a —
1351 A389 100f brt yel & multi 2.00 1.25
1352 A389 150f blue & multi 3.25 2.00
*a.* Booklet pane of 4 —
Complete booklet, #1352a —
1353 A389 200f pink & multi 4.50 3.25
1354 A389 250f dp bl & multi 5.50 4.00
1355 A389 350f blue & multi 7.50 5.00
*Nos. 1346-1355 (10)* 25.25 17.65
Set of 3 booklets, #1349a-1350a, 1352a *31.00*

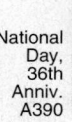

National Day, 36th Anniv. A390

**1997, Feb. 25 Litho.** *Perf. 14½*

1356 A390 25f blue & multi .40 .40
1357 A390 50f lilac & multi .75 .75
1358 A390 150f orange & multi 2.25 2.00
*Nos. 1356-1358 (3)* 3.40 3.15

Liberation Day, 6th Anniv. A391

**1997, Feb. 26** *Perf. 13x13½*

1359 A391 25f tan & multi .40 .40
1360 A391 50f lilac & multi .75 .75
1361 A391 150f blue & multi 2.25 2.00
*Nos. 1359-1361 (3)* 3.40 3.15

Marine Life — A392

No. 1368: Various views of a school of shrimp: a, b, c, d, 25f. e, f, g, h, 50f. i, j, k, l, 100f. m, n, o, p, 150f.

**1997, Jan. 15** *Perf. 14½*

1362 A392 25f Maid .40 .40
1363 A392 50f Sheim .75 .75
1364 A392 100f Hamoor 1.50 1.50
1365 A392 150f Sobaity 2.25 2.25
1366 A392 200f Nagroor 3.25 3.25
1367 A392 350f Zobaidy 5.50 5.50
*Nos. 1362-1367 (6)* 13.65 13.65

**Sheet of 16**

1368 A392 Sheet of 16, #a.-p. 19.00 19.00

Montreal Protocol on Substances that Deplete Ozone Layer, 10th Anniv. — A393

**1997, Sept. 16 Litho.** *Perf. 13½x13*

1369 A393 25f blue & multi .40 .40
1370 A393 50f violet & multi .75 .75
1371 A393 150f bl grn & multi 2.25 2.00
*Nos. 1369-1371 (3)* 3.40 3.15

Industries Exhibition A394

**1997, Oct. 1**

1372 A394 25f brt pink & multi .40 .40
1373 A394 50f green & multi .75 .75
1374 A394 150f blue & multi 2.25 2.00
*Nos. 1372-1374 (3)* 3.40 3.15

22nd Kuwait Arabic Book Exhibition A395

**1997, Nov. 19 Litho.** *Perf. 13½x13*

**Border Color**

1375 A395 25f pink .40 .40
1376 A395 50f blue .75 .75
1377 A395 150f blue green 2.25 2.00
*Nos. 1375-1377 (3)* 3.40 3.15

Cultural History A396

a, 50f, Qibliya Girls School, 1937. b, 50f, Scissors cutting ribbon, Fine Arts Exhibition, 1959. c, 150f, Folk Theatre Group, 1956. d, 25f, 1st Book Fair, 1975. e, 25f, Kuwait Magazine, 1928. f, 50f, Mubarakiya School, 1912. g, 50f, Kuwait Natl. Museum, 1958. h, 150f, Academy of Music, 1972. i, 25f, A'lam Al-Fikr (periodical), 1970. j, 25f, Al'Bitha Magazine, 1946. k, 50f, Building complex, 1953 (Al-Arabi Magazine). l, 50f, Building, 1959. m, 150f, Al-Sharqiya Cinema, 1955. n, 25f, Al'Lam Al Ma'rifa (periodical), 1978. o, 25f, Dalil Almohtar Fi Alaam al-Bihar (boat), 1923. p, 50f, Alma'had Aldini (arabesques), 1947. q, 50f, Folklore Center, 1956. r, 150f, Theatrical Academy, 1967. s, 25f, Al-Arabi Magazine, 1958. t, 25f, Public Library (book), 1923. u, 50f, Al Ma'Arif Printing Press (Arabic writing), 1947. v, 50f, Literary Club, 1924. w, 150f, Bas Ya Bahar (1st Kuwaitii feature film), 1970. x, 25f, Al Thaqafa Al-Alamiya (periodical), 1981. y, 25f, The World Theatre (periodical), 1969.

**1997, Nov. 30**

1378 A396 Sheet of 25, #a.-y. 25.00 25.00

Nos. 1378a-1378y each contain year date of event depicted.

Educational Science Museum, 25th Anniv. A397

Designs: 25f, Whale, quadrant, vert. 50f, Space exploration, whale, dinosaur. No. 1381, Astronaut, dinosaur, satellite dish, airplane, globe, skeleton encircling whale, vert.

No. 1382, Coelacanth.

*Perf. 13½x13, 13x13½*

**1997, Nov. 1 Litho.**

1379 A397 25f multicolored .40 .40
1380 A397 50f multicolored .75 .75
1381 A397 150f multicolored 2.75 2.25
*Nos. 1379-1381 (3)* 3.90 3.40

**Souvenir Sheet**

1382 A397 150f multicolored 15.00 15.00

No. 1382 is a continuous design and sold for 1d.

18th Summit of Gulf Cooperation Countries — A398

Designs: 25f, Flags of member countries, doves, vert. 50f, Map, birds with flag colors. 150f, Doves perched atop flags, vert.

**1997, Dec. 20** *Perf. 13½x14*

1383 A398 25f multicolored .50 .50
1384 A398 50f multicolored 1.00 1.00
1385 A398 150f multicolored 3.25 2.75
*a.* Bklt. pane of 3, #1383-1385 *14.00*
Complete booklet, #1385a *14.00*
*Nos. 1383-1385 (3)* 4.75 4.25

National Day, 37th Anniv. A399

**1998, Feb. 25 Litho.** *Perf. 13x13½*

1386 A399 25f yellow & multi .50 .50
1387 A399 50f pink & multi 1.00 1.00
1388 A399 150f blue & multi 3.25 2.75
*Nos. 1386-1388 (3)* 4.75 4.25

Liberation Day, 7th Anniv. A400

**1998, Feb. 26**

1389 A400 25f yellow & multi .50 .50
1390 A400 50f orange & multi 1.00 1.00
1391 A400 150f green & multi 3.25 2.75
*Nos. 1389-1391 (3)* 4.75 4.25

Say No to Drugs — A401

**1998, Mar. 16 Litho.** *Perf. 13½x13*

1392 A401 25f tan & multi .50 .50
1393 A401 50f blue & multi 1.00 1.00
1394 A401 150f white & multi 3.25 2.75
*Nos. 1392-1394 (3)* 4.75 4.25

Chernobyl disaster, 10th Anniv. — A402

**1997, May 2 Litho.** *Perf. 13½x13*

1395 A402 25f orange & multi .50 .50
1396 A402 50f blue & multi 1.00 1.00
1397 A402 150f red & multi 3.25 2.75
*Nos. 1395-1397 (3)* 4.75 4.25

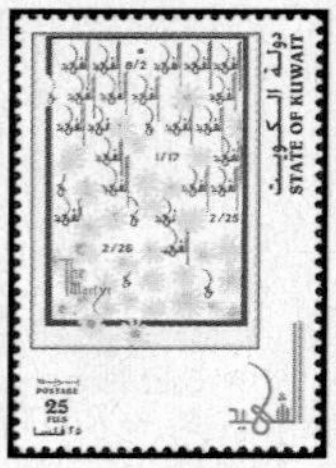


Martyrs — A403

25f, Dates, 1/17, 2/25, 2/26, flowers. 50f, Stylized tree. 150f, Lines, inscriptions.

No. 1401: a, Man with hands in dirt. b, Three boys emptying basket of dirt.

**1998, Mar. 31 Litho.** *Perf. 14*

1398 A403 25f multicolored .50 .50
1399 A403 50f multicolored 1.00 1.00
1400 A403 150f multicolored 3.50 3.00
*a.* Bklt. pane, 2 ea #1398-1400 16.00
Complete booklet, #1400a 16.00

***Perf. 14½ Between***

**Size: 31x54mm**

1401 A403 500f Pair, a.-b. 17.50 17.50
*Nos. 1398-1401 (4)* 22.50 22.00

Ban Land Mines — A405

Stylized amputees using crutches for support: 25f, Two people. 50f, One person. 150f, Two people, nurse.

500f, Three people, nurse.

**1998, Aug. 2** *Perf. 14½*

1402 A405 25f multicolored .50 .50
1403 A405 50f multicolored 1.00 1.00
1404 A405 150f multicolored 2.50 2.50

**Size: 89x82mm**

***Imperf***

1405 A405 500f multicolored 11.00 11.00
*Nos. 1402-1405 (4)* 15.00 15.00

Life in Pre-Oil Kuwait — A406

Designs: 25f, Seated at ceremonial meal. 50f, Building boat. 100f, Weaving. 150f, Loading boat. 250f, Pouring water from water skin into bowl. 350f, Man with pigeons.

**1998, Apr. 14 Litho.** *Perf. 14*

**Booklet Stamps**

1406 A406 25f multicolored .50 .50
1407 A406 50d multicolored 1.00 1.00
1408 A406 100f multicolored 2.00 2.00
1409 A406 150f multicolored 3.00 3.00
1410 A406 250f multicolored 5.00 5.00
1411 A406 350f multicolored 7.00 7.00
*a.* Booklet pane, #1406-1411 27.50
Complete booklet, #1411a 27.50

**1998, Sept. 1 Litho.** *Perf. 14*

25f, Man shaving another man's head. 50f, Woman using grindstone. 100f, Man pulling thread through cloth. 150f, Man gluing artifacts together. 250f, Potter. 350f, Veiled woman holding rope.

**Booklet Stamps**

1412 A406 25f multicolored .50 .50
1413 A406 50f multicolored 1.00 1.00
1414 A406 100f multicolored 2.00 2.00
1415 A406 150f multicolored 3.00 3.00
1416 A406 250f multicolored 5.00 5.00
1417 A406 350f multicolored 7.00 7.00
*a.* Booklet pane, #1412-1417 27.50
Complete booklet, #1417a 27.50

Emblem of Kuwait Post A407

**1998, Oct. 3 Litho. *Perf. 13x13½***

| | | | | | |
|---|---|---|---|---|---|
| 1418 | A407 | 25f green & multi | .40 | .40 |
| 1419 | A407 | 50f blue & multi | .80 | .80 |
| 1420 | A407 | 100f brt pink & multi | 1.25 | 1.25 |
| 1421 | A407 | 150f orange & multi | 2.25 | 2.25 |
| 1422 | A407 | 250f brick red & multi | 3.50 | 3.00 |
| | | *Nos. 1418-1422 (5)* | 8.20 | 7.70 |

Intl. Year of the Ocean — A408

**1998, June 1 Litho. *Perf. 13½***

| | | | | |
|---|---|---|---|---|
| 1423 | A408 | 25f green & multi | .50 | .50 |
| 1424 | A408 | 50f blue & multi | 1.00 | 1.00 |
| 1425 | A408 | 150f lilac & multi | 3.25 | 3.00 |
| | | *Nos. 1423-1425 (3)* | 4.75 | 4.50 |

No. 1424 is 27x37mm.

Union of Consumer Co-operative Societies, 25th Anniv. — A409

**1998, July 1 Litho. *Perf. 13½x13***

| | | | | |
|---|---|---|---|---|
| 1426 | A409 | 25f buff & multi | .50 | .50 |
| 1427 | A409 | 50f blue & multi | 1.00 | 1.00 |
| 1428 | A409 | 150f multicolored | 3.25 | 3.00 |
| | | *Nos. 1426-1428 (3)* | 4.75 | 4.50 |

Children's Cultural House — A410

**1998, Nov. 28 Litho. *Perf. 13½x13***

| | | | | |
|---|---|---|---|---|
| 1429 | A410 | 25f yellow & multi | .50 | .50 |
| 1430 | A410 | 50f grn, yel & multi | 1.00 | 1.00 |
| 1431 | A410 | 150f green & multi | 3.00 | 2.75 |
| | | *Nos. 1429-1431 (3)* | 4.50 | 4.25 |

A411

**1998, Dec. 10 *Perf. 14x14½***

| | | | | |
|---|---|---|---|---|
| 1432 | A411 | 25f multicolored | .50 | .50 |
| 1433 | A411 | 50f multicolored | 1.00 | 1.00 |
| 1434 | A411 | 150f multicolored | 3.00 | 2.75 |
| | | *Nos. 1432-1434 (3)* | 4.50 | 4.25 |

Universal Declaration of Human Rights, 50th anniv.

A412

**1998 Litho. *Perf. 14x14½***

| | | | | |
|---|---|---|---|---|
| 1435 | A412 | 25f orange & multi | .40 | .40 |
| 1436 | A412 | 50f violet & multi | .80 | .80 |
| 1437 | A412 | 150f green & multi | 2.50 | 2.25 |
| | | *Nos. 1435-1437 (3)* | 3.70 | 3.45 |

The Public Authority for Applied Education and Training, 25th anniv.

Organ Transplantation in Kuwait, 20th Anniv. — A413

**1999 Litho. *Perf. 13x13½***

| | | | | |
|---|---|---|---|---|
| 1438 | A413 | 50f Liver | .75 | .75 |
| 1439 | A413 | 150f Heart | 2.25 | 2.00 |

Liberation Day, 8th Anniv. A414

**1999, Feb. 26**

| | | | | |
|---|---|---|---|---|
| 1440 | A414 | 50f Building | .75 | .75 |
| 1441 | A414 | 150f Building, diff. | 2.25 | 2.00 |

Sief Palace Complex — A415

Various buildings in complex.

**1999 *Perf. 15x14***

| | | | | |
|---|---|---|---|---|
| 1442 | A415 | 25f multicolored | .30 | .30 |
| 1443 | A415 | 50f multicolored | .50 | .50 |
| 1444 | A415 | 100f multicolored | 1.25 | 1.25 |
| 1445 | A415 | 150f multicolored | 2.00 | 2.00 |
| 1446 | A415 | 250f multicolored | 3.75 | 3.75 |
| 1447 | A415 | 350f multicolored | 5.00 | 5.00 |
| *a.* | | Booklet pane, #1442-1447 | 16.00 | |
| | | Complete booklet, #1447a | 16.00 | |
| | | *Nos. 1442-1447 (6)* | 12.80 | 12.80 |

Al Arabi Magazine A416

**1999 *Perf. 13½x13***

| | | | | |
|---|---|---|---|---|
| 1448 | A416 | 50f violet & multi | .75 | .75 |
| 1449 | A416 | 150f green & multi | 2.25 | 2.00 |

Natl. Day, 38th Anniv. A417

**1999 *Perf. 13x13½***

| | | | | |
|---|---|---|---|---|
| 1450 | A417 | 50f brown & multi | .75 | .75 |
| 1451 | A417 | 150f blue & multi | 2.25 | 2.00 |

Hawk A418

Sailing Ship A419

50f, Camel. 100f, Traditional Boat.

**1999(?)-2003 Litho. *Perf. 14½x14***

| | | | | |
|---|---|---|---|---|
| 1452 | A418 | 25f multicolored | .75 | .75 |
| 1453 | A418 | 50f multicolored | 1.50 | 1.50 |

**Coil Stamp**

| | | | | |
|---|---|---|---|---|
| 1453A | A419 | 100f multicolored | 2.00 | 2.00 |
| 1454 | A419 | 150f multicolored | 4.50 | 4.50 |
| | | *Nos. 1452-1454 (4)* | 8.75 | 8.75 |

Issued: 100f, Jan. 2003.

Science Club, 25th Anniv. A420

Background color: 50f, Blue. 150f, Green. 350f, Red.

**1999, Oct. 20 Litho. *Perf. 13x13¼***

| | | | | |
|---|---|---|---|---|
| 1455-1457 | A420 | Set of 3 | 8.50 | 8.50 |

Intl. Civil Aviation Day — A421

**1999, Dec. 7 Litho. *Perf. 13x13¼***

| | | | | |
|---|---|---|---|---|
| 1458 | A421 | 50f multi | 1.00 | 1.00 |
| 1459 | A421 | 150f multi | 2.75 | 2.75 |
| 1460 | A421 | 250f multi | 4.50 | 4.00 |
| | | *Nos. 1458-1460 (3)* | 8.25 | 7.75 |

UPU, 125th Anniv. — A421a

Panel colors: 50f, Orange. 150f, Purple. 350f, Green.

1d, Two hemispheres.

**1999 Litho. *Perf. 13¼x13***

| | | | | |
|---|---|---|---|---|
| 1460A-1460C | A421a | Set of 3 | 8.50 | 8.50 |
| *1460Ce* | | Booklet pane, #1460A-1460C + label | 8.50 | |
| | | Booklet, #1460Ce | 8.50 | |

**Size: 100x75mm**

***Imperf***

| | | | | |
|---|---|---|---|---|
| 1460D | A421a | 1d multi | 14.50 | 14.50 |

Kuwait Intl. Airport — A422

**2000, Jan. 2 *Perf. 13¼x13***

| | | | | |
|---|---|---|---|---|
| 1461 | A422 | 50f multi | .75 | .75 |
| 1462 | A422 | 150f multi | 1.75 | 1.75 |
| 1463 | A422 | 250f multi | 4.00 | 3.75 |
| | | *Nos. 1461-1463 (3)* | 6.50 | 6.25 |

National Day, 39th Anniv. — A423

**2000**

| | | | | |
|---|---|---|---|---|
| 1464 | A423 | 25f multi | .50 | .50 |
| 1465 | A423 | 50f multi | 1.00 | 1.00 |
| 1466 | A423 | 150f multi | 3.25 | 3.00 |
| | | *Nos. 1464-1466 (3)* | 4.75 | 4.50 |

Liberation Day, 9th Anniv. — A424

**2000**

| | | | | |
|---|---|---|---|---|
| 1467 | A424 | 25f multi | 1.00 | 1.00 |
| 1468 | A424 | 50f multi | 2.75 | 2.75 |
| 1469 | A424 | 150f multi | 3.75 | 3.75 |
| | | *Nos. 1467-1469 (3)* | 7.50 | 7.50 |

Kuwait Conference for Autism and Communication Deficits — A425

Designs: 25f, Puzzle pieces, three children, Kuwait Tower. 50f, Puzzle pieces, children. 150f, Children, Kuwait Tower, flowers.

**2000 *Perf. 13x13¼***

| | | | | |
|---|---|---|---|---|
| 1470 | A425 | 25f multi | .50 | .50 |
| 1471 | A425 | 50f multi | 1.00 | 1.00 |
| 1472 | A425 | 150f multi | 3.25 | 3.00 |
| | | *Nos. 1470-1472 (3)* | 4.75 | 4.50 |

Kuwait City — A425a

Background colors: 50f, Blue. 150f, Green. 350f, Red violet.

**2000, Apr. 24 Litho. *Perf. 14x14½***

| | | | | |
|---|---|---|---|---|
| 1472A-1472C | A425a | Set of 3 | 6.50 | 6.50 |

Third Special Education Week — A425b

Background color: 50f, Yellow. 150f, Salmon. 350f, Blue.

**2000, May 10 *Perf. 13¼x13***

| | | | | |
|---|---|---|---|---|
| 1472D-1472F | A425b | Set of 3 | 6.50 | 6.50 |

2000 Summer Olympics, Sydney
A425c

Emblems of 2002 Olympics, Kuwait Olympic Committee and: 25f, Judo. 50f, Shooting. 150f, Swimming. 200f, Weight lifting. 250f, Hurdles. 350f, Soccer.

No. 1472M, Emblems of 2002 Olympics, Kuwait Olympic Committee and judo, swimming, shooting, weight lifting, hurdles and soccer.

**2000 Litho. *Perf. 13x13¼***
**1472G-1472L** A425c Set of 6 15.00 15.00

**Souvenir Sheet**

**Size: 98x69mm**

**1472M** A425c 1d multi *65.00 65.00*

Sixth Gulf Cooperation Council Countries Joint Stamp Exhibition, Kuwait
A425d

Denomination color: 25f, Blue. 50f, Red. 150f, Green.

1d, Emblems of previous exhibitions.

**2000 Litho. *Perf. 14¼***
**1472N-1472P** A425d Set of 3 4.50 4.50

**Size: 146x112mm**

***Imperf***

**1472Q** A425d 1d multi 17.00 17.00

Intl. Investment Forum
A426

Background colors: 25f, Gray. 50f, White. 150f, Black.

**2000, Mar. 4 Litho. *Perf. 13x13¼***
**1473-1475** A426 Set of 3 4.50 4.50

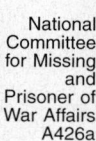

National Committee for Missing and Prisoner of War Affairs
A426a

Designs: 25f, Emblem. 50f, Emblem and chains. 150f, Emblem and years.

**2000, Aug. 2 Litho. *Perf. 13x13¼***
**1475A-1475C** A426a Set of 3 3.25 3.25

Kuwaiti Dental Association, 25th Anniv. — A426b

Frame color: 50f, Pink. 150f, Light blue. 350f, Lilac.

**2000, Oct. 15 *Perf. 13¼x13***
**1475D-1475F** A426b Set of 3 6.50 6.50

World Environment Day — A427

Denominations, 50f, 150f, 350f.

**2000 Litho. *Perf. 13x13¼***
**1476-1478** A427 Set of 3 7.00 7.00

Gulf Investment Corporation, 15th Anniv. — A428

New Gulf Investment Corporation headquarters, emblem, "15" and frame color of: 25f, Green. 50f, Blue. 150f, Red.

**2000, Oct. 31 Litho. *Perf. 13x13¼***
**1479-1481** A428 Set of 3 4.75 4.75

General Administration of Customs, Cent. — A429

Denominations: 50f, 150f, 350f.

**2000 Litho. *Perf. 13¼x14***
**1482-1484** A429 Set of 3 6.75 6.75
*a.* Booklet pane, #1482-1484 15.00
Complete booklet, #1484a 15.00

***Imperf***

**Size: 100x75mm**

**1485** A429 1d multi 13.50 13.50

No. 1485 contains one 47x28mm perf. 13¼x14 non-denominated label.

Hala Fibrayar — A430

Panel colors: 25f, Purple. 50f, Red violet. 150f, Blue.

**2001 Litho. *Perf. 13¼x13***
**1486-1488** A430 Set of 3 4.75 4.75

Prisoners of War — A431

Background colors: 25f, White. 50f, Blue & blue green. 150f, Multicolored.

**2001 *Perf. 13x13¼***
**1489-1491** A431 Set of 3 4.25 4.25

UN High Commissioner for Refugees, 50th Anniv. — A432

Various depictions of anniversary emblem: 25f, 50f, 150f.

**2001**
**1492-1494** A432 Set of 3 4.75 4.75

Kuwait, 2001 Arab Cultural Capital
A433

Background colors: 25f, Yellow. 50f, Green. 150f, Blue.

**2001**
**1495-1497** A433 Set of 3 4.75 4.75

Liberation Day, 10th Anniv. — A434

Frame color: 25f, Lilac. 50f, Blue. 150f, Yellow.

**2001 *Perf. 13¼x13***
**1498-1500** A434 Set of 3 4.75 4.75

National Day, 40th Anniv. — A435

Frame color: 25f, Orange. 50f, Yellow. 150f, Blue green.

**2001**
**1501-1503** A435 Set of 3 4.75 4.75

Kuwait Diving Team, 10th Anniv.
A436

"10" and: 25f, Fish. 50f, Divers. 150f, Shark, turtle, vert.

**2001 *Perf. 13x13¼, 13¼x13***
**1504-1506** A436 Set of 3 4.75 4.75

Radio Kuwait, 50th Anniv.
A437

Frame color: 25f, Yellow brown. 50f, Blue, vert. 150f, Red, vert.

**2001 *Perf. 13x13¼, 13¼x13***
**1507-1509** A437 Set of 3 4.75 4.75

Intifada
A438

Dome of the Rock, Jerusalem: 25f, 50f, 150f.

**2001 *Perf. 13x13¼***
**1510-1512** A438 Set of 3 5.00 5.00

Year of Dialogue Among Civilizations
A439

Background colors: 25f, Orange & yellow. 50f, Dark & light green. 150f, Rose & pink.

**2001 *Perf. 13¼x13***
**1513-1515** A439 Set of 3 4.75 4.75

Human Rights
A440

Designs: 25f, Hands covering man's face, vert. 50f, Barbed wire, clock, man's face. 150f, Chains, globe, child, woman.

**2001 *Perf. 13¼x13, 13x13¼***
**1516-1518** A440 Set of 3 4.75 4.75

A441

A442

AWQAF Foundation
A443

**2001 *Perf. 14x13***
**1519** A441 25f multi .50 .50
**1520** A442 50f multi 1.00 1.00
**1521** A443 150f multi 3.25 3.25
*Nos. 1519-1521 (3)* 4.75 4.75

Kuwait Fund for Arab Economic Development, 40th Anniv. — A444

Background colors: 25f, Yellow. 50f, Green & gray.

**2001** ***Perf. 13¼x13***
**1522-1523** A444 Set of 2 1.75 1.75

Touristic Enterprises Company, 25th Anniv. — A445

Stylistic flora: 25f, 50f, 100f, 150f. 250f, Combined designs of four stamps.

**2001** ***Perf. 13¼x13***
**1524-1527** A445 Set of 4 7.50 7.50

**Size: 60x80mm**

***Imperf***

**1528** A445 250f multi 6.00 6.00

National Bank of Kuwait, 50th Anniv. A447

Emblem and: 25f, Facade of old building. 50f, Modern building. 150f, Camels.

**2002, Jan. 16** **Litho.** ***Perf. 13x13¼***
**1532-1534** A447 Set of 3 4.75 4.75

Liberation Day, 11th Anniv. — A448

Background color: 25f, Light blue. 50f, Light yellow. 150f, White.

**2002, Feb. 26** ***Perf. 13¼x13***
**1535-1537** A448 Set of 3 4.75 4.75

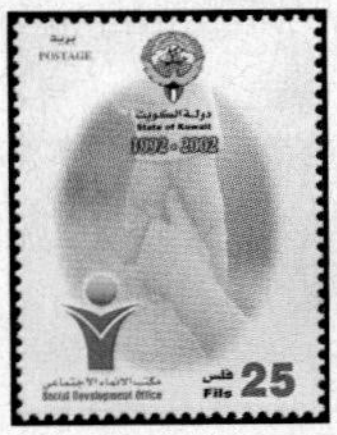

Social Development Office, 10th Anniv. — A449

Background color: 25f, Light yellow. 50f, Light blue.

**2002, Apr. 21**
**1538-1539** A449 Set of 2 1.75 1.75

41st National Day — A450

Frame color: 25f, Orange. 50f, Green. 150f, Purple.

**2002, Feb. 25** **Litho.** ***Perf. 13¼x13***
**1540-1542** A450 Set of 3 4.50 4.50

Nomadism From the Hejaz to Africa — A451

Top panel color: 25f, Pale orange. 50f, Blue. 150f, Purple.

**2002, Mar. 11**
**1543-1545** A451 Set of 3 5.00 5.00

Rehabilitation of Al-Qurain Landfill Site — A452

Panel color: 25f, Blue. 50f, Purple. 150f, Green.

**2002, Apr. 1**
**1546-1548** A452 Set of 3 4.50 4.50

Kuwait Scientific Center — A453

Designs; Nos. 1549a, 1550e, Lapwing. Nos. 1549b, 1550d, Spur-winged plover. Nos. 1549c, 1550c, Eurasian river otter. Nos. 1549d, 1550b, Saltwater crocodile. Nos. 1549e, 1550i, Fennec fox. Nos. 1549f, 1550h, Caracal. Nos. 1549g, 1550g, Cushion sister starfish. Nos. 1549h, 1550f, Cuttlefish. Nos. 1549i, 1550m, Sand tiger shark. Nos. 1549j, 1550l, Lionfish. Nos. 1549k, 1550k, Kestrel. Nos. 1549l, 1550j, Egyptian fruit bat. Nos. 1549m, 1550a, Science center.

***Perf. 13¼x13¾, 14x13¼ (#1550k)***

**2002, Apr. 17**
**1549** Sheet of 13 24.00 24.00
*a.-l.* A453 25f Any single .25 .25
*m.* A453 50f multi .30 .30
**1550** Booklet of 13 panes 40.00
*a.-m.* A453 50f Any single pane .30 .30

***Imperf***

**Size: 80x60mm**

**1551** A453 250f shown 12.00 12.00

Stamp sizes: Nos. 1549a-1549l, 30x25mm; No. 1549m, 45x27mm. Nos. 1550a-1550j, 1550l-1550m, 50x36mm; No. 1550k, 32x48mm.

Kuwait Foundation for the Advancement of Sciences, 25th Anniv. (in 2001) — A454

Foundation emblem and: 25f, 25th anniversary emblem. 50f, 25th anniversary emblem and building. 150f, Map of Kuwait, vert.

***Perf. 13x13¼, 13¼x13***

**2002 ?** **Litho.**
**1552-1554** A454 Set of 3 4.75 4.75

Intl. Volunteers Year (in 2001) — A455

Background colors: 25f, White. 50f, Lilac. 150f, Yellow.

**2002 ?** ***Perf. 13¼x13***
**1555-1557** A455 Set of 3 4.50 4.50

National Council for Culture, Arts and Letters, 25th Anniv. — A456

Panel color: 25f, Lilac. 50f, Olive green. 150f, Bright blue. 500f, Lilac.

**2002 ?** ***Perf. 13¼x13***
**1558-1560** A456 Set of 3 4.50 4.50

**Souvenir Sheet**

***Imperf***

**1561** A456 500f multi 10.00 10.00

No. 1561 contains one 42x58mm stamp.

Kuwait Society of Engineers, 40th Anniv. A457

Panel color at LR: 25f, Brown. 50f, Bright green. 150f, Yellow green.

**2002** ***Perf. 13x13¼***
**1562-1564** A457 Set of 3 4.50 4.50

Public Authority for Applied Education and Training, 20th Anniv. — A458

"20," "1982-2002" and: 25f, Men at work. 50f, Surgeon. 100f, Man with machine. 150f, Building and Kuwait flag. 250f, Ironworkers.

**2002** ***Perf. 13¼x13***
**1565-1569** A458 Set of 5 10.00 10.00

42nd National Day — A459

Frame color: 25f, Green. 50f, Red. 150f, Blue.

**2003, Feb. 25** **Litho.** ***Perf. 13x13¼***
**1570-1572** A459 Set of 3 6.00 6.00

Martyr's Bureau A460

Emblem and: 25f, Ship. 50f, Flag on Qarow Island. 150f, Fingerprint. 350f, Map of Kuwait.

**2003**
**1573-1576** A460 Set of 4 14.00 14.00
*1576a* Booklet pane, #1573-1576 14.00 —
Complete booklet, #1576a 14.00

Intl. Day Against Desertification A461

Designs: 25f, Dead tree. 50f, Log. 150f, Palm trees.

**2003** **Litho.** ***Perf. 13¼x13***
**1577-1579** A461 Set of 3 4.75 4.75

Commercial Bank of Kuwait, 43rd Anniv. — A462

"43" and: 25f, Geometric design. 50f, Old bank building. 150f, New bank building.

**2003** ***Perf. 13***
**1580-1582** A462 Set of 3 4.50 4.50

Kuwait Awqaf Public Foundation, 10th Anniv. A463

Emblem, "10," and: 50f, Building, family. 100f, Fingers. 150f, Man, minaret.

**2004, Jan. 19**
**1583-1585** A463 Set of 3 5.50 5.50

A464

A465

Ministry of Information, 50th Anniv. — A466

**2003**

**1586** A464 25f multi .60 .60
**1587** A465 100f multi 2.00 2.00
**1588** A466 150f multi 3.25 3.25
*Nos. 1586-1588 (3)* 5.85 5.85

43rd National Day — A467

Designs: 25f, Palm tree. 50f, Pearl in shell. 150f, Fortress, flags. 350f, Buildings, dhow.

**2004, Feb. 25** ***Perf. 13¼x13***
**1589-1592** A467 Set of 4 10.00 10.00

Kuwait Airways, 50th Anniv. A468

Various airplanes: 25f, 50f, 75f, 100f, 125f, 150f.

**2004, Dec. 18 Litho.** ***Perf. 13x13¼***
**1593-1598** A468 Set of 6 8.00 8.00

Kuwait Petroleum Corporation, 25th Anniv. — A469

Headquarters: 50f, In daytime. 75f, With sun on horizon. 125f, At night.

**2005, Jan. 1** ***Perf. 14½***
**1599-1601** A469 Set of 3 5.00 5.00

44th National Day — A470

Sheikhs, dhow, eagle and: 75f, Towers. 125f, Truck at port.

**2005, Feb. 25** ***Perf. 14***
**1602-1603** A470 Set of 2 3.00 3.00

Liberation Day, 14th Anniv. — A471

Sheikhs, flag and: 50f, Airplane, satellite dish. 150f, Tower.

**2005, Feb. 26**
**1604-1605** A471 Set of 2 4.00 4.00

Technical Education, 50th Anniv. — A472

Background color: 25f, Purple. 50f, Red. 75f, Orange. 125f, Green.

**2005, Mar. 15**
**1606-1609** A472 Set of 4 4.25 4.25

Flags and Emblems A473

Designs: No. 1610, Triangular 1961 ship and harbor flag. No. 1611, 1940 official flag. No. 1612, 1903 special event flag. No. 1613, 1940-50 ruling family flag. No. 1614, Two 1914 right triangle flags. No. 1615, 1921-40, 1956-62 and 1962 emblems.

No. 1616, 1962-56 emblem. No. 1617, 1921-40 emblem.

No. 1618, Right triangle flag of 1914 with Arabic script and emblem in center and script along short side like that on #1613. No. 1619, Right triangle flag of 1914 with Arabic script in center. No. 1620, Right triangle flag of 1914 with Arabic script in center and script along short side.

No. 1621, Triangular 1921 ship and harbor flag. No. 1622, Like #1610. No. 1623, Rectangular 1961 ship and harbor flag. No. 1624, Rectangular 1921 ship and harbor flag.

No. 1625, 1914-61 official flag. No. 1626, 1871-1914 official flag. No. 1627, 1746-1871 official flag. No. 1628, Like #1611. No. 1629, 1921-61 official flag.

No. 1630, 1903 special event flag. No. 1631, 1866 special event flag. No. 1632, 1921 special event flag.

No. 1633, 1921-40 ruling family flag with two white stripes. No. 1634, Like #1613, with colored background. No. 1635, 1921-40 ruling family flag with one white stripe.

**2005, Oct. 15 Litho.** ***Perf. 14x13¾***
**1610** A473 200f multi 2.25 2.25
**1611** A473 250f multi 3.25 3.25

***Perf. 14***

**Size: 40x30mm**

**1612** A473 350f multi 4.00 4.00
**1613** A473 500f multi 6.50 6.50

***Perf. 14x13¾***

**Size: 60x30mm**

**1614** A473 1d multi 11.00 11.00
**1615** A473 1d multi 11.00 11.00
*Nos. 1610-1615 (6)* 38.00 38.00

**Booklet Stamps**

**Self-Adhesive**

***Die Cut Perf. 13***

**Size:40x34mm**

**1616** A473 100f multi 2.00 2.00
**1617** A473 100f multi 2.00 2.00
*a.* Booklet pane, #1616-1617 4.00

***Die Cut Perf. 13x13¼***

**Size: 40x30mm**

**1618** A473 175f multi 3.75 3.75
**1619** A473 175f multi 3.75 3.75
**1620** A473 175f multi 3.75 3.75
*a.* Booklet pane, #1618-1620 11.50

***Die Cut Perf. 10x10¾***

**Size: 30x20mm**

**1621** A473 200f multi 3.75 3.75
**1622** A473 200f multi 3.75 3.75
**1623** A473 200f multi 3.75 3.75
**1624** A473 200f multi 3.75 3.75
*a.* Booklet pane, #1621-1624 15.00
**1625** A473 250f multi 3.75 3.75
**1626** A473 250f multi 3.75 3.75
**1627** A473 250f multi 3.75 3.75
**1628** A473 250f multi 3.75 3.75
**1629** A473 250f multi 3.75 3.75
*a.* Booklet pane #1625-1629 19.00

***Die Cut Perf. 13x13¼***

**Size: 40x30mm**

**1630** A473 350f multi 5.75 5.75
**1631** A473 350f multi 5.75 5.75
**1632** A473 350f multi 5.75 5.75
*a.* Booklet pane, #1630-1632 17.50
**1633** A473 500f multi 9.50 9.50
**1634** A473 500f multi 9.50 9.50
**1635** A473 500f multi 9.50 9.50
*a.* Booklet pane, #1633-1635 28.50
Complete booklet, #1617a, 1620a, 1624a, 1629a, 1632a, 1635a 97.50
*Nos. 1616-1635 (20)* 94.75 94.75

Civil Defense A474

Designs: 50f, Civil defense workers and emergency vehicles. 75f, Civil defense workers and children. 125f, Civil defene workers.

**2005, Nov. 15 Litho.** ***Perf. 14½***
**1636-1638** A474 Set of 3 3.75 3.75

Al-Arabi Al-Saghir Children's Magazine, 20th Anniv. A475

Background colors: 100f, Blue. 200f, Yellow. 350f, Red.

**2006, Feb. 1 Litho.** ***Perf. 14¼x13¾***
**1639-1641** A475 Set of 3 11.50 11.50

45th National Day — A476

Frame color: 75f, Purple. 200f, Green. 250f, Black. 350f, Red.

**2006, Feb. 25** ***Perf. 13¼***
**1642-1645** A476 Set of 4 13.00 13.00

A477

Gulf Cooperation Council, 25th Anniv. — A478

**Litho. With Foil Application**

**2006, May 25** ***Perf. 14***
**1646** A477 50f multi 4.00 4.00

***Imperf***

**Size: 165x105mm**

**1647** A478 500f multi 14.00 14.00

See Bahrain Nos. 628-629, Oman Nos. 477-478, Qatar Nos. 1007-1008, Saudi Arabia No. 1378, and United Arab Emirates Nos. 831-832.

Emblem A479

A480

A481

A482

A483

A484

A485

A486

A487

A488

A489

A490

A491

A492

A493

A494

A495

A496

A497

A498

A499

A500

A501

A502

A503

A504

A505

A506

A507

A508

A509

A510

A511

A512

A513

A514

A515

A516

A517

A518

A519

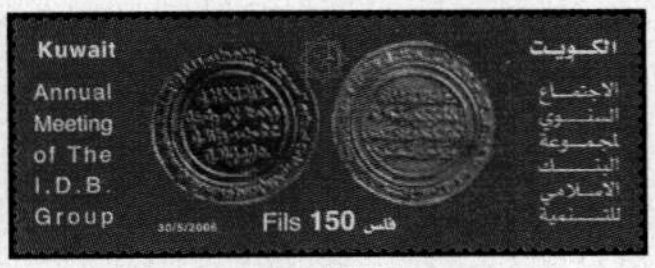

A520

Coins — A521

**2006, May 30** **Litho.** ***Perf. 13¼***

| | | | |
|---|---|---|---|
| **1648** | Sheet of 28, #1648b-1648v, 7#1648a | 20.00 | 20.00 |
| *a.* | A479 50f lt blue & multi | .60 | .60 |
| *b.* | A480 50f multi | .60 | .60 |
| *c.* | A481 50f multi | .60 | .60 |
| *d.* | A482 50f multi | .60 | .60 |
| *e.* | A483 50f multi | .60 | .60 |
| *f.* | A484 50f multi | .60 | .60 |
| *g.* | A485 50f multi | .60 | .60 |
| *h.* | A486 50f multi | .60 | .60 |
| *i.* | A487 50f multi | .60 | .60 |
| *j.* | A488 50f multi | .60 | .60 |
| *k.* | A489 50f multi | .60 | .60 |
| *l.* | A490 50f multi | .60 | .60 |
| *m.* | A491 50f multi | .60 | .60 |
| *n.* | A492 50f multi | .60 | .60 |
| *o.* | A493 50f multi | .60 | .60 |
| *p.* | A494 50f multi | .60 | .60 |
| *q.* | A495 50f multi | .60 | .60 |
| *r.* | A496 50f multi | .60 | .60 |
| *s.* | A497 50f multi | .60 | .60 |
| *t.* | A498 50f multi | .60 | .60 |
| *u.* | A499 50f multi | .60 | .60 |
| *v.* | A500 50f multi | .60 | .60 |
| **1649** | Sheet of 28, #1649b-1649v, 7#1649a | 55.00 | 55.00 |
| *a.* | A479 150f pink & multi | 1.75 | 1.75 |
| *b.* | A501 150f multi | 1.75 | 1.75 |
| *c.* | A502 150f multi | 1.75 | 1.75 |
| *d.* | A503 150f multi | 1.75 | 1.75 |
| *e.* | A504 150f multi | 1.75 | 1.75 |
| *f.* | A505 150f multi | 1.75 | 1.75 |
| *g.* | A506 150f multi | 1.75 | 1.75 |
| *h.* | A507 150f multi | 1.75 | 1.75 |
| *i.* | A508 150f multi | 1.75 | 1.75 |
| *j.* | A509 150f multi | 1.75 | 1.75 |
| *k.* | A510 150f multi | 1.75 | 1.75 |
| *l.* | A511 150f multi | 1.75 | 1.75 |
| *m.* | A512 150f multi | 1.75 | 1.75 |
| *n.* | A513 150f multi | 1.75 | 1.75 |
| *o.* | A514 150f multi | 1.75 | 1.75 |
| *p.* | A515 150f multi | 1.75 | 1.75 |
| *q.* | A516 150f multi | 1.75 | 1.75 |
| *r.* | A517 150f multi | 1.75 | 1.75 |
| *s.* | A518 150f multi | 1.75 | 1.75 |
| *t.* | A519 150f multi | 1.75 | 1.75 |
| *u.* | A520 150f multi | 1.75 | 1.75 |
| *v.* | A521 150f multi | 1.75 | 1.75 |

Islamic Development Bank Group annual meeting.

15th Asian Games, Doha, Qatar
A522

Designs: 25f, Tennis. 50f, Bowling. 150f, Shooting. 250f, Equestrian. 350f, Fencing.

| | | | | |
|---|---|---|---|---|
| **2006** | **Litho.** | | ***Perf. 14½*** | |
| **1650-1654** | A522 | Set of 5 | 13.00 | 13.00 |

Campaign Against Hypertension
A523

Frame colors: 50f, Green. 150f, Red. 350f, Brown.

| | | | | |
|---|---|---|---|---|
| **2007, Jan. 15** | | | ***Perf. 13¼x13*** | |
| **1655-1657** | A523 | Set of 3 | 9.25 | 9.25 |

46th National Day — A524

Sky color: 25f, Dark blue. 50f, Blue. 150f, Orange brown.

**2007, Feb. 25**

**1658-1660** A524 Set of 3 4.00 4.00

Liberation Day, 16th Anniv. A525

Frame color: 25f, Red. 50f, Dark blue. 150f, Purple.

**2007, Feb. 26 Litho.** ***Perf. 13x13¼***

**1661-1663** A525 Set of 3 4.00 4.00

Kuwait University, 40th Anniv. (in 2006) A526

Color behind emblem: 25f, Blue. 50f, Yellow. 150f, Green. 350f, Red.

**2007, Mar. 20**

**1664-1667** A526 Set of 4 10.00 10.00

Kuwait Oil Tanker Company, 50th Anniv. A527

Background colors: 25f, Pale blue. 50f, Pale green. 150f, Gray.

**Litho. & Embossed With Foil Application**

**2007, Nov. 25** ***Perf. 13***

**1668-1670** A527 Set of 3 5.25 5.25

Kuwait Philatelic & Numismatic Society, 1st Anniv. — A528

**2007, Dec. 5 Litho.** ***Perf. 13¼***

| | | | |
|---|---|---|---|
| **1671** | A528 Horiz. strip of 3 | 5.25 | 5.25 |
| *a.* | 25f Coin | .70 | .70 |
| *b.* | 50f Kuwait #146 | 1.10 | 1.10 |
| *c.* | 150f Society emblem | 3.00 | 3.00 |

No. 1671c is 60x35mm.

47th National Day — A529

Designs: 25f, Women voting. 150f, Stylized people, dhows, fish, towers, horiz.

***Perf. 13¼x13, 13x13¼***

**2008, Feb. 25 Litho.**

**1672-1673** A529 Set of 2 3.75 3.75

Liberation Day, 17th Anniv. A530

Hand holding map of Kuwait with background color of: 25f, Dull rose. 50f, Purple.

**2008, Feb. 26 Litho.** ***Perf. 13x13¼***

**1674-1675** A530 Set of 2 2.00 2.00

First Gulf Cooperation Council Women's Sports Tournament A531

No. 1676 — Emblem and: a, Gymnastics. b, Running. c, Shooting. d, Basketball. e, Tennis.

No. 1677, horiz. — Emblem, five sports with background color of: a, Orange. b, Red. c, Purple. d, Olive green. e, Red violet.

**2008, Mar. 5 Litho.** ***Perf. 13¼x13***

| | | | |
|---|---|---|---|
| **1676** | Vert. strip of 5 | 2.50 | 2.50 |
| *a.-e.* | A531 25f Any single | .40 | .40 |

***Perf. 13x13¼***

| | | | |
|---|---|---|---|
| **1677** | Horiz strip of 5 | 8.00 | 8.00 |
| *a.-e.* | A531 150f Any single | 1.25 | 1.25 |

Diplomatic Relations Between Kuwait and Romania, 45th Anniv. — A532

No. 1678: a, Kuwaiti man building ship model. b, Romanian woman weaving.

500f, Flags of Romania and Kuwait, handshake, vert.

**2008, June 21** ***Perf. 13¼x13***

| | | | |
|---|---|---|---|
| **1678** | Horiz. pair + 2 labels | *10.00* | *10.00* |
| *a.-b.* | A532 150f Either single + label | *4.75* | *4.75* |
| *c.* | Miniature sheet, 4 #1678 | *40.00* | — |

**Souvenir Sheet**

***Perf. 13x13¼***

**1679** A532 500f multi *20.00 20.00*

Labels of Nos. 1678a and 1678b are separated from stamps by a partial row of perforations. The labels, which have different designs, are to the left of No. 1678a and to the right of No. 1678b. The labels are adjacent to each other on half of the pairs on No. 1678c. No. 1678 was also printed in sheets containing 6 pairs, two of which have the labels adjacent. Value, $60.

See Romania Nos. 5053-5054.

Old Kuwait A533

Designs: 25f, Drummer and swordsmen. 50f, Drummers and boat painter. 100f, Street with thatched roof. 150f, Fair. 200f, Man and minarets. 250f, Donkey riders at town gate. 350f, Boats in harbor. 500f, People at town gate.

**2008, Aug. 1** ***Perf. 13***

| | | | | |
|---|---|---|---|---|
| **1680** | A533 | 25f multi | .25 | .25 |
| **1681** | A533 | 50f multi | .40 | .40 |
| **1682** | A533 | 100f multi | .75 | .75 |
| **1683** | A533 | 150f multi | 1.10 | 1.10 |
| **1684** | A533 | 200f multi | 1.50 | 1.50 |
| **1685** | A533 | 250f multi | 1.90 | 1.90 |
| **1686** | A533 | 350f multi | 2.75 | 2.75 |
| **1687** | A533 | 500f multi | 3.75 | 3.75 |
| | *Nos. 1680-1687 (8)* | | 12.40 | 12.40 |

48th National Day — A534

Frame color: 25f, Black. 50f, Green. 150f, Red.

250f, No frame.

**2009, Feb. 25 Litho.** ***Perf. 13¼***

**1688-1690** A534 Set of 3 3.00 3.00

**Size: 100x66mm**

***Imperf***

**1691** A534 250f multi 3.00 3.00

Liberation Day, 18th Anniv. — A535

Denomination color: 25f, Green. 50f, Red. 150f, Black.

**2009, Feb. 26** ***Perf. 13¾***

**1692-1694** A535 Set of 3 3.00 3.00

Kuwait Finance House A536

Denomination color: 25f, White. 50f, Silver. 150f, Gold.

**Litho. & Embossed**

**2009, June 21** ***Perf. 13¾***

**1695-1697** A536 Set of 3 2.75 2.75

Kuwait Chamber of Commerce and Industry, 50th Anniv. — A537

Designs: 25f, Building. 50f, Dhow. 150f, Cogwheels.

**2009 Granite Paper Litho.**

**1698-1700** A537 Set of 3 2.75 2.75

49th National Day — A538

Designs: 25f, Buildings and falcon. 50f, Sheikhs and falcon. 150f, Sheikhs and buildings.

**2010, Feb. 25 Litho.** ***Perf. 13¼x13***

**1701-1703** A538 Set of 3 4.25 4.25

Liberation Day, 19th Anniv. A539

Designs: 25f, Children's drawing of people waving flags in car and on side of road. 50f, Child waving flags. 150f, Fabric art of girls wearing dresses in colors of Kuwait flag.

**2010, Feb. 26** ***Perf. 13x13¼***

**1704-1706** A539 Set of 3 4.25 4.25

Jerusalem, Capital of Arab Culture — A540

Denomination color: 25f, Green. 50f, Red.

**2010, Mar. 26** ***Perf. 13¼x13***

**1707-1708** A540 Set of 2 2.00 2.00

Kuwait E-Gate A541

Frame color: 25f, Pink. 50f, Yellow. 150f, Light green.

**2010, Apr. 20** ***Perf. 14x13¼***

**1709-1711** A541 Set of 3 4.00 4.00

Organization of the Petroleum Exporting Countries, 50th Anniv. A542

Background color: 25f, Gray. 50f, Light blue. 150f, White.

**Litho. & Embossed With Foil Application**

**2010, May 23** ***Perf. 13¾***

**1712-1714** A542 Set of 3 3.75 3.75

A543

Liberation Day, 20th Anniv. and National Day, 50th Anniv. — A544

No. 1715: a, Flag, shiekh, "20." b, Dove, sheikhs, flag, "20." c, Flag, sheikh, "50." d, Flag, sheikh, "50," diff.

**Litho. & Embossed With Foil Application**

**2011, Feb. 25** ***Perf. 13¼***

| | | | |
|---|---|---|---|
| **1715** | Horiz. strip of 4 | 1.00 | 1.00 |
| *a.* | A543 25f silver & multi | .25 | .25 |
| *b.* | A544 25f silver & multi | .25 | .25 |
| *c.* | A543 25f gold & multi | .25 | .25 |
| *d.* | A544 25f gold & multi | .25 | .25 |

A souvenir sheet with a lithographed 250f stamp was produced in limited quantities.

A545

A546

A547

A548

Commercial Bank of Kuwait, 50th Anniv. (in 2010) — A549

**2011, Sept.** **Litho.** ***Perf. 13¼***

| | | | |
|---|---|---|---|
| **1716** | Horiz. strip of 5 | 2.50 | 2.50 |
| *a.* | A545 50f multi | .50 | .50 |
| *b.* | A546 50f multi | .50 | .50 |
| *c.* | A547 50f multi | .50 | .50 |
| *d.* | A548 50f multi | .50 | .50 |
| *e.* | A549 50f multi | .50 | .50 |

15th General Assembly of Arab Towns Organization, Kuwait (in 2010) — A550

No. 1717 — Stylized tree and man emblem, Arab Towns Organization emblem, and background color of: a, Rose brown. b, Yellow. c, Chocolate. d, Yellow green. e, Blue. f, Gray green. g, Gray. h, Tan. i, Orange brown. j, Brown.

**2011, Nov. 5** ***Perf. 13½***

| | | | |
|---|---|---|---|
| **1717** | Block of 10 | 5.00 | 5.00 |
| *a.-j.* | A550 50f Any single | .50 | .50 |

Miniature Sheet

Kuwait Fund for Arab Economic Development, 50th Anniv. — A551

No. 1718: a, 50th anniversary emblem, red background. b, Airport terminal with overhanging roof. c, Airport runway. d, Airplane at Banjul Intl. Airport, Gambia. e, Pipeline. f, Offshore oil rig. g, Workers examining produce. h, Farm. i, Well. j, Water works. k, Dump truck on hill. l, Culvert, hill in background. m, Electrical station. n, Ships in harbor. o, Highway bridge in populated area. p, Highway interchange. q, Elevated highway near hill. r, Culvert with three round holes. s, Elevated highway, diff.

**2011, Dec.** ***Perf. 14¼***

**1718** A551 150f Sheet of 20, 2 #1718a, 1 each #1718b-1718s 22.00 22.00

Emir Abdullah III (1895-1965) A552

Emir Sabah III (1913-77) A553

Emir Jaber III (1926-2006) A554

Emir Saad (1930-2008) A555

Crown Prince Nawaf — A556

Emir Sabah IV — A557

Sheikh Ahmad (1885-1950) A558

Sheikh Salim (1864-1921) A559

Sheikh Jaber II (1860-1917) A560

Sheikh Mubarak (1840-1915) A561

Independence, 51st Anniv. — A562

No. 1720 — Flags and scenes of of Kuwait and: a, Sheikh Mubarak (40x30mm). b, Sheikh Jaber II (40x30mm). c, Emir Abdullah III (80x30mm). d, Emir Sabah III (40x30mm). e, Emir Jaber III (40x30mm). f, Sheikh Salim (40x30mm). g, Sheikh Ahmad (40x30mm). h, Nine ruling sheikhs and emirs (80x30mm). i, Emir Saad (40x30mm). j, Emir Sabah IV (40x30mm).

**2012, Feb. 25** ***Perf. 13***

| | | | |
|---|---|---|---|
| **1719** | Sheet of 10 | *25.00* | *25.00* |
| *a.* | A552 100f multi | *2.50* | *2.50* |
| *b.* | A553 100f multi | *2.50* | *2.50* |
| *c.* | A554 100f multi | *2.50* | *2.50* |
| *d.* | A555 100f multi | *2.50* | *2.50* |
| *e.* | A556 100f multi | *2.50* | *2.50* |
| *f.* | A557 100f multi | *2.50* | *2.50* |
| *g.* | A558 100f multi | *2.50* | *2.50* |
| *h.* | A559 100f multi | *2.50* | *2.50* |
| *i.* | A560 100f multi | *2.50* | *2.50* |
| *j.* | A561 100f multi | *2.50* | *2.50* |

***Perf. 13x13¼***

| | | | |
|---|---|---|---|
| **1720** | A562 Sheet of 10 | *25.00* | *25.00* |
| *a.-j.* | 150f Any single | *2.50* | *2.50* |

A563

A564

A565

A566

A567

A568

A569

A570

A571

Liberation Day, 21st Anniv. — A572

**2012, Feb. 26** ***Perf. 13¼x13***

| | | | |
|---|---|---|---|
| **1721** | Sheet of 10 | *12.50* | *12.50* |
| *a.* | A563 50f multi | *1.25* | *1.25* |
| *b.* | A564 50f multi | *1.25* | *1.25* |

| | | | |
|---|---|---|---|
| *c.* | A565 50f multi | *1.25* | *1.25* |
| *d.* | A566 50f multi | *1.25* | *1.25* |
| *e.* | A567 50f multi | *1.25* | *1.25* |
| *f.* | A568 50f multi | *1.25* | *1.25* |
| *g.* | A569 50f multi | *1.25* | *1.25* |
| *h.* | A570 50f multi | *1.25* | *1.25* |
| *i.* | A571 50f multi | *1.25* | *1.25* |
| *j.* | A572 50f multi | *1.25* | *1.25* |

Miniature Sheet

Membership in UNESCO, 50th Anniv. (in 2010) — A573

No. 1722 — UNESCO membership 50th anniv. emblem and: a, Kuwaiti flag, emblems of Intangible Cultural Heritage, Intl. Festival of Cultural Diversity, Italian National UNESCO Commission, and UNESCO Associated Schools, white background. b, Emblem of Italian National UNESCO Commission, bister and olive background, denomination 3mm tall at UR. c, Intl. Festival of Cultural Diversity emblem, lilac background. d, Stylized "U" and "O", green and red stripes at bottom. e, Stylized figure of man with arms raised, dull orange background. f, Intl. Astronomical Union emblem, orange and green background. g, Man and Biosphere (MaB) emblem, blue and white background. h, Intangible Cultural Heritage emblem, gray and white background. i, Global Geoparks Network emblem, orange background with blue and white concentric circles. j, Multicolored squares below UNESCO emblem, blue and lilac background. k, UNESCO Associated Schools emblem, blue background with brown stripe at bottom. l, Kuwaiti flag, emblems of Global Geoparks Network, Intl. Festival of Cultural Diversity (with French inscription) and Intl. Bureau of Education, white background. m, UNESCO Institute for Lifelong Learning emblem, red, white and blue background. n, Intl. Bureau of Education (IBE) emblem, white background in blue frame. o, World Heritage emblem, orange background with yellow circle. p, Stylized dove, olive and bister background, denomination 2½mm tall at UR. q, Circle and blue stripes, light blue background. r, UNESCO Chair in Sustainable Mountain Development emblem, UHI Millennium Institute emblem, pink and white background with brown stripes at top and bottom. s, Intl. Festival of Cultural Diversity emblem with French inscription, gray background. t, UNESCO spiral emblem, blue and dull orange background.

**2012, June 6** ***Perf. 14***

**1722** A573 150f Sheet of 20, #a-t *38.00 38.00*

A574

A575

A576

A577

A578

A579

A580

A581

A582

A583

A584

A585

A586

A587

A588

A589

A590

A591

A592

Children's Art — A593

**2012, Nov.**

| | | | |
|---|---|---|---|
| **1723** | Sheet of 20 | *16.00* | *16.00* |
| *a.* | A574 50f multi | *.80* | *.80* |
| *b.* | A575 50f multi | *.80* | *.80* |
| *c.* | A576 50f multi | *.80* | *.80* |
| *d.* | A577 50f multi | *.80* | *.80* |
| *e.* | A578 50f multi | *.80* | *.80* |
| *f.* | A579 50f multi | *.80* | *.80* |
| *g.* | A580 50f multi | *.80* | *.80* |
| *h.* | A581 50f multi | *.80* | *.80* |
| *i.* | A582 50f multi | *.80* | *.80* |
| *j.* | A583 50f multi | *.80* | *.80* |
| *k.* | A584 50f multi | *.80* | *.80* |
| *l.* | A585 50f multi | *.80* | *.80* |
| *m.* | A586 50f multi | *.80* | *.80* |
| *n.* | A587 50f multi | *.80* | *.80* |
| *o.* | A588 50f multi | *.80* | *.80* |
| *p.* | A589 50f multi | *.80* | *.80* |
| *q.* | A590 50f multi | *.80* | *.80* |
| *r.* | A591 50f multi | *.80* | *.80* |
| *s.* | A592 50f multi | *.80* | *.80* |
| *t.* | A593 50f multi | *.80* | *.80* |

Kuwait Society for the Handicapped.

Miniature Sheet

Partnership Between Kuwait and United Nations, 50th Anniv. — A594

No. 1724 — 50th anniversary emblem and: a, United Nations Headquarters, flags of United Nations and member nations, emblem of Kuwait (60x30mm). b, United Nations House, Kuwait, emblems of various United Nations ororganizations (60x30mm). c, United Nations Secretary General Ban Ki-moon and Sheikh Sabah (30x40mm). d, Emblems of Kuwait and United Nations, national flags (30x40mm). e, Hoisting of Kuwaiti flag at United Nations Headquarters (30x40mm). f, Sheikh Sabah at podium at United Nations (30x40mm). g, United Nations House, and United Nations flag (30x40mm). h, Dhow (30x40mm). i, Kuwait Towers (30x40mm). j, Emblem at United Nations House (30x40mm).

***Perf. 13¼x13¼x14x13¼ (#1724a-1724b), 14***

**2013, Dec. 1** **Litho.**

**1724** A594 50f Sheet of 10, #a-j 7.50 7.50

A595

A596

A597

A598

A599

A600

A601

A602

A603

53rd National Day — A604

*Perf. 13¾x13½*

**2014, Feb. 25** **Litho.**

| | | | |
|---|---|---|---|
| **1725** | Sheet of 10 | 40.00 | 40.00 |
| *a.* | A595 350f multi | 4.00 | 4.00 |
| *b.* | A596 350f multi | 4.00 | 4.00 |
| *c.* | A597 350f multi | 4.00 | 4.00 |
| *d.* | A598 350f multi | 4.00 | 4.00 |
| *e.* | A599 350f multi | 4.00 | 4.00 |
| *f.* | A600 350f multi | 4.00 | 4.00 |
| *g.* | A601 350f multi | 4.00 | 4.00 |
| *h.* | A602 350f multi | 4.00 | 4.00 |
| *i.* | A603 350f multi | 4.00 | 4.00 |
| *j.* | A604 350f multi | 4.00 | 4.00 |

A605

A606

A607

A608

A609

A610

A611

A612

A613

Liberation Day, 23rd Anniv. — A614

*Perf. 13¾x13½*

**2014, Feb. 26** **Litho.**

| | | | |
|---|---|---|---|
| **1726** | Sheet of 10 | 40.00 | 40.00 |
| *a.* | A605 350f multi | 4.00 | 4.00 |
| *b.* | A606 350f multi | 4.00 | 4.00 |
| *c.* | A607 350f multi | 4.00 | 4.00 |
| *d.* | A608 350f multi | 4.00 | 4.00 |
| *e.* | A609 350f multi | 4.00 | 4.00 |
| *f.* | A610 350f multi | 4.00 | 4.00 |
| *g.* | A611 350f multi | 4.00 | 4.00 |
| *h.* | A612 350f multi | 4.00 | 4.00 |
| *i.* | A613 350f multi | 4.00 | 4.00 |
| *j.* | A614 350f multi | 4.00 | 4.00 |

19th Gulf Cooperation Council Stamp Exhibition, Kuwait — A615

**2014, May 4** **Litho.** ***Perf. 13***

**1727** A615 25f multi *1.10 1.10*

No. 1727 was printed in sheets of 10 with each stamp in sheet having a different background.

Modern Schools — A616

Opening Schools Abroad — A617

Female Education A618

Nutrition and Health Care — A619

Sheikh Abdullah Al Jabir Al Sabah (1895-1965) A620

Student Activities A621

Girl Scouts — A622

Heritage Arts — A623

Boy Scouts — A624

Sheikh Abdullah Al Jabir Al Sabah — A625

***Perf. 14, 13¼ (#1728j)***

**2014, Nov. 5** **Litho.**

| | | | |
|---|---|---|---|
| **1728** | Sheet of 10 | 8.50 | 8.50 |
| *a.* | A616 50f multi | .85 | .85 |
| *b.* | A617 50f multi | .85 | .85 |
| *c.* | A618 50f multi | .85 | .85 |
| *d.* | A619 50f multi | .85 | .85 |
| *e.* | A620 50f multi | .85 | .85 |
| *f.* | A621 50f multi | .85 | .85 |
| *g.* | A622 50f multi | .85 | .85 |
| *h.* | A623 50f multi | .85 | .85 |
| *i.* | A624 50f multi | .85 | .85 |
| *j.* | A625 50f multi | .85 | .85 |

**Souvenir Sheets**

***Perf. 13x13½***

**1729** A625 250f multi *5.00 5.00*

**Litho. With Foil Application**

**1730** A625 250f gold & multi *5.00 5.00*

Nos. 1729-1730 each contain one 40x60mm stamp.

A626

A627

A628

A629

A630

A631

A632

A633

A634

Kuwait Awqaf Public Foundation, 20th Anniv. A635

**2014, Nov. 10 Litho. *Perf. 13x13¼***

| | | | |
|---|---|---|---|
| **1731** | Sheet of 10 | *11.00* | *11.00* |
| *a.* | A626 25f multi | *1.10* | *1.10* |
| *b.* | A627 25f multi | *1.10* | *1.10* |
| *c.* | A628 25f multi | *1.10* | *1.10* |
| *d.* | A629 25f multi | *1.10* | *1.10* |
| *e.* | A630 25f multi | *1.10* | *1.10* |
| *f.* | A631 25f multi | *1.10* | *1.10* |
| *g.* | A632 25f multi | *1.10* | *1.10* |
| *h.* | A633 25f multi | *1.10* | *1.10* |
| *i.* | A634 25f multi | *1.10* | *1.10* |
| *j.* | A635 25f multi | *1.10* | *1.10* |

A636

A637

A638

A639

A640

A641

A642

A643

A644

International Autism Conference, Kuwait — A645

**2014, Nov. 11 Litho. *Perf. 13¾x14***

| | | | |
|---|---|---|---|
| **1732** | Sheet of 10 | *10.00* | *10.00* |
| *a.* | A636 50f multi | *1.00* | *1.00* |
| *b.* | A637 50f multi | *1.00* | *1.00* |
| *c.* | A638 50f multi | *1.00* | *1.00* |
| *d.* | A639 50f multi | *1.00* | *1.00* |
| *e.* | A640 50f multi | *1.00* | *1.00* |
| *f.* | A641 50f multi | *1.00* | *1.00* |
| *g.* | A642 50f multi | *1.00* | *1.00* |
| *h.* | A643 50f multi | *1.00* | *1.00* |
| *i.* | A644 50f multi | *1.00* | *1.00* |
| *j.* | A645 50f multi | *1.00* | *1.00* |

Towers — A646

No. 1733: a, Post Tower. b, Liberation Tower.

**2014, Nov. 23 Litho. *Perf. 14¼***

**1733** A646 1d Horiz. pair, #a-b *22.50 22.50*

### Miniature Sheet

52nd National Day (in 2013) — A647

No. 1734: a, Musician and dancers (60x30mm). b, Children surrounding sheikh (60x30mm). c, Male dancers wearing waist sashes (30x45mm). d, Female dancers wearing yellow and black costume (30x45mm). e, Male dancers wearing black vests (30x45mm). f, Female dancers wearing purple and yellow costumes (30x45mm). g, Musician and male dancers (30x45mm). h, Girls wearing turquoise green dresses (30x45mm). i, Boys wearing violet and blue costumes, girls in background (30x45mm). j, Female dancers with striped skirts (30x45mm).

**2014, Dec. 21 Litho. *Perf. 13x13¼***

**1734** A647 150f Sheet of 10, #a-j *17.50 17.50*

Miniature Sheet

Liberation Day, 22nd Anniv. (in 2013) — A648

No. 1735: a, Soldiers and black vehicles with flags (90x30mm). b, Ships (90x30mm). c, Sheikh meeting troops (45x30mm). d, Soldiers in personnel carriers in parade (45x30mm). e, Soldiers carrying guns (45x30mm). f, Helicopter and flag (45x30mm). g, Soldiers with white boots marching in parade (45x30m). h, Airplanes in flight with colored contrails (45x30mm). i, Police on motorcycles in parade (45x30mm). j, Soldiers on small boat (45x30mm).

**2014, Dec. 21 Litho. *Perf. 14¼***

**1735** A648 50f Sheet of 10, #a-j *6.00 6.00*

Miniature Sheet

Diplomatic Relations Between Kuwait and European Countries, 50th Anniv. — A649

No. 1736: a, Netherlands. b, Spain. c, Coat of arms of Kuwait. d, Germany. e, Hungary. f, Denmark. g, Greece. h, Turkey. i, Belgium. j, Italy.

**2014, Dec. 21 Litho. *Perf. 13¼***

**1736** A649 150f Sheet of 10, #a-j *18.00 18.00*

A650

A651

A652

A653

A654

A655

A656

A657

A658

Constitution, 50th Anniv. — A659

***Perf. 13¾x14, 14x13¾ (#1737j)***

**2014, Dec. 21 Litho.**

| | | | | |
|---|---|---|---|---|
| **1737** | | Sheet of 10 | *55.00* | *55.00* |
| *a.* | A650 500f multi | | *5.50* | *5.50* |
| *b.* | A651 500f multi | | *5.50* | *5.50* |
| *c.* | A652 500f multi | | *5.50* | *5.50* |
| *d.* | A653 500f multi | | *5.50* | *5.50* |
| *e.* | A654 500f multi | | *5.50* | *5.50* |
| *f.* | A655 500f multi | | *5.50* | *5.50* |
| *g.* | A656 500f multi | | *5.50* | *5.50* |
| *h.* | A657 500f multi | | *5.50* | *5.50* |
| *i.* | A658 500f multi | | *5.50* | *5.50* |
| *j.* | A659 500f multi | | *5.50* | *5.50* |

Miniature Sheet

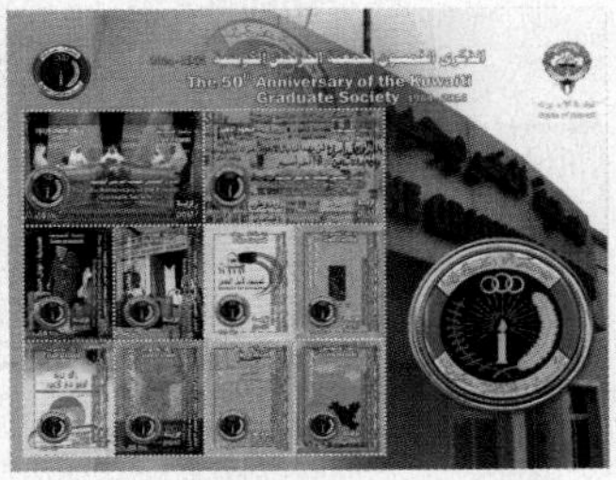


Kuwaiti Graduate Society, 50th Anniv. — A660

No. 1738 — Emblem and: a, Five men at circular dais (60x40mm). b, Pictures of Kuwaiti prisoners of war (60x40mm). c, Man in army uniform, woman with hands over mouth (30x40mm). d, Men at Kuwaiti Graduate Society Symposium (30x40mm). e, Kuwaitis for Jerusalem emblem (30x40mm). f, Book cover with Arabic text and "2007" (30x40mm). g, Book cover with Arabic text, broken pencil and "1995-2007" (30x40mm). h, Book cover depicting stylized head and neck (30x40mm). i, Page of Arabic text (30x40mm). j, Jigsaw puzzle with missing pieces (30x40mm).

**2014, Dec. 27 Litho. *Perf. 13¼x13***

**1738** A660 50f Sheet of 10, #a-j *7.00 7.00*

Emir Sabah IV — A661

Background color: 350f, Blue. 500f, Olive green. 750f, Light blue. 1d, Light gray. 250f, Brown.

**Litho. With Foil Application**

**2014, Dec. 30 *Perf. 13¾x13½***

**1739-1742** A661 Set of 4 *30.00 30.00*

**Souvenir Sheet**

***Perf. 13x14x14x14***

**1743** A661 250f multi *5.00 5.00*

No. 1743 contains one 120x90mm stamp.

Miniature Sheet

54th National Day — A662

No. 1744: a, Towers, children wearing red, white and green caps. b, Male dancers. c, Female dancers. d, Child with flag of Kuwait painted on face.

**2015, Feb. 25 Litho. *Perf. 13¼***

**1744** A662 150f Sheet of 4, #a-d 7.50 7.50

Martyrs — A663

No. 1745: a, Ahmad S. Alenezi. b, Ahmad K. Alenezi. c, Edris B. Alshammari. d, Ebrahim A. Alsubaie. e, Ebrahim J. Naif. f, Hamed K. Alshammari. g, Jamal S. Alsalem. h, Jshai'aan A. Almutairi. i, Jasem N. Alfadhli. j, Ahmad N. Alenezi. k, Khalaf A. Alenezi. l, Humoud S. Rashdan. m, Hamad Y. Alsultan. n, Hasan T. Alfadegh. o, Hasan R. Alshammari. p, Zakariya A. Bohamad. q, Refa'ie A. Almutairi. r, Rajaan W. Alazmi. s, Ra'ed M. Sabri. t, Daham H. Alshammari. u, Diaa A. Alsayegh. v, Safnan M. Althaferi. w, Sulaiman A. Sulaiman. x, Salman N. Alazmi. y, Salem M. Alenezi.

No. 1746: a, Abdulrahman N. Abdulrahman. b, Abduljaleel E. Khaleel. c, Abbas A. Muhammad. d, Ayed K. Albraikan. e, Tareq M. Alfadhli. f, Faleh S. Althaferi. g, Ghazwan H. Hawas. h, Obaid S. Alshammari. i, Abdullah E. Saleh. j, Abdulkareem T. Ali. k, Kulaib S. Farhan. l, Kamil R. Jabr. m, Fahad A. Alsabah. n, Fraih B. Alshammari. o, Fayez A. Arashidi. p, Muhammad Q. Alenezi. q, Muhammad O. Muhammad. r, Muhammad J. Alaibany. s, Mohsen A. Alenezi. t, Mut'eb S. Alshammari. u, Mutlaq M. Almutairi. v, Mus'heb M. Mutlaq. w, Meshael N. Aladwani. x, Mur'ie N. Alenezi. y, Muhammad H. Althaydi.

No. 1747: a, Khalid A. Alb'aijan. b, Hamdan M. Alenezi. c, Jamal S. Allengawi. d, Anwar A. Alrefai. e, Warid M. Jadran. f, Muhammad M. Alobaid. g, Majed R. Alkhseli. h, Fahad R. Althaferi. i, Farhan S. Alruwaili. j, Sahmi M. Alsubaie. k, Adel A. Alhaie. l, Abdulaziz S. Kashaan. m, Mufreh K. Alenezi. n, Mansour G. Alkhseli. o, Matar G. Almajdi. p, Sana A. Alfudari. q, Rashid K. Althaferi. r, Mussayer F. Alshammari. s, Abdulrahman M. Abdullah. t, Muhammad S. Alenezi. u, Ali E. Alraihan. v, Ibrahim E. Abdullah. w, Ali A. Alsa'baa. x, Wahid M. Safri, y, Musaed A. Alaskari.

No. 1748: a, Abdullatif A. Alhamdan. b, Bassam M. Sadeq. c, Nawaf M. Alhashan. d, Abdulhusain A. Albughbish. e, Muhammad J. Jaber. f, Jafar A. Taqi. g, Habib M. Alsheikh. h, Abdulrasoul H. Husain. i, Mansour H. Mansour. j, Faisal B. Albahar. k, Salem A. Alkanderi. l, Baqer A. Almousawi. m, Khalid A. Alsamhan. n, Nasser G. Aladwani, o, Mahmoud K. Aljasem. p, Mubarak F. Alnout. q, Bader R. Abdulwahab. r, Ghazi F. Aloutaibi. s, Sabbar A. Alenezi. t, Saleh H. Saleh. u, Ahmad A. Kherallah. v, Ibrahim A. Meshael. w, Muhammad H. Altawash. x, Saad S. Alshammari. y, Hammad S. Alshammari.

**2015, Feb. 26 Litho. *Perf. 14***

| | | | |
|---|---|---|---|
| **1745** | Sheet of 25 | 7.50 | 7.50 |
| *a.-y.* | A663 25f Any single | .30 | .30 |
| **1746** | Sheet of 25 | 7.50 | 7.50 |
| *a.-y.* | A663 25f Any single | .30 | .30 |
| **1747** | Sheet of 25 | 7.50 | 7.50 |
| *a.-y.* | A663 25f Any single | .30 | .30 |
| **1748** | Sheet of 25 | 7.50 | 7.50 |
| *a.-y.* | A663 25f Any single | .30 | .30 |
| | *Nos. 1745-1748 (4)* | 30.00 | 30.00 |

Liberation Day, 24th anniv.

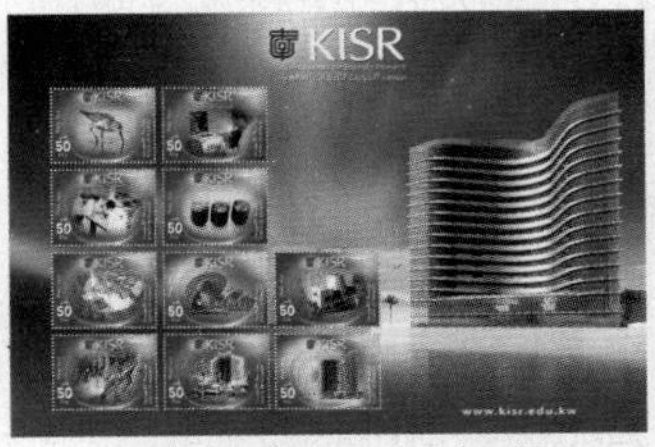


Kuwait Institute for Scientific Research — A664

No. 1749: a, Brid. b, Technician adjusting scientific equipment. c, Scientists in laboratory. d, Three test tubes. e, Fish. f, Satellite dishes. g, Building, cars parked at left. h, Bottles. i, Headquarters and relecting pond. j, Headquarters, diff.

**2015, Mar. Litho. *Perf. 13x13½***

**1749** A664 50f Sheet of 10, #a-j 7.00 7.00

## AIR POST STAMPS

**Air Post Stamps of India, 1929-30, Overprinted type "c"**

**1933-34 Wmk. 196 *Perf. 14***

| | | | |
|---|---|---|---|
| **C1** | AP1 2a dull green | 24.00 | *27.50* |
| **C2** | AP1 3a deep blue | 5.00 | *3.50* |
| **C3** | AP1 4a gray olive | 160.00 | *225.00* |
| **C4** | AP1 6a bister ('34) | 8.00 | *4.50* |
| | *Nos. C1-C4 (4)* | 197.00 | *260.50* |

Counterfeits of Nos. C1-C4 exist.

**Catalogue values for unused stamps in this section, from this point to the end of the section, are for Never Hinged items.**

Dakota and Comet Planes AP1

*Perf. 11x11½*

**1964, Nov. 29 Litho. Unwmk.**

| | | | | | |
|---|---|---|---|---|---|
| C5 | AP1 | 20f multicolored | | 1.00 | .30 |
| C6 | AP1 | 25f multicolored | | 1.10 | .40 |
| C7 | AP1 | 30f multicolored | | 1.25 | .60 |
| C8 | AP1 | 45f multicolored | | 2.00 | .80 |
| | | *Nos. C5-C8 (4)* | | 5.35 | 2.10 |

10th anniversary of Kuwait Airways.

## POSTAGE DUE STAMPS

**Catalogue values for unused stamps in this section are for Never Hinged items.**

D1

*Perf. 14x15*

**1963, Oct. 19 Unwmk. Litho.**

**Inscriptions in Black**

| | | | | |
|---|---|---|---|---|
| J1 | D1 | 1f ocher | .60 | .30 |
| J2 | D1 | 2f lilac | .70 | .45 |
| J3 | D1 | 5f blue | 1.00 | .30 |
| J4 | D1 | 8f pale green | 1.60 | .55 |
| J5 | D1 | 10f yellow | 2.00 | 1.00 |
| J6 | D1 | 25f brick red | 3.25 | *3.25* |
| | | *Nos. J1-J6 (6)* | 9.15 | 5.85 |

D2

**1965, Apr. 1** *Perf. 13*

| | | | | |
|---|---|---|---|---|
| J7 | D2 | 4f rose & yellow | .50 | .30 |
| J8 | D2 | 15f dp rose & blue | 1.75 | .55 |
| J9 | D2 | 40f blue & brt yel grn | 3.00 | 1.25 |
| J10 | D2 | 50f green & pink | 3.75 | 1.75 |
| J11 | D2 | 100f dk blue & yel | 5.50 | 3.25 |
| | | *Nos. J7-J11 (5)* | 14.50 | 7.10 |

## OFFICIAL STAMPS

**Stamps of India, 1911-23, Overprinted**

Nos. O1-O9

Nos. O10-O14

**1923-24 Wmk. 39** *Perf. 14*

| | | | | |
|---|---|---|---|---|
| O1 | A47 | ½a green | 6.50 | *50.00* |
| O2 | A48 | 1a brown | 5.50 | *27.50* |
| O3 | A58 | 1½a chocolate | 5.00 | *65.00* |
| O4 | A49 | 2a violet | 11.00 | *50.00* |
| O5 | A57 | 2a6p ultra | 7.00 | *80.00* |
| O6 | A51 | 3a brown org | 7.50 | *75.00* |
| O7 | A51 | 3a ultra ('24) | 7.75 | *75.00* |
| O8 | A52 | 4a olive grn | 6.25 | *75.00* |
| O9 | A54 | 8a red violet | 9.50 | *110.00* |
| O10 | A56 | 1r grn & brn | 35.00 | *190.00* |
| O11 | A56 | 2r brn & car rose | 37.50 | *275.00* |
| O12 | A56 | 5r vio & ultra | 125.00 | *475.00* |
| O13 | A56 | 10r car & grn | 250.00 | *440.00* |
| O14 | A56 | 15r ol grn & ultra | 400.00 | *675.00* |
| | | *Nos. O1-O14 (14)* | 913.50 | *2,663.* |

**Stamps of India, 1926-30, Overprinted**

Nos. O15-O20

Nos. O21-O25

**1929-33 Wmk. 196**

| | | | | |
|---|---|---|---|---|
| O15 | A48 | 1a dk brown | 6.50 | *42.50* |
| O16 | A60 | 2a violet | 70.00 | *250.00* |
| O17 | A51 | 3a blue | 6.00 | *55.00* |
| O18 | A61 | 4a ol green | 6.75 | *90.00* |
| O19 | A54 | 8a red violet | 9.00 | *130.00* |
| O20 | A55 | 12a claret | 45.00 | *225.00* |
| O21 | A56 | 1r green & brn | 14.00 | *275.00* |
| O22 | A56 | 2r buff & car rose | 18.00 | *400.00* |
| O23 | A56 | 5r dk vio & ultra | 50.00 | *500.00* |
| O24 | A56 | 10r car & green | 85.00 | *850.00* |
| O25 | A56 | 15r olive grn & ultra | 300.00 | *1,450.* |
| | | *Nos. O15-O25 (11)* | 610.25 | *4,268.* |

# KYRGYZSTAN

ˌkir-gi-ˈstan

(Kirghizia)

LOCATION — Bounded by Kazakhstan, Uzbekistan, Tadjikistan and China.
GOVT. — Independent republic, member of the Commonwealth of Independent States.
AREA — 77,180 sq. mi.
POP. — 4,546,055 (1999 est.)
CAPITAL — Bishkek

With the breakup of the Soviet Union on Dec. 26, 1991, Kyrgyzstan and ten former Soviet republics established the Commonwealth of Independent States.

In 2013, the Universal Postal Union announced that a second postal organization, Kyrgyz Express Post, was granted permission to provide unrestricted postal services throughout the country. This allowed for competition between the state corporation, Kyrgyz Pochtasy, the original UPU-designated postal operator in Kyrgyzstan having post offices nationwide, and Kyrgyz Express Post for postal business. Listings for stamps issued by Kyrgyz Express Post follow those of the listings for stamps from Kyrgyz Pochtasy.

100 Kopecks = 1 Ruble
100 Tyiyn = 1 Som

**Catalogue values for all unused stamps in this country are for Never Hinged items.**

## ISSUES OF KYRGYZ POCHTASY

Sary-Chelek Nature Preserve — A1

**Unwmk.**

**1992, Feb. 4 Litho.** *Perf. 12*

| | | | | |
|---|---|---|---|---|
| 1 | A1 | 15k multicolored | .55 | .55 |

Hawk — A2

**1992, Aug. 31 Litho.** *Perf. 12½x12*

| | | | | |
|---|---|---|---|---|
| 2 | A2 | 50k multicolored | .65 | .65 |

Man with Cattle, by G.A. Aytiev — A3

**1992, Aug. 31**

| | | | | |
|---|---|---|---|---|
| 3 | A3 | 1r multicolored | .40 | .40 |

Handicrafts A4

**1992, Dec. 1 Litho.** *Perf. 12x11½*

| | | | | |
|---|---|---|---|---|
| 4 | A4 | 1.50r multicolored | .55 | .55 |

Sites and Landmarks A5

Designs: 10k, Petroglyphs. 50k, 11th Cent. tower, vert. 1r + 25k, Mausoleum, vert. 2r + 50k, 12th Cent. mausoleum. 3r, Yurt. 5r + 50k, Statue of epic hero Manas, Pishpek. 9r, Commercial complex, Pishpek. 10r, Native jewelry.

**1993, Mar. 21 Litho.** *Perf. 12*

| | | | | |
|---|---|---|---|---|
| 5 | A5 | 10k multicolored | .25 | .25 |
| 6 | A5 | 50k multicolored | .25 | .25 |
| 7 | A5 | 1r +25k multi | .25 | .25 |
| 8 | A5 | 2r +50k multi | .25 | .25 |
| 9 | A5 | 3r multicolored | .25 | .25 |
| 10 | A5 | 5r +50k multi | .30 | .30 |
| 11 | A5 | 9r multi | .50 | .50 |
| | | *Nos. 5-11 (7)* | 2.05 | 2.05 |

**Souvenir Sheet**

| | | | | |
|---|---|---|---|---|
| 12 | A5 | 10r multicolored | 1.00 | 1.00 |

Nos. 5-11 exist imperf. Value, set *$22.50.*

Independence and Admission to UN, 2nd Anniv. — A6

50t, Map. 60t, UN emblem, flag, building, vert.

No. 15a, 120t, like #13. No. 15b, 130t, like #14.

*Perf. 13x12½, 12½x13*

**1993, Aug. 31 Litho.**

| | | | | |
|---|---|---|---|---|
| 13 | A6 | 50t multicolored | 1.00 | 1.00 |
| 14 | A6 | 60t multicolored | 1.25 | 1.25 |

**Souvenir Sheet**

*Imperf*

| | | | | |
|---|---|---|---|---|
| 15 | A6 | Sheet of 2, #a.-b. | 5.25 | 5.25 |

Nos. 15a-15b have simulated perforations.

Russia Nos. 4598, 5838, 5984 Surcharged in Violet Blue, Prussian Blue or Black

**Methods and Perfs as Before**

**1993, Apr. 6**

| | | | | |
|---|---|---|---|---|
| 16 | A2765 | 10r on 1k #5838 (VB) | .30 | .25 |
| 17 | A2765 | 20r on 2k #5984 (PB) | .35 | *.50* |
| 18 | A2139 | 30r on 3k #4598 (Blk) | .45 | *.70* |
| | | *Nos. 16-18 (3)* | 1.10 | *1.45* |

Russia Nos. 4599-4600 Surcharged in Blue or Red

**Methods and Perfs as Before**

**1993, June 29**

| | | | | |
|---|---|---|---|---|
| 19 | A2138 | 20t on 4k #4599 (Bl) | .70 | .70 |
| 20 | A2139 | 30t on 6k #4600 (R) | 1.00 | 1.00 |

New Year 1994 (Year of the Dog) — A7

**1994, Feb. 10 Litho.** *Perf. 12x12½*

| | | | | |
|---|---|---|---|---|
| 26 | A7 | 60t multicolored | .80 | .80 |

No. 26 exists imperf. Value, $1.75.

Musical Instrument — A8

**1993, Dec. 30 Litho.** *Perf. 13x12½*

| | | | | |
|---|---|---|---|---|
| 27 | A8 | 30t Komuz | .40 | .40 |

**Souvenir Sheet**

*Perf. 13*

| | | | | |
|---|---|---|---|---|
| 28 | A8 | 140t multi | 16.00 | 16.00 |

No. 28 exists imperf. Value $45.
Issued: No. 27, 12/30; No. 28, 4/4/94.

Panthera Uncia A9

**1994, Mar. 21 Litho.** *Perf. 12½x12*

| | | | | |
|---|---|---|---|---|
| 29 | A9 | 10t shown | .35 | .35 |
| 30 | A9 | 20t Lying down | .40 | .40 |
| 31 | A9 | 30t Seated | .65 | .65 |
| 32 | A9 | 40t Up close | .85 | .85 |
| | | *Nos. 29-32 (4)* | 2.25 | 2.25 |

World Wildlife Fund.

Flowers — A10

*Perf. 12x12½, 12½x12*

**1994, Aug. 31** Litho.

**Color of Flower**

33 A10 1t violet & white .25 .25
34 A10 3t white & yellow, horiz. .25 .25
 a. Miniature sheet of 6 1.60 1.60
35 A10 10t red & yellow .40 .40
36 A10 16t white & yellow .40 .40
37 A10 20t pink & yellow .50 .50
38 A10 30t white & yellow .55 .55
39 A10 40t yellow & brown .65 .65
 a. Miniature sheet of 6, #33, #35-39 6.50 6.50
 b. Strip of 7, #33-39 4.00 4.00
 *Nos. 33-39 (7)* 3.00 3.00

**Souvenir Sheet**

40 A10 50t yellow & orange 1.60 1.60

Nos. 33-39 exist imperf. Value, set $4.75.
For surcharge see No. 141.

Minerals — A11

**1994, Dec. 1** Litho. *Perf. 13½x13*

41 A11 80t Fluorite-Cinnabar .65 .65
42 A11 90t Calcite .70 .70
43 A11 100t Getchellite .80 .80
44 A11 110t Barite .85 .85
45 A11 120t Orpiment .90 .90
46 A11 140t Stibnite 1.25 1.25
 *Nos. 41-46 (6)* 5.15 5.15

**Souvenir Sheet**

47 A11 200t Cinnabar 3.50 3.50
 a. Miniature sheet of 6 10.00 10.00

No. 47a contains Nos. 42-46 and single from No. 47.

Fish — A12

Designs: 110t, Glyptosternum reticulatum. 120t, Leuciscus schmidti. 130t, Piptychus dybowskii. 140t, Nemachilus strauchi. 200t, Cyprinus carpio.

**1994, Dec. 1** *Perf. 13x13½*

48 A12 110t multicolored .55 .55
49 A12 120t multicolored .60 .60
50 A12 130t multicolored .65 .65
51 A12 140t multicolored .80 .80
 a. Miniature sheet, #48-51 2.75 2.75
 *Nos. 48-51 (4)* 2.60 2.60

**Souvenir Sheet**

52 A12 200t multicolored 2.25 2.25

Wild Animals — A13

No. 60: a, 130t, Raptor, diff. b, 170t, Bighorn sheep.

*Perf. 12x12½, 12½x12*

**1995, Apr. 21** Litho.

53 A13 110t Bear .30 .30
54 A13 120t Snow leopard, horiz. .30 .30
55 A13 130t Raptor .35 .35
56 A13 140t Woodchuck, horiz. .40 .40
57 A13 150t Raptor, horiz. .45 .45
58 A13 160t Vulture .50 .50
59 A13 190t Fox, horiz. .65 .65
 *Nos. 53-59 (7)* 2.95 2.95

**Souvenir Sheet**

60 A13 Sheet of 2, #a.-b. 1.50 1.50

Nos. 53-60 exist imperf. Value, set $6.50.

Natl. Costumes — A14

**1995, Mar. 24** *Perf. 12x12½*

61 A14 50t shown .30 .30
62 A14 50t Man with mandolin .30 .30
63 A14 100t Man with falcon .45 .45
64 A14 100t Woman seated .45 .45
 *Nos. 61-64 (4)* 1.50 1.50

Nos. 61-64 exist imperf. Value, set $2.50.

Traffic Safety — A15

**1995, Mar. 24** *Perf. 12*

65 A15 200t multicolored .85 .85

Souvenir Sheet

End of World War II, 50th Anniv. — A16

**1995, May 4** Litho. *Perf. 12x12½*

66 A16 150t multicolored 1.40 1.40

UPU Intl. Letter Week A17

**1995, Oct. 3** Litho. *Perf. 12x12½*

67 A17 200t multicolored 1.10 1.10

Natl. Arms — A18

**1995, Oct. 13** *Perf. 12*

68 A18 20t purple .35 .35
69 A18 50t blue .35 .35
70 A18 100t brown .45 .45
71 A18 500t green 1.50 1.50
 *Nos. 68-71 (4)* 2.65 2.65

Compare with design A37.

Horses A19

Various adult, juvenile horses.

**1995, Oct. 16** *Perf. 12½x12, 12x12½*

**Background Color**

72 A19 10t olive brown .25 .25
73 A19 50t light brown, vert. .25 .25
74 A19 100t tan, vert. .25 .25
75 A19 140t yellow brown, vert. .40 .40
76 A19 150t lilac .60 .60
77 A19 200t gray .60 .60
78 A19 300t yellow green .65 .65
 *Nos. 72-78 (7)* 3.00 3.00

**Souvenir Sheet**

79 A19 600t Herd of horses, vert. 2.50 2.50

Raptors — A20

**1995, Sept. 12** *Perf. 12x12½*

80 A20 10t Pandion haliaetus .25 .25
81 A20 50t Aquila rapax .30 .30
82 A20 100t Gyps himalayensis .35 .35
83 A20 140t Falco cherrug .40 .40
84 A20 150t Circaetus gallicus .45 .45
85 A20 200t Gypaetus barbatus .50 .50
86 A20 300t Aquila chrysaetos .70 .70
 *Nos. 80-86 (7)* 2.95 2.95

**Souvenir Sheet**

87 A20 600t Halliaeetus albicilla 2.75 2.75

"Aquila" spelled wrong on No. 86.
Nos. 80-87 exist imperf. Value: Nos. 80-86, $4.25; No. 87, $3.

Souvenir Sheet

UN, 50th Anniv. — A21

Designs: a, UN headquarters, NYC. b, Mountains, rainbow.

**1995, Oct. 24** Litho. *Perf. 12½x12*

88 A21 100t Sheet of 2, #a.-b. 1.10 1.10

Natural Wonders of the World — A22

10t, Nile River. 50t, Kilimanjaro. 100t, Sahara Desert. 140t, Amazon River, vert. 150t, Grand Canyon, vert. 200t, Victoria Falls, vert. 350t, Mount Everest. 400t, Niagara Falls.
Issyk-Kul Lake, Kyrgyzstan: No. 97, Raptor, row boat, sail boats. No. 98, Water bird, motor boat, row boat.

**1995, Dec. 29** *Perf. 11½*

89 A22 10t multicolored .30 .30
90 A22 50t multicolored .35 .35
91 A22 100t multicolored .45 .45
92 A22 140t multicolored .50 .50
93 A22 150t multicolored .55 .55
94 A22 200t multicolored .70 .70
95 A22 350t multicolored .90 .90
96 A22 400t multicolored 1.25 1.25
 *Nos. 89-96 (8)* 5.00 5.00

**Souvenir Sheets**

97 A22 600t multicolored 2.00 2.00
98 A22 600t multicolored 2.00 2.00

Reptiles A23

Designs: 20t, Psammophis lineolatum. No. 100, Natrix tessellata. No. 101, Eublepharis macularius. 100t, Agkistrodon halys. 150t, Eremias arguta. 200t, Elaphe dione. 250t, Asymblepharus. 500t, Lacerta agilis.

**1996, Feb. 2** *Perf. 12½x12*

99 A23 20t multicolored .25 .25
100 A23 50t multicolored .30 .30
101 A23 50t multicolored .30 .30
102 A23 100t multicolored .30 .30
103 A23 150t multicolored .50 .50
104 A23 200t multicolored .60 .60
105 A23 250t multicolored .65 .65
 *Nos. 99-105 (7)* 2.90 2.90

**Souvenir Sheet**

106 A23 500t multicolored 2.25 2.25

Souvenir Sheet

Save the Aral Sea — A24

Designs: a, Felis caracal. b, Salmo trutta aralensis. c, Hyaena hyaena. d, Pseudoscaphirhynchus kaufmanni. e, Aspiolucius esocinus.

**1996, Apr. 29** Litho. *Perf. 14*

107 A24 100t Sheet of 5, #a.-e. 4.00 4.00

See Kazakhstan No. 145. Tadjikistan No. 91, Turkmenistan No. 52, Uzbekistan No. 113.

Fauna — A27

a, Aquila chrysaetos. b, Capra falconeri. c, Ovis ammon. d, Gyps himalayensis. e, Equus hemionus. f, Canis lupus. g, Ursus arctor. h, Saiga tatarica.

**1997, Aug. 29 Litho. *Perf. 12x12½***
**114** A27 600t Sheet of 8, #a.-h. 7.00 7.00

See No. 117.

New Year 1998 (Year of the Tiger) A28

**1998, June 5 Litho. *Perf. 13½x14***
**115** A28 600t multicolored 1.40 1.40

Butterflies — A29

Designs: a, Parnasius actius. b, Colias christophi. c, Papilio machaon. d, Colias thisoa. e, Parnassius delphius. f, Panassius tianschanicus.

**1998, June 5**
**116** A29 600t Sheet of 6, #a.-f. 4.50 4.50

**Fauna Type of 1997**

a, 600t, Capreolus capreolus. b, 1000t, Oriolus oriolus. c, 600t, Pandion haliaetus. d, 1000t, Uncia uncia. e, 600t, Upupa epops. f, 600t, Ciconia ciconia. g, 1000t, Alcedo atthis. h, 1000t, Falco tinnunculus.

**1998, June 5 Litho. *Perf. 12x12½***
**117** A27 Sheet of 8, #a-h *10.00 10.00*

Dinosaurs — A31

Designs: a, Saurolophus, vert. b, Euoplocephalus. c, Velociraptor. d, Tyrannosaurus, vert. e, Gallimimus. f, Protoceratops.

***Perf. 14x13½, 13½x14***
**1998, Dec. 4 Litho.**
**118** A31 10s Sheet of 6, #a.-f. 6.00 6.00

Universal Declaration of Human Rights, 50th Anniv. — A32

a, Andrei Sakharov (1921-89). b, Crowd of people raising their arms. c, Martin Luther King, Jr. d, Mahatma Gandhi. e, Eleanor Roosevelt.

**1998, Dec. 4 *Perf. 14x13½***
**119** A32 10s Sheet of 5, #a.-e. + label 4.75 4.75

No. 119 exists with 2 different inscriptions on label.

Constitution, 5th Anniv. — A33

**1998, Dec. *Perf. 12***
**120** A33 1000t multi 1.60 1.60

***Imperf***
**Size: 120x90mm**
**120A** A33 10,000t multi *50.00 50.00*

No. 120A, issued 2/5/99.

Fauna A34

Designs: a, 600t, Fish, denomination UR. b, 1000t, Duck standing beside rocks. c, 1000t, Two birds. d, 1000t, Duck standing beside water. e, 1000t, Duck swimming. f, 1000t, Rodent. g, 1000t, Bird. h, 600t, Fish, denomination UL.

**1998, Dec. Litho. *Perf. 12***
**121** A34 Sheet of 8, #a.-h. 7.50 7.50

No. 121 exists imperf. Value, $9.50.

Corsac Fox (Vulpes Corsac) A35

World Wildlife Fund: Nos. 122a, 123a, 10s, Adult sitting. Nos. 122b, 123b, 10s, Adult sleeping. Nos. 122c, 123c, 30s, Two standing. Nos. 122d, 123d, 50s, Adult with young.

**1999, Apr. 27 Litho. *Perf. 12½x12***
**122** A35 Block of 4, #a.-d. 5.50 5.50

**Size: 48x34mm**
***Perf. 13½***
**123** A35 Block of 4, #a.-d. 7.50 7.50

Nos. 123a-123d each contain a holographic image. Soaking in water may affect the hologram. IBRA '99, World Philatelic Exhibition, Nuremberg (No. 123). No. 123 was issued in sheets of 8 stamps.
For overprints and surcharges, see Nos. 175, 384.

Aleksandr Pushkin (1799-1837), Poet — A36

No. 124: a, 36t, Knight, giant. b, 6s, Man, woman, fish. c, 10s, Archer, angel. d, 10s, King in carriage.
20s, Portrait of Pushkin.

**1999, June Litho. *Perf. 12x12½***
**124** A36 Strip of 4, #a.-d. 3.75 3.75

**Souvenir Sheet**
**125** A36 20s multicolored 3.75 3.75

No. 124 printed in sheets of 8 stamps.
Nos. 124-125 exist imperf. Value, set $10.

Natl. Arms — A37

**1999, July Litho. *Perf. 11¼x11½***
**126** A37 20t dark blue .80 .80

**Souvenir Sheet**

China 1999 World Philatelic Exhibition — A38

No. 131: a, 10s, Ailuropoda melanoleuca. b, 15s, Strix leptogrammica.

**1999, Aug. 21 Litho. *Perf. 13x12½***
**131** A38 Sheet of 2, #a.-b. 2.50 2.50

Exists imperf. Value $3.25.

12th World Kickboxing Championships, Bishkek — A39

Emblem, globe and: No. 132, White background. No. 133, Blue panel. c, No. 134, Green, red, and black panels.
No. 135: a, Black background. b, Yellow and brown panels.

**1999, Oct. 7 Litho. *Perf. 13¼***
**132** A39 3s multi *.70 .70*
**133** A39 3s multi *.70 .70*
**134** A39 3s multi *.70 .70*
*Nos. 132-134 (3) 2.10 2.10*

**Souvenir Sheet**
***Perf. 12½***
**135** A39 6s Sheet of 2, #a.-b., + label *2.00 2.00*

No. 135 contains 37x26mm stamps.

UPU, 125th Anniv. A40

6s, Airplane, man on horse.

**1999, Oct. *Perf. 14x14¼***
**136** A40 3s shown *.55 .55*
**137** A40 6s multicolored *1.10 1.10*

Dogs — A41

No. 138: a, 3s, Taigan. b, 6s, Tasy. c, 6s, Afghan hound. d, 10s, Saluki. e, 15s, Mid-Asian shepherd. f, 15s, Akbash dog. g, 20s, Chow chow. h, 25s, Akita.

**2000, Mar. 18 Litho. *Perf. 12¼x12***
**138** A41 Sheet of 8, #a-h 7.50 7.50

Exists imperf. Value $12.

Kyrgyzstan postal officials have declared as "not authentic and not valid" stamps with a face value of 20s depicting the Beatles, Madonna, Pop music stars, Tiger Woods, 2000 French Olympic gold medal winners, Mushrooms, American Political Cartoons concerning the 2000 Presidential election, The Simpsons, Superman, and Warner Brothers cartoon characters.

Bulat Minzhilkiev(1940-98), Opera Singer — A42

**2000, Apr. 20 Litho. *Perf. 14x14¼***
**139** A42 5s multi *1.25 1.25*

Victory in World War II, 55th Anniv. A43

Heroes: a, Cholponbay Tuleberdiev (1922-42). b, I. V. Panfilov (1893-1941), vert. c, Duyshenkul Shopokov (1915-41).

***Perf. 14x14¼ (#140a, 140c), 14¼x14 (#140b)***
**2000, May 20 Litho.**
**140** A43 6s Vert. strip of 3, #a-c *2.75 2.75*

Issued in sheets of 2 each Nos. 140a-140c.

No. 33 Surcharged

**2000, Sept. 22 Litho.** ***Perf. 12x12½***
**141** A10 36t on 1t multi .50 *.90*

No. 141 exists with bar obliterators with smaller numerals and with thinner numerals and rosette obliterators in magenta. Value: each, $13.

2000 Summer Olympics, Sydney A44

Designs: 1s, Wrestling. 3s, Hurdles, vert. 6s, Boxing. 10s, Weight lifting, vert.

***Perf. 14x14¼, 14¼x14***
**2000, Sept. 23**
**142-145** A44 Set of 4 *3.75 3.75*

Kyrgyzstan postal officials have declared as "not authentic and not valid" a sheet of nine 20s stamps depicting the History of Golf.

Atay Ogunbaev, Composer A45

**2000, Oct. 28 Litho.** ***Perf. 14x14¼***
**146** A45 6s multi .85 .85

Butterflies — A46

Designs: No. 147, 3s, Aglais urticae. No. 148, 3s, Argynnis aglaja. No. 149, 3s, Colias thisoa. No. 150, 3s, Inachis io. No. 151, 3s, Papilio machaon. No. 152, 3s, Parnassius apollo.

**2000, Nov. 18** ***Perf. 13½***
**147-152** A46 Set of 6 *4.50 4.50*

Kyrgyzstan postal officials have declared as "not authentic and not valid" stamps with a face value of 20s in sheets of 6 depicting Jennifer Aniston and Tennis, and sheets of 9 depicting Backstreet Boys, Beverly Hills 90210, Minerals, Penguins, Tom and Jerry, Prince William, Babylon 5 and the End of Mir.

Intl. Year of Mountains (in 2002) — A47

Designs: No. 153, 10s, Khan-Tengri Mountain, 7,010 meters. No. 154, 10s, Victory Peak, 7,439 meters. No. 155, 10s, Lenin Peak, 7,134 meters.

**2000, Dec. 23 Litho.** ***Perf. 13½***
**153-155** A47 Set of 3 *3.25 3.25*
*a.* Souvenir sheet, #153-155 + label *3.25 3.25*

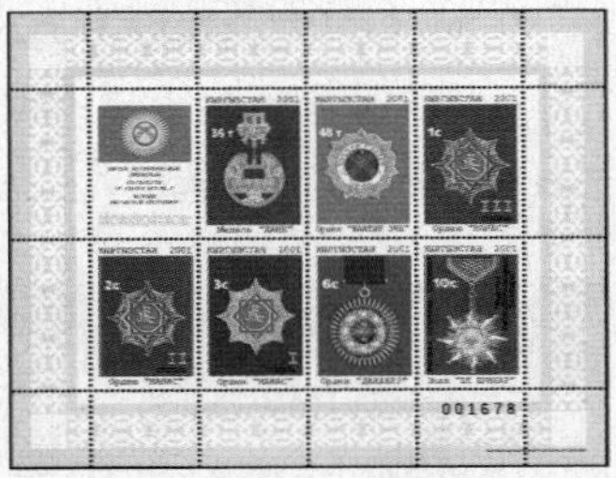


Medals — A48

No. 156: a, 36t, Dank. b, 48t, Baatyr Jene. c, 1s, Manas (third class). d, 2s, Manas (second class). e, 3s, Manas (first class). f, 6s, Danaker. g, 10s, Ak Shumkar.

**2001, Jan. 20 Litho.** ***Perf. 14¼x14***
**156** A48 Sheet of 7, #a-g, + label *3.25 3.25*

UN High Commissioner for Refugees — A49

**2001, Mar. 10 Litho.** ***Perf. 14x14¼***
**157** A49 10s multi .95 .95

New Year 2001 (Year of the Snake) A50

**2001, Mar. 17**
**158** A50 6s multi .80 .80

Exists imperf. Value $2.25.

Year of Dialogue Among Civilizations A51

**2001, Apr. 14** ***Perf. 13½***
**159** A51 10s multi *1.25 1.25*

Intl. Year of Mountains A52

Mountains and: Nos. 160, 163a, 10s, Horses crossing stream. Nos. 161, 163b, 10s, Grazing animals, yurt. Nos. 162, 163c, 10s, Valley.

**2001, July 7** ***Perf. 14x14¼***
**With White Frame**
**160-162** A52 Set of 3 *3.50 3.50*

**Souvenir Sheet**
**Without White Frame**
**163** A52 10s Sheet of 3, #a-c, + label *4.00 4.00*

Bishkek Buildings — A53

Designs: 48t, Communications Building. 1s, Town Hall. 3s, Opera House.

**2001, July 7** ***Perf. 14x13¼***
**164** A53 48t slate gray .30 .25
**165** A53 1s olive gray .30 .30
**166** A53 3s violet brown .40 .40
*a.* Horiz. strip, #164-166 *1.00 1.00*

Intl. Year of Ecotourism (in 2002) A54

Designs: No. 167, 10s, Mountains, lake. No. 168, 10s, Mountains, field of flowers. No. 169, 10s, Sailboat on lake.
No. 170, Mosque, vert.

**2001, July 21** ***Perf. 14x14¼***
**167-169** A54 Set of 3 *4.00 4.00*

**Souvenir Sheet**
***Imperf (Simulated Perfs)***
**170** A54 10s multi *2.40 2.40*

Independence, 10th Anniv. — A55

Designs: 1.50s, Eagle, mountain. 7s, Pres. Askar Akaev, flag.
11.50s, Governmental building.

**2001, Aug. 29** ***Perf. 14x14¼***
**171-172** A55 Set of 2 *4.50 4.50*

**Souvenir Sheet**
**173** A55 11.50s Sheet of 1 + 8 labels *4.75 4.75*

Kurmanbek Baatyr, 500th Anniv. of Birth — A56

**2001, Sept. 8** ***Perf. 14¼x14***
**174** A56 1.50s multi *.90 .90*

**Nos. 123a-123b Surcharged and Nos. 123c-123d Overprinted With Text Only**

No. 175: a, 25s on 10s #123a. b, 25s on 10s, #123b. c, 30s #123c. d, 50s #123d.

**Litho. With Hologram**
**2001** ***Perf. 13½***
**175** A35 Block of 4, #a-d *7.75 7.75*

Regional Communications Accord, 10th Anniv. — A57

**2001, Oct. 20 Litho.** ***Perf. 14¼x14***
**176** A57 7s multi 1.20 1.20

Commonwealth of Independent States, 10th Anniv. — A58

**2001, Dec. 8**
**177** A58 6s Prus bl & yel *1.00 1.00*

Kyrgyzstan postal officials have declared as "illegal:"
Stamps with a face value of 20s in sheets of nine depicting Shrek, Harry Potter, Concorde, Dogs, Tigers, Formula 1 racing, Mother Teresa, and The Beatles;
Stamps with various face values in sheets of nine depicting Defenders of Peace and Freedom, Superman, Green Lantern, Flash, Ironman, Legends of Baseball;
Stamps with various values in sheets of three depicting Princess Diana and Elvis Presley;
Stamps with a face value of 20s in sheets of six depicting Harley Davidson motorcycles;
Souvenir sheets of one 100s stamp depicting Harry Potter and Penguins.

2002 Winter Olympics, Salt Lake City — A59

Designs: 50t, Speed skating. 1.50s, Biathlon. 7s, Ice hockey. 10s, Ski jumping.
50s, Downhill skiing.

**2002, Feb. 23 Litho.** ***Perf. 14x14¼***
**178-181** A59 Set of 4 *2.25 2.25*

**Souvenir Sheet**
**182** A59 50s multi + label *5.50 5.50*

New Year 2002 (Year of the Horse)
A60

**2002, Mar. 23** *Perf. 14x14¼*
**183** A60 1s multi *1.10 1.10*

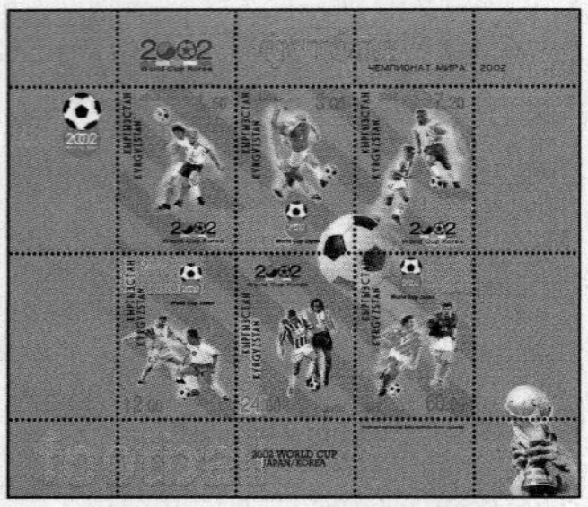

2002 World Cup Soccer Championships, Japan and Korea — A61

No. 184: a, 1.50s. b, 3s. c, 7.20s. d, 12s. e, 24s. f, 60s.

**2002, Apr. 13** *Perf. 14¼x14*
**184** A61 Sheet of 6, #a-f *11.00 11.00*

No. 184 exists with an overprint in silver or gold with scores of the final and third place matches of the tournament. Value: each, $25.

Kyrgyzstan/Pakistan Diplomatic Relations, 10th Anniv. — A62

**2002, Apr. 18** *Perf. 14¼x14*
**185** A62 12s multi *1.25 1.25*

Kyrgyzstan postal officials have declared as "illegal:"
Stamps with a face value of 20s in sheets of nine depicting Pandas, Dinosaurs, Marine Life, Cats and Scouting Emblem, and the Beatles.
Stamps with various face values in sheets of nine depicting Caricatures of World Cup Soccer Players (3 sheets).

Summer Olympics — A63

No. 186: a, 1s, Discus, Greece #125 (Athens, 1896). b, 2s, Boxing, France #113 (Paris, 1900). c, 3s, Diving, US #324 (St. Louis, 1904). d, 5s, Weight lifting, Great Britain #127 (London, 1908). e, 7s, Rowing, Sweden #97 (Stockholm, 1912). f, 7s, Hurdles, Belgium #B48 (Antwerp, 1920).
No. 187: a, 1s, Rhythmic gymnastics, France #201 (Paris, 1924). b, 2s, Diving, Netherlands #B25 (Amsterdam, 1928). c, 3s, Table tennis, US #718 (Los Angeles, 1932). d, 5s, Running, Germany #B86 (Berlin, 1936). e, 7s, Fencing, Great Britain #274 (London, 1948). f, 7s, Men's gymnastics (pommel horse), Finland #B112 (Helsinki, 1952).
No. 188: a, 1.50s, Volleyball, Australia #277 (Melbourne, 1956). b, 3s, Tennis, Italy #799 (Rome, 1960). c, 5s, Swimming, Japan #B12 (Tokyo, 1964). d, 5s, Judo, Mexico #990 (Mexico City, 1968). e, 7.20s, Kayaking, Germany #B490e (Munich, 1972). f, 12s, Yachting, Canada #B11 (Montreal, 1976).
No. 189: a, 1.50s, Men's gymnastics (rings), Russia #B99 (Moscow, 1980). b, 3s, Synchronized swimming, US #2085a (Los Angeles, 1984). c, 5s, Cycling, South Korea #B54 (Seoul, 1988). d, 5s, High jump, Spain #B197 (Barcelona, 1992). e, 7.20s, Sailboarding, US #3068a (Atlanta, 1996). f, 12s, Women's gymnastics, Australia #1779 (Sydney, 2000).

**2002, Aug. 28 Litho.** *Perf. 13x13¼*
**Sheets of 6, #a-f, + 3 labels**
**186-189** A63 Set of 4 *12.00 12.00*

Jalal-Abad
A64

Talas
A65

Osh — A66

**2002, Dec. 7** *Perf. 13½*

| | | | | | |
|---|---|---|---|---|---|
| **190** | A64 | 20t | claret | .30 | .30 |
| **191** | A65 | 50t | claret | .30 | .30 |
| **192** | A66 | 60t | claret | .30 | .30 |
| **193** | A64 | 1s | Prussian bl | .30 | .30 |
| **194** | A65 | 1.50s | Prussian bl | .30 | .30 |
| **195** | A66 | 2s | blue gray | .30 | .30 |
| **196** | A64 | 3s | blue gray | .45 | .45 |
| **197** | A65 | 7s | blue gray | .90 | .90 |
| **198** | A66 | 10s | Prussian bl | 1.25 | 1.25 |
| | | | *Nos. 190-198 (9)* | 4.40 | 4.40 |

Kyrgyzstan postal officials have declared as "illegal:"
Sheets of 9 with various denominations depicting Looney Tunes Characters (Merry Cristmas! (sic)) (2 different), Harry Potter, 71st Academy Awards, MTV Video Awards.
Sheets of 9 with 20s denominations depicting 20th Century Dreams (5 different), Chess, Teddy bears, MTV Video Awards.
Sheet of 6 with various denominations depicting Dinosaurs.
Sheet of 3 with various denominations depicting Pope John Paul II.

Nos. 33, 35 Surcharged in Red or Black

No. 34 Surcharged

**Methods and Perfs As Before**
**2002, Dec. 28**

| | | | | | |
|---|---|---|---|---|---|
| **199** | A10 | 1.50s on 1t multi (R) | .30 | .30 |
| **200** | A10 | 3.60s on 3t multi | .40 | .40 |
| **201** | A10 | 7s on 10t multi | .80 | .80 |
| | | *Nos. 199-201 (3)* | 1.50 | 1.50 |

New denomination is at left on No. 201.
Nos. 199-201 exist imperf. Value, set $3.

Olmoskhan Atabekova (1922-87) — A67

**2003, Jan. 11 Litho.** *Perf. 14¼x14*
**202** A67 7.20s multi .75 .75

Intl. Association of Academies of Science, 10th Anniv.
A68

Emblem and: 1.50s, Atom model. 7.20s, Circles.

**2003, Mar. 8** *Perf. 14x14¼*
**203-204** A68 Set of 2 1.00 1.00

Gold and Bronze Artifacts From Sakov — A69

No. 205: a, 1.50s, Two figurines of people. b, 3s, Coin. c, 3.60s, Lion. d, 5s, Idol with horns. e, 7s, Rooster. f, 10s, Goats. g, 20s, Bird on coin. h, 42s, Animal's head.
No. 206, Mask.

**2003, May 10** *Perf. 14x14¼*
**205** A69 Sheet of 8, #a-h *9.75 9.75*

**Souvenir Sheet**
***Imperf. (With Simulated Perforations)***
**206** A69 42s multi *6.00 6.00*

No. 205 exists imperf. with simulated perforations. Value $15.

Bishkek Post Office, 125th Anniv.
A70

Bishkek Post Office, emblem, dove and: 1s, Airplane. 3s, Covered wagon and Jeep. 7s, Covered wagon.
50s, "1878-2003."

**2003, May 31** *Perf. 14x14¼*
**207-209** A70 Set of 3 1.50 1.50

**Souvenir Sheet**
***Imperf. (With Simulated Perforations)***
**210** A70 50s multi 5.50 5.50

Famous Men — A71

Various men: a, 1.50s. b, 3s. c, 3.60s. d, 5s. e, 7.20s. f, 10s. g, 18s. h, 20s. i, 25s. j, 30s.

**2003, June 20** *Perf. 14x14¼*
**211** A71 Sheet of 10, #a-j 13.00 13.00

Issyk Kul — A72

No. 212: a, 1s, Rahat. b, 1.50s, Raduga. c, 2s, Teltoru. d, 3s, Kyrgyzskoe Vzmorije. e, 3.60s, Tamga. f, 5s, Solnyshko. g, 7s, Vityaz. h, 8s, Ak Bermet. i, 12s, Royal Beach. j, 20s, Luchezarnoe Poberejie.

**2003, Aug. 15** *Perf. 13½x13¾*
**212** A72 Sheet of 10, #a-j, + 10 labels *6.50 6.50*

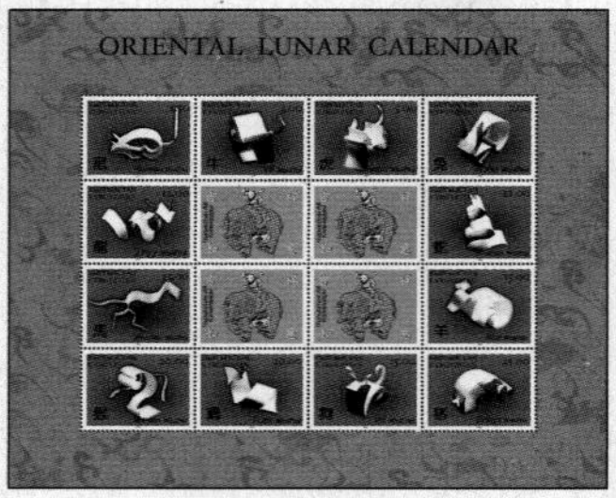

Lunar New Year Animals — A73

No. 213: a, 1.50s, Rat. b, 3s, Ox. c, 5s, Tiger. d, 7s, Hare. e, 12s, Dragon. f, 12s, Snake. g, 15s, Horse. h, 15s, Sheep. i, 20s, Monkey. j, 20s, Cock. k, 25s, Dog. l, 25s, Pig.

**2003, Aug. 25** *Perf. 13x13¼*
**213** A73 Sheet of 12, #a-l, +4 labels *14.00 14.00*

National Symbols A74

History of Syma Chan — A75

Designs: No. 214, 3s, Flag. No. 215, 3s, National anthem. 5s, Coat of arms.

**2003, Oct. 4 Litho. *Perf. 13½***

**214-216** A74 Set of 3 *1.75 1.75*
*216a* Souvenir sheet, #214-216 *1.75 1.75*

**Souvenir Sheet**

**217** A75 12s multi *2.00 2.00*

New Year 2003 (Year of the Sheep) A76

**2003, Dec. 30 Litho. *Perf. 14x14¼***

**218** A76 1.50s multi .70 .70

Meerim Fund, 10th Anniv. A77

Designs: 1.50s, Fund emblem, buildings. 7s, Fund emblem, buildings, diff. 20s, Fund emblem.

**2004, Feb. 17 Litho. *Perf. 14x14¼***

**219-220** A77 Set of 2 *1.50 1.50*

**Souvenir Sheet**

***Perf. 13½***

**221** A77 20s multi *3.00 3.00*

No. 221 contains one 37x51mm stamp.

New Year 2004 (Year of the Monkey) A78

**2004, Apr. 3 Litho. *Perf. 14x14¼***

**222** A78 3s multi .80 .80

Automobiles — A79

No. 223: a, 3.60s, 1913 Peugeot. b, 3.60s, 1999 Mercedes-Benz. c, 10s, 1996 Volvo S40. d, 10s, 1908 Ford. e, 15s, 1932 Alfa-Romeo. f, 15s, 1972 VAZ 2101. g, 25s, 1998 Nissan. h, 25s, 1950 ZIS-110.

**2004, May 1 Litho. *Perf. 14x13½***

**223** A79 Sheet of 8, #a-h *9.00 9.00*

No. 223 exists imperf. Value $16.

Insects — A80

No. 224: a, 3.60s, Insect with red wings. b, 3.60s, Grasshopper. c, 10s, Cricket. d, 10s, Ladybugs. e, 15s, Dragonfly. f, 15s, Praying mantis. g, 25s, Moth with red wings. h, 25s, Bee.

**2004, May 15**

**224** A80 Sheet of 8, #a-h *8.50 8.50*

2004 Singapore World Stamp Championship.
No. 224 exists imperf. Value $15.

FIFA (Fédération Internationale de Football Association), Cent. — A81

No. 225: a, 5s, Soccer ball. b, 6s, FIFA emblem, soccer ball, athletic shoes. c, 7s, Soccer player with red shirt. d, 10s, Soccer player with white shirt.

**2004, May 21 Litho. *Perf. 14x14¼***

**225** A81 Block of 4, #a-d *2.75 2.75*

**No. 12 Surcharged**

**2004, June 19 Litho. *Perf. 12***

**226** A5 20s on 10r #12 *2.50 2.50*

Peace and Respect Intl. Festival of Arts.

Karakol Region A82

Naryn Region A83

Tokmok Region — A84

**2004, July 6 Litho. *Perf. 13½x13¾***

| | | | | |
|---|---|---|---|---|
| **227** | A82 | 10t indigo | .25 | .25 |
| **228** | A83 | 20t dark green | .25 | .25 |
| **229** | A84 | 50t dark brown | .25 | .25 |
| **230** | A82 | 60t blue | .25 | .25 |
| **231** | A83 | 1s blue green | .25 | .25 |
| **232** | A84 | 2s brown | .25 | .25 |
| **233** | A82 | 3s violet | .50 | .50 |
| **234** | A83 | 5s green | .75 | .75 |
| **235** | A84 | 7s light brown | 1.00 | 1.00 |
| | | *Nos. 227-235 (9)* | 3.75 | 3.75 |

Chynykei Biy (1788-1874) — A85

**2004, Sept. 18 Litho. *Perf. 14x14¼***

**236** A85 3s multi .65 .65

National Academy of Sciences, 50th Anniv. A86

Emblem and: 1.50s, Old building. 3.60s, New building.

**2004, Nov. 6**

**237-238** A86 Set of 2 .95 .95

Basketball A87

Basketball player and: 1.50s, Coach Nikolay Zvenchukov. 3.60s, Coach Kubat Karabekov.

**2004, Dec. 4**

**239-240** A87 Set of 2 2.00 2.00

Falcon — A88

**2004-05 Litho. *Perf. 13¼x14***

| | | | | |
|---|---|---|---|---|
| **241** | A88 | 10t green | .40 | .40 |
| **242** | A88 | 50t blue | .40 | .40 |
| **243** | A88 | 1s brown | .75 | .75 |
| | | *Nos. 241-243 (3)* | 1.55 | 1.55 |

Issued: 1s, 12/28/04. 50t, 2/12/05. 10t, 6/16/05.

Nos. 241-243 exist imperf. Value, set $20.

New Year 2005 (Year of the Rooster) A89

**2005, Mar. 21 Litho. *Perf. 14***

**244** A89 3s multi 1.10 1.10

No. 244 exists imperf. Value, $10.

**Souvenir Sheet**

Salizhan Sharipov, Astronaut — A90

**2005, Apr. 20 Litho. *Perf. 13¾***

**245** A90 100s multi *13.50 13.50*

Folk Art — A91

Various folk art objects.

**2005, Apr. 23 *Perf. 14¼x14***

| | | | | |
|---|---|---|---|---|
| **246** | | Strip of 6 | *4.50* | *4.50* |
| *a.* | A91 | 2s orange panel | *.25* | *.25* |
| *b.* | A91 | 3.60s light blue panel | *.25* | *.25* |
| *c.* | A91 | 7s green panel | *.55* | *.55* |
| *d.* | A91 | 12s green panel | *.85* | *.85* |
| *e.* | A91 | 15s bright pink panel | *1.10* | *1.10* |
| *f.* | A91 | 20s orange panel | *1.50* | *1.50* |

**Souvenir Sheet**

**247** A91 40s multi *4.50 4.50*

End of World War II, 60th Anniv. A92

**2005, May 6** ***Perf. 14x14¼***
**248** A92 5s multi *.85 .85*

End of World War II, 60th Anniv. — A93

World War II personalities: No. 249, 5s, Gen. Tito. No. 250, 5s, Cervi Brothers. No. 251, 5s, Ferruccio Parri. No. 252, 10s, Air Marshal Sir Hugh Dowding. No. 253, 10s, Gen. George S. Patton. No. 254, 10s, Gen. Konstantin Rokossovsky. No. 255, 10s, Gen. Harold Alexander. No. 256, 10s, Gen. Omar N. Bradley. No. 257, 10s, Gen. Charles de Gaulle. No. 258, 10s, Gen. Jean Leclerc. No. 259, 10s, Field Marshal Bernard Montgomery. No. 260, 10s, Gen. Ivan Konev. No. 261, 10s, Marshal Georgy Zhukov. No. 262, 10s, Gen. Dwight D. Eisenhower. No. 263, 10s, Marshal Semyon Timoshenko. No. 264, 10s, Gen. Vasily Chuikov. No. 265, 15s, Pres. Franklin D. Roosevelt. No. 266, 15s, Prime Minister Winston Churchill. No. 267, 15s, King George VI. No. 268, 15s, Joseph Stalin.

**Embossed on Metal**
**2005, June 18** ***Die Cut Perf 12½***
**Self-Adhesive**
**249-268** A93 Set of 20 *60.00 60.00*

National Games — A94

**2005, Aug. 6 Litho.** ***Perf. 14¼x14***
**269** A94 3s multi .60 .60

World Summit on the Information Society, Tunis A95

**2005, Sept. 10** ***Perf. 14x14¼***
**270** A95 3.60s multi .75 .75

Falcon — A96

**2005, Sept. 14 Litho.** ***Perf. 13¼x14***
**271** A96 60t violet .60 .60

No. 271 exists imperf. Value $5.75.

Souvenir Sheet

Lakes — A97

No. 272: a, 7s, Lake Chatyrkul. b, 20s, Lake Sonkul. c, 25s, Lake Sarychelek. d, 30s, Lake Issyk-Kul.

**2005, Dec. 10** ***Perf. 14x14¼***
**272** A97 Sheet of 4, #a-d 6.25 6.25

Europa Stamps, 50th Anniv. (in 2006) — A98

Designs: 15s, Uzgen Minaret, Kyrgyzstan. 20s, Acropolis, Athens, Greece. 25s, Buran Tower, Kyrgyzstan. 45s, Kolossi Castle, Limassol, Cyprus. 60s, Tash Rabat, Kyrgyzstan. 85s, St. Mark's Basilica, Venice, Italy.

**2005, Dec. 29** ***Perf. 13¼x13***
**273-278** A98 Set of 6 17.50 17.50
*278a* Souvenir sheet, #273-278 17.50 17.50

Nos. 273-278 and 278a exist imperf. Values: set, $20; sheet, $20.

Tugolbai Sydykbekov (1912-97), Writer A99

**2006, Jan. 7** ***Perf. 14x14¼***
**279** A99 10s multi 1.00 1.00

New Year 2006 (Year of the Dog) A100

**2006, Feb. 4**
**280** A100 3s multi .70 .70

No. 280 exists imperf. Value, $10.

2006 Winter Olympics, Turin A101

**2006, Mar. 11**
**281** A101 5s multi .80 .80

No. 281 exists imperf. Value, $7.50.

Falcon — A102

**2006 Litho.** ***Perf. 13¼x14***
**282** A102 50t Prus blue .30 .30
**283** A102 1s car lake .40 .40
**284** A102 3s black .50 .50
*Nos. 282-284 (3)* 1.20 1.20

Issued: 50t, 4/15; 1s, 5/6; 3s, 8/5.

Nos. 282-284 exist imperf. Value, each $6.50.

2006 World Cup Soccer Championships, Germany — A103

**2006, June 9 Litho.** ***Perf. 14x14¼***
**285** A103 15s multi 1.25 1.25

Miniature Sheet

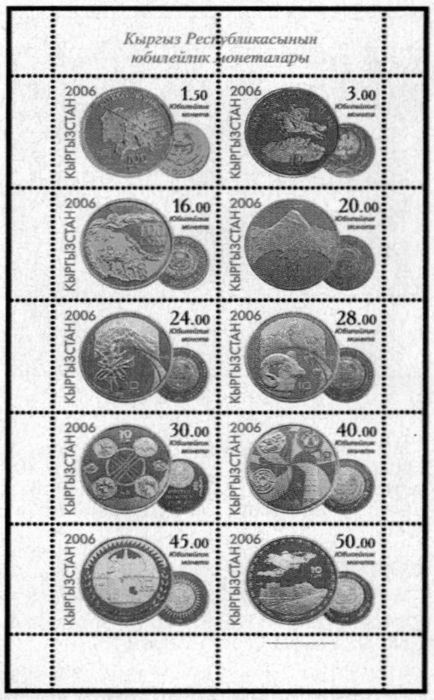

Commemorative Coins — A104

No. 286: a, 1.50s, 1995 100-som gold coin. b, 3s, 1995 10-som silver coin. c, 16s, 2000 100-som gold coin. d, 20s, 2001 10-som silver coin. e, 24s, 2002 10-som silver coin depicting flower. f, 28s, 2002 10-som silver coin depicting ram. g, 30s, 2003 10-som silver and gold coin depicting other coins. h, 40s, 2003 10-som silver and gold coin depicting national symbols. i, 45s, 2005 10-som silver coin. j, 50s, 2005 10-som silver and gold coin.

**2006, June 24**
**286** A104 Sheet of 10, #a-j *17.50 17.50*

Regional Communications Commonwealth, 15th Anniv. — A105

**2006, Sept. 23 Litho.** ***Perf. 14x14¼***
**287** A105 12s multi 1.25 1.25

Souvenir Sheet

Public Buildings in Bishkek — A106

No. 288: a, Sports arena (two word inscription, large tree at left). b, Theater (three word inscription). c, Philharmonic hall (one word inscription). d, Museum (two word inscription, no tree).

**2006, Sept. 30** ***Perf. 12¾x13¼***
**288** A106 12s Sheet of 4, #a-d 4.00 4.00

Intl. Telecommunications Union Plenipotentiary Conference, Antalya, Turkey — A107

**2006, Oct. 7 Litho.** ***Perf. 13x13½***
**289** A107 25s multi 2.25 2.25

Defense of Moscow in World War II, 65th Anniv. A108

**2006, Nov. 11** ***Perf. 14x14¼***
**290** A108 7s multi .70 .70

No. 290 exists imperf. Value, $8.

Miniature Sheet

Kyrgyz Cinema, 65th Anniv. — A109

No. 291: a, S. Chokmorov (on horse). b, B. Bejshenaliev (man wearing hat). c, T. Tursunbaeva (woman wearing headdress). d, B. Kydykeeva (two women).

**2006, Dec. 9**
**291** A109 12s Sheet of 4, #a-d 4.25 4.25

New Year 2007 (Year of the Pig) A110

**2007, Jan. 27 Litho.** ***Perf. 14x14¼***
**292** A110 3s multi .50 .50

No. 292 exists imperf. Value, $8.50.

Miniature Sheet

Paintings — A111

No. 293: a, Chingiz Aitmatov (seated man with striped shirt). b, Syimenkul Chokmorov (seated man with clasped hands). c, Kurmangazy Azykbaev (man playing flute). d, Omor Sultanov (seated man wearing light gray suit). e, Zhylkychy Zhakypov (man with dark blue shirt).

**2007, Mar. 3 Litho. *Perf. 14x14¼***
**293** A111 12s Sheet of 5, #a-e, + label 5.50 5.50

No. 293 exists imperf. Value, $30.

Kyrgyz National Games — A112

**2007, May 5 Litho. *Perf. 14x14¼***
**294** A112 7s multi .65 .65

No. 294 exists imperf. Value, $8.50.

Miniature Sheet

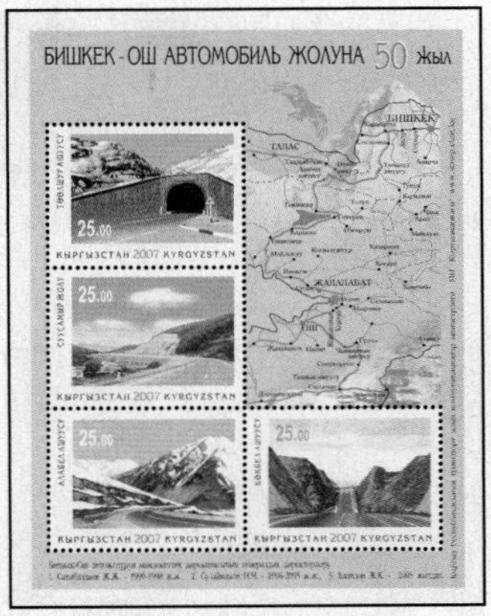


Bishkek-Osh Highway, 50th Anniv. — A113

No. 295: a, Tunnel. b, Road turning to left. c, Road turning to right. d, Straight road.

**2007, May 19 *Perf. 13x13¼***
**295** A113 25s Sheet of 4, #a-d 6.75 6.75

Aigul — A114

Flower and: 1s, Solid blue background. 100s, Mountains in background.

**2007, June 23 *Perf. 13¼x14***
**296** A114 1s multi .50 .50

**Souvenir Sheet**
***Perf. 13¼x13***

**297** A114 100s multi 8.00 8.00

No. 296 exists imperf. Value, $7.
No. 297 contains one 30x40mm stamp.

Miniature Sheet

Seventh Conference of Shanghai Cooperation Organization — A115

No. 298 — Flags of: a, Kazakhstan. b, Kyrgyzstan. c, People's Republic of China. d, Russia. e, Tajikistan. f, Uzbekistan.

**2007, Aug. 16 *Perf. 13¾x14½***
**298** A115 12s Sheet of 6, #a-f 5.75 5.75

Miniature Sheet

Birds of Prey — A116

No. 299: a, Haliaeetus albicilla. b, Falco rusticolus. c, Aquila chrysaetus. d, Accipiter gentilis. e, Milvus migrans. f, Falco peregrinus.

**2007, Nov. 30 Litho. *Perf. 14¼***
**299** A116 25s Sheet of 6, #a-f 12.00 12.00

Santa Claus — A117

**2007, Dec. 1 *Perf. 14x14¼***
**300** A117 3s multi .55 .55

No. 300 exists imperf. Value, $7.75.

New Year 2008 (Year of the Rat) — A118

**2008, Jan. 19 *Perf. 14¼x14***
**301** A118 7s multi .95 .95

No. 301 exists imperf. Value, $8.

Mammals — A119

Designs: Nos. 302, 310a, 7s, Uncia uncia. Nos. 303, 310b, 7s, Ailuropoda melanoleuca. Nos. 304, 310c, 12s, Panthera tigris. Nos. 305, 310d, 12s, Ailurus fulgens. Nos. 306, 310e, 16s, Hystrix cristata. Nos. 307, 310f, 16s, Pygathrix roxellana. Nos. 308, 310g, 25s, Otocolobus manul. Nos. 309, 310h, 25s, Ovis ammon.

**2008, Jan. 19 *Perf. 14x13½***
**Stamps With White Frames**
**302-309** A119 Set of 8 9.50 9.50

**Souvenir Sheet**
**Stamps With Colored Frames**
**310** A119 Sheet of 8, #a-h 9.25 9.25

Nos. 302-309 exist imperf. Value, set $17.

Kyrgyz National Games — A120

**2008, Mar. 1 *Perf. 14¼x14***
**311** A120 5s multi .70 .70

No. 311 exists imperf. Value, $6.50.

2008 Summer Olympics, Beijing — A121

No. 312: a, Soccer. b, Wrestling. c, Javelin. d, Basketball.

**2008, Mar. 1 *Perf. 12½x13***
**312** A121 20s Block of 4, #a-d 6.25 6.25

Souvenir Sheet

Mountains — A122

No. 313: a, Khan-Tengri, Kyrgyzstan. b, Sabalan Peak, Iran.

**2008, Mar. 8 *Perf. 13x13¼***
**313** A122 16s Sheet of 2, #a-b, + central label *4.00 4.00*

See Iran No. 2964.

Outlines of Stamps, Mountain, Kyrgyz Post Emblem — A123

**2008 Litho. *Perf. 14x13¼***

| | | | | |
|---|---|---|---|---|
| **314** | A123 50t multi | | .25 | .25 |
| **315** | A123 1s multi | | .25 | .25 |
| **316** | A123 3s multi | | .25 | .25 |
| **317** | A123 7s multi | | .65 | .65 |
| | *Nos. 314-317 (4)* | | 1.40 | 1.40 |

Issued: 1s, 3s, 4/2. 50t, 7s, 5/10.
Nos. 314-317 exist imperf. Value, set $20.

Heroes of the Kyrgyz Republic and Medals — A124

Designs: 10s, Sabira Kumushalieva (1917-2007), actress. 15s, Absamat Masaliev (1933-2004), politician.

**2008, Apr. 5 Litho. *Perf. 14x14¼***
**318-319** A124 Set of 2 2.50 2.50

Nos. 318-319 exist imperf. Value, set $12.50.

Miniature Sheets

Civil Aircraft — A125

No. 320: a, JAK-12. b, MI-2. c, AN-2. d, TU-154. e, IL-14. f, IL-18. g, AN-24. h, MI-4.
No. 321: a, AN-28. b, JAK-40. c, AN-26. d, TU-134. e, IL-76. f, A-320. g, MI-8.
No. 322: a, Sopwith. b, Air-6. c, P5. d, Po-2. e, Ju-52/3. f, ANT-9. g, Mi-1. h, Li-2.

**2008 *Perf. 14x13¼***
**320** A125 20s Sheet of 8, #a-h, + central label 11.00 11.00

***Perf. 13x13½***

**321** A125 20s Sheet of 7, #a-g, + label 10.50 10.50
**322** A125 20s Sheet of 8, #a-h, + label 10.50 10.50

Issued: No. 320, 5/24; No. 321, 9/20; No. 322, 11/1.

Hats — A126

Various hats: 6s, 7s, 12s, 50s.

**2008, June 28 Litho. *Perf. 14¼x14***
**323-326** A126 Set of 4 5.50 5.50

Nos. 323-326 exist imperf. Value, set $22.50.

Yaks — A127

No. 325: a, Buka yak (denomination on cloud). b, Mamalak yak (denomination on light blue sky and mountain). c, Inek yak facing right (denomination on purple mountain). d, Inek yak facing left (denomination on dark blue sky and mountain).

**2008, July 26 *Perf. 13x13¼***
**327** A127 25s Block of 4, #a-d 6.50 6.50

Isa Akhunbaev (1908-75), Surgeon — A128

**2008, Aug. 30 *Perf. 14¼x14***
**328** A128 12s multi .90 .90

No. 328 exists imperf. Value, $7.

**No. 312 Overprinted in Red**

No. 329: a, #312a (Soccer) with overprint at bottom. b, #312b (Wrestling) with overprint at bottom. c, #312c (Javelin) with overprint at top. d, #312d (Basketball) with overprint at top. e, #312d with overprint at bottom. f, #312c with overprint at bottom. g, #312b with overprint at top. h, #312a with overprint at top.

**2008, Nov. 22 Litho.** ***Perf. 12½x13***
**329** A121 20s Sheet of 8, #a-h 21.00 21.00

Campaign Against Drug Abuse — A129

**2008, Dec. 6** ***Perf. 14¼x14***
**330** A129 12s multi 1.25 1.25

No. 330 exists imperf. Value, $6.50.

New Year 2009 (Year of the Ox) A130

**2009, Feb. 1** ***Perf. 14x14¼***
**331** A130 25s multi 1.60 1.60

No. 331 exists imperf. Value, $6.

Ishembai Abdraimov (1914-2001), Soviet Pilot — A131

**2009, Feb. 26** ***Perf. 14¼x14***
**332** A131 10s multi .85 .85

No. 332 exists imperf. Value, $6.25.

Kok-boru (Buzkashi) A132

**2009, Apr. 25** ***Perf. 14x14¼***
**333** A132 25s multi 1.60 1.60

No. 333 exists imperf. Value, $6.

Miniature Sheet

Horses — A133

No. 334 — Various horses: a, 16s. b, 42s. c, 50s. d, 60s.

**2009, May 30** ***Perf. 13x13½***
**334** A133 Sheet of 4, #a-d 9.00 9.00

Worldwide Fund for Nature (WWF) A134

Saker falcon: 10s, Head. 15s, On nest. 25s, In flight. 50s, On nest, with chicks.

**2009, June 20** ***Perf. 13½x14***
**335-338** A134 Set of 4 5.50 5.50
*338a* Sheet, 4 each #335-338 22.00 22.00

Nos. 335-338 and 338a exist imperf. Values: set of four, $13; sheet of 16, $42.50.

Miniature Sheet

Scenes From Writings of Chynghyz Aitmatov (1928-2008) — A135

No. 339: a, 7s, Woman, horse, cart and farmer in field. b, 12s, Man and horse. c, 16s, Woman and truck. d, 21s, Women near train. e, 28s, Man carrying boy. f, 30s, Boy with binoculars, buck. g, 45s, Birds flying above horse and rider. h, 60s, Men in canoe.

**2009, Aug. 13 Litho.** ***Perf. 13x13¼***
**339** A135 Sheet of 8, #a-h, + label 11.00 11.00

Barpy Alykulov (1884-1949), Poet — A136

**2009, Aug. 22 Litho.** ***Perf. 14x13½***
**340** A136 16s multi .95 .95

No. 340 exists imperf. Value, $6.

**Horses Type of 2009**

Designs: 16s, Like #334a. 42s, Like #334b. 50s, Like #334c. 60s, Like #334d.

**2009, Sept. 19 Litho.** ***Perf. 14x14¼***
**341-344** A133 Set of 4 9.00 9.00

Nos. 341-344 were each printed in sheets of 6.

Nos. 341-344 exist imperf. Value, set $30.

National Library, 75th Anniv. A137

**2009, Sept. 30** ***Perf. 13½x14***
**345** A137 12s multi .90 .90

No. 345 exists imperf. Value, $5.75.

Miniature Sheet

Glaciers — A138

No. 346: a, 12s, Ak-Sai Glacier. b, 16s, Kotur Glacier. c, 21s, Semenovsky Glacier. d, 28s, Zvezdochka Glacier. e, 45s, North Inylchek Glacier. f, 60s, South Inylchek Glacier.

**2009, Dec. 12** ***Perf. 13x13¼***
**346** A138 Sheet of 6, #a-f 10.50 10.50

No. 346 exists imperf. Value, $32.50.

Railways of Kyrgyzstan A139

Designs: 16s, Station. 42s, Train on bridge. 50s, Train leaving tunnel. 60s, Train on bridge over highway.

**2009, Dec. 19** ***Perf. 14x14¼***
**347-350** A139 Set of 4 10.00 10.00

Nos. 347-350 exist imperf. Value, set $32.50.

United Nations Declaration of the Rights of the Child, 50th Anniv. (in 2009) — A140

**2010, Feb. 6**
**351** A140 21s multi 1.50 1.50

New Year 2010 (Year of the Tiger) A141

**2010, Feb. 6**
**352** A141 25s multi 1.60 1.60

2010 Winter Olympics, Vancouver — A142

Designs: 21s, Cross-country skiing. 28s, Biathlon. 45s, Giant slalom. 60s, Snowboarding.

**2010, Feb. 12** ***Perf. 14¼x14***
**353-356** A142 Set of 4 10.50 10.50

Peonies — A143

No. 357: a, 25s, Flowers. b, 30s, Flower.

**2010, Mar. 30** ***Perf. 12½***
**357** A143 Horiz. pair, #a-b 3.75 3.75
*c.* Souvenir sheet, #357b 2.40 2.40

Victory in World War II, 65th Anniv. A144

**2010, Apr. 10** ***Perf. 14x14¼***
**358** A144 12s multi .75 .75

Miniature Sheet

Kyrgyz National Museum of Fine Arts, 75th Anniv. — A145

No. 359 — Paintings: a, 12s, Portrait of Y. M. Vengerov, by Ilya E. Repin, 1916. b, 16s, Cabbage Field, by Robert R. Falk, 1910. c, 21s, Dishes on a Red Cloth, by Pyotr P. Konchalovsky, 1916. d, 24s, Seascape in the Crimea, by Ivan K. Ayvazovsky, 1866. e, 28s, Autumn Djailoo, by Semen A. Chuykov, 1945. f, 30s, Evening in the South of Kyrgyzstan, by Gapar A. Aitiev, 1967. g, 42s, Autumn Garden, by A. Ignatev, 1989. h, 45s, By Night, by D. N. Deymant, 1971.

**2010, Apr. 24** ***Perf. 13x13¼***
**359** A145 Sheet of 8, #a-h, + central label 13.00 13.00

2010 World Cup Soccer Championships, South Africa — A146

Players and: 24s, Emblem. 30s, World Cup. 42s, Emblem, diff. 60s, World Cup, diff.

**2010, June 26 Litho.** ***Perf. 14x14¼***
**360-363** A146 Set of 4 9.50 9.50

Ancient Silver Jewelry A147

Designs: 16s, Earrings. 24s, Buttons. 58s, Bangles. 66s, Hair ornaments.

**2010, July 31** *Perf. 13½*
**364-367** A147 Set of 4 10.00 10.00

Souvenir Sheet

Kambar-Ata 2 Hydroelectric Station — A148

No. 368: a, 28s, Explosion. b, 42s, Station under construction. c, 60s, Station under construction, diff.

**2010, Aug. 31** *Perf. 13x13¼*
**368** A148 Sheet of 3, #a-c 7.50 7.50

Souvenir Sheet

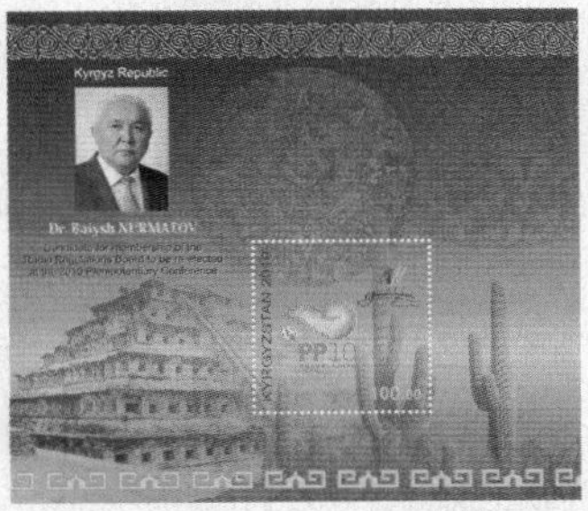

Intl. Telecommunications Union Plenipotentiary Conference, Guadalajara, Mexico — A149

**2010, Sept. 25** *Perf. 13*
**369** A149 100s multi 6.00 6.00

Famous Men — A150

Designs: 12s, Togolok Moldo (1860-1942), poet. 16s, Murataly Kurenkeev (1860-1949), composer. 21s, Zhenizhok Coco Uulu (1860-1918), poet. 28s, Itzhak Razzakov (1910-79), statesman.

**2010** *Perf. 14¼x14*
**370-373** A150 Set of 4 4.00 4.00

Issued: 28s, 10/25; others, 10/23.

Turtles A151

Designs: 16s, Agrionemys horstieldi. 24s, Pseudemys scripta. 48s, Geochelone elegans. 72s, Testudo kleinmanni.

**2010, Dec. 11** *Perf. 14x14¼*
**374-377** A151 Set of 4 9.00 9.00

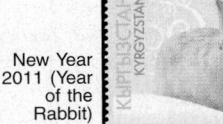

New Year 2011 (Year of the Rabbit) A152

**2011, Jan. 29**
**378** A152 24s multi 1.40 1.40

Miniature Sheet

Animals and National Reserves — A153

No. 379: a, 7s, Eagle, Ala-Archa Reserve. b, 12s, Bear, Chon-Kemin Reserve. c, 16s, Buck, Naryn Reserve. d, 21s, Ram, Sary-Chelek Reserve. e, 24s, Fish, Issyk-Kul Reserve. f, 28s, Duck, Karatal-Zhapryk Reserve. g, 42s, Falcon, Besh-Tash Reserve. h, 45s, Cat, Sarychat-Ertash Reserve. i, 60s, Pheasant, Padysha-Ata Reserve.

**2011, Feb. 25** *Perf. 13x13¼*
**379** A153 Sheet of 9, #a-i 13.50 13.50

Souvenir Sheet

First Man in Space, 50th Anniv. — A154

No. 380: a, 60s, Vostok 1. b, 90s, Yuri Gagarin (1934-68), first cosmonaut.

**2011, Apr. 2** *Perf. 13¼x13*
**380** A154 Sheet of 2, #a-b 8.00 8.00

2011 Intl. Ice Hockey Federation Championships, Slovakia — A155

Intl. Ice Hockey Federation emblem and: 28s, Player approaching goalie with puck. 42s, Two players and puck.

**2011, May 14** *Perf. 14x14¼*
**381-382** A155 Set of 2 4.00 4.00
*382a* Miniature sheet of 6, 3 each #381-382 12.50 12.50

Miniature Sheet

Bishkek Bus Station, 30th Anniv. — A156

No. 383 — Vehicles: a, 12s, PAZ-672 bus, RAF-22038 van. b, 16s, Ikarus-256 bus, GAZ-M24 Volga taxi. c, 21s, LAZ 697R Tourist bus, UAZ-2206 van. d, 24s, Ford E series van, Volvo B12B bus. e, 30s, Volkswagen Transporter T4 van, Setra S 431 dt bus. f, 42s, Mercedes Sprinter 313 van, Mitsubishi Fuso Aero Queen bus.

**2011, July 21** *Perf. 13x13¼*
**383** A156 Sheet of 6, #a-f + central label 8.50 8.50

**No. 123 Overprinted in Gold with Nos. 123c and 123d Surcharged in Metallic Red**

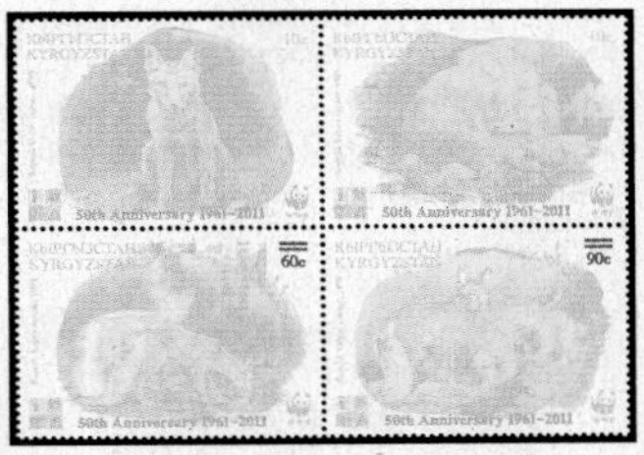

No. 384: a, Overprint on #123a. b, Overprint on #123b. c, 60s on 20s #123c. d, 90s on 50s #123d.

**Litho. With Hologram**

**2011, Aug. 5** *Perf. 13½*
**384** A35 Block of 4, #a-d *20.00 20.00*

Plum Blossoms — A157

No. 385: a, 16s, Denomination at UL. b, 60s, Denomination at UR.

**2011, Aug. 15** **Litho.** *Perf. 13*
**385** A157 Horiz. pair, #a-b 4.50 4.50

Regional Communications Commonwealth, 20th Anniv. — A158

**2011, Oct. 1** *Perf. 14x14¼*
**386** A158 28s multi 1.75 1.75

Souvenir Sheet

Independence, 20th Anniv. — A159

**2011, Oct. 1** *Perf. 14*
**387** A159 100s multi 6.00 6.00

Commonwealth of Independent States, 20th Anniv. — A160

**2011, Oct. 8** *Perf. 14x14¼*
**388** A160 42s multi 2.75 2.75

Mushrooms A161

Designs: 16s, Agaricus. 28s, Pleurotus. 42s, Marasmius oreades. 72s, Lycoperdon.

**2011, Nov. 12** **Litho.** *Perf. 14¼x14*
**389-392** A161 Set of 4 9.00 9.00

Musical Instruments A162

Designs: 16s, Surnai (wind instrument). 24s, Dobulbas (drum). 48s, Kyl kayak (stringed instrument with bow). 60s, Ooz komuz (mouth harp).

**2011, Nov. 26**
**393-396** A162 Set of 4 8.25 8.25

Airships A163

Designs: 12s, Dirigible of Henri Giffard. 28s, LZ-127 Graf Zeppelin. 45s, AU-30 Argus dirigible. 48s, Dirigible of the future.

**2011, Dec. 17** *Perf. 14x14¼*
**397-400** A163 Set of 4 7.75 7.75

New Year 2012 (Year of the Dragon) A164

**2012, Jan. 14** *Perf. 13¼*

**401** A164 36s multi 2.10 2.10

Printed in sheets of 4.

Miniature Sheet

Oriental Lunar Calendar Animals — A165

No. 402: a, Dog. b, Boar. c, Rat. d, Ox. e, Rooster. f, Tiger. g, Monkey. h, Rabbit. i, Sheep. j, Horse. k, Snake. l, Dragon.

**2012, Jan. 14** *Perf. 13¾x13½*

**402** A165 25s Sheet of 12, #a-l, + central label 18.00 18.00

Women's Headdresses A166

Various headdresses: 16s, 28s, 45s, 60s.

**2012, Feb. 25** *Perf. 13*

**403-406** A166 Set of 4 8.50 8.50

Helianthus A167

**2012, Mar. 29** *Perf. 14¼x14*

**407** A167 42s multi 2.50 2.50

Bolot Beishenaliev (1937-2002), Actor — A168

Gapar Aitiev (1912-84), Artist — A169

**2012, Apr. 28** **Litho.**

**408** A168 23s multi 1.25 1.25

**409** A169 49s multi 2.75 2.75

Miniature Sheet

Inventions — A170

No. 410: a, 21s, Writing. b, 23s, Bread. c, 45s, Wheel. d, 49s, Money.

**2012, June 2** *Perf. 14*

**410** A170 Sheet of 4, #a-d 8.25 8.25

2012 World Stamp Championship, Jakarta, Indonesia.

United Nations Environment Program, 40th Anniv. — A171

**2012, June 5** *Perf. 14x14¼*

**411** A171 45s multi 2.75 2.75

National Games A172

**2012, Aug. 4** **Litho.** *Perf. 14x14¼*

**412** A172 28s multi 1.75 1.75

Battle of Borodino, Bicent. — A173

No. 413: a, 12s, Battlefield Monument, Borodino. b, 45s, Triumphal Arch, Moscow.

**2012, Aug. 25** *Perf. 14¼x14*

**413** A173 Pair, #a-b 3.50 3.50

Snow Leopard A174

Designs: 17s, Leopard. 20s, Leopard, diff. 23s, Head of leopard. 30s, Three leopards.

**2012, Sept. 15** *Perf. 14x14¼*

**414-417** A174 Set of 4 5.75 5.75

Man and Woman in Traditional Costumes and Emblem of Regional Communications Commonwealth A175

**2012, Oct. 20** *Perf. 14¼x14*

**418** A175 30s multi 1.75 1.75

Inscribed Tablets — A176

No. 419 — Tablet from: a, 35s, 8th cent. b, 40s, 9th cent.

**2012, Nov. 3**

**419** A176 Horiz. pair, #a-b 4.50 4.50

Gen. Ysakbek Monuev (1902-49) — A177

Ormon Khan (1792-1854), Kyrgyz Tribal Leader — A178

**2012, Nov. 24**

**420** A177 35s multi 2.25 2.25

**421** A178 40s multi 2.50 2.50

Prehistoric Animals A179

Designs: 23s, Kyrgyzsaurus. 30s, Xenacanthidae. 40s, Longisquama. 52s, Mammoth.

**2012, Dec. 8** *Perf. 14x14¼*

**422-425** A179 Set of 4 9.50 9.50

Souvenir Sheet

Mayan Calendar — A180

No. 426: a, 29s, Mayan calendar. b, 52s, Mayan pyramid.

**2012, Dec. 21** *Perf. 14*

**426** A180 Sheet of 2, #a-b 5.25 5.25

New Year 2013 (Year of the Snake) A181

**2013, Feb. 16** *Perf. 14x14¼*

**427** A181 30s multi 2.00 2.00

2012 Universal Postal Congress International Stamp Exhibition, Doha, Qatar — A182

No. 428: a, 28s, Gold medal diploma awarded to Kyrgyzstan. b, 43s, Exhibition emblem.

**2013, Feb. 23**

**428** A182 Pair, #a-b 4.25 4.25

No. 428 was printed in sheets containing three pairs.

Miniature Sheet

Walnuts — A183

No. 429: a, 17s, Cluster of walnuts on tree branch. b, 20s, Walnuts with opened husks. c, 23s, Walnut in husk, walnuts in shell, opened walnut, jar of product containing walnuts. d, 29s, Walnut in shell, kernels. e, 35s, Basket of walnuts. f, 40s, Walnut grove, mountains.

**2013, Mar. 9**

**429** A183 Sheet of 6, #a-f 9.50 9.50

National Horse Games A184

**2013, Mar. 23**

**430** A184 35s multi 2.25 2.25

Spaceflight of Valentina Tereshkova, First Woman in Space, 50th Anniv. A185

**2013, Apr. 13**

**431** A185 50s multi 3.25 3.25

Introduction of Som Currency, 20th Anniv. A186

**2013, Apr. 27**
**432** A186 28s multi 1.75 1.75

Marco Polo Argali (Mountain Sheep) A187

Design: 29s, Head of ram. 35s, Adult and juveniles grazing. 40s, Ram on mountain ledge. 52s, Ram in winter.

**2013, May 18**
**433-436** A187 Set of 4 11.00 11.00
*436a* Souvenir sheet of 4, #433-436 11.00 11.00

Kozhomkul (1888-1955), Wrestler — A188

**2013, June 8**
**437** A188 30s multi 1.75 1.75

Sulayman Mountain A189

**2013, June 22**
**438** A189 45s multi 3.00 3.00

Miniature Sheet

Worldwide Fund for Nature (WWF) — A190

No. 439 — Snow leopard: a, 29s, Resting on rock. b, 35s, Leaping. c, 43s, Standing on rock. d, 52s, Kittens.

**2013, July 13**
**439** A190 Sheet of 4, #a-d 10.50 10.50

Intl. Forum on Snow Leopard Conservation, Bishkek.

Regional Communications Commonwealth Emblem, Train, Airplane, Satellite Dish, Cover and Tablet — A191

**2013, Aug. 17 Litho.** ***Perf. 14x14¼***
**440** A191 36s multi 1.90 1.90

Miniature Sheet

13th Shanghai Cooperation Organization Council of Heads of State Session, Bishkek — A192

No. 441 — Emblems or coat of arms of: a, 12s, Kazakhstan. b, 17s, Kyrgyzstan. c, 20s, People's Republic of China. d, 23s, Russia. e, 30s, Tajikistan. f, 35s, Uzbekistan.

**Litho. With Foil Application**
**2013, Sept. 13** ***Perf. 13½x13¼***
**441** A192 Sheet of 6, #a-f 6.50 6.50

Nasirdin Isanov (1943-91), First Prime Minister of Kyrgyzstan A193

**2013, Oct. 1 Litho.** ***Perf. 14x14¼***
**442** A193 17s multi 1.25 1.25

Kyrgyz Khaganate, 1170th Anniv. — A194

No. 443: a, 20s, Kyrgyz soldier wearing helmet, map of Khaganate. b, 23s, Mounted soldiers. c, 30s, Mounted soildier and petroglyphs.

**2013, Nov. 16 Litho.** ***Perf. 14¼x14***
**443** A194 Horiz. strip of 3, #a-c 4.25 4.25

Printed in sheets of 6 containing two of each stamp.

Medicinal Plants — A195

Designs: 20s, Capparis spinosa. 30s, Aconitum leucostomum. 35s, Hippophae rhamnoides. 52s, Glycyrrhiza glabra.

**2013, Dec. 14 Litho.** ***Perf. 14¼x14***
**444-447** A195 Set of 4 9.25 9.25

New Year 2014 (Year of the Horse) A196

**2014, Feb. 16 Litho.** ***Perf. 14x14¼***
**448** A196 35s multi 2.25 2.25

2014 Winter Olympics, Sochi, Russia A197

Designs: 12s, Speed skating. 21s, Cross-country skiing. 52s, Freestyle skiing. 74s, Bobsledding.

**2014, Feb. 22 Litho.** ***Perf. 14x14¼***
**449-452** A197 Set of 4 8.25 8.25

Jousting Horsemen A198

**2014, Mar. 22 Litho.** ***Perf. 14x14¼***
**453** A198 30s multi 1.90 1.90

Aykol Manas Monument, Bishkek — A199

**2014, Apr. 15 Litho.** ***Perf. 13¼x14***
**Background Color**

| | | | | | |
|---|---|---|---|---|---|
| **454** | A199 | 20s green gray | .95 | .95 |
| **455** | A199 | 23s blue gray | 1.10 | 1.10 |
| **456** | A199 | 30s lilac | 1.40 | 1.40 |
| **457** | A199 | 93s lt green | 4.50 | 4.50 |
| **458** | A199 | 100s lt orange | 4.75 | 4.75 |
| | | *Nos. 454-458 (5)* | 12.70 | 12.70 |

Children on Sleds A200

**2014, May 10 Litho.** ***Perf. 14x14¼***
**459** A200 40s multi 2.25 2.25

Medicinal Plants — A201

Designs: 20s, Tussilago farfara. 23s, Ferula foetida. 35s, Ziziphora clinopodioides. 40s, Helichrysum maracandicum.

**2014, May 31 Litho.** ***Perf. 12¼x12***
**460-463** A201 Set of 4 6.00 6.00

Worldwide Fund for Nature (WWF) A202

Aegypius monachus: 29s, Head. 35s, In flight. 62s, Adult and chick in nest. 74s, On ground.

**2014, June 21 Litho.** ***Perf. 14x14¼***
**464-467** A202 Set of 4 11.00 11.00
*467a* Block of 4, #464-467 11.00 11.00

Miniature Sheet

Soccer Players — A203

No. 468: a, 29s, Five players. b, 35s, Three players. c, 40s, Two players. d, 52s, Four players.

**2014, July 1 Litho.** ***Perf. 12x12¼***
**468** A203 Sheet of 4, #a-d 8.00 8.00

Dooronbek Sadyrbaev (1939-2008), Film Director, and Medal — A204

**2014, July 26 Litho.** ***Perf. 14x14¼***
**469** A204 35s multi 1.90 1.90

Carpets A205

UNESCO emblem and: 35s, Ala-kiyiz. 45s, Shyrdak.

**2014, Aug. 16 Litho.** ***Perf. 12x12¼***
**470-471** A205 Set of 2 4.50 4.50

Nos. 470-471 each were printed in sheets of 5 + label.

Communist Leaders — A206

Designs: 20s, Imanaly Aidarbekov (1884-1938). 29s, Abdykerim Sydykov (1889-1938). 35s, Abdykadyr Orozbekov (1889-1938).

**2014, Aug. 31 Litho.** ***Perf. 14¼x14***
**472-474** A206 Set of 3 4.00 4.00

Souvenir Sheet

Kyrgyz State Technical University, 60th Anniv. — A207

No. 475: a, 52s, University building and statue. b, 62s, University building, no statue.

**2014, Sept. 18 Litho.** ***Perf. 12x12¼***
**475** A207 Sheet of 2, #a-b 6.00 6.00

Souvenir Sheet

International Telecommunication Union Plenipotentiary Conference, Busan, South Korea — A208

**2014, Oct. 11 Litho.** ***Perf. 12x12¼***
**476** A208 30s multi 1.90 1.90

Toktogul Satylganov (1864-1933), Poet — A209

Suimenkul Chokmorov (1939-92), Film Actor — A210

**2014, Nov. 1 Litho.** ***Perf. 12¼x12***
**477** A209 35s multi 2.00 2.00
**478** A210 40s multi 2.25 2.25

Kyrgyz Flag and People — A211

**2014, Dec. 6 Litho.** ***Perf. 13x13½***
**479** A211 30s multi 1.90 1.90

Souvenir Sheet

Cotton — A212

No. 480: a, 35s, Cotton bolls and leaves. b, 52s, Cotton bolls.

**2014, Dec. 13 Litho.** ***Perf. 12x12¼***
**480** A212 Sheet of 2, #a-b 4.50 4.50

Endangered Animals — A213

Designs: 23s, Ursus arctos. 30s, Otocolobus manul. 40s, Cuon alpinus. 52s, Lynx lynx linnaeus.

**2014, Dec. 20 Litho.** ***Perf. 14x14¼***
**481-484** A213 Set of 4 7.75 7.75

New Year 2015 (Year of the Sheep) A214

**2015, Feb. 7 Litho.** ***Perf. 12x12¼***
**485** A214 40s multi 2.25 2.25

Sheep Breeds — A215

No. 486: a, 35s, Aykol. b, 52s, Mountain merino.

**2015, Feb. 21 Litho.** ***Perf. 12x12¼***
**486** A215 Pair, #a-b 4.50 4.50

Famous People — A216

No. 487: a, 29s, Korgool Dosuev (1890-1962), singer. b, 35s, Zhumamudin Sheraliev (1915-94), musician. c, 40s, Myskal Omurkanova (1915-76), singer. d, 52s, Alykul Osmonov (1915-50), poet.

**2015, Mar. 21 Litho.** ***Perf. 14¼x14***
**487** A216 Horiz. strip of 4, #a-d 7.75 7.75

Dogs and Cats A217

Designs: 29s, Ainu. 35s, Persian cat. 62s, Siamese cat. 74s, Taigan.

**2015, Apr. 4 Litho.** ***Perf. 12x12¼***
**488-491** A217 Set of 4 9.50 9.50
*491a* Souvenir sheet of 4, #488-491 9.50 9.50

Victory in World War II, 70th Anniv. A218

70th anniv. emblem and: 30s, Taranchiev Ismailbek (1923-44), fighter pilot. 40s, War memorial, soldiers, tanks, map, vert. 52s, Otorbayev Asanbek (1925-45), soldier.

***Perf. 12x12¼, 12¼x12***
**2015, May 2 Litho.**
**492-494** A218 Set of 3 6.50 6.50

No. 493 was printed in sheets of 2.

Souvenir Sheet

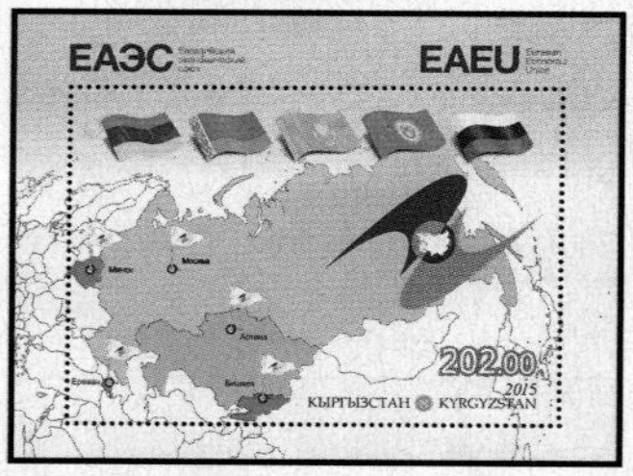

Eurasian Economic Union — A219

**2015, May 16 Litho.** ***Perf. 13***
**495** A219 202s multi 10.50 10.50

Miniature Sheet

Paintings — A220

No. 496: a, 15s, Poet, by G. Aytiev and D. Kozhakhmetov. b, 18s, Labyrinth, by D. Nurgaziev. c, 20s, Old Street of Osh City, by U. Akynov. d, 30s, Poppies, by Erbol Dogdurbek. e, 35s, Mystic Night, by D. Umetov. f, 40s, Touching Eternity, by S. A. Chuykov. g, 52s, Holiday, by S. Chokmorov. h, 59s, South Beach, by S. Torobekov.

**2015, July 18 Litho.** ***Perf. 12x12¼***
**496** A220 Sheet of 8, #a-h, + central label 13.50 13.50

Scenes From the Epic of Manas A221

No. 497 — Various scenes: a, 20s. b, 35s. c, 74s.

**2015, Aug. 1 Litho.** ***Perf. 12x12¼***
**497** A221 Vert. strip of 3, #a-c 6.75 6.75

Zhusup Balasagun, 10th Cent. Poet, and Kyrgyzstan National University A222

**2015, Aug. 22 Litho.** ***Perf. 14x14¼***
**498** A222 52s multi 2.75 2.75

Cars of the 21st Century A223

Designs: 33s, Terrafugia TF-X concept flying car. 36s, Mercedes-Benz F015 concept car. 39s, Tesla Model S. 83s, Toyota Mirai.

**2015, Oct. 10 Litho.** ***Perf. 12x12¼***
**499-502** A223 Set of 4 8.50 8.50
*502a* Sheet of 8, 2 each #499-502, + label 17.00 17.00

Nos. 499-502 were each printed in sheets of 5 + label.

Worldwide Fund for Nature (WWF) A224

Whooper swans: 36s, Three in flight. 39s, Adult and chicks in water. 48s, Adult in water. 117s, Adult extending wings.

**2015, Nov. 28 Litho.** ***Perf. 12***
**503-506** A224 Set of 4 10.00 10.00
*506a* Souvenir sheet of 8, 2 each #503-506 20.00 20.00

Souvenir Sheet

2015 Asian Juniors Chess Championship, Kyrgyzstan — A225

No. 507 — Various chess pieces on board with background colors of: a, 48s, Light green and light blue. b, 55s, Pink and light orange.

**2015, Nov. 28 Litho.** ***Perf. 12***
**507** A225 Sheet of 2, #a-b 4.25 4.25

New Year 2016 (Year of the Monkey) A226

**2016, Feb. 6 Litho.** ***Perf. 12x12¼***
**508** A226 76s multi 3.25 3.25

Flowers — A227

Designs: 36s, Tulipa kolpakovskiana. 39s, Tulip Porto. 48s, Orchid Rio Bamba. 55s, Cattleya Queen Sirikhit Diamond Crown orchid.

**2016, Feb. 13 Litho.** ***Perf. 12¼x12***
**509-512** A227 Set of 4 7.75 7.75
*512a* Souvenir sheet of 4, #509-512 7.75 7.75

Regional Communications Commonwealth, 25th Anniv. — A228

**2016, Mar. 12 Litho.** ***Perf. 14¼x14***
**513** A228 55s multi 2.25 2.25

Writers — A229

Designs: 48s, Zhakypbek Boogachy (1866-1935). 83s, Nasirdin Baytemirov (1916-96).

**2016, Mar. 26 Litho.** ***Perf. 14¼x14***
**514-515** A229 Set of 2 5.75 5.75

Commonwealth of Independent States, 25th Anniv. — A230

**2016, Apr. 30 Litho.** ***Perf. 14¼x14***
**516** A230 83s multi 4.00 4.00

Souvenir Sheet

Manned Space Flights, 55th Anniv. — A231

No. 517: a, 22s, Rocket launch. b, 117s, Docked spacecraft, spacewalker.

**2016, May 14 Litho.** ***Perf. 12***
**517** A231 Sheet of 2, #a-b 6.25 6.25

Souvenir Sheet

Bishkek Trolleybus Management, 65th Anniv. — A232

No. 518 — Trolleybuses: a, 39s, BMZ-5298.01 (56x20mm). b, 55s, MTB-82 (40x29mm). c, 83s, MTB-82D (30x27mm).

***Perf. 13 At Bottom (39s), 12 (55s), 13½x13 (83s)***

**2016, June 25 Litho.**
**518** A232 Sheet of 3, #a-c 8.00 8.00

Souvenir Sheet

Independence, 25th Anniv. — A233

**2016, July 23 Litho.** ***Perf. 12¼x12***
**519** A233 100s multi 4.75 4.75

Taylak (1796-1838), Warrior — A234

**2016, July 30 Litho.** ***Perf. 12¼x12***
**520** A234 55s multi 2.60 2.60

2016 Summer Olympics, Rio de Janeiro A235

Designs: 22s, Taekwondo. 31s, Soccer. 55s, Golf. 117s, Wrestling.

**2016, Aug. 4 Litho.** ***Perf. 12x12¼***
**521-524** A235 Set of 4 10.50 10.50

Souvenir Sheet

2016 World Nomad Games, Cholpon-Ata — A236

**2016, Sept. 3 Litho.** ***Perf. 13***
**525** A236 117s multi 5.25 5.25

Traditional Cuisine A237

**2016, Sept. 17 Litho.** ***Perf. 12x12¼***
**526** A237 76s multi 3.50 3.50

Arachnids A238

Designs: 20s, Lycosa singoriensis. 22s, Eresus collari. 31s, Solifugae. 117s, Mesobuthus eupeus.

**2016, Oct. 5 Litho.** ***Perf. 12x12¼***
**527-530** A238 Set of 4 8.50 8.50
*530a* Souvenir sheet of 4, #527-530 8.50 8.50

Paintings by Vladimir V. Obraztsov (1891-1934) — A239

No. 531: a, Return from the Red Army, 1930. b, Conspiracy, 1932.
No. 532: a, Near Globe, 1930. b, On the Way to China, 1932.
39s, The Guerrillas, 1932.

**2016, Nov. 11 Litho.** ***Perf. 13x13½***

| | | | |
|---|---|---|---|
| **531** | Vert. pair | 2.25 | 2.25 |
| *a.* | A239 20s multi | .85 | .85 |
| *b.* | A239 31s multi | 1.40 | 1.40 |
| **532** | Vert. pair | 6.25 | 6.25 |
| *a.* | A239 22s multi | 1.00 | 1.00 |
| *b.* | A239 117s multi | 5.25 | 5.25 |
| **533** | A239 39s multi | 1.75 | 1.75 |
| | *Nos. 531-533 (3)* | 10.25 | 10.25 |

Yurts A240

Designs: 22s, Guest yurt. 117s, Yurt, family and horse.

**2016, Nov. 26 Litho.** ***Perf. 12x12¼***
**534-535** A240 Set of 2 6.00 6.00

Heroism of Panfilov Division's 28 Guardsmen, 75th Anniv. A241

**2016, Dec. 10 Litho.** ***Perf. 12x12¼***
**536** A241 83s multi 4.00 4.00

No. 536 was printed in sheets of 6 + 2 labels.

New Year 2017 (Year of the Rooster) A242

**2017, Jan. 25 Litho.** ***Perf. 12x12¼***
**537** A242 76s multi 3.50 3.50

Worldwide Fund for Nature (WWF) A243

Pelecanus crispus: 22s, One bird in flight. 31s, Two birds in flight. 39s, One bird on water. 117s, Three birds on water.

**2017, Feb. 25 Litho.** ***Perf. 12x12¼***
**538-541** A243 Set of 4 9.75 9.75
*541a* Souvenir sheet of 8, 2 each #538-541 19.50 19.50

Tulipa Greigii A244

Ciconia Nigra A245

**2017, Mar. 25 Litho.** ***Perf. 12x12¼***
**542** A244 39s multi 1.90 1.90
**543** A245 48s multi 2.25 2.25
*a.* Souvenir sheet of 4, 2 each #542-543 8.50 8.50

National Horse Games A246

**2017, Apr. 15 Litho.** ***Perf. 12x12¼***
**544** A246 83s multi 4.00 4.00

Protected Natural Areas A247

No. 545 — UNESCO emblem and: a, Sary-Chelek State Natural Park. b, Besh-Aral State Natural Park. c, Padysha-Ata State Natural Park.

**2017, May 6 Litho.** ***Perf. 12x12¼***

| | | | |
|---|---|---|---|
| **545** | Vert. strip of 3 | 7.25 | 7.25 |
| *a.* | A247 39s multi | 2.00 | 2.00 |
| *b.* | A247 48s multi | 2.40 | 2.40 |
| *c.* | A247 55s multi | 2.75 | 2.75 |

Printed in sheets containing two each Nos. 545a-545c.

Famous People — A248

Designs: 39s, Saira Kiyizbaeva (1917-88), opera singer. 55s, Sagymbai Orozbakov (1867-1930), narrator of epic poem, "Manas."

**2017, May 20 Litho.** ***Perf. 12¼x12***
**546-547** A248 Set of 2 4.50 4.50

Souvenir Sheet

Abdylas Maldybaev National Opera and Ballet Theater, 75th Anniv. — A249

No. 548: a, 39s, Bulat Minzhikiev (1940-97), opera singer. b, 48s, Painting of dancers on theater ceiling. c, 55s, Dmitri Shostakovich (1906-75), composer.

**2017, June 24 Litho.** ***Perf. 12¼x12***
**548** A249 Sheet of 3, #a-c 7.00 7.00

Baitik Kanaev (1820-86), Leader of Solto People — A250

**2017, July 8 Litho. *Perf. 12¼x12***
**549** A250 76s multi 4.00 4.00

Year of Morality, Education and Culture A251

**2017, Aug. 12 Litho. *Perf. 12x12¼***
**550** A251 76s multi 4.00 4.00

Souvenir Sheet

International Snow Leopard and Ecosystem Forum, Bishkek — A252

No. 551: a, 39s, Snow leopard in grass. b, 117s, Snow leopard on rocks.

**2017, Aug. 15 Litho. *Perf. 12x12¼***
**551** A252 Sheet of 2, #a-b 6.50 6.50

Heroes of the Kyrgyz Republic A253

Medal and: 35s, Ishak Razzakov (1910-79), politician. 55s, Turdakun Usubaliev (1919-2015), politician.

**2017, Oct. 14 Litho. *Perf. 12x12¼***
**552-553** A253 Set of 2 4.75 4.75

Souvenir Sheet

Emblem of Collective Security Treaty Organization and Flags of Member Countries — A254

**2017, Oct. 21 Litho. *Perf. 12x12¼***
**554** A254 193s multi 9.75 9.75

Collective Security Treaty, 125th anniv., Collective Security Treaty Organization, 15th anniv.

Endangered Animals — A255

Designs: 36s, Lynx lynx. 39s, Marmota menzbieri. 48s, Cervus elaphus asiaticus. 55s, Martes foina.

**2017, Nov. 4 Litho. *Perf. 12¼x12***
**555-558** A255 Set of 4 9.00 9.00
*558a* Souvenir sheet of 4, #555-558 9.00 9.00

October Revolution, Cent. A256

**2017, Nov. 18 Litho. *Perf. 12x12¼***
**559** A256 83s multi 4.50 4.50

## SEMI-POSTAL STAMPS

Natl. Epic Poem, Manas, Millennium SP1

SP2

Designs: 10t+5t, Woman with bird in hand. 20t+10t, Bird on man's wrist. No. B3, Women watching as baby held up. No. B4, Woman with spear, leading horse. 40t+15t, Warrior looking at dead dragon. No. B6, Warrior on horse holding axe. No. B7, Man wearing tall hat on horseback. No. B8, Warrior with sword on horseback.

No. B9, Man in red cradling fallen warrior. No. B10, Man in black seated in desert, tornado.

***Perf. 12, Imperf***

**1995, June 16 Litho.**

| | | | | |
|---|---|---|---|---|
| **B1** | SP1 | 10t +5t blue & bis | .40 | .40 |
| **B2** | SP1 | 20t +10t blue & bis | .40 | .40 |
| **B3** | SP1 | 30t +10t blue & bis | .40 | .40 |
| **B4** | SP1 | 30t +10t blue & bis | .40 | .40 |
| **B5** | SP1 | 40t +15t blue & bis | .40 | .40 |
| **B6** | SP1 | 50t +15t blue & bis | .40 | .40 |
| **B7** | SP1 | 50t +15t blue & bis | .40 | .40 |
| **B8** | SP1 | 50t +15t blue & bis | .40 | .40 |
| *a.* | | Sheet of 8, #B1-B8 + label | 4.00 | 4.00 |

**Souvenir Sheets**

| | | | | |
|---|---|---|---|---|
| **B9** | SP2 | 2s +50t multi | 2.00 | 2.00 |
| **B10** | SP2 | 2s +50t multi | 2.00 | 2.00 |

1996 Summer Olympic Games, Atlanta SP3

Designs: 100t+20t, Equestrian events. 140t+30t, Boxing. 150t+30t, Archery. 300t+50t, Judo, hot air balloon, sailing, water skiing.

**1996, July 10 Litho. *Perf. 12½x12***

| | | | | |
|---|---|---|---|---|
| **B11** | SP3 | 100t +20t multi | .30 | .30 |
| **B12** | SP3 | 140t +30t multi | .60 | .60 |
| **B13** | SP3 | 150t +30t multi | .80 | .80 |
| **B14** | SP3 | 300t +50t multi | 1.25 | 1.25 |
| | | *Nos. B11-B14 (4)* | 2.95 | 2.95 |

Town of Osh, 3000th Anniv. — SP4

No. B15: a, Globe, mountains, mosque, "Osh" and "3000." b, Mosque with three arches, mountains (green panel at UR). c, Solomon's Throne (mosque on mountain). d, Mausoleum of Asaf ibn Burkiya (denomination at LL).

Illustration reduced.

**2000, Feb. 19 Litho. *Perf. 13½***
**B15** SP4 6s +25t Sheet of 4, #a-d *3.50 3.50*

Exists imperf. Value $5.

Kurmanzhan Datka, 190th Anniv. of Birth — SP5

**2001, Oct. 13 Litho. *Perf. 14x14¼***
**B16** SP5 10s +70t ind & gray 1.60 1.60

## KYRGYZ EXPRESS POST

On May 21, 2013, Kyrgyz Express Post was declared a designated postal operator by the Universal Postal Union, marking the first time the UPU has had two designated postal operators in one country. Kyrgyz Express Post company was created in March 2012 and granted a license from the Kyrgyzstan Ministry of Transport and Communications on Dec. 7, 2012 to offer all types of postal services to customers and to compete with the state corporation Kyrgyz Pochtasy, which has post offices across the country. At the time Kyrgyz Express Post issued its first stamps, it had two post offices and a philatelic bureau in Bishkek.

A1

Methods of Postal Conveyance — A2

Designs: 500s, Jet airplane.

No. 2: a, 25s, Post rider. b, 50s, Locomotive. c, 250s, Mail van.

700s, Dove carrying letter, Universal Postal Union emblem.

**2014, Nov. 18 Litho. *Perf. 14x14½***
**1** A1 500s multi 15.00 15.00
**2** A1 Sheet of 4, #1, 2a-2c 24.00 24.00

**Souvenir Sheet of 1 + 8 Labels**

***Perf. 13 Syncopated***

**3** A2 700s multi 20.00 20.00

No. 1 was printed in panes of 4.

Wild Animals — A3

Designs: 250s, Panthera uncia.

No. 5: a, 15s, Falco cherrug. b, 25s, Bos grunniens. c, 125s, Capra sibirica alaiana.

**2014, Nov. 19 Litho. *Perf. 14x14¾***
**4** A3 250s multi 7.50 7.50
**5** A3 Sheet of 4, #4 & 5a-5c 15.00 15.00

No. 4 was printed in sheets of 4.

Falconry — A4

Designs: No. 6, 75s, Falcon in flight, denomination at LR. No. 7, 75s, Falcon in flight, denomination at LL. No. 8, 75s, Falcon approaching rabbit.

***Perf. 13 Syncopated***

**2015, May 14 Litho.**
**6-8** A4 Set of 3 8.00 8.00
*8a* Souvenir sheet of 3, #6-8 8.00 8.00

Souvenir Sheet

First Walks in Space, 50th Anniv. — A5

Spacewalker: a, 50s, Alexei Leonov. b, 150s, Edward White.

**2015, July 2 Litho. *Perf.***
**9** A5 Sheet of 2, #a-b 6.75 6.75

Souvenir Sheet

Penny Black, 175th Anniv. — A6

**2015, July 2 Litho. *Perf. 13¼x13***
**10** A6 250s multi 8.25 8.25

Famous Men — A7

Designs: 50s, Dante Alighieri (1265-1321), writer. 100s, Pyotr Ilyich Tchaikovsky (1840-93), composer.

***Perf. 13 Syncopated***

**2015, Sept. 2 — Litho.**

**11-12** A7 Set of 2 5.00 5.00

International Years — A8

Designs: 50s, Intl. Year of Soils. 75s, Intl. Year of Light.

***Perf. 13 Syncopated***

**2015, Sept. 2 — Litho.**

**13-14** A8 Set of 2 4.25 4.25
*14a* Vert. pair, #13-14 4.25 4.25

Nos. 13-14 were each printed in sheets of 8. No. 14a was printed in sheets containing 4 pairs.

Souvenir Sheet

Horses — A9

No. 15: a, Chestnut horse. b, Chestnut horse with white blaze.

**2015, Dec. 21 — Litho. — *Perf. 14¾x14***

**15** A9 100s Sheet of 2, #a-b 5.50 5.50

Minerals A10

Designs: No. 16, 50s, Aragonite. No. 17, 50s, Realgar. 75s, Stibnite. 100s, Kyanite.

**2016, Jan. 6 — Litho. — *Perf. 14x14¾***

**16-19** A10 Set of 4 8.00 8.00
*19a* Souvenir sheet of 4, #16-19 8.00 8.00

A11

Yeti A12

**Litho. With Foil Application**

***Serpentine Die Cut 12¾***

**2016, May 19 — Self-Adhesive**

**Coil Stamps**

**20** A11 (150s) multi 4.50 4.50
**21** A12 (250s) multi 7.50 7.50
*a.* Booklet pane of 4, 2 each #20-21 24.00 —
Complete booklet, #21a 24.00

Souvenir Sheets

Philataipei 2016 World Stamp Exhibition, Taipei — A13

2016 World Stamp Show, New York — A14

**2016, June 3 — Litho. — *Perf. 14x14½***

**22** A13 150s multi 4.50 4.50
**23** A14 250s multi 7.50 7.50

Taigan Hunting Dogs — A15

Designs: 50s, Black dog. 100s, Mottled dog. 150s, Dog chasing wolf.

***Perf. 13 Syncopated***

**2016, July 28 — Litho.**

**24-26** A15 Set of 3 9.00 9.00
*26a* Souvenir sheet of 3, #24-26 9.00 9.00

Flowers A16

Designs: No. 27, 50s, Iris orchioides. No. 28, 50s, Leontopodium ochroleucum. No. 29, 100s, Primula turkestanica. No. 30, 100s, Tulipa greigii.
200s, Papaver rhoeas.

**2016, July 29 — Litho. — *Perf. 14x14½***

**27-30** A16 Set of 4 9.00 9.00
*30a* Souvenir sheet of 4, #27-30 9.00 9.00

**Souvenir Sheet**

**31** A16 200s multi 6.00 6.00

2016 Summer Olympics, Rio de Janeiro — A17

Designs: 50s, Cycling. 150s, Tennis.

**2016, Aug. 5 — Litho. — *Perf. 14x14½***

**32-33** A17 Set of 2 6.00 6.00

Nos. 32-33 each were printed in sheets of 4+2 labels.

2016 World Nomad Games, Cholpon-Ata — A18

No. 34: a, Mounted archery. b, Equestrian wrestling. c, Burning horseman.

**2016, Aug. 8 — Litho. — *Perf. 14x14½***

**34** Horiz. strip of 3 9.00 9.00
*a.* A18 50s multi 1.50 1.50
*b.* A18 100s multi 3.00 3.00
*c.* A18 150s multi 4.50 4.50

Souvenir Sheet

Independence of Kyrgyzstan, 25th Anniv. — A19

***Perf. 13 Syncopated***

**2016, Aug. 30 — Litho.**

**35** A19 150s multi 4.50 4.50

42nd Chess Olympiad, Baku, Azerbaijan — A20

**2016, Sept. 1 — Litho. — *Perf. 14x14½***

**36** A20 100s multi 3.00 3.00

No. 36 was printed in sheets of 4 + 2 labels.

Composers and Musicians — A21

Designs: No. 37, 50s, Sergei Prokofiev (1891-1953), composer. No. 38, 50s, Yehudi Menuhin (1916-99), violinist. No. 39, 100s, Antonin Dvorák (1841-1904), composer. No. 40, 100s, Wolfgang Amadeus Mozart (1756-1791), composer.

**2016, Sept. 8 — Litho. — *Perf. 14x14½***

**37-40** A21 Set of 4 9.00 9.00
*40a* Souvenir sheet of 4, #37-40 9.00 9.00

Nos. 37-40 each were printed in sheets of 4 + 2 labels.

Schooner Issyk-Kul — A22

Ship Progress of Kyrgyzstan — A23

President of Kyrgyzstan's Cruiser Moscow — A24

Torpedo Boat A25

**2016, Nov. 25 — Litho. — *Perf. 14x14½***

**41** A22 50s multi 1.50 1.50
**42** A23 50s multi 1.50 1.50
**43** A24 100s multi 3.00 3.00
**44** A25 100s multi 3.00 3.00
*a.* Souvenir sheet of 4, #41-44 9.00 9.00
*Nos. 41-44 (4)* 9.00 9.00

New Year 2017 — A26

Designs: 50s, Christmas tree and sleigh. 100s, Rooster.

***Perf. 13 Syncopated***

**2017, Feb. 3 — Litho.**

**45-46** A26 Set of 2 4.50 4.50

Nos. 45-46 each were printed in sheets of 5 + label.

Mushrooms — A27

Designs: No. 47, 50s, Pleurotus ostreatus. No. 48, 50s, Leccinum scabrum. No. 49, 100s, Morchella conica. No. 50, 100s, Pleurotus eryngii.

**2017, Apr. 6 — Litho. — *Perf. 14½x14***

**47-50** A27 Set of 4 9.00 9.00
*50a* Souvenir sheet of 4, #47-50 9.00 9.00

Fourth Islamic Solidarity Games, Baku, Azerbaijan — A28

Designs: No. 51, 50s, Wrestling. No. 52, 50s, Weight lifting. 75s, Table tennis. 100s, Soccer.

**2017, May 26 — Litho. — *Perf. 14x14½***

**51-54** A28 Set of 4 8.00 8.00
*54a* Souvenir sheet of 4, #51-54, + 2 labels 8.00 8.00

Souvenir Sheet

Historic and Cultural Ties With China — A29

No. 55: a, 50s, Li Bai (701-62), poet. b, 100s, Illustration for poem "The Ching-Ting Mountain."

***Perf. 13 Syncopated***

**2017, June 29** **Litho.**
**55** A29 Sheet of 2, #a-b 4.50 4.50

Horses A30

No. 56: a, 50s, Trakehner horse. b, 100s, New Kirgiz horse.

**2017, June 30 Litho.** ***Perf. 14x14½***
**56** A30 Pair, #a-b 4.50 4.50

See Belarus No. 1052.

Flowers — A31

Designs: 50s, Peony. 100s, Chrysanthemum.

***Perf. 13 Syncopated***

**2017, July 7** **Litho.**
**57-58** A31 Set of 2 4.50 4.50

19th International Botanical Congress, Shenzen, People's Republic of China.

Traditional Hunting — A32

Designs: 50s, Archer on horseback. 75s, Hunter on horseback releasing falcon. 100s, Taigan hunting dog chasing fox.

***Perf. 13 Syncopated***

**2017, July 14** **Litho.**
**59-61** A32 Set of 3 6.50 6.50
*61a* Souvenir sheet of 3, #59-61 6.50 6.50

Space Exploration, 60th Anniv. — A33

Designs: 50s, Sputnik. 1. 75s, Apollo Lunar Rover. 100s, Tiangong-2 Space Laboratory.

**2017, Nov. 15 Litho.** ***Perf. 14x14½***
**62-64** A33 Set of 3 6.50 6.50
*64a* Souvenir sheet of 3, #62-64 6.50 6.50

Souvenir Sheet

National Bank of the Kyrgyz Republic, 25th Anniv. — A34

No. 65: a, 50s, 2013 10-som coin depicting Gazella subgutturosa (34x34mm). b, 100s, 2016 500-som banknote and 1-som, 3-som and 10-som coins (34x68mm). c, 100s, 2015 10-som coin depicting Otis tarda (34x34mm).

***Perf. 13 Syncopated***

**2017, Nov. 17 Litho. & Embossed**
**65** A34 Sheet of 3, #a-c, + label 7.25 7.25

Souvenir Sheet

International Year of Sustainable Tourism for Development — A35

No. 65: a, 50s, Manas Peak. b, 100s, Kel-Suu Lake.

**2017, Nov. 20 Litho.** ***Perf. 14x14½***
**66** A35 Sheet of 2, #a-b 5.75 5.75

Armed Forces of Kyrgyzstan, 25th Anniv. — A36

Designs: No. 67, 50s, Truck-mounted missile launchers. No. 68, 50s, Soldier and armored troop carrier. 75s, Soldiers searching for land mines. 100s, Helicopter and tank.

**2017, Nov. 22 Litho.** ***Perf. 14x14½***
**67-70** A36 Set of 4 8.00 8.00
*70a* Sheet of 4, #67-70, + 2 labels 8.00 8.00

Souvenir Sheet

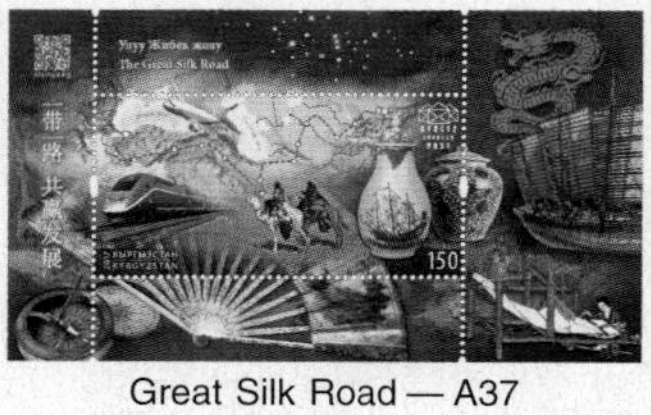

Great Silk Road — A37

***Perf. 13 Syncopated***

**2017, Nov. 24 Litho. & Embossed**
**71** A37 150s multi 4.50 4.50

Famous People A38

Designs: No. 72, 50s, Jonathan Swift (1667-1745), writer. No. 73, 50s, Sir Arthur C. Clarke (1917-2008), science fiction writer. 75s, Marie Sklodowska-Curie (1867-1934), chemist and physicist. No. 75, 100s, Gioachino Rossini (1792-1868), composer. No. 76, 100s, J. R. R. Tolkien (1892-1973), writer.

**2017, Dec. 31 Litho.** ***Perf. 14x14½***
**72-76** A38 Set of 5 11.00 11.00
*76a* Sheet of 5, #72-76, + label 11.00 11.00

Nos. 72-76 were each printed in sheets of 4 + 2 labels.

New Year 2018 (Year of the Dog) — A39

**Litho. With Foil Application**

**2018, Jan. 30** ***Perf. 13 Syncopated***
**77** A39 100s gold & multi 3.00 3.00

No. 77 was printed in sheets of 5 + label.

Souvenir Sheet

2018 Winter Olympics, PyeongChang, South Korea — A40

No. 78: a, 50s, Alpine skiing. b, 50s, Biathlon.

**2018, Feb. 23 Litho.** ***Perf. 14x14½***
**78** A40 Sheet of 2, #a-b 6.00 6.00

## LABUAN

lə-'bü-ən

LOCATION — An island in the East Indies, about six miles off the northwest coast of Borneo
GOVT. — A British possession, administered as a part of the North Borneo Colony
AREA — 35 sq. mi.
POP. — 8,963 (estimated)
CAPITAL — Victoria

The stamps of Labuan were replaced by those of Straits Settlements in 1906.

100 Cents = 1 Dollar

Queen Victoria — A1

On Nos. 1, 2, 3, 4 and 11 the watermark is 32mm high. It is always placed sideways and extends over two stamps.

**1879, May Engr. Wmk. 46** ***Perf. 14***

| | | | | |
|---|---|---|---|---|
| **1** | A1 | 2c green | 1,625. | 975.00 |
| **2** | A1 | 6c orange | 240.00 | 225.00 |
| **3** | A1 | 12c carmine | 1,925. | 850.00 |
| **4** | A1 | 16c blue | 77.50 | *200.00* |
| | | *Nos. 1-4 (4)* | 3,868. | 2,250. |

See Nos. 5-10, 16-24, 33-39, 42-48. For surcharges see Nos. 12-15, 25, 31, 40-41.

**1880-82** **Wmk. 1**

| | | | | |
|---|---|---|---|---|
| **5** | A1 | 2c green | 34.00 | *57.50* |
| **6** | A1 | 6c orange | 145.00 | *160.00* |
| **7** | A1 | 8c carmine ('82) | 135.00 | *135.00* |
| **8** | A1 | 10c yel brown | 210.00 | *100.00* |
| **9** | A1 | 12c carmine | 330.00 | *400.00* |
| **10** | A1 | 16c blue ('81) | 100.00 | 130.00 |
| | | *Nos. 5-10 (6)* | 954.00 | *982.50* |

A2

A3

A3a

A4

**1880-83** **Wmk. 46**

| | | | | |
|---|---|---|---|---|
| **11** | A2 | 6c on 16c blue (with additional "6" across original value) R) | 4,200. | 1,325. |

**Wmk. 1**

| | | | | |
|---|---|---|---|---|
| **12** | A2 | 8c on 12c car | 1,825. | 1,000. |
| *a.* | | Original value not obliterated | 3,600. | 2,000. |
| *b.* | | Additional surcharge "8" across original value | 2,300. | 1,450. |
| *c.* | | "8" inverted | 2,100. | 1,200. |
| *d.* | | As "a," "8" inverted | *4,200.* | — |
| **13** | A3 | 8c on 12c car ('81) | 475.00 | 525.00 |
| **14** | A3a | 8c on 12c car ('81) | 160.00 | 170.00 |
| *a.* | | "Eighr" | *22,500.* | |
| *b.* | | Inverted surcharge | *16,000.* | |
| *c.* | | Double surcharge | 2,900. | 2,400. |
| **15** | A4 | $1 on 16c blue (R) ('83) | *4,800.* | |

On No. 12 the original value is obliterated by a pen mark in either black or red.

**Types of 1879 Issue**

**1883-86** **Wmk. 2**

| | | | | |
|---|---|---|---|---|
| **16** | A1 | 2c green | 30.00 | *55.00* |
| *a.* | | Horiz. pair, imperf. btwn. | 18,500. | |
| **17** | A1 | 2c rose red ('85) | 4.25 | *20.00* |
| **18** | A1 | 8c carmine | 325.00 | 120.00 |
| **19** | A1 | 8c dk violet ('85) | 50.00 | 9.25 |
| **20** | A1 | 10c yellow brn | 62.50 | *57.50* |
| **21** | A1 | 10c black brn ('86) | 40.00 | *72.50* |
| **22** | A1 | 16c blue | 115.00 | *215.00* |
| **23** | A1 | 16c gray blue ('86) | 125.00 | *180.00* |
| **24** | A1 | 40c ocher | 37.50 | *145.00* |
| | | *Nos. 16-24 (9)* | 789.25 | *874.25* |

Nos. 1-10, 16-24 are in sheets of 10. For surcharges see Nos. 26-30, 32.

A5

A6

A7

**1885** **Wmk. 1**

| | | | | |
|---|---|---|---|---|
| **25** | A5 | 2c on 16c blue | 1,150. | *1,100.* |

**Wmk. 2**

| | | | | |
|---|---|---|---|---|
| **26** | A5 | 2c on 8c car | 275.00 | *550.00* |
| *a.* | | Double surcharge | | — |
| **27** | A6 | 2c on 16c blue | 135.00 | *200.00* |
| *a.* | | Double surcharge | | *7,500.* |
| **28** | A7 | 2c on 8c car | 80.00 | *145.00* |

A8

**1891** **Black or Red Surcharge**

| | | | | |
|---|---|---|---|---|
| **29** | A8 | 6c on 8c violet | 16.50 | 17.00 |
| *a.* | | 6c on 8c dark violet | 625.00 | 210.00 |
| *b.* | | Double surcharge | 390.00 | — |
| *c.* | | As "a," "Cents" omitted | 550.00 | 550.00 |
| *d.* | | Inverted surcharge | 90.00 | *85.00* |
| *e.* | | Dbl. surch., one inverted | 1,100. | — |
| *f.* | | Dbl. surch., both inverted | 1,100. | — |
| *g.* | | "6" omitted | 625.00 | |
| *h.* | | Pair, one without surcharge | 2,000. | 2,000. |

| | | | |
|---|---|---|---|
| **30** | A8 6c on 8c dk vio (R) | 1,550. | 825.00 |
| *a.* | Inverted surcharge | 1,850. | 925.00 |

**Wmk. 46**

| | | | |
|---|---|---|---|
| **31** | A8 6c on 16c blue | 2,800. | 2,300. |
| *a.* | Inverted surcharge | 15,500. | 8,250. |

**Wmk. 2**

| | | | |
|---|---|---|---|
| **32** | A8 6c on 40c ocher | 14,000. | 5,750. |
| *a.* | Inverted surcharge | 12,000. | 9,000. |

### Types of 1879 Issue

**1892 Engr. Unwmk.**

| | | | |
|---|---|---|---|
| **33** | A1 2c rose | 7.25 | 4.25 |
| **34** | A1 6c yellow green | 14.50 | 5.75 |
| **35** | A1 8c violet | 13.50 | *19.50* |
| **36** | A1 10c brown | 30.00 | 9.50 |
| **37** | A1 12c deep ultra | 16.00 | 8.00 |
| **38** | A1 16c gray | 30.00 | *45.00* |
| **39** | A1 40c ocher | 27.50 | *45.00* |
| | *Nos. 33-39 (7)* | 138.75 | 137.00 |

The 2c, 8c and 10c are in sheets of 30; others in sheets of 10.

Nos. 39 and 38 Surcharged

**1893**

| | | | |
|---|---|---|---|
| **40** | A1 2c on 40c ocher | 200.00 | 110.00 |
| *a.* | Inverted surcharge | 500.00 | *675.00* |
| **41** | A1 6c on 16c gray | 450.00 | 180.00 |
| *a.* | Inverted surcharge | 675.00 | 350.00 |
| *b.* | Surcharge sideways | 675.00 | 375.00 |
| *c.* | "Six" omitted | — | — |
| *d.* | "Cents" omitted | — | — |
| *e.* | Handstamped "Six Cents" | *2,275.* | |

Surcharges on Nos. 40-41 each exist in 10 types. Counterfeits exist.

No. 41e was handstamped on examples of No. 41 on which the surcharge failed to print or was printed partially or completely albino.

From Jan. 1, 1890, to Jan. 1, 1906, Labuan was administered by the British North Borneo Co. Late in that period, unused remainders of Nos. 42-83, 53a, 63a, 64a, 65a, 66a, 68a, 85-86, 96-118, 103a, 107a, J1-J9, J3a and J6a were canceled to order by bars forming an oval. Values for these stamps used are for those with this form of cancellation, unless described as postally used, which are for stamps with dated town cancellations. Nos. 63b, 64b, 65b, 104a, J6a, and possibly others, only exist c.t.o.

For detailed listings of Labuan, see the *Scott Classic Specialized Catalogue.*

### Types of 1879 Issue

**1894, Apr. Litho.**

| | | | |
|---|---|---|---|
| **42** | A1 2c bright rose | 2.00 | .65 |
| **43** | A1 6c yellow green | 27.50 | .65 |
| *a.* | Horiz. pair, imperf. btwn. | *11,250.* | |
| **44** | A1 8c bright violet | 29.00 | .65 |
| **45** | A1 10c brown | 60.00 | .65 |
| **46** | A1 12c light ultra | 37.50 | .80 |
| **47** | A1 16c gray | 40.00 | .65 |
| **48** | A1 40c orange | 60.00 | .65 |
| | *Nos. 42-48 (7)* | 256.00 | 4.70 |

Counterfeits exist.

Dyak Chieftain — A9

Malayan Sambar — A10

Sago Palm A11

Argus Pheasant A12

Arms of North Borneo — A13

Dhow — A14

Saltwater Crocodile — A15

Mt. Kinabalu — A16

Arms of North Borneo — A17

### Perf. 12 to 16 and Compound

**1894 Engr.**

| | | | |
|---|---|---|---|
| **49** | A9 1c lilac & black | 2.00 | .65 |
| *a.* | Vert. pair, imperf. between | 1,300. | 575.00 |
| **50** | A10 2c blue & black | 3.00 | .65 |
| *a.* | Imperf., pair | 725.00 | |
| **51** | A11 3c bister & black | 4.50 | .65 |
| **52** | A12 5c green & black | 38.50 | 1.10 |
| *a.* | Horiz. pair, imperf. between | *1,800.* | |
| **53** | A13 6c brn red & blk | 3.00 | .65 |
| *a.* | Imperf., pair | 725.00 | 350.00 |
| **54** | A14 8c rose & black | 13.00 | .65 |
| **55** | A15 12c orange & black | 27.50 | .65 |
| **56** | A16 18c ol brn & blk | 29.00 | .65 |
| *b.* | Vert. pair, imperf. between | | *2,500.* |
| **57** | A17 24c lilac & blue | 22.50 | 1.30 |
| | *Nos. 49-57 (9)* | 143.00 | 6.95 |

A18

**1895, June Litho. *Perf. 14***

| | | | |
|---|---|---|---|
| **58** | A18 4c on $1 red | 4.25 | .50 |
| **59** | A18 10c on $1 red | 11.50 | .50 |
| **60** | A18 20c on $1 red | 52.50 | .50 |
| **61** | A18 30c on $1 red | 57.50 | 1.50 |
| **62** | A18 40c on $1 red | 57.50 | 1.50 |
| | *Nos. 58-62 (5)* | 183.25 | 4.50 |

A19

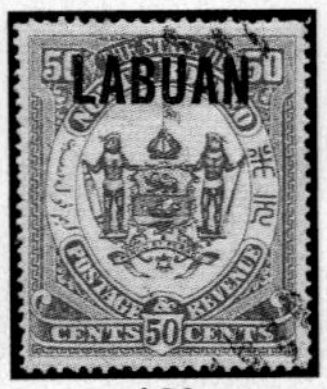

A20

A21

**1896**

| | | | |
|---|---|---|---|
| **63** | A19 25c blue green | 45.00 | .80 |
| *a.* | Imperf., pair | | 72.50 |
| *b.* | Without overprint | 35.00 | 2.00 |
| *c.* | As "b," imperf, pair | 60.00 | |
| **64** | A20 50c claret | 42.50 | .80 |
| *a.* | Imperf., pair | | 72.50 |
| *b.* | Without overprint | 32.50 | 2.00 |
| *c.* | As "b," imperf, pair | 52.50 | |
| **65** | A21 $1 dark blue | 82.50 | 1.25 |
| *a.* | Imperf., pair | | 72.50 |
| *b.* | Without overprint | 50.00 | 3.00 |
| *c.* | As "b," imperf, pair | 60.00 | |
| | *Nos. 63-65 (3)* | 170.00 | 2.85 |

For surcharges and overprint see Nos. 93-95, 116-118, 120.

Nos. 49-54 Overprinted

**1896 *Perf. 12 to 15 and Compound***

| | | | |
|---|---|---|---|
| **66** | A9 1c lilac & black | 26.00 | 1.75 |
| *a.* | "JEBILEE" | 1,450. | 360.00 |
| *b.* | "JUBILE" | *3,000.* | |
| *c.* | Orange overprint | 325.00 | 24.00 |
| *e.* | Double overprint | 450.00 | — |
| **67** | A10 2c blue & black | 52.50 | 1.75 |
| *a.* | Vert. pair, imperf. btwn. | 1,525. | — |
| *b.* | "JEBILEE" | 1,850. | — |
| *c.* | "JUBILE" | *3,500.* | |
| *d.* | Vert. strip of 3, imperf between | *8,000.* | |
| **68** | A11 3c bister & black | 50.00 | 1.50 |
| *a.* | "JEBILEE" | 2,250. | 850.00 |
| *b.* | "JUBILE" | — | — |
| *g.* | Double overprint | 425.00 | 195.00 |
| *h.* | Triple overprint | 775.00 | — |
| **69** | A12 5c green & black | 72.50 | 1.50 |
| *a.* | Double overprint | 975.00 | |
| **70** | A13 6c brown red & blk | 47.50 | 1.00 |
| *a.* | Double overprint | 975.00 | — |
| *b.* | "JUBILE" | *3,600.* | |
| **71** | A14 8c rose & black | 57.50 | 1.00 |
| *a.* | Double overprint | — | *3,000.* |
| | *Nos. 66-71 (6)* | 306.00 | 8.50 |

Cession of Labuan to Great Britain, 50th anniv.

Dyak Chieftain A22

Malayan Sambar A23

Sago Palm A24

Argus Pheasant A25

A26

Dhow — A27

Saltwater Crocodile — A28

Mt. Kinabalu "Postal Revenue" — A29

Coat of Arms — A30

### Perf. 13½ to 16 and Compound

**1897-1900 Engr.**

| | | | |
|---|---|---|---|
| **72** | A22 1c lilac & black | 8.00 | .60 |
| **72A** | A22 1c red brn & blk | 3.75 | .80 |
| **73** | A23 2c blue & black | 32.50 | .90 |
| *a.* | Vert. pair, imperf between | | 1,125. |
| *b.* | Horiz. pair, imperf between | | 1,550. |
| **74** | A23 2c grn & blk ('00) | 4.50 | .35 |
| *a.* | Horiz. pair, imperf between | *3,100.* | 1,550. |
| **75** | A24 3c bister & blk | 10.00 | .60 |
| *a.* | Vert. pair, imperf between | 1,325. | 675.00 |
| **76** | A25 5c green & blk | 67.50 | .85 |
| **77** | A25 5c lt bl & blk ('00) | 27.50 | .80 |
| **78** | A26 6c brn red & blk | 16.00 | .60 |
| *a.* | Vert. pair, imperf between | | 850.00 |
| **79** | A27 8c red & black | 25.00 | .60 |
| **80** | A28 12c red & black | 40.00 | 2.50 |
| **81** | A29 18c ol bis & blk | 125.00 | 2.40 |
| *a.* | Vert. pair, imperf between | | 3,750. |
| **82** | A30 24c gry lil & bl | 14.50 | .60 |
| | *Nos. 72-82 (12)* | 374.25 | 11.00 |

"Postage & Revenue" — A31

"Postage & Revenue" — A32

### Perf. 13½ to 16 and Compound

**1897**

| | | | |
|---|---|---|---|
| **83** | A31 18c bister & black | 95.00 | 2.40 |
| **84a** | A32 24c ocher & blue | — | 4.75 |

"Postage & Revenue" — A33

"Postage & Revenue" — A34

**1898**

| | | | |
|---|---|---|---|
| **85** | A33 12c red & black | — | 4.00 |
| **86a** | A34 18c bister & black | 42.50 | 3.75 |

No. 85a cto is always perf. 13½x14.

For surcharges see Nos. 90-91, 113-114.

Regular Issue Surcharged in Black

**1899**

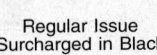

| | | | |
|---|---|---|---|
| **87** | A25 4c on 5c grn & blk | 62.50 | 30.00 |
| **88** | A26 4c on 6c brn red & blk | 34.00 | 22.50 |
| **89** | A27 4c on 8c red & blk | 72.50 | 52.50 |
| **90** | A33 4c on 12c red & blk | 67.50 | 42.50 |
| **91** | A34 4c on 18c bis & blk | 40.00 | 21.50 |
| *a.* | Double surcharge | 575.00 | *675.00* |

| | | | | |
|---|---|---|---|---|
| 92a | A32 | 4c on 24c lil & bl | 50.00 | 36.00 |
| 93 | A19 | 4c on 25c blue grn | 7.25 | 8.00 |
| 94 | A20 | 4c on 50c claret | 8.75 | 8.00 |
| 95 | A21 | 4c on $1 dk blue | 8.75 | 8.00 |
| | | Nos. 87-95 (9) | 351.25 | 229.00 |

Orangutan
A35

Sun Bear
A36

Railroad
Train — A37

*Perf. 12 to 16 and Compound*

**1899-1901**

| | | | | |
|---|---|---|---|---|
| 96 | A35 | 4c yel brn & blk | 10.00 | .75 |
| a. | | Vert. pair, imperf. btwn. | 1,450. | |
| 97a | A35 | 4c car & blk ('00) | 6.00 | .60 |
| 98 | A36 | 10c gray vio & dk brn ('01) | 60.00 | .75 |
| 99 | A37 | 16c org brn & grn (G) ('01) | 60.00 | 3.00 |
| | | Nos. 96-99 (4) | 136.00 | 5.10 |

Crown — A38

*Perf. 12½ to 16 and Compound*

**1902-03** **Engr.**

| | | | | |
|---|---|---|---|---|
| 99A | A38 | 1c vio & black | 6.75 | .60 |
| 100 | A38 | 2c grn & blk | 5.00 | .35 |
| 100A | A38 | 3c sepia & blk | 4.00 | .35 |
| 101 | A38 | 4c car & blk | 4.00 | .35 |
| 102 | A38 | 8c org & blk | 15.00 | .80 |
| 103 | A38 | 10c sl blue & brn | 4.00 | .35 |
| a. | | Vert. pair, imperf. between | 925.00 | |
| 104 | A38 | 12c yel & black | 16.00 | .35 |
| a. | | Vert. strip of 3, imperf. horiz. | | 4,000. |
| 105 | A38 | 16c org brn & grn | 5.75 | .35 |
| a. | | Vert. pair, imperf. between | — | 2,300. |
| 106 | A38 | 18c bis brn & blk | 4.00 | .35 |
| 107 | A38 | 25c grnsh bl & grn | 12.00 | .60 |
| a. | | 25c greenish blue & black | 625.00 | |
| 108 | A38 | 50c gray lil & vio | 12.00 | 2.75 |
| 109 | A38 | $1 org & red brn | 10.00 | 2.75 |
| | | Nos. 99A-109 (12) | 98.50 | 9.95 |

There are 3 known examples of No. 104a, all cto. A 16c vertical pair, imperf between has been reported. The editors would like to receive evidence of the existence of this item.

Regular Issue of 1896-97 Surcharged in Black

**1904**

| | | | | |
|---|---|---|---|---|
| 110 | A25 | 4c on 5c grn & blk | 57.50 | 17.00 |
| 111 | A26 | 4c on 6c brn red & blk | 14.50 | 17.00 |
| 112 | A27 | 4c on 8c red & blk | 30.00 | 17.00 |
| 113 | A33 | 4c on 12c red & blk | 50.00 | 17.00 |
| 114 | A34 | 4c on 18c bis & blk | 30.00 | 17.00 |
| 115 | A32 | 4c on 24c brn lil & bl | 19.25 | 17.00 |
| 116 | A19 | 4c on 25c blue grn | 10.00 | 17.00 |
| 117 | A20 | 4c on 50c clar | 10.00 | 17.00 |
| a. | | Double surcharge | 400.00 | |
| 118 | A21 | 4c on $1 dark blue | 14.00 | 17.00 |
| | | Nos. 110-118 (9) | 235.25 | 153.00 |

**Stamps of North Borneo, 1893, and Labuan No. 65a Overprinted in Black**

a

b

c

**1905**

| | | | | |
|---|---|---|---|---|
| 119 | A30(a) | 25c slate bl | 1,325. | 1,100. |
| 120 | A21(c) | $1 blue | | 1,050. |
| 121 | A33(b) | $2 gray grn | 4,000. | |
| 122 | A34(c) | $5 red vio | 7,250. | 1,850. |
| a. | | $5 dull purple | 7,000. | 1,800. |
| 123 | A35(c) | $10 brown | 55,000. | 14,500. |

## POSTAGE DUE STAMPS

Regular Issues Overprinted

**1901** **Unwmk.** ***Perf. 14***

| | | | | |
|---|---|---|---|---|
| J1 | A23 | 2c grn & blk | 27.50 | 1.10 |
| a. | | Double overprint | 425.00 | |
| J2 | A24 | 3c bis & blk | 37.50 | 1.00 |
| J3b | A35 | 4c car & black | 60.00 | .60 |
| a. | | Double overprint | | 875.00 |
| J4 | A25 | 5c lt blue & blk | 57.50 | 1.50 |
| J5 | A26 | 6c brn red & blk | 50.00 | 1.10 |
| J6 | A27 | 8c red & black | 110.00 | 3.00 |
| a. | | Center inverted, ovpt. reading down | | 12,000. |
| J7 | A33 | 12c red & black | 170.00 | 6.75 |
| a. | | Overprint reading down | | 1,125. |
| J8 | A34 | 18c ol bis & blk | 40.00 | 1.75 |
| J9 | A32 | 24c brn lil & bl | 77.50 | 7.75 |
| | | Nos. J1-J9 (9) | 630.00 | 24.55 |

See note after No. 41.

The stamps of Labuan were superseded by those of Straits Settlements in 1906.

# LAGOS

'lā-,gäs

LOCATION — West Africa, bordering on the former Southern Nigeria Colony

GOVT. — British Crown Colony and Protectorate

AREA — 3,460 sq. mi. (approx.)

POP. — 1,500,000 (1901)

CAPITAL — Lagos

This territory was purchased by the British in 1861 and placed under the Governor of Sierra Leone. In 1874 it was detached and formed part of the Gold Coast Colony until 1886 when the Protectorate of Lagos was established. In 1899 Lagos and the territories of the Royal Niger Company were surrendered to the Crown of Great Britain and formed into the Northern and Southern Nigeria Protectorates. In 1906 Lagos and Southern Nigeria were united to form the Colony and Protectorate of Southern Nigeria.

12 Pence = 1 Shilling

Queen Victoria — A1

**1874-75** **Typo.** **Wmk. 1** ***Perf. 12½***

| | | | | |
|---|---|---|---|---|
| 1 | A1 | 1p lilac | 80.00 | 50.00 |
| 2 | A1 | 2p blue | 80.00 | 45.00 |
| 3 | A1 | 3p red brown ('75) | 130.00 | 45.00 |
| 4 | A1 | 4p rose | 150.00 | 50.00 |
| 5 | A1 | 6p blue green | 150.00 | 20.00 |
| 6 | A1 | 1sh orange ('75) | 425.00 | 70.00 |
| a. | | Value 15½mm instead of 16½mm long | 700.00 | 160.00 |
| | | Nos. 1-6 (6) | 1,015. | 280.00 |

**1876** ***Perf. 14***

| | | | | |
|---|---|---|---|---|
| 7 | A1 | 1p lilac | 50.00 | 21.00 |
| 8 | A1 | 2p blue | 80.00 | 15.00 |
| 9 | A1 | 3p red brown | 120.00 | 30.00 |
| 10 | A1 | 4p rose | 225.00 | 12.50 |
| 11 | A1 | 6p green | 130.00 | 7.00 |
| 12 | A1 | 1sh orange | 950.00 | 95.00 |
| | | Nos. 7-12 (6) | 1,555. | 180.50 |

The 4p exists with watermark sideways.

**1882-1902** **Wmk. 2**

| | | | | |
|---|---|---|---|---|
| 13 | A1 | ½p green ('86) | 2.25 | .95 |
| 14 | A1 | 1p lilac | 42.50 | 27.50 |
| 15 | A1 | 1p car rose | 2.25 | .95 |
| 16 | A1 | 2p blue | 200.00 | 8.50 |
| 17 | A1 | 2p gray | 100.00 | 9.50 |
| 18 | A1 | 2p lil & bl ('87) | 8.50 | 3.25 |
| 19 | A1 | 2½p ultra ('91) | 8.00 | 2.00 |
| a. | | 2½p blue | 90.00 | 57.50 |
| 20 | A1 | 3p orange brn | 30.00 | 8.75 |
| 21 | A1 | 3p lil & brn org ('91) | 3.00 | 3.75 |
| 22 | A1 | 4p rose | 225.00 | 14.00 |
| 23 | A1 | 4p violet | 160.00 | 12.50 |
| 24 | A1 | 4p lil & blk ('87) | 2.50 | 2.00 |
| 25 | A1 | 5p lil & grn ('94) | 3.00 | 12.50 |
| 26 | A1 | 6p olive green | 9.00 | 55.00 |
| 27 | A1 | 6p lil & red vio ('87) | 5.50 | 3.50 |
| 28 | A1 | 6p lilac & car rose ('02) | 5.75 | 13.50 |
| 29 | A1 | 7½p lilac & car rose ('94) | 4.50 | 40.00 |
| 30 | A1 | 10p lil & yel ('94) | 4.50 | 15.00 |
| 31 | A1 | 1sh org ('85) | 21.00 | 25.00 |
| 32 | A1 | 1sh yel grn & blk ('87) | 6.50 | 32.50 |
| 33 | A1 | 2sh6p ol brn ('86) | 375.00 | 325.00 |
| 34 | A1 | 2sh6p green & car rose ('87) | 27.50 | 92.50 |
| 35 | A1 | 5sh blue ('86) | 750.00 | 550.00 |
| 36 | A1 | 5sh grn & ultra ('87) | 50.00 | 175.00 |
| 37 | A1 | 10sh brn vio ('86) | 2,750. | 2,000. |
| 38 | A1 | 10sh grn & brn ('87) | 120.00 | 275.00 |

Excellent forgeries exist of Nos. 33, 35 and 37 on paper with genuine watermark.

No. 24 Surcharged in Black

**1893**

| | | | | |
|---|---|---|---|---|
| 39 | A1 | ½p on 4p lilac & blk | 11.50 | 4.00 |
| a. | | Double surcharge | 70.00 | 62.50 |
| b. | | Triple surcharge | 175.00 | |
| c. | | ½p on 2p lilac & blue (#18) | — | 27,500. |

Four settings of surcharge.

Only one used example is known of No. 39c. The two unused examples are in museums.

King Edward VII — A3

**1904, Jan. 22**

| | | | | |
|---|---|---|---|---|
| 40 | A3 | ½p grn & bl grn | 3.00 | 6.25 |
| 41 | A3 | 1p vio & blk, *red* | 1.25 | .25 |
| 42 | A3 | 2p violet & ultra | 6.75 | 7.00 |
| 43 | A3 | 2½p vio & ultra, *bl* | 1.50 | 1.75 |
| 44 | A3 | 3p vio & org brn | 3.25 | 2.00 |
| 45 | A3 | 6p vio & red vio | 40.00 | 11.50 |
| 46 | A3 | 1sh green & blk | 40.00 | 47.50 |
| 47 | A3 | 2sh6p grn & car rose | 160.00 | 325.00 |
| 48 | A3 | 5sh grn & ultra | 150.00 | 350.00 |
| 49 | A3 | 10sh green & brn | 350.00 | 975.00 |
| | | Nos. 40-49 (10) | 755.75 | 1,726. |

**1904-05** **Wmk. 3**

**Ordinary or Chalky Paper**

| | | | | |
|---|---|---|---|---|
| 50 | A3 | ½p grn & bl grn | 14.50 | 3.00 |
| 51a | A3 | 1p vio & blk, *red* | 1.75 | .25 |
| 52 | A3 | 2p violet & ultra | 5.50 | 3.50 |
| 53a | A3 | 2½p vio & ultra, *bl* | 2.00 | 18.50 |
| 54 | A3 | 3p vio & org brn | 4.00 | 1.50 |
| 55a | A3 | 6p vio & red vio | 5.00 | 1.75 |
| 56 | A3 | 1sh green & blk | 22.50 | 30.00 |
| 57 | A3 | 2sh6p grn & car rose | 27.50 | 75.00 |
| 58 | A3 | 5sh grn & ultra | 27.50 | 110.00 |
| 59 | A3 | 10sh green & brn | 100.00 | 275.00 |
| | | Nos. 50-59 (10) | 210.25 | 518.50 |

See *Scott Classic Specialized Catalogue of Stamps & Covers* for detailed listings of ordinary and chalky paper varieties.

The stamps of Lagos were superseded by those of Southern Nigeria.

# LAOS

'laus

LOCATION — In northwestern Indo-China
GOVT. — Republic
AREA — 91,400 sq. mi.
POP. — 5,407,453 (1999 est.)
CAPITAL — Vientiane

Before 1949, Laos was part of the French colony of Indo-China and used its stamps until 1951. The kingdom was replaced by the Lao Peoples Democratic Republic Dec. 2, 1975.

100 Cents = 1 Piaster
100 Cents = 1 Kip (1955)

### Imperforates

Most Laos stamps issued during 1951-75 exist as imperforate proofs in issued and trial colors, and also as proofs in small presentation sheets in issued colors. Many post-1975 issues exist imperforate.

### Paper

Most Laos stamps issued before 1976 exist on both white and yellowish papers in approximately equal quantities. Souvenir sheets from this period were printed primarily on yellowish paper. Souvenir sheets printed on white paper are scarce.

**Catalogue values for all unused stamps in this country are for Never Hinged items.**

Boat on Mekong River — A1

King Sisavang-Vong A2

Laotian Woman A3

Designs: 50c, 60c, 70c, Luang Prabang. 1pi, 2pi, 3pi, 5pi, 10pi, Temple at Vientiane.

**1951-52 Unwmk. Engr. *Perf. 13***

| | | | | |
|---|---|---|---|---|
| 1 | A1 | 10c dk grn & emer | .60 | .25 |
| 2 | A1 | 20c dk car & car | .60 | .25 |
| 3 | A1 | 30c ind & dp ultra | 2.00 | 1.25 |
| 4 | A3 | 30c ind & pur ('52) | 1.00 | .30 |
| 5 | A1 | 50c dark brown | .50 | .50 |
| 6 | A1 | 60c red & red org | .50 | .50 |
| 7 | A1 | 70c ultra & bl grn | 1.25 | .50 |
| 8 | A3 | 80c brt grn & dk bl green ('52) | 1.25 | .60 |
| 9 | A1 | 1pi dk pur & pur | 1.25 | .50 |
| 10 | A3 | 1.10pi dark plum & carmine ('52) | 1.25 | 1.25 |
| 11 | A2 | 1.50pi blk brn & vio brown | 1.60 | 1.25 |
| 12 | A3 | 1.90pi indigo & dp blue ('52) | 1.50 | 1.25 |
| 13 | A1 | 2pi dk grn & gray green | 20.00 | 9.00 |
| 14 | A1 | 3pi dk car & red | 2.50 | 1.50 |
| 15 | A3 | 3pi choc & black brown ('52) | 1.75 | 1.50 |
| 16 | A1 | 5pi ind & dp ultra | 3.25 | 1.75 |
| 17 | A1 | 10pi blk brn & vio brown | 4.25 | 2.00 |
| | | *Nos. 1-17 (17)* | 45.05 | 24.15 |
| | | Set, hinged | 25.00 | |

A booklet containing 26 souvenir sheets was issued in 1952 on the anniversary of the first issue of Laos stamps. Each sheet contains a single stamp in the center (Nos. 1-17, C2-C4, J1-J6). Value $300.
See No. 223.

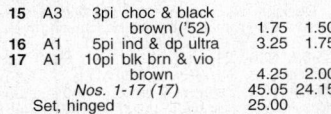

UPU Monument and King Sisavang-Vong — A4

**1952, Dec. 7**

| | | | | |
|---|---|---|---|---|
| 18 | A4 | 80c ind, blue & pur | .90 | .80 |
| 19 | A4 | 1pi dk car, car & org brown | .90 | .80 |
| 20 | A4 | 1.20pi dk pur, pur & ultra | 1.00 | .90 |
| 21 | A4 | 1.50pi dk grn, bl grn & dk brn | 1.25 | 1.00 |
| 22 | A4 | 1.90pi blk brn, vio brn & dk Prus grn | 1.50 | 1.25 |
| | | *Nos. 18-22,C5-C6 (7)* | 16.55 | 14.75 |

Laos' admission to the UPU, May 13, 1952.

Court of Love — A5

**1953, July 14**

| | | | | |
|---|---|---|---|---|
| 23 | A5 | 4.50pi indigo & bl grn | .85 | .55 |
| 24 | A5 | 6pi gray & dark brn | 1.25 | .55 |

Composite of Laotian Temples — A6

**1954, Mar. 4**

| | | | | |
|---|---|---|---|---|
| 25 | A6 | 2pi indigo & purple | 27.50 | 20.00 |
| 26 | A6 | 3pi blk brn & dk red | 27.50 | 20.00 |
| | | *Nos. 25-26,C13 (3)* | 175.00 | 135.00 |

Accession of King Sisavang-Vong, 50th anniv.
See No. C13.

Buddha Statue and Monks — A7

**1956, May 24 Engr. *Perf. 13***

| | | | | |
|---|---|---|---|---|
| 27 | A7 | 2k reddish brown | 2.50 | 1.75 |
| 28 | A7 | 3k black | 3.00 | 2.00 |
| 29 | A7 | 5k chocolate | 4.50 | 3.00 |
| | | *Nos. 27-29,C20-C21 (5)* | 64.00 | 51.75 |

2500th anniversary of birth of Buddha.
See Nos. C20-C21.

UN Emblem — A8

**1956, Dec. 14 *Perf. 13½x13***

| | | | | |
|---|---|---|---|---|
| 30 | A8 | 1k black | .65 | .45 |
| 31 | A8 | 2k blue | .90 | .70 |
| 32 | A8 | 4k bright red | 1.25 | .95 |
| 33 | A8 | 6k purple | 1.40 | 1.10 |
| | | *Nos. 30-33,C22-C23 (6)* | 13.95 | 12.95 |

Admission of Laos to the UN, 1st anniv.

Khouy Player — A9

Khene Player — A10

Musical Instrument: 8k, Ranat.

**1957, Mar. 25 Unwmk. *Perf. 13***

| | | | | |
|---|---|---|---|---|
| 34 | A9 | 2k multicolored | 1.75 | 1.10 |
| 35 | A10 | 4k multicolored | 2.00 | 1.25 |
| 36 | A9 | 8k org, bl & red brn | 2.50 | 2.00 |
| | | *Nos. 34-36,C24-C26 (6)* | 14.75 | 10.45 |

See Nos. 224, C24-C26.

Harvesting Rice — A11

Drying Rice — A12

**1957, July 22 Engr. *Perf. 13***

| | | | | |
|---|---|---|---|---|
| 37 | A11 | 3k shown | .90 | .60 |
| 38 | A12 | 5k shown | 1.25 | .75 |
| 39 | A12 | 16k Winnowing rice | 2.00 | 1.50 |
| 40 | A11 | 26k Polishing rice | 4.00 | 2.00 |
| | | *Nos. 37-40 (4)* | 8.15 | 4.85 |

Elephants — A13

Various Elephants: 30c, 5k, 10k, 13k, vert.

**1958, Mar. 17**

| | | | | |
|---|---|---|---|---|
| 41 | A13 | 10c multi | 1.00 | .50 |
| 42 | A13 | 20c multi | 1.00 | .50 |
| 43 | A13 | 30c multi | 1.00 | .50 |
| 44 | A13 | 2k multi | 1.50 | .90 |
| 45 | A13 | 5k multi | 2.75 | 1.50 |
| 46 | A13 | 10k multi | 3.00 | 2.00 |
| 47 | A13 | 13k multi | 5.00 | 2.50 |
| | | *Nos. 41-47 (7)* | 15.25 | 8.40 |

For surcharge see No. B5.

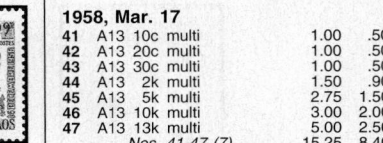

Globe and Goddess — A14

UNESCO Building and Mother with Children — A15

Designs: 70c, UNESCO building, globe and mother with children. 1k, UNESCO building and Eiffel tower.

**1958, Nov. 3 Engr. *Perf. 13***

| | | | | |
|---|---|---|---|---|
| 48 | A14 | 50c multicolored | .50 | .25 |
| 49 | A15 | 60c emer, vio & maroon | .65 | .25 |
| 50 | A15 | 70c ultra, rose red & brn | .65 | .25 |
| 51 | A14 | 1k ol bis, cl & grnsh bl | 1.00 | .60 |
| | | *Nos. 48-51 (4)* | 2.80 | 1.35 |

UNESCO Headquarters in Paris opening, Nov. 3.

King Sisavang-Vong — A16

**1959, Sept. 16 Unwmk.**

| | | | | |
|---|---|---|---|---|
| 52 | A16 | 4k rose claret | .35 | .35 |
| 53 | A16 | 6.50k orange red | .35 | .35 |
| 54 | A16 | 9k bright pink | .35 | .35 |
| 55 | A16 | 13k green | .75 | .60 |
| | | *Nos. 52-55 (4)* | 1.80 | 1.65 |

For surcharges see Nos. 112-113, B4.

Dancers A17

Student and Torch of Learning — A18

Education and Fine Arts: 3k, Globe, key of knowledge and girl student. 5k, Dancers and temple.

**1959, Oct. 1 Engr. *Perf. 13***

| | | | | |
|---|---|---|---|---|
| 56 | A17 | 1k vio blk, ol & bl | .50 | .30 |
| 57 | A18 | 2k maroon & black | .55 | .30 |
| 58 | A17 | 3k slate grn & vio | .85 | .30 |
| 59 | A18 | 5k rose vio, yel & brt grn | 1.10 | .60 |
| | | *Nos. 56-59 (4)* | 3.00 | 1.50 |

Portal of Wat Phou, Pakse — A19

Historic Monuments: 1.50k, That Inghang, Savannakhet, horiz. 2.50k, Phou Temple, Pakse, horiz. 7k, That Luang, Vientiane. 11k, That Luang, Vientiane, horiz. 12.50k, Phousi, Luang Prabang.

**1959, Nov. 2 Unwmk. *Perf. 13***

| | | | | |
|---|---|---|---|---|
| **60** | A19 | 50c sepia, grn & org | .25 | .25 |
| **61** | A19 | 1.50k multi | .35 | .25 |
| **62** | A19 | 2.50k pur, vio bl & ol | .50 | .40 |
| **63** | A19 | 7k vio, olive & claret | .75 | .50 |
| **64** | A19 | 11k brn, car & grn | .90 | .75 |
| **65** | A19 | 12.50k bl, vio & bister | 1.25 | .80 |
| | | *Nos. 60-65 (6)* | 4.00 | 2.95 |

Due to poor quality control, numerous color varieties exist.

Funeral Urn and Monks — A20

King Sisavang-Vong A21

Designs: 6.50k, Urn under canopy. 9k, Catafalque on 7-headed dragon carriage.

**1961, Apr. 29 Engr. *Perf. 13***

| | | | | |
|---|---|---|---|---|
| **66** | A20 | 4k black, bis & org | .85 | .75 |
| **67** | A20 | 6.50k black & bister | 1.00 | .75 |
| **68** | A20 | 9k black & bister | 1.10 | .85 |
| **69** | A21 | 25k black | 3.00 | 2.25 |
| | | *Nos. 66-69 (4)* | 5.95 | 4.60 |

King Sisavang-Vong's (1885-1959) funeral, Apr. 23-29, 1961.

King Savang Vatthana — A22

**1962, Apr. 16 *Perf. 13***

**Portrait in Brown and Carmine**

| | | | | |
|---|---|---|---|---|
| **70** | A22 | 1k ultramarine | .50 | .25 |
| **71** | A22 | 2k lilac rose | .60 | .25 |
| **72** | A22 | 5k greenish blue | .70 | .30 |
| **73** | A22 | 10k olive | .85 | .40 |
| | | *Nos. 70-73 (4)* | 2.65 | 1.20 |

Boy and Malaria Eradication Emblem — A23

9k, Girl. 10k, Malaria eradication emblem.

**1962, July 19 Engr.**

| | | | | |
|---|---|---|---|---|
| **74** | A23 | 4k bluish grn, blk & buff | .60 | .25 |
| **75** | A23 | 9k lt bl, blk & lt brn | .80 | .40 |
| **76** | A23 | 10k ol, bis & rose red | 1.25 | .45 |
| | | *Nos. 74-76 (3)* | 2.65 | 1.10 |

WHO drive to eradicate malaria.

Nos. 74-76 exist imperf.

An imperf. souvenir sheet on white paper with light blue inscription exists. Value, $300. Three other varieties of this sheet also exist: off white paper with light blue inscription, value, $500; white paper with dark blue inscription, value, $350; and off white paper with dark blue inscription, value, $650.

A24

A25

Designs: 50c, Modern mail service (truck, train, plane). 70c, Globe, stamps, dancer. 1k, Ancient mail service (messenger on elephant). 1.50k, Royal Messenger

**1962, Nov. 15 Unwmk. *Perf. 13***

| | | | | |
|---|---|---|---|---|
| **77** | A24 | 50c multicolored | .60 | .60 |
| **78** | A24 | 70c multicolored | .60 | .60 |
| **79** | A25 | 1k dp clar, grn & blk | 1.25 | 1.25 |
| **80** | A25 | 1.50k multicolored | 1.00 | 1.00 |
| | | *Nos. 77-80 (4)* | 3.45 | 3.45 |

Souvenir sheets exist. One contains the 50c and 70c; the other, the 1k and 1.50k. The sheets exist both perf and imperf in a souvenir booklet of four sheets. Value intact booklet, $350.

Fishermen with Nets — A26

Threshing Rice — A27

Designs: 5k, Plowing and planting in rice paddy. 9k, Woman with infant harvesting rice.

**1963, Mar. 21 *Perf. 13***

| | | | | |
|---|---|---|---|---|
| **81** | A26 | 1k grn, bister & pur | .35 | .30 |
| **82** | A27 | 4k bister, bl & grn | .45 | .35 |
| **83** | A26 | 5k grn, bis & indigo | .65 | .45 |
| **84** | A27 | 9k grn, vio bl & ocher | 1.00 | .50 |
| *a.* | | Min. sheet of 4, #81-84, imperf. | 5.00 | 5.00 |
| *b.* | | As "a," left panel of No. 83 green instead of brown | 100.00 | 100.00 |
| | | *Nos. 81-84 (4)* | 2.45 | 1.60 |

FAO "Freedom from Hunger" campaign.

No. 84a exists on yellowish and white papers; No. 84b exists only on yellowish paper.

No. 84b exists with gold inscriptions. Value $450.

Queen Khamphouy Handing out Gifts — A28

**1963, Oct. 10 Engr.**

| | | | | |
|---|---|---|---|---|
| **85** | A28 | 4k brn, dp car & blue | .50 | .40 |
| **86** | A28 | 6k grn, red, yel & bl | .60 | .50 |
| **87** | A28 | 10k bl, dp car & dk brn | .90 | .65 |
| *a.* | | Miniature sheet of 3, #85-87 | 4.00 | 4.00 |
| | | *Nos. 85-87 (3)* | 2.00 | 1.55 |

Centenary of the International Red Cross.

Man Holding UN Emblem A29

**1963, Dec. 10 Unwmk. *Perf. 13***

**88** A29 4k dk bl, dp org & vio brn 1.50 .80

15th anniv. of the Universal Declaration of Human Rights.

No. 88 also was issued imperf. Value, $15.

Temple of That Luang, Map of Nubia and Ramses II — A30

**1964, Mar. 8 Engr.**

| | | | | |
|---|---|---|---|---|
| **89** | A30 | 4k multicolored | .40 | .40 |
| **90** | A30 | 6k multicolored | .60 | .60 |
| **91** | A30 | 10k multicolored | .75 | .75 |
| *a.* | | Miniature sheet of 3, #89-91 | 3.00 | 3.00 |
| | | *Nos. 89-91 (3)* | 1.75 | 1.75 |

UNESCO world campaign to save historic monuments in Nubia. No. 91a sold for 25k.

Ceremonial Chalice A31

Designs: 15k, Buddha. 20k, Soldier leading people through Mekong River Valley. 40k, Royal Palace, Luang Prabang.

**1964, July 30 Unwmk. *Perf. 13***

| | | | | |
|---|---|---|---|---|
| **92** | A31 | 10k multicolored | .40 | .30 |
| **93** | A31 | 15k multicolored | .60 | .40 |
| **94** | A31 | 20k multicolored | .80 | .60 |
| **95** | A31 | 40k multicolored | 1.25 | .75 |
| *a.* | | Miniature sheet of 4, #92-95 | 3.50 | 3.50 |
| | | *Nos. 92-95 (4)* | 3.05 | 2.05 |

"Neutral and Constitutional Laos." When the stamps are arranged in a block of four with 40k and 15k in first row and 10k and 20k in second row, the map of Laos appears.

A souvenir booklet containing No. 95a exists. Value, $45.

Prince Vet and Wife Mathie — A32

Scenes from Buddhist Legend of Phra Vet Sandone: 32k, God of the Skies sending his son to earth. 45k, Phaune's daughter with beggar husband. 55k, Beggar cornered by guard and dogs.

**1964, Nov. 17 Photo. *Perf. 13x12½***

| | | | | |
|---|---|---|---|---|
| **96** | A32 | 10k multicolored | .50 | .50 |
| **97** | A32 | 32k multicolored | .75 | .75 |
| **98** | A32 | 45k multicolored | 1.00 | 1.00 |
| **99** | A32 | 55k multicolored | 1.25 | 1.25 |
| *a.* | | Miniature sheet of 4 | 5.00 | 3.75 |
| | | *Nos. 96-99 (4)* | 3.50 | 3.50 |

No. 99a contains 4 imperf. stamps similar to Nos. 96-99.

A souvenir booklet containing No. 99a without the sheet number exists. Value, $100.

Lao Women — A33

**1964, Dec. 15 Engr. *Perf. 13***

| | | | | |
|---|---|---|---|---|
| **100** | A33 | 25k blk, org brn & pale ol | .75 | .75 |
| | | *Nos. 100,C43-C45 (4)* | 3.45 | 2.35 |

Butterflies A34

10k, Cethosia biblis. 25k, Precis cebrene. 40k, Dysphania militaris.

**1965, Mar. 13 Unwmk. *Perf. 13***

**Size: 36x36mm**

| | | | | |
|---|---|---|---|---|
| **101** | A34 | 10k multi | 2.25 | 1.25 |
| **102** | A34 | 25k multi | 4.25 | 1.75 |

**Size: 48x27mm**

| | | | | |
|---|---|---|---|---|
| **103** | A34 | 40k multi | 10.50 | 2.50 |
| | | *Nos. 101-103,C46 (4)* | 22.50 | 8.00 |

See. No. C46.

Teacher and School, American Aid — A35

Designs: 25k, Woman at Wattay Airport, French aid, horiz. 45k, Woman bathing child and food basket, Japanese aid. 55k, Musicians broadcasting, British aid, horiz.

**1965, Mar. 30 Engr. *Perf. 13***

**104** A35 25k bl grn, brn & car rose .45 .30
**105** A35 45k ol grn & brn .95 .50
**106** A35 55k brt bl & bister 1.25 .65
**107** A35 75k multicolored 1.75 .80
*Nos. 104-107 (4)* 4.40 2.25

Issued to publicize foreign aid to Laos.

Hophabang Temple A36

**1965, Apr. 23 Unwmk. *Perf. 13***

**108** A36 10k multicolored .75 .35

Telewriter, Map of Laos and Globe A37

30k, Communication by satellite & map of Laos. 50k, Globe, map of Laos & radio.

**1965, June 15 Engr. *Perf. 13***

**109** A37 5k vio bl, brn & red lil .25 .25
**110** A37 30k bl, org brn & sl grn .65 .50
**111** A37 50k crim, lt bl & bis 1.25 .90
*a.* Miniature sheet of 3, #109-111 4.75 4.75
*Nos. 109-111 (3)* 2.15 1.65

ITU, centenary.

A souvenir booklet containing No. 111a exists. Value, $35.

**Nos. 52-53 Surcharged in Dark Blue with New Value and Bars**

**1965, July 5 Unwmk. *Perf. 13***

**112** A16 1k on 4k rose claret .70 .25
**113** A16 5k on 6.50k org red .70 .25

Mother and Child, UNICEF and WHO Emblems — A38

**1965, Sept. 1 Engr. *Perf. 13***

**114** A38 35k lt ultra & dk red .85 .70
*a.* Miniature sheet 4.75 4.75

Mother and Child Protection movement, 6th anniv.

Map of Laos and UN Emblem — A39

**1965, Nov. 3 *Perf. 12½x13***

**115** A39 5k emer, gray & vio bl .30 .25
**116** A39 25k lil rose, gray & vio bl .45 .35
**117** A39 40k bl, gray & vio bl .70 .50
*Nos. 115-117 (3)* 1.45 1.10

UN, 20th anniv. Although first day covers were canceled "Oct. 24," the actual day of issue is reported to have been Nov. 3.

Tikhy (Hockey) A40

Pastimes: 10k, Two bulls fighting. 25k, Canoe race. 50k, Rocket festival.

**1965, Dec. 23 Engr. *Perf. 13***

**118** A40 10k org, brn & gray .30 .25
**119** A40 20k grn, ver & dk bl .40 .30
**120** A40 25k brt blue & multi .40 .35
**121** A40 50k orange & multi .90 .50
*Nos. 118-121 (4)* 2.00 1.40

Slaty-headed Parakeet — A41

Birds: 15k, White-crested laughing thrush. 20k, Osprey. 45k, Bengal roller.

**1966, Feb. 10 Engr. *Perf. 13***

**122** A41 5k car rose, ol & brn .85 .50
**123** A41 15k bluish grn, brn & blk 1.25 .60
**124** A41 20k dl bl, sep & bister 2.10 1.00
**125** A41 45k vio, Prus bl & sepia 4.25 2.40
*Nos. 122-125 (4)* 8.45 4.50

WHO Headquarters, Geneva — A42

**1966, May 3 Engr. *Perf. 13***

**126** A42 10k bl grn & indigo .25 .25
**127** A42 25k car & dk green .40 .30
**128** A42 50k ultra & black .85 .70
*a.* Miniature sheet of 3, #126-128 19.00 19.00
*Nos. 126-128 (3)* 1.50 1.25

Inauguration of the WHO Headquarters, Geneva. No. 128a sold for 150k.

Ordination of Buddhist Monk — A43

Folklore: 25k, Women building ceremonial sand hills. 30k, Procession of the Wax Pagoda, vert. 40k, Wrist-tying ceremony (3 men, 3 women), vert.

**1966, May 20 *Perf. 13***

**129** A43 10k multicolored .30 .25
**130** A43 25k multicolored .45 .30
**131** A43 30k multicolored .75 .50
**132** A43 40k multicolored 1.00 .70
*Nos. 129-132 (4)* 2.50 1.75

UNESCO Emblem A44

**1966, July 7 Engr. *Perf. 13***

**133** A44 20k ocher & gray .25 .25
**134** A44 30k brt blue & gray .40 .30
**135** A44 40k brt green & gray .55 .30
**136** A44 60k crimson & gray .80 .45
*a.* Miniature sheet, #133-136 6.00 6.00
*Nos. 133-136 (4)* 2.00 1.30

UNESCO, 20th anniv. No. 136a sold for 250k.

Addressed Envelope Carrier Pigeon, Globe and Hand with Quill Pen — A45

**1966, Sept. 7 Engr. *Perf. 13***

**137** A45 5k red, brn & bl .25 .25
**138** A45 20k bl grn, blk & lil .45 .30
**139** A45 40k bl, red brn & dk ol bister .55 .35
**140** A45 45k brt rose lil, bl grn & black .75 .50
*a.* Min. sheet of 4, #137-140 6.00 6.00
*Nos. 137-140 (4)* 2.00 1.40

Intl. Letter Writing Week, Oct. 6-12. No. 140a sold for 250k.

Sculpture from Siprapouthbat Temple — A46

Sculptures: 20k, from Visoun Temple. 50k, from Xiengthong Temple. 70k, from Visoun Temple.

**1967, Feb. 21 Engr. *Perf. 12½x13***

**141** A46 5k olive grn & grn .30 .25
**142** A46 20k brn ol & gray bl .70 .40
**143** A46 50k dk brn & dp claret 1.25 .50
**144** A46 70k dk brn & dk magenta 1.50 .80
*Nos. 141-144 (4)* 3.75 1.95

General Post Office A47

**1967, Apr. 6 Engr. *Perf. 13***

**145** A47 25k brn, grn & vio brn .35 .25
**146** A47 50k ind, brt blue & grn .55 .40
**147** A47 70k dk red, grn & brn 1.25 .75
*Nos. 145-147 (3)* 2.15 1.40

Inauguration of the new Post and Telegraph Headquarters.

Snakehead A48

Fish: 35k, Giant catfish. 45k, Spiny eel. 60k, Knifefish.

**1967, June 8 Engr. *Perf. 13x12½***

**148** A48 20k dl bl, bis & blk 1.25 .50
**149** A48 35k aqua, bis & gray 1.50 .60
**150** A48 45k pale grn, bis & ol brn 2.50 .70
**151** A48 60k sl grn, bis & blk 3.75 .80
*Nos. 148-151 (4)* 9.00 2.60

Drumstick Tree Flower — A49

Blossoms: 55k, Turmeric. 75k, Peacock flower. 80k, Pagoda tree.

**1967, Aug. 10 Engr. *Perf. 12½x13***

**152** A49 30k red lil, yel & grn .60 .35
**153** A49 55k org, mag & lt grn .90 .45
**154** A49 75k bl, red & lt grn 1.25 .65
**155** A49 80k brt grn, mag & yel 1.50 .75
*Nos. 152-155 (4)* 4.25 2.20

Banded Krait — A50

Reptiles: 40k, Marsh crocodile. 100k, Malayan moccasin. 200k, Water monitor.

**1967, Dec. 7 Engr. *Perf. 13***

**156** A50 5k emer, ind & yel .85 .40
**157** A50 40k sep, lt grn & yel 1.75 .60
**158** A50 100k lt grn, brn & ocher 3.50 1.75
**159** A50 200k grn, blk & bister 8.50 5.00
*Nos. 156-159 (4)* 14.60 7.75

Human Rights Flame — A51

**1968, Feb. 8 Engr. *Perf. 13***

**160** A51 20k brt grn, red & grn .30 .25
**161** A51 30k brn, red & grn .40 .30
**162** A51 50k brt bl, red & grn .80 .60
*a.* Souv. sheet of 3, #160-162 5.00 5.00
*Nos. 160-162 (3)* 1.50 1.15

Intl. Human Rights Year. No. 162a sold for 250k.

WHO Emblem — A52

**1968, July 5 Engr. *Perf. 12½x13***

| | | | | | |
|---|---|---|---|---|---|
| **163** | A52 | 15k rose vio, ver & ocher | .25 | .25 |
| **164** | A52 | 30k brt bl, brt grn & ocher | .25 | .25 |
| **165** | A52 | 70k ver, plum & ocher | .55 | .40 |
| **166** | A52 | 110k brn, brt rose lil & ocher | .90 | .55 |
| **167** | A52 | 250k brt grn, brt bl & ocher | 2.40 | 1.50 |
| *a.* | | Souv. sheet of 5, #163-167 | 6.50 | 6.50 |
| | | *Nos. 163-167 (5)* | 4.35 | 2.95 |

WHO, 20th anniv. No. 167a sold for 500k.

Parade and Memorial Arch — A53

Designs: 20k, Armored Corps with tanks. 60k, Three soldiers with Laotian flag.

**1968, July 15 *Perf. 13***

| | | | | |
|---|---|---|---|---|
| **168** | A53 | 15k multicolored | .35 | .25 |
| **169** | A53 | 20k multicolored | .45 | .35 |
| **170** | A53 | 60k multicolored | .90 | .45 |
| | | *Nos. 168-170,C52-C53 (5)* | 5.95 | 3.15 |

Laotian Army. For souvenir sheet see No. C53a.

Chrysochroa Mnizechi — A54

Insects: 50k, Aristobia approximator. 90k, Eutaenia corbetti.

**1968, Aug. 28 Engr. *Perf. 13***

| | | | | |
|---|---|---|---|---|
| **171** | A54 | 30k vio bl, grn & yel | .90 | .35 |
| **172** | A54 | 50k lil, blk & ocher | 1.50 | .50 |
| **173** | A54 | 90k bis, blk & org | 2.25 | 1.25 |
| | | *Nos. 171-173,C54-C55 (5)* | 8.40 | 4.20 |

See. Nos. C54-C55.

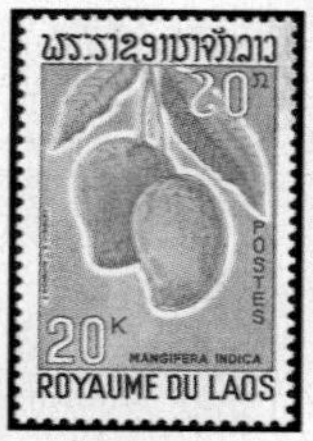


Mangoes — A55

Fruits: 50k, Tamarind. 180k, Jackfruit, horiz. 250k, Watermelon, horiz.

**1968, Oct. 3 Engr. *Perf. 13***

| | | | | |
|---|---|---|---|---|
| **174** | A55 | 20k ind, lt bl & emer | .40 | .25 |
| **175** | A55 | 50k lt bl, emer & brn | .70 | .40 |
| **176** | A55 | 180k sep, org & yel grn | 2.00 | 1.10 |
| **177** | A55 | 250k sep, bis & emer | 2.75 | 1.60 |
| | | *Nos. 174-177 (4)* | 5.85 | 3.35 |

Hurdling — A56

**1968, Nov. 15 Engr. *Perf. 13***

| | | | | |
|---|---|---|---|---|
| **178** | A56 | 15k shown | .50 | .50 |
| **179** | A56 | 80k Tennis | 1.00 | .50 |
| **180** | A56 | 100k Soccer | 1.00 | .50 |
| **181** | A56 | 110k High jump | 1.50 | 1.00 |
| | | *Nos. 178-181 (4)* | 4.00 | 2.50 |

19th Olympic Games, Mexico City, 10/12-27.

Wedding of Kathanam and Nang Sida A57

Design: 200k, Thao Khathanam battling the serpent Ngou Xouang and the giant bird Phanga Houng. Design from panels of the central gate of Ongtu Temple, Vientiane. Design of 150k is from east gate.

**1969, Feb. 28 Photo. *Perf. 12x13***

| | | | | |
|---|---|---|---|---|
| **182** | A57 | 150k blk, gold & red | 2.00 | 1.25 |
| **183** | A57 | 200k blk, gold & red | 2.75 | 1.75 |

Soukhib Ordered to Attack — A58

Scenes from Royal Ballet: 15k, Pharak pleading for Nang Sita. 20k, Thotsakan reviewing his troops. 30k, Nang Sita awaiting punishment. 40k, Pharam inspecting troops. 60k, Hanuman preparing to rescue Nang Sita.

**1969 Photo. *Perf. 14***

| | | | | |
|---|---|---|---|---|
| **184** | A58 | 10k multicolored | .50 | .25 |
| **185** | A58 | 15k blue & multi | .70 | .40 |
| **186** | A58 | 20k lt bl & multi | .70 | .50 |
| **187** | A58 | 30k salmon & multi | 1.00 | .55 |
| **188** | A58 | 40k salmon & multi | 1.60 | .70 |
| **189** | A58 | 60k pink & multi | 2.00 | 1.10 |
| | | *Nos. 184-189,C56-C57 (8)* | 17.00 | 8.50 |

See Nos. C56-C57. For surcharges see Nos. B12-B17, CB1-CB2.

ILO Emblem and Basket Weavers at Vientiane Vocational Center A59

**1969, May 7 Engr. *Perf. 13***

| | | | | |
|---|---|---|---|---|
| **190** | A59 | 30k claret & violet | .50 | .40 |
| **191** | A59 | 60k slate grn & vio brn | 1.00 | .75 |
| | | *Nos. 190-191,C58 (3)* | 7.00 | 4.40 |

ILO, 50th anniv.

Chinese Pangolin — A60

**1969, Nov. 6 Photo. *Perf. 13x12***

| | | | | |
|---|---|---|---|---|
| **192** | A60 | 15k multicolored | .60 | .25 |
| **193** | A60 | 30k multicolored | 1.00 | .50 |
| | | *Nos. 192-193,C59-C61 (5)* | 7.85 | 3.85 |

See Nos. C59-C61.

That Luang, Luang Prabang A61

King Sisavang-Vong — A62

**1969, Nov. 19 Engr. *Perf. 13***

| | | | | |
|---|---|---|---|---|
| **194** | A61 | 50k dk brn, bl & bister | .80 | .60 |
| **195** | A62 | 70k maroon & buff | 1.40 | 1.00 |
| *a.* | | Pair, #194-195 + label | 3.50 | 3.50 |

Death of King Sisavang-Vong, 10th anniv.

Carved Capital from Wat Xiengthong A63

**1970, Jan. 10 Photo. *Perf. 12x13***

| | | | | |
|---|---|---|---|---|
| **196** | A63 | 70k multicolored | 1.75 | 1.25 |
| | | *Nos. 196,C65-C66 (3)* | 5.15 | 2.90 |

Kongphene (Midday) Drum — A64

Designs: 55k, Kongthong (bronze) drum.

**1970, Mar. 30 Engr. *Perf. 13***

| | | | | |
|---|---|---|---|---|
| **197** | A64 | 30k bl gray, ol & org | 1.00 | .60 |
| **198** | A64 | 55k ocher, blk & yel grn | 1.75 | 1.35 |
| | | *Nos. 197-198,C67 (3)* | 5.75 | 3.45 |

See No. C67.

Lenin Explaining Electrification Plan, by L. Shmatko — A65

**1970, Apr. 22 Litho. *Perf. 12½x12***

| | | | | |
|---|---|---|---|---|
| **199** | A65 | 30k blue & multi | 1.10 | .55 |
| **200** | A65 | 70k rose red & multi | 1.40 | .75 |

Lenin (1870-1924), Russian communist leader.

Silk Weaver and EXPO Emblem A66

**1970, July 7 Engr. *Perf. 13***

| | | | | |
|---|---|---|---|---|
| **201** | A66 | 30k shown | .70 | .30 |
| **202** | A66 | 70k Woman winding thread | 1.00 | .80 |
| | | *Nos. 201-202,C69 (3)* | 3.45 | 2.35 |

Laotian silk industry; EXPO '70 Intl. Exposition, Osaka, Japan, Mar. 15-Sept. 13.

See No. C69.

Wild Boar A67

**1970, Sept. 7 Engr. *Perf. 13***

| | | | | |
|---|---|---|---|---|
| **203** | A67 | 20k green & dp brn | .55 | .25 |
| **204** | A67 | 60k dp brn & ol bis | 1.00 | .45 |
| | | *Nos. 203-204,C70-C71 (4)* | 9.30 | 4.45 |

See Nos. C70-C71.

Buddha, UN Headquarters and Emblem — A68

**1970, Oct. 24 Size: 22x36mm**

| | | | | |
|---|---|---|---|---|
| **205** | A68 | 30k ultra, brn & rose red | .70 | .40 |
| **206** | A68 | 70k brt grn, sep & vio | 1.40 | .60 |
| | | *Nos. 205-206,C75 (3)* | 4.50 | 2.10 |

UN, 25th anniv.

See No. C75.

Nakhanet, Symbol of Arts and Culture — A69

85k, Rahu swallowing the moon.

**1971, Feb. 5**

| | | | | |
|---|---|---|---|---|
| **207** | A69 | 70k shown | 1.00 | .60 |
| **208** | A69 | 85k multicolored | 1.40 | .85 |
| | | *Nos. 207-208,C76 (3)* | 4.80 | 2.45 |

Silversmithing — A70

**1971, Apr. 12 Engr. *Perf. 13***

**Size: 36x36mm**

**209** A70 30k shown .35 .25
**210** A70 50k Pottery .55 .35

**Size: 47x36mm**

**211** A70 70k Boat building 1.10 .40
*Nos. 209-211 (3)* 2.00 1.00

Laotian and African Children, UN Emblem — A71

60k, Women musicians, elephants, UN emblem.

**1971, May 1 Engr. *Perf. 13***

**212** A71 30k lt grn, brn & blk .50 .30
**213** A71 60k yel, pur & dull red 1.10 .50

Intl. year against racial discrimination.

Miss Rotary, Wat Ho Phrakeo — A72

Design: 30k, Monk on roof of That Luang and Rotary emblem, horiz.

**1971, June 28 Engr. *Perf. 13***

**214** A72 30k purple & ocher .60 .40
**215** A72 70k gray ol, dk bl & rose 1.25 .55

Rotary International, 50th anniversary.

Dendrobium Aggregatum A73

50k, Asocentrum ampullaceum, horiz. 70k, Trichoglottis fasciata, horiz.

***Perf. 12½x13, 13x12½***

**1971, July 7 Photo.**

**Size: 26x36, 36x26mm**

**216** A73 30k shown 1.00 .50
**217** A73 50k multicolored 1.40 .95
**218** A73 70k multicolored 2.00 1.25
*Nos. 216-218,C79 (4)* 8.90 4.20

See Nos. 230-232, C79, C89.

Palm Civet A74

Animals: 40k, like 25k. 50k, Lesser mouse deer. 85k, Sika deer.

**1971, Sept. 16 Engr. *Perf. 13***

**219** A74 25k pur, dk bl & blk .80 .45
**220** A74 40k grn, ol bis & blk 1.00 .60
**221** A74 50k brt grn & ocher 1.50 .70
**222** A74 85k sl grn, grn & brn orange 2.50 1.25
*Nos. 219-222,C83 (5)* 10.05 5.75

See No. C83.

**Types of 1952-57 with Ornamental Panels and Inscriptions**

Designs: 30k, Laotian woman. 40k, So player (like #C25). 50k, Rama (like #C19).

**1971, Oct. 31**

**223** A3 30k brn vio & brn .50 .30
**224** A10 40k sepia, blk & ver .70 .50
**225** AP7 50k ultra, blk & salmon 1.00 .70
*Nos. 223-225,C84 (4)* 4.20 2.90

Souvenir Sheet

*223A* A3 Sheet of 3 6.00 6.00
*b.* 60k 2.00 2.00
*c.* 85k 2.00 2.00

20th anniv. of Laotian independent postal service. All stamps inscribed: "Vingtième Anniversaire de la Philatélie Lao," "Postes" and "1971." No. 223A contains No. 223 and 60k and 85k in design of 30k, sold for 250k.

Children Learning to Read A75

70k, Scribe writing on palm leaves.

**1972, Jan. 30 Engr. *Perf. 13***

**Size: 36x22mm**

**226** A75 30k shown .35 .30
**227** A75 70k multicolored .70 .50
*Nos. 226-227,C87 (3)* 2.80 1.80

Intl. Book Year.

See No. C87.

Nam Ngum Hydroelectric Dam, Monument and ECAFE Emblem — A76

**1972, Mar. 28 Engr. *Perf. 13***

**228** A76 40k grn, ultra & lt brn .35 .25
**229** A76 80k grn, brn ol & dk bl .70 .40
*Nos. 228-229,C88 (3)* 2.45 1.45

25th anniv. of the Economic Commission for Asia and the Far East (ECAFE), which helped build the Nam Ngum Hydroelectric Dam.
See No. C88.

**Orchid Type of 1971**

Orchids: 40k, Hynchostylis giganterum. 60k, Paphiopedilum exul. 80k, Cattleya, horiz.

**1972, May 5 Photo. *Perf. 13***

**Size: 26x36mm, 36x26mm**

**230** A73 40k lt bl & multi .95 .35
**231** A73 60k multicolored 1.60 .45
**232** A73 80k lt bl & multi 2.00 .50
*Nos. 230-232,C89 (4)* 8.55 2.80

Woman Carrying Water, UNICEF Emblem — A77

Children's drawings: 80k, Child learning bamboo-weaving, UNICEF emblem.

**1972, July 20 Engr. *Perf. 13***

**233** A77 50k blue & multi .70 .50
**234** A77 80k brown & multi 1.00 .65
*Nos. 233-234,C90 (3)* 3.10 2.15

25th anniv. (in 1971) of UNICEF.
See No. C90.

Attopeu Costume, Religious Ceremony — A78

Design: 90k, Phongsaly festival costume.

**1973, Feb. 16 Engr. *Perf. 13***

**235** A78 40k maroon & multi .50 .30
**236** A78 90k multicolored 1.10 .50
*Nos. 235-236,C101-C102 (4)* 4.90 2.60

See Nos. C101-C102.

Lion from Wat That Luang and Lions Emblem — A79

**1973, Mar. 30 Engr. *Perf. 13***

**237** A79 40k vio bl, rose cl & lil .70 .25
**238** A79 80k pur, org brn & yel 1.10 .40
*Nos. 237-238,C103 (3)* 3.70 1.40

Lions International of Laos.

Dr. Hansen, Map of Laos, "Dok Hak" Flowers — A80

**1973, June 28 Engr. *Perf. 13***

**239** A80 40k multicolored .60 .30
**240** A80 80k multicolored 1.25 .45

Centenary of the discovery by Dr. Armauer G. Hansen of the Hansen bacillus, the cause of leprosy.

Wat Vixun, Monk Blessing Girl Scouts — A81

**1973, Sept. 1 Engr. *Perf. 13***

**241** A81 70k ocher & brown .90 .40
*Nos. 241,C106-C107 (3)* 3.25 1.10

25th anniv. of Laotian Scout Movement.

INTERPOL Headquarters — A82

**1973, Dec. 22 Engr. *Perf. 13x12½***

**242** A82 40k greenish bl .45 .25
**243** A82 80k brown .75 .60
*Nos. 242-243,C110 (3)* 2.60 1.45

Intl. Criminal Police Org., 50th anniv.

Boy Mailing Letter — A83

**1974, Apr. 30 Engr. *Perf. 13***

**244** A83 70k bl, lt grn & ocher 1.00 .25
**245** A83 80k lt grn, bl & ocher 1.20 .40
*Nos. 244-245,C114-C115 (4)* 11.95 3.65

UPU, cent.

Blue Sage — A84

50k, Water lilies, horiz. 80k, Scheffler's kapokier, horiz.

**1974, May 17**

**Size: 26x36mm, 36x26mm**

**246** A84 30k grn & vio .55 .40
**247** A84 50k multicolored .90 .50
**248** A84 80k multicolored 1.25 .75
*Nos. 246-248,C116 (4)* 8.20 4.65

See No. C116.

Mekong River Ferry — A85

90k, Samlo (passenger tricycle), vert.

**1974, July 31 Engr. *Perf. 13***

**249** A85 25k red brn & choc .40 .40
**250** A85 90k brown ol & lt ol 1.25 1.25
*Nos. 249-250,C117 (3)* 4.15 3.15

See No. C117.

Marconi, Indigenous Transmission Methods, Transistor Radio — A86

**1974, Aug. 28 Engr. *Perf. 13***

**251** A86 60k multicolored .50 .50
**252** A86 90k multicolored .75 .75
*Nos. 251-252,C118 (3)* 3.50 2.35

Guglielmo Marconi (1874-1937), Italian electrical engineer and inventor.
See No. C118.

Diastocera Wallichi Tonkinensis A87

90k, Macrochenus isabellunus. 100k, Purpuricenus malaccensis.

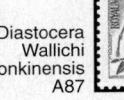

**1974, Oct. 23 Engr. *Perf. 13***

| | | | |
|---|---|---|---|
| **253** | A87 | 50k shown | .90 .60 |
| **254** | A87 | 90k multicolored | 1.40 .85 |
| **255** | A87 | 100k multicolored | 1.75 .90 |
| | | *Nos. 253-255,C119 (4)* | 5.80 3.35 |

See No. C119.

Temple, Houeisai, and Sapphire A88

110k, Sapphire panning at Attopeu.

**1975, Feb. 12 Engr. *Perf. 13x12½***

| | | | |
|---|---|---|---|
| **256** | A88 | 100k bl, brn & grn | 1.50 .50 |
| **257** | A88 | 110k multicolored | 1.75 .75 |

King Sisavang-Vong, Princes Souvanna Phouma and Souphanou-Vong — A89

**1975, Feb. 21 Engr. *Perf. 13***

| | | | |
|---|---|---|---|
| **258** | A89 | 80k olive & multi | 1.00 .40 |
| **259** | A89 | 300k multicolored | 1.75 .90 |
| **260** | A89 | 420k multicolored | 2.00 1.25 |
| | | *Nos. 258-260 (3)* | 4.75 2.55 |

1st anniv. of Peace Treaty of Vientiane.

A souvenir sheet exists, embossed on paper with a foil application. Value, $10.

Fortuneteller Working on Forecast for New Year (Size of pair: 100x27mm) — A90

New Year Riding Rabbit, and Tiger (Old Year) — A92

Designs: 40k, Chart of New Year symbols. 200k, Fortune teller. 350k, As shown.

**1975, Apr. 14 Engr. *Perf. 13***

| | | | |
|---|---|---|---|
| **261** | | 40k bister & red brn | .50 .25 |
| **262** | | 200k bis, red brn & sl | 1.40 .80 |
| *a.* | | A90 Pair, #261-262 | 2.25 1.75 |
| **263** | A92 | 350k blue & multi | 2.50 1.60 |
| | | *Nos. 261-263 (3)* | 4.40 2.65 |

New Year 1975, Year of the Rabbit.

UN Emblem, "Equality" — A93

200k, IWY emblem, man and woman.

**1975, June 19 Engr.**

| | | | |
|---|---|---|---|
| **264** | A93 | 100k dl bl & vio bl | .55 .40 |
| **265** | A93 | 200k multi | 1.20 .85 |
| *a.* | | Miniature sheet of 2, #264-265 | 5.50 5.50 |

International Women's Year.

UPU, Cent. — A93a

Designs: 15k, Runner, rocket reaching orbit, vert. 30k, Docked Soyuz capsules, chariot, vert. 40k, Biplane, Concorde. 1000k, Apollo spacecraft in orbit. 1500k, Apollo spacecraft, astronaut, vert. No. 266F, Wagon train, Lunar Rover. No. 266G, Mail truck, Concorde. No. 266H, stagecoach. No. 266I, Zeppelin, locomotive.

***Perf. 13x14, 14x13***

**1975, July 7 Litho.**

| | | | |
|---|---|---|---|
| **266** | A93a | 10k multi | .30 .25 |
| *b.* | | Souvenir sheet of 1 | *12.50 12.50* |
| **266A** | A93a | 15k multi | .50 .25 |
| *b.* | | Souvenir sheet of 1 | *12.50 12.50* |
| **266B** | A93a | 30k multi | .70 .35 |
| *a.* | | Souvenir sheet of 1 | *12.50 12.50* |
| **266C** | A93a | 40k multi | .90 .60 |
| *a.* | | Souvenir sheet of 1 | *12.50 12.50* |
| **266D** | A93a | 1000k multi | 2.75 2.00 |
| *a.* | | Souvenir sheet of 1 | *12.50 12.50* |
| **266E** | A93a | 1500k multi | 4.75 3.00 |
| *a.* | | Souvenir sheet of 1 | *12.50 12.50* |
| | | *Nos. 266-266E (6)* | 9.90 6.45 |

**Litho. & Embossed**

***Perf. 13½***

| | | | |
|---|---|---|---|
| **266F** | A93a | 2500k gold & multi | 11.00 11.00 |
| *a.* | | Souvenir sheet of 1 | *95.00 95.00* |
| **266G** | A93a | 3000k gold & multi | 11.00 11.00 |
| *a.* | | Souvenir sheet of 1 | *90.00 90.00* |

**Souvenir Sheets**

| | | | |
|---|---|---|---|
| **266H** | A93a | 2500k gold & multi | *35.00 35.00* |
| **266I** | A93a | 3000k gold & multi | *30.00 30.00* |

Nos. 266D-266E, 266G-266I are airmail.

Nos. 266-266E also exist imperf. Value, set of six pairs $150. Nos. 266b, 266Ab and 266Ba-266Ea also exist imperf. Value, set of six sheets $375. Nos. 266Fa, 266Ga and 266H-266I also exist imperf. Value, set of four sheets $550.

Both perforated and imperforate souvenir sheets with blue space images in the selvage exist for 266D and 266E. Value for set of four $35.

No. 266F exists perf and imperf. in sheets of 4.

Apollo-Soyuz Mission — A93b

Designs: 125k, Astronauts, Thomas Stafford, Vance D. Brand, Donald Slayton. 150k, Cosmonauts Alexei Leonov, Valery Koubasov. 200k, Apollo-Soyuz link-up. 300k, Handshake in space. 450k, Preparation for re-entry. 700k, Apollo splashdown.

**1975, July 7 Litho. *Perf. 14x13***

| | | | |
|---|---|---|---|
| **267** | A93b | 125k multicolored | .80 .75 |
| **267A** | A93b | 150k multicolored | .95 .75 |
| **267B** | A93b | 200k multicolored | 1.50 1.00 |
| **267C** | A93b | 300k multicolored | 2.00 1.50 |
| **267D** | A93b | 450k multicolored | 3.25 1.75 |
| **267E** | A93b | 700k multicolored | 3.75 1.50 |
| | | *Nos. 267-267E (6)* | 12.25 7.25 |

Nos. 267D-267E are airmail.

Nos. 267-267E exist imperf. Value, set $55.00

Nos. 267-267E exist in souvenir sheets of 1. Value, set perf. $75., set imperf. $150.

Scene from Vet Sandone Legend — A94

Designs: Scenes from Buddhist legend of Prince Vet Sandone.

**1975, July 22 Photo. *Perf. 13***

| | | | |
|---|---|---|---|
| **268** | A94 | 80k multicolored | .65 .30 |
| **268A** | A94 | 110k multicolored | .70 .40 |
| **268B** | A94 | 120k multicolored | .90 .50 |
| **268C** | A94 | 130k multicolored | 1.50 .60 |
| | | *Nos. 268-268C (4)* | 3.75 1.80 |

American Revolution, Bicent. — A94a

Presidents: 10k, Washington, J. Adams, Jefferson, Madison. 15k, Monroe, J.Q. Adams, Jackson, Van Buren. 40k, Harrison, Tyler, Polk, Taylor. 50k, Filmore, Pierce, Buchanon, Lincoln. 100k, Johnson, Grant, Hayes, Garfield. 123k, Arthur, Cleveland, Harrison. 150k, McKinley, Roosevelt, Taft, Wilson. 200k, Harding, Coolidge, Hoover, Roosevelt. 1000k, Truman, Eisenhower, Kennedy. 1500k, L. Johnson, Nixon, Ford.

**1975, June Litho. *Perf. 13½***

| | | | |
|---|---|---|---|
| **269** | A94a | 10k multicolored | *5.00* — |
| **269A** | A94a | 15k multicolored | *5.00* — |
| **269B** | A94a | 40k multicolored | *5.00* — |
| **269C** | A94a | 50k multicolored | *5.00* — |
| **269D** | A94a | 100k multicolored | *5.00* — |
| **269E** | A94a | 123k multicolored | *5.00* — |
| **269F** | A94a | 150k multicolored | *5.00* — |
| **269G** | A94a | 200k multicolored | *5.00* — |
| **269H** | A94a | 1000k multicolored | *5.00* — |
| **269I** | A94a | 1500k multicolored | *5.00* — |
| | | *Nos. 269-269I (10)* | *50.00* |

Nos. 269H-269I are airmail. These stamps were not approved by the Laotian government, however they were offered for sale at the Laotian post offices and used as valid postage for a brief period before being withdrawn. There is some question as to whether 269C-269G were sold in the Laotian post offices, however in period covers indicate that they probably were. Also exists imperf., set of 10, $200. Souvenir sheets of one exist both perforated, value $235, and imperforate, value $2,650.

Buddha, Stupas of Borobudur — A95

Design: 200k, Borobudur sculptures and UNESCO emblem.

**1975, Aug. 20 Engr. *Perf. 13***

| | | | |
|---|---|---|---|
| **270** | A95 | 100k indigo & multi | .85 .40 |
| **271** | A95 | 200k multicolored | 1.60 .85 |
| *a.* | | Miniature sheet of 2, #270-271 | 2.50 2.50 |

UNESCO campaign to save Borobudur Temple, Java.

Coat of Arms of Republic — A96

**1976, Dec. 2 Litho. *Perf. 14***

| | | | |
|---|---|---|---|
| **272** | A96 | 1k blue & multi | .30 .25 |
| **273** | A96 | 2k rose & multi | .30 .25 |
| **274** | A96 | 5k brt grn & multi | .30 .25 |
| **275** | A96 | 10k lilac & multi | .50 .40 |
| **276** | A96 | 200k orange & multi | 3.50 2.25 |
| *a.* | | Min. sheet of 5, #272-276 | 10.00 10.00 |
| | | *Nos. 272-276 (5)* | 4.90 3.40 |

Miniature sheets of 1 exist. Value $100.

Nos. 272-276 exist imperf. Value, set $70.

For overprints and surcharges, see Nos. 426A, 426V, 508C, 676H, 1903.

Thathiang Pagoda, Vientiane — A97

Designs: 2k, 80k, 100k, Phonsi Pagoda, Luang Prabang. 30k, 300k, like 1k.

**1976, Dec. 18 *Perf. 13½***

| | | | |
|---|---|---|---|
| **277** | A97 | 1k multicolored | .25 .25 |
| **278** | A97 | 2k multicolored | .40 .25 |
| **279** | A97 | 30k multicolored | .85 .50 |
| **280** | A97 | 80k multicolored | 1.75 1.00 |
| **281** | A97 | 100k multicolored | 2.50 1.40 |
| *a.* | | Souv. sheet of 3, #278, 280-281 | 5.25 |
| *b.* | | As a, imperf. | 12.00 |
| **282** | A97 | 300k multicolored | 4.00 2.50 |
| *a.* | | Souv. sheet of 3, #277, 279, 282 | 5.25 |
| *b.* | | As a, imperf. | 12.00 |
| | | *Nos. 277-282 (6)* | 9.75 5.90 |

Nos. 277-282 exist imperf. Value, set $45.

Silversmith — A98

***Perf. 13x12½, 12½x13***

**1977, Apr. 1 Litho.**

| | | | |
|---|---|---|---|
| **283** | A98 | 1k shown | .25 .25 |
| **284** | A98 | 2k Weaver | .25 .25 |
| **285** | A98 | 20k Potter | .65 .25 |
| **286** | A98 | 50k Basket weaver, vert. | 1.25 .40 |
| | | *Nos. 283-286 (4)* | 2.40 1.15 |

Miniature sheets of 2 exist, perf. and imperf. Values: perf, $13; imperf. $16.

For overprints, see Nos. 426B, 426C, 426D, 426E, 426R, 676B.

Cosmonauts A.A. Gubarev, G.M. Grechko A99

Government Palace, Vientiane, Kremlin, Moscow — A100

20k, 50k, Lenin speaking on Red Square.

***Perf. 12x12½, 12½x12***

**1977, Oct. 25** **Litho.**

| | | | | |
|---|---|---|---|---|
| **287** | A99 | 5k multicolored | .25 | .25 |
| **288** | A99 | 20k multicolored | .40 | .25 |
| **289** | A99 | 50k multicolored | .70 | .30 |
| **290** | A99 | 60k multicolored | .90 | .40 |
| **291** | A100 | 100k multicolored | 1.40 | .65 |
| *a.* | | Souv. sheet of 3, #288, 290-291 | 6.00 | 6.00 |
| **292** | A100 | 250k multicolored | 2.25 | 1.50 |
| *a.* | | Souv. sheet of 3, #287, 289, 292 | 6.00 | 6.00 |
| | | *Nos. 287-292 (6)* | 5.90 | 3.35 |

60th anniv. of Russian October Revolution.
Nos. 287-292 exist imperf. Value, set $15.
For overprints, see Nos. 426F, 426N, 676C, 676F, 676I.

Natl. Arms — A101

**1978, May 26** **Litho.** ***Perf. 12½***

| | | | | |
|---|---|---|---|---|
| **293** | A101 | 5k dull org & blk | .30 | .25 |
| **294** | A101 | 10k tan & black | .35 | .25 |
| **295** | A101 | 50k brt pink & blk | .50 | .25 |
| **296** | A101 | 100k yel grn & blk | 1.25 | .45 |
| **297** | A101 | 250k violet & blk | 2.00 | .85 |
| | | *Nos. 293-297 (5)* | 4.40 | 2.05 |

For overprints, see Nos. 426G, 676J.

A102

Army Day: 20k, Soldiers with flag. 40k, Fighters and burning house, horiz. 300k, Anti-aircraft battery.

***Perf. 12½x12¼, 12½x12¾***

**1978, Sept. 15** **Litho.**

| | | | | |
|---|---|---|---|---|
| **298** | A102 | 20k multicolored | .30 | .25 |
| **299** | A102 | 40k multicolored | .55 | .25 |
| **300** | A102 | 300k multicolored | 2.10 | 1.00 |
| | | *Nos. 298-300 (3)* | 2.95 | 1.50 |

Nos. 298-300 exist imperf. Value, set $55.
For overprints see No. 426O, 426Q, 676A, 676L.

Marchers with Banner A103

**1978, Dec. 2** **Litho.** ***Perf. 11½***

| | | | | |
|---|---|---|---|---|
| **301** | A103 | 20k shown | .50 | .25 |
| **302** | A103 | 50k Women with flag | .70 | .25 |
| **303** | A103 | 400k Dancer | 2.25 | 1.40 |
| *a.* | | Sheet of 3, #301-303, imperf. | 4.25 | |
| | | *Nos. 301-303 (3)* | 3.45 | 1.90 |

National Day. A second printing in slightly different colors and with rough perforation exists; values the same. Stamps in souvenir sheet are in reverse order.

Electronic Tree, Map of Laos, ITU Emblem — A104

Design: 250k, Electronic tree, map of Laos and broadcast tower.

**1979, Jan. 18** **Litho.** ***Perf. 12½***

| | | | | |
|---|---|---|---|---|
| **304** | A104 | 30k multicolored | .30 | .25 |
| **305** | A104 | 250k multicolored | 2.50 | 1.00 |

World Telecommunications Day, 1978.
Nos. 304-305 exist imperf. Value, set $10.
For overprints, see Nos. 426P, 426W, 676K.

Woman Mailing Letter A105

10k, 80k, Processing mail. 100k, like 5k.

**1979, Jan. 18**

| | | | | |
|---|---|---|---|---|
| **306** | A105 | 5k multicolored | .25 | .25 |
| **307** | A105 | 10k multicolored | .25 | .25 |
| **308** | A105 | 80k multicolored | 1.00 | .30 |
| **309** | A105 | 100k multicolored | 1.40 | .40 |
| | | *Nos. 306-309 (4)* | 2.90 | 1.20 |

Asian-Oceanic Postal Union, 15th anniv.
Nos. 306-309 exist imperf. Value, set $12.50.
For overprints, see Nos. 426H, 426J, 426K, 426T, 426U, 676E, 676G.

Intl. Year of the Child A106

No. 310, Playing with ball, vert. No. 311, Studying. No. 312, Playing musical instruments. No. 313, Breast-feeding, vert. No. 314, Map, globe, vert. No. 315, Immunization, vert. No. 316, Girl dancing, vert.

**1979** **Litho.** ***Perf. 11***
**Without Gum**

| | | | | |
|---|---|---|---|---|
| **310** | A106 | 20k multicolored | .25 | .25 |
| **311** | A106 | 50k multicolored | .40 | .25 |
| **312** | A106 | 100k multicolored | 1.00 | .35 |
| **313** | A106 | 200k multicolored | 2.00 | .65 |
| **314** | A106 | 200k multicolored | 1.75 | .65 |
| **315** | A106 | 500k multicolored | 6.00 | 1.50 |
| **316** | A106 | 600k multicolored | 4.00 | 1.50 |
| | | *Nos. 310-316 (7)* | 15.40 | 5.15 |

Issued: Nos. 310-311, 313, 315, 8/1; others, 12/25.
Imperf sheets of 4 containing Nos. 310-311, 313, 315 and of 3 containing Nos. 312, 314, 316 exist. Value for both sheets $25.
Two varieties of imperf sheet of 3 exist: inscribed "1979" or "1975" on No. 314 vignette. Sheet with "1975" imprint is very scarce.
Nos. 310-316 exist with double perfs, part perfs, and imperf between. Value $35 each.

Traditional Modes of Transportation — A107

**1979, Oct. 9** ***Perf. 12½x13***

| | | | | |
|---|---|---|---|---|
| **317** | A107 | 5k Elephants, buffalo, pirogues | .25 | .25 |
| **318** | A107 | 10k Buffalo, carts | .30 | .35 |
| **319** | A107 | 70k like 10k | .65 | 1.50 |
| **320** | A107 | 500k like 5k | 2.50 | 2.00 |
| | | *Nos. 317-320 (4)* | 3.70 | 4.10 |

Nos. 317-320 exist imperf. Value, set $15.
For overprints, see Nos. 426I, 426L, 426M, 426S, 676D.

5th Anniv. of the Republic — A108

30c, Agriculture, vert. 50c, Education, health services. 1k, Three women, vert. 2k, Hydroelectric energy.

**1980, May 30** ***Perf. 11***

| | | | | |
|---|---|---|---|---|
| **321** | A108 | 30c multicolored | .35 | .25 |
| **322** | A108 | 50c multicolored | .60 | .25 |
| **323** | A108 | 1k multicolored | .75 | .40 |
| **324** | A108 | 2k multicolored | 1.75 | 1.10 |
| | | *Nos. 321-324 (4)* | 3.45 | 2.00 |

Imperf. souvenir sheet of 4 exists in three types. Values: vowel missing above first Lao word at top of sheet, $20; vowel 9mm above first Lao word, $10; vowel 7.5mm above first Lao word, $10.

Lenin, 110th Birth Anniv. A109

**1980, July 5** ***Perf. 12x12½, 12½x12***

| | | | | |
|---|---|---|---|---|
| **325** | A109 | 1k Lenin reading | .25 | .25 |
| **326** | A109 | 2k Writing | .45 | .25 |
| **327** | A109 | 3k Lenin, red flag, vert. | .65 | .40 |
| **328** | A109 | 4k Orating, vert. | 1.25 | .55 |
| | | *Nos. 325-328 (4)* | 2.60 | 1.45 |

Nos. 325-328 exist imperf. Value, set $12.50.
Imperf. souvenir sheet of 4 exists. Value $5.

**From this point to No. 1365, used values are for CTO stamps. For Nos. 426A-426W, 676A-676L, 1318A-1318C, 1359, used values are for postally used stamps.**

5th Anniv. of the Republic — A110

50c, Threshing rice. 1.60k, Logging. 4.60k, Veterinary medicine. 5.40k, Rice paddy.

**1980, Dec. 2** ***Perf. 11***
**Without Gum**

| | | | | |
|---|---|---|---|---|
| **329** | A110 | 50c multicolored | .30 | .25 |
| **330** | A110 | 1.60k multicolored | .70 | .30 |
| **331** | A110 | 4.60k multicolored | 1.40 | .50 |
| **332** | A110 | 5.40k multicolored | 1.75 | .80 |
| | | *Nos. 329-332 (4)* | 4.15 | 1.85 |

Imperf. souvenir sheet of 4 exists. Value $10. Without inscription, value $100.

26th Communist Party (PCUS) Congress A111

4.60k, Globe, broken chains. 5.40k, Grain, cracked bomb.

**1981, June 26** ***Perf. 12x12½***
**Without Gum**

| | | | | |
|---|---|---|---|---|
| **333** | A111 | 60c shown | .30 | .25 |
| **334** | A111 | 4.60k multicolored | 1.75 | .80 |
| **335** | A111 | 5.40k multicolored | 2.00 | .85 |
| *a.* | | Souv. sheet of 3, #333-335, imperf. | 7.00 | 7.00 |
| | | *Nos. 333-335 (3)* | 4.05 | 1.90 |

No. 335a sold for 15k.

Souvenir Sheet

PHILATOKYO '81 — A112

**1981, Sept. 20** ***Perf. 13***
**Without Gum**

| | | | | |
|---|---|---|---|---|
| **336** | A112 | 10k Pandas | 6.00 | 4.00 |

1982 World Cup Soccer Championships, Spain — A113

**1981, Oct. 15** ***Perf. 12½***
**Without Gum**

| | | | | |
|---|---|---|---|---|
| **337** | A113 | 1k Heading ball | .25 | .25 |
| **338** | A113 | 2k Dribble | .40 | .25 |
| **339** | A113 | 3k Kick | .55 | .25 |
| **340** | A113 | 4k Goal, horiz. | .75 | .25 |
| **341** | A113 | 5k Dribble, diff. | 1.00 | 1.00 |
| **342** | A113 | 6k Kick, diff. | 1.40 | .80 |
| | | *Nos. 337-342 (6)* | 4.35 | 2.80 |

Intl. Year of the Disabled A114

3k, Office worker. 5k, Teacher. 12k, Weaver, fishing net.

**1981** **Without Gum** ***Perf. 13***

| | | | | |
|---|---|---|---|---|
| **343** | A114 | 3k multicolored | 1.60 | .40 |
| **344** | A114 | 5k multicolored | 2.00 | .80 |
| **345** | A114 | 12k multicolored | 4.00 | 2.00 |
| | | *Nos. 343-345 (3)* | 7.60 | 3.20 |

Wildcats — A115

10c, Felis silvestris ornata. 20c, Felis viverrinus. 30c, Felis caracal. 40c, Neofelis nebulosa. 50c, Felis planiceps. 9k, Felis chaus.

**1981 Without Gum *Perf. 12½***

| | | | | |
|---|---|---|---|---|
| **346** | A115 10c multicolored | .25 | .25 |
| **347** | A115 20c multicolored | .25 | .25 |
| **348** | A115 30c multicolored | .35 | .25 |
| **349** | A115 40c multicolored | .40 | .25 |
| **350** | A115 50c multicolored | .45 | .25 |
| **351** | A115 9k multicolored | 3.50 | 1.25 |
| | *Nos. 346-351 (6)* | 5.20 | 2.50 |

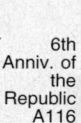

6th Anniv. of the Republic A116

3k, Satellite dish, flag. 4k, Soldier, flag. 5k, Map, flag, women, soldier.

**1981, Dec. Without Gum *Perf. 13***

| | | | |
|---|---|---|---|
| **352** | A116 3k multicolored | *65.00* | .30 |
| **353** | A116 4k multicolored | *80.00* | .40 |
| **354** | A116 5k multicolored | *110.00* | .50 |
| | *Nos. 352-354 (3)* | *255.00* | 1.20 |

Indian Elephants A117

1k, Head. 2k, Carrying log in trunk. 3k, Transporting people. 4k, In trap. 5k, Adult and young. 5.50k, Herd.

**1982, Jan. 23 *Perf. 12½x13***
**Without Gum**

| | | | |
|---|---|---|---|
| **355** | A117 1k multicolored | .30 | .25 |
| **356** | A117 2k multicolored | .60 | .25 |
| **357** | A117 3k multicolored | .80 | .30 |
| **358** | A117 4k multicolored | 1.10 | .30 |
| **359** | A117 5k multicolored | 1.50 | .55 |
| **360** | A117 5.50k multicolored | 2.25 | .70 |
| | *Nos. 355-360 (6)* | 6.55 | 2.35 |

Laotian Wrestling A118

Various moves.

**1982, Jan. 30 *Perf. 13***
**Without Gum**

| | | | |
|---|---|---|---|
| **361** | A118 50c multicolored | .25 | .25 |
| **362** | A118 1.20k multi, diff. | .25 | .25 |
| **363** | A118 2k multi, diff. | .30 | .25 |
| **364** | A118 2.50k multi, diff. | .35 | .25 |
| **365** | A118 4k multi, diff. | .60 | .35 |
| **366** | A118 5k multi, diff. | 1.00 | .55 |
| | *Nos. 361-366 (6)* | 2.75 | 1.90 |

Water Lilies A119

30c, Nymphaea zanzibariensis. 40c, Nelumbo nucifera gaertn rose. 60c, Nymphaea rosea. 3k, Nymphaea nouchali. 4k, Nymphaea white. 7k, Nelumbo nucifera gaertn white.

**1982, Feb. 10 *Perf. 12½x13***
**Without Gum**

| | | | |
|---|---|---|---|
| **367** | A119 30c multicolored | .25 | .25 |
| **368** | A119 40c multicolored | .25 | .25 |
| **369** | A119 60c multicolored | .25 | .25 |
| **370** | A119 3k multicolored | .65 | .25 |
| **371** | A119 4k multicolored | 1.00 | .25 |
| **372** | A119 7k multicolored | 1.75 | .30 |
| | *Nos. 367-372 (6)* | 4.15 | 1.55 |

Birds A120

50c, Hirundo rustica, vert. 1k, Upupa epops, vert. 2k, Alcedo atthis, vert. 3k, Hypothymis azurea. 4k, Motacilla cinerea. 10k, Orthotomus sutorius.

**1982, Mar. 9 *Perf. 13***
**Without Gum**

| | | | |
|---|---|---|---|
| **373** | A120 50c multicolored | .25 | .25 |
| **374** | A120 1k multicolored | .25 | .25 |
| **375** | A120 2k multicolored | .50 | .25 |
| **376** | A120 3k multicolored | .65 | .25 |
| **377** | A120 4k multicolored | 1.25 | .25 |
| **378** | A120 10k multicolored | 2.75 | .80 |
| | *Nos. 373-378 (6)* | 5.65 | 2.05 |

A121

1982 World Cup Soccer Championships, Spain — A122

Various match scenes.

**1982, Apr. 7 Without Gum**

| | | | |
|---|---|---|---|
| **379** | A121 1k multicolored | .25 | .25 |
| **380** | A121 2k multicolored | .40 | .25 |
| **381** | A121 3k multicolored | .55 | .30 |
| **382** | A121 4k multicolored | .70 | .40 |
| **383** | A121 5k multicolored | 1.00 | .45 |
| **384** | A121 6k multicolored | 1.25 | .55 |
| | *Nos. 379-384 (6)* | 4.15 | 2.20 |

**Souvenir Sheet**

| | | | |
|---|---|---|---|
| **385** | A122 15k multicolored | 4.00 | 4.00 |

Nos. 379-384 exist imperf.

Butterflies A123

1k, Herona marathus. 2k, Neptis paraka. 3k, Euripus halitherses. 4k, Lebadea martha. 5k, Iton semamora. 6k, Elymnias hypermnestra.

**1982, May 5 *Perf. 12½x13***
**Without Gum**

| | | | |
|---|---|---|---|
| **386** | A123 1k multicolored | .25 | .25 |
| **387** | A123 2k multicolored | .60 | .25 |
| **388** | A123 3k multicolored | .75 | .30 |
| **389** | A123 4k multicolored | 1.25 | .30 |

**Size: 42x26mm**
***Perf. 12½***

| | | | |
|---|---|---|---|
| **390** | A123 5k multicolored | 2.00 | .70 |

**Size: 54x36½mm**
***Perf. 13x12½***

| | | | |
|---|---|---|---|
| **391** | A123 6k multicolored | 2.50 | .70 |
| | *Nos. 386-391 (6)* | 7.35 | 2.50 |

Souvenir Sheet

PHILEXFRANCE '82 — A124

10k, Temple, Vientiane.

**1982, June 9 *Perf. 13***
**Without Gum**

| | | | |
|---|---|---|---|
| **392** | A124 10k multicolored | 2.75 | 2.75 |

River Vessels A125

50c, Raft. 60c, River punt. 1k, Houseboat. 2k, Passenger steamer. 3k, Ferry. 8k, Self-propelled barge.

**1982, June 24 Without Gum**

| | | | |
|---|---|---|---|
| **393** | A125 50c multicolored | .25 | .25 |
| **394** | A125 60c multicolored | .25 | .25 |
| **395** | A125 1k multicolored | .25 | .25 |
| **396** | A125 2k multicolored | .35 | .25 |
| **397** | A125 3k multicolored | .55 | .40 |
| **398** | A125 8k multicolored | 1.50 | .70 |
| | *Nos. 393-398 (6)* | 3.15 | 2.10 |

Pagodas A126

**1982, Aug. 2 Without Gum**

| | | | |
|---|---|---|---|
| **399** | A126 50c Chanh | .25 | .25 |
| **400** | A126 60c Inpeng | .25 | .25 |
| **401** | A126 1k Dong Mieng | .25 | .25 |
| **402** | A126 2k Ho Tay | .35 | .25 |
| **403** | A126 3k Ho Pha Keo | .60 | .30 |
| **404** | A126 8k Sisaket | 1.60 | .65 |
| | *Nos. 399-404 (6)* | 3.30 | 1.95 |

Dogs A127

**1982, Oct. 13 Without Gum**

| | | | |
|---|---|---|---|
| **405** | A127 50c Poodle | .25 | .25 |
| **406** | A127 60c Samoyed | .25 | .25 |
| **407** | A127 1k Boston terrier | .25 | .25 |
| **408** | A127 2k Cairn terrier | .40 | .25 |
| **409** | A127 3k Chihuahua | .75 | .40 |
| **410** | A127 8k Bulldog | 2.50 | .65 |
| | *Nos. 405-410 (6)* | 4.40 | 2.05 |

World Food Day — A128

**1982, Oct. 16 Without Gum**

| | | | |
|---|---|---|---|
| **411** | A128 7k Watering seedlings | 1.75 | .65 |
| **412** | A128 8k Planting rice | 2.00 | .80 |

Classic Automobiles — A129

**1982, Nov. 7 Without Gum**

| | | | |
|---|---|---|---|
| **413** | A129 50c 1925 Fiat | .25 | .25 |
| **414** | A129 60c 1925 Peugeot | .25 | .25 |
| **415** | A129 1k 1925 Berliet | .25 | .25 |
| **416** | A129 2k 1925 Ballot | .40 | .25 |
| **417** | A129 3k 1926 Renault | .75 | .40 |
| **418** | A129 8k 1925 Ford | 2.00 | .65 |
| | *Nos. 413-418 (6)* | 3.90 | 2.05 |

7th Anniv. of the Republic A130

50c, Kaysone Phomvihan, vert. 1k, Tractors, field, industry. 2k, Cows, farm. 3k, Truck, microwave dish. 4k, Nurse, child, vert. 5k, Education. 6k, Folk dancer, vert.

**1982, Dec. 2 Without Gum**

| | | | |
|---|---|---|---|
| **419** | A130 50c multicolored | .25 | .25 |
| **420** | A130 1k multicolored | .25 | .25 |
| **421** | A130 2k multicolored | .45 | .25 |
| **422** | A130 3k multicolored | .65 | .25 |
| **423** | A130 4k multicolored | .90 | .40 |
| **424** | A130 5k multicolored | 1.10 | .40 |
| **425** | A130 6k multicolored | 1.40 | .50 |
| | *Nos. 419-425 (7)* | 5.00 | 2.30 |

Nos. 419-425 exist imperf.

Bulgarian Flag, Coat of Arms and George Dimitrov (1882-1949), Bulgarian Statesman — A131

**1982, Dec. 15 *Perf. 12½***
**Without Gum**

| | | | |
|---|---|---|---|
| **426** | A131 10k multicolored | 1.90 | 1.10 |

Nos. 272, 276, 283, 284, 286-288, 293, 298, 299, 304-309, 317-319 Ovptd. in Red or Black

**Methods and Perfs as before**

**1982**

| | | | | | |
|---|---|---|---|---|---|
| **426A** | A96 | 1k multi | | *70.00* | *70.00* |
| **426B** | A98 | 1k multi (Bk) | | *75.00* | *75.00* |
| **426C** | A98 | 1k multi | | *55.00* | *55.00* |
| **426D** | A98 | 2k multi | | *50.00* | *50.00* |
| **426E** | A98 | 2k multi (Bk) | | *65.00* | *65.00* |
| **426F** | A99 | 5k multi | | *85.00* | *85.00* |
| **426G** | A101 | 5k dull org & blk | | *75.00* | *75.00* |
| **426H** | A105 | 5k multi | | *55.00* | *55.00* |
| **426I** | A107 | 5k multi | | *35.00* | *35.00* |
| **426J** | A105 | 10k multi (Bk) | | *70.00* | *70.00* |
| **426K** | A105 | 10k multi | | *70.00* | *70.00* |
| **426L** | A107 | 10k multi (Bk) | | *65.00* | *65.00* |
| **426M** | A107 | 10k multi | | *175.00* | *175.00* |
| **426N** | A99 | 20k multi | | — | — |
| **426O** | A102 | 20k multi | | *175.00* | *175.00* |
| **426P** | A104 | 30k multi | | *75.00* | *75.00* |
| **426Q** | A102 | 40k multi | | *85.00* | *85.00* |
| **426R** | A98 | 50k multi | | *85.00* | *85.00* |
| **426S** | A107 | 70k multi | | *115.00* | *115.00* |
| **426T** | A105 | 80k multi (Bk) | | *125.00* | *125.00* |
| **426U** | A105 | 100k multi | | *175.00* | *175.00* |
| **426V** | A96 | 200k org & multi (Bk) | | *275.00* | *275.00* |
| **426W** | A104 | 250k multi (Bk) | | *450.00* | *450.00* |
| | | *Nos. 426A-426W (23)* | | *2,505.* | *2,505.* |

Many overprint varieties exist.

Nos. 426A, 426B, 426E, 426H, 426J, 426L, 426Q, 426R, 426S, 426T, 426U, and 426V exist with inverted "8".

Nos. 426C and 426D exist with "l" instead of "1".

No. exists 426C with "a" instead of "2".

No. 426F exists with double overprint. Nos. 426J, 426N, and 426V exist with double overprint, one inverted. No. 426J exists with double overprint, one inverted, with the "1" in the upright overprint inverted.

No. 426N exists with inverted overprint.

No. 426H exists with "1" inverted.

Nos. 426O and 426P exist with small "2".

Both the "9" and the "2" wore out to the point where these numbers are almost invisible in some overprints. These seeming omission errors appear most prominently with the missing "9" in No. 426E, and the missing "2" in No. 426H.

Constitution of the USSR, 60th Anniv. — A132

**1982, Dec. 30** — **Without Gum**

| | | | | |
|---|---|---|---|---|
| **427** | A132 | 3k Kremlin | .65 | .40 |
| **428** | A132 | 4k Maps | .90 | .55 |

**Souvenir Sheet**

***Perf. 13½x13***

| | | | |
|---|---|---|---|
| **428A** | Sheet of 2 | 3.75 | 2.00 |
| *b.* | A132 5k like 3k | 1.25 | .65 |
| *c.* | A132 10k like 4k | 2.50 | 1.75 |

Nos. 428Ab-428Ac not inscribed in Laotian at top; buff and gold decorative margin contains the inscription.

1984 Summer Olympics, Los Angeles A133

**1983, Jan. 25** — ***Perf. 13***

**Without Gum**

| | | | | |
|---|---|---|---|---|
| **429** | A133 | 50c Hurdling | .25 | .25 |
| **430** | A133 | 1k Women's javelin | .25 | .25 |
| **431** | A133 | 2k Basketball | .35 | .25 |
| **432** | A133 | 3k Diving | .55 | .25 |
| **433** | A133 | 4k Gymnastics | .75 | .40 |
| **434** | A133 | 10k Weight lifting | 2.10 | .80 |
| | | *Nos. 429-434 (6)* | 4.25 | 2.20 |

**Souvenir Sheet**

| | | | | |
|---|---|---|---|---|
| **435** | A133 | 15k Soccer | 3.25 | 2.00 |

No. 435 contains one stamp 32x40mm. Nos. 429-434 exist imperf.

Horses A134

Various breeds.

**1983, Feb. 1** — **Without Gum**

| | | | | |
|---|---|---|---|---|
| **436** | A134 | 50c multicolored | .25 | .25 |
| **437** | A134 | 1k multi, diff. | .25 | .25 |
| **438** | A134 | 2k multi, diff. | .40 | .25 |
| **439** | A134 | 3k multi, diff. | .65 | .25 |
| **440** | A134 | 4k multi, diff. | .80 | .30 |
| **441** | A134 | 10k multi, diff. | 2.75 | .80 |
| | | *Nos. 436-441 (6)* | 5.10 | 2.10 |

Nos. 436-441 exist imperf.

A135

Raphael, 500th Birth Anniv. — A136

Paintings (details) by Raphael: 50c, St. Catherine of Alexandra, Natl. Gallery, London. 1k, Adoration of the Kings (spectators), Vatican. 2k, Granduca Madonna, Pitti Gallery, Florence. 3k, St. George and the Dragon, The Louvre, Paris. 4k, Vision of Ezekiel, Pitti Gallery. No. 447, Adoration of the Kings (Holy Family), Vatican. No. 448, Coronation of the Virgin, Vatican.

**1983, Mar. 9** — ***Perf. 12½x13***

**Without Gum**

| | | | | |
|---|---|---|---|---|
| **442** | A135 | 50c multicolored | .25 | .25 |
| **443** | A135 | 1k multicolored | .25 | .25 |
| **444** | A135 | 2k multicolored | .35 | .25 |
| **445** | A135 | 3k multicolored | .60 | .25 |
| **446** | A135 | 4k multicolored | .75 | .30 |
| **447** | A135 | 10k multicolored | 2.50 | .80 |
| | | *Nos. 442-447 (6)* | 4.70 | 2.10 |

**Souvenir Sheet**

***Perf. 13x13½***

| | | | | |
|---|---|---|---|---|
| **448** | A136 | 10k multicolored | 2.50 | 1.50 |

INTERCOSMOS Space Cooperation Program — A137

Cosmonaut and flags of USSR and participating nations.

**1983, Apr. 12** — ***Perf. 12½***

| | | | | |
|---|---|---|---|---|
| **449** | A137 | 50c Czechoslovakia | .25 | .25 |
| **450** | A137 | 50c Poland | .25 | .25 |
| **451** | A137 | 1k East Germany | .25 | .25 |
| **452** | A137 | 1k Bulgaria | .25 | .25 |
| **453** | A137 | 2k Hungary | .40 | .25 |
| **454** | A137 | 3k Mongolia | .65 | .25 |
| **455** | A137 | 4k Romania | .80 | .25 |
| **456** | A137 | 6k Cuba | 1.25 | .40 |
| **457** | A137 | 10k France | 2.25 | .80 |
| | | *Nos. 449-457 (9)* | 6.35 | 2.95 |

**Souvenir Sheet**

***Perf. 13½x13***

| | | | | |
|---|---|---|---|---|
| **458** | A137 | 10k Vietnam | 2.75 | 1.50 |

No. 458 contains one stamp 32x40mm. Date of issue: 7/24/83.

A138

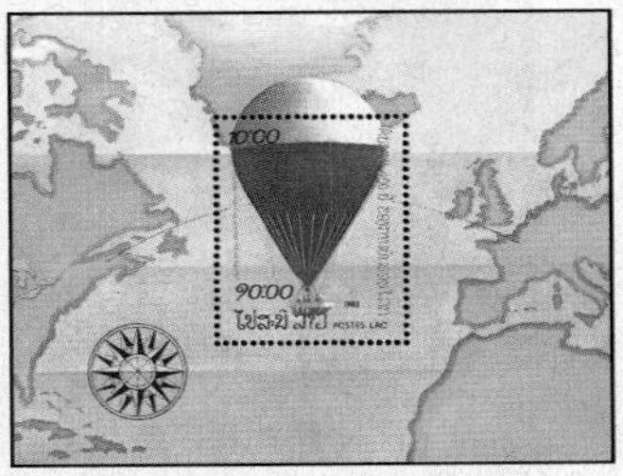

First Manned Balloon Flight, Bicent. — A139

Various balloons.

**1983, May 4** — ***Perf. 12½x13***

| | | | | |
|---|---|---|---|---|
| **459** | A138 | 50c shown | .25 | .25 |
| **460** | A138 | 1k multi, diff. | .25 | .25 |
| **461** | A138 | 2k multi, diff. | .35 | .25 |
| **462** | A138 | 3k multi, diff. | .50 | .25 |
| **463** | A138 | 4k multi, diff. | .65 | .40 |
| **464** | A138 | 10k multi, diff. | 2.25 | .80 |
| | | *Nos. 459-464 (6)* | 4.25 | 2.20 |

**Souvenir Sheet**

***Perf. 13½x13***

| | | | | |
|---|---|---|---|---|
| **465** | A139 | 10k shown | 2.40 | 1.50 |

Nos. 459-464 exist imperf.

Souvenir Sheet

TEMBAL '83, Basel — A140

10k, German Maybach.

**1983, May 21** — ***Perf. 13x13½***

**Without Gum**

| | | | | |
|---|---|---|---|---|
| **466** | A140 | 10k multi | 3.00 | 1.60 |

No. 466 exists imperf.

Flora A141

1k, Dendrobium sp. 2k, Aerides odoratum. 3k, Dendrobium aggregatum. 4k, Dendrobium. 5k, Moschatum. 6k, Dendrobium sp., diff.

**1983, June 10** — ***Perf. 13***

**Without Gum**

| | | | | |
|---|---|---|---|---|
| **467** | A141 | 1k multicolored | .25 | .25 |
| **468** | A141 | 2k multicolored | .40 | .25 |
| **469** | A141 | 3k multicolored | .60 | .25 |
| **470** | A141 | 4k multicolored | .75 | .25 |
| **471** | A141 | 5k multicolored | 1.10 | .30 |
| **472** | A141 | 6k multicolored | 1.40 | .50 |
| | | *Nos. 467-472 (6)* | 4.50 | 1.80 |

Nos. 467-472 exist imperf.

1984 Winter Olympics, Sarajevo — A142

**1983, July 2** — **Without Gum**

| | | | | |
|---|---|---|---|---|
| **473** | A142 | 50c Downhill skiing | .25 | .25 |
| **474** | A142 | 1k Slalom | .25 | .25 |
| **475** | A142 | 2k Ice hockey | .40 | .25 |
| **476** | A142 | 3k Speed skating | .70 | .25 |
| **477** | A142 | 4k Ski jumping | .85 | .30 |
| **478** | A142 | 10k Luge | 2.25 | .80 |
| | | *Nos. 473-478 (6)* | 4.70 | 2.10 |

**Souvenir Sheet**

***Perf. 13x13½***

| | | | | |
|---|---|---|---|---|
| **479** | A142 | 15k 2-Man bobsled | 3.50 | 1.50 |

No. 479 contains one 40x32mm stamp. Nos. 473-478 exist imperf.

Souvenir Sheet

BANGKOK '83 — A143

**1983, Aug. 4** — ***Perf. 13½x13***

| | | | | |
|---|---|---|---|---|
| **480** | A143 | 10k Boats on river | 2.25 | 1.50 |

No. 480 exists imperf. Value, $60.

Mekong River Fish — A144

1k, Notopterus chitala. 2k, Cyprinus carpio. 3k, Pangasius sp. 4k, Catlocarpio siamensis. 5k, Morulius sp. 6k, Tilapia nilotica.

**1983, Sept. 5** — ***Perf. 12½***

**Without Gum**

| | | | | |
|---|---|---|---|---|
| **481** | A144 | 1k multicolored | .25 | .25 |
| **482** | A144 | 2k multicolored | .40 | .25 |
| **483** | A144 | 3k multicolored | .65 | .25 |

**484** A144 4k multicolored .75 .25
**485** A144 5k multicolored 1.10 .30
**486** A144 6k multicolored 1.50 .50
*Nos. 481-486 (6)* 4.65 1.80

Nos. 481-486 exist imperf.

Explorers and Their Ships — A145

1k, Victoria, Magellan. 2k, Grand Hermine, Cartier. 3k, Santa Maria, Columbus. 4k, Cabral and caravel. 5k, Endeavor, Capt. Cook. 6k, Pourquoi-Pas, Charcot.

**1983, Oct. 8** *Perf. 13x12½*

**Without Gum**

**487** A145 1k multicolored .25 .25
**488** A145 2k multicolored .40 .25
**489** A145 3k multicolored .65 .25
**490** A145 4k multicolored .75 .25
**491** A145 5k multicolored 1.10 .30
**492** A145 6k multicolored 1.50 .50
*Nos. 487-492 (6)* 4.65 1.80

No. 492 incorrectly inscribed "CABOT."

Domestic Cats A146

**1983, Nov. 9** *Perf. 12½x13*

**Without Gum**

**493** A146 1k Tabby .25 .25
**494** A146 2k Long-haired Persian .60 .25
**495** A146 3k Siamese .75 .25
**496** A146 4k Burmese .85 .25
**497** A146 5k Persian 1.25 .30
**498** A146 6k Tortoiseshell 1.75 .50
*Nos. 493-498 (6)* 5.45 1.80

Nos. 493-498 exist imperf.

Karl Marx (1818-1883) — A147

4k, Marx, 3 flags, diff., vert. 6k, Marx, flag of Laos.

**1983, Nov. 30** *Perf. 13*

**Without Gum**

**499** A147 1k shown .25 .25
**500** A147 4k multi 1.00 .25
**501** A147 6k multi 1.60 .55
*Nos. 499-501 (3)* 2.85 1.05

8th Anniv. of the Republic — A148

1k, Elephant dragging log, vert. 4k, Oxen, pig. 6k, Produce, vert.

**1983, Dec. 2** *Perf. 12½x13, 13x12½*

**Without Gum**

**502** A148 1k multicolored .25 .25
**503** A148 4k multicolored 1.00 .25
**504** A148 6k multicolored 1.60 .55
*Nos. 502-504 (3)* 2.85 1.05

Nos. 502-504 exist imperf.

World Communications Year — A149

50c, Teletype. 1k, Telephone. 4k, Television. 6k, Satellite, dish receiver.

**1983, Dec. 15** *Perf. 13*

**505** A149 50c multicolored .25 .25
**506** A149 1k multicolored .25 .25
**507** A149 4k multicolored .65 .30
**508** A149 6k multicolored 1.00 .55
*Nos. 505-508 (4)* 2.15 1.35

Nos. 275, 306 Overprinted in Red

**1983** **Method and Perf. As Before**

**508B** A105 5k multi *450.00* —
**508C** A96 10k lilac & multi *575.00* —

1984 Winter Olympics, Sarajevo — A150

50c, Women's figure skating. 1k, Speed skating. 2k, Biathlon. 4k, Luge. 5k, Downhill skiing. 6k, Ski jumping. 7k, Slalom. 10k, Ice hockey.

**1984, Jan. 16**

**509** A150 50c multicolored .25 .25
**510** A150 1k multicolored .25 .25
**511** A150 2k multicolored .40 .25
**512** A150 4k multicolored .80 .30
**513** A150 5k multicolored 1.00 .30
**514** A150 6k multicolored 1.25 .50
**515** A150 7k multicolored 1.50 .55
*Nos. 509-515 (7)* 5.45 2.40

**Souvenir Sheet**

*Perf. 13½x13*

**516** A150 10k multicolored 2.25 1.50

Nos. 509-511, 514-515 vert. No. 516 contains one stamp 32x40mm.

World Wildlife Fund A151

Panthera tigris.

**1984, Feb. 1** *Perf. 13*

**517** A151 25c Adult, vert. *.50* .25
**518** A151 25c shown *.50* .25
**519** A151 3k Nursing cubs *5.00* 1.25
**520** A151 4k Two cubs, vert. *8.00* 1.75
*Nos. 517-520 (4)* *14.00* 3.50

1984 Summer Olympics, Los Angeles A152

Gold medals awarded during previous games, and athletes. 50c, Athens 1896, women's diving. 1k, Paris 1900, women's volleyball. 2k, St. Louis 1904, running. 4k, London 1908, basketball. 5k, Stockholm 1912, judo. 6k, Antwerp 1920, soccer. 7k, Paris 1924, gymnastics. 10k, Moscow 1980, wrestling.

**1984, Mar 26**

**521** A152 50c multicolored .25 .25
**522** A152 1k multicolored .25 .25
**523** A152 2k multicolored .60 .25
**524** A152 4k multicolored 1.10 .25
**525** A152 5k multicolored 1.25 .30
**526** A152 6k multicolored 1.60 .40
**527** A152 7k multicolored 1.90 .50
*Nos. 521-527 (7)* 6.95 2.20

**Souvenir Sheet**

*Perf. 12½*

**528** A152 10k multicolored 2.75 1.50

No. 528 contains one stamp 32x40mm.

Musical Instruments — A153

**1984, Mar. 27** *Perf. 13*

**529** A153 1k Tuned drums .25 .25
**530** A153 2k Xylophone .40 .25
**531** A153 3k Pair of drums .65 .25
**532** A153 4k Hand drum .90 .30
**533** A153 5k Barrel drum 1.10 .30
**534** A153 6k Pipes, string instrument 1.25 .50
*Nos. 529-534 (6)* 4.55 1.85

Natl. Day — A154

**1984, Mar. 30** *Perf. 12½*

**535** A154 60c Natl. flag .35 .25
**536** A154 1k Natl. arms .50 .25
**537** A154 2k like 1k .75 .25
*Nos. 535-537 (3)* 1.60 .75

For surcharges, see Nos. 1884-1886, 1899-1901.

Chess A155

Illustrations of various medieval and Renaissance chess games.
10k, Royal game, human chessmen.

**1984, Apr. 14** *Perf. 12½x13*

**538** A155 50c multi .25 .25
**539** A155 1k multi, diff. .25 .25
**540** A155 2k multi, red brn board, diff. .50 .25
**541** A155 2k multi, blk board, diff. .50 .25
**542** A155 3k multi, diff. .70 .30
**543** A155 4k multi, diff. 1.25 .30
**544** A155 8k multi, diff. 2.25 .50
*a.* Souv. sheet of 6, #538-540, 542-544, with gutter between — —
*Nos. 538-544 (7)* 5.70 2.10

**Souvenir Sheet**

*Perf. 13½x13*

**545** A155 10k multi 3.25 2.50

World Chess Federation, 60th anniv. No. 545 contains one stamp 32x40mm.

ESPANA '84, Madrid — A156

Paintings: 50c, Cardinal Nino de Guevara, by El Greco. 1k, Gaspar de Guzman, Duke of Olivares, on Horseback, byVelazquez. No. 548, The Annunciation, by Murillo. No. 549, Portrait of a Lady, by Francisco de Zurburan (1598-1664). 3k, The Family of Charles IV, by Goya. 4k, Two Harlequins, by Picasso. 8k, Abstract, by Miro. 10k, Burial of the Count of Orgaz, by El Greco.

**1984, Apr. 27** *Perf. 12½*

**546** A156 50c multicolored .25 .25
**547** A156 1k multicolored .25 .25
**548** A156 2k multicolored .45 .25
**549** A156 2k multicolored .45 .25
**550** A156 3k multicolored .65 .30
**551** A156 4k multicolored .90 .30
**552** A156 8k multicolored 1.75 .50
*Nos. 546-552 (7)* 4.70 2.10

**Souvenir Sheet**

*Perf. 13½x13*

**553** A156 10k multicolored 4.75 2.50

No. 553 contains one stamp 32x40mm and also exists imperf.

Woodland Flowers — A157

50c, Adonis aestivalis. 1k, Alpinia speciosa. No. 556, 2k, Aeschynanthus speciosus. No. 557, 2k, Cassia lechenaultiana. 3k, Datura meteloides. 4k, Quamoclit pennata. 8k, Commelina benghalensis.

**1984, May 11** *Perf. 13*

**554** A157 50c multicolored .25 .25
**555** A157 1k multicolored .25 .25
**556** A157 2k multicolored .45 .25
**557** A157 2k multicolored .45 .25
**558** A157 3k multicolored .65 .30
**559** A157 4k multicolored .90 .30
**560** A157 8k multicolored 1.75 .50
*Nos. 554-560 (7)* 4.70 2.10

Nos. 554-560 exist imperf.

A158

19th UPU Congress, Hamburg — A159

Classic sport and race cars.

**1984, June 19**

| | | | | |
|---|---|---|---|---|
| **561** | A158 | 50c Nazzaro | .25 | .25 |
| **562** | A158 | 1k Daimler | .25 | .25 |
| **563** | A158 | 2k Delage | .35 | .25 |
| **564** | A158 | 2k Fiat S 57/14B | .35 | .25 |
| **565** | A158 | 3k Bugatti | .50 | .30 |
| **566** | A158 | 4k Itala | .65 | .30 |
| **567** | A158 | 8k Blitzen Benz | 1.40 | .50 |
| | | *Nos. 561-567 (7)* | 3.75 | 2.10 |

**Souvenir Sheet**

***Perf. 12½***

| | | | | |
|---|---|---|---|---|
| **568** | A159 | 10k Winton Bullet | 1.90 | 1.25 |

Paintings by Correggio (1494-1534) A160

Designs: 50c, Madonna and Child (Holy Family). 1k, Madonna and Child (spectators). No. 571, Madonna and Child (Holy Family, diff.). No. 572, Mystical Marriage of St. Catherine (Catherine, child, two women). 3k, The Four Saints. 4k, Noli Me Tangere. 8k, Christ Bids Farewell to the Virgin Mary. 10k, Madonna and Child, diff.

**1984, June 26** ***Perf. 13***

| | | | | |
|---|---|---|---|---|
| **569** | A160 | 50c multicolored | .25 | .25 |
| **570** | A160 | 1k multicolored | .25 | .25 |
| **571** | A160 | 2k multicolored | .45 | .25 |
| **572** | A160 | 2k multicolored | .45 | .25 |
| **573** | A160 | 3k multicolored | .65 | .30 |
| **574** | A160 | 4k multicolored | .75 | .30 |
| **575** | A160 | 8k multicolored | 1.40 | .50 |
| | | *Nos. 569-575 (7)* | 4.20 | 2.10 |

**Souvenir Sheet**

***Perf. 13½x13***

| | | | | |
|---|---|---|---|---|
| **576** | A160 | 10k multicolored | 3.25 | 1.75 |

No. 576 contains one stamp 32x40mm, and exists imperforate.

Space Exploration A161

No. 577, Luna 1. No. 578, Luna 2. No. 579, Luna 3. No. 580, Sputnik 2, Kepler, horiz. No. 581, Lunokhod 2, Newton, horiz. No. 582, Luna 13, Jules Verne, horiz. No. 583, Space station, Copernicus, horiz.

**1984, July 12** ***Perf. 13***

| | | | | |
|---|---|---|---|---|
| **577** | A161 | 50c multicolored | .25 | .25 |
| **578** | A161 | 1k multicolored | .25 | .25 |
| **579** | A161 | 2k multicolored | .35 | .25 |
| **580** | A161 | 2k multicolored | .35 | .25 |
| **581** | A161 | 3k multicolored | .75 | .25 |
| **582** | A161 | 4k multicolored | 1.00 | .40 |
| **583** | A161 | 8k multicolored | 1.75 | .65 |
| | | *Nos. 577-583 (7)* | 4.70 | 2.30 |

Reptiles A162

No. 584, Malaclemys terrapin. No. 585, Bungarus fasciatus. No. 586, Python reticulatus. No. 587, Python molurus, vert. No. 588, Gekko gecko. No. 589, Natrix subminiata. No. 590, Eublepharis macularius.

**1984, Aug. 20**

| | | | | |
|---|---|---|---|---|
| **584** | A162 | 50c multicolored | .25 | .25 |
| **585** | A162 | 1k multicolored | .25 | .25 |
| **586** | A162 | 2k multicolored | .40 | .25 |
| **587** | A162 | 2k multicolored | .40 | .25 |
| **588** | A162 | 3k multicolored | .75 | .25 |
| **589** | A162 | 4k multicolored | 1.00 | .40 |
| **590** | A162 | 8k multicolored | 1.90 | .65 |
| | | *Nos. 584-590 (7)* | 4.95 | 2.30 |

Marsupials — A163

No. 591, Schoinobates volans. No. 592, Ornithorhynchus anatinus. No. 593, Sarcophilus harrisii. No. 594, Lasiorhinus latifrons. No. 595, Thylacinus cynocephalus. No. 596, Dasyurops maculatus. No. 597, Wallabia isabelinus.

10k, Macropus rufus.

**1984, Sept. 21**

| | | | | |
|---|---|---|---|---|
| **591** | A163 | 50c multicolored | .25 | .25 |
| **592** | A163 | 1k multicolored | .25 | .25 |
| **593** | A163 | 2k multicolored | .40 | .25 |
| **594** | A163 | 2k multicolored | .40 | .25 |
| **595** | A163 | 3k multicolored | .75 | .25 |
| **596** | A163 | 4k multicolored | 1.00 | .40 |
| **597** | A163 | 8k multicolored | 1.90 | .65 |
| | | *Nos. 591-597 (7)* | 4.95 | 2.30 |

**Souvenir Sheet**

***Perf. 12½***

| | | | | |
|---|---|---|---|---|
| **598** | A163 | 10k multicolored | 2.75 | 1.50 |

AUSIPEX '84, Melbourne. No. 598 contains one stamp 32x40mm and also exists imperf.

Stop Polio Campaign — A164

**1984, Sept. 29** ***Perf. 13***

| | | | | |
|---|---|---|---|---|
| **599** | A164 | 5k shown | 1.10 | .55 |
| **600** | A164 | 6k Vaccinating child | 1.20 | .55 |

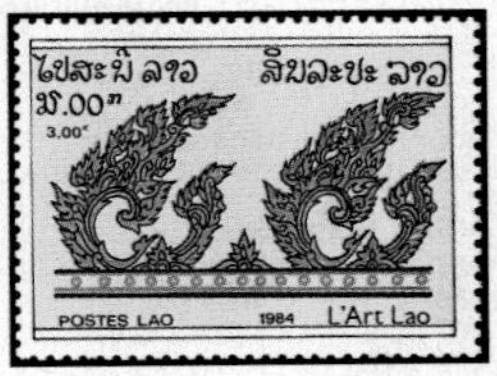


Art A165

No. 601, Dragon (hand rail). No. 602, Capital. No. 603, Oval panel. No. 604, Deity. No. 605, Leaves. No. 606, Floral pattern. No. 607, Lotus flower (round panel).

**1984, Oct. 26**

| | | | | |
|---|---|---|---|---|
| **601** | A165 | 50c multicolored | .25 | .25 |
| **602** | A165 | 1k multicolored | .25 | .25 |
| **603** | A165 | 2k multicolored | .40 | .25 |
| **604** | A165 | 2k multicolored | .40 | .25 |
| **605** | A165 | 3k multicolored | .80 | .25 |
| **606** | A165 | 4k multicolored | 1.25 | .40 |
| **607** | A165 | 8k multicolored | 2.50 | .65 |
| | | *Nos. 601-607 (7)* | 5.85 | 2.30 |

Nos. 601-604 and 607 vert.

9th Anniv. of the Republic — A166

1k, River boats. 2k, Aircraft. 4k, Bridge building. 10k, Surveying, construction.

**1984, Dec. 17**

| | | | | |
|---|---|---|---|---|
| **608** | A166 | 1k multicolored | .50 | .25 |
| **609** | A166 | 2k multicolored | .70 | .25 |
| **610** | A166 | 4k multicolored | 1.20 | .65 |
| **611** | A166 | 10k multicolored | 2.50 | .95 |
| | | *Nos. 608-611 (4)* | 4.90 | 2.10 |

1986 World Cup Soccer Championships, Mexico — A167

Various match scenes and flag of Mexico.

**1985, Jan. 18**

| | | | | |
|---|---|---|---|---|
| **612** | A167 | 50c multicolored | .25 | .25 |
| **613** | A167 | 1k multi, diff. | .25 | .25 |
| **614** | A167 | 2k multi, diff. | .50 | .25 |
| **615** | A167 | 3k multi, diff. | .65 | .25 |
| **616** | A167 | 4k multi, diff. | .85 | .30 |
| **617** | A167 | 5k multi, diff. | 1.10 | .40 |
| **618** | A167 | 6k multi, diff. | 1.40 | .65 |
| | | *Nos. 612-618 (7)* | 5.00 | 2.35 |

**Souvenir Sheet**

***Perf. 12½***

| | | | | |
|---|---|---|---|---|
| **619** | A167 | 10k multi, diff. | 2.25 | 1.50 |

No. 619 contains one stamp 32x40mm. Nos. 612-618 exist imperf.

Motorcycle, Cent. — A168

1k, 1920 Gnome Rhone. 2k, 1928 F.N. M67C. 3k, 1930 Indian Chief. 4k, 1914 Rudge Multi. 5k, 1953 Honda Benly J. 6k, 1938 CZ.

**1985, Feb. 25** ***Perf. 12½***

| | | | | |
|---|---|---|---|---|
| **620** | A168 | 50c shown | .25 | .25 |
| **621** | A168 | 1k multicolored | .25 | .25 |
| **622** | A168 | 2k multicolored | .40 | .25 |
| **623** | A168 | 3k multicolored | .60 | .25 |
| **624** | A168 | 4k multicolored | .80 | .30 |
| **625** | A168 | 5k multicolored | 1.10 | .40 |
| **626** | A168 | 6k multicolored | 1.25 | .65 |
| | | *Nos. 620-626 (7)* | 4.65 | 2.35 |

Nos. 620-626 exist imperf.

Mushrooms — A169

No. 627, Amanita muscaria. No. 628, Boletus edulis. No. 629, Coprinus comatus. No. 630, Amanita rubescens. No. 631, Xerocomus subtomentosus. No. 632, Lepiota procera. No. 633, Paxillus involutus.

**1985, Apr. 8** ***Perf. 13***

| | | | | |
|---|---|---|---|---|
| **627** | A169 | 50c multicolored | .25 | .25 |
| **628** | A169 | 1k multicolored | .25 | .25 |
| **629** | A169 | 2k multicolored | .50 | .25 |
| **630** | A169 | 2k multicolored | .50 | .25 |
| **631** | A169 | 3k multicolored | .75 | .30 |
| **632** | A169 | 4k multicolored | 1.00 | .40 |
| **633** | A169 | 8k multicolored | 2.00 | .60 |
| | | *Nos. 627-633 (7)* | 5.25 | 2.30 |

Nos. 627-633 exist imperf.

End of World War II, 40th Anniv. A169a

1k, Battle of Kursk. 2k, Red Army parade, Moscow. 4k, Battle of Stalingrad. 5k, Battle for Berlin. 6k, Victory parade through Brandenburg Gate.

**1985, May** **Litho.** ***Perf. 12½x12***

| | | | | |
|---|---|---|---|---|
| **633A** | A169a | 1k multicolored | 1.40 | .25 |
| **633B** | A169a | 2k multicolored | 2.50 | .25 |
| **633C** | A169a | 4k multicolored | 4.00 | .40 |
| **633D** | A169a | 5k multicolored | 5.00 | .50 |
| **633E** | A169a | 6k multicolored | 5.50 | .55 |
| | | *Nos. 633A-633E (5)* | 18.40 | 1.95 |

Lenin, 115th Birth Anniv. — A170

1k, Reading Pravda, horiz. 10k, Addressing revolutionaries.

**1985, June 28** ***Perf. 12½***

| | | | | |
|---|---|---|---|---|
| **634** | A170 | 1k multicolored | .35 | .25 |
| **635** | A170 | 2k shown | 2.00 | .30 |
| **636** | A170 | 10k multicolored | 2.00 | .30 |
| | | *Nos. 634-636 (3)* | 4.35 | .85 |

Orchids — A171

50c, Cattleya percivaliana. 1k, Odontoglossum luteo-purpureum. No. 639, Cattleya lueddemanniana. No. 640, Maxillaria sanderiana. 3k, Miltonia vexillaria. 4k, Oncidium varicosum. 8k, Cattleya dowiana aurea.

10k, Catasetum fimbriatum.

**1985, July 5** ***Perf. 13***

| | | | | |
|---|---|---|---|---|
| **637** | A171 | 50c multicolored | .25 | .25 |
| **638** | A171 | 1k multicolored | .25 | .25 |
| **639** | A171 | 2k multicolored | .45 | .25 |
| **640** | A171 | 2k multicolored | .45 | .25 |
| **641** | A171 | 3k multicolored | .70 | .25 |
| **642** | A171 | 4k multicolored | 1.00 | .30 |
| **643** | A171 | 8k multicolored | 2.25 | .65 |
| | | *Nos. 637-643 (7)* | 5.35 | 2.20 |

**Souvenir Sheet**

***Perf. 13½x13***

| | | | | |
|---|---|---|---|---|
| **644** | A171 | 10k multicolored | 2.75 | 1.50 |

ARGENTINA '85, Buenos Aires. No. 644 contains one stamp 32x40mm.

Fauna — A172

2k, Macaca mulatta. 3k, Bos sauveli. 4k, Hystrix leucura, horiz. 5k, Selenarctos thibotanus, horiz. 10k, Manis pentadactyla.

**1985, Aug. 15** *Perf. 13*

| | | | | |
|---|---|---|---|---|
| 645 | A172 | 2k multicolored | .35 | .25 |
| 646 | A172 | 3k multicolored | .55 | .25 |
| 647 | A172 | 4k multicolored | .80 | .30 |
| 648 | A172 | 5k multicolored | 1.00 | .30 |
| 649 | A172 | 10k multicolored | 2.00 | .65 |
| | | *Nos. 645-649 (5)* | 4.70 | 1.75 |

Nos. 645-49 exist imperf.

Apollo-Soyuz Flight, 10th Anniv. — A173

50c, Apollo launch pad, vert. 1k, Soyuz launch pad, vert. No. 652, Apollo approaching Soyuz. No. 653, Soyuz approaching Apollo. 3k, Apollo, astronauts. 4k, Soyuz, cosmonauts. 8k, Docked spacecrafts.

**1985, Sept. 6**

| | | | | |
|---|---|---|---|---|
| 650 | A173 | 50c multicolored | .25 | .25 |
| 651 | A173 | 1k multicolored | .25 | .25 |
| 652 | A173 | 2k multicolored | .40 | .25 |
| 653 | A173 | 2k multicolored | .65 | .25 |
| 654 | A173 | 3k multicolored | .80 | .25 |
| 655 | A173 | 4k multicolored | 1.00 | .30 |
| 656 | A173 | 8k multicolored | 1.60 | .65 |
| | | *Nos. 650-656 (7)* | 4.95 | 2.20 |

Nos. 650-656 exist imperf.

Aircraft A174

**1985, Oct. 25**

| | | | | |
|---|---|---|---|---|
| 657 | A174 | 50c Fiat | .25 | .25 |
| 658 | A174 | 1k Cant z.501 | .25 | .25 |
| 659 | A174 | 2k MF-5 | .40 | .25 |
| 660 | A174 | 3k Macchi Castoldi | .65 | .25 |
| 661 | A174 | 4k Anzani | .80 | .25 |
| 662 | A174 | 5k Ambrosini | 1.00 | .30 |
| 663 | A174 | 6k Piaggio | 1.10 | .35 |
| | | *Nos. 657-663 (7)* | 4.45 | 1.90 |

**Souvenir Sheet**

*Perf. 13x13½*

| | | | | |
|---|---|---|---|---|
| 664 | A174 | 10k MF-4 | 4.50 | 2.40 |

ITALIA '85, Rome. No. 664 contains one stamp 40x32mm and also exists imperf.
Nos. 657-663 exist imperf.

Miniature Sheet

Columbus's Fleet — A175

**1985, Oct. 25** *Perf. 13*

| | | | | |
|---|---|---|---|---|
| 665 | A175 | Sheet of 5 + 4 labels | 15.00 | 7.50 |
| *a.* | | 1k Pinta | .50 | .25 |
| *b.* | | 2k Nina | .75 | .25 |
| *c.* | | 3k Santa Maria | 1.25 | .30 |
| *d.* | | 4k Columbus | 1.50 | .40 |
| *e.* | | 5k Map of 1st voyage | 2.00 | 1.50 |

ITALIA '85.

UN, 40th Anniv. — A176

**1985, Oct.**

| | | | | |
|---|---|---|---|---|
| 666 | A176 | 2k UN and natl. flag | .55 | .25 |
| 667 | A176 | 3k Coats of arms | .80 | .30 |
| 668 | A176 | 10k Map, globe | 2.50 | 1.00 |
| | | *Nos. 666-668 (3)* | 3.85 | 1.55 |

Health — A177

1k, Mother feeding child. 3k, Immunization, horiz. 4k, Hospital care, horiz. 10k, Breast-feeding.

**1985, Nov. 15**

| | | | | |
|---|---|---|---|---|
| 669 | A177 | 1k multicolored | .40 | .25 |
| 670 | A177 | 3k multicolored | .80 | .25 |
| 671 | A177 | 4k multicolored | .95 | .30 |
| 672 | A177 | 10k multicolored | 2.00 | .80 |
| | | *Nos. 669-672 (4)* | 4.15 | 1.60 |

10th Anniv. of the Republic A178

**1985, Dec. 2**

| | | | | |
|---|---|---|---|---|
| 673 | A178 | 3k shown | .65 | .25 |
| 674 | A178 | 10k multi, diff. | 2.50 | 1.00 |

People's Revolutionary Party, 30th Anniv. — A179

**1985, Dec. 30**

| | | | | |
|---|---|---|---|---|
| 675 | A179 | 2k shown | .95 | .25 |
| 676 | A179 | 8k multi, diff. | 2.50 | .65 |

**Nos. 276, 286, 289, 291-292, 297, 299-300, 305, 308-309, 319 Overprinted in Red**

**Methods and Perfs As Before**

**1985**

| | | | | |
|---|---|---|---|---|
| 676A | A102 | 40k multi | 40.00 | 40.00 |
| 676B | A98 | 50k multi | 40.00 | 40.00 |
| 676C | A99 | 50k multi | 100.00 | 100.00 |
| 676D | A107 | 70k multi | 40.00 | 40.00 |
| 676E | A105 | 80k multi | 50.00 | 50.00 |
| 676F | A100 | 100k multi | 120.00 | 120.00 |
| 676G | A105 | 100k multi | 50.00 | 50.00 |
| 676H | A96 | 200k org & multi | 110.00 | 110.00 |
| 676I | A100 | 250k multi | 150.00 | 150.00 |
| 676J | A101 | 250k vio & blk | 170.00 | 170.00 |
| 676K | A104 | 250k multi | 120.00 | 120.00 |
| 676L | A102 | 300k multi | 120.00 | 120.00 |
| | | *Nos. 676A-676L (12)* | 1,110. | 1,110. |

Overprint varieties exist. An inverted "8" exists in 676A. Inverted overprints exist on 676B and 676K. An overprint reading "1895" instead of "1985" exists both upright and inverted on 676B.

1986 World Cup Soccer Championships, Mexico — A180

Various match scenes.

**1986, Jan. 20**

| | | | | |
|---|---|---|---|---|
| 677 | A180 | 50c multicolored | .25 | .25 |
| 678 | A180 | 1k multi, diff. | .25 | .25 |
| 679 | A180 | 2k multi, diff. | .40 | .25 |
| 680 | A180 | 3k multi, diff. | .50 | .25 |
| 681 | A180 | 4k multi, diff. | .70 | .25 |
| 682 | A180 | 5k multi, diff. | .80 | .30 |
| 683 | A180 | 6k multi, diff. | 1.10 | .40 |
| | | *Nos. 677-683 (7)* | 4.00 | 1.95 |

**Souvenir Sheet**

*Perf. 13x13½*

| | | | | |
|---|---|---|---|---|
| 684 | A180 | 10k multi, diff. | 2.00 | .90 |

No. 684 contains one stamp 40x32mm.

27th Congress of the Communist Party of the Soviet Union A180a

4k, Cosmonaut, spacecraft. 20k, Lenin.

**1986, Jan.** **Litho.** *Perf. 12x12½*

| | | | | |
|---|---|---|---|---|
| 684A | A180a | 4k multicolored | 2.50 | .30 |
| 684B | A180a | 20k multicolored | 7.50 | 1.00 |

Flowering Plants — A181

50c, Pelargonium grandiflorum. 1k, Aquilegia vulgaris. 2k, Fuchsia globosa. 3k, Crocus aureus. 4k, Althaea rosea. 5k, Gladiolus purpureo. 6k, Hyacinthus orientalis.

**1986, Feb. 28** *Perf. 13*

| | | | | |
|---|---|---|---|---|
| 685 | A181 | 50c multicolored | .25 | .25 |
| 686 | A181 | 1k multicolored | .25 | .25 |
| 687 | A181 | 2k multicolored | .45 | .25 |
| 688 | A181 | 3k multicolored | .65 | .25 |
| 689 | A181 | 4k multicolored | .80 | .30 |
| 690 | A181 | 5k multicolored | 1.00 | .40 |
| 691 | A181 | 6k multicolored | 1.25 | .55 |
| | | *Nos. 685-691 (7)* | 4.65 | 2.25 |

Butterflies A182

50c, Aporia hippia. 1k, Euthalia irrubescens. 2k, Japonica lutea. 3k, Pratapa ctesia. 4k, Kallina inachus. 5k, Ixias pyrene. 6k, Parantica sita.

**1986, Mar. 30**

| | | | | |
|---|---|---|---|---|
| 692 | A182 | 50c multicolored | .25 | .25 |
| 693 | A182 | 1k multicolored | .25 | .25 |
| 694 | A182 | 2k multicolored | .45 | .25 |
| 695 | A182 | 3k multicolored | .65 | .25 |
| 696 | A182 | 4k multicolored | .80 | .30 |
| 697 | A182 | 5k multicolored | 1.00 | .40 |
| 698 | A182 | 6k multicolored | 1.25 | .55 |
| | | *Nos. 692-698 (7)* | 4.65 | 2.25 |

A183

First Man in Space, 25th Anniv. — A184

Designs: 50c, Launch, Baikonur Space Center, vert. 1k, Interkosmos communications satellite, vert. 2k, Salyut space station. 3k, Yuri Gagarin, Sputnik 1 disengaging stage. 4k, Luna 3, the Moon, vert. 5k, Leonov on first space walk, vert. 6k, Luna 16 lifting off Moon, vert. 10k, Spacecrafts docking.

**1986, Apr. 12**

| | | | | |
|---|---|---|---|---|
| 699 | A183 | 50c multicolored | .25 | .25 |
| 700 | A183 | 1k multicolored | .25 | .25 |
| 701 | A183 | 2k multicolored | .40 | .25 |
| 702 | A183 | 3k multicolored | .65 | .25 |
| 703 | A183 | 4k multicolored | .80 | .25 |
| 704 | A183 | 5k multicolored | 1.00 | .40 |
| 705 | A183 | 6k multicolored | 1.10 | .50 |
| | | *Nos. 699-705 (7)* | 4.45 | 2.15 |

**Souvenir Sheet**

*Perf. 13x13½*

| | | | | |
|---|---|---|---|---|
| 706 | A184 | 10k multicolored | 2.50 | 1.00 |

No. 706 exists imperf.

Fauna — A185

50c, Giraffa camelopardalis. 1k, Panthera leo. 2k, Loxodonta africana africana. 3k, Macropus rufus. 4k, Gymnobelideus leadbeateri. 5k, Phoenicopterus ruber. 6k, Ailuropoda melanoleucus.
10k, Bison, vert.

**1986, May 22** *Perf. 12½x13, 13x12½*

| | | | | |
|---|---|---|---|---|
| 707 | A185 | 50c multicolored | .25 | .25 |
| 708 | A185 | 1k multicolored | .25 | .25 |
| 709 | A185 | 2k multicolored | .40 | .25 |
| 710 | A185 | 3k multicolored | .70 | .25 |
| 711 | A185 | 4k multicolored | 1.00 | .25 |

**712** A185 5k multicolored 1.25 .30
**713** A185 6k multicolored 1.50 .55
*Nos. 707-713 (7)* 5.35 2.10

**Souvenir Sheet**

***Perf. 13½x13***

**714** A185 10k multicolored 3.00 1.50

Nos. 707-712 vert.
No. 714 has the Ameripex '86 stamp exhibition logo in the margin.

Pheasants — A187

50c, Argusianus argus. 1k, Cennaeus nycthemerus. 2k, Phasianus colchicus. 3k, Chrysolophus amherstiae. 4k, Symaticus reevesii. 5k, Chrysolophus pictus. 6k, Syrmaticus soemmerringii.

**1986, June 29** ***Perf. 12½x13***

**715** A187 50c multicolored .25 .25
**716** A187 1k multicolored .25 .25
**717** A187 2k multicolored .45 .25
**718** A187 3k multicolored .60 .25
**719** A187 4k multicolored .80 .25
**720** A187 5k multicolored 1.00 .30
**721** A187 6k multicolored 1.25 .40
*Nos. 715-721 (7)* 4.60 1.95

Snakes — A188

No. 722, Elaphe guttata. No. 723, Thalerophis richardi. No. 724, Lampropeltis doliata annulata. No. 725, Diadophis amabilis. No. 726, Boiga dendrophila. No. 727, Python molurus. No. 728, Naja naja.

**1986, July 21** ***Perf. 12½x13, 13x12½***

**722** A188 50c multicolored .25 .25
**723** A188 1k multicolored .30 .25
**724** A188 1k multicolored .35 .25
**725** A188 2k multicolored .40 .25
**726** A188 4k multicolored .70 .25
**727** A188 5k multicolored 1.00 .30
**728** A188 8k multicolored 1.25 .40
*Nos. 722-728 (7)* 4.25 1.95

Nos. 722-723 and 728 vert.

Halley's Comet — A189

50c, Acropolis, Athens. #730a, 1k, Bayeux Tapestry. #730b, 2k, Edmond Halley. #731a, 3k, Vega space probe. #731b, 4k, Galileo. #732a, 5k, Comet. #732b, 6k, Giotto probe.

**1986, Aug. 22** ***Perf. 12½x13***

**729** A189 50c multi .25 .25
**730** A189 Pair, #a.-b. .75 .40
**731** A189 Pair, #a.-b. 1.25 .50
**732** A189 Pair, #a.-b. 2.25 .70
*Nos. 729-732 (4)* 4.50 1.85

**Souvenir Sheet**

***Perf. 13x13½***

**733** A189 10k Comet, diff. 2.50 1.25

Nos. 730-732 printed in continuous designs. Sizes of Nos. 730a, 731a, 732a: 46x25mm; Nos. 730b, 731b, 732b; 23x25mm. No. 733 contains one 40x32mm stamp.

Dogs — A190

50c, Keeshond. 1k, Elkhound. 2k, Bernese. 3k, Pointing griffon. 4k, Sheep dog (border collie). 5k, Irish water spaniel. 6k, Briard.
10k, Brittany spaniels.

**1986, Aug. 28** ***Perf. 13***

**737** A190 50c multicolored .25 .25
**738** A190 1k multicolored .25 .25
**739** A190 2k multicolored .45 .25
**740** A190 3k multicolored .65 .25
**741** A190 4k multicolored .85 .25
**742** A190 5k multicolored 1.00 .30
**743** A190 6k multicolored 1.25 .55
*Nos. 737-743 (7)* 4.70 2.10

**Souvenir Sheet**

***Perf. 13x13½***

**744** A190 10k multicolored 2.10 1.10

STOCKHOLMIA '86. Nos. 738-743 horiz. No. 744 contains one 40x32mm stamp. Nos. 737-743 exist imprf.

Cacti — A191

Designs: 50c, Mammillaria matudae. 1k, Mammillaria theresae. 2k, Ariocarpus trigonus. 3k, Notocactus crassigibbus. 4k, Astrophytum asterias hybridum. 5k, Melocactus manzanus. 6k, Astrophytum ornatum hybridum.

**1986, Sept. 28** ***Perf. 13***

**745** A191 50c multicolored .25 .25
**746** A191 1k multicolored .25 .25
**747** A191 2k multicolored .40 .25
**748** A191 3k multicolored .65 .25
**749** A191 4k multicolored .80 .25
**750** A191 5k multicolored 1.00 .30
**751** A191 6k multicolored 1.10 .40
*Nos. 745-751 (7)* 4.45 1.95

Nos. 745-751 exist imprf.

Intl. Peace Year — A192

3k, Natl, arms, dove, globe. 5k, Dove, shattered bomb. 10k, Emblem held aloft.

**1986, Oct. 24**

**752** A192 3k multicolored .75 .25
**753** A192 5k multicolored 1.10 .40
**754** A192 10k multicolored 2.25 1.00
*Nos. 752-754 (3)* 4.10 1.65

UNESCO Programs in Laos — A193

3k, Vat Phu Champasak ruins. 4k, Satellite dish, map, globe. 9k, Laotians learning to read, horiz.

**1986, Nov. 4**

**755** A193 3k multicolored .70 .25
**756** A193 4k multicolored 1.00 .30
**757** A193 9k multicolored 1.75 .65
*Nos. 755-757 (3)* 3.45 1.20

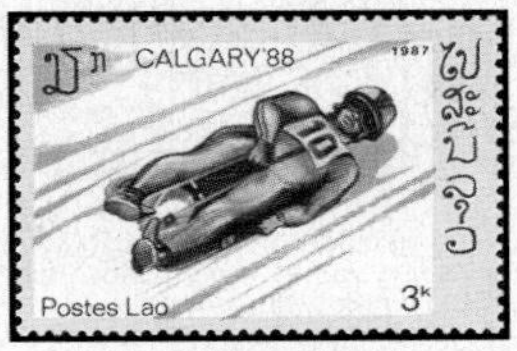


1988 Winter Olympics, Calgary — A194

**1987, Jan. 14**

**758** A194 50c Speed skating .25 .25
**759** A194 1k Biathlon .25 .25
**760** A194 2k Pairs figure skating .40 .25
**761** A194 3k Luge .60 .25
**762** A194 4k 4-Man bobsled .75 .25
**763** A194 5k Ice hockey 1.00 .30
**764** A194 6k Ski jumping 1.10 .40
*Nos. 758-764 (7)* 4.35 1.95

**Souvenir Sheet**

***Perf. 13½x13***

**765** A194 10k Slalom 2.25 1.10

Nos. 758-760 vert. No. 765 contains one stamp 32x40mm.

1988 Summer Olympics, Seoul — A195

50c, Women's gymnastics. 1k, Women's discus. 2k, Running. 3k, Equestrian. 4k, Women's javelin. 5k, High jump. 6k, Wrestling.
10k, Runners leaving start.

**1987, Feb. 2** ***Perf. 12½x13, 13x13½***

**766** A195 50c multicolored .25 .25
**767** A195 1k multicolored .25 .25
**768** A195 2k multicolored .40 .25
**769** A195 3k multicolored .65 .25
**770** A195 4k multicolored .75 .25
**771** A195 5k multicolored 1.00 .30
**772** A195 6k multicolored 1.10 .40
*Nos. 766-772 (7)* 4.40 1.95

**Souvenir Sheet**

***Perf. 12½***

**773** A195 10k multicolored 2.00 1.00

Nos. 766, 768, 770 and 772 vert. No. 773 contains one 40x32mm stamp.
Nos. 766-772 exist imperf.

Dogs A196

50c, Great Dane. 1k, Labrador retriever. 2k, St. Bernard. 3k, Schippercke. 4k, Alsatian (German shepherd). 5k, Beagle. 6k, Spaniel.

**1987, Mar. 5** ***Perf. 12½x13***

**774** A196 50c multicolored .25 .25
**775** A196 1k multicolored .25 .25
**776** A196 2k multicolored .40 .25
**777** A196 3k multicolored .65 .25
**778** A196 4k multicolored .75 .25
**779** A196 5k multicolored 1.00 .30
**780** A196 6k multicolored 1.25 .55
*Nos. 774-780 (7)* 4.55 2.10

Space Flight, 30th Anniv. A197

**1987, Apr. 12** ***Perf. 13***

**781** A197 50c Sputnik 1 .25 .25
**782** A197 1k Sputnik 2 .25 .25
**783** A197 2k Cosmos 87 .40 .25
**784** A197 3k Cosmos .50 .25
**785** A197 4k Mars .65 .25
**786** A197 5k Luna 1 .80 .30
**787** A197 9k Luna 3, vert. 1.25 .50
*Nos. 781-787 (7)* 4.10 2.05

Packet Ships and Stampless Packet Letters — A198

Canada No. 282 — A199

50c, "Montreal". 1k, "Paid Montreal". 2k, "Paid" and "Montreal Nov 24". 3k, "Williamsbvrg" and "Forwarded". 4k, "Montreal Fe 18 1844". 5k, "Paid" and "Montreal Jy 10 1848". 6k, "Paid" and "Montreal Paid Ap 16 1861 Canada".

**1987, May 12**

**788** A198 50c multicolored .25 .25
**789** A198 1k multicolored .25 .25
**790** A198 2k multicolored .35 .25
**791** A198 3k multicolored .55 .25
**792** A198 4k multicolored .75 .25
**793** A198 5k multicolored .85 .30
**794** A198 6k multicolored 1.10 .40
*Nos. 788-794 (7)* 4.10 1.95

**Souvenir Sheet**

***Perf. 12½***

**795** A199 10k multicolored 2.50 1.25

CAPEX '87.

Orchids — A200

3k, Vanda teres. 7k, Laeliocattleya. 10k, Paphiopedilum hibrido. 39k, Sobralia. 44k, Paphiopedilum hibrido, diff. 47k, Paphiopedilum hibrido, diff. 50k, Cattleya trianaei.
95k, Vanda tricolor.

**1987, Aug. 10** **Litho.** ***Perf. 13***

**796** A200 3k multicolored .25 .25
**796A** A200 7k multicolored .25 .25
**796B** A200 10k multicolored .40 .25
**796C** A200 39k multicolored .75 .25
**796D** A200 44k multicolored .80 .30
**796E** A200 47k multicolored 1.00 .40
**796F** A200 50k multicolored 1.10 .40
*Nos. 796-796F (7)* 4.55 2.10

**Souvenir Sheet**

***Perf. 12½***

**796G** A200 95k multicolored 2.25 1.10

No. 796G contains one 32x40mm stamp.
Nos. 796, 796A-796G exist imperf.

Automobiles — A201

**1987, July 2 Litho. *Perf. 12½***

| | | | | | |
|---|---|---|---|---|---|
| **797** | A201 | 50c | Toyota 480 | .25 | .25 |
| **798** | A201 | 1k | Alfa 33 | .25 | .25 |
| **799** | A201 | 2k | Ford Fiesta | .40 | .25 |
| **800** | A201 | 3k | Datsun | .65 | .25 |
| **801** | A201 | 4k | Vauxhall Cavalier | .80 | .25 |
| **802** | A201 | 5k | Renault 5 | 1.00 | .30 |
| **803** | A201 | 6k | Rover-800 | 1.25 | .55 |
| | | | *Nos. 797-803 (7)* | 4.60 | 2.10 |

**Miniature Sheet**

***Perf. 13***

| | | | | | |
|---|---|---|---|---|---|
| **804** | A201 | 10k | Talbot | 2.10 | 1.00 |

HAFNIA '87, Denmark A202

Various Indian elephants.

**1987, Sept. 2 *Perf. 13***

| | | | | | |
|---|---|---|---|---|---|
| **805** | A202 | 50c | Adult, calf | .25 | .25 |
| **806** | A202 | 1k | Two adults, calf | .25 | .25 |
| **807** | A202 | 2k | Adult eating grass | .40 | .25 |
| **808** | A202 | 3k | Adult, diff. | .60 | .25 |
| **809** | A202 | 4k | Adult, calf drinking | .75 | .25 |
| **810** | A202 | 5k | Adult, diff. | .90 | .30 |
| **811** | A202 | 6k | Adult, vert. | 1.10 | .40 |
| | | | *Nos. 805-811 (7)* | 4.25 | 1.95 |

**Souvenir Sheet**

| | | | | | |
|---|---|---|---|---|---|
| **812** | A202 | 10k | Herd, diff. | 2.25 | 1.10 |

No. 812 contains one stamp 40x32mm.

Horses — A203

***Perf. 13x12½, 12½x13***

**1987, June 3 Litho.**

| | | | | | |
|---|---|---|---|---|---|
| **813** | A203 | 50c | multicolored | .25 | .25 |
| **814** | A203 | 1k | multi, diff. | .25 | .25 |
| **815** | A203 | 2k | multi, diff. | .40 | .25 |
| **816** | A203 | 3k | multi, diff. | .60 | .25 |
| **817** | A203 | 4k | multi, diff. | .75 | .25 |
| **818** | A203 | 5k | multi, diff. | 1.00 | .30 |
| **819** | A203 | 6k | multi, diff. | 1.10 | .40 |
| | | | *Nos. 813-819 (7)* | 4.35 | 1.95 |

Nos. 814-819 vert.

Fish A204

Designs: 3k, Botia macracantha. 7k, Oxymocanthus longirostris. 10k, Adioryx caudimaculatus. 39k, Synchiropus splendidus. 44k, Cephalopolis miniatus. 47k, Dendrochirus zebra. 50k, Pomacantus semicirculatus.

**1987, Oct. 14 Litho. *Perf. 13x12½***

| | | | | | |
|---|---|---|---|---|---|
| **820** | A204 | 3k | multicolored | .25 | .25 |
| **821** | A204 | 7k | multicolored | .25 | .25 |
| **822** | A204 | 10k | multicolored | .40 | .25 |
| **823** | A204 | 39k | multicolored | .70 | .25 |
| **824** | A204 | 44k | multicolored | .80 | .30 |
| **825** | A204 | 47k | multicolored | 1.00 | .40 |
| **826** | A204 | 50k | multicolored | 1.10 | .40 |
| | | | *Nos. 820-826 (7)* | 4.50 | 2.10 |

World Food Day A205

1k, Tending crops. 3k, Harvesting corn, vert. 5k, Harvesting wheat. 63k, Youths, fish, vert. 142k, Tending pigs, chickens.

**1987, Oct. 16 *Perf. 13***

| | | | | | |
|---|---|---|---|---|---|
| **827** | A205 | 1k | multicolored | .25 | .25 |
| **828** | A205 | 3k | multicolored | .25 | .25 |
| **829** | A205 | 5k | multicolored | .30 | .25 |
| **830** | A205 | 63k | multicolored | 1.25 | .50 |
| **831** | A205 | 142k | multicolored | 2.40 | 1.00 |
| | | | *Nos. 827-831 (5)* | 4.45 | 2.25 |

Cultivation of Rice in Mountainous Regions — A206

**1987, Nov. 9 *Perf. 13***

| | | | | | |
|---|---|---|---|---|---|
| **832** | A206 | 64k | Tilling soil | 1.25 | .30 |
| **833** | A206 | 100k | Rice paddy | 1.90 | .80 |

October Revolution, Russia, 70th Anniv. A207

Paintings: 1k, Wounded soldier on battlefield. 2k, Mother and child. 4k, Storming the Winter Palace. 8k, Lenin and revolutionaries. 10k, Rebuilding Red Square.

**1987, Nov. *Perf. 12x12½***

| | | | | | |
|---|---|---|---|---|---|
| **834** | A207 | 1k | multicolored | .25 | .25 |
| **835** | A207 | 2k | multicolored | .40 | .25 |
| **836** | A207 | 4k | multicolored | .70 | .25 |
| **837** | A207 | 8k | multicolored | 1.25 | .50 |
| **838** | A207 | 10k | multicolored | 1.75 | .65 |
| | | | *Nos. 834-838 (5)* | 4.35 | 1.90 |

For surcharges, see Nos. 1882-1883.

Women Wearing Regional Costumes A208

**1987, Dec. 2**

| | | | | | |
|---|---|---|---|---|---|
| **839** | A208 | 7k | Mountain | .25 | .25 |
| **840** | A208 | 38k | Urban | .80 | .25 |
| **841** | A208 | 144k | Mountain, diff. | 2.75 | 1.10 |
| | | | *Nos. 839-841 (3)* | 3.80 | 1.60 |

Nos. 839-841 exist imperf.

A209

1988 Winter Olympics, Calgary — A210

**1988, Jan.10 *Perf. 13x12½***

| | | | | | |
|---|---|---|---|---|---|
| **842** | A209 | 1k | Bobsled | .25 | .25 |
| **843** | A209 | 4k | Biathlon | .25 | .25 |
| **844** | A209 | 20k | Skiing | .45 | .25 |
| **845** | A209 | 42k | Ice hockey | .75 | .30 |
| **846** | A209 | 63k | Speed skating | 1.10 | .50 |
| **847** | A209 | 70k | Slalom | 1.25 | .55 |
| | | | *Nos. 842-847 (6)* | 4.05 | 2.10 |

**Souvenir Sheet**

***Perf. 13***

| | | | | | |
|---|---|---|---|---|---|
| **848** | A210 | 95k | Slalom, diff. | 2.25 | 1.10 |

No. 848 contains one stamp 40x32mm.

ESSEN '88 — A211

Locomotives: 6k, Sans Pareil, vert. 15k, Rocket, vert. 20k, Royal George. 25k, Trevithick. 30k, Novelty. 100k, Tom Thumb. 95k, Locomotion.

**1988 *Perf. 12½x13, 13x12½***

| | | | | | |
|---|---|---|---|---|---|
| **849** | A211 | 6k | multicolored | .25 | .25 |
| **850** | A211 | 15k | multicolored | .25 | .25 |
| **851** | A211 | 20k | multicolored | .45 | .25 |
| **852** | A211 | 25k | multicolored | .55 | .25 |
| **853** | A211 | 30k | multicolored | .65 | .25 |
| **854** | A211 | 100k | multicolored | 1.90 | .80 |
| | | | *Nos. 849-854 (6)* | 4.05 | 2.05 |

**Souvenir Sheet**

***Perf. 13***

| | | | | | |
|---|---|---|---|---|---|
| **855** | A211 | 95k | multicolored | 2.25 | 1.10 |

No. 855 contains one stamp 40x32mm.
Nos. 849-854 exist imperf.

Intl. Year of Shelter for the Homeless — A212

1k, Building frame of house. 27k, Cutting lumber. 46k, Completed house. 70k, Community.

**1988 Litho. *Perf. 13***

| | | | | | |
|---|---|---|---|---|---|
| **856** | A212 | 1k | multicolored | .25 | .25 |
| **857** | A212 | 27k | multicolored | .55 | .25 |
| **858** | A212 | 46k | multicolored | 1.00 | .30 |
| **859** | A212 | 70k | multicolored | 1.60 | .65 |
| | | | *Nos. 856-859 (4)* | 3.40 | 1.45 |

Dinosaurs — A213

3k, Tyrannosaurus. 7k, Ceratosaurus nasicornis, vert. 39k, Iguanodon bernissartensis, vert. 44k, Scolosaurus, vert. 47k, Phororhacus, vert. 50k, Trachodon.
95k, Pteranodon.

***Perf. 13x12½, 12½x13***

**1988, Mar. 3 Litho.**

| | | | | | |
|---|---|---|---|---|---|
| **860** | A213 | 3k | multicolored | .25 | .25 |
| **861** | A213 | 7k | multicolored | .25 | .25 |
| **862** | A213 | 39k | multicolored | .75 | .25 |
| **863** | A213 | 44k | multicolored | .80 | .40 |
| **864** | A213 | 47k | multicolored | 1.00 | .40 |
| **865** | A213 | 50k | multicolored | 1.10 | .40 |
| | | | *Nos. 860-865 (6)* | 4.15 | 1.95 |

**Souvenir Sheet**

***Perf. 12½***

| | | | | | |
|---|---|---|---|---|---|
| **866** | A213 | 95k | multicolored | 2.25 | 1.10 |

JUVALUX '88. Nos. 861-864 vert.
Identifications on Nos. 860 and No. 865 are switched.
No. 866 contains one 40x32mm stamp.

WHO, 40th Anniv. A214

5k, Students, teacher. 27k, Pest control. 164k, Public water supply, vert.

**1988, Apr. 8 *Perf. 12½***

| | | | | | |
|---|---|---|---|---|---|
| **867** | A214 | 5k | multicolored | .25 | .25 |
| **868** | A214 | 27k | multicolored | .50 | .25 |
| **869** | A214 | 164k | multicolored | 3.00 | 1.25 |
| | | | *Nos. 867-869 (3)* | 3.75 | 1.75 |

Flowers — A215

8k, Plumieria rubra. 9k, Althaea rosea. 15k, Ixora coccinea. 33k, Cassia fistula. 64k, Dahlia coccinea (pink). 69k, Dahlia coccinea (yellow).
95k, Plumieria, Althaea, Ixora.

**1988 *Perf. 13x12½***

| | | | | | |
|---|---|---|---|---|---|
| **870** | A215 | 8k | multicolored | .25 | .25 |
| **871** | A215 | 9k | multicolored | .25 | .25 |
| **872** | A215 | 15k | multicolored | .40 | .25 |
| **873** | A215 | 33k | multicolored | .75 | .25 |
| **874** | A215 | 64k | multicolored | 1.25 | .50 |
| **875** | A215 | 69k | multicolored | 1.50 | .55 |
| | | | *Nos. 870-875 (6)* | 4.40 | 2.05 |

**Souvenir Sheet**

***Perf. 13***

| | | | | | |
|---|---|---|---|---|---|
| **876** | A215 | 95k | multicolored | 2.50 | 1.25 |

FINLANDIA '88. No. 876 contains one 32x40mm stamp.

Birds — A216

6k, Pelargopsis capensis. 10k, Coturnix japonica. 13k, Psittacula roseata. 44k, Treron bicincta. 63k, Pycnonotus melanicterus. 64k, Ducula badia.

**1988** ***Perf. 13***

| | | | | |
|---|---|---|---|---|
| **877** | A216 | 6k multicolored | .25 | .25 |
| **878** | A216 | 10k multicolored | .25 | .25 |
| **879** | A216 | 13k multicolored | .40 | .25 |
| **880** | A216 | 44k multicolored | .85 | .25 |
| **881** | A216 | 63k multicolored | 1.10 | .50 |
| **882** | A216 | 64k multicolored | 1.10 | .55 |
| | | *Nos. 877-882 (6)* | 3.95 | 2.05 |

1988 Summer Olympics, Seoul — A217

2k, Javelin. 5k, Long jump. 10k, Horizontal bar. 12k, Canoeing. 38k, Balance beam. 46k, Fencing. 100k, Wrestling.
95k, Horizontal bar, diff.

**1988** ***Perf. 12½x12***

| | | | | |
|---|---|---|---|---|
| **883** | A217 | 2k multicolored | .25 | .25 |
| **884** | A217 | 5k multicolored | .25 | .25 |
| **885** | A217 | 10k multicolored | .40 | .25 |
| **886** | A217 | 12k multicolored | .50 | .25 |
| **887** | A217 | 38k multicolored | .80 | .25 |
| **888** | A217 | 46k multicolored | 1.00 | .30 |
| **889** | A217 | 100k multicolored | 2.00 | .70 |
| | | *Nos. 883-889 (7)* | 5.20 | 2.25 |

**Souvenir Sheet**

***Perf. 13***

| | | | | |
|---|---|---|---|---|
| **889A** | A217 | 95k multicolored | 2.10 | 1.00 |

No. 889A contains one 40x32mm stamp.
Nos. 883-889 exist imperf.

Decorative Stencils — A218

1k, Scarf. 2k, Pagoda entrance, vert. 3k, Pagoda wall, vert. 25k, Pagoda pillar. 163k, Skirt.

**1988** ***Perf. 13***

| | | | | |
|---|---|---|---|---|
| **890** | A218 | 1k multicolored | .25 | .25 |
| **891** | A218 | 2k multicolored | .25 | .25 |
| **892** | A218 | 3k multicolored | .35 | .25 |
| **893** | A218 | 25k multicolored | .50 | .25 |
| **894** | A218 | 163k multicolored | 3.00 | 1.50 |
| | | *Nos. 890-894 (5)* | 4.35 | 2.50 |

Completion of the 5-Year Plan (1981-85) — A219

20k, Health care. 40k, Literacy. 50k, Irrigation. 100k, Communication, transport.

**1988** **Litho.** ***Perf. 13***

| | | | | |
|---|---|---|---|---|
| **895** | A219 | 20k multicolored | .40 | .25 |
| **896** | A219 | 40k multicolored | .80 | .40 |
| **897** | A219 | 50k multicolored | 1.00 | .55 |
| **898** | A219 | 100k multicolored | 1.75 | 1.00 |
| | | *Nos. 895-898 (4)* | 3.95 | 2.20 |

Intl. Red Cross and Red Crescent Organizations, 125th Annivs. — A220

Designs: 4k, Dove, 3 stylized figures representing mankind, vert. 52k, Giving aid to the handicapped, vert. 144k, Child immunization.

**1988**

| | | | | |
|---|---|---|---|---|
| **899** | A220 | 4k multi | .25 | .25 |
| **900** | A220 | 52k multi | 1.10 | .55 |
| **901** | A220 | 144k multi | 2.75 | 1.50 |
| | | *Nos. 899-901 (3)* | 4.10 | 2.30 |

Chess Champions — A220a

1k, R. Segura. 2k, Adolph Anderssen. 3k, P. Morphy. 6k, W. Steinitz. 7k, E. Lasker. 12k, J.R. Capablanca. 172k, A. Alekhine.

**1988** **Litho.** ***Perf. 13***

| | | | | |
|---|---|---|---|---|
| **901A** | A220a | 1k multicolored | .25 | .25 |
| **901B** | A220a | 2k multicolored | .25 | .25 |
| **901C** | A220a | 3k multicolored | .25 | .25 |
| **901D** | A220a | 6k multicolored | .25 | .25 |
| **901E** | A220a | 7k multicolored | .30 | .25 |
| **901F** | A220a | 12k multicolored | .40 | .25 |
| **901G** | A220a | 172k multicolored | 3.00 | 1.10 |
| | | *Nos. 901A-901G (7)* | 4.70 | 2.60 |

Nos. 901C is incorrectly inscribed "Murphy."

1990 World Cup Soccer Championships, Italy — A221

Various plays.

**1989** ***Perf. 13x12½***

| | | | | |
|---|---|---|---|---|
| **902** | A221 | 10k multi | .25 | .25 |
| **903** | A221 | 15k multi, diff. | .25 | .25 |
| **904** | A221 | 20k multi, diff. | .40 | .25 |
| **905** | A221 | 25k multi, diff. | .55 | .25 |
| **906** | A221 | 45k multi, diff. | .80 | .30 |
| **907** | A221 | 105k multi, diff. | 2.00 | .80 |
| | | *Nos. 902-907 (6)* | 4.25 | 2.10 |

**Souvenir Sheet**

***Perf. 13***

| | | | | |
|---|---|---|---|---|
| **907A** | A221 | 95k multi, diff. | 2.10 | 1.10 |

No. 907A contains one 40x32mm stamp.

INDIA '89 A222

Cats.

**1989, Jan. 7** ***Perf. 12½***

| | | | | |
|---|---|---|---|---|
| **908** | A222 | 5k multi | .25 | .25 |
| **909** | A222 | 6k multi, diff. | .25 | .25 |
| **910** | A222 | 10k multi, diff. | .40 | .25 |
| **911** | A222 | 20k multi, diff. | .60 | .25 |
| **912** | A222 | 50k multi, diff. | 1.10 | .40 |
| **913** | A222 | 172k multi, diff. | 3.25 | 1.00 |
| | | *Nos. 908-913 (6)* | 5.85 | 2.40 |

**Souvenir Sheet**

***Perf. 13***

| | | | | |
|---|---|---|---|---|
| **914** | A222 | 95k multi, diff. | 2.10 | 1.00 |

No. 914 contains one 32x40mm stamp.

1992 Winter Olympics, Albertville — A223

Various figure skaters.

**1989, May 1** ***Perf. 13***

| | | | | |
|---|---|---|---|---|
| **915** | A223 | 9k multi, vert. | .25 | .25 |
| **916** | A223 | 10k shown | .25 | .25 |
| **917** | A223 | 15k multi, diff., vert. | .35 | .25 |
| **918** | A223 | 24k multi, diff., vert. | .50 | .25 |
| **919** | A223 | 29k multi, diff., vert. | .65 | .25 |
| **920** | A223 | 114k multi, diff., vert. | 2.00 | 1.00 |
| | | *Nos. 915-920 (6)* | 4.00 | 2.25 |

**Souvenir Sheet**

***Perf. 12½***

| | | | | |
|---|---|---|---|---|
| **921** | A223 | 95k Pairs figure skating | 2.10 | 1.10 |

No. 921 contains one 32x40mm stamp.

People's Army, 40th Anniv. A224

2k, Military school, vert. 3k, Health care. 250k, Ready for combat.

**1989, Jan. 20** ***Perf. 13***

| | | | | |
|---|---|---|---|---|
| **922** | A224 | 1k shown | .25 | .25 |
| **923** | A224 | 2k multicolored | .25 | .25 |
| **924** | A224 | 3k multicolored | .25 | .25 |
| **925** | A224 | 250k multicolored | 6.00 | 1.00 |
| | | *Nos. 922-925 (4)* | 6.75 | 1.75 |

1992 Summer Olympics, Barcelona — A225

5k, Pole vault, vert. 15k, Gymnastic rings, vert. 20k, Cycling. 25k, Boxing. 70k, Archery, vert. 120k, Swimming, vert.
95k, Baseball.

***Perf. 12x12½, 12½x12***

**1989, June 1** **Litho.**

| | | | | |
|---|---|---|---|---|
| **926** | A225 | 5k multicolored | .25 | .25 |
| **927** | A225 | 15k multicolored | .25 | .25 |
| **928** | A225 | 20k multicolored | .30 | .25 |
| **929** | A225 | 25k multicolored | .40 | .30 |
| **930** | A225 | 70k multicolored | 1.10 | .55 |
| **931** | A225 | 120k multicolored | 1.75 | .65 |
| | | *Nos. 926-931 (6)* | 4.05 | 2.25 |

**Souvenir Sheet**

***Perf. 13***

| | | | | |
|---|---|---|---|---|
| **932** | A225 | 95k multicolored | 2.10 | 1.10 |

No. 932 contains one 32x40mm stamp.

PHILEXFRANCE '89 — A226

Paintings by Picasso: 5k, *Beggars by the Edge of the Sea*. 7k, *Maternity*. 8k, *Portrait of Jaime S. Le Bock*. 9k, *Harlequins*. 105k, *Dog with Boy*. 114k, *Girl Balancing on Ball*.
95k *Woman in Hat*.

**1989, July 17** ***Perf. 12½x13***

| | | | | |
|---|---|---|---|---|
| **933** | A226 | 5k multi | .25 | .25 |
| **934** | A226 | 7k multi | .25 | .25 |
| **935** | A226 | 8k multi | .25 | .25 |
| **936** | A226 | 9k multi | .35 | .25 |
| **937** | A226 | 105k multi | 1.75 | .65 |
| **938** | A226 | 114k multi | 2.00 | .80 |
| | | *Nos. 933-938 (6)* | 4.85 | 2.45 |

**Souvenir Sheet**

***Perf. 12½***

| | | | | |
|---|---|---|---|---|
| **939** | A226 | 95k multicolored | 2.10 | 1.10 |

No. 939 contains one 32x40mm stamp.

Cuban Revolution, 30th Anniv. — A227

**1989, Apr. 20** **Litho.** ***Perf. 13***

| | | | | |
|---|---|---|---|---|
| **940** | A227 | 45k shown | 1.10 | .40 |
| **941** | A227 | 50k Flags | 1.25 | .40 |

Fight the Destruction of Forests — A228

4k, Planting saplings. 10k, Fight forest fires. 12k, Do not chop down trees. 200k, Map of woodland.

**1989, Mar. 30** **Litho.** ***Perf. 13***

| | | | | |
|---|---|---|---|---|
| **942** | A228 | 4k multicolored | .25 | .25 |
| **943** | A228 | 10k multicolored | .25 | .25 |
| **944** | A228 | 12k multicolored | .25 | .25 |
| **945** | A228 | 200k multicolored | 3.25 | 1.00 |
| | | *Nos. 942-945 (4)* | 4.00 | 1.75 |

Nos. 944-945 are vert.

Jawaharlal Nehru (1889-1964), Indian Statesman A229

**1989, Nov. 9** **Litho.** ***Perf. 12½***

| | | | | |
|---|---|---|---|---|
| **946** | A229 | 1k multicolored | .25 | .25 |
| **947** | A229 | 60k multi, horiz. | 1.10 | .50 |
| **948** | A229 | 200k multi, diff. | 3.50 | 1.10 |
| | | *Nos. 946-948 (3)* | 4.85 | 1.85 |

Mani Ikara Zapota — A230

No. 950, Psidium guajava. No. 951, Annona sguamosa. No. 952, Durio zibethinus. No. 953, Punica granatum. No. 954, Moridica charautia.

**1989, Sept. 18** *Perf. 12½x13*

| | | | | | |
|---|---|---|---|---|---|
| **949** | A230 | 5k shown | .25 | .25 |
| **950** | A230 | 20k multicolored | .40 | .25 |
| **951** | A230 | 20k multicolored | .40 | .25 |
| **952** | A230 | 30k multicolored | .55 | .25 |
| **953** | A230 | 50k multicolored | .90 | .50 |
| **954** | A230 | 172k multicolored | 3.00 | 1.00 |
| | | *Nos. 949-954 (6)* | 5.50 | 2.50 |

A231

Historic Monuments: No. 955, That Sikhotabong, Khammouane. No. 956, That Dam, Vientiane. No. 957, That Ing Hang, Savannakhet. No. 958, Ho Vay Phra Thatluang, Vientiane.

**1989, Oct. 19** **Litho.** *Perf. 12½*

| | | | | |
|---|---|---|---|---|
| **955** | A231 | 5k multicolored | .25 | .25 |
| **956** | A231 | 15k multicolored | .30 | .25 |
| **957** | A231 | 61k multicolored | 1.10 | .55 |
| **958** | A231 | 161k multicolored | 2.75 | 1.25 |
| | | *Nos. 955-958 (4)* | 4.40 | 2.30 |

1992 Summer Olympics, Barcelona A232

**1990, Mar. 5** **Litho.** *Perf. 12½x13*

| | | | | |
|---|---|---|---|---|
| **959** | A232 | 10k Basketball | .25 | .25 |
| **960** | A232 | 30k Hurdles | .45 | .25 |
| **961** | A232 | 45k High jump | .65 | .25 |
| **962** | A232 | 50k Cycling | .75 | .30 |
| **963** | A232 | 60k Javelin | .90 | .50 |
| **964** | A232 | 90k Tennis | 1.40 | .80 |
| | | *Nos. 959-964 (6)* | 4.40 | 2.35 |

**Souvenir Sheet**

| | | | | |
|---|---|---|---|---|
| **965** | A232 | 95k Rhythmic gymnastics | 2.00 | 1.00 |

Nos. 959-964 exist imperf.

1992 Winter Olympics, Albertville — A233

10k, Speed skating. 25k, Cross country skiing, vert. 30k, Slalom skiing. 35k, Luge. 80k, Ice dancing, vert. 90k, Javelin.
95k, Hockey, vert.

**1990, June 20** *Perf. 13*

| | | | | |
|---|---|---|---|---|
| **966** | A233 | 10k multicolored | .25 | .25 |
| **967** | A233 | 25k multicolored | .40 | .25 |
| **968** | A233 | 30k multicolored | .45 | .25 |
| **969** | A233 | 35k multicolored | .55 | .25 |
| **970** | A233 | 80k multicolored | 1.25 | .55 |
| **971** | A233 | 90k multicolored | 1.40 | .65 |
| | | *Nos. 966-971 (6)* | 4.30 | 2.20 |

**Souvenir Sheet**

| | | | | |
|---|---|---|---|---|
| **972** | A233 | 95k multicolored | 2.00 | 1.00 |

New Zealand Birds A234

Designs: 10k, Prosthemadera novaeseelandie. 15k, Alauda arvensis. 20k, Haemotopus unicolor. 50k, Phalacrocorax carbo. 60k, Demigretta sacra. 100k Apteryx australis mantelli. 95k, Phalacrocorax corunculatus.

**1990, Aug. 24** *Perf. 12½*

| | | | | |
|---|---|---|---|---|
| **973** | A234 | 10k multicolored | .25 | .25 |
| **974** | A234 | 15k multicolored | .35 | .25 |
| **975** | A234 | 20k multicolored | .45 | .25 |
| **976** | A234 | 50k multicolored | .90 | .30 |
| **977** | A234 | 60k multicolored | 1.10 | .50 |
| **978** | A234 | 100k multicolored | 1.90 | .80 |
| | | *Nos. 973-978 (6)* | 4.95 | 2.35 |

**Souvenir Sheet**

| | | | | |
|---|---|---|---|---|
| **979** | A234 | 95k multicolored | 2.25 | 1.10 |

World Stamp Expo, New Zealand '90. No. 979 contains one 32x40mm stamp and also exists imperf.

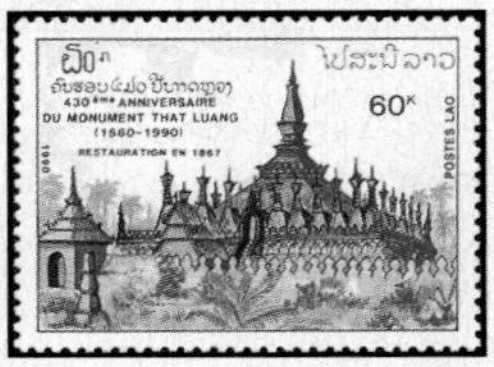


That Luang Temple, 430th Anniv. A235

**1990, July 25** *Perf. 13x12½, 12½x13*

| | | | | |
|---|---|---|---|---|
| **980** | A235 | 60k 1867 | 1.50 | .50 |
| **981** | A235 | 70k 1930 | 1.75 | .65 |
| **982** | A235 | 130k 1990, vert. | 3.25 | 1.25 |
| | | *Nos. 980-982 (3)* | 6.50 | 2.40 |

Ho Chi Minh (1890-1969), Vietnamese Leader — A236

40k, Addressing people. 60k, With Laotian President. 160k, Waving, vert.

**1990, May 11** *Perf. 13*

| | | | | |
|---|---|---|---|---|
| **983** | A236 | 40k multicolored | .90 | .30 |
| **984** | A236 | 60k multicolored | 1.40 | .45 |
| **985** | A236 | 160k multicolored | 3.75 | 1.25 |
| | | *Nos. 983-985 (3)* | 6.05 | 2.00 |

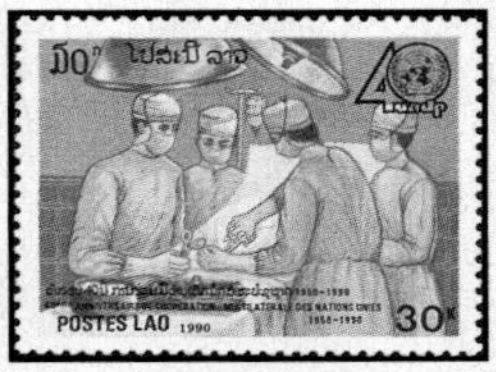


UN Development Program, 40th Anniv. — A237

30k, Surgeons. 45k, Fishermen. 80k, Flight controller, vert. 90k, Power plant.

**1990, Oct. 24** **Litho.** *Perf. 13*

| | | | | |
|---|---|---|---|---|
| **986** | A237 | 30k multicolored | .75 | .25 |
| **987** | A237 | 45k multicolored | 1.25 | .30 |
| **988** | A237 | 80k multicolored | 2.00 | .75 |
| **989** | A237 | 90k multicolored | 2.25 | .90 |
| | | *Nos. 986-989 (4)* | 6.25 | 2.20 |

15th Anniv. of the Republic A238

Designs: 15k, Placing flowers at monument. 20k, Celebratory parade. 80k, Visiting sick. 120k, Women marching with banner.

**1990, Dec. 2** **Litho.** *Perf. 13*

| | | | | |
|---|---|---|---|---|
| **990** | A238 | 15k multicolored | .40 | .25 |
| **991** | A238 | 20k multicolored | .60 | .25 |
| **992** | A238 | 80k multicolored | 2.00 | .90 |
| **993** | A238 | 120k multicolored | 3.00 | 1.25 |
| | | *Nos. 990-993 (4)* | 6.00 | 2.65 |

New Year's Day A239

**1990, Nov. 20**

| | | | | |
|---|---|---|---|---|
| **994** | A239 | 5k shown | .25 | .25 |
| **995** | A239 | 10k Parade | .30 | .25 |
| **996** | A239 | 50k Ceremony | .90 | .40 |

**Size: 40x29mm**

| | | | | |
|---|---|---|---|---|
| **997** | A239 | 150k Ceremomy, diff. | 2.50 | 1.25 |
| | | *Nos. 994-997 (4)* | 3.95 | 2.15 |

World Cup Soccer Championships, Italy — A240

Designs: Various soccer players in action.

**1990** **Litho.** *Perf. 13*

| | | | | |
|---|---|---|---|---|
| **998** | A240 | 10k multicolored | .25 | .25 |
| **999** | A240 | 15k multicolored | .30 | .25 |
| **1000** | A240 | 20k multicolored | .45 | .25 |
| **1001** | A240 | 25k multicolored | .55 | .25 |
| **1002** | A240 | 45k multicolored | .85 | .30 |
| **1003** | A240 | 105k multicolored | 1.90 | .80 |
| | | *Nos. 998-1003 (6)* | 4.30 | 2.10 |

**Souvenir Sheets**

*Perf. 12½*

| | | | | |
|---|---|---|---|---|
| **1004** | A240 | 95k multi, horiz. | 2.00 | 1.00 |

*Perf. 13*

| | | | | |
|---|---|---|---|---|
| **1004A** | A240 | 95k multi | 2.00 | 1.00 |

No. 1004 contains one 39x31mm stamp; No. 1004A one 32x40mm stamp.

Intl. Literacy Year A241

50k, Woman with child, vert. 60k, Monk teaching class. 150k, Two women, man reading.

**1990, Feb. 27** **Litho.** *Perf. 12½*

| | | | | |
|---|---|---|---|---|
| **1005** | A241 | 10k shown | .25 | .25 |
| **1006** | A241 | 50k multicolored | 1.00 | .75 |
| **1007** | A241 | 60k multicolored | 1.25 | .90 |
| **1008** | A241 | 150k multicolored | 3.00 | 1.25 |
| | | *Nos. 1005-1008 (4)* | 5.50 | 3.15 |

Stamp World London '90 — A242

Stamps, modes of mail transport: 15k, Great Britain #1, stagecoach. 20k, US #1, train. 40k, France #3, balloons. 50k, Sardinia #1, post rider. 60k, Indo-China #3, elephant. 95k, Laos #272, jet. 100k, Spain #1, sailing ship.

**1990, Apr. 26** **Litho.** *Perf. 13x12½*

| | | | | |
|---|---|---|---|---|
| **1009** | A242 | 15k multicolored | .25 | .25 |
| **1010** | A242 | 20k multicolroed | .40 | .25 |
| **1011** | A242 | 40k multicolored | .70 | .25 |
| **1012** | A242 | 50k multicolored | 1.00 | .30 |
| **1013** | A242 | 60k multicolored | 1.10 | .50 |
| **1014** | A242 | 100k multicolored | 1.90 | .75 |
| | | *Nos. 1009-1014 (6)* | 5.35 | 2.30 |

**Souvenir Sheet**

*Perf. 13*

| | | | | |
|---|---|---|---|---|
| **1015** | A242 | 95k multicolored | 2.00 | 1.00 |

No. 1015 contains one 40x32mm stamp. Nos. 1009-1014 exist imperf.

Endangered Animals — A242a

10k, Brow-antlered deer. 20k, Gaur. 40k, Wild water buffalo. 45k, Kouprey. 120k, Javan rhinoceros.

**1990, Sept. 15** **Litho.** *Perf. 12½*

| | | | | |
|---|---|---|---|---|
| **1015A** | A242a | 10k multicolored | .25 | .25 |
| **1015B** | A242a | 20k multicolored | .40 | .25 |
| **1015C** | A242a | 40k multicolored | .70 | .25 |
| **1015D** | A242a | 45k multicolored | .75 | .30 |
| **1015E** | A242a | 120k multicolored | 1.75 | 1.00 |
| | | *Nos. 1015A-1015E (5)* | 3.85 | 2.05 |

A243

1992 Olympics, Barcelona and Albertville — A244

No. 1016, 2-man canoe. No. 1017, 1-man kayak. No. 1018, Bobsled, vert. No. 1019, Cross country skiing. No. 1020, Ski jumping. No. 1021, Biathlon. No. 1022, Diving, vert. No. 1023, Sailing, vert. No. 1024, Speed skating. No. 1025, Swimming.

No. 1026, 2-man kayak. No. 1027, Slalom skiing, vert.

***Perf. 12½x12, 12x12½, 13 (A244)***

**1991, Jan. 25**

| | | | | |
|---|---|---|---|---|
| **1016** | A243 | 22k multi | .25 | .25 |
| **1017** | A243 | 32k multi | .30 | .25 |
| **1018** | A244 | 32k multi | .30 | .25 |
| **1019** | A244 | 135k multi | .50 | .25 |
| **1020** | A244 | 250k multi | .85 | .25 |
| **1021** | A244 | 275k multi | 1.00 | .30 |
| **1022** | A243 | 285k multi | 1.00 | .30 |
| **1023** | A243 | 330k multi | 1.20 | .35 |
| **1024** | A244 | 900k multi | 2.75 | 1.00 |
| **1025** | A243 | 1000k multi | 2.50 | 1.00 |
| | | *Nos. 1016-1025 (10)* | 10.65 | 4.20 |

### Souvenir Sheets
***Perf. 12½, 13½x13***

| | | | | | |
|---|---|---|---|---|---|
| **1026** | A243 | 700k | multi | 2.75 | 1.00 |
| **1027** | A244 | 700k | multi | 2.75 | 1.00 |

No. 1026 contains one 40x32mm stamp. No. 1027 contains one 32x40mm stamp.

Tourism — A245

Designs: 155k, Rapids, Champassak. 220k, Vangvieng. 235k, Waterfalls, Saravane, vert. 1000k Plain of Jars, Xieng Khouang, vert.

**1991** ***Perf. 13x12½, 12½x13***

| | | | | | |
|---|---|---|---|---|---|
| **1028** | A245 | 155k | multicolored | .55 | .25 |
| **1029** | A245 | 220k | multicolored | .80 | .30 |
| **1030** | A245 | 235k | multicolored | 1.00 | .35 |
| **1031** | A245 | 1000k | multicolored | 3.25 | 1.10 |
| | | | *Nos. 1028-1031 (4)* | 5.60 | 2.00 |

1994 World Cup Soccer Championships — A246

Designs: Various players in action.

**1991** **Litho.** ***Perf. 13***

| | | | | | |
|---|---|---|---|---|---|
| **1032** | A246 | 32k | multicolored | .25 | .25 |
| **1033** | A246 | 330k | multicolored | .75 | .35 |
| **1034** | A246 | 340k | multi, vert. | .85 | .40 |
| **1035** | A246 | 400k | multicolored | 1.00 | .45 |
| **1036** | A246 | 500k | multicolored | 1.25 | .65 |
| | | | *Nos. 1032-1036 (5)* | 4.10 | 2.10 |

### Souvenir Sheet
***Perf. 13½x13***

| | | | | | |
|---|---|---|---|---|---|
| **1037** | A246 | 700k | multi, vert. | 2.00 | 1.00 |

No. 1037 contains one 32x40mm stamp.

Espamer '91, Buenos Aires — A247

25k, Mallard 4-4-2. 32k, Pacific 231 4-6-2. 285k, American style 4-8-4. 650k, Canadian Pacific 4-6-2. 750k, Beyer-Garrant 4-8-2 2-8-4. 700k, Inter-city diesel.

**1991, June 30** **Litho.** ***Perf. 12½x12***

| | | | | | |
|---|---|---|---|---|---|
| **1038** | A247 | 25k | multicolored | .25 | .25 |
| **1039** | A247 | 32k | multicolored | .25 | .25 |
| **1040** | A247 | 285k | multicolored | .90 | .35 |
| **1041** | A247 | 650k | multicolored | 2.00 | .75 |
| **1042** | A247 | 750k | multicolored | 2.25 | 1.10 |
| | | | *Nos. 1038-1042 (5)* | 5.65 | 2.70 |

### Souvenir Sheet
***Perf. 12½***

| | | | | | |
|---|---|---|---|---|---|
| **1043** | A247 | 700k | multicolored | 2.00 | 1.00 |

Espamer '91, Buenos Aires. No. 1039 does not show denomination or country in Latin characters. Size of Nos. 1038, 1040-1042: 44x28mm.

Musical Celebrations — A248

Designs: 220k, Man playing mong, vert. 275k, Man, woman singing Siphandone, vert. 545k, Man, woman singing Khapngum. 690k, People dancing.

**1991, July 10** **Litho.** ***Perf. 13***

| | | | | | |
|---|---|---|---|---|---|
| **1044** | A248 | 20k | multicolored | .25 | .25 |
| **1045** | A248 | 220k | multicolored | .55 | .25 |
| **1046** | A248 | 275k | multicolored | .75 | .30 |
| **1047** | A248 | 545k | multicolored | 1.25 | .65 |
| **1048** | A248 | 690k | multicolored | 1.75 | 1.00 |
| | | | *Nos. 1044-1048 (5)* | 4.55 | 2.45 |

Butterflies — A248a

55k, Sasakia charonda. 90k, Luendorfia puziloi. 255k, Papilio bianor. 285k, Papilio machaon. 900k, Graphium doson. 700k, Cyrestis thyodamas.

**1991, Oct. 15** **Litho.** ***Perf. 12½x12***

| | | | | | |
|---|---|---|---|---|---|
| **1048A** | A248a | 55k | multicolored | .25 | .25 |
| **1048B** | A248a | 90k | multicolored | .30 | .25 |
| **1048C** | A248a | 255k | multicolored | .90 | .25 |
| **1048D** | A248a | 285k | multicolored | 1.00 | .30 |
| **1048E** | A248a | 900k | multicolored | 2.50 | 1.10 |
| | | | *Nos. 1048A-1048E (5)* | 4.95 | 2.15 |

### Souvenir Sheet
***Perf. 13***

| | | | | | |
|---|---|---|---|---|---|
| **1048F** | A248a | 700k | multicolored | 3.25 | 1.25 |

No. 1048F contains one 40x32mm stamp. Phila Nippon '91.

Arbor Day A249

700k, 6 people planting trees. 800k, Nursery.

**1991, June 1** ***Perf. 12½***

| | | | | | |
|---|---|---|---|---|---|
| **1049** | A249 | 250k | multicolored | .70 | .35 |
| **1050** | A249 | 700k | multicolored | 1.60 | .80 |
| **1051** | A249 | 800k | multicolored | 2.00 | 1.10 |
| | | | *Nos. 1049-1051 (3)* | 4.30 | 2.25 |

1992 Winter Olympics, Albertville A250

***Perf. 12½x12, 12x12½***

**1992, Jan. 12** **Litho.**

| | | | | | |
|---|---|---|---|---|---|
| **1052** | A250 | 200k | Bobsled | .50 | .25 |
| **1053** | A250 | 220k | Skiing | .60 | .25 |
| **1054** | A250 | 250k | Skiing, horiz. | .70 | .25 |
| **1055** | A250 | 500k | Luge | 1.25 | .30 |
| **1056** | A250 | 600k | Figure skater | 1.50 | .80 |
| | | | *Nos. 1052-1056 (5)* | 4.55 | 1.85 |

### Souvenir Sheet
***Perf. 12½***

| | | | | | |
|---|---|---|---|---|---|
| **1057** | A250 | 700k | Speed skater | 2.00 | 1.00 |

No. 1057 contains one 32x40mm stamp.

1992 Summer Olympics, Barcelona A251

**1992, Feb. 21** **Litho.** ***Perf. 12½***

| | | | | | |
|---|---|---|---|---|---|
| **1058** | A251 | 32k | Women's running | .25 | .25 |
| **1059** | A251 | 245k | Baseball | .70 | .25 |
| **1060** | A251 | 275k | Tennis | .80 | .25 |
| **1061** | A251 | 285k | Basketball | .90 | .30 |
| **1062** | A251 | 900k | Boxing, horiz. | 2.25 | 1.00 |
| | | | *Nos. 1058-1062 (5)* | 4.90 | 2.05 |

### Souvenir Sheet

| | | | | | |
|---|---|---|---|---|---|
| **1062A** | A251 | 700k | Diving | 2.00 | 1.00 |

No. 1062A contains one 40x32mm stamp.

World Health Day A252

Designs: 200k, Spraying for mosquitoes. 255k, Campaign against smoking. 330k, Receiving blood donation. 1000k, Immunizing child, vert.

**1992, Apr. 7**

| | | | | | |
|---|---|---|---|---|---|
| **1063** | A252 | 200k | multicolored | .50 | .25 |
| **1064** | A252 | 255k | multicolored | .70 | .30 |
| **1065** | A252 | 330k | multicolored | .90 | .65 |
| **1066** | A252 | 1000k | multicolored | 2.25 | 1.25 |
| | | | *Nos. 1063-1066 (4)* | 4.35 | 2.45 |

A253

Flags, ball and players: 260k, Argentina, Italy. 305k, Germany, Great Britain. 310k, US, World Cup trophy (no players). 350k, Italy, Great Britain. 800k, Germany, Argentina. 700k, Goalie.

**1992, May 1** **Litho.** ***Perf. 13***

| | | | | | |
|---|---|---|---|---|---|
| **1067** | A253 | 260k | multicolored | .60 | .25 |
| **1068** | A253 | 305k | multicolored | .65 | .25 |
| **1069** | A253 | 310k | multicolored | .70 | .30 |
| **1070** | A253 | 350k | multicolored | .80 | .50 |
| **1071** | A253 | 800k | multicolored | 1.90 | 1.00 |
| | | | *Nos. 1067-1071 (5)* | 4.65 | 2.30 |

### Souvenir Sheet
***Perf. 12½***

| | | | | | |
|---|---|---|---|---|---|
| **1072** | A253 | 700k | multicolored | 3.25 | 1.65 |

1994 World Cup Soccer Championships, US.

A254

Children playing: 220k, Playing drum. 285k, Jumping rope, horiz. 330k, Walking on stilts. 400k, Escape from line, horiz.

**1992, Nov. 8** **Litho.** ***Perf. 13***

| | | | | | |
|---|---|---|---|---|---|
| **1073** | A254 | 220k | multi | .85 | .25 |
| **1074** | A254 | 285k | multi | 1.10 | .25 |
| **1075** | A254 | 330k | multi | 1.25 | .30 |
| **1076** | A254 | 400k | multi | 1.60 | .65 |
| | | | *Nos. 1073-1076 (4)* | 4.80 | 1.45 |

For surcharge, see No. 1902.

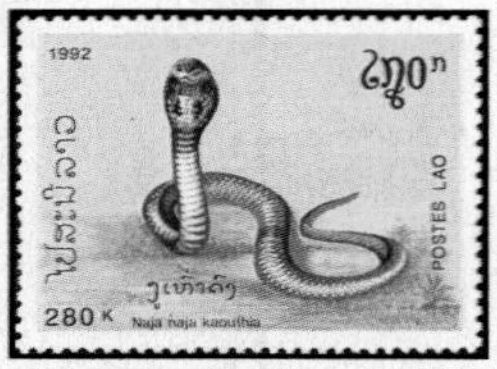

Poisonous Snakes — A255

280k, Naja naja kaouthia. 295k, Naja naja atra. 420k, Trimeresurus wagleri. 700k, Ophiophagus hannah, vert.

***Perf. 12½x13, 13x12½***

**1992, July 10** **Litho.**

| | | | | | |
|---|---|---|---|---|---|
| **1078** | A255 | 280k | multicolored | .85 | .25 |
| **1079** | A255 | 295k | multicolored | .85 | .25 |
| **1080** | A255 | 420k | multicolored | 1.25 | .35 |
| **1081** | A255 | 700k | multicolored | 2.25 | 1.00 |
| | | | *Nos. 1078-1081 (4)* | 5.20 | 1.85 |

Restoration of Wat Phou — A256

Different views of Wat Phou.

***Perf. 13x12½, 12½x13***

**1992, Aug. 22** **Litho.**

| | | | | | |
|---|---|---|---|---|---|
| **1082** | A256 | 185k | multicolored | .50 | .30 |
| **1083** | A256 | 220k | multicolored | .60 | .30 |
| **1084** | A256 | 1200k | multi, horiz. | 3.75 | 1.40 |
| | | | *Nos. 1082-1084 (3)* | 4.85 | 2.00 |

Genoa '92 — A257

Sailing ships and maps by: 100k, Juan Martinez. 300k, Piri Reis, vert. 350k, Paolo del Pozo Toscanelli. 400k, Gabriel de Vallseca. 455k, Juan Martinez, diff. 700k, Juan de la Cosa.

***Perf. 13x12½, 12½x13***

**1992, Sept. 12**

| | | | | | |
|---|---|---|---|---|---|
| **1085** | A257 | 100k | multicolored | .25 | .25 |
| **1086** | A257 | 300k | multicolored | .85 | .25 |
| **1087** | A257 | 350k | multicolored | 1.10 | .25 |
| **1088** | A257 | 400k | multicolored | 1.20 | .50 |
| **1089** | A257 | 455k | multicolored | 1.60 | .65 |
| | | | *Nos. 1085-1089 (5)* | 5.00 | 1.90 |

### Souvenir Sheet
***Perf. 13***

| | | | | | |
|---|---|---|---|---|---|
| **1090** | A257 | 700k | multicolored | 2.75 | 1.00 |

Traditional Costumes of the Montagnards A258

Various costumes.

**1992, Oct. 2 Litho. *Perf. 13***

| | | | | | |
|---|---|---|---|---|---|
| **1091** | A258 | 25k | multicolored | .25 | .25 |
| **1092** | A258 | 55k | multicolored | .25 | .25 |
| **1093** | A258 | 400k | multicolored | 1.25 | .50 |
| **1094** | A258 | 1200k | multicolored | 4.00 | 1.25 |
| | | | *Nos. 1091-1094 (4)* | 5.75 | 2.25 |

A259

UN, UNESCO emblems, stylized faces and: 330k, Drum. 1000k, Traditional flute.

**1991, Nov. 1 Litho. *Perf. 13***

| | | | | | |
|---|---|---|---|---|---|
| **1095** | A259 | 285k | shown | .85 | .35 |
| **1096** | A259 | 330k | multicolored | 1.00 | .35 |
| **1097** | A259 | 1000k | multicolored | 3.00 | 1.25 |
| | | | *Nos. 1095-1097 (3)* | 4.85 | 1.95 |

Cultural Development Decade, 1988-1997.

Apes — A260

**1992, Dec. 22**

| | | | | | |
|---|---|---|---|---|---|
| **1098** | A260 | 10k | Black gibbon | .25 | .25 |
| **1099** | A260 | 100k | Douc langur | .25 | .25 |
| **1100** | A260 | 250k | Pileated gibbon | .75 | .35 |
| **1101** | A260 | 430k | Francois langur | 1.10 | .50 |
| **1102** | A260 | 800k | Pygmy loris | 2.00 | .80 |
| | | | *Nos. 1098-1102 (5)* | 4.35 | 2.15 |

Natl. Customs A261

Designs: 100k, Woman praying before Buddha, vert. 160k, Procession. 1500k, People giving food to monks.

**1992, Dec. 2 *Perf. 12½***

| | | | | | |
|---|---|---|---|---|---|
| **1103** | A261 | 100k | multicolored | .30 | .25 |
| **1104** | A261 | 140k | multicolored | .40 | .25 |
| **1105** | A261 | 160k | multicolored | .45 | .25 |
| **1106** | A261 | 1500k | multicolored | 4.50 | 2.25 |
| | | | *Nos. 1103-1106 (4)* | 5.65 | 3.00 |

First Subway System, 130th Anniv. A262

**1993, Jan. 9 Litho. *Perf. 13***

| | | | | | |
|---|---|---|---|---|---|
| **1107** | A262 | 15k | New York | .25 | .25 |
| **1108** | A262 | 50k | Berlin | .25 | .25 |
| **1109** | A262 | 100k | Paris | .30 | .25 |
| **1110** | A262 | 200k | London | .75 | .35 |
| **1111** | A262 | 900k | Moscow | 2.75 | 1.40 |
| | | | *Nos. 1107-1111 (5)* | 4.30 | 2.50 |

**Souvenir Sheet**

***Perf. 13x13½***

| | | | | | |
|---|---|---|---|---|---|
| **1112** | A262 | 700k | Antique engine, vert. | 3.00 | 1.25 |

No. 1112 contains one 32x40mm stamp.

Frogs A263

55k, Kaloula pulchra. 90k, Xenopus muelleri. 100k, Centrolenella vireovittata, vert. 185k, Bufo marinus. 1200k, Hyla arborea, vert.

**1993, Feb. 1 Litho. *Perf. 12½***

| | | | | | |
|---|---|---|---|---|---|
| **1113** | A263 | 55k | multicolored | .25 | .25 |
| **1114** | A263 | 90k | multicolored | .30 | .25 |
| **1115** | A263 | 100k | multicolored | .35 | .25 |
| **1116** | A263 | 185k | multicolored | .70 | .35 |
| **1117** | A263 | 1200k | multicolored | 3.50 | 1.25 |
| | | | *Nos. 1113-1117 (5)* | 5.10 | 2.35 |

Animals A264

45k, Tupaia glis. 60k, Cynocephalus volans. 120k, Loris grasilis. 500k, Tarsium spectrum. 600k, Symphalangus syndactylus.

**1993, Mar. 13 Litho. *Perf. 13***

| | | | | | |
|---|---|---|---|---|---|
| **1118** | A264 | 45k | multicolored | .25 | .25 |
| **1119** | A264 | 60k | multicolored | .25 | .25 |
| **1120** | A264 | 120k | multicolored | .45 | .25 |
| **1121** | A264 | 500k | multicolored | 1.60 | .75 |
| **1122** | A264 | 600k | multicolored | 1.90 | 1.25 |
| | | | *Nos. 1118-1122 (5)* | 4.45 | 2.75 |

Native Houses A265

Various houses.

**1993, July 12 Litho. *Perf. 13***

| | | | | | |
|---|---|---|---|---|---|
| **1123** | A265 | 32k | multi, vert. | .50 | .40 |
| **1124** | A265 | 200k | multicolored | 1.50 | .60 |
| **1125** | A265 | 650k | multicolored | 5.00 | 1.00 |
| **1126** | A265 | 750k | multicolored | 6.75 | 1.75 |
| | | | *Nos. 1123-1126 (4)* | 13.75 | 3.75 |

Campaign Against Illegal Drugs — A266

Designs: 200k, Drugs, skull smoking cigarette. 430k, Burning confiscated drugs. 900k, Instructor showing danger of drugs to audience.

**1993, June 26 *Perf. 12½***

| | | | | | |
|---|---|---|---|---|---|
| **1127** | A266 | 200k | multicolored | .65 | .35 |
| **1128** | A266 | 430k | multicolored | 1.50 | .75 |
| **1129** | A266 | 900k | multicolored | 3.25 | 1.40 |
| | | | *Nos. 1127-1129 (3)* | 5.40 | 2.50 |

Shells — A267

20k, Chlamys senatorius nobilis. 30k, Epitonium prestiosum. 70k, Lambis rugosa. 500k, Conus aulicus. 1000k, Lambis millepeda.

**1993, May 29 Litho. *Perf. 12x12½***

| | | | | | |
|---|---|---|---|---|---|
| **1130** | A267 | 20k | multicolored | .25 | .25 |
| **1131** | A267 | 30k | multicolored | .25 | .25 |
| **1132** | A267 | 70k | multicolored | .30 | .25 |
| **1133** | A267 | 500k | multicolored | 1.60 | .75 |
| **1134** | A267 | 1000k | multicolored | 3.00 | 1.40 |
| | | | *Nos. 1130-1134 (5)* | 5.40 | 2.90 |

Birds of Prey — A268

10k, Aquila clanga. 100k, Athene brama. 330k, Circus melanoluecos. 1000k, Circaetus gallicus.

**1993, Aug. 10 Litho. *Perf. 13***

| | | | | | |
|---|---|---|---|---|---|
| **1135** | A268 | 10k | multicolored | .25 | .25 |
| **1136** | A268 | 100k | multicolored | .50 | .25 |
| **1137** | A268 | 330k | multicolored | 1.50 | .50 |
| **1138** | A268 | 1000k | multicolored | 4.00 | 1.40 |
| | | | *Nos. 1135-1138 (4)* | 6.25 | 2.40 |

No. 1137 is horiz.

Environmental Protection — A269

Designs: 32k, Fighting forest fire. 40k, Animals around clean river. 260k, Rice paddies. 1100k, Water buffalo, people in water.

**1993, Sept. 25 Litho. *Perf. 13***

| | | | | | |
|---|---|---|---|---|---|
| **1139** | A269 | 32k | multicolored | .25 | .25 |
| **1140** | A269 | 40k | multicolored | .25 | .25 |
| **1141** | A269 | 260k | multicolored | 1.00 | .35 |
| **1142** | A269 | 1100k | multicolored | 4.25 | 1.40 |
| | | | *Nos. 1139-1142 (4)* | 5.75 | 2.25 |

Bangkok '93 A270

Butterflies: 35k, Narathura atosia. 80k, Parides philoxenus. 150k, Euploea harrisi. 220k, Ixias pyrene. 500k, Elymnias hypermnestra. 700k, Stichopthalma louisa.

**1993, Oct. 1 Litho. *Perf. 13***

| | | | | | |
|---|---|---|---|---|---|
| **1143** | A270 | 35k | multicolored | .25 | .25 |
| **1144** | A270 | 80k | multicolored | .25 | .25 |
| **1145** | A270 | 150k | multicolored | .45 | .25 |
| **1146** | A270 | 220k | multicolored | .75 | .35 |
| **1147** | A270 | 500k | multicolored | 2.00 | .85 |
| | | | *Nos. 1143-1147 (5)* | 3.70 | 1.95 |

**Souvenir Sheet**

| | | | | | |
|---|---|---|---|---|---|
| **1148** | A270 | 700k | multicolored | 3.00 | 1.50 |

No. 1148 contains one 40x32mm stamp.

1994 World Cup Soccer Championships, US — A271

Various soccer players.

**1993, Nov. 3 *Perf. 13***

| | | | | | |
|---|---|---|---|---|---|
| **1149** | A271 | 10k | multicolored | .25 | .25 |
| **1150** | A271 | 20k | multicolored | .25 | .25 |
| **1151** | A271 | 285k | multicolored | 1.10 | .25 |
| **1152** | A271 | 400k | multicolored | 1.60 | .50 |
| **1153** | A271 | 800k | multicolored | 3.25 | 1.25 |
| | | | *Nos. 1149-1153 (5)* | 6.45 | 2.50 |

**Souvenir Sheet**

***Perf. 12½***

| | | | | | |
|---|---|---|---|---|---|
| **1154** | A271 | 700k | multicolored | 2.75 | 1.40 |

Nos. 1154 contains one 32x40mm stamp.

Prehistoric Birds — A272

10k, Hesperornis. 20k, Dronte. 150k, Archaeopterix. 600k, Phororhachos. No. 1159, 700k, Dinornis maximus.

No. 1160, 700k, Teratornis, horiz.

**1994, Jan. 20 Litho. *Perf. 13***

| | | | | | |
|---|---|---|---|---|---|
| **1155** | A272 | 10k | multi | .25 | .25 |
| **1156** | A272 | 20k | multi | .25 | .25 |
| **1157** | A272 | 150k | multi | .60 | .25 |
| **1158** | A272 | 600k | multi | 2.00 | .50 |
| **1159** | A272 | 700k | multi | 2.25 | 1.00 |
| | | | *Nos. 1155-1159 (5)* | 5.35 | 2.25 |

**Souvenir Sheet**

| | | | | | |
|---|---|---|---|---|---|
| **1160** | A272 | 700k | multi | 2.50 | 1.25 |

Intl. Olympic Committee, Cent. — A273

100k, Flag, flame. 250k, Ancient Olympians. 1000k, Baron de Coubertin, Olympic runner.

***Perf. 12x12½, 12½x12***

**1994, Mar. 15 Litho.**

| | | | | | |
|---|---|---|---|---|---|
| **1161** | A273 | 100k | multi, vert. | .25 | .25 |
| **1162** | A273 | 250k | multi | .75 | .25 |
| **1163** | A273 | 1000k | multi, vert. | 3.25 | 1.50 |
| | | | *Nos. 1161-1163 (3)* | 4.25 | 2.00 |

1994 World Cup Soccer Championships, U.S. — A274

Various soccer plays.

**1994, June 15 Litho. *Perf. 12½***

| | | | | | |
|---|---|---|---|---|---|
| **1164** | A274 | 40k | multicolored | .25 | .25 |
| **1165** | A274 | 50k | multicolored | .25 | .25 |
| **1166** | A274 | 60k | multicolored | .25 | .25 |
| **1167** | A274 | 320k | multicolored | 1.10 | .35 |
| **1168** | A274 | 900k | multicolored | 3.25 | 1.00 |
| | | | *Nos. 1164-1168 (5)* | 5.10 | 2.10 |

### Souvenir Sheet
*Perf. 13*

| | | | | |
|---|---|---|---|---|
| **1169** | A274 | 700k multicolored | 3.75 | 1.65 |

No. 1169 contains one 32x40mm stamp and is also known imperf.

Pagodas A275

Various ornate gables.

**1994, July 1 Litho. *Perf. 12½***

| | | | | |
|---|---|---|---|---|
| **1170** | A275 | 30k multicolored | .25 | .25 |
| **1171** | A275 | 150k multicolored | .55 | .25 |
| **1172** | A275 | 380k multicolored | 1.25 | .40 |
| **1173** | A275 | 1100k multicolored | 3.75 | 1.65 |
| | | *Nos. 1170-1173 (4)* | 5.80 | 2.55 |

Nos. 1170-1173 exist imperf.

World Wildlife Fund — A276

50k, Ursus Malayanus. 90k, Adult. 200k, Cub, adult. 220k, Adult standing.

**1994, July 23**

| | | | | |
|---|---|---|---|---|
| **1174** | A276 | 50k multi | .75 | .25 |
| **1175** | A276 | 90k multi | 1.00 | .40 |
| **1176** | A276 | 200k multi | 2.25 | 1.00 |
| **1177** | A276 | 220k multi | 3.25 | 1.25 |
| | | *Nos. 1174-1177 (4)* | 7.25 | 2.90 |

Reptiles — A277

70k, Natrix natrix. 80k, Natrix tessellata. 90k, Salamandra salamandra. 600k, Triturus alpestris. 700k, Triturus cristatus. 800k, Lacerta viridis.

**1994, Aug. 1 Litho. *Perf. 12½***

| | | | | |
|---|---|---|---|---|
| **1178** | A277 | 70k multi, horiz. | .30 | .25 |
| **1179** | A277 | 80k multi, horiz. | .35 | .25 |
| **1180** | A277 | 90k multi, horiz. | .40 | .25 |
| **1181** | A277 | 600k multi, horiz. | 2.50 | .50 |
| **1182** | A277 | 800k multicolored | 3.25 | 1.25 |
| | | *Nos. 1178-1182 (5)* | 6.80 | 2.50 |

### Souvenir Sheet

| | | | | |
|---|---|---|---|---|
| **1183** | A277 | 700k multi, horiz. | 3.25 | 1.25 |

No. 1183 contains one 40x32mm stamp.

Intl. Year of the Family — A278

Designs: 500k, Mother taking child to school, horiz. No. 1186, Mother walking with children. No. 1187, Family.

**1994, Sept. 24**

| | | | | |
|---|---|---|---|---|
| **1184** | A278 | 200k multicolored | .85 | .35 |
| **1185** | A278 | 500k multicolored | 2.10 | .75 |
| **1186** | A278 | 700k multicolored | 3.25 | 1.25 |
| | | *Nos. 1184-1186 (3)* | 6.20 | 2.35 |

### Souvenir Sheet

| | | | | |
|---|---|---|---|---|
| **1187** | A278 | 700k multicolored | 3.25 | 1.25 |

No. 1187 contains one 32x40mm stamp.

Drums A279

Designs: 440k, Two people with hanging drum. 450k, Barrel shaped drum. 600k, Hanging drum.

***Perf. 12½, 13x12½ (#1189)***

**1994, Oct. 20 Litho.**

| | | | | |
|---|---|---|---|---|
| **1188** | A279 | 370k multicolored | 1.60 | .40 |
| **1189** | A279 | 440k multicolored | 1.75 | .50 |
| **1190** | A279 | 450k multicolored | 1.75 | .50 |
| **1191** | A279 | 600k multicolored | 2.40 | .75 |
| | | *Nos. 1188-1191 (4)* | 7.50 | 2.15 |

No. 1189 is 40x29mm.

Elephants — A280

400k, Beside railing. 890k, Being ridden, vert.

**1994, Nov. 25**

| | | | | |
|---|---|---|---|---|
| **1192** | A280 | 140k shown | .55 | .25 |
| **1193** | A280 | 400k multi | 1.60 | .80 |
| **1194** | A280 | 890k multi | 3.25 | 1.40 |
| | | *Nos. 1192-1194 (3)* | 5.40 | 2.45 |

Peace Bridge Between Laos and Thailand — A281

**1994, Apr. 8 Litho. *Perf. 14x14½***

| | | | | |
|---|---|---|---|---|
| **1195** | A281 | 500k multicolored | 2.50 | 1.25 |

Buddha — A282

15k, Phra Xayavoraman 7. 280k, Phra Thong Souk. 390k, Phra Monolom. 800k, Phra Ongtu.

**1994, Aug. 25 Litho. *Perf. 13***

| | | | | |
|---|---|---|---|---|
| **1196** | A282 | 15k multicolored | .25 | .25 |
| **1197** | A282 | 280k multicolored | 1.25 | .35 |
| **1198** | A282 | 390k multicolored | 1.60 | .50 |
| **1199** | A282 | 800k multicolored | 3.50 | 1.40 |
| | | *Nos. 1196-1199 (4)* | 6.60 | 2.50 |

Dinosaurs A283

**1994, Dec. 8**

| | | | | |
|---|---|---|---|---|
| **1200** | A283 | 50k Theropod | .25 | .25 |
| **1201** | A283 | 380k Iguanodon | 1.75 | .65 |
| **1202** | A283 | 420k Sauropod | 2.00 | .75 |
| | | *Nos. 1200-1202 (3)* | 4.00 | 1.65 |

World Tourism Organization, 20th Anniv. — A284

60k, Traditional music. 250k, Traditional dance. 400k, Traditional food. 650k, Waterfalls, vert.

**1995, Jan. 2 Litho. *Perf. 12½***

| | | | | |
|---|---|---|---|---|
| **1203** | A284 | 60k multi | .25 | .25 |
| **1204** | A284 | 250k multi | 1.00 | .25 |
| **1205** | A284 | 400k multi | 1.75 | .50 |
| **1206** | A284 | 650k multi | 2.75 | .90 |
| | | *Nos. 1203-1206 (4)* | 5.75 | 1.90 |

### Souvenir Sheet
*Perf. 13*

| | | | | |
|---|---|---|---|---|
| **1207** | A284 | 700k like #1206, vert. | 4.00 | 2.40 |

No. 1207 contains one 32x44mm stamp.

Dinosaurs A285

**1995, Feb. 20 *Perf. 12½***

| | | | | |
|---|---|---|---|---|
| **1208** | A285 | 50k Tracodon | .25 | .25 |
| **1209** | A285 | 70k Protoceratops | .30 | .25 |
| **1210** | A285 | 300k Brontosaurus | 1.25 | .35 |
| **1211** | A285 | 400k Stegosaurus | 1.75 | .50 |
| **1212** | A285 | 600k Tyranosaurus | 2.50 | .75 |
| | | *Nos. 1208-1212 (5)* | 6.05 | 2.10 |

Birds A286

50k, Acridotheres javanicus. 150k, Starnus burmannicus. 300k, Acridotheres tristis. 700k, Gracula religiosa.

**1995, Mar. 10**

| | | | | |
|---|---|---|---|---|
| **1213** | A286 | 50k multicolored | .25 | .25 |
| **1214** | A286 | 150k multicolored | .65 | .25 |
| **1215** | A286 | 300k multicolored | 1.25 | .40 |
| **1216** | A286 | 700k multicolored | 3.00 | .90 |
| | | *Nos. 1213-1216 (4)* | 5.15 | 1.80 |

Nos. 1213-1216 exist imperf.

Francophonie, 25th Anniv. — 1216A

Designs: 50k, People with arms linked. 380k, Temple. 420k, Map of Laos.

**1995, Mar. 20 Litho. *Perf. 13***

| | | | | |
|---|---|---|---|---|
| **1216A** | A286a | 50k multi | .25 | .25 |
| **1216B** | A286a | 380k multi | 1.50 | .65 |
| **1216C** | A286a | 420k multi | 1.75 | .75 |
| | | *Nos. 1216A-1216C (3)* | 3.50 | 1.65 |

Antique Containers A287

70k, "Hanche" cup, vert. 200k, Resin bowl. 450k, Button design bowl. 600k, Loving cup.

**1995, May 1 Litho. *Perf. 12½***

| | | | | |
|---|---|---|---|---|
| **1217** | A287 | 70k multi | .30 | .25 |
| **1218** | A287 | 200k multi | .85 | .25 |
| **1219** | A287 | 450k multi | 1.90 | .55 |
| **1220** | A287 | 600k multi | 2.50 | .75 |
| | | *Nos. 1217-1220 (4)* | 5.55 | 1.80 |

1996 Atlanta Pre-Olympics A288

**1995, Apr. 5**

| | | | | |
|---|---|---|---|---|
| **1221** | A288 | 60k Pole vault | .25 | .25 |
| **1222** | A288 | 80k Javelin | .35 | .25 |
| **1223** | A288 | 200k Hammer throw | .85 | .25 |
| **1224** | A288 | 350k Long jump | 1.60 | .40 |
| **1225** | A288 | 700k High jump | 3.25 | .90 |
| | | *Nos. 1221-1225 (5)* | 6.30 | 2.05 |

### Souvenir Sheet

| | | | | |
|---|---|---|---|---|
| **1226** | A288 | 700k Baseball | 3.25 | 1.90 |

No. 1226 contains one 40x32mm stamp.

Rocket Festival A289

Designs: 80k, Launching rocket from scaffolding, vert. 160k, Carrying rocket in procession led by monk. 500k, Man carrying rocket on shoulder. 700k, People looking at rockets on tripods.

**1995, June 1 Litho. *Perf. 13***

| | | | | |
|---|---|---|---|---|
| **1227** | A289 | 80k multicolored | .30 | .25 |
| **1228** | A289 | 160k multicolored | .65 | .25 |
| **1229** | A289 | 500k multicolored | 1.90 | .55 |
| **1230** | A289 | 700k multicolored | 2.50 | .90 |
| | | *Nos. 1227-1230 (4)* | 5.35 | 1.95 |

Domestic Cats A290

Designs: 40k, Red tabby longhair. 50k, Siamese seal point. 250k, Red tabby longhair. 400k, Tortoise-shell shorthair. 650k, Tortoise-shell shorthair, vert. 700k, Tortoise-shell shorthair.

**1995, July 25 Litho. *Perf. 12½***

| | | | | | |
|---|---|---|---|---|---|
| **1231** | A290 | 40k multicolored | .25 | .25 |
| **1232** | A290 | 50k multicolored | .25 | .25 |
| **1233** | A290 | 250k multicolored | .80 | .25 |
| **1234** | A290 | 400k multicolored | 1.20 | .30 |
| **1235** | A290 | 650k multicolored | 1.40 | .75 |
| | | *Nos. 1231-1235 (5)* | 3.90 | 1.80 |

**Souvenir Sheet**

**1236** A290 700k multicolored 2.50 1.90

No. 1236 contains one 40x32mm stamp.

Insect-Eating Plants — A291

Designs: 90k, Nepenthes villosa. 100k, Dionaea muscipula. 350k, Sarracenia flava. 450k, Sarracenia purpurea. 500k, Nepenthes ampullaria.
1000k, Nepenthes gracilis.

**1995, Aug. 24**

| | | | | |
|---|---|---|---|---|
| **1237** | A291 | 90k multicolored | .30 | .25 |
| **1238** | A291 | 100k multicolored | .40 | .25 |
| **1239** | A291 | 350k multicolored | 1.20 | .35 |
| **1240** | A291 | 450k multicolored | 1.60 | .35 |
| **1241** | A291 | 500k multicolored | 2.00 | .75 |
| | | *Nos. 1237-1241 (5)* | 5.50 | 1.95 |

**Souvenir Sheet**

**1242** A291 1000k multicolored 4.50 2.00

No. 1242 contains one 40x32mm stamp.

Insects A292

Designs: 40k, Lucanus cervus. 50k, Melolontha melolontha. 500k, Xylocopa violacea. 800k, Tettigonia viridissima.

**1995, Sept. 20**

| | | | | |
|---|---|---|---|---|
| **1243** | A292 | 40k multicolored | .25 | .25 |
| **1244** | A292 | 50k multicolored | .25 | .25 |
| **1245** | A292 | 500k multicolored | 2.00 | .50 |
| **1246** | A292 | 800k multicolored | 2.75 | .90 |
| | | *Nos. 1243-1246 (4)* | 5.25 | 1.90 |

FAO, 50th Anniv. A293

Designs: 80k, Cattle grazing. 300k, Farmer tilling rice paddy. 1000k, Planting, irrigating rice paddies, stocking pond with fish.

**1995, Oct. 16 Litho. *Perf. 12½***

| | | | | |
|---|---|---|---|---|
| **1247** | A293 | 80k multicolored | .25 | .25 |
| **1248** | A293 | 300k multicolored | 1.00 | .50 |
| **1249** | A293 | 1000k multicolored | 3.50 | 1.70 |
| | | *Nos. 1247-1249 (3)* | 4.75 | 2.45 |

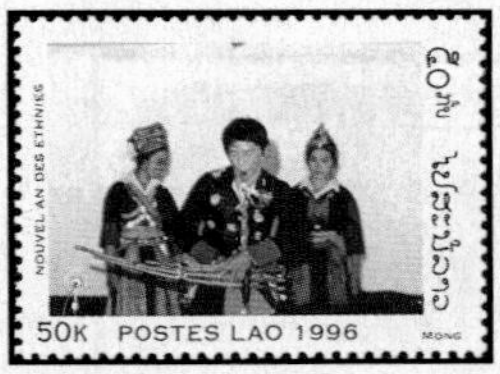

Traditional Culture — A294

Designs: 50k, Man with musical instrument, two women. 280k, Dance. 380k, Playing game with bamboo poles. 420k, Woman, man with musical instruments.

**1996, Jan. 10**

| | | | | |
|---|---|---|---|---|
| **1250** | A294 | 50k multicolored | .25 | .25 |
| **1251** | A294 | 280k multicolored | 1.40 | .35 |
| **1252** | A294 | 380k multicolored | 2.00 | .50 |
| **1253** | A294 | 420k multicolored | 2.25 | .50 |
| | | *Nos. 1250-1253 (4)* | 5.90 | 1.60 |

1996 Summer Olympics, Atlanta — A295

30k, Cycling. 150k, Soccer. 200k, Basketball, vert. 300k, Running, vert. 500k, Shooting. 1000k, Pole vault.

**1996, Feb. 20**

| | | | | |
|---|---|---|---|---|
| **1254** | A295 | 30k multi | .25 | .25 |
| **1255** | A295 | 150k multi | .75 | .25 |
| **1256** | A295 | 200k multi | 1.00 | .25 |
| **1257** | A295 | 300k multi | 1.50 | .30 |
| **1258** | A295 | 500k multi | 2.50 | .65 |
| | | *Nos. 1254-1258 (5)* | 6.00 | 1.70 |

**Souvenir Sheet**

**1259** A295 1000k multi 3.50 1.70

No. 1259 contains one 38x30mm stamp.

Fauna — A296

Designs: 40k, Helarctos malayanus. 60k, Pelecanus philippensis. 200k, Panthera pardus. 250k, Papilio machaon. 700k, Python molurus.

**1996, Feb. 26 Litho. *Perf. 13***

| | | | | |
|---|---|---|---|---|
| **1260** | A296 | 40k multicolored | .25 | .25 |
| **1261** | A296 | 60k multicolored | .35 | .25 |
| **1262** | A296 | 200k multicolored | 1.10 | .25 |
| **1263** | A296 | 250k multicolored | 1.25 | .30 |
| **1264** | A296 | 700k multicolored | 3.00 | .90 |
| | | *Nos. 1260-1264 (5)* | 5.95 | 1.95 |

Intl. Women's Day A297

20k, Weaving textile. 290k, Instructing calisthenics. 1000k, Feeding infant, vert.

**1996, Mar. 8**

| | | | | |
|---|---|---|---|---|
| **1265** | A297 | 20k multicolored | .25 | .25 |
| **1266** | A297 | 290k multicolored | 1.10 | .30 |
| **1267** | A297 | 1000k multicolored | 3.50 | 1.70 |
| | | *Nos. 1265-1267 (3)* | 4.85 | 2.25 |

A298

Various soccer plays.

**1996, May 3 Litho. *Perf. 13***

| | | | | |
|---|---|---|---|---|
| **1268** | A298 | 20k multicolored | .25 | .25 |
| **1269** | A298 | 50k multicolored | .25 | .25 |
| **1270** | A298 | 300k multicolored | .60 | .30 |
| **1271** | A298 | 400k multicolored | .75 | .50 |
| **1272** | A298 | 500k multicolored | 1.00 | .60 |
| | | *Nos. 1268-1272 (5)* | 2.85 | 1.90 |

**Souvenir Sheet**

**1273** A298 1000k multicolored 2.50 1.50

1998 World Soccer Cup Championships, France.
No. 1273 contains one 32x40mm stamp.

Rats — A299

**1996, Apr. 15 Litho. *Perf. 13½x13***

| | | | | |
|---|---|---|---|---|
| **1274** | A299 | 50k purple & multi | .25 | .25 |
| **1275** | A299 | 340k blue & multi | 1.40 | .65 |
| **1276** | A299 | 350k green & multi | 1.40 | .65 |
| **1277** | A299 | 370k red & multi | 1.50 | .75 |
| | | *Nos. 1274-1277 (4)* | 4.55 | 2.30 |

New Year 1996 (Year of the Rat).

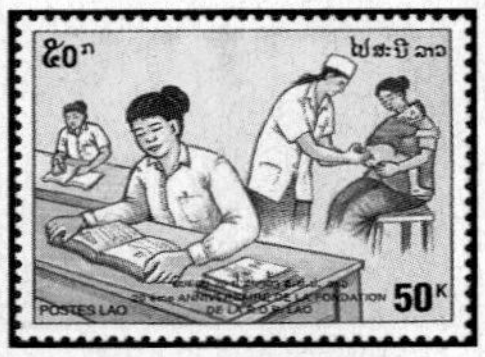

Laos Rural Development Program, 20th Anniv. — A300

50k, Instruction for giving medical care. 280k, Irrigation system. 600k, Bridge over waterway.

**1995, Dec. 2 *Perf. 13***

| | | | | |
|---|---|---|---|---|
| **1278** | A300 | 50k multicolored | .25 | .25 |
| **1279** | A300 | 280k multicolored | .55 | .50 |
| **1280** | A300 | 600k multicolored | 1.50 | 1.00 |
| | | *Nos. 1278-1280 (3)* | 2.30 | 1.75 |

UN, 50th Anniv. A301

Designs: 290k, Men seated at round table. 310k, Men playing game, checkers. 440k, Boys in swing, playing ball.

**1995, Oct. 24**

| | | | | |
|---|---|---|---|---|
| **1281** | A301 | 290k multicolored | 1.00 | .40 |
| **1282** | A301 | 310k multicolored | 1.10 | .50 |
| **1283** | A301 | 440k multicolored | 1.50 | .75 |
| | | *Nos. 1281-1283 (3)* | 3.60 | 1.65 |

Antique Aircraft A302

25k, Morane. 60k, Sopwith Camel. 150k, De Haviland DH-4. 250k, Albatros. 800k, Caudron.

**1996, July 5 Litho. *Perf. 13***

| | | | | |
|---|---|---|---|---|
| **1284** | A302 | 25k multicolored | .25 | .25 |
| **1285** | A302 | 60k multicolored | .25 | .25 |
| **1286** | A302 | 150k multicolored | .65 | .25 |
| **1287** | A302 | 250k multicolored | 1.10 | .35 |
| **1288** | A302 | 800k multicolored | 2.50 | 1.00 |
| | | *Nos. 1284-1288 (5)* | 4.75 | 2.10 |

Capex '96.

Carts A303

**1996, Aug. 21**

| | | | | |
|---|---|---|---|---|
| **1289** | A303 | 50k shown | .25 | .25 |
| **1290** | A303 | 100k Cart, diff. | .40 | .25 |
| **1291** | A303 | 440k Pulled by oxen | 1.50 | .65 |
| | | *Nos. 1289-1291 (3)* | 2.15 | 1.15 |

Flowers — A304

Designs: 50k, Dendrobium secundum. 200k, Ascocentrum miniatum. 500k, Aerides multiflorum. 520k, Dendrobium aggregatum.

**1996, Oct. 25 Litho. *Perf. 13***

| | | | | |
|---|---|---|---|---|
| **1292** | A304 | 50k multicolored | .25 | .25 |
| **1293** | A304 | 200k multicolored | .75 | .25 |
| **1294** | A304 | 500k multicolored | 1.90 | .65 |
| **1295** | A304 | 520k multicolored | 2.00 | .65 |
| | | *Nos. 1292-1295 (4)* | 4.90 | 1.80 |

Draft Horses — A305

Various breeds.

**1996, Nov. 5 Litho. *Perf. 13***

| | | | | |
|---|---|---|---|---|
| **1296** | A305 | 50k yellow & multi | .25 | .25 |
| **1297** | A305 | 80k green & multi | .25 | .25 |
| **1298** | A305 | 200k pink & multi | .55 | .25 |
| **1299** | A305 | 400k blue & multi | 1.25 | .50 |
| **1300** | A305 | 600k yellow & multi | 1.75 | .75 |
| | | *Nos. 1296-1300 (5)* | 4.05 | 2.00 |

**Souvenir Sheet**

**1301** A305 1000k pink & multi 3.00 1.50

No. 1301 contains one 32x40mm stamp.

UNICEF, 50th Anniv. A306

200k, Children in school. 500k, Child breastfeeding, vert. 600k, Woman pumping water.

**1996, Dec. 11 Litho.**

| | | | | |
|---|---|---|---|---|
| **1302** | A306 | 200k multicolored | .80 | .30 |
| **1303** | A306 | 500k multicolored | 2.00 | .90 |
| **1304** | A306 | 600k multicolored | 2.40 | 1.25 |
| | | *Nos. 1302-1304 (3)* | 5.20 | 2.45 |

Greenpeace, 25th Anniv. — A306a

Turtles: 150k, Dermochelys coriacea on sand. 250k, Dermochelys coriacea in surf. 400k, Erethochelys imbricata. 450k, Chelonia agassizi.

**1996, Dec. 27 Litho. *Perf. 13***

| | | | | |
|---|---|---|---|---|
| **1304A** | A306a 150k multicolored | .80 | .25 |
| **1304B** | A306a 250k multicolored | 1.25 | .50 |
| **1304C** | A306a 400k multicolored | 2.00 | .80 |
| **1304D** | A306a 450k multicolored | 2.25 | .90 |
| *e.* | Souvenir sheet, #1304A-1304D | 6.50 | 4.75 |
| | *Nos. 1304A-1304D (4)* | 6.30 | 2.45 |

Steam Locomotives — A307

Designs: 100k, Kinnaird, 1846, 200k, Pioneer, 1836, portrait of George Stephenson. 300k, Portrait of Robert Stephenson, Long Boiler Express, 1848. 400k, Adler, 1835. 500k, Lord of the Isles, 1851-84. 600k, The Columbine, 1845.
2000k, Best friend of Charleston, 1830.

***Perf. 12½x12, 12x13 (#1306-1309)***

**1997 Litho.**

| | | | |
|---|---|---|---|
| **1305** | A307 100k multicolored | .25 | .25 |
| **1306** | A307 200k multicolored | .40 | .25 |
| **1307** | A307 300k multicolored | .60 | .35 |
| **1308** | A307 400k multicolored | .75 | .50 |
| **1309** | A307 500k multicolored | 1.00 | .65 |
| **1310** | A307 600k multicolored | 1.25 | .75 |
| | *Nos. 1305-1310 (6)* | 4.25 | 2.75 |

**Souvenir Sheet**

***Perf. 12½***

| | | | |
|---|---|---|---|
| **1311** | A307 2000k multicolored | 3.25 | 3.00 |

Nos. 1306-1309 are 42x21mm.
No. 1311 contains one 40x32mm stamp.

Parrots — A308

Designs: 50k, Agapornis personata. 150k, Agapornis cana. 200k, Agapornis lilianae. 400k, Agapornis fischeri. 500k, Agapornis nigregenis. 800k, Agapornis roseicollis.
2000k, Agapornis taranta.

**1997 *Perf. 12½***

| | | | |
|---|---|---|---|
| **1312** | A308 50k multicolored | .25 | .25 |
| **1313** | A308 150k multicolored | .45 | .25 |
| **1314** | A308 200k multicolored | .60 | .25 |
| **1315** | A308 400k multicolored | 1.00 | .50 |
| **1316** | A308 500k multicolored | 1.10 | .65 |
| **1317** | A308 800k multicolored | 1.75 | 1.00 |
| | *Nos. 1312-1317 (6)* | 5.15 | 2.90 |

**Souvenir Sheet**

| | | | |
|---|---|---|---|
| **1318** | A308 2000k multicolored | 5.00 | 4.00 |

No. 1318 contains one 32x40mm stamp.

Year of the Ox — A308a

Designs: 300k, Ox, rider with flag, vert. 440k, Ox, rider with umbrella.

**1997 Litho. *Perf. 13x13½, 13½x13***

| | | | |
|---|---|---|---|
| **1318A** | A308a 50k multi | .25 | .25 |
| **1318B** | A308a 300k multi | 1.60 | 1.40 |
| **1318C** | A308a 440k multi | 2.25 | 1.75 |
| | *Nos. 1318A-1318C (3)* | 4.10 | 3.40 |

Cooking Utensils A309

50k, Cooking over open fire, vert. 340k, Traditional food containers. 370k, Traditional meal setting.

**1997**

| | | | |
|---|---|---|---|
| **1319** | A309 50k multicolored | .25 | .25 |
| **1320** | A309 340k multicolored | 1.00 | .55 |
| **1321** | A309 370k multicolored | 1.00 | .60 |
| | *Nos. 1319-1321 (3)* | 2.25 | 1.40 |

Orchids A310

Designs: 50k, Roeblingiana. 100k, Findlayanum. 150k, Crepidatum. 250k, Sarcanthus birmanicus. 400k, Cymbidium lowianum. 1000k, Dendrobium gratiossissimum.
2000k, Chamberlainianum.

**1997 Litho. *Perf. 12½***

| | | | |
|---|---|---|---|
| **1322** | A310 50k multicolored | .25 | .25 |
| **1323** | A310 100k multicolored | .35 | .25 |
| **1324** | A310 150k multicolored | .45 | .25 |
| **1325** | A310 250k multicolored | .60 | .35 |
| **1326** | A310 400k multicolored | .90 | .50 |
| **1327** | A310 1000k multicolored | 1.75 | 1.25 |
| | *Nos. 1322-1327 (6)* | 4.30 | 2.85 |

**Souvenir Sheet**

| | | | |
|---|---|---|---|
| **1328** | A310 2000k multicolored | 4.25 | 3.50 |

No. 1328 contains one 32x40mm stamp.

Elephants — A311

Elephas maximus: 100k, Adult, vert. 250k, Adult holding log. 300k, Adult, calf.
Loxodonta africana: 350k, Adult. 450k, Adult in water. 550k, Adult, vert. 2000k, Head of adult.

**1997 Litho. *Perf. 12½***

| | | | |
|---|---|---|---|
| **1329** | A311 100k multicolored | .30 | .25 |
| **1330** | A311 250k multicolored | .60 | .35 |
| **1331** | A311 300k multicolored | .65 | .35 |
| **1332** | A311 350k multicolored | .70 | .40 |
| **1333** | A311 450k multicolored | .85 | .55 |
| **1334** | A311 550k multicolored | 1.20 | .65 |
| | *Nos. 1329-1334 (6)* | 4.30 | 2.55 |

**Souvenir Sheet**

| | | | |
|---|---|---|---|
| **1335** | A311 2000k multicolored | 4.25 | 3.00 |

No. 1335 contains one 32x40mm stamp.

Head Pieces and Masks A312

Various designs.

**1997 Litho. *Perf. 12½***

| | | | |
|---|---|---|---|
| **1336** | A312 50k multi, vert. | .25 | .25 |
| **1337** | A312 100k multi, vert | .25 | .25 |
| **1338** | A312 150k multi | .40 | .25 |
| **1339** | A312 200k multi, vert. | .55 | .25 |
| **1340** | A312 350k multi, vert. | 1.25 | .40 |
| | *Nos. 1336-1340 (5)* | 2.70 | 1.40 |

1998 World Cup Soccer Championships, France — A313

Various soccer plays.

**1997 Litho. *Perf. 12½***

| | | | |
|---|---|---|---|
| **1341** | A313 100k multicolored | .25 | .25 |
| **1342** | A313 200k multicolored | .50 | .25 |
| **1343** | A313 250k multicolored | .55 | .30 |
| **1344** | A313 300k multicolored | .55 | .30 |
| **1345** | A313 350k multicolored | .65 | .40 |
| **1346** | A313 700k multicolored | .95 | .80 |
| | *Nos. 1341-1346 (6)* | 3.45 | 2.30 |

**Souvenir Sheet**

| | | | |
|---|---|---|---|
| **1347** | A313 2000k multicolored | 3.50 | 2.50 |

Sailing Ships A314

50k, Phoenician. 100k, 13th cent. ship. 150k, 15th cent. vessel. 200k, Portuguese caravel, 16th cent. 400k, Dutch, 17th cent. 900k, HMS Victory.
2000k, Grand Henry, 1514.

**1997 *Perf. 13***

| | | | |
|---|---|---|---|
| **1348** | A314 50k multicolored | .25 | .25 |
| **1349** | A314 100k multicolored | .25 | .25 |
| **1350** | A314 150k multicolored | .35 | .25 |
| **1351** | A314 200k multicolored | .40 | .25 |
| **1352** | A314 400k multicolored | .80 | .40 |
| **1353** | A314 900k multicolored | 1.40 | .80 |
| | *Nos. 1348-1353 (6)* | 3.45 | 2.20 |

**Souvenir Sheet**

| | | | |
|---|---|---|---|
| **1354** | A314 2000k multicolored | 3.50 | 2.50 |

No. 1354 contains one 40x28mm stamp.

Canoe Races A315

Designs: 50k, Team in red shirts, team in yellow shirts rowing upward. 100k, Crowd cheering on teams. 300k, Teams rowing left. 500k, People standing in canoe cheering on teams.

**1997 Litho. *Perf. 12½***

| | | | |
|---|---|---|---|
| **1355** | A315 50k multicolored | .25 | .25 |
| **1356** | A315 100k multicolored | .25 | .25 |
| **1357** | A315 300k multicolored | .75 | .30 |
| **1358** | A315 500k multicolored | 1.25 | .55 |
| | *Nos. 1355-1358 (4)* | 2.50 | 1.35 |

Admission of Laos to ASEAN — A316

Central flag: a, Brunei. b, Indonesia. c, Laos. d, Malaysia. e, Taiwan. f, Philippines. g, Singapore. h, Thailand. i, Viet Nam.

**1997, July 23 Litho. *Perf. 14x14½***

| | | | |
|---|---|---|---|
| **1359** | A316 550k Strip of 9, #a.-i. | 9.50 | 9.50 |
| *j.* | Sheet of 9, #1359a-1359i + label | 15.00 | 15.00 |

Nos. 1359a-1359i also exist in souvenir sheets of 1. No. 1359 was not available in the philatelic market until 8/98.

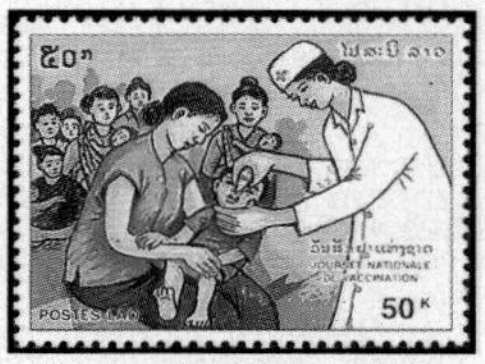


Vaccination Day — A317

Design: 50k, Child receiving oral vaccination. 340k, Child receiving shot. 370k, Child in wheelchair.

**1997, Jan. 3 Litho. *Perf. 13x13¼***

| | | | |
|---|---|---|---|
| **1363** | A317 50k multi | *.25* | .25 |
| **1364** | A317 340k multi | *1.50* | .65 |
| **1365** | A317 370k multi | *1.60* | .75 |
| | *Nos. 1363-1365 (3)* | *3.35* | 1.65 |

**Beginning with No. 1366, used values are for postally used stamps.**

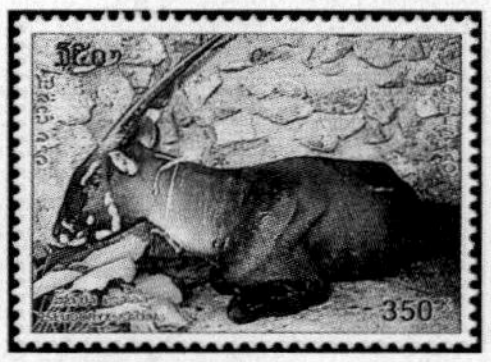


Pseudoryx Saola — A319

Various views of Pseudoryx saola.

**1997, Feb. 10 *Perf. 13x13¼, 13¼x13***

| | | | |
|---|---|---|---|
| **1366** | A319 350k multi | *1.60* | *1.60* |
| **1367** | A319 380k multi, vert. | *1.75* | *1.75* |
| **1368** | A319 420k multi | *2.00* | *2.00* |
| | *Nos. 1366-1368 (3)* | *5.35* | *5.35* |

ASEAN (Assoc. of South East Asian Nations), 30th Anniv. — A321

**1997, Aug. 8 Litho. *Perf. 13***

| | | | |
|---|---|---|---|
| **1373** | A321 150k Headquarters | .90 | .65 |
| **1374** | A321 600k Map of Laos | 3.50 | 2.75 |

Fishing A322

Designs: 50k, Holding large net with a pole, vert. 100k, Casting net. 450k, Woman using small net, vert. 600k, Placing fish traps in water.

**1997**

| | | | |
|---|---|---|---|
| **1375** | A322 50k multicolored | .30 | .25 |
| **1376** | A322 100k multicolored | .60 | .30 |
| **1377** | A322 450k multicolored | 2.00 | 1.60 |
| **1378** | A322 600k multicolored | 2.75 | 2.00 |
| | *Nos. 1375-1378 (4)* | 5.65 | 4.15 |

New Year 1998 (Year of the Tiger) A323

**1998**

**1379** A323 150k green & multi .90 .70
**1380** A323 350k gray & multi 1.75 1.60
**1381** A323 400k pale lilac & multi 1.90 1.75
*Nos. 1379-1381 (3)* 4.55 4.05

Canoes — A325

Designs: 1100k, Barque. 1200k, Covered pirogue. 2500k, Motorized pirogue.

**1998 Litho. *Perf. 14½x14***

**1387** A325 1100k multicolored 2.50 2.50
**1388** A325 1200k multicolored 2.75 2.75
**1389** A325 2500k multicolored 6.25 6.25
*Nos. 1387-1389 (3)* 11.50 11.50

A326

Various wind musical instruments.

**1998 *Perf. 14x14½***

**1390** A326 900k multicolored 2.25 2.25
**1391** A326 1200k multicolored 3.25 3.25
**1392** A326 1500k multicolored 4.00 4.00
*Nos. 1390-1392 (3)* 9.50 9.50

A327

Buddha Luang, Phabang.

**1998**

**1393** A327 3000k multicolored 7.50 7.50

Orchids — A328

Designs: 900k, Paphiopedilum callosum. 950k, Paphiopedilum concolor. 1000k, Dendrobium thyrsiflorum, vert. 1050k, Dendrobium lindleyi, vert.

**1998 *Perf. 14½x14, 14x14½***

**1394** A328 900k multicolored 2.75 2.75
**1395** A328 950k multicolored 3.00 3.00
**1396** A328 1000k multicolored 3.00 3.00
**1397** A328 1050k multicolored 3.25 3.25
*Nos. 1394-1397 (4)* 12.00 12.00

Universal Declaration of Human Rights, 50th Anniv. — A329

Designs: 170k, Women voting. 300k, Children in classroom.

**1998 *Perf. 14½x14***

**1398** A329 170k multicolored 2.25 2.25
**1399** A329 300k multicolored 3.75 3.75

Historic Sites — A330

Designs: 10,000k, Hotay Vat Sisaket, vert. 25,000k, Vat Phou. 45,000k, That Luong.

***Perf. 14x14¼, 14¼x14***

**1998, Sept. 1 Litho.**

**1400-1402** A330 Set of 3 *120.00 120.00*

People's Army, 50th Anniv. — A331

Designs: 1300k, Soldiers, flag, flowers. 1500k, Soldiers, cave, jungle, vert.

**1999, Jan. 20 Litho. *Perf. 13¼***

**1403** A331 1300k multi *4.00 1.40*
**1404** A331 1500k multi *5.00 1.50*

Souvenir Sheet

Visit Laos Year (in 2000) — A331a

Various temples: b, 2500k. c, 4000k, d, 5500k, e, 8000k.

**1999, Aug. 1 Typo. *Perf. 13¼***

**Gold Stamps**

**1404A** A331a Sheet of 4, #b-e 25.00 25.00
*f.* As 1404A, with larger margins with Thaipex 99 and China Stamp Exhibition 99 emblems 30.00 30.00
*g.* As 1404A, with larger margins with China 1999 Philatelic Exhibition emblem 30.00 30.00

No. 1404Af issued 8/2; No. 1404Ag issued 8/4.

Luang Prabang World Heritage Site — A332

Designs: 400k, Commemorative marker, vert. 1150k, Building. 1250k, Vat Xiengthong (building with curved roof).

**1999, Feb. 2**

**1405** A332 400k multi *2.50 .80*
**1406** A332 1150k multi *5.50 1.50*
**1407** A332 1250k multi *6.50 2.00*
*Nos. 1405-1407 (3)* *14.50 4.30*

Tourism — A333

Designs: 200k, Yaos, Muong Sing. 500k, Phadeang, Vangvieng District. 1050k, That Makmo, Luang Prabang. 1300k, Patuxay, Vientiane, vert.

***Perf. 14¾x14, 14x14¾***

**1999, Mar. 2 Litho.**

**1408** A333 200k multi *1.00*
**1409** A333 500k multi *1.50*
**1410** A333 1050k multi *2.50*
**1411** A333 1300k multi *3.50*
*Nos. 1408-1411 (4)* *8.50*

Nocturnal Creatures A334

Designs: 900k, Glaucidium brodiei. 1600k, Otus lempiji. 2100k, Tyto alba. 2800k, Chironax melanocephalus.

**1999, July 2 Litho. *Perf. 14x14½***

**1412** A334 900k multi *1.50 1.00*
**1413** A334 1600k multi *3.00 2.00*
**1414** A334 2100k multi *3.50 3.00*
**1415** A334 2800k multi *5.00 4.00*
*Nos. 1412-1415 (4)* *13.00 10.00*

New Year 1999 (Year of the Rabbit) — A335

1500k, Rabbit, other animals of calendar cycle. 1600k, Rabbit.

**1999, Apr. 15 Litho. *Perf. 14x14¼***

**1416** A335 1500k multi, vert. *7.00 5.00*

***Perf. 14¾x14***

**1417** A335 1600k multi, horiz. *8.00 6.00*

Farming Implements — A336

**1999, May 1 Litho. *Perf. 14¾x14***

**1418** A336 1500k Plow *2.50 1.50*
**1419** A336 2000k Yoke *3.00 2.00*
**1420** A336 3200k Plow, diff. *4.00 3.00*
*Nos. 1418-1420 (3)* *9.50 6.50*

UPU, 125th Anniv. A337

**1999, Oct. 9**

**1421** A337 2600k shown *5.00 3.00*
**1422** A337 3400k Postman *7.00 4.00*

Wildlife — A338

700k, Rhinoceros sondaicus. 900k, Bubalus bubalis. 1700k, Prionodon pardicolor. 1800k, Cervus unicolor. 1900k, Panthera leo.

***Perf. 14¾x14, 14x14¾***

**1999, Nov. 10**

**1423** A338 700k multi *1.50 .60*
**1424** A338 900k multi, vert. *1.75 .80*
**1425** A338 1700k multi *3.00 1.50*
**1426** A338 1800k multi *3.25 1.75*
**1427** A338 1900k multi, vert. *3.50 1.90*
*Nos. 1423-1427 (5)* *13.00 6.55*

Expo '99, Kunming, China — A339

Designs: 300k, Carved tree stump. 900k, China Hall. 2300k, Science and Technology Hall. 2500k, Laos traditional wooden house.

**1999, Oct. 15 *Perf. 14¾x14***

**1428** A339 300k multi *.70 .25*
**1429** A339 900k multi *1.50 .75*
**1430** A339 2300k multi *3.25 1.90*
**1431** A339 2500k multi *4.50 2.00*
*Nos. 1428-1431 (4)* *9.95 4.90*

Millennium — A340

No. 1432, 2000k: a, Airport, bus, hospital. b, Temple, tractor, elephant. c, Building, truck. d, River, waterfalls.

**2000, Jan. 1 Litho. *Perf. 13½***

**1432** A340 Block of 4, #a-d *10.00 5.50*
*e.* Souvenir sheet, #1432 *12.00 6.75*

No. 1432e sold for 10,000k. No. 1432e exists imperf. Value, $30.

New Year 2000 (Year of the Dragon) — A341

Dragons: 1800k, And other zodiac animals. 2300k, In water.

**2000, Apr. 1** *Perf. 14½x14*
**1433-1434** A341 Set of 2 5.50 1.25

Wedding Costumes A342

Designs: 800k, Lao Theung. 2300k, Lao Lum. 3400k, Lao Sung.

**2000, Oct. 30** *Perf. 14x14½*
**1435-1437** A342 Set of 3 4.50 3.00

Children's Drawings — A343

Designs: 300k, Waterfall. 400k, Forest fire. 2300k, Animals at river. 3200k, Animals at river, vert.

**2000, June 1** *Perf. 14½x14, 14x14½*
**1438-1441** A343 Set of 4 7.50 3.00

Bangkok 2000 Stamp Exhibition — A344

Orchids: 500k, Dendrobium draconis. 900k, Paphiopedilum hirsutissimum. 3000k, Dendrobium sulcatum. 3400k, Rhynchostylis gigantea.

**2000, Mar. 25** *Perf. 14x14½*
**1442-1445** A344 Set of 4 10.00 3.00
*1445a* Souv. sheet, #1442-1445, perf. 13½ 15.00 15.00

No. 1445a sold for 10,000k. No. 1445a exists imperf. Value, $80.

Peacocks A345

700k, Male with feathers down, vert., 1000k, Male with feathers up, vert., 1800k, Female. 3500k, Male and female. 10,000k, Male with feathers up, vert.

**2000, July 10** *Perf. 14x14½, 14½x14*
**1446-1449** A345 Set of 4 4.50 2.50

**Souvenir Sheet**

***Perf. 13½***

**Litho. With Foil Application**

**1450** A345 10,000k multi 7.50 7.50

2000 Summer Olympics, Sydney — A346

Designs: 500k, Cycling. 900k, Boxing. 2600k, Judo. 3600k, Kayaking.

**2000, Sept. 15 Litho.** *Perf. 14½x14*
**1451-1454** A346 Set of 4 6.00 3.00
*1454a* Souvenir sheet, #1451-1454, perf. 13½ 10.00 10.00

No. 1454a sold for 10,000k. No. 1454a exists imperf. Value, $40.

---

Laotian postal officials have declared as "illegal" a sheet of stamps for Great People of the 20th Century (Elvis Presley, Roberto Clemente, Marilyn Monroe, Dr. Martin Luther King, Jr., Pope John Paul II, Frank Sinatra, Albert Einstein, Princess Diana and Walt Disney) and stamps depicting Tiger Woods, Payne Stewart, Arnold Palmer, Elvis Presley, Marilyn Monroe, John Lennon and the Beatles.

---

Women's Costumes — A347

**2000, Mar. 8 Litho.** *Perf. 14¼x14½*

| | | | | | |
|---|---|---|---|---|---|
| **1455** | A347 | 100k | Kor Loma | .30 | .25 |
| **1456** | A347 | 200k | Kor Pchor | .40 | .25 |
| **1457** | A347 | 500k | Nhuan Krom | .50 | .25 |
| **1458** | A347 | 900k | Taidam | 2.00 | .40 |
| **1459** | A347 | 2300k | Yao | 3.00 | 1.00 |
| **1460** | A347 | 2500k | Meuy | 3.00 | 1.10 |
| **1461** | A347 | 2600k | Sila | 1.50 | 1.10 |
| **1462** | A347 | 2700k | Hmong | 3.50 | 1.25 |
| **1463** | A347 | 2800k | Yao, diff. | 3.50 | 1.25 |
| **1464** | A347 | 3100k | Kor Nukkuy | 3.50 | 1.40 |
| **1465** | A347 | 3200k | Kor Pouxang | 3.50 | 1.40 |
| **1466** | A347 | 3300k | Yao Lanten | 2.00 | 1.40 |
| **1467** | A347 | 3400k | Khir | 2.25 | 1.50 |
| **1468** | A347 | 3500k | Kor | 4.00 | 1.50 |
| **1469** | A347 | 3900k | Hmong, diff. | 4.00 | 1.75 |
| | *Nos. 1455-1469 (15)* | | | 36.95 | 15.80 |

Laotian-Japanese Bridge Project — A348

Flags, various views of bridge: 900k, 2700k, 3200k.

**2000, Aug. 2** *Perf. 14½x14*
**1470-1472** A348 Set of 3 5.00 2.75

**Souvenir Sheet**

No. 1472A: b, 4000k, Similar to #1470. c, 7500k, Similar to #1471. d, 8500k, Similar to #1472.

**2000 Typo.** *Perf. 13¼x13½*
**1472A** A348 Sheet of 3, #b-d 15.00 15.00

No. 1472A contains three 48x33mm stamps in gold. No. 1472A exists imperf. Value, $40.

Tourism — A349

Designs: 300k, Phousy Stupa, Luang Prabang. 600k, Than Chang Cave. 2800k, Inhang Stupa. 3300k, Buddha, Phiawat Temple.

**2000, Nov. 23** *Perf. 14x14½*
**1473-1476** A349 Set of 4 6.00 3.00

Lao People's Democratic Republic, 25th Anniv. — A350

**2000, Dec. 2** *Perf. 13¼*
**1477** A350 4000k multi 2.75 1.50

Mekong River at Twilight A351

Various views: 900k, 2700k, 3400k.

**2000, June 20** *Perf. 14½x14*
**1478-1480** A351 Set of 3 5.00 2.50

Anti-Drug Campaign — A352

Designs: 100k, Poppy field. 4000k, Burning of seized drugs.

**2000, June 26** **Litho.**
**1481-1482** A352 Set of 2 3.50 1.50

**Souvenir Sheet**

Route 13 Bridge Reconstruction Project — A353

Bridge in: a, Savannakhet. b, Saravane. c, Pakse.

**2000, Feb. 14** *Perf. 13¼*
**1483** A353 4000k Sheet of 3, #a-c 9.00 9.00

**Souvenir Sheet**

Anti-Polio Campaign — A354

No. 1484: a, 900k, People receiving vaccine. b, 2500k, Family, map of Laos.

**2000, June 1**
**1484** A354 Sheet of 2, #a-b 3.50 3.50

Millennium A355

Designs: 3200k, Satellite, telecommunication dishes, map of Laos, student. 4000k, High tension lines, dam.

**2001, Jan. 1** *Perf. 14x14½*
**1485-1486** A355 Set of 2 4.00 2.50

New Year 2001 (Year of the Snake) A356

Designs: 900k, Snake coiled around branch. 3500k, Snake, other zodiac animals.

**2001, Apr. 15** *Perf. 14½x14*
**1487-1488** A356 Set of 2 4.00 2.00

Cockfighting — A357

Pair of cocks fighting: 500k, 900k, 3300k, 3500k.
10,000k, Single cock, vert.

**2001, Mar. 10** *Perf. 14½x14*
**1489-1492** A357 Set of 4 5.50 3.25

**Souvenir Sheet**

***Perf. 13¼***

**1493** A357 10,000k multi 7.50 7.50

No. 1493 contains one 36x50mm stamp. No. 1493 exists imperf. Value, $40.

Laos-People's Republic of China Diplomatic Relations, 40th Anniv. — A358

**2001, Apr. 25** *Perf. 14¼x14½*

| | | | |
|---|---|---|---|
| **1494** A358 1000k multi | 1.25 | .40 |

Phila Nippon '01 A359

Birds: Nos. 1495, 1499a, 700k, Egretta intermedia. Nos. 1496, 1499b, 800k, Bubulcus ibis (36x50mm). Nos. 1497, 1499c, 3100k, Ardea cinera (36x50mm). Nos. 1498, 1499d, 3400k, Egretta alba.

*Perf. 14½x14, 13¼ (#1496-1497)*

**2001, Aug. 1 With White Frames**

| | | | |
|---|---|---|---|
| **1495-1498** A359 Set of 4 | 6.00 | 3.00 |

**Souvenir Sheet**

**Without White Frames**

*Perf. 13¼*

| | | | |
|---|---|---|---|
| **1499** A359 Sheet of 4, #a-d | 7.50 | 7.50 |

No. 1499 sold for 10,000k. No. 1499 exists imperf. Value, $50.

Mortars and Pestles — A360

Designs: 900k, Two women using large hand-held pestle, vert. 2600k, Water-driven mortar and pestle. 3500k, Woman operating mechanical mortar and pestle, vert.

*Perf. 14x14½, 14½x14*

**2001, Nov. 15**

| | | | |
|---|---|---|---|
| **1500-1502** A360 Set of 3 | 4.50 | 2.25 |

Ceremonies — A361

Designs: 300k, Pou Nyer and Nya Nyer, vert. 600k, Hae Nang Sangkhan, vert. 1000k, Sand Stupa. 2300k, Hae Prabang, vert. 4000k, Takbat, vert.

**2001, Apr. 13** *Perf. 14x14½, 14½x14*

| | | | |
|---|---|---|---|
| **1503-1507** A361 Set of 5 | 7.50 | 3.50 |

Buddhist Art — A362

Designs: 200k, Himavanta. 900k, Vanapavesa. 3200k, Kumarakanda. 3600k, Sakkapabba.

**2001, Dec. 5** *Perf. 13¼*

| | | | |
|---|---|---|---|
| **1508-1511** A362 Set of 4 | 6.00 | 3.25 |
| *1511a* Souvenir sheet, #1508-1511 | 7.00 | 7.00 |

No. 1511a exists imperf. Value, $50.

Men's Costumes — A363

Designs: 100k, Yao Mane. 200k, Gnaheun. 500k, Katou. 2300k, Hmong Dam. 2500k, Harlak. 2600k, Kui. 2700k, Krieng. 3100k, Khmu Nhuan. 3200k, Ta Oy. 3300k, Tai Theng. 3400k, Hmong Khao. 3500k, Gnor. 3600k, Phouthai Na Gnom. 4000k, Yao. 5000k, Hmong.

**2001, Feb. 20** *Perf. 14¼x14½*

| | | | | | |
|---|---|---|---|---|---|
| **1512** | A363 | 100k multi | .25 | .25 |
| **1513** | A363 | 200k multi | .25 | .25 |
| **1514** | A363 | 500k multi | .30 | .25 |
| **1515** | A363 | 2300k multi | 1.25 | .80 |
| **1516** | A363 | 2500k multi | 1.40 | .85 |
| **1517** | A363 | 2600k multi | 1.40 | .85 |
| **1518** | A363 | 2700k multi | 1.50 | .90 |
| **1519** | A363 | 3100k multi | 1.60 | 1.00 |
| **1520** | A363 | 3200k multi | 1.75 | 1.10 |
| **1521** | A363 | 3300k multi | 1.75 | 1.10 |
| **1522** | A363 | 3400k multi | 1.75 | 1.25 |
| **1523** | A363 | 3500k multi | 2.00 | 1.25 |
| **1524** | A363 | 3600k multi | 2.00 | 1.25 |
| **1525** | A363 | 4000k multi | 2.25 | 1.50 |
| **1526** | A363 | 5000k multi | 2.75 | 1.90 |
| | | *Nos. 1512-1526 (15)* | 22.20 | 14.50 |

Buddhist Temple Doors — A364

Various doors: 600k, 2300k, 2500k, 2600k.

**2001, Sept. 17 Litho.** *Perf. 14x14½*

| | | | |
|---|---|---|---|
| **1527-1530** A364 Set of 4 | 6.00 | 3.00 |

Frangipani Flowers — A365

Designs: 1000k, White flowers. 2500k, Pink flowers, vert. 3500k, Red flowers.

**2001, Oct. 2** *Perf. 14½x14, 14x14½*

| | | | |
|---|---|---|---|
| **1531-1533** A365 Set of 3 | 4.50 | 2.50 |
| *a.* Souvenir sheet, #1531-1533, perf. 13¼ | 6.00 | 4.00 |

Intl. Volunteers Year — A366

**2001, Dec. 29** *Perf. 13¼*

| | | | |
|---|---|---|---|
| **1534** A366 1000k multi | 2.50 | .40 |

Women's Costumes — A367

Designs: 200k, Meuy. 300k, Leu. 500k, Tai Kouane. 700k, Tai Dam. 1000k, Tai Men. 1500k, Lanten. 2500k, Hmong. 3000k, Phouxang. 3500k, Taitheng. 4000k, Tai O. 5000k, Tai Dam, diff.

**2002, Jan. 10** *Perf. 14x14½*

| | | | | |
|---|---|---|---|---|
| **1535** | A367 | 200k multi | .25 | .25 |
| **1536** | A367 | 300k multi | .25 | .25 |
| **1537** | A367 | 500k multi | .25 | .25 |
| **1538** | A367 | 700k multi | .30 | .25 |
| **1539** | A367 | 1000k multi | .50 | .30 |
| **1540** | A367 | 1500k multi | .70 | .45 |
| **1541** | A367 | 2500k multi | 1.25 | .75 |
| **1542** | A367 | 3000k multi | 1.50 | .95 |
| **1543** | A367 | 3500k multi | 1.75 | 1.10 |
| **1544** | A367 | 4000k multi | 2.00 | 1.25 |
| **1545** | A367 | 5000k multi | 2.25 | 1.60 |
| | | *Nos. 1535-1545 (11)* | 11.00 | 7.40 |

Intl. Year of Mountains — A368

Designs: No. 1546, 1500k, Pha Tang. No. 1547, 1500k, Phou Phamane.

**2002, Mar. 30** *Perf. 14½x14*

| | | | |
|---|---|---|---|
| **1546-1547** A368 Set of 2 | 2.50 | 1.10 |

Nos. 1546-1547 are a corrected printing. The first printing, which was erroneously inscribed "LAO PRD" instead of "LAO PDR," was removed from sale after a few panes had been sold. Value, set of 2 $100.

New Year 2002 (Year of the Horse) A369

Designs: 1500k, Horse, zodiac animals. 3500k, Galloping horse.

**2002, Apr. 14**

| | | | |
|---|---|---|---|
| **1548-1549** A369 Set of 2 | 3.00 | 1.60 |

Laos - Viet Nam Cooperation A370

Designs: 2500k, Musical instruments. 3500k, Laotian leader with Ho Chi Minh, horiz.

**2002, July 18** *Perf. 13*

| | | | |
|---|---|---|---|
| **1550-1551** A370 Set of 2 | 3.25 | 1.90 |

Phila Korea 2002 World Stamp Exhibition, Seoul — A371

Insects: Nos. 1552a, 1553a, Sagra femorata. Nos. 1552b, 1552b, Cerambycidae. Nos. 1552c, 1552c, Chrysochroa mniszechii. Nos. 1552d, 1553d, Anoplophora sp. Nos. 1552e, 1553e, Chrysochroa sandersi. Nos. 1552f, 1553f, Mouhotia batesi. Nos. 1552g, 1553g, Megaloxantha assamensis. Nos. 1552h, 1553h, Eupatorus gracillicornis.

**2002, Aug. 1** *Perf. 14½x14*

**Insects and Colored Backgrounds**

| | | | |
|---|---|---|---|
| **1552** Vert. strip of 8 | 5.00 | 5.00 |
| *a.-h.* A371 1000k Any single | .50 | .30 |

**Souvenir Sheet**

**Insects On Vegetation**

| | | | |
|---|---|---|---|
| **1553** A371 1000k Sheet of 8, #a-h | 5.00 | 5.00 |

No. 1553 exists imperf. Value, $45.

Admission to UPU, 50th Anniv. A372

**2002, May 20 Litho.** *Perf. 13x13¼*

| | | | |
|---|---|---|---|
| **1554** A372 3000k black | 2.00 | 2.00 |

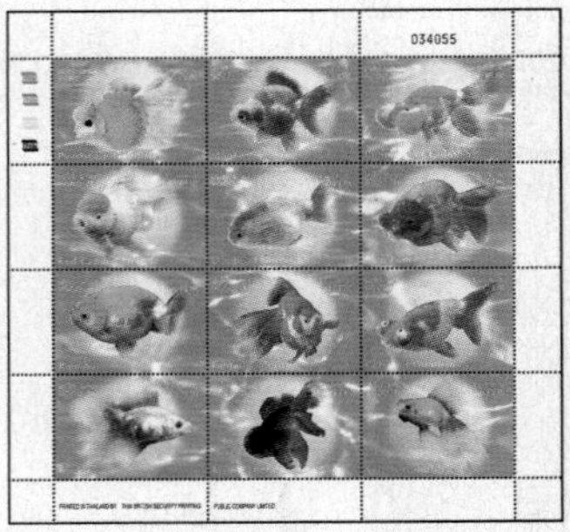

Goldfish — A373

No. 1555: a, Pearlscale goldfish. b, Moor. c, Bubble eyes goldfish. d, Red-capped oranda. e, Lionhead goldfish. f, Pom pom. g, Ranchu. h, Fantail goldfish. i, Celestial goldfish. j, Ryukin. k, Brown oranda. l, Veiltail goldfish.

**2002, Oct. 2** *Perf. 13¼*

| | | | |
|---|---|---|---|
| **1555** A373 1000k Sheet of 12, #a-l | 6.00 | 6.00 |

No. 1555 exists imperf. Value, $25.

Buffalo Fighting A374

Various buffalo: 200k, 300k, 3000k, 4000k.

**2002, Dec. 15** *Perf. 13x13¼*

| | | | |
|---|---|---|---|
| **1556-1559** A374 Set of 4 | 4.50 | 3.00 |

**Souvenir Sheet**

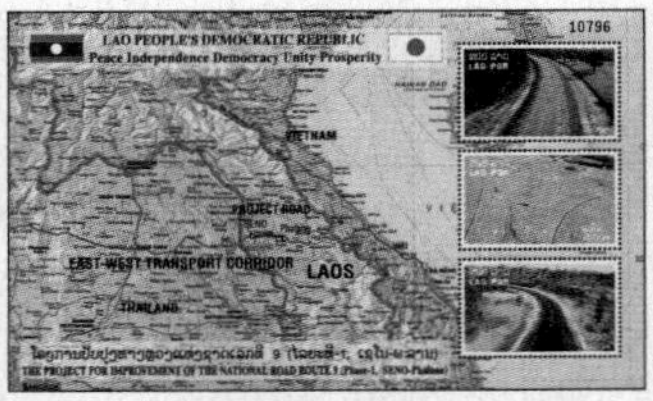

National Route 9 Improvement Project — A375

No. 1560: a, Curve. b, Interchange. c, Curve and building.

**2002, Dec. 18 Litho.** *Perf. 13¼*

| | | | |
|---|---|---|---|
| **1560** A375 1500k Sheet of 3, #a-c | 6.00 | 6.00 |

Vat Phou World Heritage Site — A376

Designs: 1500k, Temple, vert. 3000k, Temple, diff. 4000k, Statue of Buddha, vert. 10,000k, Stone carving.

**2003, Feb. 14** *Perf. 14x14½, 14½x14*

| | | | |
|---|---|---|---|
| **1561-1563** A376 Set of 3 | 4.50 | 2.60 |

**Souvenir Sheet**

*Perf. 13¼*

| | | | |
|---|---|---|---|
| **1564** A376 10,000k multi | 6.00 | 6.00 |

No. 1564 contains one 93x27mm stamp.

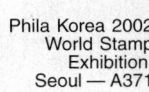

Butterflies — A377

No. 1565: a, Hasora schoenherr. b, Spindasis lohita. c, Graphium sarpedon. d, Polyura schreiber. e, Castalius rosimon. f, Dalias pasithoe. g, Pachliopta aristolochiae. h, Papilio memnon.
10,000k, Danaus genutia.

**2003, Mar. 8** ***Perf. 14½x14***

| | | | | |
|---|---|---|---|---|
| **1565** | A377 | Block of 8 | 6.00 | 6.00 |
| *a.-h.* | | 1000k Any single | .60 | .35 |

**Souvenir Sheet**

***Perf. 13¼***

| | | | | |
|---|---|---|---|---|
| **1566** | A377 | 10,000k multi | *6.00* | *6.00* |

No. 1566 exists imperf. Value, $30.

New Year 2003 (Year of the Goat) A378

Designs: 2500k, Two goats. 5000k, Goat, zodiac animals.

**2003, Apr. 15** ***Perf. 14½x14***

| | | | | |
|---|---|---|---|---|
| **1567-1568** | A378 | Set of 2 | 5.00 | 2.25 |

Orchids — A379

Designs: 200k, Phalaenopsis Paifang's Golden Lion. 300k, Coelogyne lentiginosa. 500k, Phalaenopsis sumatrana. 1000k, Phalaenopsis bellina. 1500k, Paphiopedilum appletonianum. 2000k, Vanda bensonii. 2500k, Dendrobium harveyanum. 3000k, Paphiopedilum glaucophyllum. 3500k, Paphiopedilum gratrixianum. 4000k, Vanda roeblingiana. 5000k, Phalaenopsis Lady Sakhara.

**2003, Apr. 25** ***Perf. 14½x14¼***

| | | | | |
|---|---|---|---|---|
| **1569** | A379 | 200k multi | .30 | .25 |
| **1570** | A379 | 300k multi | .40 | .25 |
| **1571** | A379 | 500k multi | .60 | .25 |
| **1572** | A379 | 1000k multi | .70 | .30 |
| **1573** | A379 | 1500k multi | .80 | .45 |
| **1574** | A379 | 2000k multi | 1.00 | .60 |
| **1575** | A379 | 2500k multi | 1.25 | .75 |
| **1576** | A379 | 3000k multi | 1.40 | .90 |
| **1577** | A379 | 3500k multi | 1.75 | 1.00 |
| **1578** | A379 | 4000k multi | 1.75 | 1.25 |
| **1579** | A379 | 5000k multi | 2.25 | 1.50 |
| | | *Nos. 1569-1579 (11)* | 12.20 | 7.50 |

Wood Handicrafts — A380

Designs: 500k, Bowl. 1500k, Pitcher and goblets. 2500k, Fluted bowl. 3500k, Bowl, vert.

**2003, May 10** ***Perf. 13***

| | | | | |
|---|---|---|---|---|
| **1580-1583** | A380 | Set of 4 | 4.75 | 2.40 |

Traditional Games A381

Designs: 1000k, Walking on stringed coconut shells. 3000k, Top spinning. 4000k, Field hockey.

**2003, June 1**

| | | | | |
|---|---|---|---|---|
| **1584-1586** | A381 | Set of 3 | 3.50 | 2.40 |

Stop Hunting Campaign A382

Designs: 1500k, Deer. 2000k, Gun. 4500k, Wild animals.

**2003, July 25** **Litho.** ***Perf. 13***

| | | | | |
|---|---|---|---|---|
| **1587-1589** | A382 | Set of 3 | 3.75 | 2.50 |

Fruit A383

Designs: 500k, Mango. 1500k, Watermelon. 2500k, Custard apple. 4000k, Pineapple.

**2003, Aug. 8** ***Perf. 14½x14***

| | | | | |
|---|---|---|---|---|
| **1590-1593** | A383 | Set of 4 | 4.50 | 2.60 |

Palm Leaf Manuscripts A384

Designs: 500k, Monk writing palm leaf manuscript. 1500k, Palm leaf manuscript. 2500k, Manuscript casket. 3000k, Ho Tai.

**2003, Sept. 12** ***Perf. 14x14½***

| | | | | |
|---|---|---|---|---|
| **1594-1597** | A384 | Set of 4 | 4.00 | 3.00 |

Bangkok 2003 Intl. Philatelic Exhibition — A385

Buddhas of Luang Prabang: 500k, Pha Sene Souk. 1500k, Pha Gnai. 3000k, Pha Ong Luang. 3500k, Pha Ong Sene.
10,000k, Pha Attharatsa.

**2003, Oct. 4** ***Perf. 14x14½***

| | | | | |
|---|---|---|---|---|
| **1598-1601** | A385 | Set of 4 | 5.00 | 3.25 |

**Souvenir Sheet**

***Perf. 13½***

| | | | | |
|---|---|---|---|---|
| **1602** | A385 | 10,000k multi | 6.00 | 6.00 |

No. 1602 contains one 30x95mm stamp. No. 1602 exists imperf. Value, $30.

Textiles — A386

Various textiles with panel colors of: 500k, Blue. 1000k, Red brown. 3000k, Green. 4000k, Yellow brown.

**2003, Dec. 1** ***Perf. 14x14½***

| | | | | |
|---|---|---|---|---|
| **1603-1606** | A386 | Set of 4 | 5.00 | 3.00 |

Installed Emerald Buddha — A387

**2004, Feb. 5** **Litho.** ***Perf. 14½x14***

| | | | | |
|---|---|---|---|---|
| **1607** | A387 | 5500k multi | 3.00 | 1.90 |

Birds — A388

Designs: 2000k, Buceros bicornis. 2500k, Pycnonotus jocosus. 3000k, Ploceus hypoxanthus. 3500k, Alcedo atthis. 4000k, Magalaima incognita. 4500k, Serilophus lunatus. 5000k, Lacedo pulchella. 5500k, Eurylaimus ochromalus.

**2004, Feb. 20** ***Perf. 14¼x14½***

| | | | | |
|---|---|---|---|---|
| **1608-1615** | A388 | Set of 8 | 13.50 | 11.00 |

Dolphins — A389

Two dolphins: 1500k With heads above water. 2500k, Leaping out of water. 3500k, Underwater.

**2004, Mar. 29** ***Perf. 14½x14***

| | | | | |
|---|---|---|---|---|
| **1616-1618** | A389 | Set of 3 | 3.50 | 2.50 |

New Year 2004 (Year of the Monkey) — A390

Designs: 500k, Two monkeys. 4500k, Monkey, zodiac animals.

**2004, Apr. 15**

| | | | | |
|---|---|---|---|---|
| **1619-1620** | A390 | Set of 2 | 2.75 | 1.75 |

FIFA (Fédération Internationale de Football Association), Cent. — A391

No. 1621 — FIFA emblem and: a, Flags of various countries. b, Soccer players.

**2004, May 21** ***Perf. 13½***

| | | | | |
|---|---|---|---|---|
| **1621** | A391 | 12,000k Pair, #a-b | 12.00 | 10.00 |

Values are for stamps with surrounding selvage,

Children's Day — A392

Designs: 3500k, Four children. 4500k, Children, globe, school.

**2004, June 1** ***Perf. 14½x14***

| | | | | |
|---|---|---|---|---|
| **1622-1623** | A392 | Set of 2 | 3.50 | 2.60 |

11th ASEAN Postal Business Meeting — A393

**2004, July 5** **Litho.** ***Perf. 14x14½***

| | | | | |
|---|---|---|---|---|
| **1624** | A393 | 5000k multi | 3.00 | 1.75 |

Worldwide Fund for Nature (WWF) — A394

No. 1625 — Cuora amboinensis: a, 5000k, In water. b, 5500k, On rock near water. c, 6000k, Pair. d, 7000k, Head, feet and shell.

**2004, Aug. 16** **Litho.** ***Perf. 13½x14***

| | | | | |
|---|---|---|---|---|
| **1625** | A394 | Block of 4, #a-d | 6.00 | 5.00 |

Dances — A395

Designs: 1000k, Tangwai. 1500k, Khabthoume Luangprabang. 2000k, Lao Lamvong. 2500k, Salavan.

**2004, Aug. 23** ***Perf. 14x14¾***

| | | | | |
|---|---|---|---|---|
| **1626-1629** | A395 | Set of 4 | 3.25 | 2.10 |
| *1629a* | | Souvenir sheet, #1626-1629, perf. 13¼ | 5.00 | 5.00 |

No. 1629a sold for 10,000k. No. 1629a exists imperf. Value, $40.

Marigolds A396

Designs: 3500k, Yellow, orange marigolds. 5000k, Red and orange marigolds. 5500k, Decorations made with marigolds.

**2004, Sept. 28** *Perf. 13¼x13*
**1630-1632** A396 Set of 3 4.75 4.75

Scenes From Ramakian — A397

Various scenes: 3500k, 4500k, 5500k, 6500k.

**2004, Oct. 10** *Perf. 13¼*
**1633-1636** A397 Set of 4 9.00 6.75

Naga Fireball — A398

Designs: 2000k, Figure above river, serpent in river. 3000k, Buildings, serpent, horiz. 3500k, Fireball in serpent's mouth, horiz. 4000k, Fireballs above serpent.

**2004, Oct. 28** *Perf. 13 Syncopated*
**1637-1640** A398 Set of 4 4.25 4.25

Betel Tray A399

Designs: 2000k, Betel nuts, bowls and containers. 4000k, Betel nut and leaf. 6000k, Betel tray.

**2004, Nov. 11** **Litho.** *Perf. 13*
**1641-1643** A399 Set of 3 4.00 4.00

Laos — Sweden Diplomatic Relations, 40th Anniv. — A400

**2004, Dec. 12** **Litho.** *Perf. 13x13½*
**1644** A400 8500k multi 4.00 2.75

Handicrafts — A401

Designs: 1000k, Short, round basket. 2000k, Paddle. 2500k, Basket with handle, vert. 5500k, Basket with handle and lid, vert.

*Perf. 14½x14, 14x14½*

**2005, Mar. 10** **Litho.**
**1645-1648** A401 Set of 4 5.25 3.25

New Year 2005 (Year of the Rooster) — A402

Rooster and: 2000k, Hen. 7500k, Zodiac animals.

**2005, Apr. 13** *Perf. 14½x14*
**1649-1650** A402 Set of 2 5.00 3.50

Daily Buddhas — A403

Buddha for: 500k, Sunday. 1000k, Monday. 1500k, Tuesday, horiz. 2000k, Wednesday. 2500k, Thursday. 3000k, Friday. 3500k, Saturday.

*Perf. 14x14½, 14½x14*

**2005, May 15** **Litho.**
**1651-1657** A403 Set of 7 6.50 4.50

Rice — A404

Designs: 1500k, Rice plants. 3000k, Cooked rice on plate, horiz. 6500k, Bundles of rice plants, horiz.

*Perf. 13 Syncopated*

**2005, June 1** **Litho.**
**1658-1660** A404 Set of 3 5.25 3.25

Mekong River Giant Catfish — A405

Designs: 3500k, Shown. 6500k, Catfish, diff.

**2005, July 13** **Litho.** *Perf. 14½x14*
**1661-1662** A405 Set of 2 4.75 3.25

Gold Panning — A406

Designs: 2000k, Pan. 7500k, Woman panning for gold, vert.

*Perf. 13 Syncopated*

**2005, Aug. 1** **Litho.**
**1663-1664** A406 Set of 2 4.00 3.00

Folk Songs — A407

Designs: 1000k, Two musicians standing. 3500k, Two musicians seated. 5500k, Four musicians, horiz.

**2005, Sept. 2**
**1665-1667** A407 Set of 3 4.50 3.00

Europa Stamps, 50th Anniv. (in 2006) A408

Designs: 6000k, Stonehenge, England, and Plain of Jars, Laos. No. 1669, 7000k, Knossos Palace, Greece, and Patuxay, Laos. No. 1670, 7000k, Colosseum, Rome, and Wat Phu, Laos. No. 1671, 7500k, Stave Church, Lom, Norway, and Wat Xieng Thong, Laos. No. 1672, 7500k, Notre Dame Cathedral, Paris, and That Luang, Laos. 8000k, Trier Cathedral, Germany, and Wat Phra Keo, Laos.

**2005, Oct. 24** **Litho.** *Perf. 14¾x14*
**1668-1673** A408 Set of 6 15.00 12.50
*1673a* Souvenir sheet, #1668-1673 30.00 30.00

No. 1673a exists imperf. Value, $60.

People's Democratic Republic, 30th Anniv. — A409

Designs: 500k, Flag and building. 1000k, Flag and people. 2000k, Flag and coat of arms. 5000k, People and coat of arms.

**2005, Dec. 2** *Perf. 13*
**1674-1677** A409 Set of 4 4.50 2.50

Diplomatic Relations with Thailand, 55th Anniv. — A410

**2005, Dec. 19**
**1678** A410 7500k multi 4.50 2.25

Laos-United Nations Cooperation, 50th Anniv. — A411

Designs: No. 1679, 3000k, Rice harvesters. No. 1679A, 3000k, Children at school gate. No. 1679B, 3000k, Infant health care.

**2005, Oct. 24** **Litho.** *Perf. 13x13¼*
**1679-1679B** A411 Set of 3 4.50 3.50
*1679Bc* Souvenir sheet, #1679-1679B 15.00 15.00

No. 1679Bc sold for 15,000k.

Lao People's Democratic Republic, 30th Anniv. — A411a

Designs: 500k, Buildings and flag. 1000k, Map, people and flag. 2000k, Flag, coat of arms. 5000k, Arms, people.

**2005, Dec. 2** **Litho.** *Perf. 13*
**1679D-1679G** A411a Set of 4 4.50 4.50

Lao People's Democratic Republic, 30th Anniv. — A411b

**2005, Dec. 16** **Litho.** *Perf. 13¼x13*
**1679H** A411b 15,500k multi 9.00 5.50

**Souvenir Sheet**

**1679I** A411b 20,000k multi 10.00 7.00

Diplomatic Relations Between Laos and Japan, 50th Anniv. — A411c

Designs: 7000k, Flowers. 20,000k, Temples.

**2005, Dec. 30** *Perf. 13*
**1679J** A411c 7000k multi 4.50 2.60

**Size: 170x130mm**

*Imperf*

**1679K** A411c 20,000k multi 15.00 15.00

Statue of King Phangum Lenglathorany A412

**2006, Mar. 9** **Litho.** *Perf. 14x14½*
**1680** A412 8500k multi 3.50 2.60

A souvenir sheet containing one perf. 13½ example of No. 1680 sold for 20,000k.

New Year 2006 (Year of the Dog) A413

Designs: 2000k, Dog. 6500k, Dog, zodiac animals.

**2006, Apr. 14** *Perf. 14½x14*
**1681-1682** A413 Set of 2 6.50 3.50

AGL Insurance in Laos, 15th Anniv. — A414

AGL Insurance emblem and: 8000k, Car, minivan and motorcycle. 8500k, Map of Laos. 9500k, Family.

**2006, May 1** *Perf. 13*
**1683-1685** A414 Set of 3 11.00 7.75

Friendship Between Vientiane and Moscow — A415

Laotian and Russian: 7500k, Women. 8500k, Sculptures and houses of worship.

**2006, May 1**

**1686-1687** A415 Set of 2 8.00 4.75
*1687a* Souvenir sheet, #1686-1687 10.00 10.00

No. 1687a sold for 20,000k.

Diplomatic Relations Between Laos and People's Republic of China, 45th Anniv. — A416

**2006, July 7** ***Perf. 13x12¾***

**1688** A416 8500k multi 5.00 5.00

No. 1688 exists imperf. Value, $20.

Shrimp A417

Various depictions of shrimp: 1000k, 2000k, 4000k, 6000k.

**2006, July 10** ***Perf. 13***

**1689-1692** A417 Set of 4 7.00 4.00
*1692a* Souvenir sheet, #1689-1692 8.50 8.50

No. 1692a sold for 15,000k.

Léopold Sédar Senghor (1906-2001), First President of Senegal — A418

**2006, Sept. 4**

**1693** A418 8500k multi 5.00 3.00

Bronze Drums A419

Various drums with background colors of: 2000k, Red brown. 3500k, Blue. 7500k, Olive green.

**2006, Oct. 9**

**1694-1696** A419 Set of 3 7.00 4.00
*1696a* Souvenir sheet, #1694-1696 9.00 9.00

No. 1696a sold for 15,000k.

Xieng Khouane Temple — A420

Various views of temple and sculptures: 1000k, 2500k, 3000k, 5000k.

**2006, June 10** **Litho.** ***Perf. 13***

**1697-1700** A420 Set of 4 6.50 4.00

Bananas A421

Designs: 1000k, Pisang Masak Hijau. 2000k, Pisang Mas. 4000k, Pisang Ambon. 8000k, Pisang Awak.

**2006, Nov. 1**

**1701-1704** A421 Set of 4 7.50 5.00

Opening of Second Thai-Lao Friendship Bridge — A422

Designs: No. 1705, 7500k, Bridge in daylight. No. 1706, 7500k, Bridge at night.

**2006, Dec. 20**

**1705-1706** A422 Set of 2 8.00 5.00

Jewelry — A423

Designs: 2000k, Pins. 5000k, Bracelet. 7000k, Earrings. 7500k, Necklace and pendant.

**2007, Jan. 15** **Litho.** ***Perf. 13¼x13***

**1707-1710** A423 Set of 4 11.00 8.00
*1710a* Souvenir sheet, #1707-1710 14.00 12.00

No. 1710a sold for 25,000k.

Crabs A424

Various crabs: 1000k, 2000k, 7000k, 7500k.

**2007, Feb. 20** ***Perf. 13x13¼***

**1711-1714** A424 Set of 4 9.00 6.50
*1714a* Souvenir sheet, #1711-1714, perf. 13½x13¾ 10.00 9.00

No. 1714a sold for 20,000k.

New Year 2007 (Year of the Pig) A425

Designs: No. 1715, 7500k, Pig and piglets. No. 1716, 7500k, Pig, zodiac animals.

**2007, Apr. 15** ***Perf. 13x13¼***

**1715-1716** A425 Set of 2 8.00 5.75

Takbat Festival — A425a

Designs: 2000k, Monks standing, women placing items on ground. 5000k, Woman reaching into monk's bowl. 7500k, Women holding bowls.

**2007, July 10** **Litho.** ***Perf. 13***

**1716A-1716C** A425a Set of 3 7.00 5.50

Association of South East Asian Nations (ASEAN), 40th Anniv. — A426

Designs: 7000k, Typical house, Laos.
No. 1718: a, Like 7000k. b, Secretariat Building, Bandar Seri Begawan, Brunei. c, National Museum of Cambodia. d, Fatahillah Museum, Jakarta, Indonesia. e, Malayan Railway Headquarters Building, Kuala Lumpur, Malaysia. f, Yangon Post Office, Myanmar. g, Malacañang Palace, Philippines. h, National Museum of Singapore. i, Vimanmek Mansion, Bangkok, Thailand. j, Presidential Palace, Hanoi, Viet Nam.

**2007, Aug. 8** **Litho.** ***Perf. 13***

**1717** A426 7000k multi 3.00 3.00
**1718** Sheet of 10 7.00 7.00
***a.-j.*** A426 700k Any single .50 .40

See Brunei No. 607, Burma No. 370, Cambodia No. 2339, Indonesia Nos. 2120-2121, Malaysia No. 1170, Philippines Nos. 3103-3105, Singapore No. 1265, Thailand No. 2315, and Viet Nam Nos. 3302-3311.

Transportation — A426a

Designs: 2000k, Airplanes. 5000k, Ferry. 7500k, Trucks.

**2007, Sept. 1** **Litho.** ***Perf. 13***

**1718K-1718M** A426a Set of 3 7.00 6.00

That Luang Festival — A426b

Designs: 2000k, Monks leading procession. 5000k, Procession with temple in background. 8000k, Temple at night.

**2007, Nov. 13**

**1718N-1718P** A426b Set of 3 7.50 5.75

Traditional Foods — A426c

Designs: 2000k, Sticky rice cooked in bamboo tubes. 5500k, Green papaya salad. 7500k, Grilled chicken.

**2007, Dec. 30**

**1718Q-1718S** A426c Set of 3 7.50 5.75

Worldwide Fund for Nature (WWF) A427

Hylobates lar: 6000k, Head. 7000k, Adult and juvenile. 8000k, With open mouth. 9000k, Two adults.

**2008** **Litho.** ***Perf. 13½x14***

**1719-1722** A427 Set of 4 12.00 7.25
*1722a* Miniature sheet, 4 each #1719-1722 120.00 120.00

Nos. 1719-1722, 1722a exist imperf. Value, Nos. 1719-1722 imperf. block of 4 $40.

2008 Summer Olympics, Beijing A428

Designs: No. 1723, 5000k, Taekwondo. No. 1724, 5000k, High jump. No. 1725, 5000k, Cycling. No. 1726, 5000k, Soccer.

**2008, Apr. 17** ***Perf. 12½x13***

**1723-1726** A428 Set of 4 8.00 4.75

Nos. 1723-1726 each were printed in sheets of 16. Two sheet varieties exist: English inscriptions in the top and bottom selvage, and a combination of English (right and bottom selvage) and Ukrainian (top and left selvage) inscriptions. Sheets with the English and Ukrainian inscriptions are scarce. Value, set of four singles of Nos. 1723-1726 each with attached Ukrainian selvage $20.

Elephant Festival — A429

Designs: 1000k, Tuskless elephant and rider. 2000k, Two elephants and riders. 3000k, Man in crowd holding rope. 5000k, Tusked elephant with rider. 7500k, Woman decorating elephant. 8500k, Elephants moving logs.
20,000k, Elephants, riders and guides.

**2008, Jan. 14** **Litho.** ***Perf. 13***

**1727-1732** A429 Set of 6 12.00 11.00

**Size: 146x110mm**

***Imperf***

**1733** A429 20,000k multi + label 12.50 8.50

Coffee — A430

Designs: Nos. 1734, 1737a, 3000k, Mug and roasted coffee beans. Nos. 1735, 1737b, 5000k, Coffee berries. Nos. 1736, 1737c, 6000k, Roasted coffee beans.

**2008, Feb. 11 Litho. *Perf. 13***
**Size: 30x45mm**

**1734-1736** A430 Set of 3 8.00 6.25

**Souvenir Sheet**
***Perf. 13¼x13***

**1737** A430 Sheet of 3, #a-c 10.00 8.00

No. 1737 contains three 32x43mm stamps and sold for 18,000k.

Cotton A432

Designs: Nos. 1739, 1742a, 1000k, Woman at cotton gin. Nos. 1740, 1742b, 5000k, Cotton plant. Nos. 1741, 1742c, 5500k, Cotton plant, diff.

**2008, Apr. 10 *Perf. 13***
**Size: 45x30mm**

**1739-1741** A432 Set of 3 7.50 5.25

**Souvenir Sheet**
***Perf. 13½x13¾***

**1742** A432 Sheet of 3, #a-c 8.50 6.75

No. 1742 contains three 42x32mm stamps and sold for 15,000k.

Bees A434

Designs: 1000k, Bees and honeycomb. 4000k, Bees on flower. 6000k, Beehive. 8500k, Bee in flight.

**2008, June 13 *Perf. 13***

**1747-1750** A434 Set of 4 11.00 8.75

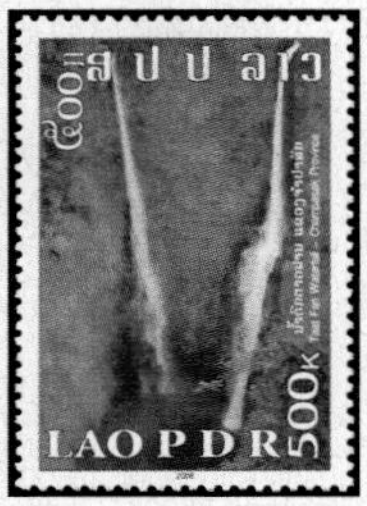

Waterfalls A435

Designs: Nos. 1751, 1755a, 500k, Taat Fan Waterfall. Nos. 1752, 1755b, 2000k, Tad Sae Waterfall, horiz. Nos. 1753, 1755c, 5000k, Kuang Si Waterfall. Nos. 1754, 1755d, 6500k, Khonphapheng Waterfall, horiz.

**2008, July 28 *Perf. 13***
**Sizes: 30x45mm, 45x30mm (Horiz. Stamps)**

**1751-1754** A435 Set of 4 9.00 6.25

**Souvenir Sheet**
***Perf. 13¾x13½, 13½x13¾***

**1755** A435 Sheet of 4, #a-d 9.50 7.25

No. 1755 contains two 32x42mm stamps and two 42x32mm stamps and sold for 16,000k.

Eggplants — A436

Designs: Nos. 1756, 1760a, 1000k, White eggplants. Nos. 1757, 1760b, 2000k, Green eggplants. Nos. 1758, 1760c, 4000k, Green, striped eggplants. Nos. 1759, 1760d, 5500k, Purple eggplants.

**2008, Oct. 1 *Perf. 13***
**Size: 45x30mm**

**1756-1759** A436 Set of 4 8.00 5.75

**Souvenir Sheet**

**1760** A436 Sheet of 4, #a-d 9.00 6.75

No. 1760 contains four 42x32mm stamps and sold for 15,000k.

Hmong New Year — A437

Designs: Nos. 1761, 1765a, 1000k, Woman. Nos. 1762, 1765b, 5500k, Two oxen, horiz. Nos. 1763, 1765c, 6000k, Musician. Nos. 1764, 1765d, 7500k, Two women holding umbrellas, horiz.

**2008, Dec. 1 *Perf. 13***
**Size: 30x45mm, 45x30mm (Horiz. Stamps)**

**1761-1764** A437 Set of 4 12.00 9.00

**Souvenir Sheet**
***Perf. 13¾x13½, 13½x13¾***

**1765** A437 Sheet of 4, #a-d 12.50 9.00

No. 1765 contains two 32x42mm stamps and two 42x32mm stamps.

Antiquities of Laos — A438

Designs: Nos. 1766, 1770a, 1000k, Haw Phra Kaew. Nos. 1767, 1770b, 2000k, Plain of Jars. Nos. 1768, 1770c, 4000k, Phat That Luang. Nos. 1769, 1770d, 7500k, Temple.

**2009, Jan. 3 *Perf. 13***
**Stamps With White Frames**

**1766-1769** A438 Set of 4 8.50 5.00

**Souvenir Sheet**
**Stamps With Colored Frames**

**1770** A438 Sheet of 4, #a-d 8.50 5.25

No. 1770 sold for 15,000k.

A439

A440

A441

Army, 60th Anniv. A442

**2009, Jan. 20**

**1771** A439 2000k multi 2.00 1.25
**1772** A440 2000k multi 2.00 1.25
**1773** A441 2000k multi 2.00 1.25
**1774** A442 2000k multi 2.00 1.25
*a.* Souvenir sheet of 4, #1771-1774 6.00 6.00
*Nos. 1771-1774 (4)* 8.00 5.00

No, 1774a sold for 10,000k.

A443

A444

Opening of Laos-Thailand Rail Link — A445

**2009, Mar. 5**

**1775** A443 3000k multi 2.00 1.50
**1776** A444 3000k multi 2.00 1.50
**1777** A445 3000k multi 2.00 1.50
*a.* Souvenir sheet of 3, #1775-1777 12.00 12.00
*Nos. 1775-1777 (3)* 6.00 4.50

No. 1777a sold for 15,000k.

China 2009 World Stamp Exhibition A446

Color of flower: No. 1778, 7500k, White. No. 1779, 7500k, Red.

**2009, Mar. 20**

**1778-1779** A446 Set of 2 8.00 6.50
*1779a* Souvenir sheet of 2, #1778-1779 12.00 12.00

No. 1779a sold for 20,000k, and exists imperf.

Flowers A447

Designs: 500k, Mari flower. 2000k, Ixora. 4000k, White Vuddish flowers (Calotropis gigantea). 7500k, Lilac Vuddish flowers (Calotropis gigantea).

**2009, May 15**

**1780-1783** A447 Set of 4 6.00 5.00
*1783a* Souvenir sheet of 4, #1780-1783 8.00 6.00

No. 1783a sold for 15,000k.

Rice Alcohol — A448

Designs: 1000k, Pots with sticks. 2000k, Horn and pot. 5500k, Man and pot.

**2009, Aug. 11**

**1784-1786** A448 Set of 3 5.00 5.00

A souvenir sheet containing Nos. 1784-1786 sold for 18,000k.

Postmarks A449

No. 1787 — Postmark of: a, R. P. Vientiane. b, Centre de Tri. c, Phongsaly. d, Luangnamtha. e, Oudomxay. f, Bokeo. g, Luangpabang. h, Huaphan. i, Sayaboury. j, Xiengkhouang. k, Vientiane. l, Bolikhamxay. m, Khammouane. n, Savannakhet. o, Saravan. p, Sekong. q, Champasack. r, Attapeu.

**2009, Oct. 9 *Perf. 13½***

**1787** Sheet of 18 17.50 17.50
*a.-r.* A449 2000r Any single .75 .50

25th South East Asian Games, Vientiane — A450

Mascots and: 5000k, Red background. 7000k, Flag, blue background.

**2009, Dec. 9** ***Perf. 14½x14***

**1788-1789** A450 Set of 2 6.50 6.50
*1789a* Souvenir sheet of 2, #1788-1789 9.00 9.00

No. 1789a sold for 15,000k.

Nos. 1788-1789 exist in a souvenir sheet of 4 containing 2 each, along with 4 labels that could be personalized.

Wat Simuong A451

Designs: 4000k, Statue. 5000k, Stone temple. 6000k, Temple.

**2009, Dec. 7** ***Perf. 13***

**1790-1792** A451 Set of 3 9.00 9.00
*1792a* Souvenir sheet of 3, #1790-1792 11.00 11.00

No. 1792a sold for 18,000k.

Flora A452

Designs: 1000k, Litsea cubeba. 3000k, Orthosiphon stamineus, vert. 4000k, Strychnos nux-vomica, vert. 5000k, Zingiber sp. 8000k, Styrax tonkinensis, vert. 9000k, Aquilaria crassna, vert.

**2010, Jun. 30** **Litho.**

**1793-1798** A452 Set of 6 25.00 25.00
*1797a* Souvenir sheet of 3 — —
*1798a* Souvenir sheet of 3 — —

No. 1797a contains Nos. 1794, 1795, and 1797. No. 1798a contains Nos. 1793, 1796, and 1798.

Rural Life A453

Designs: 1000k, Huts and people near stream. 6000k, Weavers. 12,000k, Woman and children winnowing rice.

**2010, Feb. 5**

**1799-1801** A453 Set of 3 10.00 10.00
*1801a* Souvenir sheet of 3, #1799-1801 12.00 12.00

No. 1801a sold for 20,000k.

Laotian Landscapes — A454

Designs: 1000k, Cave entrance. 3000k, Lake. 4000k, Boat on river. 10,000k, Canyon.

**2010, Apr. 1**

**1802-1805** A454 Set of 4 10.00 10.00
*1805a* Souvenir sheet of 4, #1802-1805 12.00 12.00

No. 1805a sold for 20,000k.

Rice Blessing Festival — A455

Designs: 4000k, Boy placing stick in clay pot. 5000k, Offering. 11,000k, People looking at burning candles.

**2010, July 26**

**1806-1808** A455 Set of 3 12.00 12.00
*1808a* Souvenir sheet of 3, #1806-1808 11.00 11.00
*1808b* Souvenir sheet of 1 #1808 11.00 11.00

No. 1808b sold for 15,000k.

Wild Fruit — A456

Color of fruit: 500k, Brown. 1500k, Red. 8000k, Yellow orange. 9000k, Green.

**2010. Sept. 1**

**1809-1812** A456 Set of 4 12.00 12.00
*1812a* Souvenir sheet of 4, #1809-1812 12.50 12.50

No. 1812a sold for 20,000k.

Vientiane, 450th Anniv. — A457

Emblem and Pha That Luang Stupa, Vientiane, in: 1000k, 1889. 3000k, 1910. 5000k, 1935. 6000k, 2010.

20,000k, Golden Stupa and statue, vert.

**2010, Nov. 15** **Litho.** ***Perf. 14½x14***

**1813-1816** A457 Set of 4 8.50 8.50

**Souvenir Sheet**

**Litho. & Embossed With Foil Application**

**1817** A457 20,000k gold & multi 12.00 12.00

No. 1817 contains one 48x60mm stamp.

People's Democratic Republic of Laos, 35th Anniv. — A458

Designs: 5000k, Army officer pointing. 6000k, Soldiers and large gun, vert. 10,000k, Laotian leaders and soldiers. No. 1821a, Like 10,000k.

**2010, Dec. 2** **Litho.** ***Perf. 13***

**1818-1820** A458 Set of 3 11.00 11.00
**1821** A458 Souvenir sheet of 3, #1818, 1819, 1821a 18.00 18.00
*a.* 9000k multi 5.00 5.00

Selection of Luang Prabang as UNESCO World Heritage Site, 15th Anniv. — A459

Various views of Luang Prabang festivals: 2000k, 3000k, 5000k, 10,000k.

**2010, Dec. 12**

**1822-1825** A459 Set of 4 12.00 12.00
*1825a* Souvenir sheet of 4, #1822-1825 12.00 12.00

Traditional Women's Costumes A460

Various women in traditional costumes: 1000k, 3000k, 4000k, 5000k, 8000k.

**2011, Jan. 31**

**1826-1830** A460 Set of 5 12.00 12.00

Potters and Pottery — A461

Designs: 1000k, Potter. 3000k, Clay pot. 5000k, Decorated clay pot. 6000k, Potter, diff.

**2011, Mar. 14**

**1831-1834** A461 Set of 4 10.00 10.00

Peonies — A462

No. 1835: a, 7000k, Pink peonies. b, 8000k, White peonies.

**2011, Mar. 20** ***Perf. 12½***

**1835** A462 Pair, #a-b 10.00 10.00
*c.* Souvenir sheet of 1 #1835b 7.00 7.00

Nos. 1835 and 1835a exist imperforate.

Diplomatic Relations Between Laos and Thailand, 60th Anniv. — A463

Designs: No. 1836, 8000k, Laotian woman with black skirt. No. 1837, 8000k, Thai woman with yellow dress. No. 1838, 8000k, White frangipani flowers. No. 1839, 8000k, Yellow Cassia fistula flowers.

**2011, Apr. 22** ***Perf. 13***

**1836-1839** A463 Set of 4 20.00 20.00
*1839a* Souvenir sheet of 4, #1836-1839 25.00 25.00

No. 1839a sold for 35,000k. See Thailand No. 2602.

Dipmomatic Relations Beween Laos and People's Republic of China, 50th Anniv. — A464

**2011, Apr. 25**

**1840** A464 9000k multi 5.00 5.00

A souvenir sheet containing one No. 1840 sold for 20,000k.

Orchids — A465

Paphiopedilum barbigerum var. sulivongii: 1000k, One flower. 9000k, Three flowers. 11,000k, One flower, with leaves.

**2011, May 22**

**1841-1843** A465 Set of 3 20.00 20.00
*1843a* Souvenir sheet of 3, #1841-1843 30.00 30.00

No. 1843a sold for 25,000k. Imperforate examples of No. 1843a sold for 35,000k.

Forest Products — A466

Products harvested from trees: 3000k, Lac resin. 4000k, Cinnamon. 5000k, Malva nuts. 6000k, Gurjum balsam. 11,000k, Dammar gum. 12,000k, Beeswax, horiz.

**2011, June 15** ***Perf. 13***

**1844-1849** A466 Set of 6 25.00 25.00

Wildlife Conservation — A467

Designs: 1000k, Asian elephant. 3000k, Tiger. 5000k, Saola. 8000k, Red-shanked douc langur.

**2011, July 13**

**1850-1853** A467 Set of 4 12.00 12.00
*1853a* Souvenir sheet of 4, #1850-1853 15.00 15.00

No. 1853a sold for 20,000k.

Lotus Flowers — A468

No. 1854: a, 7000k, Lotus flower. b, 8000k, Lotus flower, diff.

**2011, Aug. 12**

**1854** A468 Horiz. pair, #a-b 9.00 9.00

No. 1854 exists as a souvenir sheet of 3 pairs.

A469

A470

City Pillar, Vientiane — A471

**2011, Nov. 10**

| | | | |
|---|---|---|---|
| **1855** A469 9000k multi | | 6.00 | 6.00 |
| **1856** A470 9000k multi | | 6.00 | 6.00 |
| **1857** A471 9000k multi | | 6.00 | 6.00 |
| *a.* | Souvenir sheet of 3, #1855-1857 | 20.00 | 20.00 |
| | *Nos. 1855-1857 (3)* | 18.00 | 18.00 |

No. 1857a sold for 30,000k.

Miniature Sheet

Architecture in Vientiane and Moscow — A472

No. 1858: a, 6000k, Pha That Luang, Vientiane. b, 7000k, St. Basil's Cathedral, Moscow. c, 8000k, Temple, Vientiane. d, 9000k, Egg House, Moscow.

**2011, Dec. 3** ***Perf. 14¼x14***

**1858** A472 Sheet of 4, #a-d 25.00 25.00

No. 1858 exists imperforate. For overprint, see No. 1873.

New Year 2012 (Year of the Dragon) A473

**2012, Jan. 10** **Litho.** ***Perf. 13¼***

**1859** A473 8000k multi 4.50 4.50

No. 1859 was printed in sheets of 4.

Laos Pres. Kaysone Phomvihane (1920-92), North Viet Nam Pres. Ho Chi Minh (1890-1969), Flags of Laos and Viet Nam — A474

Buildings in Laos and Viet Nam — A475

**2012, July 18** **Litho.** ***Perf. 13x12¾***

**1860** A474 4000k multi 2.50 2.50
**1861** A475 12,000k multi 6.50 6.50

See Viet Nam Nos. 3458-3459.

Asia-Europe Summit Meeting, Vientiane — A476

Emblems for summit and: 9000k, Laotian temple. 11,000k, Map with Europe and Southeast Asis highlighted.

**2012, Nov. 5** **Litho.** ***Perf. 13x12¾***

**1862-1863** A476 Set of 2 9.00 9.00

An imperforate souvenir sheets containing No. 1862 sold for 20,000k. A souvenir sheet containing No. 1863 sold for 20,000k.

Silk Processing — A477

Designs: 2000k, Boiling of silk cocoons. 3000k, Spinning of silk. 4000k, Collection of cocoons. 5000k, Mulberries on tree.

**2013, Apr. 22** **Litho.** ***Perf. 13***

| | | | |
|---|---|---|---|
| **1864-1867** A477 | Set of 4 | 7.25 | 7.25 |
| *1867a* | Souvenir sheet of 4, #1864-1867 | 13.00 | 13.00 |

No. 1867a sold for 25,000k and exists imperforate.

Miniature Sheet

Cultural Cooperation Between Laos and Russia — A478

No. 1868: a, 6000k, Patuxai Gate, Vientiane. b, 7000k, Triumphal Arch, Moscow. c, 8000k, Pagoda, Laos. d, 9000k, Tower, Russia.

**2013, July 5** **Litho.** ***Perf. 14¼x14***

**1868** A478 Sheet of 4, #a-d 22.00 22.00

No. 1868 exists imperforate.

Fish A479

Designs: 2000k, Clupisoma sinense. 4000k, Hemibarus filamentus. 6000k, Great white catfish. 9000k, Bagarius yarrelli.

**2013, July 6** **Litho.** ***Perf. 13***

| | | | |
|---|---|---|---|
| **1869-1872** A479 | Set of 4 | 11.00 | 11.00 |
| *1872a* | Souvenir sheet of 4, #1869-1872 | 13.00 | 13.00 |

No. 1872a sold for 25,000k and exists imperforate.

**No. 1858 Overprinted in Red and Blue**

**Methods and Perfs. As Before**

**2013, July 10**

**1873** A472 Sheet of 4, #a-d *57.50 57.50*

Nos. 1873a-1873d are Nos. 1858a-1858d with a different part of the overprint covering the sheet.

Stupas A480

Designs: 1000k, Xiengkhoeng Stupa, Huaphanh. 2000k, Wat That Noi Stupa, Luang Prabang. 3000k, Makmo Stupa, Luang Prabang. 4000k, Phonphao Stupa, Luang Prabang. 10,000k, Phousi Stupa, Luang Prabang.

**2013, Nov. 11** **Litho.** ***Perf. 13***

**1874-1878** A480 Set of 5 9.75 9.75

Perforate and imperforate souvenir sheets containing one example of No. 1874 exist. Each sheet sold for 25,000k.

Fourth International Mekong Bridge — A481

Designs: No. 1879, 8000k, Border checkpoint and parking lot. No. 1880, 8000k, Bridge.

**2013, Dec. 11** **Litho.** ***Perf. 13***

| | | | |
|---|---|---|---|
| **1879-1880** A481 | Set of 2 | 7.50 | 7.50 |
| *1880a* | Souvenir sheet of 2, #1879-1880 | 12.50 | 12.50 |

No. 1880a sold for 25,000k and exists imperforate.

First Laos-Thailand Friendship Bridge, 20th Anniv. — A482

No. 1881 — Bridge and: a, Sai Buddha Image Procession Festival, Nong Khai, Thailand, and Wax Candle Procession Festival, Vientiane. b, Pho Chai Temple, Nong Khai, and On Teu Temple, Vientiane.

**2014, Apr. 8** **Litho.** ***Perf. 14½x14***

| | | | |
|---|---|---|---|
| **1881** A482 9000k | Horiz. pair, #a-b | 8.00 | 8.00 |
| *c.* | Souvenir sheet of 2, #1881a-1881b | 9.00 | 9.00 |

No. 1881c sold for 20,00k and exists imperforate. See Thailand No. 2807.

Nos. 535-537, 834-835 Handstamp Srchd.

**Methods and Perfs. As Before**

**2014, July 22**

| | | | |
|---|---|---|---|
| **1882** A207 | 5000k on 1k #834 | 3.00 | 3.00 |
| **1883** A207 | 8000k on 2k #835 | 4.75 | 4.75 |
| **1884** A154 | 10,000k on 60c #535 | 6.00 | 6.00 |
| **1885** A154 | 11,000k on 1k #536 | 6.50 | 6.50 |
| **1886** A154 | 12,000k on 2k #537 | 7.00 | 7.00 |
| | *Nos. 1882-1886 (5)* | 27.25 | 27.25 |

A483

A484

A485

Buddhas — A486

**2014, Oct. 8 Litho. *Perf. 13***

| | | | | |
|---|---|---|---|---|
| **1887** | A483 5000k multi | | 2.40 | 2.40 |
| **1888** | A484 5000k multi | | 2.40 | 2.40 |
| **1889** | A485 5000k multi | | 2.40 | 2.40 |
| **1890** | A486 5000k multi | | 2.40 | 2.40 |
| *a.* | Souvenir sheet of 4, #1887-1890 | | 12.50 | 12.50 |

No. 1890a sold for 25,000k and exists imperf.

Tourist Attractions — A487

Designs: No. 1891, 5000k, Wat Nonglamchanh, Savannakhet Province. No. 1892, 5000k, Tham Ting Cave, Luang Prabang Province. No. 1893, 5000k. Wat Sisaket Tripitaka Hall, Vientiane. No. 1894, 5000k, Sikhottabong Stupa, Khammuan Province. 9000k, Wat Phiawat, Xiengkhuang Province.

**2014, Nov. 11 Litho. *Perf. 13***

| | | | |
|---|---|---|---|
| **1891-1895** A487 | Set of 5 | 14.00 | 14.00 |
| *1895a* | Souvenir sheet of 4, #1892-1895 | 16.00 | 16.00 |

No. 1895a sold for 25,000k and exists imperf. A souvenir sheet containing No. 1891 sold for 25,000k and exists imperf.

Monuments A488

Designs: No. 1896, 5000k, King Saya Setthathirath. No. 1897, 5000k, King Chao Anouvong. 11,000k, King Fangoum Maharath.

**2014, Dec. 1 Litho. *Perf. 13***

| | | | |
|---|---|---|---|
| **1896-1898** A488 | Set of 3 | 9.75 | 9.75 |
| *1898a* | Souvenir sheet of 3, #1896-1898 | 12.50 | 12.50 |

No. 1898a sold for 25,000k and exists imperf.

Nos. 276a, 535-537 and 1073 Surcharged

**Methods and Perfs. As Before**

**2015**

| | | | |
|---|---|---|---|
| **1899** | A154 10,000k on 60c #535 | 4.50 | 4.50 |
| **1900** | A154 11,000k on 1k #536 | 5.00 | 5.00 |
| **1901** | A154 12,000k on 2k #537 | 5.50 | 5.50 |
| **1902** | A254 13,000k on 220k #1073 | 6.00 | 6.00 |
| | *Nos. 1899-1902 (4)* | 21.00 | 21.00 |

**Souvenir Sheet**

| | | | |
|---|---|---|---|
| **1903** | Sheet of 5, #1903a-1903e (#276a) | 32.50 | 32.50 |
| *a.* | A96 14,000k on 1k #272 | 6.50 | 6.50 |
| *b.* | A96 14,000k on 2k #273 | 6.50 | 6.50 |
| *c.* | A96 14,000k on 5k #274 | 6.50 | 6.50 |
| *d.* | A96 14,000k on 10k #275 | 6.50 | 6.50 |
| *e.* | A96 14,000k on 200k #276 | 6.50 | 6.50 |

Issued: 11,000k, 2/19; 10,000k, 12,000k, 13,000k, 2/26; No. 1903, 3/13.

National Posts and Telecommunications Day, 50th Anniv. — A489

Designs: No. 1904, 10,000k, Satellite dish, telegraph key, telephone, people carrying sacks, airplane, letters, mailbox. No. 1905, 10,000k, Communications workers.

**2015, Mar. 13 Litho. *Perf. 13***

| | | | |
|---|---|---|---|
| **1904-1905** A489 | Set of 2 | 9.50 | 9.50 |
| *1905a* | Souvenir sheet of 2, #1904-1905 | 12.00 | 12.00 |

No. 1905a sold for 25,000k and exists imperf.

## SEMI-POSTAL STAMPS

Laotian Children — SP1

**Unwmk.**

**1953, July 14 Engr. *Perf. 13***

| | | | | |
|---|---|---|---|---|
| **B1** | SP1 | 1.50pi + 1pi multi | 2.40 | 2.25 |
| **B2** | SP1 | 3pi + 1.50pi multi | 2.75 | 2.25 |
| **B3** | SP1 | 3.90pi + 2.50pi multi | 3.00 | 2.50 |
| | | *Nos. B1-B3 (3)* | 8.15 | 7.00 |

The surtax was for the Red Cross.

**Nos. 52 and 46 Surcharged: "1k ANNEE MONDIALE DU REFUGIE 1959-1960"**

**1960, Apr. 7**

| | | | | |
|---|---|---|---|---|
| **B4** | A16 | 4k + 1k rose claret | 3.50 | 3.50 |
| **B5** | A13 | 10k + 1k multicolored | 5.00 | 5.00 |

World Refugee Year, July 1, 1959-June 30, 1960. The surcharge was for aid to refugees.

Flooded Village SP2

40k+10k, Flooded market place and truck. 60k+15k, Flooded airport and plane.

**1967, Jan. 18 Engr. *Perf. 13***

| | | | | |
|---|---|---|---|---|
| **B6** | SP2 | 20k + 5k multi | .45 | .25 |
| **B7** | SP2 | 40k + 10k multi | .85 | .55 |
| **B8** | SP2 | 60k + 15k multi | 1.40 | 1.25 |
| *a.* | | Miniature sheet of 3 | 6.00 | 6.00 |
| | | *Nos. B6-B8 (3)* | 2.70 | 2.05 |

The surtax was for victims of the Mekong Delta flood. No. B8a contains one each of Nos. B6-B8. Size: 148x99mm. Sold for 250k.

Women Working in Tobacco Field — SP3

**1967, Oct. 5 Engr. *Perf. 13***

| | | | | |
|---|---|---|---|---|
| **B9** | SP3 | 20k + 5k multi | .75 | .40 |
| **B10** | SP3 | 50k + 10k multi | 1.25 | .75 |
| **B11** | SP3 | 60k + 15k multi | 2.00 | 1.10 |
| *a.* | | Souv. sheet of 3, #B9-B11 | 4.50 | 4.50 |
| | | *Nos. B9-B11 (3)* | 4.00 | 2.25 |

Laotian Red Cross, 10th anniv. No. B11a sold for 250k+30k.

**Nos. 184-189 Surcharged: "Soutien aux Victimes / de la Guerre / + 5k"**

**1970, May 1 Photo. *Perf. 14***

| | | | | |
|---|---|---|---|---|
| **B12** | A58 | 10k + 5k multi | .50 | .30 |
| **B13** | A58 | 15k + 5k multi | .60 | .30 |
| **B14** | A58 | 20k + 5k multi | .65 | .30 |
| **B15** | A58 | 30k + 5k multi | .85 | .30 |
| **B16** | A58 | 40k + 5k multi | 1.25 | .50 |
| **B17** | A58 | 60k + 5k multi | 1.30 | .60 |
| | | *Nos. B12-B17,CB1-CB2 (8)* | 11.65 | 6.05 |

## AIR POST STAMPS

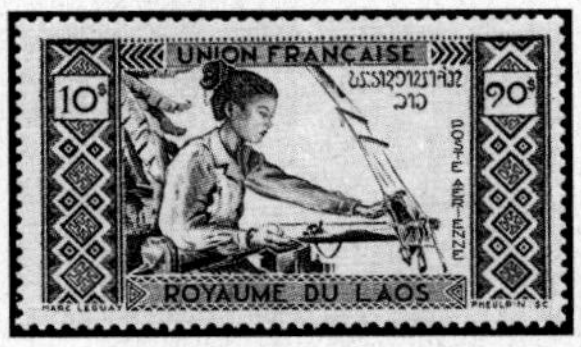


Weaving — AP1

Design: 3.30pi, Wat Pra Keo.

**Unwmk.**

**1952, Apr. 13 Engr. *Perf. 13***

| | | | | |
|---|---|---|---|---|
| **C1** | AP1 | 3.30pi dk pur & pur | 2.25 | 1.00 |
| **C2** | AP1 | 10pi ultra & bl grn | 2.00 | 1.25 |
| **C3** | AP1 | 20pi deep cl & red | 3.50 | 2.75 |
| **C4** | AP1 | 30pi blk brn & dk brn violet | 4.50 | 4.25 |
| | | *Nos. C1-C4 (4)* | 12.25 | 9.25 |

See note following No. 17.

UPU Monument and King Sisavang-Vong — AP2

**1952, Dec. 7**

| | | | | |
|---|---|---|---|---|
| **C5** | AP2 | 25pi vio bl & indigo | 5.00 | 4.50 |
| **C6** | AP2 | 50pi dk brn & vio brn | 6.00 | 5.50 |

Laos' admission to the UPU, May 13, 1952.

AP3

AP4

Designs: Various Buddha statues.

**1953, Nov. 18**

| | | | | |
|---|---|---|---|---|
| **C7** | AP3 | 4pi dark green | 1.25 | .60 |
| **C8** | AP4 | 6.50pi dk bl green | 1.25 | .60 |
| **C9** | AP4 | 9pi blue green | 1.75 | .90 |
| **C10** | AP3 | 11.50pi red, yel & dk vio brn | 2.75 | 1.25 |
| **C11** | AP4 | 40pi purple | 4.50 | 1.75 |
| **C12** | AP4 | 100pi olive | 8.00 | 4.50 |
| | | *Nos. C7-C12 (6)* | 19.50 | 9.60 |

Great Oath of Laos ceremony.

**Accession Type of Regular Issue**

**1954, Mar. 4 Unwmk.**

| | | | | |
|---|---|---|---|---|
| **C13** | A6 | 50pi indigo & bl grn | 120.00 | 95.00 |
| | | Hinged | 75.00 | |

Ravana — AP6

Sita and Rama — AP7

Scenes from the Ramayana: 4k, Hanuman, the white monkey. 5k, Ninh Laphath, the black monkey. 20k, Lucy with a friend of Ravana. 30k, Rama.

**1955, Oct. 28 Engr. *Perf. 13***

| | | | | |
|---|---|---|---|---|
| **C14** | AP6 | 2k bl grn, emer & ind | .75 | .45 |
| **C15** | AP6 | 4k red brn, dk red brn & ver | 1.20 | .90 |
| **C16** | AP6 | 5k scar, sep & olive | 1.90 | 1.40 |
| **C17** | AP7 | 10k blk, org & brn | 3.75 | 1.60 |
| **C18** | AP7 | 20k vio, dk grn & olive | 5.25 | 2.75 |
| **C19** | AP7 | 30k ultra, blk & salmon | 6.75 | 4.00 |
| | | *Nos. C14-C19 (6)* | 19.60 | 11.10 |

See No. 225.

**Buddha Type of Regular Issue, 1956**

**1956, May 24**

| | | | | |
|---|---|---|---|---|
| **C20** | A7 | 20k carmine rose | 27.00 | 20.00 |
| **C21** | A7 | 30k olive & olive bister | 27.00 | 25.00 |

2500th anniversary of birth of Buddha.

UN Emblem
AP8

**1956, Dec. 14**

| | | |
|---|---|---|
| **C22** AP8 15k light blue | 4.25 | 4.25 |
| **C23** AP8 30k deep claret | 5.50 | 5.50 |

Admission of Laos to the UN, 1st anniv.

### Types of Regular Issue, 1957

Musical Instruments: 12k, Khong vong. 14k, So. 20k, Kong.

**1957, Mar. 25 Unwmk. *Perf. 13***

| | | |
|---|---|---|
| **C24** A9 12k multicolored | 2.50 | 1.60 |
| **C25** A10 14k multicolored | 2.75 | 1.90 |
| **C26** A10 20k bl grn, yel grn & pur | 3.25 | 2.60 |
| *Nos. C24-C26 (3)* | 8.50 | 6.10 |

Monk Receiving Alms — AP9

Monks Meditating in Boat — AP10

18k, Smiling Buddha. 24k, Ancient temple painting (horse and mythological figures.)

**1957, Nov. 5**

| | | |
|---|---|---|
| **C27** AP9 10k dk pur, pale brn & dk grn | 1.25 | 1.25 |
| **C28** AP10 15k dk vio brn, brn org & yel | 1.25 | 1.25 |
| **C29** AP9 18k slate grn & ol | 1.50 | 1.50 |
| **C30** AP10 24k claret, org yel & blk | 3.25 | 3.25 |
| *Nos. C27-C30 (4)* | 7.25 | 7.25 |

No. C28 measures 48x27mm. No. C30, 48x36mm. See No. C84.

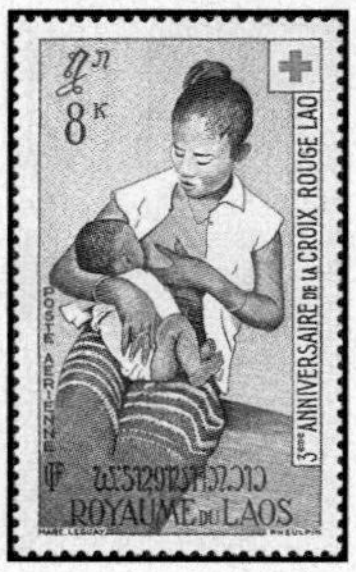

Mother Nursing Infant — AP11

**1958, May 2 Cross in Red**

| | | |
|---|---|---|
| **C31** AP11 8k lil gray & dk gray | 1.30 | .75 |
| **C32** AP11 12k red brn & brn | 1.50 | 1.00 |
| **C33** AP11 15k sl grn & bluish green | 1.60 | 1.00 |
| **C34** AP11 20k bister & vio | 2.10 | 1.50 |
| *Nos. C31-C34 (4)* | 6.50 | 4.25 |

3rd anniversary of Laotian Red Cross.

Plain of Stones, Xieng Khouang
AP12

Papheng Falls, Champassak — AP13

Natl. Tourism Industry: 15k, Buffalo cart. 19k, Buddhist monk and village.

**1960, July 1 Engr. *Perf. 13***

| | | |
|---|---|---|
| **C35** AP12 9.50k bl, ol & claret | .50 | .50 |
| **C36** AP13 12k vio bl, red brn & gray | .50 | .50 |
| **C37** AP13 15k yel grn, ol gray & cl | .75 | .75 |
| **C38** AP12 19k multicolored | 1.00 | 1.00 |
| *Nos. C35-C38 (4)* | 2.75 | 2.75 |

Pou Gneu Nha Gneu Legend — AP14

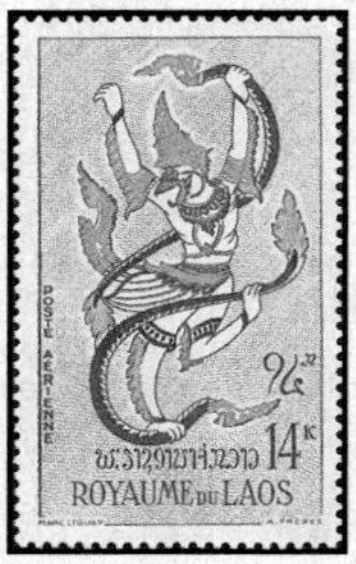

Garuda — AP15

Hanuman, the White Monkey — AP16

Nang Teng One Legend
AP17

**1962, Feb. 19 Unwmk. *Perf. 13***

| | | |
|---|---|---|
| **C39** AP14 11k grn, car & ocher | .60 | .60 |
| **C40** AP15 14k ultra & org | .60 | .60 |
| **C41** AP16 20k multicolored | .80 | .80 |
| **C42** AP17 25k multicolored | .90 | .90 |
| *Nos. C39-C42 (4)* | 2.90 | 2.90 |

Makha Bousa festival.

Yao Hunter — AP18

**1964, Dec. 15 Engr. *Perf. 13***

| | | |
|---|---|---|
| **C43** AP18 5k shown | .55 | .25 |
| **C44** AP18 10k Kha hunter | .55 | .35 |
| **C45** AP18 50k Meo woman | 1.60 | 1.00 |
| *a.* Min. sheet of 4, #100, C43-C45 | 7.50 | 6.50 |
| *Nos. C43-C45 (3)* | 2.70 | 1.60 |

No. C45a exists imperf in a booklet. Value, intact booklet $75.

### Butterfly Type of 1965

**1965, Mar. 13 Size: 48x27mm**

| | | |
|---|---|---|
| **C46** A34 20k Attacus atlas | 5.50 | 2.50 |

Phayre's Flying Squirrel — AP19

Designs: 25k, Leopard cat. 75k, Javan mongoose. 100k, Crestless porcupine. 200k, Binturong.

**1965, Oct. 7 Engr. *Perf. 13***

| | | |
|---|---|---|
| **C47** AP19 25k dk brn, yel grn & ocher | .50 | .25 |
| **C48** AP19 55k brown & blue | .75 | .35 |
| **C49** AP19 75k brt grn & brn | 1.00 | .50 |
| **C50** AP19 100k ocher, brn & blk | 1.75 | 1.10 |
| **C51** AP19 200k red & black | 3.50 | 2.50 |
| *Nos. C47-C51 (5)* | 7.50 | 4.70 |

### Army Type of Regular Issue

Design: 200k, 300k, Parading service flags before National Assembly Hall.

**1968, July 15 Engr. *Perf. 13***

| | | |
|---|---|---|
| **C52** A53 200k multicolored | 1.75 | .85 |
| **C53** A53 300k multicolored | 2.50 | 1.25 |
| *a.* Souv. sheet of 5, #168-170, C52-C53 | 6.00 | 6.00 |

No. C53a sold for 600k.

### Insect Type of Regular Issue

Insects: 120k, Dorysthenes walkeri, horiz. 160k, Megaloxantha bicolor, horiz.

**1968, Aug. 28 Engr. *Perf. 13***

| | | |
|---|---|---|
| **C54** A54 120k brn, org & blk | 1.50 | .85 |
| **C55** A54 160k rose car, Prus bl & yel | 2.25 | 1.25 |

### Ballet Type of Regular Issue

Designs: 110k, Sudagnu battling Thotsakan. 300k, Pharam dancing with Thotsakan.

**1969 Photo. *Perf. 14***

| | | |
|---|---|---|
| **C56** A58 110k multicolored | 3.50 | 1.75 |
| *a.* Souv. sheet of 4, #187-189, C56, imperf. | 24.00 | 24.00 |
| **C57** A58 300k multicolored | 7.00 | 3.25 |
| *a.* Souv. sheet of 4, #184-186, C57, imperf. | 24.00 | 24.00 |

No. C56a sold for 480k; No. C57a for 650k.
For surcharges see Nos. CB1-CB2.

Timber Industry, Paksane
AP20

**1969, May 7 Engr. *Perf. 13***

| | | |
|---|---|---|
| **C58** AP20 300k olive bister & blk | 5.50 | 3.25 |

ILO, 50th anniversary.

### Animal Type of Regular Issue

Animals: 70k, Malaysian black bear. 120k, White-handed gibbon, vert. 150k, Indochinese tiger.

**1969, Nov. 6 Photo. *Perf. 12x13***

| | | |
|---|---|---|
| **C59** A60 70k multicolored | 1.10 | .60 |
| **C60** A60 120k multicolored | 2.40 | 1.10 |
| **C61** A60 150k multicolored | 2.75 | 1.40 |
| *Nos. C59-C61 (3)* | 5.85 | 3.10 |

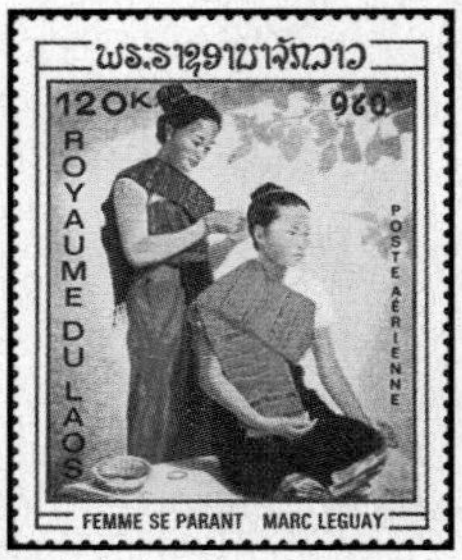

Hairdressing, by Marc Leguay — AP21

Paintings: No. C63, Village Market, by Marc Leguay, horiz. No. C64, Tree on the Bank of the Mekong, by Marc Leguay, horiz.

**1969-70 Photo. *Perf. 12x13, 13x12***

| | | |
|---|---|---|
| **C62** AP21 120k multicolored | 1.00 | .40 |
| **C63** AP21 150k multicolored | 2.00 | .65 |
| **C64** AP21 150k multi ('70) | 2.00 | .65 |
| *Nos. C62-C64 (3)* | 5.00 | 1.70 |

See Nos. C72-C74.

Wat Xiengthong, Luang Prabang — AP22

**1970, Jan. 10 *Perf. 12x13, 13x12***

| | | |
|---|---|---|
| **C65** AP22 100k Library, Wat Sisaket, vert. | 1.40 | .65 |
| **C66** AP22 120k shown | 2.00 | 1.00 |

### Drum Type of 1970

**1970, Mar. 30 Engr. *Perf. 13***

| | | |
|---|---|---|
| **C67** A64 125k Pong wooden drum, vert. | 3.00 | 1.50 |

Franklin D. Roosevelt (1882-1945) — AP23

**1970, Apr. 12**

| | | |
|---|---|---|
| **C68** AP23 120k olive & slate | 1.60 | 1.10 |

### EXPO '70 Type of Regular Issue

Design: 125k, Woman boiling cocoons in kettle, and spinning silk thread.

**1970, July 7 Engr. *Perf. 13***

**C69** A66 125k olive & multi 1.75 1.25

See note after No. 202.

### Animal Type of Regular Issue

**1970, Sept. 7 Engr. *Perf. 13***

**C70** A67 210k Leopard 2.75 1.25
**C71** A67 500k Gaur 5.00 2.50

### Painting Type of 1969-70

Paintings by Marc Leguay: 100k, Village Foot Path. 120k, Rice Field in Rainy Season, horiz. 150k, Village Elder.

***Perf. 11½x13, 13x11½***

**1970, Dec. 21 Photo.**

**C72** AP21 100k multicolored 1.10 1.10
**C73** AP21 120k multicolored 1.40 1.40
**C74** AP21 150k multicolored 1.60 1.60
*Nos. C72-C74 (3)* 4.10 4.10

### UN Type of Regular Issue

125k, Earth Goddess Nang Thorani wringing her hair; UN Headquarters and emblem.

**1970, Oct. 24 *Perf. 13***
**Size: 26x36mm**

**C75** A68 125k brt bl, pink & dk grn 2.40 1.10

Hanuman and Nang Matsa — AP24

**1971, Feb. 5 *Perf. 13***

**C76** AP24 125k multicolored 2.40 1.00

### Orchid Type of Regular Issue

Design: 125k, Brasilian cattleya.

**1971, July Photo. *Perf. 13x12½***
**Size: 48x27mm**

**C79** A73 125k multi 4.50 1.50

Laotian and French Women, That Luang Pagoda and Arms AP25

**1971, Aug. 6 Engr. *Perf. 13***

**C80** AP25 30k brn & dull red .25 .25
**C81** AP25 70k vio & lilac .50 .40
**C82** AP25 100k slate grn & grn .70 .55
*Nos. C80-C82 (3)* 1.45 1.20

Kinship between the cities Keng Kok, Laos, and Saint Astier, France.

### Animal Type of Regular Issue

**1971, Sept. 16**

**C83** A74 300k Javan rhinoceros 4.25 2.75

### Type of 1957 with Ornamental Panel and Inscription

Design: Monk receiving alms (like No. C27).

**1971, Oct. 31 Engr. *Perf. 13***

**C84** AP9 125k dk pur, pale brn & dk grn 2.00 1.40

20th anniv. of Laotian independent postal service. No. C84 inscribed: "Vingtième Anniversaire de la Philatélie Lao," "Poste Aerienne" and "1971."

Sunset Over the Mekong, by Chamnane Prisayane — AP26

Design: 150k, "Quiet Morning" (village scene), by Chamnane Prisayane.

**1971, Dec. 20 Photo. *Perf. 13x12***

**C85** AP26 125k black & multi 1.00 1.00
**C86** AP26 150k black & multi 1.25 1.25

### Book Year Type of Regular Issue

Design: 125k, Father teaching children to read palm leaf book.

**1972, Jan. 30 Engr. *Perf. 13***
**Size: 48x27mm**

**C87** A75 125k bright purple 1.75 1.00

### Dam Type of Regular Issue

Design: 145k, Nam Ngum Hydroelectric Dam and ECAFE emblem.

**1972, Mar. 28 Engr. *Perf. 13***

**C88** A76 145k brown, bl & grn 1.40 .80

### Orchid Type of Regular Issue

**1972, May 5 Photo. *Perf. 13x12½***
**Size: 48x27mm**

**C89** A73 150k Vanda teres, horiz. 4.00 1.50

### UNICEF Type of Regular Issue

Design: 120k, Boy riding buffalo to water hole (child's drawing).

**1972, July Engr. *Perf. 13***

**C90** A77 120k multicolored 1.40 1.00

Nakharath, Daughter of the Dragon King AP27

Wood carvings from Wat Sikhounvieng Dongmieng, Vientiane: 120k, Nang Kinnali, Goddess from Mt. Kailath. 150k, Norasing, Lion King from Himalayas.

**1972, Sept. 15 Engr. *Perf. 13***

**C91** AP27 100k blue green .70 .70
**C92** AP27 120k violet .80 .80
**C93** AP27 150k brn orange 1.10 1.10
*Nos. C91-C93 (3)* 2.60 2.60

That Luang Religious Festival — AP28

**1972, Nov. 18 Engr. *Perf. 13***

**C94** AP28 110k Presentation of wax castles .90 .90
**C95** AP28 125k Procession 1.10 1.10

Workers in Rice Field, by Leguay AP29

Paintings by Mark Leguay: No. C97, Women and water buffalo in rice field. Nos. C98, Rainy Season in Village (Water buffalo in water). No. C99, Rainy Season in Village (Water buffalo on land). 120k, Mother and Child.

**1972, Dec. 23 Photo. *Perf. 13***

**C96** AP29 50k multicolored .45 .45
**C97** AP29 50k multicolored .45 .45
**C98** AP29 70k multicolored .65 .65
**C99** AP29 70k multicolored .65 .65
**C100** AP29 120k yel & multi 1.25 1.25
*Nos. C96-C100 (5)* 3.45 3.45

Nos. C97, C99 have denomination and frame at right.

### Costume Type of Regular Issue

Women's Costumes: 120k, Luang Prabang marriage costume. 150k, Vientiane evening costume.

**1973, Feb. 16 Engr. *Perf. 13***

**C101** A78 120k multicolored 1.40 .80
**C102** A78 150k brown & multi 1.90 1.00

Lions Club Emblems, King Sayasettha-Thirath — AP30

**1973, Mar. 30 Engr. *Perf. 13***

**C103** AP30 150k rose & multi 1.90 .75

Lions Club of Vientiane.

Rahu with Rockets and Sputnik — AP31

Space achievements: 150k, Laotian festival rocket and US lunar excursion module.

**1973, May 11 Engr. *Perf. 13***

**C104** AP31 80k ultra & multi .55 .35
**C105** AP31 150k buff & ultra 1.00 .45

Dancing Around Campfire — AP32

Design: 125k, Boy Scouts helping during Vientiane Flood, 1966.

**1973, Sept. 1 Engr. *Perf. 13***

**C106** AP32 110k vio & orange 1.10 .30
**C107** AP32 125k Prus grn & bis 1.25 .40

Laotian Scout Movement, 25th anniv.

Sun Chariot and WMO Emblem — AP33

Design: 90k, Nang Mékhala, the weather goddess, and WMO emblem, vert.

**1973, Oct. 24 Engr. *Perf. 13***

**C108** AP33 90k vio, red & ocher .75 .35
**C109** AP33 150k ocher, red & brn ol .85 .50

Intl. meteorological cooperation, cent.

Woman in Poppy Field, INTERPOL Emblem — AP34

**1973, Dec. 22 Engr. *Perf. 13***

**C110** AP34 150k vio, yel grn & red 1.40 .60

Intl. Criminal Police Org., 50th anniv.

Phra Sratsvady, Wife of Phra Phrom AP35

Designs: 110k, Phra Indra on 3-headed elephant Erawan. 150k, Phra Phrom, the Creator, on phoenix. Designs show giant sculptures in park at Thadeua.

**1974, Mar. 23 Engr. *Perf. 13***

**C111** AP35 100k lilac, red & blk .80 .40
**C112** AP35 110k car, vio & brn 1.00 .50
**C113** AP35 150k ocher, vio & sepia 1.25 .70
*Nos. C111-C113 (3)* 3.05 1.60

UPU Emblem, Women Reading Letter — AP36

**1974 Engr. *Perf. 13***

**C114** AP36 200k lt brn & car 3.75 1.00
**C115** AP36 500k lilac & red 6.00 2.00
*a.* Souvenir sheet 5.50 5.50

Centenary of Universal Postal Union. Issue dates: 200k, Apr. 30; 500k, Oct. 9.

### Flower Type of 1974

**1974, May 17 Size: 36x36mm**

**C116** A84 500k Pitcher plant 5.50 3.00

### Transportation Type of Regular Issue

**1974, July 31 Engr. *Perf. 13***

**C117** A85 250k Sampan 2.50 1.50

### Marconi Type of 1974

Old & new means of communications.

**1974, Aug. 28 Engr. *Perf. 13***

| | | | | |
|---|---|---|---|---|
| C118 | A86 | 200k vio bl & brn | 2.25 | 1.10 |

### Insect Type of 1974

110k, Sternocera multipunctata.

**1974, Oct. 23 Engr. *Perf. 13***

| | | | | |
|---|---|---|---|---|
| C119 | A87 | 110k grn, blue & red | 1.75 | 1.00 |

Boeing 747 — AP37

**1986, June 2 Litho. *Perf. 12½***

| | | | |
|---|---|---|---|
| C120 | AP37 | 20k shown | 3.50 |
| C121 | AP37 | 50k IL86 | 8.00 |

## AIR POST SEMI-POSTAL STAMPS

### Nos. C56-C57 Surcharged: "Soutien aux Victimes / de la Guerre / + 5k"

**1970, May 1 Photo. *Perf. 13***

| | | | | |
|---|---|---|---|---|
| CB1 | A58 | 110k + 5k multi | 3.00 | 1.50 |
| CB2 | A58 | 300k + 5k multi | 3.50 | 2.25 |

The surtax was for war victims.

## POSTAGE DUE STAMPS

Vat-Sisaket Monument D1

Boat and Raft D2

***Perf. 13½x13***

**1952-53 Unwmk. Engr.**

| | | | | |
|---|---|---|---|---|
| J1 | D1 | 10c dark brown | .40 | .25 |
| J2 | D1 | 20c purple | .40 | .25 |
| J3 | D1 | 50c carmine | .50 | .25 |
| J4 | D1 | 1pi dark green | .60 | .25 |
| J5 | D1 | 2pi deep ultra | .70 | .25 |
| J6 | D1 | 5pi rose violet | 1.25 | 1.00 |
| J7 | D2 | 10pi indigo ('53) | 2.00 | .80 |
| | | *Nos. J1-J7 (7)* | 5.85 | 3.05 |

Serpent — D3

**1973, Oct. 31 Photo. *Perf. 13***

| | | | | |
|---|---|---|---|---|
| J8 | D3 | 10k yellow & multi | .40 | .25 |
| J9 | D3 | 15k emerald & multi | .45 | .25 |
| J10 | D3 | 20k blue & multi | .60 | .25 |
| J11 | D3 | 50k scarlet & multi | .75 | .40 |
| | | *Nos. J8-J11 (4)* | 2.20 | 1.15 |

## PARCEL POST STAMPS

Wat Ong Theu PP1

**2000, June 7 Litho. *Die Cut***

**Self-Adhesive**

**Serial Number in Black**

| | | | | |
|---|---|---|---|---|
| Q1 | PP1 | 5000k orange | *5.00* | *5.00* |
| Q2 | PP1 | 40,000k milky blue | *30.00* | *30.00* |
| Q3 | PP1 | 60,000k gray blue | *32.50* | *32.50* |
| Q4 | PP1 | 80,000k cerise | *55.00* | *55.00* |
| Q5 | PP1 | 100,000k carmine | *65.00* | *65.00* |
| Q6 | PP1 | 250,000k ultra | *160.00* | *160.00* |
| | | *Nos. Q1-Q6 (6)* | 347.50 | 347.50 |

Phra That Luang — PP2

**2003, Aug. 14 *Die Cut***

**Self-Adhesive**

**Serial Number in Black**

| | | | | |
|---|---|---|---|---|
| Q7 | PP2 | 5000k vio bl & bl | 5.00 | 5.00 |
| Q8 | PP2 | 40,000k claret & red | 30.00 | 30.00 |
| Q9 | PP2 | 60,000k grn & claret | 45.00 | 45.00 |
| Q10 | PP2 | 90,000k red & blue | 70.00 | 70.00 |
| | | *Nos. Q7-Q10 (4)* | 150.00 | 150.00 |

Pha That Luang, Vientiane — PP7

**2013, July 3 Litho. *Imperf.***

**Self-Adhesive**

**Frame Color**

| | | | | |
|---|---|---|---|---|
| Q17 | PP7 | 50,000k blue | 25.00 | 20.00 |
| Q18 | PP7 | 100,000k red | 45.00 | 37.50 |
| Q19 | PP7 | 200,000k green | 85.00 | 67.50 |
| | | *Nos. Q17-Q19 (3)* | 155.00 | 125.00 |

# LATAKIA

ˌla-tə-ˈkē-ə

LOCATION — A division of Syria in Western Asia
GOVT. — French Mandate
AREA — 2,500 sq. mi.
POP. — 278,000 (approx. 1930)
CAPITAL — Latakia

This territory, included in the Syrian Mandate to France under the Versailles Treaty, was formerly known as Alaouites. The name Latakia was adopted in 1930. See Alaouites and Syria.

100 Centimes = 1 Piaster

### Stamps of Syria Overprinted in Black or Red

***Perf. 12x12½, 13½***

**1931-33 Unwmk.**

| | | | | |
|---|---|---|---|---|
| 1 | A6 | 10c red violet | 1.25 | 1.25 |
| 2 | A6 | 10c vio brn ('33) | 1.60 | 1.60 |
| 3 | A7 | 20c dk blue (R) | 1.25 | 1.25 |
| 4 | A7 | 20c brn org ('33) | 1.60 | 1.60 |
| 5 | A8 | 25c gray grn (R) | 1.25 | 1.25 |
| 6 | A8 | 25c dk bl gray (R) ('33) | 1.60 | 1.60 |
| 7 | A9 | 50c violet | 2.00 | 2.00 |
| 8 | A15 | 75c org red ('32) | 3.25 | 3.25 |
| 9 | A10 | 1p green (R) | 2.40 | 2.40 |
| 10 | A11 | 1.50p bis brn (R) | 3.25 | 3.25 |
| 11 | A11 | 1.50p dp grn ('33) | 4.00 | 4.00 |
| 12 | A12 | 2p dk vio (R) | 4.00 | 4.00 |
| 13 | A13 | 3p yel grn (R) | 6.00 | 6.00 |
| 14 | A14 | 4p orange | 5.50 | 5.50 |
| 15 | A15 | 4.50p rose car | 5.75 | 5.75 |
| 16 | A16 | 6p grnsh blk (R) | 5.75 | 5.75 |
| 17 | A17 | 7.50p dl blue (R) | 5.50 | 5.50 |
| *a.* | | Inverted overprint | 650.00 | |
| 18 | A18 | 10p dp brown (R) | 9.50 | 9.50 |
| *a.* | | Inverted overprint | 650.00 | |
| 19 | A19 | 15p dp green (R) | 11.00 | 11.00 |
| 20 | A20 | 25p violet brn | 24.00 | 24.00 |
| 21 | A21 | 50p dk brown (R) | 22.50 | 22.50 |
| *a.* | | Inverted overprint | 650.00 | |
| 22 | A22 | 100p red orange | 55.00 | 55.00 |
| | | *Nos. 1-22 (22)* | 177.95 | 177.95 |

## AIR POST STAMPS

Air Post Stamps of Syria, 1931, Overprinted in Black or Red

**1931-33 Unwmk. *Perf. 13½***

| | | | | |
|---|---|---|---|---|
| C1 | AP2 | 50c ocher | 1.25 | 1.25 |
| *a.* | | Inverted overprint | 1,200. | 1,200. |
| C2 | AP2 | 50c blk brn (R) ('33) | 2.50 | 2.50 |
| C3 | AP2 | 1p ches brn | 2.50 | 2.50 |
| C4 | AP2 | 2p Prus blue (R) | 4.00 | 4.00 |
| C5 | AP2 | 3p blue grn (R) | 5.50 | 5.50 |
| C6 | AP2 | 5p red violet | 7.00 | 7.00 |
| C7 | AP2 | 10p sl grn (R) | 8.75 | 8.75 |
| C8 | AP2 | 15p orange red | 12.50 | 12.50 |
| C9 | AP2 | 25p orange brn | 24.00 | 24.00 |
| C10 | AP2 | 50p black (R) | 40.00 | 40.00 |
| C11 | AP2 | 100p magenta | 42.50 | 42.50 |
| | | *Nos. C1-C11 (11)* | 150.50 | 150.50 |

## POSTAGE DUE STAMPS

### Postage Due Stamps of Syria, 1931, Overprinted

**1931 Unwmk. *Perf. 13½***

| | | | | |
|---|---|---|---|---|
| J1 | D7 | 8p blk, *gray bl* (R) | 26.00 | 25.00 |
| J2 | D8 | 15p blk, *dl rose* (R) | 26.00 | 25.00 |

Stamps of Latakia were superseded in 1937 by those of Syria.

# LATVIA

ˈlat-vē-ə

## (Lettonia, Lettland)

LOCATION — Northern Europe, bordering on the Baltic Sea and the Gulf of Riga
GOVT. — Independent Republic
AREA — 25,395 sq. mi.
POP. — 2,353,874 (1999 est.)
CAPITAL — Riga

Latvia was created a sovereign state following World War I and was admitted to the League of Nations in 1922. In 1940 it became a republic in the Union of Soviet Socialist Republics. Latvian independence was recognized by the Soviet Union on Sept. 6, 1991.

100 Kapeikas = 1 Rublis
100 Santims = 1 Lat (1923, 1993)
100 Kopecks = 1 Ruble (1991)
100 Cents = 1 Euro (2014)

**Catalogue values for unused stamps in this country are for Never Hinged items, beginning with Scott 300 in the regular postage section, Scott B150 in the semi-postal section, and Scott 2N45 in the Russian Occupation section.**

### Watermarks

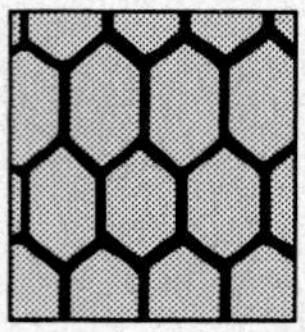
Wmk. 108 Honeycomb

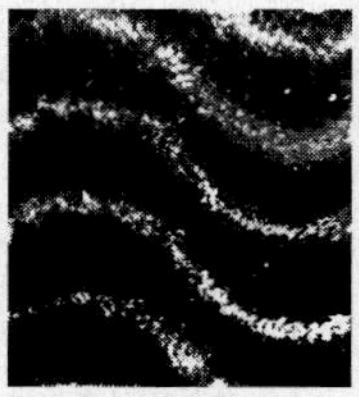
Wmk. 145 — Wavy Lines

Wmk. 181 Wavy Lines

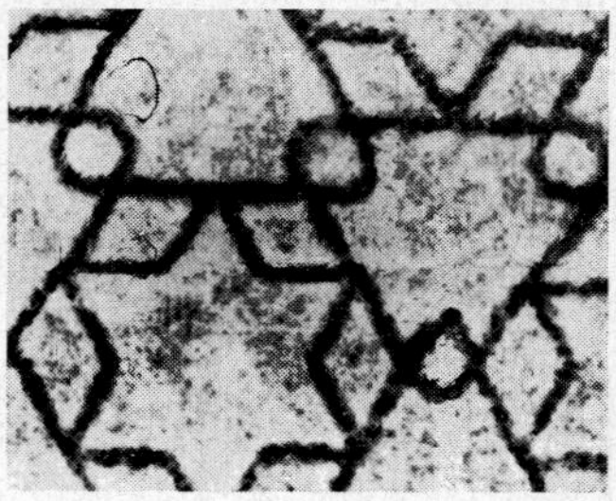
Wmk. 197 — Star and Triangles

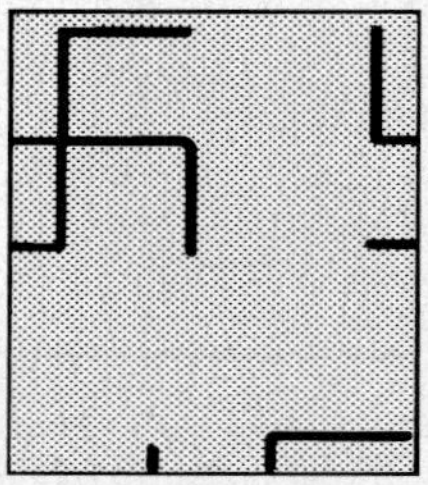
Wmk. 212 Multiple Swastikas

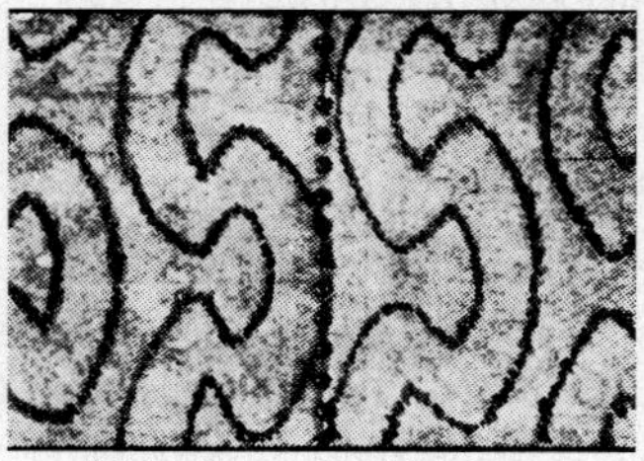
Wmk. 265 — Multiple Waves

Wmk. 387 — Squares and Rectangles

Arms — A1

**Printed on the Backs of German Military Maps**

**Unwmk.**

**1918, Dec. 18 Litho. *Imperf.***

1 A1 5k carmine .75 1.50

***Perf. 11½***

2 A1 5k carmine .75 1.50

Values given are for stamps where the map on the back is printed in brown and black. Maps printed only in black are valued at: No. 1 unused $2.00; used $5.75; No. 2 unused $1.20, used $2.50. Stamps with no map at all valued: No. 1 unused $1.50, used $3.25; No. 2 unused $1.20, used $2.25. Stamps with no printing on the back are from the outer rows of some sheets.

**Redrawn**
**Paper with Ruled Lines**

**1919 *Imperf.***

| | | | | |
|---|---|---|---|---|
| 3 | A1 | 5k carmine | .25 | .25 |
| 4 | A1 | 10k dark blue | .25 | .25 |
| 5 | A1 | 15k green | .50 | .50 |

***Perf. 11½***

| | | | | |
|---|---|---|---|---|
| 6 | A1 | 5k carmine | 2.40 | *4.00* |
| 7 | A1 | 10k dark blue | 2.40 | *4.00* |
| 8 | A1 | 15k deep green | 7.25 | *9.50* |
| | | *Nos. 3-8 (6)* | 13.05 | 18.50 |

In the redrawn design the wheat heads are thicker, the ornament at lower left has five points instead of four, and there are minor changes in other parts of the design.

The sheets of this and subsequent issues were usually divided in half by a single line of perforation gauging 10. Thus stamps are found with this perforation on one side.

**1919 Pelure Paper *Imperf.***

| | | | | |
|---|---|---|---|---|
| 9 | A1 | 3k lilac | 4.75 | 4.50 |
| 10 | A1 | 5k carmine | .25 | .25 |
| 11 | A1 | 10k deep blue | .25 | .25 |
| 12 | A1 | 15k dark green | .25 | .25 |
| 13 | A1 | 20k orange | .25 | .25 |
| 13A | A1 | 25k gray | 40.00 | *47.50* |
| 14 | A1 | 35k dark brown | .25 | .25 |
| 15 | A1 | 50k purple | .25 | .25 |
| 16 | A1 | 75k emerald | 2.50 | *2.75* |
| | | *Nos. 9-16 (9)* | 48.75 | 56.25 |

***Perf. 11½, 9½***

| | | | | |
|---|---|---|---|---|
| 17 | A1 | 3k lilac | 35.00 | 30.00 |
| 18 | A1 | 5k carmine | .80 | .80 |
| 19 | A1 | 10k deep blue | 4.00 | 3.50 |
| 20 | A1 | 15k dark green | 2.75 | *4.00* |
| 21 | A1 | 20k orange | 3.75 | *4.50* |
| 22 | A1 | 35k dark brown | 4.50 | *6.50* |
| 23 | A1 | 50k purple | 5.50 | *8.00* |
| 24 | A1 | 75k emerald | 8.00 | *11.00* |
| | | *Nos. 17-24 (8)* | 64.30 | *68.30* |

Values are for perf 11½. Examples Perf 9½ sell for more.

Nos. 17-24 are said to be unofficially perforated varieties of Nos. 9-16.

**1919 Wmk. 108 *Imperf.***

| | | | | |
|---|---|---|---|---|
| 25 | A1 | 3k lilac | .30 | .25 |
| 26 | A1 | 5k carmine | .30 | .25 |
| 27 | A1 | 10k deep blue | .30 | .25 |
| 28 | A1 | 15k deep green | .30 | .25 |
| 29 | A1 | 20k orange | .35 | .25 |
| 30 | A1 | 25k gray | .40 | .35 |
| 31 | A1 | 35k dark brown | .35 | .25 |
| 32 | A1 | 50k purple | .35 | .25 |
| 33 | A1 | 75k emerald | .35 | .25 |
| | | *Nos. 25-33 (9)* | 3.00 | 2.35 |

The variety "printed on both sides" exists for 3k, 10k, 15k, 20k and 35k. Value, $20 each.

See Nos. 57-58, 76-82. For surcharges and overprints see Nos. 86, 132-133, 2N1-2N8, 2N12-2N19.

Liberation of Riga — A2

**1919 Wmk. 108**

| | | | | |
|---|---|---|---|---|
| 43 | A2 | 5k carmine | .25 | .25 |
| 44 | A2 | 15k deep green | .25 | .25 |
| 45 | A2 | 35k brown | .35 | *.80* |
| | | *Nos. 43-45 (3)* | .85 | 1.30 |

**Unwmk.**
**Pelure Paper**

| | | | | |
|---|---|---|---|---|
| 49 | A2 | 5k carmine | 9.50 | *16.00* |
| 50 | A2 | 15k deep green | 9.50 | *16.00* |
| 51 | A2 | 35k brown | 21.00 | 16.00 |
| | | *Nos. 49-51 (3)* | 40.00 | 48.00 |

For surcharge and overprints see Nos. 87, 2N9-2N11, 2N20-2N22.

Rising Sun — A4

**1919 *Imperf.***

55 A4 10k gray blue .80 .50

***Perf. 11½***

56 A4 10k gray blue .80 *1.50*

**Type of 1918**

**1919 Laid Paper *Perf. 11½***

| | | | | |
|---|---|---|---|---|
| 57 | A1 | 3r slate & org | 1.00 | 1.00 |
| 58 | A1 | 5r gray brn & org | 1.00 | 1.00 |

**Independence Issue**

Allegory of One Year of Independence A5

**Wove Paper**
**Size: 33x45mm**

**1919, Nov. 18 Unwmk.**

59 A5 10k brown & rose 1.25 *2.00*

**Laid Paper**

60 A5 10k brown & rose 1.25 *2.00*

**Size: 28x38mm**

| | | | | |
|---|---|---|---|---|
| 61 | A5 | 10k brown & rose | .30 | *.40* |
| *a.* | | Imperf. | 50.00 | |
| 62 | A5 | 35k indigo & grn | .30 | *.40* |
| *a.* | | Vert. pair, imperf. btwn. | 50.00 | 45.00 |

Back of No. 63 Block

**Wmk. 197**
**Thick Wove Paper**
**Blue Design on Back**

| | | | | |
|---|---|---|---|---|
| 63 | A5 | 1r green & red | .45 | .45 |
| | | *Nos. 59-63 (5)* | 3.55 | 5.25 |

There are two types of Nos. 59 and 60. In type I the trunk of the tree is not outlined. In type II it has a distinct white outline.

No. 63 was printed on the backs of unfinished 5r bank notes of the Workers and Soldiers Council, Riga.

For surcharges see Nos. 83-85, 88, 94.

Warrior Slaying Dragon — A6

**Wove Paper**

| | | | | |
|---|---|---|---|---|
| 64 | A6 | 10k brown & car | .50 | .50 |
| *a.* | | Horiz. pair, imperf. btwn. | 55.00 | 45.00 |
| 65 | A6 | 25k ind & yel grn | .50 | .50 |
| *a.* | | Pair, imperf. btwn. | 55.00 | 45.00 |
| 66 | A6 | 35k black & bl ('20) | .50 | .50 |
| *a.* | | Horiz. pair, imperf. btwn. | 55.00 | 45.00 |
| 67 | A6 | 1r dk grn & brn ('20) | .50 | .50 |
| *a.* | | Horiz. pair, imperf. vert. | 50.00 | 40.00 |
| *b.* | | Horiz. pair, imperf. btwn. | 50.00 | 40.00 |
| | | *Nos. 64-67 (4)* | 2.00 | 2.00 |
| | | Set, never hinged | 5.75 | |

Issued in honor of the liberation of Kurzeme (Kurland). The paper sometimes shows impressed quadrille lines.

For surcharges see Nos. 91-93.

**Latgale Relief Issue**

Latvia Welcoming Home Latgale Province — A7

Partial Design of No. 68 Back

**Brown and Green Design on Back**

**1920, Mar.**

| | | | | |
|---|---|---|---|---|
| 68 | A7 | 50k dk green & rose | .50 | .50 |
| *a.* | | Horiz. pair, imperf. vert. | 50.00 | |
| 69 | A7 | 1r slate grn & brn | .50 | .50 |
| *a.* | | Horiz. pair, imperf. vert. | 50.00 | |
| | | Set, never hinged | 10.00 | |

No. 68-69 were printed on the backs of unfinished bank notes of the government of Colonel Bermondt-Avalov and on the so-called German "Ober-Ost" money.

For surcharges see Nos. 95-99.

**First National Assembly Issue**

Latvia Hears Call to Assemble — A8

**1920**

| | | | | |
|---|---|---|---|---|
| 70 | A8 | 50k rose | .50 | .30 |
| *a.* | | Imperf., pair | 9.00 | *11.00* |
| 71 | A8 | 1r blue | .50 | .30 |
| *a.* | | Vert. pair, imperf. btwn. | 45.00 | 45.00 |
| *b.* | | Imperf., pair | 20.00 | 15.00 |
| 72 | A8 | 3r dk brn & grn | .50 | *.80* |
| 73 | A8 | 5r slate & vio brn | 1.00 | .80 |
| | | *Nos. 70-73 (4)* | 2.50 | 2.20 |
| | | Set, never hinged | 10.00 | |

For surcharges see Nos. 90, 134.

**Type of 1918 Issue**
**Wove Paper**

**1920-21 Unwmk. *Perf. 11½***

| | | | | |
|---|---|---|---|---|
| 76 | A1 | 5k carmine | .25 | .25 |
| 78 | A1 | 20k orange | .25 | .25 |
| 79 | A1 | 40k lilac ('21) | .30 | .25 |
| 80 | A1 | 50k violet | .35 | .25 |
| 81 | A1 | 75k emerald | .35 | .25 |
| 82 | A1 | 5r gray brn & org ('21) | 1.50 | 1.00 |
| | | *Nos. 76-82 (6)* | 3.00 | 2.25 |
| | | Set, never hinged | 6.00 | |

No. 63 Surcharged in Black, Brown or Blue

**1920, Sept. 1**

| | | | | |
|---|---|---|---|---|
| 83 | A5 | 10r on 1r grn & red (Bk) | 1.00 | *1.60* |
| 84 | A5 | 20r on 1r grn & red (Br) | 2.50 | *3.25* |
| 85 | A5 | 30r on 1r grn & red (Bl) | 3.50 | *4.00* |
| | | *Nos. 83-85 (3)* | 7.00 | *8.85* |
| | | Set, never hinged | 17.50 | |

Types of 1919 Surcharged

**1920-21 Wmk. 108 *Perf. 11½***

| | | | | |
|---|---|---|---|---|
| 86 | A1 | 2r on 10k dp blue | 1.75 | *7.25* |
| 87 | A2 | 2r on 35k brown | .50 | *5.50* |
| | | Set, never hinged | 5.00 | |

No. 62 Surcharged in Red

**Unwmk.**

| | | | | |
|---|---|---|---|---|
| 88 | A5 | 2r on 35k ind & grn | .40 | *.50* |
| | | Never hinged | .80 | |

No. 70 Surcharged in Blue

**1921**

| | | | | |
|---|---|---|---|---|
| 90 | A8 | 2r on 50k rose | .50 | .60 |
| | | Never hinged | 1.00 | |

Nos. 64-66 Surcharged in Red or Blue

**1920-21**

| | | | | |
|---|---|---|---|---|
| 91 | A6 | 1r on 35k blk & bl (R) | .35 | .40 |
| 92 | A6 | 2r on 10k brn & rose (Bl) | .60 | .80 |
| 93 | A6 | 2r on 25k ind & grn (R) | .35 | .40 |
| *a.* | | Imperf. | — | |
| | | *Nos. 91-93 (3)* | 1.30 | 1.60 |
| | | Set, never hinged | 3.25 | |

On Nos. 92 and 93 the surcharge reads "DIVI 2 RUBLI."

No. 83 with Added Surcharge

**1921** **Wmk. 197**

**94** A5 10r on 10r on 1r 1.50 1.00
Never hinged 5.00

Latgale Relief Issue of 1920 Surcharged in Black or Blue

**1921, May 31** **Unwmk.**

**95** A7 10r on 50k 1.25 .80
*a.* Imperf. —
**96** A7 20r on 50k 3.75 4.00
**97** A7 30r on 50k 5.00 4.00
**98** A7 50r on 50k 7.50 5.00
**99** A7 100r on 50k (Bl) 17.50 16.00
*Nos. 95-99 (5)* 35.00 29.80
Set, never hinged 62.50

Excellent counterfeits exist.

Arms and Stars for Vidzeme, Kurzeme & Latgale — A10

Type I, slanting cipher in value.
Type II, upright cipher in value.

***Perf. 10, 11½ and Compound***
**Wmk. Similar to 181**

**1921-22** **Typo.**

**101** A10 50k violet (II) .50 .30
**102** A10 1r orange yel .50 .50
**103** A10 2r deep green .25 .25
**104** A10 3r brt green .65 .45
**105** A10 5r rose 1.40 .40
**106** A10 6r dp claret 2.00 .80
**107** A10 9r orange 1.25 .55
**108** A10 10r blue (I) 1.25 .25
**109** A10 15r ultra 3.25 .50
*a.* Printed on both sides *50.00*
**110** A10 20r dull lilac (II) 20.00 2.00

Coat of Arms — A11

**1922, Aug. 21** ***Perf. 11½***

**111** A11 50r dk brn & pale brn (I) 30.00 4.50
**112** A11 100r dk bl & pale bl (I) 35.00 4.50
*Nos. 101-112 (12)* 96.05 15.00
Set, never hinged 200.00

Nos. 101-131 sometimes show letters and numerals of the paper maker's watermark "PACTIEN LIGAT MILLS 1858." Stamps showing part of the inscription command a 100 percent premium. Pairs with the complete year "1858" command a 300 percent premium.
See Nos. 126-131, 152-154.

A12

2 SANTIMS
Type A, tail of "2" ends in an upstroke.
Type B, tail of "2" is nearly horizontal.

**1923-25** ***Perf. 10, 11, 11½***

**113** A12 1s violet .40 .25
**114** A12 2s org yel (A) .60 .35
**115** A12 4s dark green .60 .25
*a.* Horiz. pair, imperf. btwn. 55.00 50.00
**116** A12 5s lt green ('25) 2.50 .65
**117** A12 6s grn, *yel* ('25) 3.50 .25
**118** A12 10s rose red (I) 1.50 .25
*a.* Horiz. pair, imperf. btwn. 55.00 50.00
**119** A12 12s claret .25 .40
**120** A12 15s brn, *sal* 3.50 .25
*a.* Horiz. pair, imperf. btwn. 55.00 50.00
**121** A12 20s dp blue (II) 1.50 .25
**122** A12 25s ultra ('25) .50 .25
**123** A12 30s pink (I) ('25) 5.00 .25
**124** A12 40s lilac (I) 2.00 .25
**125** A12 50s lil gray (II) 3.75 .35
**126** A11 1 l dk brn & pale brn 12.50 1.00
**127** A11 2 l dk blue & blue 20.00 1.60
**130** A11 5 l dp grn & pale grn 60.00 5.00
**131** A11 10 l car rose & pale rose (I) 3.00 6.00
*Nos. 113-131 (17)* 121.10 17.60
Set, never hinged 250.00

Value in "Santims" (1s); "Santimi" (2s-6s) or "Santimu" (others).
See note after No. 112.
See Nos. 135-151, 155-157. For overprints and surcharges see Nos. 164-167, B21-B23.

Nos. 79-80 Surcharged

No. 72 Surcharged

**1927** **Unwmk.** ***Perf. 11½***

**132** A1 15s on 40k lilac .40 .40
**133** A1 15s on 50k violet 1.15 *1.50*
**134** A8 1 l on 3r brn & grn 9.00 7.00
*Nos. 132-134 (3)* 10.55 8.90
Set, never hinged 24.00

**Types of 1923-25 Issue**

**1927-33** **Wmk. 212** ***Perf. 10, 11½***

**135** A12 1s dull violet .25 .25
**136** A12 2s org yel (A) .35 .25
**137** A12 2s org yel (B) ('33) .30 .25
**138** A12 3s org red ('31) .25 .25
**139** A12 4s dk green ('29) 3.50 2.25
**140** A12 5s lt green ('31) .50 .25
**141** A12 6s grn, *yel* .25 .25
**142** A12 7s dk green ('31) .50 .25
**143** A12 10s red (I) 2.50 .70
**144** A12 10s grn, *yel* (I) ('32) 10.00 .25
**145** A12 15s brn, *sal* 3.50 .45
**146** A12 20s pink (I) 5.00 .25
**147** A12 20s pink (II) 6.00 .25
**148** A12 30s lt blue (I) 1.25 .40
**149** A12 35s dk blue ('31) 1.50 .25
**150** A12 40s dl lil (I) ('29) 2.25 .25
**151** A12 50s gray (II) 2.50 .45
**152** A11 1 l dk brn & pale brn 8.00 .30
**153** A11 2 l dk bl & bl ('31) 30.00 2.25
**154** A11 5 l grn & pale grn ('33) 140.00 30.00
*Nos. 135-154 (20)* 218.40 39.80
Set, never hinged 400.00

The paper of Nos. 141, 144 and 145 is colored on the surface only.
See note above No. 113 for types A and B, and note above No. 101 for types I and II.

**Type of 1927-33 Issue**
**Paper Colored Through**

**1931-33** ***Perf. 10***

**155** A12 6s grn, *yel* .25 .25
**156** A12 10s grn, *yel* (I) ('33) 15.00 .25
**157** A12 15s brn, *salmon* 3.00 .25
*Nos. 155-157 (3)* 18.25 .75
Set, never hinged 37.50

View of Rezekne — A13

Designs (Views of Cities): 15s, Jelgava. 20s, Cesis (Wenden). 30s, Liepaja (Libau). 50s, Riga. 1 l, Riga Theater.

**1928, Nov. 18** **Litho.** ***Perf. 10, 11½***

**158** A13 6s dp grn & vio 1.00 .40
**159** A13 15s dk brn & ol grn 1.00 .40
**160** A13 20s cerise & bl grn 1.25 .45
**161** A13 30s ultra & vio brn 1.50 .40
**162** A13 50s dk gray & plum 1.50 1.00
**163** A13 1 l blk brn & brn 3.75 1.75
*Nos. 158-163 (6)* 10.00 4.40
Set, never hinged 20.00

10th anniv. of Latvian Independence.

**Riga Exhibition Issue**

Stamps of 1927-33 Overprinted

**1932, Aug. 30** ***Perf. 10, 11***

**164** A12 3s orange 1.00 .50
**165** A12 10s green, *yel* 1.00 .50
**166** A12 20s pink (I) 2.10 1.00
**167** A12 35s dark blue 4.75 2.00
*Nos. 164-167 (4)* 8.85 4.00
Set, never hinged 30.00

Riga Castle — A19

Arms and Shield — A20

Allegory of Latvia — A21

Ministry of Foreign Affairs — A22

**1934, Dec. 15** **Litho.** ***Perf. 10½, 10***

**174** A19 3s red orange .25 .25
**175** A20 5s yellow grn .25 .25
**176** A20 10s gray grn 1.00 .25
**177** A21 20s deep rose 1.00 .25
**178** A22 35s dark blue .35 .25
**179** A19 40s brown .35 .25
*Nos. 174-179 (6)* 3.20 1.50
Set, never hinged 6.00

Atis Kronvalds A23

A. Pumpurs A24

Juris Maters A25

Mikus Krogzemis (Auseklis) A26

**1936, Jan. 4** **Wmk. 212** ***Perf. 11½***

**180** A23 3s vermilion 3.50 *4.75*
**181** A24 10s green 3.50 *4.75*
**182** A25 20s rose pink 3.50 *6.00*
**183** A26 35s dark blue 3.50 *6.00*
*Nos. 180-183 (4)* 14.00 21.50
Set, never hinged 35.00

President Karlis Ulmanis — A27

**1937, Sept. 4** **Litho.** ***Perf. 10, 11½***

**184** A27 3s org red & brn org .25 .25
**185** A27 5s yellow grn .25 .25
**186** A27 10s dk sl grn .75 .60
**187** A27 20s rose lake & brn lake 1.50 .60
**188** A27 25s black vio 2.25 1.25
**189** A27 30s dark blue 2.25 1.25
**190** A27 35s indigo 1.00 1.00
**191** A27 40s lt brown 2.00 1.25
**192** A27 50s olive blk 2.25 1.50
*Nos. 184-192 (9)* 12.50 7.95
Set, never hinged 25.00

60th birthday of President Ulmanis.

Independence Monument, Rauna (Ronneburg) A28

Monument Entrance to Cemetery at Riga A29

Independence Monument, Jelgava — A30

War Memorial, Valka — A31

Independence Monument, Iecava — A32

Independence Monument, Riga — A33

Tomb of Col. Kalpaks — A34

**Thick Paper**

**Unwmk.**

**1937, July 12 Litho. *Perf. 10***

**193** A28 3s vermilion .65 *.90*
**194** A29 5s yellow grn .65 *.90*
**195** A30 10s deep grn .65 *.50*
**196** A31 20s carmine 1.60 *1.00*
**197** A32 30s lt blue 2.25 2.00

**Wmk. 212**

**Engr. *Perf. 11½***

**Thin Paper**

**198** A33 35s dark blue 2.25 2.00
**199** A34 40s brown 3.50 3.00
*Nos. 193-199 (7)* 11.55 10.30
Set, never hinged 25.00

View of Vidzeme — A35

General J. Balodis A37

President Karlis Ulmanis A38

Views: 5s, Latgale. 30s, Riga waterfront. 35s, Kurzeme. 40s, Zemgale.

**1938, Nov. 17 *Perf. 10, 10½x10***

**200** A35 3s brown org .25 .25
*a.* Booklet pane of 4 *45.00*
**201** A35 5s yellow grn .25 .25
*a.* Booklet pane of 4 *45.00*
**202** A37 10s dk green .25 .25
*a.* Booklet pane of 2 *45.00*
**203** A38 20s red lilac .25 .25
*a.* Booklet pane of 2 *45.00*
**204** A35 30s deep blue .90 .25
**205** A35 35s indigo .90 .25
*a.* Booklet pane of 2 *45.00*
**206** A35 40s rose violet 1.25 .25
*Nos. 200-206 (7)* 4.05 1.75
Set, never hinged 12.00

The 20th anniversary of the Republic.

School, Riga — A42

Independence Monument, Riga — A45

President Karlis Ulmanis A49

Designs: 5s, Castle of Jelgava. 10s, Riga Castle. 30s, Symbol of Freedom. 35s, Community House Daugavpils. 40s, Powder Tower and War Museum, Riga.

**1939, May 13 Photo. *Perf. 10***

**207** A42 3s brown orange .25 .80
**208** A42 5s deep green .50 .80
**209** A42 10s dk slate grn .75 .80
**210** A45 20s dk car rose 1.50 1.60
**211** A42 30s brt ultra 1.00 .80
**212** A42 35s dark blue 1.50 1.60
**213** A45 40s brown violet 2.00 1.00
**214** A49 50s grnsh black 3.00 1.00
*Nos. 207-214 (8)* 10.50 8.40
Set, never hinged 20.00

5th anniv. of National Unity Day.

Harvesting Wheat — A50

Apple — A51

**1939, Oct. 8**

**215** A50 10s slate green .90 .60
**216** A51 20s rose lake .90 .65
Set, never hinged 3.00

8th Agricultural Exposition held near Riga.

Arms and Stars for Vidzeme, Kurzeme and Latgale — A52

**1940**

**217** A52 1s dk vio brn .30 .30
**218** A52 2s ocher .40 .30
**219** A52 3s red orange .25 .25
**220** A52 5s dk olive brn .25 .25
**221** A52 7s dk green .30 .30
**222** A52 10s dk blue grn .75 .25
**224** A52 20s rose brown .75 .25
**225** A52 30s dp red brn 1.25 .30
**226** A52 35s brt ultra .25 *.80*
**228** A52 50s dk slate grn 1.75 .80
**229** A52 1 l olive green 3.50 2.40
*Nos. 217-229 (11)* 9.75 6.20
Set, never hinged 25.00

**Catalogue values for unused stamps in this section, from this point to the end of the section, are for Never Hinged items.**

Natl. Arms — A70

**1991, Oct. 19 Litho. *Perf. 13x12½***

**300** A70 5k multicolored *5.00* *5.00*
**301** A70 10k multicolored .40 .40
**302** A70 15k multicolored .50 .50
**303** A70 20k multicolored .65 .65
**304** A70 40k multicolored 1.25 1.25
**305** A70 50k multicolored 1.75 1.75

**Size: 28x32mm**

***Perf. 13½x14***

**306** A70 100k silver & multi 2.75 2.75
**307** A70 200k gold & multi 5.00 5.00
*Nos. 300-307 (8)* 17.30 17.30

**Most issues, Nos. 300-342, have one blocked value that was not freely available at Latvian post offices.**

**Russia Nos. 5984, 5985a Ovptd. "LATVIJA" and Srchd. in Red Lilac, Orange, Green, Violet**

**1991, Dec. 23 Photo. *Perf. 12x11½***

**308** A2765 100k on 7k (RL) *.50* .50
*a.* Vert. pair, one without ovpt. 8.00
*b.* Litho., perf. 12x12½ *.50* .50

***Perf. 12x12½***

**Litho.**

**309** A2765 300k on 2k (O) *.85* .85
*a.* Vert. pair, one without ovpt. 8.00
**310** A2765 500k on 2k (G) *1.25* 1.25
*a.* Vert. pair, one without ovpt. 8.00
**311** A2765 1000k on 2k (V) *2.40* 2.40
*a.* Vert. pair, one without ovpt. 8.00
*Nos. 308-311 (4)* *5.00* 5.00

On Nos. 308-311 the sixth row of the sheet was not surcharged.

Forgeries exist.

Liberty Monument, Riga — A71

**1991, Dec. 28 *Perf. 12½x13***

**312** A71 10k ol brn & multi .25 .25
**313** A71 15k violet & multi *1.00* *1.00*
**314** A71 20k bl grn & multi .80 .80
**315** A71 30k ol grn & multi .90 .90
**316** A71 50k choc & multi 1.25 1.25
**317** A71 100k dp blue & multi 1.25 1.25
*Nos. 312-317 (6)* 5.45 5.45

A72

A73

Monuments — A74

**1992, Feb. 29 *Perf. 14***

**318** A72 10k black .25 .25
**319** A73 20k violet black .40 .25
**320** A73 30k brown .55 .25
**321** A72 30k purple .55 .25
**322** A74 40k violet blue .75 .25
**323** A74 50k green .90 .25
**324** A73 50k olive green .90 .25
**325** A74 100k red brown 1.75 .60
**326** A72 200k blue 2.75 1.10
*Nos. 318-326 (9)* 8.80 3.45

**Russia Nos. 4599, 5984, 5985a Ovptd. "LATVIJA" and Srchd. in Red, Brown, Emerald and Violet**

**1992, Apr. 4 Photo. *Perf. 12x11½***

**327** A2765 1r on 7k (R) .25 .25

***Perf. 12x12½***

**Litho.**

**328** A2765 3r on 2k (Br) .40 .25
**329** A2765 5r on 2k (E) .65 .35
**330** A2765 10r on 2k (V) 1.10 .75
**331** A2138 25r on 4k 2.25 1.75
*Nos. 327-331 (5)* 4.65 3.35

Surcharged denominations expressed in rubles (large numerals) and kopecks (small zeros).

Birds of the Baltic Shores — A75

**Litho. & Engr.**

**1992, Oct. 3 *Perf. 12½x13***

**Booklet Stamps**

**332** A75 5r Pandion haliaetus .35 .35
**333** A75 5r Limosa limosa .35 .35
**334** A75 5r Mergus merganser .35 .35
**335** A75 5r Tadorna tadorna .35 .35
*a.* Booklet pane of 4, #332-335 2.25

See Estonia Nos. 231-234a, Lithuania Nos. 427-430a, and Sweden Nos. 1975-1978a.

Christmas A76

2r, 10r Angels with children around Christmas tree. 3r, Angels with musical instruments, Christmas tree. 15r, Nativity scene.

**1992, Nov. 21 Litho. *Perf. 13½x13***

**336** A76 2r silver & multi *1.00* *1.00*
**337** A76 3r multicolored *.30* *.25*
**338** A76 10r gold & multi *1.00* *.60*
**339** A76 15r multicolored *1.50* *1.00*
*Nos. 336-339 (4)* *3.80* *2.85*

Russia Nos. 4728, 5107, 5109 Surcharged in Brown or Blue

***Perfs. & Printing Methods as Before***

**1993, Feb. 26**

**340** A2229 50r on 6k #4728 (Br) *.75* *.55*
**341** A2435 100r on 6k #5109 *1.60* *1.00*
**342** A2435 300r on 6k #5107 *4.25* *3.00*
*Nos. 340-342 (3)* *6.60* *4.55*

Traditional Costumes — A77

**1993, Apr. 29 Litho. *Perf. 13x13½***

**343** A77 5s Kuldiga *.25* *.25*
**344** A77 10s Alsunga *.30* *.25*
**345** A77 20s Lielvarde *.55* *.30*
**346** A77 50s Rucava *1.50* *.80*
**347** A77 100s Zemgale *3.00* *1.50*
**348** A77 500s Ziemellatgale *15.00* *12.00*
*a.* Miniature sheet of 6, #343-348 *25.00* *25.00*
*Nos. 343-348 (6)* *20.60* *15.10*

See Nos. 400-401, 415-416, 440-441, 466-467.

21st Natl. Song Festival
A78 A79

**1993, July 3 Litho. *Perf. 12½x13***

**349** A78 3s rose brn, gold & black *1.00* *.50*
**350** A78 5s purple, gold & black *1.50* *.80*
**351** A79 15s multicolored *2.00* *1.25*
*Nos. 349-351 (3)* *4.50* *2.55*

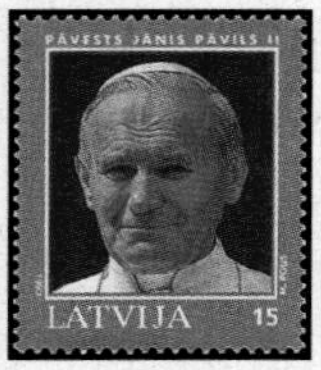

A80

**1993, Aug. 28 Litho. *Perf. 14***
**352** A80 15s Pope John Paul II *1.10 .90*

A81

**1993, Nov. 11 Litho. *Perf. 12½x13***
**353** A81 5s silver, black & red *.70 .30*
**354** A81 15s gold, black & red *1.30 .45*

Independence, 75th anniv.

A82

**1994, Apr. 2 Litho. *Perf. 14***
**355** A82 15s multicolored *1.00 .60*

Evalds Valters, actor, 100th birthday.

A83

**1994, Apr. 20 Litho. *Perf. 12½x13***
**356** A83 5s Biathlon *.40 .40*
**357** A83 10s 2-man bobsled *.85 .40*
**358** A83 15s Luge *1.00 .65*
**359** A83 100s Men's figure skating *5.75 3.25*
*Nos. 356-359 (4) 8.00 4.70*

**Souvenir Sheet**

**360** A83 200s like #357 *8.00 7.00*

1994 Winter Olympics, Lillehammer.

Ethnographical Open Air Museum — A84

**1994, Apr. 30 Litho. *Perf. 13x12½***
**361** A84 5s multicolored *.80 .35*

1994 Basketball Festival, Riga — A85

**1994, June 4 Litho. *Perf. 12½x13***
**362** A85 15s multicolored *1.10 .55*

Provincial Municipal Arms — A86

Nos. 363-377A are inscribed with the year date of issue below the design. The year noted in each description is the date that appears on the stamp.

***Perf. 13x12½, 14x14¼ (#373)***

**1994-2007**

**363** A86 1s Kurzeme, "1994" .25 .25
*a.* "1996" .25 .25
*b.* "1997" .75 .25
*c.* "1998" .25 .25
*d.* Perf 14x14¼, "1999" 1.25 .50
*e.* As "d," "2002" .25 .25
*f.* Perf. 13¼x13¾, "2006" .25 .25
*g.* As "f," "2007" .25 .25
*h.* As "d," "2011" .25 .25
*i.* As "d," "2012" .25 .25
**364** A86 2s Auce, "1996" .40 .25
*a.* "1997" .40 .25
*b.* "1998" .30 .25
*c.* Perf 14x14¼, "1999" 1.25 1.25
*d.* As "c," "2000" .40 .25
*e.* As "c," "2002" .25 .25
*f.* Perf 13¼x13¾, "2005" .25 .25
*g.* As "f," "2006" .25 .25
*h.* As "f," "2007" .25 .25
*i.* As "c," "2011" .25 .25
*j.* As "c," "2012" .25 .25
*k.* As "c," "2013" .25 .25
**365** A86 3s Zemgale, 1994 .55 .35
*a.* Perf 14x14¼, "1999" .55 .35
*b.* As "a," "2000" .55 .35
*c.* As "a," "2002" .25 .25
*d.* Perf 13¼x13¾, "2005" .25 .25
*e.* As "d," "2006" .25 .25
*f.* As "d," "2007" .25 .25
*g.* Perf. 14x14¼, "2010" .25 .25
*h.* As "g," "2011" .25 .25
*i.* As "g," "2012" .25 .25
*j.* As "g," "2013" .25 .25
**366** A86 5s Vidzeme, "1994" .55 .25
*a.* "1996" .50 .50
*b.* Perf 14x14¼, "1999" .50 .50
*c.* As "b," "2000" .50 .50
**367** A86 8s Livani, "1995" .50 .40
*a.* "1996" .50 .40
**368** A86 10s Latgale, "1994" .50 .50
*a.* "1997" 1.60 1.00
*b.* "1998" .50 .50
**369** A86 13s Preili, "1996" .70 .70
*a.* Perf. 14x14¼, "2010" .50 .50
**370** A86 16s Ainazi, "1995" .80 .80
*a.* "1996" 1.00 1.00
**371** A86 20s Grobina, "1995" 1.00 1.00
*a.* "1996" 1.00 1.00
**372** A86 24s Tukums, "1995" 1.10 1.10
*a.* "1996" 1.10 1.10
**373** A86 28s Madona, "1996" 1.75 1.50
**374** A86 30s Riga, "1994" 1.50 1.50
**375** A86 36s Priekule, "1996" 2.25 1.50
**376** A86 50s Natl. arms, "1994" 2.25 2.25

**Size: 29x24mm**

***Perf. 14***

**377** A86 100s Riga *4.25 2.50*
**377A** A86 200s Natl. arms *8.75 4.75*
*Nos. 363-377A (16)* 27.10 19.60

Issued: No. 363, 6/21/94; No. 363a, 1/30/96; No. 363b, 2/5/97; No. 363c, 1/12/98; No. 363d, 1/20/99; No. 363e, 2/6/02; No. 363f, 9/9/06; No. 363g, 6/8/07; No. 363h, 6/8/11; No. 363i, 3/15/12. No. 364, 4/12/96; No. 364a, 2/5/97; No. 364b, 2/11/98; No. 364c, 1/20/99; No. 364d, 4/26/00; No. 364e, 2/6/02; No. 364f, 9/10/05; No. 364g, 9/9/06; No. 364h, 6/8/07. No. 364i, 6/8/11; No. 364j, 3/15/12. No. 364k, 3/3/13. No. 365, 6/21/94; No. 365a, 3/16/99; No. 365b, 4/26/00; No. 365c, 2/6/02; No. 365d, 9/10/05; No. 365e, 9/9/06; No. 365f, 6/8/07; No. 365g, 2/15/10; No. 365h, 6/8/11; No. 365i, 3/15/12. No. 365j, 3/3/13. No. 366, 6/21/94; No. 366a, 1/30/96; No. 366b, 1/20/99; No. 366c, 4/26/00. No. 367, 6/1/95; No. 367a, 1/30/96. No. 368, 6/21/94; No. 368a, 8/28/97; No. 368b, 8/4/98. No. 369, 4/12/96; No. 369a, 3/12/10 No. 370, 6/1/95; No. 370a, 4/8/96. No. 371, 6/1/95; No. 371a, 9/6/96. No. 372, 6/1/95; No. 372a, 4/8/96. No. 373, 11/5/96. No. 374, 12/21/94. No. 375, 11/5/96. Nos. 376, 377, 378, 12/21/94.

See Nos. 450-451, 472-473, 482-483, 506-507, 525-526.

A87

**1994, Sept. 24 Litho. *Perf. 14***
**378** A87 5s multicolored *.80 .30*

University of Latvia, 75th anniv.

A88

Items balanced on scales (Europa): 10s, Latvian coins. 50s, Locked chest, money card.

**1994, Oct. 29 Litho. *Perf. 14x13½***
**379** A88 10s multicolored *.65 .25*
*a.* Tete-beche pair *1.75 1.75*
**380** A88 50s multicolored *2.75 1.50*
*a.* Tete-beche pair *7.00 6.00*

Dormouse A89

**1994, Nov. 19 Litho. *Perf. 13½x13***
**381** A89 5s shown *.45 .35*
**382** A89 10s Among leaves *.75 .35*
**383** A89 10s Eating berries *.75 .35*
**384** A89 15s Berry, large mouse *1.50 .50*
*Nos. 381-384 (4) 3.45 1.55*

World Wildlife Fund.

A90

Christmas: 3s, Angel. 8s, Angels playing flute & violin. 13c, Angels singing. 100s, Candles.

**1994, Dec. 3 *Perf. 14***
**385** A90 3s multicolored *.30 .25*
**386** A90 8s multicolored *.55 .25*
**387** A90 13s multicolored *1.00 .30*
**388** A90 100s multicolored *5.00 2.10*
*Nos. 385-388 (4) 6.85 2.90*

A91

Children's Fairy Tales, by Margarita Staraste: 5s, Elf with candle. No. 390, Small bear in snow. No. 391, Boy on sled.

***Perf. 13x12½ on 3 Sides***
**1994, Dec. 17 Booklet Stamps**
**389** A91 5s multicolored *.50 .50*
**390** A91 10s multicolored *.50 .50*
**391** A91 10s multicolored *.50 .50*
*a.* Booklet pane, 2 each #389-391 *3.00*
Complete booklet, #391a + label *3.25*
*Nos. 389-391 (3) 1.50 1.50*

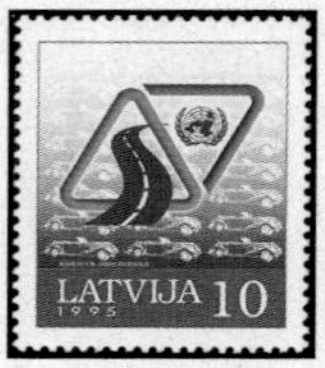

A92

**1995, Feb. 18 *Perf. 14***
**392** A92 10s multicolored *.80 .50*

European safe driving week.

A93

**1995, Mar. 4 Litho. *Perf. 14***
**393** A93 15s silver, blue & red *.75 .60*

UN, 50th anniv.

A94

Via Baltica Highway Project: Nos. 394, 395b, Castle, Bauska, Latvia. No. 395a, Beach Hotel, Parnu, Estonia. No. 395c, Kaunas, Lithuania.

**1995, Apr. 20 Litho. *Perf. 14***
**394** A94 8s multicolored *.50 .50*

**Souvenir Sheet**

**395** A94 18s Sheet of 3, #a.-c. *2.75 2.75*

See Estonia Nos. 288-289, Lithuania Nos. 508-509.

A95

8s, Dendrocopos leucotos. 20s, Crex crex. 24s, Chlidonias leucopterus.

**1995, July 8 Litho. *Perf. 12½***
**396** A95 8s multicolored *.50 .50*
**397** A95 20s multicolored *1.20 1.20*
**398** A95 24s multicolored *1.60 1.60*
*Nos. 396-398 (3) 3.30 3.30*

European nature conservation year.

Julian Cardinal Vaivods, Birth Cent. — A96

**1995, Aug. 18 Litho. *Perf. 14***
**399** A96 8s multicolored *.65 .50*

**Traditional Costume Type of 1993**

**1995, Sept. 8 Litho. *Perf. 13x13½***
**400** A77 8s Nica *.40 .40*

**Souvenir Sheet**

**401** A77 100s Like #400 4.50 4.50

Friendly Appeal, by Karlis Ulmanis, 60th Anniv. — A97

**1995, Sept. 8** ***Perf. 14***
**402** A97 8s multicolored *.50 .50*

Riga, 800th Anniv. — A98

**1995, Sept. 23** ***Perf. 13½***
**403** A98 8s Natl. Opera .40 .40
**404** A98 16s Natl. Theatre .80 .80

**Size: 45x27mm**

**405** A98 24s Academy of Arts 1.00 1.00
**406** A98 36s State Art Museum 1.50 1.50
*Nos. 403-406 (4)* 3.70 3.70

See Nos. 508-511, 529-531, 529-531.

Peace and Freedom — A99

Heroes from national epic, Lacplesis, dates of independence: 16s, Spidola with sword and shield, 1918. 50s, Lacplesis with leaves and banner, 1991.

**1995, Nov. 15** **Litho.** ***Perf. 13½***
**407** A99 16s multicolored .75 .75
*a.* Tete beche pair 2.50 2.50
**408** A99 50s multicolored 2.25 2.25
*a.* Tete beche pair 5.00 5.00

Europa.

Christmas A100

Designs: No. 409, Characters surrounding Christmas tree at night. No. 410, Santa gliding through sky holding candle. 15s, Characters outside snow-covered house. 24s, Santa standing between dog and cat.

**1995, Dec. 2**
**409** A100 6s multicolored .55 .25
**410** A100 6s multicolored .55 .25
**411** A100 15s multicolored .30 .60
**412** A100 24s multicolored 2.25 1.00
*Nos. 409-412 (4)* 3.65 2.10

Pauls Stradins (1896-1958), Physician — A101

**1996, Jan. 17** **Litho.** ***Perf. 14***
**413** A101 8s multicolored .40 .25

Zenta Maurina (1897-1978) A102

**1996, May 10** **Litho.** ***Perf. 13½x14***
**414** A102 36s multicolored *1.60 .95*
*a.* Tete beche pair 3.25 3.25

Europa.

**Traditional Costume Type of 1993**

**1996, May 18** **Litho.** ***Perf. 13x13½***
**415** A77 8s Barta *.50 .25*

**Souvenir Sheet**

**416** A77 100s like No. 415 *4.00 3.00*

Souvenir Sheet

Children's Games — A103

**1996, June 8** **Litho.** ***Perf. 14x13½***
**417** A103 48s Sheet of 1 *2.75 2.25*

1996 Summer Olympic Games, Atlanta A104

***Perf. 14x13½, 13½x14***

**1996, June 19**
**418** A104 8s Cycling,vert. .40 .25
**419** A104 16s Basketball, vert .70 .40
**420** A104 24s Walking, vert. .80 .50
**421** A104 36s Canoeing 1.50 .80
*Nos. 418-421 (4)* 3.40 1.95

**Souvenir Sheet**

**422** A104 100s Javelin *4.50 3.50*

Nature Museum, 150th Anniv. A105

Butterflies: 8s, Papilio machaon. 24s, Catocala fraxini. 80s, Pericallia matronula.

**1996, Aug. 30** ***Perf. 13***
**423** A105 8s multicolored *.35 .25*
**424** A105 24s multicolored *.90 .45*
**425** A105 80s multicolored *3.75 1.90*
*Nos. 423-425 (3)* *5.00 2.60*

Car Production in Latvia — A106

Designs: 8s, 1912 Russo-Balt fire truck. 24s, 1899 Leutner-Russia. 36s, 1939 Ford-Vairogs.

**1996, Oct. 25** **Litho.** ***Perf. 13x12½***
**426** A106 8s multicolored *.35 .25*
**427** A106 24s multicolored *1.20 .55*
**428** A106 36s multicolored *1.50 .85*
*Nos. 426-428 (3)* *3.05 1.65*

City of Riga, 800th Anniv. — A107

**1996, Dec. 5** **Litho.** ***Perf. 13½***
**429** A107 8s Building front *.40 .25*

**Size: 30x26mm**

**430** A107 16s Stained glass window *.75 .40*

**Size: 37x26mm**

**431** A107 24s Buildings *1.25 .55*
**432** A107 30s Art figures *1.25 .70*
*Nos. 429-432 (4)* *3.65 1.90*

Christmas A108

Designs: 6s, Santa's elves, presents. 14s, Santa on skis, dog, children in animal costumes. 20s, Child in front of Christmas tree, santa in chair, pets.

**1996, Dec. 7** ***Perf. 14***
**433** A108 6s multicolored *.30 .25*
**434** A108 14s multicolored *.70 .35*
**435** A108 20s multicolored *1.00 .50*
*Nos. 433-435 (3)* *2.00 1.10*

See Nos. 458-460.

Birds — A109

Designs: 10s, Caprimulgus eurpaeus. 20s, Aquila clanga. 30s, Acrocephalus paludicola.

**1997, Feb. 8** ***Perf. 13x12½***
**436** A109 10s multicolored *.50 .25*
**437** A109 20s multicolored *.90 .45*
**438** A109 30s multicolored *1.40 .70*
*Nos. 436-438 (3)* *2.80 1.40*

Turn of the Epochs — A110

**1997, Mar. 25** **Litho.** ***Perf. 14***
**439** A110 10s multicolored *.70 .35*

**Traditional Costume Type of 1993**

**1997, Apr. 3** ***Perf. 13x13½***
**440** A77 10s Rietumvidzeme *1.25 .80*

**Souvenir Sheet**

**441** A77 100s like #440 *4.25 3.50*

Stamp Day.

Legend of Rozi Turaidas — A111

**1997, Apr. 26** **Litho.** ***Perf. 12½x13***
**442** A111 32s multicolored *1.50 .70*
*a.* Tete beche pair 3.50 3.50

Europa.

Old Baltic Ships — A112

Designs: 10s, Linijkugis, 17th cent.

No. 444: a, Linijkugis, 17th cent., diff. b, Kurenas 16th cent. c, Maasilinn ship, 16th cent.

**1997, May 10** ***Perf. 14x14½***
**443** A112 10s multicolored *.50 .40*

**Souvenir Sheet**

**444** A112 20s Sheet of 3, #a.-c. *3.00 2.75*

See Estonia Nos. 322-323, Lithuania Nos. 571-572.

Port of Ventspils, Cent. — A113

**1997, May 21** **Litho.** ***Perf. 13½x14***
**445** A113 20s Hermes, Poseidon *.90 .50*

Children's Activities A114

Designs: 10s, Stamp collecting. 12s, Riding dirt bike, vert. 20s, Boy in hockey uniform, girl in skiwear, vert. 30s, Tennis, soccer, basketball.

**1997, June 7** ***Perf. 13½x13***
**446** A114 10s multicolored *.45 .25*
**447** A114 12s multicolored *.60 .30*
**448** A114 20s multicolored *.90 .45*
**449** A114 30s multicolored *1.25 .75*
*Nos. 446-449 (4)* *3.20 1.75*

**Municipal Arms Type of 1994**

**1997-2005** **Litho.** ***Perf. 13x12½***

**Date imprint below design**

**450** A86 10s Valmiera, "1997" 1.00 .50
*a.* "1998" 1.00 .50
*b.* Perf 14x14¼, "1999" 1.00 .50
*c.* "2000" 1.00 .50
*d.* Perf. 13¼x13¾, "2001" 1.00 .50
*e.* "2005" 1.00 .40
**451** A86 20s Rezekne, "1997" 2.25 1.00

Issued: No. 450, 9/6/97; No. 450a, 1/12/98; No. 450b, 1/20/99; No. 450c, 4/26/00; No. 450d, 9/12/01; No. 450e, 9/10/05. No. 451, 9/6/97.

Nature Preserves A115

**1997, Oct. 18** **Litho.** ***Perf. 13x12½***
**452** A115 10s Moricsala, 1912 *.50 .25*
**453** A115 30s Slitere, 1921 *1.50 .80*

See Nos. 464-465.

City of Riga, 800th Anniv. A116

10s, Woman, house, 12th cent. 20s, Monument to Bishop Albert, seal of the bishop, rosary, writing tool, 13th-16th cent. 30s, Riga castle, weapons used during Middle Ages. 32s, Houses, arms of Riga, statue of St. John.

**1997, Nov. 27** **Litho.** ***Perf. 13x14***
**454** A116 10s multicolored .50 .30
**455** A116 20s multicolored .85 .45
**456** A116 30s multicolored 1.25 .70

**Size: 27x26mm**

**457** A116 32s multicolored 1.40 .80
*Nos. 454-457 (4)* 4.00 2.25

See Nos. 468-471, 488-491, 508-511, 529-531.

### Christmas Type of 1996

People dressed in masks, costumes for mummery: 8s, Santa, bear. 18s, Two goats. 28s, Horse.

**1997, Nov. 29** ***Perf. 14***

**458** A108 8s multicolored .40 .25
**459** A108 18s multicolored .90 .40
**460** A108 28s multicolored 1.40 .60
*Nos. 458-460 (3)* 2.70 1.25

A117

**1998, Jan. 31 Litho.** ***Perf. 14x13½***

**461** A117 20s multicolored 1.00 *.75*

1998 Winter Olympic Games, Nagano.

A118

Statue at Spridisi, museum home of Anna Brigadere(1861-1933), writer.

**1998, Feb. 21 Litho.** ***Perf. 13½***

**462** A118 10s multicolored .65 .35

National Song Festival — A119

**1998, Mar. 28 Litho.** ***Perf. 13x14***

**463** A119 30s multicolored 2.50 1.25
*a.* Tete beche pair 5.50 5.50

Europa.

### Nature Preserves Type of 1997

**1998, Apr. 30** ***Perf. 13x12½***

**464** A115 10s Grini, 1936 .45 .25
**465** A115 30s Teici, 1982 1.25 1.00

### Traditional Costume Type of 1993

No. 467, Krustpils, man wearing crown of leaves.

**1998, May 9** ***Perf. 13x13½***

**466** A77 10s Krustpils region .75 .30

### Souvenir Sheet

**467** A77 100s multicolored 5.00 5.00

### City of Riga, 800th Anniv., Type of 1997

10s, Dannenstern House, 16th and 17th cent. coins issued by kings of Poland and Sweden, 17th cent. wooden sculpture. 20s, City Library, monument to G. Herder, poet, philosopher, teacher. 30s, 18th cent. arsenal, column celebrating defeat of Napoleon's troops, octant, compass. 40s, Sculpture of Mother Latvia at Warriors' Cemetery, entrance to Cemetery, obv. & rev. of 5 lat coin, 1930.

**1998, May 29 Litho.** ***Perf. 13x14***

**468** A116 10s multicolored .45 .25
**469** A116 20s multicolored 1.00 .45
**470** A116 30s multicolored 1.30 .60
**471** A116 40s multicolored 1.75 .85
*Nos. 468-471 (4)* 4.50 2.15

No. 468 is 30x26mm.

### Municipal Arms Type of 1994

**1998-2004 Litho.** ***Perf. 13¼x13¾***

**Date imprint below design**

**472** A86 15s Bauska, "1998" .55 .40
**473** A86 30s Liepaja, "1998" 1.25 1.00
*a.* Perf 13½x14, "2004" 1.35 1.10

Issued: No. 472, 473, 9/26/98; No. 473a, 9/7/04.

World Stamp Day — A120

**1998, Oct. 20 Litho.** ***Perf. 14***

**474** A120 30s #2, various stamps 1.25 .75

Dome Church, Riga, 1211 — A121

**1998, Oct. 23**

**475** A121 10s multicolored .70 .40

Pres. Janis Cakste (1859-1927) A122

**1998, Nov. 11** ***Perf. 14x13½***

**476** A122 10s multicolored .50 .35

See No. 497, 515, 524.

Independence, 80th Anniv. — A123

**1998, Nov. 14** ***Perf. 13x12½***

**477** A123 10s shown .45 .30
**478** A123 30s Arms, flags 1.40 .90

Christmas A124

Christmas elves: 10s, Rolling snow balls. 20s, Decorating tree, preparing presents. 30s, Pulling sled over snow.

**1998, Nov. 28** ***Perf. 13½x14***

**479** A124 10s multicolored .55 .35
**480** A124 20s multicolored 1.20 .75
**481** A124 30s multicolored 1.50 .95
*Nos. 479-481 (3)* 3.25 2.05

### Municipal Arms Type of 1994

**1999-2004 Litho.** ***Perf. 13¼x13¾***

**Date imprint below design**

**482** A86 15s Ogre, "1999" .80 .45
*a.* "2000" .90 .55
**483** A86 40s Jelgava, "1999" 2.00 1.10
*a.* "2004" 1.50 .85

Issued: No. 482, 2/12/99; No. 482a, 2/25/00. No. 483, 4/10/99; No. 483a, 9/7/04.

Nature Parks and Reserves A125

Europa: 30s, Krustkalnu Nature Reserve. 60s, Gauja Natl. Nature Park.

**1999, Mar. 20** ***Perf. 13x12½***

**484** A125 30s multicolored 1.75 1.00
**485** A125 60s multicolored 4.00 2.00

Council of Europe, 50th Anniv. — A126

**1999, Apr. 24**

**486** A126 30s multicolored 1.50 1.00

Rudolfs Blaumanis (1863-1908), Writer — A127

**1999, Apr. 24** ***Perf. 14x13***

**487** A127 110s multicolored *4.25* 2.00

### City of Riga, 800th Anniv. Type

10s, Streetcar. 30s, Schooner "Widwud." 40s, Airplane. 70s, TK-type locomotive.

***Perf. 13¼x13¾***

**1999, June 26** **Litho.**

**488** A116 10s multicolored .40 .30
**489** A116 30s multicolored 1.20 .80
**490** A116 40s multicolored 1.60 1.10
**491** A116 70s multicolored 2.50 1.75
*Nos. 488-491 (4)* 5.70 3.95

No. 488 is 30x27mm.

Aglona Basilica — A129

**1999, July 10 Litho.** ***Perf. 14x14½***

**492** A129 15s multicolored .80 .40
Complete booklet, 6 #492 12.00

"Baltic Chain," 10th Anniv. — A130

Families and flags: 15s, No. 494a, Latvian. No. 494: b, Lithuanian. c, Estonian.

**1999, Aug. 23 Litho.** ***Perf. 12½x13***

**493** A130 15s multicolored 1.25 .50

### Souvenir Sheet

**494** A130 30s Sheet of 3, #a.-c. 4.25 4.00

See Estonia Nos. 366-367, Lithuania Nos. 639-640.

Rundâle Palace — A131

**1999, Sept. 25 Litho.** ***Perf. 14***

**495** A131 20s multicolored .90 .65

See Nos. 512, 536, 578.

Landscape, by Julijs Feders (1838-1909) — A132

**1999, Oct. 13 Litho.** ***Perf. 13½***

**496** A132 15s multi .85 .55

### Presidents Type of 1998

15s, Pres. Gustavs Zemgals (1871-1939).

**1999, Nov. 16 Litho.** ***Perf. 14x13½***

**497** A122 15s multicolored .75 .55

A134

**1999, Nov. 25** ***Perf. 14x14½***

**498** A134 40s multi 2.00 1.00

UPU, 125th anniv.

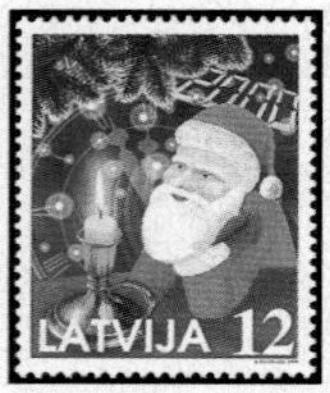

A135

Christmas and Millennium: 12s, Santa, tree, candle. 15s, Santa, tree, children. 40s, Santa, tree with ornaments.

**1999, Nov. 27** ***Perf. 14¼***

**499** A135 12s multi .65 .30
**500** A135 15s multi .80 .40
**501** A135 40s multi 2.00 1.00
*Nos. 499-501 (3)* 3.45 1.70

Nude, by J. Rozentals A136

***Perf. 14½x14¼***

**2000, Feb. 26** **Litho.**

**502** A136 40s multi 2.00 1.50

Aleksandrs Caks (1901-50), Poet — A137

**2000, Apr. 8 Litho.** ***Perf. 14x13½***

**503** A137 40s multi 2.00 .90
Booklet, 6 #503 12.50

### Europa, 2000

Common Design Type

**2000, May 9**

**504** CD17 60s multi 5.00 2.40
*a.* Tete beche pair 10.00 10.00

Ice Hockey — A138

**Wmk. 387**

**2000, June 21 Litho.** ***Perf. 14***
**505** A138 70s multi + label 3.25 1.75

Issued in sheets of 8 + 8 labels. Vertical columns of four labels, which depict players Helmut Balderis, Vitalijs Samoilovs, Sandis Ozolinsh and Arturs Irbe, flank a central block of eight stamps. Color photos of the players appear at left or right of the labels.

**Municipal Arms Type of 1994**

**2000-05 Unwmk.** ***Perf. 13¼x13¾***

**Date imprint below design**

**506** A86 15s Daugavpils, "2000" .75 .50
*a.* "2005" .65 .45
**507** A86 15s Jūrmala, "2000" .75 .50
*a.* "2001" .75 .50
*b.* "2002" .75 .50
*c.* "2005" .65 .45

Issued: No. 506, 7/6/00; No. 506a, 8/5/05. No. 507, 7/6/00; No. 507a, 9/12/01; No. 507b, 1/12/02; No. 507c, 8/5/05.

**City of Riga, 800th Anniv. Type of 1995**

Designs: 20s, Central Market. No. 509, Riga Zoo. No. 510, Riga Dome Organ. 70s, Powder Tower,

**2000, July 22** ***Perf. 13¼x14***

**Size: 40x28mm**

**508** A98 20s multi 1.00 .50

**Size: 47x28mm**

**509** A98 40s multi 1.75 1.00
Complete booklet, 6 #509 10.50

***Perf. 14x13¼***

**Size: 28x32mm**

**510** A98 40s multi 1.75 1.00
**511** A98 70s multi 3.00 1.25
*Nos. 508-511 (4)* 7.50 3.75

**Palace Type of 1999**

**2000, Aug. 12** ***Perf. 13¼x14***
**512** A131 40s Jelgava Palace 1.75 1.00
Booklet, 6 #512 11.50

2000 Summer Olympics, Sydney — A139

**2000, Sept. 15** ***Perf. 14¼x14***
**513** A139 70s multi + label 3.00 2.00

See No. 518.

Millennium — A140

No. 514: a, 15s, Freedom Monument, Riga. b, House of Blackheads, Riga.

***Perf. 14x13¼***

**2000, Sept. 28 Litho. Wmk. 387**
**514** A140 Pair + label 3.00 2.75
*a.* 15s multi .80 .40
*b.* 50s multi 2.00 1.10

**President Type of 1998**

***Perf. 13¾x13¼***

**2000, Nov. 11 Unwmk.**
**515** A122 15s Alberts Kveisis (1881-1936) .80 .50

Orthodox Cathedral — A141

**2000, Nov. 17** ***Perf. 14***
**516** A141 40s multi 1.75 1.00

See Nos. 537, 559, 573.

Red Cross — A142

**2000, Nov. 22**
**517** A142 15s multi .75 .45

**Olympics Type of 2000**

**2000, Nov. 22**
**518** A139 40s multi 1.75 1.00

Issued in sheets of 4 + 2 different labels depicting gold medal winner Igors Vihrovs.

Christmas — A143

Designs: 12s, Watch. No. 520, 15s, Angels. No. 521, 15s, Madonna and child.

**2000, Nov. 25**
**519-521** A143 Set of 3 1.90 1.00

International Recognition of Latvia, 80th Anniv. — A144

**2001, Jan. 13 Litho.** ***Perf. 14***
**522** A144 40s multi 1.75 1.25

Kad Silavas Mostas, by Vilhelmis Purvitis — A145

***Perf. 14¼x14½***

**2001, Feb. 1 Litho. Unwmk.**
**523** A145 40s multi 2.75 1.50
Booklet, 6 #523 16.50

**President Type of 1998**

**2001, Feb. 17** ***Perf. 13¾x13¼***
**524** A122 15s Karlis Ulmanis (1877-1942) .75 .40

**Municipal Arms Type of 1994**

**2001-06** ***Perf. 13¼x13¾***

**Date imprint below design**

**525** A86 5s Smiltene, "2001" .60 .30
*a.* "2002" .60 .30
*b.* "2005" .30 .30
*c.* "2006" .30 .30
*d.* Perf. 14x14¼, "2011" .30 .30
*e.* As "d," "2012" .30 .30
*f.* As "d," "2013" .30 .30
**526** A86 15s Kuldiga, "2001" .70 .40
*a.* "2002" .70 .40

Issued: No. 525, 3/5/01; No. 525a, 9/16/02; No. 525b, 9/10/05; No. 525c, 9/9/06. No. 525d, 6/8/11; No. 525e, 3/15/12; No. 525f, 3/3/13. No. 526, 3/5/01; No. 526a, 9/16/02.

Narrow Gauge Locomotive A146

**2001, Mar. 24** ***Perf. 14***
**527** A146 40s multi 1.75 1.25

Europa — A147

**2001, Apr. 14**
**528** A147 60s multi 3.50 1.75
*a.* Tete beche pair 4.50 4.50

**Riga, 800th Anniv. Type of 1995**

Riga in: No. 529a, 20th cent. No. 529b, 21st cent. 60s, 16th cent. 70s, 17th cent.

**2001, May 24 Litho.** ***Perf. 13¾x13½***

**Size: 29x33mm (each stamp)**

**529** A98 15s Horiz. pair, #a-b 1.50 .75

**Size: 47x28mm**

***Perf. 13½x13¾***

**530** A98 60s multi 2.50 1.25
**531** A98 70s multi 2.75 1.40
*Nos. 529-531 (3)* 6.75 3.40

Kakisa Dzirnavas, by Karlis Skalbe — A148

**2001, June 9** ***Perf. 13¾***
**532** A148 40s multi 1.75 1.00
Booklet, 6 #532 10.50

**Souvenir Sheet**

Mikhail Tal (1936-92), Chess Champion — A149

**2001, Aug. 18 Litho.** ***Perf. 14***
**533** A149 100s multi 4.50 3.50

Baltic Coast Landscapes A150

Designs: 15s, No. 535a, Vidzeme. No. 535b, Palanga. No. 535c, Lahemaa.

**2001, Sept. 15** ***Perf. 13½***
**534** A150 15s multi 2.00 1.00
Booklet, 6 #534 13.00

**Souvenir Sheet**

**535** Sheet of 3 4.25 3.50
*a.-c.* A150 30s Any single 1.25 .75

See Estonia Nos. 423-424, Lithuania Nos. 698-699.

**Palace Type of 1999**

**2001, Oct. 24** ***Perf. 14½x14***
**536** A131 40s Cesvaines Palace 2.00 1.25
*a.* Perf. 13¼x14 2.00 1.25
*b.* Booklet pane, 6 #536a 12.00 —
Booklet, #536b 12.00

**House of Worship Type of 2000**

**2001, Nov. 3** ***Perf. 13¾x14***
**537** A141 70s Riga Synagogue 3.00 1.50
Booklet, 6 #537 24.00

Latvian Seamen — A151

Designs: 15s, Krisjanis Valdemars (1825-91), founder of Naval College. 70s, Duke Jekabs Ketlers (1610-82), shipbuilder.

**2001, Nov. 14** ***Perf. 13¼x14***
**538-539** A151 Set of 2 3.50 2.25

Christmas A152

Designs: 12s, Rabbits. No. 541, 15s, Dog, rabbit. No. 542, 15s, Lambs.

**2001, Nov. 22** ***Perf. 13¼***
**540-542** A152 Set of 3 2.00 1.25

Town Arms — A153

**2002, Jan. 29 Litho.** ***Perf. 13¼x13¾***
**543** A153 5s Ludza .40 .35
**544** A153 10s Dobele .60 .50
*a.* Perf. 14x14¼, dated "2012" .50 .50
*b.* As "a," "2013" .40 .50
**545** A153 15s Sigulda .80 .60
*Nos. 543-545 (3)* 1.80 1.45

See Nos. 565-567, 585-587, 609-611, 638-640, 670-672, 696-698, 726-728, 753-755, 776-777, 798-800, 824-826.

Issued: No. 544a, 3/15/12; No. 544b, 3/3/13.

2002 Winter Olympics, Salt Lake City — A154

**2002, Feb. 8** ***Perf. 13¼x13¾***
**546** A154 40s multi 2.00 1.25
*a.* Booklet pane of 6, perf. 13¼x13¾ on 3 sides 17.00 —
Booklet, #546a 17.00

2002 Winter Paralympics, Salt Lake City — A155

**2002, Mar. 5** ***Perf. 14¼x13¾***
**547** A155 15s multi 1.00 .70

Refugees, by Jekabs Kazaks — A156

**2002, Apr. 20 Litho. *Perf. 14½x14¼***
**548** A156 40s multi *2.00* 1.25

Europa — A157

**2002, May 4 *Perf. 14***
**549** A157 60s multi 2.50 1.75
*a.* Tete-beche pair 6.00 6.00

Endangered Plants — A158

Designs: 15s, Cypripedium calceolus. 40s, Trapa natans.

**2002, May 25 *Perf. 13¾***
**550-551** A158 Set of 2 2.50 1.50

See Nos. 568-569, 589-590, 612-613.

Latvian Armed Forces — A159

**2002, June 15 *Perf. 13¾x13¼***
**552** A159 40s multi 1.60 1.10

Janis Jaunsudrabins (1877-1962), Writer — A160

**2002, July 6 *Perf. 13¾x13½***
**553** A160 40s multi 1.75 1.10
*a.* Booklet pane of 6, perf. 13¾x13½ on 3 sides 12.00
Booklet, #553a 12.00

Kristians Johans Dals (1839-1904) and Ship — A161

**2002, July 20 *Perf. 13¼x13¾***
**554** A161 70s multi 2.75 1.75

Fish — A162

Designs: 15s, Gadus morhua callarias. 40s, Siluris glanis.

**2002, Aug. 10 Litho. *Perf. 14***
**555-556** A162 Set of 2 2.50 1.75
*a.* Booklet pane, perf. 14 on 3 sides 15.00
Booklet, #556a 15.00

**Souvenir Sheet**

Venta River Bridge — A163

**2002, Aug. 24 *Perf. 12¾x12½***
**557** A163 100s multi 4.25 3.50

Jaunmoku Palace — A164

**2002, Sept. 14 *Perf. 14¼x13¾***
**558** A164 40s multi 1.75 1.25

**House of Worship Type of 2000**

70s, Grebenschikov Old Belief Praying House.

**2002, Oct. 12 *Perf. 13¾x14***
**559** A141 70s multicolored 3.00 1.75
*a.* Booklet pane of 6, perf. 13¾x14 on 3 sides 20.00
Booklet, #559a 20.00

Mittens A165

**2002, Nov. 2 *Perf. 13¼x13¾***
**560** A165 15s multi .85 .50

See Nos. 579, 604, 629.

Christmas — A166

Designs: 12s, Elf on sack, Christmas tree. No. 562, 15s, Angel, Christmas tree. No. 563, 15s, Elves on gift.

**2002, Nov. 23 *Perf. 13¾x13¼***
**561-563** A166 Set of 3 2.00 1.25

A Man Entering a Room, by Niklavs Strunke (1894-1966) A167

**2003, Jan. 25 Litho. *Perf. 13¼x14***
**564** A167 40s multi 1.75 1.25

**Town Arms Type of 2002**

**2003, Feb. 15 *Perf. 13¼x13¾***
**565** A153 10s Balvi .50 .25
**566** A153 15s Gulbene .65 .40
**567** A153 20s Ventspils .90 .60
*Nos. 565-567 (3)* 2.05 1.25

**Endangered Plants Type of 2002**

Designs: 15s, Ophrys insectifera. 30s, Taxus baccata.

**2003, Mar. 21 *Perf. 13¾***
**568** A158 15s multi .75 .50
**569** A158 30s multi 1.75 1.00
*a.* Perf. 14½x14¼ on 3 sides 2.00 1.00
*b.* Booklet pane, 6 #569a 12.00 —
Complete booklet, #569b 12.00

Straumeni, by Edvarts Virza (1883-1940) A168

**2003, Apr. 12 *Perf. 13¾x13¼***
**570** A168 40s multi 1.75 1.25

Europa — A169

**2003, May 3 Litho. *Perf. 13¼x13¾***
**571** A169 60s multi 2.75 1.75
*a.* Tete beche pair 6.00 6.00

Kolka Lighthouse — A170

**2003, May 17 *Perf. 13¾x13¼***
**572** A170 60s multi 2.50 1.75

See Nos. 602, 626, 662, 676, 709, 746.

**House of Worship Type of 2000**

**2003, June 6 *Perf. 13¼x13¾***
**573** A141 70s Salvation Temple, horiz. 3.00 1.75

**Souvenir Sheet**

Gauja River Bridge, Sigulda — A171

**2003, July 19**
**574** A171 100s multi 4.75 3.75

Fish — A172

Designs: 15s, Thymallus thymallus. 30s, Salmo salar.

**2003, Aug. 2 *Perf. 14x13¾***
**575** A172 15s multi .75 .50
**576** A172 30s multi 1.75 1.25
*a.* Booklet pane of 6, perf. 14x13¾ on 3 sides 13.00 —
Complete booklet, #576a 13.00

Motacilla Alba — A173

**2003, Aug. 30 *Perf. 14¾x14***
**577** A173 15s multi 1.00 .50

**Palace Type of 1999**

**2003, Sept. 27 *Perf. 14¼x13¾***
**578** A131 40s Birini Palace 1.75 1.25
*a.* Booklet pane of 6 11.00
Complete booklet, #578a 11.00

**Mittens Type of 2002**

**2003, Oct. 11 *Perf. 14x13¾***
**579** A165 15s Libiesi mittens .80 .45

Motorcycle Racing A174

**2003, Oct. 31 *Perf. 13¼x13¾***
**580** A174 70s multi 3.00 1.75
*a.* Booklet pane of 6 20.00 —
Complete booklet, #580a 20.00

Christmas — A175

Designs: 12s, Madonna and Child with two angels. No. 582, 15s, The Annunciation (golden brown frame). No. 583, 15s, Nativity (gray frame).

**2003, Nov. 22 *Perf. 13¾x14¼***
**581-583** A175 Set of 3 2.25 1.25

*Still Life with Triangle*, by Romans Suta — A176

**2004, Jan. 25 Litho. *Perf. 13¼x14***
**584** A176 40s multi 1.75 1.00

**Town Arms Type of 2002**

**2004, Feb. 14 *Perf. 13¼x13¾***
**585** A153 5s Valka .30 .30
**586** A153 15s Cesis .60 .60
**587** A153 20s Saldus .80 .80
*Nos. 585-587 (3)* 1.70 1.70

Reinis (1839-1920) and Matiss (1848-1926) Kaudzites, Writers — A177

**2004, Mar. 20 *Perf. 13¾***
**588** A177 40s multi 1.60 1.00

**Endangered Plants Type of 2002**

Designs: 15s, Gentiana cruciata. 30s, Onobrychis arenaria.

**2004, Apr. 3**
**589-590** A158 Set of 2 2.00 1.25

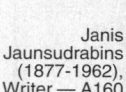

2006 World Ice Hockey Championships, Riga — A178

**2004, Apr. 17 Litho.** ***Perf. 13¼x13¾***

**591** A178 30s multi 1.50 .80

*a.* Booklet pane of 4, perf. 13¼x13¾ on 3 sides 15.00 —

Complete booklet, #591a 15.00

Admission to European Union — A179

Designs: No. 592, 30s, Stars, map of Europe, flags of newly-added countries. No. 593, 30s, Seven stars.

**2004, May 1** ***Perf. 13x13¼***

**592-593** A179 Set of 2 2.50 1.75

Europa — A180

**2004, May 8 Litho.** ***Perf. 13¼x13¾***

**594** A180 60s multi 2.50 1.75

*a.* Tete beche pair 5.50 5.50

European Soccer Championships, Portugal — A181

**2004, June 3** ***Perf. 14x13½***

**595** A181 30s multi 1.40 1.25

Fish — A182

Designs: 15s, Oncorhynchus mykiss. 30s, Psetta maxima.

**2004, June 26** ***Perf. 13¼x14***

**596** A182 15s multi .60 .40

**597** A182 30s multi 1.50 .90

*a.* Booklet pane of 6, perf. 13¼x14 on 3 sides 11.00 —

Complete booklet, #597a 11.00

See Nos. 620-621.

Visit of Pres. Bill Clinton to Latvia, 10th Anniv. — A183

**2004, July 6** ***Perf. 13¾x13¼***

**598** A183 40s multi 1.75 1.25

### Souvenir Sheet

Dzelzcela Bridge, Riga — A184

**2004, July 24** ***Perf. 13¼x13¾***

**599** A184 100s multi 4.25 4.25

2004 Summer Olympics, Athens A185

**2004, Aug. 14 Litho.** ***Perf. 14***

**600** A185 30s multi 1.25 .90

St. Jacob's Cathedral — A186

***Perf. 13¾x13¼***

**2004, Aug. 28 Litho.**

**601** A186 40s multi 1.75 1.25

### Lighthouse Type of 2003

**2004, Sept. 18**

**602** A170 60s Mikelbaka 2.75 1.50

*a.* Booklet pane of 4, perf. 13¾x13¼ on 3 sides 12.00 —

Complete booklet, #602a 12.00

Jaunpils Palace — A187

**2004, Oct. 15** ***Perf. 14¼x13¾***

**603** A187 40s multi 1.75 1.25

*a.* Booklet pane of 6, perf. 14¼x13¾ on 3 sides 11.00 —

Complete booklet, #603a 11.00

See Nos. 628, 678.

### Mittens Type of 2002

**2004, Nov. 6** ***Perf. 13¼x13¾***

**604** A165 15s Piebalga mittens .80 .50

Christmas — A188

Designs: 12s, Children, rabbit, bird, heart. No. 606, 15s, Snowman, birds. No. 607, 15s, Angel.

**2004, Dec. 4** ***Perf. 13¾x13¼***

**605-607** A188 Set of 3 1.75 1.25

1905 Revolution, Cent. A189

**2005, Jan. 13 Litho.** ***Perf. 13¾x13¼***

**608** A189 15s multi 1.10 .65

### Town Arms Type of 2002

**2005, Feb. 11** ***Perf. 13¼x13¾***

**609** A153 15s Aluksne .60 .40

**610** A153 15s Talsi .60 .40

**611** A153 40s Jekabpils 1.50 1.25

*Nos. 609-611 (3)* 2.70 2.05

### Endangered Plants Type of 2002

Designs: 20s, Pulsatilla patens. 30s, Allium ursinum.

**2005, Mar. 5** ***Perf. 13¼***

**612-613** A158 Set of 2 2.00 1.25

*613a* Booklet pane of 6 #613, perf. 13¼ on 3 sides 12.00 —

Complete booklet, #613a 12.00

Krimuldas Church, 800th Anniv. A190

**2005, Mar. 19** ***Perf. 13¼x13¾***

**614** A190 40s multi 1.60 1.00

The Adventures of Baron Munchausen, by Rudolph Erich Raspe A191

**2005, Apr. 1 Litho.** ***Perf. 13¼x13¾***

**615** A191 30s multi 1.25 .90

Europa — A192

**2005, Apr. 23**

**616** A192 60s multi 2.50 1.50

*a.* Tete beche pair 6.00 6.00

Mother and Child, by Janis Rozentals A193

**2005, May 8** ***Perf. 14x13¼***

**617** A193 40s multi 1.60 1.00

*a.* Booklet pane of 4, perf. 14x13¼ on 3 sides 7.25 —

Complete booklet, #617a 7.25

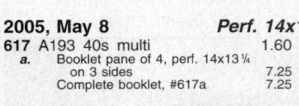

Baumanu Karlis (1835-1905), Composer of National Anthem — A194

**2005, May 21** ***Perf. 13¾x13¼***

**618** A194 20s multi .80 .50

Kaive Oak — A195

***Serpentine Die Cut 14***

**2005, June 11 Self-Adhesive**

**619** A195 15s multi 1.00 .75

Printed in sheets of 8.

### Fish Type of 2004

Designs: 15s, Lampetra fluviatilis. 40s, Clupea harengus membras.

**2005, Aug. 13 Litho.** ***Perf. 13¼x14***

**620-621** A182 Set of 2 2.25 1.50

Pope John Paul II (1920-2005) A196

**2005, Aug. 14** ***Perf. 14¼x13½***

**622** A196 15s multi .80 .50

### Souvenir Sheet

Latvian National Library — A197

**2005, Aug. 27** ***Perf. 13¼x12¾***

**623** A197 100s multi 4.00 3.75

Janis Plieksans (Rainis), (1865-1929), Writer — A198

**2005, Sept. 10** ***Perf. 14¼***

**624** A198 40s multi 1.60 1.00

*a.* Booklet pane of 6, perf. 14¼ on 3 sides 11.00 —

Complete booklet, #624a 11.00

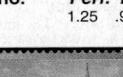

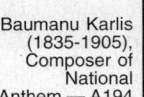

Souvenir Sheet

Bridge Over Railroad Tracks, Riga — A199

**2005, Sept. 24** ***Perf. 13¼x13¾***
**625** A199 100s multi 5.50 4.00

**Lighthouse Type of 2003**

**2005, Oct. 8 Litho.** ***Perf. 14x13¼***
**626** A170 40s Daugavgrivas 1.75 1.00
*a.* Booklet pane of 4, perf. 14x13¼ on 3 sides 8.50 —
Complete booklet, #626a 8.50

Gunars Astra (1931-88), Human Rights Activist in Soviet Union — A200

**2005, Oct. 22** ***Perf. 13½x14¼***
**627** A200 15s multi .60 .40

**Palace Type of 2004**

**2005, Nov. 5** ***Perf. 13¼x14***
**628** A187 40s Durbes Palace, horiz. 1.60 1.00

**Mittens Type of 2002**

**2005, Nov. 26** ***Perf. 13¼x13¾***
**629** A165 20s Dienvidlatgale mittens .80 .50

Christmas A201

Designs: 12s, Goat riding on wolf's back. No. 631, 15s, Woman, dog near tree, vert. No. 632, 15s, Cat, woman carrying rooster, vert.

**2005, Dec. 3** ***Serpentine Die Cut 15***
**Self-Adhesive**
**630-632** A201 Set of 3 1.75 1.25

Europa Stamps, 50th Anniv. A202

Latvian Europa stamps: Nos. 633, 637a, 10s, #414. Nos. 634, 637b, 15s, #463. Nos. 635, 637c, 15s, #442. Nos. 636, 637d, 20s, #484-485.

**2006, Jan. 7 Litho.** ***Perf. 13¾x13¼***
**633-636** A202 Set of 4 2.50 1.50

**Souvenir Sheet**
***Perf. 13½ Syncopated***
**637** A202 Sheet of 4, #a-d 2.25 2.25

No. 637 contains four 45x28mm stamps.

**Town Arms Type of 2002**

**2006, Jan. 11** ***Perf. 13¼x13¾***
**638** A153 7s Aizkraukle .30 .25
**639** A153 22s Kraslava .80 .60
**640** A153 31s Limbazi 1.25 .90
*Nos. 638-640 (3)* 2.35 1.75

2006 Winter Olympics, Turin — A203

**2006, Feb. 4** ***Perf. 14***
**641** A203 45s multi 1.75 1.25

Stamerienas Palace — A204

**2006, Feb. 25** ***Perf. 14¼x13¾***
**642** A204 95s multi 3.50 2.25

Zvartes Iezis — A205

***Serpentine Die Cut 14***
**2006, Mar. 11** **Self-Adhesive**
**643** A205 22s multi .80 .55

Printed in sheets of 8.

Souvenir Sheet

Raunu Railroad Bridge — A206

**2006, Mar. 25** ***Perf. 13½x14***
**644** A206 100s multi 3.75 3.25

2006 World Ice Hockey Championships, Riga — A207

***Perf. 13½x14¼***
**2006, Mar. 31** **Litho.**
**645** A207 55s multi + label 2.00 1.25
*a.* Booklet pane of 4, perf. 13½x14¼ on 3 sides, without labels 10.00 —
Complete booklet, #645a 10.00

Cesis, 800th Anniv. — A208

Various sites in Cesis: 22s, 31s, 45s, 55s. 45s and 55s are horiz.

***Perf. 13¼x13¾, 13¾x13¼***
**2006, Apr. 7**
**646-649** A208 Set of 4 6.00 4.00

Traditional Jewelry — A209

No. 650: a, Brooch, Latvia. b, Bracelet, Kazakhstan.

**2006, Apr. 19** ***Perf. 14x13¾***
**650** A209 22s Horiz. pair, #a-b 1.75 1.00

See Kazakhstan No. 509.

Europa — A210

**2006, May 3** ***Perf. 13½x14¼***
**651** A210 85s multi 3.25 2.50
*a.* Tete beche pair 7.00 7.00

Ciganiete ar Tamburinu, by Karlis Huns — A211

**2006, May 13** ***Perf. 13¼x14***
**652** A211 40s multi 1.50 1.00
*a.* Booklet pane of 4, perf. 13¼x14 on 3 sides 7.00 —
Complete booklet, #652a 7.00

A212

Personalizable Stamps A213

**2006, June 9** ***Perf. 13¾***
**653** A212 31s yel bister 1.25 1.00
**654** A213 31s yel bister 1.25 1.00

Stamp vignettes could be personalized by customers, presumably for an extra fee.

"Big Christopher" Statue — A214

**2006, June 16** ***Perf. 14x13½***
**655** A214 36s multi 1.40 1.00

Art by Anna Koshkina — A215

**Booklet Stamp**
***Die Cut Perf. 14½x13 on 3 Sides***
**2006, Aug. 11** **Self-Adhesive**
**656** A215 22s multi .90 .60
*a.* Booklet pane of 8 7.25

Volunteer Army, 15th Anniv. — A216

**2006, Aug. 23** ***Perf. 13½x14***
**657** A216 22s multi .90 .60

Staburags — A217

**2006, Sept. 9 Litho.** ***Perf. 14¼x13¾***
**658** A217 58s multi 2.25 1.50
*a.* Tete beche pair 5.00 5.00

Wild Animals and Their Tracks — A218

Designs: 45s, Lynx lynx. 55s, Cervus elaphus.

**2006, Sept. 23** ***Perf. 14¼x13½***
**659-660** A218 Set of 2 3.75 2.50
*659a* Booklet pane of 4 #659, perf. 14¼x13½ on 3 sides 7.50 —
Complete booklet, #659a 7.50
*659b* Tete beche pair 4.00 4.00
*660a* Tete beche pair 4.50 4.50

See Nos. 691-692, 719-720, 744-745.

Pansija Pili, Novel by Anslavs Eglitis (1906-93) A219

**2006, Oct. 14 Litho.** ***Perf. 13¼x13½***
**661** A219 67s multi 2.50 1.50

**Lighthouse Type of 2003**

**2006, Oct. 27** ***Perf. 14¼x13½***
**662** A170 40s Mersraga Lighthouse 1.50 1.00
*a.* Booklet pane of 4, perf. 14¼x13½ on 3 sides 7.00 —
Complete booklet, #662a 7.00

NATO Summit, Riga A220

**2006, Nov. 17** ***Perf. 13¾x13¼***
**663** A220 55s multi 2.25 1.25

Christmas A221

Cookies in shape of: 18s, Christmas tree. 22s, Star. 31s, Crescent moon. 45s, Bell.

***Serpentine Die Cut 14***

**2006, Nov. 17** **Self-Adhesive**

**664-667** A221 Set of 4 4.50 3.25

Oskars Kalpaks (1882-1919), First Commander-in-chief of Latvian Army — A222

**2007, Jan. 6** ***Perf. 14¼x14***

**668** A222 22s multi .85 .60

Mobile Telecommunications in Latvia, 15th Anniv. — A223

**2007, Jan. 19**

**669** A223 22s multi .85 .60
*a.* Tete beche pair 2.00 2.00

**Town Arms Type of 2002**

**2007, Feb. 3** ***Perf. 13¼x13¾***

**670** A153 5s Staicele .25 .25
*a.* Perf. 14x14¼, "2010" .25 .25
**671** A153 10s Sabile .35 .25
**672** A153 22s Vecumnieki .80 .65
*Nos. 670-672 (3)* 1.40 1.15

Issued: No. 670a, 3/12/10.

Tilts Tornkalna, Painting by Ludolfs Liberts (1895-1959) A224

**2007, Feb. 17** ***Perf. 14¼x14***

**673** A224 58s multi 2.25 1.50

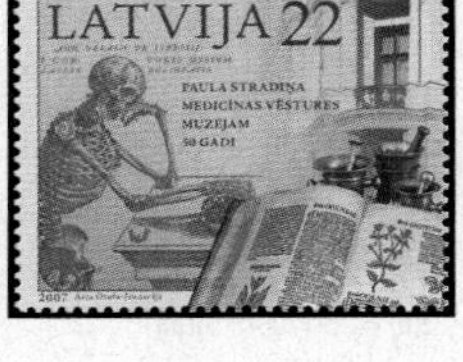


Pauls Stradins Museum of the History of Medicine, Riga, 50th Anniv. A225

**2007, Mar. 9** ***Perf. 14x14¼***

**674** A225 22s multi .85 .60

Baltic Coast — A226

***Serpentine Die Cut 14***

**2007, Mar. 24** **Self-Adhesive**

**675** A226 22s multi .85 .60

**Lighthouse Type of 2003**

**2007, Apr. 14** ***Perf. 13¾x13½***

**676** A170 67s Papes Lighthouse 2.50 1.75
*a.* Booklet pane of 4, perf. 13¾x13½ on 3 sides 12.00 —
Complete booklet, #676a 12.00

Europa — A227

**2007, Apr. 28 Litho.** ***Perf. 13½x14¼***

**677** A227 85s multi 3.25 2.50
*a.* Tete beche pair 7.50 7.50

Scouting, cent.

**Palace Type of 2004**

**2007, June 8 Litho.** ***Perf. 13½x14¼***

**678** A187 22s Krustpils, horiz. .85 .60

UNESCO World Heritage Sites — A228

Designs: 36s, Historic Center of Riga. 45s, Historic Centers of Straslund and Wismar, Germany.

**2007, July 12 Litho.** ***Perf. 14x13¾***

**679-680** A228 Set of 2 3.50 2.50

See Germany Nos. 2449-2450.

Sigulda, 800th Anniv. — A229

Designs: 22s, New Sigulda Castle. 31s, Bobsled course. 40s, Sigulda Castle ruins.

***Serpentine Die Cut 15¼***

**2007, Aug. 10** **Self-Adhesive**

**681-683** A229 Set of 3 3.75 2.50

Berries and Mushrooms A230

Designs: 22s, Vaccinium vitis-idaea. 58s, Cantharellus cibarius.

**2007, Aug. 25** ***Perf. 14x13½***

**684** A230 22s multi .80 .55
*a.* Tete beche pair 2.00 2.00

**685** A230 58s multi 2.25 1.50
*a.* Booklet pane of 4, perf. 14x13½ on 3 sides 10.00 —
Complete booklet, #685a 10.00
*b.* Tete beche pair 5.00 5.00

See Nos. 715-716, 742-743, 767-768.

Organized Soccer in Latvia, Cent. — A231

**2007, Sept. 8** ***Perf. 13¾***

**686** A231 45s multi 1.75 1.75

Values are for stamps with surrounding selvage.

**Souvenir Sheet**

Aivieksti Railroad Bridge — A232

**2007, Oct. 13** ***Perf. 14***

**687** A232 100s multi 3.75 3.75

Latvia Post, 375th Anniv. A233

Designs: 22s, Postrider. 31s, Postal worker and van.

***Serpentine Die Cut 15***

**2007, Oct. 20** **Litho.**

**Self-Adhesive**

**688-689** A233 Set of 2 2.10 1.60

13th Century Decorations A234

**2007, Nov. 3** ***Perf. 13¼x14***

**690** A234 60s multi 2.50 1.75

**Wild Animals and Their Tracks Type of 2006**

Designs: 45s, Vulpes vulpes. 55s, Alces alces.

**2007, Nov. 16** ***Perf. 14¼x13½***

**691** A218 45s multi 1.75 1.25
*a.* Tete beche pair 3.50 3.50
**692** A218 55s multi 2.25 1.50
*a.* Tete beche pair 5.00 5.00

Christmas — A235

Christmas tree and children with: 22s, Musical instruments. 31s, Cookies. 45s, Skis and sled.

***Serpentine Die Cut 15***

**2007, Nov. 24** **Self-Adhesive**

**693-695** A235 Set of 3 3.75 3.00

**Town Arms Type of 2002 With Country Name at Top**

**2008, Feb. 9** ***Perf. 13¼x13¾***

**696** A153 22s Salaspils .75 .60
**697** A153 28s Plavinas .95 .75
**698** A153 45s Saulkrasti 1.60 1.25
*Nos. 696-698 (3)* 3.30 2.60

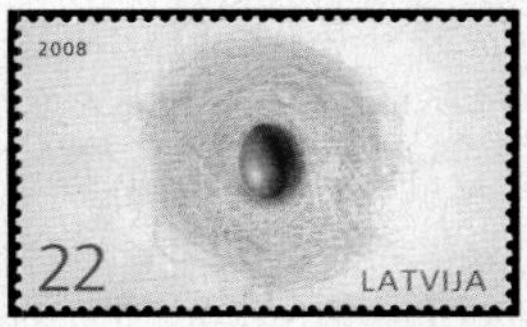


Easter A236

**2008, Feb. 23** ***Perf. 13¼x13***

**699** A236 22s multi .80 .80

Augli, by Leo Svemps A237

**2008, Mar. 8 Litho.** ***Perf. 13x13¼***

**700** A237 63s multi 2.40 2.40

State Awards of the Baltic Countries — A238

Designs: Nos. 701, 702a, Order of Three Stars, Latvia. No. 702b, Order of Vytautas the Great, Lithuania. No. 702c, Order of the National Coat of Arms, Estonia.

**2008, Mar. 15** ***Perf. 13½x13¾***

**701** A238 31s multi 1.25 1.25

**Souvenir Sheet**

**702** A238 31s Sheet of 3, #a-c 3.50 3.50

On No. 701, the second line of type above the medal is 18mm wide, while it is 15mm wide on No. 702a.

See Estonia Nos. 592-593, Lithuania Nos. 862-863.

Worldwide Fund for Nature (WWF) — A239

Bats: 22s, Barbastella barbastellus. 31s, Myotis dasycneme. 45s, Barbastella barbastellus, vert. 55s, Myotis dasycneme, vert.

***Perf. 13½x14¼, 14¼x13½***

**2008, Apr. 12**

**703** A239 22s multi .80 .80
*a.* Tete beche pair 1.75 1.75
**704** A239 31s multi 1.15 1.15
*a.* Tete beche pair 2.75 2.75
**705** A239 45s multi 1.60 1.60
*a.* Tete beche pair 3.50 3.50
**706** A239 55s multi 1.75 1.75
*a.* Tete beche pair 4.50 4.50
*Nos. 703-706 (4)* 5.30 5.30

Europa — A240

Designs: 45s, Letters and postcards. 85s, Person writing letter.

**2008, Apr. 22** *Perf. 13½*

**707** A240 45s multi 1.75 1.75
*a.* Tete beche pair 4.00 4.00
**708** A240 multi 3.25 3.25
*a.* Tete beche pair 7.50 7.50

### Lighthouse Type of 2003

**2008, May 5** *Perf. 14¼x13½*

**709** A170 63s Akmenraga Lighthouse 2.25 2.25
*a.* Booklet pane of 4, perf. 14¼x13½ on 3 sides 12.00 —
Complete booklet, #709a 12.00

European Orienteering Championships, Ventspils — A241

**2008, May 23** **Litho.** *Perf. 13x13¼*

**710** A241 45s multi 1.60 1.60
*a.* Tete beche pair 4.00 4.00

Nature Protection A242

***Serpentine Die Cut 12½***

**2008, June 7** **Self-Adhesive**

**711** A242 22s multi .85 .85

Riga Museum Foundations — A243

**2008, June 26** *Perf. 13x13½*

**712** A243 22s multi .85 .85

2008 Summer Olympics, Beijing — A244

**2008, Aug. 8** *Perf. 13½x13*

**713** A244 63s multi 2.25 2.25

Sudraba Fairy Tale — A245

***Perf. 14¼x13½***

**2008, Aug. 23** **Litho.**

**714** A245 22s multi .85 .85
*a.* Tete beche pair 1.90 1.90

### Berries and Mushrooms Type of 2007

Designs: 22s, Vaccinium myrtillus. 58s, Leccinum aurantiacum.

**2008, Sept. 6** *Perf. 14x13½*

**715** A230 22s multi .80 .80
*a.* Tete beche pair 2.00 2.00
**716** A230 58s multi 2.00 2.00
*a.* Perf. 13½x14 on 3 sides 2.25 2.25
*b.* Booklet pane of 4 #716a 9.00 —
Complete booklet, #716b 9.00
*c.* Tete beche pair 4.50 4.50

Souvenir Sheet

Kandavas Bridge — A246

**2008, Sept. 27** *Perf. 14*

**717** A246 100s multi 3.75 3.75

Tautas Fronte Newspaper, 20th Anniv. — A247

**2008, Oct. 8** *Perf. 13½*

**718** A247 22s multi .85 .85
*a.* Tete beche pair 1.75 1.75

### Wild Animals and Their Tracks Type of 2006

Designs: 45s, Martes martes. 55s, Castor fiber.

**2008, Oct. 10** *Perf. 14¼x13½*

**719** A218 45s multi 1.75 1.75
*a.* Tete beche pair 3.50 3.50
**720** A218 55s multi 2.25 2.25
*a.* Tete beche pair 5.00 5.00

Maris Strombergs, 2008 BMX Cycling Olympic Gold Medalist — A248

**2008, Oct. 24** *Perf. 13½*

**721** A248 22s multi .85 .85

Plate, Bow and Tablecloth A249

**2008, Oct. 25** *Perf. 13½x13¾*

**722** A249 28s multi 1.00 1.00

Latvian Republic, 90th Anniv. — A250

**2008, Nov. 7** *Perf. 13¼x13*

**723** A250 31s multi 1.25 1.25

Mezotnes Palace A251

**2008, Nov. 8** *Perf. 13½x14¼*

**724** A251 63s multi 2.40 2.40

Christmas — A252

**2008, Nov. 28** *Perf. 14¼x13¾*

**725** A252 25s multi .90 .90

### Town Arms Type of 2002 With Country Name at Top

**2009, Jan. 10** **Litho.** *Perf. 14x14¼*

**726** A153 33s Dagda 1.25 1.25
**727** A153 35s Balozi 1.40 1.40
**728** A153 60s Stende 2.00 2.00
*Nos. 726-728 (3)* 4.65 4.65

Brooch, 8th Cent. A. D. — A253

**2009, Jan. 24** *Perf. 14*

**729** A253 98s multi 3.50 3.50
*a.* Tete beche pair 7.50 7.50

Dancing Boy and Animals Folktale A254

**2009, Feb. 21** *Perf. 13¼*

**730** A254 40s multi 1.50 1.50

Souvenir Sheet

Preservation of Polar Regions and Glaciers — A255

No. 731: a, 35s, Polar bear. b, 55s, Penguins.

**2009, Mar. 18** **Litho.** *Perf. 13¼*

**731** A255 Sheet of 2, #a-b 3.75 3.75

Europa — A256

Designs: 50s, Janis Ikaunieks, astronomer, and Baldone Observatory telescope. 55s, Map of solar system, asteroid, University of Latvia Institute of Astronomy, radio telescope, five astronomers.

**2009, Apr. 2** *Perf. 14x13¾*

**732** A256 50s multi 2.25 2.25
*a.* Tete beche pair 4.75 4.75
**733** A256 55s multi 2.50 2.50
*a.* Tete beche pair 5.25 5.25

Intl. Year of Astronomy.

Natl. Museum of History A257

**2009, May 14** *Perf. 13½*

**734** A257 35s multi 1.40 1.40

Basketball A258

Player from opposing team and: 35s, Male Latvian team player, 1935. 40s, Female TTT Riga player. 60s, Male ASK Riga player.
120s, Latvian player in 2009 Women's European Basketball Championships.

**2009, June 6**

**735-737** A258 Set of 3 5.25 5.25

**Souvenir Sheet**

**738** A258 120s multi 4.50 4.50

Nos. 735-737 each were printed in sheets of 9 + label.

Bauska, 400th Anniv. A259

**2009, July 10** **Litho.** *Perf. 13½x14*

**739** A259 38s multi 1.35 1.35

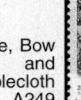

Steam Locomotive — A260

**2009, Aug. 5 Litho. *Perf. 13½***
**740** A260 35s multi 1.40 1.40

Souvenir Sheet

Dienvidu Bridge, Riga — A261

**2009, Aug. 22**
**741** A261 100s multi 4.00 4.00

### Berries and Mushrooms Type of 2007

Designs: 55s, Fragaria vesca. 60s, Russula paludosa.

**2009, Sept. 12**
**742** A230 55s multi 2.25 2.25
*a.* Tete beche pair 5.00 5.00
**743** A230 60s multi 2.50 2.50
*a.* Tete beche pair 5.50 5.50
*b.* Perf. 13½ on 3 sides 2.50 2.50
*c.* Booklet pane of 4 #743b 11.00 —
Complete booklet, #743c 11.00

### Wild Animals and Their Tracks Type of 2006

Designs: 35s, Canis lupus. 98s, Lepus europaeus.

**2009, Oct. 21 *Perf. 13½x14¼***
**744** A218 35s multi 1.25 1.25
*a.* Tete beche pair 2.75 2.75
**745** A218 98s multi 4.00 4.00
*a.* Tete beche pair 8.25 8.25

### Lighthouse Type of 2003

**2009, Nov. 5 Litho. *Perf. 13¼***
**746** A170 63s Liepaja Lighthouse 2.60 2.60

Republic of Latvia, 91st Anniv. — A262

Designs: 35s, Formation of Latvian People's Council, Nov. 17, 1918. 40s, Proclamation of Latvian Republic, Nov. 18, 1918. 100s, First meeting of Constitutional Assembly, May 1, 1920.

**2009, Nov. 14 Litho. *Perf. 14***
**747-749** A262 Set of 3 6.75 6.75

Christmas A263

Designs: 35s, Horse Christmas ornament, building. 55s, Fish Christmas ornament, building. 60s, Snowflake Christmas ornament.

**2009, Nov. 27 *Perf. 13¼***
**750-752** A263 Set of 3 5.75 5.75

### Town Arms Type of 2002 With Country Name at Top

**2010, Jan. 16 Litho. *Perf. 14x14¼***
**753** A153 35s Viesite 1.25 1.25
**754** A153 40s Ligatne 1.40 1.40
**755** A153 55s Iecava 2.00 2.00
*Nos. 753-755 (3)* 4.65 4.65

2010 Winter Olympics, Vancouver — A264

**2010, Feb. 5 *Perf. 13¼x13¾***
**756** A264 55s multi 2.10 2.10

Peonies A265

**2010, Mar. 26 *Perf. 13¼***
**757** A265 35s multi 1.25 1.25
*a.* Tete beche pair 2.75 2.75

Europa A266

Designs: 55s, Girl holding books, characters from children's books. 120s, Boy reading book, ship, castle, mountain.

**2010, Apr. 9 Litho. *Perf. 13½x13¼***
**758** A266 55s multi 2.00 2.00
*a.* Tete beche pair 4.25 4.25
**759** A266 120s multi 4.00 4.00
*a.* Tete beche pair 8.75 8.75

Expo 2010, Shanghai A267

**2010, Apr. 23 *Perf. 13¼***
**760** A267 150s multi 5.25 5.25

Declaration of May 4, 1990, 20th Anniv. A268

**2010, May 4**
**761** A268 35s multi 1.40 1.40
*a.* Tete beche pair 3.00 3.00

Fire Fighting Museum A269

**2010, May 21**
**762** A269 98s multi 3.75 3.75
*a.* Tete beche pair 7.75 7.75

Birds — A270

Designs: 35s, Coracias garrulus. 98s, Bubo bubo, vert.

***Perf. 14x13¾, 13¾x14***

**2010, June 18**
**763-764** A270 Set of 2 5.00 5.00

See Nos. 790-791.

Talsos Sports Hall — A271

**2010, July 16 *Perf. 13¼***
**765** A271 150s multi 5.75 5.75

RP Series Locomotive — A272

**2010, Aug. 5 *Perf. 13¼x13½***
**766** A272 40s multi 1.50 1.50

### Berries and Mushrooms Type of 2007

Designs: 55s, Rubus ideus. 120s, Leccinum scabrum.

**2010, Sept. 10 *Perf. 13½x13¼***
**767** A230 55s multi 2.00 2.00
*a.* Tete beche pair 4.50 4.50
**768** A230 120s multi 4.75 4.75
*a.* Tete beche pair 9.75 9.75

### Lighthouse Type of 2003

**2010, Oct. 15 Litho. *Perf. 13½x13¼***
**769** A170 98s Uzavas Lighthouse 3.75 3.75
*a.* Booklet pane of 4, perf. 13½x13¼ on 3 sides 16.00 —
Complete booklet, #769a 16.00

Republic of Latvia, 92nd Anniv. — A273

National symbols: 35s, Flag. 38s, Arms. 98s, Anthem.

**2010, Nov. 12 Litho. *Perf. 14***
**770-772** A273 Set of 3 6.50 6.50

Christmas A274

Designs: 35s, Girl, cat, Christmas tree. 60s, Boy with gift, bird in tree.

**2010, Dec. 3 *Perf. 13½x13¼***
**773** A274 35s multi 1.35 1.35
*a.* Tete beche pair 3.00 3.00
**774** A274 60s multi 2.40 2.40
*a.* Tete beche pair 5.00 5.00

New Year 2011 (Year of the Rabbit) A275

**2011, Jan. 14 Litho. *Perf. 13½x13¼***
**775** A275 35s multi 1.40 1.40

### Town Arms Type of 2002 With Country Name at Top

**2011, Feb. 25 Litho. *Perf. 14x14¼***
**776** A153 35s Ikskiles 1.10 1.10
**777** A153 98s Carnikavas 4.25 4.25

Rose — A276

**2011, Mar. 25 *Perf. 13½x13¼***
**778** A276 35s multi 1.35 1.35
*a.* Tete beche pair 3.00 3.00

Europa — A277

Animals in forest: 55s, Deer. 120s, Wolf.

**2011, Apr. 8 *Perf. 14x13¾***
**779** A277 55s multi 1.90 1.90
*a.* Tete beche pair 4.00 4.00
**780** A277 120s multi 4.00 4.00
*a.* Tete beche pair 8.50 8.50

Intl. Year of Forests.

Souvenir Sheet

Struve Geodetic Arc — A278

No. 781: a, 35s, Map of arc and stone. b, 55s, Map and Friedrich Georg Wilhelm von Struve (1793-1864), astronomer.

**2011, May 5 *Perf. 13¼x13½***
**781** A278 Sheet of 2, #a-b 3.25 3.25

First Coin of Riga, 800th Anniv. A279

**2011, May 23 *Perf. 13½x13¼***
**782** A279 98s multi 3.75 3.75
*a.* Tete beche pair 8.00 8.00

Johanna (1904-90) and Zanis Lipke (1900-87), Rescuers of Jews During World War II — A280

**2011, July 4** *Perf. 14x13¾*
**783** A280 60s multi 2.25 2.25
*a.* Tete beche pair 5.00 5.00

Phoenix III Passenger Coach — A281

**2011, Aug. 5** *Perf. 13¼x13½*
**784** A281 33s multi 1.25 1.25

A282

A283

Personalized Stamps — A284

**2011, Aug. 22** *Perf. 13¾*
**785** A282 35s yel bis & blk 1.30 1.30
**786** A283 55s yel bis & blk 2.10 2.10
**787** A284 60s yel bis & blk 2.25 2.25
*Nos. 785-787 (3)* 5.65 5.65

The generic vignettes shown for Nos. 785-787 could be personalized by customers for an extra fee.

Latvian Cycling Federation, 125th Anniv. — A285

**2011, Aug. 25** *Perf. 14x13¾*
**788** A285 35s multi 1.40 1.40

Port of Riga A286

**2011, Sept. 2 Litho.** *Perf. 13¼x13½*
**789** A286 60s multi 2.25 2.25

### Birds Type of 2010

Designs: 35s, Hippolais icterina. 98s, Circaetus gallicus, vert.

**2011, Sept. 23 Litho.** *Perf. 14x13¾*
**790** A270 35s multi 1.25 1.25
*a.* Perf. 13¾x14 on 3 sides, granite paper 1.25 1.25
*b.* Booklet pane of 4 #790a 8.50 —
Complete booklet, #790b 8.50

*Perf. 13¾x14*
**791** A270 98s multi 3.75 3.75
*a.* Perf. 13¾x14 on 3 sides, granite paper 3.75 3.75
*b.* Booklet pane of 4 #791a 15.00 —
Complete booklet, #791b 15.00

Parventa Library, Ventspils A287

**2011, Oct. 14** *Perf. 13½x13¼*
**792** A287 100s multi 4.00 4.00

Republic of Latvia, 93rd Anniv. — A288

Designs: 35s, Merchant fleet ships and their captains. 60s, Krisjanis Valdemars, founder of Latvian Naval School, Ainazi. 100s, Admiral Teodors Spade, Navy emblem, ships and sailors.

**2011, Nov. 11** *Perf. 14*
**Granite Paper**
**793-795** A288 Set of 3 7.50 7.50

Christmas A289

Designs: 35s, Reindeer with clothesline between antlers, Santa Claus with ripped bag. 60s, Santa Claus pushing reindeer and bag on dragon's back.

**2011, Dec. 2** *Perf. 13¼*
**Granite Paper**
**796-797** A289 Set of 2 3.75 1.90

### Town Arms Type of 2002 With Country Name At Top

**2012, Jan. 7** *Perf. 13¼x13¾*
**798** A153 33s Piltene 1.25 .90
**799** A153 35s Riga 1.40 1.00
**800** A153 38s Lielvardes Novads 1.50 1.10
*Nos. 798-800 (3)* 4.15 3.00

Nos. 798-800 are dated "2011."

Library No. 1 Restaurant, Riga A290

**2012, Jan. 27** *Perf. 13¼*
**801** A290 35s multi 1.40 1.40

Lilies — A291

**2012, Feb. 11**
**802** A291 35s multi 1.40 1.40
*a.* Tete beche pair 3.00 3.00

Europa — A292

Designs: 55s, Dancers. 120s, National Opera House.

**2012, Mar. 17** *Perf. 14*
**803** A292 55s multi 2.10 2.10
*a.* Tete beche pair 4.50 4.50
**804** A292 120s multi 4.50 4.50
*a.* Tete beche pair 9.50 9.50

Riga Zoo, Cent. — A293

**2012, Apr. 14** *Perf. 13¼*
**805** A293 Block or horiz. strip of 3 + label 6.00 6.00
*a.* 35s Lion 1.40 1.40
*b.* 55s Horse 2.10 2.10
*c.* 60s Frog 2.25 2.25
*d.* Booklet pane of 4 #805c, perf. 13¼ on 3 sides 9.50 —
Complete booklet, #805d 9.50

Janis Misins (1862-1945), Librarian — A294

**2012, Apr. 25** *Perf. 13¼*
**806** A294 98s multi 3.75 3.75
*a.* Tete beche pair 8.00 8.00

Port of Ventspils — A295

**2012, May 11** *Perf. 13¼x13½*
**807** A295 35s multi 1.25 1.25

Birds — A296

Designs: 35s, Hirundo rustica. 98s, Carduelis carduelis.

**2012, June 16 Litho.** *Perf. 13¾x14*
**808-809** A296 Set of 2 5.00 5.00

2012 Summer Olympics, London — A297

**2012, July 14** *Perf. 13¼x13½*
**810** A297 60s multi 2.25 2.25
*a.* Tete beche pair 5.00 5.00

Ungurmuiza Manor A298

**2012, Aug. 18**
**811** A298 98s multi 3.75 3.75

Friedrich Zander (1887-1933), Rocketry Pioneer — A299

**2012, Aug. 23** *Perf. 13¼*
**812** A299 60s multi 2.25 2.25
*a.* Tete beche pair 5.00 5.00

### Souvenir Sheet

Duchy of Courland and Semigallia, 450th Anniv. — A300

No. 813: a, 35s, Duke Ernsts Johans Birons (1690-1772). b, 55s, Duke Jekabs Kettlers (1610-82).

**Granite Paper**

**2012, Sept. 21** *Perf. 13¼x13½*
**813** A300 Sheet of 2, #a-b 3.50 3.50

Riga Technical University, 150th Anniv. — A301

**2012, Oct. 8** *Perf. 13¼*
**814** A301 98s multi 3.75 3.75

Railway Bridges A302

Train and: Nos. 815, 816a, Carnikava Bridge, Latvia. No. 816b, Lyduvenai Bridge, Lithuania. No. 816c, Narva Bridge, Estonia.

**2012** *Perf. 13¼*
**815** A302 35s multi 1.40 1.40

### Souvenir Sheet

**816** A302 55s Sheet of 3, #a-c 6.00 6.00

Issued: No. 815, 10/8; No. 816, 10/25. See Estonia Nos. 713-714, Lithuania Nos. 985-986.

Republic of Latvia, 94th Anniv. — A303

Composers: 35s, Emils Darzins (1875-1910). 60s, Jazeps Vitols (1863-1948). 100s, Talivaldis Kenins (1919-2008).

**2012, Nov. 10** **Litho.** ***Perf. 14***

**817-819** A303 Set of 3 7.25 7.25

Latvian Medalists at 2012 Summer Olympics, London — A304

Designs: No. 820, 35s, Martins Plavins and Janis Smedins, beach volleyball bronze medalists. No. 821, 35s, Maris Strombergs, BMX cycling gold medalist.

**2012, Nov. 23** ***Perf. 13¼***

**820** A304 35s multi 1.30 1.30
*a.* Tete beche pair 2.75 2.75
**821** A304 35s multi 1.30 1.30
*a.* Tete beche pair 2.75 2.75

Christmas A305

Designs: 35s, Girl, gifts, Christmas tree. 60s, Snow-covered house.

**2012, Nov. 30** ***Perf. 14x13¾***

**822** A305 35s multi 1.25 1.25
*a.* Tete beche pair 2.75 2.75
**823** A305 60s multi 2.50 2.50
*a.* Tete beche pair 5.25 5.25

**Town Arms Type of 2002 With Country Name at Top**

**2013, Jan. 13** ***Perf. 14***

**824** A153 35s Varaklani 1.40 1.40
**825** A153 60s Strencu Novads 2.40 2.40
**826** A153 98s Varkavas Novads 3.75 3.75
*Nos. 824-826 (3)* 7.55 7.55

Janis Uzraugs, Cyclist A306

**2013, Jan. 30** ***Perf. 13¾x13½***

**827** A306 35s multi 1.40 1.40

Starting with Nos. 827, 2013 stamps also have euro denominations, in anticipation of a change to the euro currency in 2014.

Dailes Theater, Riga A307

**2013, Feb. 15** ***Perf. 13¼x13½***

**828** A307 100s multi 3.75 3.75

Irises — A308

**2013, Mar. 8** ***Perf. 13¼***

**829** A308 35s multi 1.40 1.40
*a.* Tete beche pair 3.00 3.00

Europa — A309

Postal vehicles: 55s, Horse-drawn carriage, rail car. 120s, Airplane, truck, van, bicycle.

**2013, Apr. 19** ***Perf. 14x13¾***

**Granite Paper**

**830** A309 55s multi 2.10 2.10
*a.* Tete beche pair 4.50 4.50
*b.* Booklet pane of 4, perf. 14x13¼ on 3 sides 8.50 —
Complete booklet, #830b 8.50
**831** A309 120s multi 4.50 4.50
*a.* Tete beche pair 9.50 9.50

Souvenir Sheet

Paul Walden (1863-1957), Chemist — A310

**2013, May 14** ***Perf. 13¼***

**Granite Paper**

**832** A310 100s multi 4.00 4.00

Birds — A311

Designs: 35s, Clangula hyemalis. 98s, Merops apiaster, vert.

***Perf. 14x13¾, 13¾x14***

**2013, June 7** **Litho.**

**833-834** A311 Set of 2 5.25 5.25

Souvenir Sheet

25th Latvian Song and Dance Festival — A312

No. 835: a, Singers. b, Dancers.

**2013, June 28** **Litho.** ***Perf. 13¼***

**835** A312 35s Sheet of 2, #a-b 2.60 2.60

Cover With Russia (Wenden) No. L2 — A313

**2013, July 12** **Litho.** ***Perf. 13¼***

**Granite Paper**

**836** A313 100s multi 3.75 3.75

First postage stamp issued in Latvia, 150th anniv.

Cats — A314

Designs: 35s, Kittins in basket. 98s, Cats in doorway,vert.

***Perf. 14x13¾, 13¾x14***

**2013, July 29** **Litho.**

**837-838** A314 Set of 2 5.00 5.00

Port of Liepaja A315

**2013, Aug. 23** **Litho.** ***Perf. 13½***

**839** A315 98s multi 3.75 3.75

Latvia University of Agriculture, 150th Anniv. A316

**2013, Sept. 16** **Litho.** ***Perf. 13¼***

**840** A316 40s multi 1.60 1.60

Mark Rothko (1903-70), Painter — A317

**2013, Sept. 25** **Litho.** ***Perf. 13¾x14***

**841** A317 60s multi 2.40 2.40

Latvian Popular Front, 25th Anniv. — A318

**2013, Oct. 5** **Litho.** ***Perf. 13¾x14***

**842** A318 35s multi 1.40 1.40

Printing in Latvia, 425th Anniv. — A319

**2013, Oct. 22** **Litho.** ***Perf. 13¼***

**Granite Paper**

**843** A319 60s multi 2.40 2.40

No. 843 was printed in sheets of 8 + 4 labels.

Pink Ribbon and Flower — A320

**2013, Oct. 30** **Litho.** ***Perf. 14***

**844** A320 4s multi .40 .40

Breast cancer awareness.

Republic of Latvia, 95th Anniv. — A321

Writers: 35s, Rainis (1865-1929). 60s, Rudolfs Blaumanis (1863-1908). 98s, Zenta Maurina (1897-1978).

**2013, Nov. 8** **Litho.** ***Perf. 13¾***

**845-847** A321 Set of 3 7.50 7.50

Christmas A322

Falling snow and: 35s, Girl on rocking horse, Christmas gifts. 60s, Girl and cats on building's roof.

**2013, Nov. 22** **Litho.** ***Perf. 14x13¾***

**Granite Paper**

**848-849** A322 Set of 2 3.75 3.75

**100 Cents = 1 Euro**

Flowers — A323

Designs: 3c, Narcissi. 47c, Crocuses. 57c, Pansies. 78c, Cornflowers. 85c, Poppies. €1.39, Asters.

**2014, Jan. 2** **Litho.** ***Perf. 14***

**850** A323 3c multi .30 .25
*a.* Dated "2016" .30 .25
**851** A323 47c multi 1.40 .30
**852** A323 57c multi 1.75 .90
**853** A323 78c multi 2.25 1.25
**854** A323 85c multi 2.75 1.40
**855** A323 €1.39 multi 4.00 2.10
*a.* Souvenir sheet of 6, #850-855 13.00 13.00
*Nos. 850-855 (6)* 12.45 6.20

See Nos. 867-870, 895-899.
Issued: No. 850a, 1/29/16.

Imants Ziedonis (1933-2013), Poet — A324

**2014, Jan. 6** **Litho.** ***Perf. 13¼x13¾***

**856** A324 50c multi 1.40 1.10

Bildmuseet, Umea, Sweden A325

National Library, Riga, Latvia A326

**2014, Jan. 16 Litho. *Perf. 13¼***
**Granite Paper**

| | | | |
|---|---|---|---|
| **857** A325 50c multi | | 1.30 | 1.30 |
| **858** A326 78c multi | | 2.00 | 2.00 |

Selection of Umea and Riga as European Capitals of Culture. See Sweden Nos. 2720-2721.

2014 Winter Olympics, Sochi, Russia — A327

**2014, Feb. 7 Litho. *Perf. 13¼x13½***
**Granite Paper**

| | | |
|---|---|---|
| **859** A327 85c multi | 2.00 | 1.75 |

Personalized Stamp With Horizontal Orientation — A328

Personalized Stamp With Vertical Orientation A329

***Perf. 13¼x13½, 13½x13¼***
**2014, Feb. 28 Litho.**

| | | |
|---|---|---|
| **860** A328 50c multi | 1.40 | .70 |
| **861** A329 50c multi | 1.40 | .70 |
| **862** A328 78c multi | 2.25 | 1.10 |
| **863** A329 78c multi | 2.25 | 1.10 |
| **864** A328 85c multi | 2.40 | 1.25 |
| **865** A329 85c multi | 2.40 | 1.25 |
| *Nos. 860-865 (6)* | 12.10 | 6.10 |

Stamps with generic images of museums and their displays were made available on Nos. 860, 863 and 865. Stamps with generic images of airplanes were made available on Nos. 861, 862 and 864.

Tulips — A330

**2014, Mar. 7 Litho. *Perf. 13¼***

| | | |
|---|---|---|
| **866** A330 50c multi | 1.60 | 1.10 |

**Flowers Type of 2014**

Designs: 1c, Daisies. 4c, Hepatica. 7c, Marigolds. 50c, Lily of the valley.

**2014, Mar. 22 Litho. *Perf. 14***

| | | |
|---|---|---|
| **867** A323 1c multi | .30 | .30 |
| *a.* Dated "2015" | .30 | .30 |
| *b.* Dated "2016" | .30 | .30 |
| *c.* Dated "2017" | .30 | .30 |
| **868** A323 4c multi | .30 | .30 |
| *a.* Dated "2015" | .30 | .30 |
| *b.* Dated "2016" | .30 | .30 |
| *c.* Dated "2017" | .30 | .30 |
| **869** A323 7c multi | .30 | .30 |
| *a.* Dated "2015" | .30 | .30 |
| *c.* Dated "2017" | .30 | .30 |

**Granite Paper**

| | | |
|---|---|---|
| **870** A323 50c multi | 1.40 | 1.40 |
| *b.* Dated "2016," plain paper | 1.10 | 1.10 |
| *Nos. 867-870 (4)* | 2.30 | 2.30 |

Issued: Nos. 867a, 868a, 869a, 5/5/15; Nos. 867b, 870a, 1/29/16; No. 868b, 7/12/16; Nos. 867c, 868c, 869b, 1/13/17.

Diplomatic Relations With Georgia, 20th Anniv. — A331

***Perf. 13¼x13½***
**2014, Mar. 28 Litho.**
**Granite Paper**

| | | |
|---|---|---|
| **871** A331 85c multi | 2.00 | 1.25 |

See Georgia No. 491.

Europa — A332

Musical instruments: 78c, Kokle (zither). €1.71, Dudas (bagpipe).

**2014, Apr. 11 Litho. *Perf. 14x13¾***
**Granite Paper**

| | | |
|---|---|---|
| **872-873** A332 Set of 2 | 7.00 | 3.50 |
| *872a* Booklet pane of 4 #872, perf. 14x13¾ on 3 sides | 10.00 | — |
| Complete booklet, #872a | 10.00 | |

Emblem of *Te!* Television Show — A333

**2014, Apr. 17 Litho. *Perf. 13¼x13¾***
**Granite Paper**

| | | |
|---|---|---|
| **874** A333 50c deep lilac | 1.50 | 1.10 |

Birds — A334

Designs: 50c, Lymnocryptes minimus. €1.39, Upupa epops, vert.

***Perf. 13¾x14, 14x13¾***
**2014, May 16 Litho.**

| | | |
|---|---|---|
| **875-876** A334 Set of 2 | 5.25 | 2.60 |

Latvian Medalists at 2014 Winter Olympics A335

Designs: No. 877, 50c, Martin Dukurs, silver medalist in skeleton. No. 878, 50c, Daumants Dreiskens, Oskars Melbardis, Janis Strenga, Arvis Vilkaste, silver medalists in four-man bobsled. No. 879, 50c, Juris Sics, Andris Sics, bronze medalists in men's doubles luge. No. 880, 50c, Juris Sics, Andris Sics, Martins Rubenis, Eliza Tiruma, bronze medalists in Mixed team relay luge.

**2014, May 27 Litho. *Perf. 13¼***
**Granite Paper**

| | | |
|---|---|---|
| **877-880** A335 Set of 4 | 5.50 | 2.75 |

Nos. 877-880 each were printed in sheets of 4.

Janis Cimze (1814-81), Collector and Publisher of Folk Songs — A336

**2014, July 3 Litho. *Perf. 13¼x13½***
**Granite Paper**

| | | |
|---|---|---|
| **881** A336 57c multi | 1.60 | .80 |

Turaida Castle, 800th Anniv. — A337

**2014, July 11 Litho. *Perf. 13¼x13½***

| | | |
|---|---|---|
| **882** A337 50c multi | 1.40 | .70 |

Baltic Chain Demonstration, 25th Anniv. — A338

Designs: 50c, Three women.
No. 884: a, Five adults and one child. b, Like #883. c, Man and child.

**2014, Aug. 23 Litho. *Perf. 13¼***

| | | |
|---|---|---|
| **883** A338 50c multi | 1.40 | .70 |

**Souvenir Sheet**

| | | |
|---|---|---|
| **884** A338 78c Sheet of 3, #a-c | 6.25 | 3.25 |

See Estonia Nos. 764-765; Lithuania No. 1031.

Gothards Fridrihs Stenders (1714-96), Lexicographer A339

**2014, Aug. 24 Litho. *Perf. 13¼***

| | | |
|---|---|---|
| **885** A339 €1.39 multi | 3.75 | 1.90 |

No. 885 was printed in sheets of 8 + 4 labels.

Ainazu Lighthouse A340

**2014, Sept. 12 Litho. *Perf. 13¼***

| | | |
|---|---|---|
| **886** A340 71c multi | 1.90 | .95 |

Latvian Academy of Arts — A341

**2014, Oct. 17 Litho. *Perf. 13¼***

| | | |
|---|---|---|
| **887** A341 €1.42 multi | 3.50 | 1.75 |

Republic of Latvia, 96th Anniv. — A342

Designs: 57c, Painter. 64c, Graphic artist. 78c, Sculptor.

**2014, Nov. 7 Litho. *Perf. 14***

| | | |
|---|---|---|
| **888-890** A342 Set of 3 | 5.00 | 2.50 |

Christmas — A343

Designs: 50c, Forest in winter. 85c, City in winter, horiz.

**2014, Nov. 27 Litho. *Perf. 13½***

| | | |
|---|---|---|
| **891-892** A343 Set of 2 | 3.50 | 1.75 |

Singing Trees — A344

**2014, Dec. 4 Litho. *Perf. 14x13¾***

| | | |
|---|---|---|
| **893** A344 50c multi | 1.25 | .60 |

Latvian Presidency of Council of the European Union — A345

**2015, Jan. 6 Litho. *Perf. 13¾x14***

| | | |
|---|---|---|
| **894** A345 64c multi | 1.50 | .75 |

**Flowers Type of 2014**

Designs: 10c, Crocuses. 25c, Asters. 70c, Lilies. 78c, Gerbera daisies. €2.13, Pansies.

**2015, Jan. 9 Litho. *Perf. 14***
**Dated "2015"**

| | | |
|---|---|---|
| **895** A323 10c multi | .30 | .25 |
| *a.* Dated "2017" | .30 | .25 |

**896** A323 25c multi .65 .30
**897** A323 70c multi 1.75 .80
**898** A323 78c multi 2.00 .90
**899** A323 €2.13 multi 5.00 2.50
*Nos. 895-899 (5)* 9.70 4.75

Issued: No. 895a, 1/13/17.

Green Week A346

**2015, Jan. 15 Litho.** ***Perf. 13¼x13¾***
**900** A346 50c multi 1.25 .60

Arms of Riga — A347

National Arms — A348

**2015, Jan. 30 Litho.** ***Perf. 14x13¾***
**901** A347 €1 sil & multi 2.25 1.10
**902** A348 €2 sil & multi 4.50 2.25
**903** A348 €5 gold & multi 11.50 5.75
*Nos. 901-903 (3)* 18.25 9.10

Jelgava, 750th Anniv. A349

**2015, Feb. 5 Litho.** ***Perf. 13½***
**904** A349 €1.71 multi 3.75 1.90

Asterolepis Ornata and Fossils — A350

**2015, Feb. 20 Litho.** ***Perf. 13¼***
**905** A350 71c multi 1.60 .80

Helianthus A351

**2015, Mar. 6 Litho.** ***Perf. 13¼***
**906** A351 50c multi 1.10 .55

Europa — A352

Designs: 78c, Dolls. €1.71, Teddy bears.

**2015, Apr. 10 Litho.** ***Perf. 14x13¾***
**907** A352 78c multi 1.75 .90
*a.* Tete-beche pair 3.50 3.50
*b.* Booklet pane of 4, perf. 14x13¾ on 3 sides 7.00 —
Complete booklet, #907b 7.00
**908** A352 €1.71 multi 4.00 2.00

Kurzemes Literary Society, 200th Anniv. A353

**2015, Apr. 21 Litho.** ***Perf. 13¼***
**909** A353 85c multi 1.90 .95

No. 909 was printed in sheets of 10 + 2 central labels.

Independence, 25th Anniv. — A354

**2015, Apr. 29 Litho.** ***Perf. 13¼x13½***
**910** A354 50c multi 1.25 .60

World Press Freedom Day — A355

**2015, May 3 Litho.** ***Perf. 13¼x13¾***
**911** A355 57c multi 1.40 .70

Latvian Fire Services, 150th Anniv. A356

**2015, May 15 Litho.** ***Perf. 13¼***
**912** A356 €1.42 multi 3.25 1.60

Birds — A357

Designs: 71c, Oriolus oriolus. €1.42, Pluvialis apricaria, vert.

***Perf. 14x13¾, 13¾x14***
**2015, June 26 Litho.**
**913-914** A357 Set of 2 5.25 2.75

Rundales Palace A358

**2015, July 24 Litho.** ***Perf. 13¼***
**915** A358 €1.57 multi 3.50 1.75

Miniature Sheet

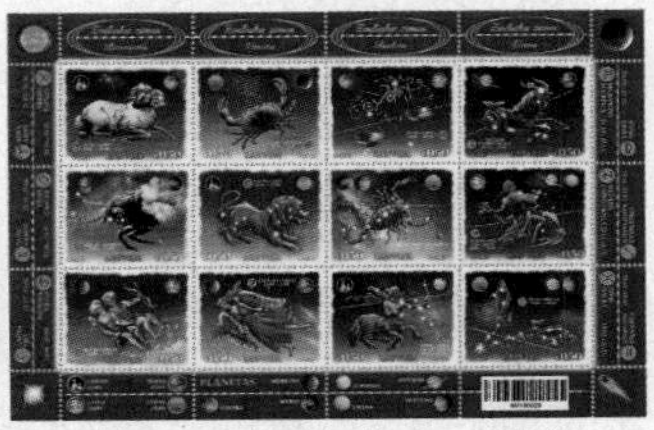

Signs of the Zodiac — A359

No. 916: a, Aries. b, Cancer. c, Libra. d, Capricorn. e, Taurus. f, Leo. g, Scorpio. h, Aquarius. i, Gemini. j, Virgo. k, Sagittarius. l, Pisces.

**2015, Aug. 7 Litho.** ***Perf. 13¼***
**916** A359 50c Sheet of 12, #a-l 13.50 6.75

Salacgrivas Lighthouse A360

***Perf. 13¼x13½***
**2015, Aug. 21 Litho.**
**917** A360 78c multi 1.75 .85

Poets — A361

No. 918: a, Rainis (1865-1929). b, Aspazija (1865-1943).

***Perf. 13¼x13½***
**2015, Sept. 11 Litho.**
**918** A361 50c Sheet of 2, #a-b 2.25 1.10

Latvian Riflemen, Cent. — A362

**2015, Oct. 25 Litho.** ***Perf. 13¼x13½***
**919** A362 €1.71 multi 3.75 1.90

Republic of Latvia, 97th Anniv. — A363

Architects: 50c, Janis Fridrihs Baumanis (1834-91). 64c, Eizens Laube (1880-1967), Janis Alksnis (1869-1939), Konstantins Peksens (1859-1928). €1.39, Marta Stana (1913-72).

**2015, Nov. 13 Litho.** ***Perf. 14***
**920-922** A363 Set of 3 5.50 2.75

Nos. 920-922 were each printed in sheets of 8 + central label.

Christmas A364

Designs: 50c, Gift box, pine cones and Christmas ornaments. 85c, Christmas ornaments and pine cones.

***Serpentine Die Cut 14¼x15 Syncopated***
**2015, Dec. 3 Litho.**
**Self-Adhesive**
**923-924** A364 Set of 2 3.00 1.50

Attack of Soviet Forces Against Latvian Barricades, 25th Anniv. A365

**2016, Jan. 13 Litho.** ***Perf. 13¼***
**925** A365 54c multi 1.25 .60

Coats of Arms of Municipalities — A366

Designs: 50c, Alsunga. 57c, Beverina. €1.39, Smiltene.

***Serpentine Die Cut 20x18 Syncopated***
**2016, Jan. 29 Litho.**
**Self-Adhesive**
**926** A366 50c red & multi 1.10 .55
**927** A366 57c blue & multi 1.25 .60
**928** A366 €1.39 tan & multi 3.00 1.50
*Nos. 926-928 (3)* 5.35 2.65

Stuffed Male and Female Tetrao Tetrix from Latvian Natural History Museum — A367

**2016, Feb. 19 Litho.** ***Perf. 13¼***
**929** A367 €1.71 multi 3.75 1.90

Nymphaea A368

**2016, Mar. 4 Litho.** ***Perf. 13¼***
**930** A368 50c multi 1.25 .60

Souvenir Sheet

Janis Rozentals (1866-1916), Painter — A369

No. 931: a, Kardinasana (Temptation), painting by Rozentals. b, Rozentals.

**2016, Mar. 18 Litho. *Perf. 13¼***
**931** A369 50c Sheet of 2, #a-b 2.25 1.10

2016 Floorball World Championships, Riga — A370

**2016, Apr. 9 Litho. *Perf. 13¼x13½***
**932** A370 64c multi 1.50 .75

A371

Europa A372

**2016, May 9 Litho. *Perf. 13¼***
**933** A371 78c multi 1.75 .85
**934** A372 78c multi 1.75 .85
*a.* Tete-beche pair 3.50 3.50
*b.* Booklet pane of 4, perf. 13¼ on 3 sides 7.00 —
Complete booklet, #934b 7.00

Think Green Issue.

Birds — A373

Designs: 71c, Glaucidium passerinum. €1.71, Dendrocopos major.

**2016, May 20 Litho. *Perf. 13¾x14***
**935-936** A373 Set of 2 5.50 2.75

Souvenir Sheet

1941 Deportation of Latvians to Siberia, 75th Anniv. — A374

No. 937 — Photographs of deportees and inscription: a, "14.06.1941." b, "Litene."

**2016, June 14 Litho. *Perf. 13¼***
**937** A374 50c Sheet of 2, #a-b 2.25 1.10

Cesis Concert Hall A375

**2016, July 15 Litho. *Perf. 13¼x13½***
**938** A375 €1.57 multi 3.50 1.75

Gustavs Erenpreiss (1891-1956), Bicycle Manufacturer A376

**2016, July 23 Litho. *Perf. 13¼***
**939** A376 50c multi 1.10 .55

Restoration of Latvian Independence, 25th Anniv. — A377

**2016, Aug. 21 Litho. *Perf. 13¼***
**940** A377 50c multi 1.10 .55

Bikernieki Race Track, 50th Anniv. — A378

**2016, Sept. 9 Litho. *Perf. 13¼x13¾***
**941** A378 57c multi 1.25 .65

Krustpils Railroad Station A379

**2016, Sept. 12 Litho. *Perf. 13¾***
**942** A379 €1.49 multi 3.50 1.75

Latvian Admission to the United Nations, 25th Anniv. — A380

**2016, Sept. 18 Litho. *Perf. 14x13¾***
**943** A380 54c multi 1.25 .60

Andrejs Pumpurs (1841-1902), Poet and Army Officer — A381

***Perf. 13¼x13½***
**2016, Sept. 22 Litho.**
**944** A381 €1.41 multi 3.25 1.60

Ovisi Lighthouse A382

**2016, Oct. 7 Litho. *Perf. 13¼***
**945** A382 90c multi 2.00 2.00
*a.* Booklet pane of 4, perf. 13¼ on 3 sides 8.00 —
Complete booklet, #945a 8.00

Archbishop Janis Pommers (1876-1934) — A383

**2016, Oct. 12 Litho. *Perf. 13¼***
**946** A383 50c multi 1.10 1.10

Barquentine Andreas Weide — A384

**2016, Oct. 28 Litho. *Perf. 13¼***
**947** A384 61c multi 1.40 1.40

Baltic Assembly, 25th Anniv. — A385

**2016, Nov. 8 Litho. *Perf. 13½x13¼***
**Stamp With White Frame**
**948** A385 50c multi 1.10 1.10

**Souvenir Sheet**
**Stamp With Multicolored Frame**
**949** A385 €1.39 multi 3.00 3.00

See Estonia Nos. 827-828, Lithuania Nos. 1088-1089.

Souvenir Sheet

Medalists at 2016 Paralympics, Rio de Janeiro — A386

No. 950: a, Diana Dadzite, javelin gold medalist. b, Aigars Apinis, discus gold medalist. c, Edgars Bergs, shot put bronze medalist.

**2016, Nov. 15 Litho. *Perf. 13¼***
**950** A386 50c Sheet of 3, #a-c, + label 3.25 3.25

Republic of Latvia, 98th Anniv. — A387

Designs: 50c, Janis Lusis, Dainis Kula and Inese Jaunzeme, Olympic gold medalists in javelin. 57c, Uljana Semjonova and Janis Krumins, Olympic medalists in basketball. €1.42, Sandis Ozolinsh, Sergejs Zoltoks, Arturs Irbe, Helmuts Balderis, Karlis Skrastins, past Latvian National Team and National Hockey League players.

**2016, Nov. 17 Litho. *Perf. 14***
**951-953** A387 Set of 3 5.50 5.50

A388

Christmas A389

***Serpentine Die Cut 14¼x15 Syncopated***
**2016, Nov. 25 Litho.**
**Self-Adhesive**
**954** A388 50c multi 1.10 1.10
**955** A389 78c multi 1.75 1.75

**Coats of Arms of Municipalities Type of 2016**

Designs: 50c, Olaine. 57c, Rojas. €1.39, Malpils.

***Serpentine Die Cut 20x18 Syncopated***
**2017, Jan. 13 Litho.**
**Self-Adhesive**
**956** A366 50c green & multi 1.10 .55
**957** A366 57c blue & multi 1.25 .60
**958** A366 €1.39 red & multi 3.00 1.50
*Nos. 956-958 (3)* 5.35 2.65

Rosa Canina — A390

**2017, Feb. 17 Litho. *Perf. 13¼***
**959** A390 €1.42 multi 3.00 1.50

Freesia — A391

**2017, Mar. 3 Litho. *Perf. 13¼***
**960** A391 64c multi 1.40 .70

Europa — A392

Designs: 78c, Cesvaine Palace. €1.71, Bauska Castle.

**2017, Apr. 21 Litho. *Perf. 14x13¾***
961 A392 78c multi 1.75 .85
a. Tete-beche pair 3.50 1.75
b. Booklet pane of 4, perf. 14x13¾ on 3 sides 7.00 —
Complete booklet, #961b 7.00
962 A392 €1.71 multi 3.75 1.90

Schooner Abraham — A393

**2017, May 9 Litho. *Perf. 13¼***
963 A393 61c multi 1.40 .70

Family Day — A394

**2017, May 15 Litho. *Perf. 13¼***
964 A394 50c multi 1.10 .55

Souvenir Sheet

Janis Tidemanis (1897-1964), Painter — A395

No. 965: a, Masks, by Tidemanis. b, Tidemanis.

**2017, May 26 Litho. *Perf. 13¼***
965 A395 50c Sheet of 2, #a-b 2.25 1.10

1903 Krastin Automobile — A396

**2017, June 2 Litho. *Perf. 13¼x13½***
966 A396 €1.39 multi 3.25 1.60

Meles Meles — A397

**2017, June 16 Litho. *Perf. 14x13¾***
967 A397 85c multi 2.00 1.00

Birds — A398

Designs: 50c, Motacilla flava. €1.41, Porzana parva.

**2017, July 14 Litho. *Perf. 14x13¾***
968-969 A398 Set of 2 5.00 2.50

Ceramic Sculpture by Dainis Pundurs A399

**2017, Aug. 18 Litho. *Perf. 13¼***
970 A399 €1.49 multi 3.75 1.90

Rojas Lighthouse A400

**2017, Sept. 8 Litho. *Perf. 13¼***
971 A400 90c multi 2.10 1.10
a. Booklet pane of 4, perf. 13¼ on 3 sides 8.50 —
Complete booklet, #971a 8.50

University of Latvia Natural Sciences Academic Center A401

**2017, Sept. 28 Litho. *Perf. 13¼***
972 A401 €1.39 multi 3.25 1.60

Eduards Veidenbaums (1867-92), Poet — A402

**2017, Oct. 3 Litho. *Perf. 13¼***
973 A402 57c multi 1.40 .70

Venta-1, First Latvian Satellite A403

**2017, Oct. 6 Litho. *Perf. 13¼x13½***
974 A403 85c multi 2.00 1.00

Anti-Corruption Campaign — A404

**2017, Oct. 10 Litho. *Perf. 13¼***
975 A404 50c multi 1.25 .60

Andreas Knopken (c. 1468-1539) and Martin Luther (1483-1546), Religious Reformers A405

**2017, Oct. 27 Litho. *Perf. 13¼***
976 A405 85c multi 2.00 1.00

Protestant Reformation, 500th anniv.

Republic of Latvia, Cent. — A406

Designs: 50s, Fridrihs Canders (1887-1933), rocket designer, Karlis Steins (1911-83), astronomer, Janis Ikaunieks (1912-69), astronomer, and Arturs Balklavs (1933-2005), astronomer. 57s, Surgeons Romans Lacis, Pauls Stradins (1896-1958) and Viktors Kalnberzs. €1.42, Chemists Pauls Valdens (1863-1957), Janis Stradins and Wilhelm Ostwald (1853-1932).

**2017, Nov. 3 Litho. *Perf. 14***
977-979 A406 Set of 3 6.00 6.00

Souvenir Sheet

Alona Ostapenko, 2017 French Open Tennis Champion — A407

**2017, Nov. 10 Litho. *Perf. 13¼***
980 A407 €1.42 multi 3.50 3.50

A408

A409

Christmas A410

***Serpentine Die Cut 14¼x14½ Syncopated***

**2017, Nov. 24 Litho.**

**Self-Adhesive**

981 A408 50c multi 1.25 1.25
982 A409 78c multi 1.90 1.90
983 A410 85c multi 2.10 2.10
*Nos. 981-983 (3)* 5.25 5.25

## SEMI-POSTAL STAMPS

"Mercy" Assisting Wounded Soldier — SP1

**Brown and Green Design on Back**

**1920 Unwmk. Typo. *Perf. 11½***
B1 SP1 20(30)k dk brn & red .50 *1.20*
B2 SP1 40(55)k dk bl & red .50 *1.20*
B3 SP1 50(70)k dk grn & red .50 *1.60*
B4 SP1 1(1.30)r dl sl & red .50 *1.60*

**Wmk. 197**

**Blue Design on Back**

B5 SP1 20(30)k dk brn & red .70 *1.20*
B6 SP1 40(55)k dk bl & red .70 *1.20*
a. Vert. pair, imperf. btwn. 40.00
B7 SP1 50(70)k dk grn & red .70 *1.60*
B8 SP1 1(1.30)r dk sl & red .70 *2.40*

**Wmk. Similar to 145**

**Pink Paper *Imperf.***

**Brown, Green and Red Design on Back**

B9 SP1 20(30)k dk brn & red 1.00 *2.50*
B10 SP1 40(55)k dk bl & red 1.00 *2.50*
B11 SP1 50(70)k dk grn & red 1.00 *2.50*
B12 SP1 1(1.30)r dk sl & red 2.00 *4.25*
*Nos. B1-B12 (12)* 9.80 *23.75*
Set, never hinged 22.50

These semi-postal stamps were printed on the backs of unfinished bank notes of the Workers and Soldiers Council, Riga, and the Bermondt-Avalov Army. Blocks of stamps showing complete banknotes on reverse are worth approximately three times the catalogue value of the stamps.

Nos. B1-B8 Surcharged

**Brown and Green Design on Back**

**1921 Unwmk. *Perf. 11½***
B13 SP1 20k + 2r dk brn & red 2.50 *4.00*
B14 SP1 40k + 2r dk bl & red 2.50 *4.00*
B15 SP1 50k + 2r dk grn & red 2.50 *4.00*
B16 SP1 1r + 2r dk sl & red 2.50 *4.00*

**Wmk. 197**

**Blue Design on Back**

B17 SP1 20k + 2r dk brn & red 10.00 *40.00*
B18 SP1 40k + 2r dk bl & red 10.00 *40.00*
B19 SP1 50k + 2r dk grn & red 10.00 *40.00*
B20 SP1 1r + 2r dk sl & red 10.00 *40.00*
*Nos. B13-B20 (8)* 50.00 *176.00*
Set, never hinged 150.00

Regular Issue of 1923-25 Surcharged in Blue

**1923 Wmk. Similar to 181 *Perf. 10***
B21 A12 1s + 10s violet .70 *1.75*
B22 A12 2s + 10s yellow .70 *1.75*
B23 A12 4s + 10s dk green .70 *1.75*
*Nos. B21-B23 (3)* 2.10 *5.25*
Set, never hinged 5.00

The surtax benefited the Latvian War Invalids Society.

Lighthouse and Harbor, Liepaja (Libau) SP2

Church at Liepaja — SP5

Coat of Arms of Liepaja — SP6

Designs: 15s (25s), City Hall, Liepaja. 25s (35s), Public Bathing Pavilion, Liepaja.

**1925, July 23** ***Perf. 11½***

| | | | | |
|---|---|---|---|---|
| **B24** SP2 | 6s | (12s) red brn & dp blue | 3.75 | *5.50* |
| **B25** SP2 | 15s | (25s) dk bl & brn | 2.25 | *4.00* |
| **B26** SP2 | 25s | (35s) vio & dk grn | 3.75 | *4.00* |
| **B27** SP5 | 30s | (40s) dk blue & lake | 6.75 | *12.00* |
| **B28** SP6 | 50s | (60s) dk grn & vio | 9.75 | *16.00* |
| | | *Nos. B24-B28 (5)* | 26.25 | *41.50* |
| | | Set, never hinged | 55.00 | |

Tercentenary of Liepaja (Libau). The surtax benefited that city. Exist imperf. Value, unused set $500.

President Janis Cakste — SP7

**1928, Apr. 18** **Engr.**

| | | | | |
|---|---|---|---|---|
| **B29** SP7 | 2s | (12s) red orange | 2.25 | *3.25* |
| **B30** SP7 | 6s | (16s) deep green | 2.25 | *3.25* |
| **B31** SP7 | 15s | (25s) red brown | 2.25 | *3.25* |
| **B32** SP7 | 25s | (35s) deep blue | 2.25 | *3.25* |
| **B33** SP7 | 30s | (40s) claret | 2.25 | *3.25* |
| | | *Nos. B29-B33 (5)* | 11.25 | *16.25* |
| | | Set, never hinged | 35.00 | |

The surtax helped erect a monument to Janis Cakste, 1st pres. of the Latvian Republic.

Venta River — SP8

Allegory, "Latvia" — SP9

View of Jelgava SP10

National Theater, Riga — SP11

View of Cesis (Wenden) SP12

Riga Bridge and Trenches SP13

***Perf. 11½, Imperf.***

**1928, Nov. 18** **Wmk. 212** **Litho.**

| | | | | |
|---|---|---|---|---|
| **B34** SP8 | 6s | (16s) green | 2.50 | *2.75* |
| **B35** SP9 | 10s | (20s) scarlet | 2.50 | *2.75* |
| **B36** SP10 | 15s | (25s) maroon | 2.50 | *2.75* |
| **B37** SP11 | 30s | (40s) ultra | 2.50 | *2.75* |
| **B38** SP12 | 50s | (60s) dk gray | 2.50 | *2.75* |
| **B39** SP13 | 1 l | (1.10 l) choc | 2.50 | *2.75* |
| | | *Nos. B34-B39 (6)* | 15.00 | *16.50* |
| | | Set, never hinged | 35.00 | |

The surtax was given to a committee for the erection of a Liberty Memorial.

Z. A. Meierovics SP14

**1929, Aug. 22** ***Perf. 11½, Imperf.***

| | | | | |
|---|---|---|---|---|
| **B46** SP14 | 2s | (4s) orange | 3.00 | 3.00 |
| **B47** SP14 | 6s | (12s) dp grn | 3.00 | 3.00 |
| **B48** SP14 | 15s | (25s) red brown | 3.00 | 3.00 |
| **B49** SP14 | 25s | (35s) deep blue | 3.00 | 3.00 |
| **B50** SP14 | 30s | (40s) ultra | 3.00 | 3.00 |
| | | *Nos. B46-B50 (5)* | 15.00 | 15.00 |
| | | Set, never hinged | 42.50 | |

The surtax was used to erect a monument to Z. A. Meierovics, Latvian statesman.

Tuberculosis Cross — SP15

Allegory of Hope for the Sick — SP16

Gustavs Zemgals — SP17

Riga Castle — SP18

Daisies and Double-barred Cross — SP20

Tuberculosis Sanatorium, near Riga — SP22

Cakste, Kviesis and Zemgals SP23

Designs: No. B61, Janis Cakste, 1st pres. of Latvia. No. B63, Pres. Alberts Kviesis.

**1930, Dec. 4** **Typo.** ***Perf. 10, 11½***

| | | | | |
|---|---|---|---|---|
| **B56** SP15 | 1s | (2s) dk vio & red org | .75 | *.85* |
| **B57** SP15 | 2s | (4s) org & red org | .75 | *.85* |
| **B58** SP16 | 4s | (8s) dk grn & red | .75 | *.85* |
| **B59** SP17 | 5s | (10s) brt grn & dk brn | 1.50 | *1.75* |
| **B60** SP18 | 6s | (12s) ol grn & bister | 1.50 | *1.75* |
| **B61** SP17 | 10s | (20s) dp red & blk | 2.20 | *2.25* |
| **B62** SP20 | 15s | (30s) mar & dl green | 2.25 | *2.25* |
| **B63** SP17 | 20s | (40s) rose lake & ind | 2.25 | *2.25* |
| **B64** SP22 | 25s | (50s) multi | 3.00 | *3.50* |
| **B65** SP23 | 30s | (60s) multi | 3.50 | *4.00* |
| | | *Nos. B56-B65 (10)* | 18.45 | *20.30* |
| | | Set, never hinged | 55.00 | |

Surtax for the Latvian Anti-Tuberculosis Soc.
For surcharges see Nos. B72-B81.

J. Rainis and New Buildings, Riga SP24

Character from Play and Rainis SP25

Characters from Plays — SP26

Rainis and Lyre SP27

Flames, Flag and Rainis SP28

**1930, May 23** **Wmk. 212** ***Perf. 11½***

| | | | | |
|---|---|---|---|---|
| **B66** SP24 | 1s | (2s) dull violet | .75 | *3.25* |
| **B67** SP25 | 2s | (4s) yellow org | .75 | *3.25* |
| **B68** SP26 | 4s | (8s) dp green | .75 | *3.25* |
| **B69** SP27 | 6s | (12s) yel grn & red brown | .75 | *3.25* |
| **B70** SP28 | 10s | (20s) dark red | 22.50 | *47.50* |
| **B71** SP27 | 15s | (30s) red brn & yel grn | 22.50 | *47.50* |
| | | *Nos. B66-B71 (6)* | 48.00 | *108.00* |
| | | Set, never hinged | 95.00 | |

Sold at double face value, surtax going to memorial fund for J. Rainis (Jan Plieksans, 1865-1929), writer and politician.

Exist imperf. Value twice that of perf. stamps.

Nos. B56 to B65 Surcharged in Black With Bars

Nos. B56 to B65 Surcharged in Black Without Bars

**1931, Aug. 19** ***Perf. 10, 11½***

| | | | | |
|---|---|---|---|---|
| **B72** SP18 | 9s on 6s | (12s) | 1.00 | *2.00* |
| **B73** SP15 | 16s on 1s | (2s) | 12.50 | 24.00 |
| **B74** SP15 | 17s on 2s | (4s) | 1.25 | *2.00* |
| **B75** SP16 | 19s on 4s | (8s) | 3.75 | *8.50* |
| **B76** SP17 | 20s on 5s | (10s) | 2.50 | *8.50* |
| **B77** SP20 | 23s on 15s | (30s) | 1.00 | *1.50* |
| **B78** SP17 | 25s on 10s | (20s) | 2.50 | *4.50* |
| **B79** SP17 | 35s on 20s | (40s) | 3.75 | *7.00* |
| **B80** SP22 | 45s on 25s | (50s) | 10.00 | *20.00* |
| **B81** SP23 | 55s on 30s | (60s) | 12.50 | *32.50* |
| | *Nos. B72-B81 (10)* | | 50.75 | *110.50* |
| | Set, never hinged | | 110.00 | |

The surcharge replaces the original total price, including surtax.

Nos. B73-B81 have no bars in the surcharge. The surtax aided the Latvian Anti-Tuberculosis Society.

Lacplesis, the Deliverer SP29

Designs: 1s, Kriva telling stories under Holy Oak. 2s, Enslaved Latvians building Riga under knight's supervision. 4s, Death of Black Knight. 5s, Spirit of Lacplesis over freed Riga.

**Inscribed: "AIZSARGI" (Army Reserve)**

**1932, Feb. 10** ***Perf. 10½, Imperf.***

| | | | | |
|---|---|---|---|---|
| **B82** SP29 | 1s | (11s) vio brn & bluish | 2.50 | 2.50 |
| **B83** SP29 | 2s | (17s) ocher & ol green | 2.50 | 2.50 |
| **B84** SP29 | 3s | (23s) red brn & org brown | 2.50 | 2.50 |
| **B85** SP29 | 4s | (34s) dk grn & green | 2.50 | 2.50 |
| **B86** SP29 | 5s | (45s) grn & emerald | 2.50 | 2.50 |
| | | *Nos. B82-B86 (5)* | 12.50 | 12.50 |
| | | Set, never hinged | 22.00 | |

Surtax aided the Militia Maintenance Fund.

Marching Troops SP30

Infantry in Action SP31

Nurse Binding Soldier's Wound — SP32

Army Soup Kitchen — SP33

Gen. J. Balodis — SP34

**1932, May** ***Perf. 10½, Imperf.***

**B87** SP30 6s (25s) ol brn & red violet 4.00 *6.50*
**B88** SP31 7s (35s) dk bl grn & dark blue 4.00 *6.50*
**B89** SP32 10s (45s) ol grn & blk brn 4.00 *6.50*
**B90** SP33 12s (55s) lake & ol green 4.00 *6.50*
**B91** SP34 15s (75s) red org & brn vio 4.00 *6.50*
*Nos. B87-B91 (5)* 20.00 *32.50*
Set, never hinged 45.00

The surtax aided the Latvian Home Guards.

Symbolical of Unified Latvia — SP35

Symbolical of the Strength of the Latvian Union — SP36

Aid to the Sick SP37

"Charity" SP38

**Wmk. 212**

**1936, Dec. 28 Litho.** ***Perf. 11½***

**B92** SP35 3s orange red 1.50 *2.50*
**B93** SP36 10s green 1.50 *2.50*
**B94** SP37 20s rose pink 1.50 *3.00*
**B95** SP38 35s blue 1.50 *3.00*
*Nos. B92-B95 (4)* 6.00 *11.00*
Set, never hinged 12.00

Souvenir Sheets

SP39

**1938, May 12 Wmk. 212** ***Perf. 11***

**B96** SP39 Sheet of 2 12.00 *50.00*
Never hinged 22.50
*a.* 35s Justice Palace, Riga 2.00 *5.00*
*b.* 40s Power Station, Kegums 2.00 *5.00*

Sold for 2 l. The surtax of 1.25 l was for the National Reconstruction Fund.
No. B96 exists imperf.

**Overprinted in Blue with Dates 1934 1939 and "15" over "V"**

**1939**

**B97** SP39 Sheet of 2 15.00 *75.00*
Never hinged 40.00

5th anniv. of Natl. Unity Day. Sold for 2 lats. Surtax for the Natl. Reconstruction Fund.

Natl. Olympic Committee SP50

**1992, Feb. 8 Litho.** ***Perf. 13½x13***

**Background Color**

**B150** SP50 50k +25k gray .60 .60
**B151** SP50 50k +25k buff 1.25 1.25
**B152** SP50 100k +50k bister .80 .80
*Nos. B150-B152 (3)* 2.65 2.65

No. B150 inscribed "Berlin 18.09.91."

## AIR POST STAMPS

Blériot XI — AP1

**Wmk. Wavy Lines Similar to 181**

**1921, July 30 Litho.** ***Perf. 11½***

**C1** AP1 10r emerald 3.00 4.50
*a.* Imperf. 6.00 *35.00*
**C2** AP1 20r dark blue 3.00 4.50
*a.* Imperf. 6.00 *35.00*
Set, perf, never hinged 12.00
Set, imperf, never hinged 25.00

**1928, May 1**

**C3** AP1 10s deep green 4.50 1.60
**C4** AP1 15s red 2.00 1.60
**C5** AP1 25s ultra 3.75 2.50
*a.* Pair, imperf. btwn. 35.00
*Nos. C3-C5 (3)* 10.25 5.70
Set, never hinged 16.00

Nos. C1-C5 sometimes show letters of a paper maker's watermark "PACTIEN LIGAT MILLS."

**1931-32 Wmk. 212** ***Perf. 11½***

**C6** AP1 10s deep green 1.00 .90
*a.* Perf. 11 12.00 *14.50*
**C7** AP1 15s red 1.50 1.00
*a.* Perf. 11 120.00 32.50
**C8** AP1 25s deep blue ('32) 8.50 1.25
*a.* Perf. 11 28.00 14.50
*Nos. C6-C8 (3)* 11.00 3.15
Set, never hinged 22.50

**Type of 1921 Overprinted or Surcharged in Black**

**1933, May 26 Wmk. 212** ***Imperf.***

**C9** AP1 10s deep green 40.00 *80.00*
**C10** AP1 15s red 40.00 *80.00*
**C11** AP1 25s deep blue 40.00 *80.00*
**C12** AP1 50s on 15s red 200.00 *525.00*
**C13** AP1 100s on 25s dp blue 200.00 *525.00*
*Nos. C9-C13 (5)* 520.00 *1,290.*
Set, never hinged 825.00

Honoring and financing a flight from Riga to Bathurst, Gambia. The plane crashed at Neustettin, Germany.
Counterfeits exist of Nos. C1-C13.

## AIR POST SEMI-POSTAL STAMPS

Durbes Castle, Rainis Birthplace — SPAP1

**Wmk. 212**

**1930, May 26 Litho.** ***Perf. 11½***

**CB1** SPAP1 10s (20s) red & olive green 6.50 *14.50*
**CB2** SPAP1 15s (30s) dk yel grn & cop red 6.50 *14.50*
Set, never hinged 25.00

Surtax for the Rainis Memorial Fund.

**Imperf.**

*CB1a* SPAP1 10s (20s) 10.00 *27.50*
*CB2a* SPAP1 15s (30s) 10.00 *27.50*
Set, never hinged 40.00

**Nos. C6-C8 Surcharged in Magenta, Blue or Red**

**1931, Dec. 5**

**CB3** AP1 10s + 50s dp grn (M) 6.50 *7.50*
**CB4** AP1 15s + 1 l red (Bl) 6.50 *7.50*
**CB5** AP1 25s + 1.50 l dp blue 6.50 *7.50*
*Nos. CB3-CB5 (3)* 19.50 *22.50*
Set, never hinged 40.00

Surtax for the Latvian Home Guards.

**Imperf.**

*CB3a* AP1 10s + 50s 10.00 *11.00*
*CB4a* AP1 15s + 1 l 10.00 *11.00*
*CB5a* AP1 25s + 1.50 l 10.00 *11.00*
*Nos. CB3a-CB5a (3)* 30.00 *33.00*
Set, never hinged 55.00

SPAP2

**1932, June 17** ***Perf. 10½***

**CB6** SPAP2 10s (20s) dk sl grn & grn 12.50 *25.00*
**CB7** SPAP2 15s (30s) brt red & buff 12.50 *25.00*
**CB8** SPAP2 25s (50s) dp bl & gray 12.50 *25.00*
*Nos. CB6-CB8 (3)* 37.50 *75.00*
Set, never hinged 75.00

Surtax for the Latvian Home Guards.

**Imperf.**

*CB6a* SPAP2 10s (20s) 12.50 *25.00*
*CB7a* SPAP2 15s (30s) 12.50 *25.00*
*CB8a* SPAP2 25s (50s) 12.50 *25.00*
*Nos. CB6a-CB8a (3)* 37.50 *75.00*
Set, never hinged 75.00

Icarus — SPAP3

Leonardo da Vinci — SPAP4

Charles Balloon — SPAP5

Wright Brothers Biplane SPAP6

Bleriot Monoplane SPAP7

**1932, Dec.** ***Perf. 10, 11½***

**CB9** SPAP3 5s (25s) ol bis & grn 17.50 *20.00*
**CB10** SPAP4 10s (50s) ol brn & gray grn 17.50 *20.00*
**CB11** SPAP5 15s (75s) red brn & gray grn 17.50 *20.00*
**CB12** SPAP6 20s (1 l) gray grn & lil rose 17.50 *20.00*
**CB13** SPAP7 25s (1.25 l) brn & bl 17.50 *20.00*
*Nos. CB9-CB13 (5)* 87.50 100.00
Set, never hinged 150.00

Issued to honor pioneers of aviation. The surtax of four times the face value was for wounded Latvian aviators.

**Imperf.**

*CB9a* SPAP3 5s (25s) 17.50 *20.00*
*CB10a* SPAP4 10s (50s) 17.50 *20.00*
*CB11a* SPAP5 15s (75s) 17.50 *20.00*
*CB12a* SPAP6 20s (1 l) 17.50 *20.00*
*CB13a* SPAP7 25s (1.25 l) 17.50 *20.00*
*Nos. CB9a-CB13a (5)* 87.50 100.00
Set, never hinged 175.00

Icarus Falling SPAP8

Monument to Aviators SPAP9

Proposed Tombs for Aviators
SPAP10 SPAP11

**1933, Mar. 15** ***Perf. 11½***

**CB14** SPAP8 2s (52s) blk & ocher 14.00 *20.00*
**CB15** SPAP9 3s (53s) blk & red org 14.00 *20.00*
**CB16** SPAP10 10s (60s) blk & dk yel green 14.00 *20.00*
**CB17** SPAP11 20s (70s) blk & cerise 14.00 *20.00*
*Nos. CB14-CB17 (4)* 56.00 *80.00*
Set, never hinged 125.00

50s surtax for wounded Latvian aviators.

### Imperf.

| | | | | |
|---|---|---|---|---|
| *CB14a* | SPAP8 | 2s (52s) | 15.00 | *21.00* |
| *CB15a* | SPAP9 | 3s (53s) | 15.00 | *21.00* |
| *CB16a* | SPAP10 | 10s (60s) | 15.00 | *21.00* |
| *CB17a* | SPAP11 | 20s (70s) | 15.00 | *21.00* |
| | | *Nos. CB14a-CB17a (4)* | 60.00 | 84.00 |
| | | Set, never hinged | 135.00 | |

Biplane Taking Off SPAP12

Designs: 7s (57s), Biplane under fire at Riga. 35s (1.35 l), Map and planes.

**1933, June 15 Wmk. 212 *Perf. 11½***

| | | | | |
|---|---|---|---|---|
| **CB18** | SPAP12 | 3s (53s) org & sl blue | 19.00 | *40.00* |
| **CB19** | SPAP12 | 7s (57s) sl bl & dk brn | 19.00 | *40.00* |
| **CB20** | SPAP12 | 35s (1.35 l) dp ultra & ol blk | 19.00 | *40.00* |
| | | *Nos. CB18-CB20 (3)* | 57.00 | *120.00* |
| | | Set, never hinged | 135.00 | |

Surtax for wounded Latvian aviators. Counterfeits exist.

### Imperf.

| | | | | |
|---|---|---|---|---|
| *CB18a* | SPAP12 | 3s (53s) | 22.50 | *42.50* |
| *CB19a* | SPAP12 | 7s (57s) | 22.50 | *42.50* |
| *CB20a* | SPAP12 | 35s (1.35 l) | 22.50 | *42.50* |
| | | *Nos. CB18a-CB20a (3)* | 67.50 | *127.50* |
| | | Set, never hinged | 140.00 | |

American Gee-Bee SPAP13

English Seaplane S6B SPAP14

Graf Zeppelin over Riga SPAP15

DO-X SPAP16

**1933, Sept. 5 *Perf. 11½***

| | | | | |
|---|---|---|---|---|
| **CB21** | SPAP13 | 8s (68s) brn & gray blk | 40.00 | *85.00* |
| **CB22** | SPAP14 | 12s (1.12 l) brn car & ol grn | 40.00 | *85.00* |
| **CB23** | SPAP15 | 30s (1.30 l) bl & gray blk | 50.00 | *90.00* |
| **CB24** | SPAP16 | 40s (1.90 l) brn vio & indigo | 40.00 | *85.00* |
| | | *Nos. CB21-CB24 (4)* | 170.00 | 345.00 |
| | | Set, never hinged | 275.00 | |

Surtax for wounded Latvian aviators.

### Imperf.

| | | | | |
|---|---|---|---|---|
| *CB21a* | SPAP13 | 8s (68s) | 40.00 | *85.00* |
| *CB22a* | SPAP14 | 12s (1.12 l) | 40.00 | *85.00* |
| *CB23a* | SPAP15 | 30s (1.30 l) | 50.00 | *95.00* |
| *CB24a* | SPAP16 | 40s (1.90 l) | 40.00 | *90.00* |
| | | *Nos. CB21a-CB24a (4)* | 170.00 | *355.00* |
| | | Set, never hinged | 275.00 | |

## OCCUPATION STAMPS

### Issued under German Occupation

German Stamps of 1905-18 Handstamped

### Red Overprint

**1919 Wmk. 125 *Perf. 14, 14½***

| | | | | |
|---|---|---|---|---|
| **1N1** | A22 | 2½pf gray | 275.00 | *325.00* |
| **1N2** | A16 | 5pf green | 225.00 | 100.00 |
| **1N3** | A22 | 15pf dk vio | 375.00 | 100.00 |
| **1N4** | A16 | 20pf blue vio | 135.00 | 65.00 |
| **1N5** | A16 | 25pf org & blk, *yel* | 475.00 | 325.00 |
| **1N6** | A16 | 50pf pur & blk, *buff* | 475.00 | 325.00 |

### Violet Blue Overprint

| | | | | |
|---|---|---|---|---|
| **1N7** | A22 | 2½pf gray | 275.00 | *325.00* |
| **1N8** | A16 | 5pf green | 225.00 | 120.00 |
| **1N9** | A16 | 10pf carmine | 190.00 | 47.50 |
| **1N10** | A22 | 15pf dk vio | 325.00 | 325.00 |
| **1N11** | A16 | 20pf bl vio | 135.00 | 65.00 |
| **1N12** | A16 | 25pf org & blk, *yel* | 675.00 | 525.00 |
| **1N13** | A16 | 50pf pur & blk, *buff* | 675.00 | 525.00 |
| | | *Nos. 1N1-1N13 (13)* | 4,460. | 3,173. |

Inverted and double overprints exist, as well as counterfeit overprints.

Some experts believe that Nos. 1N1-1N7 were not officially issued. All used examples are canceled to order.

Russian Stamps Overprinted

**1941, July**

| | | | | |
|---|---|---|---|---|
| **1N14** | A331 | 5k red (#734) | 1.00 | *4.25* |
| **1N15** | A109 | 10k blue (#616) | 1.00 | *4.25* |
| **1N16** | A332 | 15k dk grn (#735) | 32.50 | *72.50* |
| **1N17** | A97 | 20k dull grn (#617) | 1.00 | *4.25* |
| **1N18** | A333 | 30k dp blue (#736) | 1.00 | *4.25* |
| **1N19** | A111 | 50k dp brn (#619A) | 3.50 | *10.00* |
| | | *Nos. 1N14-1N19 (6)* | 40.00 | *99.50* |
| | | Set, never hinged | 77.50 | |

Issued: 20k, 30k, 7/17; 5k, 10k, 7/18; 15k, 7/19; 50k, 7/23.

Nos. 1N14-1N19 were replaced by German stamps in mid-October. On Nov. 4, 1941, German stamps overprinted "Ostland" (Russia Nos. N9-N28) were placed into use.

The overprint exists on imperf examples of the 10k and 50k stamps. Value, each $800.

Counterfeit overprints exist.

### KURLAND

German Stamps Surcharged

**1945, Apr. 20**

| | | | | |
|---|---|---|---|---|
| **1N20** | A115 | 6pf on 5pf dp yel grn (#509) | 37.50 | *72.50* |
| | | Never hinged | 72.50 | |
| **1N21** | A115 | 6 pf on 10pf dk brn (#511A) | 15.00 | *30.00* |
| | | Never hinged | 27.50 | |
| *a.* | | Inverted surcharge | 100.00 | *175.00* |
| | | Never hinged | 175.00 | |
| *b.* | | Double surcharge | 85.00 | *150.00* |
| | | Never hinged | 150.00 | |
| **1N22** | A115 | 6 pf on 20pf blue | 8.50 | *14.50* |
| | | Never hinged | 16.00 | |
| *a.* | | Inverted surcharge | 100.00 | *175.00* |
| | | Never hinged | 175.00 | |
| *b.* | | Double surcharge | 85.00 | *150.00* |
| | | Never hinged | 150.00 | |

Germany Nos. MQ1 & MQ1a Surcharged

### *Perf 13½*

| | | | | |
|---|---|---|---|---|
| **1N23** | MPP1 | 12pf on (-) red brn, (#MQ1) | 42.50 | *72.50* |
| | | Never hinged | 82.50 | |
| *a.* | | Inverted surcharge | 150.00 | *275.00* |
| | | Never hinged | 275.00 | |
| *b.* | | Double surcharge | 150.00 | *275.00* |
| | | Never hinged | 275.00 | |

### *Rouletted*

| | | | | |
|---|---|---|---|---|
| **1N24** | MPP1 | 12pf on (-) red brn, (#MQ1a) | 6.50 | *16.00* |
| | | Never hinged | 16.00 | |
| *a.* | | Inverted surcharge | 75.00 | *135.00* |
| | | Never hinged | 135.00 | |
| *b.* | | Double surcharge | 67.50 | *120.00* |
| | | Never hinged | 120.00 | |
| | | *Nos. 1N20-1N24 (5)* | 110.00 | *205.50* |
| | | Set, never hinged | 200.00 | |

Nos. 1N20-1N24 were used in the German-held enclave of Kurland (Courland) from April 20-May 8, 1945.

Counterfeit surcharges are plentiful.

## ISSUED UNDER RUSSIAN OCCUPATION

Fake overprints/surcharges exist on Nos. 2N1-2N36.

The following stamps were issued at Mitau during the occupation of Kurland by the West Russian Army under Colonel Bermondt-Avalov.

Stamps of Latvia Handstamped

### On Stamps of 1919

**1919 Wmk. 108 *Imperf.***

| | | | | |
|---|---|---|---|---|
| **2N1** | A1 | 3k lilac | 40.00 | *52.50* |
| **2N2** | A1 | 5k carmine | 40.00 | *52.50* |
| **2N3** | A1 | 10k dp blue | 140.00 | *240.00* |
| **2N4** | A1 | 20k orange | 40.00 | *52.50* |
| **2N5** | A1 | 25k gray | 40.00 | *52.50* |
| **2N6** | A1 | 35k dk brown | 40.00 | *52.50* |
| **2N7** | A1 | 50k purple | 40.00 | *52.50* |
| **2N8** | A1 | 75k emerald | 40.00 | *80.00* |

### On Riga Liberation Stamps

| | | | | |
|---|---|---|---|---|
| **2N9** | A2 | 5k carmine | 40.00 | *52.50* |
| **2N10** | A2 | 15k dp green | 20.00 | *40.00* |
| **2N11** | A2 | 35k brown | 20.00 | *40.00* |

Stamps of Latvia Overprinted

### On Stamps of 1919

| | | | | |
|---|---|---|---|---|
| **2N12** | A1 | 3k lilac | 6.00 | *9.50* |
| **2N13** | A1 | 5k carmine | 6.00 | *9.50* |
| **2N14** | A1 | 10k dp blue | 120.00 | *200.00* |
| **2N15** | A1 | 20k orange | 12.00 | *20.00* |
| **2N16** | A1 | 25k gray | 27.50 | *60.00* |
| **2N17** | A1 | 35k dk brown | 20.00 | *27.50* |
| **2N18** | A1 | 50k purple | 20.00 | *27.50* |
| **2N19** | A1 | 75k emerald | 20.00 | *27.50* |

### On Riga Liberation Stamps

| | | | | |
|---|---|---|---|---|
| **2N20** | A2 | 5k carmine | 4.00 | *8.00* |
| **2N21** | A2 | 15k dp green | 4.00 | *8.00* |
| **2N22** | A2 | 35k brown | 4.00 | *8.00* |
| *a.* | | Inverted overprint | *200.00* | |
| | | *Nos. 2N1-2N22 (22)* | 743.50 | *1,173.* |

The letters "Z. A." are the initials of "Zapadnaya Armiya"-i.e. Western Army.

Russian Stamps of 1909-17 Surcharged

### On Stamps of 1909-12

**_Perf. 14, 14½x15_**

**Unwmk.**

| | | | | |
|---|---|---|---|---|
| **2N23** | A14 | 10k on 2k grn | 6.00 | *8.00* |
| *a.* | | Inverted surcharge | *30.00* | |
| **2N24** | A15 | 30k on 4k car | 8.00 | *8.00* |
| **2N25** | A14 | 40k on 5k cl | 8.00 | *9.50* |
| **2N26** | A15 | 50k pn 10k dk bl | 6.00 | *8.00* |
| **2N27** | A11 | 70k on 15k red brn & bl | 6.00 | *8.00* |
| *a.* | | Inverted surcharge | *200.00* | |
| **2N28** | A8 | 90k on 20k bl & car | 12.00 | *16.00* |
| **2N29** | A11 | 1r on 25k grn & vio | 6.00 | 8.00 |
| **2N30** | A11 | 1½r on 35k red brn & grn | 47.50 | 65.00 |
| **2N31** | A8 | 2r on 50k vio & grn | 12.00 | 16.00 |
| *a.* | | Inverted surcharge | *120.00* | |
| **2N32** | A11 | 4r on 70k brn & org | 20.00 | 27.50 |

### *Perf. 13½*

| | | | | |
|---|---|---|---|---|
| **2N33** | A9 | 6r on 1r pale brn, brn & org | 27.50 | 40.00 |

### On Stamps of 1917

### *Imperf*

| | | | | |
|---|---|---|---|---|
| **2N34** | A14 | 20k on 3k red | 6.00 | *8.00* |
| **2N35** | A14 | 40k on 5k claret | 95.00 | *100.00* |
| **2N36** | A12 | 10r on 3.50r mar & lt grn | 80.00 | *80.00* |
| *a.* | | Inverted surcharge | *300.00* | |
| | | *Nos. 2N23-2N36 (14)* | 340.00 | *402.00* |

Eight typographed stamps of this design were prepared in 1919, but never placed in use. They exist both perforated and imperforate. Value, set, imperf. $1, perf. $2.

Reprints and counterfeits exist.

**Catalogue values for unused stamps in this section, from this point to the end of the section, are for Never Hinged items.**

Arms of Soviet Latvia — OS1

**1940 Typo. Wmk. 265 *Perf. 10***

| | | | | |
|---|---|---|---|---|
| **2N45** | OS1 | 1s dk violet | .25 | .25 |
| **2N46** | OS1 | 2s orange yel | .25 | .25 |
| **2N47** | OS1 | 3s orange ver | .25 | .25 |
| **2N48** | OS1 | 5s dk olive grn | .25 | .25 |
| **2N49** | OS1 | 7s turq green | .25 | .80 |
| **2N50** | OS1 | 10s slate green | 2.00 | .40 |
| **2N51** | OS1 | 20s brown lake | 1.20 | .25 |
| **2N52** | OS1 | 30s light blue | 2.40 | .40 |
| **2N53** | OS1 | 35s brt ultra | .25 | *.40* |
| **2N54** | OS1 | 40s chocolate | 2.00 | 1.20 |
| **2N55** | OS1 | 50s lt gray | 2.50 | 1.20 |
| **2N56** | OS1 | 1 l lt brown | 3.25 | 1.50 |
| **2N57** | OS1 | 5 l brt green | 24.00 | 13.50 |
| | | *Nos. 2N45-2N57 (13)* | 38.85 | 20.65 |

Used values of Nos. 2N45-2N57 are for CTOs. Commercially used examples are worth three times as much.

# LEBANON

'le-bə-nən

## (Grand Liban)

LOCATION — Asia Minor, bordering on the Mediterranean Sea
GOVT. — Republic
AREA — 4,036 sq. mi.
POP. — 3,562,699 (1999 est.)
CAPITAL — Beirut

Formerly a part of the Syrian province of Turkey, Lebanon was occupied by French forces after World War I. It was mandated to France after it had been declared a separate state. Limited autonomy was granted in 1927 and full independence achieved in 1941. The French issued two sets of occupation stamps (with T.E.O. overprint) for Lebanon in late 1919. The use of these and later occupation issues (of 1920-24, with overprints "O.M.F." and "Syrie-Grand Liban") was extended to Syria, Cilicia, Alaouites and Alexandretta. By custom, these are all listed under Syria.

100 Centimes = 1 Piaster
100 Piasters = 1 Pound

**Watermark**

Wmk. 400

**Catalogue values for unused stamps in this country are for Never Hinged items, beginning with Scott 177 in the regular postage section, Scott B13 in the semi-postal section, Scott C97 in the airpost section, Scott CB5 in the airpost semi-postal section, Scott J37 in the postage due section, and Scott RA11 in the postal tax section.**

### Issued under French Mandate

Stamps of France 1900-21 Surcharged

**1924 Unwmk. *Perf. 14x13½***

| | | | | |
|---|---|---|---|---|
| 1 | A16 | 10c on 2c vio brn | 1.60 | 1.60 |
| *a.* | | Inverted surcharge | 45.00 | 45.00 |
| 2 | A22 | 25c on 5c orange | 1.60 | 1.60 |
| 3 | A22 | 50c on 10c green | 1.60 | 1.60 |
| 4 | A20 | 75c on 15c sl grn | 2.75 | 2.40 |
| 5 | A22 | 1p on 20c red brn | 1.60 | 1.60 |
| *a.* | | Double surcharge | 45.00 | 45.00 |
| *b.* | | Inverted surcharge | 45.00 | 45.00 |
| 6 | A22 | 1.25p on 25c blue | 4.50 | 2.40 |
| *a.* | | Double surcharge | 40.00 | 40.00 |
| 7 | A22 | 1.50p on 30c org | 2.75 | 2.00 |
| 8 | A22 | 1.50p on 30c red | 2.75 | 2.40 |
| 9 | A20 | 2.50p on 50c dl bl | 2.40 | 2.00 |
| *a.* | | Inverted surcharge | 35.00 | 35.00 |

Surcharged

| | | | | |
|---|---|---|---|---|
| 10 | A18 | 2p on 40c red & pale bl | 5.50 | 3.75 |
| *a.* | | Inverted surcharge | 27.50 | 27.50 |
| 11 | A18 | 3p on 60c vio & ultra | 8.00 | 6.75 |
| 12 | A18 | 5p on 1fr cl & ol grn | 10.00 | 7.50 |
| 13 | A18 | 10p on 2fr org & pale bl | 15.00 | 12.00 |
| *a.* | | Inverted surcharge | 50.00 | 50.00 |
| 14 | A18 | 25p on 5fr dk bl & buff | 22.50 | 19.00 |
| *a.* | | Inverted surcharge | 85.00 | 85.00 |
| | | *Nos. 1-14 (14)* | 82.55 | 66.60 |

Broken and missing letters and varieties of spacing are numerous in these surcharges.

For overprints see Nos. C1-C4.

### Stamps of France, 1923, (Pasteur) Surcharged "GRAND LIBAN" and New Values

| | | | | |
|---|---|---|---|---|
| 15 | A23 | 50c on 10c green | 3.50 | 1.10 |
| *a.* | | Inverted surcharge | 35.00 | 25.00 |
| 16 | A23 | 1.50p on 30c red | 4.50 | 2.25 |
| 17 | A23 | 2.50p on 50c blue | 3.75 | 1.10 |
| *a.* | | Inverted surcharge | 30.00 | 27.50 |
| | | *Nos. 15-17 (3)* | 11.75 | 4.45 |

### Commemorative Stamps of France, 1924, (Olympic Games) Surcharged "GRAND LIBAN" and New Values

| | | | | |
|---|---|---|---|---|
| 18 | A24 | 50c on 10c gray grn & yel grn | 32.50 | *32.50* |
| *a.* | | Inverted surcharge | 350.00 | |
| 19 | A25 | 1.25p on 25c rose & dk rose | 32.50 | *32.50* |
| *a.* | | Inverted surcharge | 350.00 | |
| 20 | A26 | 1.50p on 30c brn red & blk | 32.50 | *32.50* |
| *a.* | | Inverted surcharge | 350.00 | |
| 21 | A27 | 2.50p on 50c ultra & dk bl | 32.50 | *32.50* |
| *a.* | | Inverted surcharge | 350.00 | |
| | | *Nos. 18-21 (4)* | 130.00 | 130.00 |

Stamps of France, 1900-24, Surcharged

**1924-25**

| | | | | |
|---|---|---|---|---|
| 22 | A16 | 0.10p on 2c vio brn | 1.00 | .50 |
| 23 | A22 | 0.25p on 5c orange | 1.25 | .75 |
| 24 | A22 | 0.50p on 10c green | 2.00 | 1.40 |
| 25 | A20 | 0.75p on 15c gray grn | 1.75 | 1.10 |
| 26 | A22 | 1p on 20c red brn | 1.50 | .95 |
| 27 | A22 | 1.25p on 25c blue | 2.25 | 1.60 |
| 28 | A22 | 1.50p on 30c red | 2.00 | 1.25 |
| 29 | A22 | 1.50p on 30c orange | 62.50 | 57.50 |
| 30 | A22 | 2p on 35c vio ('25) | 2.25 | 1.60 |
| 31 | A20 | 3p on 60c lt vio ('25) | 3.00 | 2.10 |
| 32 | A20 | 4p on 85c ver | 3.50 | 2.50 |

Surcharged

| | | | | |
|---|---|---|---|---|
| 33 | A18 | 2p on 40c red & pale bl | 2.25 | 1.60 |
| *a.* | | 2nd line of Arabic reads "2 Piastre" (singular) | 2.50 | .50 |
| 34 | A18 | 2p on 45c grn & bl ('25) | 27.50 | 22.50 |
| 35 | A18 | 3p on 60c vio & ultra | 3.50 | 2.50 |
| 36 | A18 | 5p on 1fr cl & ol grn | 4.25 | 3.25 |
| 37 | A18 | 10p on 2fr org & pale bl | 9.75 | 8.50 |
| 38 | A18 | 25p on 5fr dk bl & buff | 15.00 | 13.50 |
| | | *Nos. 22-38 (17)* | 145.25 | 123.10 |

Last line of surcharge on No. 33 has four characters, with a 9-like character between the third and fourth in illustration. Last line on No. 33a is as illustrated.

The surcharge may be found inverted on most of Nos. 22-38, and double on some values.

For overprints see Nos. C5-C8.

### Stamps of France 1923-24 (Pasteur) Surcharged as Nos. 22-32

| | | | | |
|---|---|---|---|---|
| 39 | A23 | 0.50p on 10c green | 2.00 | .85 |
| *a.* | | Inverted surcharge | 35.00 | 25.00 |
| *b.* | | Double surcharge | 40.00 | 21.00 |
| 40 | A23 | 0.75p on 15c green | 2.25 | 1.40 |
| 41 | A23 | 1.50p on 30c red | 2.75 | 1.40 |
| *a.* | | Inverted surcharge | 35.00 | 25.00 |
| 42 | A23 | 2p on 45c red | 5.00 | 3.50 |
| *a.* | | Inverted surcharge | 35.00 | 21.00 |
| 43 | A23 | 2.50p on 50c blue | 2.00 | .95 |
| *a.* | | Inverted surcharge | 35.00 | 21.00 |
| *b.* | | Double surcharge | 40.00 | 21.00 |
| 44 | A23 | 4p on 75c blue | 5.00 | 3.50 |
| | | *Nos. 39-44 (6)* | 19.00 | 11.60 |

France Nos. 198 to 201 (Olympics) Surcharged as Nos. 22-32

| | | | | |
|---|---|---|---|---|
| 45 | A24 | 0.50p on 10c | 32.50 | *32.50* |
| 46 | A25 | 1.25p on 25c | 32.50 | *32.50* |
| 47 | A26 | 1.50p on 30c | 32.50 | *32.50* |
| 48 | A27 | 2.50p on 50c | 32.50 | *32.50* |
| | | *Nos. 45-48 (4)* | 130.00 | 130.00 |

France No. 219 (Ronsard) Surcharged

| | | | | |
|---|---|---|---|---|
| 49 | A28 | 4p on 75c bl, *bluish* | 3.50 | 3.50 |
| *a.* | | Inverted surcharge | 65.00 | 50.00 |

Cedar of Lebanon — A1

Crusader Castle, Tripoli — A3

View of Beirut — A2

Designs: 50c, Crusader Castle, Tripoli. 75c, Beit-ed-Din Palace. 1p, Temple of Jupiter, Baalbek. 1.25p, Mouktara Palace. 1.50p, Harbor of Tyre. 2p, View of Zahle. 2.50p, Ruins at Baalbek. 3p, Square at Deir-el-Kamar. 5p, Castle at Sidon. 25p, Square at Beirut.

**1925 Litho. *Perf. 12½, 13½***

| | | | | |
|---|---|---|---|---|
| 50 | A1 | 0.10p dark violet | .50 | .25 |

**Photo.**

| | | | | |
|---|---|---|---|---|
| 51 | A2 | 0.25p olive black | .95 | .25 |
| 52 | A2 | 0.50p yellow grn | .75 | .25 |
| 53 | A2 | 0.75p brn orange | .75 | .25 |
| 54 | A2 | 1p magenta | 2.00 | .80 |
| 55 | A2 | 1.25p deep green | 2.25 | 1.40 |
| 56 | A2 | 1.50p rose red | 1.00 | .25 |
| 57 | A2 | 2p dark brown | 1.25 | .25 |
| 58 | A2 | 2.50p peacock bl | 2.00 | .80 |
| 59 | A2 | 3p orange brn | 2.75 | 1.10 |
| 60 | A2 | 5p violet | 3.00 | 1.40 |
| 61 | A3 | 10p violet brn | 7.50 | 2.10 |
| 62 | A2 | 25p ultramarine | 20.00 | 12.00 |
| | | *Nos. 50-62 (13)* | 44.70 | 21.10 |

For surcharges and overprints see Nos. 63-107, B1-B12, C9-C38, CB1-CB4.



Stamps of 1925 with Bars and Surcharged

**1926**

| | | | | |
|---|---|---|---|---|
| 63 | A2 | 3.50p on 0.75p brn org | 1.50 | 1.50 |
| 64 | A2 | 4p on 0.25p ol blk | 2.50 | 2.50 |
| 65 | A2 | 6p on 2.50p pck bl | 2.00 | 2.00 |
| 66 | A2 | 12p on 1.25p dp grn | 1.40 | 1.40 |
| 67 | A2 | 20p on 1.25p dp grn | 6.75 | 6.75 |

Stamps of 1925 with Bars and Surcharged

| | | | | |
|---|---|---|---|---|
| 68 | A2 | 4.50p on 0.75p brn org | 2.75 | 2.75 |
| 69 | A2 | 7.50p on 2.50p pck bl | 2.75 | 2.75 |
| 70 | A2 | 15p on 25p ultra | 2.75 | 2.75 |
| | | *Nos. 63-70 (8)* | 22.40 | 22.40 |

No. 51 with Bars and Surcharged

**1927**

| | | | | |
|---|---|---|---|---|
| 71 | A2 | 4p on 0.25p ol blk | 2.50 | 2.50 |

### Issues of Republic under French Mandate

Stamps of 1925 Issue Overprinted in Black or Red

**1927**

| | | | | |
|---|---|---|---|---|
| 72 | A1 | 0.10p dark vio (R) | .55 | .25 |
| *a.* | | Black overprint | 35.00 | |
| 73 | A2 | 0.50p yellow grn | .55 | .25 |
| 74 | A2 | 1p magenta | .55 | .25 |
| 75 | A2 | 1.50p rose red | .80 | .60 |
| 76 | A2 | 2p dark brown | 1.10 | .90 |
| 77 | A2 | 3p orange brn | .90 | .25 |
| 78 | A2 | 5p violet | 1.75 | 1.00 |
| 79 | A3 | 10p violet brn | 2.25 | 1.10 |
| 80 | A2 | 25p ultramarine | 19.00 | 8.00 |
| | | *Nos. 72-80 (9)* | 27.45 | 12.60 |

On Nos. 72 and 79 the overprint is set in two lines. On all stamps the double bar obliterates GRAND LIBAN.

### Same Overprint on Provisional Issues of 1926-27

15 PIASTERS ON 25 PIASTERS

TYPE I — "République Libanaise" at foot of stamp.

TYPE II — "République Libanaise" near top of stamp.

| | | | | |
|---|---|---|---|---|
| 81 | A2 | 4p on 0.25p ol blk | .75 | .25 |
| 82 | A2 | 4.50p on 0.75p brn org | .85 | .25 |
| 83 | A2 | 7.50p on 2.50p pck bl | 1.10 | .25 |

84 A2 15p on 25p ultra (I) 7.50 5.25
a. Type II 11.50 8.00
*Nos. 81-84 (4)* 10.20 6.00

Most of Nos. 72-84 are known with overprint double, inverted or on back as well as face.

Stamps of 1927 Overprinted in Black or Red

**1928**
86 A1 0.10p dark vio (R) .80 .60
a. French overprint omitted, on #50
87 A2 0.50p yel grn (Bk) 2.00 1.50
a. Arabic overprint inverted 35.00 25.00
88 A2 1p magenta (Bk) 1.00 .70
a. Inverted overprint 35.00 25.00
89 A2 1.50p rose red (Bk) 2.00 1.50
90 A2 2p dk brn (R) 2.75 2.10
90A A2 2p dk brn (Bk+R) 110.00 110.00
91 A2 3p org brn (Bk) 1.90 1.40
92 A2 5p violet (Bk+R) 3.50 2.75
93 A2 5p violet (R) 3.00 2.40
a. French ovpt. below Arabic 30.00 14.00
94 A3 10p vio brn (Bk) 5.00 4.25
a. Double overprint 100.00 90.00
b. Double overprint inverted
c. Inverted overprint 100.00 70.00
95 A2 25p ultra (Bk+R) 11.50 10.50
95A A2 25p ultra (R) 13.00 13.00
*Nos. 86-95A (12)* 156.45 150.70

On all stamps the double bar with Arabic overprint obliterates Arabic inscription.

**Same Overprint on Nos. 81-84**
96 A2 4p on 0.25p (Bk+R) 2.00 1.50
97 A2 4.50p on 0.75p (Bk) 2.00 1.50
98 A2 7.50p on 2.50p (Bk+R) 4.50 3.50
99 A2 7.50p on 2.50p (R) 7.00 6.00
100 A2 15p on 25p (II) (Bk+R) 11.00 9.50
a. Arabic overprint inverted
101 A2 15p on 25p (I) (R) 14.00 12.00
*Nos. 96-101 (6)* 40.50 34.00

The new values are surcharged in black. The initials in ( ) refer to the colors of the overprints.

Stamps of 1925 Srchd. in Red or Black

**1928-29** *Perf. 13½*
102 A2 50c on 0.75p brn org (Bk) ('29) 1.50 1.90
103 A2 2p on 1.25p dp grn 1.50 1.90
104 A2 4p on 0.25p ol blk 1.50 1.90
a. Double surcharge 35.00 25.00
105 A2 7.50p on 2.50p pck bl 2.50 2.75
a. Double surcharge 40.00 25.00
b. Inverted surcharge 55.00 25.00
106 A2 15p on 25p ultra 22.50 10.00
*Nos. 102-106 (5)* 29.50 18.45

On Nos. 103, 104 and 105 the surcharged numerals are 3¼mm high, and have thick strokes.

No. 86 Surcharged in Red

**1928**
107 A1 5c on 0.10p dk vio 1.75 .30

Silkworm, Cocoon and Moth — A4

**1930, Feb. 11** **Typo.** *Perf. 11*
108 A4 4p black brown 15.00 15.00
109 A4 4½p vermilion 15.00 15.00
110 A4 7½p dark blue 15.00 15.00
111 A4 10p dk violet 15.00 15.00
112 A4 15p dark green 15.00 15.00
113 A4 25p claret 15.00 15.00
*Nos. 108-113 (6)* 90.00 90.00

Sericultural Congress, Beirut. Presentation imperfs exist.

Pigeon Rocks, Ras Beirut — A5

View of Bickfaya A8

Beit-ed-Din Palace A10

Crusader Castle, Tripoli A11

Ruins of Venus Temple, Baalbek A12

Ancient Bridge, Dog River A13

Belfort Castle A14

Afka Falls — A19

20c, Cedars of Lebanon. 25c, Ruins of Bacchus Temple, Baalbek. 1p, Crusader Castle, Sidon Harbor. 5p, Arcade of Beit-ed-Din Palace. 6p, Tyre Harbor. 7.50p, Ruins of Sun Temple, Baalbek. 10p, View of Hasbeya. 25p, Government House, Beirut. 50p, View of Deir-el-Kamar. 75c, 100p, Ruins at Baalbek.

**1930-35** **Litho.** *Perf. 12½, 13½*
114 A5 0.10p brn org .60 .25
115 A5 0.20p yellow brn .60 .25
116 A5 0.25p deep blue .75 .45

**Photo.**
117 A8 0.50p orange brn 3.00 1.50
118 A11 0.75p ol brn ('32) 1.50 1.00
119 A8 1p deep green 1.75 1.25
120 A8 1p brn vio ('35) 3.00 1.00
121 A10 1.50p violet brn 3.25 1.90
122 A10 1.50p dp grn ('32) 3.50 1.50
123 A11 2p Prussian bl 4.50 1.60
124 A12 3p black brown 4.50 1.60
125 A13 4p orange brn 4.75 1.60
126 A14 4.50p carmine 5.00 1.60
127 A13 5p greenish blk 3.00 1.50
128 A13 6p brn violet 5.25 2.75
129 A10 7.50p deep blue 5.00 1.60
130 A10 10p dk ol grn 9.00 1.60
131 A19 15p blk violet 11.50 3.50
132 A19 25p blue green 20.00 6.00
133 A8 50p apple grn 60.00 15.00
134 A11 100p black 65.00 19.00
*Nos. 114-134 (21)* 215.45 66.45

See Nos. 135, 144, 152-155. For surcharges see Nos. 147-149, 161, 173-174.

**Pigeon Rocks Type of 1930-35 Redrawn**

**1934** **Litho.** *Perf. 12½x12*
135 A5 0.10p dull orange 6.75 4.00

Lines in rocks and water more distinct. Printer's name "Hélio Vaugirard, Paris," in larger letters.

Cedar of Lebanon A23

President Emile Eddé A24

Dog River Panorama A25

**1937-40** **Typo.** *Perf. 14x13½*
137 A23 0.10p rose car .50 .25
137A A23 0.20p aqua ('40) .50 .25
137B A23 0.25p pale rose lilac ('40) .50 .25
138 A23 0.50p magenta .50 .25
138A A23 0.75p brown ('40) .50 .25

**Engr.**
*Perf. 13*
139 A24 3p dk violet 4.00 .75
140 A24 4p black brown .75 .25
141 A24 4.50p carmine 1.00 .25
142 A25 10p brn carmine 2.25 .25
142A A25 12½p dp ultra ('40) 1.00 .25
143 A25 15p dk grn ('38) 4.00 .75
143A A25 20p chestnut ('40) 1.00 .25
143B A25 25p crimson ('40) 1.50 .60
143C A25 50p dk vio ('40) 5.00 1.60
143D A25 100p sepia ('40) 3.50 2.25
*Nos. 137-143D (15)* 26.50 8.45

Nos. 137A, 137B, 138A, 142A, 143A, 143B, 143C, and 143D exist imperforate.
For surcharges see Nos. 145-146A, 150-151, 160, 162, 175-176.

View of Bickfaya A26

**Type A8 Redrawn**

**1935 (?)** **Photo.** *Perf. 13½*
144 A26 0.50p orange brown 17.50 9.75

Arabic inscriptions more condensed.

Stamps of 1930-37 Surcharged in Black or Red

**1937-42** *Perf. 13, 13½*
145 A24 2p on 3p dk vio 1.50 1.50
146 A24 2½p on 4p blk brn 1.50 1.50
146A A24 2½p on 4p black brown (R) ('42) 1.50 1.50
147 A10 6p on 7.50p dp bl (R) 4.00 4.00

**Stamps of 1930-35 and Type of 1937-40 Surcharged in Black or Red**

*Perf. 13½, 13*
148 A8 7.50p on 50p ap grn 2.50 2.50
149 A11 7.50p on 100p blk (R) 2.50 2.50
150 A25 12.50p on 7.50p dk bl (R) 5.00 5.00

Type of 1937-40 Srchd. in Red

**1939** **Engr.** *Perf. 13*
151 A25 12½p on 7.50p dk bl 2.00 2.00
*Nos. 145-151 (8)* 20.50 20.50

**Type of 1930-35 Redrawn**
**Imprint: "Beiteddine-Imp.-Catholique-Beyrouth-Liban."**

**1939** **Litho.** *Perf. 11½*
152 A10 1p dk slate grn 2.25 .25
153 A10 1.50p brn violet 2.25 .75
154 A10 7.50p carmine lake 2.25 1.10
*Nos. 152-154 (3)* 6.75 2.10

**Bridge Type of 1930-35**
**Imprint: "Degorce" instead of "Hélio Vaugirard"**

**1940** **Engr.** *Perf. 13*
155 A13 5p grnsh blue 1.50 .25

Exists imperforate.

**Independent Republic**

Amir Beshir Shehab — A27

**1942, Sept. 18** **Litho.** *Perf. 11½*
156 A27 0.50p emerald 3.00 3.00
157 A27 1.50p sepia 3.00 3.00
158 A27 6p rose pink 3.00 3.00
159 A27 15p dull blue 3.00 3.00
*Nos. 156-159 (4)* 12.00 12.00

1st anniv. of the Proclamation of Independence, Nov. 26, 1941. See Nos. C80-C81.
Nos. 156-159 exist imperforate.

Nos. 140, 154 and 142A Surcharged in Blue, Green or Black

**1943** *Perf. 13, 11½*
160 A24 2p on 4p (Bl) 6.00 *6.25*
161 A10 6p on 7.50p (G) 2.60 .85
162 A25 10p on 12½p (Bk) 2.60 .85
*Nos. 160-162 (3)* 11.20 7.95

The surcharge is arranged differently on each value.

Parliament Building A28

Government House, Beirut — A29

**1943 Litho. Perf. 11½**

| | | | | |
|---|---|---|---|---|
| 163 | A28 | 25p salmon rose | 12.00 | 5.00 |
| 164 | A29 | 50p bluish green | 12.00 | 5.00 |
| 165 | A28 | 150p light ultra | 12.00 | 5.00 |
| 166 | A29 | 200p dull vio brn | 12.00 | 5.00 |
| | | *Nos. 163-166 (4)* | 48.00 | 20.00 |
| | | *Nos. 163-166,C82-C87 (10)* | 137.25 | 93.00 |

2nd anniv. of Proclamation of Independence. Nos. 163-166 exist imperforate. For overprints see Nos. 169-172.

Quarantine Station, Beirut A30

**Black Overprint**

**1943, July 8 Photo.**

| | | | | |
|---|---|---|---|---|
| 167 | A30 | 10p cerise | 5.50 | 3.50 |
| 168 | A30 | 20p light blue | 5.50 | 3.50 |
| | | *Nos. 167-168,C88-C90 (5)* | 25.00 | 17.75 |

Arab Medical Congress, Beirut.

**Nos. 163 to 166 Overprinted in Blue, Violet, Red or Black**

**1944**

| | | | | |
|---|---|---|---|---|
| 169 | A28 | 25p sal rose (Bl) | 15.00 | 15.00 |
| 170 | A29 | 50p bluish grn (V) | 15.00 | 15.00 |
| 171 | A28 | 150p lt ultra (R) | 15.00 | 15.00 |
| 172 | A29 | 200p dull vio brn (Bk) | 17.50 | 15.00 |
| | | *Nos. 169-172,C91-C96 (10)* | 218.25 | 208.25 |

Return to office of the president and his ministers, Nov. 22, 1943.

**Type of 1930 and No. 142A Surcharged in Violet, Black or Carmine**

**1945 Unwmk. Engr. Perf. 13**

| | | | | |
|---|---|---|---|---|
| 173 | A13 | 2p on 5p dk bl grn (V) | 1.25 | .25 |
| 174 | A13 | 3p on 5p dk bl grn (Bk) | 1.25 | .25 |
| 175 | A25 | 6p on 12½p deep ultra (Bk) | 1.50 | .35 |
| 176 | A25 | 7½p on 12½p deep ultra (C) | 2.50 | .95 |
| | | *Nos. 173-176 (4)* | 6.50 | 1.80 |

Trees at bottom on Nos. 175 and 176.

**Catalogue values for unused stamps in this section, from this point to the end of the section, are for Never Hinged items.**

Citadel of Jubayl (Byblos) A31

Crusader Castle, Tripoli A32

**1945 Litho. Perf. 11½**

| | | | | |
|---|---|---|---|---|
| 177 | A31 | 15p violet brown | 4.50 | 3.50 |
| 178 | A31 | 20p deep green | 4.50 | 3.50 |
| 179 | A32 | 25p deep blue | 4.50 | 3.50 |
| 180 | A32 | 50p dp carmine | 7.50 | 4.00 |
| | | *Nos. 177-180,C97-C100 (8)* | 72.00 | 35.10 |

See Nos. 229-233.

Soldiers and Flag of Lebanon A33

**1946 Litho.**

**Stripes of Flag in Red Orange**

| | | | | |
|---|---|---|---|---|
| 181 | A33 | 7.50p red & pale lil | 1.40 | .25 |
| 182 | A33 | 10p lil & pale lilac | 2.40 | .25 |
| 183 | A33 | 12.50p choc & yel grn | 3.25 | .25 |
| 184 | A33 | 15p sepia & pink | 4.00 | .25 |
| 185 | A33 | 20p ultra & pink | 3.50 | .30 |
| 186 | A33 | 25p dk grn & yel grn | 5.50 | .35 |
| 187 | A33 | 50p dk bl & pale bl | 12.00 | 1.25 |
| 188 | A33 | 100p gray blk & pale bl | 16.00 | 2.50 |
| | | *Nos. 181-188 (8)* | 48.05 | 5.40 |

Type of 1946 Ovptd. in Red

**1946, May 8**

**Stripes of Flag in Red**

| | | | | |
|---|---|---|---|---|
| 189 | A33 | 7.50p choc & pink | 1.50 | .25 |
| 190 | A33 | 10p dk vio & pink | 1.75 | .25 |
| 191 | A33 | 12.50p brn red & pale lilac | 2.00 | .45 |
| 192 | A33 | 15p lt grn & yel grn | 3.25 | .65 |
| 193 | A33 | 20p sl grn & yel grn | 3.00 | .70 |
| 194 | A33 | 25p sl bl & pale bl | 5.00 | .95 |
| 195 | A33 | 50p ultra & gray | 7.50 | .90 |
| 196 | A33 | 100p blk & pale bl | 11.00 | 2.25 |
| | | *Nos. 189-196 (8)* | 35.00 | 6.40 |

See Nos. C101-C106, note after No. C106.

Cedar of Lebanon — A34

Night Herons over Mt. Sanin A35

**1946-47 Unwmk. Perf. 10½**

| | | | | |
|---|---|---|---|---|
| 197 | A34 | 0.50p red brn ('47) | .80 | .25 |
| 198 | A34 | 1p purple ('47) | 1.20 | .25 |
| 199 | A34 | 2.50p violet | 2.75 | .25 |
| 200 | A34 | 5p red | 3.25 | .25 |
| 201 | A34 | 6p gray ('47) | 4.00 | .25 |

***Perf. 11½***

| | | | | |
|---|---|---|---|---|
| 202 | A35 | 12.50p deep car | 24.00 | .25 |
| | | *Nos. 197-202,C107-C110 (10)* | 113.50 | 10.85 |

For surcharge see No. 246.

A36

Crusader Castle, Tripoli A37

**1947 Litho. Perf. 14x13½**

| | | | | |
|---|---|---|---|---|
| 203 | A36 | 0.50p dark brown | 1.50 | .25 |
| 204 | A36 | 2.50p bright green | 2.00 | .25 |
| 205 | A36 | 5p car rose | 4.00 | .25 |

***Perf. 11½***

| | | | | |
|---|---|---|---|---|
| 206 | A37 | 12.50p rose pink | 10.50 | .50 |
| 207 | A37 | 25p ultramarine | 10.50 | .55 |
| 208 | A37 | 50p turq green | 30.00 | 1.10 |
| 209 | A37 | 100p violet | 40.00 | 5.75 |
| | | *Nos. 203-209 (7)* | 98.50 | 8.65 |

A38

Zubaida Aqueduct A39

**1948 Perf. 14x13½**

| | | | | |
|---|---|---|---|---|
| 210 | A38 | 0.50p blue | .65 | .25 |
| 211 | A38 | 1p yel brown | .75 | .25 |
| 212 | A38 | 2.50p rose violet | .95 | .25 |
| 213 | A38 | 3p emerald | 2.40 | .25 |
| 214 | A38 | 5p crimson | 2.75 | .25 |

***Perf. 11½***

| | | | | |
|---|---|---|---|---|
| 215 | A39 | 7.50p rose red | 6.00 | .25 |
| 216 | A39 | 10p dl violet | 4.25 | .25 |
| 217 | A39 | 12.50p blue | 9.00 | .40 |
| 218 | A39 | 25p blue vio | 15.00 | .90 |
| 219 | A39 | 50p green | 27.50 | 4.75 |
| | | *Nos. 210-219 (10)* | 69.25 | 7.80 |

See Nos. 227A-228A, 234-237. For surcharge see No. 245.

Europa A40

Avicenna — A41

**1948 Litho.**

| | | | | |
|---|---|---|---|---|
| 220 | A40 | 10p dk red & org red | 4.75 | 1.40 |
| 221 | A40 | 12.50p pur & rose | 5.50 | 1.90 |
| 222 | A40 | 25p ol grn & pale green | 6.50 | 1.50 |
| 223 | A41 | 30p org brn & buff | 7.25 | 1.50 |
| 224 | A41 | 40p Prus grn & buff | 10.50 | 1.50 |
| | | *Nos. 220-224 (5)* | 34.50 | 7.80 |

UNESCO. Nos. 220 to 224 exist imperforate (see note after No. C145).

Camel Post Rider A42

**1949, Aug. 16 Unwmk. Perf. 11½**

| | | | | |
|---|---|---|---|---|
| 225 | A42 | 5p violet | 1.60 | .40 |
| 226 | A42 | 7.50p red | 2.40 | .60 |
| 227 | A42 | 12.50p blue | 3.25 | 1.00 |
| | | *Nos. 225-227,C148-C149 (5)* | 27.25 | 10.50 |

UPU, 75th anniv. See note after No. C149.

**Cedar Type of 1948 Redrawn and Jubayl Type of 1945**

Original

Redrawn

**1949 Litho. Perf. 14x13½**

| | | | | |
|---|---|---|---|---|
| 227A | A38 | 0.50p blue | 2.75 | .25 |
| 228 | A38 | 1p red orange | 2.75 | .25 |
| 228A | A38 | 2.50p rose lilac | 13.00 | .35 |

***Perf. 11½***

| | | | | |
|---|---|---|---|---|
| 229 | A31 | 7.50p rose red | 4.00 | .25 |
| 230 | A31 | 10p violet brn | 7.00 | .25 |
| 231 | A31 | 12.50p deep blue | 14.00 | .25 |
| 232 | A31 | 25p violet | 25.00 | .40 |
| 233 | A31 | 50p green | 47.50 | 1.90 |
| | | *Nos. 227A-233 (8)* | 116.00 | 3.90 |

On No. 227A in left numeral tablet, top of "P" stands higher than flag of the 1¼mm high "5." On No. 210, tops of "P" and the 2mm "5" are on same line.

On No. 228, "1 P." is smaller than on No. 211, and has no line below "P."

On No. 228A, the "O" does not touch tablet frame; on No. 212, it does. No. 228A exists on gray paper.

**Cedar Type of 1948 Redrawn and**

Ancient Bridge across Dog River — A43

**1950 Litho. Perf. 14x13½**

| | | | | |
|---|---|---|---|---|
| 234 | A38 | 0.50p rose red | .40 | .25 |
| 235 | A38 | 1p salmon | 1.00 | .25 |
| 236 | A38 | 2.50p violet | 1.50 | .25 |
| 237 | A38 | 5p claret | 3.50 | .25 |

Cedar slightly altered and mountains eliminated.

***Perf. 11½***

| | | | | |
|---|---|---|---|---|
| 238 | A43 | 7.50p rose red | 3.50 | .25 |
| 239 | A43 | 10p rose vio | 5.00 | .25 |
| 240 | A43 | 12.50p light blue | 11.00 | .25 |
| 241 | A43 | 25p deep blue | 15.00 | 1.25 |
| 242 | A43 | 50p emerald | 35.00 | 5.00 |
| | | *Nos. 234-242 (9)* | 75.90 | 8.00 |

See Nos. 251-255, 310-312.

Flags and Building A44

**1950, Aug. 8 Perf. 11½**

| | | | | |
|---|---|---|---|---|
| 243 | A44 | 7.50p gray | 2.00 | .25 |
| 244 | A44 | 12.50p lilac rose | 2.00 | .25 |
| | | *Nos. 243-244,C150-C153 (6)* | 15.25 | 4.20 |

Conf. of Emigrants, 1950. See note after No. C153.

**Nos. 213 and 201 Surcharged with New Value and Bars in Carmine**

**1950 Unwmk. Perf. 14x13½, 10½**

| | | | | |
|---|---|---|---|---|
| 245 | A38 | 1p on 3p emerald | 1.25 | .25 |
| 246 | A34 | 2.50p on 6p gray | 1.25 | .25 |

Cedar — A45

**1951 Litho. *Perf. 14x13½***

| | | | | |
|---|---|---|---|---|
| **247** A45 | 0.50p | rose red | .40 | .25 |
| **248** A45 | 1p | light brown | .80 | .25 |
| **249** A45 | 2.50p | slate gray | 3.75 | .25 |
| **250** A45 | 5p | rose lake | 4.50 | .25 |

### Bridge Type of 1950, Redrawn

**Typo. *Perf. 11½***

| | | | | |
|---|---|---|---|---|
| **251** A43 | 7.50p | red | 4.50 | .25 |
| **252** A43 | 10p | dl rose vio | 6.00 | .25 |
| **253** A43 | 12.50p | blue | 11.00 | .25 |
| **254** A43 | 25p | dull blue | 20.00 | .50 |
| **255** A43 | 50p | green | 40.00 | 3.75 |
| | | *Nos. 247-255 (9)* | 90.95 | 6.00 |

Nos. 238-242 are lithographed from a fine-screen halftone; "P" in the denomination has serifs. Nos. 251-255 are typographed and much coarser; "P" without serifs.

Cedar — A46

Ruins at Baalbek A47

Design: 50p, 100p, Beaufort Castle.

**1952 Litho. *Perf. 14x13½***

| | | | | |
|---|---|---|---|---|
| **256** A46 | 0.50p | emerald | 1.00 | .25 |
| **257** A46 | 1p | orange brn | 1.10 | .25 |
| **258** A46 | 2.50p | grnsh blue | 2.50 | .25 |
| **259** A46 | 5p | car rose | 3.75 | .25 |

***Perf. 11½***

| | | | | |
|---|---|---|---|---|
| **260** A47 | 7.50p | red | 4.50 | .25 |
| **261** A47 | 10p | brt violet | 6.25 | .70 |
| **262** A47 | 12.50p | blue | 7.00 | .70 |
| **263** A47 | 25p | violet bl | 7.75 | 1.40 |
| **264** A47 | 50p | dk blue grn | 21.00 | 2.75 |
| **265** A47 | 100p | chocolate | 42.50 | 7.50 |
| | | *Nos. 256-265 (10)* | 97.35 | 14.30 |

Cedar of Lebanon A48

Postal Administration Building A49

**1953 *Perf. 14x13½***

| | | | | |
|---|---|---|---|---|
| **266** A48 | 0.50p | blue | .85 | .25 |
| **267** A48 | 1p | rose lake | 1.10 | .25 |
| **268** A48 | 2.50p | lilac | 1.25 | .25 |
| **269** A48 | 5p | emerald | 2.25 | .25 |

***Perf. 11½***

| | | | | |
|---|---|---|---|---|
| **270** A49 | 7.50p | car rose | 3.25 | .25 |
| **271** A49 | 10p | dp yel grn | 4.50 | .65 |
| **272** A49 | 12.50p | aquamarine | 6.25 | .75 |
| **273** A49 | 25p | ultra | 8.25 | 1.40 |
| **274** A49 | 50p | violet brn | 16.50 | 3.00 |
| | | *Nos. 266-274 (9)* | 44.20 | 7.05 |

See No. 306.

A50

Gallery, Beit-ed-Din Palace — A51

**1954 *Perf. 14x13½***

| | | | | |
|---|---|---|---|---|
| **275** A50 | 0.50p | blue | .30 | .25 |
| **276** A50 | 1p | dp orange | .50 | .25 |
| **277** A50 | 2.50p | purple | .80 | .25 |
| **278** A50 | 5p | blue green | 1.75 | .25 |

***Perf. 11½***

| | | | | |
|---|---|---|---|---|
| **279** A51 | 7.50p | dp carmine | 2.75 | .25 |
| **280** A51 | 10p | dl ol grn | 4.00 | .35 |
| **281** A51 | 12.50p | blue | 7.00 | 1.00 |
| **282** A51 | 25p | vio blue | 9.00 | 2.75 |
| **283** A51 | 50p | aqua | 17.00 | 5.00 |
| **284** A51 | 100p | black brn | 37.50 | 9.00 |
| | | *Nos. 275-284 (10)* | 80.60 | 19.35 |

### Arab Postal Union Issue

Globe — A52

**1955, Jan. 1 Litho. *Perf. 13½x13***

| | | | | |
|---|---|---|---|---|
| **285** A52 | 12.50p | blue green | 1.25 | .25 |
| **286** A52 | 25p | violet | 1.75 | .25 |
| | | *Nos. 285-286,C197 (3)* | 4.50 | .75 |

Founding of the APU, July 1, 1954.

Cedar A53

Jeita Cave A54

**1955 *Perf. 14x13½***

| | | | | |
|---|---|---|---|---|
| **287** A53 | 0.50p | violet blue | .50 | .25 |
| **288** A53 | 1p | vermilion | .60 | .25 |
| **289** A53 | 2.50p | purple | .90 | .25 |
| **290** A53 | 5p | emerald | 1.10 | .25 |

***Perf. 11½***

| | | | | |
|---|---|---|---|---|
| **291** A54 | 7.50p | deep orange | 1.75 | .25 |
| **292** A54 | 10p | yellow grn | 2.00 | .25 |
| **293** A54 | 12.50p | blue | 2.50 | .25 |
| **294** A54 | 25p | dp vio blue | 4.50 | .25 |
| **295** A54 | 50p | dk gray grn | 8.50 | .45 |
| | | *Nos. 287-295 (9)* | 22.35 | 2.45 |

See Nos. 308-309, 315-318, 341-343A. For overprint see No. 351.

Cedar of Lebanon A55

Globe and Columns A56

**1955 Unwmk. *Perf. 13x13½***

| | | | | |
|---|---|---|---|---|
| **296** A55 | 0.50p | dark blue | .25 | .25 |
| **297** A55 | 1p | deep orange | .50 | .25 |
| **298** A55 | 2.50p | deep violet | .65 | .25 |
| **299** A55 | 5p | green | 1.25 | .25 |
| **300** A56 | 7.50p | yel org & cop red | 1.50 | .25 |
| **301** A56 | 10p | emer & sal | 1.75 | .25 |
| **302** A56 | 12.50p | ultra & bl grn | 2.00 | .25 |
| **303** A56 | 25p | dp ultra & brt pink | 3.50 | .25 |
| **304** A56 | 50p | dk grn & lt bl | 4.50 | .25 |
| **305** A56 | 100p | dk brn & sal | 7.00 | .50 |
| | | *Nos. 296-305 (10)* | 22.90 | 2.75 |

For surcharge see No. 333.

### Cedar Type of 1953 Redrawn

**1956 Litho. *Perf. 13x13½***

| | | | | |
|---|---|---|---|---|
| **306** A48 | 2.50p | violet | 10.00 | 1.75 |

No. 306 measures 17x20½mm. The "2p.50" is in Roman (upright) type face.

### Cedar Type of 1955 Redrawn & Bridge Type of 1950, Second Redrawing

**1957 Litho. *Perf. 13x13½***

| | | | | |
|---|---|---|---|---|
| **308** A53 | 0.50p | light ultra | .45 | .25 |
| **309** A53 | 2.50p | claret | .90 | .25 |

***Perf. 11½***

| | | | | |
|---|---|---|---|---|
| **310** A43 | 7.50p | vermilion | 2.00 | .40 |
| **311** A43 | 10p | brn orange | 2.75 | .50 |
| **312** A43 | 12.50p | blue | 3.50 | .75 |
| | | *Nos. 308-312 (5)* | 9.60 | 2.15 |

On Nos. 308 and 309 numerals are slanted and clouds slightly changed.

Nos. 310-312 inscribed "Liban" instead of "Republique Libanaise," and different Arabic characters.

Runners — A57

**1957, Sept. 12 Litho. *Perf. 13***

| | | | | |
|---|---|---|---|---|
| **313** A57 | 2.50p | shown | 1.50 | .25 |
| **314** A57 | 12.50p | Soccer players | 2.25 | .35 |
| | | *Nos. 313-314,C243-C244 (4)* | 11.00 | 4.35 |

Second Pan-Arab Games, Beirut.

A souvenir sheet of 4 contains Nos. 313-314, C243-C244. Value, $130.

### Cedar Type of 1955 Redrawn and

Workers — A58

Ancient Potter — A59

**1957 Unwmk. *Perf. 13x13½***

| | | | | |
|---|---|---|---|---|
| **315** A53 | 0.50p | light blue | .25 | .25 |
| **316** A53 | 1p | light brown | .50 | .25 |
| **317** A53 | 2.50p | bright vio | .50 | .25 |
| **318** A53 | 5p | light green | .80 | .25 |

***Perf. 11½, 13½x13 (A59)***

| | | | | |
|---|---|---|---|---|
| **319** A58 | 7.50p | crim rose | 1.25 | .25 |
| **320** A58 | 10p | dull red brn | 1.25 | .25 |
| **321** A58 | 12.50p | bright blue | 1.50 | .25 |
| **322** A59 | 25p | dull blue | 5.00 | .25 |
| **323** A59 | 50p | yellow grn | 6.00 | .30 |
| **324** A59 | 100p | sepia | 7.00 | .75 |
| | | *Nos. 315-324 (10)* | 24.05 | 3.05 |

The word "piaster" is omitted on No. 315; on Nos. 316 and 318 there is a line below "P"; on No. 317 there is a period between "2" and "50."

Nos. 315-318 are 16mm wide and have three shading lines above tip of cedar. See No. 343A and footnote.

For surcharges see Nos. 334-335, 339.

Cedar of Lebanon A60

Soldier and Flag A61

**1958 Litho. *Perf. 13***

| | | | | |
|---|---|---|---|---|
| **325** A60 | 0.50p | blue | .50 | .25 |
| **326** A60 | 1p | dull orange | .75 | .25 |
| **327** A60 | 2.50p | violet | 1.00 | .25 |
| **328** A60 | 5p | yellow grn | 1.50 | .25 |
| **329** A61 | 12.50p | bright blue | 2.25 | .25 |
| **330** A61 | 25p | dark blue | 2.50 | .25 |
| **331** A61 | 50p | orange brn | 2.75 | .25 |
| **332** A61 | 100p | black brn | 4.00 | .40 |
| | | *Nos. 325-332 (8)* | 15.25 | 2.15 |

For surcharges see Nos. 336-338.

No. 304 Surcharged

**1959, Sept. 1**

| | | | | |
|---|---|---|---|---|
| **333** A56 | 30p | on 50p dk grn & lt bl | 2.00 | .25 |

Arab Lawyers Congress. See No. C265.

No. 323 Surcharged

**1959 *Perf. 13½x13***

| | | | | |
|---|---|---|---|---|
| **334** A59 | 30p | on 50p yel grn | 1.75 | .25 |
| **335** A59 | 40p | on 50p yel grn | 2.50 | .35 |

Convention of the Assoc. of Arab Emigrants in the United States.

### Nos. 329-330 and 323 Surcharged with New Value and Bars

**1959 *Perf. 13, 13½x13***

| | | | | |
|---|---|---|---|---|
| **336** A61 | 7.50p | on 12.50p brt bl | 1.25 | .25 |
| **337** A61 | 10p | on 12.50p brt bl | 1.50 | .25 |
| **338** A61 | 15p | on 25p dark blue | 1.60 | .25 |
| **339** A59 | 40p | on 50p yel grn | 2.25 | .25 |
| | | *Nos. 336-339,C271 (5)* | 9.60 | 1.30 |

Arab League Center, Cairo A62

***Perf. 13x13½***

**1960, May 23 Unwmk. Litho.**

| | | | | |
|---|---|---|---|---|
| **340** A62 | 15p | lt blue green | 1.00 | .25 |

Opening of the Arab League Center and the Arab Postal Museum in Cairo.

For overprint see No. 352.

### Cedar Type of 1955, Second Redrawing

**1960 Litho. *Perf. 13x13½***

| | | | | |
|---|---|---|---|---|
| **341** A53 | 0.50p | light violet | 1.25 | .25 |
| **342** A53 | 1p | rose claret | 1.25 | .25 |
| **343** A53 | 2.50p | ultramarine | 1.50 | .25 |
| **343A** A53 | 5p | light green | 1.75 | .25 |
| | | *Nos. 341-343A (4)* | 5.75 | 1.00 |

Nos. 341-343A are 16½-17mm wide and have two shading lines above cedar. In other details they resemble the redrawn A53 type of 1957 (Nos. 315-318).

President Fuad Chehab — A63

**1960 Photo. *Perf. 13½***

| | | | | | |
|---|---|---|---|---|---|
| **344** | A63 | 0.50p | deep green | .25 | .25 |
| **345** | A63 | 2.50p | olive | .25 | .25 |
| **346** | A63 | 5p | green | .25 | .25 |
| **347** | A63 | 7.50p | rose brown | .35 | .25 |
| **348** | A63 | 15p | bright blue | .85 | .25 |
| **349** | A63 | 50p | lilac | 1.75 | .25 |
| **350** | A63 | 100p | brown | 4.25 | .25 |
| | | | *Nos. 344-350 (7)* | 7.95 | 1.75 |

Nos. 343A and 340 Overprinted in Red

**1960, Nov. Litho. *Perf. 13x13½***

| | | | | | |
|---|---|---|---|---|---|
| **351** | A53 | 5p | light green | .85 | .25 |
| **352** | A62 | 15p | lt blue green | 1.75 | .25 |

Arabian Oil Conference, Beirut.

President Fuad Chehab — A64

**1961, Feb. Litho. *Perf. 13½x13***

| | | | | | |
|---|---|---|---|---|---|
| **353** | A64 | 2.50p | blue & light bl | .50 | .25 |
| **354** | A64 | 7.50p | dark vio & pink | 1.00 | .25 |
| **355** | A64 | 10p | red brn & yel | 1.50 | .25 |
| | | | *Nos. 353-355 (3)* | 3.00 | .75 |

Cedar — A65

Post Office, Beirut A66

**1961 Unwmk. Litho. *Perf. 13***

| | | | | | |
|---|---|---|---|---|---|
| **356** | A65 | 2.50p | green | .75 | .25 |

**Redrawn**

| | | | | | |
|---|---|---|---|---|---|
| **357** | A65 | 2.50p | orange | 1.25 | .25 |
| **358** | A65 | 5p | maroon | 1.25 | .25 |
| **359** | A65 | 10p | black | 1.50 | .25 |

Nos. 357-359 have no clouds.

***Perf. 11½***

| | | | | | |
|---|---|---|---|---|---|
| **361** | A66 | 2.50p | rose carmine | .75 | .25 |
| **362** | A66 | 5p | bright green | 1.40 | .25 |
| **363** | A66 | 15p | dark blue | 2.10 | .25 |
| | | | *Nos. 356-363 (7)* | 9.00 | 1.75 |

Cedars — A67

10p, 15p, 50p, 100p, View of Zahle.

**1961 Litho. *Perf. 13***

| | | | | | |
|---|---|---|---|---|---|
| **365** | A67 | 0.50p | yellow green | .45 | .25 |
| **366** | A67 | 1p | brown | .45 | .25 |
| **367** | A67 | 2.50p | ultramarine | .45 | .25 |
| **368** | A67 | 5p | carmine | .65 | .25 |
| **369** | A67 | 7.50p | violet | .85 | .25 |
| **370** | A67 | 10p | dark brown | 2.25 | .25 |
| **371** | A67 | 15p | dark blue | 2.50 | .25 |
| **372** | A67 | 50p | dark green | 2.75 | .25 |
| **373** | A67 | 100p | black | 3.25 | .35 |
| | | | *Nos. 365-373 (9)* | 13.60 | 2.35 |

See Nos. 381-384.

Unknown Soldier Monument — A68

**1961, Dec. 30 Unwmk. *Perf. 12***

| | | | | | |
|---|---|---|---|---|---|
| **374** | A68 | 10p | shown | 3.00 | .25 |
| **375** | A68 | 15p | Soldier & flag | 3.75 | .25 |

Anniv. of Lebanon's independence; evacuation of foreign troops, Dec. 31, 1946.
See Nos. C329-C330.

Bugler — A69

Scout Carrying Flag and Scout Emblem A70

Designs: 2.50p, First aid. 6p, Lord Baden-Powell. 10p, Scouts building campfire.

**1962, Mar. 1 Litho. *Perf. 12***

| | | | | | |
|---|---|---|---|---|---|
| **376** | A69 | 0.50p | yel grn, blk & yel | 1.50 | .25 |
| **377** | A70 | 1p | multicolored | 1.50 | .25 |
| **378** | A70 | 2.50p | dk red, blk & grn | 1.50 | .25 |
| **379** | A69 | 6p | multicolored | 1.50 | .25 |
| **380** | A70 | 10p | dp bl, blk & yel | 1.50 | .25 |
| | | | *Nos. 376-380,C331-C333 (8)* | 10.75 | 2.15 |

50th anniversary of Lebanese Boy Scouts.

Type of 1961 Redrawn

Designs as before.

**1962 Unwmk. *Perf. 13***

| | | | | | |
|---|---|---|---|---|---|
| **381** | A67 | 0.50p | yellow green | 1.50 | .25 |
| **382** | A67 | 1p | brown | 1.50 | .25 |
| **383** | A67 | 2.50p | ultramarine | 1.60 | .25 |
| **384** | A67 | 15p | dark blue | 4.00 | .25 |
| | | | *Nos. 381-384,C341-C342 (6)* | 15.95 | 1.65 |

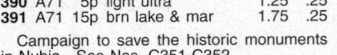

Temple of Nefertari, Abu Simbel — A71

**1962, Aug. 1 Unwmk. *Perf. 13***

| | | | | | |
|---|---|---|---|---|---|
| **390** | A71 | 5p | light ultra | 1.25 | .25 |
| **391** | A71 | 15p | brn lake & mar | 1.75 | .25 |

Campaign to save the historic monuments in Nubia. See Nos. C351-C352.

Cherries — A72

Designs: 50c, 2.50p, 7.50p, Cherries. 1p, 5p, Figs. 10p, 17.50p, 30p, Grapes. 50p, Oranges. 100p, Pomegranates.

**1962 Vignette Multicolored Litho.**

| | | | | | |
|---|---|---|---|---|---|
| **392** | A72 | 0.50p | violet blue | 1.50 | .25 |
| **393** | A72 | 1p | gray blue | 1.50 | .25 |
| **394** | A72 | 2.50p | brown | 1.50 | .25 |
| **395** | A72 | 5p | bright blue | 1.50 | .25 |
| **396** | A72 | 7.50p | lilac rose | 1.50 | .25 |
| **397** | A72 | 10p | chocolate | 1.75 | .25 |
| **398** | A72 | 17.50p | slate | 2.50 | .25 |
| **399** | A72 | 30p | slate grn | 2.75 | .25 |
| **400** | A72 | 50p | green | 3.00 | .25 |
| **401** | A72 | 100p | brown blk | 5.00 | .50 |
| | | | *Nos. 392-401,C359-C366 (18)* | 31.65 | 5.05 |

Elementary Schoolboy — A73

**1962, Oct. 1 Litho. *Perf. 12***

| | | | | | |
|---|---|---|---|---|---|
| **404** | A73 | 30p | multicolored | 1.50 | .25 |

Students' Day, Oct. 1. See No. C355.

Cedar of Lebanon
A74 A75

**1963-64 Unwmk. *Perf. 13x13½***

| | | | | | |
|---|---|---|---|---|---|
| **405** | A74 | 0.50p | green | 7.00 | .25 |
| **406** | A75 | 0.50p | gray grn ('64) | 1.50 | .25 |
| **407** | A75 | 2.50p | ultra ('64) | 1.50 | .25 |
| **408** | A75 | 5p | brt pink ('64) | 1.60 | .25 |
| **409** | A75 | 7.50p | orange ('64) | 1.75 | .25 |
| **410** | A75 | 17.50p | rose lil ('64) | 2.25 | .25 |
| | | | *Nos. 405-410 (6)* | 15.60 | 1.50 |

Bicyclist — A76

**1964, Feb. 11 Litho. *Perf. 13***

| | | | | | |
|---|---|---|---|---|---|
| **415** | A76 | 2.50p | shown | 1.50 | .25 |
| **416** | A76 | 5p | Basketball | 1.50 | .25 |
| **417** | A76 | 10p | Track | 1.50 | .25 |
| | | | *Nos. 415-417,C385-C387 (6)* | 6.70 | 1.50 |

4th Mediterranean Games, Naples, Sept. 21-29, 1963.

Hyacinth — A77

**1964 Unwmk. *Perf. 13x13½***

**Size: 26x27mm**

| | | | | | |
|---|---|---|---|---|---|
| **418** | A77 | 0.50p | shown | 1.50 | .25 |
| **419** | A77 | 1p | Hyacinth | 1.50 | .25 |
| **420** | A77 | 2.50p | Hyacinth | 1.50 | .25 |
| **421** | A77 | 5p | Cyclamen | 1.50 | .25 |
| **422** | A77 | 7.50p | Cyclamen | 1.50 | .25 |

***Perf. 13***

**Size: 26x37mm**

| | | | | | |
|---|---|---|---|---|---|
| **423** | A77 | 10p | Poinsettia | 1.50 | .25 |
| **424** | A77 | 17.50p | Anemone | 2.50 | .25 |
| **425** | A77 | 30p | Iris | 3.50 | .25 |
| **426** | A77 | 50p | Poppy | 7.00 | .45 |
| | | | *Nos. 418-426,C391-C397 (16)* | 29.20 | 4.25 |

See Nos. C391-C397.

Temple of the Sun, Baalbek A78

**1965, Jan. 11 Litho. *Perf. 13x13½***

| | | | | | |
|---|---|---|---|---|---|
| **429** | A78 | 2.50p | blk & red org | 2.00 | .25 |
| **430** | A78 | 7.50p | black & blue | 2.75 | .25 |
| | | | *Nos. 429-430,C420-C423 (6)* | 9.10 | 1.85 |

International Festival at Baalbek.

Swimmer A79

**1965, Jan. 23 Engr. *Perf. 13***

| | | | | | |
|---|---|---|---|---|---|
| **431** | A79 | 2.50p | shown | 2.50 | .25 |
| **432** | A79 | 7.50p | Fencer | 2.75 | .25 |
| **433** | A79 | 10p | Basketball, vert. | 4.00 | .25 |
| | | | *Nos. 431-433,C424-C426 (6)* | 11.10 | 1.50 |

18th Olympic Games, Tokyo, Oct. 10-25, 1964.

Golden Oriole A80

5p, Bullfinch. 10p, European goldfinch. 15p, Hoopoe. 17.50p, Rock partridge. 32.50p, European bee-eater.

**1965 Engr. *Perf. 13***

| | | | | | |
|---|---|---|---|---|---|
| **434** | A80 | 5p | multicolored | 8.00 | .25 |
| **435** | A80 | 10p | multicolored | 13.00 | .25 |
| **436** | A80 | 15p | multicolored | 10.00 | .25 |
| **437** | A80 | 17.50p | multicolored | 12.00 | .25 |
| **438** | A80 | 20p | shown | 15.00 | .25 |
| **439** | A80 | 32.50p | multicolored | 20.00 | .25 |
| | | | *Nos. 434-439 (6)* | 78.00 | 1.50 |

For surcharge see No. 459.

Cow and Calf — A81

**1965 Photo. *Perf. 11x12***

| | | | | | |
|---|---|---|---|---|---|
| **440** | A81 | 0.50p | shown | 2.00 | .25 |
| **441** | A81 | 1p | Rabbit | 2.25 | .25 |
| **442** | A81 | 2.50p | Ewe & lamb | 2.50 | .25 |
| | | | *Nos. 440-442 (3)* | 6.75 | .75 |

Hippodrome, Beirut — A82

1p, Pigeon Rocks. 2.50p, Tabarja. 5p, Ruins, Beit-Méry. 7.50p, Statue and ruins, Anjar.

**1966 Unwmk. *Perf. 12x11½***

| | | | | | |
|---|---|---|---|---|---|
| **443** | A82 | 0.50p | gold & multi | 1.75 | .25 |
| **444** | A82 | 1p | gold & multi | 2.00 | .25 |
| **445** | A82 | 2.50p | gold & multi | 2.25 | .25 |

**446** A82 5p gold & multi 2.50 .25
**447** A82 7.50p gold & multi 2.75 .25
*Nos. 443-447 (5)* 11.25 1.25

See Nos. C486-C492. For surcharge see No. 460.

ITY Emblem and Cedars A83

**1967 Photo. *Perf. 11x12***
**448** A83 0.50p lem, blk & brt bl 4.00 .25
**449** A83 1p sal, blk & brt bl 4.00 .25
**450** A83 2.50p gray, blk & brt bl 4.00 .25
**451** A83 5p lt rose lil, blk & brt bl 4.00 .25
**452** A83 7.50p yel, blk & brt bl 4.00 .25
*Nos. 448-452 (5)* 20.00 1.25

Intl. Tourist Year; used as a regular issue.
See Nos. C515-C522. For surcharge see No. 461.

Goat and Kid A84

**1968, Feb. Photo. *Perf. 12x11½***
**453** A84 0.50p shown 3.00 .25
**454** A84 1p Cattle 4.00 .25
**455** A84 2.50p Sheep 5.00 .25
**456** A84 5p Camels 6.00 .25
**457** A84 10p Donkey 7.00 .25
**458** A84 15p Horses 9.00 .25
*Nos. 453-458 (6)* 34.00 1.50

See Nos. C534-C539.

**No. 439 Surcharged in Black**

**1972, Apr. Engr. *Perf. 13***
**459** A80 25p on 32.50p multi 22.50 .25

**Nos. 447 and 452 Surcharged with New Value and Bars**
***Perf. 12x11½, 11x12***
**1972, May Photo.**
**460** A82 5p on 7.50p multi *4.50* .25
**461** A83 5p on 7.50p multi *4.50* .25

Cedar — A85

**1974 Litho. *Perf. 11***
**462** A85 0.50p orange & olive *.25* .25

Army Badge — A86

**1980, Dec. 28 Litho. *Perf. 11½***
**463** A86 25p multicolored 2.50 .25

Army Day. See Nos. C792-C793.

Pres. Elias Sarkis — A87

**1981, Sept. 23 Photo. *Perf. 14x13½***
**464** A87 125p multicolored 2.75 .80
**465** A87 300p multicolored 2.75 1.60
**466** A87 500p multicolored 7.50 2.40
*Nos. 464-466 (3)* 13.00 4.80

World Food Day, Oct. 16, 1981 A88

**1982, Nov. 23 Photo. *Perf. 12x11½***
**467** A88 50p Stork carrying food packages 1.75 .30
**468** A88 75p Wheat, globe 2.00 .50
**469** A88 100p Produce 2.25 .65
*Nos. 467-469 (3)* 6.00 1.45

World Communications Year — A89

**1983, Dec. 19 Photo. *Perf. 14***
**470** A89 300p multicolored 6.00 1.75

Illustrations from Khalil Gibran's The Prophet A90

**1983, Dec. 19 *Perf. 13½x14***
**471** A90 200p The Soul Is Back 2.75 1.00
**472** A90 300p The Family 4.25 1.75
**473** A90 500p Self-portrait 7.50 2.40
**474** A90 1000p The Prophet 15.00 4.75
*a.* Souvenir sheet, #471-474 37.50 37.50
*Nos. 471-474 (4)* 29.50 9.90

No. 474a sold for £25.

Scouting Year — A91

**1983, Dec. 19 *Perf. 14***
**475** A91 200p Rowing 3.50 .65
**476** A91 300p Signaling 4.00 .80
**477** A91 500p Camp 7.25 1.25
*Nos. 475-477 (3)* 14.75 2.70

Cedar of Lebanon — A93

**1984, Dec. Photo. *Perf. 14½x13½***
**481** A93 5p multicolored 2.00 .25

Flowers — A94

**1984, Dec. Photo. *Perf. 14½x13½***
**482** A94 10p Iris of Sofar 2.00 .25
**483** A94 25p Periwinkle 3.00 .30
**484** A94 50p Flowering thorn 4.00 .40
*Nos. 482-484 (3)* 9.00 .95

For surcharges see Nos. 531-532.

Defense — A95

**1984, Dec. Photo. *Perf. 14½x13½***
**485** A95 75p Dove over city 3.50 .90
**486** A95 150p Soldier, cedar 4.75 1.90
**487** A95 300p Olive wreath, cedar 6.25 3.50
*Nos. 485-487 (3)* 14.50 6.30

Temple Ruins A96

**1985 Photo. *Perf. 13½x14½***
**488** A96 100p Fakra 3.00 .55
**489** A96 200p Bziza 3.50 1.10
**490** A96 500p Tyre 6.50 2.75
*Nos. 488-490 (3)* 13.00 4.40

Pres. Gemayel, Map of Lebanon, Dove, Text — A97

**1988, Feb. 1 Litho. *Perf. 14***
**491** A97 £50 multicolored 5.00 2.00

Pres. Gemayel, Military Academy Graduate — A98

**1988, Mar. 9**
**492** A98 £25 multicolored 5.50 1.50

Arab Scouts, 75th Anniv. A99

**1988, Mar. 9 *Perf. 13½x14½***
**493** A99 £20 multicolored 5.50 1.25

UN Child Survival Campaign A100

**1988, Mar. 9 *Perf. 14½x13½***
**494** A100 £15 multicolored 3.50 .75

Prime Minister Rashid Karame (1921-1987), Satellite, Flags, Earth A101

**1988, Mar. 9 *Perf. 13½x14½***
**495** A101 £10 multicolored 2.50 .60

1st World Festival for Youths of Lebanese Descent in Uruguay A102

**1988, Mar. 9**
**496** A102 £5 multicolored 3.25 .50

Cedar — A103

**1989 Photo. *Perf. 13x13½***
**497** A103 £50 dk grn & vio 3.00 .35
**498** A103 £70 dk grn & brn 3.50 .50
**499** A103 £100 dk grn & brt yel 4.00 .50
**500** A103 £200 dk grn & bluish grn 6.00 1.25
**501** A103 £500 dk grn & brt yel grn 11.00 3.00
*Nos. 497-501 (5)* 27.50 5.60

Independence, 50th Anniv. — A104

Designs: £200, Al Muntazah Restaurant, Zahle, 1883. £300, Sea Castle, Sidon, vert. £500, Presidential Palace, Baabda. £1000, Army graduation ceremony, vert. £3000, Beirut 2000, architectural plan. £5000, Pres. Elias Harawi, Lebanese flag, vert.

**1993** **Litho.** ***Perf. 14***

**502** A104 £200 multi 1.75 .25
**503** A104 £300 multi 2.25 .55
**504** A104 £500 multi 3.50 .85
**505** A104 £1000 multi 5.00 1.75
**506** A104 £3000 multi 9.25 3.00
**507** A104 £5000 multi 17.50 8.25
*Nos. 502-507 (6)* 39.25 14.65

For overprints, see Nos. 533B, 533C, 533G.

**Size: 126x150mm**

***Imperf***

**508** A104 £10,000 multi 57.50 57.50

A105

Environmental Protection: £100, Stop polluting atmosphere. £200, Stop fires. £500, Trees, building. £1000, Birds, trees in city. £2000, Mosaic of trees. £5000, Green tree in middle of polluted city.

**1994, May 7** **Litho.** ***Perf. 13½x13***

**509** A105 £100 multicolored 1.75 .25
**510** A105 £200 multicolored 2.00 .45
**511** A105 £500 multicolored 3.25 .95
**512** A105 £1000 multicolored 5.25 1.60
**513** A105 £2000 multicolored 8.75 2.75
**514** A105 £5000 multicolored 20.00 6.50
*Nos. 509-514 (6)* 41.00 12.50

For overprints see Nos. 533D, 533H, 537.

A106

**1995, May 6** **Litho.** ***Perf. 13½x13***

**515** A106 £1500 Martyr's Day 7.00 3.00

For overprint see No. 534.

Anniversaries and Events — A107

£500, UNICEF, 50th anniv., horiz. £1000, Intl. Year of the Family (1994), horiz. £2000, ILO, 75th anniv. (in 1994), horiz. £3000, Bar Association (Berytus Nutrix Legum), 75th anniv.

**1996, Feb. 21** **Litho.** ***Perf. 14***

**516** A107 £500 multi, horiz. 4.25 1.10
**517** A107 £1000 multi, horiz. 6.75 2.25
**518** A107 £2000 multi, horiz. 12.00 4.25
**519** A107 £3000 multicolored 17.50 6.75
*Nos. 516-519 (4)* 40.50 14.35

For overprints, see Nos. 533E, 534A, 535A.

Anniversaries and Events of 1995 — A108

£100, Opening of Museum of Arab Postage Stamps. £500, FAO, 50th anniv. £1000, UN, 50th anniv. £2000, Arab League, 50th anniv. £3000, Former Pres. René Moawad (1925-89).

**1996, Feb. 21** ***Perf. 13½x13***

**520** A108 £100 multicolored 2.75 .25
**521** A108 £500 multicolored 4.25 1.10
**522** A108 £1000 multicolored 7.00 2.10
**523** A108 £2000 multicolored 11.50 4.00
**524** A108 £3000 multicolored 17.50 6.50
*Nos. 520-524 (5)* 43.00 13.95

For overprints see Nos. 533A, 533F, 533I, 535-536.

Massacre at Cana A109

**1997, Oct. 13** **Litho.** ***Perf. 14***

**525** A109 £1100 multicolored 11.00 2.75

For overprint, see No. 533J.

1997 Visit of Pope John Paul II to Lebanon A110

**1997** **Litho.** ***Perf. 13½x13***

**526** A110 £10,000 multi 110.00 35.00

For overprint see Nos. 533O, 538.

Fakhr al-Din Palace, Deir-el-Kamar — A111

£100, Chehab Palace, Hasbaya, vert. £300, ESCWA Building, Beirut, vert. £1100, Grand Seraglio, Beirut.

**1999** **Litho.** ***Perf. 12***

**527** A111 £100 multicolored 1.50 .25
**528** A111 £300 multicolored 2.50 .45
**529** A111 £500 shown 3.00 .80
**530** A111 £1100 multicolored 6.00 1.75
*Nos. 527-530 (4)* 13.00 3.25

Nos. 484, 485 and C775 Surcharged in Silver and Black

**Methods and Perfs. as before**

**1999**

**531** A94 £100 on 50p (#484) 1.75 .25
**532** A95 £300 on 75p (#485) 2.50 .45
**533** AP154 £1100 on 70p (#C775) 6.00 1.75
*Nos. 531-533 (3)* 10.25 2.45

Nos. 502, 504-505, 511-512, 516, 518-522, 525 Overprinted in Gold

Similar to Nos. 534-538 but with Symbol Oriented as a Cross

**Methods and Perfs As Before**

**1999**

**533A** A108 £100 multi 17.50
**533B** A104 £200 multi 17.50
**533C** A104 £500 multi (#504) 27.50 —
**533D** A105 £500 multi (#501) 30.00 —
**533E** A107 £500 multi 30.00
**533F** A108 £500 multi (#521) 30.00 —
**533G** A104 £1000 multi (#505) 60.00 —
**533H** A105 £1000 multi 55.00
**533I** A108 £1000 multi (#522) 35.00 —
**533J** A109 £1100 multi (#525) 350.00 —
**533K** A106 £1500 multi 45.00
**533L** A107 £2000 multi 85.00
**533M** A107 £3000 multi (#519) 125.00 —
**533N** A105 £5000 multi 240.00
**533O** A110 £10,000 multi (#526) 475.00 —
*Nos. 533A-533O (15)* 1,623.

Nos. 514, 515, 523, 524 and 526 Overprinted in Gold or Silver

**Methods and Perfs As Before**

**1999**

**534** A106 £1500 multi 7.50 5.00
**535** A108 £2000 multi 11.50 9.00
**536** A108 £3000 multi (S) 15.00 12.50
**537** A105 £5000 multi 20.00 17.50
**538** A110 £10,000 multi 40.00 40.00
*Nos. 534-538 (5)* 94.00 84.00

Cedar of Lebanon — A112

***Perf. 13x13¼, 11x11¼ (£500, £1000, £1100)***

**2000 ?** **Litho.** **Unwmk.**

**539** A112 £100 dark red .50 .25
**540** A112 £300 Prus blue 1.00 .35

**Wmk. 400**

**541** A112 £500 green 1.50 .65
*a.* Perf. 13x13¼ 1.50 .65
*b.* Booklet pane, 10 #541a 15.00
Booklet, #541b 15.00
**542** A112 £1000 blue 3.50 1.25
**543** A112 £1100 olive brn 3.75 1.40
*a.* Perf. 13x13¼ 3.75 1.40
*b.* Booklet pane, 10 #543a 37.50
Booklet, #543b 37.50
**544** A112 £1500 vio blue 4.50 1.90
*a.* Booklet pane, 10 #544 45.00
Booklet, #544a 45.00
*b.* Perf. 11x11¼ 4.50 1.90
*Nos. 539-544 (6)* 14.75 5.80

**Cedar of Lebanon Type of 2000 Redrawn**

***Perf. 11x11¼, 13x13¼ (£1000)***

**2001 ?** **Litho.** **Unwmk.**

**Numerals 1½mm Tall**

**544C** A112 £500 olive grn —
**544D** A112 £1000 blue —
**544E** A112 £1100 brown —
**544F** A112 £1500 purple —
*g.* Perf. 13x13¼ —

On Nos. 539-544, numerals are 2mm tall.

A113

**2001** **Litho.** ***Perf. 11¼x11***

**545** A113 £1100 multi 4.00 1.50

Geneva Conventions, 50th Anniv. (in 1999) — A114

Red Cross/Red Crescent A115

**2001** **Litho.** ***Perf. 11x11½***

**546** A114 £500 shown 2.00 .70
**547** A114 £1100 "50," fist 4.00 1.50
**548** A115 £1500 shown 5.00 2.10
*Nos. 546-548 (3)* 11.00 4.30

SOS Children's Villages A116

**2001**

**549** A116 £300 multi 1.25 .40

Prisoners in Israel A117

**2001**

**550** A117 £500 multi 2.00 .70

Ibrahim Abd el Al (1908-59), Hydrologist
A118

**2001**
**551** A118 £1000 multi 3.50 1.40

Abdallah Zakher (1680-1748), Printer — A119

**2001**
**552** A119 £1000 multi 3.50 1.40

Elias Abu Chabke (1904-49), Poet — A120

**2001** ***Perf. 11½x11***
**553** A120 £1500 multi 5.00 2.10

Saint Joseph University, 125th Anniv. (in 2000)
A121

**2001** ***Perf. 11x11½***
**554** A121 £5000 multi 15.00 7.00

Economic & Social Commission for Western Asia, 25th Anniv. (in 1999) — A122

**2001** ***Perf. 11½x11***
**555** A122 £10,000 multi 32.50 20.00

Arab Woman's Day — A123

**2002, Feb. 1 Litho.** ***Perf. 13¼x13½***
**556** A123 £1000 multi 3.25 2.60

Arab League Summit Conference, Beirut — A124

Arab League member flags and: £2000, Emblem. £3000, Cedar tree, Lebanese Pres. Emile Lahoud.

**2002, Mar. 27**
**557-558** A124 Set of 2 11.00 9.25

Souvenir Sheet

Israeli Withdrawal From Southern Lebanon, 2nd Anniv. — A125

No. 559: a, Pres. Emile Lahoud, flag. b, Pres. Lahoud holding book. c, Pres. Lahoud and map. d, Pres. Lahoud receiving sword.

**2002, Mar. 27** ***Perf. 13¼***
**559** A125 £1100 Sheet of 4, #a-d 10.50 9.50

Souvenir Sheet

Martyrs of Justice — A126

**2002, June 14** ***Perf. 13¼x13½***
**560** A126 £3000 multi 7.00 5.75

UPU, 125th Anniv. (in 1999)
A127

**2002, Oct. 11 Litho.** ***Perf. 13½x13¼***
**561** A127 £2000 multi 7.00 5.75

City Views — A128

Ruins — A129

Paleontonlogy — A130

Designs: £100 Old souk, Zouk Mikael. £300, Old souk, Sidon. £500, Byblos. £1000, Souk, Tripoli. £1100, Bziza. £1500, Arqa. £2000, Niha. £3000, Mousailaha Citadel. £5000, Libanobythus milkii in amber. £10,000, Nematonotus longispinus fossil.

***Perf. 13¼x13½, 13½x13¼***

| **2002-03** | | | | **Litho.** | |
|---|---|---|---|---|---|
| **562** | A128 | £100 | multi | .50 | .25 |
| **563** | A128 | £300 | multi | .90 | .50 |
| **564** | A128 | £500 | multi | 1.75 | .90 |
| **565** | A128 | £1000 | multi | 2.50 | 1.75 |
| **566** | A129 | £1100 | multi | 3.00 | 2.00 |
| **567** | A129 | £1500 | multi | 3.50 | 2.75 |
| **568** | A129 | £2000 | multi | 4.50 | 3.75 |
| **569** | A129 | £3000 | multi | 7.25 | 5.75 |
| **570** | A130 | £5000 | multi | 10.50 | 9.25 |
| **571** | A130 | £10,000 | multi | 21.00 | 18.00 |
| | *Nos. 562-571 (10)* | | | 55.40 | 44.90 |

Issued: £100, £300, 10/11; £1000, £1500, £2000, £3000, £10,000, 11/20; £500, £1100, 12/20; £5000, 1/8/03.

Ninth Francophone Summit, Beirut — A131

Summit emblem and: No. 572, £1500, Mountains. No. 573, £1500, Pres. Emile Lahoud.

**2002, Oct. 23** ***Perf. 13¼x13½***
**572-573** A131 Set of 2 7.00 5.50

Beirut, 1999 Arab Cultural Capital — A132

**2002, Nov. 13**
**574** A132 £2000 multi 5.00 4.00

Independence, 60th Anniv. (in 2001) — A133

Stylized flag and: No. 575, £1250, Crowd viewing horse and rider. No. 576, £1250, Men and flag on staff. No. 577, £1750, Arabic text. No. 578, £1750, Soldier saluting group of men. £6000, Vignettes of Nos. 575-578.

**2003, Dec. 5 Litho.** ***Perf. 12¾x13***
**575-578** A133 Set of 4 14.00 14.00

***Imperf***

**Size: 160x110mm**

**579** A133 £6000 multi 14.00 14.00

Faqra Ski Resort
A134

**2004 Litho.** ***Perf. 11x11¼***
**580** A134 £500 multi 1.25 1.25

General Post Office, Beirut — A135

Post office in: £100, 1953. £300, 2002.

**2004** ***Perf. 11¼x11***
**581-582** A135 Set of 2 1.00 1.00

Al Bustan Festival
A136

**2004 Litho.** ***Perf. 11x11¼***
**583** A136 £1000 multi 2.50 2.50

St. George's Hospital, Beirut, 125th Anniv. (in 2003) — A137

**2004, Oct. 28 Litho.** ***Perf. 11x11¼***
**584** A137 £3000 multi 4.00 4.00

Ski Resorts
A138

**2004 Litho.** ***Perf. 11x11¼, 11¼x11***

| | | | | | |
|---|---|---|---|---|---|
| **585** | A138 | £100 | Kamouaa | — | — |
| **586** | A138 | £100 | Aayoun Siman | .25 | .25 |
| **587** | A138 | £250 | Laklouk, vert. | .35 | .35 |
| **588** | A138 | £300 | Zaarour | | — |
| **589** | A138 | £300 | Kanat Bakish | .40 | .40 |
| **590** | A138 | £1000 | Cedres | 1.40 | 1.40 |
| | *Nos. 585-590 (5)* | | | 2.40 | 2.40 |

Issued: No. 585, 10/28; £250, 11/26; No. 588, 10/28; Nos. 586, 589, £1000, 12/10.

Baalbeck Intl. Festival
A139

Tyre Festival — A140

Beiteddine Festival — A141

Byblos Intl. Festival — A142

*Perf. 11x11¼, 11¼x11*

**2004, Nov. 26** **Litho.**

| | | | | |
|---|---|---|---|---|
| **591** | A139 | £500 multi | .70 | .70 |
| **592** | A140 | £1250 multi | 1.75 | 1.75 |
| **593** | A141 | £1400 multi | 1.90 | 1.90 |
| **594** | A142 | £1750 multi | 2.40 | 2.40 |
| | *Nos. 591-594 (4)* | | 6.75 | 6.75 |

Rotary International, Cent. — A143

**2005, Feb. 23** ***Perf. 11¼x11***

**595** A143 £3000 multi 4.00 4.00

Beirut Buildings A144

Designs: £100, Rafiq Hariri Intl. Airport. £250, Parliament. £300, Camille Chamoun Sports Center. £500, National Museum. £1000, Governmental Palace. £1250, Bank of Lebanon. £1400, St. Paul's Cathedral. £1750, Bahaeddine Hariri Mosque. £2000, Presidential Palace.

**2005** **Litho.** ***Perf. 13x13½***

**596-604** A144 Set of 9 15.00 15.00

Issued: £100, £300, £500, £1000, 10/11; others, 11/11.

Pres. Rafiq Hariri (1944-2005) — A145

Designs: No. 605, £1250, Pres. Hariri, flag. No. 606, £1250, Pres. Hariri, mosque, church and statues. No. 607, £1750, Pres. Hariri, mosque. No. 608, £1750, Child kissing picture of Pres. Hariri.

**2006, Feb. 13** ***Perf. 13¼x13***

**605-608** A145 Set of 4 10.50 10.50

*608a* Souvenir sheet, #605-608, imperf. 10.50 10.50

No. 608a has embossed margin and simulated perforations between stamps.

Arabic Book Exhibition A146

**2007, Apr. 18** **Litho.** ***Perf. 13x13¼***

**609** A146 £1000 multi 1.40 1.40

Basil Fuleihan (1963-2005), Economy Minister — A147

Fuleihan: £500, Wearing cap and gown, suit and tie. £1500, With flags of Lebanon and European Union. £2000, With flag of Lebanon. £4000, Vignettes of Nos. 610-612, map and flag of Lebanon.

**2007, Apr. 18** ***Perf. 13¼x13***

**610-612** A147 Set of 3 5.75 5.75

**Size: 160x100mm**

***Imperf***

**613** A147 £4000 multi 5.75 5.75

Pres. Fouad Chehab (1902-73) — A148

**2007, June 4** ***Perf. 13¼x13***

**614** A148 £1400 multi 1.90 1.90

World Summit on the Information Society, Tunis (in 2005) A149

**2007, July 2** ***Perf. 13x13¼***

**615** A149 £100 multi .25 .25

Léopold Sédar Senghor (1906-2001), First President of Senegal — A150

**2007, July 2** ***Perf. 13¼x13***

**616** A150 £300 multi .45 .45

Intl. Year of Sports and Physical Education (in 2005) A151

**2007, July 2** ***Perf. 13x13¼***

**617** A151 £500 multi .70 .70

OPEC Development Fund, 30th Anniv. — A152

**2007, July 2**

**618** A152 £1400 multi 1.90 1.90

Baalbeck Intl. Festival, 50th Anniv. — A153

50th anniv. emblem and: £1000, Names of performers. £5000, Female performers.

**2007, July 2** ***Perf. 13¼x13***

**619-620** A153 Set of 2 7.50 7.50

Islamic Makassed Association of Sidon, 125th Anniv. (in 2004) — A154

Emblem and: £1400, Pres. Rafiq Hariri. £1750, Prime Minister Riad El Solh.

**2007, July 2**

**621-622** A154 Set of 2 4.00 4.00

Islamic Makassed Association of Beirut, 125th Anniv. (in 2003) — A155

Emblem and: £250, "125" in Arabian script. £500, Prime Minister Saeb Salam. £1400, Pres. Rafiq Hariri. £1750, Omar El Daouk.

**2007, July 2**

**623-626** A155 Set of 4 5.00 5.00

**Souvenir Sheet**

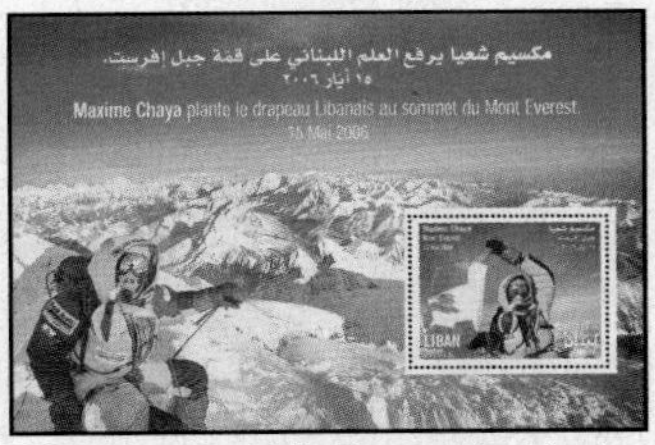

2006 Ascent of Mt. Everest by Maxime Chaya — A156

**2007, July 2**

**627** A156 £3000 multi 3.75 3.75

2004 Return of Freed Prisoners — A157

**2007, July 2** ***Imperf.***

**628** A157 £5000 multi 6.25 6.25

**Souvenir Sheet**

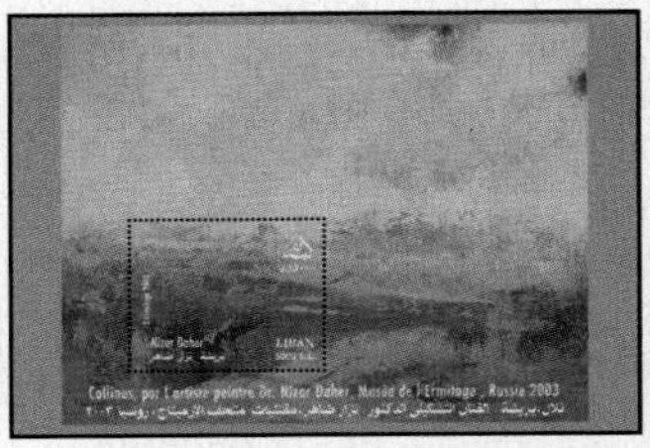

Hills, by Nizar Daher — A158

**2007, July 2** **Litho.** ***Perf. 13¼x13***

**629** A158 £5000 multi 6.25 6.25

Rotary International District 2450 Conference, Beirut — A159

**2008, Apr. 30 Litho.** ***Perf. 13¼x13***
**630** A159 £2000 multi 3.00 3.00

Kahlil Gibran (1883-1931), Writer and Artist — A160

Designs: £100, Mother and Her Child. £500, Sultana. £1400, Gibran Museum, Bsharri. £2000, Gibran.
£4000, Gibran and vignettes of Nos. 631-634, horiz.

**2008, Apr. 30** ***Perf. 13x13¼***
**631-634** A160 Set of 4 5.75 5.75

***Imperf***

**Size: 160x110mm**

**635** A160 £4000 multi 5.75 5.75

Army Day A161

Emblem and: £500, Soldier and flag of Lebanon. £1000, Stylized flag of Lebanon. £1250, Soldier holding wheat stalks. £1750, Eye.
£4500, Soldiers and vignettes of Nos. 636-639.

**2008 Litho.** ***Perf. 13¼x13***
**636-639** A161 Set of 4 6.00 6.00

**Size: 160x110mm**

***Imperf***

**640** A161 £4500 multi 6.00 6.00

Souvenir Sheet

Arab Postal Day — A162

No. 641 — Emblem and: a, World map and pigeon. b, Camel caravan.

***Perf. 13¼ Vert. Through Center***
**2008**
**641** A162 £5000 Sheet of 2, #a-b 13.50 13.50

Stamps have simulated perforations on three sides.

Lebanon Post, 10th Anniv. — A163

Simulated postmarks, Lebanon Post emblem, streamers, airplane and: £1250, "10" in Arabian script. £1750, Open envelope and "10th anniversary."
£3000, Simulated postmarks, Lebanon Post emblem, streamers, airplane and vignettes of Nos. 642-643.

**2008** ***Perf. 13¼x13***
**642-643** A163 Set of 2 4.00 4.00

**Size: 160x110mm**

***Imperf***

**644** A163 £3000 multi 4.00 4.00

Trees and Map of Mediterranean Area — A164

**2008, Nov. 20** ***Perf. 13***
**645** A164 £1750 multi 2.40 2.40

See France No. 3569.

Gen. François El Hajj (1953-2007) — A165

**2009, Jan. 8** ***Perf. 13x13¼***
**646** A165 £1750 multi 2.60 2.60

Universal Declaration of Human Rights, 60th Anniv. — A166

**2009, Jan. 8** ***Perf. 13¼x13***
**647** A166 £2000 multi 3.00 3.00

Dated 2008.

Beirut, World Book Capital A167

**2009, Sept. 17 Litho.** ***Perf. 13x13¼***
**648** A167 £750 multi 1.25 1.25

Jerusalem, Capital of Arab Culture — A168

**2009, Sept. 17** ***Perf. 13¼x13***
**649** A168 £1000 multi 1.60 1.60

Pierre Deschamps (1873-1958), Founder of French Lay Mission — A169

**2009, Sept. 17**
**650** A169 £500 blue & black .85 .85

Sixth Francophone Games, Beirut — A170

**2009, Sept. 28**
**651** A170 £1000 multi 1.60 1.60

Fire Fighters A171

Fire fighters with panel color of: £100, Green. £250, Red.

**2010, Aug. 2 Litho.** ***Perf. 13x13¼***
**652-653** A171 Set of 2 .50 .50

Nature Reserves A172

**2010, Aug. 2**
**654** A172 £300 multi .45 .45

Architecture A173

Various buildings with frame color of: £500, Red. £1000, Blue. £1200, Red.

**2010, Aug. 2** ***Perf. 13¼x13***
**655-657** A173 Set of 3 3.75 3.75

Soap Production A174

**2010, Aug. 2** ***Perf. 13x13¼***
**658** A174 £1400 multi 1.90 1.90

Soldier, Map of Lebanon A175

**2010, Aug. 2**
**659** A175 £1750 multi 2.40 2.40

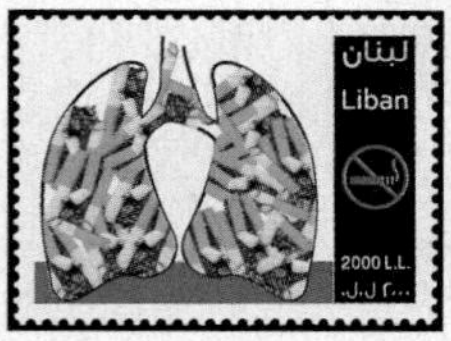


Lungs and Cigarette Butts A176

**2010, Aug. 2**
**660** A176 £2000 multi 2.75 2.75

Syringe and Arrows — A177

**2010, Aug. 2** ***Perf. 13¼x13***
**661** A177 £5000 black & red 7.00 7.00

Imam Al Ouzaai (707-74) — A178

**2010, Oct. 9**
**662** A178 £1000 multi 1.40 1.40

Grand Mufti Hassan Khaled (1921-89) — A179

Musa as-Sadr (1929-78), Religious Leader A180

**2010, Oct. 9** ***Perf. 13¼x13***
**663** A179 £1400 multi 2.00 2.00

***Perf. 13x13¼***
**664** A180 £1400 multi 2.00 2.00

Assassinated Political Leaders — A181

Designs: No. 665, £1400, Kamal Jumblatt (1917-77). No. 666, £1400, Prime Minister Rashid Karami (1921-87). No. 667, £1400, President René Moawad (1925-89). No. 668, £1400, President Bachir Gemayel (1947-82), horiz.

**2010, Oct. 9** ***Perf. 13x13¼, 13¼x13***
**665-668** A181 Set of 4 8.00 8.00

World Tourism Day A182

**2010, Oct. 9** ***Perf. 13x13¼***
**669** A182 £2000 multi 3.00 3.00

Dove and Flowers A183

**2010, Oct. 9**
**670** A183 £3000 multi 4.25 4.25

Source of the Alphabet A184

Arab Permanent Postal Commission — A185

Famous People A186

Designs: £1750, Sabah, singer and actress. £2250, Nabih Abou El-Hossn, actor. £2750, Hassan Alaa Eddine (1939-75), comedian. £3000, Caracalla Dance Ensemble. £5000, Alfred (1924-2006), Michel (1921-1981) and Youssef (1926-2001) Basbous, sculptors. £10,000, Said Akl, poet.

**2011, May 23 Litho.** ***Perf. 13x13¼***

| | | | | | |
|---|---|---|---|---|---|
| **671** | A184 | £250 | multi | .35 | .35 |
| **672** | A185 | £500 | multi | .70 | .70 |
| **673** | A186 | £1750 | multi | 2.50 | 2.50 |
| **674** | A186 | £2250 | multi | 3.25 | 3.25 |
| **675** | A186 | £2750 | multi | 4.00 | 4.00 |
| **676** | A186 | £3000 | multi | 4.25 | 4.25 |
| **677** | A186 | £5000 | multi | 7.00 | 7.00 |
| **678** | A186 | £10,000 | multi | 14.00 | 14.00 |
| | *Nos. 671-678 (8)* | | | 36.05 | 36.05 |

**Famous People Type of 2011 and**

Ehden Reserve A187

Pres. Suleiman Franjieh (1910-92) A188

Designs: £1500, Fayrouz, singer. £2000, Wadih El-Safi, singer.

***Perf. 13x13¼, 13¼x13 (£1000)***
**2011, June 27**

| | | | | | |
|---|---|---|---|---|---|
| **679** | A187 | £750 | multi | 1.10 | 1.10 |
| **680** | A188 | £1000 | multi | 1.40 | 1.40 |
| **681** | A186 | £1500 | multi | 2.10 | 2.10 |
| **682** | A186 | £2000 | multi | 3.00 | 3.00 |
| | *Nos. 679-682 (4)* | | | 7.60 | 7.60 |

Pres. Michel Suleiman — A189

Pres. Suleiman and: £750, Cedar trees. £1750, People at President's Summer Residence, Beiteddine. £2500, Dove with flags of Syria and Lebanon on wings. £2750, United Nations emblem.

**2011, Nov. 5** ***Perf. 13¼x13***
**683-686** A189 Set of 4 12.00 12.00

Mother's Day A190

**2012, Mar. 12** ***Perf. 13x13¼***
**687** A190 £2000 multi *72.50 72.50*

Lions International in Lebanon, 60th Anniv. — A191

**2012, Apr. 2**
**688** A191 £750 multi 1.60 1.60

Pope Benedict XVI and Pres. Michel Suleiman — A192

**2012, Sept. 15** ***Perf. 13¼x13***
**689** A192 £1250 multi 2.10 2.10

Visit of Pope Benedict XVI to Lebanon.

Beirut Marathon, 10th Anniv. — A193

**2012, Nov. 12**
**690** A193 £750 multi 1.25 1.25

Christmas A194

**2012, Nov. 13** ***Perf. 13x13¼***
**691** A194 £2000 multi 3.25 3.25

World Map and Statue of Lebanese Man A195

**2012, Nov. 21 Litho.** ***Perf. 13x13¼***
**692** A195 £500 multi *16.00 16.00*

Adel Osseiran (1905-98), Politician — A196

**2012, Nov. 21 Litho.** ***Perf. 13¼x13***
**693** A196 £1000 multi 1.60 1.60

National Scientific Research Council, 50th Anniv. — A197

**2012, Dec. 10**
**694** A197 £250 multi .45 .45

Pres. Michel Suleiman A198

**2012, Dec. 13** ***Perf. 13x13¼***
**695** A198 £250 multi *37.50 37.50*

Ghassan Tueni (1926-2012), Journalist and Politician — A199

**2012, Dec. 14**
**696** A199 £750 multi 1.25 1.25

100th Birthday (in 2011) of Said Akl, Poet — A200

**2012, Dec. 26** *Perf. 13¼x13*
**697** A200 £500 multi .80 .80

Mother's Day A201

**2013, Mar. 20** *Perf. 13x13¼*
**698** A201 £2000 multi *7.00 7.00*

Lebanon Post, 15th Anniv. A202

**2013, Nov. 11 Litho.** *Perf. 13x13¼*
**699** A202 £3000 multi 4.75 4.75

Amin Maalouf, Member of French Academy — A203

**2013, Nov. 19 Litho.** *Perf. 13¼x13*
**700** A203 £100 multi 1.75 1.75

Independence, 70th Anniv. — A204

**2013, Nov. 27 Litho.** *Perf. 13x13¼*
**701** A204 £1000 multi 1.75 1.75

Christmas A205

**2013, Dec. 16 Litho.** *Perf. 13¼x13*
**702** A205 £2000 multi 3.50 3.50

Armenian Genocide Monument, Bikfaya — A206

**2014, Apr. 15 Litho.** *Perf. 13¼x13*
**703** A206 £2000 multi 5.00 5.00

Medicine, Law and Engineering Faculties of St. Joseph University, Cent. A207

**2014, Apr. 29 Litho.** *Perf. 13x13¼*
**704** A207 £500 multi .85 .85

Famous Women — A208

Designs: No. 705, £2000, Laure Moughhaizel (1929-97), women's rights advocate. No. 706, £2000, Mounira el Solh (1911-2010), advocate for women's rights and the disabled. No. 707, £2000, Alexandra Issa el Khoury, President of Lebanese Red Cross. No. 708, £2000, Anissa Najjar, founder of Al Ahlia Magazine.

**2014, May 22 Litho.** *Perf. 13¼x13*
**705-708** A208 Set of 4 14.00 14.00

Bank of Lebanon, 50th Anniv. A209

**2014, June 2 Litho.** *Perf. 13x13¼*
**709** A209 £1750 multi 3.00 3.00

Father's Day — A210

**2014, June 17 Litho.** *Perf. 13¼x13*
**710** A210 £1750 multi 3.00 3.00

Euromed Postal Emblem and Mediterranean Sea — A211

**2014, July 9 Litho.** *Perf. 13x13¼*
**711** A211 £1000 multi 1.90 1.90

2014 World Cup Soccer Championships, Brazil — A212

Designs: £1750, Mascot. £2000, Emblem.

**2014, July 12 Litho.** *Perf. 13¼x13*
**712-713** A212 Set of 2 7.25 7.25

Monsignor Germanos Mouakkad (1853-1912), Missionary A213

**2014, Sept. 5 Litho.** *Perf. 13¼x13*
**714** A213 £250 multi .60 .60

Youssef Bey Karam (1823-89), Leader of 1866-67 Rebellion Against Ottoman Rule — A214

**2014, Nov. 10 Litho.** *Perf. 13¼x13*
**715** A214 £1750 multi 3.25 3.25

Writers — A215

Designs: No. 716, £1750, Kamal Youssef El-Hage (1917-76). No. 717, £1750, Ounsi El-Hage (1937-2014). No. 718, £1750, Joseph Harb (1941-2014).

**2014, Nov. 10 Litho.** *Perf. 13¼x13*
**716-718** A215 Set of 3 8.75 8.75

Independence, 71st Anniv. — A216

**2014, Nov. 22 Litho.** *Perf. 13¼x13*
**719** A216 £2750 multi 5.00 5.00

Christmas and New Year's Day — A217

**2014, Dec. 16 Litho.** *Perf. 13¼x13*
**720** A217 £5000 multi 9.25 9.25

Monastery of Saints Cyprian and Justina, Kfifane A218

Monastery of Saint Saviour, Joun A219

Monastery of St. John Castle, Beit Mery — A220

**2015, Jan. 15 Litho.** *Perf. 13x13¼*
**721** A218 £250 multi .50 .50
**722** A219 £250 multi .50 .50

*Perf. 13¼x13*
**723** A220 £250 multi .50 .50
*Nos. 721-723 (3)* 1.50 1.50

Said Freiha (1912-78), Founder and Publisher of Dar Assayad News Magazine A221

**2015, Jan. 20 Litho.** *Perf. 13x13¼*
**724** A221 £1750 multi 3.25 3.25

Emblem of General Security Forces — A222

Emblem of Internal Security Forces — A223

**2015, Mar. 17 Litho.** ***Perf. 13¼x13***
**725** A222 £1750 multi 3.25 3.25
**726** A223 £1750 multi 3.25 3.25

Mother's Day — A224

**2015, Mar. 20 Litho.** ***Perf. 13¼x13***
**727** A224 £2000 multi 3.75 3.75

Pierre Sadek (1938-2013), Political Cartoonist — A225

**2015, May 26 Litho.** ***Perf. 13x13¼***
**728** A225 £2250 multi 4.00 4.00

Famous People — A226

Designs: No. 729, £1750, Amin al-Hafez (1926-2009), prime minister. No. 730, £1750, Leila Osseiran (1934-2007), writer and wife of Amin al-Hafez.

**2015, July 7 Litho.** ***Perf. 13¼x13***
**729-730** A226 Set of 2 6.50 6.50

Euromed Postal Emblem, Boats of the Mediterranean Sea — A227

**2015, July 9 Litho.** ***Perf. 13x13¼***
**731** A227 £5000 multi 9.25 9.25

Politicians A228

Designs: No. 732, £1750, Riad El Solh (1894-1951), first prime minister. No. 733, £1750, Bechara El Khoury (1890-1964), prime minister and president.

**2015, July 14 Litho.** ***Perf. 13x13¼***
**732-733** A228 Set of 2 6.50 6.50

The Red Sunset, by Saliba Douaihy (1915-94) — A229

**2015, Aug. 11 Litho.** ***Perf. 13¼x13***
**734** A229 £2000 multi 3.75 3.75

Flag Day A230

**2015, Nov. 21 Litho.** ***Perf. 13x13¼***
**735** A230 £2000 multi 3.75 3.75

End of 2015 — A231

**2015, Dec. 30 Litho.** ***Perf. 13¼x13***
**736** A231 £2000 multi 3.75 3.75

Jawad Boulos (1900-82), Historian — A232

Hani Fahs (1946-2014), Shiite Cleric — A233

**2016, Feb. 17 Litho.** ***Perf. 13¼x13***
**737** A232 £2000 multi 3.75 3.75
**738** A233 £2000 multi 3.75 3.75

Flags and Church of Saidet et Tallé, Deir al-Qamar — A234

**2016, Apr. 2 Litho.** ***Perf. 13¼x13***
**739** A234 £250 multi .50 .50

Labor Day A235

**2016, Apr. 30 Litho.** ***Perf. 13x13¼***
**740** A235 £2000 multi 3.75 3.75

Martyr's Day A236

**2016, May 5 Litho.** ***Perf. 13x13¼***
**741** A236 £2000 multi 3.75 3.75

Fish of the Mediterranean Sea — A237

**2016, July 9 Litho.** ***Perf. 13x13¼***
**742** A237 £2250 multi 4.25 4.25

Baalbek International Festival, 60th Anniv. — A238

**2016, July 26 Litho.** ***Perf. 13x13¼***
**743** A238 £2000 multi 3.75 3.75

Lebanese Olympic Committee A239

**2016, Aug. 5 Litho.** ***Perf. 13¼x13***
**744** A239 £250 multi .50 .50

Elie Snaifer (1935-2005), Comedian A240

**2016, Sept. 6 Litho.** ***Perf. 13¼x13***
**745** A240 £250 multi .50 .50

Admittance to Universal Postal Union, 70th Anniv. A241

**2016, Oct. 8 Litho.** ***Perf. 13x13¼***
**746** A241 £2000 multi 3.75 3.75

Université la Sagesse, 140th Anniv. (in 2015) — A242

**2016, Oct. 22 Litho.** ***Perf. 13¼x13***
**747** A242 £2000 multi 3.75 3.75

Arab Postal Day — A243

Globe at: No. 748, £10,000, Right (blue background). No. 749, £10,000, Left (blue green background).

**2016, Nov. 4 Litho.** ***Perf. 13¼x13***
**748-749** A243 Set of 2 37.50 37.50

Famous Men A244

Contributors to Lebanese independence: No. 750, £250, Habib Abou Chahla, Speaker of Parliament. No. 751, £250, Adnan Al Hakim, member of Parliament. No. 752, £250, Saadi Al Mounla (1890-1975), Prime minister. No. 753, £250, Majid Arslan (1908-83), governmental minister. No. 754, £250, Rashid Baydoun (1889-1971), governmental minister. No. 755, £250, Camille Chamoun (1900-87), President. No. 756, £250, Mohamad El Fadi, member of Parliament. No. 757, £250, Hamid Frangieh (1907-81), member of Parliament. No. 758, £250, Pierre Gemayel (1905-84), member of Parliament. No. 759, £250, Sabri Hamadeh (1902-76), Speaker of Parliament. No. 760, £250, Maroun Kanaan (1890-1981), deputy of Jezzine. No. 761, £250, Abdul Hamid Karami (1890-1950), Prime minister. No. 762, £250, Henri Pharaon (1901-93), foreign minister. No. 763, £250, Saeb Salam (1905-2000), Prime minister. No. 764, £250, Selim Takla (1895-1945), foreign minister.

**2016, Nov. 18 Litho.** ***Perf. 13x13¼***
**750-764** A244 Set of 15 7.25 7.25

Independence Day.

American University of Beirut, 150th Anniv. A245

**2016, Dec. 3 Litho.** ***Perf. 13x13¼***
**765** A245 £2000 multi 3.75 3.75

Zaki Nassif (1918-2004), Composer
A246

**2016, Dec. 15 Litho. *Perf. 13¼x13***
**766** A246 £2000 multi 3.75 3.75

New Year 2017 — A247

**2016, Dec. 29 Litho. *Perf. 13¼x13***
**767** A247 £5000 multi 9.50 9.50

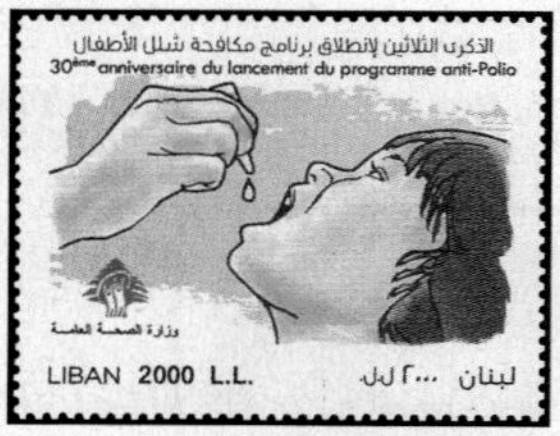


Anti-Polio Campaign, 30th Anniv. — A248

**2017, Jan. 20 Litho. *Perf. 13¼x13***
**768** A248 £2000 multi 3.75 3.75

International Women's Day — A249

**2017, Mar. 29 Litho. *Perf. 13¼x13***
**769** A249 £10,000 multi 20.00 20.00

Museums
A250

Designs: No. 770, £2000, Sursock Museum. No. 771, £2000, Minerals from Mineral Museum, Beirut. No. 772, £2000, Sculptures from National Museum, Beirut.

**2017, May 16 Litho. *Perf. 13x13¼***
**770-772** A250 Set of 3 12.00 12.00

National Museum, 75th anniv. (No. 772).

Dar Al Aytam Al Islamiya Orphanage
A251

**2017, June 13 Litho. *Perf. 13x13¼***
**773** A251 £2000 multi 4.00 4.00

World Music Day — A252

**2017, June 21 Litho. *Perf. 13¼x13***
**774** A252 £250 multi .65 .65

Cedar of Lebanon — A253

**2017, July 8 Litho. *Perf. 13¼x13***
**775** A253 £2250 multi 5.50 5.50

Mikhail Naimy (1889-1998), Writer — A254

**2017, July 22 Litho. *Perf. 13x13¼***
**776** A254 £250 multi .65 .65

Army Day
A255

**2017, July 31 Litho. *Perf. 13¼x13***
**777** A255 £2000 multi 4.00 4.00

Carlos Ghosn, Automobile Industry Executive — A256

**2017, Aug. 28 Litho. *Perf. 13¼x13***
**778** A256 £2000 multi 4.00 4.00

Zalfa Chamoun (1910-71), Wife of Pres. Camille Chamoun
A257

**2017, Oct. 6 Litho. *Perf. 13x13¼***
**779** A257 £2000 multi 4.00 4.00

Nasri Chamessedine (1927-83), Singer — A258

**2017, Oct. 19 Litho. *Perf. 13x13¼***
**780** A258 £250 multi .65 .65

Caritas Lebanon Charity — A259

**2017, Nov. 3 Litho. *Perf. 13¼x13***
**781** A259 £2000 multi 4.00 4.00

Mohamad Baalbaki (1921-2017), Journalist — A260

**2017, Nov. 9 Litho. *Perf. 13¼x13***
**782** A260 £2000 multi 4.00 4.00

Pres. Michel Aoun
A261

Pres. Aoun and Crowd — A262

People Carrying Large Flag of Lebanon — A263

**2017, Dec. 6 Litho. *Perf. 13x13¼***
**783** A261 £5000 multi 10.00 10.00

***Perf. 13¼x13***

**784** A262 £5000 multi 10.00 10.00
**785** A263 £5000 multi 10.00 10.00
*Nos. 783-785 (3)* 30.00 30.00

## SEMI-POSTAL STAMPS

Stamps of 1925 Srchd. in Red or Black

**1926 Unwmk. *Perf. 14x13½***
**B1** A2 0.25p + 0.25p ol blk 4.25 4.25
**B2** A2 0.25p + 0.50p yel grn (B) 4.25 4.25
**B3** A2 0.25p + 0.75p brn org (B) 4.25 4.25
**B4** A2 0.50p + 1p mag 4.75 4.75
**B5** A2 0.50p 1.25p 5.00 5.00
**B6** A2 0.50p + 1.50p rose red (B) 5.00 5.00
*a.* Double surcharge 40.00 30.00
**B7** A2 0.75p + 2.50p dk brn 5.00 5.00
**B8** A2 0.75p + 72.50p pck bl 5.50 5.50
**B9** A2 1p + 3p org brn 5.50 5.50
**B10** A2 1p + 5p vio (B) 5.50 5.50
**B11** A3 2p + 10p vio brn (B) 5.50 5.50
**B12** A2 5p + 25p ultra 5.50 5.50
*Nos. B1-B12 (12)* 60.00 60.00

On No. B11 the surcharge is set in six lines to fit the shape of the stamp. All values of this series exist with inverted surcharge. Value each, $17.50.

See Nos. CB1-CB4.

**Catalogue values for unused stamps in this section, from this point to the end of the section, are for Never Hinged items.**

Boxing — SP1

**1961, Jan. 12 Litho. *Perf. 13***

| | | | | |
|---|---|---|---|---|
| **B13** | SP1 | 2.50p + 2.50p shown | .50 | .25 |
| **B14** | SP1 | 5p + 5p Wrestling | .50 | .25 |
| **B15** | SP1 | 7.50p + 7.50p Shot put | .50 | .25 |
| | | *Nos. B13-B15,CB12-CB14 (6)* | 13.50 | 5.55 |

17th Olympic Games, Rome, Aug. 25-Sept. 11, 1960.

### Nos. B13-B15 with Arabic and French Overprint in Black, Blue or Green and two Bars through Olympic Inscription: "CHAMPIONNAT D'EUROPE DE TIR, 2 JUIN 1962"

**1962, June 2**

| | | | | |
|---|---|---|---|---|
| **B16** | SP1 | 2.50p + 2.50p blue & brn (Bk) | .50 | .25 |
| **B17** | SP1 | 5p + 5p org & brn (G) | .90 | .25 |
| **B18** | SP1 | 7.50p + 7.50p vio & brn (Bl) | 1.00 | .40 |
| | | *Nos. B16-B18,CB15-CB17 (6)* | 9.40 | 4.35 |

European Marksmanship Championships held in Lebanon.

Red Cross SP2

No. B20, Stylized profile. No. B21, Globe, emblems, dove.

**1988, June 8 Litho. *Perf. 14***

| | | | |
|---|---|---|---|
| **B19** | SP2 | £10 + £1 shown | 1.75 |
| **B20** | SP2 | £20 + £2 multi | 2.75 |
| **B21** | SP2 | £30 + £3 multi | 3.75 |
| | | *Nos. B19-B21 (3)* | 8.25 |

## AIR POST STAMPS

Nos. 10-13 with Additional Overprint

**1924 Unwmk. *Perf. 14x13½***

| | | | | |
|---|---|---|---|---|
| **C1** | A18 | 2p on 40c | 13.00 | *13.00* |
| *a.* | | Double surcharge | 52.50 | 52.50 |
| **C2** | A18 | 3p on 60c | 13.00 | *13.00* |
| *a.* | | Invtd. surch. and ovpt. | 87.50 | 87.50 |
| **C3** | A18 | 5p on 1fr | 13.00 | *13.00* |
| *a.* | | Dbl. surch. and ovpt. | 72.50 | 72.50 |
| *b.* | | "5" omitted | 300.00 | |
| **C4** | A18 | 10p on 2fr | 13.00 | *13.00* |
| *a.* | | Invtd. surch. and ovpt. | 110.00 | 110.00 |
| *b.* | | Dbl. surch. and ovpt. | 60.00 | 60.00 |
| | | *Nos. C1-C4 (4)* | 52.00 | *52.00* |

Nos. 33, 35-37 Overprinted

| | | | | |
|---|---|---|---|---|
| **C5** | A18 | 2p on 40c | 13.00 | 13.00 |
| *a.* | | Overprint reversed | 45.00 | |
| **C6** | A18 | 3p on 60c | 13.00 | 13.00 |
| *a.* | | Overprint reversed | 45.00 | |
| **C7** | A18 | 5p on 1fr | 13.00 | 13.00 |
| *a.* | | Overprint reversed | 45.00 | |
| **C8** | A18 | 10p on 2fr | 13.50 | 13.50 |
| *a.* | | Overprint reversed | 45.00 | |
| *b.* | | Double surcharge | 45.00 | |
| | | *Nos. C5-C8 (4)* | 52.50 | 52.50 |

Nos. 57, 59-61 Overprinted in Green

**1925**

| | | | | |
|---|---|---|---|---|
| **C9** | A2 | 2p dark brown | 5.00 | 5.00 |
| **C10** | A2 | 3p orange brown | 5.00 | 5.00 |
| **C11** | A2 | 5p violet | 5.00 | 5.00 |
| *a.* | | Inverted overprint | | |
| **C12** | A3 | 10p violet brown | 5.00 | 5.00 |
| | | *Nos. C9-C12 (4)* | 20.00 | 20.00 |

Nos. 57, 59-61 Ovptd. in Red — c

**1926**

| | | | | |
|---|---|---|---|---|
| **C13** | A2 | 2p dark brown | 5.25 | 5.25 |
| **C14** | A2 | 3p orange brown | 5.25 | 5.25 |
| **C15** | A2 | 5p violet | 5.25 | 5.25 |
| **C16** | A3 | 10p violet brown | 5.25 | 5.25 |
| | | *Nos. C13-C16 (4)* | 21.00 | 21.00 |

Airplane pointed down on No. C16.

Exist with inverted overprint. Value, each $45.

### Issues of Republic under French Mandate

Nos. C13-C16 Overprinted — d

**1927**

| | | | | |
|---|---|---|---|---|
| **C17** | A2 | 2p dark brown | 5.50 | 5.50 |
| **C18** | A2 | 3p orange brown | 5.50 | 5.50 |
| **C19** | A2 | 5p violet | 5.50 | 5.50 |
| **C20** | A3 | 10p violet brown | 5.50 | 5.50 |
| | | *Nos. C17-C20 (4)* | 22.00 | 22.00 |

On No. C19 "Republique Libanaise" is above the bars. Overprint set in two lines on No. C20.

Nos. C17-C20 with Additional Ovpt. — e

**1928 Black Overprint**

| | | | | |
|---|---|---|---|---|
| **C21** | A2 | 2p brown | 12.50 | 10.00 |
| *a.* | | Double overprint | 65.00 | 65.00 |
| *b.* | | Inverted overprint | 65.00 | 65.00 |
| **C22** | A2 | 3p orange brown | 12.50 | 10.00 |
| *a.* | | Double overprint | 65.00 | 65.00 |
| **C23** | A2 | 5p violet | 12.50 | 10.00 |
| *a.* | | Double overprint | 65.00 | 65.00 |
| **C24** | A3 | 10p violet brown | 12.50 | 10.00 |
| *a.* | | Double overprint | 65.00 | 65.00 |
| | | *Nos. C21-C24 (4)* | 50.00 | 40.00 |

On Nos. C21-C24 the airplane is always in red.

Nos. 52, 54, 57, 59-62 Ovptd. in Red or Black — f

**1928**

| | | | | |
|---|---|---|---|---|
| **C25** | A2 | 2p dark brown | 4.50 | 4.50 |
| **C26** | A2 | 3p orange brown | 3.00 | 3.00 |
| **C27** | A2 | 5p violet | 4.50 | 4.50 |
| **C28** | A3 | 10p violet brown | 4.50 | 4.50 |

**1929**

| | | | | |
|---|---|---|---|---|
| **C33** | A2 | 0.50p yellow green | 1.25 | 1.25 |
| *a.* | | Inverted overprint | 45.00 | 45.00 |
| **C34** | A2 | 1p magenta (Bk) | 1.00 | 1.00 |
| *a.* | | Inverted overprint | 45.00 | 45.00 |
| **C35** | A2 | 25p ultra | 190.00 | 160.00 |
| *a.* | | Inverted overprint | 525.00 | 525.00 |
| | | *Nos. C25-C34 (6)* | 18.75 | 18.75 |
| | | *Nos. C25-C35 (7)* | 208.75 | 178.75 |

On Nos. C25-C28 the airplane is always in red.

On No. C28 the overprinted orientation is horizontal. The bars covering the old country names are at the left.

The red overprint of a silhouetted plane and "Republique Libanaise," as on Nos. C25-C27, was also applied to Nos. C9-C12. These are believed to have been essays, and were not regularly issued.

No. 62 with Surcharge Added in Red

Two types of surcharge:

I — The "5" of "15 P." is italic. The "15" is 4mm high. Arabic characters for "Lebanese Republic" and for "15 P." are on same line in that order.

II — The "5" is in Roman type (upright) and smaller; "15" is 3½mm high. Arabic for "Lebanese Republic" is centered on line by itself, with Arabic for "15 P." below right end of line.

| | | | | |
|---|---|---|---|---|
| **C36** | A2 | 15p on 25p ultra (I) | 225.00 | 175.00 |
| *a.* | | Type II (#106) | *800.00* | *800.00* |

### Nos. 102 Overprinted Type "c" in Blue

| | | | | |
|---|---|---|---|---|
| **C37** | A2 | 0.50p on 0.75p | 1.00 | 1.00 |
| *a.* | | Airplane inverted | 45.00 | |
| *b.* | | French and Arabic surch. invtd. | | |
| *c.* | | "P" omitted | | |
| *d.* | | Airplane double | 50.00 | |

### No. 55 Surcharged in Red

**1930**

| | | | | |
|---|---|---|---|---|
| **C38** | A2 | 2p on 1.25p dp green | 1.75 | 1.25 |
| *a.* | | Inverted surcharge | 72.50 | 45.00 |

Airplane over Racheya AP2

Designs: 1p, Plane over Broumana. 2p, Baalbek. 3p, Hasroun. 5p, Byblos. 10p, Kadicha River. 15p, Beirut. 25p, Tripoli. 50p, Kabeljas. 100p, Zahle.

**1930-31 Photo. *Perf. 13½***

| | | | | |
|---|---|---|---|---|
| **C39** | AP2 | 0.50p dk violet ('31) | .50 | .50 |
| **C40** | AP2 | 1p yellow grn ('31) | .80 | .80 |
| **C41** | AP2 | 2p dp orange ('31) | 2.50 | 2.50 |
| **C42** | AP2 | 3p magenta ('31) | 2.50 | 2.50 |
| **C43** | AP2 | 5p indigo | 2.50 | 2.50 |
| **C44** | AP2 | 10p orange red | 3.25 | 3.25 |
| **C45** | AP2 | 15p orange brn | 3.25 | 3.25 |
| **C46** | AP2 | 25p gray vio ('31) | 4.75 | 4.75 |
| **C47** | AP2 | 50p dp claret | 9.00 | 9.00 |
| **C48** | AP2 | 100p olive brown | 12.00 | 12.00 |
| | | *Nos. C39-C48 (10)* | 41.05 | 41.05 |

Nos. C39-C48 exist imperforate. Value, set $200.

### Tourist Publicity Issue

Skiing in Lebanon AP12

Bay of Jounie AP13

**1936, Oct. 12**

| | | | | |
|---|---|---|---|---|
| **C49** | AP12 | 0.50p slate grn | 3.00 | 3.00 |
| **C50** | AP13 | 1p red orange | 3.75 | 3.75 |
| **C51** | AP12 | 2p black violet | 3.75 | 3.75 |
| **C52** | AP13 | 3p yellow grn | 4.00 | 4.00 |
| **C53** | AP12 | 5p brown car | 4.00 | 4.00 |
| **C54** | AP13 | 10p orange brn | 4.00 | 4.00 |
| **C55** | AP13 | 15p dk carmine | 37.50 | 37.50 |
| **C56** | AP12 | 25p green | 125.00 | 125.00 |
| | | *Nos. C49-C56 (8)* | 185.00 | 185.00 |

Nos. C49-C56 exist imperforate. Value, set $650.

Lebanese Pavilion at Exposition AP14

**1937, July 1 *Perf. 13½***

| | | | | |
|---|---|---|---|---|
| **C57** | AP14 | 0.50p olive black | 1.50 | 1.50 |
| **C58** | AP14 | 1p yellow green | 1.50 | 1.50 |
| **C59** | AP14 | 2p dk red orange | 1.50 | 1.50 |
| **C60** | AP14 | 3p dk olive grn | 1.50 | 1.50 |
| **C61** | AP14 | 5p deep green | 2.00 | 2.00 |
| **C62** | AP14 | 10p carmine lake | 9.00 | 9.00 |
| **C63** | AP14 | 15p rose lake | 10.00 | 10.00 |
| **C64** | AP14 | 25p orange brn | 17.50 | 17.50 |
| | | *Nos. C57-C64 (8)* | 44.50 | 44.50 |

Paris International Exposition.

Arcade of Beit-ed-Din Palace AP15

Ruins of Baalbek AP16

**1937-40 Engr. *Perf. 13***

| | | | | |
|---|---|---|---|---|
| **C65** | AP15 | 0.50p ultra ('38) | .35 | .25 |
| **C66** | AP15 | 1p hen brn ('40) | .35 | .25 |
| **C67** | AP15 | 2p sepia ('40) | .35 | .25 |
| **C68** | AP15 | 3p rose ('40) | 3.25 | 1.25 |
| **C69** | AP15 | 5p lt green ('40) | .35 | .25 |
| **C70** | AP16 | 10p dull violet | .35 | .25 |
| **C71** | AP16 | 15p turq bl ('40) | 2.75 | 1.75 |
| **C72** | AP16 | 25p violet ('40) | 6.00 | 5.00 |
| **C73** | AP16 | 50p yel grn ('40) | 11.00 | 7.00 |
| **C74** | AP16 | 100p brown ('40) | 6.00 | 3.50 |
| | | *Nos. C65-C74 (10)* | 30.75 | 19.75 |

Nos. C65-C74 exist imperforate.

Medical College of Beirut AP17

**1938, May 9 Photo. *Perf. 13***

| | | | | |
|---|---|---|---|---|
| **C75** | AP17 | 2p green | 3.00 | *3.50* |
| **C76** | AP17 | 3p orange | 3.00 | *3.50* |
| | | Never hinged | 6.00 | |
| **C77** | AP17 | 5p lilac gray | 5.50 | *6.50* |
| **C78** | AP17 | 10p lake | 10.50 | *12.00* |
| | | *Nos. C75-C78 (4)* | 22.00 | *25.50* |

Medical Congress.

Maurice Noguès and View of Beirut — AP18

**1938, July 15 *Perf. 11***

| | | | | |
|---|---|---|---|---|
| **C79** | AP18 | 10p brown carmine | 4.00 | 1.50 |
| *a.* | | Souv. sheet of 4, perf. 13½ | 35.00 | 20.00 |
| *b.* | | Perf. 13½ | 7.50 | 4.00 |

10th anniversary of first Marseille-Beirut flight, by Maurice Noguès.

No. C79a has marginal inscriptions in French and Arabic. Exists imperf.; value $250.

### Independent Republic

Plane Over Mt. Lebanon AP19

**1942, Sept. 18 Litho. *Perf. 11½***

| | | | | |
|---|---|---|---|---|
| **C80** | AP19 | 10p dk brown vio | 7.00 | *8.00* |
| **C81** | AP19 | 50p dk gray grn | 7.00 | *8.00* |

1st anniv. of the Proclamation of Independence, Nov. 26, 1941.

Nos. C80 and C81 exist imperforate.

Bechamoun AP20

Rachaya Citadel AP21

Air View of Beirut AP22

**1943, May 1** *Perf. 11½*

| | | | | | |
|---|---|---|---|---|---|
| **C82** | AP20 | 25p yellow grn | | 4.75 | 4.75 |
| **C83** | AP20 | 50p orange | | 6.50 | 5.50 |
| **C84** | AP21 | 100p buff | | 6.50 | 5.50 |
| **C85** | AP21 | 200p blue vio | | 8.00 | 7.25 |
| **C86** | AP22 | 300p sage green | | 21.00 | 17.50 |
| **C87** | AP22 | 500p sepia | | 42.50 | 32.50 |
| | | *Nos. C82-C87 (6)* | | 89.25 | 73.00 |

2nd anniv. of the Proclamation of Independence. Nos. C82-C87 exist imperforate.

See Nos. 163-166. For overprints see Nos. C91-C96.

Bhannes Sanatorium AP23

**1943, July 8** **Photo.**

**Black Overprint**

| | | | | |
|---|---|---|---|---|
| **C88** | AP23 | 20p orange | 3.75 | 2.75 |
| **C89** | AP23 | 50p steel blue | 4.25 | 3.50 |
| **C90** | AP23 | 100p rose violet | 6.00 | 4.50 |
| | | *Nos. C88-C90 (3)* | 14.00 | 10.75 |

Arab Medical Congress, Beirut.

Nos. C82 to C87 Overprinted in Red, Blue or Violet

**1944, Nov. 23**

| | | | | |
|---|---|---|---|---|
| **C91** | AP20 | 25p yel grn (R) | 7.25 | 7.25 |
| **C92** | AP20 | 50p orange (Bl) | 12.00 | 12.00 |
| **C93** | AP21 | 100p buff (V) | 14.00 | 14.00 |
| **C94** | AP21 | 200p blue vio (R) | 25.00 | 25.00 |
| **C95** | AP22 | 300p sage grn (R) | 32.50 | 30.00 |
| **C96** | AP22 | 500p sepia (Bl) | 65.00 | 60.00 |
| | | *Nos. C91-C96 (6)* | 155.75 | 148.25 |

Return to office of the President and his ministers, Nov. 22, 1943.

**Catalogue values for unused stamps in this section, from this point to the end of the section, are for Never Hinged items.**

Falls of Litani — AP24

The Cedars AP25

**1945, July** **Unwmk.** **Litho.**

| | | | | |
|---|---|---|---|---|
| **C97** | AP24 | 25p gray brown | 3.50 | 2.10 |
| **C98** | AP24 | 50p rose violet | 5.00 | 2.75 |
| **C99** | AP25 | 200p violet | 15.00 | 5.25 |
| **C100** | AP25 | 300p brown black | 27.50 | 10.50 |
| | | *Nos. C97-C100 (4)* | 51.00 | 20.60 |

Lebanese Soldiers at Bir Hacheim AP26

**1946, May 8**

| | | | | |
|---|---|---|---|---|
| **C101** | AP26 | 15p bl blk, org & red org | 1.00 | .25 |
| **C102** | AP26 | 20p red, lil & bl | 1.00 | .60 |
| **C103** | AP26 | 25p brt bl, org & red | 1.25 | .25 |
| **C104** | AP26 | 50p gray blk, bl & red | 1.75 | .50 |
| **C105** | AP26 | 100p pur, pink & red | 5.00 | 1.25 |
| **C106** | AP26 | 150p brn, pink & red | 6.00 | 3.75 |
| | | *Nos. C101-C106 (6)* | 16.00 | 6.60 |

Victory of the Allied Nations in WWII, 1st anniv.

Three imperf. souvenir sheets of 14 exist. They contain one each of Nos. C101-C106 and 189-196 in changed colors. One has sepia inscriptions, and one on thin white card has blue inscriptions. Value $30 each. The third, with blue inscriptions, is on thick honeycombed chamois card. Value $110.

**Night Herons Type**

**1946, Sept. 11**

| | | | | |
|---|---|---|---|---|
| **C107** | A35 | 10p orange | 7.00 | 1.00 |
| **C108** | A35 | 25p ultra | 8.00 | .25 |
| **C109** | A35 | 50p blue green | 25.00 | 1.60 |
| **C110** | A35 | 100p dk vio brn | 37.50 | 6.50 |
| | | *Nos. C107-C110 (4)* | 77.50 | 9.35 |

Symbols of Communications — AP28

**1946, Nov. 22**

| | | | | |
|---|---|---|---|---|
| **C111** | AP28 | 25p deep blue | 1.75 | .70 |
| **C112** | AP28 | 50p green | 2.50 | .80 |
| **C113** | AP28 | 75p orange red | 4.25 | 1.75 |
| **C114** | AP28 | 150p brown black | 6.00 | 2.75 |
| | | *Nos. C111-C114 (4)* | 14.50 | 6.00 |

Arab Postal Congress, Sofar, 1946.

Stone Tablet, Dog River and Pres. Bechara el-Khoury AP29

**1947, Feb. 11**

| | | | | |
|---|---|---|---|---|
| **C115** | AP29 | 25p ultra | 7.00 | .35 |
| **C116** | AP29 | 50p dull rose | 9.00 | .60 |
| **C117** | AP29 | 75p gray black | 11.00 | .65 |
| **C118** | AP29 | 150p blue green | 17.50 | 1.40 |
| | | *Nos. C115-C118 (4)* | 44.50 | 3.00 |

Evacuation of foreign troops from Lebanon, Dec. 31, 1946.

Bay of Jounie AP30

Government House, Beirut — AP31

**1947, Feb. 11** **Grayish Paper**

| | | | | |
|---|---|---|---|---|
| **C119** | AP30 | 5p dp blue grn | .60 | .25 |
| **C120** | AP30 | 10p rose vio | .90 | .25 |
| **C121** | AP30 | 15p vermilion | 2.25 | .25 |
| **C122** | AP30 | 20p orange | 2.50 | .25 |
| *a.* | | 20p red orange, white paper | 2.25 | .25 |
| **C123** | AP30 | 25p deep blue | 3.00 | .25 |
| **C124** | AP30 | 50p henna brn | 5.00 | .25 |
| **C125** | AP30 | 100p chocolate | 10.50 | .30 |
| **C126** | AP31 | 150p dk vio brn | 18.00 | .50 |
| **C127** | AP31 | 200p slate | 27.50 | 2.40 |
| **C128** | AP31 | 300p black | 45.00 | 6.00 |
| | | *Nos. C119-C128 (10)* | 115.25 | 10.70 |

See Nos. C145A-C147B.

Post Horn and Letter — AP32

Phoenician Galley AP33

**1947, June 17** **Litho.**

| | | | | |
|---|---|---|---|---|
| **C129** | AP32 | 10p brt ultra | 1.75 | .50 |
| **C130** | AP32 | 15p rose car | 2.00 | .50 |
| **C131** | AP32 | 25p bright blue | 2.50 | .80 |
| **C132** | AP33 | 50p dk slate grn | 5.75 | .90 |
| **C133** | AP33 | 75p purple | 7.00 | 1.90 |
| **C134** | AP33 | 100p dark brown | 9.00 | 2.50 |
| | | *Nos. C129-C134 (6)* | 28.00 | 7.10 |

Lebanon's participation in the 12th UPU congress, Paris.

Lebanese Village AP34

**1948, Sept. 1** *Perf. 11½*

| | | | | |
|---|---|---|---|---|
| **C135** | AP34 | 5p dp orange | .75 | .25 |
| **C136** | AP34 | 10p rose lilac | 1.75 | .25 |
| **C137** | AP34 | 15p orange brn | 3.50 | .25 |
| **C138** | AP34 | 20p slate | 4.50 | .25 |
| **C139** | AP34 | 25p Prus blue | 10.50 | 1.00 |
| **C140** | AP34 | 50p gray black | 17.50 | 1.40 |
| | | *Nos. C135-C140 (6)* | 38.50 | 3.40 |

Apollo — AP35

Minerva AP36

**1948, Nov. 23** **Unwmk.**

| | | | | |
|---|---|---|---|---|
| **C141** | AP35 | 7.50p blue & lt blue | 4.00 | 1.00 |
| **C142** | AP35 | 15p black & gray | 5.00 | 1.25 |
| **C143** | AP35 | 20p rose brn & rose | 5.25 | 1.90 |
| **C144** | AP36 | 35p car rose & rose | 8.00 | 2.50 |
| **C145** | AP36 | 75p bl grn & lt green | 15.00 | 5.00 |
| | | *Nos. C141-C145 (5)* | 37.25 | 11.65 |

UNESCO. Nos. C141-C145 exist imperforate, and combined with Nos. 220-224 in an imperforate souvenir sheet on thin buff cardboard, with black inscriptions in top margin in Arabic and at bottom in French. Value $275.

**Bay Type of 1947 Redrawn**

**1949** **White Paper**

| | | | | |
|---|---|---|---|---|
| **C145A** | AP30 | 10p rose lilac | 9.00 | 1.00 |
| **C146** | AP30 | 15p dark green | 11.00 | 1.25 |
| **C147** | AP30 | 20p orange | 25.00 | 9.00 |
| **C147A** | AP30 | 25p dark blue | 65.00 | 3.25 |
| **C147B** | AP30 | 50p brick red | 275.00 | 35.00 |
| | | *Nos. C145A-C147B (5)* | 385.00 | 49.50 |

In the redrawn designs, Nos. C145A, C147 and C147B have zeros with broader centers than in the 1947 issue (Nos. C120, C122 and C124).

Helicopter Mail Delivery — AP37

**1949, Aug. 16** **Unwmk.** *Perf. 11½*

| | | | | |
|---|---|---|---|---|
| **C148** | AP37 | 25p deep blue | 8.00 | 4.00 |
| **C149** | AP37 | 50p green | 12.00 | 4.50 |
| *a.* | | Souvenir sheet of 5, #225-227, C148-C149 | 75.00 | 35.00 |

UPU, 75th anniv. No. 149a exists on thin cardboard. Value $250.

Homing Birds AP38

Pres. Bechara el-Khoury AP39

**1950, Aug. 8** **Litho.**

| | | | | |
|---|---|---|---|---|
| **C150** | AP38 | 5p violet blue | 2.75 | .65 |
| **C151** | AP38 | 15p rose vio | 3.00 | .70 |
| **C152** | AP39 | 25p chocolate | 2.25 | .95 |
| **C153** | AP39 | 35p gray green | 3.25 | 1.40 |
| *a.* | | Souvenir sheet of 6, #243-244, C150-C153, chamois paper | 70.00 | 55.00 |
| | | *Nos. C150-C153 (4)* | 11.25 | 3.70 |

Conference of Emigrants, 1950.

Crusader Castle, Sidon Harbor AP40

**1950, Sept. 7**

| | | | | |
|---|---|---|---|---|
| **C154** | AP40 | 10p chocolate | 1.00 | .25 |
| **C155** | AP40 | 15p dark green | 2.00 | .25 |
| **C156** | AP40 | 20p crimson | 4.00 | .25 |
| **C157** | AP40 | 25p ultra | 7.00 | .80 |
| **C158** | AP40 | 50p gray black | 10.00 | 2.25 |
| | | *Nos. C154-C158 (5)* | 24.00 | 3.80 |

**1951, June 9** **Redrawn** **Typo.**

| | | | | |
|---|---|---|---|---|
| **C159** | AP40 | 10p grnsh black | 2.00 | .25 |
| **C160** | AP40 | 15p black brown | 3.00 | .25 |
| **C161** | AP40 | 20p vermilion | 3.00 | .25 |
| **C162** | AP40 | 25p deep blue | 4.00 | .25 |
| **C163** | AP40 | 35p lilac rose | 8.00 | 2.40 |
| **C164** | AP40 | 50p indigo | 11.00 | 2.40 |
| | | *Nos. C159-C164 (6)* | 31.00 | 5.80 |

Nos. C154-C158 are lithographed from a fine-screen halftone; Nos. C159-C164 are typographed and much coarser, with larger plane and many other differences.

Khaldé International Airport, Beirut — AP41

Design: 50p to 300p, Amphitheater, Byblos.

**1952 Litho. *Perf. 11½***

| | | | | |
|---|---|---|---|---|
| **C165** | AP41 | 5p crimson | 1.50 | .25 |
| **C166** | AP41 | 10p dark gray | 1.50 | .25 |
| **C167** | AP41 | 15p rose lilac | 1.75 | .25 |
| **C168** | AP41 | 20p brown org | 2.00 | .25 |
| **C169** | AP41 | 25p grnsh blue | 2.00 | .25 |
| **C170** | AP41 | 35p violet bl | 2.75 | .25 |
| **C171** | AP41 | 50p blue green | 14.00 | .60 |
| **C172** | AP41 | 100p deep blue | 55.00 | 2.40 |
| **C173** | AP41 | 200p dk blue grn | 35.00 | 3.50 |
| **C174** | AP41 | 300p black brn | 52.50 | 7.50 |
| | | *Nos. C165-C174 (10)* | 168.00 | 15.50 |

Lockheed Constellation — AP42

**1953, Oct. 1**

| | | | | |
|---|---|---|---|---|
| **C175** | AP42 | 5p yellow green | .90 | .25 |
| **C176** | AP42 | 10p deep plum | 1.25 | .25 |
| **C177** | AP42 | 15p scarlet | 1.75 | .25 |
| **C178** | AP42 | 20p aqua | 2.25 | .25 |
| **C179** | AP42 | 25p blue | 4.00 | .25 |
| **C180** | AP42 | 35p orange brn | 5.75 | .25 |
| **C181** | AP42 | 50p violet blue | 11.00 | .30 |
| **C182** | AP42 | 100p black brown | 16.00 | 2.40 |
| | | *Nos. C175-C182 (8)* | 42.90 | 4.20 |

Ruins at Baalbek AP43

Irrigation Canal, Litani AP44

**1954, Mar.**

| | | | | |
|---|---|---|---|---|
| **C183** | AP43 | 5p yel green | .75 | .25 |
| **C184** | AP43 | 10p dull purple | .90 | .25 |
| **C185** | AP43 | 15p carmine | 1.50 | .25 |
| **C186** | AP43 | 20p brown | 2.00 | .25 |
| **C187** | AP43 | 25p dull blue | 2.50 | .25 |
| **C188** | AP43 | 35p black brn | 3.00 | .25 |
| **C189** | AP44 | 50p dk olive grn | 10.00 | .25 |
| **C190** | AP44 | 100p dp car | 19.00 | .35 |
| **C191** | AP44 | 200p dark brown | 27.50 | .70 |
| **C192** | AP44 | 300p dk gray blue | 50.00 | 1.50 |
| | | *Nos. C183-C192 (10)* | 117.15 | 4.30 |

See Nos. C229-C232.

Khaldé International Airport, Beirut — AP45

**1954, Apr. 23 *Perf. 11½***

| | | | | |
|---|---|---|---|---|
| **C193** | AP45 | 10p pink & rose red | 1.25 | .25 |
| **C194** | AP45 | 25p dp bl & gray bl | 2.75 | .50 |
| **C195** | AP45 | 35p dl brn & yel brn | 4.25 | .90 |
| **C196** | AP45 | 65p dp grn & grn | 6.25 | 1.60 |
| | | *Nos. C193-C196 (4)* | 14.50 | 3.25 |

Opening of Beirut's Intl. Airport. Exist imperf.

**Arab Postal Union Type of Regular Issue, 1955**

**1955, Jan. 1 *Perf. 13½x13***

| | | | | |
|---|---|---|---|---|
| **C197** | A52 | 2.50p yellow brn | 1.50 | .25 |

Rotary Emblem AP47

**1955, Feb. 23 *Perf. 11½***

| | | | | |
|---|---|---|---|---|
| **C198** | AP47 | 35p dull green | 1.50 | .40 |
| **C199** | AP47 | 65p dull blue | 2.50 | .55 |

Rotary International, 50th anniversary.

Skiing Among the Cedars AP48

**1955, Feb. 24 Litho.**

| | | | | |
|---|---|---|---|---|
| **C200** | AP48 | 5p blue green | 2.00 | .25 |
| **C201** | AP48 | 15p crimson | 2.25 | .25 |
| **C202** | AP48 | 20p lilac | 2.75 | .25 |
| **C203** | AP48 | 25p blue | 5.00 | .25 |
| **C204** | AP48 | 35p olive brn | 6.50 | .25 |
| **C205** | AP48 | 50p chocolate | 11.00 | .70 |
| **C206** | AP48 | 65p deep blue | 17.50 | 2.10 |
| | | *Nos. C200-C206 (7)* | 47.00 | 4.05 |

See Nos. C233-C235. For surcharge see No. C271.

Tourist — AP49

**1955, Sept. 10 Unwmk. *Perf. 13***

| | | | | |
|---|---|---|---|---|
| **C207** | AP49 | 2.50p brn vio & lt bl | .50 | .25 |
| **C208** | AP49 | 12.50p ultra & lt bl | .65 | .25 |
| **C209** | AP49 | 25p indigo & lt bl | 1.50 | .25 |
| **C210** | AP49 | 35p ol grn & lt bl | 1.75 | .25 |
| *a.* | | Sheet of 4, #C207-C210, imperf. | 22.50 | 7.75 |
| | | *Nos. C207-C210 (4)* | 4.40 | 1.00 |

Tourist Year. No. C210a is printed on cardboard.

Oranges AP50

Designs: 25p, 35p, 50p, Grapes, vert. 65p, 100p, 200p, Apples.

**1955, Oct. 15**

| | | | | |
|---|---|---|---|---|
| **C211** | AP50 | 5p yel grn & yel | 1.10 | .25 |
| **C212** | AP50 | 10p dk grn & dp orange | 1.25 | .25 |
| **C213** | AP50 | 15p yel grn & red orange | 1.40 | .25 |
| **C214** | AP50 | 20p olive & yel org | 2.00 | .25 |
| **C215** | AP50 | 25p blue & vio bl | 2.75 | .25 |
| **C216** | AP50 | 35p green & cl | 3.25 | .25 |
| **C217** | AP50 | 50p blk brn & dl yel | 3.25 | .25 |
| **C218** | AP50 | 65p green & lemon | 6.50 | .25 |
| **C219** | AP50 | 100p yel grn & dp orange | 8.50 | .85 |
| **C220** | AP50 | 200p green & car | 15.00 | 4.25 |
| | | *Nos. C211-C220 (10)* | 45.00 | 7.10 |

For surcharge see No. C265.

United Nations Emblem AP52

**1956, Jan. 23 *Perf. 11½***

| | | | | |
|---|---|---|---|---|
| **C221** | AP52 | 35p violet blue | 5.25 | 1.90 |
| **C222** | AP52 | 65p green | 6.50 | 2.25 |

UN, 10th anniv. (in 1955).

An imperf. souvenir sheet contains one each of Nos. C221 and C222. Value $90.

Temple of the Sun Colonnade, Masks and Lion's Head — AP53

Temple of Bacchus, Baalbek AP54

Design: 35p, 65p, Temple of the Sun colonnade, masks and violincello.

**1956, Dec. 10 Litho. *Perf. 13***

| | | | | |
|---|---|---|---|---|
| **C223** | AP53 | 2.50p dark brown | .85 | .25 |
| **C224** | AP53 | 10p green | 1.10 | .25 |
| **C225** | AP54 | 12.50p light blue | 1.10 | .25 |
| **C226** | AP54 | 25p brt vio bl | 1.60 | .35 |
| **C227** | AP53 | 35p red lilac | 3.00 | .45 |
| **C228** | AP53 | 65p slate blue | 4.25 | .90 |
| | | *Nos. C223-C228 (6)* | 11.90 | 2.45 |

International Festival at Baalbek.

**Skiing Type of 1955 Redrawn and**

Irrigation Canal, Litani AP55

**1957 Litho. *Perf. 11½***

| | | | | |
|---|---|---|---|---|
| **C229** | AP55 | 10p brt violet | .65 | .25 |
| **C230** | AP55 | 15p orange | .90 | .25 |
| **C231** | AP55 | 20p yel green | 1.00 | .25 |
| **C232** | AP55 | 25p slate blue | 1.10 | .25 |
| **C233** | AP48 | 35p gray green | 2.50 | .25 |
| **C234** | AP48 | 65p dp claret | 4.00 | .25 |
| **C235** | AP48 | 100p brown | 6.00 | .65 |
| | | *Nos. C229-C235 (7)* | 16.15 | 2.15 |

Different Arabic characters used for the country name; letters in "Liban" larger.

For surcharge see No. C271.

Pres. Camille Chamoun and King Saud AP56

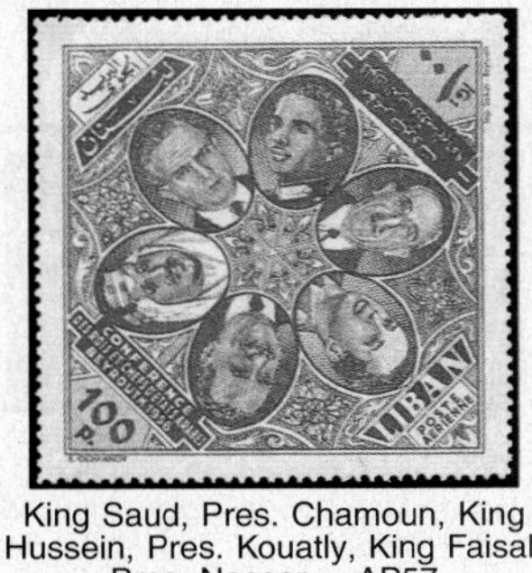


King Saud, Pres. Chamoun, King Hussein, Pres. Kouatly, King Faisal, Pres. Nasser — AP57

Pres. Chamoun and: No. C237, King Hussein. No. C238, Pres. Kouatly. No. C239, King Faisal. No. C240, Pres. Nasser. 25p, Map of Lebanon.

**1957, July 15 Litho. *Perf. 13***

| | | | | |
|---|---|---|---|---|
| **C236** | AP56 | 15p green | .75 | .25 |
| **C237** | AP56 | 15p blue | .75 | .25 |
| **C238** | AP56 | 15p red lilac | .75 | .25 |
| **C239** | AP56 | 15p red orange | .75 | .25 |
| **C240** | AP56 | 15p claret | .75 | .25 |
| **C241** | AP56 | 25p blue | .75 | .25 |
| **C242** | AP57 | 100p dl red brn | 6.00 | 1.50 |
| | | *Nos. C236-C242 (7)* | 10.50 | 3.00 |

Congr. of Arab Leaders, Beirut, 11/12-15/56.

Fencing AP58

50p, Pres. Chamoun and stadium with flags.

**1957, Sept. 12 Unwmk. *Perf. 13***

| | | | | |
|---|---|---|---|---|
| **C243** | AP58 | 35p claret | 3.25 | 1.50 |
| **C244** | AP58 | 50p lt green | 4.00 | 2.25 |

2nd Pan-Arab Games, Beirut. See note on souvenir sheet below No. 314.

Symbols of Communications — AP59

Power Plant, Chamoun AP60

**1957 *Perf. 13x13½, 11½ (AP60)***

| | | | | |
|---|---|---|---|---|
| **C245** | AP59 | 5p brt green | .55 | .25 |
| **C246** | AP59 | 10p yel orange | .60 | .25 |
| **C247** | AP59 | 15p brown | .60 | .25 |
| **C248** | AP59 | 20p maroon | .80 | .25 |
| **C249** | AP59 | 25p violet blue | 1.10 | .25 |
| **C250** | AP60 | 35p violet brn | 1.40 | .25 |
| **C251** | AP60 | 50p green | 1.60 | .25 |
| **C252** | AP60 | 65p sepia | 2.25 | .25 |
| **C253** | AP60 | 100p dark gray | 3.00 | .55 |
| | | *Nos. C245-C253 (9)* | 11.90 | 2.55 |

Plane at Airport AP61

Cogwheel AP62

**1958-59 Unwmk. *Perf. 13***

| | | | | |
|---|---|---|---|---|
| **C254** | AP61 | 5p green | .55 | .25 |
| **C255** | AP61 | 10p magenta | .75 | .25 |
| **C256** | AP61 | 15p dull violet | .90 | .25 |
| **C257** | AP61 | 20p orange ver | 1.10 | .25 |
| **C258** | AP61 | 25p dk vio bl | 1.40 | .25 |
| **C259** | AP62 | 35p grnsh gray | 1.60 | .25 |
| **C260** | AP62 | 50p aquamarine | 2.25 | .25 |
| **C261** | AP62 | 65p pale brown | 3.75 | .30 |
| **C262** | AP62 | 100p brt ultra | 4.25 | .25 |
| | | *Nos. C254-C262 (9)* | 16.55 | 2.30 |

Nos. C259 and C261 Srchd. in Black or Dark Blue

**1959 Unwmk. Litho. *Perf. 13***

| | | | | |
|---|---|---|---|---|
| **C263** | AP62 | 30p on 35p grnsh gray | 1.00 | .25 |
| **C264** | AP62 | 40p on 65p pale brn (Bl) | 1.40 | .45 |

Arab Engineers Congress.

No. C217 Surcharged

**1959, Sept. 1**
**C265** AP50 40p on 50p blk brn & dull yel 1.50 .50

Arab Lawyers Congress.

Myron's Discobolus — AP63

Wreath and Hand Holding Torch AP64

**1959, Oct. 11 Litho. *Perf. 11½***
**C266** AP63 15p shown 1.00 .25
**C267** AP63 30p Weight lifter 1.25 .30
**C268** AP64 40p shown 1.90 .40
*Nos. C266-C268 (3)* 4.15 .95

3rd Mediterranean Games, Beirut.
A souvenir sheet on white cardboard contains one each of Nos. C266-C268, imperf. Sold for 100p. Value *$67.50*

Soldiers and Flag — AP65

**1959, Nov. 25 *Perf. 13½x13***
**C269** AP65 40p sep, brick red & sl 1.50 .30
**C270** AP65 60p sep, dk grn & brick red 2.00 .35

Lebanon's independence, 1941-1959.

**No. C234 Surcharged with New Value and Bars**

**1959, Dec. 15 *Perf. 11½***
**C271** AP48 40p on 65p dp claret 3.00 .30

Hands Planting Tree — AP66

**1960, Jan. 18 Litho. *Perf. 11½***
**C272** AP66 20p rose vio & grn 1.00 .25
**C273** AP66 40p dk brn & green 1.25 .40

Friends of the Tree Society, 25th anniv.

Postal Administration Building — AP67

**1960, Feb. Unwmk. *Perf. 13***
**C274** AP67 20p green .90 .25

President Fuad Chehab — AP68

**1960, Mar. 12 Photo. *Perf. 13½***
**C275** AP68 5p green .50 .25
**C276** AP68 10p Prus blue .50 .25
**C277** AP68 15p orange brn .50 .25
**C278** AP68 20p brown .55 .25
**C279** AP68 30p olive .80 .25
**C280** AP68 40p dull red .90 .25
**C281** AP68 50p blue 1.00 .25
**C282** AP68 70p red lilac 1.10 .25
**C283** AP68 100p dark green 2.00 .40
*Nos. C275-C283 (9)* 7.85 2.40

Uprooted Oak Emblem — AP69

**1960, Apr. 7 Litho. *Perf. 13½x13***
**Size: 20½x36½mm**
**C284** AP69 25p yellow brn 1.00 .25
**C285** AP69 40p green 1.25 .30
*a.* Souv. sheet of 2, #C284-C285, imperf. 45.00 19.00

**Size: 20x36mm**
*C284b* AP69 25p yellow brown 1.00 .40
*C285b* AP69 40p green 1.75 .65

World Refugee Year, 7/1/59-6/30/60.
No. C285a sold for 150p.
Nos. C284b-C285b appear fuzzy and pale when compared to the bolder, clear-cut printing of Nos. C284-C285. Issue date: July 18.
Nos. C284b-C285b exist with carmine surcharges of "30P.+15P." (on C284b) and "20P.+10P." (on C285b), repeated in Arabic, with ornaments covering original denominations.

Martyrs' Monument — AP70

Martyrs of May 6th: 70p, Statues from Martyrs' monument, vert.

**1960, May 6 *Perf. 13x13½, 13½x13***
**C286** AP70 20p rose lilac & grn .80 .25
**C287** AP70 40p Prus grn & dk grn 1.00 .30
**C288** AP70 70p gray olive & blk 2.00 .50
*Nos. C286-C288 (3)* 3.80 1.05

Pres. Chehab and King of Morocco AP71

**1960, June 1 *Perf. 13x13½***
**C289** AP71 30p choc & dk brn 1.00 .30
**C290** AP71 70p blk, dk brn & buff 2.00 .35

Visit of King Mohammed V of Morocco.
A souvenir sheet of 2 on white cardboard contains Nos. C289-C290, imperf. Value $72.50.

Child Learning to Walk — AP72

**1960, Aug. 16 Litho. *Perf. 13½x13***
**C291** AP72 20p shown 1.00 .25
**C292** AP72 60p Mother & child 2.00 .40
*Nos. C291-C292,CB10-CB11 (4)* 6.50 1.50

Day of Mother and Child, Mar. 21-22.

Bird, Ribbon of Flags and Map of Beirut — AP73

40p, Cedar & birds. 70p, Globes & cedar, horiz.

***Perf. 13½x13, 13x13½***
**1960, Sept. 20 Unwmk.**
**C293** AP73 20p multicolored .50 .25
**C294** AP73 40p vio, bl & grn .75 .25
**C295** AP73 70p multicolored 1.00 .25
*Nos. C293-C295 (3)* 2.25 .75

Union of Lebanese Emigrants in the World.
A souvenir sheet of 3 contains Nos. C293-C295, imperf., printed on cardboard. Sold for 150p. Value $22.50.

Pres. Chehab and Map of Lebanon — AP74

**1961, Feb. Litho. *Perf. 13½x13***
**C296** AP74 5p bl grn & yel grn .50 .25
**C297** AP74 10p brown & bister .50 .25
**C298** AP74 70p vio & rose lilac 1.25 .35

Casino, Maameltein Lebanon AP75

**1961 *Perf. 13x13½***
**C299** AP75 15p rose claret .60 .25
**C300** AP75 30p greenish blue 1.00 .25
**C301** AP75 40p brown 1.25 .25
**C302** AP75 200p bis brn & dl bl 5.25 1.40
*Nos. C296-C302 (7)* 10.35 3.00

On Nos. C299-C301, the denomination, inscription and trees differ from No. C302.

UN, 15th Anniv. (in 1960) — AP76

20p, UN Emblem & map of Lebanon, vert. 30p, UN Emblem & symbolic building, vert. 50p, UN Headquarters, New York.

**1961, May 5 *Perf. 13½x13, 13x13½***
**C306** AP76 20p lake & lt blue .70 .25
**C307** AP76 30p green & beige .85 .25
**C308** AP76 50p vio bl & grnsh bl 1.40 .25
*a.* Souvenir sheet of 3 9.00 9.00
*Nos. C306-C308 (3)* 2.95 .75

No. C308a contains one each of Nos. C306-C308, imperf., against a light blue background showing UN emblem. Sold for 125p.

Pottery Workers AP77

**1961, July 11 Litho. *Perf. 13x13½***
**C309** AP77 30p shown 2.75 .25
**C310** AP77 70p Weaver 1.60 .25

Issued for Labor Day, 1961.

Fireworks AP78

Water Skiing AP79

70p, Tourists on boat ride through cave.

**1961, Aug. 8 *Perf. 13½x13, 13x13½***
**C311** AP78 15p lt pur & dk bl 1.50 1.00
**C312** AP79 40p blue & pink 2.10 1.25
**C313** AP79 70p dull brn & pink .90 .50
*Nos. C311-C313 (3)* 4.50 2.75

Issued to publicize tourist month.

Highway Circle at Dora, Beirut Suburb AP80

**1961, Aug. *Perf. 11½***
**C314** AP80 35p yellow green 1.00 .30
**C315** AP80 50p orange brown 1.25 .45
**C316** AP80 100p gray 1.25 .55
*Nos. C314-C316 (3)* 3.50 1.30

Beach at Tyre — AP81

Afka Falls — AP82

**1961, Sept. Litho. *Perf. 13***

| | | | | | |
|---|---|---|---|---|---|
| **C317** | AP81 | 5p | carmine rose | .50 | .25 |
| **C318** | AP81 | 10p | brt violet | .75 | .25 |
| **C319** | AP81 | 15p | bright blue | .80 | .25 |
| **C320** | AP81 | 20p | orange | 1.00 | .25 |
| **C321** | AP81 | 30p | brt green | 1.25 | .25 |
| **C322** | AP82 | 40p | dp claret | 1.00 | .25 |
| **C323** | AP82 | 50p | ultramarine | 1.10 | .25 |
| **C324** | AP82 | 70p | yellow green | 1.50 | .25 |
| **C325** | AP82 | 100p | dark brown | 2.00 | .35 |
| | | | *Nos. C317-C325 (9)* | 9.90 | 2.35 |

See Nos. C341-C342.

Entrance to UNESCO Building AP83

"UNESCO" and Cedar — AP84

Design: 50p, UNESCO headquarters, Paris.

**1961, Nov. 20 Unwmk. *Perf. 12***

| | | | | | |
|---|---|---|---|---|---|
| **C326** | AP83 | 20p | bl, buff & blk | .65 | .25 |
| **C327** | AP84 | 30p | lt grn, blk & mag | .80 | .25 |
| **C328** | AP83 | 50p | multicolored | 1.25 | .25 |
| | | | *Nos. C326-C328 (3)* | 2.70 | .75 |

UNESCO, 15th anniv.

Emir Bechir and Fakhr-el-Din El Maani — AP85

**1961, Dec. 30 Litho.**

| | | | | | |
|---|---|---|---|---|---|
| **C329** | AP85 | 25p | Cedar emblem | .65 | .25 |
| **C330** | AP85 | 50p | shown | 1.00 | .30 |

See note after No. 375.

### Scout Types of Regular Issue, 1962

15p, Trefoil & cedar emblem. 20p, Hand making Scout sign. 25p, Lebanese Scout emblem.

**1962, Mar. 1 Unwmk. *Perf. 12***

| | | | | | |
|---|---|---|---|---|---|
| **C331** | A70 | 15p | grn, blk & red | .80 | .25 |
| **C332** | A69 | 20p | lil, blk & yel | .95 | .25 |
| **C333** | A70 | 25p | multicolored | 1.50 | .40 |
| | | | *Nos. C331-C333 (3)* | 3.25 | .90 |

Arab League Building, Cairo — AP86

**1962, Mar. 20 *Perf. 13***

| | | | | | |
|---|---|---|---|---|---|
| **C334** | AP86 | 20p | ultra & lt bl | .60 | .25 |
| **C335** | AP86 | 30p | red brn & pink | .75 | .25 |
| **C336** | AP86 | 50p | grn & grnsh bl | 1.00 | .30 |
| | | | *Nos. C334-C336 (3)* | 2.35 | .80 |

Arab League Week, Mar. 22-28. See Nos. C372-C375.

Blacksmith AP87

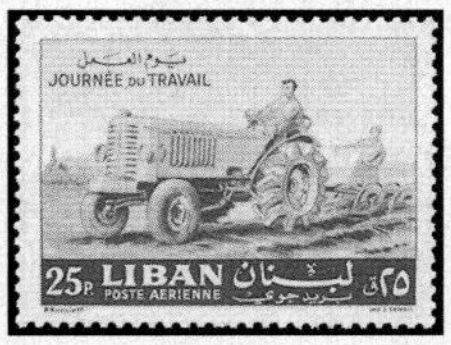


Farm Tractor AP88

***Perf. 13½x13, 13x13½***

**1962, May 1 Litho.**

| | | | | | |
|---|---|---|---|---|---|
| **C337** | AP87 | 5p | green & lt blue | .50 | .25 |
| **C338** | AP87 | 10p | blue & pink | .50 | .25 |
| **C339** | AP88 | 25p | brt vio & pink | .75 | .25 |
| **C340** | AP88 | 35p | car rose & blue | 1.00 | .25 |
| | | | *Nos. C337-C340 (4)* | 2.75 | 1.00 |

Issued for Labor Day.

### Types of 1961 Redrawn with Large Numerals Similar to Redrawn Regular Issue of 1962

**1962 *Perf. 13***

| | | | | | |
|---|---|---|---|---|---|
| **C341** | AP81 | 5p | carmine rose | 1.10 | .25 |
| **C342** | AP82 | 40p | deep claret | 6.25 | .40 |

Hand Reaching for Malaria Eradication Emblem — AP89

Design: 70p, Malaria eradication emblem.

**1962, July 2 Litho. *Perf. 13½x13***

| | | | | | |
|---|---|---|---|---|---|
| **C349** | AP89 | 30p | tan & brown | 1.00 | .25 |
| **C350** | AP89 | 70p | bluish lil & vio | 1.25 | .50 |

WHO drive to eradicate malaria.

Bas-relief of Isis, Kalabsha Temple, Nubia — AP90

**1962, Aug. 1 Unwmk. *Perf. 13***

| | | | | | |
|---|---|---|---|---|---|
| **C351** | AP90 | 30p | yellow green | 2.00 | .25 |
| **C352** | AP90 | 50p | slate | 4.00 | .60 |

Campaign to save historic monuments in Nubia.

Spade, Heart, Diamond, Club — AP91

**1962, Sept.**

| | | | | | |
|---|---|---|---|---|---|
| **C353** | AP91 | 25p | car rose, blk & red | 3.25 | 1.25 |
| **C354** | AP91 | 40p | multicolored | 4.50 | 1.25 |

European Bridge Championship Tournament.

College Student — AP92

**1962, Oct. 1 *Perf. 12***

| | | | | | |
|---|---|---|---|---|---|
| **C355** | AP92 | 45p | multicolored | .90 | .25 |

Issued for Students' Day, Oct. 1.

Sword Severing Chain — AP93

**1962, Nov. 22 Litho. *Perf. 13***

| | | | | | |
|---|---|---|---|---|---|
| **C356** | AP93 | 25p | vio, lt bl & red | 1.00 | .25 |
| **C357** | AP93 | 25p | bl, lt bl & red | 1.00 | .25 |
| **C358** | AP93 | 25p | grn, lt bl & red | 1.00 | .25 |
| | | | *Nos. C356-C358 (3)* | 3.00 | .75 |

19th anniversary of independence.

### Fruit Type of Regular Issue, 1962

5p, Apricots. 10p, 30p, Plums. 20p, 40p, Apples. 50p, Pears. 70p, Medlar. 100p, Lemons.

**1962 Vignette Multicolored**

| | | | | | |
|---|---|---|---|---|---|
| **C359** | A72 | 5p | orange brown | .50 | .25 |
| **C360** | A72 | 10p | black | .55 | .25 |
| **C361** | A72 | 20p | brown | .60 | .25 |
| **C362** | A72 | 30p | gray | .75 | .25 |
| **C363** | A72 | 40p | dark gray | 1.00 | .25 |
| **C364** | A72 | 50p | light brown | 1.25 | .25 |
| **C365** | A72 | 70p | gray olive | 1.50 | .30 |
| **C366** | A72 | 100p | blue | 3.00 | .50 |
| | | | *Nos. C359-C366 (8)* | 9.15 | 2.30 |

Harvest — AP94

Design: 15p, 20p, UN Emblem and hand holding Wheat Emblem, horiz.

**1963, Mar. 21 Litho. *Perf. 13***

| | | | | | |
|---|---|---|---|---|---|
| **C367** | AP94 | 2.50p | ultra & yel | .50 | .25 |
| **C368** | AP94 | 5p | gray grn & yel | .50 | .25 |
| **C369** | AP94 | 7.50p | rose lil & yel | .50 | .25 |
| **C370** | AP94 | 15p | rose brn & pale grn | .80 | .25 |
| **C371** | AP94 | 20p | rose & pale grn | 1.00 | .25 |
| | | | *Nos. C367-C371 (5)* | 3.30 | 1.25 |

FAO "Freedom from Hunger" campaign.

### Redrawn Type of 1962, Dated "1963"

Design: Arab League Building, Cairo.

**1963, Mar. Unwmk. *Perf. 12***

| | | | | | |
|---|---|---|---|---|---|
| **C372** | AP86 | 5p | violet & lt blue | .50 | .25 |
| **C373** | AP86 | 10p | green & lt blue | .50 | .25 |
| **C374** | AP86 | 15p | claret & lt blue | .55 | .25 |
| **C375** | AP86 | 20p | gray & lt blue | .70 | .25 |
| | | | *Nos. C372-C375 (4)* | 2.25 | 1.00 |

Issued for Arab League Week.

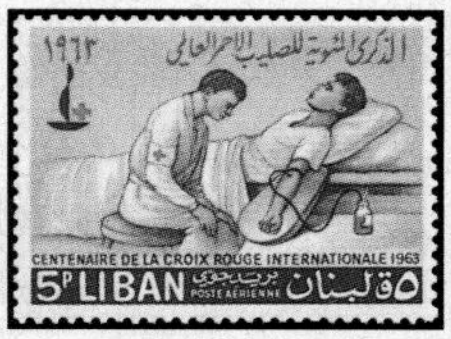


Blood Transfusion AP95

Design: 35p, 40p, Nurse and infant, vert.

**1963, Oct. 5 Unwmk. *Perf. 13***

| | | | | | |
|---|---|---|---|---|---|
| **C376** | AP95 | 5p | green & red | .50 | .25 |
| **C377** | AP95 | 20p | grnsh bl & red | .55 | .25 |
| **C378** | AP95 | 35p | org, red & blk | .70 | .25 |
| **C379** | AP95 | 40p | purple & red | 1.00 | .25 |
| | | | *Nos. C376-C379 (4)* | 2.75 | 1.00 |

Centenary of International Red Cross.

Lyre Player and Columns — AP96

**1963, Nov. 7 Unwmk. *Perf. 13***

| | | | | | |
|---|---|---|---|---|---|
| **C380** | AP96 | 35p | lt bl, org & blk | 1.50 | .30 |

International Festival at Baalbek.

Lebanon Flag, Rising Sun — AP97

**1964, Jan. 8 Litho.**

| | | | | | |
|---|---|---|---|---|---|
| **C381** | AP97 | 5p | bluish grn, ver & yel | .50 | .25 |
| **C382** | AP97 | 10p | yel grn, ver & yel | .55 | .25 |
| **C383** | AP97 | 25p | ultra, ver & yel | .75 | .25 |
| **C384** | AP97 | 40p | gray, ver & yel | 1.10 | .35 |
| | | | *Nos. C381-C384 (4)* | 2.90 | 1.10 |

20th anniversary of Independence.

### Sports Type of Regular Issue, 1964

**1964, Feb. 11 Unwmk. *Perf. 13***

| | | | | | |
|---|---|---|---|---|---|
| **C385** | A76 | 15p | Tennis | .55 | .25 |
| **C386** | A76 | 17.50p | Swimming, horiz. | .65 | .25 |
| **C387** | A76 | 30p | Skiing, horiz. | 1.00 | .25 |
| *a.* | | | Souvenir sheet of 3 | 13.50 | 10.50 |
| | | | *Nos. C385-C387 (3)* | 2.20 | .75 |

No. C387a contains three imperf. stamps similar to Nos. C385-C387 with simulated orange brown perforations and green marginal inscription. Sold for 100p.

Anemone AP98

**1964, June 9 Unwmk. *Perf. 13***

| | | | | | |
|---|---|---|---|---|---|
| **C391** | AP98 | 5p | Lily | .50 | .25 |
| **C392** | AP98 | 10p | Ranunculus | .60 | .25 |
| **C393** | AP98 | 20p | shown | .75 | .25 |
| **C394** | AP98 | 40p | Tuberose | 1.00 | .25 |
| **C395** | AP98 | 45p | Rhododendron | 1.10 | .25 |
| **C396** | AP98 | 50p | Jasmine | 1.25 | .25 |
| **C397** | AP98 | 70p | Yellow broom | 2.00 | .30 |
| | | | *Nos. C391-C397 (7)* | 7.20 | 1.80 |

Girls Jumping Rope AP99

Children's Day: 20p, 40p, Boy on hobby-horse, vert.

**1964, Apr. 8**

| | | | | |
|---|---|---|---|---|
| **C398** | AP99 | 5p emer, org & red | .50 | .25 |
| **C399** | AP99 | 10p yel brn, org & red | .55 | .25 |
| **C400** | AP99 | 20p dp ultra, lt bl & org | .60 | .25 |
| **C401** | AP99 | 40p lil, lt bl & yel | 1.00 | .30 |
| | | *Nos. C398-C401 (4)* | 2.65 | 1.05 |

Flame and UN Emblem — AP100

40p, Flame, UN emblem and broken chain.

**1964, May 15 Litho. Unwmk.**

| | | | | |
|---|---|---|---|---|
| **C402** | AP100 | 20p sal, org & brn | .50 | .25 |
| **C403** | AP100 | 40p lt bl, gray bl & org | .75 | .25 |

15th anniv. (in 1963) of the Universal Declaration of Human Rights.

Arab League Conference — AP101

**1964, Apr. 20** ***Perf. 13x13½***

| | | | | |
|---|---|---|---|---|
| **C404** | AP101 | 5p blk & pale sal | 1.00 | .25 |
| **C405** | AP101 | 10p black | 1.25 | .35 |
| **C406** | AP101 | 15p green | 1.75 | .50 |
| **C407** | AP101 | 20p dk brn & pink | 2.25 | .65 |
| | | *Nos. C404-C407 (4)* | 6.25 | 1.75 |

Arab League meeting.

Child in Crib — AP102

Beit-ed-Din Palace and Children — AP103

**1964, July 20** ***Perf. 13½x13, 13½***

| | | | | |
|---|---|---|---|---|
| **C408** | AP102 | 2.50p multicolored | .50 | .25 |
| **C409** | AP102 | 5p multicolored | .50 | .25 |
| **C410** | AP102 | 15p multicolored | .60 | .25 |
| **C411** | AP103 | 17.50p multicolored | .80 | .25 |
| **C412** | AP103 | 20p multicolored | .90 | .25 |
| **C413** | AP103 | 40p multicolored | 1.00 | .25 |
| | | *Nos. C408-C413 (6)* | 4.30 | 1.50 |

Ball of the Little White Beds, Beirut, for the benefit of children's hospital beds.

Clasped Hands and Map of Lebanon AP104

**1964, Oct. 16 Litho.** ***Perf. 13½x13***

| | | | | |
|---|---|---|---|---|
| **C414** | AP104 | 20p yel grn, yel & gray | .65 | .25 |
| **C415** | AP104 | 40p slate, yel & gray | 1.10 | .40 |

Congress of the Intl. Lebanese Union.

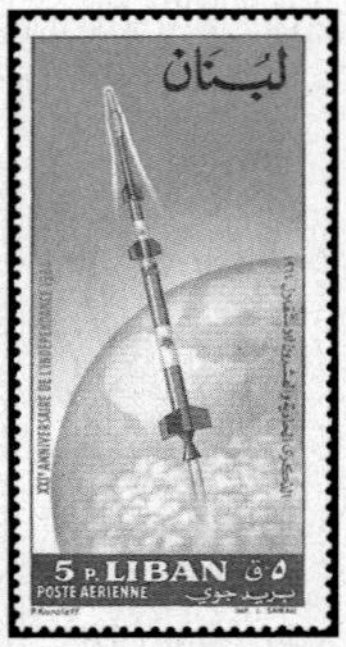


Rocket Leaving Earth — AP105

Battle Scene — AP106

**1964, Nov. 24 Unwmk.** ***Perf. 13½***

| | | | | |
|---|---|---|---|---|
| **C416** | AP105 | 5p multicolored | .50 | .25 |
| **C417** | AP105 | 10p multicolored | .50 | .25 |
| **C418** | AP106 | 40p sl blue & blk | 1.00 | .30 |
| **C419** | AP106 | 70p dp claret & blk | 2.00 | .50 |
| | | *Nos. C416-C419 (4)* | 4.00 | 1.30 |

21st anniversary of independence.

Woman in Costume AP107

Design: 10p, 15p, Man in costume.

**1965, Jan. 11 Litho.** ***Perf. 13½***

| | | | | |
|---|---|---|---|---|
| **C420** | AP107 | 10p multicolored | .70 | .25 |
| **C421** | AP107 | 15p multicolored | .90 | .25 |
| **C422** | AP107 | 25p green & multi | 1.25 | .35 |
| **C423** | AP107 | 40p brown & multi | 1.50 | .50 |
| | | *Nos. C420-C423 (4)* | 4.35 | 1.35 |

International Festival at Baalbek.

Equestrian AP108

25p, Target shooting, vert. 40p, Gymnast on rings.

**1965, Jan. 23 Engr.** ***Perf. 13***

| | | | | |
|---|---|---|---|---|
| **C424** | AP108 | 15p shown | .50 | .25 |
| **C425** | AP108 | 25p mutlicolored | .60 | .25 |
| **C426** | AP108 | 40p multicolored | .75 | .25 |
| *a.* | | Souvenir sheet of 3, #C424-C426, imperf. | 18.00 | 9.25 |
| | | *Nos. C424-C426 (3)* | 1.85 | .75 |

18th Olympic Games, Tokyo, Oct. 10-25, 1964. No. 426a sold for 100p.

Heliconius Cybria AP109

30p, Pericallia matronula. 40p, Red admiral. 45p, Satyrus semele. 70p, Machaon. 85p, Aurore. 100p, Morpho cypris. 200p, Erasmia sanguiflua. 300p, Papilio crassus. 500p, Charaxes ameliae.

**1965 Unwmk.** ***Perf. 13***

**Size: 36x22mm**

| | | | | |
|---|---|---|---|---|
| **C427** | AP109 | 30p multi | *2.75* | .25 |
| **C428** | AP109 | 35p multi | *4.00* | .35 |
| **C429** | AP109 | 40p multi | *5.00* | .35 |
| **C430** | AP109 | 45p multi | *5.50* | .50 |
| **C431** | AP109 | 70p multi | *6.75* | .75 |
| **C432** | AP109 | 85p multi | *7.50* | .90 |
| **C433** | AP109 | 100p multi | *11.00* | 1.00 |
| **C434** | AP109 | 200p multi | *18.00* | 1.25 |
| **C435** | AP109 | 300p multi | *24.50* | 3.50 |

**Engr. and Litho.**

***Perf. 12***

**Size: 35x25mm**

| | | | | |
|---|---|---|---|---|
| **C436** | AP109 | 500p lt ultra & blk | *50.00* | 7.00 |
| | | *Nos. C427-C436 (10)* | *135.00* | 15.85 |

For surcharges see Nos. C654-C656.

Pope Paul VI and Pres. Charles Helou — AP110

**1965, June 28 Photo.** ***Perf. 12***

| | | | | |
|---|---|---|---|---|
| **C437** | AP110 | 45p gold & brt vio | 5.25 | 1.00 |
| *a.* | | Souv. sheet of 1, imperf. | 52.50 | 32.50 |

Visit of Pope Paul VI to Lebanon. No. C437a sold for 50p.

Cedars of Friendship AP111

**1965, Oct. 16 Photo.** ***Perf. 13x12½***

| | | | | |
|---|---|---|---|---|
| **C438** | AP111 | 40p multicolored | 1.50 | .25 |

Cocoon, Spindle and Silk — AP112

15p, 30p, 40p, 50p, Silk weaver at loom.

**1965, Oct. 16** ***Perf. 12½x13***

**Design in Buff and Bright Green**

| | | | | |
|---|---|---|---|---|
| **C439** | AP112 | 2.50p brown | 1.25 | .25 |
| **C440** | AP112 | 5p dk olive grn | 1.25 | .25 |
| **C441** | AP112 | 7.50p Prus blue | 1.25 | .25 |
| **C442** | AP112 | 15p deep ultra | 1.25 | .25 |
| **C443** | AP112 | 30p deep claret | 1.50 | .25 |
| **C444** | AP112 | 40p brown | 2.40 | .25 |
| **C445** | AP112 | 50p rose brown | 3.50 | .60 |
| | | *Nos. C439-C445 (7)* | 12.40 | 2.10 |

Parliament Building AP113

**1965, Oct. 26** ***Perf. 13x12½***

| | | | | |
|---|---|---|---|---|
| **C446** | AP113 | 35p red, buff & brn | .80 | .25 |
| **C447** | AP113 | 40p emer, buff & brn | 1.00 | .25 |

Centenary of the Lebanese parliament.

UN Headquarters, NYC, UN Emblem and Lebanese Flags — AP114

**1965, Nov. 10 Engr.** ***Perf. 12***

| | | | | |
|---|---|---|---|---|
| **C448** | AP114 | 2.50p dull blue | .50 | .25 |
| **C449** | AP114 | 10p magenta | .50 | .25 |
| **C450** | AP114 | 17.50p dull violet | .50 | .25 |
| **C451** | AP114 | 30p green | .60 | .25 |
| **C452** | AP114 | 40p brown | .85 | .25 |
| | | *Nos. C448-C452 (5)* | 2.95 | 1.25 |

UN, 20th anniv. A souvenir sheet contains one 40p imperf. stamp in bright rose lilac. Sold for 50p. Value $15.

Playing Card King, Laurel and Cedar — AP115

**1965, Nov. 15 Photo.** ***Perf. 12½x13***

| | | | | |
|---|---|---|---|---|
| **C453** | AP115 | 2.50p multicolored | .70 | .25 |
| **C454** | AP115 | 15p multicolored | 1.10 | .25 |
| **C455** | AP115 | 17.50p multicolored | 1.25 | .25 |
| **C456** | AP115 | 40p multicolored | 1.40 | .25 |
| | | *Nos. C453-C456 (4)* | 4.45 | 1.00 |

Intl. Bridge Championships. A souvenir sheet contains two imperf. stamps similar to Nos. C454 and C456. Sold for 75p. Value $22.50.

Dagger in Map of Palestine — AP116

**1965, Dec. 12** ***Perf. 12½x11***

| | | | | |
|---|---|---|---|---|
| **C457** | AP116 | 50p multicolored | 4.50 | .55 |

Deir Yassin massacre, Apr. 9, 1948.

ITU Emblem, Old and New Communication Equipment and Early Bird Satellite — AP117

**1966, Apr. 15** ***Perf. 13x12½***

| | | | | |
|---|---|---|---|---|
| **C458** | AP117 | 2.50p multi | .50 | .25 |
| **C459** | AP117 | 15p multi | .55 | .25 |
| **C460** | AP117 | 17.50p multi | .60 | .25 |
| **C461** | AP117 | 25p multi | 1.00 | .25 |
| **C462** | AP117 | 40p multi | 1.25 | .25 |
| | | *Nos. C458-C462 (5)* | 3.90 | 1.25 |

ITU, centenary (in 1965).

Folk Dancers Before Temple of Bacchus — AP118

Designs: 7.50p, 15p, Dancers before Temple of Jupiter, vert. 30p, 40p, Orchestra before Temple of Bacchus.

**1966, July 20 Unwmk. *Perf. 12***

**Gold Frame**

| | | | | |
|---|---|---|---|---|
| **C463** | AP118 | 2.50p brn vio, bl & orange | .50 | .25 |
| **C464** | AP118 | 5p mag, bl & org | .50 | .25 |
| **C465** | AP118 | 7.50p vio bl, bl & pink | .50 | .25 |
| **C466** | AP118 | 15p pur, bl & pink | .60 | .25 |
| **C467** | AP118 | 30p dk grn, org & blue | .65 | .25 |
| **C468** | AP118 | 40p vio, org & bl | 1.10 | .25 |
| | | *Nos. C463-C468 (6)* | 3.85 | 1.50 |

11th International Festival at Baalbek.

Opening of WHO Headquarters, Geneva — AP119

**1966, Aug. 25 Engr. *Perf. 12***

| | | | | |
|---|---|---|---|---|
| **C469** | AP119 | 7.50p dp yel grn | .50 | .25 |
| **C470** | AP119 | 17.50p car rose | .60 | .25 |
| **C471** | AP119 | 25p blue | 1.00 | .25 |
| | | *Nos. C469-C471 (3)* | 2.10 | .75 |

Skier AP120

Designs: 5p, Children on toboggan. 17.50p, Cedar in snow. 25p, Ski lift.

**1966, Sept. 15 Photo. *Perf. 12x11½***

| | | | | |
|---|---|---|---|---|
| **C472** | AP120 | 2.50p multi | .50 | .25 |
| **C473** | AP120 | 5p multi | .50 | .25 |
| **C474** | AP120 | 17.50p multi | .75 | .25 |
| **C475** | AP120 | 25p multi | 1.00 | .25 |
| | | *Nos. C472-C475 (4)* | 2.75 | 1.00 |

International Festival of Cedars.

Sarcophagus of King Ahiram with Early Alphabet — AP121

15p, Phoenician ship. 20p, Map of the Mediterranean Sea showing Phoenician travel routes, and ship. 30p, Phoenician with alphabet tablet.

**Litho. & Engr.**

**1966, Sept. 25 *Perf. 12***

| | | | | |
|---|---|---|---|---|
| **C476** | AP121 | 10p dl grn, blk & lt brn | .50 | .25 |
| **C477** | AP121 | 15p rose lil, brn & ocher | .50 | .25 |
| **C478** | AP121 | 20p tan, dk brn & bl | .60 | .25 |
| **C479** | AP121 | 30p org, dk brn & yel | 1.00 | .25 |
| | | *Nos. C476-C479 (4)* | 2.60 | 1.00 |

Invention of alphabet by Phoenicians.

Child in Bathtub and UNICEF Emblem AP122

5p, Boy in rowboat. 7.50p, Girl skier. 12p, Girl feeding bird. 20p, Boy doing homework. 50p, Children of various races, horiz.

**1966, Oct. 10 Photo. *Perf. 11½x12***

| | | | | |
|---|---|---|---|---|
| **C480** | AP122 | 2.50p multi | .50 | .25 |
| **C481** | AP122 | 5p multi | .50 | .25 |
| **C482** | AP122 | 7.50p multi | .60 | .25 |
| **C483** | AP122 | 15p multi | .75 | .25 |
| **C484** | AP122 | 20p multi | 1.00 | .25 |
| | | *Nos. C480-C484 (5)* | 3.35 | 1.25 |

**Miniature Sheet**

***Imperf***

| | | | | |
|---|---|---|---|---|
| **C485** | AP122 | 50p dl yellow & multi | 7.50 | 3.50 |

UNICEF; World Children's Day. No. C485 contains one horizontal stamp 43x33mm.

**Scenic Type of Regular Issue, 1966**

Designs: 10p, Waterfall, Djezzine. 15p, Castle of the Sea, Saida. 20p, Amphitheater, Jubayl (Byblos). 30p, Temple of the Sun, Baalbek. 50p, Beit-ed-Din Palace. 60p, Church of Christ the King, Nahr-el-Kalb. 75p, Abu Bakr Mosque, Tripoli.

**1966, Oct. 12 *Perf. 12x11½***

| | | | | |
|---|---|---|---|---|
| **C486** | A82 | 10p gold & multi | .50 | .25 |
| **C487** | A82 | 15p gold & multi | .60 | .25 |
| **C488** | A82 | 20p gold & multi | .75 | .25 |
| **C489** | A82 | 30p gold & multi | 1.00 | .25 |
| **C490** | A82 | 50p gold & multi | 1.75 | .25 |
| **C491** | A82 | 60p gold & multi | 2.00 | .25 |
| **C492** | A82 | 75p gold & multi | 3.00 | .25 |
| | | *Nos. C486-C492 (7)* | 9.60 | 1.75 |

Symbolic Water Cycle — AP123

15p, 20p, Different wave pattern without sun.

**1966, Nov. 15 Photo. *Perf. 12½***

| | | | | |
|---|---|---|---|---|
| **C493** | AP123 | 5p red, bl & vio bl | .50 | .25 |
| **C494** | AP123 | 10p org, bl & brn | .50 | .25 |
| **C495** | AP123 | 15p org, emer & dk brn | .60 | .25 |
| **C496** | AP123 | 20p org, emer & grnsh blue | .75 | .25 |
| | | *Nos. C493-C496 (4)* | 2.35 | 1.00 |

Hydrological Decade (UNESCO), 1965-74.

Daniel Bliss — AP124

Designs: 30p, Chapel, American University, Beirut. 50p, Daniel Bliss, D.D., and American University, horiz.

**1966, Dec. 3**

| | | | | |
|---|---|---|---|---|
| **C497** | AP124 | 20p grn, yel & brn | .50 | .25 |
| **C498** | AP124 | 30p red brn, grn & blue | .60 | .25 |

**Souvenir Sheet**

***Imperf***

| | | | | |
|---|---|---|---|---|
| **C499** | AP124 | 50p grn, brn & org brown | 2.50 | 1.00 |

Cent. of American University, Beirut, founded by the Rev. Daniel Bliss (1823-1916). Nos. C497-C498 are printed each with alternating labels showing University emblem.

No. C499 contains one stamp 59x37mm.

Flags of Arab League Members, Hand Signing Scroll — AP125

**1967, Aug. 2 Photo. *Perf. 12x11½***

| | | | | |
|---|---|---|---|---|
| **C500** | AP125 | 5p brown & multi | .50 | .25 |
| **C501** | AP125 | 10p multicolored | .50 | .25 |
| **C502** | AP125 | 15p black & multi | .55 | .25 |
| **C503** | AP125 | 20p multicolored | .65 | .25 |
| | | *Nos. C500-C503 (4)* | 2.20 | 1.00 |

Signing of Arab League Pact in 1945.

Veteran's War Memorial Building, San Francisco — AP126

10p, 20p, 30p, Scroll, flags of Lebanon & UN.

**1967, Sept. 1 Photo. *Perf. 12x11½***

| | | | | |
|---|---|---|---|---|
| **C504** | AP126 | 2.50p blue & multi | .50 | .25 |
| **C505** | AP126 | 5p multicolored | .50 | .25 |
| **C506** | AP126 | 7.50p multicolored | .50 | .25 |
| **C507** | AP126 | 10p blue & multi | .50 | .25 |
| **C508** | AP126 | 20p multicolored | .60 | .25 |
| **C509** | AP126 | 30p multicolored | .75 | .25 |
| | | *Nos. C504-C509 (6)* | 3.35 | 1.50 |

San Francisco Pact (UN Charter), 22nd anniv.

Ruins at Baalbek — AP127

Intl. Tourist Year: 10p, Ruins at Anjar. 15p, Bridge over Ibrahim River and ruins. 20p, Boat on underground lake, Jaita cave. 50p, St. George's Bay, Beirut.

**1967, Sept. 25 *Perf. 12½***

| | | | | |
|---|---|---|---|---|
| **C510** | AP127 | 5p multicolored | .50 | .25 |
| **C511** | AP127 | 10p multicolored | .60 | .25 |
| **C512** | AP127 | 15p violet & multi | .80 | .25 |
| **C513** | AP127 | 20p brn & multi | .95 | .25 |
| | | *Nos. C510-C513 (4)* | 2.85 | 1.00 |

**Souvenir Sheet**

***Imperf***

| | | | | |
|---|---|---|---|---|
| **C514** | AP127 | 50p multicolored | *27.50* | *20.00* |

View of Tabarja AP128

Views: 15p, Pigeon Rock and shore, Beirut. 17.50p, Beit-ed-Din Palace. 20p, Ship at Sidon. 25p, Tripoli. 30p, Beach at Byblos. 35p, Ruins, Tyre. 40p, Temple of Bacchus, Baalbek.

**1967, Oct. *Perf. 12x11½***

| | | | | |
|---|---|---|---|---|
| **C515** | AP128 | 10p multi | *.50* | .25 |
| **C516** | AP128 | 15p multi | *1.00* | .25 |
| **C517** | AP128 | 17.50p multi | *1.50* | .25 |
| **C518** | AP128 | 20p multi | *1.50* | .25 |
| **C519** | AP128 | 25p multi | *1.50* | .25 |
| **C520** | AP128 | 30p multi | *2.00* | .25 |
| **C521** | AP128 | 35p multi | *2.50* | .25 |
| **C522** | AP128 | 40p multi | *3.50* | .25 |
| | | *Nos. C515-C522 (8)* | *14.00* | 2.00 |

Intl. Tourist Year; used as a regular airmail issue.

India Day — AP129

**1967, Oct. 30 Engr. *Perf. 12***

| | | | | |
|---|---|---|---|---|
| **C523** | AP129 | 2.50p orange | .50 | .25 |
| **C524** | AP129 | 5p magenta | .50 | .25 |
| **C525** | AP129 | 7.50p brown | .50 | .25 |
| **C526** | AP129 | 10p blue | .55 | .25 |
| **C527** | AP129 | 15p green | .60 | .25 |
| | | *Nos. C523-C527 (5)* | 2.65 | 1.25 |

Globe and Arabic Inscription — AP130

Design: 10p, 20p, 30p, UN emblem.

**1967, Nov. 25 Engr. *Perf. 12***

| | | | | |
|---|---|---|---|---|
| **C528** | AP130 | 2.50p rose | .50 | .25 |
| **C529** | AP130 | 5p gray blue | .50 | .25 |
| **C530** | AP130 | 7.50p green | .50 | .25 |
| **C531** | AP130 | 10p brt carmine | .50 | .25 |
| **C532** | AP130 | 20p violet blue | .60 | .25 |
| **C533** | AP130 | 30p dark green | .80 | .25 |
| | | *Nos. C528-C533 (6)* | 3.40 | 1.50 |

Lebanon's admission to the UN. A 100p rose red souvenir sheet in the globe design exists. Value $6.25.

Basking Shark AP131

Fish: 30p, Needlefish. 40p, Pollack. 50p, Cuckoo wrasse. 70p, Red mullet. 100p, Rainbow trout.

**1968, Feb. Photo. *Perf. 12x11½***

| | | | | |
|---|---|---|---|---|
| **C534** | AP131 | 20p multi | 1.90 | .25 |
| **C535** | AP131 | 30p multi | 1.90 | .25 |
| **C536** | AP131 | 40p multi | 2.75 | .25 |
| **C537** | AP131 | 50p multi | 4.00 | .25 |
| **C538** | AP131 | 70p multi | 7.00 | .25 |
| **C539** | AP131 | 100p multi | 9.00 | .25 |
| | | *Nos. C534-C539 (6)* | 26.55 | 1.50 |

Ski Jump — AP132

5p, 7.50p, 10p, Downhill skiers (various). 25p, Congress emblem (skis and cedar).

**1968** ***Perf. 12½x11½***

| | | | | |
|---|---|---|---|---|
| **C540** | AP132 | 2.50p multicolored | .50 | .25 |
| **C541** | AP132 | 5p multicolored | .50 | .25 |
| **C542** | AP132 | 7.50p multicolored | .50 | .25 |
| **C543** | AP132 | 10p multicolored | .50 | .25 |
| **C544** | AP132 | 25p multicolored | .75 | .25 |
| | | *Nos. C540-C544 (5)* | 2.75 | 1.25 |

26th Intl. Ski Congress, Beirut. A 50p imperf. souvenir sheet exists in design of the 25p. Value $7.25.

Emir Fakhr al-Din II — AP133

2.50p, Emira Khaskiah. 10p, Citadel of Sidon, horiz. 15p, Citadel of Chekif & grazing sheep, horiz. 17.50p, Citadel of Beirut & harbor, horiz.

***Perf. 11½x12, 12x11½***

**1968, Feb. 20** **Litho.**

| | | | | |
|---|---|---|---|---|
| **C546** | AP133 | 2.50p multicolored | .50 | .25 |
| **C547** | AP133 | 5p multicolored | .50 | .25 |
| **C548** | AP133 | 10p multicolored | .50 | .25 |
| **C549** | AP133 | 15p multicolored | .75 | .25 |
| **C550** | AP133 | 17.50p multicolored | .75 | .25 |
| | | *Nos. C546-C550 (5)* | 3.00 | 1.25 |

In memory of the Emir Fakhr al-Din II. A 50p imperf. souvenir sheet exists showing the Battle of Anjar. Value $11.50.

Roman Bust AP134

Ruins of Tyre: 5p, Colonnade, horiz. 7.50p, Arch, horiz. 10p, Banquet, bas-relief.

**Litho. & Engr.**

**1968, Mar. 20** ***Perf. 12***

| | | | | |
|---|---|---|---|---|
| **C552** | AP134 | 2.50p pink, brn & buff | .50 | .25 |
| **C553** | AP134 | 5p yel, brn & lt bl | .60 | .25 |
| **C554** | AP134 | 7.50p lt grnsh bl, brn & yel | .80 | .25 |
| **C555** | AP134 | 10p sal, brn & lt bl | .95 | .25 |
| *a.* | | Souvenir sheet | 22.50 | 17.50 |
| | | *Nos. C552-C555 (4)* | 2.85 | 1.00 |

No. C555a contains one dark brown and light blue stamp, perf. 10½x11½. Sold for 50p. Exists imperf. Value $22.50.

For surcharge see No. C657.

Emperor Justinian AP135

Design: 15p, 20p, Justinian and map of the Mediterranean, horiz.

***Perf. 11½x12, 12x11½***

**1968, May 10** **Photo.**

| | | | | |
|---|---|---|---|---|
| **C556** | AP135 | 5p blue & multi | .50 | .25 |
| **C557** | AP135 | 10p blue & multi | .50 | .25 |
| **C558** | AP135 | 15p red & multi | .55 | .25 |
| **C559** | AP135 | 20p blue & multi | .60 | .25 |
| | | *Nos. C556-C559 (4)* | 2.15 | 1.00 |

Beirut, site of one of the greatest law schools in antiquity; Emperor Justinian (483-565), who compiled and preserved the Roman law.

Arab League Emblem AP136

**1968, June 6** **Photo.** ***Perf. 12x11½***

| | | | | |
|---|---|---|---|---|
| **C560** | AP136 | 5p orange & multi | .50 | .25 |
| **C561** | AP136 | 10p multicolored | .50 | .25 |
| **C562** | AP136 | 15p pink & multi | .60 | .25 |
| **C563** | AP136 | 20p multicolored | .75 | .25 |
| | | *Nos. C560-C563 (4)* | 2.35 | 1.00 |

Issued for Arab League Week.

Cedar and Globe Emblem — AP137

**1968, July 10**

| | | | | |
|---|---|---|---|---|
| **C564** | AP137 | 2.50p sal pink, brn & green | .50 | .25 |
| **C565** | AP137 | 5p gray, brn & grn | .55 | .25 |
| **C566** | AP137 | 7.50p brt bl, brn & grn | .60 | .25 |
| **C567** | AP137 | 10p yel grn, brn & grn | .75 | .25 |
| | | *Nos. C564-C567 (4)* | 2.40 | 1.00 |

3rd Congress of Lebanese World Union.

Temple of Jupiter, Baalbek AP138

Designs: 10p, Fluted pilasters, cella of Bacchus Temple. 15p, Corniche, south peristyle of Jupiter Temple, horiz. 20p, Gate, Bacchus Temple. 25p, Ceiling detail, south peristyle of Bacchus Temple.

**1968, Sept. 25** **Photo.** ***Perf. 12½***

| | | | | |
|---|---|---|---|---|
| **C568** | AP138 | 5p gold & multi | .50 | .25 |
| **C569** | AP138 | 10p gold & multi | .50 | .25 |
| **C570** | AP138 | 15p gold & multi | .60 | .25 |
| **C571** | AP138 | 20p gold & multi | .75 | .25 |
| **C572** | AP138 | 25p gold & multi | 1.00 | .25 |
| | | *Nos. C568-C572 (5)* | 3.35 | 1.25 |

13th Baalbek International Festival.

Broad Jump and Phoenician Statue — AP139

Designs: 10p, High jump and votive stele, Phoenician, 6th century B.C. 15p, Fencing and Olmec jade head, 500-400 B.C. 20p, Weight lifting and axe in shape of human head, Vera Cruz region. 25p, Aztec stone calendar and Phoenician ship.

**1968, Oct. 19** **Photo.** ***Perf. 12x11½***

| | | | | |
|---|---|---|---|---|
| **C573** | AP139 | 5p lt ultra, yel & gray | .50 | .25 |
| **C574** | AP139 | 10p mag, lt ultra & blk | .50 | .25 |
| **C575** | AP139 | 15p cit, ocher & brn | .50 | .25 |
| **C576** | AP139 | 20p dp org, brn & ocher | .60 | .25 |
| **C577** | AP139 | 25p light brown | 1.00 | .25 |
| | | *Nos. C573-C577 (5)* | 3.10 | 1.25 |

19th Olympic Games, Mexico City, 10/12-27.

Human Rights Flame and Tractor AP140

Human Rights Flame and: 15p, People. 25p, Boys of 3 races placing hands on globe.

**1968, Dec. 10** **Litho.** ***Perf. 11½***

| | | | | |
|---|---|---|---|---|
| **C578** | AP140 | 10p multicolored | .50 | .25 |
| **C579** | AP140 | 15p yellow & multi | .60 | .25 |
| **C580** | AP140 | 25p lilac & multi | 1.00 | .25 |
| | | *Nos. C578-C580 (3)* | 2.10 | .75 |

International Human Rights Year.

Minshiya Stairs, Deir El-Kamar AP141

Views in Deir El-Kamar: 15p, The Seraglio Kiosk. 25p, Old paved city road.

**1968, Dec. 26**

| | | | | |
|---|---|---|---|---|
| **C581** | AP141 | 10p multicolored | .50 | .25 |
| **C582** | AP141 | 15p multicolored | .60 | .25 |
| **C583** | AP141 | 25p multicolored | .80 | .25 |
| | | *Nos. C581-C583 (3)* | 1.90 | .75 |

1st Municipal Council in Lebanon, established in Deir El-Kamar by Daoud Pasha, cent.

Nurse Treating Child, and UN Emblem — AP142

Designs: 10p, Grain, fish, grapes and jug. 15p, Mother and children. 20p, Reading girl and Phoenician alphabet. 25p, Playing children.

**1969, Jan. 20** **Litho.** ***Perf. 12***

| | | | | |
|---|---|---|---|---|
| **C584** | AP142 | 5p blk, lt bl & sepia | .50 | .25 |
| **C585** | AP142 | 10p blk, brt yel & grn | .50 | .25 |
| **C586** | AP142 | 15p blk, red lil & ver | .50 | .25 |
| **C587** | AP142 | 20p blk, citron & bl | .50 | .25 |
| **C588** | AP142 | 25p blk, pink & bis brn | .70 | .25 |
| | | *Nos. C584-C588 (5)* | 2.70 | 1.25 |

UNICEF, 22nd anniversary.

Silver Coin from Byblos, 5th Century B.C. — AP143

National Museum, Beirut: 5p, Gold dagger, Byblos, 18th cent. B.C. 7.50p, King Dining in the Land of the Dead, sarcophagus of Ahiram, 13-12th cent. B.C. 30p, Breastplate with cartouche of Amenemhat III (1849-1801 B.C.). 40p, Phoenician bird vase from Khalde, 8th cent. B.C.

**Photogravure; Gold Impressed**

**1969, Feb. 20** ***Perf. 12***

| | | | | |
|---|---|---|---|---|
| **C589** | AP143 | 2.50p grn, yel & lt bl | .50 | .25 |
| **C590** | AP143 | 5p vio, brn & yel | .60 | .25 |
| **C591** | AP143 | 7.50p dl yel, brn & pink | .80 | .25 |
| **C592** | AP143 | 30p blue & multi | 1.00 | .25 |
| **C593** | AP143 | 40p multicolored | 1.10 | .25 |
| | | *Nos. C589-C593 (5)* | 4.00 | 1.25 |

Intl. Congress of Museum Councils; 20th anniv. of the Intl. Council of Museums.

Water Skier AP144

Designs: 5p, Water ballet. 7.50p, Parachutist, vert. 30p, Yachting, vert. 40p, Regatta.

**1969, Mar. 3** **Litho.** ***Perf. 11½***

| | | | | |
|---|---|---|---|---|
| **C594** | AP144 | 2.50p multicolored | .50 | .25 |
| **C595** | AP144 | 5p multicolored | .50 | .25 |
| **C596** | AP144 | 7.50p multicolored | .50 | .25 |
| **C597** | AP144 | 30p multicolored | 1.00 | .25 |
| **C598** | AP144 | 40p multicolored | 1.25 | .25 |
| | | *Nos. C594-C598 (5)* | 3.75 | 1.25 |

Tomb of Unknown Soldier at Military School — AP145

2.50p, Frontier guard. 7.50p, Soldiers doing forestry work. 15p; Army engineers building road. 30p, Ambulance and helicopter. 40p, Ski patrol.

**1969, Aug. 1** **Litho.** ***Perf. 12x11½***

| | | | | |
|---|---|---|---|---|
| **C599** | AP145 | 2.50p multicolored | .50 | .25 |
| **C600** | AP145 | 5p multicolored | .50 | .25 |
| **C601** | AP145 | 7.50p multicolored | .50 | .25 |
| **C602** | AP145 | 15p multicolored | .50 | .25 |
| **C603** | AP145 | 30p multicolored | .60 | .25 |
| **C604** | AP145 | 40p multicolored | .75 | .25 |
| | | *Nos. C599-C604 (6)* | 3.35 | 1.50 |

25th anniversary of independence.

Crosses and Circles AP146

**1971, Jan. 6 Photo.** *Perf. 11½x12*

**C605** AP146 15p shown .50 .25
**C606** AP146 85p Crosses, cedar 1.75 .45

Lebanese Red Cross, 25th anniversary.

Foil Fencing AP147

10p, Flags of participating Arab countries. 15p, Flags of participating non-Arab countries. 40p, Sword fencing. 50p, Saber fencing.

**1971, Jan. 15 Litho.** *Perf. 12*

**C607** AP147 10p yellow & multi .50 .25
**C608** AP147 15p yellow & multi .50 .25
**C609** AP147 35p yellow & multi .60 .25
**C610** AP147 40p yellow & multi .80 .25
**C611** AP147 50p yellow & multi .95 .25
*Nos. C607-C611 (5)* 3.35 1.25

10th World Fencing Championships, held in Lebanon.

Agricultural Workers, Arab Painting, 12th Century — AP148

**1971, Feb. 1**

**C612** AP148 10p silver & multi 1.00 .25
**C613** AP148 40p gold & multi 1.75 .25

International Labor Organization.

UPU Building and Monument, Bern — AP149

**1971, Feb. 15 Litho.** *Perf. 12*

**C614** AP149 15p yel, blk & dp org 1.00 .25
**C615** AP149 35p dp org, yel & blk 1.75 .35

Opening of new UPU Headquarters in Bern, Switzerland.

Ravens Burning Owls — AP150

Children's Day: 85p, Jackal and lion. Designs of the 15p and 85p are after 13th-14th century paintings, illustrations for the "Kalila wa Dumna."

**1971, Mar. 1 Photo.** *Perf. 11*
**Size: 30x30mm**

**C616** AP150 15p gold & multi .25 .25

*Perf. 12x11½*
**Size: 38½x29mm**

**C617** AP150 85p gold & multi 2.75 .70

Map and Flag of Arab League AP151

**1971, Mar. 20** *Perf. 12x11½*

**C618** AP151 30p orange & multi .55 .25
**C619** AP151 70p yellow & multi 1.25 .35

Arab League, 25th anniv.

Bechara el Khoury AP152

Famous Lebanese Men: No. C620, Symbolic design for Imam al Ouzai. No. C622, Hassan Kamel al Sabbah. No. C623, Kahlil Gibran.

**1971, Apr. 10**

**C620** AP152 25p lt grn, gold & brn .25 .25
**C621** AP152 25p yel, gold & brn .40 .25
**C622** AP152 25p yel, gold & brn .40 .25
**C623** AP152 25p lt grn, gold & brn .40 .25
*Nos. C620-C623 (4)* 1.45 1.00

Education Year Emblem, Computer Card — AP153

**1971, Apr. 30 Photo.** *Perf. 11½x12*

**C624** AP153 10p blk, vio & bl .35 .25
**C625** AP153 40p blk, org & yel .70 .25

Intl. Education Year.

Maameltein Bridge — AP154

5p, Jamhour Substation. 15p, Hotel Management School. 20p, Litani Dam. 25p, Television set wiring. 35p, Temple of Bziza. 40p, Jounieh Port. 45p, Airport radar. 50p, Flower. 70p, New School of Sciences. 85p, Oranges. 100p, Arbanieh earth satellite station.

**1971, May Litho.** *Perf. 12*

**C626** AP154 5p multicolored .25 .25
**C627** AP154 10p multicolored .25 .25
**C628** AP154 15p multicolored .45 .25
**C629** AP154 20p multicolored .85 .25
**C630** AP154 25p multicolored 1.25 .25
**C631** AP154 35p multicolored 1.60 .25
**C632** AP154 40p multicolored 1.60 .25
**C633** AP154 45p multicolored 1.75 .25
**C634** AP154 50p multicolored 2.75 .25
**C635** AP154 70p multicolored 4.00 .25
**C636** AP154 85p multicolored 5.50 .25
**C637** AP154 100p multicolored 7.00 .40
*Nos. C626-C637 (12)* 27.25 3.15

For overprints and surcharges see Nos. C771, C775, C779, 533.

Dahr-el-Bacheq Sanatorium AP155

**1971, June 1**

**C638** AP155 50p shown 1.25 .25
**C639** AP155 100p multi, diff. 1.75 .60

Campaign against tuberculosis.

Solar Wheel (Festival Emblem) AP156

**1971, July 1 Photo.** *Perf. 11*

**C640** AP156 15p ultra & org .25 .25
**C641** AP156 85p Corinthian capital 1.25 .35

16th Baalbek International Festival.

Mirage Fighters Flying Over Baalbek Ruins AP157

Army Day: 15p, 155mm Cannon. 40p, Army Headquarters. 70p, Naval patrol boat.

**1971, Aug. 1** *Perf. 12x11½*

**C642** AP157 15p gold & multi 3.25 .25
**C643** AP157 25p gold & multi 5.75 .25
**C644** AP157 40p gold & multi 7.75 .25
**C645** AP157 70p gold & multi 13.00 .25
*Nos. C642-C645 (4)* 29.75 1.00

Wooden Console, Al Aqsa Mosque AP158

**1971, Aug. 21** *Perf. 12*

**C646** AP158 15p dk brn & ocher .75 .25
**C647** AP158 35p dk brn & ocher 1.25 .25

2nd anniversary of the burning of Al Aqsa Mosque in Jerusalem.

Lenin (1870-1924) — AP159

**1971, Oct. 1** *Perf. 12x11½*

**C648** AP159 30p gold & multi .60 .25
**C649** AP159 70p multicolored 1.40 .30

UN Emblem, World Map AP160

**1971, Oct. 24** *Perf. 13x12½*

**C650** AP160 15p multicolored .35 .25
**C651** AP160 85p multicolored 1.25 .35

UN, 25th anniv. (in 1970).

The Rape of Europa, Mosaic from Byblos AP161

**1971, Nov 20 Litho.** *Perf. 12*

**C652** AP161 10p slate & multi .50 .25
**C653** AP161 40p gold & multi 2.50 .25

Publicity for World Lebanese Union (ULM).

**Nos. C435-C436 Surcharged**

**Engr.; Engr. & Litho.**

**1972, May** *Perf. 13, 12*

**C654** AP109 100p on 300p 20.00 .40
**C655** AP109 100p on 500p 20.00 .40
**C656** AP109 200p on 300p 35.00 .80
*Nos. C654-C656 (3)* 75.00 1.60

The numerals on No. C655 are taller (5mm) and bars spaced 1½mm apart.

**No. C554 Surcharged**

**1972, June Litho. & Engr.** *Perf. 12*

**C657** AP134 5p on 7.50p multi 3.00 .25

Hibiscus — AP162

**1973 Litho.** *Perf. 12*

**C658** AP162 2.50p shown .25 .25
**C659** AP162 5p Roses .25 .25
**C660** AP162 15p Tulips .35 .25
**C661** AP162 25p Lilies 1.00 .25
**C662** AP162 40p Carnations 1.10 .25
**C663** AP162 50p Iris 1.60 .25
**C664** AP162 70p Apples 1.25 .25
**C665** AP162 75p Grapes 1.40 .25
**C666** AP162 100p Peaches 1.90 .35
**C667** AP162 200p Pears 6.75 .25
**C668** AP162 300p Cherries 7.25 .55
**C669** AP162 500p Oranges 12.00 .90
*Nos. C658-C669 (12)* 35.10 4.05

For overprints see Nos. C758-C759, C763, C766, C769, C772, C776, C778, C782, C785-C787.

Lebanese House AP163

Designs: Old Lebanese houses.

**1973** ***Perf. 14***

| | | | | | |
|---|---|---|---|---|---|
| **C670** | AP163 | 35p | yel & multi | *2.50* | .25 |
| **C671** | AP163 | 50p | lt bl & multi | *3.50* | .25 |
| **C672** | AP163 | 85p | buff & multi | *5.75* | .30 |
| **C673** | AP163 | 100p | multicolored | *7.75* | .40 |
| | | | *Nos. C670-C673 (4)* | *19.50* | 1.20 |

For overprints see Nos. C768, C773, C780, C783.

Woman with Rose — AP164

Lebanese Costumes: 10p, Man. 20p, Man on horseback. 25p, Woman playing mandolin.

**1973, Sept. 1** **Litho.** ***Perf. 14***

| | | | | | |
|---|---|---|---|---|---|
| **C674** | AP164 | 5p | yellow & multi | *1.25* | .25 |
| **C675** | AP164 | 10p | yellow & multi | *3.75* | .25 |
| **C676** | AP164 | 20p | yellow & multi | *5.75* | .25 |
| **C677** | AP164 | 25p | yellow & multi | *8.25* | .25 |
| | | | *Nos. C674-C677 (4)* | *19.00* | 1.00 |

For overprints see Nos. C760-C761, C764, C767.

Swimming, Temple at Baalbek — AP165

Designs: 10p, Running and portal. 15p, Woman athlete and castle. 20p, Women's volleyball and columns. 25p, Basketball and aqueduct. 50p, Women's table tennis and buildings. 75p, Handball and building. 100p, Soccer and cedar.

**1973, Sept. 25** **Photo.** ***Perf. 11½x12***

| | | | | | |
|---|---|---|---|---|---|
| **C678** | AP165 | 5p | multicolored | .25 | .25 |
| **C679** | AP165 | 10p | multicolored | .25 | .25 |
| **C680** | AP165 | 15p | grn & multi | .35 | .25 |
| **C681** | AP165 | 20p | multicolored | .35 | .25 |
| **C682** | AP165 | 25p | ultra & multi | .50 | .25 |
| **C683** | AP165 | 50p | org & multi | 1.25 | .30 |
| **C684** | AP165 | 75p | vio & multi | 1.50 | .40 |
| **C685** | AP165 | 100p | multicolored | 2.75 | .80 |
| *a.* | | | Souvenir sheet | 3.75 | 1.75 |
| | | | *Nos. C678-C685 (8)* | 7.20 | 2.75 |

5th Pan-Arabic Scholastic Games, Beirut. No. C685a contains one stamp with simulated perforations similar to No. C685; gold inscription and denomination.

View of Brasilia — AP166

20p, Old Salvador (Bahia). 25p, Lebanese sailing ship enroute from the Old World to South America. 50p, Dom Pedro I & Emir Fakhr al-Din II.

**1973, Nov. 15** **Litho.** ***Perf. 12***

| | | | | | |
|---|---|---|---|---|---|
| **C686** | AP166 | 5p | gold & multi | .40 | .25 |
| **C687** | AP166 | 20p | gold & multi | 2.25 | .35 |
| **C688** | AP166 | 25p | gold & multi | 2.25 | .35 |
| **C689** | AP166 | 50p | gold & multi | 4.75 | .65 |
| | | | *Nos. C686-C689 (4)* | 9.65 | 1.60 |

Sesquicentennial of Brazil's independence.

Inlay Worker AP167

**1973, Dec. 1**

| | | | | | |
|---|---|---|---|---|---|
| **C690** | AP167 | 10p | shown | *.80* | .25 |
| **C691** | AP167 | 20p | Weaver | *1.25* | .25 |
| **C692** | AP167 | 35p | Glass blower | *2.00* | .35 |
| **C693** | AP167 | 40p | Potter | *2.75* | .50 |
| **C694** | AP167 | 50p | Metal worker | *3.00* | .50 |
| **C695** | AP167 | 70p | Cutlery maker | *5.00* | .65 |
| **C696** | AP167 | 85p | Lace maker | *7.00* | 1.00 |
| **C697** | AP167 | 100p | Handicraft Museum | *8.00* | 1.40 |
| | | | *Nos. C690-C697 (8)* | *29.80* | 4.90 |

Lebanese handicrafts.
For overprints see Nos. C762, C765, C770, C774, C777, C781, C784.

Camp Site, Log Fire and Scout Emblem — AP168

Designs: 5p, Lebanese Scout emblem and map. 7½p, Lebanese Scout emblem and map of Middle East. 10p, Lord Baden-Powell, ruins of Baalbek. 15p, Girl Guide, camp and emblem. 20p, Lebanese Girl Guide and Scout emblems. 25p, Scouts around camp fire. 30p, Symbolic globe with Lebanese flag and Scout emblem. 35p, Flags of participating nations. 50p, Old man, and Scout chopping wood.

**1974, Aug. 24** **Litho.** ***Perf. 12***

| | | | | | |
|---|---|---|---|---|---|
| **C698** | AP168 | 2.50p | multi | .75 | .25 |
| **C699** | AP168 | 5p | multi | .75 | .25 |
| **C700** | AP168 | 7.50p | multi | *1.40* | .25 |
| **C701** | AP168 | 10p | multi | *1.40* | .25 |
| **C702** | AP168 | 15p | multi | *1.75* | .55 |
| *a.* | | | Vert. strip of 5, #C698-C702 | *7.00* | |
| **C703** | AP168 | 20p | multi | *2.50* | .65 |
| **C704** | AP168 | 25p | multi | *3.50* | .65 |
| **C705** | AP168 | 30p | multi | *4.75* | .65 |
| **C706** | AP168 | 35p | multi | *5.75* | .90 |
| **C707** | AP168 | 50p | multi | *7.00* | 1.40 |
| *a.* | | | Vert. strip of 5, #C703-C707 | *25.00* | |
| | | | *Nos. C698-C707 (10)* | *29.55* | 5.80 |

11th Arab Boy Scout Jamboree, Smar-Jubeil, Aug. 1974. Nos. C702-C703 are for the 5th Girl Guide Jamboree, Deir-el-Kamar.

Mail Train and Postman Loading Mail, UPU Emblem — AP169

UPU Emblem and: 20p, Postal container hoisted onto ship. 25p, Postal Union Congress Building, Lausanne, and UPU Headquarters, Bern. 50p, Fork-lift truck loading mail on plane.

**1974, Nov. 4** **Photo.** ***Perf. 11½x12***

| | | | | | |
|---|---|---|---|---|---|
| **C708** | AP169 | 5p | multicolored | .45 | .25 |
| **C709** | AP169 | 20p | multicolored | *2.00* | .25 |
| **C710** | AP169 | 25p | multicolored | *3.00* | .25 |
| **C711** | AP169 | 50p | ultra & multi | *6.25* | .70 |
| | | | *Nos. C708-C711 (4)* | *11.70* | 1.45 |

Centenary of Universal Postal Union.

Congress Building, Sofar — AP170

Arab Postal Union Emblem and: 20p, View of Sofar. 25p, APU Headquarters, Cairo. 50p, Ministry of Post, Beirut.

**1974, Dec. 4** **Litho.** ***Perf. 13x12½***

| | | | | | |
|---|---|---|---|---|---|
| **C712** | AP170 | 5p | orange & multi | *.35* | .25 |
| **C713** | AP170 | 20p | yellow & multi | *.60* | .25 |
| **C714** | AP170 | 25p | blue & multi | *.90* | .25 |
| **C715** | AP170 | 50p | multicolored | *4.25* | 1.00 |
| | | | *Nos. C712-C715 (4)* | *6.10* | 1.75 |

Arab Postal Union, 25th anniversary.

Mountain Road, by Omar Onsi — AP171

Paintings by Lebanese artists: No. C717, Clouds, by Moustapha Farroukh. No. C718, Woman, by Gebran Kahlil Gebran. No. C719, Embrace, by Cesar Gemayel. No. C720, Self-portrait, by Habib Serour. No. C721, Portrait of a Man, by Daoud Corm.

**1974, Dec. 6** **Litho.** ***Perf. 13x12½***

| | | | | | |
|---|---|---|---|---|---|
| **C716** | AP171 | 50p | lilac & multi | *2.00* | .50 |
| **C717** | AP171 | 50p | blue & multi | *2.00* | .50 |
| **C718** | AP171 | 50p | green & multi | *2.00* | .50 |
| **C719** | AP171 | 50p | lt vio & multi | *2.00* | .50 |
| **C720** | AP171 | 50p | brown & multi | *2.00* | .50 |
| **C721** | AP171 | 50p | gray brn & multi | *2.00* | .50 |
| | | | *Nos. C716-C721 (6)* | *12.00* | 3.00 |

Hunter Spearing Lion — AP172

Excavations at Hermel: 10p, Statue of Astarte. 25p, Dogs hunting boar, tiled panel. 35p, Greco-Roman tomb.

**1974, Dec. 13**

| | | | | | |
|---|---|---|---|---|---|
| **C722** | AP172 | 5p | blue & multi | *.40* | .25 |
| **C723** | AP172 | 10p | lilac & multi | *.90* | .25 |
| **C724** | AP172 | 25p | multicolored | *2.25* | .25 |
| **C725** | AP172 | 35p | multicolored | *2.75* | .40 |
| | | | *Nos. C722-C725 (4)* | *6.30* | 1.15 |

UNESCO Emblems and Globe AP173

**1974, Dec. 16** ***Perf. 12½x13***

| | | | | | |
|---|---|---|---|---|---|
| **C726** | AP173 | 5p | violet & multi | .40 | .25 |
| **C727** | AP173 | 10p | bister & multi | .85 | .25 |
| **C728** | AP173 | 25p | blue & multi | 2.00 | .30 |
| **C729** | AP173 | 35p | multicolored | 2.50 | .40 |
| | | | *Nos. C726-C729 (4)* | 5.75 | 1.20 |

International Book Year.

Symbolic Stamp under Magnifying Glass — AP174

Designs (Symbolic): 10p, Post horns. 15p, Stamp printing. 20p, Mounted stamp.

**1974, Dec. 20** ***Perf. 13x12½***

| | | | | | |
|---|---|---|---|---|---|
| **C730** | AP174 | 5p | blue & multi | .25 | .25 |
| **C731** | AP174 | 10p | olive & multi | .40 | .25 |
| **C732** | AP174 | 15p | brown & multi | .80 | .25 |
| **C733** | AP174 | 20p | lilac & multi | 1.00 | .25 |
| | | | *Nos. C730-C733 (4)* | 2.45 | 1.00 |

Georgina Rizk — AP175

5p, 25p, Georgina Rizk in Lebanese costume.

**1974, Dec. 21**

| | | | | | |
|---|---|---|---|---|---|
| **C734** | AP175 | 5p | multicolored | .25 | .25 |
| **C735** | AP175 | 20p | violet & multi | .55 | .25 |
| **C736** | AP175 | 25p | yellow & multi | .75 | .25 |
| **C737** | AP175 | 50p | blue & multi | 1.50 | .25 |
| *a.* | | | Souvenir sheet of 4 | 8.00 | 4.25 |
| | | | *Nos. C734-C737 (4)* | 3.05 | 1.00 |

Georgina Rizk, Miss Universe 1971. No. C737a contains 4 stamps similar to Nos. C734-C737 with simulated perforations.

UNICEF Emblem, Helicopter, Camel, Supplies — AP176

UNICEF Emblem and: 25p, Child welfare clinic. 35p, Kindergarten class. 70p, Girls in chemistry laboratory.

**1974, Dec. 28** **Litho.** ***Perf. 12½x13***

| | | | | | |
|---|---|---|---|---|---|
| **C738** | AP176 | 20p | multicolored | .25 | .25 |
| **C739** | AP176 | 25p | multicolored | .25 | .25 |
| **C740** | AP176 | 35p | blue & multi | .75 | .25 |
| **C741** | AP176 | 70p | blue & multi | 1.75 | .25 |
| *a.* | | | Souvenir sheet of 4 | 5.75 | 3.00 |
| | | | *Nos. C738-C741 (4)* | 3.00 | 1.00 |

UNICEF, 25th anniv. No. C741a contains 4 stamps similar to Nos. C738-C741 with simulated perforations. Sold for 200p.

Discus and Olympic Rings — AP177

**1974, Dec. 30** ***Perf. 13x12½***

| | | | | | |
|---|---|---|---|---|---|
| **C742** | AP177 | 5p | shown | .25 | .25 |
| **C743** | AP177 | 10p | Shot put | .30 | .25 |
| **C744** | AP177 | 15p | Weight lifting | .40 | .25 |
| **C745** | AP177 | 35p | Running | .85 | .25 |
| **C746** | AP177 | 50p | Wrestling | 1.25 | .25 |
| **C747** | AP177 | 85p | Javelin | 2.00 | .35 |
| *a.* | | | Souvenir sheet of 6 | 8.00 | 5.25 |
| | | | *Nos. C742-C747 (6)* | 5.05 | 1.60 |

20th Olympic Games, Munich, Aug. 26-Sept. 11, 1972. No. C747a contains 6 stamps similar to Nos. C742-C747 with simulated perforations.

Clouds and Environment Emblem AP178

**1975**

| | | | | |
|---|---|---|---|---|
| **C748** | AP178 | 5p shown | .25 | .25 |
| **C749** | AP178 | 25p Landscape | .55 | .25 |
| **C750** | AP178 | 30p Flowers and tree | .55 | .25 |
| **C751** | AP178 | 40p Waves | .85 | .25 |
| *a.* | | Souvenir sheet of 4 | 7.00 | 4.75 |
| | | *Nos. C748-C751 (4)* | 2.20 | 1.00 |

UN Conf. on Human Environment, Stockholm, June 5-16, 1972. No. C751a contains four stamps similar to Nos. C748-C751 with simulated perforations. Sold for 150p.

Archaeology — AP179

Symbols of: 25p, Science & medicine. 35p, Justice & commerce. 70p, Industry & commerce.

**1975, Aug. Litho. *Perf. 12½x13***

| | | | | |
|---|---|---|---|---|
| **C752** | AP179 | 20p multicolored | *.90* | .25 |
| **C753** | AP179 | 25p multicolored | *1.25* | .25 |
| **C754** | AP179 | 35p blue & multi | *1.75* | .40 |
| **C755** | AP179 | 70p buff & multi | *4.00* | .70 |
| | | *Nos. C752-C755 (4)* | *7.90* | 1.60 |

Beirut, University City.

Stamps of 1971-73 Ovptd. with Various Overall Patterns Including Cedars in Blue, Red, Orange, Lilac, Brown or Green

**1978 Litho. *Perf. 12, 14***

| | | | | |
|---|---|---|---|---|
| **C758** | AP162 | 2.50p (#C658;B) | .25 | .25 |
| **C759** | AP162 | 5p (#C659;R) | .25 | .25 |
| **C760** | AP164 | 5p (#C674;B) | .25 | .25 |
| **C761** | AP164 | 10p (#C675;B) | .25 | .25 |
| **C762** | AP167 | 10p (#C690;O) | .25 | .25 |
| **C763** | AP162 | 15p (#C660;R) | 1.00 | .25 |
| **C764** | AP164 | 20p (#C676;B) | .70 | .25 |
| **C765** | AP167 | 20p (#C691;B) | .70 | .25 |
| **C766** | AP162 | 25p (#C661;L) | .70 | .25 |
| **C767** | AP164 | 25p (#C677;B) | 1.40 | .25 |
| **C768** | AP163 | 35p (#C670;Br) | 1.60 | .25 |
| **C769** | AP162 | 40p (#C662;L) | 1.60 | .25 |
| **C770** | AP167 | 40p (#C693;G) | 1.60 | .25 |
| **C771** | AP154 | 45p (#C633;L) | 1.60 | .25 |
| **C772** | AP162 | 50p (#C663;L) | 2.50 | .25 |
| **C773** | AP163 | 50p (#C671;L) | 2.50 | .25 |
| **C774** | AP167 | 50p (#C694;Br) | 2.50 | .25 |
| **C775** | AP154 | 70p (#C635;L) | 2.75 | .55 |
| **C776** | AP162 | 70p (#C664;L) | 2.75 | .55 |
| **C777** | AP167 | 70p (#C695;B) | 2.75 | .55 |
| **C778** | AP162 | 75p (#C665;B) | 4.50 | .55 |
| **C779** | AP154 | 85p (#C636;R) | 3.25 | .60 |
| **C780** | AP163 | 85p (#C672;B) | 3.25 | .60 |
| **C781** | AP167 | 85p (#C696;G) | 3.25 | .60 |
| **C782** | AP162 | 100p (#C666;O) | 5.00 | .80 |
| **C783** | AP163 | 100p (#C673;B) | 5.00 | .80 |
| **C784** | AP167 | 100p (#C697;L) | 5.00 | .80 |
| **C785** | AP162 | 200p (#C667;O) | 10.00 | 2.75 |
| **C786** | AP162 | 300p (#C668;O) | 14.50 | 5.25 |
| **C787** | AP162 | 500p (#C669;O) | 21.00 | 7.50 |
| | | *Nos. C758-C787 (30)* | 102.65 | 26.15 |

Heart and Arrow — AP180

**1978, Apr. 7 Litho. *Perf. 12***

| | | | | |
|---|---|---|---|---|
| **C788** | AP180 | 50p blue, blk & red | 1.00 | .80 |

World Health Day; drive against hypertension.

Poet Mikhail Naimy and Sannine Mountains — AP181

Designs: 50p, Naimy and view of Al Chakhroub Baskinta. 75p, Naimy portrait in sunburst, vert.

**1978, May 17**

| | | | | |
|---|---|---|---|---|
| **C789** | AP181 | 25p gold & multi | *.90* | .25 |
| **C790** | AP181 | 50p gold & multi | *1.60* | .55 |
| **C791** | AP181 | 75p gold & multi | *2.50* | .80 |
| | | *Nos. C789-C791 (3)* | *5.00* | 1.60 |

Mikhail Naimy Festival.

### Army Day Type of 1980

Designs: 50p, Emir Fakhr al-Din statue, vert. 75p, Soldiers and flag.

**1980, Dec. 28 Litho. *Perf. 11½***

| | | | | |
|---|---|---|---|---|
| **C792** | A86 | 50p multicolored | *1.50* | .25 |
| **C793** | A86 | 75p multicolored | *2.00* | .40 |

28th UPU Congress, Rio de Janeiro, 1979 — AP182

**1981, Feb. 17 Photo. *Perf. 12x11½***

| | | | | |
|---|---|---|---|---|
| **C794** | AP182 | 25p multicolored | 1.10 | .25 |
| **C795** | AP182 | 50p multicolored | 2.40 | .70 |
| **C796** | AP182 | 75p multicolored | 3.50 | 1.00 |
| | | *Nos. C794-C796 (3)* | 7.00 | 1.95 |

Intl. Year of the Child (1979) AP183

**1981, Mar. 25 Litho. *Perf. 12x11½***

| | | | | |
|---|---|---|---|---|
| **C797** | AP183 | 100p multicolored | 4.50 | 1.40 |

1974 Chess Championships — AP184

Various chess pieces. Nos. C799-C802 vert.

***Perf. 12x11½, 11½x12***

**1980-81 Photo.**

| | | | | |
|---|---|---|---|---|
| **C798** | AP184 | 50p multicolored | 1.90 | .65 |
| **C799** | AP184 | 75p multicolored | 2.25 | .85 |
| **C800** | AP184 | 100p multicolored | 2.75 | 1.25 |
| **C801** | AP184 | 150p multicolored | 4.50 | 2.40 |
| **C802** | AP184 | 200p multicolored | 5.75 | 3.25 |
| | | *Nos. C798-C802 (5)* | 17.15 | 8.40 |

Makassed Islamic Institute Centenary (1978) AP185

**1981 Photo. *Perf. 13½x14***

| | | | | |
|---|---|---|---|---|
| **C803** | AP185 | 50p Children | 1.00 | .25 |
| **C804** | AP185 | 75p Institute | 1.50 | .25 |
| **C805** | AP185 | 100p Makassed | 1.75 | .40 |
| | | *Nos. C803-C805 (3)* | 4.25 | .90 |

## AIR POST SEMI-POSTAL STAMPS

### Nos. C13-C16 Surcharged Like Nos. B1-B12

**1926 *Perf. 13½***

| | | | | |
|---|---|---|---|---|
| **CB1** | A2 | 1p + 2p dk brn | 15.00 | 8.00 |
| **CB2** | A2 | 2p + 3p org brn | 15.00 | 8.00 |
| **CB3** | A2 | 3p + 5p violet | 15.00 | 8.00 |
| **CB4** | A3 | 5p + 10p vio brn | 15.00 | 8.00 |
| | | *Nos. CB1-CB4 (4)* | 60.00 | 32.00 |

These stamps were sold for their combined values, original and surcharged. The latter represented their postal franking value and the former was a contribution to the relief of refugees from the Djebel Druze War.

**Catalogue values for unused stamps in this section, from this point to the end of the section, are for Never Hinged items.**

### Independent Republic

Natural Bridge, Faraya SPAP1

Bay of Jounie SPAP2

***Perf. 11½***

**1947, June 27 Unwmk. Litho.**

**Cross in Carmine**

| | | | | |
|---|---|---|---|---|
| **CB5** | SPAP1 | 12.50 + 25pi brt bl grn | 12.50 | 3.75 |
| **CB6** | SPAP1 | 25 + 50pi blue | 15.00 | 4.50 |
| **CB7** | SPAP2 | 50 + 100pi choc | 17.50 | 5.25 |
| **CB8** | SPAP2 | 75 + 150pi brt pur | 35.00 | 10.00 |
| **CB9** | SPAP2 | 100 + 200pi sl | 65.00 | 14.00 |
| | | *Nos. CB5-CB9 (5)* | 145.00 | 37.50 |

The surtax was for the Red Cross.

### Mother & Child Type of Air Post Stamps, 1960

**1960, Aug. 16 *Perf. 13½x13***

| | | | | |
|---|---|---|---|---|
| **CB10** | AP72 | 20p + 10p dk red & buff | 1.00 | .25 |
| **CB11** | AP72 | 60p + 15p bl & lt bl | 2.50 | .60 |

### Olympic Games Type of Semi-Postal Issue, 1961

**1961, Jan. 12 Unwmk. *Perf. 13***

| | | | | |
|---|---|---|---|---|
| **CB12** | SP1 | 15p + 15p Fencing | 4.00 | 1.60 |
| **CB13** | SP1 | 25p + 25p Bicycling | 4.00 | 1.60 |
| **CB14** | SP1 | 35p + 35p Swimming | 4.00 | 1.60 |
| | | *Nos. CB12-CB14 (3)* | 12.00 | 4.80 |

An imperf. souvenir sheet exists, containing one each of Nos. CB12-CB14. Value $32.50.

### Nos. CB12-CB14 with Arabic and French Overprint in Green, Red or Maroon

**1962, June 2**

| | | | | |
|---|---|---|---|---|
| **CB15** | SP1 | 15p + 15p (G) | 1.50 | .60 |
| **CB16** | SP1 | 25p + 25p (M) | 2.50 | 1.25 |
| **CB17** | SP1 | 35p + 35p (R) | 3.00 | 1.60 |
| | | *Nos. CB15-CB17 (3)* | 7.00 | 3.45 |

European Marksmanship Championships held in Lebanon.

## POSTAGE DUE STAMPS

### Postage Due Stamps of France, 1893-1920, Surcharged like Regular Issue

**1924 Unwmk. *Perf. 14x13½***

| | | | | |
|---|---|---|---|---|
| **J1** | D2 | 50c on 10c choc | 6.75 | 4.25 |
| **J2** | D2 | 1p on 20c ol grn | 6.75 | 4.25 |
| **J3** | D2 | 2p on 30c red | 6.75 | 4.25 |
| **J4** | D2 | 3p on 50c vio brn | 6.75 | 4.25 |
| **J5** | D2 | 5p on 1fr red brn, *straw* | 6.75 | 4.25 |
| | | *Nos. J1-J5 (5)* | 33.75 | 21.25 |

Postage Due Stamps of France, 1893-1920, Surcharged

**1924**

| | | | | |
|---|---|---|---|---|
| **J6** | D2 | 0.50p on 10c choc | 7.25 | 4.00 |
| **J7** | D2 | 1p on 20c ol grn | 7.25 | 4.00 |
| **J8** | D2 | 2p on 30c red | 7.25 | 4.00 |
| **J9** | D2 | 3p on 50c vio brn | 7.25 | 4.00 |
| **J10** | D2 | 5p on 1fr red brn, *straw* | 7.25 | 4.00 |
| | | *Nos. J6-J10 (5)* | 36.25 | 20.00 |

Ancient Bridge across Dog River — D3

Designs: 1p, Village scene. 2p, Pigeon Rocks, near Beirut. 3p, Belfort Castle. 5p, Venus Temple at Baalbek.

**1925 Photo. *Perf. 13½***

| | | | | |
|---|---|---|---|---|
| **J11** | D3 | 0.50p brown, *yellow* | .95 | .45 |
| **J12** | D3 | 1p violet, *rose* | 1.35 | .65 |
| **J13** | D3 | 2p black, *blue* | 2.25 | .90 |
| **J14** | D3 | 3p black, *red org* | 3.50 | 2.00 |
| **J15** | D3 | 5p black, *bl grn* | 5.75 | 3.75 |
| | | *Nos. J11-J15 (5)* | 13.80 | 7.75 |
| | | Set, never hinged | 42.50 | |

Nos. J11 to J15 Overprinted

**1927**

| | | | | |
|---|---|---|---|---|
| **J16** | D3 | 0.50p brown, *yellow* | 1.50 | .40 |
| **J17** | D3 | 1p violet, *rose* | 2.50 | .85 |
| **J18** | D3 | 2p black, *blue* | 3.50 | 1.25 |
| **J19** | D3 | 3p black, *red org* | 7.25 | 3.00 |
| **J20** | D3 | 5p black, *bl grn* | 9.50 | 4.50 |
| | | *Nos. J16-J20 (5)* | 24.25 | 10.00 |
| | | Set, never hinged | 35.00 | |

Nos. J16-J20 with Additional Ovpt.

**1928**

**J21** D3 0.50p brn, *yel* (Bk+R) 1.75 1.25
**J22** D3 1p vio, *rose* (Bk) 1.75 1.25
**J23** D3 2p blk, *bl* (Bk+R) 3.00 2.00
**J24** D3 3p blk, *red org* (Bk) 6.00 3.50
**J25** D3 5p blk, *bl grn* (Bk+R) 6.75 4.25
*Nos. J21-J25 (5)* 19.25 12.25
Set, never hinged 65.00

No. J23 has not the short bars in the upper corners.

### Postage Due Stamps of 1925 Overprinted in Red like Nos. J21-J25

**1928**

**J26** D3 0.50p brn, *yel* (R) 1.00 .50
**J27** D3 2p blk, *bl* (R) 4.25 3.50
**J28** D3 5p blk, *bl grn* (R) 11.50 7.50
*Nos. J26-J28 (3)* 16.75 11.50
Set, never hinged 32.50

No. J28 has not the short bars in the upper corners.

D4

Bas-relief of a Ship — D5

D6

D7

D8

Bas-relief from Sarcophagus of King Ahiram — D9

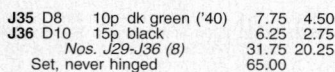

D10

**1930-40 Photo.; Engr. (No. J35)**

**J29** D4 0.50p black, *rose* .75 .50
**J30** D5 1p blk, *gray bl* 1.25 1.00
**J31** D6 2p blk, *yellow* 1.75 1.25
**J32** D7 3p blk, *bl grn* 1.75 1.25
**J33** D8 5p blk, *orange* 7.25 5.50
**J34** D9 8p blk, *lt rose* 5.00 3.50
**J35** D8 10p dk green ('40) 7.75 4.50
**J36** D10 15p black 6.25 2.75
*Nos. J29-J36 (8)* 31.75 20.25
Set, never hinged 65.00

Nos. J29-J36 exist imperf.

**Catalogue values for unused stamps in this section, from this point to the end of the section, are for Never Hinged items.**

### Independent Republic

National Museum, Beirut D11

**1945 Unwmk. Litho. *Perf. 11½***

**J37** D11 2p brn black, *yel* 8.25 2.00
**J38** D11 5p ultra, *rose* 10.00 2.50
**J39** D11 25p blue, *bl green* 14.00 4.00
**J40** D11 50p dark bl, *blue* 17.50 6.00
*Nos. J37-J40 (4)* 49.75 14.50

D12

**1947**

**J41** D12 5p black, *green* 6.00 1.25
**J42** D12 25p blk, *yellow* 60.00 3.50
**J43** D12 50p black, *blue* 30.00 6.00
*Nos. J41-J43 (3)* 96.00 10.75

Hermel Monument D13

**1948**

**J44** D13 2p blk, *yellow* 4.75 3.75
**J45** D13 3p black, *pink* 9.00 3.00
**J46** D13 10p black, *blue* 22.50 5.50
*Nos. J44-J46 (3)* 36.25 12.25

D14

**1950**

**J47** D14 1p carmine rose 3.50 .30
**J48** D14 5p violet blue 13.00 .60
**J49** D14 10p gray green 27.50 1.50
*Nos. J47-J49 (3)* 44.00 2.40

D15

**1952**

**J50** D15 1p dp rose lilac .75 .30
**J51** D15 2p bright violet .75 .30
**J52** D15 3p dk blue green 1.50 .30
**J53** D15 5p blue 2.00 .35
**J54** D15 10p chocolate 2.75 .55
**J55** D15 25p black 20.00 1.25
*Nos. J50-J55 (6)* 27.75 3.05

D16

**1953**

**J56** D16 1p carmine rose .35 .30
**J57** D16 2p blue green .35 .30
**J58** D16 3p orange .35 .30
**J59** D16 5p lilac rose .60 .30
**J60** D16 10p brown .95 .35
**J61** D16 15p deep blue 2.00 .75
*Nos. J56-J61 (6)* 4.60 2.30

D17

**1955 Unwmk. *Perf. 13***

**J62** D17 1p orange brown .40 .25
**J63** D17 2p yellow green .40 .25
**J64** D17 3p blue green .40 .25
**J65** D17 5p carmine lake .40 .25
**J66** D17 10p gray green .60 .25
**J67** D17 15p ultramarine .70 .30
**J68** D17 25p red lilac 1.50 .80
*Nos. J62-J68 (7)* 4.40 2.35

Cedar of Lebanon — D18

**1966 Photo. *Perf. 11½***

**J69** D18 1p bright green .60 .25
**J70** D18 5p rose lilac .60 .25
**J71** D18 15p ultramarine .75 .55
*Nos. J69-J71 (3)* 1.95 1.05

Emir Fakhr al-Din II — D19

**1968 Litho. *Perf. 11***

**J72** D19 1p dk & lt gray .65 .25
**J73** D19 2p dk & lt blue grn .65 .25
**J74** D19 3p deep org & yel .65 .25
**J75** D19 5p brt rose lil & pink .65 .25
**J76** D19 10p olive & lemon .65 .25
**J77** D19 15p vio & pale violet .95 .50
**J78** D19 25p brt & lt blue 1.50 1.25
*Nos. J72-J78 (7)* 5.70 3.00

---

## POSTAL TAX STAMPS

Fiscal Stamp Surcharged in Violet

**Wmk. A T 39 Multiple**

**1945 *Perf. 13½***

**RA1** R1 5pi on 30c red brn 350.00 1.50

The tax was for the Lebanese Army.

No. RA1 Overprinted in Black

**1948**

**RA2** R1 5pi on 30c red brn 17.50 1.40

Fiscal Stamps Surcharged in Various Colors

**RA3** R1 5pi on 15pi dk vio bl (R) 15.00 1.60
*a.* Brown surcharge 18.00 2.25
**RA4** R1 5pi on 25c dk blue green (R) 15.00 1.60
**RA5** R1 5pi on 30c red brn (Bl) 17.50 1.60
**RA6** R1 5pi on 60c lt ultra (Br) 24.00 1.60
**RA7** R1 5pi on 3pi salmon rose (Ult) 15.00 1.60

No RA4 exists with watermarks "AT37" or "AT38."

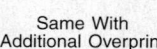

Same With Additional Overprint

**RA8** R1 5pi on 10pi red *70.00* 5.00

Fiscal Stamp Surcharged Like Nos. RA3-RA7 with Top Arabic Characters Replaced by

**RA9** R1 5pi on 3pi rose (Bk+V) 18.00 1.40

Fiscal Stamp Surcharged in Black and Violet

**RA10** R1 5pi on 3pi sal rose *200.00* 15.00

The tax was to aid the war in Palestine.

**Catalogue values for unused stamps in this section, from this point to the end of the section, are for Never Hinged items.**

Family among Ruins — R2

**1956 Unwmk. Litho. *Perf. 13***

**RA11** R2 2.50pi brown 5.00 .25

The tax was for earthquake victims. These stamps were obligatory on all inland mail and all mail going to Arab countries.

Building a House — R3

**1957-58 *Perf. 13½x13***

**RA12** R3 2.50p brown 4.25 .25
**RA13** R3 2.50p dk blue grn ('58) 2.50 .25

### Type of 1957 Redrawn

**1959**

| | | | |
|---|---|---|---|
| **RA14** | R3 2.50p light brown | 2.75 | .25 |

On No. RA14 the denomination is on top and the Arabic lines are at the bottom of design.

R4

**1961 Unwmk.** ***Perf. 13½x13***

| | | | |
|---|---|---|---|
| **RA15** | R4 2.50p yellow brown | 2.50 | .25 |

Building a House — R5

**1962** ***Perf. 13½x14***

| | | | |
|---|---|---|---|
| **RA16** | R5 2.50p blue green | 4.00 | .25 |

The tax was for the relief of earthquake victims.

## LEEWARD ISLANDS

'lē-wərd 'ī-ləndz

LOCATION — A group of islands in the West Indies, southeast of Puerto Rico
GOVT. — British Colony
AREA — 423 sq. mi.
POP. — 108,847 (1946)
CAPITAL — St. John

While stamps inscribed "Leeward Islands" were in use, 1890-1956, the colony consisted of the presidencies (now colonies) of Antigua, Montserrat, St. Christopher (St. Kitts) with Nevis and Anguilla, the British Virgin Islands and Dominica (which became a separate colony in 1940).

Each presidency issued its own stamps, using them along with the Leeward Islands general issues. The Leeward Islands federation was abolished in 1956.

12 Pence = 1 Shilling
20 Shillings = 1 Pound
100 Cents = 1 Dollar

**Catalogue values for unused stamps in this country are for Never Hinged items, beginning with Scott 116.**

Queen Victoria — A1

**1890 Typo. Wmk. 2** ***Perf. 14***

| | | | |
|---|---|---|---|
| **1** | A1 ½p lilac & green | 3.75 | 1.40 |
| **2** | A1 1p lilac & car | 8.75 | .25 |
| **3** | A1 2½p lilac & ultra | 9.50 | .30 |
| **4** | A1 4p lilac & org | 12.00 | 9.50 |
| **5** | A1 6p lilac & brown | 13.50 | 15.50 |
| **6** | A1 7p lilac & slate | 12.00 | *21.00* |
| **7** | A1 1sh green & car | 24.00 | *62.50* |
| **8** | A1 5sh green & ultra | 145.00 | *330.00* |
| | *Nos. 1-8 (8)* | 228.50 | *440.45* |

Denomination of Nos. 7-8 are in color on plain tablet: "ONE SHILLING" or "FIVE SHILLINGS."

For overprints and surcharges see Nos. 9-19.

### Jubilee Issue

Regular Issue of 1890 Handstamp Overprinted

**1897, July 22**

| | | | |
|---|---|---|---|
| **9** | A1 ½p lilac & green | 8.25 | *26.00* |
| **10** | A1 1p lilac & car | 9.25 | *26.00* |
| **11** | A1 2½p lilac & ultra | 9.75 | *26.00* |
| **12** | A1 4p lilac & org | 57.50 | *80.00* |
| **13** | A1 6p lilac & brown | 62.50 | *130.00* |
| **14** | A1 7p lilac & slate | 62.50 | *130.00* |
| **15** | A1 1sh green & car | 130.00 | *275.00* |
| **16** | A1 5sh green & ultra | 525.00 | *850.00* |
| | *Nos. 9-16 (8)* | 864.75 | *1,543.* |

### Double Overprints

| | | | |
|---|---|---|---|
| *9a* | A1 ½p | *1,400.* | |
| ***b.*** | Triple overprint | *9,000.* | |
| *10a* | A1 1p | *1,150.* | |
| ***b.*** | Triple overprint | *6,250.* | |
| *11a* | A1 2½p | *1,350.* | |
| *12a* | A1 4p | *1,350.* | |
| *13a* | A1 6p | *1,700.* | 4,500. |
| *14a* | A1 7p | *1,700.* | *2,100.* |
| *15a* | A1 1sh | *2,250.* | |
| *16a* | A1 5sh | *6,000.* | |

60th year of Queen Victoria's reign.
Excellent counterfeits of Nos. 9-16 exist.

### Stamps of 1890 Surcharged in Black or Red

b

c

**1902, Aug.**

| | | | |
|---|---|---|---|
| **17** | A1(b) 1p on 4p lilac & org | 7.00 | *12.00* |
| ***a.*** | Tall narrow "O" in "One" | 47.50 | *87.50* |
| ***b.*** | Double surcharge | 6,000. | |
| **18** | A1(b) 1p on 6p lilac & brn | 8.00 | *19.00* |
| ***a.*** | Tall narrow "O" in "One" | 67.50 | *150.00* |
| **19** | A1(c) 1p on 7p lilac & sl | 7.00 | *15.00* |
| | *Nos. 17-19 (3)* | 22.00 | 46.00 |

King Edward VII — A4

Numerals of ¼p, 2p, 3p and 2sh6p of type A4 are in color on plain tablet. The 1sh and 5sh denominations are expressed as "ONE SHILLING" and "FIVE SHILLINGS" on plain tablet.

**1902**

| | | | |
|---|---|---|---|
| **20** | A4 ½p violet & green | 6.00 | 1.10 |
| **21** | A4 1p vio & car rose | 11.00 | .25 |
| **22** | A4 2p violet & bister | 3.00 | *4.50* |
| **23** | A4 2½p violet & ultra | 6.75 | 2.50 |
| **24** | A4 3p violet & black | 11.50 | *8.00* |
| **25** | A4 6p violet & brown | 3.00 | *9.00* |
| **26** | A4 1sh grn & car rose | 11.50 | *30.00* |
| **27** | A4 2sh6p green & blk | 32.50 | *80.00* |
| **28** | A4 5sh green & ultra | 65.00 | *95.00* |
| | *Nos. 20-28 (9)* | 150.25 | *230.35* |

**1905-11 Wmk. 3**
**Chalky Paper (Ordinary Paper #29, 33)**

| | | | |
|---|---|---|---|
| **29** | A4 ½p vio & grn ('06) | 5.25 | 2.75 |
| ***a.*** | Chalky paper ('08) | 32.50 | 23.00 |
| **30** | A4 1p vio & car rose | 11.50 | .90 |
| **31** | A4 2p vio & bis ('08) | 14.00 | *27.00* |
| **32** | A4 2½p vio & ultra | 80.00 | 50.00 |
| **33** | A4 3p violet & black | 25.00 | *62.50* |
| ***a.*** | Chalky paper ('08) | 60.00 | 100.00 |
| **34** | A4 3p violet, *yel* ('10) | 3.75 | *8.00* |
| **35** | A4 6p vio & brn ('08) | 55.00 | *100.00* |
| **36** | A4 6p violet & red violet ('11) | 10.00 | *11.00* |
| **37** | A4 1sh grn & car rose ('08) | 55.00 | *140.00* |
| **38** | A4 1sh blk, *grn* ('11) | 12.00 | *22.50* |
| **39** | A4 2sh6p blk & red, *blue* ('11) | 45.00 | *55.00* |
| **40** | A4 5sh grn & red, *yel* ('11) | 50.00 | *70.00* |
| | *Nos. 29-40 (12)* | 366.50 | *549.65* |

**1907-11 Ordinary Paper**

| | | | |
|---|---|---|---|
| **41** | A4 ¼p brown ('09) | 3.00 | 1.90 |
| **42** | A4 ½p green | 6.25 | 1.90 |
| **43** | A4 1p red | 16.50 | .85 |
| ***a.*** | 1p rose carmine | 50.00 | 3.75 |
| **44** | A4 2p gray ('11) | 5.50 | *14.50* |
| **45** | A4 2½p ultramarine | 9.00 | 4.50 |
| | *Nos. 41-45 (5)* | 40.25 | *23.65* |

King George V — A5

For description of dies I and II, see "Dies of British Colonial Stamps" in Table of Contents.

The ½p, 1p, 2½p and 6p denominations of type A5 show the numeral on horizontally-lined tablet. The 1sh and 5sh denominations are expressed as "ONE SHILLING" and "FIVE SHILLINGS" on plain tablet.

**Die I**

**1912 Ordinary Paper**

| | | | |
|---|---|---|---|
| **46** | A5 ¼p brown | 1.90 | 1.10 |
| **47** | A5 ½p green | 5.50 | 2.00 |
| **48** | A5 1p carmine | 5.25 | 1.10 |
| ***a.*** | 1p scarlet | 15.00 | 1.10 |
| **49** | A5 2p gray | 4.25 | *5.75* |
| **50** | A5 2½p ultramarine | 3.50 | *7.25* |

**1912-22 Chalky Paper**

| | | | |
|---|---|---|---|
| **51** | A5 3p violet, *yel* | 4.00 | *26.00* |
| **52** | A5 4p blk & red, *yel* (Die II) ('22) | 8.00 | *24.00* |
| **53** | A5 6p vio & red vio | 4.75 | *9.25* |
| **54** | A5 1sh blk, *bl grn*, ol back | 17.50 | *8.50* |
| ***a.*** | 1sh black, *green* | 3.75 | *8.50* |
| **55** | A5 2sh vio & ultra, *bl* (Die II) ('22) | 18.00 | *65.00* |
| **56** | A5 2sh6p black & red, *blue* ('14) | 24.00 | *57.50* |
| **57** | A5 5sh grn & red, *yel* ('14) | 65.00 | *120.00* |
| ***a.*** | 5sh green & red, *lemon* ('15) | 50.00 | *85.00* |
| | *Nos. 46-57 (12)* | 161.65 | *327.45* |

**1913, Nov. Surface-colored Paper**

| | | | |
|---|---|---|---|
| **58** | A5 3p violet, *yel* | 95.00 | *180.00* |
| **59** | A5 1sh black, *green* | 90.00 | 40.00 |
| **60** | A5 5sh green & red, *yel* | 55.00 | *90.00* |
| | *Nos. 58-60 (3)* | 240.00 | 310.00 |

King George V — A6

**Die II**

**1921-32 Wmk. 4 Ordinary Paper**

| | | | |
|---|---|---|---|
| **61** | A5 ¼p dk brn ('22) | 2.50 | 1.10 |
| ***a.*** | ¼p dark brown (I) ('32) | 16.50 | *21.00* |
| **62** | A5 ½p green | 1.25 | .80 |
| ***a.*** | ½p green (I) ('32) | 27.50 | *65.00* |
| **63** | A5 1p carmine | 2.50 | .60 |
| ***a.*** | 1p rose red (I) ('32) | 45.00 | 1.00 |
| ***b.*** | 1p bright scarlet (II) ('29) | 15.00 | 2.50 |
| **64** | A5 1p dp violet ('22) | 2.50 | 1.10 |
| **65** | A5 1½p rose red ('26) | 9.25 | 1.50 |
| **66** | A5 1½p red brn ('29) | 2.25 | .25 |
| ***a.*** | 1½p red brown (I) ('32) | 4.50 | *3.00* |
| **68** | A5 2p gray ('22) | 3.25 | .85 |
| **69** | A5 2½p orange ('23) | 14.00 | *67.50* |
| **70** | A5 2½p ultra ('27) | 3.75 | 1.40 |
| ***a.*** | Die I ('32) | 7.50 | 3.75 |
| **71** | A5 3p ultra ('23) | 17.50 | *42.50* |
| ***a.*** | 3p deep ultramarine ('25) | 65.00 | 65.00 |

**Chalky Paper**

| | | | |
|---|---|---|---|
| **72** | A5 3p violet, *yel* | *8.50* | *6.75* |
| **73** | A5 4p blk & red, *yel* ('23) | 4.00 | *24.00* |
| **74** | A5 5p vio & ol grn ('22) | 2.75 | *4.50* |
| **75** | A5 6p vio & red vio ('23) | 19.00 | *50.00* |
| ***a.*** | Die I ('32) | 32.50 | *100.00* |
| **76** | A5 1sh blk, *emer* ('23) | 11.00 | *8.50* |
| ***a.*** | 1sh black, *green* (I) ('32) | 60.00 | *85.00* |
| **77** | A5 2sh vio & ultra, *bl* ('22) | 25.00 | *45.00* |
| ***a.*** | 2sh red purple & blue, *blue* ('26) | 14.00 | *52.50* |
| **78** | A5 2sh6p blk & red, *bl* ('23) | 13.00 | *27.00* |
| **79** | A5 3sh green & vio | 12.50 | *42.50* |
| **80** | A5 4sh black & scar | 21.00 | *42.50* |
| **81** | A5 5sh grn & red, *yel* | 50.00 | *85.00* |
| **82** | A6 10sh red & grn, *emer* ('28) | 80.00 | *140.00* |

**Wmk. 3**

| | | | |
|---|---|---|---|
| **83** | A6 £1 black & vio, *red* ('28) | 240.00 | 325.00 |
| | *Nos. 61-66,68-83 (22)* | 545.50 | *918.35* |

Common Design Types pictured following the introduction.

### Silver Jubilee Issue
Common Design Type

***Perf. 11x12***

**1935, May 6 Engr. Wmk. 4**

| | | | |
|---|---|---|---|
| **96** | CD301 1p car & dk blue | 1.75 | *3.25* |
| **97** | CD301 1½p blk & ultra | 2.75 | 1.60 |
| **98** | CD301 2½p ultra & brn | 4.75 | 4.75 |
| **99** | CD301 1sh brn vio & ind | 26.50 | *40.00* |
| | *Nos. 96-99 (4)* | 35.75 | 49.60 |
| | Set, never hinged | 45.00 | |

### Coronation Issue
Common Design Type

**1937, May 12** ***Perf. 13½x14***

| | | | |
|---|---|---|---|
| **100** | CD302 1p carmine | .50 | 1.00 |
| **101** | CD302 1½p brown | .50 | 1.50 |
| **102** | CD302 2½p bright ultra | .55 | 1.50 |
| | *Nos. 100-102 (3)* | 1.55 | 4.00 |
| | Set, never hinged | 3.00 | |

A7

King George VI — A8

**1938-51 Typo.** ***Perf. 14***

| | | | |
|---|---|---|---|
| **103** | A7 ¼p brown | .40 | 1.50 |
| ***a.*** | ¼p deep brown, chalky paper ('49) | .25 | *1.75* |
| **104** | A7 ½p green | .75 | .75 |
| **105** | A7 1p carmine | 1.25 | 1.75 |
| ***a.*** | 1p scarlet ('42) | 1.40 | 12.50 |
| ***b.*** | 1p red ('48) | 3.75 | *6.75* |
| **106** | A7 1½p red brown | .80 | .50 |
| **107** | A7 2p gray | 2.00 | 2.25 |
| ***a.*** | 2p slate gray ('42) | 4.00 | 3.75 |
| **108** | A7 2½p ultramarine | .60 | *4.00* |
| ***a.*** | 2½p bright blue | 18.00 | 1.20 |
| **109** | A7 3p dl org ('42) | .40 | *.90* |
| ***a.*** | 3p brown orange | 22.50 | 2.75 |
| **110** | A7 6p vio & red vio | 6.00 | 3.50 |
| ***a.*** | 6p deep dull purple & bright purple | 16.00 | 7.00 |
| ***b.*** | 6p purple & deep magenta ('47) | 9.00 | 5.50 |
| **111** | A7 1sh blk, *emer* ('42) | 3.50 | 1.50 |
| ***a.*** | 1sh black, *emerald*, chalky paper | 10.00 | 5.50 |
| **112** | A7 2sh vio & ultra, *bl* | 7.75 | 2.25 |
| ***a.*** | 2sh reddish purple & blue, *blue*, chalky paper | 17.00 | 3.00 |
| **113** | A7 5sh grn & red, *yel* | 21.00 | *18.00* |
| ***a.*** | 5sh green & red, *yel*, chalky paper | 30.00 | 22.50 |
| **114** | A8 10sh dp ver & dp grn, *emer*, ordinary paper ('47) | 82.50 | 100.00 |
| ***a.*** | 10sh dp red & bluish grn, *green*, chalky paper | 125.00 | *140.00* |
| ***b.*** | 10sh dull red & pale grn, *green*, ordinary paper ('44) | 475.00 | 375.00 |
| ***c.*** | 10sh red & green, *green*, ordinary paper ('45) | 100.00 | 90.00 |

Two dies were used for the 1p, differing in thickness of shading line at base of "1."

**Wmk. 3** ***Perf. 13***

| | | | |
|---|---|---|---|
| **115** | A8 £1 blk & vio, *scar* ('51) | 22.50 | *37.50* |
| ***a.*** | £1 black & brown purple, *red*, perf. 14 | 225.00 | *375.00* |
| | Never hinged | 375.00 | |
| ***b.*** | £1 black & purple, *carmine*, perf. 14 ('41) | 55.00 | 55.00 |
| | Never hinged | 90.00 | |
| ***c.*** | £1 black & brown purple, *salmon*, perf. 14 ('43) | 27.50 | 29.00 |
| | Never hinged | 45.00 | |
| ***d.*** | Wmkd. sideways (as #115, perf. 13) | *4,000.* | |
| | Never hinged | 7,000. | |
| | *Nos. 103-115 (13)* | 149.45 | 174.40 |
| | Set, never hinged | 750.00 | |

The 3p-£1 were issued on chalky paper in 1938 and on ordinary paper in 1942. Values are for the most common varieties.

Issued: #115, 12/13/51; others, 11/25/38.
See Nos. 120-125.

**Catalogue values for unused stamps in this section, from this point to the end of the section, are for Never Hinged items.**

### Peace Issue
Common Design Type
*Perf. 13½x14*

| 1946, Nov. 1 | | Wmk. 4 | Engr. | |
|---|---|---|---|---|
| **116** | CD303 | 1½p brown | .25 | .75 |
| **117** | CD303 | 3p deep orange | .25 | .75 |

### Silver Wedding Issue
Common Design Types

| 1949, Jan. 2 | | Photo. | *Perf. 14x14½* | |
|---|---|---|---|---|
| **118** | CD304 | 2½p bright ultra | .25 | .25 |

*Perf. 11½x11*

**Engr.; Name Typographed**

| | | | | |
|---|---|---|---|---|
| **119** | CD305 | 5sh green | 6.75 | 8.00 |

### George VI Type of 1938

| 1949, July 1 | | Typo. | *Perf. 13½x14* | |
|---|---|---|---|---|
| **120** | A7 | ½p gray | 2.00 | 1.50 |
| **121** | A7 | 1p green | .55 | .25 |
| **122** | A7 | 1½p orange & black | 1.75 | .40 |
| **123** | A7 | 2p crimson rose | 1.40 | 1.25 |
| **124** | A7 | 2½p black & plum | 1.00 | .25 |
| **125** | A7 | 3p ultramarine | 1.00 | .25 |
| | | *Nos. 120-125 (6)* | 7.70 | 3.90 |

### UPU Issue
Common Design Types

**Engr.; Name Typo. on 3p and 6p**

| 1949, Oct. 10 | | *Perf. 13½, 11x11½* | | |
|---|---|---|---|---|
| **126** | CD306 | 2½p slate | .25 | *2.40* |
| **127** | CD307 | 3p indigo | 2.00 | 2.40 |
| **128** | CD308 | 6p red lilac | .40 | *2.40* |
| **129** | CD309 | 1sh blue green | .40 | *2.40* |
| | | *Nos. 126-129 (4)* | 3.05 | *9.60* |

### University Issue
Common Design Types
*Perf. 14x14½*

| 1951, Feb. 16 | | Engr. | Wmk. 4 | |
|---|---|---|---|---|
| **130** | CD310 | 3c gray black & org | .35 | *2.00* |
| **131** | CD311 | 12c lilac & rose car | 1.00 | *2.00* |

### Coronation Issue
Common Design Type

| 1953, June 2 | | | *Perf. 13½x13* | |
|---|---|---|---|---|
| **132** | CD312 | 3c dk green & black | 1.00 | *2.25* |

A9

Queen Elizabeth II — A10

| 1954, Feb. 22 | | Typo. | *Perf. 14* | |
|---|---|---|---|---|
| **133** | A9 | ½c brown | .25 | .60 |
| **134** | A9 | 1c gray | 1.25 | 1.50 |
| **135** | A9 | 2c green | 1.75 | .25 |
| **136** | A9 | 3c orange & blk | 2.50 | 1.50 |
| **137** | A9 | 4c rose red | 1.75 | .25 |
| **138** | A9 | 5c blk & claret | 2.25 | 1.50 |
| **139** | A9 | 6c orange | 2.25 | .65 |
| **140** | A9 | 8c deep ultra | 2.75 | .25 |
| **141** | A9 | 12c rose vio & mag | 2.00 | .25 |
| **142** | A9 | 24c black & green | 2.00 | .30 |
| **143** | A9 | 48c rose vio & ultra | 8.00 | 4.00 |
| **144** | A9 | 60c brown & green | 6.00 | 3.25 |
| **145** | A9 | $1.20 yel grn & rose red | 7.00 | 4.50 |

*Perf. 13*

| | | | | |
|---|---|---|---|---|
| **146** | A10 | $2.40 red & blue grn | 12.00 | 7.75 |
| **147** | A10 | $4.80 black & claret | 16.00 | 11.00 |
| | | *Nos. 133-147 (15)* | 67.75 | *37.55* |

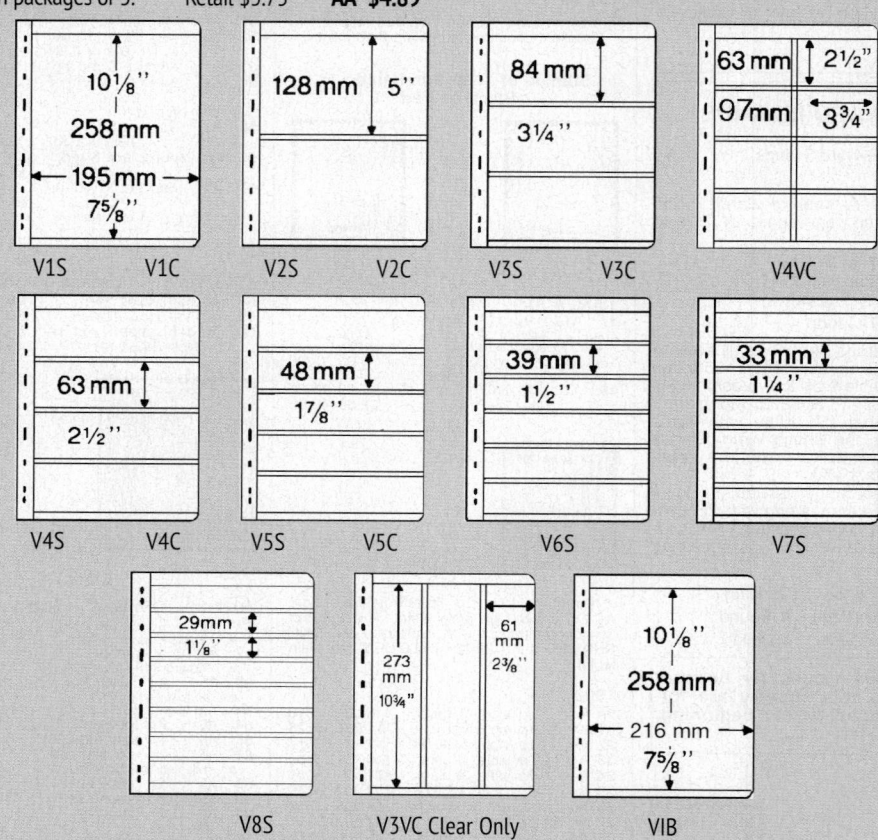

# LESOTHO

lə-'sō-ₒₕtō

LOCATION — An enclave within the Republic of South Africa
GOVT. — Independent state in British Commonwealth
AREA — 11,720 sq. mi.
POP. — 2,128,950 (1999 est.)
CAPITAL — Maseru

Basutoland, the British Crown Colony, became independent, October 4, 1966, taking the name Lesotho.

100 Cents = 1 Rand
100 Lisente (s) = 1 Maloti (1979)

**Catalogue values for all unused stamps in this country are for Never Hinged items.**

**Watermark**

Wmk. 362 — Basotho Hat Multiple

Moshoeshoe I and II — A1

*Perf. 12½x13*

| 1966, Oct. 4 | Photo. | Unwmk. | |
|---|---|---|---|
| **1** A1 | 2½c red brn, blk & red | .25 | .25 |
| **2** A1 | 5c red brn, blk & brt bl | .25 | .25 |
| **3** A1 | 10c red brn, blk & brt green | .25 | .25 |
| **4** A1 | 20c red brn, blk & red lilac | .30 | .30 |
| | *Nos. 1-4 (4)* | 1.05 | 1.05 |

Lesotho's independence, Oct. 4, 1966.

Basutoland Nos. 72-74, 76-82 Overprinted

*Perf. 13½*

| 1966, Nov. 1 | Wmk. 4 | Engr. | |
|---|---|---|---|
| **5** A7 | ½c dk brown & gray | .25 | .25 |
| **6** A7 | 1c dp grn & gray blk | .25 | .25 |
| **7** A7 | 2c orange & dp blue | .90 | .25 |
| **8** A7 | 3½c dp blue & indigo | .50 | .25 |
| **9** A7 | 5c dk grn & org brn | .30 | .25 |
| **10** A7 | 10c rose vio & dk ol | .35 | .25 |
| **11** A7 | 12½c aqua & brown | 6.00 | .35 |
| **12** A7 | 25c lil rose & dp ultra | .70 | .25 |
| **13** A7 | 50c dp car & black | 1.60 | .75 |
| | *Perf. 11½* | | |
| **14** A8 | 1r dp claret & blk | 2.25 | *3.50* |
| *a.* | "Lseotho" | 85.00 | |
| | *Nos. 5-14 (10)* | 13.10 | 6.35 |

**Same Overprint on Nos. 87-91 and Type of 1954**

| Wmk. 314 | | Perf. 13½ | |
|---|---|---|---|
| **15** A7 | 1c green & gray blk | .25 | .25 |
| **16** A7 | 2½c car & ol green | .65 | .25 |
| **17** A7 | 5c dk grn & org brn | .30 | .25 |
| **18** A7 | 12½c aqua & brown | .50 | .25 |
| **19** A7 | 50c dp car & black | .95 | .45 |
| | *Perf. 11½* | | |
| **20** A8 | 1r dp claret & blk | .95 | .90 |
| *a.* | "Lseotho" | 50.00 | *70.00* |
| | *Nos. 15-20 (6)* | 3.60 | 2.35 |

UNESCO Emblem, Microscope, Book, Violin and Retort — A2

**Unwmk.**

| 1966, Dec. 1 | Litho. | Perf. 14 | |
|---|---|---|---|
| **21** A2 | 2½c green & ocher | .25 | .25 |
| **22** A2 | 5c olive & brt green | .25 | .25 |
| **23** A2 | 12½c ver & lt blue | .30 | .25 |
| **24** A2 | 25c dull blue & orange | .50 | .60 |
| | *Nos. 21-24 (4)* | 1.30 | 1.35 |

20th anniv. of UNESCO.

King Moshoeshoe II and Corn — A3

King Moshoeshoe II — A4

Designs: 1c, Bull. 2c, Aloes. 2½c, Basotho hat. 3½c, Merino sheep. 5c, Basotho pony. 10c, Wheat. 12½c, Angora goat. 25c, Maletsunyane Falls. 50c, Diamonds. 1r, Coat of Arms.

*Perf. 13½x14½*

| 1967, Apr. 1 | Photo. | Unwmk. | |
|---|---|---|---|
| **25** A3 | ½c violet & green | .25 | .25 |
| **26** A3 | 1c dk red & brown | .25 | .25 |
| **27** A3 | 2c green & yellow | .25 | *.80* |
| **28** A3 | 2½c yel bister & blk | .25 | .25 |
| **29** A3 | 3½c yellow & black | .25 | .25 |
| **30** A3 | 5c brt blue & yel bis | .25 | .25 |
| **31** A3 | 10c gray & ocher | .35 | .25 |
| **32** A3 | 12½c orange & blk | .30 | .30 |
| **33** A3 | 25c ultra & blk | .60 | .50 |
| **34** A3 | 50c Prus green & blk | 5.00 | 2.00 |
| **35** A3 | 1r gray & multi | 1.00 | 1.00 |
| | *Perf. 14½x13½* | | |
| **36** A4 | 2r mag, blk & gold | 1.25 | *1.75* |
| | *Nos. 25-36 (12)* | 10.00 | 7.85 |

See Nos. 47-59.

University Buildings and Graduates — A4a

| 1967, Apr. 7 | | Perf. 14x14½ | |
|---|---|---|---|
| **37** A4a | 1c yel, sep & dp blue | .25 | .25 |
| **38** A4a | 2½c blue, sep & dp bl | .25 | .25 |
| **39** A4a | 12½c dl rose, sep & dp bl | .25 | .25 |
| **40** A4a | 25c lt vio, sep & dp bl | .25 | .25 |
| | *Nos. 37-40 (4)* | 1.00 | 1.00 |

1st conferment of degrees by the Univ. of Botswana, Lesotho and Swaziland at Roma, Lesotho.

Statue of Moshoeshoe I — A5

1st Anniv. of Independence: 12½c, Flag of Lesotho. 25c, Crocodile.

| 1967, Oct. 4 | Photo. | Perf. 14 | |
|---|---|---|---|
| **41** A5 | 2½c apple green & black | .25 | .25 |
| **42** A5 | 12½c multicolored | .45 | .45 |
| **43** A5 | 25c tan, blk & dp green | .80 | .80 |
| | *Nos. 41-43 (3)* | 1.50 | 1.50 |

Boy Scout and Lord Baden-Powell — A6

| 1967, Nov. 1 | Unwmk. | Perf. 14x14½ | |
|---|---|---|---|
| **44** A6 | 15c lt ol grn, dk grn & brn | .35 | .25 |

60th anniversary of the Boy Scouts.

World Map and WHO Emblem A7

20th anniv. of WHO: 25c, Nurse and child, arms of Lesotho and WHO emblem.

| 1968, Apr. 8 | Photo. | Perf. 14x14½ | |
|---|---|---|---|
| **45** A7 | 2½c dp bl, car rose & gold | .25 | .25 |
| **46** A7 | 25c gold, gray grn & redsh brown | .45 | .40 |

**Types of 1967**

Design: 3c, Sorghum. Others as before.

*Perf. 13½x14½*

| 1968-69 | Photo. | Wmk. 362 | |
|---|---|---|---|
| **47** A3 | ½c violet & green | .25 | .25 |
| **48** A3 | 1c dk red & brown | .25 | .25 |
| **49** A3 | 2c green & yellow | .25 | .25 |
| **50** A3 | 2½c yel bister & blk | .25 | .25 |
| **51** A3 | 3c lt brn, dk brn & green | .25 | .25 |
| **52** A3 | 3½c yellow & black | .25 | .25 |
| **53** A3 | 5c brt bl & yel bis | .50 | .25 |
| **54** A3 | 10c gray & ocher | .30 | .60 |
| **55** A3 | 12½c org & blk ('69) | .80 | .90 |
| **56** A3 | 25c ultra & blk ('69) | 1.75 | 1.15 |
| **57** A3 | 50c Prussian grn & black ('69) | 12.50 | 3.00 |
| **58** A3 | 1r gray & multi | 2.25 | 2.25 |
| | *Perf. 14½x13½* | | |
| **59** A4 | 2r magenta, blk & gold ('69) | 9.00 | *11.50* |
| | *Nos. 47-59 (13)* | 28.60 | 21.15 |

Hunters, Rock Painting A8

Rock Paintings: 3½c, Baboons. 5c, Javelin thrower, vert. 10c, Archers. 15c, Cranes, vert. 20c, Eland. 25c, Hunting scene.

*Perf. 14½x14, 14x14½*

| 1968, Nov. 1 | Photo. | Wmk. 362 | |
|---|---|---|---|
| **60** A8 | 3c dk & lt green & brn | .35 | .25 |
| **61** A8 | 3½c dk brown & yel | .45 | .25 |
| **62** A8 | 5c sepia, yel & red brn | .50 | .25 |
| **63** A8 | 10c black, brt rose & org | .60 | .30 |
| **64** A8 | 15c olive brn & buff | .85 | .45 |
| **65** A8 | 20c black, yel & lt grn | 1.00 | .60 |
| **66** A8 | 25c dk brown, yel & org | 1.10 | .90 |
| | *Nos. 60-66 (7)* | 4.85 | 3.00 |

Protection for Lesotho's rock paintings.

Queen Elizabeth II Hospital A9

Designs: 10c, Radio Lesotho. 12½c, Leabua Jonathan Airport. 25c, Royal Palace.

| 1969, Mar. 11 | Litho. | Perf. 14x13½ | |
|---|---|---|---|
| **67** A9 | 2½c multicolored | .25 | .25 |
| **68** A9 | 10c multicolored | .25 | .25 |
| **69** A9 | 12½c multicolored | .25 | .25 |
| **70** A9 | 25c multicolored | .25 | .25 |
| | *Nos. 67-70 (4)* | 1.00 | 1.00 |

Centenary of Maseru, capital of Lesotho.

Mosotho Horseman and Car — A10

Designs: 12½c, Car on mountain pass. 15c, View from Sani Pass and signal flags. 20c, Map of Lesotho and Independence Trophy.

| 1969, Sept. 26 | Photo. | Perf. 14½x14 | |
|---|---|---|---|
| **71** A10 | 2½c brown & multi | .25 | .25 |
| **72** A10 | 12½c multicolored | .25 | .25 |
| **73** A10 | 15c multicolored | .30 | .30 |
| **74** A10 | 20c yellow & multi | .30 | .30 |
| | *Nos. 71-74 (4)* | 1.10 | 1.10 |

Roof of Africa Auto Rally, Sept. 19-20.

Gryponyx A11

Prehistoric Reptile Footprints, Moyeni: 3c, Dinosaur. 10c, Plateosauravus and Footprints. 15c, Tritylodon. 25c, Massospondylus.

*Perf. 14½x14*

| 1970, Jan. 5 | | Wmk. 362 | |
|---|---|---|---|
| | **Size: 60x23mm** | | |
| **75** A11 | 3c brown, yel & black | 1.00 | .75 |
| | *Perf. 15x14* | | |
| | **Size: 40x23mm** | | |
| **76** A11 | 5c maroon, blk & pink | 1.40 | .40 |
| **77** A11 | 10c sepia, blk & yel | 1.50 | .45 |
| **78** A11 | 15c slate grn, blk & yel | 2.00 | 2.50 |
| **79** A11 | 25c gray blue, blk & bl | 3.00 | 2.50 |
| | *Nos. 75-79 (5)* | 8.90 | 6.60 |

Moshoeshoe I A12

Design: 25c, Moshoeshoe I with top hat.

*Perf. 14x13½*

| 1970, Mar. 11 | Litho. | Wmk. 362 | |
|---|---|---|---|
| **80** A12 | 2½c brt grn & car rose | .25 | .25 |
| **81** A12 | 25c lt blue & org brn | .25 | .25 |

Cent. of the death of Moshoeshoe I, chief of the Bakoena clan of the Basothos.

UN Headquarters, New York — A13

2½c, UN emblem. 12½c, UN emblem, people. 25c, UN emblem, peace dove.

| 1970, June 26 | Litho. | Perf. 14½x14 | |
|---|---|---|---|
| **82** A13 | 2½c pink, red brn & bl | .25 | .25 |
| **83** A13 | 10c blue & multi | .25 | .25 |
| **84** A13 | 12½c olive, ver & lt blue | .25 | .25 |
| **85** A13 | 25c tan & multi | .25 | .25 |
| | *Nos. 82-85 (4)* | 1.00 | 1.00 |

25th anniversary of the United Nations.

Basotho Hat Gift Shop, Maseru
A14

Tourism: 5c, Trout fishing. 10c, Horseback riding. 12½c, Skiing, Maluti Mountains. 20c, Holiday Inn, Maseru.

**1970, Oct. 27** ***Perf. 14x14½***

| | | | | |
|---|---|---|---|---|
| **86** | A14 | 2½c multicolored | .25 | .25 |
| **87** | A14 | 5c multicolored | .25 | .25 |
| **88** | A14 | 10c multicolored | .30 | .30 |
| **89** | A14 | 12½c multicolored | .30 | .30 |
| **90** | A14 | 20c multicolored | .35 | .35 |
| | | *Nos. 86-90 (5)* | 1.45 | 1.45 |

Corn — A15

Designs: 1c, Bull. 2c, Aloes. 2½c, Basotho hat. 3c, Sorghum. 3½c, Merino sheep. 4c, National flag. 5c, Basotho pony. 10c, Wheat. 12½c, Angora goat. 25c, Maletsunyane Falls. 50c, Diamonds. 1r, Coat of Arms. 2r, Statue of King Moshoeshoe I in Maseru, vert.

**1971** **Litho.** **Wmk. 362** ***Perf. 14***

| | | | | |
|---|---|---|---|---|
| **91** | A15 | ½c lilac & green | .25 | .25 |
| **92** | A15 | 1c brn red & brn | .25 | .25 |
| **93** | A15 | 2c yel brn & yel | .25 | .25 |
| **94** | A15 | 2½c dull yel & blk | .25 | .25 |
| **95** | A15 | 3c bis, brn & grn | .25 | .25 |
| **96** | A15 | 3½c yellow & black | .25 | .25 |
| **97** | A15 | 4c ver & multi | .25 | .25 |
| **98** | A15 | 5c blue & brown | .25 | .25 |
| **99** | A15 | 10c gray & ocher | .35 | .30 |
| **100** | A15 | 12½c orange & brn | .45 | .35 |
| **101** | A15 | 25c ultra & black | .75 | .60 |
| **102** | A15 | 50c lt bl grn & blk | 6.50 | 4.00 |
| **103** | A15 | 1r gray & multi | 1.90 | 1.75 |
| **104** | A15 | 2r ultra & brown | 1.40 | *2.25* |
| *a.* | | Unwmkd. ('80) | 2.25 | *3.50* |
| | | *Nos. 91-104 (14)* | 13.35 | 11.25 |

Issue dates: 4c, Apr. 1; others, Jan. 4.

For overprints and surcharges see Nos. 132-135, 245, 312.

Lammergeier
A16

Birds: 5c, Bald ibis. 10c, Rufous rock jumper. 12½c, Blue korhaan (bustard). 15c, Painted snipe. 20c, Golden-breasted bunting. 25c, Ground woodpecker.

**1971, Mar. 1** ***Perf. 14***

| | | | | |
|---|---|---|---|---|
| **105** | A16 | 2½c multicolored | 2.75 | .25 |
| **106** | A16 | 5c multicolored | 3.75 | 2.10 |
| **107** | A16 | 10c multicolored | 4.00 | 1.60 |
| **108** | A16 | 12½c multicolored | 4.25 | 3.25 |
| **109** | A16 | 15c multicolored | 4.75 | 4.25 |
| **110** | A16 | 20c multicolored | 4.75 | 4.25 |
| **111** | A16 | 25c multicolored | 5.25 | 4.25 |
| | | *Nos. 105-111 (7)* | 29.50 | 19.95 |

Lionel Collett Dam
A17

Designs: 10c, Contour farming. 15c, Earth dams. 25c, Beaver dams.

**1971, July 15** **Litho.** **Wmk. 362**

| | | | | |
|---|---|---|---|---|
| **112** | A17 | 4c multicolored | .25 | .25 |
| **113** | A17 | 10c multicolored | .25 | .25 |
| **114** | A17 | 15c multicolored | .25 | .25 |
| **115** | A17 | 25c multicolored | .25 | .25 |
| | | *Nos. 112-115 (4)* | 1.00 | 1.00 |

Soil conservation and erosion control.

Diamond Mining
A18

10c, Potter. 15c, Woman weaver at loom. 20c, Construction worker and new buildings.

**1971, Oct. 4**

| | | | | |
|---|---|---|---|---|
| **116** | A18 | 4c olive & multi | 1.40 | .40 |
| **117** | A18 | 10c ocher & multi | .55 | .25 |
| **118** | A18 | 15c red & multi | .85 | .60 |
| **119** | A18 | 20c dk brown & multi | 1.10 | 1.40 |
| | | *Nos. 116-119 (4)* | 3.90 | 2.65 |

Mail Cart, 19th Century
A19

Designs: 10c, Postal bus. 15c, Cape of Good Hope No. 17, vert. 20c, Maseru Post Office.

**1972, Jan. 3**

| | | | | |
|---|---|---|---|---|
| **120** | A19 | 5c pink & black | .25 | .25 |
| **121** | A19 | 10c lt blue & multi | .25 | .25 |
| **122** | A19 | 15c gray, black & blue | .25 | .25 |
| **123** | A19 | 20c yellow & multi | .35 | .60 |
| | | *Nos. 120-123 (4)* | 1.10 | 1.35 |

Centenary of mail service between Maseru and Aliwal North in Cape Colony.

Runner and Olympic Rings — A20

**1972, Sept. 1**

| | | | | |
|---|---|---|---|---|
| **124** | A20 | 4c shown | .25 | .25 |
| **125** | A20 | 10c Shot put | .25 | .25 |
| **126** | A20 | 15c Hurdles | .40 | .35 |
| **127** | A20 | 25c Broad jump | .60 | .60 |
| | | *Nos. 124-127 (4)* | 1.50 | 1.45 |

20th Olympic Games, Munich, 8/26-9/11.

Adoration of the Shepherds, by Matthias Stomer — A21

**1972, Dec. 1** **Litho.** ***Perf. 14***

| | | | | |
|---|---|---|---|---|
| **128** | A21 | 4c blue & multi | .25 | .25 |
| **129** | A21 | 10c red & multi | .25 | .25 |
| **130** | A21 | 25c emerald & multi | .25 | .25 |
| | | *Nos. 128-130 (3)* | .75 | .75 |

Christmas.

WHO Emblem — A22

**1973, Apr. 7** **Litho.** ***Perf. 13½***

| | | | | |
|---|---|---|---|---|
| **131** | A22 | 20c blue & yellow | .60 | .60 |

WHO, 25th anniversary.

**Nos. 94, 97-99 ovptd. "O.A.U. / 10th Anniversary / Freedom in Unity"**

**1973, May 25** **Wmk. 362** ***Perf. 14***

| | | | | |
|---|---|---|---|---|
| **132** | A15 | 2½c dull yellow & black | .25 | .25 |
| **133** | A15 | 4c vermilion & multi | .25 | .25 |
| **134** | A15 | 5c blue & brown | .25 | .25 |
| **135** | A15 | 10c gray & ocher | .25 | .25 |
| | | *Nos. 132-135 (4)* | 1.00 | 1.00 |

Basotho Hat, WFP/FAO Emblem — A23

Designs: 15c, School lunch. 20c, Child drinking milk and cow. 25c, Map of mountain roads and farm workers.

**1973, June 1** ***Perf. 13½***

| | | | | |
|---|---|---|---|---|
| **136** | A23 | 4c ultra & multi | .25 | .25 |
| **137** | A23 | 15c buff & multi | .25 | .25 |
| **138** | A23 | 20c yellow & multi | .25 | .25 |
| **139** | A23 | 25c violet & multi | .25 | .25 |
| | | *Nos. 136-139 (4)* | 1.00 | 1.00 |

World Food Program, 10th anniversary.

Christmas Butterfly
A24

Designs: Butterflies of Lesotho.

**1973, Sept. 3** ***Perf. 14x14½***

| | | | | |
|---|---|---|---|---|
| **140** | A24 | 4c Mountain Beauty | 1.10 | .25 |
| **141** | A24 | 5c shown | 1.25 | .60 |
| **142** | A24 | 10c Painted lady | 2.00 | .60 |
| **143** | A24 | 15c Yellow pansy | 3.25 | 2.00 |
| **144** | A24 | 20c Blue pansy | 3.25 | 2.10 |
| **145** | A24 | 25c African monarch | 3.50 | 2.75 |
| **146** | A24 | 30c Orange tip | 3.50 | 3.75 |
| | | *Nos. 140-146 (7)* | 17.85 | 12.05 |

Map of Northern Lesotho and Location of Diamond Mines — A25

Designs: 15c, Kimberlite (diamond-bearing) rocks. 20c, Diagram of Kimberlite volcano, vert. 30c, Diamond prospector, vert.

***Perf. 13½x14, 14x13½***

**1973, Oct. 1** **Litho.** **Wmk. 362**

| | | | | |
|---|---|---|---|---|
| **147** | A25 | 10c gray & multi | 2.25 | .50 |
| **148** | A25 | 15c multicolored | 2.50 | 2.25 |
| **149** | A25 | 20c multicolored | 2.50 | 2.50 |
| **150** | A25 | 30c multicolored | 3.75 | 7.00 |
| | | *Nos. 147-150 (4)* | 11.00 | 12.25 |

International Kimberlite Conference.

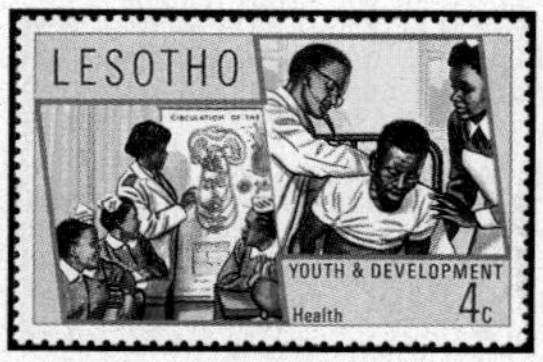


Nurses' Training and Medical Care — A26

Designs: 10c, Classroom, student with microscope. 20c, Farmers with tractor and bullock team and crop instruction. 25c, Potter and engineers with lathe. 30c, Boy scouts and young bricklayers.

**1974, Feb. 18** **Litho.** ***Perf. 13½x14***

| | | | | |
|---|---|---|---|---|
| **151** | A26 | 4c lt blue & multi | .25 | .25 |
| **152** | A26 | 10c ocher & multi | .25 | .25 |
| **153** | A26 | 20c multicolored | .25 | .25 |
| **154** | A26 | 25c bister & multi | .25 | .25 |
| **155** | A26 | 30c yellow & multi | .25 | .25 |
| | | *Nos. 151-155 (5)* | 1.25 | 1.25 |

Youth and development.

Open Book and Wreath — A27

Designs: 15c, Flags of Botswana, Lesotho and Swaziland; cap and diploma. 20c, Map of Africa and location of Botswana, Lesotho and Swaziland. 25c, King Moshoeshoe II, Chancellor of UBLS, capping graduate.

**1974, Apr. 7** **Litho.** ***Perf. 14***

| | | | | |
|---|---|---|---|---|
| **156** | A27 | 10c multicolored | .25 | .25 |
| **157** | A27 | 15c multicolored | .25 | .25 |
| **158** | A27 | 20c multicolored | .25 | .25 |
| **159** | A27 | 25c multicolored | .25 | .50 |
| | | *Nos. 156-159 (4)* | 1.00 | 1.25 |

10th anniversary of the University of Botswana, Lesotho and Swaziland.

Senqunyane River Bridge, Marakabei — A28

5c, Tsoelike River Bridge. 10c, Makhaleng River Bridge. 15c, Seaka Bridge, Orange/Senqu River. 20c, Masianokeng Bridge, Phuthiatsana River. 25c, Mahobong Bridge, Hlotse River.

**1974, June 26** **Wmk. 362** ***Perf. 14***

| | | | | |
|---|---|---|---|---|
| **160** | A28 | 4c multicolored | .25 | .25 |
| **161** | A28 | 5c multicolored | .25 | .25 |
| **162** | A28 | 10c multicolored | .25 | .25 |
| **163** | A28 | 15c multicolored | .50 | .40 |
| **164** | A28 | 20c multicolored | .55 | .55 |
| **165** | A28 | 25c multicolored | .60 | .60 |
| | | *Nos. 160-165 (6)* | 2.40 | 2.30 |

Bridges and rivers of Lesotho.

UPU Emblem
A29

**1974, Sept. 6** **Litho.** ***Perf. 14x13***

| | | | | |
|---|---|---|---|---|
| **166** | A29 | 4c shown | .25 | .25 |
| **167** | A29 | 10c Map of Lesotho | .25 | .25 |
| **168** | A29 | 15c GPO, Maseru | .25 | .40 |
| **169** | A29 | 20c Rural mail delivery | .80 | 1.00 |
| | | *Nos. 166-169 (4)* | 1.55 | 1.90 |

Centenary of Universal Postal Union.

Siege of Thaba-Bosiu — A30

King Moshoeshoe I
A31

5c, King Moshoeshoe II laying wreath at grave of Moshoeshoe I. 20c, Makoanyane, warrior hero.

*Perf. 12½x12, 12x12½*

**1974, Nov. 25**

**170** A30 4c multicolored .25 .25
**171** A30 5c multicolored .25 .25
**172** A31 10c multicolored .25 .25
**173** A31 20c multicolored .60 .40
*Nos. 170-173 (4)* 1.35 1.15

Sesquicentennial of Thaba-Bosiu becoming the capital of Basutoland and Lesotho.

Mamokhorong — A32

Musical Instruments of the Basotho: 10c, Lesiba. 15c, Setolotolo. 20c, Meropa (drums).

*Perf. 14x14½*

**1975, Jan. 25** **Wmk. 362**

**174** A32 4c multicolored .25 .25
**175** A32 10c multicolored .25 .25
**176** A32 15c multicolored .30 .30
**177** A32 20c multicolored .50 .50
*a.* Souvenir sheet of 4, #174-177 1.75 2.00
*Nos. 174-177 (4)* 1.30 1.30

View, Sehlabathebe National Park — A33

5c, Natural arch. 15c, Mountain stream. 20c, Lake and mountains. 25c, Waterfall.

**1975, Apr. 8** **Litho.** ***Perf. 14***

**178** A33 4c multicolored .35 .25
**179** A33 5c multicolored .35 .25
**180** A33 15c multicolored .70 .70
**181** A33 20c multicolored .70 .70
**182** A33 25c multicolored .90 .90
*Nos. 178-182 (5)* 3.00 2.80

Sehlabathebe National Park.

Moshoeshoe I (1824-1870) A34

Mofumahali Mantsebo Seeiso (1940-1960) A35

Leaders of Lesotho: 4c, Moshoeshoe II. 5c, Letsie I (1870-1891). 6c, Lerotholi (1891-1905). 10c, Letsie II (1905-1913). 15c, Griffith (1913-1939). 20c, Seeiso Griffith Lerotholi (1939-1940).

**1975, Sept. 10** **Litho.** **Wmk. 362**

**183** A34 3c dull blue & black .25 .25
**184** A34 4c lilac rose & black .25 .25
**185** A34 5c pink & black .25 .25
**186** A34 6c brown & black .25 .25
**187** A34 10c rose car & black .25 .25
**188** A34 15c orange & black .25 .25
**189** A34 20c olive & black .25 .30
**190** A35 25c lt blue & black .25 .40
*Nos. 183-190 (8)* 2.00 2.20

No. 190 issued for Intl. Women's Year.

Mokhibo, Women's Dance
A36

Traditional Dances: 10c, Ndlamo, men's dance. 15c, Raleseli, men and women. 20c, Mohobelo, men's dance.

**1975, Dec. 17** ***Perf. 14x14½***

**191** A36 4c blue & multi .25 .25
**192** A36 10c black & multi .25 .25
**193** A36 15c black & multi .30 .40
**194** A36 20c blue & multi .40 .70
*a.* Souvenir sheet of 4, #191-194 5.00 5.00
*Nos. 191-194 (4)* 1.20 1.60

Enrollment in Junior Red Cross — A37

Designs: 10c, First aid team and truck. 15c, Red Cross nurse on horseback in rural area. 25c, Supplies arriving by plane.

**1976, Feb. 20** **Litho.** ***Perf. 14***

**195** A37 4c red & multi .55 .40
**196** A37 10c red & multi .80 .60
**197** A37 15c red & multi 1.05 1.00
**198** A37 25c red & multi 1.60 2.00
*Nos. 195-198 (4)* 4.00 4.00

Lesotho Red Cross, 25th anniversary.

Mosotho Horseman — A38

King Moshoeshoe II
A39

2c, Tapestry (weavers and citation). 4c, Map of Lesotho. 5c, Hand holding Lesotho brown diamond. 10c, Lesotho Bank. 15c, Flags of Lesotho and Organization of African Unity. 25c, Sehlabathebe National Park. 40c, Pottery. 50c, Pre-historic rock painting.

**1976, June 2** ***Perf. 14***

**199** A38 2c multicolored .25 .35
**200** A38 3c multicolored .25 .30
**201** A38 4c multicolored 1.40 .25
**202** A38 5c multicolored .50 .90
**203** A38 10c multicolored .30 .30
**204** A38 15c multicolored 1.60 .80
**205** A38 25c multicolored .50 .60
*a.* Unwmkd. ('80) 1.60 *4.00*
**206** A38 40c multicolored .70 1.25
*a.* Unwmkd. ('80) 4.25 *11.00*
**207** A38 50c multicolored 2.25 2.00
*a.* Unwmkd. ('80) 6.00 *10.00*
**208** A39 1r multicolored 1.00 *1.75*
*Nos. 199-208 (10)* 8.75 8.50

For surcharges see Nos. 302-311.

Soccer — A40

Olympic Rings and: 10c, Weight lifting. 15c, Boxing. 25c, Discus.

**1976, Aug. 9** **Litho.** **Wmk. 362**

**209** A40 4c citron & multi .25 .25
**210** A40 10c lilac & multi .25 .25
**211** A40 15c salmon & multi .30 .30
**212** A40 25c blue & multi .65 .65
*Nos. 209-212 (4)* 1.45 1.45

21st Olympic Games, Montreal, Canada, July 17-Aug. 1.

Rising Sun of Independence
A41

Designs: 10c, Opening gates. 15c, Broken chain. 25c, Plane over Molimo Restaurant.

**1976, Oct. 4** ***Perf. 14***

**213** A41 4c yellow & multi .25 .25
**214** A41 10c pink & multi .25 .25
**215** A41 15c blue & multi .50 .25
**216** A41 25c dull blue & multi .60 .50
*Nos. 213-216 (4)* 1.60 1.25

Lesotho's independence, 10th anniversary.

Telephones, 1876 and 1976 — A42

Designs: 10c, Woman using telephone, and 1895 telephone. 15c, Telephone operators and wall telephone. 25c, A.G. Bell and 1905 telephone.

*Perf. 13x13½*

**1976, Dec. 6** **Wmk. 362**

**217** A42 4c multicolored .25 .25
**218** A42 10c multicolored .25 .25
**219** A42 15c multicolored .35 .35
**220** A42 25c multicolored .50 .50
*Nos. 217-220 (4)* 1.35 1.35

Centenary of first telephone call by Alexander Graham Bell, Mar. 10, 1876.

Aloe Striatula — A43

Aloes and Succulents: 4c, Aloe aristata. 5c, Kniphofia caulescens. 10c, Euphorbia pulvinata. 15c, Aloe saponaria. 20c, Caralluma lutea. 25c, Aloe polyphylla.

**1977, Feb. 14** **Litho.** ***Perf. 14***

**221** A43 3c multicolored .30 .25
**222** A43 4c multicolored .35 .25
**223** A43 5c multicolored .40 .25
**224** A43 10c multicolored .55 .25
**225** A43 15c multicolored 1.50 .40
**226** A43 20c multicolored 1.50 .60
**227** A43 25c multicolored 1.75 .80
*Nos. 221-227 (7)* 6.35 2.80

Rock Rabbits
A44

*Perf. 14x14½*

**1977, Apr. 25** **Wmk. 362**

**228** A44 4c shown *6.00* .55
**229** A44 5c Porcupine *6.00* .75
**230** A44 10c Polecat *6.00* .60
**231** A44 15c Klipspringers *18.50* 2.75
**232** A44 25c Baboons *20.00* 3.00
*Nos. 228-232 (5)* *56.50* 7.65

Man with Cane, Concentric Circles — A45

Man with Cane: 10c, Surrounded by flames of pain. 15c, Surrounded by chain. 25c, Man and globe.

**1977, July 4** **Litho.** ***Perf. 14***

**233** A45 4c red & yellow .25 .25
**234** A45 10c dk blue & lt blue .25 .25
**235** A45 15c blue green & yellow .40 .25
**236** A45 25c black & orange .50 .60
*Nos. 233-236 (4)* 1.40 1.35

World Rheumatism Year.

Small-mouthed Yellow-fish — A46

Fresh-water Fish: 10c, Orange River mud fish. 15c, Rainbow trout. 25c, Oreodaimon quathlambae.

**1977, Sept. 28** **Wmk. 362** ***Perf. 14***

**237** A46 4c multicolored .40 .25
**238** A46 10c multicolored .75 .25
**239** A46 15c multicolored 1.50 .60
**240** A46 25c multicolored 1.60 1.25
*Nos. 237-240 (4)* 4.25 2.35

White and Black Equal — A47

Designs: 10c, Black and white jigsaw puzzle. 15c, White and black cogwheels. 25c, Black and white handshake.

**1977, Dec. 12** **Litho.** ***Perf. 14***

**241** A47 4c lilac rose & black .25 .25
**242** A47 10c brt blue & black .25 .25
**243** A47 15c orange & black .25 .25
**244** A47 25c lt green & black .30 .30
*Nos. 241-244 (4)* 1.05 1.05

Action to Combat Racism Decade.

No. 99 Surcharged

**1977, Dec. 7**

**245** A15 3c on 10c gray & ocher 1.75 1.50

Poppies — A48

Flowers of Lesotho: 3c, Diascia integerrima. 4c, Helichrysum trilineatum. 5c, Zaluzianskya maritima. 10c, Gladioli. 15c, Chironia krebsii. 25c, Wahlenbergia undulata. 40c, Brunsvigia radulosa.

**1978, Feb. 13 Litho. Wmk. 362**

| | | | | |
|---|---|---|---|---|
| **246** | A48 | 2c multicolored | .25 | .30 |
| **247** | A48 | 3c multicolored | .25 | .30 |
| **248** | A48 | 4c multicolored | .25 | .25 |
| **249** | A48 | 5c multicolored | .25 | .25 |
| **250** | A48 | 10c multicolored | .25 | .30 |
| **251** | A48 | 15c multicolored | .25 | .45 |
| **252** | A48 | 25c multicolored | .80 | 1.00 |
| **253** | A48 | 40c multicolored | 1.40 | 2.00 |
| | | *Nos. 246-253 (8)* | 3.70 | 4.85 |

Edward Jenner Vaccinating Child — A49

Global Eradication of Smallpox: 25c, Child's head and WHO emblem.

**1978, May 8 Litho. *Perf. 13½x13***

| | | | | |
|---|---|---|---|---|
| **254** | A49 | 5c multicolored | .40 | .25 |
| **255** | A49 | 25c multicolored | 1.40 | 1.50 |

Tsoloane Falls — A50

Lesotho Waterfalls: 10c, Qiloane Falls. 15c, Tsoelikana Falls. 25c, Maletsunyane Falls.

**1978, July 28 Litho. *Perf. 14***

| | | | | |
|---|---|---|---|---|
| **256** | A50 | 4c multicolored | .25 | .25 |
| **257** | A50 | 10c multicolored | .30 | .30 |
| **258** | A50 | 15c multicolored | .55 | .55 |
| **259** | A50 | 25c multicolored | .85 | .85 |
| | | *Nos. 256-259 (4)* | 1.95 | 1.95 |

Flyer 1 A51

25c, Orville and Wilbur Wright, Flyer 1.

**1978, Oct. 9 Wmk. 362 *Perf. 14½***

| | | | | |
|---|---|---|---|---|
| **260** | A51 | 5c multicolored | .25 | .25 |
| **261** | A51 | 25c multicolored | 1.00 | 1.00 |

75th anniversary of 1st powered flight.

Dragonflies — A52

Insects: 10c, Winged grasshopper. 15c, Wasps. 25c, Praying mantis.

**1978, Dec. 18 Litho. *Perf. 14***

| | | | | |
|---|---|---|---|---|
| **262** | A52 | 4c multicolored | .25 | .25 |
| **263** | A52 | 10c multicolored | .30 | .30 |
| **264** | A52 | 15c multicolored | .45 | .45 |
| **265** | A52 | 25c multicolored | .75 | .75 |
| | | *Nos. 262-265 (4)* | 1.75 | 1.75 |

Trees — A53

**1979, Mar. 26 Litho. *Perf. 14***

| | | | | |
|---|---|---|---|---|
| **266** | A53 | 4c Leucosidea Sericea | .25 | .25 |
| **267** | A53 | 10c Wild olive | .25 | .25 |
| **268** | A53 | 15c Blinkblaar | .40 | .40 |
| **269** | A53 | 25c Cape holly | .55 | .55 |
| | | *Nos. 266-269 (4)* | 1.45 | 1.45 |

Reptiles A54

**1979, June 4 Wmk. 362 *Perf. 14***

| | | | | |
|---|---|---|---|---|
| **270** | A54 | 4s Agama Lizard | .35 | .35 |
| **271** | A54 | 10s Berg adder | .45 | .40 |
| **272** | A54 | 15s Rock lizard | .65 | .55 |
| **273** | A54 | 25s Spitting snake | 1.15 | 1.00 |
| | | *Nos. 270-273 (4)* | 2.60 | 2.30 |

A55

**1979, Oct. 22 Litho. *Perf. 14½***

| | | | | |
|---|---|---|---|---|
| **274** | A55 | 4s Basutoland No. 2 | .25 | .25 |
| **275** | A55 | 15s Basutoland No. 72 | .30 | .30 |
| **276** | A55 | 25s Penny Black | .45 | .45 |
| | | *Nos. 274-276 (3)* | 1.00 | 1.00 |

**Souvenir Sheet**

| | | | | |
|---|---|---|---|---|
| **277** | A55 | 50s Lesotho No. 122 | .90 | .90 |

Sir Rowland Hill (1795-1879), originator of penny postage.

Intl. Year of the Child — A56

Children's Games, by Brueghel the Elder, and IYC emblem: 4s, Children Climbing Tree. 10s, Follow the leader. 15s, Three cup montie. 25s, Entire painting.

**1979, Dec. 10 Wmk. 362 *Perf. 14½***

| | | | | |
|---|---|---|---|---|
| **278** | A56 | 4s multicolored | .25 | .25 |
| **279** | A56 | 10s multicolored | .25 | .25 |
| **280** | A56 | 15s multicolored | .25 | .25 |
| | | *Nos. 278-280 (3)* | .75 | .75 |

**Souvenir Sheet**

| | | | | |
|---|---|---|---|---|
| **281** | A56 | 25s multicolored | .75 | .75 |

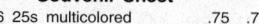

Beer Strainer, Brooms and Mat A57

**1980, Feb. 18 Litho. *Perf. 14½***

| | | | | |
|---|---|---|---|---|
| **282** | A57 | 4s shown | .25 | .25 |
| **283** | A57 | 10s Winnowing basket | .25 | .25 |
| **284** | A57 | 15s Basotho hat | .30 | .30 |
| **285** | A57 | 25s Grain storage pots | .50 | .50 |
| | | *Nos. 282-285 (4)* | 1.30 | 1.30 |

Qalabane Ambush A58

Gun War Centenary: 4s, Praise poet, text. 5s, Basotho army commander Lerotholi. 15s, Snider and Martini-Henry rifles. 25s, Map of Basutoland showing battle sites.

**1980, May 6 Litho. *Perf. 14***

| | | | | |
|---|---|---|---|---|
| **286** | A58 | 4s multicolored | .25 | .25 |
| **287** | A58 | 5s multicolored | .25 | .25 |
| **288** | A58 | 10s multicolored | .30 | .30 |
| **289** | A58 | 15s multicolored | .65 | .40 |
| **290** | A58 | 25s multicolored | .80 | .65 |
| | | *Nos. 286-290 (5)* | 2.25 | 1.85 |

St. Basil's, Moscow, Olympic Torch A59

No. 292, Torch and flags. No. 293, Soccer. No. 294, Running. No. 295, Misha and stadium.
No. 296,

**1980, Sept. 20 Litho. *Perf. 14½***

| | | | | |
|---|---|---|---|---|
| **291** | A59 | 25s shown | .35 | .35 |
| **292** | A59 | 25s multicolored | .35 | .35 |
| **293** | A59 | 25s multicolored | .35 | .35 |
| **294** | A59 | 25s multicolored | .35 | .35 |
| **295** | A59 | 25s multicolored | .35 | .35 |
| *a.* | | Strip of 5, #291-295 | 2.25 | 2.25 |

**Souvenir Sheet**

| | | | | |
|---|---|---|---|---|
| **296** | A59 | 1.40m multicolored | 2.00 | 2.00 |

22nd Summer Olympic Games, Moscow, July 19-Aug. 3.

Beer Mug and Man Drinking A60

Prince Philip — A61

**Wmk. 362**

**1980, Oct. 1 Litho. *Perf. 14***

| | | | | |
|---|---|---|---|---|
| **297** | A60 | 4s shown | .25 | .25 |
| **298** | A60 | 10s Beer brewing pot | .25 | .25 |
| **299** | A60 | 15s Water pot | .25 | .25 |
| **300** | A60 | 25s Pots and jugs | .30 | .25 |
| | | *Nos. 297-300 (4)* | 1.05 | 1.00 |

**Souvenir Sheet**

***Perf. 14x14½***

| | | | | |
|---|---|---|---|---|
| **301** | | Sheet of 4 | 1.25 | 1.25 |
| *a.* | A61 | 40s shown | .30 | .30 |
| *b.* | A61 | 40s Queen Elizabeth | .30 | .30 |
| *c.* | A61 | 40s Prince Charles | .30 | .30 |
| *d.* | A61 | 40s Princess Anne | .30 | .30 |

Traditional pottery; 250th birth anniversary of Josiah Wedgewood, potter.

**Nos. 104, 199-208 Surcharged**

Nos. 302-303, 304, 306-308, 310

No. 304a

No. 305

No. 309

Nos. 311-312

**Wmk. 362**

**1980, Oct. 20 Litho. *Perf. 14***

| | | | | |
|---|---|---|---|---|
| **302** | A38 | 2s on 2c multi | .25 | .25 |
| **303** | A38 | 3s on 3c multi | .25 | .25 |
| **304** | A38 | 5s on 5c multi | .25 | .25 |
| *a.* | | 6s on 5s on 5c multi | .25 | .25 |
| **305** | A38 | 6s on 4c multi | .25 | .25 |
| **306** | A38 | 10s on 10c multi | .25 | .25 |
| **307** | A38 | 25s on 25s multi | .35 | .35 |
| **308** | A38 | 40s on 40c multi | .55 | .55 |
| **309** | A38 | 50s on 50c multi | .80 | .80 |
| **310** | A38 | 75s on 15c multi | 2.00 | 2.00 |
| **311** | A39 | 1m on 1r multi | 2.40 | 2.40 |
| **312** | A15 | 2m on 2r multi | 4.50 | 4.50 |
| | | *Nos. 302-312 (11)* | 11.85 | 11.85 |

Numerous surcharge errors exist (double triple, inverted, etc.).

Queen Mother Elizabeth and Prince Charles — A62

Basutoland No. 36, Flags of Lesotho and Britain — A63

**1980, Dec. 1 Unwmk. *Perf. 14½***

| | | | |
|---|---|---|---|
| **313** | Sheet of 9 | 3.75 | 3.75 |
| *a.* | A62 5s shown | .25 | .25 |
| *b.* | A62 10s Portrait | .25 | .25 |
| *c.* | A63 1m shown | 1.10 | 1.10 |

Queen Mother Elizabeth, 80th birthday. No. 313 contains 3 each Nos. 313a-313c.

St. Agnes' Anglican Church, Teyateyaneng — A63a

Nativity — A64

4s, Lesotho Evangelical Church, Morija. 25s, Our Lady's Victory Cathedral, Maseru. 75s, University Chapel, Roma.

**1980, Dec. 8 *Perf. 14x14½***

| | | | | |
|---|---|---|---|---|
| **314** | A63a | 4s multicolored | .25 | .25 |
| **315** | A63a | 15s shown | .25 | .25 |
| **316** | A63a | 25s multicolored | .25 | .25 |
| **317** | A63a | 75s multicolored | .25 | .25 |
| | | *Nos. 314-317 (4)* | 1.00 | 1.00 |

**Souvenir Sheet**

| | | | | |
|---|---|---|---|---|
| **318** | A64 | 1.50m shown | .90 | .90 |

Christmas.

Voyager Satellite and Saturn — A65

**1981, Mar. 15 Litho. *Perf. 14***

| | | | |
|---|---|---|---|
| **319** | Strip of 5 | 2.50 | 2.50 |
| *a.* | A65 25s Voyager, planet | .40 | .40 |
| *b.* | A65 25s shown | .40 | .40 |
| *c.* | A65 25s Voyager, Saturn's rings | .40 | .40 |
| *d.* | A65 25s Columbia space shuttle | .40 | .40 |
| *e.* | A65 25s Columbia, diff. | .40 | .40 |

**Souvenir Sheet**

| | | | | |
|---|---|---|---|---|
| **320** | A65 | 1.40m Saturn | 2.50 | 2.50 |

Voyager expedition to Saturn and flight of Columbia space shuttle.

Rock Pigeons — A66

1s, Greater kestrel, vert. 3s, Crowned cranes, vert. 5s, Bokmakierie, vert. 6s, Cape robins, vert. 7s, Yellow canary, vert. 10s, Red-billed teal. 25s, Malachite kingfisher, vert. 40s, Malachite sunbirds. 60s, Orange-throated longclaw. 75s, African hoopoe. 1m, Red bishops. 2m, Egyptian goose. 5m, Lilac-breasted rollers.

**1981, Apr. 20 Unwmk. *Perf. 14½***

| | | | | |
|---|---|---|---|---|
| **321** | A66 | 1s mutlicolored | .25 | .25 |
| **322** | A66 | 2s shown | .25 | .25 |
| **323** | A66 | 3s multicolored | .25 | .25 |
| **324** | A66 | 5s multicolored | .25 | .25 |
| **325** | A66 | 6s multicolored | .40 | .25 |
| **326** | A66 | 7s multicolored | .40 | .25 |
| **327** | A66 | 10s multicolored | .40 | .25 |
| **328** | A66 | 25s multicolored | 1.00 | .60 |
| **329** | A66 | 40s multicolored | 1.25 | 1.00 |
| **330** | A66 | 60s multicolored | 1.60 | 1.50 |
| **331** | A66 | 75s multicolored | 2.00 | 1.75 |
| **332** | A66 | 1m multicolored | 2.50 | 2.50 |
| **333** | A66 | 2m multicolored | 4.75 | 4.75 |
| **334** | A66 | 5m multicolored | 9.00 | 9.00 |
| | | *Nos. 321-334 (14)* | 24.30 | 22.85 |

For surcharges see Nos. 558A, 561-563, 598A, 599, 600B, 600C.

**1981 *Perf. 13***

| | | | | |
|---|---|---|---|---|
| *321a* | A66 | 1s | 1.40 | .70 |
| *322a* | A66 | 2s | 1.60 | .70 |
| *324a* | A66 | 5s | 2.00 | .70 |
| *327a* | A66 | 10s | 2.00 | .70 |
| | | *Nos. 321a-327a (4)* | 7.00 | 2.80 |

**1982, June 14 Wmk. 373 *Perf. 14½***

| | | | | |
|---|---|---|---|---|
| *321b* | A66 | 1s | .25 | .40 |
| *322b* | A66 | 2s | .25 | .40 |
| *323a* | A66 | 3s | .35 | .40 |
| *324b* | A66 | 5s | .35 | .45 |
| *325a* | A66 | 6s | .35 | .25 |
| *326a* | A66 | 7s | .35 | .25 |
| *327b* | A66 | 10s | .35 | .25 |
| *328a* | A66 | 25s | 1.00 | .45 |
| *329a* | A66 | 40s | 1.10 | .50 |
| *330a* | A66 | 60s | 1.50 | .90 |
| *331a* | A66 | 75s | 2.00 | .90 |
| *332a* | A66 | 1m | 2.40 | *2.75* |
| *333a* | A66 | 2m | 3.00 | *4.00* |
| *334a* | A66 | 5m | 6.00 | *10.00* |
| | | *Nos. 321b-334a (14)* | 19.25 | 21.90 |

Common Design Types pictured following the introduction.

**Royal Wedding Issue**

Common Design Type and

Royal Wedding — A66a

**Unwmk.**

**1981, July 22 Litho. *Perf. 14***

| | | | | |
|---|---|---|---|---|
| **335** | CD331 25s Bouquet | | .25 | .25 |
| *a.* | Booklet pane of 3 + label | | .80 | |
| **336** | CD331 50s Charles | | .25 | .25 |
| *a.* | Booklet pane of 3 + label | | 1.40 | |
| **337** | CD331 75s Couple | | .40 | .40 |
| *b.* | Booklet pane of 3 + label | | 1.60 | |
| *c.* | Bklt. pane of 3, #335-337 + label | | 1.25 | |
| | *Nos. 335-337 (3)* | | .90 | .90 |

**1981 Litho. *Perf. 14½***

**Souvenir Sheet**

| | | | | |
|---|---|---|---|---|
| **337A** | A66a | 1.50m Couple | 1.75 | 1.75 |

Nos. 335-337A exist imperf. Value, set $8.

Tree Planting A67

6s, Duke of Edinburgh and flags. 25s, Digging. 40s, Mountain climbing. 75s, Emblem. 1.40m, Duke of Edinburgh.

**1981, Oct. 30 Litho. *Perf. 14½***

| | | | | |
|---|---|---|---|---|
| **338** | A67 | 6s multicolored | .25 | .25 |
| **339** | A67 | 7s shown | .25 | .25 |
| **340** | A67 | 25s multicolored | .25 | .25 |
| **341** | A67 | 40s multicolored | .40 | .40 |
| **342** | A67 | 75s multicolored | .65 | .65 |
| | | *Nos. 338-342 (5)* | 1.80 | 1.80 |

**Souvenir Sheet**

| | | | | |
|---|---|---|---|---|
| **343** | A67 | 1.40m multi | 1.75 | 1.75 |

Duke of Edinburgh's Awards, 25th anniv. No. 343 contains 1 45x29mm stamp, perf. 13½.

Santa Claus at Globe, by Norman Rockwell A68

The Mystic Nativity, by Botticelli — A69

Christmas: Saturday Evening Post covers by Norman Rockwell.

**1981, Oct. 5 *Perf. 13½x14***

| | | | | |
|---|---|---|---|---|
| **344** | A68 | 6s multicolored | .25 | .25 |
| **345** | A68 | 10s multicolored | .25 | .25 |
| **346** | A68 | 15s multicolored | .25 | .25 |
| **347** | A68 | 20s multicolored | .30 | .30 |
| **348** | A68 | 25s multicolored | .35 | .35 |
| **349** | A68 | 60s multicolored | .65 | .65 |
| | | *Nos. 344-349 (6)* | 2.05 | 2.05 |

**Souvenir Sheet**

| | | | | |
|---|---|---|---|---|
| **350** | A69 | 1.25m multicolored | 2.00 | 2.00 |

Chacma Baboons A70

***Perf. 14x13½, 14½ (20s, 40s, 50s)***

**1982, Jan. 15 Litho.**

| | | | | |
|---|---|---|---|---|
| **351** | A70 | 6s African wild cat | *3.75* | .50 |
| **352** | A70 | 20s shown | *4.75* | 1.25 |
| **353** | A70 | 25s Cape eland | *5.75* | 1.90 |
| **354** | A70 | 40s Porcupine | *6.75* | 2.50 |
| **355** | A70 | 50s Oribi | *7.00* | 3.25 |
| | | *Nos. 351-355 (5)* | *28.00* | 9.40 |

**Souvenir Sheet**

***Perf. 14***

| | | | | |
|---|---|---|---|---|
| **356** | A70 | 1.50m Black-backed jackal | 10.50 | 8.50 |

6s, 25s; 50x37mm. No. 356 contains one stamp 48x31mm.

Scouting Year — A71

**1982, Mar. 5 Litho. *Perf. 14x13½***

| | | | | |
|---|---|---|---|---|
| **357** | A71 | 6s Bugle call | .25 | .25 |
| **358** | A71 | 30s Hiking | .50 | .50 |
| **359** | A71 | 40s Drawing | .70 | .70 |
| **360** | A71 | 50s Holding flag | .90 | .90 |
| **361** | A71 | 75s Salute | 1.30 | 1.30 |
| *a.* | | Booklet pane of 10 + sheet | 11.00 | |
| | | *Nos. 357-361 (5)* | 3.65 | 3.65 |

**Souvenir Sheet**

| | | | | |
|---|---|---|---|---|
| **362** | A71 | 1.50m Baden-Powell | 2.40 | 2.40 |

No. 361a contains 2 each Nos. 357-361 with gutter and No. 362.

Nos. 357-361 issued in sheets of 8 with gutter.

1982 World Cup Soccer A72

Championships, 1930-1978: a, Uruguay, 1930. b, Italy, 1934. c, France, 1938. d, Brazil, 1950. e, Switzerland, 1954. f, Sweden, 1958. g, Chile, 1962. h, England, 1966. i, Mexico, 1970. j, Germany, 1974. k, Argentina, 1978. l, World Cup.

**1982, Apr. 14 *Perf. 14½***

| | | | |
|---|---|---|---|
| **363** | Sheet of 12 | 4.00 | 4.00 |
| *a.-l.* | A72 15s any single | .25 | .25 |

**Souvenir Sheet**

| | | | | |
|---|---|---|---|---|
| **364** | A72 | 1.25m Stadium | 2.00 | 2.00 |

Nos. 363b, 363c, 363f, 363g, 363j, 363k exist se-tenant in sheets of 72.

George Washington's Birth Bicentenary — A73

Paintings: 6s, Portrait. 7s, With children. 10s, Indian Chief's Prophecy. 25s, With troops. 40s, Arriving at New York. 1m, Entry into New York.

1.25m, Crossing Delaware.

**1982, June 7**

| | | | | |
|---|---|---|---|---|
| **365** | A73 | 6s multicolored | .25 | .25 |
| **366** | A73 | 7s multicolored | .25 | .25 |
| **367** | A73 | 10s multicolored | .25 | .25 |
| **368** | A73 | 25s multicolored | .35 | .35 |
| **369** | A73 | 40s multicolored | .45 | .45 |
| **370** | A73 | 1m multicolored | .90 | .90 |
| | | *Nos. 365-370 (6)* | 2.45 | 2.45 |

**Souvenir Sheet**

| | | | | |
|---|---|---|---|---|
| **371** | A73 | 1.25m multicolored | 1.75 | 1.75 |

**Princess Diana Issue**

Common Design Type

**Wmk. 373**

**1982, July 1 Litho. *Perf. 14***

| | | | | |
|---|---|---|---|---|
| **372** | CD333 | 30s Arms | .75 | .75 |
| **373** | CD333 | 50s Diana | .75 | .75 |
| **374** | CD333 | 75s Wedding | 1.00 | 1.00 |
| **375** | CD333 | 1m Portrait | 1.50 | 1.50 |
| | | *Nos. 372-375 (4)* | 4.00 | 4.00 |

Sesotho Bible Centenary A74

6s, Man reading bible. 15s, Angels, bible. 1m, Bible, Maseru Cathedral.

**1982, Aug. 20 Litho. *Perf. 14½***

| | | | | |
|---|---|---|---|---|
| **376** | A74 | 6s multi | .25 | .25 |
| **377** | A74 | 15s multi | .25 | .25 |

**Size: 59½x40½mm**

| | | | | |
|---|---|---|---|---|
| **378** | A74 | 1m multi | .40 | .40 |
| | | *Nos. 376-378 (3)* | .90 | .90 |

Issued in sheets of 9 (3 each Nos. 376-378).

Birth of Prince William of Wales, June 21 — A75

**1982, Sept. 30**

| | | | | |
|---|---|---|---|---|
| **379** | A75 | 6s Congratulation | 3.25 | 3.25 |
| **380** | A75 | 60s Diana, William | 1.75 | 1.75 |

Issued in sheets of 6 (No. 379, 5 No. 380).

Christmas — A76

Designs: Scenes from Walt Disney's The Twelve Days of Christmas. Stamps of same denomination se-tenant.

**1982, Dec. 1 Litho. *Perf. 11***

| | | | | |
|---|---|---|---|---|
| **381** | A76 | 2s multicolored | .25 | .25 |
| **382** | A76 | 2s multicolored | .25 | .25 |
| **383** | A76 | 3s multicolored | .25 | .25 |
| **384** | A76 | 3s multicolored | .25 | .25 |
| **385** | A76 | 4s multicolored | .25 | .25 |
| **386** | A76 | 4s multicolored | .25 | .25 |
| **387** | A76 | 75s multicolored | 1.40 | 2.00 |
| **388** | A76 | 75s multicolored | 1.40 | 2.00 |
| | | *Nos. 381-388 (8)* | 4.30 | 5.50 |

**Souvenir Sheet**

***Perf. 14x13½***

| | | | | |
|---|---|---|---|---|
| **389** | A76 | 1.50m multicolored | 4.00 | 4.00 |

Local Mushrooms — A77

10s, Lepista caffrorum. 30s, Broomexia congregate. 50s, Afroboletus luteolus. 75s, Lentinus tuberregium.

**1983, Jan. 11 *Perf. 14½***

| | | | | |
|---|---|---|---|---|
| **390** | A77 | 10s multicolored | .25 | .25 |
| **391** | A77 | 30s multicolored | .50 | .40 |
| *a.* | | Booklet pane of 2, #390, 391 | 1.05 | |
| **392** | A77 | 50s multicolored | .90 | .80 |
| **393** | A77 | 75s multicolored | 1.25 | 1.10 |
| *a.* | | Booklet pane of 4, #390-393 | 4.00 | |
| | | *Nos. 390-393 (4)* | 2.90 | 2.55 |

Commonwealth Day — A78

**1983, Mar. 14 Litho. *Perf. 14½***

| | | | | |
|---|---|---|---|---|
| **394** | A78 | 5s Ba-Leseli dance | .25 | .25 |
| **395** | A78 | 30s Tapestry weaving | .25 | .25 |
| **396** | A78 | 60s Elizabeth II | .35 | .35 |
| **397** | A78 | 75s Moshoeshoe II | .40 | .40 |
| | | *Nos. 394-397 (4)* | 1.25 | 1.25 |

Trance Dancers A79

Hunters — A79a

Rock Paintings: 25s, Baboons, Sehonghong Thaba Tseka. 60s, Hunter attacking mountain reedbuck, Makhetha Berera. 75s, Eland, Leribe.

**1983, May 20 Litho. *Perf. 14½***

| | | | | |
|---|---|---|---|---|
| **398** | A79 | 6s multicolored | .35 | .35 |
| **399** | A79 | 25s multicolored | .70 | .70 |
| **400** | A79 | 60s multicolored | .80 | .80 |
| **401** | A79 | 75s multicolored | .90 | .90 |
| | | *Nos. 398-401 (4)* | 2.75 | 2.75 |

**Souvenir Sheet**

| | | | | |
|---|---|---|---|---|
| **402** | | Sheet of 5, #398-401, 402a | 3.00 | 3.00 |
| *a.* | | A79a 10s multicolored | .30 | .25 |

Manned Flight Bicentenary — A80

**1983, July 11 Litho. *Perf. 14½***

| | | | | |
|---|---|---|---|---|
| **403** | A80 | 7s Montgolfier, 1783 | .25 | .25 |
| **404** | A80 | 30s Wright brothers | .45 | .35 |
| **405** | A80 | 60s 1st airmail plane | .85 | .75 |
| **406** | A80 | 1m Concorde | 2.50 | 2.50 |
| | | *Nos. 403-406 (4)* | 4.05 | 3.85 |

**Souvenir Sheet**

| | | | | |
|---|---|---|---|---|
| **407** | | Sheet of 5 | 3.00 | 3.00 |
| *a.* | | A80 6s Dornier 228 | .30 | .30 |

No. 407 contains Nos. 403-406, 407a (60x60mm).

Sesquicentennial of French Missionaries' Arrival — A81

6s, Rev. Eugene Casalis, flags. 25s, Morija, 1833. 40s, Baptism of Libe. 75s, Map of Basutoland, 1834.

**1983, Sept. 5 Litho. *Perf. 13½x14***

| | | | | |
|---|---|---|---|---|
| **408** | A81 | 6s multicolored | .30 | .30 |
| **409** | A81 | 25s multicolored | .30 | .30 |
| **410** | A81 | 40s multicolored | .30 | .30 |
| **411** | A81 | 75s multicolored | .65 | .65 |
| | | *Nos. 408-411 (4)* | 1.55 | 1.55 |

Christmas — A82

Scenes from Disney's Old Christmas, from Washington Irving's Sketch Book: 2s, Christmas Eve, diff. 3s, Christmas Day. 4s, Christmas Day, diff. 5s, Christmas dinner. 6s, Christmas dinner, diff. 75s, Christmas games. 1m, Christmas dancers.

1.75m, Christmas Eve.

**1983, Dec. Litho. *Perf. 14***

| | | | | |
|---|---|---|---|---|
| **412** | A82 | 1s shown | .25 | .25 |
| **413** | A82 | 2s multicolored | .25 | .25 |
| **414** | A82 | 3s multicolored | .25 | .25 |
| **415** | A82 | 4s multicolored | .25 | .25 |
| **416** | A82 | 5s multicolored | .25 | .25 |
| **417** | A82 | 6s multicolored | .25 | .25 |
| **418** | A82 | 75s multicolored | 2.25 | 2.25 |
| **419** | A82 | 1m multicolored | 2.50 | 2.50 |
| | | *Nos. 412-419 (8)* | 6.25 | 6.25 |

**Souvenir Sheet**

| | | | | |
|---|---|---|---|---|
| **420** | A82 | 1.75m multicolored | 5.00 | 5.00 |

African Monarch A83

Butterflies: 2s, Mountain Beauty. 3s, Orange Tip. 4s, Blue Pansy. 5s, Yellow Pansy. 6s, African Migrant. 7s, African Leopard. 10s, Suffused Acraea. 15s, Painted Lady. 20s, Lemon Traveller. 30s, Foxy Charaxes. 50s, Broad-Bordered Grass Yellow. 60s, Meadow White. 75s, Queen Purple Tip. 1m, Diadem. 5m, Christmas Butterfly.

**1984, Jan. 20 Litho.**

| | | | | |
|---|---|---|---|---|
| **421** | A83 | 1s shown | .50 | .35 |
| **422** | A83 | 2s multicolored | .50 | .35 |
| **423** | A83 | 3s multicolored | .60 | .40 |
| **424** | A83 | 4s multicolored | .60 | .40 |
| **425** | A83 | 5s multicolored | .60 | .40 |
| **426** | A83 | 6s multicolored | .60 | .40 |
| **427** | A83 | 7s multicolored | .60 | .40 |
| **428** | A83 | 10s multicolored | .70 | .50 |
| **429** | A83 | 15s multicolored | 1.10 | 1.10 |
| **430** | A83 | 20s multicolored | 1.50 | 1.25 |
| **431** | A83 | 30s multicolored | 1.75 | 1.75 |
| **432** | A83 | 50s multicolored | 1.75 | 1.75 |
| **433** | A83 | 60s multicolored | 1.75 | 1.75 |
| **434** | A83 | 75s multicolored | 1.90 | 2.00 |
| **435** | A83 | 1m multicolored | 1.90 | 2.00 |
| **436** | A83 | 5m multicolored | 3.00 | 4.50 |
| | | *Nos. 421-436 (16)* | 19.35 | 19.30 |

For surcharges see Nos. 559-560, 561A, 564-566, 600, 600A, 600D, 617A-617B.

Easter A84

Designs: Nos. 437a-437j, The Ten Commandments. 1.50m, Moses holding tablets.

**1984, Mar. 30 Litho. *Perf. 14***

| | | | | |
|---|---|---|---|---|
| **437** | | Sheet of 10 + 2 labels | 6.50 | 6.50 |
| *a.-j.* | | A84 20s any single | .30 | .30 |

**Souvenir Sheet**

| | | | | |
|---|---|---|---|---|
| **438** | A84 | 1.50m multicolored | 1.75 | 1.75 |

No. 438 contains one stamp 45x29mm.

1984 Summer Olympics — A85

10s, Torch bearer. 30s, Equestrian. 50s, Swimming. 75s, Basketball. 1m, Running.

1.50m, Flags, flame, stadium.

**1984, May 5 Litho. *Perf. 13½***

| | | | | |
|---|---|---|---|---|
| **439** | A85 | 10s multicolored | .25 | .25 |
| **440** | A85 | 30s multicolored | .25 | .25 |
| **441** | A85 | 50s multicolored | .25 | .25 |
| **442** | A85 | 75s multicolored | .35 | .35 |
| **443** | A85 | 1m multicolored | .45 | .45 |
| | | *Nos. 439-443 (5)* | 1.55 | 1.55 |

**Souvenir Sheet**

| | | | | |
|---|---|---|---|---|
| **444** | A85 | 1.50m multicolored | 1.60 | 1.60 |

Prehistoric Footprints — A86

10s, Sauropodomorph. 30s, Lesothosaurus. 50s, Carnivorous dinosaur.

**1984, July 2 Litho. *Perf. 13½***

| | | | | |
|---|---|---|---|---|
| **445** | A86 | 10s multicolored | .25 | .25 |
| **446** | A86 | 30s multicolored | .80 | .80 |
| **447** | A86 | 50s multicolored | 1.45 | 1.45 |
| | | *Nos. 445-447 (3)* | 2.50 | 2.50 |

Mail Coach Bicentenary and Ausipex '84 — A87

6s, Wells Fargo, 1852. 7s, Basotho mail cart, 1900. 10s, Bath mail coach, 1784. 30s, Cobb coach, 1853. 50s, Exhibition buildings. 1.75m, Penny Black, Basutoland #O4, Western Australia #3.

**1984, Sept. 5 Litho. *Perf. 14***

| | | | | |
|---|---|---|---|---|
| **448** | A87 | 6s multicolored | .25 | .25 |
| *a.* | | Sheet of 4 #448, 1 #451A | 1.00 | 1.00 |
| **449** | A87 | 7s multicolored | .25 | .25 |
| *a.* | | Sheet of 4 #449, 1 #451A | 1.00 | 1.00 |
| **450** | A87 | 10s multicolored | .25 | .25 |
| *a.* | | Sheet of 4 #450, 1 #451A | 1.00 | 1.00 |
| **451** | A87 | 30s multicolored | .25 | .25 |
| *b.* | | Sheet of 4 #451, 1 #451A | 1.00 | 1.00 |

**Size: 82x26mm**

| | | | | |
|---|---|---|---|---|
| **451A** | A87 | 50s multicolored | .45 | .45 |
| | | *Nos. 448-451A (5)* | 1.45 | 1.45 |

**Souvenir Sheet**

| | | | | |
|---|---|---|---|---|
| **452** | A87 | 1.75m multicolored | 3.25 | 3.25 |

No. 452 contains one stamp 82x26mm.

Trains — A88

6s, Orient Express, 1900. 15s, 05.001, Class 5, 1935. 30s, Cardean, Caledonian, 1906. 60s, Santa Fe, Super Chief, 1940. 1m, Flying Scotsman, 1934.

2m, The Blue Train, 1972.

**1984, Nov. 5 Litho. *Perf. 13½***

| | | | | |
|---|---|---|---|---|
| **453** | A88 | 6s multicolored | .25 | .25 |
| **454** | A88 | 15s multicolored | .30 | .30 |
| **455** | A88 | 30s multicolored | .40 | .40 |
| **456** | A88 | 60s multicolored | .80 | 1.25 |
| **457** | A88 | 1m multicolored | 1.60 | 2.00 |
| | | *Nos. 453-457 (5)* | 3.35 | 4.20 |

**Souvenir Sheet**

***Perf. 14x13½***

| | | | | |
|---|---|---|---|---|
| **458** | A88 | 2m multicolored | 2.10 | 2.10 |

Indigenous Young Animals — A89

15s, Cape Eland calf. 20s, Chacma baboons. 30s, Oribo calf. 75s, Red rock hares. 1m, Black-backed jackals.

**1984, Dec. 20 *Perf. 14½***

| | | | | |
|---|---|---|---|---|
| **459** | A89 | 15s multicolored | .25 | .25 |
| **460** | A89 | 20s multicolored | .30 | .30 |
| **461** | A89 | 30s multicolored | .45 | .45 |
| **462** | A89 | 75s multicolored | .90 | 1.25 |

**Size: 47x28mm**

*Perf. 13½*

| | | | | |
|---|---|---|---|---|
| **463** | A89 1m multicolored | | 1.25 | 1.75 |
| | *Nos. 459-463 (5)* | | 3.15 | 4.00 |

King Moshoeshoe II — A90

6s, Royal crown, 1974. 30s, Moshoeshoe II, 1966. 75s, In Basotho dress. 1m, In military uniform.

**1985, Jan. 30** **Litho.** ***Perf. 15***

| | | | |
|---|---|---|---|
| **464** | A90 6s multicolored | .25 | .25 |
| **465** | A90 30s multicolored | .25 | .25 |
| **466** | A90 75s multicolored | .45 | .45 |
| **467** | A90 1m multicolored | .65 | .65 |
| | *Nos. 464-467 (4)* | 1.60 | 1.60 |

25th anniversary of reign.

Miniature Sheet

Easter — A91

Stations of the Cross: a, Condemned to death. b, Bearing cross. c, Falls the first time. d, Meets his mother. e, Cyrenean helps carry cross. f, Veronica wipes His face. g, Second fall. h, Consoles women of Jerusalem. i, Third fall. j, Stripped. k, Nailed to cross. l, Dies on cross. m, Taken down from cross. n, Laid in sepulchre.

No. 469, The Crucifixion, detail, by Mathias Grunewald (c. 1460-1528).

**1985, Mar. 8** ***Perf. 11***

| | | | |
|---|---|---|---|
| **468** | A91 Sheet of 14 + label | 6.50 | 6.50 |
| ***a.-n.*** | 20s any single | .25 | .25 |

**Souvenir Sheet**

***Perf. 14***

| | | | |
|---|---|---|---|
| **469** | A91 2m multicolored | 2.25 | 2.25 |

Queen Mother, 85th Birthday — A92

Photographs: 10s, Queen Mother, Princess Elizabeth, 1931. 30s, 75th birthday portrait. 60s With Queen Elizabeth II and Princess Margaret, 80th birthday. No. 473, With Queen Elizabeth II, Princess Diana, Princes Henry and Charles, christening of Prince Henry.

No. 474, like No. 473, with Prince William.

**1985, May 30** ***Perf. 13½x14***

| | | | |
|---|---|---|---|
| **470** | A92 10s multicolored | .25 | .25 |
| **471** | A92 30s multicolored | .90 | .90 |
| **472** | A92 60s multicolored | 1.00 | 1.00 |
| **473** | A92 2m multicolored | 1.75 | 1.75 |
| | *Nos. 470-473 (4)* | 3.90 | 3.90 |

**Souvenir Sheet**

| | | | |
|---|---|---|---|
| **474** | A92 2m multicolored | 2.00 | 2.00 |

No. 474 contains one stamp 38x51mm.

Automobile Centenary — A93

Luxury cars: 6s, BMW 732i. 10s, Ford LTD Crown Victoria. 30s, Mercedes-Benz 500SE. 90s, Cadillac Eldorado Biarritz. No. 479, Rolls Royce Silver Spirit.

No. 480, 1907 Rolls Royce Silver Ghost Tourer, vert.

**1985, June 10** ***Perf. 14***

| | | | |
|---|---|---|---|
| **475** | A93 6s multicolored | .35 | .25 |
| **476** | A93 10s multicolored | .50 | .25 |
| **477** | A93 30s multicolored | .80 | .60 |
| **478** | A93 90s multicolored | 1.50 | 1.50 |
| **479** | A93 2m multicolored | 3.00 | 3.00 |
| | *Nos. 475-479 (5)* | 6.15 | 5.60 |

**Souvenir Sheet**

| | | | |
|---|---|---|---|
| **480** | A93 2m multicolored | 5.50 | 5.50 |

No. 480 contains one stamp 38x51mm.

Audubon Birth Bicentenary — A94

Illustrations of North American bird species by artist and naturalist John J. Audubon: 5s, Cliff swallow, vert. 6s, Great crested grebe. 10s, Vesper sparrow. 30s, Greenshank. 60s, Stilt sandpiper. 2m, Glossy ibis.

**1985, Aug. 5** ***Perf. 14½***

| | | | |
|---|---|---|---|
| **481** | A94 5s multicolored | .55 | .45 |
| **482** | A94 6s multicolored | .70 | .45 |
| **483** | A94 10s multicolored | 1.25 | .60 |
| **484** | A94 30s multicolored | 1.75 | 1.75 |
| **485** | A94 60s multicolored | 2.25 | 2.25 |
| **486** | A94 2m multicolored | 3.50 | 3.50 |
| | *Nos. 481-486 (6)* | 10.00 | 9.00 |

Nos. 481-486 printed in sheets of 5 with labels picturing various birds.

Intl. Youth Year, Girl Guides 75th Anniv. — A95

10s, Mountain climbing. 30s, Medical research. 75s, Guides on parade. No. 490, 2m, Guide saluting.

No. 491, Lady Baden-Powell, World Chief Guide.

**1985, Sept. 26** ***Perf. 15***

| | | | |
|---|---|---|---|
| **487** | A95 10s multicolored | .25 | .25 |
| **488** | A95 30s multicolored | .60 | .60 |
| **489** | A95 75s multicolored | 1.25 | 1.25 |
| **490** | A95 2m multicolored | 2.50 | 2.50 |
| | *Nos. 487-490 (4)* | 4.60 | 4.60 |

**Souvenir Sheet**

| | | | |
|---|---|---|---|
| **491** | A95 2m multicolored | 3.50 | 3.50 |

UN, 40th Anniv. — A96

Designs: 10s, UN No. 1, flag, horiz. 30s, Dish satellite, Ha Sofonia Earth Satellite Station, ITU emblem. 50s, Aircraft, Maseru Airport, ICAO emblem, horiz. 2m, Maimonides (1135-1204), medieval Jewish scholar, WHO emblem.

**1985, Oct. 15** **Litho.** ***Perf. 15***

| | | | |
|---|---|---|---|
| **492** | A96 10s multicolored | .30 | .30 |
| **493** | A96 30s multicolored | .50 | .50 |
| **494** | A96 50s multicolored | .90 | .90 |
| **495** | A96 2m multicolored | 4.50 | 4.50 |
| | *Nos. 492-495 (4)* | 6.20 | 6.20 |

Wildflowers — A97

6s, Cosmos. 10s, Small agapanthus. 30s, Pink witchweed. 60s, Small iris. 90s, Wild geranium. 1m, Large spotted orchid.

**1985, Nov. 11** ***Perf. 11***

| | | | |
|---|---|---|---|
| **496** | A97 6s multicolored | .45 | .25 |
| **497** | A97 10s multicolored | .60 | .25 |
| **498** | A97 30s multicolored | 1.10 | .75 |
| **499** | A97 60s multicolored | 1.75 | 1.75 |
| **500** | A97 90s multicolored | 2.25 | 2.25 |
| **501** | A97 1m multicolored | 3.00 | 3.00 |
| | *Nos. 496-501 (6)* | 9.15 | 8.25 |

Mark Twain, Author, Jacob and Wilhelm Grimm, Fabulists A98

Disney characters acting out Mark Twain quotes or portraying characters from The Wishing Table, by the Grimm Brothers.

**1985, Dec. 2** ***Perf. 11***

| | | | |
|---|---|---|---|
| **502** | A98 6s multicolored | .25 | .25 |
| **503** | A98 10s multicolored | .25 | .25 |
| **504** | A98 50s multicolored | 1.40 | 1.40 |
| **505** | A98 60s multicolored | 1.90 | 1.90 |
| **506** | A98 75s multicolored | 2.25 | 2.25 |
| **507** | A98 90s multicolored | 2.75 | 2.75 |
| **508** | A98 1m multicolored | 3.00 | 3.00 |
| **509** | A98 1.50m multicolored | 5.00 | 5.00 |
| | *Nos. 502-509 (8)* | 16.80 | 16.80 |

**Souvenir Sheets**

***Perf. 14***

| | | | |
|---|---|---|---|
| **510** | A98 1.25m multicolored | 6.00 | 6.00 |
| **511** | A98 1.50m multicolored | 6.00 | 6.00 |

Christmas. Nos. 505, 507 printed in sheets of 8.

World Wildlife Fund — A99

Lammergeier vulture.

**1986, Jan. 20** ***Perf. 15***

| | | | |
|---|---|---|---|
| **512** | A99 7s Male | 2.00 | .75 |
| **513** | A99 15s Male, female | 3.75 | 1.00 |
| **514** | A99 50s Male in flight | 5.50 | 2.00 |
| **515** | A99 1m Adult, young | 7.00 | 3.50 |
| | *Nos. 512-515 (4)* | 18.25 | 7.25 |

Flora and Fauna — A100

9s, Prickly pear. 12s, Stapelia. 35s, Pig's ears. No. 519, 2m, Columnar cereus.

No. 520, 2m, Black eagle.

**1986, Jan. 20**

| | | | |
|---|---|---|---|
| **516** | A100 9s multicolored | .50 | .25 |
| **517** | A100 12s multicolored | .50 | .25 |
| **518** | A100 35s multicolored | .75 | .50 |
| **519** | A100 2m multicolored | 2.75 | 2.50 |
| | *Nos. 516-519 (4)* | 4.50 | 3.50 |

**Souvenir Sheet**

| | | | |
|---|---|---|---|
| **520** | A100 2m multicolored | 9.75 | 9.75 |

1986 World Cup Soccer Championships, Mexico — A101

Various soccer plays.

**1986, Mar. 17** ***Perf. 14***

| | | | |
|---|---|---|---|
| **521** | A101 35s multicolored | 1.25 | 1.25 |
| **522** | A101 50s multicolored | 1.75 | 1.75 |
| **523** | A101 1m multicolored | 3.50 | 3.50 |
| **524** | A101 2m multicolored | 7.00 | 7.00 |
| | *Nos. 521-524 (4)* | 13.50 | 13.50 |

**Souvenir Sheet**

| | | | |
|---|---|---|---|
| **525** | A101 3m multicolored | 10.00 | 10.00 |

New Currency, 1st Anniv. (in 1980) A101a

No. 525A — Both sides of: b, 1979 Intl. Year of the Child gold coin. c, Five-maloti banknote. d, 1979 50-lisente coin. e, Ten-maloti banknote. f, 1979 1-sente coin.

**1986, Apr. 1** **Litho.** ***Perf. 13¾x14***

| | | | |
|---|---|---|---|
| **525A** | Horiz. strip of 5 | 30.00 | 32.50 |
| ***b.-f.*** | A101a 30s Any single | 6.00 | 6.50 |

A102

Halley's Comet — A103

Designs: 9s, Hale Telescope, Mt. Palomar, Galileo. 15s, Pioneer Venus 2 probe, 1985 sighting. 70s, 684 sighting illustration, Nuremberg Chronicles. 3m, 1066 sighting, Norman conquest of England. 4m, Comet over Lesotho.

**1986, Apr. 5**

**526** A102 9s multicolored .65 .25
**527** A102 15s multicolored .90 .25
**528** A102 70s multicolored 2.00 .75
**529** A102 3m multicolored 5.50 6.00
*Nos. 526-529 (4)* 9.05 7.25

**Souvenir Sheet**

**530** A103 4m multicolored 8.50 8.50

**Queen Elizabeth II, 60th Birthday**
Common Design Type

Designs: 90s, In pantomime during youth. 1m, At Windsor Horse Show, 1971. 2m, At Royal Festival Hall, 1971. 4m, Age 8.

**1986, Apr. 21**

**531** CD339 90s lt yel bis & black .55 .55
**532** CD339 1m pale grn & multi .65 .65
**533** CD339 2m dull vio & multi 1.30 1.30
*Nos. 531-533 (3)* 2.50 2.50

**Souvenir Sheet**

**534** CD339 4m tan & black 2.75 2.75

For overprints see Nos. 636-639.

Statue of Liberty, Cent. A104

Statue and famous emigrants: 15s, Bela Bartok (1881-1945), composer. 35s, Felix Adler (1857-1933), philosopher. 1m, Victor Herbert (1859-1924), composer. No. 538, David Niven (1910-1983), actor. No. 539, Statue, vert.

**1986, May 1**

**535** A104 15s multicolored .90 .25
**536** A104 35s multicolored .90 .35
**537** A104 1m multicolored 3.25 1.75
**538** A104 3m multicolored 5.00 3.00
*Nos. 535-538 (4)* 10.05 5.35

**Souvenir Sheet**

**539** A104 3m multicolored 6.50 6.50

AMERIPEX '86 — A105

Walt Disney characters: 15s, Goofy, Mickey. 35s, Mickey, Pluto. 1m, Goofy. 2m, Donald, Pete. 4m, Goofy, Chip'n'Dale.

**1986, May 22** *Perf. 11*

**540** A105 15s multicolored 1.10 .25
**541** A105 35s multicolored 1.40 .45
**542** A105 1m multicolored 3.00 1.90
**543** A105 2m multicolored 3.50 2.50
*Nos. 540-543 (4)* 9.00 5.10

**Souvenir Sheet**
***Perf. 14***

**544** A105 4m multicolored 11.00 11.00

**Royal Wedding Issue, 1986**
Common Design Type

Designs: 50s, Prince Andrew and Sarah Ferguson. 1m, Andrew. 3m, Andrew at helicopter controls. 4m, Couple, diff.

**1986, July 23** *Perf. 14*

**545** CD340 50s multicolored .50 .50
**546** CD340 1m multicolored .95 .95
**547** CD340 3m multicolored 2.25 2.25
*Nos. 545-547 (3)* 3.70 3.70

**Souvenir Sheet**

**548** CD340 4m multicolored 3.75 3.75

Natl. Independence, 20th Anniv. — A106

9s, Basotho pony, rider. 15s, Mohair spinning. 35s, River crossing.
4m, Moshoeshoe I.

**1986, Oct. 20** **Litho.** *Perf. 15*

**549** A106 9s multicolored .25 .25
**550** A106 15s multicolored .25 .25
**551** A106 35s multicolored .35 .35
**552** A106 3m Thaba Tseka P.O. 2.25 2.25
*Nos. 549-552 (4)* 3.10 3.10

**Souvenir Sheet**

**553** A106 4m multicolored 7.00 7.00

Christmas A107

Walt Disney characters: 15s, Chip'n'Dale. 35s, Mickey, Minnie. 1m, Pluto. 2m, Aunt Matilda.
5m, Huey and Dewey.

**1986, Nov. 4** **Litho.** *Perf. 11*

**554** A107 15s multicolored .85 .25
**555** A107 35s multicolored 1.25 .40
**556** A107 1m multicolored 1.75 1.60
**557** A107 2m multicolored 2.50 2.50
*Nos. 554-557 (4)* 6.35 4.75

**Souvenir Sheet**
***Perf. 14***

**558** A107 5m multicolored 10.00 10.00

**Butterfly and Bird Type of 1981-84 Surcharged**

**1986** **Litho.** *Perf. 14, 14½*

**558A** A66 9s on 10s #327b *6.00 1.75*
*b.* 9s on 10s #327 *4.00 4.00*
**559** A83 9s on 30s No. 431 .25 .25
*a.* 9s on 30s #431 (surcharge smaller & sans serif) *7.50 5.00*
**560** A83 9s on 60s No. 433 .25 .25
**561** A66 15s on 1s No. 321 *85.00*
*b.* 15s on 1s #321a *7.00 8.50*
*c.* 15s on 1s #321b *10.00 4.50*
**561A** A83 15s on 1s No. 421 2.50 2.50
**562** A66 15s on 2s No. 322 .30 .25
**563** A66 15s on 60s No. 330 .30 .25
*a.* 15s on 60s #330a *4.50 5.00*
**564** A83 15s on 2s No. 422 .30 .25
**565** A83 15s on 3s No. 423 .30 .25
**566** A83 35s on 75s No. 434 *24.00 17.50*
*a.* 35s on 75s #434, small "s" *50.00 52.50*
*Nos. 558A-566 (10)* 119.20 23.25

Issued: Nos. 559-560, July 1. Nos. 561-563, Aug. 22. Nos. 561A, 564-566, June 25.
See Nos. 617A-617B.

Roof of Africa Rally — A108

**1987, Apr. 28** **Litho.** *Perf. 14*

**567** A108 9s White car .45 .25
**568** A108 15s Motorcycle #26 .55 .25
**569** A108 35s Motorcycle #25 .75 .35
**570** A108 4m Red car 3.25 3.25
*Nos. 567-570 (4)* 5.00 4.10

1988 Summer Olympics, Seoul — A109

**1987, May 29** *Perf. 14*

**571** A109 9s Tennis .80 .25
**572** A109 15s Judo .80 .25
**573** A109 20s Running .90 .25
**574** A109 35s Boxing 1.00 .45
**575** A109 1m Diving 1.25 1.10
**576** A109 3m Bowling 3.00 3.00
*Nos. 571-576 (6)* 7.75 5.30

**Souvenir Sheet**

**577** A109 2m Tennis, diff. 2.75 2.75
**577A** A109 4m Soccer 5.25 5.25

See Nos. 606-611.
No. 577A shows green at lower left diagonal half of the flag.

Inventors and Innovators A110

Designs: 5s, Sir Isaac Newton, reflecting telescope. 9s, Alexander Graham Bell, telephone. 75s, Robert H. Goddard, liquid fuel rocket. 4m, Chuck Yeager (b. 1923), test pilot. No. 582, Mariner 10 spacecraft.

**1987, June 30** *Perf. 15*

**578** A110 5s multicolored .45 .25
**579** A110 9s multicolored .45 .25
**580** A110 75s multicolored 1.00 .75
**581** A110 4m multicolored 3.50 3.50
*Nos. 578-581 (4)* 5.40 4.75

**Souvenir Sheet**

**582** A110 4m multicolored 4.75 4.75

Fauna and Flora A111

5s, Gray rhebuck. 9s, Cape clawless otter. 15s, Cape gray mongoose. 20s, Free state daisy. 35s, River bells. 1m, Turkey flower. 2m, Sweet briar. 3m, Mountain reedbuck.
No. 591, Pig-lily. No. 592, Cape wildebeest.

**1987, Aug. 14**

**583** A111 5s multicolored .50 .25
**584** A111 9s multicolored .50 .25
**585** A111 15s multicolored .70 .25
**586** A111 20s multicolored .80 .25
**587** A111 35s multicolored .90 .35
**588** A111 1m multicolored 2.00 1.00
**589** A111 2m multicolored 2.50 2.00
**590** A111 3m multicolored 3.00 3.00
*Nos. 583-590 (8)* 10.90 7.35

**Souvenir Sheet**

**591** A111 2m multicolored 3.00 3.00
**592** A111 4m multicolored 5.25 5.25

Nos. 586-589 and 591 vert.

16th World Scout Jamboree, Australia, 1987-88 — A112

**1987, Sept. 10** **Litho.** *Perf. 14*

**593** A112 9s Orienteering .25 .25
**594** A112 15s Playing soccer .25 .25
**595** A112 35s Kangaroos .65 .65
**596** A112 75s Salute, flag 1.25 1.25
**597** A112 4m Windsurfing 6.25 6.25
*Nos. 593-597 (5)* 8.65 8.65

**Souvenir Sheet**

**598** A112 4m Map, flag of Australia 5.25 5.25

Nos. 324, 425, 424, 328 and 427 Surcharged

**1987** **Litho.** *Perf. 14½, 14*

**598A** A66 9s on 5s No. 324 .75 .25
**599** A66 15s on 5s No. 324 2.00 .25
**600** A83 15s on 5s No. 425 .25 .25
**600A** A83 20s on 4s No. 424 .25 .25
**600B** A66 35s on 25s No. 328 1.50 .60
*e.* 35s on 25s #328, small "s"
*f.* 35s on 25s #328a
*g.* 35s on 25s #328a, small "s"
**600C** A66 35s on 75s #331
*h.* 35s on 75s #331, small "s"
**600D** A83 40s on 7s No. 427 .40 .40

Issued: Nos. 599-600, 11/16; No. 600B, 12/15; Nos. 598A, 600A, 600D, 12/30.

A113

A114

Religious paintings (details) by Raphael: 9s, Madonna and Child. 15s, Marriage of the Virgin. 35s, Coronation of the Virgin. 90s, Madonna of the Chair. 3m, Madonna and Child Enthroned with Five Saints.

**1987, Dec. 21** *Perf. 14*

**601** A113 9s multicolored .25 .25
**602** A113 15s multicolored .25 .25
**603** A113 35s multicolored 1.25 1.25
**604** A113 90s multicolored 3.00 3.00
*Nos. 601-604 (4)* 4.75 4.75

**Souvenir Sheet**

**605** A114 3m multicolored 4.50 4.50

Christmas.

**Summer Olympics Type of 1987**

**1987, Nov. 30** **Litho.** *Perf. 14*

**606** A109 5s like 9s .25 .25
**607** A109 10s like 15s .25 .25
**608** A109 25s like 20s .25 .25
**609** A109 40s like 35s .35 .35
**610** A109 50s like 1m .50 .50
**611** A109 3.50m like 3m 3.25 3.25
*Nos. 606-611 (6)* 4.85 4.85

**Souvenir Sheet**

**612** A109 4m Soccer 4.00 4.00

No. 612 shows green at lower right diagonal half of the flag.

Discovery of America, 500th Anniv. (in 1992) A115

Columbus's fleet and marine life: 9s, Spotted trunkfish. 15s, Green sea turtle. 35s, Common dolphin. 5m, White-tailed tropicbird. 4m, Ship.

**1987, Dec. 14 Litho. *Perf. 14***

| | | | | | |
|---|---|---|---|---|---|
| **613** | A115 | 9s multicolored | | .25 | .25 |
| **614** | A115 | 15s multicolored | | .25 | .25 |
| **615** | A115 | 35s multicolored | | .60 | .60 |
| **616** | A115 | 5m multicolored | | 8.00 | 8.00 |
| | | *Nos. 613-616 (4)* | | 9.10 | 9.10 |

**Souvenir Sheet**

| | | | | |
|---|---|---|---|---|
| **617** | A115 | 4m multicolored | 6.50 | 6.50 |

Nos. 328, 559 Surcharged

**1988**

**Methods and Perfs as Before**

| | | | | |
|---|---|---|---|---|
| **617A** | A83 | 3s on 9s on 30s | | |
| **617B** | A83 | 7s on 9s on 30s | | |
| **617C** | A66 | 16s on 25s No. 328 | — | — |

Issued: Nos. 617A, 617B, 2/2/88; No. 617C, 3/88.

Birds A116

2s, Pied kingfisher. 3s, Three-banded plover. 5s, Spurwing goose. 10s, Clapper lark. 12s, Red-eyed bulbul. 16s, Cape weaver. 20s, Red-headed finch. 30s, Mountain chat. 40s, Stone chat. 55s, Pied barbet. 60s, Cape glossy starling. 75s, Cape sparrow. 1m, Cattle egret. 3m, Giant kingfisher. 10m, Crowned guinea fowl.

**1988, Apr. 5 Litho. *Perf. 15***

| | | | | |
|---|---|---|---|---|
| **618** | A116 | 2s multicolored | .25 | .25 |
| **619** | A116 | 3s multicolored | .25 | .25 |
| **620** | A116 | 5s multicolored | .25 | .25 |
| **621** | A116 | 10s multicolored | .25 | .25 |
| **622** | A116 | 12s multicolored | .25 | .25 |
| **623** | A116 | 16s multicolored | .25 | .25 |
| **624** | A116 | 20s multicolored | .25 | .25 |
| **625** | A116 | 30s multicolored | .30 | .30 |
| **626** | A116 | 40s multicolored | .40 | .40 |
| **627** | A116 | 55s multicolored | .55 | .55 |
| **628** | A116 | 60s multicolored | .60 | .60 |
| **629** | A116 | 75s multicolored | .75 | .75 |
| **630** | A116 | 1m multicolored | .85 | .85 |
| **631** | A116 | 3m multicolored | 2.50 | 2.50 |
| **632** | A116 | 10m multicolored | 9.00 | 9.00 |
| | | *Nos. 618-632 (15)* | 16.70 | 16.70 |

For surcharges see Nos. 755, 805-806.

**1989, Sept. 18 *Perf. 14***

| | | | | |
|---|---|---|---|---|
| *620a* | A116 | 5s multicolored | .25 | .25 |
| *622a* | A116 | 12s multicolored | .25 | .25 |
| *623a* | A116 | 16s multicolored | .25 | .25 |
| *624a* | A116 | 20s multicolored | .25 | .25 |
| *630a* | A116 | 1m multicolored | .80 | .80 |
| *631a* | A116 | 3m multicolored | 2.40 | 2.40 |
| *632a* | A116 | 10m multicolored | 8.00 | 8.00 |
| | | *Nos. 620a-632a (7)* | 12.20 | 12.20 |

Dated 1989.

**1990 *Perf. 12½x12***

| | | | | |
|---|---|---|---|---|
| *620b* | A116 | 5s multicolored | .25 | .25 |
| *622b* | A116 | 12s multicolored | .25 | .25 |
| *623b* | A116 | 16s multicolored | .25 | .25 |
| *624b* | A116 | 20s multicolored | .25 | .25 |
| *630b* | A116 | 1m multicolored | .80 | .80 |
| *631b* | A116 | 3m multicolored | 2.40 | 2.40 |
| *632b* | A116 | 10m multicolored | 8.00 | 8.00 |
| | | *Nos. 620b-632b (7)* | 12.20 | 12.20 |

Dated 1989.

**1991 (?) *Perf. 11½x13***

| | | | | |
|---|---|---|---|---|
| *620c* | A116 | 5s multicolored | .25 | .25 |
| *622c* | A116 | 12s multicolored | .25 | .25 |
| *623c* | A116 | 16s multicolored | .25 | .25 |
| *624c* | A116 | 20s multicolored | .25 | .25 |
| *630c* | A116 | 1m multicolored | .80 | .80 |
| *631c* | A116 | 3m multicolored | 2.40 | 2.40 |
| *632c* | A116 | 10m multicolored | 8.00 | 8.00 |
| | | *Nos. 620c-632c (7)* | 12.20 | 12.20 |

Dated 1989.

**Nos. 531-534 Ovptd. "40th WEDDING ANNIVERSARY / H.M. QUEEN ELIZABETH II / H.R.H. THE DUKE OF EDINBURGH" in Silver**

**1988, May 3 *Perf. 14***

| | | | | |
|---|---|---|---|---|
| **636** | CD339 | 90s lt yel bis & blk | .90 | .90 |
| **637** | CD339 | 1m pale grn & multi | 1.00 | 1.00 |
| **638** | CD339 | 2m dull vio & multi | 2.00 | 2.00 |
| | | *Nos. 636-638 (3)* | 3.90 | 3.90 |

**Souvenir Sheet**

| | | | | |
|---|---|---|---|---|
| **639** | CD339 | 4m tan & black | 4.00 | 4.00 |

FINLANDIA '88, Helsinki, June 1-12 — A117

Disney animated characters and Helsinki sights: 1s, Touring President's Palace. 2s, Sauna. 3s, Lake Country fishing. 4s, Finlandia Hall. 5s, Photographing Sibelius Monument. 10s, Pony trek, youth hostel. 3m, Olympic Stadium. 5m, Santa Claus, Arctic Circle.

No. 648, Market Square. No. 649, Lapp encampment, vert.

**1988, June 2 Litho. *Perf. 14x13½***

| | | | | |
|---|---|---|---|---|
| **640** | A117 | 1s multicolored | .25 | .25 |
| **641** | A117 | 2s multicolored | .25 | .25 |
| **642** | A117 | 3s multicolored | .25 | .25 |
| **643** | A117 | 4s multicolored | .25 | .25 |
| **644** | A117 | 5s multicolored | .25 | .25 |
| **645** | A117 | 10s multicolored | .30 | .30 |
| **646** | A117 | 3m multicolored | 4.25 | 3.50 |
| **647** | A117 | 5m multicolored | 5.25 | 4.75 |
| | | *Nos. 640-647 (8)* | 11.05 | 9.80 |

**Souvenir Sheets**

***Perf. 14x13½, 13½x14***

| | | | | |
|---|---|---|---|---|
| **648** | A117 | 4m multicolored | 4.50 | 4.50 |
| **649** | A117 | 4m multicolored | 4.50 | 4.50 |

Mickey Mouse, 60th anniv.

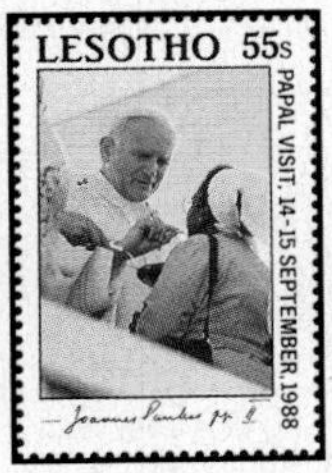


A118

55s, Pope giving communion. 2m, Leading procession. 3m, Walking in garden. 4m, Wearing scullcap.

5m, Pope, Archbishop Morapeli of Lesotho, horiz.

**1988, Sept. 1 Litho. *Perf. 14***

| | | | | |
|---|---|---|---|---|
| **650** | A118 | 55s multicolored | .50 | .50 |
| **651** | A118 | 2m multicolored | 1.60 | 1.60 |
| **652** | A118 | 3m multicolored | 2.50 | 2.50 |
| **653** | A118 | 4m multicolored | 3.50 | 3.50 |
| | | *Nos. 650-653 (4)* | 8.10 | 8.10 |

**Souvenir Sheet**

| | | | | |
|---|---|---|---|---|
| **654** | A118 | 5m multicolored | 8.00 | 8.00 |

Visit of Pope John Paul II, Sept. 14-16.

A119

Small indigenous mammals: 16s, Rock hyrax. 40s, Honey badger. 75s, Genet. 3m, Yellow mongoose.

4m, Meerkat.

**1988, Oct. 13 Litho. *Perf. 14***

| | | | | |
|---|---|---|---|---|
| **655** | A119 | 16s multicolored | .25 | .25 |
| **656** | A119 | 40s multicolored | .85 | .85 |
| **657** | A119 | 75s multicolored | 1.50 | 1.50 |
| **658** | A119 | 3m multicolored | 5.75 | 5.75 |
| | | *Nos. 655-658 (4)* | 8.35 | 8.35 |

**Souvenir Sheet**

| | | | | |
|---|---|---|---|---|
| **659** | A119 | 4m multicolored | 5.25 | 5.25 |

Birth of Venus, 1480, by Botticelli A120

Paintings: 25s, View of Toledo, 1608, by El Greco. 40s, Maids of Honor, 1656, by Diego Velazquez. 50s, The Fifer, 1866, by Manet. 55s, The Starry Night, 1889, by Van Gogh. 75s, Prima Ballerina, 1876, by Degas. 2m, Bridge over Water Lilies, 1899, by Monet. 3m, Guernica, 1937, by Picasso. No. 668, The Presentation of the Virgin in the Temple, c. 1534, by Titian. No. 669, The Miracle of the Newborn Infant, 1511, by Titian.

**1988, Oct. 17 Litho. *Perf. 13½x14***

| | | | | |
|---|---|---|---|---|
| **660** | A120 | 15s multicolored | .40 | .25 |
| **661** | A120 | 25s multicolored | .55 | .25 |
| **662** | A120 | 40s multicolored | .65 | .40 |
| **663** | A120 | 50s multicolored | .75 | .50 |
| **664** | A120 | 55s multicolored | .80 | .55 |
| **665** | A120 | 75s multicolored | .90 | .90 |
| **666** | A120 | 2m multicolored | 2.00 | 2.00 |
| **667** | A120 | 3m multicolored | 2.50 | 2.50 |
| | | *Nos. 660-667 (8)* | 8.55 | 7.35 |

**Souvenir Sheets**

| | | | | |
|---|---|---|---|---|
| **668** | A120 | 4m multicolored | 3.50 | 3.50 |
| **669** | A120 | 4m multicolored | 3.50 | 3.50 |

1988 Summer Olympics, Seoul — A121

12s, Wrestling, horiz. 16s, Equestrian. 55s, Shooting, horiz.

4m, Olympic flame.

**1988, Nov. 11 Litho. *Perf. 14***

| | | | | |
|---|---|---|---|---|
| **670** | A121 | 12s multicolored | .25 | .25 |
| **671** | A121 | 16s multicolored | .25 | .25 |
| **672** | A121 | 55s multicolored | .40 | .40 |
| **673** | A121 | 3.50m like 16s | 2.10 | 2.10 |
| | | *Nos. 670-673 (4)* | 3.00 | 3.00 |

**Souvenir Sheet**

| | | | | |
|---|---|---|---|---|
| **674** | A121 | 4m multicolored | 4.75 | 4.75 |

Intl. Tennis Federation, 75th Anniv. — A122

Tennis champions, views of cities or landmarks: 12s, Yannick Noah, Eiffel Tower, horiz. 20s, Rod Laver, Sydney Opera House and Harbor Bridge, horiz. 30s, Ivan Lendl, Prague, horiz. 65s, Jimmy Connors, Tokyo. 1m, Arthur Ashe, Barcelona. 1.55m, Althea Gibson, NYC. 2m, Chris Evert, Vienna. 2.40m, Boris Becker, London. 3m, Martina Navratilova, Golden Gate Bridge, horiz. 4m, Steffi Graf, Berlin, West Germany.

**1988, Nov. 18**

| | | | | |
|---|---|---|---|---|
| **675** | A122 | 12s multi | .70 | .25 |
| **676** | A122 | 20s multi | .90 | .25 |
| **677** | A122 | 30s multi | .80 | .35 |
| **678** | A122 | 65s multi | .95 | .80 |
| **679** | A122 | 1m multi | 1.25 | 1.25 |
| **680** | A122 | 1.55m multi | 1.50 | 1.50 |
| **681** | A122 | 2m multi | 2.25 | 2.25 |
| **682** | A122 | 2.40m multi | 2.50 | 2.50 |
| **683** | A122 | 3m multi | 3.00 | 3.00 |
| | | *Nos. 675-683 (9)* | 13.85 | 12.15 |

**Souvenir Sheet**

| | | | | |
|---|---|---|---|---|
| **684** | A122 | 4m multi | 4.50 | 4.50 |

No. 676 has "Sidney" instead of "Sydney." No. 679 has "Ash" instead of "Ashe."

Paintings by Titian A123

Designs: 12s, The Averoldi Polyptych. 20s, Christ and the Adulteress (Christ). 35s, Christ and the Adulteress (adultress). 45s, Angel of the Annunciation. 65s, Saint Dominic. 1m, The Vendramin Family. 2m, Mary Magdalen. 3m, The Tribute Money. No. 693, Christ and the Woman Taken in Adultery. No. 694, The Mater Dolorosa.

**1988, Dec. 1 *Perf. 14x13½***

| | | | | |
|---|---|---|---|---|
| **685** | A123 | 12s multicolored | .40 | .25 |
| **686** | A123 | 20s multicolored | .50 | .25 |
| **687** | A123 | 35s multicolored | .60 | .35 |
| **688** | A123 | 45s multicolored | .70 | .45 |
| **689** | A123 | 65s multicolored | .70 | .65 |
| **690** | A123 | 1m multicolored | .90 | .90 |
| **691** | A123 | 2m multicolored | 1.75 | 1.75 |
| **692** | A123 | 3m multicolored | 2.50 | 2.50 |
| | | *Nos. 685-692 (8)* | 8.05 | 7.10 |

**Souvenir Sheets**

| | | | | |
|---|---|---|---|---|
| **693** | A123 | 5m multicolored | 4.50 | 4.50 |
| **694** | A123 | 5m multicolored | 4.50 | 4.50 |

Birth of Titian, 500th anniv. Nos. 685-693 inscribed "Christmas 1988."

Intl. Red Cross, 125th Anniv. A124

Anniv. emblem, supply and ambulance planes: 12s, Pilatus PC-6 Turbo Porter. 20s, Cessna Caravan. 55s, De Havilland DHC-6 Otter. 3m, Douglas DC-3 in thunderstorm. 4m, Douglas DC-3, diff.

**1989, Jan. 30 Litho. *Perf. 14***

| | | | | |
|---|---|---|---|---|
| **695** | A124 | 12s multicolored | .25 | .25 |
| **696** | A124 | 20s multicolored | .25 | .25 |
| **697** | A124 | 55s multicolored | 1.25 | 1.25 |
| **698** | A124 | 3m multicolored | 5.25 | 5.25 |
| | | *Nos. 695-698 (4)* | 7.00 | 7.00 |

**Souvenir Sheet**

| | | | | |
|---|---|---|---|---|
| **699** | A124 | 4m multi, vert. | 9.00 | 9.00 |

Landscapes by Hiroshige — A125

Designs: 12s, Dawn Mist at Mishima. 16s, Night Snow at Kambara. 20s, Wayside Inn at Mariko Station. 35s, Shower at Shono. 55s, Snowfall on the Kisokaido Near Oi. 1m, Autumn Moon at Seba. 3.20m, Evening Moon at Ryogaku Bridge. 5m, Cherry Blossoms, Arashiyama. No. 708, Listening to the Singing Insects at Dokanyama. No. 709, Moonlight, Nagakubo.

**1989, June 19 Litho. *Perf. 14x13½***

| | | | | | |
|---|---|---|---|---|---|
| **700** | A125 | 12s | multi | .40 | .25 |
| **701** | A125 | 16s | multi | .45 | .25 |
| **702** | A125 | 20s | multi | .45 | .25 |
| **703** | A125 | 35s | multi | .45 | .30 |
| **704** | A125 | 55s | multi | .70 | .45 |
| **705** | A125 | 1m | multi | 1.00 | .80 |
| **706** | A125 | 3.20m | multi | 2.25 | 2.25 |
| **707** | A125 | 5m | multi | 3.75 | 3.75 |
| | | | *Nos. 700-707 (8)* | 9.45 | 8.30 |

**Souvenir Sheets**

| | | | | | |
|---|---|---|---|---|---|
| **708** | A125 | 4m | multi | 4.25 | 4.25 |
| **709** | A125 | 4m | multi | 4.25 | 4.25 |

Hirohito (1901-1989) and enthronement of Akihito as emperor of Japan.

PHILEXFRANCE '89, French Revolution Bicent. — A126

Disney characters wearing insurgent uniforms: 1s, General. 2s, Infantry. 3s, Grenadier. 4s, Cavalry. 5s, Hussar. 10s, Marine. 3m, Natl. guard. 5m, Admiral.

No. 718, Natl. guard, royal family, horiz. No. 719, La Marseillaise.

**1989, July 10 *Perf. 13½x14, 14x13½***

| | | | | | |
|---|---|---|---|---|---|
| **710** | A126 | 1s | multicolored | .25 | .25 |
| **711** | A126 | 2s | multicolored | .25 | .25 |
| **712** | A126 | 3s | multicolored | .25 | .25 |
| **713** | A126 | 4s | multicolored | .25 | .25 |
| **714** | A126 | 5s | multicolored | .25 | .25 |
| **715** | A126 | 10s | multicolored | .25 | .25 |
| **716** | A126 | 3m | multicolored | 3.00 | 3.00 |
| **717** | A126 | 5m | multicolored | 4.75 | 4.75 |
| | | | *Nos. 710-717 (8)* | 9.25 | 9.25 |

**Souvenir Sheets**

| | | | | | |
|---|---|---|---|---|---|
| **718** | A126 | 4m | multicolored | 5.00 | 5.00 |
| **719** | A126 | 4m | multicolored | 5.00 | 5.00 |

Maloti Mountains — A127

No. 720: a, Sotho thatched dwellings. b, Two trees, cliff edge. c, Waterfall. d, Tribesman.

**1989, Sept. Litho. *Perf. 14***

| | | | |
|---|---|---|---|
| **720** | Strip of 4 | 4.00 | 4.00 |
| ***a.-d.*** | A127 1m any single | .75 | .75 |

**Souvenir Sheet**

| | | | | |
|---|---|---|---|---|
| **721** | A127 | 4m Flora | 4.25 | 4.25 |

Mushrooms A128

12s, Paxillus involutus. 16s, Ganoderma applanatum. 55s, Suillus granulatus. 5m, Stereum hirsutum.

4m, Scleroderma flavidum.

**1989, Sept. 8 Litho. *Perf. 14***

| | | | | | |
|---|---|---|---|---|---|
| **722** | A128 | 12s | multicolored | .35 | .25 |
| **723** | A128 | 16s | multicolored | .35 | .25 |
| **723A** | A128 | 55s | multicolored | .65 | .55 |
| **724** | A128 | 5m | multicolored | 4.50 | 4.50 |
| | | | *Nos. 722-724 (4)* | 5.85 | 5.55 |

**Souvenir Sheet**

| | | | | | |
|---|---|---|---|---|---|
| **725** | A128 | 4m | multicolored | 6.25 | 6.25 |

Birds A129

12s, Marsh sandpipers. 65s, Little stints. 1m, Ringed plovers. 4m, Curlew sandpipers.

5m, Ruff, vert.

**1989, Oct. 23 Litho. *Perf. 14***

| | | | | | |
|---|---|---|---|---|---|
| **726** | A129 | 12s | multicolored | .25 | .25 |
| **727** | A129 | 65s | multicolored | 1.10 | 1.10 |
| **728** | A129 | 1m | multicolored | 1.75 | 1.75 |
| **729** | A129 | 4m | multicolored | 6.25 | 6.25 |
| | | | *Nos. 726-729 (4)* | 9.35 | 9.35 |

**Souvenir Sheet**

| | | | | | |
|---|---|---|---|---|---|
| **730** | A129 | 5m | multicolored | 11.00 | 11.00 |

1st Moon Landing, 20th Anniv. A130

Highlights of the Apollo 11 mission: 12s, Liftoff. 16s, Eagle landing. 40s, Astronaut on ladder. 55s, Buzz Aldrin. 1m, Solar wind experiment. 2m, Eagle lifting off. 3m, Columbia in orbit. 4m, Splashdown.

5m, Astronaut, Eagle.

**1989, Nov. 6 *Perf. 14***

| | | | | | |
|---|---|---|---|---|---|
| **731** | A130 | 12s | multicolored | .25 | .25 |
| **732** | A130 | 16s | multicolored | .25 | .25 |
| **733** | A130 | 40s | multicolored | .40 | .40 |
| **734** | A130 | 55s | multicolored | .60 | .60 |
| **735** | A130 | 1m | multicolored | .90 | .90 |
| **736** | A130 | 2m | multicolored | 1.75 | 1.75 |
| **737** | A130 | 3m | multicolored | 2.40 | 2.40 |
| **738** | A130 | 4m | multicolored | 3.50 | 3.50 |
| | | | *Nos. 731-738 (8)* | 10.05 | 10.05 |

**Souvenir Sheet**

| | | | | | |
|---|---|---|---|---|---|
| **739** | A130 | 5m | multicolored | 6.75 | 6.75 |

Nos. 731, 733, 738-739 vert.

World Stamp Expo '89 — A131

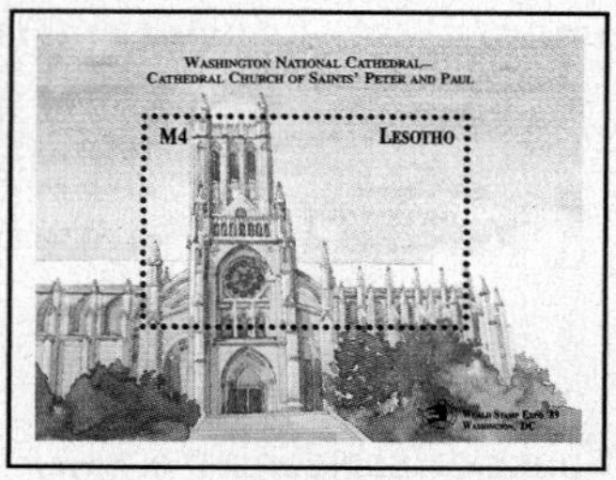


Cathedral Church of Sts. Peter and Paul, Washington, DC — A132

No. 740: a, Postal marking, England, 1680. b, Wax seal and feather, Germany, 1807. c, Crete #1. d, Perot postmaster's provisional, Bermuda, 1848. e, Pony Express handstamp, US, 1860. f, Finland #1. g, Fiji #1. h, Swedish newspaper handstamp, 1823. i, Bhor #1.

**1989, Nov. 17 Litho. *Perf. 14***

| | | | | |
|---|---|---|---|---|
| **740** | A131 | Sheet of 9 | 8.25 | 8.25 |
| ***a.-i.*** | | 75s any single | .35 | .35 |

**Souvenir Sheet**

| | | | | |
|---|---|---|---|---|
| **741** | A132 | 4m shown | 4.00 | 4.00 |

Christmas — A133

Religious paintings by Velazquez: 12s, The Immaculate Conception. 20s, St. Anthony Abbot and St. Paul the Hermit. 35s, St. Thomas the Apostle. 55s, Christ in the House of Martha and Mary. 1m, St. John Writing the Apocalypse on Patmos. 3m, The Virgin Presenting the Chasuble to St. Ildephonsus. 4m, The Adoration of the Magi. 5m, The Coronation of the Virgin.

**1989, Dec. 18**

| | | | | | |
|---|---|---|---|---|---|
| **742** | A133 | 12s | multicolored | .25 | .25 |
| **743** | A133 | 20s | multicolored | .25 | .25 |
| **744** | A133 | 35s | multicolored | .35 | .35 |
| **745** | A133 | 55s | multicolored | .55 | .55 |
| **746** | A133 | 1m | multicolored | .80 | .80 |
| **747** | A133 | 3m | multicolored | 2.25 | 2.25 |
| **748** | A133 | 4m | multicolored | 3.00 | 3.00 |
| | | | *Nos. 742-748 (7)* | 7.45 | 7.45 |

**Souvenir Sheet**

| | | | | | |
|---|---|---|---|---|---|
| **749** | A133 | 5m | multicolored | 9.00 | 9.00 |

1990 World Cup Soccer Championships, Italy — A134

Various athletes, emblem and name of previous championship host nations: 12s, England, 1966. 16s, Mexico, 1970. 55s, West Germany, 1974. 5m, Spain, 1982.

4m, Diego Maradona, Argentina.

**1989, Dec. 27**

| | | | | | |
|---|---|---|---|---|---|
| **750** | A134 | 12s | multicolored | .25 | .25 |
| **751** | A134 | 16s | multicolored | .25 | .25 |
| **752** | A134 | 55s | multicolored | 1.00 | 1.00 |
| **753** | A134 | 5m | multicolored | 6.50 | 6.50 |
| | | | *Nos. 750-753 (4)* | 8.00 | 8.00 |

**Souvenir Sheet**

| | | | | | |
|---|---|---|---|---|---|
| **754** | A134 | 4m | multicolored | 7.50 | 7.50 |

**No. 622a Surcharged**

**1990 Litho. *Perf. 14***

| | | | | |
|---|---|---|---|---|
| **755** | A116 | 16s on 12s multi | — | — |

Orchids A135

Designs: 12s, Satyrium princeps. 16s, Huttonaea pulchra. 55s, Herschelia graminifolia. 1m, Ansellia gigantea. 1.55m, Polystachya pubescens. 2.40m, Penthea filicornis. 3m, Disperis capensis. 4m, Disa uniflora.

5m, Stenoglottis longifolia.

**1990, Mar. 12 Litho. *Perf. 14***

| | | | | | |
|---|---|---|---|---|---|
| **756** | A135 | 12s | multicolored | .25 | .25 |
| **757** | A135 | 16s | multicolored | .25 | .25 |
| **758** | A135 | 55s | multicolored | .90 | .90 |
| **759** | A135 | 1m | multicolored | 1.60 | 1.60 |
| **760** | A135 | 1.55m | multicolored | 2.25 | 2.25 |
| **761** | A135 | 2.40m | multicolored | 3.50 | 3.50 |
| **762** | A135 | 3m | multicolored | 4.25 | 4.25 |
| **763** | A135 | 4m | multicolored | 6.00 | 6.00 |
| | | | *Nos. 756-763 (8)* | 19.00 | 19.00 |

**Souvenir Sheet**

| | | | | | |
|---|---|---|---|---|---|
| **764** | A135 | 5m | multicolored | 10.00 | 10.00 |

Expo '90.

Butterflies — A136

12s, Pseudo ergolid. 16s, Painted lady. 55s, Ringed pansy. 65s, False acraea. 1m, Eyed pansy. 2m, Golden pansy. 3m, African monarch. 4m, African giant swallowtail.

5m, Citrus swallowtail.

**1990, Feb. 26 Litho. *Perf. 14***

| | | | | | |
|---|---|---|---|---|---|
| **765** | A136 | 12s | multicolored | .95 | .25 |
| **766** | A136 | 16s | multicolored | 1.10 | .25 |
| **767** | A136 | 55s | multicolored | 1.60 | .55 |
| **768** | A136 | 65s | multicolored | 1.75 | .65 |
| **769** | A136 | 1m | multicolored | 2.40 | 1.10 |
| **770** | A136 | 2m | multicolored | 3.75 | 2.25 |
| **771** | A136 | 3m | multicolored | 5.25 | 3.25 |
| **772** | A136 | 4m | multicolored | 6.50 | 5.50 |
| | | | *Nos. 765-772 (8)* | 23.30 | 13.80 |

**Souvenir Sheet**

| | | | | | |
|---|---|---|---|---|---|
| **773** | A136 | 5m | multicolored | 11.00 | 11.00 |

Queen Mother, 90th Birthday — A137

**1990, July 5 Litho. *Perf. 14***

| | | | |
|---|---|---|---|
| **774** | 1.50m In hat | 1.25 | 1.25 |
| **775** | 1.50m Two children | 1.25 | 1.25 |
| **776** | 1.50m Young woman | 1.25 | 1.25 |
| ***a.*** | A137 Strip of 3, #774-776 | 4.50 | 4.50 |
| | *Nos. 774-776 (3)* | 3.75 | 3.75 |

**Souvenir Sheet**

| | | | | |
|---|---|---|---|---|
| **777** | A137 | 5m Child | 5.50 | 5.50 |

A139

Designs: 12s, King Moshoeshoe II, Prince Mohato wearing blankets. 16s, Prince Mohato in Seana-Marena blanket. 1m, Pope John Paul II in Seana-Marena blanket. 3m, Basotho men on horses.
5m, Pope with blanket and hat.

**1990, Aug. 17 Litho. *Perf. 14***

| | | | | |
|---|---|---|---|---|
| **778** | A139 | 12s multicolored | .25 | .25 |
| **779** | A139 | 16s multicolored | .25 | .25 |
| **780** | A139 | 1m multicolored | 1.40 | 1.40 |
| **781** | A139 | 3m multicolored | 3.50 | 3.50 |
| | | *Nos. 778-781 (4)* | 5.40 | 5.40 |

**Souvenir Sheet**

| | | | | |
|---|---|---|---|---|
| **782** | A139 | 5m multi, horiz. | 7.50 | 7.50 |

Highland Water Project — A140

16s, Moving gravel. 20s, Fuel truck. 55s, Piers for bridge construction. 2m, Road construction.
5m, Drilling blasting holes.

**1990, Aug. 24**

| | | | | |
|---|---|---|---|---|
| **783** | A140 | 16s multicolored | .25 | .25 |
| **784** | A140 | 20s multicolored | .25 | .25 |
| **785** | A140 | 55s multicolored | .90 | .90 |
| **786** | A140 | 2m multicolored | 2.75 | 2.75 |
| | | *Nos. 783-786 (4)* | 4.15 | 4.15 |

**Souvenir Sheet**

| | | | | |
|---|---|---|---|---|
| **787** | A140 | 5m multicolored | 7.25 | 7.25 |

UNICEF Save the Children Campaign — A141

12s, Breastfeeding. 55s, Oral rehydration. 1m, Baby being weighed.

**1990, Sept. 26 Litho. *Perf. 14***

| | | | | |
|---|---|---|---|---|
| **788** | A141 | 12s multicolored | .25 | .25 |
| **789** | A141 | 55s multicolored | 1.75 | 1.75 |
| **790** | A141 | 1m multicolored | 2.50 | 2.50 |
| | | *Nos. 788-790 (3)* | 4.50 | 4.50 |

1992 Summer Olympics, Barcelona — A142

16s, Triple jump. 55s, 200-meter race. 1m, 5000-meter race. 4m, Equestrian show jumping.
5m, Lighting Olympic flame.

**1990, Oct. 5**

| | | | | |
|---|---|---|---|---|
| **791** | A142 | 16s multicolored | .25 | .25 |
| **792** | A142 | 55s multicolored | 1.00 | 1.00 |
| **793** | A142 | 1m multicolored | 1.50 | 1.50 |
| **794** | A142 | 4m multicolored | 5.50 | 5.50 |
| | | *Nos. 791-794 (4)* | 8.25 | 8.25 |

**Souvenir Sheet**

| | | | | |
|---|---|---|---|---|
| **795** | A142 | 5m multicolored | 8.50 | 8.50 |

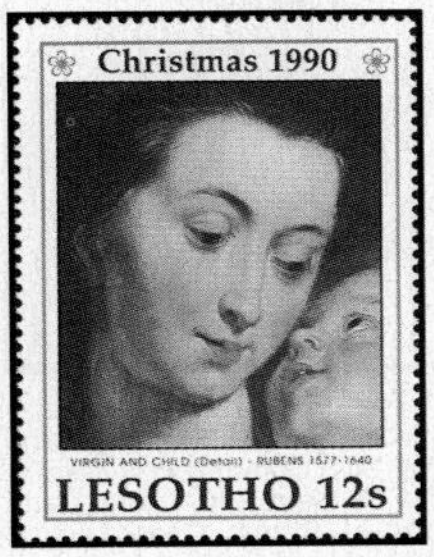

Christmas A143

Different details from paintings by Rubens: 12s, 1m, 3m, Virgin and Child. 16s, 80s, 2m, 4m, Adoration of the Magi. 55s, Head of One of the Three Kings, diff. 5m, Assumption of the Virgin.

**1990, Dec. 5 Litho. *Perf. 13½x14***

| | | | | |
|---|---|---|---|---|
| **796** | A143 | 12s multicolored | .25 | .25 |
| **797** | A143 | 16s multicolored | .25 | .25 |
| **798** | A143 | 55s multicolored | .55 | .55 |
| **799** | A143 | 80s multicolored | .85 | .85 |
| **800** | A143 | 1m multicolored | 1.00 | 1.00 |
| **801** | A143 | 2m multicolored | 2.10 | 2.10 |
| **802** | A143 | 3m multicolored | 2.75 | 2.75 |
| **803** | A143 | 4m multicolored | 3.75 | 3.75 |
| | | *Nos. 796-803 (8)* | 11.50 | 11.50 |

**Souvenir Sheet**

| | | | | |
|---|---|---|---|---|
| **804** | A143 | 5m multicolored | 7.25 | 7.25 |

**Nos. 625-626 Surcharged**

**1991, Jan. 18 Litho. *Perf. 15***

| | | | | |
|---|---|---|---|---|
| **805** | A116 | 16s on 30s #625 | — | — |
| **806** | A116 | 16s on 40s #626 | — | — |

Phila Nippon '91 — A144

Walt Disney characters visit Japan: 20s, Mickey at Nagasaki Peace Park. 30s, Mickey at Kamakura Beach. 40s, Mickey, Donald entertain at Bunraku Puppet Theater. 50s, Mickey, Donald eat soba at noodle shop. 75s, Minnie, Mickey at tea house. 1m, Mickey, Bullet Train. 3m, Mickey, deer at Todaiji Temple. 4m, Mickey, Minnie before Imperial Palace. No. 815, Mickey skiing at Happo-One, Nagano. No. 816, Mickey, Minnie at Suizenji Park.

**1991, June 10 Litho. *Perf. 14x13½***

| | | | | |
|---|---|---|---|---|
| **807** | A144 | 20s multicolored | .25 | .25 |
| **808** | A144 | 30s multicolored | .25 | .25 |
| **809** | A144 | 40s multicolored | .50 | .50 |
| **810** | A144 | 50s multicolored | .70 | .70 |
| **811** | A144 | 75s multicolored | 1.40 | 1.40 |
| **812** | A144 | 1m multicolored | 1.40 | 1.40 |
| **813** | A144 | 3m multicolored | 3.75 | 3.75 |
| **814** | A144 | 4m multicolored | 5.00 | 5.00 |
| | | *Nos. 807-814 (8)* | 13.25 | 13.25 |

**Souvenir Sheets**

| | | | | |
|---|---|---|---|---|
| **815** | A144 | 6m multicolored | 5.50 | 5.50 |
| **816** | A144 | 6m multicolored | 5.50 | 5.50 |

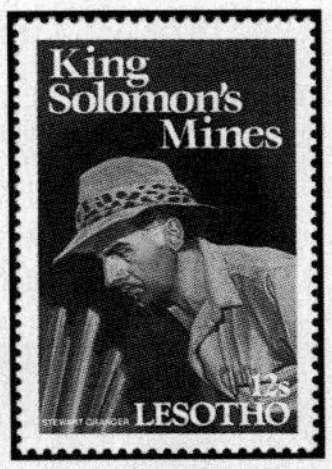

Entertainers in Films About Africa — A145

Designs: 12s, Stewart Granger, King Solomon's Mines. 16s, Johnny Weissmuller, Tarzan, the Ape Man. 30s, Clark Gable, Grace Kelly, Mogambo. 55s, Sigourney Weaver, Gorillas in the Mist. 70s, Humphrey Bogart, Katharine Hepburn, The African Queen. 1m, John Wayne, Hatari. 2m, Meryl Streep, Out of Africa. 4m, Eddie Murphy, Arsenio Hall, Coming to America. 5m, Elsa, Born Free.

**1991, June 20 Litho. *Perf. 14***

| | | | | |
|---|---|---|---|---|
| **817** | A145 | 12s multicolored | .65 | .25 |
| **818** | A145 | 16s multicolored | .65 | .25 |
| **819** | A145 | 30s multicolored | .80 | .25 |
| **820** | A145 | 55s multicolored | .95 | .70 |
| **821** | A145 | 70s multicolored | 1.25 | .90 |
| **822** | A145 | 1m multicolored | 1.60 | 1.25 |
| **823** | A145 | 2m multicolored | 2.50 | 2.50 |
| **824** | A145 | 4m multicolored | 4.25 | 4.25 |
| | | *Nos. 817-824 (8)* | 12.65 | 10.35 |

**Souvenir Sheet**

| | | | | |
|---|---|---|---|---|
| **825** | A145 | 5m multicolored | 6.75 | 6.75 |

Butterflies A146

2s, Satyrus aello. 3s, Erebia medusa. 5s, Melanargia galathea. 10s, Erebia aethiops. 20s, Coenonympha pamphilus. 25s, Pyrameis atalanta. 30s, Charaxes jasius. 40s, Colias palaeno. 50s, Colias cliopatra. 60s, Colias philodice. 70s, Rhumni gonepterix. 1m, Colias caesonia. 2m, Pyrameis cardui. 3m, Danaus chrysippus. 10m, Apatura iris.

**No date inscription below design**

**1991, Aug. 1 Litho. *Perf. 13½***

| | | | | |
|---|---|---|---|---|
| **827** | A146 | 2s multicolored | .25 | .25 |
| **828** | A146 | 3s multicolored | .25 | .25 |
| **829** | A146 | 5s multicolored | .25 | .25 |
| **830** | A146 | 10s multicolored | .25 | .25 |
| **831** | A146 | 20s multicolored | .30 | .25 |
| **832** | A146 | 25s multicolored | .30 | .25 |
| **833** | A146 | 30s multicolored | .45 | .30 |
| **834** | A146 | 40s multicolored | .45 | .35 |
| **835** | A146 | 50s multicolored | .50 | .45 |
| **836** | A146 | 60s multicolored | .60 | .55 |
| **837** | A146 | 70s multicolored | .60 | .60 |
| **838** | A146 | 1m multicolored | .90 | .90 |
| **839** | A146 | 2m multicolored | 1.75 | 1.75 |
| **840** | A146 | 3m multicolored | 2.50 | 2.50 |
| **840A** | A146 | 10m multicolored | 8.75 | 8.75 |
| | | *Nos. 827-840A (15)* | 18.10 | 17.65 |

For surcharge see No. 1062.

**1992, Apr. Inscribed "1992"**

| | | | | |
|---|---|---|---|---|
| *827a* | A146 | 2s multicolored | .25 | .25 |
| *828a* | A146 | 3s multicolored | .25 | .25 |
| *829a* | A146 | 5s multicolored | .25 | .25 |
| *830a* | A146 | 10s multicolored | .25 | .25 |
| *831a* | A146 | 20s multicolored | .30 | .25 |
| *832a* | A146 | 25s multicolored | .30 | .25 |
| *833a* | A146 | 30s multicolored | .45 | .30 |
| *834a* | A146 | 40s multicolored | .50 | .35 |
| *835a* | A146 | 50s multicolored | .65 | .45 |
| *836a* | A146 | 60s multicolored | .70 | .70 |
| *837a* | A146 | 70s multicolored | 1.00 | 1.00 |
| *838a* | A146 | 1m multicolored | 1.25 | 1.25 |
| *839a* | A146 | 2m multicolored | 2.75 | 2.75 |
| *840a* | A146 | 3m multicolored | 4.00 | 4.00 |
| *840Aa* | A146 | 10m multicolored | 8.75 | 8.75 |
| | | *Nos. 827a-840Aa (15)* | 21.65 | 21.05 |

SADCC, 10th Anniv. A147

Tourism: 12s, Wattled cranes. 16s, Butterfly, flowers in national parks. 25s, Tourist bus and Mukurub, the Finger of God. 3m, People in traditional dress.

**1991, Oct. 10 Litho. *Perf. 14x13½***

| | | | | |
|---|---|---|---|---|
| **841** | A147 | 12s multicolored | 1.75 | 1.75 |
| **842** | A147 | 16s multicolored | 1.75 | 1.75 |
| **843** | A147 | 25s multicolored | 1.75 | 1.75 |
| | | *Nos. 841-843 (3)* | 5.25 | 5.25 |

**Souvenir Sheet**

| | | | | |
|---|---|---|---|---|
| **844** | A147 | 3m multicolored | 5.50 | 5.50 |

Say No to Drugs A148

**1991, Oct. 10**

| | | | | |
|---|---|---|---|---|
| **845** | A148 | 16s multicolored | 2.25 | 2.25 |

Charles de Gaulle, Birth Cent. — A149

DeGaulle: 40s, Wearing brigadier general's kepi. 50s, Facing left. 60s, Facing right. 4m, In later years.

**1991, Dec. 6 Litho. *Perf. 14***

| | | | | |
|---|---|---|---|---|
| **846** | A149 | 20s black & brown | .25 | .25 |
| **847** | A149 | 40s black & violet | .65 | .65 |
| **848** | A149 | 50s black & olilve | .85 | .85 |
| **849** | A149 | 60s black & dk blue | 1.00 | 1.00 |
| **850** | A149 | 4m black & brn org | 6.75 | 6.75 |
| | | *Nos. 846-850 (5)* | 9.50 | 9.50 |

Christmas A150

Engravings by Albrecht Durer: 20s, St. Anne with Mary and the Child Jesus. 30s, Mary on the Grass Bench. 50s, Mary with the Crown of Stars. 60s, Mary with Child beside a Tree. 70s, Mary with Child beside the Wall. 1m, Mary in a Halo on the Crescent Moon. 2m, Mary Breastfeeding Her Child. 4m, Mary with the Infant in Swaddling Clothes. No. 859, Holy Family with the Dragonfly. No. 860, The Birth of Christ.

**1991, Dec. 13 Litho. *Perf. 12***

| | | | | |
|---|---|---|---|---|
| **851** | A150 | 20s rose & black | .25 | .25 |
| **852** | A150 | 30s blue & black | .50 | .50 |
| **853** | A150 | 50s green & black | .80 | .80 |
| **854** | A150 | 60s red & black | 1.00 | 1.00 |
| **855** | A150 | 70s yellow & black | 1.10 | 1.10 |
| **856** | A150 | 1m yel org & black | 1.60 | 1.60 |
| **857** | A150 | 2m violet & black | 2.75 | 2.75 |
| **858** | A150 | 4m dk blue & black | 5.75 | 5.75 |
| | | *Nos. 851-858 (8)* | 13.75 | 13.75 |

**Souvenir Sheets**

***Perf. 14½***

| | | | | |
|---|---|---|---|---|
| **859** | A150 | 5m blue & black | 5.00 | 5.00 |
| **860** | A150 | 5m pink & black | 5.00 | 5.00 |

Games A151

Walt Disney characters playing games: 20s, Mickey, Pluto playing pin the tail on the donkey. 30s, Mickey enjoying board game, Mancala. 40s, Mickey hoop rolling. 50s, Minnie with hula hoops. 70s, Mickey throwing Frisbee to Pluto. 1m, Donald trying to play Diabolo. 2m, Huey, Dewey and Louie playing marbles. 3m, Donald frustrated by Rubik's cube. No. 869, Donald and Mickey's nephews in tug-of-war. No. 870, Mickey, Donald stick fighting.

**1991, Dec. 16** *Perf. 13½x14*

| | | | | |
|---|---|---|---|---|
| **861** | A151 | 20s multicolored | .25 | .25 |
| **862** | A151 | 30s multicolored | .55 | .55 |
| **863** | A151 | 40s multicolored | .65 | .65 |
| **864** | A151 | 50s multicolored | .90 | .90 |
| **865** | A151 | 70s multicolored | 1.25 | 1.25 |
| **866** | A151 | 1m multicolored | 1.75 | 1.75 |
| **867** | A151 | 2m multicolored | 3.25 | 3.25 |
| **868** | A151 | 3m multicolored | 5.00 | 5.00 |
| | | *Nos. 861-868 (8)* | 13.60 | 13.60 |

**Souvenir Sheets**

| | | | | |
|---|---|---|---|---|
| **869** | A151 | 5m multicolored | 6.00 | 6.00 |
| **870** | A151 | 5m multicolored | 6.00 | 6.00 |

**Royal Family Birthday, Anniversary**

Common Design Type

**1991, Dec. 9** **Litho.** *Perf. 14*

| | | | | |
|---|---|---|---|---|
| **871** | CD347 | 50s multicolored | .70 | .70 |
| **872** | CD347 | 70s multicolored | .95 | .95 |
| **873** | CD347 | 1m multicolored | 1.40 | 1.40 |
| **874** | CD347 | 3m multicolored | 4.25 | 4.25 |
| | | *Nos. 871-874 (4)* | 7.30 | 7.30 |

**Souvenir Sheet**

| | | | | |
|---|---|---|---|---|
| **875** | CD347 | 4m Charles, Diana, sons | 6.25 | 6.25 |

Charles and Diana, 10th wedding anniversary.

**Queen Elizabeth II's Accession to the Throne, 40th Anniv.**

Common Design Type

**1992, Feb. 6** **Litho.** *Perf. 14*

| | | | | |
|---|---|---|---|---|
| **881** | CD348 | 20s multicolored | .25 | .25 |
| **882** | CD348 | 30s multicolored | .40 | .40 |
| **883** | CD348 | 1m multicolored | 1.25 | 1.25 |
| **884** | CD348 | 4m multicolored | 4.00 | 4.00 |
| | | *Nos. 881-884 (4)* | 5.90 | 5.90 |

**Souvenir Sheet**

| | | | | |
|---|---|---|---|---|
| **885** | CD348 | 5m multicolored | 6.00 | 6.00 |

Birds — A152

Designs: a, Lanner falcon. b, Bataleur. c, Red-headed finch. d, Lesser-striped swallow. e, Alpine swift. f, Diederik cuckoo. g, Malachite sunbird. h, Crimson-breasted shrike. i, Pin-tailed whydah. j, Lilac-breasted roller. k, Black korhaan. l, Black-collared barbet. m, Secretary bird. n, Red-billed quelea. o, Red bishop. p, Ring-necked dove. q, Yellow canary. r, Orange-throated longclaw. s, Blue waxbill. t, Golden bishop.

**1992, Feb. 10** *Perf. 14½*

| | | | | |
|---|---|---|---|---|
| **886** | A152 | 30s Sheet of 20, #a.-t. | 17.50 | 17.50 |

World Columbian Stamp Expo '92, Chicago A153

Walt Disney characters depicting native Americans: 30s, Donald Duck making arrowheads. 40s, Goofy playing lacrosse. 1m, Mickey, Donald planting corn. 3m, Minnie Mouse mastering art of beading. No. 891, Mickey as "Blackhawk" hunting for moose.

**1992, Apr.** **Litho.** *Perf. 13½x14*

| | | | | |
|---|---|---|---|---|
| **887** | A153 | 30s multicolored | .55 | .55 |
| **888** | A153 | 40s multicolored | .65 | .65 |
| **889** | A153 | 1m multicolored | 1.75 | 1.75 |
| **890** | A153 | 3m multicolored | 4.50 | 4.50 |
| | | *Nos. 887-890 (4)* | 7.45 | 7.45 |

**Souvenir Sheet**

| | | | | |
|---|---|---|---|---|
| **891** | A153 | 5m multicolored | 7.75 | 7.75 |

Granada '92 — A154

Walt Disney characters in Spanish costumes: 20s, Minnie Mouse as Lady of Rank, 1540-1660. 50s, Mickey as conqueror of Lepanto, 1571. 70s, Donald Duck from Galicia, 1880. 2m, Daisy Duck from Aragon, 1880. No. 901, Goofy as bullfighter.

**1992, Apr. 13** **Litho.** *Perf. 13½x14*

| | | | | |
|---|---|---|---|---|
| **897** | A154 | 20s multicolored | .25 | .25 |
| **898** | A154 | 50s multicolored | 1.25 | 1.25 |
| **899** | A154 | 70s multicolored | 1.60 | 1.60 |
| **900** | A154 | 2m multicolored | 4.00 | 4.00 |
| | | *Nos. 897-900 (4)* | 7.10 | 7.10 |

**Souvenir Sheet**

| | | | | |
|---|---|---|---|---|
| **901** | A154 | 5m multicolored | 7.75 | 7.75 |

Dinosaurs A155

20s, Stegosaurus. 30s, Ceratosaurus. 40s, Procompsognathus. 50s, Lesothosaurus. 70s, Plateosaurus. 1m, Gasosaurus. 2m, Massospondylus. 3m, Archaeopteryx.

No. 915, Archaeopteryx, diff. No. 916, Lesothosaurus, diff.

**1992, June 9** *Perf. 14*

| | | | | |
|---|---|---|---|---|
| **907** | A155 | 20s multicolored | .25 | .25 |
| **908** | A155 | 30s multicolored | .65 | .65 |
| **909** | A155 | 40s multicolored | .75 | .75 |
| **910** | A155 | 50s multicolored | 1.00 | 1.00 |
| **911** | A155 | 70s multicolored | 1.40 | 1.40 |
| **912** | A155 | 1m multicolored | 2.00 | 2.00 |
| **913** | A155 | 2m multicolored | 3.50 | 3.50 |
| **914** | A155 | 3m multicolored | 5.25 | 5.25 |
| | | *Nos. 907-914 (8)* | 14.80 | 14.80 |

**Souvenir Sheet**

| | | | | |
|---|---|---|---|---|
| **915** | A155 | 5m multicolored | 7.75 | 7.75 |
| **916** | A155 | 5m multicolored | 7.75 | 7.75 |

No. 915 printed in continuous design.

1992 Olympics, Barcelona and Albertville — A156

Designs: 20s, Discus. 30s, Long jump. 40s, Women's 4x100-meter relay. 70s, Women's 100-meter dash. 1m, Parallel bars. 2m, Two-man luge, horiz. 3m, Women's cross-country skiing, horiz. 4m, Biathlon.

No. 925, Ice hockey, horiz. No. 926, Women's figure skating.

**1992, Aug. 5** **Litho.** *Perf. 14*

| | | | | |
|---|---|---|---|---|
| **917** | A156 | 20s multicolored | .25 | .25 |
| **918** | A156 | 30s multicolored | .25 | .25 |
| **919** | A156 | 40s multicolored | .30 | .30 |
| **920** | A156 | 70s multicolored | .65 | .65 |
| **921** | A156 | 1m multicolored | .95 | .95 |
| **922** | A156 | 2m multicolored | 1.75 | 1.75 |
| **923** | A156 | 3m multicolored | 2.50 | 2.50 |
| **924** | A156 | 4m multicolored | 3.50 | 3.50 |
| | | *Nos. 917-924 (8)* | 10.15 | 10.15 |

**Souvenir Sheet**

| | | | | |
|---|---|---|---|---|
| **925** | A156 | 5m multicolored | 5.25 | 5.25 |
| **926** | A156 | 5m multicolored | 5.25 | 5.25 |

Christmas A158

Details or entire paintings: 20s, Virgin and Child, by Sassetta. 30s, Coronation of the Virgin, by Master of Bonastre. 40s, Virgin and Child, by Master of Saints Cosmas and Damian. 70s, The Virgin of Great Panagia, by Russian School, 12th cent. 1m, Madonna and Child, by Vincenzo Foppa. 2m, Madonna and Child, by School of Lippo Memmi. 3m, Virgin and Child, by Barnaba da Modena. 4m, Virgin and Child, by Simone Dei Crocifissi.

No. 935, Virgin & Child Enthroned & Surrounded by Angels, by Cimabue. No. 936, Virgin and Child with Saints (entire triptych), by Dei Crocifissi.

**1992, Nov. 2** **Litho.** *Perf. 13½x14*

| | | | | |
|---|---|---|---|---|
| **927** | A158 | 20s multicolored | .25 | .25 |
| **928** | A158 | 30s multicolored | .45 | .45 |
| **929** | A158 | 40s multicolored | .55 | .55 |
| **930** | A158 | 70s multicolored | 1.10 | 1.10 |
| **931** | A158 | 1m multicolored | 1.50 | 1.50 |
| **932** | A158 | 2m multicolored | 2.75 | 2.75 |
| **933** | A158 | 3m multicolored | 4.25 | 4.25 |
| **934** | A158 | 4m multicolored | 5.75 | 5.75 |
| | | *Nos. 927-934 (8)* | 16.60 | 16.60 |

**Souvenir Sheets**

| | | | | |
|---|---|---|---|---|
| **935** | A158 | 5m multicolored | 6.50 | 6.50 |
| **936** | A158 | 5m multicolored | 6.50 | 6.50 |

Souvenir Sheet

World Trade Center, New York City — A159

**1992, Oct. 28** **Litho.** *Perf. 14*

| | | | | |
|---|---|---|---|---|
| **937** | A159 | 5m multicolored | 10.00 | 10.00 |

Postage Stamp Mega Event '92, NYC.

Anniversaries and Events — A160

Designs: 20s, Baby harp seal. 30s, Giant panda. 40s, Graf Zeppelin, globe. 70s, Woman grinding corn. 4m, Zeppelin shot down over Cuffley, UK by Lt. Leefe Robinson flying BE 2c, WWI. No. 943, Valentina Tereshkova, first woman in space. No. 944, West African crowned cranes. No. 945, Dr. Ronald McNair.

**1993, Jan.** **Litho.** *Perf. 14*

| | | | | |
|---|---|---|---|---|
| **938** | A160 | 20s multicolored | .25 | .25 |
| **939** | A160 | 30s multicolored | .40 | .40 |
| **940** | A160 | 40s multicolored | .50 | .50 |
| **941** | A160 | 70s multicolored | .90 | .90 |
| **942** | A160 | 4m multicolored | 4.75 | 4.75 |
| **943** | A160 | 5m multicolored | 5.75 | 5.75 |
| | | *Nos. 938-943 (6)* | 12.55 | 12.55 |

**Souvenir Sheets**

| | | | | |
|---|---|---|---|---|
| **944** | A160 | 5m multicolored | 6.50 | 6.50 |
| **945** | A160 | 5m multicolored | 6.50 | 6.50 |

Earth Summit, Rio de Janeiro (Nos. 938-939, 944). Count Zeppelin, 75th death anniv. (Nos. 940, 942). Intl. Conference on Nutrition, Rome (No. 941). Intl. Space Year (Nos. 943, 945).

Louvre Museum, Bicent. A161

No. 947 — Details or entire paintings, by Nicolas Poussin: a, Orpheus and Eurydice. b-c, Rape of the Sabine Women (left, right). d-e, The Death of Sapphira (left, right). f-g, Echo and Narcissus (left, right). h, Self-portrait.

No. 948, The Moneychanger and His Wife, by Quentin Metsys.

**1993, Mar. 19** **Litho.** *Perf. 12*

| | | | | |
|---|---|---|---|---|
| **947** | A161 | 70s Sheet of 8, #a.-h. + label | 8.75 | 8.75 |

**Souvenir Sheet**

*Perf. 14½*

| | | | | |
|---|---|---|---|---|
| **948** | A161 | 5m multicolored | 7.25 | 7.25 |

No. 948 contains one 55x88mm stamp.

Flowers — A162

**1993, June** **Litho.** *Perf. 14*

| | | | | |
|---|---|---|---|---|
| **949** | A162 | 20s Healing plant | .25 | .25 |
| **950** | A162 | 30s Calla lily | .25 | .25 |
| **951** | A162 | 40s Bird of Paradise | .30 | .30 |
| **952** | A162 | 70s Belladonna | .75 | .75 |
| **953** | A162 | 1m African lily | 1.00 | 1.00 |
| **954** | A162 | 2m Veldt lily | 2.00 | 2.00 |
| **955** | A162 | 4m Watsonia | 3.75 | 3.75 |
| **956** | A162 | 5m Gazania | 4.50 | 4.50 |
| | | *Nos. 949-956 (8)* | 12.80 | 12.80 |

**Souvenir Sheets**

| | | | | |
|---|---|---|---|---|
| **957** | A162 | 7m Leadwort | 5.75 | 5.75 |
| **958** | A162 | 7m Desert rose | 5.75 | 5.75 |

Miniature Sheet

Coronation of Queen Elizabeth II, 40th Anniv. — A163

No. 959: a, 20s, Official coronation photograph. b, 40s, St. Edward's Crown, Scepter with the Crosss. c, 1m, Queen Mother. d, 5m, Queen, family.

7m, Conversation Piece at Royal Lodge, Windsor, by Sir James Gunn, 1950.

**1993, June 2** **Litho.** *Perf. 13½x14*

| | | | | |
|---|---|---|---|---|
| **959** | A163 | Sheet, 2 each, #a.-d. | 8.00 | 8.00 |

**Souvenir Sheet**

*Perf. 14*

| | | | | |
|---|---|---|---|---|
| **960** | A163 | 7m multicolored | 15.00 | 15.00 |

Butterflies A164

20s, Bi-colored pansy. 40s, Golden pansy. 70s, Yellow pansy. 1m, Pseudo ergolid. 2m, African giant swallowtail. 5m, False acraea.

No. 967, 7m, Seasonal pansy. No. 968, 7m, Ringed pansy.

**1993, June 30 Litho. *Perf. 14***

| | | | | |
|---|---|---|---|---|
| **961** | A164 20s multicolored | .25 | .25 |
| **962** | A164 40s multicolored | .35 | .35 |
| **963** | A164 70s multicolored | .55 | .55 |
| **964** | A164 1m multicolored | .90 | .90 |
| **965** | A164 2m multicolored | 1.75 | 1.75 |
| **966** | A164 5m multicolored | 3.75 | 3.75 |
| | *Nos. 961-966 (6)* | 7.55 | 7.55 |

**Souvenir Sheets**

| | | | |
|---|---|---|---|
| **967** | A164 7m multicolored | 5.50 | 5.50 |
| **968** | A164 7m multicolored | 5.50 | 5.50 |

African Trains A165

Designs: 20s, East African Railways Vulcan 2-8-2, 1929. 30s, Zimbabwe Railways Class 15A, 1952. 40s, South African Railways Class 25 4-8-4, 1953. 70s, East African Railways A58 Class Garratt. 1m, South Africa Class 9E Electric. 2m, East African Railways Class 87, 1971. 3m, East African Railways Class 92, 1971. 5m, South Africa Class 26 2-D-2, 1982.
No. 977, Algeria 231-132BT Class, 1937. No. 978, South African Railway Class 6E Bo-Bo, 1969.

**1993, Sept. 24 Litho. *Perf. 14***

| | | | |
|---|---|---|---|
| **969** | A165 20s multicolored | .25 | .25 |
| **970** | A165 30s multicolored | .40 | .40 |
| **971** | A165 40s multicolored | .45 | .45 |
| **972** | A165 70s multicolored | .90 | .90 |
| **973** | A165 1m multicolored | 1.25 | 1.25 |
| **974** | A165 2m multicolored | 2.40 | 2.40 |
| **975** | A165 3m multicolored | 3.25 | 3.25 |
| **976** | A165 5m multicolored | 5.25 | 5.25 |
| | *Nos. 969-976 (8)* | 14.15 | 14.15 |

**Souvenir Sheets**

| | | | |
|---|---|---|---|
| **977** | A165 7m multicolored | 6.75 | 6.75 |
| **978** | A165 7m multicolored | 6.75 | 6.75 |

Taipei '93 — A166

Disney characters in Taiwan: 20s, Chung Cheng Park, Keelung. 30s, Chiao-Tienkung Temple Festival. 40s, Procession. 70s, Temple Festival. 1m, Queen's Head Rock Formation, Yehliu, vert. 1.20m, Natl. Concert Hall, Taiwan, vert. 2m, C.K.S. Memorial Hall, Taiwan, vert. 2.50m, Grand Hotel, Taipei.
No. 987, 5m, Natl. Palace Museum, Taipei. No. 988, 6m, Presidential Palace Museum, Taipei, vert.

**1993 Litho. *Perf. 14x13½, 13½x14***

| | | | | |
|---|---|---|---|---|
| **979-986** | A166 | Set of 8 | 13.00 | 13.00 |

**Souvenir Sheets**

| | | | | |
|---|---|---|---|---|
| **987-988** | A166 | Set of 2 | 11.00 | 11.00 |

Domestic Cats — A167

Various cats: 20s, 30s, 70s, 5m.
No. 992A, Brown cat eating mouse, vert.

**1993, Oct. 29 Litho. *Perf. 14***

| | | | | |
|---|---|---|---|---|
| **989-992** | A167 | Set of 4 | 6.50 | 6.50 |

**Souvenir Sheet**

| | | | |
|---|---|---|---|
| **992A** | A167 5m multicolored | 5.50 | 5.50 |

Traditional Houses A168

Designs: 20s, Khoaling, Khotla. 30s, Lelapa le seotloana morao ho, 1833. 70s, Thakaneng, Baroetsana. 4m, Mohlongoafatse pele ho, 1833.
No. 996A, Lelapa litema le mekhabiso.

**1993, Sept. 24**

| | | | | |
|---|---|---|---|---|
| **993-996** | A168 | Set of 4 | 7.25 | 7.25 |

**Souvenir Sheet**

| | | | |
|---|---|---|---|
| **996A** | A168 4m multicolored | 5.50 | 5.50 |

A169

Players, country: 20s, Khomari, Lesotho. 30s, Mohale, Lesotho. 40s, Davor, Yugoslavia; Rincon, Colombia. 50s, Lekhotla, Lesotho. 70s, Khali, Lesotho. 1m, Milla, Cameroun. 1.20m, Platt, England. 2m, Rummenigge, Germany; Lerby, Denmark.
No. 1005, Stejskal & Hasek, Czechoslovakia; Baresi, Italy, horiz. No. 1006, Lindenberger, Czechoslovakia; Schillaci, Italy.

**1993 Litho. *Perf. 13½x14***

| | | | | |
|---|---|---|---|---|
| **997-1004** | A169 | Set of 8 | 9.50 | 9.50 |

**Souvenir Sheets**
***Perf. 13***

| | | | | |
|---|---|---|---|---|
| **1005-1006** | A169 6m | Set of 2 | 11.00 | 11.00 |

1994 World Cup Soccer Championships, US.

A170

New Democratic Government: 20s, King Letsie III signs oath of office under new constitution. 30s, Parliament building. 50s, Dr. Ntsu Mokhehle sworn in as prime minister. 70s, Transfer of power from Major Gen. P. Ramaema to Dr. Mokhehle.
30s, 50s, 70s are horizontal.

**1994, Apr. 2 Litho. *Perf. 14***

| | | | |
|---|---|---|---|
| **1007** | A170 20s multicolored | .25 | .25 |
| **1008** | A170 30s multicolored | .45 | .45 |
| **1009** | A170 50s multicolored | .65 | .65 |
| **1010** | A170 70s multicolored | .90 | .90 |
| | *Nos. 1007-1010 (4)* | 2.25 | 2.25 |

A171

PHILAKOREA '94 — A172

Frogs: 35s, Aquatic river. 50s, Bubbling kassina. 1m, Guttural toad. 1.50m, Common river.
No. 1015, 5m, Green frog statue. No. 1016, 5m, Black spotted frog, oriental white-eye bird, vert.

**1994, Aug. 16 Litho. *Perf. 14***

| | | | | |
|---|---|---|---|---|
| **1011-1014** | A171 | Set of 4 | 3.25 | 3.25 |

**Souvenir Sheets**

| | | | | |
|---|---|---|---|---|
| **1015-1016** | A172 | Set of 2 | 11.00 | 11.00 |

ICAO, 50th Anniv. A173

Designs: 35s, Airplane, passengers on ground. 50s, Airplane, control tower. 1m, Airplane banking, terminal, control tower. 1.50m, Airplane ascending.

**1994 Litho. *Perf. 14***

| | | | |
|---|---|---|---|
| **1017** | A173 35s multicolored | .25 | .25 |
| **1018** | A173 50s multicolored | .65 | .65 |
| **1019** | A173 1m multicolored | 1.25 | 1.25 |
| **1020** | A173 1.50m multicolored | 2.00 | 2.00 |
| | *Nos. 1017-1020 (4)* | 4.15 | 4.15 |

Medicinal Plants — A174

Designs: 35s, Tagetes minuta. 50s, Plantago lanceolata. 1m, Amaranthus spinosus. 1.50m, Taraxacum officinale. 5m, Datura stramonium.

**1995, May 22 Litho. *Perf. 14***

| | | | | |
|---|---|---|---|---|
| **1021-1024** | A174 | Set of 4 | 2.25 | 2.25 |

**Souvenir Sheet**

| | | | |
|---|---|---|---|
| **1025** | A174 5m multicolored | 2.75 | 2.75 |

Pius XII Natl. University, 50th Anniv. A175

Designs: 35s, Pius XII College, 1962. 50s, Univ. of Basutoland, Bechuanaland Protectorate & Swaziland, 1965. 70s, Univ. of Botswana, Lesotho & Swaziland, 1970. 1m, Univ. of Bostswana, Lesotho & Swaziland, 1975. 1.50m, Natl. Univ. of Lesotho, 1988. 2m, Natl. Univ. of Lesotho, procession of vice-chancellors at celebration.

**1995, July 26 Litho. *Perf. 14***

| | | | | |
|---|---|---|---|---|
| **1026-1031** | A175 | Set of 6 | 4.25 | 4.25 |

World Tourism Organization, 20th Anniv. — A176

Designs: 35s, Qiloane Pinnacle, Thaba-Bosiu, horiz. 50s, Rock Formation, Ha Mohalenyane, horiz. 1m, Botsoela Falls, Malealea. 1.50m, Backpacking, Makhaleng River Gorge, horiz.
4m, Red hot pokers.

**1995, Aug. 28 Litho. *Perf. 14***

| | | | | |
|---|---|---|---|---|
| **1032-1035** | A176 | Set of 4 | 2.75 | 2.75 |

**Souvenir Sheet**

| | | | |
|---|---|---|---|
| **1036** | A176 4m multicolored | 2.50 | 2.50 |

No. 1036 contains one 38x58mm stamp.
No. 1036 withdrawn 9/15 because "Pokers" was misspelled "Porkers."

UN, 50th Anniv. — A177

UN emblem and: 35s, Peace dove. 50s, Scales of justice. 1.50m, Handshake of reconciliation, horiz.

**1995, Sept. 26**

| | | | | |
|---|---|---|---|---|
| **1037-1039** | A177 | Set of 3 | 2.25 | 2.25 |

Christmas A178

Roses: 35s, Sutter's Gold. 50s, Michele Meilland. 1m, J. Otto Thilow. 2m, Papa Meilland.

**1995, Nov. 1 Litho. *Perf. 14***

| | | | | |
|---|---|---|---|---|
| **1040-1043** | A178 | Set of 4 | 2.75 | 2.75 |

A179

UNICEF, 50th Anniv.: 35s, Using iodized salt. 50s, Taking care of livestock, horiz. 70s, Children in classroom. horiz. 1.50m, Children learning traditional dance, singing, horiz.

**1996, July 30 Litho. *Perf. 14***

| | | | | |
|---|---|---|---|---|
| **1044-1047** | A179 | Set of 4 | 2.50 | 2.50 |

A180

1996 Summer Olympic Games, Atlanta: 1m, US Basketball team, 1936, horiz. 1.50m, Olympic Stadium, Brandenburg Gate, Berlin, horiz. 2m, Jesse Owens, 1936. 3m, Motor boating, horiz.
Past Olympic medalists: No. 1052a, Glen Morris, long jump, decathlon, 1936. b, Said Aouita, 5000-meters, 1984. c, Arnie Robinson, long jump, 1976. d, Hans Woellke, shot put, 1936. e, Renate Stecher, 100-meters, 1972. f, Evelyn Ashford, 100-meters, 1984. g, Willie Davenport, 110-meter hurdles, 1968. h, Bob Beamon, long jump, 1968. i, Heidi Rosendhal, long jump, 1972.
No. 1053, 8m, Michael Gross, swimming, 1984. No. 1054, 8m, Kornelia Ender, swimming, 1976.

**1996, Aug. 1**

| | | | | |
|---|---|---|---|---|
| **1048-1051** | A180 | Set of 4 | 4.00 | 4.00 |
| **1052** | A180 1.50m | Sheet of 9, #a.-i. | 10.50 | 10.50 |

**Souvenir Sheets**

| | | | | |
|---|---|---|---|---|
| **1053-1054** | A180 | Set of 2 | 11.50 | 11.50 |

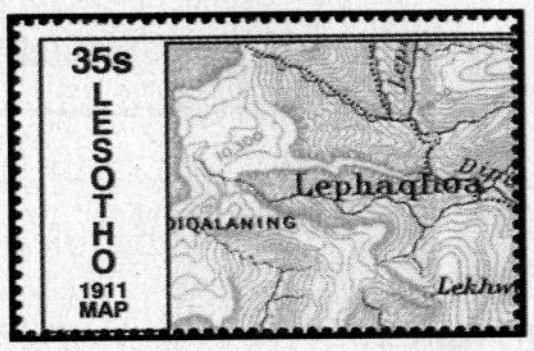

Maps of Lesotho — A181

No. 1055 — 1911 map: a, Lephaqlioa. b, Maqaleng. c, Molapo. d, Nkeu. e, No area specified. f, Rafanyane. g, No area specified (7800). h, Madibomatso River. i, Konyani. j, Semena River.

No. 1056 — 1978 map: a, No area specified. b, Lepaqoa. c, Mamoha (name). d, Ha Nkisi. e, Ha Rafanyan, Ha Thoora. f, Ha Mikia, Ha Ntseli. g, Ha Kosetabole, Ha Mpeli. h, Ha Selebeli, Ha Theko. i, Ha Rapooane, Ha Ramabotsa. j, Ha Ramani, Khohlontso (Kolberg).

No. 1057 — Locations on 1994 Map: a, Mafika-Lisiu Pass. b, Rampai's Pass, Ha Lesaoana. c, Ha Masaballa. d, Ha Nkisi, Ha Molotanyan. e, Ha Rafanyane, Kobong. f, Laitsoka Pass. g, Katse Reservoir. h, Seshote. i, Ha Rapoeea, Ha Kennan. j, Katse (i, name), Ha Mense.

**1996** **Sheets of 10, #a-j**

**1055-1057** A181 35s Set of 3 15.00 15.00

Trains A182

No. 1058, 1.50m: a, ETR 450, Italy. b, TGV, France. c, XPT, Australia. d, Blue Train, South Africa. e, IC 255, Great Britain. f, Bullet Train, Japan.

No. 1059, 1.50m: a, WP Streamlined 4-6-2, India. b, Canadian Pacific 2471, Canada. c, The Caledonian 4-2-2, Scotland. d, William Mason 4-4-0, US. e, Trans-Siberian Express, Russia. f, Swiss Federal 4-6-0, Switzerland.

No. 1060, 8m, 52 Class, Germany. No. 1061, 8m, ICE, Germany.

**1996, Sept. 1** **Litho.** ***Perf. 14***

**Sheets of 6, #a-f**

**1058-1059** A182 Set of 2 11.50 11.50

**Souvenir Sheets**

**1060-1061** A182 Set of 2 9.50 9.50

Nos. 1060-1061 each contain one 56x42mm stamp.

**No. 833 Surcharged**

**1996** **Litho.** ***Perf. 13½***

**1062** A146 20s on 30s multi *2.00 1.00*

Christmas — A183

Women from Mother's Unions: 35s, Methodist Church. 50s, Roman Catholic Church. 1m, Lesotho Evangelical Church. 1.50m, Anglican Church.

**1996, Dec. 10** **Litho.** ***Perf. 14***

**1063-1066** A183 Set of 4 2.75 2.75

Highlands Water Project A184

Designs: 35s, "Cooperation for Development." 50s, "Nature and Heritage." 1m, "An Engineering Feat." 1.50m, "LHDA 10th Anniv., 1986-1996."

**1997, Apr. 21** **Litho.** ***Perf. 14***

**1067-1070** A184 Set of 4 3.25 3.25

No. 1070 is 72x25mm.

Environmental Protection — A184a

Emblem of National Environment Secretariat and: 35s, Animals grazing on reclaimed land. 50s, Person throwing trash in can. 1m, Hands holding globe with tree. 1.20m, Trash and recycling emblem. 1.50m, Collection of rainwater.

**1997, June 30**

**1070A-1070E** A184a Set of 5 3.00 3.00

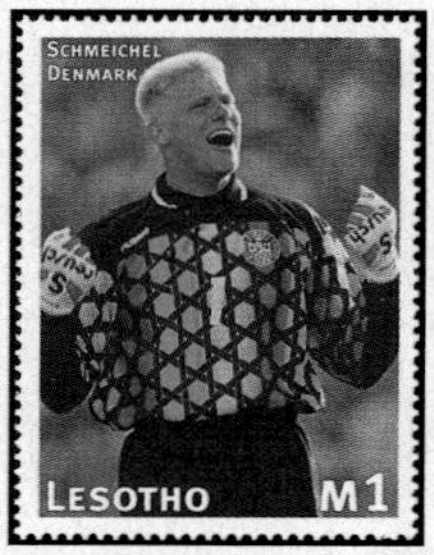


1998 World Cup Soccer Championships, France — A185

Players: 1m, Schmeichel, Denmark. 1.50m, Bergkamp, Holland. 2m, Southgate, England. 2.50m, Asprilla, Colombia. 3m, Gascoigne, England. 4m, Giggs, Wales.

No. 1077: Various action scenes of Argentina vs. Holland, 1978.

No. 1078, 8m, Littbarski, W. Germany, horiz. No. 1079, 8m, Shearer, England.

**1997, Oct. 31** ***Perf. 13½***

**1071-1076** A185 Set of 6 6.50 6.50

**1077** A185 1.50m Sheet of 6, #a.-f. 11.00 11.00

**Souvenir Sheets**

**1078-1079** A185 Set of 2 9.00 9.00

Butterflies A186

No. 1080: a, Spialia spio. b, Cyclyrius pirithous. c, Acraea satis. d, Belenois aurota. e, Spindasis natalensis. f, Torynesis orangica. g, Lepidochrysops variabilis. h, Pinacopteryx eriphea. i, Anthene butleri.

No. 1081, 8m, Bematistes aganice. No. 1082, 8m, Papilio demodocus.

**1997, Nov. 28** ***Perf. 14***

**1080** A186 1.50m Sheet of 9, #a.-i. 7.75 7.75

**Souvenir Sheets**

**1081-1082** A186 Set of 2 11.00 11.00

Morija Museum and Archives, 40th Anniv. A187

Designs: 35s, Rock paintings, child, vert. 45s, Lower jaw of hippopotamus, hippo walking in water. 50s, Traditional attire, vert. 1m, Traditional musical instruments, vert. 1.50m, Award, Man with ceremonial garb, vert. 2m Boy riding bull.

***Perf. 14½ Syncopated Type A***

**1998, Jan. 30** **Litho.**

**1083-1088** A187 Set of 6 3.25 3.25

Diana, Princess of Wales (1961-97) — A188

Designs: No. 1089, Various portaits. No. 1090, Taking flowers from child.

**1998, Mar. 16** **Litho.** ***Perf. 13½***

**1089** A188 3m Sheet of 6, #a.-f. 9.00 9.00

**Souvenir Sheet**

**1090** A188 9m multicolored 9.00 9.00

A189

A190

Wildlife — A191

No. 1091 — Cape vulture: a, Head. b, Perched on rock with head down. c, Looking left. d, Looking right.

No. 1092: a, Atitlan grebe. b, Cabot's tragopan. c, Spider monkey. d, Dibatag. e, Right whale. f, Imperial parrot. g, Cheetah. h, Brown-eared pheasant. i, Leatherback turtle. j, Imperial woodpecker. k, Andean condor. l, Barbary deer. m, Grey gentle lemur. n, Cuban parrot. o, Numbat. p, Short-tailed albatross. q, Green turtle. r, White rhinoceros. s, Diademed sifaka. t, Galapagos penguin.

No. 1093: a, Impala. b, Black bear. c, Buffalo. d, Elephant. e, Kangaroo. f, Lion. g, Panda. h, Tiger. i, Zebra.

No. 1094, 8m, Nectarinia talatala. No. 1095, 8m, Psephotus chrysopterygius. No. 1096, 8m, Percina tanasi.

No. 1097, 8m, Monkey.

**1998, Apr. 27** **Litho.** ***Perf. 14***

**1091** A189 1m Strip of 4, #a.-d. 4.50 4.50

**1092** A190 1m Sheet of 20, #a.-t. 11.00 11.00

**1093** A191 1.50m Sheet of 9, #a.-i. 7.00 7.00

**Souvenir Sheets**

**1094-1096** A190 Set of 3 12.00 12.00

**1097** A191 8m multicolored 4.00 4.00

No. 1091 was issued in sheets of 12 stamps. World Wildlife Fund (No. 1091).

Cats A192

Designs: 70s, Siamese. 1m, Chartreux. 2m, Korat. 3m, Egyptian mau. 4m, Bombay. 5m, Burmese.

No. 1104, 2m: a, Japanese bobtail. b, British white. c, Bengal. d, Abyssinian. e, Snowshoe. f, Scottish fold.

No. 1105, 2m: a, Maine coon. b, Balinese. c, Persian. d, Javanese. e, Turkish angora. f, Tiffany.

No. 1106, 8m, Singapura. No. 1107, 8m, Tonkinese.

**1998, May 18**

**1098-1103** A192 Set of 6 7.75 7.75

**Sheets of 6, #a-f**

**1104-1105** A192 Set of 2 16.00 16.00

**Souvenir Sheets**

**1106-1107** A192 Set of 2 10.00 10.00

Mushrooms — A193

Designs: 70s, Laccaria laccata. 1m, Mutinus caninus. 1.50m, Tricholoma lascivum. 2m, Clitocybe geotrapa. 3m, Amanita excelsa. 4m, Red-capped bolete.

No. 1114: a, Parrot wax cap. b, Cortinarius obtusus. c, Volvariella bombycina. d, Continarius caerylescens. e, Laccaria amethystea. f, Tricholoma aurantium. g, Amanita excelsa. h, Clavaria helvola. i, Cortinarius caerylescens. j, Russula queletii. k, Amanita phalloides. l, Lactarius delicious.

No. 1115, 8m, Amanita pantherina. No. 1116, 8m, Boletus satanus.

**1998, June 15** **Litho.** ***Perf. 14***

**1108-1113** A193 Set of 6 6.50 6.50

**1114** A193 1m Sheet of 12, #a.-l. 6.50 6.50

**Souvenir Sheets**

**1115-1116** A193 Set of 2 9.00 9.00

Japanese Film Stars A194

No. 1117: a, Takamine Hideko. b, James Shigeta. c, Miyoshi Umeki. d, May Ishimara. e, Sessue Hayakawa. f, Miiko Taka. g, Mori Masayuki. h, Hara Setsuko. i, Kyo Machiko. 10m, Toshiro Mifune.

**1998, July 14** **Litho.** ***Perf. 14***

**1117** A194 2m Sheet of 9, #a.-i. 7.50 7.50

**Souvenir Sheet**

**1118** A194 10m multicolored 4.00 4.00

Prehistoric Animals — A195

No. 1119, 2m: a, Nyctosaurus (b). b, Volcanoes, wings of nyctosaurus, eudimorphadon. c, Eudimorphodon (b). d, Apatosaurus (g). e, Peteinosaurus (d, f, i). f, Tropeognathus. g, Pteranodon ingens (d). h, Ornithodesmus (g, i). i, Wuerhosaurus.

No. 1120, 2m: a, Ceresiosaurus (b, c, d). b, Rhomaleosaurus (d, e, f). c, Anomalocaris (b, f). d, Mixosaurus (e, g, h). e, Stethacanthus. f, Dunklosteus (c, e, i). g, Tommotia. h, Sanctacaris. i, Ammonites (a, f, h).

No. 1121, 2m: a, Rhamphorhynchus (b, d). b, Brachiosaurus (c, f). c, Mamenchisaurus hochuanensis (a, d, e, f). d, Ceratosaurus nasicornis (e, g, h). e, Archaeopteryx (b). f, Leaellynasaura amicargraphica (e, h, i). g, Chasmosaurus belli (h). h, Deinonychus, Pachyrhinosaurus (g). i, Deinonychus (h).

No. 1122, 10m, Woolly rhinoceros. No. 1123, 10m, Tyrannosaurus. No. 1124, 10m, Coelophysis.

**1998, Aug. 10** **Sheets of 9, #a-i**
**1119-1121** A195 Set of 3 24.00 24.00

**Souvenir Sheets**
**1122-1124** A195 Set of 3 14.00 14.00

Intl. Year of the Ocean A196

Fish: No. 1125, 1m, Treefish. No. 1126, 1m, Tiger barb. No. 1127, 1m, Bandtail puffer. No. 1128, 1m, Cod. No. 1129, 1.50m, Filefish. No. 1130, 1.50m, Clown loach. No. 1131, 1.50m, Sicklefin killie. No. 1132, 1.50m, Christy's lyretail. No. 1133, 2m, Brook trout. No. 1134, 2m, Pacific electric ray. No. 1135, 2m, Big-head searobin. No. 1136, 2m, Emerald betta. 3m, Harlequin tuskfish. 4m, Half-moon angelfish. 5m, Spotted trunkfish. 6m, Wolf-eel. 7m, Cherubfish.

No. 1142, 2m: a, Platy variatus. b, Archerfish. c, Clown knifefish. d, Angelicus. e, Black arowana. f, Spotted scat. g, Kribensis. h, Golden pheasant.

No. 1143, 2m: a, Bluegill. b, Grayling. c, Walleye. d, Brown trout. e, Atlantic salmon. f, Northern pike. g, Large mouth bass. h, Rainbow trout.

No. 1144, 2m: a, Purple firefish. b, Halequin sweetlips. c, Clown wrasse. d, Bicolor angelfish. e, False cleanerfish. f, Mandarinfish. g, Regal tang. h, Clownfish.

No. 1145, 2m: a, Weakfish. b, Red drum. c, Blue marlin. d, Yellowfin tuna. e, Barracuda. f, Striped bass. g, White shark. h, Permit.

No. 1146, 12m, Cyprinus carpio. No. 1147, 12m, Oncorhychus. No. 1148, 12m, Pseudopleuronectes americanus. No. 1149, 12m, Heterodontus francisci.

**1998, Oct. 15** **Litho.** ***Perf. 14***
**1125-1141** A196 Set of 17 17.50 17.50

**Sheets of 8, #a-h**
**1142-1145** A196 Set of 4 26.00 26.00

**Souvenir Sheets**
**1146-1149** A196 Set of 4 19.00 19.00

Africa in Films A197

No. 1150: a, "Simba." b, "Call to Freedom." c, "Cry the Beloved Country." d, "King Solomon's Mines." e, "Flame and the Fire." f, "Cry Freedom." g, "Bopha!" h, "Zulu."
10m "Born Free," horiz.

**1998, July 14** **Litho.** ***Perf. 14***
**1150** A197 2m Sheet of 8, #a.-h. 7.50 7.50

**Souvenir Sheet**
**1151** A197 10m multicolored 4.00 4.00

Flowers — A198

Designs: 10s, Pelargonium sidoides. 15s, Aponogeton ranunculiflorus. 20s, Sebaea leiostyla. 40s, Sebaea grandis. 50s, Satyrium neglectum. 60s, Massonia jasminiflora. 70s, Ajuga ophrydis. 80s, Nemesia fruticans. 1m, Aloe broomii. 2m, Wahlenbergia androsacea. 2.50m, Phygelius capensis. 3m, Dianthus basuticus. 4.50m, Rhodohypoxis baurii. 5m, Turbina oblongata. 6m, Hibiscus microcarpus. 10m, Lobelia erinus, moraea stricta.

**1998** **Litho.** ***Perf. 14***
**1152** A198 10s multicolored .25 .25
**1153** A198 15s multicolored .25 .25
**1154** A198 20s multicolored .25 .25
**1155** A198 40s multicolored .25 .25
**1156** A198 50s multicolored .25 .25
**1157** A198 60s multicolored .25 .25
**1158** A198 70s multicolored .25 .25
**1159** A198 80s multicolored .40 .40
**1160** A198 1m multicolored .50 .50
**1161** A198 2m multicolored 1.00 1.00
**1162** A198 2.50m multicolored 1.25 1.25
**1163** A198 3m multicolored 1.50 1.50
**1164** A198 4.50m multicolored 2.25 2.25
**1165** A198 5m multicolored 2.40 2.40
**1166** A198 6m multicolored 3.00 3.00
**1167** A198 10m multicolored 4.50 4.50
*Nos. 1152-1167 (16)* 18.55 18.55

Nos. 1152-1167 are dated 1997.

Coronation of King Letsie III, 1st Anniv. — A199

No. 1168: a, Receiving crown. b, Waving. c, Facing left.

**1998, Oct. 31**
**1168** A199 1m Strip of 3, #a.-c. 2.25 2.25

Dogs A200

Designs: 70s, Akita. 1m, Canaan. 2m, Eskimo. 4.50m, Norwegian elkhound.

No. 1173, 2m: a, Cirneco dell'etna. b, Afghan hound. c, Finnish spitz. d, Dalmatian. e, Basset hound. f, Shar-pei.

No. 1174, 2m: a, Boxer. b, Catalan sheepdog. c, English toy spaniel. d, Greyhound. e, Keeshond. f, Bearded collie.

No. 1175, 8m, Rough collie. No. 1176, 8m, Borzoi.

**1999, May 18** **Litho.** ***Perf. 14***
**1169-1172** A200 Set of 4 4.00 4.00

**Sheets of 6, #a-f**
**1173-1174** A200 Set of 2 11.00 11.00

**Souvenir Sheets**
**1175-1176** A200 Set of 2 10.00 10.00

Birds A201

Designs: 70s, Belted kingfisher. 1.50m, Palm cockatoo, vert. 2m, Red-tailed hawk. 3m, Tufted puffin. 4m, Reddish egret. 5m, Hoatzin, vert.

No. 1183, 2m: a, Evening grosbeak. b, Lesser blue-winged pitta. c, Altamira oriole. d, Rose-breasted grosbeak. e, Yellow warbler. f, Akiapolaau. g, American goldfinch. h, Northern flicker. i, Western tanager.

No. 1184, 2m, vert: a, Blue jay. b, Northern cardinal. c, Yellow-headed blackbird. d, Red crossbill. e, Cedar waxwing. f, Vermilion flycatcher. g, Pileated woodpecker. h, Western meadowlark. i, Kingfisher.

No. 1185, 8m, Great egret. No. 1186, 8m, Zosterops erythropleura.

**1999, June 28** **Litho.** ***Perf. 14***
**1177-1182** A201 Set of 6 8.00 8.00

**Sheets of 9, #a-i**
**1183-1184** A201 Set of 2 19.00 19.00

**Souvenir Sheets**
**1185-1186** A201 Set of 2 10.00 10.00

No. 1183c is incorrectly inscribed "Atlamira."

Orchids — A202

Designs: 1.50m, Cattleya dowiana. 3m, Diurus behri. 4m, Ancistrochilus rothchildianus. 5m, Aerangis curnowiana. 7m, Arachnis flos-aeris. 8m, Aspasia principissa.

No. 1193, 2m: a, Dendrobium bellaudum. b, Dendrobium trigonopus. c, Dimerandra emarginata. d, Dressleria eburnea. e, Dracula tubeana. f, Disa kirstenbosch. g, Encyclia alata. h, Epidendrum pseudepidendrum. i, Eriopsis biloba.

No. 1194, 2m: a, Apasia epidendroides. b, Barkaria lindleyana. c, Bifrenaria terragona. d, Bulbophyllum graveolens. e, Brassavola flagellaris. f, Bollea lawrenceana. g, Caladenia carnea. h, Catasetum macrocarpum. i, Cattleya aurantiaca.

No. 1195, 2m: a, Cochleanthes discolor. b, Cischweinfia dasyandra. c, Ceratostylis retisquama. d, Comparettia speciosa. e, Cryptostylis subulata. f, Cycnoches ventricsum. g, Dactylorhiza maculata. h, Cypripedium calceolus. i, Cymbidium finlaysonianum.

No. 1196, 10m, Paphiopedilum tonsum. No. 1197, 10m, Laelia rubescens. No. 1198, 10m, Ansellium africana. No. 1199, 10m, Ophrys apifera.

**1999, July 30** **Litho.** ***Perf. 14***
**1187-1192** A202 Set of 6 13.00 13.00

**Sheets of 9, #a-i**
**1193-1195** A202 Set of 3 22.50 22.50

**Souvenir Sheets**
**1196-1199** A202 Set of 4 15.00 15.00

Chinese Art — A203

No. 1200 — Paintings by Pan Tianshou (1897-1971): a, Water Lily at Night. b, Hen and Chicks. c, Plum Blossom and Orchid. d, Plum Blossom and Banana Tree. e, Crane and Pine. f, Swallows. g, Eagle on the Pine (black eagle). h, Palm Tree. i, Eagle on the Pine (gray eagle). j, Orchids.

No. 1201: a, Sponge Gourd. b, Dragonfly.

**1999, Aug. 16** ***Perf. 13x13¼***
**1200** A203 1.50m Sheet of 10, #a.-j. 8.50 8.50

**Souvenir Sheet**
**1201** A203 6m Sheet of 2, #a.-b. 6.50 6.50

China 1999 World Philatelic Exhibition.
No. 1201 contains two 51x40mm stamps.

Souvenir Sheet

UN Rights of the Child Convention, 10th Anniv. — A204

No. 1202: a, Black boy. b, Asian girl. c, Caucasian boy.

**1999, Aug. 16** ***Perf. 14***
**1202** A204 2m Sheet of 3, #a.-c. 3.00 3.00

Paintings by Hokusai (1760-1849) — A205

No. 1203, 3m: a, Nakamaro Watching the Moon from a Hill. b, Peonies and Butterfly. c, The Blind (bald man, both eyes open). d, The Blind (bald man, one eye shut). e, People Crossing an Arched Bridge (two at crest). f, People Crossing an Arched Bridge (river).

No. 1204, 3m: a, A View of Sumida River in Snow. b, Two Carp. c, The Blind (man with hair, both eyes shut). d, The Blind (man with hair, one eye open). e, Fishing by Torchlight. f, Whaling off the Goto Islands.

No. 1205, 10m, The Moon Above Yodo River and Osaka Castle, vert. No. 1206, 10m, Bellflower and Dragonfly, vert.

**1999, Aug. 16** ***Perf. 13¾***

**Sheet of 6, #a-f**
**1203-1204** A205 Set of 2 14.00 14.00

**Souvenir Sheets**
**1205-1206** A205 Set of 2 8.00 8.00

Queen Mother (b. 1900) — A206

No. 1207: a, Wearing hat, 1938. b, With King George VI, 1948. c, Wearing tiara, 1963. d, Wearing hat, 1989.
15m, Waving at Clarence House.

**1999, Aug. 16** ***Perf. 14***
**1207** A206 5m Sheet of 4, #a.-d., + label 7.50 7.50

**Souvenir Sheet**
***Perf. 13¾***
**1208** A206 15m multicolored 6.25 6.25

No. 1208 contains one 38x51mm stamp.

Johann Wolfgang von Goethe (1749-1832) — A207

No. 1209: a, Mephistopheles appears as a dog in Faust's study. b, Portraits of Goethe and Friedrich von Schiller. c, Mephistopheles disguised as dog scorching the earth.
12m, Mephistopheles.

**1999, Aug. 16** ***Perf. 14***

**1209** A207 6m Sheet of 3, #a.-c. 6.25 6.25

**Souvenir Sheet**

**1210** A207 12m multicolored 4.50 4.50

IBRA '99, Nuremberg, Germany — A208

Designs: 7m, Austerity 2-10-10 locomotive, building in Frankfurt am Main. 8m, Adler locomotive, Brandenburg Gate.

**1999, Aug. 16** ***Perf. 14x14½***

**1211** A208 7m multicolored 2.75 2.75
**1212** A208 8m multicolored 3.25 3.25

Ships A209

No. 1213, 4m: a, James Watt. b, Savannah. c, Amistad. d, Brick. e, Great Briain. f, Sirius.
No. 1214, 4m: a, France. b, Queen Elizabeth II. c, United States. d, Queen Elizabeth I. e, Michelangelo. f, Mauretania.
No. 1215, 4m: a, New Jersey. b, Aquila. c, De Zeven Provincien. d, Formidable. e, Vittorio Veneto. f, Hampshire.
No. 1216, 4m: a, Shearwater. b, British submarine. c, Hovercraft SRN 130. d, Italian submarine. e, Sr. N/3. f, Soucoupe Plongeante.
No. 1217, 15m, E. W. Morrison. No. 1218, 15m, Titanic. No. 1219, 15m, German U-boat. No. 1220, 15m, Enterprise.

**1999, Dec. 31** **Litho.** ***Perf. 14***

**Sheets of 6, #a.-f.**

**1213-1216** A209 Set of 4 30.00 30.00

**Souvenir Sheets**

**1217-1220** A209 Set of 4 21.00 21.00

Names of ships are only found on sheet margins.

Millennium A210

No. 1221 — Highlights of the 12th century: a, Chinese make first rocket. b, Burmese temple guardian. c, Troubador. d, Abbé Suger. e, Pope Adrian IV. f, King Henry II of England. g, Holy Roman Emperor Barbarossa. h, Yoritomo establishes shogunate in Japan. i, Crusader monument. j, Ibn Rushd translates Aristotle. k, Archbishop Thomas Becket. l, Leaning Tower of Pisa. m, Pivot windmill. n, Saladin. o, Richard the Lion-Hearted. p, Easter Island statues (60x40mm) q, Third Crusade begins.

**1999, Dec. 31** ***Perf. 12¾x12½***

**1221** A210 1.50m Sheet of 17, #a.-q. 11.00 11.00

Wedding of King Letsie III to Karabo Anne Motsoeneng A211

No. 1222: a, King, bride in Western attire. b, Bride. c, King. d, King, bride in native attire.

**2000, Feb. 18** **Litho.** ***Perf. 14***

**1222** A211 1m Sheet of 4, #a.-d., + label 3.75 3.75

Prince William, 18th Birthday — A212

No. 1223: a, Wearing bow tie. b, Wearing scarf. c, Wearing striped shirt. d, Wearing sweater, holding car door.
15m, Wearing sweater, diff.

**2000, June 21** **Litho.** ***Perf. 14***

**1223** A212 4m Sheet of 4, #a-d 6.50 6.50

**Souvenir Sheet**

***Perf. 13¾***

**1224** A212 15m multi 6.50 6.50

No. 1223 contains four 28x42mm stamps.

First Zeppelin Flight, Cent. — A213

No. 1225 — Ferdinand von Zeppelin and: a, LZ- 127. b, LZ-130. c, LZ-10.
15m, LZ-130, diff.

**2000, July 6** ***Perf. 14***

**1225** A213 8m Sheet of 3, #a-c 8.50 8.50

**Souvenir Sheet**

**1226** A213 15m multi 6.50 6.50

No. 1225 contains three 42x28mm stamps.

Berlin Film Festival, 50th Anniv. — A214

No. 1227: a, Gena Rowlands. b, Vlastimil Brodsky. c, Carlos Saura. d, La Collectioneuse. e, Le Depart. f, Le Diable Probablement.
15m, Stammheim.

**2000, July 6**

**1227** A214 6m Sheet of 6, #a-f 12.00 12.00

**Souvenir Sheet**

**1228** A214 15m multi 6.50 6.50

Souvenir Sheets

2000 Summer Olympics, Sydney — A215

No. 1229: a, Nedo Nadi. b, Swimming. c, Aztec Stadium, Mexico City and Mexican flag. d, Ancient Greek boxers.

**2000, July 6**

**1229** A215 6m Sheet of 4, #a-d 8.50 8.50

Public Railways, 175th Anniv. — A216

No. 1230: a, George Stephenson. b, Stephenson's patent locomotive engine. c, Stephenson's Britannia Tubular Bridge.

**2000, July 6**

**1230** A216 8m Sheet of 3, #a-c 8.50 8.50

Johann Sebastian Bach (1685-1750) — A217

**2000, July 6**

**1231** A217 15m multi 6.50 6.50

Flowers — A218

Designs: 4m, Moore's crinum. 5m, Flame lily. 6m, Cape clivia. 8m, True sugarbush.
No. 1236, 3m: a, Spotted leaved arum. b, Christmas bells. c, Lady Monson. d, Wild pomegranate. e, Blushing bride. f, Bot River protea.
No. 1237, 3m: a, Starry gardenia. b, Pink hibiscus. c, Dwarf poker. d, Coast kaffirboom. e, Rose cockade. f, Pride of Table Mountain.
No. 1238, 3m: a, Drooping agpanthus. b, Yellow marsh afrikander. c, Weak stemmed painted lady. d, Impala lily. e, Beatrice watsonia. f, Pink arum.
No. 1239, 15m, Green arum. No. 1240, 15m, Red hairy erica, horiz.

**2000, July 12**

**1232-1235** A218 Set of 4 9.00 9.00

**Sheets of 6, #a-f**

**1236-1238** A218 Set of 3 21.00 21.00

**Souvenir Sheets**

**1239-1240** A218 Set of 2 15.00 15.00

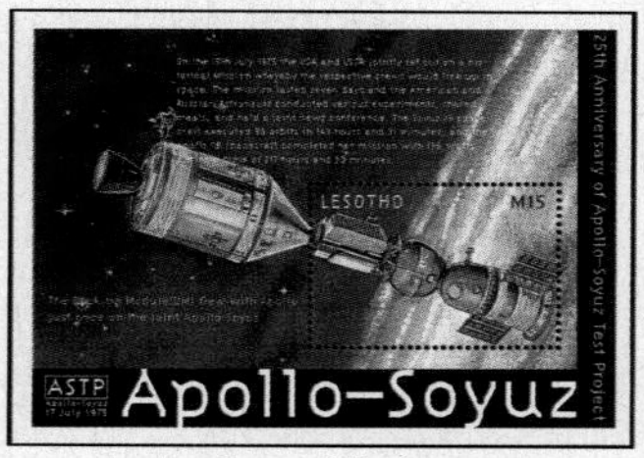


Apollo-Soyuz Mission, 25th Anniv. — A219

No. 1241: a, Apollo 18 and Soyuz 19 docked. b, Apollo 18. c, Soyuz 19.

**2000, July 6** **Litho.** ***Perf. 14***

**1241** A219 8m Sheet of 3, #a-c 9.00 9.00

**Souvenir Sheet**

**1242** A219 15m shown 6.50 6.50

Souvenir Sheet

Albert Einstein (1879-1955) — A220

**2000, July 6** *Perf. 14¼*
**1243** A220 15m multi 6.50 6.50

Endangered Wildlife — A221

No. 1244, 4m, horiz.: a, Alethe. b, Temminck's pangolin. c, Cheetah. d, African elephant. e, Chimpanzee. f, Northern white rhinoceros.

No. 1245, 4m, horiz.: a, African black rhinoceros. b, Leopard. c, Roseate tern. d, Mountain gorilla. e, Mountain zebra. f, Zanzibar red colobus monkey.

No. 1246, horiz: a, Wildebeest. b, Tree hyrax. c, Red lechwe. d, Eland.

No. 1247, 15m, Dugong. No. 1248, 15m, West African manatee.

**2000, Aug. 10** **Litho.** *Perf. 14*

**Sheets of 6, #a-f**

**1244-1245** A221 Set of 2 18.00 18.00
**1246** A221 5m Sheet of 4, #a-d 7.75 7.75

**Souvenir Sheets**

**1247-1248** A221 Set of 2 16.00 16.00

The Stamp Show 2000, London.

Automobiles — A222

No. 1249, 3m: a, 1960 Cadillac El Dorado Seville. b, 1955-75 Citroen DS. c, 1961 Ford Zephyr Zodiac Mk II. d, 1945-55 MG TF. e, 1949-65 Porsche 356. f, 1955 Ford Thunderbird.

No. 1250, 3m: a, 1948-52 Cisitalia 202 Coupe. b, 1990s Dodge Viper. c, 1968-69, TVR Vixen SI. d, 1957-70 Lotus 7. e, 1964-68 Ferrari 275 GTB/4. f, 1951 Pegasus Touring Spider.

No. 1251, 4m: a, 1913 Fiat Type O. b, 1914 Stutz Bearcat. c, 1924 French Levat. d, 1888 Benz Motorwagen. e, 1925 Isota Fraschini Type 8A. f, 1887 Markus Motor Carriage.

No. 1252, 4m: a, 1951 Morris Minor. b, 1935 Hispano-Suiza Type 68. c, 1949 MG TC. d, 1955 Morgan 4/4. e, 1950 Jaguar XK120. f, 1946-49 Triumph 1800/2000 Roadster.

No. 1253, 15m, 1896 Bersey Electric Car. No. 1254, 15m, 1948-71 Morris Minor 1000. No. 1255, 15m, 1953-63 AC Ace. No. 1256, 15m, Ferrari F40, vert.

Illustration reduced.

**2000, Sept. 1** **Sheets of 6, #a-f**
**1249-1252** A222 Set of 4 30.00 30.00

**Souvenir Sheets**

**1253-1256** A222 Set of 4 25.00 25.00

Fight Against AIDS A223

Designs: 70s, "Fight AIDS, not people living with it." 1m, "Speed kills, so does AIDS. Go Slow!" 1.50m, "People with AIDS need friends, not rejection," vert. 2.10m, "Even when you're off duty, protect the nation."

**2001, Jan. 22** **Litho.** *Perf. 14*
**1257-1260** A223 Set of 4 5.00 5.00

Butterflies A224

Designs: 70s, Great orange tip. 1m, Red-banded pereute. 1.50m, Sword grass brown. No. 1264, 2m, Striped blue crow. No. 1265, 3m, Alfalfa. 4m, Doris.

No. 1267, 2m: a, African migrant. b, Large oak blue. c, Wanderer. d, Tiger swallowtail. e, Union jack. f, Saturn. g, Broad-bordered grass yellow. h, Hewitson's uraneis.

No. 1268, 2m: a, Orange-banded sulfur. b, Large wood nymph. c, Postman. d, Palmfly. e, Gulf fritillary. f, Cairns birdwing. g, Common morpho. h, Common dotted border.

No. 1269, 3m: a, Bertoni's antwren (bird). b, Clorinde. c, Iolas blue. d, Mocker swallowtail. e, Common Indian crow. f, Grecian shoemaker. g, Small flambeau. h, Orchid swallowtail.

No. 1270, 15m, Crimson tip. No. 1271, 15m, Forest queen.

**2001, Mar. 1** **Litho.** *Perf. 13¼x13¾*
**1261-1266** A224 Set of 6 7.00 7.00

**Sheets of 8, #a-h**

**1267-1269** A224 Set of 3 24.00 24.00

**Souvenir Sheets**

**1270-1271** A224 Set of 2 22.00 22.00

Phila Nippon '01, Japan A225

Designs: 1.50m, Man in carriage from The Battle of Lepanto and the Map of the World, by unknown artist. 2m, Battle scene from The Battle of Lepanto and the Map of the World. 3m, Crane from Birds and Flowers of the Four Seasons, by Eitoku Kano. 4m, The Four Elegant Pastimes. 7m, Maple Viewing at Mount Takao, by unknown artist. 8m, The Four Accomplishments, by Yusho Kaiho.

No. 1278, 5m: a, Portrait of a Lady, by unknown artist. b, Portrait of Tadakatsu Honda, by unknown artist. c, Portrait of the Wife of Tokujo Goto, by unknown aritst. d, Portrait of Emperor Go-yosei, by Takanobu Kano. e, Portrait of Tenzuiin, Hideyoshi's Mother, by Sochin Hoshuku.

No. 1279, 6m:: a, Portrait of Yusai Hosokawa, by Suden Ishin. b, Portrait of Sen No Rikyu, attributed to Tohaku Hasegawa. c, Portrait of Oichi No Kata, by unknown artist. d, Portrait of Ittetsu Inaba, attributed to Hasegawa. e, Portrait of Nobunaga Oda, by Sochin Kokei.

No. 1280, 15m, Portrait of Ieyasu Tokugawa, by unknown artist. No. 1281, 15m, Portrait of Hideyoshi Toyotomi, by unknown artist.

*Perf. 13¾, 14 (#1278-1279)*

**2001, May 31** **Litho.**
**1272-1277** A225 Set of 6 6.00 6.00

**Sheets of 5, #a-e**

**1278-1279** A225 Set of 2 30.00 30.00

**Souvenir Sheets**

**1280-1281** A225 Set of 2 14.50 14.50

Size of stamps on Nos. 1278-1279: 85x28mm.

Nos. 1274-1275 are incorrectly inscribed. No. 1274 actually depicts "Landscape with Flowers and Birds." No. 1275 shows a detail from"The Four Elegant Pastimes," by Eitoku Kano.

Mushrooms A226

Designs: No. 1282, 5m, Bell-shaped panaeolus. No. 1283, 5m, Golden false pholiota. No. 1284, 5m, Shiny cap. No. 1285, 5m, Sooty brown waxy cap.

No. 1286, 3m: a, Violet cortinarius. b, Angel's wings. c, Collybia velutibes. d, Lentinellus. e, Anthurus aseroiformis. f, Caesar's mushroom.

No. 1287, 4m: a, Pungent cortinarius. b, Peziza sarcosphaera. c, Emetic russula. d, Questionable stropharia. e, Apricot jelly mushroom. f, Anise-scented clitocybe.

No. 1288, 15m, Cone-shaped waxy cap, horiz. No. 1289, 15m, Boletus, horiz.

**2001, June 29** *Perf. 14*
**1282-1285** A226 Set of 4 9.00 9.00

**Sheets of 6, #a-f**

**1286-1287** A226 Set of 2 19.00 19.00

**Souvenir Sheets**

**1288-1289** A226 Set of 2 14.00 14.00

Belgica 2001 Intl. Stamp Exhibition, Brussels (Nos. 1286-1289).

UN High Commissioner for Refugees, 50th Anniv. — A227

Designs: 70s, Silhouette of woman and child. 1m, Child and animal. 1.50m, Woman, vert. 2.10m, Information technology, vert.

**2001, Aug. 20** *Perf. 14*
**1290-1293** A227 Set of 4 4.75 4.75

Birds of Prey — A228

Designs: 70s, Black kite. 1m, Martial eagle. 1.50m, Bateleur. 2.10m, African goshawk. 2.50m, Bearded vulture. 3m, Jackal buzzard.

**2001, Oct. 1** **Litho.** *Perf. 14*
**1294-1299** A228 Set of 6 6.00 6.00

Southern African Wildlife A229

Designs: 1m, Grass owl. 2.10m, Klipspringer. 3m, Saddlebacked jackal. 5m, Black wildebeest.

No. 1304, 4m: a, Damara zebra. b, Bontebok. c, Eland. d, Lion. e, Saddlebacked jackal, diff. f, Yellow-billed kite.

No. 1305, 4m: a, Aardvark. b, Rock kestrel. c, Black-footed cat. d, Springhare. e, Aardwolf. f, Rock hyrax.

No. 1306, 15m, black-shouldered kite. No. 1307, 15m, Caracal, vert.

**2001, Oct. 15** **Litho.** *Perf. 14*
**1300-1303** A229 Set of 4 6.00 6.00

**Sheets of 6, #a-f**

**1304-1305** A229 Set of 2 21.00 21.00

**Souvenir Sheets**

**1306-1307** A229 Set of 2 15.00 15.00

Reign of Queen Elizabeth II, 50th Anniv. — A230

No. 1308: a, Queen seated. b, Queen with Prince Philip and British flag. c, Queen with man. c, Prince Philip.

20m, Queen wearing black suit.

**2002, Feb. 6** **Litho.** *Perf. 14¼*
**1308** A230 8m Sheet of 4, #a-d 13.00 13.00

**Souvenir Sheet**

**1309** A230 20m multi 10.00 10.00

United We Stand — A231

**2002, Aug. 13** *Perf. 14*
**1310** A231 7m multi 4.00 4.00

Printed in sheets of 4.

SOS Children's Village, Lithabaneng — A232

**2002, Aug. 13**
**1311** A232 10m multi 4.50 4.50

Rotary International in Lesotho, 25th Anniv. — A233

Designs: 8m, Horner Wood. 10m, Paul Harris.
No. 1314, 25m, Stylized globe and clasped hands. No. 1315, 25m, Golden Gate Bridge, horiz.

**2002, Aug. 13**

1312-1313 A233 Set of 2 7.00 7.00

**Souvenir Sheets**

1314-1315 A233 Set of 2 18.00 18.00

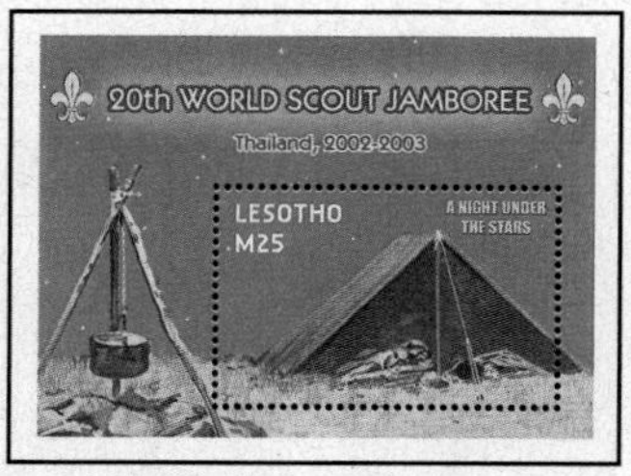


20th World Scout Jamboree, Thailand — A234

No. 1316: a, Sheet bend knots. b, Pup and forester tents. c, Canoeing. d, Water rescue.
25m, A night under the stars.

**2002, Aug. 13**

1316 A234 9m Sheet of 4, #a-d 11.50 11.50

**Souvenir Sheet**

1317 A234 25m multi 11.00 11.00

Intl. Year of Mountains — A235

No. 1318, horiz.: a, Mt. Machache. b, Mt. Thabana Li-Mèle. c, Mt. Qiloane. d, Mt. Thaba Bosiu.
25m, Mt. Rainier, US.

**2002, Aug. 13**

1318 A235 8m Sheet of 4, #a-d 11.50 11.50

**Souvenir Sheet**

1319 A235 25m multi 11.50 11.50

Intl. Year of Ecotourism — A236

No. 1320, horiz.: a, Plant. b, Flowers. c, Man and horses. d, Lion. e, Frog. f, House.
20m, Bird.

**2002, Aug. 13**

1320 A236 6m Sheet of 6, #a-f 13.00 13.00

**Souvenir Sheet**

1321 A236 20m multi 8.50 8.50

Flowers, Insects and Spiders — A237

No. 1322, 6m — Flowers: a, Angel's fishing rod. b, Marigold. c, Joan's blood. d, Mule pink. e, Tiger lily. f, Comtesse de Bouchaud.
No. 1323, 6m — Orchids: a, Phragmipedium besseae. b, Cypripedium calceolus. c, Cattleya Louise Georgiana. d, Brassocattleya binosa. e, Laelia gouldiana. f, Paphiopedilum maudiae.
No. 1324, 6m, horiz. — Insects: a, Leaf grasshopper. b, Golden-ringed dragonfly. c, Weevil-hunting wasp. d, European grasshopper. e, Thread-waisted wasp. f, Mantid.
No. 1325, 20m, Bleeding heart. No. 1326, 20m, Brassavola tuberculata. No. 1327, 20m, Orb web spider.

**2002, Aug. 30** ***Perf. 14***

**Sheets of 6, #a-f**

1322-1324 A237 Set of 3 35.00 35.00

**Souvenir Sheets**

1325-1327 A237 Set of 3 25.00 25.00

Coronation of Queen Elizabeth II, 50th Anniv. (in 2003) — A238

No. 1328: a, Wearing blue hat. b, Wearing white hat. c, Wearing black hat.
15m, Wearing red hat.

**2004, May 17** **Litho.** ***Perf. 14***

1328 A238 8m Sheet of 3, #a-c 7.00 7.00

**Souvenir Sheet**

1329 A238 15m multi 4.50 4.50

Prince William, 21st Birthday (in 2003) — A239

No. 1330: a, Wearing sunglasses. b, Wearing suit and tie c, Wearing sports shirt.
15m, As young boy.

**2004, May 17**

1330 A239 8m Sheet of 3, #a-c 8.00 8.00

**Souvenir Sheet**

1331 A239 15m multi 4.75 4.75

Intl. Year of Fresh Water (in 2003) — A240

No. 1332: a, Top of Qiloane Falls (gray water at top). b, Middle portion of Qiloane Falls (narrow at top). c, Bottom portion of Qiloane Falls.
15m, Orange River.

**2004, May 17** ***Perf. 14¼***

1332 A240 8m Sheet of 3, #a-c 12.00 12.00

**Souvenir Sheet**

1333 A240 15m multi 7.50 7.50

Powered Flight, Cent. (in 2003) — A241

No. 1334: a, Louis Blériot's Canard at Bagatelle, 1906. b, Blériot's Double-winged Libellule, 1907. c, Cross-country flight of Blériot VIII, Toury to Artenay, 1908. d, Blériot XII test flight, 1909.
15m, Blériot XI.

**2004, May 17**

1334 A241 6m Sheet of 4, #a-d 9.00 9.00

**Souvenir Sheet**

1335 A241 15m multi 6.75 6.75

Worldwide Fund for Nature (WWF) — A242

No. 1336 — Southern bald ibis: a, On nest, country name in white at LR. b, Flying to right, black denomination. c, Standing on rock, black denomination. d, Facing left.
No. 1337 — Southern bald ibis: a, Standing on rock, red denomination. b, Flying to left, red denomination. c, On nest, country name in black at UR.

**2004, May 17** ***Perf. 14***

1336 Horiz. strip of 4 4.00 4.00
*a.-d.* A242 3m Any single .80 .80
1337 Horiz. strip of 4, #1336d, 1337a-1337c 4.00 4.00
*a.-c.* A242 3m Any single .80 .80

No. 1336 printed in sheets of 4 strips. No. 1337 printed in sheets of 2 strips.

Mammals A243

Designs: 1m, Cape porcupine. 1.50m, Brown rat. 2.10m, Springhare, vert. No. 1341, 5m, South African galago, vert.
No. 1342, 5m: a, Striped grass mouse. b, Greater galago. c, Ground pangolin. d, Banded mongoose.
15m, Egyptian rousette, vert.

**2004, May 17**

1338-1341 A243 Set of 4 7.00 7.00
1342 A243 5m Sheet of 4, #a-d 9.50 9.50

**Souvenir Sheet**

1343 A243 15m multi 8.00 8.00

Birds — A244

Designs: 1.50m, Secretary bird. 2.10m, Gray-crowned crane. 3m, Pied avocet. 5m, Common kestrel.
No. 1348: a, European roller. b, Common cuckoo. c, Great spotted cuckoo. d, Pel's fishing owl.
15m, Kori bustard.

**2004, May 17**

1344-1347 A244 Set of 4 8.00 8.00
1348 A244 6m Sheet of 4, #a-d 12.00 12.00

**Souvenir Sheet**

1349 A244 15m multi 9.50 9.50

Butterflies A245

Designs: 1.50m, Acraea rabbaiae. 2.10m, Alaena margaritacea. 4m, Bematistes aganice. No. 1353, 6m, Acraea quirina.
No. 1354, 6m: a, Bematistes excisa male. b, Bematistes excisa female. c, Bematistes epiprotea. d, Bematistes poggei.
15m, Acraea satis.

**2004, May 17**

1350-1353 A245 Set of 4 8.00 8.00

**1354** A245 6m Sheet of 4, #a-d 11.00 11.00

**Souvenir Sheet**

**1355** A245 15m multi 7.50 7.50

Flowers — A246

Designs: 1.50m, Sparaxis grandiflora. 2.10m, Agapanthus africanus. 3m, Protea linearis. No. 1359, 5m, Nerine cultivars.
No. 1360, 5m: a, Kniphofia uvaria. b, Amaryllis belladonna. c, Cazania splendens. d, Erica coronata.
15m, Saintpaulia cultivars.

**2004, May 17**

**1356-1359** A246 Set of 4 6.75 6.75
**1360** A246 5m Sheet of 4, #a-d 9.00 9.00

**Souvenir Sheet**

**1361** A246 15m multi 6.00 6.00

Houses A247

Designs: 70s, Mokhoro. 1m, Heisi. 1.50m, Lesotho. 2.10m, Mohlongoa-Fat'se.

**2005, Feb. 21 Litho. *Perf. 14***

**1362-1365** A247 Set of 4 4.00 4.00

Girl Guides A248

Girl Guides: 70s, Dancing. 1m, Marching in parade. 1.50m, Collecting cans, vert. 2.10m, Standing near building.
10m, Leader holding microphone, vert.

**2005, May 20 Litho. *Perf. 14***

**1366-1369** A248 Set of 4 4.75 4.75

**Souvenir Sheet**

**1370** A248 10m multi 6.25 6.25

Pope John Paul II (1920-2005) A249

**2005, Aug. 22 *Perf. 12¾***

**1371** A249 10m multi 6.25 6.25

Printed in sheets of 4.

**Souvenir Sheet**

Rotary International, Cent. — A250

No. 1372: a, Alleviating poverty. b, Advancement of literacy. c, Helping at-risk children.

**2005, Aug. 22**

**1372** A250 8m Sheet of 3, #a-c 7.75 7.75

World Cup Soccer Championships, 75th Anniv. — A251

No. 1373, horiz. — Players from final match from: a, 1930. b, 1938. c, 1990.
15m, Bodo Illgner, 1990 goalie for Germany.

**2005, Aug. 22 *Perf. 12***

**1373** A251 8m Sheet of 3, #a-c 9.50 9.50

**Souvenir Sheet**

**1374** A251 15m multi 6.50 6.50

Hans Christian Andersen (1805-75), Author — A252

No. 1375: a, Statue of Andersen, Copenhagen. b, Childhood home of Andersen, Odense, Denmark. c, Scene from "The Steadfast Tin Soldier".
15m, Little Mermaid statue, Copenhagen.

**2005, Aug. 22 *Perf. 12¾***

**1375** A252 8m Sheet of 3, #a-c 9.75 9.75

**Souvenir Sheet**

**1376** A252 15m multi 6.50 6.50

Jules Verne (1828-1905), Writer — A253

No. 1377, horiz.: a, Journey to the Center of the Earth. b, Verne, without hat. c, 20,000 Leagues Under the Sea.
15m, Verne wearing hat.

**2005, Aug. 22**

**1377** A253 8m Sheet of 3, #a-c 10.00 10.00

**Souvenir Sheet**

**1378** A253 15m multi 6.50 6.50

Albert Einstein (1879-1955), Physicist — A254

No. 1379, horiz. — Einstein and: a, Country name in black. b, Nikola Tesla, Charles Steinmetz. c, Country name in red violet.
15m, Time Magazine "Person of the Century" cover.

**2005, Aug. 22**

**1379** A254 8m Sheet of 3, #a-c 10.00 10.00

**Souvenir Sheet**

**1380** A254 15m multi 6.50 6.50

Battle of Trafalgar, Bicent. — A255

No. 1381: a, HMS Victory. b, Admiral Horatio Nelson facing left. c, Nelson wounded in battle. d, Ships in battle.
25m, Nelson facing right.

**2005, Aug. 22 *Perf. 12¾***

**1381** A255 8m Sheet of 4, #a-d 19.00 19.00

**Souvenir Sheet**

***Perf. 12***

**1382** A255 25m multi 19.00 19.00

No. 1381 contains four 42x28mm stamps.

End of World War II, 60th Anniv. — A256

No. 1383, 4m — V-E Day: a, U.S. troops land on Omaha Beach, 1944. b, Gen. George C. Marshall. c, German Field Marshal Wilhelm Keitel signing surrender. d, Generals Dwight D. Eisenhower and George S. Patton. e, Soldiers sifting through war damage.
No. 1384, 4m — V-J Day: a, USS Arizona. b, Bunker, Chula Beach, Tinian Island. c, Bockscar flight crew. d, Newspaper announcing Japanese surrender. e, Historic marker commemorating loading of second atomic bomb on Tinian Island.

**2005, Aug. 22 *Perf. 12¾***

**Sheets of 5, #a-e**

**1383-1384** A256 Set of 2 13.00 13.00

A257

People and Livestock — A258

Designs: 70 l, Boy riding calf. 1m, Man feeding cattle. 1.50m, Cattle tenders playing game. 2.10m, Shepherd carrying lamb.
10m, Dancers.

**2006, Mar. 13 Litho. *Perf. 14***

**1385-1388** A257 Set of 4 4.00 4.00

**Souvenir Sheet**

**1389** A258 10m multi 6.50 6.50

A259

Women Balancing Items on Heads — A260

Women carrying: 70 l, Sticks. 1m, Cooking pot. 1.50m, Water jar. 2.10m, Bowl of fruit.
10m, Bowl of grain.

**2006, June 19**

**1390-1393** A259 Set of 4 4.00 4.00

**Souvenir Sheet**

**1394** A260 10m multi 5.75 5.75

A261

Handicrafts — A262

Designs: 70 l, Baskets. 1m, Artist and drawing, vert. 1.50m, Painted pottery. 2.10m, Figurines of stork and fish, decorated bull's horn.

10m, Boy, native costume.

**2006, Oct. 9 Litho. *Perf. 14¼***
**1395-1398** A261 Set of 4 4.00 4.00

**Souvenir Sheet**

**1399** A262 10m multi 6.50 6.50

Birds — A263

Designs: 1m, Crested caracara. 1.50m, Wood storks. 2.10m, Tawny-shouldered blackbird. No. 1403, 15m, Jabiru.

No. 1404: a, Great blue heron. b, Anna's hummingbird. c, Gray silky flycatcher. d, Limpkin.

No. 1405, 15m, Western reef heron. No. 1406, 15m, Monk parakeet.

**2007, Aug. 20 Litho. *Perf. 14***
**1400-1403** A263 Set of 4 24.00 24.00
**1404** A263 6m Sheet of 4, #a-d 8.00 8.00

**Souvenir Sheets**

**1405-1406** A263 Set of 2 10.00 10.00

Butterflies — A264

Designs: 1m, Mylothris erlangeri. 1.50m, Papilio nireus. 2.10m, Acraea terpiscore. 10m, Salamis temora.

No. 1411: a, Danaus chrysippus. b, Myrina silenus. c, Chrysiridia madagascariensis. d, Hypolimnas dexithea.

No. 1412, 15m, P. demodocus. No. 1413, 15m, Amphicallia tigris.

**2007, Aug. 20**
**1407-1410** A264 Set of 4 9.00 9.00
**1411** A264 6m Sheet of 4, #a-d 7.00 7.00

**Souvenir Sheets**

**1412-1413** A264 Set of 2 9.00 9.00

Orchids — A265

Designs: 1.50m, Spiranthes laciniata. 2.10m, Triphora craigheadii. 3m, Arethusa bulbosa. 10m, Calypso bulbosa.

No. 1418: a, Encyclia tampensis. b, Prosthechea cochleata. c, Vanilla pompona. d, Cypripedium acaule.

No. 1419, 15m, Vanilla barbellata. No. 1420, 15m, Epidendrum radicans.

**2007, Aug. 20**
**1414-1417** A265 Set of 4 22.50 22.50
**1418** A265 6m Sheet of 4, #a-d 7.50 7.50

**Souvenir Sheets**

**1419-1420** A265 Set of 2 10.00 10.00

A266

A267

Mushrooms — A268

Designs: 1m, Amanita pantherina. 1.50m, Agaricus xanthodermus. 2.10m, Amanita rubescens. No. 1424, 15m, Amanita phalloides.

No. 1425: a, Amanita phalloides, diff. b, Amanita pantherina, diff. c, Panaeolus papilionaceus. d, Amanita rubescens, diff.

No. 1426, 15m, Amanite panther. No. 1427, 15m, Podaxis pistillaris.

**2007, Aug. 20**
**1421-1424** A266 Set of 4 12.00 12.00
**1425** A267 6m Sheet of 4, #a-d 12.00 12.00

**Souvenir Sheets**

**1426** A267 15m multi 9.00 9.00
**1427** A268 15m multi 9.00 9.00

Miniature Sheet

2008 Summer Olympics, Beijing — A269

No. 1428: a, Rowing. b, Softball. c, Wrestling. d, Volleyball.

**2008, Aug. 18 Litho. *Perf. 12***
**1428** A269 3.50m Sheet of 4, #a-d 6.50 6.50

In 2015 Lesotho postal officials declared as "illegal" a number of souvenir sheets of 1 depicting subjects such as wild mammals, wild cats, dogs, frogs, turtles, insects, penguins, Marie Curie and Brigitte Bardot.

Independence, 50th Anniv. — A270

Designs: 10m, Thaba Bosiu National Monument. 15m, National flags of Lesotho mounted on the Basotho hat.

**2016, Oct. 4 Litho. *Perf. 13¼***
**1429** A270 10m multi — —
**1430** A270 15m multi — —

An additional stamp was issued in this set. The editors would like to examine any example of it.

World Post Day — A271

Inscriptions: 2m, Mail sorting and packaging. 5m, Mail delivery. 10m, Lesotho Central Post Office. 15m, Morija Post Office. 20m, Maseru Main Post Office. 25m, Maseru Central Post Office.

**2016, Oct. 9 Litho. *Perf. 13¼***
**1432-1437** A271 Set of 6 — —

## POSTAGE DUE STAMPS

Basutoland Nos. J9-J10 Overprinted

**Wmk. 314**

**1966, Nov. 1 Typo. *Perf. 14***
**J1** D2 1c carmine .30 *.75*
 *a.* "Lseotho" *35.00*
**J2** D2 5c dark purple .30 *.90*
 *a.* "Lseotho" *55.00*

D1

***Perf. 13½***

**1967, Apr. 1 Unwmk. Litho.**
**J3** D1 1c dark blue .25 *3.00*
**J4** D1 2c dull rose .25 *3.50*
**J5** D1 5c emerald .40 *3.50*
 *Nos. J3-J5 (3)* .90 *10.00*

**1976, Nov. 30 Wmk. 362**
**J7** D1 2c dull rose 3.00 3.00
**J8** D1 5c emerald 3.00 3.00

D2

**1986 Litho. *Perf. 13x13½***
**J9** D2 2s green .55 .55
**J10** D2 5s blue .55 .55
**J11** D2 25s purple .55 .55
 *Nos. J9-J11 (3)* 1.65 1.65

# LIBERIA

lī-ˈbir-ē-ə

LOCATION — West coast of Africa, between Ivory Coast and Sierra Leone
GOVT. — Republic
AREA — 43,000 sq. mi.
POP. — 2,602,100 (1997 est.)
CAPITAL — Monrovia

100 Cents = 1 Dollar

**Catalogue values for unused stamps in this country are for Never Hinged items, beginning with Scott 330 in the regular postage section, Scott B19 in the semi-postal section, Scott C67 in the airpost section, and Scott CB4 in the airpost semi-postal section.**

Values for unused stamps are for examples with original gum as defined in the catalogue introduction. Any exceptions will be noted. Very fine examples of Nos. 1-3, 13-21 and 157-159 will have perforations just clear of the design due to the narrow spacing of the stamps on the plates and/or imperfect perforating methods.

**Watermarks**

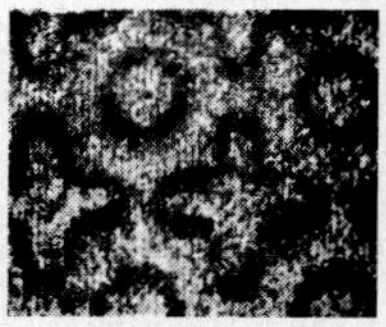

Wmk. 116 — Crosses and Circles

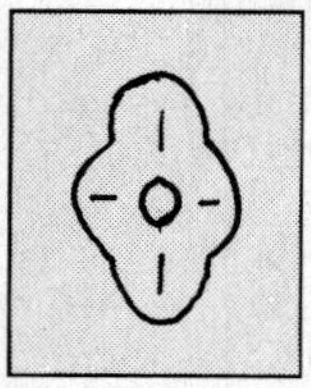

Wmk. 143

For watermarks 373 and 384 see British Watermark page.

"Liberia" — A1

A1a

**Thick Paper**

**1860 Unwmk. Litho. *Perf. 12***
**1** A1 6c red 400.00 *300.00*
 *a.* Imperf, pair 500.00
**2** A1 12c deep blue 25.00 *50.00*
 *a.* Imperf, pair 250.00
**3** A1a 24c green 50.00 *50.00*
 *a.* Imperf, pair 300.00
 *Nos. 1-3 (3)* 475.00 *400.00*

Stamps set very close together. Examples of the 12c occasionally show traces of a frame line around the design.

**Medium to Thin Paper**
**With a single-line frame around each stamp, about 1mm from the border**

**1864 *Perf. 11, 12***
**7** A1 6c red 62.50 *85.00*
 *a.* Imperf, pair 225.00
**8** A1 12c blue 80.00 *95.00*
 *a.* Imperf, pair 225.00
**9** A1a 24c lt green 87.50 *100.00*
 *a.* Imperf, pair 225.00
 *Nos. 7-9 (3)* 230.00 *280.00*

Stamps set about 5mm apart. Margins large and perforation usually outside the frame line.

**1866-69 Without Frame Line**
**13** A1 6c lt red 25.00 *40.00*
**14** A1 12c lt blue 25.00 *40.00*
**15** A1a 24c lt yellow grn 25.00 *40.00*
 *Nos. 13-15 (3)* 75.00 *120.00*

Stamps set 2-2½mm apart with small margins. Stamps are usually without frame line but those from one transfer show broken and irregular parts of a frame.

**1880 With Frame Line** ***Perf. 10½***

| | | | | |
|---|---|---|---|---|
| 16 | A1 | 1c ultra | 5.00 | 8.00 |
| 17 | A1 | 2c rose | 5.00 | *5.25* |
| *a.* | | Imperf, pair | 175.00 | |
| 18 | A1 | 6c violet | 5.00 | 5.25 |
| 19 | A1 | 12c yellow | 5.00 | *5.25* |
| 20 | A1a | 24c rose red | 6.00 | 5.50 |
| | | *Nos. 16-20 (5)* | 26.00 | 29.25 |

Unused values for Nos. 16-20 are for stamps without gum.

For surcharges see Nos. 157-159.

Counterfeits

Counterfeits exist of Nos. 1-28, 32 and 64.

From Arms of Liberia — A2

**1881**

| | | | | |
|---|---|---|---|---|
| 21 | A2 | 3c black | 15.00 | 10.00 |

Unused value is for a stamp without gum.

A3

A4

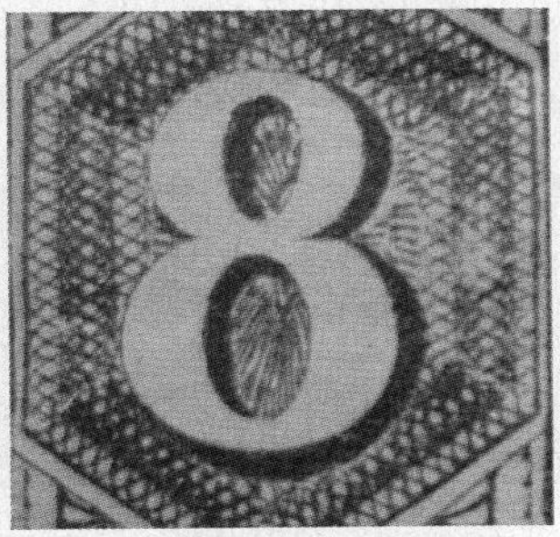

Slanting Lines

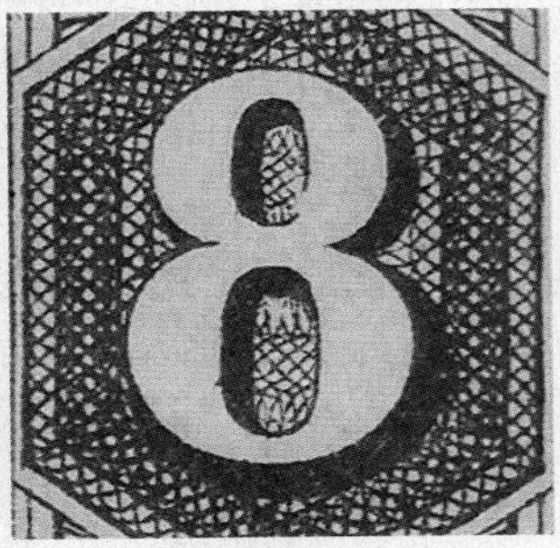

Network Lines

On No. 22 the openings in the figure "8" enclose a pattern of slanting lines. Compare with No. 32.

**1882** ***Perf. 11½, 12, 14***

| | | | | |
|---|---|---|---|---|
| 22 | A3 | 8c blue | 50.00 | 10.00 |
| 23 | A4 | 16c red | 8.00 | 5.00 |

Canceled to Order

Beginning with the issue of 1885, values in the used column are for "canceled to order" stamps. Postally used examples sell for much more.

A5

A6

From Arms of Liberia — A7

***Perf. 10½, 11, 12, 11½x10½, 14, 14½***

**1885**

| | | | | |
|---|---|---|---|---|
| 24 | A5 | 1c carmine | 2.00 | 2.00 |
| *a.* | | 1c rose | 2.00 | 2.00 |
| 25 | A5 | 2c green | 2.00 | 2.00 |
| 26 | A5 | 3c violet | 2.00 | 2.00 |
| 27 | A5 | 4c brown | 2.00 | 2.00 |
| 28 | A5 | 6c olive gray | 2.00 | 2.00 |
| 29 | A6 | 8c bluish gray | 4.00 | 4.00 |
| *a.* | | 8c lilac | 7.00 | 7.00 |
| 30 | A6 | 16c yellow | 15.00 | 12.00 |
| 31 | A7 | 32c deep blue | 35.00 | 29.00 |
| | | *Nos. 24-31 (8)* | 64.00 | 55.00 |

In the 1885 printing, the stamps are spaced 2mm apart and the paper is medium. In the 1892 printing, the stamps are 4½mm apart.

For surcharges see Nos. J1-J2.

**Imperf., Pair**

| | | | | |
|---|---|---|---|---|
| *24b* | A5 | 1c | 3.00 | |
| *25a* | A5 | 2c | 4.75 | |
| *26a* | A5 | 3c | 5.00 | |
| *27a* | A5 | 4c | 5.00 | |
| *28a* | A5 | 6c | 4.25 | 4.25 |
| *29b* | A6 | 8c | 12.50 | |
| *30a* | A6 | 16c | 30.00 | |
| *31a* | A7 | 32c | 50.00 | |

Imperf. pairs with 2mm spacing sell for higher prices.

A8

The openings in the figure "8" are filled with network lines.

**1889** ***Perf. 12, 14***

| | | | | |
|---|---|---|---|---|
| 32 | A8 | 8c blue | 4.25 | 4.25 |
| *a.* | | Imperf., pair | 20.00 | |

See No. 22.

A9

Elephant — A10

Oil Palm — A11

Pres. Hilary R. W. Johnson — A12

Vai Woman in Full Dress — A13

Coat of Arms — A14

Liberian Star — A15

Coat of Arms — A16

Hippopotamus A17

Liberian Star — A18

President Johnson — A19

**1892-96 Wmk. 143 Engr.** ***Perf. 15***

| | | | | |
|---|---|---|---|---|
| 33 | A9 | 1c vermilion | .50 | .40 |
| *a.* | | 1c blue (error) | 40.00 | |
| 34 | A9 | 2c blue | .50 | .40 |
| *a.* | | 2c vermilion (error) | 40.00 | |
| 35 | A10 | 4c green & blk | 2.00 | 1.25 |
| *a.* | | Center inverted | 225.00 | |
| 36 | A11 | 6c blue green | .70 | .50 |
| 37 | A12 | 8c brown & blk | .95 | .95 |
| *a.* | | Center inverted | 500.00 | 500.00 |
| *b.* | | Center sideways | 750.00 | |
| 38 | A12 | 10c chrome yel & indigo ('96) | .95 | .65 |
| 39 | A13 | 12c rose red | .95 | .65 |
| 40 | A13 | 15c slate ('96) | .95 | .65 |
| 41 | A14 | 16c lilac | 3.50 | 1.75 |
| *a.* | | 16c deep greenish blue (error) | 110.00 | |
| 42 | A14 | 20c vermilion ('96) | 3.50 | 1.75 |
| 43 | A15 | 24c ol grn, *yel* | 2.00 | 1.10 |
| 44 | A15 | 25c yel grn ('96) | 2.00 | 1.40 |
| 45 | A16 | 30c steel bl ('96) | 6.25 | 4.50 |
| 46 | A16 | 32c grnsh blue | 3.50 | 2.75 |
| *a.* | | 32c lilac (error) | *110.00* | |
| 47 | A17 | $1 ultra & blk | 12.00 | 9.00 |
| *a.* | | $1 blue & black | 13.50 | 11.00 |
| 48 | A18 | $2 brown, *yel* | 9.00 | 8.00 |
| 49 | A19 | $5 carmine & blk | 10.00 | 10.00 |
| *a.* | | Center inverted | 400.00 | 400.00 |
| | | *Nos. 33-49 (17)* | 59.25 | 45.70 |

Many imperforates, part-perforated and misperforated varieties exist.

The 1c, 2c and 4c were issued in sheets of 60; 6c, sheet of 40; 8c, 10c, sheets of 30; 12c, 15c, 24c, 25c, sheets of 20; 16c, 20c, 30c, sheets of 15; $1, $2, $5, sheets of 10.

For overprints & surcharges see Nos. 50, 64B-64F, 66, 71-77, 79-81, 85-93, 95-100, 160, O1-O13, O15-O25, O37-O41, O44-O45.

**No. 36 Surcharged**

a

b

**1893**

| | | | | |
|---|---|---|---|---|
| 50 | A11 (a) | 5c on 6c blue grn | 1.75 | 1.10 |
| *a.* | | "5" with short flag | 6.00 | 6.00 |
| *b.* | | Both 5's with short flags | 5.00 | 5.00 |
| *c.* | | "i" dot omitted | 19.00 | 19.00 |
| *d.* | | Surcharge "b" | 30.00 | 30.00 |

"Commerce," Globe and Krumen — A22

**1894 Unwmk. Engr.** ***Imperf.***

| | | | | |
|---|---|---|---|---|
| 52 | A22 | 5c carmine & blk | 5.00 | 5.00 |

***Rouletted***

| | | | | |
|---|---|---|---|---|
| 53 | A22 | 5c carmine & blk | 10.00 | 7.50 |

For overprints see Nos. 69, O26-O27.

Oil Palm A23

Hippopotamus A24

Elephant — A25

Liberty — A26

**1897-1905 Wmk. 143** ***Perf. 14 to 16***

| | | | | |
|---|---|---|---|---|
| 54 | A23 | 1c lilac rose | 1.00 | .65 |
| *a.* | | 1c violet | 1.00 | .65 |
| 55 | A23 | 1c dp grn ('00) | 1.25 | .95 |
| 56 | A23 | 1c lt green ('05) | 3.00 | 1.60 |
| 57 | A24 | 2c bister & blk | 3.00 | 1.60 |
| 58 | A24 | 2c org red & blk ('00) | 6.00 | 2.10 |
| 59 | A24 | 2c rose & blk ('05) | 3.00 | 1.60 |
| 60 | A25 | 5c lake & black | 3.00 | 1.60 |
| *a.* | | 5c lilac rose & black | 3.00 | 1.60 |
| 61 | A25 | 5c gray bl & blk ('00) | 6.00 | 5.00 |
| 62 | A25 | 5c ultra & blk ('05) | 4.25 | 2.75 |
| *a.* | | Center inverted | 1,600. | |
| 63 | A26 | 50c red brn & blk | 4.00 | 3.50 |
| | | *Nos. 54-63 (10)* | 34.50 | 21.35 |

For overprints & surcharges see Nos. 65, 66A-68. 70, 78, 82-84, M1, O28-O36, O42, O92.

A27

Two types:

I — 13 pearls above "Republic Liberia."

II — 10 pearls.

**1897 Unwmk. Litho.** ***Perf. 14***

| | | | | |
|---|---|---|---|---|
| 64 | A27 | 3c red & green (I) | .25 | *.60* |
| *a.* | | Type II | *20.00* | .25 |

No. 64a is considered a reprint, unissued. "Used" examples are CTO.

For surcharge see No. 128.

Official Stamps Handstamped in Black

**1901-02 Wmk. 143**

**On Nos. O7-O8, O10-O12**

| | | | | |
|---|---|---|---|---|
| 64B | A14 | 16c lilac | *525.00* | *525.00* |
| 64C | A15 | 24c ol grn, *yel* | *575.00* | *400.00* |
| 64D | A17 | $1 blue & blk | *3,000.* | *2,000.* |
| 64E | A18 | $2 brown, *yel* | — | — |
| 64F | A19 | $5 car & blk | — | — |

### On Stamps with "O S" Printed

| | | | | |
|---|---|---|---|---|
| 65 | A23 | 1c green | 37.50 | 40.00 |
| 66 | A9 | 2c blue | 100.00 | 100.00 |
| 66A | A24 | 2c bister & blk | — | 150.00 |
| 67 | A24 | 2c org red & blk | 45.00 | 40.00 |
| 68 | A25 | 5c gray bl & blk | 37.50 | 35.00 |
| 69 | A22 | 5c vio & grn (No. O26) | 300.00 | 300.00 |
| 70 | A25 | 5c lake & blk | 275.00 | 225.00 |
| 71 | A12 | 10c yel & blue blk | 37.50 | 60.00 |
| a. | | "O S" omitted | — | |
| 72 | A13 | 15c slate | 40.00 | 60.00 |
| 73 | A14 | 16c lilac | 550.00 | 350.00 |
| 74 | A14 | 20c vermilion | 42.50 | 50.00 |
| 75 | A15 | 24c ol grn, *yel* | 52.50 | 50.00 |
| 76 | A15 | 25c yellow grn | 42.50 | 50.00 |
| a. | | "O S" omitted | 750.00 | |
| 77 | A16 | 30c steel blue | 42.50 | 40.00 |
| 78 | A26 | 50c red brn & blk | 100.00 | 52.50 |
| 79 | A17 | $1 ultra & blk | 325.00 | 275.00 |
| a. | | "O S" omitted | | |
| 80 | A18 | $2 brn, *yel* | 2,000. | 1,800. |
| 81 | A19 | $5 car & blk | 2,500. | 2,000. |
| a. | | "O S" omitted | 3,000. | 2,750. |

### On Stamps with "O S" Handstamped

| | | | | |
|---|---|---|---|---|
| 82 | A23 | 1c deep green | 62.50 | — |
| 83 | A24 | 2c org red & blk | 75.00 | — |
| 84 | A25 | 5c lake & blk | 200.00 | — |
| 85 | A12 | 10c yel & bl blk | 125.00 | — |
| 86 | A14 | 20c vermilion | 140.00 | — |
| 87 | A15 | 24c ol grn, *yel* | 140.00 | — |
| 88 | A15 | 25c yel grn | 160.00 | — |
| 89 | A16 | 30c steel blue | 525.00 | — |
| 90 | A16 | 32c grnsh blue | 210.00 | — |

Varieties of Nos. 65-90 include double and inverted overprints.

Nos. 47, O10, O23a Surcharged in Carmine

**1902**

| | | | | |
|---|---|---|---|---|
| 91 | A17 | 75c on $1 #47 | 15.00 | 13.00 |
| a. | | Thin "C" and comma | 25.00 | 25.00 |
| b. | | Inverted surcharge | 62.50 | 62.50 |
| c. | | As "a," inverted | | |
| 92 | A17 | 75c on $1 #O10 | 2,750. | |
| a. | | Thin "C" and comma | 4,250. | |
| 93 | A17 | 75c on $1 #O23a | 4,000. | |
| a. | | Thin "C" and comma | 5,250. | |

Liberty — A29

**1903 Unwmk. Engr. *Perf. 14***

| | | | | |
|---|---|---|---|---|
| 94 | A29 | 3c black | .30 | .25 |
| a. | | Printed on both sides | 50.00 | |
| b. | | Perf. 12 | 20.00 | 6.00 |

For overprint see No. O43.

**Stamps of 1892 Surcharged in Blue**

a

b

**1903 Wmk. 143**

| | | | | |
|---|---|---|---|---|
| 95 | A14 (a) | 10c on 16c lilac | 3.00 | 5.00 |
| 96 | A15 (b) | 15c on 24c ol grn, *yel* | 4.50 | 6.00 |
| 97 | A16 (b) | 20c on 32c grnsh bl | 6.25 | 8.50 |
| | | *Nos. 95-97 (3)* | 13.75 | 19.50 |

**Nos. 50, O3 and 45 Surcharged in Black or Red**

**1904**

| | | | | |
|---|---|---|---|---|
| 98 | A11 | 1c on 5c on 6c bl grn | .70 | .55 |
| a. | | "5" with short flag | 4.25 | 4.25 |
| b. | | Both 5's with short flags | 8.75 | 8.75 |
| c. | | "i" dot omitted | 10.00 | 10.00 |
| d. | | Surcharge on #50d | 15.00 | 15.00 |
| e. | | Inverted surcharge | 7.50 | 7.50 |
| 99 | A10 | 2c on 4c grn & blk | 2.75 | 4.00 |
| a. | | Pair, one without surcharge | 35.00 | |
| b. | | Double surcharge | 50.00 | |
| c. | | Double surcharge, red and blk | 62.50 | |
| d. | | Surcharged on back also | 25.00 | |
| e. | | "Official" overprint missing | 35.00 | |
| 100 | A16 | 2c on 30c stl bl (R) | 9.50 | 15.00 |
| | | *Nos. 98-100 (3)* | 12.95 | 19.55 |

African Elephant — A33

Mercury — A34

Chimpanzee A35

Great Blue Touraco — A36

Agama — A37

Egret — A38

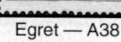

Head of Liberty From Coin — A39

A40

Liberian Flag — A41

Pygmy Hippopotamus A42

Liberty with Star of Liberia on Cap — A43

Mandingos — A44

Executive Mansion and Pres. Arthur Barclay — A45

**1906 Unwmk. Engr. *Perf. 14***

| | | | | |
|---|---|---|---|---|
| 101 | A33 | 1c green & blk | 1.75 | .50 |
| 102 | A34 | 2c carmine & blk | .35 | .25 |
| 103 | A35 | 5c ultra & blk | 3.00 | .85 |
| 104 | A36 | 10c red brn & blk | 14.00 | .85 |
| 105 | A37 | 15c pur & dp grn | 10.00 | 3.00 |
| 106 | A38 | 20c orange & blk | 9.00 | 2.50 |
| 107 | A39 | 25c dull blue & gray | 1.00 | .25 |
| 108 | A40 | 30c deep violet | 1.00 | .25 |
| 109 | A41 | 50c dp grn & blk | 1.25 | .25 |
| 110 | A42 | 75c brown & blk | 13.00 | 2.50 |
| 111 | A43 | $1 rose & gray | 3.50 | .25 |
| 112 | A44 | $2 dp grn & blk | 5.00 | .35 |
| 113 | A45 | $5 red brn & blk | 10.00 | .50 |
| | | *Nos. 101-113 (13)* | 72.85 | 12.30 |

For surcharges see Nos. 114, 129, 130, 141, 145-149, 161, M2, M5, O72-O73, O82-O85, O96. For overprints see Nos. O46-O58.

**Center Inverted**

| | | | | |
|---|---|---|---|---|
| 101a | A33 | 1c | 110.00 | 55.00 |
| 102a | A34 | 2c | 120.00 | 35.00 |
| 103a | A35 | 5c | 175.00 | 175.00 |
| 104a | A36 | 10c | 80.00 | 80.00 |
| 105a | A37 | 15c | 175.00 | 175.00 |
| 106b | A38 | 20c | 175.00 | 175.00 |
| 107a | A39 | 25c | 75.00 | 75.00 |
| 109b | A41 | 50c | 75.00 | 75.00 |
| 110b | A42 | 75c | 125.00 | 125.00 |
| 111a | A43 | $1 | 100.00 | 100.00 |
| 112a | A44 | $2 | 95.00 | 95.00 |

**Imperf., Pairs**

| | | | | |
|---|---|---|---|---|
| 101b | A33 | 1c | 13.50 | |
| 102b | A34 | 2c | 5.50 | |
| 106a | A38 | 20c | 20.00 | |
| 107b | A39 | 25c | 55.00 | 45.00 |
| 109a | A41 | 50c | 20.00 | |
| 110a | A42 | 75c | 20.00 | |
| 113a | A45 | $5 | 27.00 | |

No. 104 Surcharged in Black

**1909**

| | | | | |
|---|---|---|---|---|
| 114 | A36 | 3c on 10c red brn & blk | 6.00 | 6.00 |

Coffee Plantation — A46

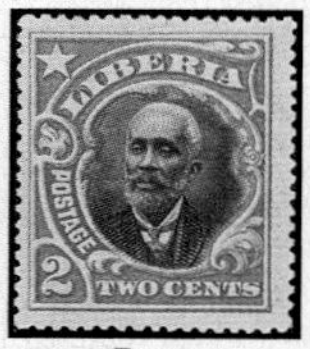

Pres. Barclay — A47

S. S. Pres. Daniel E. Howard, former Gunboat Lark — A48

Commerce with Caduceus — A49

Vai Woman Spinning Cotton — A50

Blossom and Fruit of Pepper Plants — A51

Circular House — A52

President Barclay — A53

Men in Canoe — A54

Liberian Village — A55

**1909-12 *Perf. 14***

| | | | | |
|---|---|---|---|---|
| 115 | A46 | 1c yel grn & blk | .70 | .55 |
| 116 | A47 | 2c lake & blk | .70 | .55 |
| 117 | A48 | 5c ultra & blk | .70 | .55 |
| 118 | A49 | 10c plum & blk, perf. 12½ ('12) | .70 | .55 |
| a. | | Imperf., pair | 19.00 | |
| b. | | Perf 14 ('12) | 2.25 | 2.25 |
| c. | | As "b," pair, imperf between | 27.50 | |
| d. | | Perf 12½x14 | 2.75 | 2.25 |
| 119 | A50 | 15c indigo & blk | 3.50 | .60 |
| 120 | A51 | 20c rose & grn | 4.50 | .60 |
| b. | | Imperf. | | |
| 121 | A52 | 25c dk brn & blk | 1.40 | .60 |
| a. | | Imperf. | | |

| | | | |
|---|---|---|---|
| **122** | A53 30c dark brown | 4.50 | .60 |
| **123** | A54 50c green & blk | 4.50 | .60 |
| **124** | A55 75c red brn & blk | 4.50 | .60 |
| | *Nos. 115-124 (10)* | 25.70 | 5.80 |

***Rouletted***

| | | | |
|---|---|---|---|
| **125** | A49 10c plum & blk | .75 | .45 |

For surcharges see Nos. 126-127E, 131-133, 136-140, 142-144, 151-156, 162, B1-B2, M3-M4, M6-M7, O70-O1, O74-O81, O86-O91, O97.

For overprints see Nos. O59-O69.

**Center Inverted**

| | | | | |
|---|---|---|---|---|
| *116a* | A47 | 2c | 70.00 | 60.00 |
| *117a* | A48 | 5c | 62.50 | 55.00 |
| *119a* | A50 | 15c | 100.00 | 60.00 |
| *120a* | A51 | 20c | 70.00 | 55.00 |
| *121b* | A52 | 25c | 47.50 | 42.50 |
| *123a* | A54 | 50c | 95.00 | 80.00 |

**Stamps and Types of 1909-12 Surcharged in Blue or Red**

**1910-12** ***Rouletted***

| | | | |
|---|---|---|---|
| **126** | A49 3c on 10c plum & blk (Bl) | .40 | .25 |
| *a.* | "3" inverted | | |
| **126B** | A49 3c on 10c blk & ultra (R) | 30.00 | 5.00 |

No. 126B is roulette 7. It also exists in roulette 13.

***Perf. 12½, 14, 12½x14***

| | | | |
|---|---|---|---|
| **127** | A49 3c on 10c plum & blk (Bl) ('12) | .40 | .25 |
| *a.* | Imperf., pair | 22.50 | |
| *b.* | Double surcharge, one invtd. | 22.50 | |
| *c.* | Double vertical surcharge | | |
| **127E** | A49 3c on 10c blk & ultra (R) ('12) | 17.00 | .55 |
| | *Nos. 126-127E (4)* | 47.80 | 6.05 |

Nos. 64, 64a Surcharged in Dark Green

**1913**

| | | | |
|---|---|---|---|
| **128** | A27 8c on 3c red & grn (I) | .30 | .25 |
| *a.* | Surcharge on No. 64a | 3.00 | .25 |
| *b.* | Double surcharge | 6.25 | |
| *c.* | Imperf., pair | 20.00 | |
| *d.* | Inverted surcharge | 25.00 | |

**Stamps of Preceding Issues Surcharged**

a

b

**1914** **On Issue of 1906**

| | | | |
|---|---|---|---|
| **129** | A39 (a) 2c on 25c dl bl & gray | 11.50 | 3.25 |
| **130** | A40 (b) 5c on 30c dp vio | 11.50 | 3.25 |

**On Issue of 1909**

| | | | |
|---|---|---|---|
| **131** | A52 (a) 2c on 25c brn & blk | 11.50 | 3.25 |
| **132** | A53 (b) 5c on 30c dk brown | 11.50 | 3.25 |
| **133** | A54 (a) 10c on 50c grn & blk | 11.50 | 3.25 |
| | *Nos. 129-133 (5)* | 57.50 | 16.25 |

Liberian House A57

Providence Island, Monrovia Harbor A58

**1915** **Engr.** **Wmk. 116** ***Perf. 14***

| | | | |
|---|---|---|---|
| **134** | A57 2c red | .25 | .25 |
| **135** | A58 3c dull violet | .25 | .25 |

For overprints see Nos. 196-197, O113-O114, O128-O129.

**Nos. 109, 111-113, 119-124 Surcharged in Dark Blue, Black or Red**

c

d

e

f

g

**1915-16** **Unwmk.**

| | | | |
|---|---|---|---|
| **136** | A50 (c) 2c on 15c (R) | .90 | .90 |
| **137** | A52 (d) 2c on 25c (R) | 8.50 | 8.50 |
| **138** | A51 (e) 5c on 20c (Bk) | 1.10 | 6.25 |
| **139** | A53 (f) 5c on 30c (R) | 4.50 | 4.50 |
| *a.* | Double surcharge | 15.00 | 15.00 |
| **140** | A53 (g) 5c on 30c (R) | 40.00 | 40.00 |

h

i

j

| | | | |
|---|---|---|---|
| **141** | A41 (h) 10c on 50c (R) | 8.00 | 8.00 |
| *a.* | Double surch., one invtd. | | |
| **142** | A54 (i) 10c on 50c (R) | 15.00 | 15.00 |
| *a.* | Double surcharge red & blk | 50.00 | 35.00 |
| *b.* | Blue surcharge | 35.00 | 35.00 |
| **143** | A54 (i) 10c on 50c (Bk) | 20.00 | 15.00 |

k

| | | | |
|---|---|---|---|
| **144** | A55 (j) 20c on 75c (Bk) | 4.00 | 7.50 |
| **145** | A43 (k) 25c on $1 (Bk) | 42.50 | 42.50 |

l

m

| | | | |
|---|---|---|---|
| **146** | A44 (l) 50c on $2 (R) | 12.00 | 12.00 |
| *a.* | "Ceuts" | 30.00 | 22.50 |
| **147** | A44 (m) 50c on $2 (R) | 800.00 | 800.00 |

n

| | | | |
|---|---|---|---|
| **148** | A45 $1 on $5 (Bk) | 65.00 | 65.00 |
| *a.* | Double surcharge | 90.00 | 90.00 |

o

| | | | |
|---|---|---|---|
| **149** | A45 $1 on $5 (R) | 52.50 | 52.50 |

The color of the red surcharge varies from light dull red to almost brown.

**Handstamped Surcharge, Type "i"**

| | | | |
|---|---|---|---|
| **150** | A54 10c on 50c (Dk Bl) | 14.00 | 14.00 |

No. 119 Surcharged in Black

| | | | |
|---|---|---|---|
| **151** | A50 2c on 15c | 650.00 | 650.00 |

No. 119 Surcharged in Red

| | | | |
|---|---|---|---|
| **152** | A50 2c on 15c | 45.00 | 40.00 |
| *a.* | Double surcharge | 92.50 | |

**Nos. 116-117 Surcharged in Black or Red**

a

b

c

d

e

f

g

h

i

j

k

l

m

n

o

p

q

r

s

t

Types A-J are for No. 153. Types K-T are for No. 154.

**153** A47 1c on 2c lake & blk 2.50 2.50
*a.* Strip of 10 types 35.00
**154** A48 2c on 5c ultra & blk (R) 3.50 2.50
*a.* Black surcharge 14.00 14.00
*b.* Strip of 10 types (R) 35.00
*c.* Strip of 10 types (Bk) 175.00

The 10 types of surcharge are repeated in illustrated sequence on 1c on 2c in each horiz. row and on 2c on 5c in each vert. row of sheets of 100 (10x10).

No. 116 and Type of 1909 Surcharged

**155** A47 1c on 2c lake & blk 190.00 190.00

No. 117 Surcharged

**156** A48 2c on 5c turq & blk 140.00 140.00

Nos. 18-20 Surcharged

**1916**

**157** A1 3c on 6c violet 45.00 45.00
*a.* Inverted surcharge 100.00 75.00
**158** A1 5c on 12c yellow 3.00 3.00
*a.* Inverted surcharge 17.50 17.50
*b.* Surcharge sideways 17.50
**159** A1 10c on 24c rose red 2.75 3.00
*a.* Inverted surcharge 15.00 15.00
*b.* Surcharge sideways *20.00*
*Nos. 157-159 (3)* 50.75 51.00

Unused values for Nos. 157-159 are for examples without gum.

**Nos. 44 and 108 Surcharged**

p

r

**1917** **Wmk. 143**

**160** A15 (p) 4c on 25c yel grn 12.00 12.00
*a.* "OUR" 27.50 27.50
*b.* "FCUR" 27.50 27.50

**Unwmk.**

**161** A40 (r) 5c on 30c dp vio 90.00 90.00

**No. 118 Surcharged in Red**

**1918**

**162** A49 3c on 10c plum & blk 2.75 4.25
*a.* "3" inverted 9.25 9.25

Bongo Antelope — A59

Symbols of Liberia — A61

Two-spot Palm Civet A60

A62

Palm-nut Vulture — A66

Oil Palm — A63

Mercury — A64

Traveler's Tree — A65

"Mudskipper" or Bommi Fish — A67

Mandingos A68

"Liberia" A71

Coast Scene A69

Liberia College A70

**1918** **Engr.** ***Perf. 12½, 14***

**163** A59 1c dp grn & blk .75 .25
**164** A60 2c rose & blk .90 .25
**165** A61 5c gray bl & blk .25 .25
**166** A62 10c dark green .30 .25
**167** A63 15c blk & dk grn 3.50 .25
**168** A64 20c claret & blk .40 .25
**169** A65 25c dk grn & grn 3.75 .25
**170** A66 30c red vio & blk 17.00 .80
**171** A67 50c ultra & blk 30.00 3.50
**172** A68 75c ol bis & blk 3.00 .25
**173** A69 $1 yel brn & bl 7.50 .25
**174** A70 $2 lt vio & blk 8.00 .25
**175** A71 $5 dark brown 8.50 .40
*Nos. 163-175 (13)* 83.85 7.20

For surcharges see Nos. 176-177, 228-229, 248-270, B3-B15, O111-O112, O155-O157.
For overprints see Nos. O98-O110.

**Nos. 163-164, F10-F14 Surcharged**

**1920**

**176** A59 3c on 1c grn & blk 1.10 1.10
*a.* "CEETS" 17.00 17.00
*b.* Double surcharge 10.00 10.00
*c.* Triple surcharge 15.00 15.00
**177** A60 4c on 2c rose & blk 1.10 1.10
*a.* Inverted surcharge 20.00 20.00
*b.* Double surcharge 10.00 10.00
*c.* Double surcharge, one invtd. 18.00
*d.* Triple surcharge, one inverted 25.00 25.00
*e.* Quadruple surcharge 30.00 30.00
*f.* Typewritten surcharge
*g.* Same as "f" but inverted
*h.* Printed and typewritten surcharges, both inverted
**178** R6 5c on 10c bl & blk 2.50 2.75
*a.* Inverted surcharge 10.00 10.00
*b.* Double surcharge 10.00 10.00
*c.* Double surcharge, one invtd. 15.00 15.00
*d.* Typewritten surcharge ("five") 100.00
*e.* Printed and typewritten surcharges 100.00
**179** R6 5c on 10c org red & blk 2.50 2.75
*a.* 5c on 10c orange & black 4.00 2.75
*b.* Inverted surcharge 15.00
*c.* Double surcharge 15.00
*d.* Double surcharge, one invtd. 18.00 15.00
*e.* Typewritten surch. in violet 100.00 100.00
*f.* Typewritten surch. in black
*g.* Printed and typewritten surcharges 100.00
**180** R6 5c on 10c grn & blk 2.50 2.75
*a.* Double surcharge 10.00 10.00
*b.* Double surcharge, one invtd. 18.00 18.00
*c.* Inverted surcharge 18.00
*d.* Quadruple surcharge 25.00 25.00
*e.* Typewritten surcharge 100.00
*f.* Printed and typewritten surcharges
**181** R6 5c on 10c vio & blk (Monrovia) 4.00 5.00
*a.* Double surcharge, one invtd. 25.00 25.00
**182** R6 5c on 10c mag & blk (Robertsport) 2.25 2.40
*a.* Double surcharge 15.00 15.00
*b.* Double surcharge, one invtd. 15.00 15.00
*c.* Double surcharge, both invtd. 25.00
*Nos. 176-182 (7)* 15.95 17.85

Cape Mesurado A75

Pres. Daniel E. Howard — A76

Arms of Liberia — A77

Crocodile A78

Pepper Plant — A79

Leopard A80

Village Scene — A81

Krumen in Dugout A82

Rapids in St. Paul's River — A83

Bongo Antelope A84

Hornbill A85

Elephant A86

**1921 Wmk. 116 *Perf. 14***

| | | | | | |
|---|---|---|---|---|---|
| 183 | A75 | 1c | green | .25 | .25 |
| 184 | A76 | 5c | dp bl & blk | .25 | .25 |
| 185 | A77 | 10c | red & dl bl | .25 | .25 |
| 186 | A78 | 15c | dl vio & grn | 6.50 | .55 |
| 187 | A79 | 20c | rose red & grn | 2.75 | .25 |
| 188 | A80 | 25c | org & blk | 7.50 | .55 |
| 189 | A81 | 30c | grn & dl vio | .40 | .25 |
| 190 | A82 | 50c | org & ultra | .45 | .25 |
| 191 | A83 | 75c | red & blk brn | .80 | .25 |
| *a.* | | | Center inverted | | 70.00 |
| 192 | A84 | $1 | red & blk | 20.00 | 1.75 |
| 193 | A85 | $2 | yel & ultra | 16.00 | 1.25 |
| 194 | A86 | $5 | car rose & vio | 32.50 | 1.50 |
| | | | *Nos. 183-194 (12)* | 87.65 | 7.35 |

For overprints see Nos. 195, 198-208, O115-O127, O130-O140.

Nos. 134-135, 183-194 Ovptd.

| | | | | | |
|---|---|---|---|---|---|
| 195 | A75 | 1c | green | 22.50 | .40 |
| 196 | A57 | 2c | red | 22.50 | .40 |
| 197 | A58 | 3c | dull violet | 32.50 | .40 |
| 198 | A76 | 5c | dp bl & blk | 3.50 | .30 |
| 199 | A77 | 10c | red & dull bl | 50.00 | .40 |
| 200 | A78 | 15c | dull vio & grn | 22.50 | 1.40 |
| 201 | A79 | 20c | rose red & grn, ovpt. invtd. | 7.25 | .75 |
| 202 | A80 | 25c | orange & blk | 22.50 | 1.40 |
| 203 | A81 | 30c | grn & dull vio | 2.50 | .30 |
| 204 | A82 | 50c | orange & ultra | 3.50 | .30 |
| 205 | A83 | 75c | red & blk brn | 4.75 | .30 |
| 206 | A84 | $1 | red & blk | 62.50 | 2.10 |
| 207 | A85 | $2 | yellow & ultra | 22.50 | 2.10 |
| 208 | A86 | $5 | car rose & vio | 60.00 | 2.75 |
| | | | *Nos. 195-208 (14)* | 339.00 | 13.30 |

Overprint exists inverted in Nos. 195-208 and normal on No. 201.

First Settlers Landing at Cape Mesurado from U. S. S. Alligator A87

**1923 Litho.**

| | | | | | |
|---|---|---|---|---|---|
| 209 | A87 | 1c | lt blue & blk | 18.00 | .45 |
| 210 | A87 | 2c | claret & ol gray | 26.00 | .45 |
| 211 | A87 | 5c | ol grn & ind | 26.00 | .45 |
| 212 | A87 | 10c | bl grn & vio | 1.00 | .45 |
| 213 | A87 | $1 | rose & brn | 3.25 | .45 |
| | | | *Nos. 209-213 (5)* | 74.25 | 2.25 |

Centenary of founding of Liberia.

Memorial to J. J. Roberts, 1st Pres. — A88

Hall of Representatives, Monrovia — A89

Liberian Star — A90

A91

Pres. Charles Dunbar Burgess King — A92

Hippopotamus — A93

Antelope A94

West African Buffalo A95

Grebos Making Dumboy A96

Pineapple A97

Carrying Ivory Tusk A98

Rubber Planter's House — A99

Stockton Lagoon — A100

Grebo Houses — A101

**1923 *Perf. 13½x14½, 14½x13½***
**White Paper**

| | | | | | |
|---|---|---|---|---|---|
| 214 | A88 | 1c | yel grn & dp grn | 7.50 | 1.25 |
| 215 | A89 | 2c | claret & brn | 7.50 | .25 |
| 216 | A90 | 3c | lilac & blk | .35 | .25 |
| 217 | A91 | 5c | bl vio & blk | 115.00 | .25 |
| 218 | A92 | 10c | slate & brn | .35 | .25 |
| 219 | A93 | 15c | bister & bl | 35.00 | .50 |
| 220 | A94 | 20c | bl grn & vio | 2.50 | .35 |
| 221 | A95 | 25c | org red & brn | 160.00 | .60 |
| 222 | A96 | 30c | dk brn & vio | .60 | .25 |
| 223a | A97 | 50c | dull vio & brn, *brnsh* | 1.00 | .25 |
| 224 | A98 | 75c | gray & bl | 1.90 | .40 |
| 225a | A99 | $1 | dp red & dk vio, *brnsh* | 4.50 | .60 |
| 226 | A100 | $2 | orange & blue | 7.50 | .80 |
| 227a | A101 | $5 | dp grn & brn, *brnsh* | 8.00 | .90 |
| | | | *Nos. 214-227a (14)* | 351.70 | 6.90 |

No. 163 Surcharged in Black

**1926 Unwmk. *Perf. 14***

| | | | | |
|---|---|---|---|---|
| 228 | A59 2c on 1c dp grn & blk | 3.50 | 3.50 |
| *a.* | Surcharge with ornamental design as on #O155 | 17.00 | |

No. 163 Surcharged in Red

**1927**

| | | | |
|---|---|---|---|
| 229 | A59 2c on 1c dp grn & blk | 9.50 | 9.50 |
| *a.* | "Ceuts" | 14.00 | |
| *b.* | "Vwo" | 14.00 | |
| *c.* | "Twc" | 14.00 | |
| *d.* | Double surcharge | 27.50 | |
| *e.* | Wavy lines omitted | 17.50 | |

Palms A102

Map of Africa — A103

President Burgess King — A104

**1928 Engr. *Perf. 12***

| | | | | | |
|---|---|---|---|---|---|
| 230 | A102 | 1c | green | .75 | .50 |
| 231 | A102 | 2c | dark violet | .50 | .35 |
| 232 | A102 | 3c | bister brn | .50 | .35 |
| *a.* | | | Horiz. pair, imperf vert. | | — |
| 233 | A103 | 5c | ultra | 1.00 | .55 |
| 234 | A104 | 10c | olive gray | 1.40 | .55 |
| 235 | A103 | 15c | dull violet | 6.25 | 2.25 |
| 236 | A103 | $1 | red brown | 77.50 | 26.50 |
| | | | *Nos. 230-236 (7)* | 87.90 | 31.05 |

For surcharges & overprints see Nos. 288A, 289A, 290A-291, 292A, C1-C3, O158-O165.

**Nos. 164-168, 170-175 Surcharged in Various Colors and Styles**

No. 248

No. 250

**1936 *Perf. 12½, 14***

| | | | | | |
|---|---|---|---|---|---|
| 248 | A60 | 1c on 2c (Bl) | | .50 | *3.50* |
| 249 | A61 | 3c on 5c (Bl) | | .45 | *2.00* |
| 250 | A62 | 4c on 10c (Br) | | .45 | *2.00* |
| 251 | A63 | 6c on 15c (Bl) | | .50 | *3.50* |
| 252 | A64 | 8c on 20c (V) | | .45 | *2.00* |
| 253 | A66 | 12c on 30c (V) | | 1.25 | *9.75* |
| 254 | A67 | 14c on 50c (Bl) | | 1.40 | *11.00* |
| 255 | A68 | 16c on 75c (Br) | | .70 | *5.50* |
| 256 | A69 | 18c on $1 (Bk) | | .70 | *5.50* |
| *a.* | | 22c on $1 yellow brown & blue | | *8.00* | |
| 257 | A70 | 22c on $2 (V) | | .85 | *7.75* |
| 258 | A71 | 24c on $5 (Bk) | | 1.50 | *9.75* |
| | | *Nos. 248-258 (11)* | | 8.75 | 62.25 |

**Official Stamps, Nos. O99-O110, Srchd. or Ovptd. in Various Colors & Styles**

**1936**

| | | | | |
|---|---|---|---|---|
| **259** | A60 | 1c on 2c (Bl) | .45 | *4.00* |
| **260** | A61 | 3c on 5c (Bl) | .45 | *4.00* |
| **261** | A62 | 4c on 10c (Bl) | .45 | *4.00* |
| **262** | A63 | 6c on 15c (Bl) | .45 | *4.00* |
| **263** | A64 | 8c on 20c (V) | .45 | *4.00* |
| **264** | A66 | 12c on 30c (V) | 1.65 | *20.00* |
| *a.* | | "193" instead of "1936" | 20.00 | |
| **265** | A67 | 14c on 50c (Bl). | 2.25 | *21.00* |
| **266** | A68 | 16c on 75c (Bk) | 1.10 | *12.00* |
| **267** | A69 | 18c on $1 (Bk) | 1.10 | *12.00* |
| **268** | A70 | 22c on $2 (Bl) | 1.40 | *15.00* |
| **269** | A71 | 24c on $5 (Bk) | 1.75 | *17.00* |
| **270** | A65 | 25c (Bk) | 2.25 | *21.00* |
| | | *Nos. 259-270 (12)* | 13.75 | 138.00 |

Hornbill — A106

Designs: 2c, Bushbuck. 3c, West African dwarf buffalo. 4c, Pygmy hippopotamus. 5c, Lesser egret. 6c, Pres. E. J. Barclay.

***Perf. Compound of 11½, 12, 12½, 14***

**1937, Apr. 10 Engr. Unwmk.**

| | | | | |
|---|---|---|---|---|
| **271** | A106 | 1c yel grn & blk | 1.50 | .45 |
| **272** | A106 | 2c carmine & blk | 1.50 | .45 |
| **273** | A106 | 3c violet & blk | 1.50 | .45 |
| **274** | A106 | 4c orange & blk | 2.25 | .70 |
| **275** | A106 | 5c blue & blk | 2.25 | .65 |
| **276** | A106 | 6c green & blk | .80 | .25 |
| | | *Nos. 271-276 (6)* | 9.80 | 2.95 |

Coast Line of Liberia, 1839 A107

Seal of Liberia, Map and Farming Scenes A108

Thomas Buchanan and Residence at Bassa Cove — A109

**1940, July 29 Engr. *Perf. 12***

| | | | | |
|---|---|---|---|---|
| **277** | A107 | 3c dark blue | .35 | .35 |
| **278** | A108 | 5c dull red brn | .35 | .35 |
| **279** | A109 | 10c dark green | .35 | .35 |
| | | *Nos. 277-279 (3)* | 1.05 | 1.05 |

100th anniv. of the founding of the Commonwealth of Liberia.

For overprints & surcharges see Nos. 280-282, B16-B18, C14-C16, CB1-CB3, CE1, CF1, E1, F35.

Imperforates

Many stamps of Liberia exist imperforate or with various perforation errors, in issued and trial colors, and also in small presentation sheets in issued colors.

**Nos. 277-279 Overprinted in Red or Blue**

**1941, Feb. 21**

| | | | | |
|---|---|---|---|---|
| **280** | A107 | 3c dk blue (R) | 2.50 | 2.50 |
| **281** | A108 | 5c dull red brn (Bl) | 2.50 | 2.50 |
| **282** | A109 | 10c dark green (R) | 2.50 | 2.50 |
| | | *Nos. 280-282,C14-C16 (6)* | 15.75 | 15.75 |

Royal Antelope A110

Bay-thighed Diana Monkey — A115

2c, Water chevrotain. 3c, White-shouldered duiker. 4c, Bushbuck. 5c, Zebra antelope.

**1942 Engr.**

| | | | | |
|---|---|---|---|---|
| **283** | A110 | 1c violet & fawn | 1.10 | .25 |
| **284** | A110 | 2c brt ultra & yel brn | 1.40 | .25 |
| **285** | A110 | 3c brt grn & yel brn | 1.90 | .90 |
| **286** | A110 | 4c blk & red org | 2.40 | 1.90 |
| **287** | A110 | 5c olive & fawn | 3.00 | 1.90 |
| **288** | A115 | 10c red & black | 5.25 | 2.40 |
| | | *Nos. 283-288 (6)* | 15.05 | 7.60 |

**Nos. 231, 233-234, 271-276 Srchd. with New Values and Bars or X's in Violet, Black, Red Brown or Blue**

No. 288A

No. 289A

No. 292A

No. 295

***Perf. 12, 12x12½, 14***

**1944-46 Unwmk.**

| | | | | |
|---|---|---|---|---|
| **288A** | A102 | 1c on 2c (Bk) | 9.25 | 6.50 |
| **289** | A106 | 1c on 4c (Bk) | 60.00 | 47.50 |
| **289A** | A104 | 1c on 10c (R Br) | 12.50 | 9.50 |
| *b.* | | Double surcharge, one red brown, one violet | 25.00 | 19.00 |
| **290** | A106 | 2c on 3c | 70.00 | 50.00 |
| **290A** | A103 | 2c on 5c (Bk) | 2.75 | 2.75 |
| **290B** | A103 | 2c on 5c (Bl) | 21.00 | 9.25 |
| **291** | A102 | 3c on 2c | 30.00 | 35.00 |
| **292** | A106 | 4c on 5c | 11.00 | 7.25 |
| **292A** | A104 | 4c on 10c (Bk) | 3.25 | 3.25 |
| *b.* | | Double surch., one inverted | | |
| **293** | A106 | 5c on 1c (Bk) | 100.00 | 50.00 |
| **294** | A106 | 6c on 2c (Bk) | 11.00 | 9.50 |
| **295** | A106 | 10c on 6c | 11.00 | 9.50 |
| | | *Nos. 288A-295 (12)* | 341.75 | 240.00 |

Surcharges on Nos. 289, 290, 293, 294 are found double or inverted. Such varieties command a small premium.

Pres. Franklin D. Roosevelt Reviewing Troops — A116

**1945, Nov. 26 Engr. *Perf. 12½***

**Grayish Paper**

| | | | | |
|---|---|---|---|---|
| **296** | A116 | 3c brt violet & blk | .25 | .25 |
| **297** | A116 | 5c dk blue & blk | .45 | .45 |
| | | *Nos. 296-297,C51 (3)* | 2.95 | 2.10 |

In memory of Pres. Franklin D. Roosevelt (1882-1945).

Monrovia Harbor A117

**1947, Jan. 2**

| | | | | |
|---|---|---|---|---|
| **298** | A117 | 5c deep blue | .25 | .25 |

Opening of the Monrovia Harbor Project, Feb. 16, 1946. See No. C52.

**Without Inscription at Top**

**1947, May 16**

| | | | | |
|---|---|---|---|---|
| **299** | A117 | 5c violet | .25 | .25 |

See No. C53.

1st US Postage Stamps and Arms of Liberia — A118

**1947, June 6**

| | | | | |
|---|---|---|---|---|
| **300** | A118 | 5c carmine rose | .25 | .25 |
| | | *Nos. 300,C54-C56 (4)* | 1.20 | 1.00 |

Cent. of US postage stamps and the 87th anniv. of Liberian postal issues.

Matilda Newport Firing Cannon A119

**1947, Dec. 1 Engr. & Photo.**

**Center in Gray Black**

| | | | | |
|---|---|---|---|---|
| **301** | A119 | 1c brt blue green | .25 | .25 |
| **302** | A119 | 3c brt red violet | .25 | .25 |
| **303** | A119 | 5c brt ultra | .60 | .25 |
| **304** | A119 | 10c yellow | 3.25 | .80 |
| | | *Nos. 301-304,C57 (5)* | 5.60 | 1.85 |

125th anniv. of Matilda Newport's defense of Monrovia, Dec. 1, 1822.

Liberian Star — A120

Cent. of Independence: 2c, Liberty. 3c, Liberian Arms. 5c, Map of Liberia.

**1947, Dec. 22 Engr.**

| | | | | |
|---|---|---|---|---|
| **305** | A120 | 1c dark green | .55 | .25 |
| **306** | A120 | 2c brt red vio | .55 | .25 |
| **307** | A120 | 3c brt purple | .55 | .25 |
| **308** | A120 | 5c dark blue | .55 | .25 |
| | | *Nos. 305-308,C58-C60 (7)* | 3.80 | 1.95 |

Centenary of independence.

Natives Approaching Village — A124

Rubber Tapping and Planting A125

Landing of First Colonists A126

Jehudi Ashmun and Defenders — A127

**1949, Apr. 4 Litho. *Perf. 11½***

| | | | | |
|---|---|---|---|---|
| **309** | A124 | 1c multicolored | .45 | .75 |
| **310** | A125 | 2c multicolored | .45 | .75 |
| **311** | A126 | 3c multicolored | .45 | .75 |
| **312** | A127 | 5c multicolored | .45 | .75 |
| | | *Nos. 309-312,C63-C64 (6)* | 2.50 | 4.30 |

Nos. 309-312 exist perf. 12½ and sell at a much lower price. The status of the perf. 12½ set is indefinite.

Stephen Benson A128

Liberian Presidents: 1c, Pres. Joseph J. Roberts. 3c, Daniel B. Warner. 4c, James S. Payne. 5c, Executive mansion. 6c, Edward J. Roye. 7c, A. W. Gardner and A. F. Russell. 8c, Hilary R. W. Johnson. 9c, Joseph J. Cheeseman. 10c, William D. Coleman. 15c, Garretson W. Gibson. 20c, Arthur Barclay. 25c, Daniel E. Howard. 50c, Charles D. B. King. $1, Edwin J. Barclay.

**1948-50 Unwmk. Engr. *Perf. 12½***

**Caption and Portrait in Black**

| | | | | |
|---|---|---|---|---|
| **313** | A128 | 1c green ('48) | 2.75 | *7.00* |
| **314** | A128 | 2c salmon pink | .40 | *.65* |
| **315** | A128 | 3c rose violet | .40 | *.65* |
| *a.* | | "1876-1878" added | 16.00 | *40.00* |
| **316** | A128 | 4c lt olive grn | .90 | .90 |
| **317** | A128 | 5c ultra | .50 | *.90* |
| **318** | A128 | 6c red orange | .90 | *1.75* |
| **319** | A128 | 7c lt blue ('50) | 1.10 | *2.10* |

**320** A128 8c carmine 1.10 *2.40*
**321** A128 9c red violet 1.25 *2.10*
**322** A128 10c yellow ('50) .85 .55
**323** A128 15c yellow orange 1.00 .70
**324** A128 20c blue gray 1.40 1.40
**325** A128 25c cerise 2.00 2.10
**326** A128 50c aqua 3.75 1.40
**327** A128 $1 rose lilac 6.25 1.40
*Nos. 313-327,C65 (16)* 25.15 *26.65*

Issued: 1c, 11/18; 7c, 10c, 1950; others, 7/21/49.

See Nos. 328, 371-378, C65, C118.

Pres. Joseph J. Roberts A129

**1950**

**328** A129 1c green & blk .25 .25

Hand Holding Book — A130

**1950, Feb. 14**

**329** A130 5c deep blue .45 .25

National Literacy Campaign. See No. C66.

**Catalogue values for unused stamps in this section, from this point to the end of the section, are for Never Hinged items.**

UPU Monument — A131

First UPU Building, Bern A132

**1950, Apr. 21 Engr. Unwmk.**

**330** A131 5c green & blk .25 .25
**331** A132 10c red vio & blk .25 .25
*Nos. 330-331,C67 (3)* 3.25 3.25

UPU, 75th anniv. (in 1949).

Exist imperf. Value, $6.50.

Jehudi Ashmun and Seal of Liberia — A133

John Marshall, Ashmun and Map of Town of Marshall A134

Designs (Map or View and Two Portraits): 2c, Careysburg, Gov. Lott Carey (1780-1828), freed American slave, and Jehudi Ashmun (1794-1828), American missionary credited as founder of Liberia. 3c, Town of Harper, Robert Goodloe Harper (1765-1825), American statesman, and Ashmun. 5c, Upper Buchanan, Gov. Thomas Buchanan and Ashmun. 10c, Robertsport, Pres. Joseph J. Roberts and Ashmun.

**1952, Apr. 10** ***Perf. 10½***

**332** A133 1c deep green .25 .25
**333** A133 2c scarlet & ind .30 .25
**334** A133 3c purple & grn .30 .25
**335** A134 4c brown & grn .30 .25
**336** A133 5c ultra & org red .30 .25
**337** A134 10c org red & dk bl .30 .25
*Nos. 332-337,C68-C69 (8)* 2.70 2.45

Nos. 332-337 exist imperf. Value about two and one-half times that of the perf. set.

No. 334 exists with center inverted. Value $50.

See No. C69a.

UN Headquarters Building — A135

Scroll and Flags A136

10c, Liberia arms, letters "UN" and emblem.

**1952, Dec. 20 Unwmk.** ***Perf. 12½***

**338** A135 1c ultra .30 .30
**339** A136 4c car & ultra .30 .30
**340** A136 10c red brn & yel .30 .30
*a.* Souvenir sheet of 3, #338-340 2.00 2.00
*Nos. 338-340,C70 (4)* 1.80 1.55

Nos. 338-340 and 340a exist imperforate. Values: set $5; souvenir sheet $3.50.

Pepper Bird — A137

Roller A138

Hornbill — A138a

Kingfisher — A138b

Jacana — A138c

Weaver — A138d

**1953, Nov. 18** ***Perf. 10½***

**341** A137 1c shown 1.00 .25
**342** A138 3c shown 1.00 .25
**343** A138a 4c yellow & brown 1.60 .25
**344** A138b 5c mauve & bl grn 1.75 .25
**345** A138c 10c grn & dp mag 1.90 .25
**346** A138d 12c brn & org 2.50 .25
*Nos. 341-346 (6)* 9.75 1.50

Exist imperf. Value, set unused $12.

Tennis — A139

**1955, Jan. 26 Litho.** ***Perf. 12½***

**347** A139 3c shown .25 .25
**348** A139 5c Soccer .25 .25
**349** A139 25c Boxing .40 .25
*Nos. 347-349,C88-C90 (6)* 1.80 1.65

Callichilia Stenosepala A140

Various Native Flowers: 7c, Gomphia subcordata. 8c, Listrostachys caudata. 9c, Musaenda isertiana.

**1955, Sept. 28** **Unwmk.**

**350** A140 6c yel grn, org & yel .30 .25
**351** A140 7c emer, yel & car .30 .25
**352** A140 8c yel grn, buff & bl .30 .25
**353** A140 9c orange & green .40 .25
*Nos. 350-353,C91-C92 (6)* 2.10 1.50

Rubber Tapping A141

**1955, Dec. 5** ***Perf. 12½***

**354** A141 5c emerald & yellow .25 .25
*Nos. 354,C97-C98 (3)* 1.20 .75

50th anniv. of Rotary Intl. No. 354 exists printed entirely in emerald.

Statue of Liberty — A142

Coliseum, New York City — A143

Design: 6c, Globe inscribed FIPEX.

**1956, Apr. 28** ***Perf. 12***

**355** A142 3c brt grn & dk red brn .25 .25
**356** A143 4c Prus grn & bis brn .25 .25
**357** A143 6c gray & red lilac .25 .25
*Nos. 355-357,C100-C102 (6)* 2.15 1.50

Fifth International Philatelic Exhibition (FIPEX), NYC, Apr. 28-May 6, 1956.

Kangaroo and Emu — A144

Discus Thrower A145

Designs: 8c, Goddess of Victory and Olympic symbols. 10c, Classic chariot race.

**1956, Nov. 15 Litho. Unwmk.**

**358** A144 4c lt ol grn & gldn brn .25 .25
**359** A145 6c emerald & gray .25 .25
**360** A144 8c lt ultra & redsh brn .25 .25
**361** A144 10c rose red & blk .40 .25
*Nos. 358-361,C104-C105 (6)* 2.15 2.00

16th Olympic Games at Melbourne, Nov. 22-Dec. 8, 1956.

Nos. 358-361 exist imperf.

Idlewild Airport, New York
A146

Roberts Field, Liberia, plane & Pres. Tubman — A146a

**Lithographed and Engraved**

**1957, May 4** *Perf. 12*

**362** A146 3c orange & dk blue .25 .25
**363** A146a 5c red lilac & blk .25 .25
*Nos. 362-363,C107-C110 (6)* 3.15 1.50

1st anniv. of direct air service between Roberts Field, Liberia, and Idlewild (Kennedy), NY. See Nos. C107-C110.

Orphanage Playground — A147

Orphanage and: 5c, Teacher and pupil. 6c, Singing boys and natl. anthem. 10c, Children and flag.

**1957, Nov. 25** **Litho.** *Perf. 12*

**364** A147 4c green & red .25 .25
**365** A147 5c bl grn & red brn .25 .25
**366** A147 6c brt vio & bis .25 .25
**367** A147 10c ultra & rose car .25 .25
*Nos. 364-367,C111-C112 (6)* 2.25 1.50

Founding of the Antoinette Tubman Child Welfare Foundation.

Windmill and Dutch Flag
A148

Designs: No. 369, German flag and Brandenburg Gate. No. 370, Swedish flag, palace and crowns.

**Engraved and Lithographed**

**1958, Jan. 10** **Unwmk.** *Perf. 10½*

**Flags in Original Colors**

**368** A148 5c reddish brn .25 .25
**369** A148 5c blue .25 .25
**370** A148 5c lilac rose .25 .25
*Nos. 368-370,C114-C117 (7)* 2.55 2.55

European tour of Pres. Tubman in 1956. Exist imperf.

**Presidential Types of 1948-50**

Designs as before.

**1958-60** **Engr.** *Perf. 12*

**Caption and Portrait in Black**

**371** A129 1c salmon pink .45 .25
**372** A128 2c brt yellow .45 .25
**373** A128 10c blue gray .55 .55
**374** A128 15c brt bl & blk ('59) .25 .25
**375** A128 20c dark red .65 .65
**376** A128 25c blue .65 .65
**377** A128 50c red lil & blk ('59) .75 .65
**378** A128 $1 bister brn ('60) 5.75 .75
*Nos. 371-378,C118 (9)* 10.75 4.90

Many shades of 1c.

Open Globe Projection — A149

Designs: 5c, UN Emblem and building. 10c, UN Emblem. 12c, UN Emblem and initials of agencies.

**1958, Dec. 10** **Litho.** *Perf. 12*

**379** A149 3c gray, bl & blk .30 .25
**380** A149 5c blue & choc .25 .25
**381** A149 10c black & org .40 .25
**382** A149 12c black & car 1.10 1.10
*Nos. 379-382 (4)* 2.05 1.85

10th anniv. of the Universal Declaration of Human Rights. See No. C119.

People of Africa on the March — A150

**1959, Apr. 15**

**383** A150 20c orange & brown .45 .45

African Freedom Day, Apr. 15. Exists imperf. See No. C120.

Symbols of UNESCO — A151

**1959, May 11** **Unwmk.**

**384** A151 25c dp plum & emer .55 .55

Opening of UNESCO Headquarters in Paris, Nov. 3, 1958. Exists imperf. See Nos. C121, C121a.

Abraham Lincoln — A152

**1959, Nov. 20** **Engr.** *Perf. 12*

**385** A152 10c ultra & blk .40 .40
**386** A152 15c orange & blk .40 .40
*a.* Souv. sheet of 3, Nos. 385-386, C122, imperf. 2.50 4.00
*Nos. 385-386,C122 (3)* 1.70 1.70

150th anniv. of the birth of Abraham Lincoln.

Touré, Tubman and Nkrumah
A153

**1960, Jan. 27** **Litho.** **Unwmk.**

**387** A153 25c crimson & blk .55 .55

1959 "Big Three" conference of Pres. Sékou Touré of Guinea, Pres. William V. S. Tubman of Liberia and Prime Minister Kwame Nkrumah of Ghana at Saniquellie, Liberia. See No. C123.

World Refugee Year Emblem — A154

**1960, Apr. 7** *Perf. 11½*

**388** A154 25c emerald & blk .70 1.00

World Refuge Year, July 1, 1959-June 30, 1960. See No. C124, C124a. Exist imperf.

Map of Africa — A155

**1960, May 11** **Litho.** *Perf. 11½*

**389** A155 25c green & black .60 .60

10th anniv. of the Commission for Technical Cooperation in Africa South of the Sahara (C.C.T.A.). See No. C125.

Weight Lifter and Porter — A156

Designs: 10c, Rower and canoeists, horiz. 15c, Walker and porter.

**1960, Sept. 6** **Unwmk.**

**390** A156 5c dk brn & emer .25 .25
**391** A156 10c brown & red lil .25 .25
**392** A156 15c brown & org .70 .75
*Nos. 390-392,C126 (4)* 2.10 1.95

17th Olympic Games, Rome, 8/25-9/11. Exist imperf.

Liberian Stamps of 1860 — A157

**1960, Dec. 1** **Litho.** *Perf. 11½*

**393** A157 5c multicolored .25 .25
**394** A157 20c multicolored .70 .70
*Nos. 393-394,C128 (3)* 1.95 1.95

Liberian postage stamps, cent.

Laurel Wreath — A158

**1961, May 19** **Unwmk.** *Perf. 11½*

**395** A158 25c red & dk blue .60 .60

Liberia's membership in the UN Security Council. Exists imperf. Value, Nos. 395, C130 $6.

See Nos. C130-C131 and note after No. C131.

Anatomy Class — A159

**1961, Sept. 8** *Perf. 11½*

**396** A159 25c green & brown .60 .60

15th anniv. of UNESCO. Nos. 396 and C132 exist imperf. Value, $3.
See Nos. C132-C133.

Joseph J. Roberts Monument, Monrovia — A160

Design: 10c, Pres. Roberts and old and new presidential mansions, horiz.

**1961, Oct. 25** **Litho.**

**397** A160 5c orange & sepia .25 .25
**398** A160 10c ultra & sepia .45 .25
*Nos. 397-398,C134 (3)* 1.40 1.20

150th anniv. of the birth of Joseph J. Roberts, 1st pres. of Liberia. Exist imperf.

Boy Scout
A161

Design: Insignia and Scouts camping.

**1961, Dec. 4** **Unwmk.** *Perf. 11½*

**399** A161 5c lilac & sepia .25 .25
**400** A161 10c ultra & bister .50 .50
*Nos. 399-400,C135 (3)* 2.15 2.15

Boy Scouts of Liberia. Exist imperf. Value, $5.50.

Dag Hammarskjold and UN Emblem — A162

**1962, Feb. 1** *Perf. 12*

**401** A162 20c black & ultra .45 .45

Dag Hammarskjold, Secretary General of the UN, 1953-61. See Nos. C137-C138.

Malaria Eradication Emblem — A163

**1962, Apr. 7** **Litho.** *Perf. 12½*

**402** A163 25c dk green & red .55 .45

WHO drive to eradicate malaria. Nos. 402, C137 exist imperf. Value, $5.
See Nos. C139-C140.

United Nations Emblem A164

**1962, Oct. 22** *Perf. 12x12½*

**403** A164 20c green & yel bister .35 .35

Issued to mark the observance of United Nations Day, Oct. 24, as a national holiday.

See Nos. C144-C145.

Executive Mansion, Monrovia A165

1c, 80c, Executive Mansion, Monrovia. 5c, Treasury Department Building, Monrovia. 10c, Information Service. 15c, Capitol.

**1962-64**

**403A** A165 1c vio bl & dp org ('64) .25 .25
**404** A165 5c lt blue & pur .25 .25
**405** A165 10c bister & brn .25 .25
**406** A165 15c salmon & dk bl .40 .30
**406A** A165 80c brn & yel ('64) 1.75 1.20
*Nos. 403A-406A,C146-C148 (9)* 8.35 6.30

See Nos. C146-C148.

"FAO" Emblem and Food Bowl — A166

**1963, Mar. 21** *Perf. 12½*

**407** A166 5c aqua & dk car .40 .25

FAO "Freedom from Hunger" campaign. See Nos. C149-C150.

Rocket in Space A167

Design: 15c, Space capsule and globe.

**1963, May 27** **Litho.** *Perf. 12½*

**408** A167 10c dp vio bl & yel .25 .25
**409** A167 15c blue & red brn .60 .60
*Nos. 408-409,C151 (3)* 1.40 1.25

Achievements in space exploration for peaceful purposes. Exist imperf. Value, $8.

Red Cross A168

10c, Centenary emblem and torch, vert.

**1963, Aug. 26** **Unwmk.** *Perf. 11½*

**410** A168 5c blue grn & red .25 .25
**411** A168 10c gray & red .25 .25
*Nos. 410-411,C153-C154 (4)* 1.60 1.60

Intl. Red Cross, cent. See Nos. C153-C154.

Palm Tree and Scroll — A169

**1963, Oct. 28** *Perf. 12½*

**412** A169 20c brown & green .40 .40

Conference of African heads of state for African Unity, Addis Ababa, May, 1963. See No. C156.

Ski Jump — A170

**1963, Dec. 11** **Unwmk.** *Perf. 12½*

**413** A170 5c rose red & dk vio bl .25 .25
*Nos. 413,C157-C158 (3)* 1.30 1.30

9th Winter Olympic Games, Innsbruck, Austria, Jan. 29-Feb. 9, 1964. Exist imperf. Value, $6.

John F. Kennedy A171

**1964, Apr. 6** **Litho.**

**414** A171 20c blk & brt blue .35 .35

John F. Kennedy (1917-63). Nos. 414, C160 exist imperf. Value, set $5.

See Nos. C160-C161.

Syncom Satellite A172

Satellites: 15c, Relay I, vert. 25c, Mariner II.

**1964, June 22** **Unwmk.** *Perf. 12½*

**415** A172 10c orange & emer .30 .25
**416** A172 15c brt car rose & vio .40 .25
**417** A172 25c blue, org & blk .40 .70
*Nos. 415-417 (3)* 1.10 1.20

Progress in space communications and the peaceful uses of outer space. See No. C162. Exist imperf. Value, set $9.

Mt. Fuji — A173

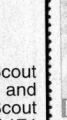

Designs: 15c, Torii and Olympic flame. 25c, Cherry blossoms and stadium.

**1964, Sept. 15** **Litho.**

**418** A173 10c orange yel & emer .25 .25
**419** A173 15c lt red & purple .25 .25
**420** A173 25c ocher & red .95 .95
*Nos. 418-420 (3)* 1.45 1.45

Issued for the 18th Olympic Games, Tokyo, Oct. 10-25, 1964. See No. C163. Exist imperf. Value, set $9.

Boy Scout Emblem and Scout Sign — A174

10c, Bugle and Liberian Scout emblem, horiz.

**1965, Mar. 8** **Litho.** *Perf. 12½*

**421** A174 5c lt blue & brown .30 .25
**422** A174 10c dk green & ocher .40 .25
*Nos. 421-422,C164 (3)* 1.50 1.30

Liberian Boy Scouts. Exist imperf. Value, set $8.

"Emancipation" by Thomas Ball — A175

Designs: 20c, Abraham Lincoln and John F. Kennedy, horiz. 25c, Lincoln by Augustus St. Gaudens, Lincoln Park, Chicago.

**1965, May 3** **Unwmk.** *Perf. 12½*

**423** A175 5c dk gray & brn org .25 .25
**424** A175 20c emer & lt gray .50 .50
**425** A175 25c maroon & blue .65 .65
*Nos. 423-425 (3)* 1.40 1.40

Centenary of the death of Abraham Lincoln. Exist imperf. Value, set $9.

See No. C166.

ICY Emblem A176

**1965, June 21** **Litho.** *Perf. 12½*

**426** A176 12c orange & brn .40 .25
**427** A176 25c vio blue & brn .75 .40
**428** A176 50c emerald & brn 1.50 .85
*Nos. 426-428 (3)* 2.65 1.50

Intl. Cooperation Year. See No. C167.

ITU Emblem, Old and New Communication Equipment — A177

**1965, Sept. 21** **Unwmk.** *Perf. 12½*

**429** A177 25c brt grn & red brn .40 .40
**430** A177 35c black & car rose .50 .50
*Nos. 429-430,C168 (3)* 1.70 1.60

Cent. of the ITU.

Pres. Tubman and Liberian Flag — A178

**1965, Nov. 29** **Litho.**

**431** A178 25c red, ultra & brn .60 .60

Pres. William V. S. Tubman's 70th birthday. See No. C169, C169a.

Churchill in Admiral's Uniform A179

Designs: 15c, Churchill giving "V" sign, vert.

**1966, Jan. 18** **Litho.** *Perf. 12½*

**432** A179 15c orange & blk .40 .25
**433** A179 20c black & brt grn .90 .90
*Nos. 432-433,C170 (3)* 2.00 1.70

Issued in memory of Sir Winston Spencer Churchill (1874-1965), statesman and World War II leader. Exist imperf. Value, set $6.

Pres. Joseph J. Roberts — A180

Presidents: 2c, Stephen Benson. 3c, Daniel Bashiel Warner. 4c, James S. Payne. 5c, Edward James Roye. 10c, William D. Coleman. 25c, Daniel Edward Howard. 50c, Charles Dunbar Burgess King. 80c, Hilary R. W. Johnson. $1, Edwin J. Barclay. $2, Joseph James Cheeseman ("Cheesman" on stamp).

**1966-69** **Litho.** *Perf. 12½*

**434** A180 1c black & brick red .25 .25
**435** A180 2c black & yellow .25 .25
**436** A180 3c black & lilac .25 .25
**437** A180 4c ap grn & blk ('67) .25 .25
**438** A180 5c black & dull org .25 .25
**439** A180 10c pale grn & blk ('67) .25 .25
**440** A180 25c black & lt blue .60 .25
**441** A180 50c blk & brt lil rose 1.25 .90
**442** A180 80c dp rose & blk ('67) 1.90 1.10
**443** A180 $1 black & ocher 2.25 .25

*Perf. 11½x11*

**443A** A180 $2 blk & dp red lil ('69) 4.50 3.00
*Nos. 434-443A,C182 (12)* 12.60 7.30

Soccer Players and Globe A181

Designs: 25c, World Championships Cup, ball and shoes, vert. 35c, Soccer player dribbling, vert.

**1966, May 3** **Litho.** *Perf. 12½*

**444** A181 10c brt green & dk brn .40 .25
**445** A181 25c brt pink & brn .60 .30
**446** A181 35c brown & orange .80 .45
*Nos. 444-446 (3)* 1.80 1.00

World Cup Soccer Championships, Wembley, England, July 11-30. Exist imperf. Value, $14.

See No. C172.

Pres. Kennedy Taking Oath of Office A182

20c, 1964 Kennedy stamps, #414, C160.

**1966, Aug. 16** **Litho.** *Perf. 12½*

**447** A182 15c red & blk .25 .25
**448** A182 20c brt bl & red lil .30 .30
*Nos. 447-448,C173-C174 (4)* 1.45 1.05

3rd anniv. of Pres. Kennedy's death (Nov. 22). Exist imperf. Value, set $12.

Children on Seesaw and UNICEF Emblem
A183

Design: 80c, Boy playing doctor.

**1966, Oct. 25 Unwmk. *Perf. 12½***

| | | | | |
|---|---|---|---|---|
| **449** | A183 | 5c brt blue & red | .35 | .25 |
| **450** | A183 | 80c org brn & yel grn | .90 | .90 |

20th anniv. of UNICEF.

Giraffe — A184

Designs: 3c, Lion. 5c, Slender-nosed crocodile, horiz. 10c, Baby chimpanzees. 15c, Leopard, horiz. 20c, Black rhinoceros, horiz. 25c, Elephant.

**1966, Dec. 20**

| | | | | |
|---|---|---|---|---|
| **451** | A184 | 2c multicolored | 1.00 | .25 |
| **452** | A184 | 3c multicolored | 1.00 | .25 |
| **453** | A184 | 5c multicolored | 1.00 | .25 |
| *a.* | | Black omitted ("5¢ LIBERIA" and imprint) | *50.00* | |
| **454** | A184 | 10c multicolored | 1.00 | .25 |
| **455** | A184 | 15c multicolored | 1.10 | .30 |
| **456** | A184 | 20c multicolored | 1.75 | .55 |
| **457** | A184 | 25c multicolored | 2.40 | .65 |
| | | *Nos. 451-457 (7)* | 9.25 | 2.50 |

Jamboree Badge — A185

Designs: 25c, Boy Scout emblem and various sports, horiz. 40c, Scout at campfire and vision of moon landing, horiz.

**1967, Mar. 23 Litho. *Perf. 12½***

| | | | | |
|---|---|---|---|---|
| **458** | A185 | 10c brt lil rose & grn | .25 | .25 |
| **459** | A185 | 25c brt red & blue | .55 | .55 |
| **460** | A185 | 40c brt grn & brn org | 1.00 | .85 |
| | | *Nos. 458-460 (3)* | 1.80 | 1.65 |

12th Boy Scout World Jamboree, Farragut State Park, Idaho, Aug. 1-9. Exist imperf. Value, set $9.

See No. C176.

A186

Pre-Hispanic Sculpture of Mexico: 25c, Aztec Calendar and Olympic rings. 40c, Mexican pottery, sombrero and guitar, horiz.

**1967, June 20 Litho. *Perf. 12½***

| | | | | |
|---|---|---|---|---|
| **461** | A186 | 10c ocher & violet | .25 | .25 |
| **462** | A186 | 25c lt bl, org & blk | .50 | .25 |
| **463** | A186 | 40c yel grn & car | .75 | .50 |
| | | *Nos. 461-463 (3)* | 1.50 | 1.00 |

Issued to publicize the 19th Olympic Games, Mexico City. Exist imperf. Value, set $8.

See No. C177.

A187

Designs: 5c, WHO Office for Africa, horiz. 80c, WHO Office for Africa.

**1967, Aug. 28 Litho. *Perf. 12½***

| | | | | |
|---|---|---|---|---|
| **464** | A187 | 5c blue & ol bister | .25 | .25 |
| **465** | A187 | 80c emer & ol bister | 1.50 | 1.50 |

Inauguration of the WHO Regional Office for Africa in Brazzaville, Congo.

Boy Playing African Rattle — A188

Africans Playing Native Instruments: 3c, Tom-tom and soko violin, horiz. 5c, Mang harp, horiz. 10c, Alimilim. 15c, Xylophone drums. 25c, Large tom-toms. 35c, Large harp.

**1967, Oct. 16 Litho. *Perf. 14***

| | | | | |
|---|---|---|---|---|
| **466** | A188 | 2c violet & multi | .25 | .25 |
| **467** | A188 | 3c blue & multi | .25 | .25 |
| **468** | A188 | 5c lilac rose & multi | .25 | .25 |
| **469** | A188 | 10c yel grn & multi | .25 | .25 |
| **470** | A188 | 15c violet & multi | .40 | .25 |
| **471** | A188 | 25c ocher & multi | .80 | .40 |
| **472** | A188 | 35c dp rose & multi | 1.25 | .65 |
| | | *Nos. 466-472 (7)* | 3.45 | 2.30 |

Ice Hockey — A189

Designs: 25c, Ski jump. 40c, Bobsledding.

**1967, Nov. 20 Litho. *Perf. 12½***

| | | | | |
|---|---|---|---|---|
| **473** | A189 | 10c emer & vio bl | .25 | .25 |
| **474** | A189 | 25c grnsh bl & dp plum | .35 | .25 |
| **475** | A189 | 40c ocher & org brn | .60 | .50 |
| | | *Nos. 473-475 (3)* | 1.20 | 1.00 |

10th Winter Olympic Games, Grenoble, France, Feb. 6-18, 1968. See No. C178.

Pres. William Tubman — A190

**1967, Dec. 22 Litho. *Perf. 12½***

| | | | | |
|---|---|---|---|---|
| **476** | A190 | 25c ultra & brown | .75 | .30 |

**Souvenir Sheet**

***Imperf***

| | | | | |
|---|---|---|---|---|
| **477** | A190 | 50c ultra & brown | 2.00 | 2.00 |

Inauguration of President Tubman, Jan. 1, 1968. No. 476 exists imperf. No. 477 contains one stamp with simulated perforations and picture frame.

Human Rights Flame — A191

**1968, Apr. 26 Litho. *Perf. 12½***

| | | | | |
|---|---|---|---|---|
| **478** | A191 | 3c ver & dp bl | .25 | .25 |
| **479** | A191 | 80c brown & emer | 1.25 | 1.25 |

Intl. Human Rights Year. See No. C179. Exist imperf.

Martin Luther King, Jr. — A192

Designs: 15c, Mule-drawn hearse and Dr. King. 35c, Dr. King and Lincoln monument by Daniel Chester French, horiz.

**1968, July 11 Unwmk. *Perf. 12½***

| | | | | |
|---|---|---|---|---|
| **480** | A192 | 15c brt bl & brn | .25 | .25 |
| **481** | A192 | 25c indigo & brn | .40 | .25 |
| **482** | A192 | 35c olive & blk | .65 | .40 |
| | | *Nos. 480-482 (3)* | 1.30 | .90 |

Rev. Dr. Martin Luther King, Jr. (1929-1968), American civil rights leader. Value, set $8.

See No. C180. Exist imperf.

Javelin and Diana Statue, Mexico City — A193

Designs: 25c, Discus, pyramid and serpent god Quetzalcoatl. 35c, Woman diver and Xochicalco from ruins near Cuernavaca.

**1968, Aug. 22 Litho. *Perf. 12½***

| | | | | |
|---|---|---|---|---|
| **483** | A193 | 15c dp vio & org brn | .30 | .25 |
| **484** | A193 | 25c red & brt blue | .50 | .25 |
| **485** | A193 | 35c brown & emer | .85 | .45 |
| | | *Nos. 483-485 (3)* | 1.65 | .95 |

19th Olympic Games, Mexico City, Oct. 12-27. Exist imperf. Value, set $7.

See No. C181.

Pres. Wm. V. S. Tubman
A194

Unification Monument, Voinjama-Lofa County — A195

**1968, Dec. 30 Unwmk. *Perf. 12½***

| | | | | |
|---|---|---|---|---|
| **486** | A194 | 25c silver, blk & brn | 1.25 | .55 |

**Souvenir Sheet**

***Imperf***

| | | | | |
|---|---|---|---|---|
| **487** | A195 | 80c silver, ultra & red | 2.00 | 2.00 |

25th anniv. of Pres. Tubman's administration.

"ILO" with Cogwheel and Wreath
A196

**1969, Apr. 16 Litho. *Perf. 12½***

| | | | | |
|---|---|---|---|---|
| **488** | A196 | 25c lt blue & gold | .55 | .40 |

50th anniv. of the ILO. Exists imperf. See No. C183.

Red Roofs, by Camille Pissarro — A197

Paintings: 3c, Prince Balthasar Carlos on Horseback, by Velazquez, vert. 10c, David and Goliath, by Caravaggio. 12c, Still Life, by Jean Baptiste Chardin. 15c, The Last Supper, by Leonardo da Vinci. 20c, Regatta at Argenteuil, by Claude Monet. 25c, Judgment of Solomon, by Giorgione. 35c, Sistine Madonna, by Raphael.

**1969, June 26 Litho. *Perf. 11***

| | | | | |
|---|---|---|---|---|
| **489** | A197 | 3c gray & multi | .25 | .25 |
| **490** | A197 | 5c gray & multi | .25 | .25 |
| **491** | A197 | 10c lt blue & multi | .25 | .25 |
| **492** | A197 | 12c gray & multi | .40 | .25 |
| **493** | A197 | 15c gray & multi | .40 | .25 |
| **494** | A197 | 20c gray & multi | .55 | .25 |
| **495** | A197 | 25c gray & multi | .75 | .25 |
| **496** | A197 | 35c gray & multi | 1.10 | .35 |
| | | *Nos. 489-496 (8)* | 3.95 | 2.10 |

See Nos. 502-509.

African Development Bank Emblem — A198

**1969, Aug. 12 Litho. *Perf. 12½***

| | | | | |
|---|---|---|---|---|
| **497** | A198 | 25c blue & brown | .55 | .35 |
| **498** | A198 | 80c yel grn & red | 1.40 | .65 |

5th anniversary of the African Development Bank. Exist imperf.

Moon Landing and Liberia No. C174 — A199

15c, Memorial tablet left on moon, rocket, earth & moon, horiz. 35c, Take-off from moon.

**1969, Oct. 15 Litho. *Perf. 12½***

| | | | | |
|---|---|---|---|---|
| **499** | A199 | 15c blue & bister | .55 | .25 |
| **500** | A199 | 25c dk vio bl & org | .80 | .25 |
| **501** | A199 | 35c gray & red | 1.25 | .25 |
| | | *Nos. 499-501 (3)* | 2.60 | .75 |

Man's 1st landing on the moon, July 20, 1969. US astronauts Neil A. Armstrong and Col. Edwin E. Aldrin, Jr., with Lieut. Col. Michael Collins piloting Apollo 11. Exist imperf. Value, set $10.

See No. C184.

### Painting Type of 1969

Paintings: 3c, The Gleaners, by Francois Millet. 5c, View of Toledo, by El Greco, vert. 10c, Heads of Negroes, by Rubens. 12c, The Last Supper, by El Greco. 15c, Dancing Peasants, by Brueghel. 20c, Hunters in the Snow, by Brueghel. 25c, Detail from Descent from the Cross, by Rogier van der Weyden, vert. 35c, The Ascension, by Murillo (inscribed "The Conception"), vert.

**1969, Nov. 18 Litho. *Perf. 11***

| | | | | |
|---|---|---|---|---|
| **502** | A197 | 3c lt blue & multi | .25 | .25 |
| **503** | A197 | 5c lt blue & multi | .25 | .25 |
| **504** | A197 | 10c lt blue & multi | .25 | .25 |
| **505** | A197 | 12c gray & multi | .40 | .25 |
| **506** | A197 | 15c gray & multi | .45 | .25 |
| **507** | A197 | 20c lt blue & multi | .55 | .25 |
| **508** | A197 | 25c gray & multi | .80 | .30 |
| **509** | A197 | 35c lt blue & multi | 1.00 | .30 |
| | | *Nos. 502-509 (8)* | 3.95 | 2.10 |

Peace Dove, UN Emblem and Atom — A200

**1970, Apr. 16 Litho. *Perf. 12½***

| | | | | |
|---|---|---|---|---|
| **510** | A200 | 5c green & silver | .25 | .25 |

25th anniv. of the UN. Exists imperf.

See No. C185.

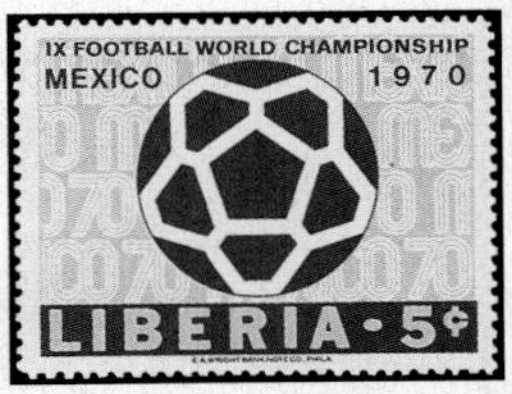


Official Emblem A201

Designs: 10c, Statue of rain god Tlaloc, vert. 25c, Jules Rimet cup and sculptured wall, vert. 35c, Sombrero and soccer ball. 55c, Two soccer players.

**1970, June 10 Litho. *Perf. 12½***

| | | | | |
|---|---|---|---|---|
| **511** | A201 | 5c pale blue & brn | .25 | .25 |
| **512** | A201 | 10c emerald & ocher | .30 | .25 |
| **513** | A201 | 25c dp rose lil & gold | .55 | .25 |
| **514** | A201 | 35c ver & ultra | .80 | .35 |
| | | *Nos. 511-514 (4)* | 1.90 | 1.10 |

**Souvenir Sheet**

***Perf. 11½***

| | | | | |
|---|---|---|---|---|
| **515** | A201 | 55c brt bl, yel & grn | 1.60 | 1.25 |

9th World Soccer Championships for the Jules Rimet Cup, Mexico City, May 30-June 21, 1970. Exist imperf.

EXPO '70 Emblem, Japanese Singer and Festival Plaza — A202

Designs (EXPO '70 Emblem and): 3c, Male Japanese singer, EXPO Hall and floating stage. 5c, Tower of the Sun and view of exhibition. 7c, Tanabata Festival. 8c, Awa Dance Festival. 25c, Sado-Okesa Dance Festival. 50c, Ricoh Pavilion with "eye," and Mt. Fuji, vert.

**1970, July Litho. *Perf. 11***

| | | | | |
|---|---|---|---|---|
| **516** | A202 | 2c multicolored | .25 | .25 |
| **517** | A202 | 3c multicolored | .25 | .25 |
| **518** | A202 | 5c multicolored | .30 | .25 |
| **519** | A202 | 7c multicolored | .45 | .25 |
| **520** | A202 | 8c multicolored | .55 | .25 |
| **521** | A202 | 25c multicolored | 1.40 | .30 |
| | | *Nos. 516-521 (6)* | 3.20 | 1.55 |

**Souvenir Sheet**

| | | | | |
|---|---|---|---|---|
| **522** | A202 | 50c multicolored | 2.50 | .75 |

Issued to publicize EXPO '70 International Exhibition, Osaka, Japan, Mar. 15-Sept. 13.

UPU Headquarters and Monument, Bern — A203

Design: 80c, Like 25c, vert.

**1970, Aug. 25 *Perf. 12½***

| | | | | |
|---|---|---|---|---|
| **523** | A203 | 25c blue & multi | 1.00 | .35 |
| **524** | A203 | 80c multicolored | 1.60 | .90 |

Inauguration of the new UPU Headquarters in Bern. Exist imperf.

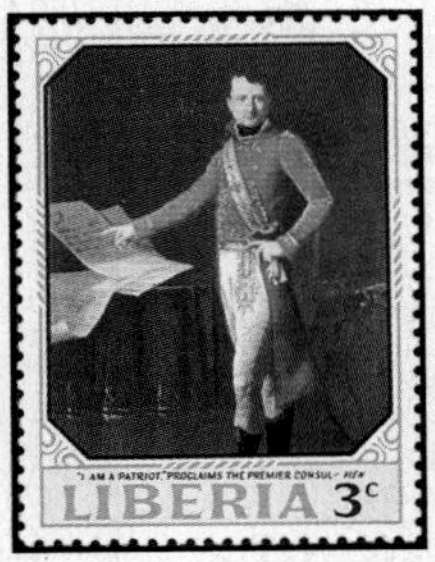


Napoleon as Consul, by Joseph Marie Vien, Sr. — A204

Paintings of Napoleon: 5c, Visit to a School, by unknown painter. 10c, Napoleon Bonaparte, by François Pascal Gerard. 12c, The French Campaign, by Ernest Meissonier. 20c, Napoleon Signing Abdication at Fontainebleau, by François Bouchot. 25c, Napoleon Meets Pope Pius VII, by Jean-Louis Demarne. 50c, Napoleon's Coronation, by Jacques Louis David.

**1970, Oct. 20 Litho. *Perf. 11***

| | | | | |
|---|---|---|---|---|
| **525** | A204 | 3c blue & multi | .25 | .25 |
| **526** | A204 | 5c blue & multi | .25 | .25 |
| **527** | A204 | 10c blue & multi | .45 | .25 |
| **528** | A204 | 12c blue & multi | .65 | .25 |
| **529** | A204 | 20c blue & multi | .95 | .25 |
| **530** | A204 | 25c blue & multi | 1.75 | .25 |
| | | *Nos. 525-530 (6)* | 4.30 | 1.50 |

**Souvenir Sheet**

***Imperf***

| | | | | |
|---|---|---|---|---|
| **531** | A204 | 50c blue & multi | 2.50 | .50 |

200th anniv. of the birth of Napoleon Bonaparte (1769-1821). No. 531 contains one stamp with simulated perforations.

Pres. Tubman A205

**1970, Nov. 20 Litho. *Perf. 13½***

| | | | | |
|---|---|---|---|---|
| **532** | A205 | 25c multicolored | .90 | .35 |

**Souvenir Sheet**

***Imperf***

| | | | | |
|---|---|---|---|---|
| **533** | A205 | 50c multicolored | 1.60 | 1.10 |

Pres. Tubman's 75th birthday. No. 533 contains one imperf. stamp with simulated perforations.

Adoration of the Kings, by Rogier van der Weyden — A206

Paintings (Adoration of the Kings, by): 5c, Hans Memling. 10c, Stefan Lochner. 12c, Albrecht Altdorfer, vert. 20c, Hugo van der Goes, Adoration of the Shepherds. 25c, Hieronymus Bosch, vert. 50c, Andrea Mantegna (triptych).

***Perf. 13½x14, 14x13½***

**1970, Dec. 21 Litho.**

| | | | | |
|---|---|---|---|---|
| **534** | A206 | 3c multicolored | .25 | .25 |
| **535** | A206 | 5c multicolored | .25 | .25 |
| **536** | A206 | 10c multicolored | .30 | .25 |
| **537** | A206 | 12c multicolored | .40 | .25 |
| **538** | A206 | 20c multicolored | .40 | .25 |
| **539** | A206 | 25c multicolored | .70 | .25 |
| | | *Nos. 534-539 (6)* | 2.30 | 1.50 |

**Souvenir Sheet**

***Imperf***

| | | | | |
|---|---|---|---|---|
| **540** | A206 | 50c multicolored | 2.50 | .60 |

Christmas 1970.
No. 540 contains one 60x40mm stamp.

Dogon Tribal Mask A207

African Tribal Ceremonial Masks: 2c, Bapendé. 5c, Baoulé. 6c, Dédougou. 9c, Dan. 15c, Bamiléké. 20c, Bapendé mask and costume. 25c, Bamiléké mask and costume.

**1971, Feb. 24 Litho. *Perf. 11***

| | | | | |
|---|---|---|---|---|
| **541** | A207 | 2c lt green & multi | .25 | .25 |
| **542** | A207 | 3c pink & multi | .25 | .25 |
| **543** | A207 | 5c lt blue & multi | .25 | .25 |
| **544** | A207 | 6c lt green & multi | .25 | .25 |
| **545** | A207 | 9c lt blue & multi | .25 | .25 |
| **546** | A207 | 15c pink & multi | .45 | .25 |
| **547** | A207 | 20c lt green & multi | .55 | .35 |
| **548** | A207 | 25c pink & multi | .75 | .35 |
| | | *Nos. 541-548 (8)* | 3.00 | 2.20 |

Astronauts on Moon — A208

Designs: 5c, Astronaut and lunar transport vehicle. 10c, Astronaut with US flag on moon. 12c, Space capsule in Pacific Ocean. 20c, Astronaut leaving capsule. 25c, Astronauts Alan B. Shepard, Stuart A. Roosa and Edgar D. Mitchell.

**1971, May 20 Litho. *Perf. 13½***

| | | | | |
|---|---|---|---|---|
| **549** | A208 | 3c vio blue & multi | .25 | .25 |
| **550** | A208 | 5c vio blue & multi | .25 | .25 |
| **551** | A208 | 10c vio blue & multi | .35 | .25 |
| **552** | A208 | 12c vio blue & multi | .50 | .25 |
| **553** | A208 | 20c vio blue & multi | .75 | .25 |
| **554** | A208 | 25c vio blue & multi | .90 | .35 |
| | | *Nos. 549-554 (6)* | 3.00 | 1.60 |

Apollo 14 moon landing, Jan. 31-Feb. 9. Exist imperf.

See No. C186.

Map, Liberian Women and Pres. Tubman A209

3c, Pres. Tubman & women at ballot box, vert.

**1971, May 27 *Perf. 12½***

| | | | | |
|---|---|---|---|---|
| **555** | A209 | 3c ultra & brn | .25 | .25 |
| **556** | A209 | 80c green & brn | 1.75 | 1.75 |

25th anniversary of women's suffrage.

Hall of Honor, Munich, and Olympic Flag — A210

Munich Views and Olympic Flag: 5c, General view. 10c, National Museum. 12c, Max Joseph's Square. 20c, Propylaeum on King's Square. 25c, Liesel-Karlstadt Fountain.

**1971, June 28 Litho. *Perf. 11***

| | | | | |
|---|---|---|---|---|
| **557** | A210 | 3c multicolored | .25 | .25 |
| **558** | A210 | 5c multicolored | .25 | .25 |
| **559** | A210 | 10c multicolored | .25 | .25 |
| **560** | A210 | 12c multicolored | .30 | .25 |
| **561** | A210 | 20c multicolored | .55 | .25 |
| **562** | A210 | 25c multicolored | .80 | .35 |
| | | *Nos. 557-562 (6)* | 2.40 | 1.60 |

Publicity for the 20th Summer Olympic Games, Munich, Germany, 1972. Exist imperf. Value, set $7.50.

See No. C187.

Boy Scout, Emblem and US Flag — A211

Boy Scout, Natl. Flag & Boy Scout Emblem of: 5c, German Federal Republic. 10c, Australia. 12c, Great Britain. 20c, Japan. 25c, Liberia.

**1971, Aug. 6 Litho. *Perf. 13½***

| | | | | |
|---|---|---|---|---|
| **563** | A211 | 3c multicolored | .25 | .25 |
| **564** | A211 | 5c multicolored | .25 | .25 |
| **565** | A211 | 10c multicolored | .25 | .25 |
| **566** | A211 | 12c multicolored | .30 | .25 |
| **567** | A211 | 20c multicolored | .50 | .25 |
| **568** | A211 | 25c multicolored | .75 | .25 |
| | | *Nos. 563-568 (6)* | 2.30 | 1.50 |

13th Boy Scout World Jamboree, Asagiri Plain, Japan, Aug. 2-10. Exist imperf.
See No. C188.

Pres. Tubman (1895-1971) A212

**1971, Aug. 23 *Perf. 12½***

| | | | | |
|---|---|---|---|---|
| **569** | A212 | 3c black, ultra & brn | .25 | .25 |
| **570** | A212 | 25c blk, brt rose lil & brn | .80 | .80 |

Zebra and UNICEF Emblem — A213

Animals (UNICEF Emblem and Animals with their Young): 7c, Koala. 8c, Llama. 10c, Red fox. 20c, Monkey. 25c, Brown bear.

**1971, Oct. 1 *Perf. 11***

| | | | | |
|---|---|---|---|---|
| **571** | A213 | 5c multicolored | .25 | .25 |
| **572** | A213 | 7c multicolored | .40 | .25 |
| **573** | A213 | 8c multicolored | .40 | .25 |
| **574** | A213 | 10c multicolored | .55 | .25 |
| **575** | A213 | 20c multicolored | 1.00 | .35 |
| **576** | A213 | 25c multicolored | 1.25 | .45 |
| | | *Nos. 571-576 (6)* | 3.85 | 1.80 |

25th anniv. of UNICEF. See No. C189.

Sapporo 72 Emblem, Long-distance Skiing, Sika Deer — A214

3c, Sledding & black woodpecker. 5c, Ski Jump & brown bear. 10c, Bobsledding & murres. 15c, Figure skating & pikas. 25c, Downhill skiing & Japanese cranes.

**1971, Nov. 4 *Perf. 13x13½***

| | | | | |
|---|---|---|---|---|
| **577** | A214 | 2c multicolored | .25 | .25 |
| **578** | A214 | 3c multicolored | .25 | .25 |
| **579** | A214 | 5c multicolored | .25 | .25 |
| **580** | A214 | 10c multicolored | .30 | .25 |
| **581** | A214 | 15c multicolored | .50 | .25 |
| **582** | A214 | 25c multicolored | 2.10 | .25 |
| | | *Nos. 577-582 (6)* | 3.65 | 1.50 |

11th Winter Olympic Games, Sapporo, Japan, Feb. 3-13, 1972. Exist imperf. Value, set $10.
See No. C190.

Dove Carrying Letter, APU Emblem A215

**1971, Dec. 9 *Perf. 12½***

| | | | | |
|---|---|---|---|---|
| **583** | A215 | 25c ultra & dp org | .60 | .55 |
| **584** | A215 | 80c gray & dp brn | 1.60 | 1.25 |

10th anniversary of African Postal Union.

Pioneer Fathers' Monument, Monrovia — A216

Designs: 3c, 25c, Sailing ship "Elizabeth," Providence Island, horiz. 35c, as 20c.

**1972, Jan. 1**

| | | | | |
|---|---|---|---|---|
| **585** | A216 | 3c blue & brt grn | .25 | .25 |
| **586** | A216 | 20c orange & blue | .80 | .60 |
| **587** | A216 | 25c orange & purple | .80 | .65 |
| **588** | A216 | 35c lil rose & brt grn | 1.40 | 1.00 |
| | | *Nos. 585-588 (4)* | 3.25 | 2.50 |

Founding of Liberia, sesqui. See No. C191.

Pres. Tolbert and Map of Liberia A217

Pres. William R. Tolbert, Jr. — A217a

**1972, Jan. 1**

| | | | | |
|---|---|---|---|---|
| **589** | A217 | 25c brt grn & brown | .65 | .40 |
| **590** | A217a | 80c blue & brown | 1.75 | .70 |

Inauguration of William R. Tolbert, Jr. as 19th president of Liberia.

Soccer and Swedish Flag — A218

Olympic Rings, "Motion" Symbol and: 5c, Swimmers at start, Italian flag. 10c, Equestrian, British flag. 12c, Bicycling, French flag. 20c, Long jump, US flag. 25c, Running and Liberian flag.

**1972, May 19 Litho. *Perf. 11***

| | | | | |
|---|---|---|---|---|
| **591** | A218 | 3c lemon & multi | .25 | .25 |
| **592** | A218 | 5c lt lilac & multi | .25 | .25 |
| **593** | A218 | 10c multicolored | .55 | .25 |
| **594** | A218 | 12c gray & multi | .75 | .25 |
| **595** | A218 | 20c lt blue & multi | 1.00 | .30 |
| **596** | A218 | 25c pink & multi | 1.20 | .35 |
| | | *Nos. 591-596 (6)* | 4.00 | 1.65 |

20th Olympic Games, Munich, Aug. 26-Sept. 10. Exist imperf. Value, set $10.
See No. C192.

Y's Men's Club Emblem, Map — A219

Design: 90c, Y's Men's Club emblem and globe; inscribed "fifty and forward."

**1972, June 12 *Perf. 13½***

| | | | | |
|---|---|---|---|---|
| **597** | A219 | 15c purple & gold | .40 | .25 |
| **598** | A219 | 90c vio bl & emer | 2.10 | 1.50 |

Intl. Y's Men's Club, 50th anniv.

Astronaut and Lunar Rover — A220

5c, Moon scene reflected in astronaut's helmet. 10c, Astronauts with cameras. 12c, Astronauts placing scientific equipment on moon. 20c, Apollo 16 badge. 25c, Astronauts riding lunar rover.

**1972, June 26**

| | | | | |
|---|---|---|---|---|
| **599** | A220 | 3c lt blue & multi | .25 | .25 |
| **600** | A220 | 5c red org & multi | .25 | .25 |
| **601** | A220 | 10c pink & multi | .35 | .25 |
| **602** | A220 | 12c yellow & multi | .65 | .25 |
| **603** | A220 | 20c lt vio & multi | .80 | .25 |
| **604** | A220 | 25c emerald & multi | 1.40 | .25 |
| | | *Nos. 599-604 (6)* | 3.70 | 1.50 |

Apollo 16 US moon mission, Apr. 15-27, 1972. Exist imperf. Value, set $10.
See No. C193.

Emperor Haile Selassie — A221

**1972, July 21 *Perf. 14x14½***

| | | | | |
|---|---|---|---|---|
| **605** | A221 | 20c olive grn & yel | .55 | .55 |
| **606** | A221 | 25c maroon & yel | .75 | .75 |
| **607** | A221 | 35c brown & yel | .80 | .80 |
| | | *Nos. 605-607 (3)* | 2.10 | 2.10 |

80th birthday of Emperor Haile Selassie of Ethiopia.

Ajax, 1809, and Figurehead — A222

Famous sailing ships and their figureheads: 5c, Hogue, 1811. 7c, Ariadne, 1816. 15c, Royal Adelaide, 1828. 20c, Rinaldo, 1860. 25c, Nymphe, 1888.

**1972, Sept. 6 *Perf. 11***

| | | | | |
|---|---|---|---|---|
| **608** | A222 | 3c shown | .25 | .25 |
| **609** | A222 | 5c multicolored | .35 | .25 |
| **610** | A222 | 7c multicolored | .55 | .25 |
| **611** | A222 | 15c multicolored | .75 | .25 |
| **612** | A222 | 20c multicolored | .95 | .25 |
| **613** | A222 | 25c multicolored | 1.25 | .45 |
| | | *Nos. 608-613 (6)* | 4.10 | 1.70 |

See No. C194.

Pres. Tolbert Taking Oath, Richard A. Henries — A223

**1972, Oct. 23 Litho. *Perf. 13½***

| | | | | |
|---|---|---|---|---|
| **614** | A223 | 15c green & multi | .65 | .65 |
| **615** | A223 | 25c vio blue & multi | .95 | .95 |

Pres. William R. Tolbert, Jr. sworn in as 19th President of Liberia, July 23, 1971. See No. C195.

Klaus Dibiasi, Italy, Diving — A224

8c, Valery Borzov, USSR, running. 10c, Hideaki Yanagida, Japan, wrestling. 12c, Mark Spitz, US, swimming. 15c, Kipchoge Keino, Kenya, 3000-meter steeplechase. 25c, Richard Meade, Great Britain, equestrian. 55c, Hans Winkler, Germany, grand prix jumping.

**1973, Jan. 5 Litho. *Perf. 11***

| | | | | |
|---|---|---|---|---|
| **616** | A224 | 5c lt blue & multi | .25 | .25 |
| **617** | A224 | 8c violet & multi | .30 | .25 |
| **618** | A224 | 10c multicolored | .40 | .25 |
| **619** | A224 | 12c green & multi | .50 | .25 |
| **620** | A224 | 15c orange & multi | .60 | .25 |
| **621** | A224 | 25c pale salmon & multi | 1.00 | .30 |
| | | *Nos. 616-621 (6)* | 3.05 | 1.55 |

**Souvenir Sheet**

| | | | | |
|---|---|---|---|---|
| **622** | A224 | 55c multicolored | 3.25 | 1.50 |

Gold medal winners in 20th Olympic Games. Exist imperf. Values: set $10; souvenir sheet $8.

Astronaut on Moon and Apollo 17 Badge — A225

Designs (Apollo 17 Badge and): 3c, Astronauts on earth in lunar rover. 10c, Astronauts collecting yellow lunar dust. 15c, Astronauts in lunar rover exploring moon crater. 20c, Capt. Eugene A. Cernan, Dr. Harrison H. Schmitt and Comdr. Ronald E. Evans on launching pad. 25c, Astronauts on moon with scientific equipment.

**1973, Mar. 28 Litho. *Perf. 11***

| | | | | |
|---|---|---|---|---|
| **623** | A225 | 2c blue & multi | .30 | .25 |
| **624** | A225 | 3c blue & multi | .30 | .25 |
| **625** | A225 | 10c blue & multi | .30 | .25 |
| **626** | A225 | 15c blue & multi | .50 | .25 |
| **627** | A225 | 20c blue & multi | .90 | .30 |
| **628** | A225 | 25c blue & multi | .90 | .40 |
| | | *Nos. 623-628 (6)* | 3.20 | 1.70 |

Apollo 17 US moon mission, Dec. 7-19, 1972. Exist imperf. Value, set $10.
See No. C196.

Locomotive, England — A226

Designs: Locomotives, 1895-1905.

**1973, May 4**

| | | | | |
|---|---|---|---|---|
| **629** | A226 | 2c shown | .25 | .25 |
| **630** | A226 | 3c Netherlands | .35 | .25 |
| **631** | A226 | 10c France | .65 | .25 |
| **632** | A226 | 15c United States | .85 | .25 |
| **633** | A226 | 20c Japan | 1.75 | .25 |
| **634** | A226 | 25c Germany | 2.50 | .35 |
| | | *Nos. 629-634 (6)* | 6.35 | 1.60 |

See No. C197.

OAU Emblem and Flags — A227

**1973, May 24 Litho. *Perf. 13½***

| | | | | |
|---|---|---|---|---|
| **635** | A227 | 3c multicolored | .25 | .25 |
| **636** | A227 | 5c multicolored | .25 | .25 |
| **637** | A227 | 10c multicolored | .25 | .25 |
| **638** | A227 | 15c multicolored | .30 | .25 |
| **639** | A227 | 25c multicolored | .55 | .45 |
| **640** | A227 | 50c multicolored | 1.25 | .95 |
| | | *Nos. 635-640 (6)* | 2.85 | 2.40 |

10th anniv. of the Organization for African Unity.

WHO Emblem, Edward Jenner and Roses — A228

Designs (WHO Emblem and): 4c, Sigmund Freud and pansies. 10c, Jonas E. Salk and chrysanthemums. 15c, Louis Pasteur and scabiosa caucasia. 20c, Emil von Behring and rhododendron. 25c, Alexander Fleming and tree mallows.

**1973, June 26 Litho. *Perf. 11***

| | | | | |
|---|---|---|---|---|
| **641** | A228 | 1c gray & multi | .25 | .25 |
| **642** | A228 | 4c orange & multi | .25 | .25 |
| **643** | A228 | 10c lt blue & multi | .25 | .25 |
| **644** | A228 | 15c rose & multi | .35 | .25 |
| **645** | A228 | 20c blue & multi | .40 | .25 |
| **646** | A228 | 25c yel grn & multi | .50 | .40 |
| | | *Nos. 641-646 (6)* | 2.00 | 1.65 |

25th anniv. of WHO. See No. C198.

Stanley Steamer, 1910 — A229

Classic automobiles: 3c, Cadillac, 1903. 10c, Clement-Bayard, 1904. 15c, Rolls Royce, 1907. 20c, Maxwell, 1905. 25c, Chadwick, 1907.

**1973, Sept. 11 Litho. *Perf. 11***

| | | | | |
|---|---|---|---|---|
| **647** | A229 | 2c shown | .25 | .25 |
| **648** | A229 | 3c multicolored | .25 | .25 |
| **649** | A229 | 10c multicolored | .30 | .25 |
| **650** | A229 | 15c multicolored | .40 | .25 |
| **651** | A229 | 20c multicolored | .55 | .25 |
| **652** | A229 | 25c multicolored | .65 | .35 |
| | | *Nos. 647-652 (6)* | 2.40 | 1.60 |

See No. C199.

Copernicus, Armillary Sphere, Satellite Communication — A230

Portraits of Copernicus and: 4c, Eudoxus solar system. 10c, Aristotle, Ptolemy, Copernicus and satellites. 15c, Saturn and Apollo spacecraft. 20c, Orbiting astronomical observatory. 25c, Satellite tracking station.

**1973, Dec. 14 Litho. *Perf. 13½***

| | | | | |
|---|---|---|---|---|
| **653** | A230 | 1c yellow & multi | .25 | .25 |
| **654** | A230 | 4c lt violet & multi | .25 | .25 |
| **655** | A230 | 10c lt blue & multi | .25 | .25 |
| **656** | A230 | 15c yel grn & multi | .40 | .25 |
| **657** | A230 | 20c bister & multi | .55 | .25 |
| **658** | A230 | 25c pink & multi | .60 | .30 |
| | | *Nos. 653-658 (6)* | 2.30 | 1.55 |

Nicolaus Copernicus (1473-1543), Polish astronomer. Exist imperf.
See No. C200.

Radio Tower, Map of Africa A231

15c, 25c, Map of Liberia, Radio tower and man listening to broadcast. 17c, like 13c.

**1974, Jan. 16 Litho. *Perf. 13½***

| | | | | |
|---|---|---|---|---|
| **659** | A231 | 13c mag & multi | .45 | .45 |
| **660** | A231 | 15c yellow & multi | .45 | .45 |
| **661** | A231 | 17c lt gray & multi | .60 | .50 |
| **662** | A231 | 25c brt green & multi | .75 | .50 |
| | | *Nos. 659-662 (4)* | 2.25 | 1.90 |

20th anniv. of Radio ELWA, Monrovia.

Thomas Coutts, 1817; Aureal, 1974; UPU Emblem — A232

Designs (UPU Emblem and): 3c, Jet, satellite, Post Office, Monrovia, ship. 10c, US and USSR telecommunication satellites. 15c, Mail runner and jet. 20c, Futuristic mail train and mail truck. 25c, American Pony Express rider.

**1974, Mar. 4 Litho. *Perf. 13½***

| | | | | |
|---|---|---|---|---|
| **663** | A232 | 2c ocher & multi | .25 | .25 |
| **664** | A232 | 3c lt green & multi | .25 | .25 |
| **665** | A232 | 10c lt blue & multi | .25 | .25 |
| **666** | A232 | 15c pink & multi | .35 | .25 |
| **667** | A232 | 20c gray & multi | .80 | .25 |
| **668** | A232 | 25c lt lilac & multi | .75 | .40 |
| | | *Nos. 663-668 (6)* | 2.65 | 1.65 |

Cent. of UPU. Exist imperf. Value, set $15.
See No. C201.

Fox Terrier — A233

**1974, Apr. 16 Litho. *Perf. 13½***

| | | | | |
|---|---|---|---|---|
| **669** | A233 | 5c shown | .25 | .25 |
| **670** | A233 | 10c Boxer | .25 | .25 |
| **671** | A233 | 16c Chihuahua | .45 | .25 |
| **672** | A233 | 19c Beagle | .55 | .25 |
| **673** | A233 | 25c Golden retriever | .60 | .25 |
| **674** | A233 | 50c Collie | 1.40 | .25 |
| | | *Nos. 669-674 (6)* | 3.50 | 1.50 |

Exist imperf. See No. C202.

1974 World Cup Soccer Championships, Munich. — A234

Flags and scenes from games played by: 1c, West Germany and Chile. 2c, Australia and East Germany. 5c, Brazil and Yugoslavia. 10c, Zaire and Scotland. 12c, Netherlands and Uruguay. 15c, Sweden and Bulgaria. 20c, Italy and Haiti. 25c, Poland and Argentina.

**1974, June 4 Litho. *Perf. 11***

| | | | | |
|---|---|---|---|---|
| **675** | A234 | 1c shown | .25 | .25 |
| **676** | A234 | 2c multicolored | .25 | .25 |
| **677** | A234 | 5c multicolored | .25 | .25 |
| **678** | A234 | 10c multicolored | .25 | .25 |
| **679** | A234 | 12c multicolored | .30 | .25 |
| **680** | A234 | 15c multicolored | .40 | .25 |
| **681** | A234 | 20c multicolored | .55 | .25 |
| **682** | A234 | 25c multicolored | .30 | .45 |
| | | *Nos. 675-682 (8)* | 2.55 | 2.20 |

Exist imperf. Value, set $20:
See No. C203.

Chrysiridia Madagascariensis — A235

Tropical Butterflies: 2c, Catagramma sorana. 5c, Erasmia pulchella. 17c, Morpho cypris. 25c, Agrias amydon. 40c, Vanessa cardui.

**1974, Sept. 11 Litho. *Perf. 13½***

| | | | | |
|---|---|---|---|---|
| **683** | A235 | 1c gray & multi | .25 | .25 |
| **684** | A235 | 2c gray & multi | .25 | .25 |
| **685** | A235 | 5c gray & multi | .25 | .25 |
| **686** | A235 | 17c gray & multi | .75 | .25 |
| **687** | A235 | 25c gray & multi | 1.00 | .30 |
| **688** | A235 | 40c gray & multi | 1.90 | .45 |
| | | *Nos. 683-688 (6)* | 4.40 | 1.75 |

See No. C204.

Pres. Tolbert and Medal — A236

$1, Pres. Tolbert, medal & Liberian flag.

**1974, Dec. 10 Litho. *Perf. 13½***

| | | | | |
|---|---|---|---|---|
| **689** | A236 | 3c multi | .25 | .25 |
| **690** | A236 | $1 multi, vert. | 1.75 | 1.50 |

Pres. William R. Tolbert, Jr., recipient of 1974 Family of Man Award.

Winston Churchill, 1940 — A237

Churchill and: 10c, RAF planes in dog fight. 15c, In naval launch on way to Normandy. 17c, In staff car reviewing troops in desert. 20c, Aboard landing craft crossing Rhine. 25c, In conference with Pres. Roosevelt.

**1975, Jan. 17 Litho. *Perf. 13½***

| | | | | |
|---|---|---|---|---|
| **691** | A237 | 3c multicolored | .25 | .25 |
| **692** | A237 | 10c multicolored | .25 | .25 |
| **693** | A237 | 15c multicolored | .25 | .25 |
| **694** | A237 | 17c multicolored | .40 | .25 |
| **695** | A237 | 20c multicolored | .50 | .25 |
| **696** | A237 | 25c multicolored | .75 | .30 |
| | | *Nos. 691-696 (6)* | 2.40 | 1.55 |

Sir Winston Churchill (1874-1965), birth centenary. Exist imperf. Value, set $10.
See No. C205.

Women's Year Emblem and Marie Curie — A238

3c, Mahalia Jackson with microphone. 5c, Joan of Arc. 10c, Eleanor Roosevelt and children. 25c, Matilda Newport firing cannon. 50c, Valentina Tereshkova in space suit.

**1975, Mar. 14 Litho. *Perf. 14½***

| | | | | |
|---|---|---|---|---|
| **697** | A238 | 2c citron & multi | .25 | .25 |
| **698** | A238 | 3c dull orange & multi | .25 | .25 |
| **699** | A238 | 5c lilac rose & multi | .25 | .25 |
| **700** | A238 | 10c yellow & multi | .25 | .25 |
| **701** | A238 | 25c yellow grn & multi | .55 | .25 |
| **702** | A238 | 50c lilac & multi | .90 | .65 |
| | | *Nos. 697-702 (6)* | 2.45 | 1.90 |

Intl. Women's Year 1975. Exist imperf. Value, set $10.
See No. C206.

Old State House, Boston, US No. 627 — A239

10c, George Washington, US #645. 15c, Town Hall & Court House, Philadelphia, US #798. 20c, Benjamin Franklin, US #835. 25c, Paul Revere's Ride, US #618. 50c, Santa Maria, US #231.

**1975, Apr. 25 Litho. *Perf. 13½***

| | | | | |
|---|---|---|---|---|
| **703** | A239 | 5c multicolored | .25 | .25 |
| **704** | A239 | 10c multicolored | .35 | .25 |
| **705** | A239 | 15c multicolored | .55 | .25 |
| **706** | A239 | 20c multicolored | .60 | .25 |
| **707** | A239 | 25c multicolored | .90 | .25 |
| **708** | A239 | 50c multicolored | 2.00 | .50 |
| | | *Nos. 703-708 (6)* | 4.65 | 1.75 |

American Revolution Bicentennial. Exist imperf. Value, set $10.
See No. C207.

Dr. Schweitzer, Hospital and Baboon Mother — A240

Designs (Dr. Schweitzer and): 3c, Elephant, and tribesmen poling boat. 5c, Water buffalo, egret, man and woman paddling canoe. 6c, Antelope and dancer. 25c, Lioness, woman cooking outdoors. 50c, Zebra and colt, doctor's examination at clinic.

**1975, June 26 Litho. *Perf. 13½***

| | | | | |
|---|---|---|---|---|
| **709** | A240 | 1c multicolored | .25 | .25 |
| **710** | A240 | 3c multicolored | .25 | .25 |
| **711** | A240 | 5c multicolored | .25 | .25 |
| **712** | A240 | 6c multicolored | .25 | .25 |
| **713** | A240 | 25c multicolored | .55 | .25 |
| **714** | A240 | 50c multicolored | 1.25 | .65 |
| | | *Nos. 709-714 (6)* | 2.80 | 1.90 |

Dr. Albert Schweitzer (1875-1965), medical missionary, birth centenary. Exist imperf. Value, set $10.
See No. C208.

American-Russian Handshake in Space — A241

Designs (Apollo-Soyuz Emblem and): 5c, Apollo. 10c, Soyuz. 20c, Flags and maps of US and USSR. 25c, A. A. Leonov, and V. N. Kubasov. 50c, D. K. Slayton, V. D. Brand, T. P. Stafford.

**1975, Sept. 18 Litho. *Perf. 13½***

| | | | | |
|---|---|---|---|---|
| **715** | A241 | 5c multicolored | .25 | .25 |
| **716** | A241 | 10c multicolored | .25 | .25 |
| **717** | A241 | 15c multicolored | .30 | .25 |
| **718** | A241 | 20c multicolored | .45 | .25 |
| **719** | A241 | 25c multicolored | .50 | .25 |
| **720** | A241 | 50c multicolored | 1.10 | .45 |
| | | *Nos. 715-720 (6)* | 2.85 | 1.70 |

Apollo Soyuz space test project (Russo-American cooperation), launching July 15; link-up, July 17. Exist imperf. Value, set $10.

See No. C209.

Presidents Tolbert, Siaka Stevens; Treaty Signing; Liberia and Sierra Leone Maps — A242

**1975, Oct. 3 Litho. *Perf. 13½***

| | | | | |
|---|---|---|---|---|
| **721** | A242 | 2c gray & multi | .25 | .25 |
| **722** | A242 | 3c gray & multi | .25 | .25 |
| **723** | A242 | 5c gray & multi | .25 | .25 |
| **724** | A242 | 10c gray & multi | .25 | .25 |
| **725** | A242 | 25c gray & multi | .50 | .30 |
| **726** | A242 | 50c gray & multi | .90 | .55 |
| | | *Nos. 721-726 (6)* | 2.40 | 1.85 |

Mano River Union Agreement between Liberia and Sierra Leone, signed Oct. 3, 1973.

Figure Skating — A243

Designs (Winter Olympic Games Emblem and): 4c, Ski jump. 10c, Slalom. 25c, Ice hockey. 35c, Speed skating. 50c, Two-man bobsled.

**1976, Jan. 23 Litho. *Perf. 13½***

| | | | | |
|---|---|---|---|---|
| **727** | A243 | 1c lt blue & multi | .25 | .25 |
| **728** | A243 | 4c lt blue & multi | .25 | .25 |
| **729** | A243 | 10c lt blue & multi | .35 | .25 |
| **730** | A243 | 25c lt blue & multi | .75 | .25 |
| **731** | A243 | 35c lt blue & multi | 1.10 | .25 |
| **732** | A243 | 50c lt blue & multi | 1.50 | .75 |
| | | *Nos. 727-732 (6)* | 4.20 | 2.00 |

12th Winter Olympic Games, Innsbruck, Austria, Feb. 4-15. Exist imperf. Value, set $11.

See No. C210.

Pres. Tolbert Taking Oath of Office — A244

25c, Pres. Tolbert at his desk, vert. $1, Seal & flag of Liberia, $400 commemorative gold coin.

**1976, Apr. 5 Litho. *Perf. 13½***

| | | | | |
|---|---|---|---|---|
| **733** | A244 | 3c multicolored | .25 | .25 |
| **734** | A244 | 25c multicolored | .50 | .50 |
| **735** | A244 | $1 multicolored | 2.00 | 1.75 |
| | | *Nos. 733-735 (3)* | 2.75 | 2.50 |

Inauguration of President William R. Tolbert, Jr., Jan. 5, 1976.

Weight Lifting and Olympic Rings — A245

Designs (Olympic Rings and): 3c, Pole vault. 10c, Hammer and shot put. 25c, Yachting. 35c, Women's gymnastics. 50c, Hurdles.

**1976, May 4 Litho. *Perf. 13½***

| | | | | |
|---|---|---|---|---|
| **736** | A245 | 2c gray & multi | .25 | .25 |
| **737** | A245 | 3c orange & multi | .25 | .25 |
| **738** | A245 | 10c lt violet & multi | .30 | .25 |
| **739** | A245 | 25c lt green & multi | .60 | .25 |
| **740** | A245 | 35c yellow & multi | .90 | .60 |
| **741** | A245 | 50c pink & multi | 1.20 | .60 |
| | | *Nos. 736-741 (6)* | 3.50 | 2.20 |

21st Olympic Games, Montreal, Canada, July 17-Aug. 1. Exist imperf. Value, set $11.

See No. C211.

A. G. Bell, Telephone and Receiver, 1876, UPU Emblem — A246

UPU Emblem and: 4c, Horsedrawn mail coach and ITU emblem. 5c, Intelsat IV satellite, radar and ITU emblem. 25c, A. G. Bell, ship laying underwater cable, 1976 telephone. 40c, A. G. Bell, futuristic train, telegraph and telephone wires. 50c, Wright brothers' plane, Zeppelin and Concorde.

**1976, June 4 Litho. *Perf. 13½***

| | | | | |
|---|---|---|---|---|
| **742** | A246 | 1c green & multi | .25 | .25 |
| **743** | A246 | 4c ocher & multi | .25 | .25 |
| **744** | A246 | 5c orange & multi | .25 | .25 |
| **745** | A246 | 25c green & multi | .90 | .25 |
| **746** | A246 | 40c lilac & multi | 1.10 | .25 |
| **747** | A246 | 50c blue & multi | 1.25 | .70 |
| | | *Nos. 742-747 (6)* | 4.00 | 1.95 |

Cent. of 1st telephone call by Alexander Graham Bell, Mar. 10, 1876. Exist imperf. Value, set $25.

See No. C212.

Gold Nugget on Chain, Gold Panner A247

1c, Mano River Bridge. 5c, "V" ring. 10c, Rubber tire, tree. 15c, Harvesting. 20c, Hydroelectric plant. 25c, Mesurado shrimp. 27c, Woman tie-dying cloth. 55c, Lake Piso, barracuda. $1, Train hauling iron ore.

**1976-81 Litho. *Perf. 14½***

| | | | | |
|---|---|---|---|---|
| **749** | A247 | 1c multicolored | .25 | .25 |
| **750** | A247 | 3c shown | .25 | .25 |
| **751** | A247 | 5c multicolored | .25 | .25 |
| **752** | A247 | 7c like 5c ('81) | .75 | .25 |
| **753** | A247 | 10c multicolored | .30 | .25 |
| **754** | A247 | 15c multicolored | .55 | .45 |
| **755** | A247 | 17c like 55c ('81) | 1.75 | .60 |
| **756** | A247 | 20c multicolored | .65 | .45 |
| **757** | A247 | 25c multicolored | .85 | .25 |
| **758** | A247 | 27c multicolored | .90 | .65 |
| **759** | A247 | 55c multicolored | 2.75 | .75 |
| **760** | A247 | $1 multicolored | 3.25 | 2.50 |
| | | *Nos. 749-760 (12)* | 12.50 | 6.90 |

See Nos. 945-953.

Rhinoceros — A249

African Animals: 3c, Zebra antelope. 5c, Chimpanzee, vert. 15c, Pigmy hippopotamus. 25c, Leopard. $1, Gorilla, vert.

**1976, Sept. 1 Litho. *Perf. 13½***

| | | | | |
|---|---|---|---|---|
| **763** | A249 | 2c orange & multi | .25 | .25 |
| **764** | A249 | 3c gray & multi | .25 | .25 |
| **765** | A249 | 5c blue & multi | .25 | .25 |
| **766** | A249 | 15c brt blue & multi | .45 | .25 |
| **767** | A249 | 25c ultra & multi | 1.00 | .45 |
| **768** | A249 | $1 multicolored | 3.50 | 1.10 |
| | | *Nos. 763-768 (6)* | 5.70 | 2.55 |

See No. C213.

Maps of US and Liberia; Statue of Liberty, Unification Monument, Voinjama and Liberty Bell — A250

$1, George Washington, Gerald R. Ford, Joseph J. Roberts (1st Pres. of Liberia), William R. Tolbert, Jr., Bicentennial emblem, US & Liberian flags.

**1976, Sept. 21 Litho. *Perf. 13½***

| | | | | |
|---|---|---|---|---|
| **769** | A250 | 25c multicolored | .40 | .30 |
| **770** | A250 | $1 multicolored | 1.40 | .75 |

American Bicentennial and visit of Pres. William R. Tolbert, Jr. to the US, Sept. 21-30. See No. C214.

Baluba Masks and Festival Emblem A251

Tribal Masks: 10c, Bateke. 15c, Basshilele. 20c, Igungun. 25c, Masai. 50c, Kifwebe.

**1977, Jan. 20 Litho. *Perf. 13½***

| | | | | |
|---|---|---|---|---|
| **771** | A251 | 5c yellow & multi | .25 | .25 |
| **772** | A251 | 10c green & multi | .30 | .25 |
| **773** | A251 | 15c salmon & multi | .45 | .25 |
| **774** | A251 | 20c lt blue & multi | .45 | .25 |
| **775** | A251 | 25c violet & multi | .60 | .25 |
| **776** | A251 | 50c lemon & multi | 1.20 | .30 |
| | | *Nos. 771-776 (6)* | 3.25 | 1.55 |

FESTAC '77, 2nd World Black and African Festival, Lagos, Nigeria, Jan. 15-Feb. 12. See No. C215.

Latham's Francolin — A252

Birds of Liberia: 10c, Narina trogon. 15c, Rufous-crowned roller. 20c, Brown-cheeked hornbill. 25c, Common bulbul. 50c, Fish eagle. 80c, Gold Coast touraco.

**1977, Feb. 18 Litho. *Perf. 14***

| | | | | |
|---|---|---|---|---|
| **777** | A252 | 5c multicolored | .30 | .25 |
| **778** | A252 | 10c multicolored | .45 | .25 |
| **779** | A252 | 15c multicolored | .65 | .25 |
| **780** | A252 | 20c multicolored | .95 | .25 |
| **781** | A252 | 25c multicolored | 1.20 | .25 |
| **782** | A252 | 50c multicolored | 2.40 | .65 |
| | | *Nos. 777-782 (6)* | 5.95 | 1.90 |

**Souvenir Sheet**

| | | | | |
|---|---|---|---|---|
| **783** | A252 | 80c multicolored | 3.50 | 1.75 |

Edmund Coffin, Combined Training, US — A253

Designs: 15c, Alwin Schockemohle, single jump. Germany, vert. 20c, Christine Stuckelberger, Switzerland, individual dressage. 25c, Prix de Nations (team), France.

**1977, Apr. 22 Litho. *Perf. 13½***

| | | | | |
|---|---|---|---|---|
| **784** | A253 | 5c ocher & multi | .35 | .25 |
| **785** | A253 | 15c ocher & multi | .70 | .25 |
| **786** | A253 | 20c ocher & multi | .85 | .25 |
| **787** | A253 | 25c ocher & multi | 1.10 | .35 |
| | | *Nos. 784-787,C216 (5)* | 5.40 | 1.70 |

Equestrian gold medal winners in Montreal Olympic Games. Exist imperf. Value, set $10.

See No. C217.

Elizabeth II Wearing Crown — A254

Designs: 25c, Elizabeth II Prince Philip, Pres. and Mrs. Tubman. 80c, Elizabeth II, Prince Philip, royal coat of arms.

**1977, May 23 Litho. *Perf. 13½***

| | | | | |
|---|---|---|---|---|
| **788** | A254 | 15c silver & multi | .35 | .25 |
| **789** | A254 | 25c silver & multi | .55 | .25 |
| **790** | A254 | 80c silver & multi | 1.75 | .55 |
| | | *Nos. 788-790 (3)* | 2.65 | 1.05 |

25th anniversary of the reign of Queen Elizabeth II. Nos. 788-790 exist imperf. Value, set $8.

See No. C218.

Jesus Blessing Children A255

Christmas: 25c, The Good Shepherd. $1, Jesus and the Samaritan Woman. Designs after stained-glass windows, Providence Baptist Church, Monrovia.

**1977, Nov. 3 Litho. *Perf. 13½***

| | | | | |
|---|---|---|---|---|
| **791** | A255 | 20c lt blue & multi | .30 | .25 |
| **792** | A255 | 25c lt blue & multi | .45 | .35 |
| **793** | A255 | $1 lt blue & multi | 1.40 | .75 |
| | | *Nos. 791-793 (3)* | 2.15 | 1.35 |

Dornier DOX, 1928 — A256

Progress of Aviation: 3c, Piggyback space shuttle, 1977. 5c, Eddie Rickenbacker and Douglas DC 3. 25c, Charles A. Lindbergh and Spirit of St. Louis. 35c, Louis Bleriot and Bleriot XI. 50c, Orville and Wilbur Wright and flying machine, 1903. 80c, Concorde landing at night at Dulles Airport, Washington, DC.

**1978, Jan. 6 — Litho. — *Perf. 13½***

| | | | | |
|---|---|---|---|---|
| **794** | A256 | 2c multicolored | .25 | .25 |
| **795** | A256 | 3c multicolored | .25 | .25 |
| **796** | A256 | 5c multicolored | .25 | .25 |
| **797** | A256 | 25c multicolored | .55 | .25 |
| **798** | A256 | 35c multicolored | .90 | .55 |
| **799** | A256 | 50c multicolored | 1.25 | .50 |
| | | *Nos. 794-799 (6)* | 3.45 | 2.05 |

**Souvenir Sheet**

| | | | | |
|---|---|---|---|---|
| **800** | A256 | 80c multicolored | 2.75 | 1.00 |

Exist imperf. Values, set $10, souvenir sheet $15.

Baladeuse by Santos-Dumont, 1903 — A257

Airships: 3c, Baldwin's, 1908, and US flag. 5c, Tissandier brothers', 1883. 25c, Parseval PL VII, 1912. 40c, Nulli Secundus II, 1908. 50c, R34 rigid airship, 1919.

**1978, Mar. 9 — Litho. — *Perf. 13½***

| | | | | |
|---|---|---|---|---|
| **801** | A257 | 2c multicolored | .25 | .25 |
| **802** | A257 | 3c multicolored | .25 | .25 |
| **803** | A257 | 5c multicolored | .25 | .25 |
| **804** | A257 | 25c multicolored | .50 | .25 |
| **805** | A257 | 40c multicolored | .70 | .25 |
| **806** | A257 | 50c multicolored | 1.10 | .25 |
| | | *Nos. 801-806 (6)* | 3.05 | 1.50 |

75th anniv. of the Zeppelin. Exist imperf. Value, set $12.

See No. C219.

Soccer, East Germany and Brazil — A258

Soccer Games: 2c, Poland and Argentina, vert. 10c, West Germany and Netherlands. 25c, Yugoslavia and Brazil. 35c, Poland and Italy, vert. 50c, Netherlands and Uruguay.

**1978, May 16 — Litho. — *Perf. 13½***

| | | | | |
|---|---|---|---|---|
| **807** | A258 | 2c multicolored | .25 | .25 |
| **808** | A258 | 3c multicolored | .25 | .25 |
| **809** | A258 | 10c multicolored | .25 | .25 |
| **810** | A258 | 25c multicolored | .70 | .25 |
| **811** | A258 | 35c multicolored | .90 | .45 |
| **812** | A258 | 50c multicolored | 1.40 | .60 |
| | | *Nos. 807-812 (6)* | 3.75 | 2.05 |

11th World Cup Soccer Championships, Argentina, June 1-25. Exist imperf. Value, set $15.

See No. C220.

Coronation Chair — A259

Designs: 25c, Imperial state crown. $1, Buckingham Palace, horiz.

**1978, June 12**

| | | | | |
|---|---|---|---|---|
| **813** | A259 | 5c multicolored | .25 | .25 |
| **814** | A259 | 25c multicolored | .55 | .25 |
| **815** | A259 | $1 multicolored | 2.10 | .75 |
| | | *Nos. 813-815 (3)* | 2.90 | 1.25 |

25th anniversary of coronation of Queen Elizabeth II. Exist imperf. Value, set $9.

See No. C221.

Jinnah, Liberian and Pakistani Flags — A260

**1978, June — Litho. — *Perf. 13***

| | | | | |
|---|---|---|---|---|
| **816** | A260 | 30c multicolored | *37.50* | 8.25 |

Mohammed Ali Jinnah (1876-1948), first Governor General of Pakistan.

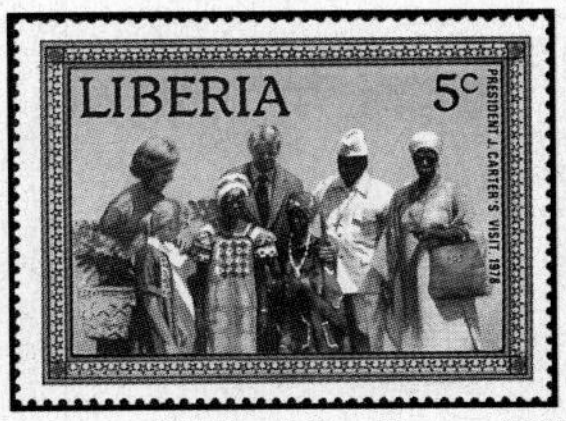


Carter and Tolbert Families — A261

Designs: 25c, Pres. Tolbert, Rosalynn Carter and Pres. Carter at microphone, Robertsfield Airport. $1, Jimmy Carter and William R. Tolbert, Jr. in motorcade from airport.

**1978, Oct. 26 — Litho. — *Perf. 13½***

| | | | | |
|---|---|---|---|---|
| **817** | A261 | 5c multicolored | .25 | .25 |
| **818** | A261 | 25c multicolored | .65 | .65 |
| **819** | A261 | $1 multicolored | 2.50 | 2.50 |
| | | *Nos. 817-819 (3)* | 3.40 | 3.40 |

Pres. Carter's visit to Liberia, Apr. 1978.

Soccer Game: Italy-France A262

Soccer Games: 1c, Brazil-Spain, horiz. 10c, Poland-West Germany, horiz. 27c, Peru-Scotland. 35c, Austria-West Germany. 50c, Argentina the victor.

**1978, Dec. 8 — Litho. — *Perf. 13½***

| | | | | |
|---|---|---|---|---|
| **820** | A262 | 1c multicolored | .25 | .25 |
| **821** | A262 | 2c multicolored | .25 | .25 |
| **822** | A262 | 10c multicolored | .30 | .25 |
| **823** | A262 | 27c multicolored | .70 | .50 |
| **824** | A262 | 35c multicolored | .90 | .60 |
| **825** | A262 | 50c multicolored | 1.25 | .90 |
| | | *Nos. 820-825 (6)* | 3.65 | 2.75 |

1978 World Cup Soccer winners. Exist imperf. Value, set $10.

See No. C222.

Liberian Lumbermen — A263

Designs: 10c, Hauling timber by truck, vert. 25c, Felling trees with chain saw. 50c, Moving logs.

**1978, Dec. 15 — Litho. — *Perf. 13½x14***

| | | | | |
|---|---|---|---|---|
| **826** | A263 | 5c multicolored | .25 | .25 |
| **827** | A263 | 10c multicolored | .30 | .25 |
| **828** | A263 | 25c multicolored | .65 | .40 |
| **829** | A263 | 50c multicolored | 1.40 | .90 |
| | | *Nos. 826-829 (4)* | 2.60 | 1.80 |

8th World Forestry Congress, Djakarta, Indonesia.

"25" and Waves — A264

Design: $1, Radio tower and waves.

**1979, Apr. 6 — Litho. — *Perf. 14x13½***

| | | | | |
|---|---|---|---|---|
| **830** | A264 | 35c multicolored | .65 | .65 |
| **831** | A264 | $1 multicolored | 1.75 | 1.75 |

25th anniversary of Radio ELWA.

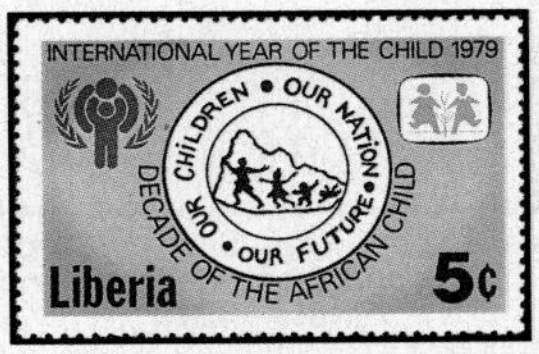


Emblems of IYC, African Child's Decade and SOS Village — A265

Designs: 25c, $1, like 5c, with UNICEF emblem replacing SOS emblem. 35c, like 5c.

**1979, Apr. 6 — *Perf. 13½x14***

| | | | | |
|---|---|---|---|---|
| **832** | A265 | 5c multicolored | .25 | .25 |
| **833** | A265 | 25c multicolored | .25 | .25 |
| **834** | A265 | 35c multicolored | .60 | .60 |
| **835** | A265 | $1 multicolored | 1.40 | 1.40 |
| | | *Nos. 832-835 (4)* | 2.50 | 2.50 |

IYC and Decade of the African Child.

Presidents Gardner and Tolbert, and Post Office, Monrovia — A266

Design: 35c, Anthony W. Gardner, William R. Tolbert, Jr. and UPU emblem.

**1979, Apr. 2 — Litho. — *Perf. 13½x14***

| | | | | |
|---|---|---|---|---|
| **836** | A266 | 5c multicolored | .25 | .25 |
| **837** | A266 | 35c multicolored | .95 | .95 |

Cent. of Liberia's joining UPU.

Unity Problem, Map of Africa, Torches — A267

Designs: 27c, Masks. 35c, Elephant, giraffe, lion, antelope, cheetah and map of Africa. 50c, Huts, pepper birds and map of Africa.

**1979, July 6 — Litho. — *Perf. 14x13½***

| | | | | |
|---|---|---|---|---|
| **838** | A267 | 5c multicolored | .30 | .25 |
| **839** | A267 | 27c multicolored | .50 | .35 |
| **840** | A267 | 35c multicolored | .75 | .45 |
| **841** | A267 | 50c multicolored | 1.10 | 1.10 |
| | | *Nos. 838-841 (4)* | 2.65 | 2.15 |

Organization for African Unity, 16th anniversary, and OAU Summit Conference.

Liberia No. 666, Rowland Hill — A268

10c, Pony Express rider, 1860. 15c, British mail coach, 1800. 25c, Mail steamship John Penn, 1860. 27c, Stanier Pacific train, 1939. 50c, Concorde. $1, Curtiss Jenny, 1916.

**1979, July 20**

| | | | | |
|---|---|---|---|---|
| **842** | A268 | 3c multicolored | .25 | .25 |
| **843** | A268 | 10c multicolored | .25 | .25 |
| **844** | A268 | 15c multicolored | .35 | .35 |
| **845** | A268 | 25c multicolored | .60 | .50 |
| **846** | A268 | 27c multicolored | .65 | .50 |
| **847** | A268 | 50c multicolored | 1.10 | 1.00 |
| | | *Nos. 842-847 (6)* | 3.20 | 2.85 |

**Souvenir Sheet**

| | | | | |
|---|---|---|---|---|
| **848** | A268 | $1 multicolored | 2.25 | 1.60 |

Sir Rowland Hill (1795-1879), originator of penny postage. Exist imperf. Value, set $20.

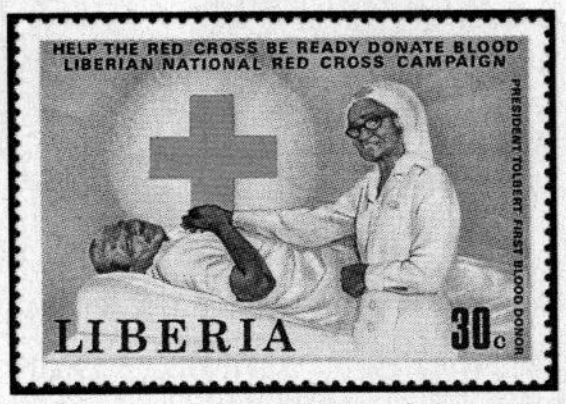


Red Cross, Pres. Tolbert Donating Blood — A269

Design: 50c, Red Cross, Pres. Tolbert.

**1979, Aug. 15 — Litho. — *Perf. 13½***

| | | | | |
|---|---|---|---|---|
| **849** | A269 | 30c multicolored | .50 | .50 |
| **850** | A269 | 50c multicolored | 1.25 | 1.25 |

National Red Cross, 30th anniversary and blood donation campaign.

M.S. World Peace — A270

Design: $1, M.S. World Peace, diff.

**1979, Aug. 15**

| | | | | |
|---|---|---|---|---|
| **851** | A270 | 5c multicolored | .25 | .25 |
| **852** | A270 | $1 multicolored | 2.40 | 2.40 |

2nd World Maritime Day, March 16; Liberia Maritime Program, 30th anniversary.

A Good Turn, by Norman Rockwell
A271

Paintings — Scouting through the eyes of Norman Rockwell (1925-76): No. 853: a, Stories. b, 3 branches of Scouts. c, camping. d, Church. e, Animal care. f, advancements. g, Scout, Lincoln. h, First aid on puppy. i, Reading with elderly and dog. j, Scout teaching cubs..

No. 854: a, "1910." b, Feeding dog. c, Man, dog, Scout on top of rock. d, Merit badges. e, Hiking in mountains. f, With explorer and eagle. g, Wearing new uniform. h, Indian lore. i, First camping. j, Group saluting.

No. 855: a, Eagle ceremony. b, Hiking with compass. c, The Scouting Trail. d, Phyical fitness. e, Prayer. f, Tales of the sea. g, Foreign and US scouts dancing. h, Building a birdhouse. i, In front of flag. j, Rescueing girl and kitten.

No. 856: a, Painting outdoors. b, Scout saluting in front of flag. c, Scout, Lincoln, Washington, eagle. d, Starting on hike. e, Knot tying. f, Reading instructions. g, Scouts of 6 nations. h, Boy, Girl Scouts and leaders. i, "On my honor..." j, Cooking outdoors.

No. 857: a, Portaging. b, "Spirit of '76." c, Saluting flag with astronaut. d, 5 branches of scouting. e, Planting trees. f, Washington praying. g, First aid on dog. h, Saying grace in mess tent. i, First time in Scout uniform. j, Rock climbing.

**1979, Sept. 1 Litho. *Perf. 11***

**853** A271 5c #a.-j, any single .40 .25
**854** A271 10c #a.-j, any single .40 .25
**855** A271 15c #a.-j, any single .65 .35
**856** A271 25c #a.-j, any single 1.20 .40
**857** A271 35c #a.-j, any single 1.75 .70
Nos. 853-857, Set of 50 in 5 strips of 10 45.00 20.00

Exist imperf. Value, set of 5 strips $55.

Mrs. Tolbert, Children, Children's Village Emblem — A272

40c, Mrs. Tolbert, children, emblem, vert.

**1979, Nov. 14 Litho. *Perf. 14***

**858** A272 25c multicolored .60 .60
**859** A272 40c multicolored 1.00 1.00

SOS Children's Village in Monrovia, Liberia.

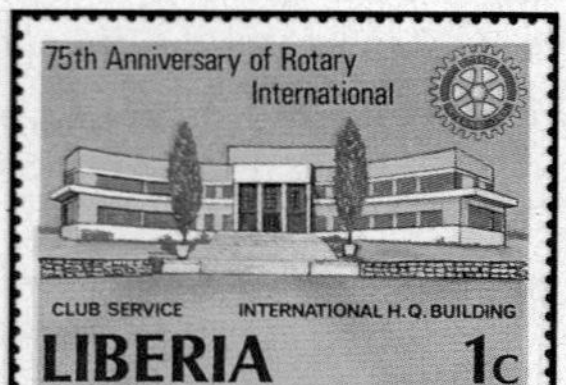


Rotary International Headquarters, Evanston, Ill., Emblem — A273

Rotary Emblem and: 5c, Vocational services. 17c, Man in wheelchair, nurse, vert. 27c, Flags of several nations. 35c, People of various races holding hands around globe. 50c, Pres. Tolbert, map of Africa, vert. $1, "Gift of Life."

**1979, Dec. 28 *Perf. 11***

**860** A273 1c multicolored .25 .25
**861** A273 5c multicolored .25 .25
**862** A273 17c multicolored .40 .40
**863** A273 27c multicolored .70 .70
**864** A273 35c multicolored .75 .75
**865** A273 50c multicolored 1.40 1.40
*Nos. 860-865 (6)* 3.75 3.75

**Souvenir Sheet**

**866** A273 $1 multicolored 2.75 2.75

Rotary International, 75th anniversary. Exist imperf. Values: set $14.; souvenir sheet $11.

Ski Jump, Lake Placid '80 Emblem — A274

Lake Placid '80 Emblem and: 5c, Figure skating. 17c, Bobsledding. 27c, Cross-country skiing. 35c, Women's speed skating. 50c, Ice hockey. $1, Slalom.

**1980, Jan. 21**

**867** A274 1c multicolored .30 .25
**868** A274 5c multicolored .30 .25
**869** A274 17c multicolored .75 .45
**870** A274 27c multicolored 1.50 .90
**871** A274 35c multicolored 1.50 .90
**872** A274 50c multicolored 2.10 1.25
*Nos. 867-872 (6)* 6.45 4.00

**Souvenir Sheet**

**873** A274 $1 multicolored 2.75 2.00

13th Winter Olympic Games, Lake Placid, NY, Feb. 12-24. Exist imperf. Values: set $12.50; souvenir sheet $12.50.

Pres. Tolbert, Pres. Stevens, Maps of Liberia and Sierra Leone, Mano River — A275

**1980, Mar. 6 Litho. *Perf. 14x13½***

**874** A275 8c multicolored .25 .25
**875** A275 27c multicolored .65 .65
**876** A275 35c multicolored .75 .75
**877** A275 80c multicolored 1.90 1.90
*Nos. 874-877 (4)* 3.55 3.55

Mano River Agreement, 5th anniversary; Mano River Postal Union, 1st anniversary.

Redemption Horn
A276

10c, Sgt. Doe and Soldiers, Clenched Hands Angel, horiz. 14c, Citizens, map, Flag, horiz. $2, Sgt. Samuel Doe.

**1981, Feb. 6 Litho. *Perf. 14***

**878** A276 1c multicolored .25 .25
**879** A276 6c like 1c .25 .25
**880** A276 10c multicolored .25 .25
**881** A276 14c multicolored .30 .25
**882** A276 23c like 10c .35 .35
**883** A276 31c like 14c .60 .60
**884** A276 41c like $2 .75 .75
**885** A276 $2 multicolored 4.00 4.00
*Nos. 878-885 (8)* 6.75 6.70

Establishment of new government under the People's Redemption Council, Apr. 12, 1980.

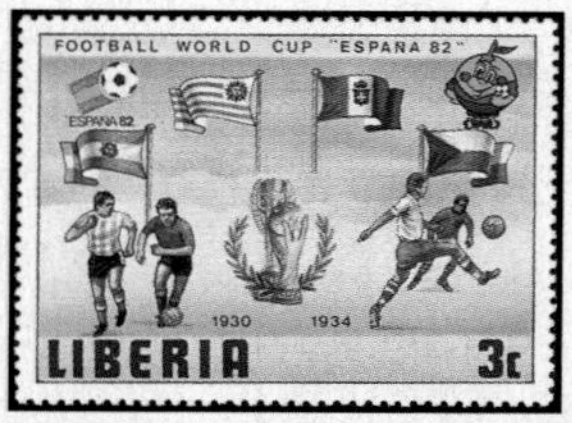


Soccer Players, World Cup, Flags of 1930 and 1934 Finalists — A277

Soccer Players, Cup, Flags of Finalists from: 5c, 1938, 1950. 20c, 1954, 1958. 27c, 1962, 1966. 40c, 1970, 1974. 55c. 1978. $1, Spanish team.

**1981, Mar. 4 Litho. *Perf. 14***

**886** A277 3c multicolored .25 .25
**887** A277 5c multicolored .25 .25
**888** A277 20c multicolored .45 .45
**889** A277 27c multicolored .65 .65
**890** A277 40c multicolored .90 .90
**891** A277 55c multicolored 1.25 1.25
*Nos. 886-891 (6)* 3.75 3.75

**Souvenir Sheet**

**892** A277 $1 multicolored 2.50 1.75

ESPANA '82 World Cup Soccer Championship.

Sgt. Samuel Doe and Citizens — A278

27c, Doe, Liberian flag. 30c, Clasped arms. $1, Doe, soldiers, Justice.

**1981, Apr. 7 Litho. *Perf. 14***

**893** A278 22c shown .50 .50
**894** A278 27c multicolored .65 .65
**895** A278 30c multicolored .90 .90
**896** A278 $1 multicolored 2.50 2.50
*Nos. 893-896 (4)* 4.55 4.55

People's Redemption Council government, first anniversary.

Royal Wedding
A279

31c, Couple. 41c, Initials, roses. 62c, St. Paul's Cathedral.
$1, Couple, horiz.

**1981, Aug. 12 Litho. *Perf. 14x13½***

**897** A279 31c multicolored .65 .65
**898** A279 41c multicolored .85 .85
**899** A279 62c multicolored 1.50 1.50
*Nos. 897-899 (3)* 3.00 3.00

**Souvenir Sheet**

**900** A279 $1 multicolored 2.50 2.50

Nos. 897-899 exist imperf. Value, set $7.

John Adams, US President, 1797-1801
A280

Washington Crossing the Delaware — A281

5c, Wm. H. Harrison. 10c, Martin Van Buren. 17c, James Monroe. 20c, John Q. Adams. 22c, James Madison. 27c, Thomas Jefferson. 30c, Andrew Jackson. 40c, John Tyler. 80c, George Washington.

**1981, July 4 *Perf. 11***

**901** A280 4c shown *.25 .25*
**902** A280 5c multicolored *.25 .25*
**903** A280 10c multicolored *.25 .25*
**904** A280 17c multicolored *.40 .30*
**905** A280 20c multicolored *.45 .35*
**906** A280 22c multicolored *.55 .45*
**907** A280 27c multicolored *.60 .55*
**908** A280 30c multicolored *.70 .60*
**909** A280 40c multicolored *.90 .85*
**910** A280 80c multicolored *1.90 1.60*
*Nos. 901-910 (10) 6.25 5.45*

**Souvenir Sheet**

**911** A281 $1 multicolored *2.75 2.75*

**1981, Nov. 26 Litho. *Perf. 11***

6c, Rutherford B. Hayes. 12c, Ulysses S. Grant. 14c, Millard Fillmore. 15c, Zachary Taylor. 20c, Abraham Lincoln. 27c, Andrew Johnson. 31c, James Buchanan. 41c, James A. Garfield. 50c, James K. Polk. 55c, Franklin Pierce.
$1, Washington at Valley Forge.

**912** A280 6c multicolored *.25 .25*
**913** A280 12c multicolored *.25 .25*
**914** A280 14c multicolored *.25 .25*
**915** A280 15c multicolored *.30 .25*
**916** A280 20c multicolored *.45 .30*
**917** A280 27c multicolored *.50 .45*
**918** A280 31c multicolored *.60 .45*
**919** A280 41c multicolored *.90 .75*
**920** A280 50c multicolored *1.10 .85*
**921** A280 55c multicolored *1.20 .90*
*Nos. 912-921 (10) 5.80 4.70*

**Souvenir Sheet**

**922** A281 $1 multicolored *4.25 4.25*

**1982, Apr. 7 Litho. *Perf. 11***

4c, William H. Taft. 5c, Calvin Coolidge. 6c, Benjamin Harrison. 10c, Warren G. Harding. 22c, Grover Cleveland. 27c, Chester Arthur. 31c, Woodrow Wilson. 41c, William McKinley. 80c, Theodore Roosevelt.
$1, Signing Constitution, horiz.

**923** A280 4c multicolored *.25 .25*
**924** A280 5c multicolored *.25 .25*
**925** A280 6c multicolored *.25 .25*
**926** A280 10c multicolored *.25 .25*
**927** A280 22c multicolored *.60 .50*
**928** A280 27c multicolored *.75 .75*
**929** A280 31c multicolored *.85 .85*
**930** A280 41c multicolored *1.00 1.00*
**931** A280 80c multicolored *1.60 1.60*
*Nos. 923-931 (9) 5.80 5.70*

**Souvenir Sheet**

**932** A281 $1 multicolored *2.75 2.75*

**1982, July 15 Litho. *Perf. 11***

4c, Jimmy Carter. 6c, Gerald Ford. 14c, Harry Truman. 17c, F. D. Roosevelt. 23c, L. B. Johnson. 27c, Richard Nixon. 31c, John F. Kennedy. 35c, Ronald Reagan. 50c, Herbert Hoover. 55c, Dwight D. Eisenhower.
$1, Battle of Yorktown.

**933** A280 4c multicolored *.25 .25*
**934** A280 6c multicolored *.25 .25*
**935** A280 14c multicolored *.30 .30*
**936** A280 17c multicolored *.40 .40*
**937** A280 23c multicolored *.45 .45*
**938** A280 27c multicolored *.50 .50*
**939** A280 31c multicolored *.60 .60*
**940** A280 35c multicolored *.75 .75*
**941** A280 50c multicolored *1.00 1.00*
**942** A280 55c multicolored *1.20 1.20*
*Nos. 933-942 (10) 5.70 5.70*

**Souvenir Sheet**

***Perf. 14x13½***

**943** A281 $1 multicolored *2.75 2.75*

See No. 1113.

**Type of 1976**

**1981-83 Litho. *Perf. 14½x13½***

**Size: 34x20mm**

| | | | | |
|---|---|---|---|---|
| **945** | A247 | 1c like #749 | .25 | .25 |
| **946** | A247 | 3c like #750 | .25 | .25 |
| **947** | A247 | 6c like #753 | .25 | .25 |
| **948** | A247 | 15c like #754 | .60 | .60 |
| **949** | A247 | 25c like #757 | 1.00 | 1.00 |
| **950** | A247 | 31c like #756 | 1.25 | 1.25 |
| **951** | A247 | 41c like #758 | 1.75 | 1.75 |
| **952** | A247 | 80c like #759 | 3.50 | 3.50 |
| **953** | A247 | $1 like #760 | 5.00 | 5.00 |
| | | *Nos. 945-953 (9)* | 13.85 | 13.85 |

Issued: Nos. 946-947, 949, 950, 11/27/81; Nos. 945, 953, 10/12/82; Nos. 948, 951, 12/10/82; No. 952, 11/3/83.

Intl. Year of the Disabled (1981) — A282

Designs: Various disabled people.

**1982, Mar. 24 Litho. *Perf. 14***

| | | | | |
|---|---|---|---|---|
| **954** | A282 | 23c multi, vert. | .45 | .45 |
| **955** | A282 | 62c multicolored | 1.00 | 1.00 |

30th Anniv. of West African Examinations Council — A283

**1982, Mar. 24**

| | | | | |
|---|---|---|---|---|
| **956** | A283 | 6c multicolored | .25 | .25 |
| **957** | A283 | 31c multicolored | 1.00 | 1.00 |

21st Birthday of Princess Diana — A284

31c, 41c, 62c, Diana portraits. $1, Wedding.

**1982, July 1 *Perf. 14x13½***

| | | | | |
|---|---|---|---|---|
| **958** | A284 | 31c multicolored | .65 | .65 |
| **959** | A284 | 41c multicolored | .90 | .90 |
| **960** | A284 | 62c multicolored | 1.50 | 1.50 |
| | | *Nos. 958-960 (3)* | 3.05 | 3.05 |

**Souvenir Sheet**

| | | | | |
|---|---|---|---|---|
| **961** | A284 | $1 multicolored | 2.50 | 2.50 |

Nos. 958-961 Overprinted in Silver

**1982, Aug. 30 Litho. *Perf. 14x13½***

| | | | | |
|---|---|---|---|---|
| **962** | A284 | 31c multicolored | .65 | .65 |
| **963** | A284 | 41c multicolored | .90 | .90 |
| **964** | A284 | 62c multicolored | 1.50 | 1.50 |
| | | *Nos. 962-964 (3)* | 3.05 | 3.05 |

**Souvenir Sheet**

| | | | | |
|---|---|---|---|---|
| **965** | A284 | $1 multicolored | 2.50 | 2.50 |

Birth of Prince William of Wales, June 21.

3rd Natl. Redemption Day — A285

3c, Fallah Varney. 6c, Samuel Doe. 10c, Jlatoh N. Podier, Jr. 15c, Jeffry S. Gbatu. 31c, Thomas G. Quiwonkpa. 41c, Abraham D. Kollie.

**1983, Apr. 5 Litho. *Perf. 13½***

| | | | | |
|---|---|---|---|---|
| **966** | A285 | 3c multicolored | .25 | .25 |
| **967** | A285 | 6c multicolored | .25 | .25 |
| **968** | A285 | 10c multicolored | .25 | .25 |
| **969** | A285 | 15c multicolored | .30 | .30 |
| **970** | A285 | 31c multicolored | .85 | .85 |
| **971** | A285 | 41c multicolored | 1.40 | 1.40 |
| | | *Nos. 966-971 (6)* | 3.30 | 3.30 |

**Souvenir Sheet**

| | | | | |
|---|---|---|---|---|
| **972** | A285 | $1 like 6c | 2.60 | 2.60 |

Natl. Archives Opening — A286

Building views.

**1983, Apr. 5**

| | | | | |
|---|---|---|---|---|
| **973** | A286 | 6c multicolored | *1.25* | *1.25* |
| **974** | A286 | 31c multicolored | *2.00* | *2.00* |

Christmas 1983 A287

Raphael Paintings: 6c, Circumcision of Christ. 15c, Adoration of the Magi. 25c, Announcement to Mary. 31c, Madonna with Baldachin. 41c, Holy Family. 62c, Detail of Madonna with Child Surrounded by Five Saints. $1.25 Madonna of Foligno.

**1983, Dec. 14 Litho. *Perf. 13½***

| | | | | |
|---|---|---|---|---|
| **975** | A287 | 6c multicolored | .25 | .25 |
| **976** | A287 | 15c multicolored | .25 | .25 |
| **977** | A287 | 25c multicolored | .45 | .35 |
| **978** | A287 | 31c multicolored | .60 | .50 |
| **979** | A287 | 41c multicolored | .75 | .65 |
| **980** | A287 | 62c multicolored | 1.00 | 1.00 |
| | | *Nos. 975-980 (6)* | 3.30 | 3.00 |

**Souvenir Sheet**

| | | | | |
|---|---|---|---|---|
| **981** | A287 | $1.25 multicolored | 2.60 | 1.90 |

Sheets of 1 showing entire painting exist.

Mano River Union, 10th Anniv. (1983) — A288

6c, Training school graduates. 25c, Emblem. 31c, Maps, leaders. 41c, Guinea's accession. 75c, Guinea's accession, diff.

**1984, Apr. 6 Litho. *Perf. 14x13½***

| | | | | |
|---|---|---|---|---|
| **982** | A288 | 6c multicolored | .25 | .25 |
| **983** | A288 | 25c multicolored | .70 | .70 |
| **984** | A288 | 31c multicolored | .90 | .90 |
| **985** | A288 | 41c multicolored | 1.25 | 1.25 |
| | | *Nos. 982-985 (4)* | 3.10 | 3.10 |

**Souvenir Sheet**

| | | | | |
|---|---|---|---|---|
| **986** | A288 | 75c multicolored | 2.60 | 2.60 |

4th Natl. Redemption Day — A289

3c, Hospital, New Kru Town. 10c, Ganta-Harper Highway construction. 20c, Constitution Assembly opening. 31c, Doe at highway construction. 41c, Draft Constitution presentation.

**1984, Apr. 12 *Perf. 14½***

| | | | | |
|---|---|---|---|---|
| **987** | A289 | 3c multicolored | .25 | .25 |
| **988** | A289 | 10c multicolored | .25 | .25 |
| **989** | A289 | 20c multicolored | .45 | .45 |
| **990** | A289 | 31c multicolored | 1.00 | 1.00 |
| **991** | A289 | 41c multicolored | 1.40 | 1.40 |
| | | *Nos. 987-991 (5)* | 3.35 | 3.35 |

Adoration of the Wise Men, by Rubens (1577-1640) A290

15c, Crowning of Katharina. 25c, Mother and Child Adored by Wise Men. 31c, Madonna and Child with Halo. 41c, Adoration of the Shepherds. 62c, Madonna and Child with Saints.

$1.25, Madonna Adored by Saints.

**1984, June 1 Litho. *Perf. 13½***

| | | | | |
|---|---|---|---|---|
| **992** | A290 | 6c shown | .25 | .25 |
| **993** | A290 | 15c multicolored | .30 | .30 |
| **994** | A290 | 25c multicolored | .45 | .45 |
| **995** | A290 | 31c multicolored | .60 | .60 |
| **996** | A290 | 41c multicolored | .75 | .75 |
| **997** | A290 | 62c multicolored | 1.20 | 1.20 |
| | | *Nos. 992-997 (6)* | 3.55 | 3.55 |

**Souvenir Sheet**

| | | | | |
|---|---|---|---|---|
| **998** | A290 | $1.25 multicolored | *4.25* | *4.25* |

Sheets of 1 showing entire painting exist.

1984 Summer Olympics A291

3c, Jesse Owens, 1936. 4c, Rafer Johnson, 1960. 25c, Miruts Yifter, 1980. 41c, Kipchoge Keino, 1968, 1972. 62c, Muhammad Ali, 1960.

$1.25, Wilma Rudolph, 1960, horiz.

**1984, July 2 *Perf. 13½x14***

| | | | | |
|---|---|---|---|---|
| **999** | A291 | 3c multicolored | .25 | .25 |
| **1000** | A291 | 4c multicolored | .25 | .25 |
| **1001** | A291 | 25c multicolored | .75 | .75 |
| **1002** | A291 | 41c multicolored | 1.20 | 1.20 |
| **1003** | A291 | 62c multicolored | 2.00 | 2.00 |
| | | *Nos. 999-1003 (5)* | 4.45 | 4.45 |

**Souvenir Sheet**

***Perf. 14x13½***

| | | | | |
|---|---|---|---|---|
| **1004** | A291 | $1.25 multicolored | 4.25 | 4.25 |

1984 Louisiana Expo — A292

6c, Water birds. 31c, Ship, Buchanan Harbor. 41c, Fish. 62c, Train carrying iron ore.

**1984, July 24 *Perf. 14½***

| | | | | |
|---|---|---|---|---|
| **1005** | A292 | 6c multicolored | .25 | .25 |
| **1006** | A292 | 31c multicolored | 1.00 | 1.00 |
| **1007** | A292 | 41c multicolored | 1.25 | 1.25 |
| **1008** | A292 | 62c multicolored | 2.00 | 2.00 |
| | | *Nos. 1005-1008 (4)* | 4.50 | 4.50 |

Pygmy Hippopotamus, World Wildlife Fund Emblem — A293

Various pygmy hippopotomi.

**1984, Nov. 22 Litho. *Perf. 14½***

| | | | | |
|---|---|---|---|---|
| **1009** | A293 | 6c multicolored | .75 | .75 |
| **1010** | A293 | 10c multicolored | 1.00 | 1.00 |
| **1011** | A293 | 20c multicolored | 2.75 | 2.75 |
| **1012** | A293 | 31c multicolored | 4.00 | 4.00 |
| | | *Nos. 1009-1012 (4)* | 8.50 | 8.50 |

Exist imperf.

Indigent Children Home, Bensonville — A294

First Lady Mrs. Nancy Doe and various children.

**1984, Dec. 14**

| | | | | |
|---|---|---|---|---|
| **1013** | A294 | 6c multicolored | .25 | .25 |
| **1014** | A294 | 31c multicolored | 1.00 | 1.00 |

Natl. Redemption Day, Apr. 12 — A295

6c, Army barracks, Monrovia. 31c, Pan-African Plaza, Monrovia.

**1985, Apr. 5 Litho. *Perf. 14½***

| | | | | |
|---|---|---|---|---|
| **1015** | A295 | 6c multicolored | .25 | .25 |
| **1016** | A295 | 31c multicolored | 1.00 | 1.00 |

Liberian Revolution, fifth anniv.

Audubon Birth Bicentenary — A296

Illustrations by artist/naturalist J. J. Audubon: 1c, Bohemian waxwing. 3c, Bay-breasted warbler. 6c, White-winged crossbill. 31c, Red phalarope. 41c, Eastern bluebird. 62c, Northern cardinal.

**1985, Apr. 5**

| | | | | |
|---|---|---|---|---|
| **1017** | A296 | 1c multicolored | .25 | .25 |
| **1018** | A296 | 3c multicolored | .25 | .25 |
| **1019** | A296 | 6c multicolored | .30 | .25 |
| **1020** | A296 | 31c multicolored | 1.10 | 1.00 |

| | | | | |
|---|---|---|---|---|
| **1021** | A296 | 41c multicolored | 1.60 | .75 |
| **1022** | A296 | 62c multicolored | 2.25 | 2.00 |
| | | *Nos. 1017-1022 (6)* | 5.75 | 4.50 |

Venus and Mirror
A297

Paintings (details) by Rubens: 15c, Adam & Eve in Paradise. 25c, Andromeda. 31c, The Three Graces. 41c, Venus & Adonis. 62c, The Daughters of Leucippus. $1.25, The Judgement of Paris.

**1985, Nov. 14** **Litho.** ***Perf. 14***

| | | | | |
|---|---|---|---|---|
| **1023** | A297 | 6c multicolored | .25 | .25 |
| **1024** | A297 | 15c multicolored | .55 | .55 |
| **1025** | A297 | 25c multicolored | .85 | .85 |
| **1026** | A297 | 31c multicolored | 1.00 | 1.00 |
| **1027** | A297 | 41c multicolored | 1.40 | 1.40 |
| **1028** | A297 | 62c multicolored | 2.40 | 2.40 |
| | | *Nos. 1023-1028 (6)* | 6.45 | 6.45 |

**Souvenir Sheet**

| | | | | |
|---|---|---|---|---|
| **1029** | A297 | $1.25 multicolored | 3.25 | 3.25 |

Sheets of 1 showing entire painting exist.

1986 World Cup Soccer Championships, Mexico — A298

6c, Germany-Morocco, 1970. 15c, Zaire-Brazil, 1974. 25c, Tunisia-Germany, 1978. 31c, Cameroun-Peru, 1982, vert. 41c, Algeria-Germany, 1982. 62c, 1986 Senegal team. $1.25, Liberia-Nigeria.

**1985, Nov. 14**

| | | | | |
|---|---|---|---|---|
| **1030** | A298 | 6c multicolored | .25 | .25 |
| **1031** | A298 | 15c multicolored | .35 | .35 |
| **1032** | A298 | 25c multicolored | .60 | .60 |
| **1033** | A298 | 31c multicolored | .85 | .85 |
| **1034** | A298 | 41c multicolored | 1.10 | 1.10 |
| **1035** | A298 | 62c multicolored | 1.60 | 1.60 |
| | | *Nos. 1030-1035 (6)* | 4.75 | 4.75 |

**Souvenir Sheet**

| | | | | |
|---|---|---|---|---|
| **1036** | A298 | $1.25 multicolored | 3.25 | 3.25 |

Queen Mother, 85th Birthday — A299

31c, Elizabeth in garter robes. 41c, At the races. 62c, In garden, waving. $1.25, Wearing diadem.

**1985, Dec. 12** **Litho.** ***Perf. 14½***

| | | | | |
|---|---|---|---|---|
| **1037** | A299 | 31c multicolored | .60 | .60 |
| **1038** | A299 | 41c multicolored | .85 | .85 |
| **1039** | A299 | 62c multicolored | 1.20 | 1.20 |
| | | *Nos. 1037-1039 (3)* | 2.65 | 2.65 |

**Souvenir Sheet**

| | | | | |
|---|---|---|---|---|
| **1040** | A299 | $1.25 multicolored | 2.25 | 2.25 |

World Food Day — A300

**1985, Dec. 12**

| | | | | |
|---|---|---|---|---|
| **1041** | A300 | 25c multicolored | .70 | .70 |
| **1042** | A300 | 31c multicolored | 1.00 | 1.00 |

AMERIPEX '86 — A301

25c, The Alamo. 31c, Liberty Bell. 80c, #344, 802, C102.

**1986, June 10** **Litho.** ***Perf. 14½***

| | | | | |
|---|---|---|---|---|
| **1043** | A301 | 25c multicolored | 1.00 | .65 |
| **1044** | A301 | 31c multicolored | 1.10 | .85 |
| **1045** | A301 | 80c multicolored | 2.90 | 2.10 |
| | | *Nos. 1043-1045 (3)* | 5.00 | 3.60 |

Statue of Liberty, Cent. — A302

20c, Unveiling, 1886. 31c, Frederic A. Bartholdi. $1, Statue close-up.

**1986, June 10**

| | | | | |
|---|---|---|---|---|
| **1046** | A302 | 20c multicolored | .50 | .50 |
| **1047** | A302 | 31c multicolored | .90 | .90 |
| **1048** | A302 | $1 multicolored | 2.75 | 2.75 |
| | | *Nos. 1046-1048 (3)* | 4.15 | 4.15 |

1988 Winter Olympics, Calgary — A303

1984 Gold medalists: 3c, Max Julen, Switzerland, men's giant slalom. 6c, Debbie Armstrong, U.S., women's giant slalom. 31c, Peter Angerer, West Germany, biathlon. 60c, Bill Johnson, U.S., men's downhill. 80c, East Germany, 4-man bobsled. $1.25, H. Stangassinger, F. Wembacher, West Germany, 2-man luge.

**1987, Aug. 21** **Litho.** ***Perf. 14***

| | | | | |
|---|---|---|---|---|
| **1049** | A303 | 3c multicolored | .25 | .25 |
| **1050** | A303 | 6c multicolored | .25 | .25 |
| **1051** | A303 | 31c multicolored | .70 | .70 |
| **1052** | A303 | 60c multicolored | 1.40 | 1.40 |
| **1053** | A303 | 80c multicolored | 1.60 | 1.60 |
| | | *Nos. 1049-1053 (5)* | 4.20 | 4.20 |

**Souvenir Sheet**

| | | | | |
|---|---|---|---|---|
| **1054** | A303 | $1.25 multicolored | 2.25 | 2.25 |

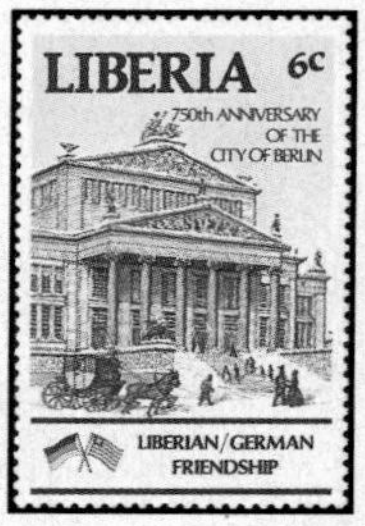


City of Berlin, 750th Anniv. — A304

6c, State (Royal) Theater in the Gendarmenmarkt, c. 1820, architect Schinkel. 31c, Kaiser Friedrich Museum, Museum Is. on River Spree. 60c, Charlottenburg Castle, 17th cent. 80c, Modern church bell tower & Kaiser Wilhelm Gedachtniskirche. $1.50, MIRAK rocket development, Spaceship Society Airfield, Reinickendorf, 1930.

**1987, Sept. 4**

| | | | | |
|---|---|---|---|---|
| **1055** | A304 | 6c multicolored | .25 | .25 |
| **1056** | A304 | 31c multicolored | .70 | .70 |
| **1057** | A304 | 60c multicolored | 1.40 | 1.40 |
| **1058** | A304 | 80c multicolored | 1.60 | 1.60 |
| | | *Nos. 1055-1058 (4)* | 3.95 | 3.95 |

**Souvenir sheet**

***Perf. 11½***

| | | | | |
|---|---|---|---|---|
| **1059** | A304 | $1.50 buff & dk brown | 3.50 | 3.50 |

No. 1059 contains one 25x61mm stamp.

Shakespearean Plays — A305

**1987, Nov. 6** **Litho.** ***Perf. 14***

| | | | |
|---|---|---|---|
| **1060** | Sheet of 8 | 6.50 | 6.50 |
| *a.* | A305 3c Othello | .25 | .25 |
| *b.* | A305 6c Romeo & Juliet | .25 | .25 |
| *c.* | A305 10c The Merry Wives of Windsor | .25 | .25 |
| *d.* | A305 15c Henry IV | .25 | .25 |
| *e.* | A305 31c Hamlet | .45 | .45 |
| *f.* | A305 60c Macbeth | .90 | .90 |
| *g.* | A305 80c King Lear | 1.10 | 1.10 |
| *h.* | A305 $2 Shakespeare and the Globe Theater, 1598 | 2.75 | 2.75 |

Amateur Radio Association, 25th Anniv. — A306

No. 1061, Emblem. No. 1062, Village. No. 1063, On-the-Air certificate. No. 1064, Globe, flags.

**1987, Nov. 23** **Litho.** ***Perf. 14***

| | | | | |
|---|---|---|---|---|
| **1061** | A306 | 10c multicolored | .35 | .35 |
| **1062** | A306 | 10c multicolored | .35 | .35 |
| **1063** | A306 | 35c multicolored | 1.20 | 1.20 |
| **1064** | A306 | 35c multicolored | 1.20 | 1.20 |
| | | *Nos. 1061-1064 (4)* | 3.10 | 3.10 |

Miniature Sheets

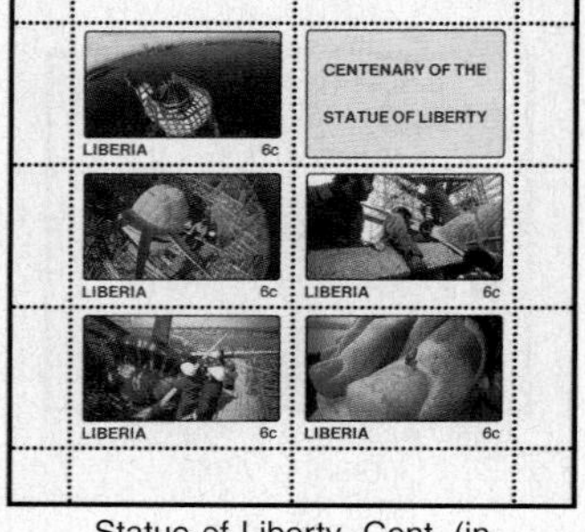


Statue of Liberty, Cent. (in 1986) — A307

No. 1065: a, Torch, southern view of NYC. b, Overhead view of crown and scaffold. c, 4 workmen repairing crown. d, 5 workmen, crown. e, Statue's right foot.

No. 1066: a, Tall ship, statue. b, Bay Queen ferry. c, Statue on poster at a construction site, NYC. d, Tug boat, tall ship. e, Building frieze.

No. 1067: a, Statue flanked by fireworks. b, Lighting of the statue. c, Crown observatory illuminated. d, Statue surrounded by fireworks. e, Crown and torch observatories illuminated.

No. 1068: a, Liberty "Happy Birthday" poster at a construction site. b, Ships in NY Harbor. c, Woman renovating statue nose. d, Man & woman renovating nose. e, Man, nose. #1068a-1068e vert.

**1987, Dec. 10** ***Perf. 13½***

| | | | | |
|---|---|---|---|---|
| **1065** | A307 | Sheet of 5 + label | 1.10 | 1.10 |
| *a.-e.* | | 6c any single | .25 | .25 |
| **1066** | A307 | Sheet of 5 + label | 2.25 | 2.25 |
| *a.-e.* | | 15c any single | .40 | .40 |
| **1067** | A307 | Sheet of 5 + label | 4.25 | 4.25 |
| *a.-e.* | | 31c any single | .80 | .80 |
| **1068** | A307 | Sheet of 5 + label | 7.50 | 7.50 |
| *a.-e.* | | 60c any single | 1.40 | 1.40 |
| | | *Nos. 1065-1068 (4)* | 15.10 | |

Nos. 1065-1068 contain label inscribed "CENTENARY OF THE STATUE OF LIBERTY" in two or five lines.

Second Republic, 2nd Anniv. A308

Design: Natl. flag, coat of arms, hand grip, Pres. Doe and Vice Pres. Moniba.

**1988, Jan. 6** ***Perf. 14½***

| | | | | |
|---|---|---|---|---|
| **1069** | A308 | 10c multicolored | .45 | .45 |
| **1070** | A308 | 35c multicolored | .90 | .90 |

UN Child Survival Campaign A309

3c, Breast-feeding. 6c, Oral rehydration therapy, vert. 31c, Immunization. $1, Growth monitoring, vert.

**1988, Jan. 15** ***Perf. 13x13½, 13½x13***

| | | | | |
|---|---|---|---|---|
| **1071** | A309 | 3c multicolored | .25 | .25 |
| **1072** | A309 | 6c multicolored | .25 | .25 |
| **1073** | A309 | 31c multicolored | 1.60 | 1.60 |
| **1074** | A309 | $1 multicolored | 4.50 | 2.90 |
| | | *Nos. 1071-1074 (4)* | 6.60 | 5.00 |

Inauguration of the Second Republic — A310

Design: Pres. Doe greeting Chief Justice Emmanuel N. Gbalazeh.

**1988, Jan. 15** ***Perf. 13x13½***

| | | | | |
|---|---|---|---|---|
| **1075** | A310 | 6c multicolored | .30 | .30 |

Samuel Kanyon Doe Sports Complex, Opened Apr. 12, 1986 A311

**1988, Jan. 15**

| | | | | |
|---|---|---|---|---|
| **1076** | A311 | 31c multicolored | .90 | .90 |

Green (Agricultural) Revolution — A312

**1988, Apr. 4** ***Perf. 15***

| | | | | | |
|---|---|---|---|---|---|
| **1077** | A312 | 10c multicolored | | .35 | .35 |
| **1078** | A312 | 35c multicolored | | 1.20 | 1.20 |

US Peace Corps in Liberia, 25th Anniv. A313

**1988, Apr. 4**

| | | | | |
|---|---|---|---|---|
| **1079** | A313 | 10c multicolored | .35 | .35 |
| **1080** | A313 | 35c multicolored | 1.20 | 1.20 |

Souvenir Sheet

1988 Summer Olympics, Seoul — A314

**1988, Apr. 14** ***Perf. 14***

| | | | | |
|---|---|---|---|---|
| **1081** | A314 | $3 multicolored | 7.50 | 7.50 |

Organization of African Unity, 25th Anniv. — A315

**1988, May 25**

| | | | | |
|---|---|---|---|---|
| **1082** | A315 | 10c multicolored | .35 | .35 |
| **1083** | A315 | 35c multicolored | 1.10 | 1.10 |
| **1084** | A315 | $1 multicolored | 3.50 | 3.50 |
| | | *Nos. 1082-1084 (3)* | 4.95 | 4.95 |

Rail Transport A316

10c, GP10 at Nimba. 35c, Triple-headed iron ore train.

No. 1087, King Edward II, 1930. No. 1088, GWR 57 No. 3697, 1941. No. 1089, GWR 0-4-2T No. 1408, 1932. No. 1090, GWR No. 7034 Ince Castle, 1950.

**1988, July 30** **Litho.** ***Perf. 14½***

| | | | | |
|---|---|---|---|---|
| **1085** | A316 | 10c multicolored | .50 | .50 |
| **1086** | A316 | 35c multicolored | 1.40 | 1.40 |

**Souvenir Sheets**

***Perf. 11***

| | | | | |
|---|---|---|---|---|
| **1087** | A316 | $2 multicolored | *4.25* | *4.25* |
| **1088** | A316 | $2 multicolored | *4.25* | *4.25* |
| **1089** | A316 | $2 multicolored | *4.25* | *4.25* |
| **1090** | A316 | $2 multicolored | *4.25* | *4.25* |

Nos. 1087-1090 contain one 64x44mm stamp each.

**Nos. 1087-1090 with Added Text**

**1993, Aug. 3** **Souvenir Sheets**

| | | | |
|---|---|---|---|
| *1087a* | With added text in margin | 6.00 | 6.00 |
| *1088a* | With added text in margin | 6.00 | 6.00 |
| *1089a* | With added text in margin | 6.00 | 6.00 |
| *1090a* | With added text in margin | 6.00 | 6.00 |

Added text on Nos. 1087a-1090a reads: "25th ANNIVERSARY OF THE LAST STEAM TRAIN TO / RUN ON BRITISH RAIL 1968-1993."

1988 Summer Olympics, Seoul — A317

10c, Baseball. 35c, Hurdles. 45c, Fencing. 80c, Synchronized swimming. $1, Yachting. $1.50, Tennis.

**1988, Sept. 13** **Litho.**

| | | | | |
|---|---|---|---|---|
| **1091** | A317 | 10c multicolored | .25 | .25 |
| **1092** | A317 | 35c multicolored | .65 | .65 |
| **1093** | A317 | 45c multicolored | .90 | .90 |
| **1094** | A317 | 80c multicolored | 1.50 | 1.50 |
| **1095** | A317 | $1 multicolored | 2.00 | 2.00 |
| | | *Nos. 1091-1095 (5)* | 5.30 | 5.30 |

**Souvenir Sheet**

| | | | | |
|---|---|---|---|---|
| **1096** | A317 | $1.50 multicolored | 2.25 | 2.25 |

Intl. Tennis Federation, 75th anniv. ($1.50).

St. Joseph's Catholic Hospital, 25th Anniv. — A318

No. 1098, Hospital, 4 staff members. No. 1099, St. John of God. No. 1100, Doctor, nurse, map.

**1988, Aug. 26** **Litho.** ***Perf. 14½***

| | | | | |
|---|---|---|---|---|
| **1097** | A318 | 10c shown | .25 | .25 |
| **1098** | A318 | 10c multicolored | .25 | .25 |
| **1099** | A318 | 35c multicolored | .70 | .70 |
| **1100** | A318 | $1 multicolored | 2.00 | 2.00 |
| | | *Nos. 1097-1100 (4)* | 3.20 | 3.20 |

Common Design Types pictured following the introduction.

**Lloyds of London, 300th Anniv.**

Common Design Type

CD341

Designs: 10c, Royal Exchange destroyed by fire, 1838, vert. 35c, Air Liberia BN2A aircraft. 45c, Supertanker Chevron Antwerp. $1, Lakonia on fire off Madeira, 1963, vert.

**1988, Oct. 31** **Litho.** ***Perf. 14***

| | | | | |
|---|---|---|---|---|
| **1101** | CD341 | 10c multicolored | .25 | .25 |
| **1102** | CD341 | 35c multicolored | .75 | .75 |
| **1103** | CD341 | 45c multicolored | 1.00 | 1.00 |
| **1104** | CD341 | $1 multicolored | 2.25 | 2.25 |
| | | *Nos. 1101-1104 (4)* | 4.25 | 4.25 |

Sasa Players A319

10c, Monkey bridge, vert. 45c, Snake dancers, vert.

***Perf. 14x14½, 14½x14***

**1988, Sept. 30** **Litho.**

| | | | | |
|---|---|---|---|---|
| **1105** | A319 | 10c multicolored | .35 | .35 |
| **1106** | A319 | 35c shown | 1.00 | 1.00 |
| **1107** | A319 | 45c multicolored | 1.40 | 1.40 |
| | | *Nos. 1105-1107 (3)* | 2.75 | 2.75 |

Intl. Fund for Agricultural Development, 10th Anniv. — A320

10c, Crops. 35c, Spraying crops, livestock.

**1988, Oct. 7** **Litho.** ***Perf. 14x14½***

| | | | | |
|---|---|---|---|---|
| **1108** | A320 | 10c multicolored | .40 | .40 |
| **1109** | A320 | 35c multicolored | 1.50 | 1.50 |

3rd Anniv. of the 2nd Republic — A321

10c, Pres. Doe, officials. 50c, Pres. Doe, doctor.

**1989, Jan. 6** **Litho.** ***Perf. 14***

| | | | | |
|---|---|---|---|---|
| **1110** | A321 | 10c multicolored | .35 | .35 |
| **1111** | A321 | 35c like 10c | 1.10 | 1.10 |
| **1112** | A321 | 50c multicolored | 1.75 | 1.75 |
| | | *Nos. 1110-1112 (3)* | 3.20 | 3.20 |

**US Presidents Type of 1981-82**

**1989, Jan. 20** ***Perf. 13½x14***

| | | | | |
|---|---|---|---|---|
| **1113** | A280 | $1 George Bush | 2.60 | 2.60 |

Rissho Kosei-Kai Buddhist Assoc., Tokyo, 50th Anniv. — A322

Natl. flags and: No. 1114, "Harmony" in Japanese. No. 1115, Organization headquarters, Tokyo. No. 1116, Nikkyo Niwano, founder. 50c, Statue of Buddha in the Great Sacred Hall.

**1989, Feb. 28** **Litho.** ***Perf. 14x14½***

| | | | | |
|---|---|---|---|---|
| **1114** | A322 | 10c multicolored | .45 | .45 |
| **1115** | A322 | 10c multicolored | .45 | .45 |
| **1116** | A322 | 10c multicolored | .45 | .45 |
| **1117** | A322 | 50c multicolored | 2.00 | 2.00 |
| | | *Nos. 1114-1117 (4)* | 3.35 | 3.35 |

Liberian-Japanese friendship.

Souvenir Sheet

Emperor Hirohito of Japan (1901-1989) — A323

Commemorative coins: a, Silver. b, Gold.

**1989, Feb. 28** **Unwmk.** ***Perf. 14½***

| | | | | |
|---|---|---|---|---|
| **1118** | A323 | Sheet of 2 | 6.00 | 6.00 |
| ***a.-b.*** | | 75c any single | 2.50 | 2.50 |

For overprint see No. 1147.

Mano River Union, 15th Anniv. A324

Natl. flag, crest and: 10c, Union Glass Factory, Gardnersville, Monrovia. 35c, Pres. Doe, Momoh of Sierra Leone and Conte of Guinea. 45c, Monrovia-Freetown Highway. 50c, Sierra Leone-Guinea land postal services. $1, Communique, 1988 summit.

**Unwmk.**

**1989, May 8** **Litho.** ***Perf. 14***

| | | | | |
|---|---|---|---|---|
| **1119** | A324 | 10c multicolored | .30 | .30 |
| **1120** | A324 | 35c multicolored | 1.00 | 1.00 |
| **1121** | A324 | 45c multicolored | 1.25 | 1.25 |
| **1122** | A324 | 50c multicolored | 1.40 | 1.40 |
| **1123** | A324 | $1 multicolored | 2.75 | 2.75 |
| | | *Nos. 1119-1123 (5)* | 6.70 | 6.70 |

World Telecommunications Day — A325

**1989, May 17** **Litho.** ***Perf. 12½***

| | | | | |
|---|---|---|---|---|
| **1124** | A325 | 50c multicolored | 1.25 | 1.25 |

Common Design Type

Moon Landing, 20th Anniv. — CD342

Apollo 11: 10c, Recovery ship USS Okinawa. 35c, Buzz Aldrin, Neil Armstrong and Michael Collins. 45c, Mission emblem. $1, Aldrin steps on the Moon. $2, Aldrin preparing to conduct experiments on the Moon's surface.

***Perf. 14x13½, 14 (35c, 45c)***

**1989, July 20** **Litho.** **Wmk. 384**

**Size of Nos. 1126-1127: 29x29mm**

| | | | | |
|---|---|---|---|---|
| **1125** | CD342 | 10c multicolored | .25 | .25 |
| **1126** | CD342 | 35c multicolored | .75 | .75 |
| **1127** | CD342 | 45c multicolored | 1.00 | 1.00 |
| **1128** | CD342 | $1 multicolored | 2.25 | 2.25 |
| | | *Nos. 1125-1128 (4)* | 4.25 | 4.25 |

**Souvenir Sheet**

| | | | | |
|---|---|---|---|---|
| **1129** | CD342 | $2 multicolored | 4.25 | 4.25 |

Souvenir Sheet

The Women's March on Versailles — A326

**1989, July 7** **Wmk. 384** ***Perf. 14***

| | | | | |
|---|---|---|---|---|
| **1130** | A326 | $1.50 multicolored | 3.00 | 3.00 |

French revolution, bicent., PHILEXFRANCE '89.

Souvenir Sheet

Renovation and Re-dedication of the Statue of Liberty, 1986 — A327

Photographs: a, Workman. b, French dignitary, US flag. c, Dignitaries at ceremony, statue.

*Perf. 14x13½*

**1989, Oct. 2 Litho. Wmk. 373**

| | | | |
|---|---|---|---|
| 1131 A327 Sheet of 3 | | 1.75 | 1.75 |
| *a.-c.* 25c any single | | .55 | .55 |

World Stamp Expo '89 and PHILEXFRANCE '89.

Souvenir Sheet

A328

**1989, Nov. 17 Unwmk. *Perf. 14½***

| | | |
|---|---|---|
| 1132 A328 $2 black | 4.50 | 4.50 |

World Stamp Expo '89, Washington, DC.

Jawaharlal Nehru, 1st Prime Minister of Independent India — A329

45c, Nehru, signature, flag. 50c, Nehru, signature.

**1989, Dec. 22 Unwmk. *Perf. 14***

| | | |
|---|---|---|
| 1133 A329 45c multicolored | .75 | .75 |
| 1134 A329 50c multicolored | 1.90 | 1.90 |

New Standard-A Earth Satellite Station — A330

**1990, Jan. 5**

| | | |
|---|---|---|
| 1135 A330 10c shown | .25 | .25 |
| 1136 A330 35c multi, diff. | 1.00 | 1.00 |

US Educational & Cultural Foundation in Liberia, 25th Anniv. (in 1989) — A331

**1990, Jan. 5**

| | | |
|---|---|---|
| 1137 A331 10c multicolored | .25 | .25 |
| 1138 A331 45c multicolored | 1.10 | 1.10 |

Pan-African Postal Union, 10th Anniv. — A332

**1990, Jan. 18 *Perf. 13x12½***

| | | |
|---|---|---|
| 1139 A332 35c multicolored | .80 | .80 |

Flags of Liberian Counties — A333

Designs: a, Bomi. b, Bong. c, Grand Bassa. d, Grand Cape Mount. e, Grand Gedeh. f, Grand Kru. g, Lofa. h, Margibi. i, Maryland. j, Montserrado. k, Nimba. l, Rivercess. m, Sinoe.

*Perf. 14x13½*

**1990, Mar. 2 Litho. Unwmk.**

| | | |
|---|---|---|
| 1140 Strip of 13 | 5.00 | 5.00 |
| *a.-m.* A333 10c any single | .30 | .30 |
| 1141 Strip of 13 | 13.00 | 13.00 |
| *a.-m.* A333 35c any single | 1.00 | 1.00 |
| 1142 Strip of 13 | 15.00 | 15.00 |
| *a.-m.* A333 45c any single | 1.10 | 1.10 |
| 1143 Strip of 13 | 20.00 | 20.00 |
| *a.-m.* A333 50c any single | 1.40 | 1.40 |
| 1144 Strip of 13 | 37.50 | 37.50 |
| *a.-m.* A333 $1 any single | 2.75 | 2.75 |
| *Nos. 1140-1144 (5)* | 90.50 | 90.50 |

**Queen Mother, 90th Birthday**
Common Design Types

Designs: 10c, At age 6. $2, At age 22.

*Perf. 14x15*

**1991, Oct. 28 Wmk. 384**

| | | |
|---|---|---|
| 1145 CD343 10c multicolored | .25 | .25 |

*Perf. 14½*

| | | |
|---|---|---|
| 1146 CD344 $2 brn & blk | 3.00 | 3.00 |

For overprints see Nos. 1162-1163.

**No. 1118 Overprinted**

*Perf. 14½*

**1991, Nov. 16 Litho. Unwmk.**

| | | |
|---|---|---|
| 1147 A323 Sheet of 2 | 3.50 | 3.50 |
| *a.-b.* 75c any single | 1.50 | 1.50 |

National Unity — A334

Designs: 35c, Hands clasp over map of Liberia. 45c, Liberian flag, hands, African map. 50c, All Liberia conference, March 1991, conferees, flag, map.

**1991, Dec. 30 *Perf. 13½***

| | | |
|---|---|---|
| 1148 A334 35c multicolored | 1.00 | 1.00 |
| 1149 A334 45c multicolored | 1.25 | 1.25 |
| 1150 A334 50c multicolored | 1.40 | 1.40 |
| *Nos. 1148-1150 (3)* | 3.65 | 3.65 |

1992 Summer Olympics, Barcelona — A335

**1992, Aug. 7 Litho. *Perf. 14***

| | | |
|---|---|---|
| 1151 A335 45c Boxing | 1.50 | 1.25 |
| 1152 A335 50c Soccer | 1.60 | 1.40 |
| 1153 A335 $1 Weight lifting | 3.25 | 2.75 |
| 1154 A335 $2 Water polo | 6.00 | 5.50 |
| *Nos. 1151-1154 (4)* | 12.35 | 10.90 |

**Souvenir Sheet**

| | | |
|---|---|---|
| 1155 A335 $1.50 Running | 6.00 | 6.00 |

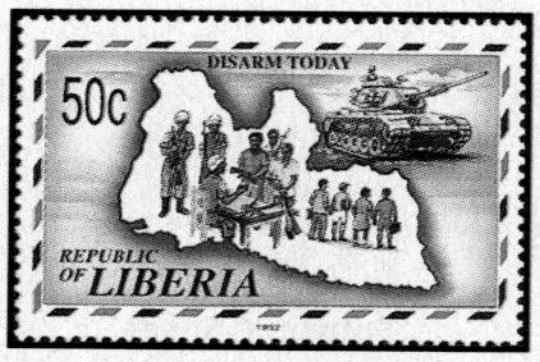


Disarmament — A336

Designs: 50c, Disarm today. $1, Join your parents & build Liberia. $2, Peace must prevail in Liberia.

**1993, Feb. 10 Litho. *Perf. 13½x14***

| | | |
|---|---|---|
| 1156 A336 50c multicolored | 1.50 | 1.50 |
| 1157 A336 $1 multicolored | 2.90 | 2.90 |
| 1158 A336 $2 multicolored | 5.50 | 5.50 |
| *Nos. 1156-1158 (3)* | 9.90 | 9.90 |

See Nos. 1237-1239.

Miniature Sheets

Flora and Fauna — A337

No. 1159 — Flora: a, Papaya. b, Sausage tree. c, Angraecum eichlerianum. d, Arachnis flos-aeris. e, Screw pine. f, African tulip tree. g, Coffee tree. h, Bolusiella talbotii. i, Bulbophyllum lepidum. j, Oeceoclades maculata. k, Plectrelminthus caudatus. l, Diaphananthe rutila.

No. 1160 — Fauna: a, Diana monkey. b, Flying squirrel. c, Egyptian rousette. d, Serval. e, Potto. f, Chimpanzee. g, African horned chameleon. h, Royal python. i, Golden cat. j, Banded duiker. k, Pygmy hippopotamus. l, Water chevrotain.

No. 1161 — Birds: a, Grey heron. b, Bat hawk. c, Martial eagle. d, Little sparrow hawk. e, Hoopoe. f, Red bishop. g, Purple-throated sunbird. h, African fish eagle. i, African grey parrot. j, Black-crowned night heron. k, Swallow. l, Great white egret.

**1993-94 Litho. *Perf. 14***

| | | |
|---|---|---|
| 1159 A337 70c Sheet of 12, #a.-l. | 25.00 | 25.00 |
| 1160 A337 90c Sheet of 12, #a.-l. | 27.50 | 27.50 |
| 1161 A337 $1 Sheet of 12, #a.-l. | 24.00 | 24.00 |
| *Nos. 1159-1161 (3)* | 76.50 | 76.50 |

Issued: 70c, 10/14; 90c, 11/18; $1, 1/14/94.

Nos. 1145-1146 Ovptd. with Hong Kong '94 Emblem

*Perf. 14x15*

**1994, Feb. 18 Litho. Wmk. 384**

| | | |
|---|---|---|
| 1162 CD343 10c multicolored | .35 | .35 |

*Perf. 14½*

| | | |
|---|---|---|
| 1163 CD344 $2 multicolored | 5.25 | 5.25 |

Miniature Sheet

Roberts Field, Monrovia, 50th Anniv. — A338

No. 1164: a, Vickers Supermarine Spitfire Mk IX. b, Boeing B-17G. c, Douglas A-20 Boston. d, North American B-25J Mitchell. e, Beech C-45 Expeditor. f, Douglas C-54. g, Piper L4 Cub. h, Martin PBM-3C.

**1994, July 11 Litho. *Perf. 13½x13***

| | | |
|---|---|---|
| 1164 A338 35c Sheet of 8, #a.-h. + label | 10.00 | 10.00 |

Souvenir Sheets

Locomotives — A339

Designs: No. 1165, $1, Class A3 #60044 Melton, Class A4 #60017 Silver Fox. No. 1166, $1, GWR 2-6-2 Prairie Tank #4561. No. 1167, $1, GWR 2-6-2 Small Prairie. No. 1168, $1, GWR Castle Class 4-6-0 No. Kinswear Castle. No. 1169, $1, GWR 0-6-0 Pannier Tank. No. 1170, $1, Bong Mining Company diesel hauling iron ore.

**1994, Aug. 16 Litho. *Perf. 14***

| | | |
|---|---|---|
| 1165-1170 A339 Set of 6 | 14.00 | 14.00 |

See Nos. 1194-1199, 1205.

Liberian Natl. Red Cross, 75th Anniv. — A340

Designs: 70c, No. 1172, Globe. No. 1173, $2, Jean-Henri Dunant.

**1994, Oct. 3 Litho. *Perf. 14½x14***
**1171** A340 70c multicolored 1.90 1.90
**1172** A340 $1 multicolored 2.25 2.25
**1173** A340 $1 multicolored 2.25 2.25
**1174** A340 $2 multicolored 5.00 5.00
*Nos. 1171-1174 (4)* 11.40 11.40

### End of World War II, 50th Anniv.
Common Design Types

Designs: 70c, Sunderland on U-boat patrol. 90c, US Army Engineer Task Force. $1, MV Abosso sunk off Liberia, 1942. No. 1178, MV Adda sunk off Liberia, 1941.

No. 1179, Obverse of U.S. Victory Medal depicting Liberty.

**1995, May 8 Litho. *Perf. 13½***
**1175** CD351 70c multicolored 1.75 1.00
**1176** CD351 90c multicolored 2.00 1.40
**1177** CD351 $1 multicolored 2.50 1.50
**1178** CD351 $2 multicolored 4.50 2.75
*Nos. 1175-1178 (4)* 10.75 6.65

**Souvenir Sheet**
***Perf. 14***
**1179** CD352 $2 multicolored 4.50 4.50

Wild Animals — A341

**1995, June 1 *Perf. 14***
**1180** A341 70c Cheetah 2.00 2.00
**1181** A341 70c Giraffe 2.00 2.00
**1182** A341 90c Rhinoceros 2.00 2.00
**1183** A341 $1 Elephant 3.00 3.00
**1184** A341 $2 Lion 6.00 6.00
*Nos. 1180-1184 (5)* 15.00 15.00

Souvenir Sheet

1995 IAAF World Track & Field Championships, Gothenburg — A342

No. 1185: a, Merlene Ottey. b, Heike Drechsler.

**1995, Aug. 4 Litho. *Perf. 14***
**1185** A342 $1 Sheet of 2, #a.-b. 8.50 8.50

Miniature Sheet

Orchids — A343

No. 1186: a, Ancistrochilus rothschildianus. b, Disa uniflora. c, Polystachya ottoniana. d, Aerangis brachycarpa. e, Plectrelminthus caudatus. f, Polystachya bella. g, Ansellia africana. h, Bulbophyllum cochleatum.

**1995, Sept. 1 *Perf. 13***
**1186** A343 70c Sheet of 8, #a.-h. + label 17.00 17.00

Singapore '95.

### UN, 50th Anniv.
Common Design Type

Designs: 25c, UN Land Rovers. 50c, Delivering food supplies. $1, Ilyushin IL-76 freighter airlifting supplies. $2, MIL MI-8 helicopter.

**1995, Oct. 24 Litho. *Perf. 14***
**1187** CD353 25c multicolored .90 .90
**1188** CD353 50c multicolored 1.25 1.25
**1189** CD353 $1 multicolored 2.50 2.50
**1190** CD353 $2 multicolored 5.00 5.00
*Nos. 1187-1190 (4)* 9.65 9.65

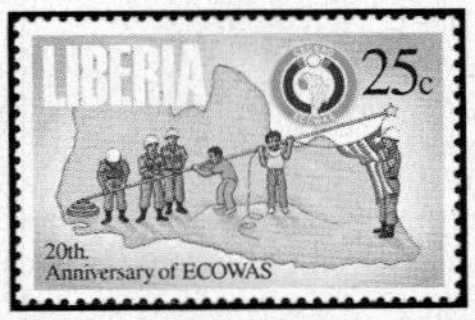

Economic Community of West African States, 20th Anniv. — A344

Designs: 25c, Map, Liberian flag, soldiers, civilians. 50c, Soldier carrying child, vert. $1, Logo, vert.

***Perf. 13½x13, 13½x13***
**1995, Nov. 10 Litho.**
**1191** A344 25c multicolored .75 .75
**1192** A344 50c multicolored 1.50 1.50
**1193** A344 $1 multicolored 3.00 3.00
*Nos. 1191-1193 (3)* 5.25 5.25

### Train Type of 1994
Souvenir Sheets

Designs: No. 1194, $1, 4-4-0 locomotive 11 "The Reno," galloping horses. No. 1195, $1, Halwill station, Southern Region T9 class locomotive #30719. No. 1196, $1, GWR 0-4-2T "1400" class locomotive #1408, cricket match. No. 1197, $1, LMS Jubilee class 4-6-0, #45684 "Jutland," Kettering station. No. 1198, $1, GWR 2-6-2 "Prairie" locomotive #4547, Lustleigh station. No. 1199, $1, Wainwright "H" class 0-4-4T locomotive, winter countryside.

**1996, Feb. 29 Litho. *Perf. 14x15***
**1194-1199** A339 Set of 6 14.00 14.00

Modern Olympic Games, Cent. — A345

**1996, Apr. 22 Litho. *Perf. 13***
**1200** A345 20c Runners .60 .60
**1201** A345 35c Boxing 1.00 1.00
**1202** A345 50c Javelin 1.40 1.40
**1203** A345 $1 Hurdles 2.75 2.75
*Nos. 1200-1203 (4)* 5.75 5.75

Butterflies A346

No. 1204: a, Papilio zalmoxis. b, Papilio dardanus. c, Charaxes varanes. d, Acraea natalica. e, Euphaedra neophron. f, Craphium antheus. g, Salamis anacardii. h, Kallima cymodoce. i, Precis hierta.

**1996, May 22 Litho. *Perf. 13½***
**1204** A346 70c Sheet of 9, #a.-i. 14.00 14.00

### Train Type of 1994
Souvenir Sheet

Design: G4a Class Pacific locomotive, Canadian Pacific Railroad.

**1996, June 8 Litho. *Perf. 14x15***
**1205** A339 $1 multi 2.25 2.25

CAPEX '96.

Fish — A347

No. 1206: a, Atlantic Sailfish. b, Guinean flyingfish. c, Blue marlin. d, Little tunny (e). e, Common dolphinfish (f). f, Guachanche barracuda. g, Guinean parrotfish. h, Cadenat's chromis (g). i, Dusky grouper (h). j, Hoefler's butterflyfish (k). k, African hind (l). l, West African Angelfish.

**1996, July 15 Litho. *Perf. 14***
**1206** A347 90c Sheet of 12, #a.-l. 20.00 20.00

Butterflies A348

No. 1207: a, Euphaedra judith. b, Euphaedra eleus. c, Acraea encedon. d, Euphaedra neophron. e, Liptena praestans. f, Neptis exalenca. g, Palla decius. h, Salamis cytora. i, Pseudacraea dolomena. j, Anaphaeis eriphia. k, Euphaedra themis. l, Hadrodontes varanes.

No. 1208: a, Papilio mnestheus. b, Papilio nobilis. c, Graphium antheus. d, Asterope benguelae. e, Graphium illyris. f, Emphaedra eupalus. g, Charaxes protoclea. h, Cymothoe beckeri. i, Euphaedra cyparissa. j, Coliades chalybe. k, Mimacraea neokoton. l, Charaxes ethalion.

$2, Charaxes pelias.

**1996 Litho. *Perf. 14***
**1207** A348 20c Sheet of 12, #a.-l. 5.50 5.50
**1208** A348 25c Sheet of 12, #a.-l. 6.50 6.50

**Souvenir Sheet**
**1209** A348 $2 multicolored 4.50 4.50

Birds — A349

Designs, horiz: 35c, African jacana. 50c, Pel's fishing owl. $1, Paradise whydah.

No. 1213: a, Turtle dove. b, Bee-eater. c, Golden oriole. d, Pied flycatcher. e, Sardinian warbler. f, Goliath heron. g, Rock thrush. h, Kestrel. i, Cattle egret. j, Woodchat shrike. k, Hoopoe. l, Great egret.

No. 1214, horiz: a, Red faced crimsonwing. b, Egyptian goose. c, African pitta. d, Paradise flycatcher. e, Garganey. f, Southern carmine bee-eater. g, Fulvous whistling duck. h, Village weaver. i, Martial eagle.

$2, Pintail duck, horiz.

**1996**
**1210-1212** A349 Set of 3 4.50 4.50
**1213** A349 25c Sheet of 12, #a.-l. 7.25 7.25
**1214** A349 35c Sheet of 9, #a.-i. 8.00 8.00

**Souvenir Sheet**
**1215** A349 $2 multicolored 4.75 4.75

Marilyn Monroe (1926-62) — A350

**1996**
**1216** A350 20c multicolored .70 .70

No. 1216 was issued in sheets of 16.

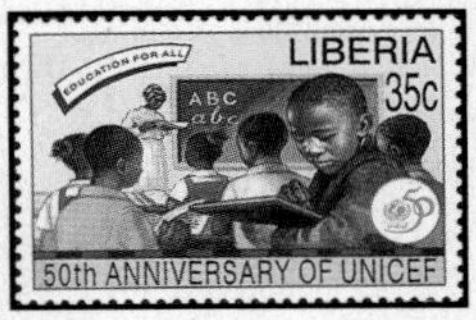

UNICEF, 50th Anniv. A351

Designs: 35c, Education for all. 70c, Health care. $1, Children first.

**1996, Sept. 16 *Perf. 13½x13***
**1217-1219** A351 35c Set of 3 5.50 5.50

1996 Summer Olympic Games, Atlanta A352

Designs: No. 1220, 20c, Cricket (discontinued sport), vert. No. 1221, 20c, Babe Didrikson, vert. No. 1222, 35c, Vitaly Scherbo, winner of 6 gold medals, 1992, vert. No. 1223, 35c, Betty Robinson, vert. No. 1224, 50c, Cuban baseball team, gold medal, 1992. No. 1225, 50c, Ancient Greek wall painting of boxers, vert. No. 1226, $1, Stadium, Barcelona, 1992. No. 1227, $1, Stadium, Amsterdam, 1928, vert.

No. 1228, 35c, vert. — Olympic events: a, Men's athletics. b, Men's gymnastics. c, Weight lifting. d, Women's volleyball. e, Women's diving. f, Women's gymnastics. g, Women's track. h, Women's tennis. i, Discus.

No. 1229, 35c, vert. — Boxing gold medalists, boxing: a, Tyrell Biggs, U.S. b, Isan Gura, Tanzania (no medal). c, Mark Breland, U.S. d, Teofilo Stevenson, Cuba. e, Ray Leonard, U.S. f, Michael Spinks, U.S. g, Joe Frazier, U.S. h, Floyd Patterson, US. i, George Foreman, US.

$2, Evelyn Ashford.

**1996 Litho. *Perf. 14***
**1220-1227** A352 Set of 8 14.00

**Sheets of 9, #a-i**
**1228-1229** A352 Set of 2 22.50

**Souvenir Sheet**
**1230** A352 $2 multicolored 7.00

Flowers and Flowering Trees — A353

No. 1231: a, Olive tree. b, Olive flower. c, Fig tree. d, Almond tree. e, Almug tree. f, Cedar. g, Pomegranate (b). h, Citron. i, Date palm (d, e, j). j, Date palm (fruit). k, Cedar of Lebanon. l, Rock rose. m, Narcissus. n, Oleander (i). o, Date palm (flower). p, Shittah tree. q, Hyacinth. r, Barley, flax (s). s, Grape vine. t, Lily of the field. u, Mandrake. v, Caper desire. w, Madonna lily. x, Aloe (s). y, Date palm tree.

**1996**
**1231** A353 25c Sheet of 25, #a.-y. 25.00 25.00

History of Rock and Roll — A354

No. 1232: a, Wilson Pickett. b, Bill Haley. c, Otis Redding. d, Fats Domino. e, Buddy Holly. f, Chubby Checker. g, Marvin Gaye. h, Jimi Hendrix.

**1996 *Perf. 13½x14***
**1232** A354 35c Sheet of 8, #a.-h. + label 8.00 8.00

Kingfisher — A355

No. 1233 — Kingfishers: a, Striped. b, Grey-headed. c, Pied. d, Giant. e, Shining-blue.

**1996, Oct. 7 Litho. *Perf. 13½***
**1233** A355 75c Strip of 5, #a.-e. 7.50 7.50

See No. 1236.

Mao Zedong, 20th Anniv. of Death — A356

**1996, Nov. 1 Litho. *Perf. 14½x14***
**1234** A356 $1 shown 2.50 2.50
**1235** A356 $1 As older man 2.50 2.50

**Kingfisher Type of 1996**
Souvenir Sheet

**1997, Feb. 3 Litho. *Perf. 14***
**1236** A355 $1 Like #1233b 2.00 2.00

Hong Kong '97. No. 1236 contains one 29x43mm stamp.

**Disarmament Type of 1993**
Inscribed "PEACE TODAY"

**1997 Litho. 13½x14**
**1237** A336 $1 Like #1157 3.00 3.00
**1238** A336 $2 Like #1158 5.00 5.00
**1239** A336 $3 Like #1156 9.00 9.00
*Nos. 1237-1239 (3)* 17.00

Nos. 1237-1239 are dated 1996.

Wildlife — A357

No. 1240: a, Olive baboon. b, Leopard. c, African tree pangolin. d, Vervet. e, Aardvark. f, Spotted hyena. g, Hunting dog. h, Thomson's gazelle. i, Warthog. j, African civet. k, Nile crocodile. l, African polecat.

**1997, Apr. 2 Litho. *Perf. 14***
**1240** A357 50c Sheet of 12, #a.-l. 15.00 15.00

Deng Xiaoping (1904-97), British Transfer of Hong Kong — A358

Different portraits of Deng Xiaoping, "July 1, 1997," Hong Kong: 70c, In daylight, vert. $1, At night.
No. 1243: a, 50c. b, 70c. c, $1.20.

**1997 Litho. *Perf. 14***
**1241** A358 70c multicolored 2.00
**1242** A358 $1 multicolored 3.25
**1243** A358 Sheet of 3, #a.-c. 7.75

No. 1241 is 28x44mm, and was issued in sheets of 4. No. 1242 was issued in sheets of 3.

UNESCO, 50th Anniv. — A359

No. 1244, 50c, vert.: a, Canals, Venice, Italy. b, Mosque of Badshahi, Gardens of Shalamar, Lahore, Pakistan. c, Palace of Orando, Spain. d, Grounds of Temple of Hera, Greece. e, Church and Monastery of Daphni, Greece. f, Fraser Island, Australia. g, Canadian Rocky Mountains Park, Canada. h, Church of Santo Domingo Puebla, Mexico.
No. 1245, 50c, vert.: a, City of Ohrid and lake, Macedonia. b, Thracian Tomb of Sveshtari, Bulgaria. c, Monastery of Hossios Luckas, Greece. d, Church of Santa Cristina of Lena, Spain. e, Church of Santa Maria Della Salute, Venice, Italy. f, Center of Puebla, Mexico. g, Bagrati Cathedral, Georgia. h, Quebec City, Canada.
No. 1246: a, Ngorongoro Conservation Area, Tanzania. b, Garamba Natl. Park, Zaire. c, Canaima Natl. Park, Venezuela. d, Simien Natl. Park, Ethiopia. e, Mana Pools Natl. Park, Zimbabwe.
No. 1247, $2, Palace of Diocletian, Split, Croatia. No., 1248, $2, Monument of Nubia at Abu Simbel, Egypt. No. 1249, $2, Quedlinberg, Germany.

***Perf. 13½x14, 14x13½***
**1997, June 17 Litho.**
**Sheets of 8, #a-h + Label**
**1244-1245** A359 Set of 2 27.50
**1246** A359 70c Sheet of 5, #a-e, + label 12.50

**Souvenir Sheets**
**1247-1249** A359 Set of 3 21.00

Queen Elizabeth II, Prince Philip, 50th Wedding Anniv. A360

No. 1250: a, Queen holding umbrella. b, Royal arms. c, Prince in white uniform, Queen. d, Queen waving, Prince. e, Windsor Castle. f, Prince Philip.
No. 1251, $2, Queen seated on sofa. No. 1252, $2, Queen, Prince wearnig robes of Order of the Garter.

**1997, June 17 *Perf. 14***
**1250** A360 50c Sheet of 6, #a.-f. 11.00

**Souvenir Sheet**
**1251-1252** A360 $2 Set of 2 14.00

Grimm's Fairy Tales A361

Mother Goose — A362

No. 1253 — Scenes from Rapunzel: a, Girl. b, Wicked person, raven. c, Prince.
No. 1254, Prince rescuing girl.
No. 1255, Little Bo Peep, sheep.

**1997, June 17 *Perf. 13½x14***
**1253** A361 $1 Sheet of 3, #a.-c. 10.00

**Souvenir Sheets**
**1254** A361 $2 multicolored 7.00

***Perf. 14***
**1255** A362 $2 multicolored 7.00

1998 Winter Olympics, Nagano — A363

Designs: 50c, Olympic Stadium, Lillehammer, 1994. 70c, Johann Koss, speed skating. $1, Katarina Witt, figure skating. $1.50, Sonia Henie, figure skating.
No. 1260: a, K. Seizinger, Alpine downhill skiing. b, J. Weissflog, 120-m ski jump. c, T. Kono, Nordic combined. d, G. Hackl, luge.
No. 1261: a, E. Bredesen, 90-m ski jump. b, L. Kjus, downhill skiing. c, B. Daehlie, cross-country skiing. d, P. Wiberg, combined Alpine skiing. e, S.L. Hattestad, freestyle skiing. f, G. Weder, D. Acklin, 2-man bobsled. g, Swedish hockey player. h, T. Alsgaard, cross-country skiing.
No. 1262, $2, German biathlete, 1994. No. 1263, $2, M. Wasmeier, giant slalom. No. 1264, $2, J. Koss, speed skating, diff. No. 1265, $2, V. Schneider, slalom.

**1997, June 23 *Perf. 14***
**1256-1259** A363 Set of 4 13.00
**1260** A363 50c Strip or block of 4, #a.-d. 7.00
**1261** A363 50c Sheet of 8, #a.-h. 14.00

**Souvenir Sheets**
**1262-1265** A363 Set of 4 27.50

No. 1260 was issued in sheets of 8 stamps.

Flowers — A364

No. 1266, 50c: a, Sugar cane dahlia. b, Windsor tall phlox. c, Creative art daylily. d, Columbine. e, Infinite Grace bearded iris. f, Fairy lilies mini amaryllis.
No. 1267, 50c: a, White coneflower. b, Peggy Lee hybrid tea rose. c, Daffodil. d, Bowl of Beauty peony. e. Hardy lily. f, Windflower.
No. 1268, $2, Lily-flowered tulip. No. 1269, $2, Chrysanthemum Potomac.

**1997, July 1 Litho. *Perf. 14***
**Sheets of 6, #a-f**
**1266-1267** A364 Set of 2 20.00 20.00

**Souvenir Sheets**
**1268-1269** A364 Set of 2 16.00 16.00

Flora and Fauna A365

No. 1270: a, Lovebirds. b, Genet. c, Leopard, crowned night heron. d, Gorilla. e, Giant wild boar. f, Elephant. g, Sterculia flower, skink. h, Ladybugs, bush baby. i, Cape primroses, ground hornbill.
No. 1271, $2, Rufus-crowned roller. No. 1272, $2, Gray heron.

**1997, July 1**
**1270** A365 50c Sheet of 9, #a.-i. 13.00 13.00

**Souvenir Sheets**
**1271-1272** A365 Set of 2 12.00 12.00

Chernobyl Disaster, 10th Anniv. A366

**1997, June 17 Litho. *Perf. 13½x14***
**1273** A366 $1 UNESCO 3.25 3.25

Marcello Mastroianni (1923-96), Actor A367

No. 1274 — Scenes from motion pictures: a, Casanova, 1970. b, Divorce Italian Style. c, 8½. d, La Dolce Vita.

**1997, Sept. 3**
**1274** A367 75c Sheet of 4, #a.-d. 10.00 10.00

Contemporary Artists and Paintings — A368

No. 1275, 50c: a, Andy Warhol (1927-87). b, "Multicolored Retropective," by Warhol, 1979. c, "The Three Muscians," by Picasso, 1921. d, Pablo Picasso (1881-1973). e, Henri Matisse (1869-1954). f, "The Dance," by Matisse, 1910. g, "Lavender Mist," by Pollock, 1950. h, Jackson Pollock (1912-56).
No. 1276, 50c: a, Piet Mondrian (1872-1944). b, "Broadway Boogie Woogie," by Mondrian, 1942-43. c, "Persistence of Memory," by Dali, 1931. d, Salvador Dali (1904-89). e, Roy Lichtenstein (1923-97). f, "Artist's Studio: The Dance," by Lichtenstein, 1974. g, "Europe After the Rain," by Ernst, 1940-42. h, Max Ernst (1891-1976).

**1997, Sept. 3** *Perf. 14*

**Sheets of 8, #a-h**

**1275-1276** A368 Set of 2 27.50 27.50

Nos. 1275b-1275c, 1275f-1275g, 1276b-1276c, 1276f-1276g are 53x38mm.

Owls — A369

No. 1277: a, Akun eagle owl. b, Shelley's eagle owl. c, African wood owl. d, Rufous fishing owl. e, Maned owl. f, Sandy scops owl.

**1997**

**1277** A369 50c Sheet of 6, #a.-f. 9.00 9.00

Birds — A370

Designs: 1c, Black bee-eater. 2c, Yellow-billed barbet. 3c, Carmine bee-eater. 4c, Malachite kingfisher. 5c, Emerald cuckoo. 10c, Blue-throated roller. 15c, Blue-headed bee-eater. 20c, Black-collared lovebird. 25c, Broad-billed roller. 50c, Blue-breasted kingfisher. 70c, Little bee-eater. 75c, Yellow spotted barbet. 90c, White-throated bee-eater. $1, Double-toothed barbet. $2, Blue-cheeked bee-eater. $3, Narina's trogon.

**1997**

| | | | | |
|---|---|---|---|---|
| **1278** | A370 | 1c multicolored | .25 | .25 |
| **1279** | A370 | 2c multicolored | .25 | .25 |
| **1280** | A370 | 3c multicolored | .25 | .25 |
| **1281** | A370 | 4c multicolored | .25 | .25 |
| **1282** | A370 | 5c multicolored | .25 | .25 |
| **1283** | A370 | 10c multicolored | .25 | .25 |
| **1284** | A370 | 15c multicolored | .40 | .40 |
| **1285** | A370 | 20c multicolored | .50 | .50 |
| **1286** | A370 | 25c multicolored | .65 | .65 |
| **1287** | A370 | 50c multicolored | 1.25 | 1.25 |
| **1288** | A370 | 70c multicolored | 1.90 | 1.90 |
| **1289** | A370 | 75c multicolored | 2.00 | 2.00 |
| **1290** | A370 | 90c multicolored | 2.40 | 2.40 |
| **1291** | A370 | $1 multicolored | 2.75 | 2.75 |
| **1292** | A370 | $2 multicolored | 5.25 | 5.25 |
| **1293** | A370 | $3 multicolored | 7.75 | 7.75 |
| | | *Nos. 1278-1293 (16)* | 26.35 | 26.35 |

1998 World Cup Soccer — A371

Players, country, vert: 50c, Salenko, Russia. 70c, Schillaci, Italy. $1, Lineker, England. $1.50, Pele, Brazil. $2, Fontaine, France. $2, Rahn, W. Germany.

No. 1300, 50c, vert: a, Ardiles, Argentina. b, Romario, Brazil. c, Rummenigge, Germany. d, Charlton, England. e, Villa, Argentina. f, Matthäus, Germany. g, Maradona, Argentina. h, Lineker, England.

No. 1301, 50c: a, Paulo Rossi, Italy. b, Ademir, Brazil. c, Grzegorz Lato, Poland. d, Gary Lineker, England. e, Gerd Muller, W. Germany. f, Johan Cruyff, Holland. g, Karl-Heinz Rummenigge, Germany. h, Mario Kempes, Argentina.

No. 1302, $6, Beckenbauer, W. Germany, vert. No. 1303, $6, Maier, W. Germany, vert.

***Perf. 13½x14, 14x13½***

**1997, Oct. 1** **Litho.**

**1294-1299** A371 Set of 6 18.00 18.00

**Sheets of 8, #a-h, + Label**

**1300-1301** A371 Set of 2 27.50 27.50

**Souvenir Sheets**

**1302-1303** A371 Set of 2 40.00 40.00

Marine Life A372

No. 1304: a, Flamingoes (beach, palm trees). b, Six flamingoes. c, Sailfish (d). d, Egret. e, Yellow-tail snapper. f, Manatee. g, Clown coris. h, White-collar butterflyfish. i, Royal angelfish. j, Titan triggerfish. k, Three-striped wrasse. l, Pacific blue-eye. m, Wobbegono. n, Jellyfish. o, Sea urchin, red sea triggerfish. p, Harlequin fish.

No. 1305, $2, Seahorses, vert. No. 1306, $2, Anemone fish.

**1998, Mar. 9** **Litho.** *Perf. 14*

**1304** A372 20c Sheet of 16, #a.-p. 9.50 9.50

**Souvenir Sheets**

***Perf. 13½x14, 14x13½***

**1305-1306** A372 Set of 2 12.00 12.00

No. 1305 contains one 38x51mm stamp, No. 1306 contains one 51x38mm stamp.

Butterflies A373

Designs: No. 1307, 50c, Orange tip. No. 1308, 50c, Saturn. No. 1309, 50c, Queen of Spain fritillary. No. 1310, 50c, Plain tiger. No. 1311, 50c, Doris. No. 1312, 50c, Forest queen. No. 1313, 50c, Figure-of-eight. No. 1314, 50c, Orange-barred sulphur.

No. 1315, 50c: a, Alfalfa. b, Orange-barred sulphur, diff. c, Union jack. d, Mocker swallowtail. e, Large green-banded blue. f, Common dotted border.

No. 1316, 50c: a, Cairns birdwing. b, Leafwing. c, Banded kin shoemaker. d, Tiger swallowtail. e, Adonis blue. f, Palmfly.

No. 1317, $2, Great orange tip. No. 1318, $2, Japanese emperor.

**1998, Apr. 6** **Litho.** *Perf. 14*

**1307-1314** A373 Set of 8 12.00 12.00

**Sheets of 6, #a-f**

**1315-1316** A373 Set of 2 18.00 18.00

**Souvenir Sheets**

**1317-1318** A373 Set of 2 12.00 12.00

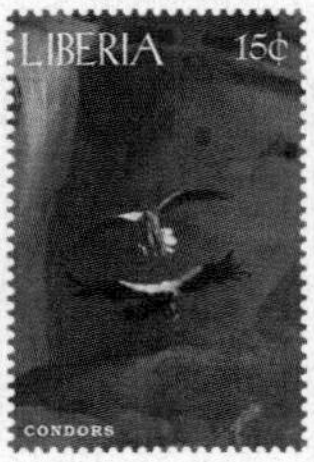


Noah's Ark — A374

No. 1319: a, Condors. b, Giraffes, skunks. c, Mallard ducks. d, Snowy owl. e, Snowy owl (face forward). f, Noah. g, Noah's wife. h, Polar bears. i, Elephants. j, Zebras. k, Rhinoceros. l, Sheep. m. Ruby-throated hummingbird. n, Wives of Noah's sons. o, Bats. p, Ring-necked pheasant. q, Tiger. r, Deer. s, Kangaroos. t, Camels. u, Red-eyed frogs. v, Raccoons. w, Rooster, hen. x, Marmosets. y, Lions.

$2, Black-legged kittiwake gull, ark on top of mountain, horiz.

**1998, May 4** **Litho.** *Perf. 14*

**1319** A374 15c Sheet of 25, #a.-y. 11.00 11.00

**Souvenir Sheet**

**1320** A374 $2 multicolored 6.00 6.00

World Wildlife Fund — A375

No. 1321 — Liberian Mongoose: a, Looking straight ahead. b, Holding object between front paws. c, With front legs on branch. d, With mouth wide open.

**1998, June 16** **Litho.** *Perf. 14*

**1321** A375 32c Block or strip of 4, #a.-d. 5.50 5.50

Issued in sheets of 12 stamps.

Mushrooms A376

Designs: 10c, Lepiota cristata. 15c, Russula emetica. 20c, Coprinus comatus. 30c, Russula cyanoxantha. 50c, Cortinarius violaceus. 75c, Amanita cothurnata. $1, Stropharia cyanea. $1.20, Panaeolus semiovatus.

No. 1330, 40c: a, Collybia butryacea. b, Asterophora parasitica. c, Tricholomopsis rutilans. d, Marasmius alliaceus. e, Mycena crocata. f, Mycena polygramma. g, Oudemansiella mucida. h, Entoloma conferendum. i, Entoloma serrulatum.

No. 1331, 40c: a, Cordyceps militaris. b, Xylaria hypoxlon. c, Sarcoscypha austriaca. d, Auriscalpium. e, Fomitopsis pinicola. f, Pleurotus ostreatus. g, Lepista flaccida. h, Clitocybe metachroa. i, Hygrocybe conica.

No. 1332, $2, Gomphidus roseus. No. 1333, $2, Paxillus atrotomentosus. No. 1334, $2, Russula occidentalis. No. 1335, $2, Cantharellus cibarius.

**1998, July 1**

**1322-1329** A376 Set of 8 14.00 14.00

**Sheets of 9, #a-i**

**1330-1331** A376 Set of 2 24.00 24.00

**Souvenir Sheets**

**1332-1335** A376 Set of 4 27.50 27.50

Monarchs — A377

No. 1336, 50c: a, Kaiser Wilhelm II, Germany. b, Qabus Bin Said, Oman. c, King Albert, Belgium. d, Haile Selassie, Ethiopia. e, King Hussein, Jordan. f, Sheik Jaber Al-Ahmad Al-Sabah, Kuwait.

No. 1337, 50c: a, Alexander the Great, Greece. b, Charlemagne, France. c, Cleopatra, Egypt. d, Henry VIII, England. e, Peter the Great, Russia. f, Frederick the Great, Prussia.

No. 1338, 50c: a, Queen Beatrix, Netherlands. b, King Juan Carlos, Spain. c, Queen Elizabeth II, England. d, Franz Joseph I, Austria-Hungary. e, Princess Grace, Monaco. f, King Carl XVI Gustaf, Sweden.

No. 1339, $2, Empress Michiko, Japan. No. 1340, $2, Emperor Akihito, Japan. No. 1341, $2, Kublai Khan, China.

**1998, July 27** **Litho.** *Perf. 14*

**Sheets of 6, #a-f**

**1336-1338** A377 Set of 3 24.00 24.00

**Souvenir Sheets**

**1339-1341** A377 Set of 3 21.00 21.00

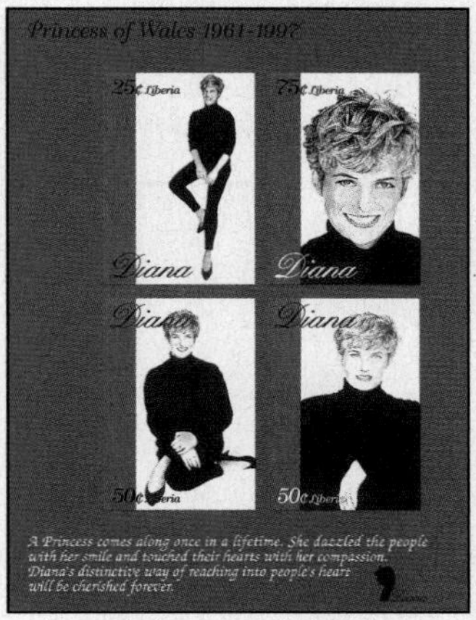


Diana, Princess of Wales (1961-97) — A378

Various portraits of Diana in black outfit.

**1998** ***Imperf.***

**1342** A378 50c Sheet of 4, #a.-d. 4.00 4.00

Birds A379

No. 1343, 32c, Great green macaw. No. 1344, 32c, Crowned pigeon, vert. No. 1345, 32c, Blue-gray tanager. No. 1346, 32c, Roseate spoonbill, vert. No. 1347, 32c, Red-capped manakin. No. 1348, 32c, Groove-billed ani. No. 1349, 32c, South African crowned crane, vert.

No. 1350, vert: a, African sunbird. b, Seven-colored tanager. c, Red-throated bee-eater. d, Blue-crowned motmot. e, Duvaucel's trogon. f, Green bulbul. g, Grass-green tanager. h, Turaco. i, Hammer-head. j, Sarus crane. k, Limpkin. l, Ground hornbill.

No. 1351, $2, Red-crested touraco. No. 1352, $2, Flamingo, vert.

**1998, Aug. 31** **Litho.** *Perf. 14*

**1343-1349** A379 Set of 7 7.00 7.00

**1350** A379 32c Sheet of 12, #a.-l. 12.00 12.00

**Souvenir Sheets**

**1351-1352** A379 Set of 2 12.00 12.00

Children's Stories — A380

No. 1354: a, Tom Sawyer, by Mark Twain. b, Peter Rabbit, by Beatrix Potter. c, The Nutcracker, by E.T.A. Hoffman. d, Hansel & Gretel, by The Brothers Grimm. e, The Princess and the Pea, by Hans Christian Andersen. f, Oliver Twist, by Charles Dickens. g, Little Red Riding Hood, by The Brothers Grimm. h, Rumpelstiltskin, by The Brothers Grimm. i, The Wind & the Willows, by Kenneth Grahame.

$2, Rapunzel, by Brothers Grimm.

**1998, Sept. 16** **Litho.** *Perf. 14½*

**1354** A380 40c Sheet of 9, #a.-i. 12.00 12.00

**Souvenir Sheet**

***Perf. 13½***

**1355** A380 $2 multicolored 7.00 7.00

No. 1355 contains one 38x51mm stamp.

Island, Marine Life A381

No. 1356: a, Litoria peronii. b, Volcano, denomination UL. c, Volcano, denomination UR. d, Egretta alba. e, Graphium antiphates itamputi. f, Rhododendron zoelleri. g, Boat. h, Lava flow. i, Cormorants. j, Vaccinium. k, Caranx latus. l, Dugongs. m, Underwater lava flow. n, Cetocarus bicolor. o, Chilomycterus spilostylus. p, Lienardella fasliatus. q, Aerobatus. r, Gray reef shark. s, Acanthurus leucosternon, denomination UR. t, Hippocampus kuda. u, Coral, denomination UR. v, Chelonia. w, Myripristis hexogona. x, Coral, denomination, UL. y, Acanthurus leucosternon, denonination UL.

No. 1357: a, Sperm whale (b, c). b, Lollipop tang. c, Bottlenose dolphin (b, f). d, Jackass penguin (h). e, Harlequin tuskfish. f, Manta ray (a, b, e, j). g, Sealion. h, Grouper (g, l). i, Hammerhead shark (m). j, Butterfly fish. k, Garibaldi (g). l, Marine iguana (p). m, Loggerhead turtle (n). n, Seahorse. o, Horseshow crab (n, p). p, Moray eel.

No. 1358, 32c: a, Walrus. b, Pockfish-harlequin. c, Striped marlin. d, Whale shark. e, Spiny boxfish. f, Porcupine fish. g, Octopus. h, Dragonfish. i, Sea krait.

No. 1359, 32c: a, Snapping turtle. b, Atlantic spadefish. c, Bottlenose dolphin. d, Humpback whale. e, Whitetip shark. f, Twilight and deep seafish. g, Moorish idol. h, American lobster. i, Stingrays.

No. 1360, $2, Great white shark. No. 1361, $2, Banner fish. No. 1362, $2, Killer whale. No. 1363, $2, Surgeon fish.

**1998, Oct. 15** ***Perf. 14***

**1356** A381 15c Sheet of 25, #a.-y. 12.00 12.00
**1357** A381 20c Sheet of 16, #a.-p. 10.00 10.00

**Sheets of 9, #a-i**

**1358-1359** A381 Set of 2 18.00 18.00

**Souvenir Sheets**

**1360-1363** A381 Set of 4 22.50 22.50

International Year of the Ocean.

Diana, Princess of Wales (1961-97) A382

No. 1364: a, Inscription panel at left. b, Panel at right.

**1998, Oct. 26 Litho.** ***Perf. 14½x14***

**1364** A382 50c Horiz. pair, #a-b 3.25 3.25

No. 1364 was issued in sheets of 3 pairs.

Pablo Picasso (1881-1973) — A383

Entire paintings or details: 50c, Woman Throwing a Stone, 1931. 70c, Man with Sword and Flower, 1969, vert. $1, Large Bather with a Book, 1937, vert.

$2, French Cancan, 1901.

**1998, Oct. 26** ***Perf. 14½***

**1365-1367** A383 Set of 3 7.50 7.50

**Souvenir Sheet**

**1368** A383 $2 multicolored 7.00 7.00

Mahatma Gandhi (1869-1948) A384

**1998, Oct. 26** ***Perf. 14***

**1369** A384 50c shown 1.75 1.75

**Souvenir Sheet**

**1370** A384 $2 Portrait, diff. 7.00 7.00

No. 1369 was issued in sheets of 4.

1998 World Scout Jamboree, Chile — A385

No. 1371: a, Daniel Carter Beard, Ernest Thompson Seton, award scouts, 1912. b, Robert Baden-Powell in Matabeleland, 1896. c, Scout repairing small girl's wagon.

**1998, Oct. 26**

**1371** A385 $1 Sheet of 3, #a.-c. 10.00 10.00

Enzo Ferrari (1898-1988), Automobile Manufacturer — A386

No. 1372: a, King Leopold Cabriolet. b, 195 S. c, 250 GTO 64.

$2, 250MM Cabriolet.

**1998, Oct. 26 Litho.** ***Perf. 14***

**1372** A386 $1 Sheet of 3, #a.-c. 9.00 9.00

**Souvenir Sheet**

**1373** A386 $2 multicolored 8.50 8.50

No. 1373 contains one 91x35mm stamp.

Royal Air Force, 80th Anniv. A387

No. 1374: a, Hawker Hurricane XII. b, Avro Lancaster in flight. c, Avro Lancaster B2. d, Supermarine Spitfire HG Mk 1XB.

No. 1375, $2, Bristol F2B fighter, Eurofighter. No. 1376, $2, Hawk, biplane.

**1998, Oct. 26**

**1374** A387 70c Sheet of 4, #a.-d. 9.50 9.50

**Souvenir Sheet**

**1375-1376** A387 Set of 2 14.00 14.00

Famous People and Events of the Twentieth Cent. — A388

No. 1380, 40c: a, Mao Tse-tung. b, Cultural Revolution begins. c, Promoting Third World unity. d, Zhou Enlai. e, Deng Xiaoping. f, Hong Kong returns to China, 1997. g, Shanghai, an Asian metropolis. h, Jiang Zemin.

No. 1381, 40c: a, Robert E. Peary. b, Expedition to the North Pole. c, Climbing Mt. Everest. d, Sir Edmund Hillary. e, Neil Armstrong. f, Walking on the moon. g, Expedition to the South Pole. h, Roald Amundsen.

$2, Matthew Henson.

**1998, Dec. 1 Litho.** ***Perf. 14***

**Sheets of 8, #a-h**

**1380-1381** A388 Set of 2 22.50 22.50

**Souvenir Sheet**

**1382** A388 $2 multicolored 6.50 6.50

Nos. 1380b-1380c, 1380f-1380g, 1381b-1381c, 1380f-1381g are each 53x38mm.

Classic Cars A389

Designs: No. 1383, 32c, 1966-72 Lamborghini Miura. No. 1384, 32c, 1966-93 Alfa Romeo Spider. No. 1385, 32c, 1948-61 Jaguar XK140. No. 1386, 32c, 1959-63 Lotus Elite.

No. 1387, 50c: a, 1949-53 Bristol 401. b, 1952-55 Bentley Continental R. c, 1973-75 Lancia stratos. d, 1963-67 Chevrolet Corvette Stingray. e, 1948-52 Austin A90 Atlantic. f, 1969-90 Aston Martin V8.

No. 1388, 50c: a, 1961-75 Jaguar E-Type. b, 1955-57 Ford Thunderbird. c, 1964-73, Ford Mustang GT350. d, 1957-77 Fiat 500. e, 1955-59 BMW 507. f, 1963-65 Buick Riviera.

No. 1389, $2, 1945-55 MG TD. No. 1390, $2, 1959-65 Rolls Royce Silver Cloud.

**1998, Dec. 24**

**1383-1386** A389 Set of 4 4.00 4.00

**Sheets of 6, #a-f**

**1387-1388** A389 Set of 2 20.00 20.00

**Souvenir Sheets**

**1389-1390** A389 Set of 2 13.00 13.00

New Year 1999 (Year of the Rabbit) — A390

Paintings, by Liu Jiyou (1918-83): No. 1391, Two rabbits. No. 1392, Three rabbits.

No. 1393, Two rabbits, flowers, vert.

**1999, Jan. 5**

**1391** A390 50c multicolored 1.75 1.75
**1392** A390 50c multicolored 1.75 1.75

**Souvenir Sheet**

**1393** A390 $2 multicolored 6.50 6.50

Nos. 1391-1392 were issued in sheets of 2 each. No. 1393 contains one 43x52mm stamp.

US Presidents — A391

No. 1394, 75c, Various portraits of Abraham Lincoln. No. 1395, 75c, Various portraits of Bill Clinton.

**1998, Dec. 1 Litho.** ***Perf. 14***

**Sheets of 4, #a-d**

**1394-1395** A391 Set of 2 20.00 20.00

Zhou Enlai (1898-1976), Chinese Premier A392

Various portraits.

**1999 Litho.** ***Perf. 14***

**1396** A392 50c Sheet of 6, #a.-f. 10.00 10.00

**Souvenir Sheet**

**1397** A392 $2 multicolored 7.00 7.00

Raptors — A393

Designs: 50c, Snowy owl. 70c, Barn owl. $1, American kestrel $1.50, Golden eagle.

No. 1402, 50c: a, Eurasian eagle owl. b, Osprey. c, Egyptian vulture. d, Lizard buzzard. e, Pale chanting goshawk. f, Bald eagle.

No. 1403, 50c: a, Goshawk. b, Laughing falcon. c, Oriental bay-owl. d, Swallow-tailed kite. e, Secretary bird. f, Brown falcon.

No. 1404, $2, Northern harrier. No. 1405, $2, Peregrine falcon.

**1999, Jan. 4**

**1398-1401** A393 Set of 4 11.00 11.00

**Sheets of 6, #a-f**

**1402-1403** A393 Set of 2 20.00 20.00

**Souvenir Sheets**

**1404-1405** A393 Set of 2 13.00 13.00

Dinosaurs A395

No. 1406, 50c, Pachyrinosaur. No. 1407, 50c, Centrosaurus, vert. No. 1408, 70c, Pentaceratops, vert. No. 1409, 70c, Oviraptor, vert. $1, Corythosaur. $1.50, Stegosaurus, vert.

No. 1412, 40c: a, Baryonyx (e). b, Pachycephalosaur (a, c). c, Homalocephale. d, Pterodustro (c, g). e, Pycnosteroides. f, Giant nautiloid. g, Kronosaur (e, f). h, Giant cephalopod (g).

No. 1413, 40c: a, Camarasaur. b, Albertosaur (c, f, g). c, Eudimorhodon (b, d). d, Dimorphodon (c). e, Compsognathus. f, Torosaurus. g, Nodosaurid (h). h, Probactrosaurus.

No. 1414, $2, Tarbosaurus, vert. No. 1415, $2, Shunosaurus, vert.

**1999, Jan. 18**

**1406-1411** A395 Set of 6 12.00 12.00

**Sheets of 8, #a-h**

**1412-1413** A395 Set of 2 22.50 22.50

**Souvenir Sheets**

**1414-1415** A395 Set of 2 13.00 13.00

Dinosaurs A396

Designs: 50c, Brachiosaurus, vert. 70c, Tyrannosaurus, vert. $1, Mosasaurus. $1.50, Triceratops.

No. 1420: a, Albertosaurus. b, Parasaurolophus. c, Styracosaurus. d, Struthiomimus. e, Ankylosaurus. f, Chasmosaurus.
No. 1421, $2, Deinonychus. No. 1422, $2, Stegosaurus.

**1999**

**1416-1419** A396 Set of 4 9.00 9.00
**1420** A396 50c Sheet of 6, #a.-f. 10.00 10.00

**Souvenir Sheets**

**1421-1422** A396 Set of 2 13.00 13.00

Flowers — A397

Designs: No. 1423, 50c, Tecophilaea cyanocrocus. 70c, Nymphoides peltata. $1, Angraecum scottianum. $1.50, Grevillea dielsiana.
No. 1427, 50c: a, Cyrtopodium parvilforum. b, Catharanthus roseus. c, Acacia acuminata. d, Herbertia lahue. e, Protea venusta. f, Clianthus formosus.
No. 1428, 50c: a, Dendrobium rarum. b, Cyrtorchis arcuata. c, Zygopetalum intermedium. d, Cassia fistula. e, Saintpaulia ionantha. f, Heliconia collinsiana.
No. 1429, $2, Hibiscus tilliaceus. No. 1430, $2, Rhododendron thomsonii.

**1999, Feb. 8**

**1423-1426** A397 Set of 4 11.00 11.00

**Sheets of 6, #a-f**

**1427-1428** A397 Set of 2 20.00 20.00

**Souvenir Sheets**

**1429-1430** A397 Set of 2 13.00 13.00

Orchids — A398

Designs: No. 1431, 50c, Tridactyle bicaudata. No. 1432, 50c, Angraecum infundibulare. No. 1433, 70c, Oeceoclades maculata. No. 1434, 70c, Ophyrs fusca. No. 1435, $1, Sobennikoffia robusta. No. 1436, $1, Stenoglottis fimbriata. No. 1437, $1.50, Plectrelminthus caudatus. No. 1438, $1.50, Satyrium erectum.
No. 1439, 50c: a, Angraecrum eichlerianum. b, Ansellia africana. c, Cymbidiella pardalina. d, Angraecum eburnium. e, Ancistrochilus rothchildianus. f, Aerangis luteoalba.
No. 1440, 50c: a, Dis cardinalis. b, Cytorchus arcuata. c, Cynorkis compacta. d, Disa kewensis. e, Eulophia guineensis. f, Eulophia speciosa.
No. 1441, $2, Angraecum compactum. No. 1442, $2, Calanthe vestita.

**1999, Mar. 13**

**1431-1438** A398 Set of 8 22.50 22.50

**Sheets of 6, #a-f**

**1439-1440** A398 Set of 2 19.00 19.00

**Souvenir Sheets**

**1441-1442** A398 Set of 2 13.00 13.00

Orchids — A399

Designs: No. 1443, 50c, Calypso bulbosa. No. 1444, 50c, Maclellanara pagan lovesong. No. 1445, 70c, Masdevallia chimaera. No. 1446, 70c, Yamadara midnight. $1, Cleistes divaricata. $1.50, Oncidium golden sunset.
No. 1449: a, Trichopilia tortilis. b, Stenoglottis longifolia. c, Telipogon pulcher. d, Esmeralda clarkei. e, Papilionanthe teres. f, Mormodes rolfeanum. g, Cypripedium acaule. h, Serapias lingua.

**1999, Mar. 13**

**1443-1448** A399 Set of 6 15.00 15.00
**1449** A399 30c Sheet of 8, #a.-h. 9.00 9.00

Wildlife — A400

No. 1450: a, Mink. b, Arctic fox. c, Lynx. d, Snowy owl. e, Polar bear. f, Golden eagle.
$2, Big horn sheep.

**1999, Feb. 24** **Litho.** ***Perf. 14***

**1450** A400 50c Sheet of 6, #a.-f. 7.00 7.00

**Souvenir Sheet**

**1451** A400 $2 multicolored 5.00 5.00

Flora and Fauna A401

No. 1452: a, Madgascan red fody. b, Indri (e). c, Coral-billed nuthatch. d, Sifaka (g, j). e, Golden piper. f, Aye aye (i). g, Broad-bordered grass yellow butterfly. h, Ring-tailed lemur (g, j, k). i, Parson's chameleon. j, Madagascar day gecko. k, Leaf-tailed gecko. l, Orchid.
No. 1453, $2, Wattled false sunbird. No. 1454, $2, Parson's chameleon. No. 1455, $2, Ring-tailed lemur.

**1999, Apr. 1**

**1452** A401 20c Sheet of 12, #a.-l. 7.00 7.00

**Souvenir Sheets**

**1453-1455** A401 Set of 3 15.00 15.00

Seabirds A402

Designs: No. 1456, 50c, Harlequin duck. No. 1457, 50c, Eleonor's falcon, vert. No. 1458, 70c, Wilson's plover. No. 1459, 70c, Common eider. No. 1460, $1, Little tern. No. 1461, $1, American oystercatcher. No. 1462, $1.50, Herring gull, vert. No. 1463, $1.50, Brown pelican, vert.
No. 1464, 30c, vert: a, Great cormorant. b, Crested cormorant. c, Red faced cormorant. d, Whimbrel. e, Tufted puffin. f, Ivory gull. g, Common murre. h, Shelduck. i, Razorbill.
No. 1465, 30c: a, Common tern. b, Black-legged kittiwake. c, Bernacle goose. d, Black-headed gull. e, Semipalmated plover. f, Northern gannet. g, King eider. h, Iceland gull. i, Ring-billed gull.
No. 1466, $2, Arctic loon. No. 1467, $2, Atlantic puffin. No. 1468, $2, California gull, vert.

**1999, Apr. 1** **Litho.** ***Perf. 14***

**1456-1463** A402 Set of 8 17.00 17.00

**Sheets of 9, #a-i**

**1464-1465** A402 Set of 2 13.00 13.00

**Souvenir Sheets**

**1466-1468** A402 Set of 3 15.00 15.00

Queen Mother (b. 1900) — A404

No. 1475: a, With King George VI at wedding, 1923. b, In Nairobi, 1959. c, Wearing tiara, 1953. d, Wearing hat, 1990.
$2, Wearing hat, 1990, diff.

**1999, Aug. 4** ***Perf. 14***

**1475** A404 $1 Sheet of 4, #a.-d., + label 9.00 9.00

**Souvenir Sheet**

***Perf. 13¾***

**1476** A404 $2 multicolored 5.00 5.00

No. 1476 contains one 38x51mm stamp.

Trains A405

Designs: 32c, Nozomi Train, Japan. 40c, 401 Intercity Express, Germany. 50c, C53, Japan Railways. 70c, Beuth 2-2-2, Germany.
No. 1481, 40c: a, "Adler," Germany. b, Suburban EMU, Japan. c, Class 01, 4-6-2, Germany. d, Class 120 Bo-Bo, Germany. e, Class P8, 4-6-0, Germany. f, Fujikawa Express, Japan. g, Class 081, Germany. h, Kodama 8-car train, Japan. i, Class C62, 4-6-4, Japan.
No. 1482, 40c: a, KF Type, 4-8-4, China. b, Minobu Line train, Japan. c, Class S34-40, Germany. d, Class EF81, Bo-Bo, Japan. e, V200, B-B, Germany. f, SVT 877 "Flying Hamburger," Japan. g, C51, 4-6-2 Japan Railways. h, AEO Single rail car, Germany. i, Class D51, Japan.
No. 1483, $2, Yamonote Line train, Japan. No. 1484, $2, Class B8, Germany.

**1999, Aug. 25** **Litho.** ***Perf. 14***

**1477-1480** A405 Set of 4 4.50 4.50

**Sheets of 9, #a-i**

**1481-1482** A405 Set of 2 17.00 17.00

**Souvenir Sheets**

**1483-1484** A405 Set of 2 10.00 10.00

Dogs A406

No. 1485, Lhasa apso. 70c, Samoyed.
No. 1487, vert.: a, Dalmatian. b, Pyrennean Mountain dog. c, Golden retriever. d, Bearded collie. e, Basset hound. f, Bernese Mountain dog.
No. 1488, Beagle, vert.

**1999, Aug. 30** ***Perf. 14***

**1485** A406 50c multicolored 1.25 1.25
**1486** A406 70c multicolored 1.75 1.75
**1487** A406 50c Sheet of 6, #a.-f. 7.50 7.50

**Souvenir Sheet**

**1488** A406 $2 multicolored 5.00 5.00

During 1999-2004 Liberia was torn by a brutal and chaotic civil war that reduced the nation to a state of anarchy. Government services, including postal operations, functioned erratically, if at all, for months at a time. During this period, overseas stamp agents continued to produce stamps under pre-war contracts, and a large number of issues appeared that were marketed to overseas collectors. It appears that some of these stamps have been released in Liberia since the end of hostilities. These will be listed when their sale and postal use has been confirmed.

Paintings by Norman Rockwell A580

Paintings: $15, Playing Party Games. $30, Saturday Night Out. $35, The Portrait. No, 2328, $50, Grandpa's Little Ballerina.
No. 2329, $50: a, The Cave of the Winds. b, Redhead Loves Hatty. c, The Rivals. d, Three's Company.
No. 2330, $50: a, Distortion. b, Summer Vacation. c, Runaway Pants. d, Tumble.
No. 2331, $50: a, Daydreams. b, A Patient Friend. c, Lands of Enchantment. d, The Little Spooners.
No. 2332, $50: a, The Skating Lesson. b, The Fortune Teller. c, God Bless You. d, Knowledge is Power.

**2005, Jan. 10** **Litho.** ***Perf. 14¼***

**2325-2328** A580 Set of 4 7.00 7.00

**Sheets of 4, #a-d**

**2329-2332** A580 Set of 4 40.00 40.00

Jules Verne (1828-1905), Writer — A581

No. 2333, $30: a, The Adventures of Captain Hatteras. b, The Mysterious Island (deflated balloon). c, The Mysterious Island (Men looking at ape). d, 20,000 Leagues Under the Sea (spotlights on ship).
No. 2334, $30: a, Around the World in Eighty Days. b, From the Earth to the Moon (people watching man on space capsule ladder). c, Paris in the Twentieth Century. d, Master of the World (ship captain at wheel).
No. 2335, $30: a, The Chase of the Golden Meteor. b, Master of the World (flying machine, country name in white). c, Five Weeks in a Balloon. d, From the Earth to the Moon (rocket in space).
No. 2336, $30: a, The Mysterious Island (People in balloon basket). b, Robur the Conqueror. c, Round the Moon. d, Master of the World (flying machine, country name in black).
No. 2337, $30: Scenes from 20,000 Leagues Under the Sea: a, Ships on water. b, Shark and octopus attacking ship. c, Shark attacking diver. d, Squid attacking ship.
No. 2338, $100, Deep sea divers. No. 2339, $100, Admiral Richard E. Byrd. No. 2340, $100, Radio satellite communication. No. 2341, $100, Long range ballistic missile. No. 2342, $100, Extravehicular satellite repair.

**2005, Jan. 11** ***Perf. 13¼x13½***

**Sheets of 4, #a-d**

**2333-2337** A581 Set of 5 32.50 32.50

**Souvenir Sheets**

**2338-2342** A581 Set of 5 27.50 27.50

Marilyn Monroe (1926-62), Actress — A582

**2005, Jan. 26** ***Perf. 14***

**2343** A582 $12 multi .70 .70

Prehistoric Animals — A583

No. 2344, $50: a, Torosaurus. b, Tyrannosaurus. c, Polacanthus. d, Stegosaurus.
No. 2345, $50: a, Smilodon. b, Brontothere. c, Doedicurus. d, Moeritherium.
No. 2346, $50: a, Cymbospondylus. b, Archelon. c, Xiphactinus. d, Dunkleosteus.
No. 2347, $120, Stegosaurus, diff. No. 2348, $120, Woolly rhinoceros. No. 2349, $120, Odobenocetops.

**2005, Jan. 26** ***Perf. 13¼x13½***
**Sheets of 4, #a-d**

**2344-2346** A583 Set of 3 32.50 32.50

**Souvenir Sheet**

**2347-2349** A583 Set of 3 18.00 18.00

Battle of Trafalgar, Bicent. — A584

Various ships: $10, $20, $40, $50.
$100, Death of Admiral Horatio Nelson.

**2005, May 4** ***Perf. 14¼***

**2350-2353** A584 Set of 4 6.00 6.00

**Souvenir Sheet**

**2354** A584 $100 multi 5.50 5.50

Hans Christian Andersen (1805-75), Author — A585

No. 2355: a, Medal. b, Open book. c, Andersen.
$100, Sketch of Little Mermaid.

**2005, May 4** ***Perf. 14¼***

**2355** A585 $50 Sheet of 3, #a-c 7.50 7.50

**Souvenir Sheet**

**2356** A585 $100 multi 5.50 5.50

Friedrich von Schiller (1759-1805), Writer — A586

No. 2357: a, Bust of Schiller on round pedestal. b, Bust and foliage. c, Bust on monument.
$100, Statue of Schiller, Chicago.

**2005, May 4** ***Perf. 14¼***

**2357** A586 $50 Sheet of 3, #a-c 7.50 7.50

**Size: 48x67mm**

***Imperf***

**2358** A586 $100 multi 5.50 7.50

No. 2357 contains three 28x42mm stamps.

Miniature Sheets

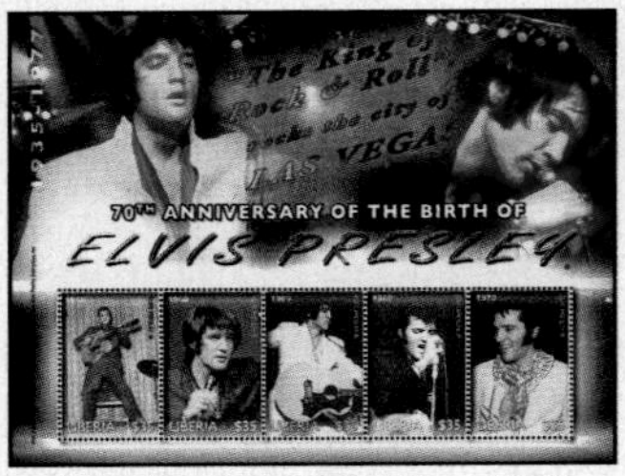


Elvis Presley (1935-77) — A587

No. 2359, $35 — Presley in: a, 1956. b, 1969. c, 1969 (country name in yellow). d, 1969 (country name in pink). e, 1970.
No. 2360, $35 — Presley wearing: a, Red suit and white shirt. b, Yellow sweater. c, Red shirt. d, Brown suit. e, Gray suit.

**2005, May 19** ***Perf. 13½x13¼***
**Sheets of 5, #a-e**

**2359-2360** A587 Set of 2 19.00 19.00

Pope John Paul II (1920-2005) A588

**2005, Aug. 22** ***Perf. 12¾***

**2361** A588 $50 multi 2.50 2.50

Printed in sheets of 4.

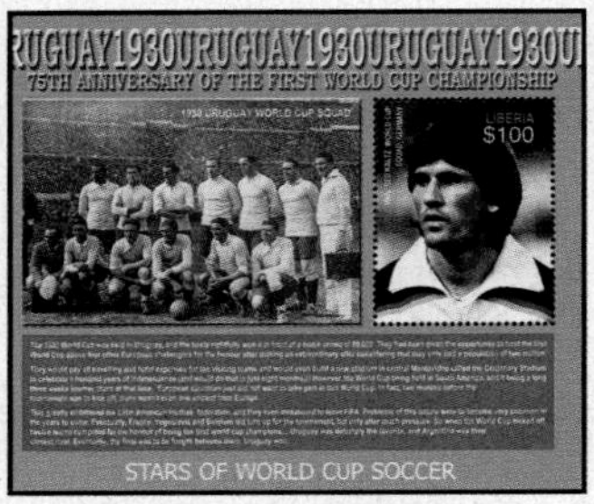


World Cup Soccer Championships, 75th Anniv. — A589

No. 2362: a, Norbert Eder. b, Paul Breitner. c, Thomas Helmer.
$100, Manfred Kaltz.

**2005, Aug. 22** ***Perf. 13¼***

**2362** A589 $60 Sheet of 3, #a-c 10.00 10.00

**Souvenir Sheet**

***Perf. 12***

**2363** A589 $100 multi 5.50 5.50

Albert Einstein (1879-1955), Physicist — A590

No. 2364 — Einstein and: a, Charlie Chaplin. b, Max Planck. c, William Allen White.
$100, J. Robert Oppenheimer

**2005, Aug. 22** ***Perf. 12¾***

**2364** A590 $60 Sheet of 3, #a-c 9.00 9.00

**Souvenir Sheet**

**2365** A590 $100 multi 5.00 5.00

End of World War II, 60th Anniv. — A591

No. 2366, $40 — V-E Day: a, Gen. Dwight D. Eisenhower. b, Prime Minister Winston Churchill. c, Gen. George Patton. d, Field Marshal Bernard Montgomery.
No. 2367, $40 — V-E Day: a, Air Marshal Sir Arthur "Bomber" Harris. b, Gen. Douglas MacArthur. c, Field Marshal Alan Brooke. d, Pres. Franklin D. Roosevelt.
No. 2368, $40 — V-J Day: a, RAF Wellington bomber. b, Mitsubishi A6M Zero. c, RAF Hudson bomber. d, B-17 bomber.
No. 2369, $40 — V-J Day: a, P-51 Mustang. b, RAF Hamilcar glider. c, P-38 Lightning. d, RAF Supermarine Spitfire.

**2005, Aug. 22** ***Perf. 13¼x13½***
**Sheets of 4, #a-d**

**2366-2369** A591 Set of 4 26.00 26.00

Worldwide Fund for Nature (WWF) — A592

No. 2370: a, Jentink's duiker. b, Head of Ogilby's duiker. c, Ogilby's duiker. d, Head of Jentink's duiker.

**2005, Aug. 31** ***Perf. 14***

**2370** A592 $20 Block or vert. strip of 4, #a-d 4.00 4.00

*e.* Miniature sheet, 2 each #2370a-2370d 6.50 6.50

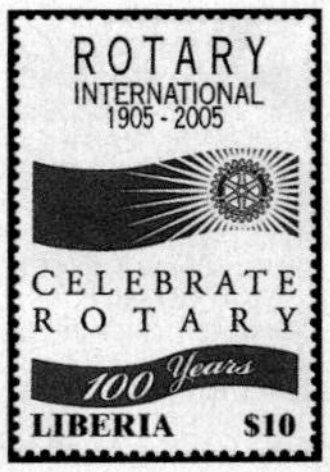


Rotary International, Cent. — A593

Emblem: $10, $25, $35, $50.
$100, Mother Teresa.

**2005, Sept. 22** ***Perf. 14***

**2371-2374** A593 Set of 4 5.00 5.00

**Souvenir Sheet**

**2375** A593 $100 multi 5.00 5.00

Christmas — A594

Paintings: $20, Glory to God, by Kim Ki-chang. $25, Flight Into Egypt, by Fra Angelico. $30, Christmas Mom, by Will Hickock Low. $50, The Nativity, by Bernadino Luini.
$100, Adoration of the Magi, by Nicolas Poussin.

**2005, Dec. 1**

**2376-2379** A594 Set of 4 6.00 6.00

**Souvenir Sheet**

**2380** A594 $100 multi 5.00 5.00

Elvis Presley (1935-77) — A595

***Variable Serpentine Die Cut***

**2006, Jan. 17** **Litho. & Embossed**
**Without Gum**

**2381** A595 $350 gold & multi 20.00 20.00

African Antelopes — A596

No. 2382: a, Gemsbok. b, Kudu. c, Sable antelope. d, Impala.
$100, Springbok.

**2006, Jan. 17** **Litho.** ***Perf. 13½***

**2382** A596 $45 Sheet of 4, #a-d 9.00 9.00

**Souvenir Sheet**

**2383** A596 $100 multi 5.00 5.00

Mammals — A597

No. 2384: a, Jackal. b, Fox. c, Wolf. d, Coyote.
$100, Hyena.

**2006, Jan. 17**

**2384** A597 $45 Sheet of 4, #a-d 9.00 9.00

**Souvenir Sheet**

**2385** A597 $100 multi 5.00 5.00

Wild Cats — A598

No. 2386: a, Jaguar. b, Lion. c, Puma. d, Cheetah.

$100, Siberian tiger.

**2006, Jan. 17**
**2386** A598 $45 Sheet of 4, #a-d 9.00 9.00

**Souvenir Sheet**

**2387** A598 $100 multi 5.00 5.00

Animals of the Bible — A599

No. 2388, $45: a, Lions. b, Camels. c, Doves. d, Donkey.
No. 2389, $45: a, Foxes. b, Vultures. c, Turtles. d, Ducks.
No. 2390, $45: a, Goat. b, Bear. c, Ravens. d, Sheep.
No. 2391, $120, Pig. No. 2392, $120, Whale. No. 2393, $120, Snake.

**2006, Jan. 17** **Sheets of 4, #a-d**
**2388-2390** A599 Set of 3 25.00 25.00

**Souvenir Sheets**

**2391-2393** A599 Set of 3 20.00 20.00

Snakes — A600

No. 2394: a, Rough green snake. b, Speckled king snake. c, Garter snake. d, Brown snake.
$100, Red milk snake.

**2006, Jan. 27**
**2394** A600 $45 Sheet of 4, #a-d 9.00 9.00

**Souvenir Sheet**

**2395** A600 $100 multi 5.00 5.00

2006 Winter Olympics, Turin — A601

Designs: $20, Austria #B337. $25, Poster for 1976 Innsbruck Winter Olympics, vert. $35, Austria #B338. $50, Austria #B335. $70, US #3555. $100, Poster for 2002 Salt Lake City Winter Olympics, vert.

**2006, Apr. 6** ***Perf. 13½***
**2396-2399** A601 Set of 4 8.00 8.00
**2399A** A601 $70 multi 4.00 4.00
**2399B** A601 $100 multi 6.00 6.00

Nos. 2399A-2399B were not made available until 2007.

**Souvenir Sheet**

Benjamin Franklin (1706-90), Statesman — A602

**2006, May 27** ***Perf. 13½***
**2400** A602 $120 multi 7.50 7.50

Washington 2006 World Philatelic Exhibition.

Queen Elizabeth II, 80th Birthday — A603

No. 2401 — Hat color: a, Green. b, Blue. c, Beige. d, Black.
$120, Queen wearing tiara.

**2006, June 13** ***Perf. 14¼***
**2401** A603 $40 Sheet of 4, #a-d 9.00 9.00

**Souvenir Sheet**

**2402** A603 $120 multi 7.00 7.00

Rembrandt (1606-69), Painter A604

Artwork: $15, Young Man in a Turban. $30, Man Leaning on a Windowsill. $40, Officer with a Gold Chain. $45, The Art Dealer Clement de Jonghe.
No. 2407, $60: a, Self-portrait, 1633. b, Self-portrait, 1634. c, Self-portrait, 1639. d, Self-portrait, 1640.
No. 2408, $60: a, Christ and the Canaanite Woman. b, The Mocking of Christ. c, Head of an Old Man (Three-quarters view). d, Head of an Old Man (profile).
No. 2409, $60: a, David and Jonathan. b, Nude Woman with a Snake. c, The Abduction of Europa. d, Daniel and Cyrus Before the Idol Bel.
No. 2410, $60: a, Shah Jahan and Dara Shikoh. b, Farm Building Surrounded by Trees. c, Two Thatched Cottages with Figures at Window. d, A Sailing Boat on Wide Expanse of Water.
No. 2411, $120, Bearded Old Man with a Gold Chain. No. 2412, $120, A Scholar in His Study. No. 2413, $120, Rembrandt's Mother. No. 2414, $120, Portrait of Jan Six.

**2006, June 13** **Litho.**
**2403-2406** A604 Set of 4 7.00 7.00

**Sheets of 4, #a-d**

**2407-2410** A604 Set of 4 50.00 50.00

***Imperf***

**Size: 76x103mm**

**2411-2414** A604 Set of 4 30.00 30.00

**Souvenir Sheet**

Wolfgang Amadeus Mozart (1756-91), Composer — A605

**2006, July 25** ***Perf. 12¾***
**2415** A605 $120 multi 7.50 7.50

**Miniature Sheet**

Chinese Ceramics — A606

No. 2416: a, Bowl with red, black and white exterior, brown interior. b, Bowl with blue and white exterior, blue, red and white interior. c, Bowl with green on white exterior, square opening. d, Bowl with red, white and blue exterior, brown interior. e, Bowl with green on white exterior, circular opening. f, Bowl with red, white and green exterior, square opening.

**2006, Aug. 16** ***Perf. 12x12¼***
**2416** A606 $35 Sheet of 6, #a-f 12.00 12.00

Inauguration of Pres. Ellen Johnson-Sirleaf — A607

Designs: $10, Pres. Johnson-Sirleaf and flag. $25, Certification by National Election Commission, horiz. $30, Casting of ballots. $40, Pres. Johnson-Sirleaf holding child, horiz.
$100, Pres. Johnson-Sirleaf at microphone.

**2006, Aug. 22** ***Perf. 13¼***
**2417-2420** A607 Set of 4 6.00 6.00

**Souvenir Sheet**

**2421** A607 $100 multi 6.00 6.00

Millennium Development Goals — A608

Goals: No. 2422, $10, Achieve universal primary education (graduates). No. 2423, $10, Promote gender equality and empower women. No. 2424, $25, Eradicate extreme hunger and poverty. No. 2425, $25, Reduce child mortality. No. 2426, $30, Develop a global partnership for development (map). No. 2427, $30, Develop a global partnership for development (ships and airplane). $40, Improve maternal health. $50, Achieve universal primary education (classroom). No. 2430, $100, Ensure environmental sustainability. No. 2431, $100, Combat HIV/AIDS, malaria and other diseases.
No. 2432, Achieve universal primary education (classroom), vert.

**2006, Sept. 22**
**2422-2431** A608 Set of 10 25.00 25.00

**Souvenir Sheet**

**2432** A608 $100 multi 6.00 6.00

Space Achievements — A609

No. 2433, $40 — Intl. Space Station: a, Country name and denomination in black, at top. b, Country name in black, denomination in white. c, Country name and denomination in white, at top. d, Country name and denomination in black, at bottom. e, Space shuttle (country name and denomination in white, at bottom). f, Astronaut (country name and denomination in white, at bottom.
No. 2434, $40, vert. — Apollo 11: a, Lunar module. b, Rocket on launch pad. c, Nose cone of rocket. d, Astronaut on moon. e, Command module. f, Astronauts and rocket.
No. 2435, $55, vert. — First Flight of Space Shuttle Columbia: a, Astronaut Bob Crippen. b, Front of space shuttle. c, Astronaut John Young. d, Tail of space shuttle.
No. 2436, $55 — Space Shuttle returns to space: a, Wing. b, Fuselage, reflection of sunlight. c, Wing inscribed "Discovery." d, Fuselage and Earth.
No. 2437, $120, Apollo-Soyuz. No. 2438, $120, Mars Reconnaissance Orbiter. No. 2439, $120, Venus Express. No. 2440, $120, Deep Impact Probe.

**2006, Oct. 3** **Litho.** ***Perf. 12¾***

**Sheets of 6, #a-f**

**2433-2434** A609 Set of 2 30.00 30.00

**Sheets of 4, #a-d**

**2435-2436** A609 Set of 2 25.00 25.00

**Souvenir Sheets**

**2437-2440** A609 Set of 4 25.00 25.00

Christopher Columbus (1451-1506), Explorer — A610

Designs: $25, Columbus, drawings of ships. $50, Columbus, ships, horiz. $70, Columbus and Santa Maria, horiz. $100, Ship, crew encountering natives, horiz.
$120, Men on shore.

**2006, Nov. 15**
**2441-2444** A610 Set of 4 12.50 12.50

**Souvenir Sheet**

**2445** A610 $120 multi 7.00 7.00

**Souvenir Sheet**

Christmas — A611

No. 2446 — Details from The Adoration of the Magi, by Peter Paul Rubens: a, Man and boy. b, Mary. c, Man with headcovering. d, Infant Jesus.

**2006, Dec. 21 Litho. *Perf. 14***

**2446** A611 $40 Sheet of 4, #a-d 9.00 9.00

A612

Concorde — A613

No. 2447, $30 — Concorde: a, G-BOAF. b, G-BOAB.

No. 2448, $35 — Concorde: a, F-BVFA on runway. b, G-BOAA taking off.

**2007, Mar. 1 Litho. *Perf. 13½***

**Horiz. Pairs, #a-b**

**2447-2448** A612 Set of 2 7.50 7.50

**Litho. & Embossed**

**Without Gum**

***Irregular Serpentine Die Cut***

**2449** A613 $350 gold & multi 20.00 20.00

Souvenir Sheet

Ludwig Durr (1878-1956), Engineer — A614

No. 2450: a, Durr and Zeppelin. b, Interior cabin plan for LZ-127. c, Count Ferdinand von Zeppelin.

**2007, Mar. 1 Litho. *Perf. 13¼***

**2450** A614 $60 Sheet of 3, #a-c 10.00 10.00

Souvenir Sheet

Marilyn Monroe (1926-62), Actress — A615

Various portraits.

**2007, Mar. 1**

**2451** A615 $50 Sheet of 4, #a-d 12.00 12.00

Pres. John F. Kennedy (1917-62) — A616

No. 2452, $45: a, Signing executive order establishing the Peace Corps. b, With Sargent Shriver. c, Peace Corps volunteers in Tanganyika. d, Jack Hood Vaughn, second director of Peace Corps.

No. 2453, $45 — Kennedy: a, And Eleanor Roosevelt. b, Delivering Alliance for Progress speech. c, With Mrs. Kennedy in Venezuela. d, And Secretary of State Dean Rusk.

**2007, Mar. 1 Litho.**

**Sheets of 4, #a-d**

**2452-2453** A616 Set of 2 20.00 20.00

Mushrooms A617

Designs: $25, Boletus edulis. $35, Begriipt russula. No. 2456, $45, Lactarius helvus. $50, Amanita pantherina.

No. 2458, $45: a, Russula cyanoxantha. b, Cantharellus subalbidus. c, Leccinum oxydalile. d, Boletus badius.

No. 2459, $45: a, Amanita bingensis. b, Chlorophyllum molybdites. c, Calvatia utriformis. d, Amanita loosii.

No. 2460, $100, Amanita muscaria. No. 2461, $100, Chlorophyllum molybdites, diff. No. 2462, $100, Agaricus silvaticus.

**2007, Mar. 1**

**2454-2457** A617 Set of 4 9.00 9.00

**Sheets of 4, #a-d**

**2458-2459** A617 Set of 2 20.00 20.00

**Souvenir Sheets**

**2460-2462** A617 Set of 3 18.00 18.00

Scouting, Cent. A618

Designs: $50, Scouts and 2006 World Jamboree emblem. $150, Scouts, horiz.

**2007, Mar. 15**

**2463** A618 $50 multi 3.00 3.00

**Souvenir Sheet**

**2464** A618 $150 multi 9.00 9.00

No. 2463 was printed in sheets of 4.

Pope Benedict XVI — A619

**2007, Nov. 30 Litho. *Perf. 13¼***

**2465** A619 $30 multi 1.75 1.75

Miniature Sheet

New Year 2007 (Year of the Boar) — A620

No. 2466 — Wild Boar, by Liu Jiyou with text "Year of the Boar" in: a, Red. b, Green. c, Brown. d, Blue.

**2007, Nov. 30**

**2466** A620 $30 Sheet of 4, #a-d 7.00 7.00

Miniature Sheet

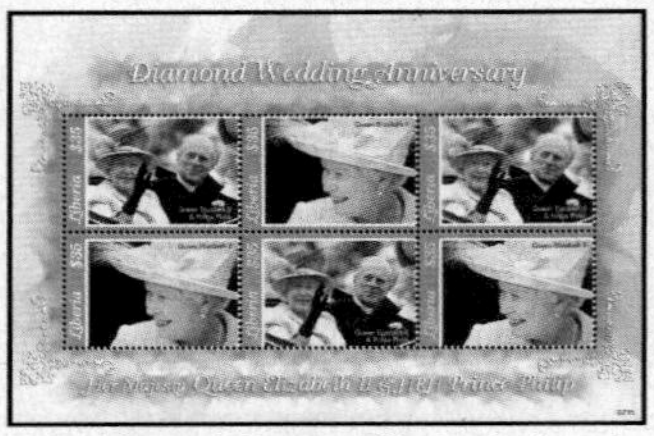


Wedding of Queen Elizabeth II and Prince Philip, 60th Anniv. — A621

No. 2467: a, Couple, denomination in white. b, Queen, denomination in yellow. c, Couple, denomination in lilac. d, Queen, denomination in white. e, Couple, denomination in yellow. f, Queen, denomination in lilac.

**2007, Nov. 30**

**2467** A621 $35 Sheet of 6, #a-f 12.00 12.00

Princess Diana (1961-97) — A622

No. 2468 — Various depictions of Diana with denomination in: a, Red violet. b, Blue. c, Green. d, Red.

$125, Red denomination.

**2007, Nov. 30**

**2468** A622 $45 Sheet of 4, #a-d 10.00 10.00

**Souvenir Sheet**

**2469** A622 $125 multi 7.50 7.50

Souvenir Sheets

Pres. Ellen Johnson-Sirleaf and Foreign Dignitaries — A623

Pres. Johnson-Sirleaf meeting with: No. 2470, $100, Chinese Pres. Hu Jintao. No. 2471, $100, U.S. Pres. George W. Bush.

**2007, Nov. 30**

**2470-2471** A623 Set of 2 12.00 12.00

Miniature Sheet

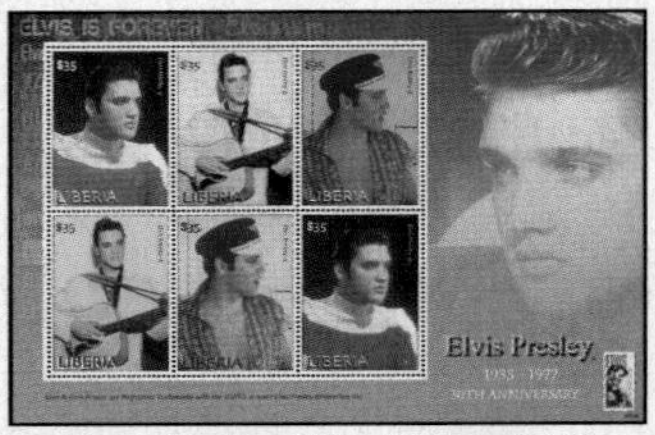


Elvis Presley (1935-77) — A624

No. 2472 — Presley: a, Wearing red and white sweater, country name in white. b, Holding guitar, country name in blue. c, Wearing cap, country name in white. d, Holding guitar, country name in purple. e, Wearing cap, country name in red violet. f, Wearing red and white sweater, country name in yellow.

**2007, Nov. 30**

**2472** A624 $35 Sheet of 6, #a-f 12.00 12.00

Souvenir Sheet

Japanese Prime Minister Junchiro Koizumi, U.S. Pres. George W. Bush and Wife at Graceland — A625

**2007, Nov. 30**

**2473** A625 $100 multi 6.00 6.00

New Year 2008 (Year of the Rat) A626

**2007, Dec. 26 Litho. *Perf. 11½x12***

**2474** A626 $25 multi 1.50 1.50

Printed in sheets of 4.

Birds — A627

Designs: $20, Pin-tailed whydahs. $30, Lesser honeyguides. $40, African jacanas. $50, Malachite sunbirds.

No. 2479, $45, horiz.: a, White-brown sparrow weavers. b, Parasitic weavers. c, Black-winged orioles. d, Crested guineafowl.

No. 2480, $45, horiz.: a, Red-billed francolins. b, Rufous-crowned rollers. c, African golden orioles. d, Black-crowned tchagras.

No. 2481, $100, Kori bustard. No. 2482, $100, Ostrich. No. 2483, $100, Great white pelican, horiz.

**2007, Dec. 26** ***Perf. 14***

**2475-2478** A627 Set of 4 8.00 8.00

**Sheets of 4, #a-d**

**2479-2480** A627 Set of 2 20.00 20.00

**Souvenir Sheets**

**2481-2483** A627 Set of 3 18.00 18.00

Butterflies — A628

Designs: $20, Appias epaphia. $30, Papilio bromius. $40, Charaxes jasius. $50, Mimacraea marshalli dohertyi.

No. 2488, $45: a, Belenois thysa. b, Papilio pelodorus. c, Cymothoe sangaris. d, Colotis aurigineus.

No. 2489, $45: a, Junonia hierta. b, Myrina silenus. c, Byblia ilithyia. d, Argyrogrammana attsonii.

No. 2490, $100, Iolaus menas. No. 2491, $100, Leptomyrina hirundo. No. 2492, $100, Pinacopteryx eriphia.

**2007, Dec. 26**

**2484-2487** A628 Set of 4 8.00 8.00

**Sheets of 4, #a-d**

**2488-2489** A628 Set of 2 20.00 20.00

**Souvenir Sheets**

**2490-2492** A628 Set of 3 18.00 18.00

Orchids — A629

Designs: $20, Neobenthamia gracilis. $30, Eulophia guineensis. $40, Aerangis curnowiana. $50, Cymbidiella pardalina.

No. 2497, $45: a, Ophrys lutea. b, Ophrys holoserica. c, Ophrys fusca. d, Ophrys scolopax.

No. 2498, $45: a, Disa veitchii. b, Disa racemosa. c, Disa kewensis. d, Disa diores.

No. 2499, $100, Disa crassicornis. No. 2500, $100, Aerangis citrata. No. 2501, $100, Angraecum sororium.

**2007, Dec. 26**

**2493-2496** A629 Set of 4 8.00 8.00

**Sheets of 4, #a-d**

**2497-2498** A629 Set of 2 20.00 20.00

**Souvenir Sheets**

**2499-2501** A629 Set of 3 18.00 18.00

Christmas A630

Designs: $30, Madonna and Child. $40, Holy Family. $45, Flight into Egypt. $50, The Three Magi, horiz.

**2007, Dec. 26** ***Perf. 14x14¾, 14¾x14***

**2502-2505** A630 Set of 4 10.00 10.00

Miniature Sheet

2008 Summer Olympics, Beijing — A631

No. 2506: a, Babe Didrikson. b, 1932 Summer Olympics poster. c, Helene Madison. d, Chuhei Nambu.

**2008, Apr. 8** ***Perf. 12¾***

**2506** A631 $30 Sheet of 4, #a-d 7.00 7.00

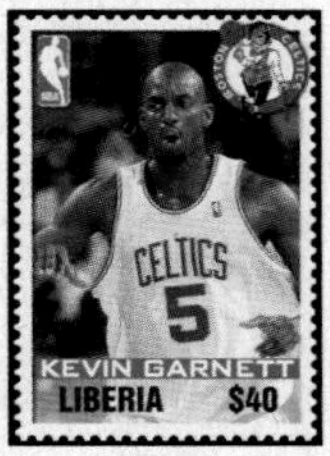


National Basketball Association Players — A632

No. 2507 — NBA and Boston Celtics emblems and Kevin Garnett: a, Wearing white uniform, not holding basketball. b, Wearing green uniform. c, Wearing white uniform, holding basketball.

No. 2508 — NBA and Boston Celtics emblems and Paul Pierce: a, Wearing white uniform, hands at side. b, Wearing green uniform. c, Wearing white uniform, pointing.

No. 2509 — NBA and Washington Wizards emblems and Gilbert Arenas: a, Wearing white uniform, hands on hips. b, Wearing blue uniform. c, Wearing white uniform, with basketball.

No. 2510 — NBA and Milwaukee Bucks emblems and Yi Jianlian: a, Wearing white uniform, basketball at left. b, Wearing blue green uniform. c, Wearing white uniform, basketball at right.

**2008, Apr. 30** ***Perf. 13½x13¼***

**2507** Vert. strip of 3 7.00 7.00
*a.-c.* A632 $40 Any single 1.25 1.25
**2508** Vert. strip of 3 7.00 7.00
*a.-c.* A632 $40 Any single 1.25 1.25
**2509** Vert. strip of 3 7.00 7.00
*a.-c.* A632 $40 Any single 1.25 1.25
**2510** Vert. strip of 3 7.00 7.00
*a.-c.* A632 $40 Any single 1.25 1.25
*Nos. 2507-2510 (4)* 28.00 28.00

Nos. 2507-2510 each printed in sheets of 6 containing 2 of each stamp in strip.

Souvenir Sheet

Meeting of Liberian Pres. Ellen Johnson-Sirleaf and US Pres. George W. Bush. — A633

No. 2511: a, Pres. Bush. b, Pres. Johnson-Sirleaf.

**2008, June 12** ***Perf. 13¼***

**2511** A633 $125 Sheet of 2, #a-b 12.00 12.00

Elvis Presley (1935-77) — A634

No. 2512 — Presley: a, Holding microphone, red background. b, Holding microphone, "Elvis" in lights. c, Holding microphone, blue background. d, Wearing glasses.

**2008, June 12** ***Perf. 13¼***

**2512** A634 $60 Sheet of 4, #a-d 12.00 12.00

Space Achievements — A635

No. 2513, $40 — International Space Station with denomination at: a, UR. b, UL. c, LR.

No. 2514, $40 — Chandra X-ray Observatory: a, Observatory below nebula. b, Interior of Observatory. c, Observatory above nebula.

No. 2515: a, Callisto, Europa, Voyager I, Jupiter and Io. b, Lift-off of Voyager I. c, Voyager I record cover. d, Voyager I, Titan and Saturn.

No. 2516, $150, International Space Station, horiz. No. 2517, $150, Chandra X-ray Observatory, horiz. No. 2518, $150, Voyager I and rings of Saturn, horiz.

Illustration reduced.

**2008, June 12** ***Perf. 13¼***

**Horiz. Strips of 3, #a-c**

**2513-2514** A635 Set of 2 18.00 18.00

**Miniature Sheet**

**2515** A635 $60 Sheet of 4, #a-d 18.00 18.00

**Souvenir Sheets**

**2516-2518** A635 Set of 3 24.00 24.00

Nos. 2513-2514 were each printed in sheets of 6 containing 2 of each stamp in strip.

Pope Benedict XVI — A636

**2008, June 30** **Litho.**

**2519** A636 $45 multi 2.00 2.00

Printed in sheets of 4.

County Flags A637

Flag of: No. 2520, $10, Maryland County. No. 2521, $10, Montserrado County. No. 2522, $25, Gbarpolu County. No. 2523, $25, Grand Bassa County. No. 2524, $30, Grand Cape Mount County. No. 2525, $30, Nimba County. No. 2526, $40, Lofa County. No. 2527, $40, Sinoe County. No. 2528, $50, Bong County. No. 2529, $50, Margibi County. No. 2530, $100, Bomi County. No. 2531, $100, Grand Gedeh County. No. 2532, $100, Grand Kru County. No. 2533, $100, River Cess County. No. 2534, $100, River Gee County.

**2008, June 30**

**2520-2534** A637 Set of 15 26.00 26.00

Miniature Sheet

Ferrari F2008 — A638

No. 2535: a, "F" under "E" of "Liberia." b, "F" under "B" of Liberia. c, Side view of car. d, Car straddling yellow line on track.

**2008, Sept. 5** **Litho.** ***Perf. 13½***

**2535** A638 $60 Sheet of 4, #a-d 12.00 12.00

A639

Election of Barack Obama as US President — A640

Inscriptions: No. 2537, Joseph Biden. No. 2539a, Joseph Robinette Biden, Jr.

No. 2539B: c, Barack Obama. d, Joseph Biden.

***Perf. 14¼x14¾, 12¼x11¾ (#2538)***

**2008, Nov. 5**

**2536** A639 $45 shown 1.50 1.50
**2537** A639 $45 multi 1.50 1.50
**2538** A640 $65 shown 2.10 2.10
*Nos. 2536-2538 (3)* 5.10 5.10

**Souvenir Sheet**

**2539** Sheet of 2, #2536, 2539a 3.00 3.00
*a.* A639 $45 multi 1.50 1.50
**2539B** Sheet of 2 17.00 17.00
*c.-d.* A639 $160 Either single 8.50 8.50

No. 2536 was printed in sheets of 9 and in No. 2539. No. 2537 was printed in sheets of 9. No. 2538 was printed in sheets of 4.

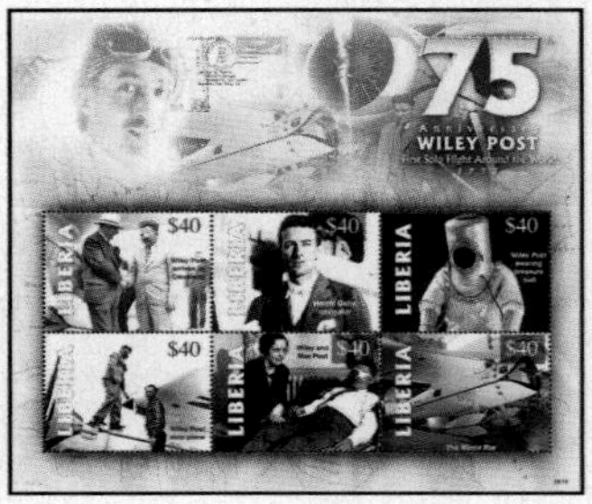


A641

Solo Aerial Circumnavigation of the World by Wiley Post, 75th Anniv. — A642

No. 2540: a, Post arriving in Cleveland. b, Harold Gatty, navigator. c, Post wearing pressure suit. d, Post atop plane. e, Post and wife Mae. f, The Winnie Mae.
$100, Post and map of flight.

**2008, Nov. 24** ***Perf. 13¼***

**2540** A641 $40 Sheet of 6, #a-f 12.00 12.00

**Souvenir Sheet**

**2541** A642 $100 multi 6.00 6.00

Christmas — A643

Paintings: $10, The Nativity, by Martin Schongauer. $25, Birth of Christ, by Robert Campin. $30, Adoration of the Magi, by Geertgen tot Sint Jans. $40, The Birth of Christ, by Sandro Botticelli.

**2008, Dec. 1 Litho.** ***Perf. 14¼x14¾***

**2542-2545** A643 Set of 4 3.50 3.50

New Year 2009 (Year of the Ox) A644

**2009, Jan. 2** ***Perf. 12***

**2546** A644 $60 multi 1.90 1.90

Printed in sheets of 4.

Blindness A645

Designs: $10, Blind student reading Braille. $30, Blind man in crosswalk. $45, Blind man, map of Liberia. $100, Sighted man leading blind man.

**2009, Jan. 4** ***Perf. 14¾x14¼***

**2547-2550** A645 Set of 4 5.75 5.75

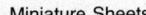

Miniature Sheets

Star Trek — A646

No. 2551: a, Captain Kirk. b, USS Enterprise. c, Scotty. d, Uhura. e, Spock. f, Spock, Rand and Kirk.

No. 2552: a, Scotty. b, Spock and Kirk. c, Dr. McCoy. d, Sulu.

**2009, Jan. 14** ***Perf. 11½***

**2551** A646 $35 Sheet of 6, #a-f 6.75 6.75

***Perf. 13½x13¼***

**2552** A646 $60 Sheet of 4, #a-d 7.50 7.50

No. 2552 contains four 38x51mm stamps.

Miniature Sheet

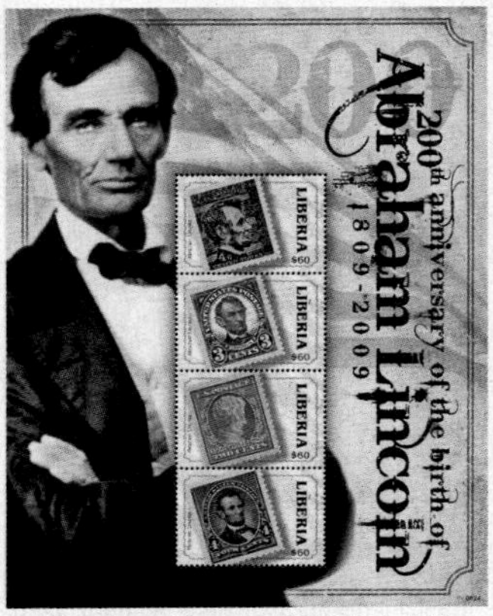


Abraham Lincoln (1809-65), US President — A647

No. 2553: a, US #1282. b, US #555. c, US #367. d, US #222.

**2009, Feb. 2** ***Perf. 13¼x13½***

**2553** A647 $60 Sheet of 4, #a-d 7.50 7.50

Miniature Sheet

John F. Kennedy (1917-63), US President — A648

No. 2554 — Kennedy: a, Greeting Cuban-exile Bay of Pigs invasion force, with wife Jackie, shaking hand. b, Standing with Jackie. c, In White House. d, With Jackie at stadium.

**2009, Feb. 25** ***Perf. 11¼x11½***

**2554** A648 $50 Sheet of 4, #a-d 6.25 6.25

A649

Peonies — A650

No. 2556: a, White peony, tan background. b, Pink peony, white background.

**2009, Apr. 10** ***Perf. 13¼***

**2555** A649 $32 multi 1.00 1.00

**Souvenir Sheet**

**2556** A650 $65 Sheet of 2, #a-b 4.00 4.00

No. 2555 was printed in sheets of 6.

Miniature Sheets

A651

A652

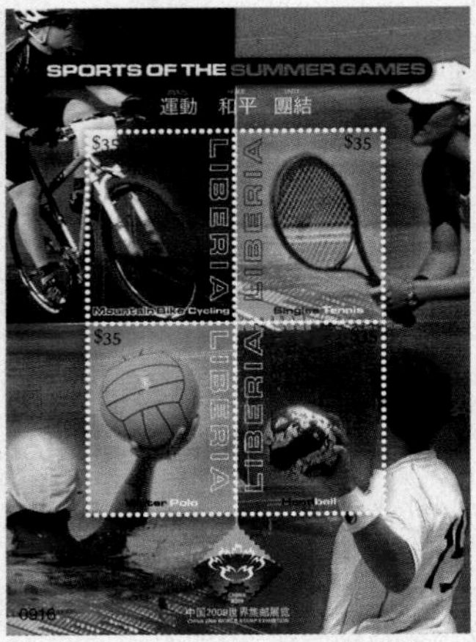


China 2009 World Stamp Exhibition, Luoyang — A653

No. 2557: a, Panda, Chengdu. b, West Lake, Hangzhou. c, Bonsai Garden, Suzhou. d, Fuzi Miao and Qinhuai River, Nanjing.

No. 2558: a, Ornamental plaque (770-476 B.C.). b, Vessel (206 B.C.-A.D. 8). c, Covered jar (1279-1368). d, Head of a Bodhisattva (618-907).

No. 2559: a, Wheel of mountain bike. b, Hand holding tennis racquet. c, Hand holding water polo ball. d, Hand holding handball.

**2009, Apr. 10** ***Perf. 12½***

**2557** A651 $35 Sheet of 4, #a-d 4.50 4.50

***Perf. 12***

**2558** A652 $35 Sheet of 4, #a-d 4.50 4.50

**2559** A653 $35 Sheet of 4, #a-d 4.50 4.50

*Nos. 2557-2559 (3)* 13.50 13.50

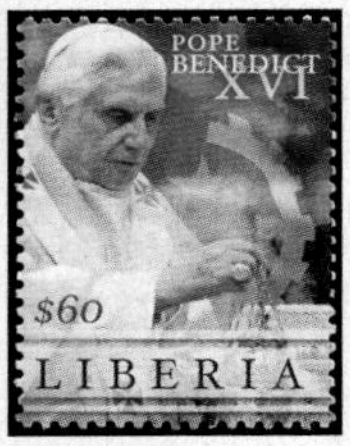


Pope Benedict XVI — A654

**2009, May 4** ***Perf. 11¼x11½***

**2560** A654 $60 multi 1.75 1.75

Printed in sheets of 4.

Miniature Sheet

Felix Mendelssohn (1809-47), Composer — A655

No. 2561: a, Portrait of young Mendelssohn, by Carl Begas. b, Fanny Mendelssohn, sister of Felix. c, Mendelssohn's sketch of Thomasschule, Leipzig. d, Leipzig Conservatory. e, Portrait of Mendelssohn, by James Warren Childe. f, Mendelssohn drawing made during visit to Scotland.

**2009, May 4** ***Perf. 11¼x11½***

**2561** A655 $50 Sheet of 6, #a-f 8.75 8.75

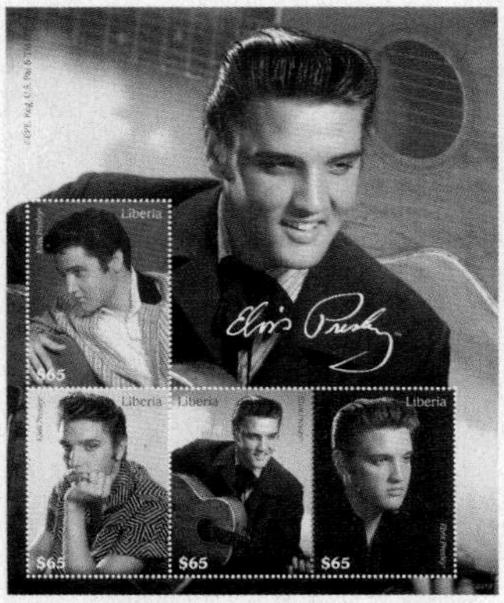


A656

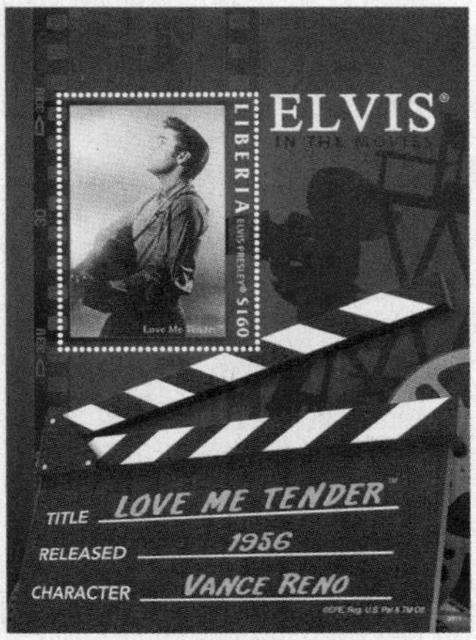


A657

A658

A659

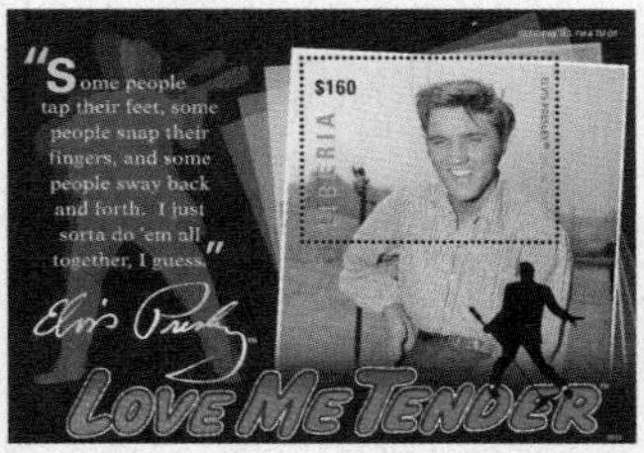


Elvis Presley (1935-77) — A660

No. 2562 — Background color: a, Red brown. b, Tan. c, Gray green. d, Black.

**2009, May 4** *Perf. 13¼*

| | | | | |
|---|---|---|---|---|
| **2562** | A656 | $65 Sheet of 4, #a-d | 7.50 | 7.50 |

### Souvenir Sheets

*Perf. 14¼*

| | | | | |
|---|---|---|---|---|
| **2563** | A657 | $160 multi | 4.75 | 4.75 |
| **2564** | A658 | $160 multi | 4.75 | 4.75 |
| **2565** | A659 | $160 multi | 4.75 | 4.75 |
| **2566** | A660 | $160 multi | 4.75 | 4.75 |
| | | *Nos. 2563-2566 (4)* | 19.00 | 19.00 |

US Presidents — A661

No. 2567, $20, vert.: a, George Washington. b, John Adams. c, Thomas Jefferson. d, James Madison. e, James Monroe. f, John Quincy Adams. g, Andrew Jackson. h, Martin Van Buren. i, William Henry Harrison. j, John Tyler. k, James K. Polk. l, Zachary Taylor. m, Millard Fillmore. n, Franklin Pierce. o. James Buchanan.

No. 2568, $20, vert.: a, Abraham Lincoln. b, Andrew Johnson. c, Ulysses S. Grant. d, Rutherford B. Hayes. e, James A. Garfield. f, Chester A. Arthur. g, Grover Cleveland (1885-89). h, Benjamin Harrison. i, Grover Cleveland (1893-97). j, William McKinley. k, Theodore Roosevelt. l, William Howard Taft. m, Woodrow Wilson. n, Warren G. Harding. o, Calvin Coolidge.

No. 2569, $20, vert.: a, Herbert Hoover. b, Franklin D. Roosevelt. c, Harry S Truman. d, Dwight D. Eisenhower. e, John F. Kennedy. f, Lyndon B. Johnson. g, Richard M. Nixon. h, Gerald R. Ford. i, Jimmy Carter. j, Ronald Reagan. k, George H. W. Bush (1989-93). l, William J. Clinton. m, George W. Bush (2001-09). n, Barack H. Obama. o, Presidential seal.

$320, Barack Obama.

**2009, May 4** *Perf. 13¼*

### Sheets of 15, #a-o

| | | | | |
|---|---|---|---|---|
| **2567-2569** | A661 | Set of 3 | 26.00 | 26.00 |
| *2568p* | | Sheet of 9 #2568a | 5.25 | 5.25 |
| *2569p* | | Miniature sheet, #2569o, 14 #2569n | 8.50 | 8.50 |

### Souvenir Sheet

*Perf. 14¼*

| | | | | |
|---|---|---|---|---|
| **2570** | A661 | $320 multi | 9.25 | 9.25 |

Nos. 2567-2569 each contain fifteen 28x42mm stamps. Issued: No. 2568p, 3/23/10. 2569p, 9/4.

Famous People — A662

Designs: No. 2571, $50, Madame Suakoko (1816-1927), first female paramount chief. No. 2572, $50, Chief Flomo Doughba Barwulor.

**2009, Aug. 2 Litho.** *Perf. 11¼x11½*

| | | | | |
|---|---|---|---|---|
| **2571-2572** | A662 | Set of 2 | 2.75 | 2.75 |

Masks — A663

Designs: $10, Korkpor mask. $25, Landa mask. $35, Borwhoo mask. $45, Zoba mask. $100, Kote mask.

**2009, Aug. 2** *Perf. 13¼*

| | | | | |
|---|---|---|---|---|
| **2573-2577** | A663 | Set of 5 | 6.00 | 6.00 |

Dance — A664

Designs: $30, Traditional dancers. $40, Traditional dancers, diff. $45, Poro dancers.

**2009, Aug. 2**

| | | | | |
|---|---|---|---|---|
| **2578-2580** | A664 | Set of 3 | 3.25 | 3.25 |

### Souvenir Sheet

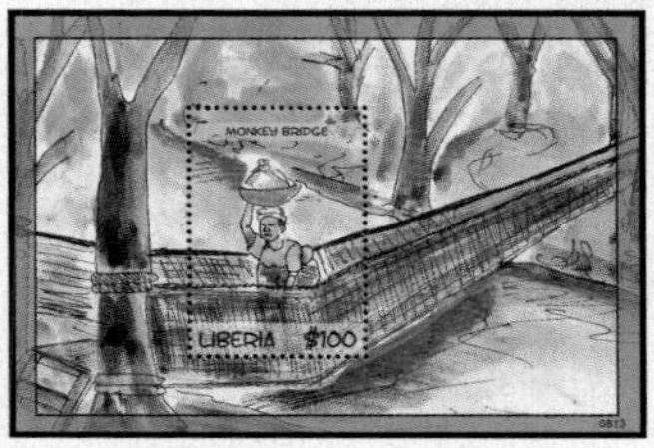


Monkey Bridge — A665

**2009, Aug. 2**

| | | | | |
|---|---|---|---|---|
| **2581** | A665 | $100 multi | 2.75 | 2.75 |

### Miniature Sheets

Players in 2009 National Basketball Association All-Star Game — A666

No. 2582, $30 — Eastern All-stars: a, Ray Allen. b, Kevin Garnett. c, Danny Granger. d, Devin Harris. e, Dwight Howard. f, Allen Iverson. g, LeBron James. h, Joe Johnson. i, Rashard Lewis. j, Paul Pierce. k, Dwayne Wade. l, Mo Williams.

No. 2583, $30 — Western All-stars: a, Chauncey Billups. b, Kobe Bryant. c, Tim Duncan. d, Pau Gasol. e, Yao Ming. f, Dirk Nowitzki. g, Shaquille O'Neal. h, Tony Parker. i, Chris Paul. j, Brandon Roy. k, Amar'e Stoudemire. l, David West.

**2009, Aug. 2** *Perf. 11¼x11½*

### Sheets of 12, #a-l

| | | | | |
|---|---|---|---|---|
| **2582-2583** | A666 | Set of 2 | 20.00 | 20.00 |

Liberian Presidents — A667

Designs: $10, Ellen Johnson-Sirleaf. $25, Moses Z. Blah. $35, Charles M.G. Taylor. $45, Samuel K. Doe. $50, William Richard Tolbert. $70, William V.S. Tubman.

Nos. 2590, 2611, Joseph Jenkins Roberts. Nos. 2591, 2612, Stephen Allen Benson. Nos. 2592, 2613, Daniel Bashiel Warner. Nos. 2593, 2614, James Spriggs Payne. Nos. 2594, 2615, Edward James Roye. Nos. 2595, 2616, Anthony Williams Gardiner. Nos. 2596, 2617, Alfred Francis Russell. Nos. 2597, 2618, Hilary R.W. Johnson. Nos. 2598, 2619, Joseph James Cheeseman. Nos. 2599, 2620, William David Coleman. Nos. 2600, 2621, Garretson W. Gibson. Nos. 2601, 2622, Arthur Barclay. Nos. 2602, 2623, Daniel E. Howard. Nos. 2603, 2624, Charles D.B. King. Nos. 2604, 2625, Edwin James Barclay. No. 2605, Tubman. No. 2606, Tolbert. No. 2607, Doe. No. 2608, Taylor. No. 2609, Blah. No. 2610, Johnson-Sirleaf.

**2009, Aug. 22** *Perf. 12¾*

| | | | | |
|---|---|---|---|---|
| **2584** | A667 | $10 multi | .30 | .30 |
| **2585** | A667 | $25 multi | .70 | .70 |
| **2586** | A667 | $35 multi | 1.00 | 1.00 |
| **2587** | A667 | $45 multi | 1.25 | 1.25 |
| **2588** | A667 | $50 multi | 1.40 | 1.40 |
| **2589** | A667 | $70 multi | 2.00 | 2.00 |
| **2590** | A667 | $100 multi | 2.75 | 2.75 |
| **2591** | A667 | $100 multi | 2.75 | 2.75 |
| **2592** | A667 | $100 multi | 2.75 | 2.75 |
| **2593** | A667 | $100 multi | 2.75 | 2.75 |
| **2594** | A667 | $100 multi | 2.75 | 2.75 |
| **2595** | A667 | $100 multi | 2.75 | 2.75 |
| **2596** | A667 | $100 multi | 2.75 | 2.75 |
| **2597** | A667 | $100 multi | 2.75 | 2.75 |
| **2598** | A667 | $100 multi | 2.75 | 2.75 |
| **2599** | A667 | $100 multi | 2.75 | 2.75 |
| **2600** | A667 | $100 multi | 2.75 | 2.75 |
| **2601** | A667 | $100 multi | 2.75 | 2.75 |
| **2602** | A667 | $100 multi | 2.75 | 2.75 |
| **2603** | A667 | $100 multi | 2.75 | 2.75 |
| **2604** | A667 | $100 multi | 2.75 | 2.75 |
| **2605** | A667 | $100 multi | 2.75 | 2.75 |
| **2606** | A667 | $100 multi | 2.75 | 2.75 |
| **2607** | A667 | $100 multi | 2.75 | 2.75 |
| **2608** | A667 | $100 multi | 2.75 | 2.75 |
| **2609** | A667 | $100 multi | 2.75 | 2.75 |
| **2610** | A667 | $100 multi | 2.75 | 2.75 |
| **2611** | A667 | $500 multi | 14.00 | 14.00 |
| **2612** | A667 | $500 multi | 14.00 | 14.00 |
| **2613** | A667 | $500 multi | 14.00 | 14.00 |
| **2614** | A667 | $500 multi | 14.00 | 14.00 |
| **2615** | A667 | $500 multi | 14.00 | 14.00 |
| **2616** | A667 | $500 multi | 14.00 | 14.00 |
| **2617** | A667 | $500 multi | 14.00 | 14.00 |
| **2618** | A667 | $500 multi | 14.00 | 14.00 |
| **2619** | A667 | $500 multi | 14.00 | 14.00 |
| **2620** | A667 | $500 multi | 14.00 | 14.00 |
| **2621** | A667 | $500 multi | 14.00 | 14.00 |
| **2622** | A667 | $500 multi | 14.00 | 14.00 |
| **2623** | A667 | $500 multi | 14.00 | 14.00 |
| **2624** | A667 | $500 multi | 14.00 | 14.00 |
| **2625** | A667 | $500 multi | 14.00 | 14.00 |
| | | *Nos. 2584-2625 (42)* | 274.40 | 274.40 |

Chinese Aviation, Cent. — A668

No. 2626: a, H-2 missiles. b, H-2B missiles. c, H-12 missiles on trucks. d, H-12 missiles on truck.

$150, H-9 missiles.

**2009, Nov. 12** *Perf. 14*

| | | | | |
|---|---|---|---|---|
| **2626** | A668 | $50 Sheet of 4, #a-d | 6.00 | 6.00 |

### Souvenir Sheet

*Perf. 14¼*

| | | | | |
|---|---|---|---|---|
| **2627** | A668 | $150 multi | 4.50 | 4.50 |

No. 2626 contains four 42x32mm stamps.

Miniature Sheet

Charles Darwin (1809-82), Naturalist — A669

No. 2628: a, Rhea darwinii. b, Proctotretus fitzingerii. c, Vespertilio chiloensis. d, Geospiza fortis.

**2009, Dec. 10** ***Perf. 12x11½***
**2628** A669 $60 Sheet of 4, #a-d 7.50 7.50

Miniature Sheet

The Three Stooges — A670

No. 2629: a, Stooges with open book. b, Moe sticking drill into Curly's mouth. c, Stooges at table looking at book. d, Curly pointing stick at man.

**2009, Dec. 10** ***Perf. 11½x12***
**2629** A670 $60 Sheet of 4, #a-d 7.50 7.50

Miniature Sheet

Pres. John F. Kennedy and Wife, Jacqueline — A671

No. 2630: a, Pres. Kennedy with Jacqueline, wearing cape. b, Pres. Kennedy. c, Pres. Kennedy with Jacqueline in limousine. d, Jacqueline Kennedy and crowd. e, Pres. Kennedy and wife (Jacqueline holding arm of husband). f, Jacqueline Kennedy.

**2009, Dec. 10** ***Perf. 11¼x11½***
**2630** A671 $60 Sheet of 6, #a-f 11.00 11.00

Intl. Year of Astronomy — A672

No. 2631, horiz.: a, Sergei Korolev and Luna 9. b, Luna 9 horizontal on transporter. c, Lift-off of Luna 9. d, Luna 9 over Moon. e, Luna 9 open, with antennae erect. f, Luna 9 open, antennae not erect.
$160, Lift-off of Apollo 11.

**2009, Dec. 10** ***Perf. 13½***
**2631** A672 $40 Sheet of 6, #a-f 7.50 7.50

**Souvenir Sheet**

**2632** A672 $160 multi 5.00 5.00

Nos. 2631a, 2631b and 2631d have country name misspelled as "Libeira."

Christmas A673

Paintings: $25, Nativity (Holy Night), by Correggio. $40, Adoration of the Magi, by Bartolomé Esteban Murillo. $50, Adoration of the Magi, by Vicente Gil. $100, Adoration of the Magi, by Peter Paul Rubens.

**2009, Dec. 10** ***Perf. 13¼x13***
**2633-2636** A673 Set of 4 6.50 6.50

Miniature Sheet

Awarding of Nobel Peace Prize to US Pres. Barack Obama — A674

No. 2637 — Pres. Obama wearing: a, Red tie, facing right. b, Red tie, facing forward. c, Blue tie, facing forward. d, Blue tie, facing left.

**2009, Dec. 30 Litho.** ***Perf. 12x11½***
**2637** A674 $60 Sheet of 4, #a-d 7.00 7.00

Miniature Sheet

Chinese Zodiac Animals — A675

No. 2638: a, Dragon. b, Snake. c, Horse. d, Goat. e, Monkey. f, Rooster. g, Dog. h, Pig. i, Rat. j, Ox. k, Tiger. l, Rabbit.

**2010, Jan. 4** ***Perf. 12½***
**2638** A675 $15 Sheet of 12, #a-l 6.00 6.00

Souvenir Sheet

New Year 2010 (Year of the Tiger) — A676

No. 2639: a, Tiger. b, Tiger and Chinese characters.

**2010, Jan. 4** ***Perf. 14¾x14¼***
**2639** A676 $130 Sheet of 2, #a-b 7.50 7.50

Miniature Sheets

Dogs — A677

No. 2640, $65 — German shorthaired pointer: a, At duckpond. b, With trees and building in background. c, On rocks. d, Sniffing flowers.
No. 2641, $65 — Chihuahua: a, On pink dog bed. b, Standing. c, At pond. d, In small pot.

**2010, Jan. 19** ***Perf. 11½x12***
**Sheets of 4, #a-d**
**2640-2641** A677 Set of 2 15.00 15.00

Miniature Sheets

A678

Visit of Pope Benedict XVI to Great Synagogue of Rome — A679

No. 2642: a, Great Synagogue. b, Pope Benedict XVI and Rome's Chief Rabbi Riccardo Di Segni. c, Pope Benedict XVI and Cardinal. d, Rabbi Di Segni and man wearing white yarmulke.
No. 2643: a, Pope Benedict XVI and Rabbi Di Segni seated. b, Rome's former Chief Rabbi Elio Toaff. c, Pope Benedixt XVI, standing and reaching for Toaff. d, Pope Benedict XVI with hands clasped.

**2010, Mar. 23** ***Perf. 12x11½***
**2642** A678 $110 Sheet of 4, #a-d 12.50 12.50
***Perf. 11½***
**2643** A679 $110 Sheet of 4, #a-d 12.50 12.50

Miniature Sheets

Boy Scouts of America, Cent. — A680

No. 2644, $55 — Merit badges: a, Swimming, First Aid. b, Environmental Science, Family Life. c, Citizenship in the Community, Personal Management. d, Camping, Lifesaving. e, Citizenship in the Nation, Communications. f, Personal Fitness, Citizenship in the World.
No. 2645, $55 — Merit badges: a, Aviation, Fishing. b, Engineering, Electronics. c, Medicine, Music. d, Graphic Arts, Soil and Water Conservation. e, Cinematography, Oceanography. f, Animal Science, Art.

**2010, Mar. 23** ***Perf. 13¼***
**Sheets of 6, #a-f**
**2644-2645** A680 Set of 2 19.00 19.00

Whales and Dolphins — A681

No. 2646: a, Harbor porpoise. b, Killer whale. c, Sowerby's beaked whale. d, Atlantic spotted dolphin. e, Atlantic hump-backed dolphin. f, Clymene dolphin.
$180, Gervais beaked whale.

**2010, Apr. 26** ***Perf. 14¾x14¼***

**2646** A681 $60 Sheet of 6, #a-f 10.50 10.50

**Souvenir Sheet**

**2647** A681 $180 multi 5.25 5.25

US Pres. Barack Obama and Wife, Michelle — A682

No. 2648: a, Pres. Obama. b, Pres Obama with arm around wife's waist. c, Pres. Obama and wife dancing. d, Michelle Obama.
No. 2649, Head of Michelle Obama. No. 2650, Michelle Obama (30x81mm).

**2010, Apr. 26** ***Perf. 14¼x14¾***

**2648** A682 $60 Sheet of 4, #a-d 7.00 7.00

**Souvenir Sheets**

**2649** A682 $100 multi 3.00 3.00
**2650** A682 $100 multi 3.00 3.00

Miniature Sheets

A683

Pres. Abraham Lincoln (1809-65) — A684

No. 2651, $80 — Lincoln: a, Facing right, hand visible at LR. b, Facing left. c, Facing right, no hand visible. d, Facing right, hand visible at center bottom.
No. 2652, $80 — Lincoln: a, Photograph without hat. b, Photograph with hat. c, Lincoln Memorial sculpture. d, Mount Rushmore sculpture.

**2010, June 25** ***Perf. 12x11½***

**2651** A683 $80 Sheet of 4, #a-d 9.00 9.00
**2652** A684 $80 Sheet of 4, #a-d 9.00 9.00

Girl Guides, Cent. — A685

No. 2653, horiz.: a, Three Girl Guides, one wearing cap. b, Three Girl Guides wearing neckerchiefs. c, Three Girl Guides. d, Five Girl Guides in uniform.
$160, Girl Guide wearing cap.

**2010, June 25** ***Perf. 13x13¼***

**2653** A685 $65 Sheet of 4, #a-d 7.25 7.25

**Souvenir Sheet**

***Perf. 13¼x13***

**2654** A685 $160 multi 4.50 4.50

Lech Kaczynski (1949-2010), President of Poland — A686

**2010, Aug. 27** ***Perf. 11½***

**2655** A686 $75 multi 2.10 2.10

Printed in sheets of 4.

Paintings by Michelangelo Merisi da Caravaggio (1573-1610) — A687

No. 2656, horiz.: a, The Beheading of St. John the Baptist. b, Judith Beheading Holofernes. c, Abraham's Sacrifice. d, Medusa.
$180, The Penitent Mary Magdalene.

**2010, Aug. 27** ***Perf. 11½x11¼***

**2656** A687 $80 Sheet of 4, #a-d 9.00 9.00

**Souvenir Sheet**

***Perf. 11¼x11½***

**2657** A687 $180 multi 5.25 5.25

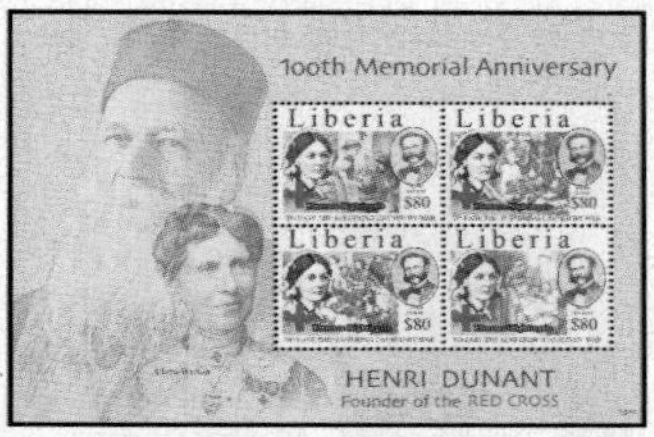


Henri Dunant (1828-1910), Founder of the Red Cross — A688

No. 2658 — Red Cross, Florence Nightingale, depictions of war casualties and nurses, and portrait of Dunant in: a, Gray green. b, Brown. c, Purple. d, Gray blue.
$180, Red Cross, Nightingale, war casualties at Red Cross station, Dunant in purple.

**2010, Aug. 27** ***Perf. 11½x12***

**2658** A688 $80 Sheet of 4, #a-d 9.00 9.00

**Souvenir Sheet**

***Perf. 11½x11¼***

**2659** A688 $180 multi 5.25 5.25

Miniature Sheets

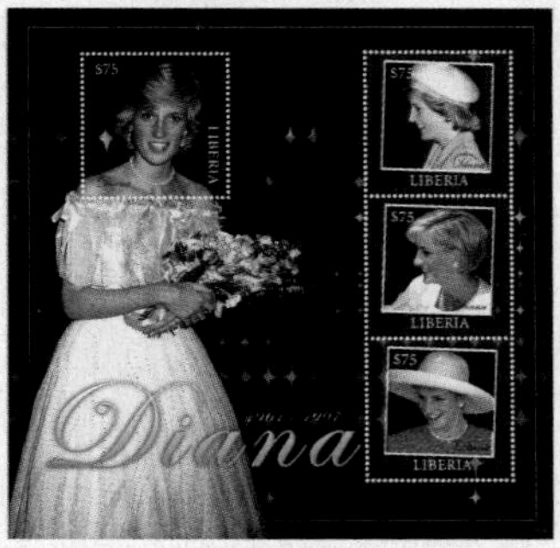


A689

A690

Princess Diana (1961-97) — A691

No. 2660 — Princess Diana with: a, Bare shoulders and single-stand pearl necklace. b, Pink and white hat. c, White dress, earrings, no hat. d, White hat, dark blue and white dress.
No. 2661 — Princess Diana with: a, Tiara. b, Pink hat and dress. c, Green sweater, white blouse. d, Red and white jacket, white blouse.
No. 2662 — Princess Diana with: a, Red dress and flower bouquet. b, White dress, pendant earrings, no hat. c, Bare shoulders and multi-strand pearl necklace. d, White dress, pearl necklace, no hat.

**2010, Aug. 27** ***Perf. 13¼***

**2660** A689 $75 Sheet of 4, #a-d 8.50 8.50
**2661** A690 $75 Sheet of 4, #a-d 8.50 8.50
**2662** A691 $75 Sheet of 4, #a-d 8.50 8.50
*Nos. 2660-2662 (3)* 25.50 25.50

Miniature Sheets

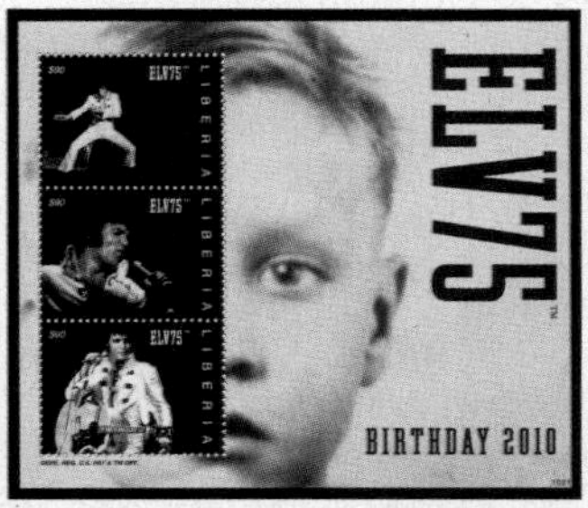


A692

A693

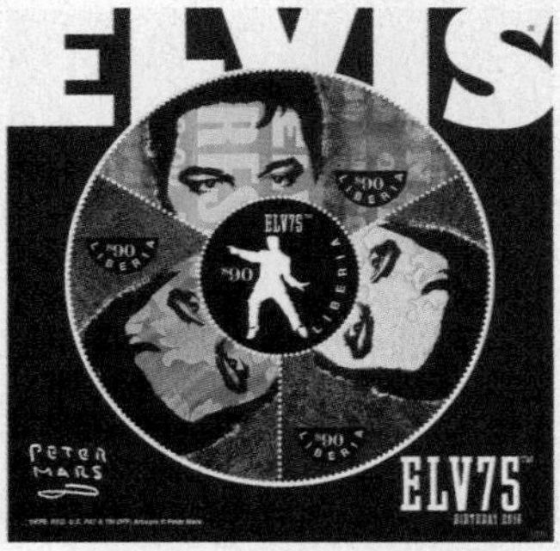


Elvis Presley (1935-77) — A694

No. 2663 — Presley: a, With hands pointing left. b, Holding microphone. c, With guitar, holding microphone.
No. 2664 — Paintings of Presley with backgrounds of: a, Green and black. b, Orange and bister. c, Black and red.
No. 2665: a, Presley's face in orange and yellow. b, Presley's face in light blue and

white. c, Presley's face in blue and gray. d, Silhouette of Presley.

**2010, Aug. 27** ***Perf. 11½x11¼***
**2663** A692 $90 Sheet of 3, #a-c 7.75 7.75

***Perf. 11¼x11½***
**2664** A693 $90 Sheet of 3, #a-c 7.75 7.75

***Perf. 13***
**2665** A694 $90 Sheet of 4, #a-d 10.00 10.00
*Nos. 2663-2665 (3)* 25.50 25.50

Cats — A695

No. 2666, vert.: a, Siberian. b, Turkish Angora. c, British shorthair. d, Maine coon. e, Abyssinian. f, Scottish fold.
$180, Bluepoint Himalayan.

**2010, Oct. 27** ***Perf. 11¼x11½***
**2666** A695 $60 Sheet of 6, #a-f 10.50 10.50

**Souvenir Sheet**
***Perf. 11½x11¼***
**2667** A695 $180 multi 5.25 5.25

Nos. 2666-2667 exist imperf. Value, set $25.

Miniature Sheets

Pres. John F. Kennedy (1917-63) — A696

No. 2668, $80 — Olive bister frames with Kennedy: a, Walking with Vice-president Lyndon B. Johnson. b, On telephone. c, At lectern. d, Looking upwards.
No. 2669, $80 — Blue frames with Kennedy: a, At lectern. b, Walking with McGeorge Bundy. c, Campaigning in New York City. d, With hands clasped.
No. 2670, $80 — Red frames with Kennedy: a, With Dr. Wernher von Braun. b, With wife, Jacqueline, watching space flight on television. c, At lectern. d, Viewing Friendship 7 space capsule.

**2010, Oct. 27** ***Perf. 12x11½***
**Sheets of 4, #a-d**
**2668-2670** A696 Set of 3 28.00 28.00

Christmas — A697

Paintings: $25, The Annunciation, by Fra Angelico. $40, The Angelic Announcement to the Shepherds, by Taddeo Gaddi. $50, Adoration of the Shepherds, by Guido Reni. $100, Virgin and Child with Angels and Saints, by Felice Torelli.

**2010, Oct. 27** **Litho.** ***Perf. 11½***
**2671-2674** A697 Set of 4 6.25 6.25

Liberian Politicians A698

Designs: $25, Pres. Ellen Johnson-Sirleaf receiving gift. $45, Pres. Johnson Sirleaf standing with Chinese Pres. Hu Jintao, vert. No. 2677, $50, Pres. Johnson-Sirleaf reading. No. 2678, $50, Vice-president Joseph N. Boakai. No. 2679, $100, Pres. Johnson-Sirleaf sitting with Pres. Hu. No. 2680, $100, Pres. Johnson-Sirleaf shaking hands with Vice-president Boakai. No. 2681, $100, Pres. Johnson-Sirleaf wearing sash of office, vert. No. 2682, $500, Pres. Johnson-Sirleaf meeting with international investors. No. 2683, $500, Pres. Johnson-Sirleaf with Vice-president Boakai and cabinet.

**2010, Dec. 16** ***Perf. 12***
**2675-2683** A698 Set of 9 *5.00 5.00*

Nos. 2675-2683 were sold to the philatelic trade at prices well below that indicated by currency exchange rates at the date of issue.

Mother Teresa (1910-97), Humanitarian A699

Various photos with frame color of: No. 2684, $80, Olive bister. No. 2685, $80, Blue.

**2010, Dec. 16**
**2684-2685** A699 Set of 2 4.50 4.50

Nos. 2684-2685 each were printed in sheets of 4.

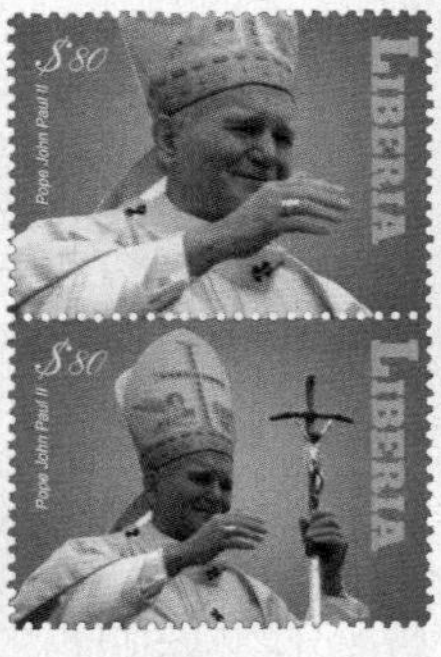


Pope John Paul II (1920-2005) A700

No. 2686 — Red background: a, Without crucifix. b, With crucifix.
No. 2687 — Purple background: a, With crucifix. b, Without crucifix.

**2010, Dec. 16**
**2686** A700 $80 Pair, #a-b 4.50 4.50
**2687** A700 $80 Horiz. pair, #a-b 4.50 4.50

Nos. 2686-2687 each were printed in sheets containing two pairs.

Paintings of Sandro Botticelli (1455-1510) — A701

No. 2688 — Details from The Birth of Venus: a, Head of Venus. b, Reversed image of torso of winged zephyrs. c, Reversed image of heads of winged zephyrs. d, Nymph.
$160, Portrait of St. Augustine, vert.

**2010, Dec. 16** ***Perf. 12***
**2688** A701 $80 Sheet of 4, #a-d 9.00 9.00

**Souvenir Sheet**
***Perf. 12½x12¾***
**2689** A701 $160 multi 4.50 4.50

No. 2689 contains one 38x50mm stamp.

A702

Michael Jackson (1958-2009), Singer — A703

No. 2690 — Jackson: a, With arched back, holding microphone. b, Moving hat to cover face. c, Wearing white glove and hat. d, With arched back, arms stretched outward.
No. 2691 — Jackson: a, Wearing red shirt. b, Holding microphone. c, With arm outstretched. d, With spotlights in background, holding microphone.
$180, Jackson singing.

**2010, Dec. 16** ***Perf. 12***
**2690** A702 $80 Sheet of 4, #a-d 9.00 9.00
**2691** A703 $80 Sheet of 4, #a-d 9.00 9.00

**Souvenir Sheet**
**2692** A703 $180 multi 5.00 5.00

Miniature Sheets

Mao Zedong (1893-1976), Chairman of People's Republic of China — A704

Hu Jintao, President of People's Republic of China — A705

No. 2693 — Mao: a, Without cap, no pockets shown on jacket. b, Wearing cap, pockets shown on jacket. c, Without cap, pockets shown on jacket. d, With cap, no pockets shown on jacket.
No. 2694 — Pres. Hu: a, Ear at left visible, tie over jacket. b, Both ears visible. c, Ear at right visible. d, Ear at left visible, tie under jacket.

**2010, Nov. 7** **Litho.** ***Perf. 12***
**2693** A704 $90 Sheet of 4, #a-d 10.50 10.50
**2694** A705 $90 Sheet of 4, #a-d 10.50 10.50

Beijing 2010 Intl. Philatelic Exhibition.

Miniature Sheet

Anti-Apartheid Activists of South Africa — A706

No. 2695: a, Helen Suzman (1917-2009). b, Eli Weinberg (1908-81). c, Hymie Barsel (1920-87). d, Esther Barsel (1924-2008), and South African Pres. Nelson Mandela.

**2011, Mar. 1**
**2695** A706 $75 Sheet of 4, #a-d 8.50 8.50

Chinese Zodiac Animals — A707

New Year 2011 (Year of the Rabbit) — A708

No. 2696: a, Rat. b, Ox. c, Tiger. d, Rabbit. e, Dragon. f, Snake. g, Horse. h, Sheep. i, Monkey. j, Rooster. k, Dog. l, Pig.

**2011, Mar. 28**
**2696** A707 $25 Sheet of 12, #a-l 8.50 8.50

**Souvenir Sheet**

**2697** A708 Sheet of 2 #2697a 5.75 5.75
*a.* $100 Single stamp 2.75 2.75

British Monarchs A709

Designs: No. 2698, $80, King George V (1865-1936). No. 2699, $80, King Edward VIII (1894-1972). No. 2700, $80, King George VI (1895-1952). No. 2701, $80, Queen Elizabeth II.

***Perf. 13 Syncopated, 12 (#2700)***
**2011, Mar. 28**
**2698-2701** A709 Set of 4 9.00 9.00

Nos. 2698-2701 each were printed in sheets of 4.

Princess Diana (1961-97) in India — A710

No. 2702, vert. — Princess Diana: a, Greeting girl with hands together, red background. b, Touching woman on cot, red background. c, Talking with Mother Teresa, red background. d, Shaking hands with seated man, purple background. e, With woman and small boy, purple background. f, At Taj Mahal, purple background.

$360, Princess Diana talking with seated people.

**2011, Mar. 28** ***Perf. 13 Syncopated***
**2702** A710 $60 Sheet of 6, #a-f 10.00 10.00

**Souvenir Sheet**

**2703** A710 $360 multi 10.00 10.00

Indipex 2011 Intl. Philatelic Exhibition, New Delhi.

Engagement of Prince William and Catherine Middleton A711

Deisgns: No. 2704, $65, Couple, dull green background. No. 2705, $65, Couple, gray background.

No. 2706, $100: a, Catherine Middleton. b, Prince William.

No. 2707, $100, horiz.: a, Couple, Middleton touching hat. b, Couple, Middleton not touching hat.

***Perf. 12, 13 Syncopated (#2707)***
**2011, Mar. 28**
**2704-2705** A711 Set of 2 3.75 3.75

**Sheets of 2, #a-b**

**2706-2707** A711 Set of 2 11.50 11.50

Pres. John F. Kennedy (1917-63) — A712

No. 2708 — Kennedy: a, Oval portrait. b, Close-up of head. c, Wearing patterned tie. d, Wearing pinstripe suit and solid tie.

$180, Kennedy, diff.

**2011, Mar. 28** ***Perf. 12***
**2708** A712 $80 Sheet of 4, #a-d 9.00 9.00

**Souvenir Sheet**

**2709** A712 $180 multi 5.00 5.00

Miniature Sheets

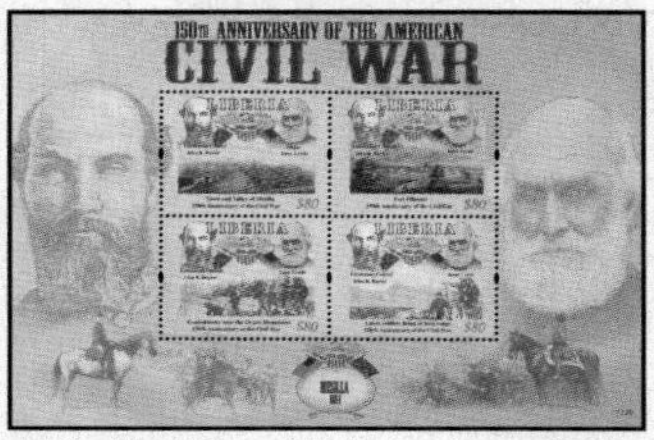


U.S. Civil War, 150th Anniv. — A713

No. 2710, $80 — Lieutenant Colonel John B. Baylor, Major Isaac Lynde and Battle of Mesilla image: a, Town and valley of Mesilla. b, Fort Fillmore. c, Confederates near the Organ Mountains. d, Union soldiers firing at long range.

No. 2711, $80 — Colonel Martin E. Green, Colonel David Moore and Battle of Athens image: a, Confederates near the Fabius River. b, Col. Moore leads Union troops. c, Cavalries clash at Athens encounter. d, Col. Green's Missouri State Guard.

No. 2712, $80 — Major General Sterling Price, Captain Nathaniel Lyon and Battle of Wilson's Creek image: a, Missouri State Guardsmen on Bloody Hill. b, Confederate battery in action. c, Lt. Omar Weaver is wounded. d, 2nd Kansas Infantry on Bloody Hill.

No. 2713, $80 — Brigadier General John B. Floyd, Colonel Erastus Tyler and Battle of Kessler's Cross Lanes image: a, Confederate forces in the Kanawha Valley. b, 7th Ohio Regiment at Kessler's Cross Lanes. c, The Union forces surprised and routed. d, Confederate forces near the Gauley River.

No. 2714, $80 — Captain Samuel Barron, Major General Benjamin F. Butler and Battle of Hatteras Inlet image: a, Capture of Fort Hatteras. b, Union Atlantic blockading squadron. c, USS Harriet Lane. d, USS Cumberland.

**2011, Mar. 28** ***Perf. 13 Syncopated***

**Sheets of 4, #a-d**

**2710-2714** A713 Set of 5 45.00 45.00

Mushrooms — A714

No. 2715: a, Penny bun. b, Ola'h. c, The miller. d, False ink cap. e, The blusher. f, Glistening ink cap.

No. 2716: a, Death cap. b, Panther cap.

**2011, Mar. 28** ***Perf. 12***
**2715** A714 $65 Sheet of 6, #a-f 11.00 11.00

**Souvenir Sheet**

**2716** A714 $65 Sheet of 2, #a-b 3.75 3.75

Birds — A715

No. 2717: a, Red-faced cisticola. b, Orange-cheeked waxbill. c, Zebra waxbill. d, African firefinch.

No. 2718, $180, Guinea turaco. No. 2719, $180, Lavender waxbill, vert.

***Perf. 12, 13 Syncopated (#2718)***
**2011, Mar. 28**
**2717** A715 $80 Sheet of 4, #a-d 9.00 9.00

**Souvenir Sheets**

**2718-2719** A715 Set of 2 10.00 10.00

Miniature Sheets

Zodiac Constellations — A716

No. 2720, $100: a, Aries. b, Leo. c, Sagittarius.

No. 2721, $100: a, Gemini. b, Libra. c, Aquarius.

No. 2722, $100: a, Cancer. b, Scorpio. c, Pisces.

No. 2723, $100: a, Virgo. b, Taurus. c, Capricorn.

**2011, Mar. 28** ***Perf. 12***

**Sheets of 3, #a-c**

**2720-2723** A716 Set of 4 34.00 34.00

Souvenir Sheets

Pres. Ellen Johnson-Sirleaf — A717

Designs: $45, Pres. Johnson-Sirleaf and Chinese President Hu Jintao. No. 2725, $100, Pres. Johnson-Sirleaf. No. 2726, $100, Pres. Johnson-Sirleaf and Pres. Hu, horiz.

**2011, Mar. 28** ***Perf. 13¼x13, 13x13¼***
**2724-2726** A717 Set of 3 7.00 7.00

Souvenir Sheets

Popes and Their Arms — A718

No. 2727, $250: a, Pope Pius XII (1876-1958). b, Arms of Pope Pius XII.

No. 2728, $250: a, Pope John XXIII (1881-1963). b, Arms of Pope John XXIII.

**2011, Mar. 28** ***Imperf.***

**Sheets of 2, #a-b Without Gum**

**2727-2728** A718 Set of 2 28.00 28.00

Visit of Chinese President Hu Jintao to Washington, D.C. — A719

No. 2729 — Presidents Hu Jintao and Barack Obama: a, Shaking hands. b, Standing near lectern. c, Greeting crowd. d, Walking outside of White House.

$180, Reviewing troops.

**2011, Mar. 28** **Litho.** ***Perf. 12***
**2729** A719 $75 Sheet of 4, #a-d 8.50 8.50

**Souvenir Sheet**

**2730** A719 $180 multi 5.25 5.25

Back to the Soil — A720

Inscriptions: $25, Invest in the Soil Rubber Farm. $45, Women scratching rice, horiz. $50, Rice nursery in Bong County. $70, The soil is a bank. $100, President Ellen Johnson-Sirleaf harvesting rice, horiz. No. 2736, $500, Fresh fruits and vegetables. No. 2737, $500, Harvesting rice, horiz.

***Perf. 12¾x12½, 12½x12¾***
**2011, Mar. 28**
**2731-2737** A720 Set of 7 37.50 37.50

Worldwide Fund for Nature (WWF) — A721

No. 2738 — Water chevrotain: a, Standing in foliage. b, In water. c, Eating. d, Pair in foliage.

**2011, June 30** ***Perf. 13¼***

| | | | |
|---|---|---|---|
| **2738** | Strip of 4 | 5.75 | 5.75 |
| *a.-d.* | A721 $50 Any single | 1.40 | 1.40 |
| *e.* | Souvenir sheet of 8, 2 each #2738a-2738d | 11.50 | 11.50 |

Miniature Sheet

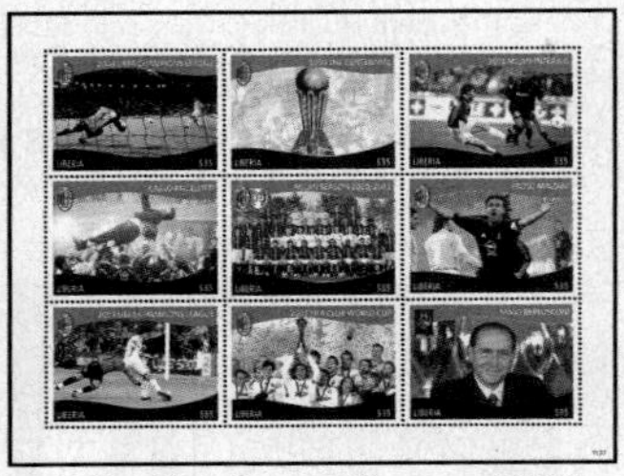

A.C. Milan Soccer Team — A722

No. 2739 — Team emblem and photographs of: a, 2003 UEFA Champions League match. b, Centennial emblem, 1999. c, 2001 6-0 A.C. Milan- Milan Inter match. d, Carlo Ancelloti. e, 2010-11 team. f, Paolo Maldini. g, 2007 UEFA Champions League match. h, Team members with 2007 FIFA Club World Cup. i, Team owner Italian Prime Minister Silvio Berlusconi.

**2011, June 30** ***Perf. 13½***

**2739** A722 $35 Sheet of 9, #a-i 8.75 8.75

Miniature Sheets

A723

Chocolate Candy — A724

No. 2740: a, Cacao pods. b, Sun. c, Ship. d, Fires. e, Mound of cocoa powder. f, Milk and butter. g, Chocolate bar and wrapped candy. h, Cash register and chocolate bar. i, Mouth and chocolate bar.

No. 2741 — Piece of candy with: a, Chocolate coating with white chocolate swirls. b, Dark chocolate coating with walnut. c, White chocolate coating with dark chocolate swirls. d, White chocolate coating with chocolate swirls. e, Chocolate coating with dark chocolate ribbons. f, Dark chocolate coating with choclolate sprinkles. g, Chocolate coating with chocolate rosette. h, Dark chocolate coating with almond. i, White chocolate coating with candy heart.

**2011, June 30** ***Perf. 13 Syncopated***

**2740** A723 $30 Sheet of 9, #a-i 7.50 7.50
**2741** A724 $30 Sheet of 9, #a-i 7.50 7.50

Nos. 2740-2741 each are impregnated with a chocolate aroma.

A725

U.S. Civil War, 150th Anniv. — A726

No. 2742: a, Union General Ulysses S. Grant. b, Drum, rifles, Union and Confederate flags. c, Confederate General Robert E. Lee. d, Pres. Abraham Lincoln. e, Cannons.

No. 2743 — Paintings depicting Lincoln: a, Abraham Lincoln, by William F. Cogswell. b, The Peacemakers, by George Healy. c, President Lincoln Writing the Proclamation of Freedom, by David Gilmour Blythe.

**2011, June 30** ***Perf. 12¾x13***

**2742** A725 $70 Sheet of 5, #a-e 9.75 9.75

***Perf. 13¼x13***

**2743** A726 $100 Sheet of 3, #a-c 8.25 8.25

Jane Goodall's Roots and Shoots, 25th Anniv. — A727

No. 2744: a, Adult showing group of children how to plant seedlings. b, Two children planting seedlings. c, Children holding sign. d, Children and teachers in classroom.
$180, Children.

**2011, June 30** ***Perf. 13x13¼***

**2744** A727 $90 Sheet of 4, #a-d 10.00 10.00

**Souvenir Sheet**

**2745** A727 $180 multi 5.00 5.00

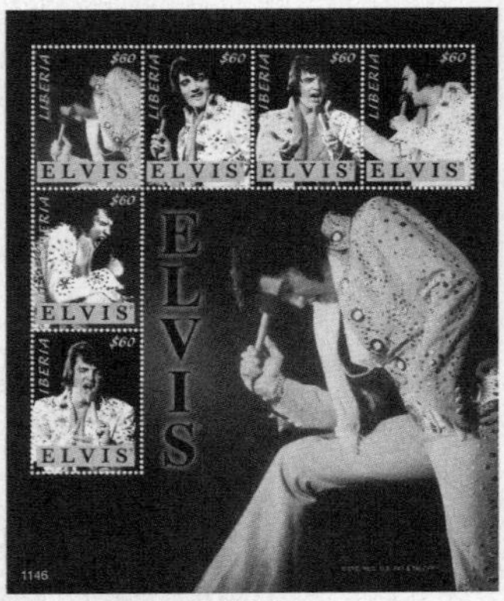


A728

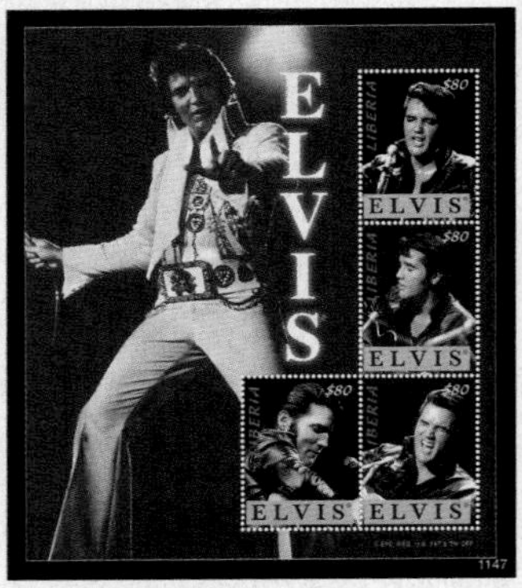


A729

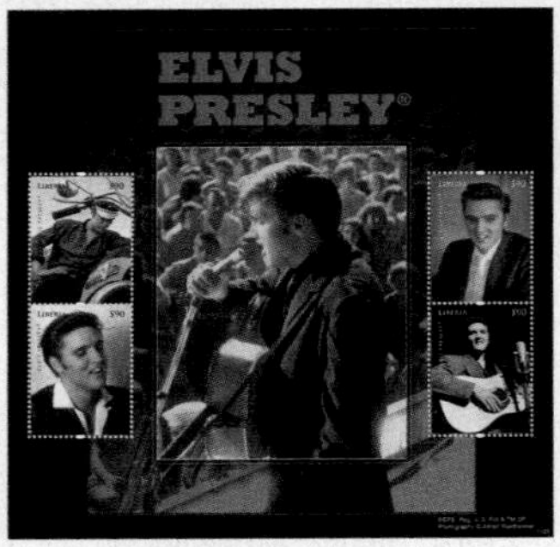


A730

A731

A732

A733

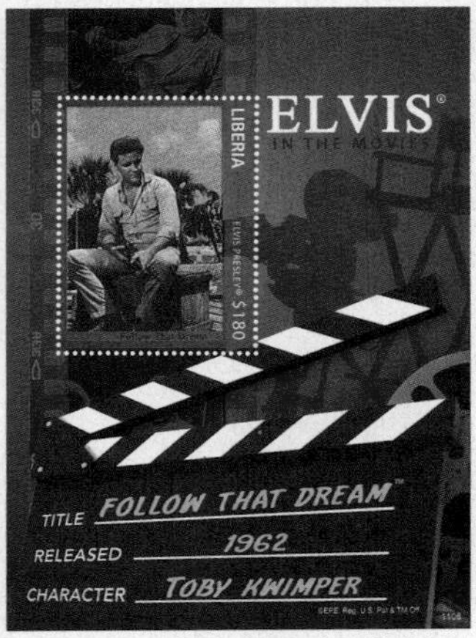


Elvis Presley (1935-77) — A734

No. 2746: a, Face in color. b, Face in black and white, microphone cord above "E." c, As "b," microphone between "I" and "S." d, As "b," microphone cord above "L." e, As "b," microphone cord above "S." f, As "b," microphone cord between "V" and "I."

No. 2747: a, Head of microphone above shoulder. b, Head of microphone even with edge of guitar. c, Head of microphone at right. d, Head of microphone even with tip of chin.

No. 2748 — Presley: a, On motorcycle. b, Wearing white tie. c, Wearing white shirt open at neck. d, Playing guitar.

**2011, June 30** ***Perf. 12¾x13***

**2746** A728 $60 Sheet of 6, #a-f 10.00 10.00

***Perf. 13¼x13***

**2747** A729 $80 Sheet of 4, #a-d 8.75 8.75

***Perf. 13 Syncopated***

**2748** A730 $90 Sheet of 4, #a-d 10.00 10.00
*Nos. 2746-2748 (3)* 28.75 28.75

**Souvenir Sheets**

***Perf. 12¾***

| | | | |
|---|---|---|---|
| **2749** | A731 $180 multi | 5.00 | 5.00 |
| **2750** | A732 $180 multi | 5.00 | 5.00 |
| **2751** | A733 $180 multi | 5.00 | 5.00 |
| **2752** | A734 $180 multi | 5.00 | 5.00 |
| | *Nos. 2749-2752 (4)* | 20.00 | 20.00 |

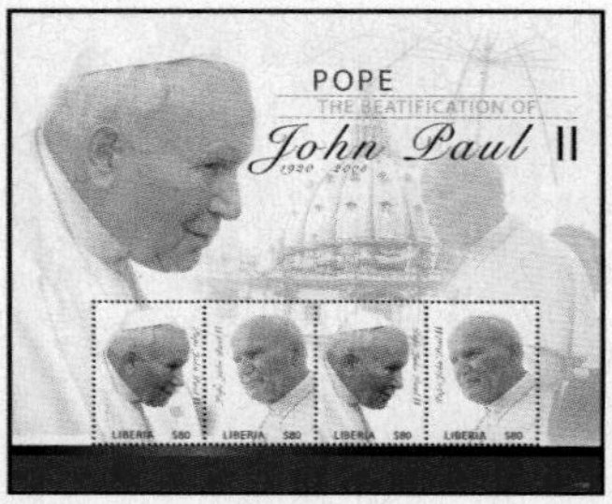


Beatification of Pope John Paul II — A735

No. 2753 — Pope John Paul II facing: a, Right, gray area at LR. b, Left, gray area at top. c, Right, no gray area at LR. d, Left, no gray area at top.
$180, Pope John Paul II wearing miter and green stole.

**2011, Aug. 5 Litho. *Perf. 12***

**2753** A735 $80 Sheet of 4, #a-d 9.00 9.00

**Souvenir Sheet**

**2754** A735 $180 multi 5.00 5.00

Statue of Liberty, 125th Anniv. — A736

No. 2755 — Inscription at right: a, National Monument. b, Lighting the Night Sky. c, Liberty Island, New York Harbor. d, Designed by Frédéric Auguste Bartholdi. e, Enlightening the World, 1886, by Edward Moran. f, Under Construction in Paris, France.
$180, Statue of Liberty and Manhattan buildings, horiz.

**2011, Aug. 5 *Perf. 12***

**2755** A736 $60 Sheet of 6, #a-f 10.00 10.00

**Souvenir Sheet**

***Perf. 12½***

**2756** A736 $180 multi 5.00 5.00

No. 2756 contains one 51x38mm stamp.

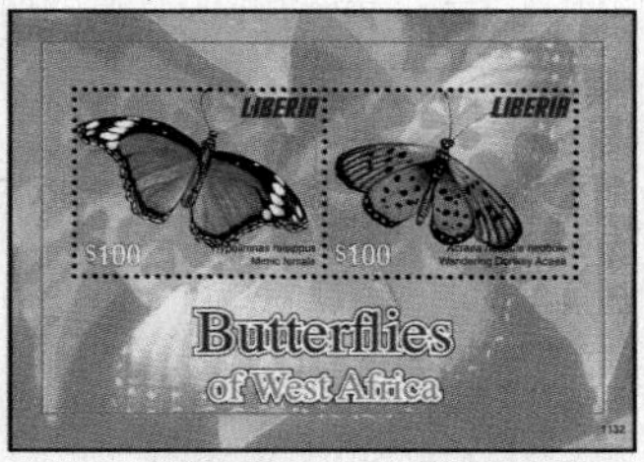


Butterflies — A737

No. 2757: a, Gaudy commodore. b, Yellow pansy. c, White lady swallowtail. d, Broad-bordered grass yellow. e, Blue pansy. f, Citrus swallowtail.
No. 2758: a, Mimic female. b, Wandering donkey acaea.

**2011, Aug. 5 *Perf. 12***

**2757** A737 $65 Sheet of 6, #a-f 11.00 11.00

**Souvenir Sheet**

**2758** A737 $100 Sheet of 2, #a-b 5.50 5.50

Miniature Sheets

A738

Princess Diana (1961-97) — A739

No. 2759: a, Wearing hat with veil. b, Wearing dark hat and winter jacket. c, Without hat. d, Wearing dark hat and white dress.
No. 2760: a, Wearing blue dress and necklace. b, Wearing blue hat. c, Wearing blue jacket, no necklace. d, Wearing white hat.

**2011, Aug. 5 *Perf. 13 Syncopated***

**2759** A738 $75 Sheet of 4, #a-d 8.25 8.25
**2760** A739 $75 Sheet of 4, #a-d 8.25 8.25

First Man in Space, 50th Anniv. — A740

No. 2761, $80: a, Statue of Yuri Gagarin. b, American astronaut John Glenn. c, Gagarin on medal. d, Vostok spacecraft in orbit.
No. 2762, $80, horiz.: a, Gagarin souvenir medal. b, Mosaic of Gagarin. c, Vostok rocket on train. d, American astronauts Virgil Grissom and John Young.
No. 2763, $180, Gagarin. No. 2764, $180, Vostok spacecraft, horiz.

**2011, Aug. 5 *Perf. 13 Syncopated***

**Sheets of 4, #a-d**

**2761-2762** A740 Set of 2 18.00 18.00

**Souvenir Sheets**

**2763-2764** A740 Set of 2 10.00 10.00

Orchids — A741

No. 2765: a, Polystachya longiscapa. b, Vanilla polylepis. c, Ansellia africana. d, Bolusiella maudiae.
No. 2766, $180, Polystachya zambesiaca. No. 2767, $180, Polystachya bella.

**2011, Aug. 5 *Perf. 12***

**2765** A741 $80 Sheet of 4, #a-d 9.00 9.00

**Souvenir Sheets**

**2766-2767** A741 Set of 2 10.00 10.00

Sept. 11, 2001 Terrorist Attacks, 10th Anniv. — A742

No. 2768: a, World Trade Center. b, September 11 Memorial, New York. c, Tribute in Light. d, The Pentagon.
$200, World Trade Center and Brooklyn Bridge, vert.

**2011, Sept. 11 *Perf. 13 Syncopated***

**2768** A742 $75 Sheet of 4, #a-d 8.25 8.25

**Souvenir Sheet**

**2769** A742 $200 multi 5.50 5.50

Chinese Civil Engineering A743

Designs: $40, Qingdao Cross-sea Bridge.
No. 2771 — Qingdao Jiaozhouwan Undersea Tunnel: a, Entrance. b, Cross-sectional diagram.

**2011, Oct. 11 Litho.**

**2770** A743 $40 multi 1.10 1.10
**2771** A743 $25 Sheet of 6, 3 each #2771a-2771b 4.25 4.25

No. 2770 was printed in sheets of 4.

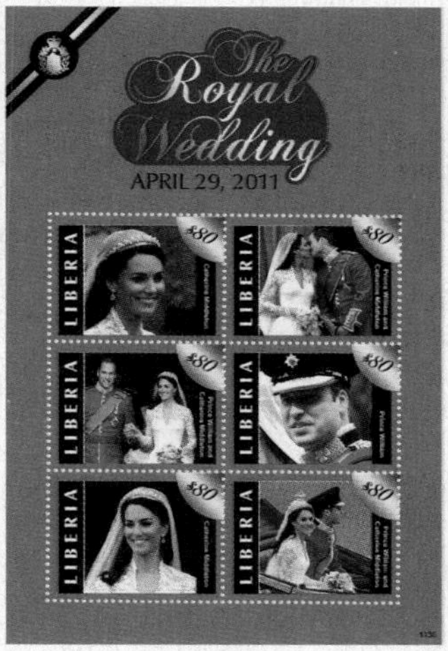


A744

Wedding of Prince William and Catherine Middleton — A745

No. 2772 — Red frames: a, Bride facing right. b, Couple kissing. c, Couple holding hands. d, Groom. e, Bride facing left. f, Couple in coach.
No. 2773 — Blue frames: a, Couple holding hands. b, Groom waving. c, Bride facing left. d, Couple in coach, groom waving. e, Couple standing, bride waving. f, Groom facing right.
$180, Couple in coach, bride waving.

**2011, Oct. 11 *Perf. 12***

**2772** A744 $80 Sheet of 6, #a-f 13.50 13.50
**2773** A745 $80 Sheet of 6, #a-f 13.50 13.50

**Souvenir Sheet**

**2774** A745 $180 multi 5.00 5.00

Christmas A746

Paintings: $25, Madonna with Members of the Pesaro Family, by Titian. $40, The Nativity, by Prero della Francesca. $50, The Virgin of the Rocks, by Leonardo da Vinci. $100, Madonna with Child, by Fra Filippo Lippi.

**2011, Oct. 11 *Perf. 13 Syncopated***

**2775-2778** A746 Set of 4 6.00 6.00

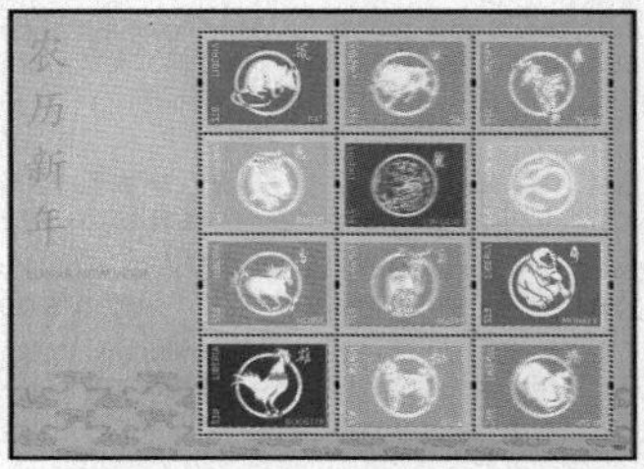

Chinese Zodiac Animals — A747

New Year 2012 (Year of the Dragon) — A748

No. 2779: a, Rat. b, Ox. c, Tiger. d, Rabbit. e, Dragon. f, Snake. g, Horse. h, Sheep. i, Monkey. j, Rooster. k, Dog. l, Boar.

**Litho. With Foil Application**

**2011, Oct. 11 *Perf. 13 Syncopated***

**2779** A747 $18 Sheet of 12, #a-l 6.00 6.00

**Souvenir Sheet**

**Litho.**

***Perf. 13¼***

**2780** A748 $200 multi 5.75 5.75

China 2011 World Philatelic Exhibition, Wuxi (No. 2780).

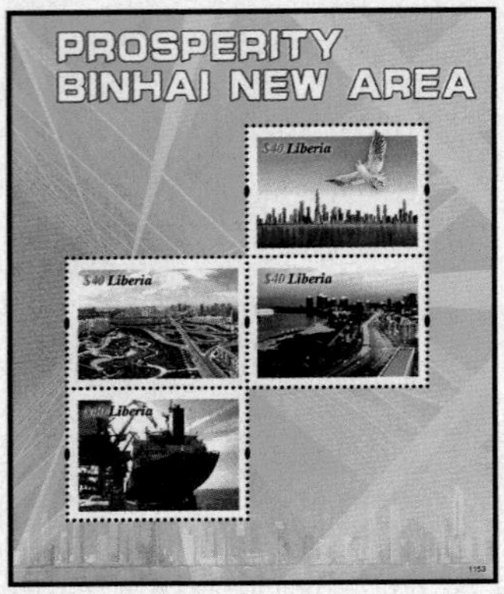


Binhai New Area, People's Republic of China — A749

No. 2781: a, Dove, city. b, Highway cloverleaf interchange. c, City at nightfall. d, Ship at dock.
$160, City, ship, airplanes, rocket.

***Perf. 13 Syncopated***

**2011, Oct. 26** **Litho.**

**2781** A749 $40 Sheet of 4, #a-d 4.50 4.50

**Souvenir Sheet**

**2782** A749 $160 multi 4.50 4.50

No. 2782 contains one 119x40mm stamp.

Peking Opera — A750

No. 2783 — Character with: a, Two sharp teeth, (gray, red and pink face). b, Beard (black and red face). c, Heart-shaped nose (pink, red and black face). d, Ten teeth (red, black and gray face). $180, Character with red, dark red and black face.

**2011, Oct. 26** ***Perf. 13¼***

**2783** A750 $50 Sheet of 4, #a-d 5.75 5.75

**Souvenir Sheet**

**2784** A750 $180 multi 5.00 5.00

China 2011 Intl. Philatelic Exhibition, Wuxi. No. 2784 contains one 44x44mm stamp.

Pres. Ronald Reagan (1911-2004) A751

Flags and Pres. Reagan wearing suit: No. 2785, $100, Without handkerchief in suit pocket. No. 2786, $100, With handkerchief in suit pocket.

**2011, Dec. 16** ***Perf. 13 Syncopated***

**2785-2786** A751 Set of 2 5.50 5.50

Nos. 2785-2786 each were printed in sheets of 3.

Awarding of Nobel Peace Prize to Pres. Ellen Johnson-Sirleaf A752

Designs: $75, Shown. $250, Pres. Johnson-Sirleaf, horiz.

**2011, Dec. 5** ***Perf. 12***

**2787** A752 $75 multi 2.10 2.10

**Souvenir Sheet**

**2788** A752 $250 multi 7.00 7.00

No. 2787 was printed in sheets of 6. No. 2788 contains one 50x30mm stamp.

Reptiles — A753

No. 2789: a, Natal green snake. b, African tree snake. c, African python.
No. 2790: a, African spiny-tailed lizard. b, Western Cape crag lizard. c, Eastern Cape crag lizard. d, Armadillo lizard.
No. 2791: a, African tent tortoise. b, Serrated tortoise.
No. 2792: a, Underside of Nile crocodile. b, Top of Nile crocodile.

**2011, Dec. 16** ***Perf. 12***

**2789** A753 $90 Sheet of 3, #a-c 7.50 7.50

**2790** A753 $90 Sheet of 4, #a-d 10.00 10.00

**Souvenir Sheets**

**2791** A753 $180 Sheet of 2, #a-b 10.00 10.00

**2792** A753 $180 Sheet of 2, #a-b 10.00 10.00

No. 2790 contains four 50x30mm stamps. No. 2792 contains two 80x30mm stamps.

Completion of St. Paul's Cathedral, London, 300th Anniv. — A754

No. 2793: a, Plan of Cathedral. b, Building St. Paul's by J. Seymour Lucas. c, Architect Sir Christopher Wren. d, Pope Clement XI. e, St. Paul's Cathedral. f, Pope Benedict XVI.
No. 2794: a, Pope Clement XI, diff. b, Pope Benedict XVI, diff.

**2011, Dec. 16** ***Perf. 13 Syncopated***

**2793** A754 $50 Sheet of 6, #a-f 8.25 8.25

**Souvenir Sheet**

**2794** A754 $150 Sheet of 2, #a-b 8.25 8.25

St. Paul's Cathedral is an Anglican cathedral and was not visited by Pope Benedict XVI in his travels to the United Kingdom.

Sinking of the Titanic, Cent. — A755

No. 2795: a, Titanic Captain Edward J. Smith. b, Cross-section of the Titanic. c, Iceberg. d, Titanic sinking.
$250, Titanic sinking, vert.

**2012, Jan. 1** ***Perf. 13¼***

**2795** A755 $90 Sheet of 4, #a-d 10.00 10.00

**Souvenir Sheet**

***Perf. 12***

**2796** A755 $250 multi 7.00 7.00

No. 2796 contains one 38x50mm stamp.

Souvenir Sheet

Pope Benedict XVI, 85th Birthday — A756

No. 2797: a, Joseph Ratzinger as young boy (44x25mm). b, Pope Benedict XVI, vert. (30x44mm). c, Birthplace of Pope Benedict XV I(44x25mm)

**2012, Feb. 22** ***Imperf.***

**2797** A756 $250 Sheet of 3, #a-c 21.00 21.00

Mao Zedong (1893-1976), Chairman of People's Republic of China — A757

Photograph of Mao Zedong: No. 2798, $25, No. 2802a, $90, With blue background. No. 2799, $25, No. 2802b, $90, Reading in library. No. 2800, $25, No. 2802c, $90, Waving. No. 2801, $25, No. 2802d, $90, Seated.

**2012, Feb. 22** **Litho.** ***Perf. 14***

**2798-2801** A757 Set of 4 2.75 2.75

**2802** A757 $90 Sheet of 4, #a-d 9.75 9.75

Premiere of *The Three Stooges* Movie — A758

No. 2803: a, Chris Diamantopolous as Moe, denomination in yellow. b, Diamantopolous as Moe, denomination in orange. c, Sean Hayes as Larry, denomination in yellow. d, Hayes as Larry, denomination in orange. e, Will Sasso as Curly, denomination in yellow. f, Sasso as Curly, denomination in orange.
No. 2804: a, Stooges, denomination in blue. b, Stooges, denomination in red violet.

**2012, Mar. 13** ***Perf. 13 Syncopated***

**2803** A758 $75 Sheet of 6, #a-f 12.50 12.50

**Souvenir Sheet**

**2804** A758 $125 Sheet of 2, #a-b 7.00 7.00

Meeting of U.S. Pres. Barack Obama and Xi Jinping, Vice-President of People's Republic of China — A759

No. 2805: a, Xi Jinping. b, Temple, Beijing. c, Pres. Obama. d, Washington Monument.
No. 2806: a, Xi Jinping, diff. b, Pres. Obama, diff.

**2012, Apr. 4** ***Perf. 12***

**2805** A759 $90 Sheet of 4, #a-d 10.00 10.00

**Souvenir Sheet**

**2806** A759 $125 Sheet of 2, #a-b 7.00 7.00

African Wildlife — A760

No. 2807: a, West African giraffe (30x80mm). b, Dorcas gazelle (30x40mm). c, Blue duiker (30x40mm). d, Red river hog (30x40mm). e, Hartebeest (30x40mm).
No. 2808, horiz.: a, Spotted hyena. b, Side-striped jackal. c, Serval.
No. 2809, African bush elephant. No. 2810, Patas monkey.

**2012, May 3** ***Perf. 14***

**2807** A760 $75 Sheet of 5, #a-e 10.50 10.50

***Perf. 12***

**2808** A760 $100 Sheet of 3, #a-c 8.25 8.25

**Souvenir Sheets**

**2809** A760 $250 multi 7.00 7.00

**2810** A760 $250 multi 7.00 7.00

Miniature Sheet

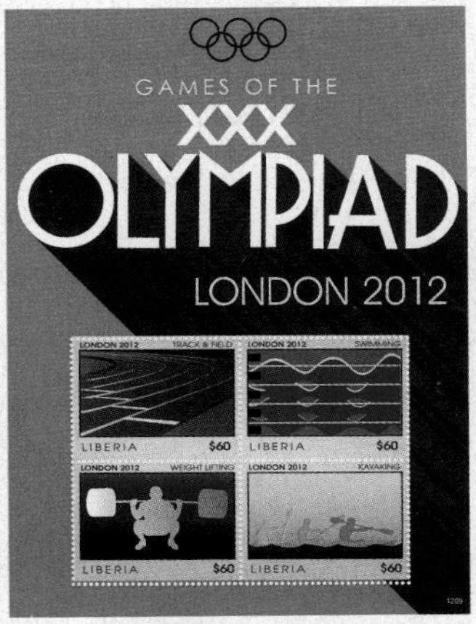


2012 Summer Olympics, London — A761

No. 2811: a, Track and field. b, Swimming. c, Weight lifting. d, Kayaking.

**2012, May 30** ***Perf. 14***
**2811** A761 $60 Sheet of 4, #a-d 6.50 6.50

Dinosaurs — A762

No. 2812, horiz.: a, Albertaceratops. b, Zuniceratops. c, Prestosaurus. d, Saurolophus. e, Ampelosaurus. f, Euoplocephalus.
No. 2813: a, Pachyrhinosaurus. b, Hypsilophodon.

**2012, June 27** ***Perf. 13 Syncopated***
**2812** A762 $75 Sheet of 6, #a-f 12.50 12.50

**Souvenir Sheet**

**2813** A762 $125 Sheet of 2, #a-b 7.00 7.00

Dogs — A763

No. 2814, $120: a, Afghan hound. b, Dalmatian. c, Greyhound.
No. 2815, $120: a, English bulldog. b, Bichon Frise. c, Dachshund.
No. 2816, $250, Scottish terrier. No. 2817, $250, Poodle.

**2012, June 27** ***Perf. 14, 12 (#2816)***

**Sheets of 3, #a-c**

**2814-2815** A763 Set of 2 20.00 20.00

**Souvenir Sheets**

**2816-2817** A763 Set of 2 14.00 14.00

SOS Children's Village, Liberia, 30th Anniv. (in 2011) A764

SOS Children's Village emblem, map of Liberia and: $45, Inscription and slogan. $55, Inscription and palm tree.

**2012, Feb. 14** ***Perf. 14***
**2818-2819** A764 Set of 2 2.75 2.75

Miniature Sheet

Apes — A765

No. 2820: a, Barbary macaque. b, Bonobo. c, Silverback gorilla. d, Chacma baboon.

**2012, Aug. 9** ***Perf. 12***
**2820** A765 $90 Sheet of 4, #a-d 9.75 9.75

Souvenir Sheets

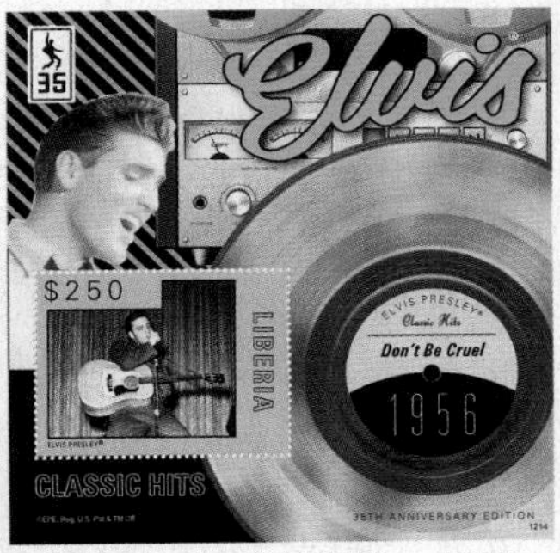


Elvis Presley (1935-77) — A766

Designs: No. 2821, $250, Presley with guitar, light blue frame. No. 2822, $250, Presley behind microphone, light blue frame. No. 2823, $250, Two black-and white photographs of Presley, dull red frame. No. 2824, $250, Color and black-and-white photographs of Presley, red frame. No. 2825, $250, Presley in army uniform, red frame.

**2012, Aug. 9** ***Perf. 12½***
**2821-2825** A766 Set of 5 35.00 35.00

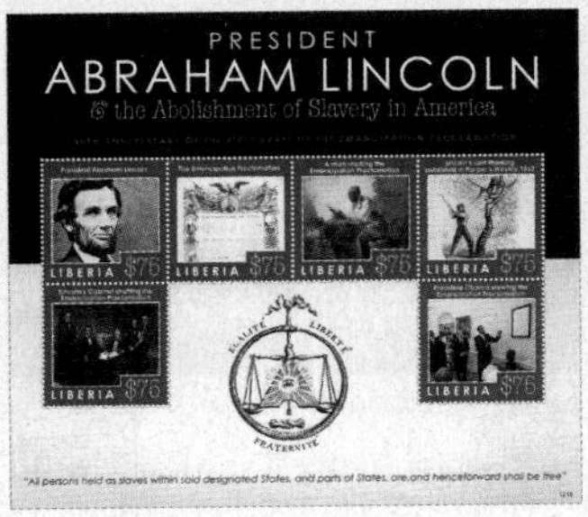

PRESIDENT
ABRAHAM LINCOLN
& the Abolishment of Slavery in America


First Draft of the Emancipation Proclamation, 150th Anniv. — A767

No. 2826: a, Pres. Abraham Lincoln. b, Printed copy of Emancipation Proclamation. c, Man reading Emancipation Proclamation. d, Lincoln's Last Warning, political cartoon from Harper's Weekly, 1862. e, First Reading of the Emacipation Proclamation of President Lincoln, by Francis Bicknell Carpenter. f, Pres. Barack Obama viewing Emancipation Proclamation.
$250, President Lincoln Writing the Proclamation of Freedom, by David Gilmour Blythe, horiz.

**2012, Sept. 21** ***Perf. 13¾***
**2826** A767 $75 Sheet of 6, #a-f 12.50 12.50

**Souvenir Sheet**

***Perf. 12½***

**2827** A767 $250 multi 7.00 7.00

No. 2827 contains one 51x38mm stamp.

Chinese Zodiac Animals — A768

Designs: No. 2828, $15, Monkeys. No. 2829. $15, Cock.

**2012, Sept. 27** ***Perf. 13¼x13***
**2828-2829** A768 Set of 2 .85 .85

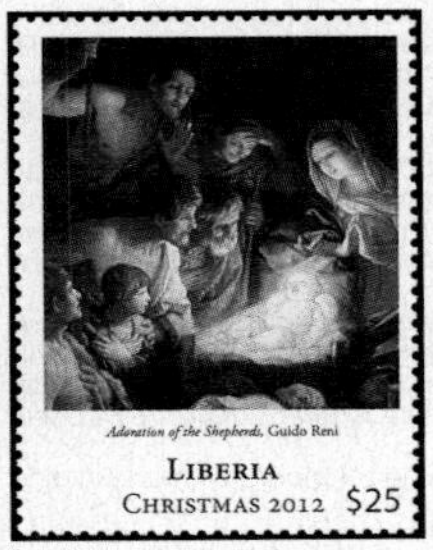


Christmas A769

Paintings: $25, Adoration of the Shepherds, by Guido Reni. $35, Adoration of the Shepherds, by Correggio. $40, Holy Family with St. John the Baptist, by Michelangelo. $45, Tempi Madonna (detail), by Raphael. $50, The Annunciation, by Francisco Goya. $100, Virgin and Child Before an Archway, by Albrecht Dürer.

**2012, Oct. 1** ***Perf. 12½***
**2830-2835** A769 Set of 6 8.25 8.25

Giant Pandas — A770

No. 2836 — Giant Panda: a, On tree, facing left. b, Eating. c, Walking, foliage at right. d, With log at right.
$220, Panda on tree, vert.

**2012, Nov. 15** ***Perf. 13 Syncopated***
**2836** A770 $85 Sheet of 4, #a-d 7.00 7.00

**Souvenir Sheet**

**2837** A770 $220 multi 6.00 6.00

Beijing 2012 Intl. Stamp Exhibition.

Aircraft Carriers — A771

No. 2838: a, Admiral Gorshkov, Russia. b, Dédalo, Spain. c, Foch (R99), France. d, USS Philippine Sea. e, USS Intrepid. f, HTMS Chakri Naruebet, Thailand.
$250, USS Ticonderoga, horiz.

**2012, Nov. 28** ***Perf. 13¾***
**2838** A771 $75 Sheet of 6, #a-f 12.50 12.50

**Souvenir Sheet**

***Perf. 12½***

**2839** A771 $250 multi 6.75 6.75

No. 2839 contains one 51x38mm stamp.

Flowers — A772

No. 2840: a, Nymphaea lotus. b, Papaver somniferum. c, Protea repens. d, Liparia splendens. e, Tulipa florenskyi. f, Gladiolus carmineus.
$280, Zantedeschia aethiopica, vert.

**2013, Jan. 8** ***Perf. 13¾***
**2840** A772 $70 Sheet of 6, #a-f 11.50 11.50

**Souvenir Sheet**

***Perf. 12½***

**2841** A772 $280 multi 7.75 7.75

No. 2841 contains one 38x51mm stamp.

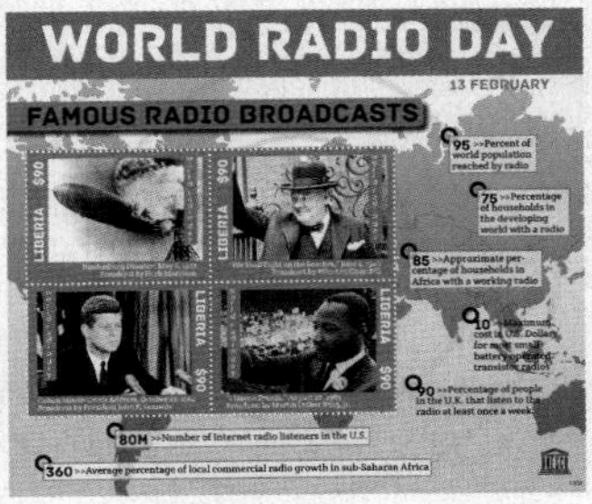


World Radio Day — A773

No. 2842: a, Hindenburg disaster reporting, 1937. b, Winston Churchill's "We Shall Fight on the Beaches" broadcast, 1940. c, Pres. John F. Kennedy's Cuban Missile Crisis address, 1962. d, Dr. Martin Luther King, Jr.'s "I Have a Dream" speech, 1963.
$250, Orson Welles' "War of the Worlds" broadcast, 1938.

**2013, Jan. 8** ***Perf. 12½***
**2842** A773 $90 Sheet of 4, #a-d 9.75 9.75

**Souvenir Sheet**

***Perf.***

**2843** A773 $250 multi 6.75 6.75

No. 2843 contains one 38mm diameter stamp.

Gems and Rocks — A774

No. 2844, $100: a, Aquamarine. b, Euclase. c, Rainbow garnet.
No. 2845, $100: a, Rhodochrosite. b, Opal. c, Tanzanite.
Mo. 2846: a, Agate with red inner rings, small hole. b, Agate with white inner rings, large hole.

**2013, Jan. 8** *Perf. 13¾*

**Sheets of 3, #a-c**

**2844-2845** A774 Set of 2 16.50 16.50

**Souvenir Sheet**

*Perf. 12½*

**2846** A774 $140 Sheet of 2, #a-b 7.75 7.75

Nos. 2844-2845 each contain three 35x35mm stamps.

American Civil Rights Leaders — A775

No. 2847, $85: a, Harriet Tubman (c. 1820-1913), abolitionist (without head covering). b, Frederick Douglass (1818-95), abolitionist. c, John Brown (1800-59), abolitionist. d, Martha Coffin Wright (1806-75), abolitionist.

No. 2848, $85: a, Union Major General David Hunter (1802-86). b, Pres. Abraham Lincoln (1809-65). c, Susan B. Anthony (1820-1906), suffragist. d, Tubman (with head covering).

No. 2849, $280, Tubman and slave capture reward notice. No. 2850, $280, Tubman, daughter Gertie and husband Nelson Davis, horiz.

**2013, Mar. 20** *Perf. 12½*

**Sheets of 4, #a-d**

**2847-2848** A775 Set of 2 18.50 18.50

**Souvenir Sheets**

*Perf. 12*

**2849-2850** A775 Set of 2 15.50 15.50

No. 2849 contains on 30x40mm stamp. No. 2850 contains one 40x30mm stamp.

African Wildlife — A776

No. 2851: a, Acionyx jubatus. b, Aepyceros melampus. c, Diceros bicornis. d, Equus grevyi. e, Panthera leo. f, Phacochoerus africanus.

No. 2852, vert.: a, Giraffa camelopardalis. b, Loxodonta africana. c, Connochaetes taurinus.

$280, Panthera pardus pardus, horiz.

**2013, Apr. 3** *Perf. 13¾*

**2851** A776 $70 Sheet of 6, #a-f 11.50 11.50

*Perf. 12*

**2852** A776 $100 Sheet of 3, #a-c 8.25 8.25

**Souvenir Sheet**

*Perf. 12½*

**2853** A776 $280 multi 7.75 7.75

No. 2852 contains three 30x50mm stamps. No. 2853 contains one 51x38mm stamp.

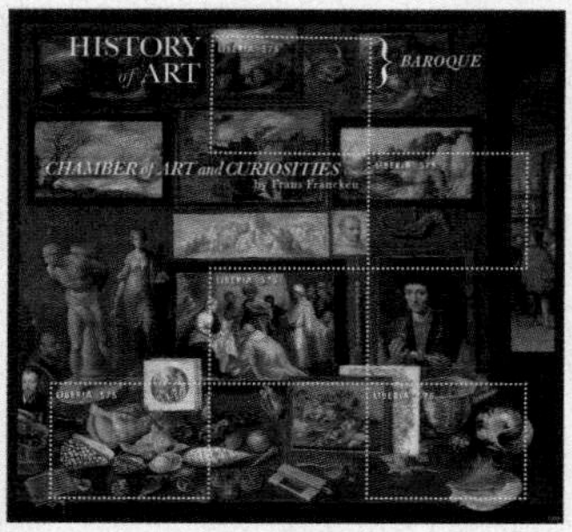


History of Art — A777

No. 2854 — Chamber of Art and Curiosities, by Frans Francken (details) with: a, Fish at UR. b, Seahorse at L. c, Religious painting and tasselled cord. d, Shells, book at LL. e, Shells, bowl at top.

No. 2855, $100, vert.: a, Girl with a Pearl Earring, by Johannes Vermeer. b, A Commander Being Armed for Battle, by Peter Paul Rubens. c, David with the Head of Goliath, by Caravaggio.

No. 2856, $100, vert.: a, Still-life with Flowers, by Rachel Ruysch. b, Maddalena Penitente, by Artemisia Gentileschi. c, The Fruit and Vegetable Costermonger, by Louise Moillon.

$280, La Gamme d'Amour, by Jean-Antoine Watteau.

**2013, Apr. 4** **Litho.** *Perf. 12½*

**2854** A777 $75 Sheet of 5, #a-e 10.50 10.50

**Sheets of 3, #a-c**

**2855-2856** A777 Set of 2 16.50 16.50

**Souvenir Sheet**

**2857** A777 $280 multi 7.75 7.75

Pope Benedict XVI — A778

No. 2858, $85 — Pope Benedict XVI at Beatification Ceremony for Pope John Paul II: a, Wearing miter, with two assistants. b, Wearing miter, waving. c, Kissing glass object. d, Holding censer.

No. 2859, $85 — Pope Benedict XVI visiting Germany: a, Meeting Chancellor Angela Merkel. b, Waving. c, With German President Christian Wulff and wife. d, Facing left.

No. 2860, $280, Pope Benedict XVI seated at beatification ceremony. No. 2861, $280, Pope Benedict XVI with Wulff and Merkel.

**2013, Apr. 29** *Perf. 12*

**Sheets of 4, #a-d**

**2858-2859** A778 Set of 2 18.50 18.50

**Souvenir Sheets**

**2860-2861** A778 Set of 2 15.50 15.50

Lady Margaret Thatcher (1925-2013), British Prime Minister — A779

No. 2862 — Thatcher: a, At microphone. b, Wearing black dress, facing left. c, With Pres. Ronald Reagan. d, With hand on chin.

$280, Thatcher, vert.

**2013, June 1** *Perf. 12*

**2862** A779 $85 Sheet of 4, #a-d 9.25 9.25

**Souvenir Sheet**

*Perf. 12½*

**2863** A779 $280 multi 7.50 7.50

No. 2863 contains one 38x51mm stamp.

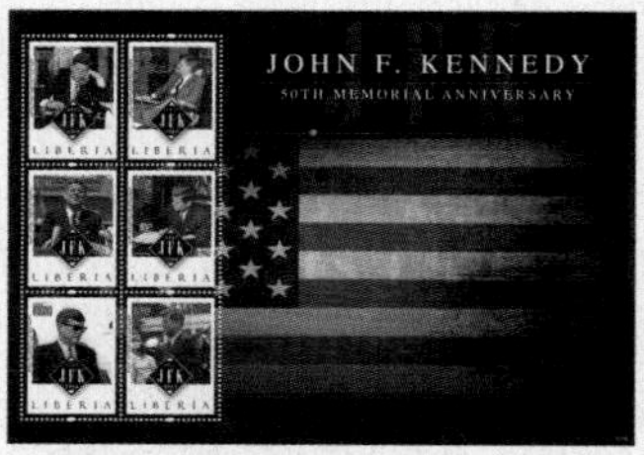


Pres. John F. Kennedy (1917-63) — A780

No. 2864 — Pres Kennedy: a, On telephone. b, Sitting in rocking chair. c, Standing behind microphone. d, Signing document. e, Wearing sunglasses. f, Standing in crowd.

$280, Pres. Kennedy on yacht.

*Perf. 13 Syncopated*

**2013, June 25** **Litho.**

**2864** A780 $70 Sheet of 6, #a-f 11.00 11.00

**Souvenir Sheet**

**2865** A780 $280 multi 7.50 7.50

Medicinal Plants — A781

No. 2866: a, Acacia. b, Rooibos. c, Buchu. d, Caralluma. e, Common myrrh. f, Shea tree.

$280, Aloe, vert.

**2013, June 25** **Litho.** *Perf. 13¾*

**2866** A781 $70 Sheet of 6, #a-f 11.00 11.00

**Souvenir Sheet**

*Perf. 12¾*

**2867** A781 $280 multi 7.50 7.50

No. 2867 contains one 38x51mm stamp.

Birds — A782

No. 2868, $85: a, Barnacle geese. b, Brown pelican. c, Long-billed curlew. d, Eurasian griffon.

No. 2869, $85: a, Eastern great egret. b, Red and green macaw. c, Roseate spoonbill. d, Mute swan.

No. 2870, $280, Blue peafowl. No. 2871, $280, Crowned crane, vert.

*Perf. 14, 12 (#2871)*

**2013, July 30** **Litho.**

**Sheets of 4, #a-d**

**2868-2869** A782 Set of 2 17.50 17.50

**Souvenir Sheets**

**2870-2871** A782 Set of 2 14.50 14.50

Birth of Prince George of Cambridge — A783

No. 2872: a, Duchess of Cambridge handing Prince George to Duke of Cambridge. b, Duke of Cambridge holding Prince George. c, Duchess of Cambridge holding Prince George. d, Duke and Duchess of Cambridge, Prince George.

$280, Duke and Duchess of Cambridge, Prince George.

**2013, Sept. 17** **Litho.** *Perf. 12x12½*

**2872** A783 $85 Sheet of 4, #a-d 8.50 8.50

**Souvenir Sheet**

*Perf. 13¼*

**2873** A783 $280 multi 7.00 7.00

No. 2873 contains one 38x51mm stamp.

Coronation of Queen Elizabeth II, 60th Anniv. — A784

No. 2874 — Queen Elizabeth II wearing: a, Pink jacket and hat. b, Pink jacket, pink and white hat, fur coat. c, Gray hat and dress. d, Black hat and coat.

$280, Queen Elizabeth II wearing black feathered hat.

**2013, Oct. 7** **Litho.** *Perf. 13¾*

**2874** A784 $85 Sheet of 4, #a-d 8.50 8.50

**Souvenir Sheet**

**2875** A784 $280 multi 7.00 7.00

Miniature Sheet

2014 Intl. Horiticultural Exposition, Qingdao, People's Republic of China — A785

No. 2876: a, Exposition emblem. b, Mascot waving. c, Mascot with watering can. d, Mascot snorkeling. e, Mascot surfing. f, Mascot teaching.

**2013, Jan. 1 Litho. *Perf. 14***

**2876** A785 $50 Sheet of 6, #a-f 8.25 8.25

Miniature Sheet

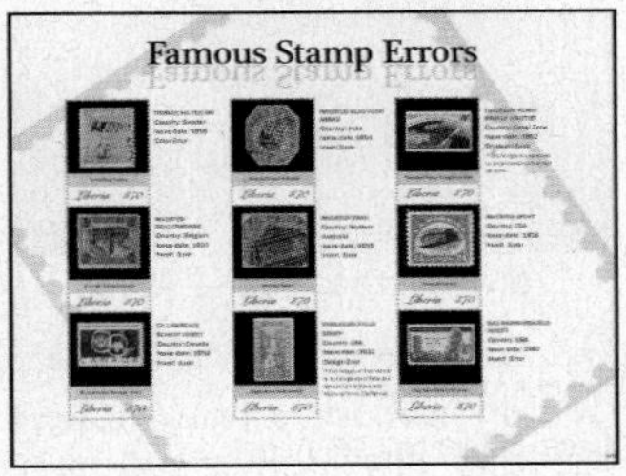


Famous Stamp Errors — A786

No. 2877: a, Sweden #1a. b, India #6c. c, Canal Zone #157a. d, Belgium #139a. e, Western Australia #3a. f, United States #C3a. g, Canada #387a. h, Philippines #357. i, United States #1204.

**2013, Jan. 1 Litho. *Perf. 14***

**2877** A786 $70 Sheet of 9, #a-i 17.50 17.50

New Year 2014 (Year of the Horse) — A787

No. 2878 — Six steeds of Zhaoling from the Mausoleum of Tang Emperor Taizong: a, Horse and attendant. b, Horse facing left, galloping. c, Horse facing left, walking. d, Horse facing right, galloping, diagonal crack running from denomination to horse's head. e, Horse facing right, walking. f, Horse facing right, galloping, vertical crack behind horse's head running to bottom.

$280, Horse's head.

**2013, Nov. 25 Litho. *Perf. 14***

**2878** A787 $70 Sheet of 6, #a-f 10.50 10.50

**Souvenir Sheet**

***Perf. 12***

**2879** A787 $280 multi 7.00 7.00

Intl. Red Cross, 150th Anniv. — A788

No. 2880: a, Horse-drawn ambulances at Red Cross site. b, Red Cross equipment bag. c, Red Cross volunteer tending to prisoners near train. d, Red Cross stenciled on wall.

$280, Jean-Henri Dunant, Red Cross founder.

**2013, Dec. 2 Litho. *Perf. 14***

**2880** A788 $85 Sheet of 4, #a-d 8.50 8.50

**Souvenir Sheet**

**2881** A788 $280 multi 7.00 7.00

Trains — A789

No. 2882: a, 20th Century Limited, United States. b, Ghan, Australia. c, Flying Scotsman, Great Britain. d, Indian Pacific, Australia.

$280, Super Chief, United States, vert.

**2013, Dec. 2 Litho. *Perf. 14***

**2882** A789 $85 Sheet of 4, #a-d 8.50 8.50

**Souvenir Sheet**

**2883** A789 $280 multi 7.00 7.00

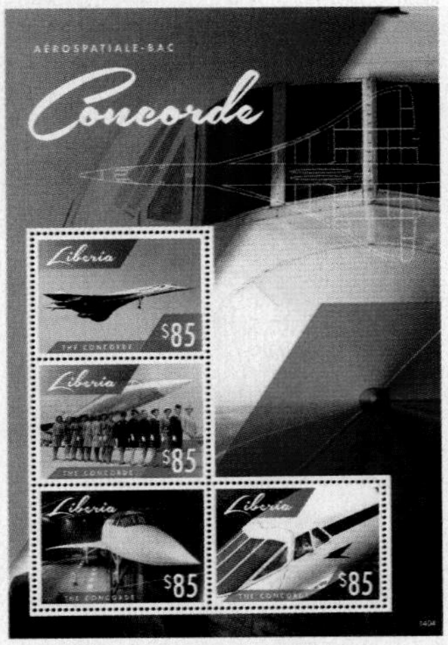


Concorde — A790

No. 2884: a, Concorde in flight. b, Concorde and flight attendants. c, Nose of Concorde. d, Pilot in cockpit window of Concorde.

$280, Concorde in flight in front of clouds.

**2013, Dec. 2 Litho. *Perf. 14***

**2884** A790 $85 Sheet of 4, #a-d 8.50 8.50

**Souvenir Sheet**

***Perf. 12***

**2885** A790 $280 multi 7.00 7.00

No. 2885 contains one 50x30mm stamp.

Miniature Sheets

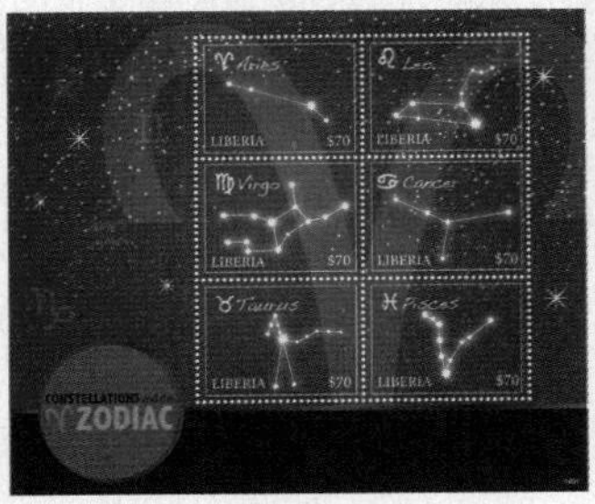


Zodiac Constellations — A791

No. 2886, $70: a, Aries. b, Leo. c, Virgo. d, Cancer. e, Taurus. f, Pisces.

No. 2887, $70: a, Gemini. b, Libra. c, Sagittarius, d, Scorpio. e, Aquarius. f, Capricorn.

**2013, Dec. 2 Litho. *Perf. 12***

**Sheets of 6, #a-f**

**2886-2887** A791 Set of 2 21.00 21.00

Military Vehicles — A792

No. 2888: a, Light utility vehicle. b, Armored personnel carrier. c, Half-track armored personnel carrier. d, Amphibious vehicle.

$280, Amphibious transport.

**2013, Dec. 23 Litho. *Perf. 14***

**2888** A792 $85 Sheet of 4, #a-d 8.50 8.50

**Souvenir Sheet**

***Perf. 12***

**2889** A792 $280 multi 7.00 7.00

Christmas A793

Paintings: $25, Madonna and Child, by Taddeo di Bartolo. $40, Madonna and Saints, by Giovanni Bellini. $50, Nativity, by Lorenzo Lotto. $175, San Marco Altarpiece, by Fra Angelico.

**2013, Dec. 2 Litho. *Perf. 12½***

**2890-2893** A793 Set of 4 7.25 7.25

A794

A795

Nelson Mandela (1918-2013), President of South Africa — A796

No. 2894 — Mandela: a, Wearing green and red shirt, denomination in black. b, Close-up of head. c, With clenched fist, two people in background. d, Wearing flowered shirt, brick wall in background. e, With fist raised, crowd in background. f, Sitting in chair, flag in background.

No. 2895 — Mandela: a, Wearing gray blue shirt, pen in breast pocket. b, Wearing suit and tie, curtains in background. c, Wearing shirt with gray squares, black background. d, Wearing blue and white shirt with red AIDS ribbon under collar button. e, Wearing brown and red shirt. f, Wearing suit and tie, with fist raised.

$280, Mandela in suit and tie, diff. $765, Mandela waving.

**2013, Dec. 15 Litho. *Perf. 14***

**2894** A794 $70 Sheet of 6, #a-f 10.50 10.50

**2895** A795 $70 Sheet of 6, #a-f 10.50 10.50

**Souvenir Sheets**

***Perf. 12***

**2896** A795 $280 multi 7.00 7.00

**Litho., Margin Embossed With Foil Application**

**Without Gum**

***Imperf***

**2897** A796 $765 multi 19.00 19.00

Christening of Prince George of Cambridge — A797

No. 2898: a, Prince George. b, Duchess of Cambridge holding Prince George. c, Duke of Cambridge holding Prince George. d, Duke and Duchess of Cambridge, Prince George.

$280, Prince George, diff.

**2013, Dec. 31 Litho. *Perf. 14***

**2898** A797 $85 Sheet of 4, #a-d 8.50 8.50

**Souvenir Sheet**

***Perf. 12***

**2899** A797 $280 multi 7.00 7.00

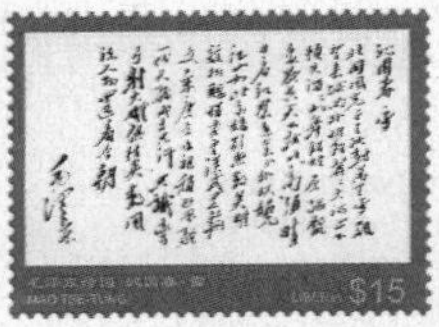

Poems by Mao Zedong A798

A799

Mao Zedong (1893-1976), Chinese Communist Leader — A800

No. 2900 — Poem with: a, 13 vertical columns of characters. b, 12 vertical columns of characters. c, 11 vertical columns of characters.
No. 2901 — Mao Zedong: a, With other people, building's roof visible. b, With Jawaharlal Nehru. c, With Kwame Nkrumah at dinner table. d, Surrounded by people from different countries.
No. 2902: a, Painting of Mao Zedong carrying scroll. b, Black-and-white photograph of Mao Zedong without hat. c, Painting of Mao Zedong with cap. d, Black-and-white photograph of Mao Zedong with cap. e, Painting of Mao Zedong without cap. f, Great Wall of China.

**2013, Mar. 7 Litho. *Perf. 14***

| | | | | |
|---|---|---|---|---|
| **2900** | | Horiz. strip of 3 | 1.25 | 1.25 |
| *a.-c.* | | A798 $15 Any single | .40 | .40 |
| **2901** | A799 | $15 Sheet of 4, #a-d | 1.60 | 1.60 |
| **2902** | A800 | $15 Sheet of 6, #a-f | 2.50 | 2.50 |

No. 2900 was printed in sheets of 6, containing two of each stamp.

World Leaders — A800a

Designs: No. 2902A, $100, Liberian Pres. Ellen Johnson Sirleaf, People's Republic of China Premier Xi Jinping, U.S. Pres. Barack Obama. No. 2902B, $100, Former leaders of People' Republic of China Hu Jintao and Mao Zedong. $125, Mao Zedong and first Liberian Pres. Joseph Jenkins Roberts. $150, Xi Jinping and Ellen Johnson Sirleaf.

**2013, Dec. 6 Litho. *Perf. 12***

| | | | | |
|---|---|---|---|---|
| **2902A-2902D** | A800a | Set of 4 | 12.00 | 12.00 |

Souvenir Sheet

Elvis Presley (1935-77) — A801

**Litho., Sheet Margin Embossed**

**2014, Jan. 1 *Imperf.***

| | | | | |
|---|---|---|---|---|
| **2903** | A801 | $740 multi | 18.50 | 18.50 |

Yosemite National Park — A802

No. 2904: a, Cathedral Rocks. b, Yosemite Falls. c, Giant sequoias. d, Tenaya Lake. e, Hetch Hetchy Reservoir. f, Half Dome.
$280, El Capitan.

**2014, Jan. 2 Litho. *Perf. 14***

| | | | | |
|---|---|---|---|---|
| **2904** | A802 | $70 Sheet of 6, #a-f | 10.50 | 10.50 |

**Souvenir Sheet**

***Perf. 12¾***

| | | | | |
|---|---|---|---|---|
| **2905** | A802 | $280 multi | 7.00 | 7.00 |

Yosemite Grant, 150th anniv. No. 2905 contains one 51x38mm stamp.

Miniature Sheets

Winter Games — A803

No. 2906, $85: a, Snowboarding. b, Alpine skiing. c, Curling. d, Freestyle skiing. e, Figure skating.
No. 2907, $85: a, Ski jumping. b, Ice hockey. c, Bobsled. d, Cross-country skiing. e, Speed skating.

**2014, Mar. 5 Litho. *Perf. 13¾***

**Sheets of 5, #a-e**

| | | | | |
|---|---|---|---|---|
| **2906-2907** | A803 | Set of 2 | 20.00 | 20.00 |

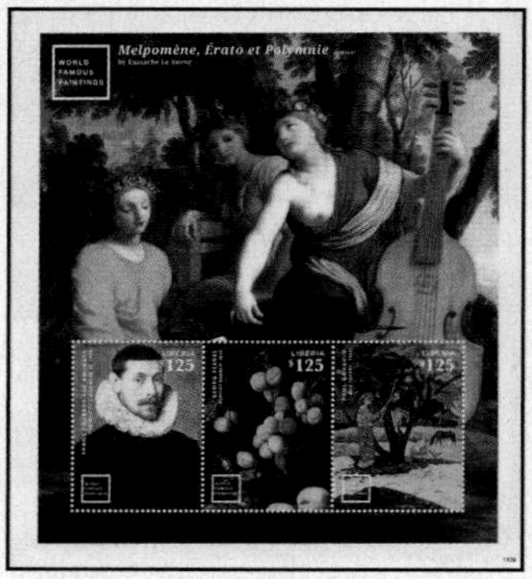


Paintings — A804

No. 2908, $125: a, Portrait of a Man Aged 32, by Frans Pourbus the Younger. b, Apricot Branch, by Georg Flegel. c, Meu Taporo, by Paul Gauguin.
No. 2909, $125: a, Portrait of a Woman, by Antonio del Pollaiuolo. b, A World, by Maximilian Lenz. c, Woman Carrying a Pitcher on Her Head, by Camille Pissarro.
No. 2910, $350, The Piano Lesson, by Pierre-Auguste Renoir. No. 2911, $350, The Japanese Bridge, by Claude Monet.

**2014, Mar. 10 Litho. *Perf. 12¾***

**Sheets of 3, #a-c**

| | | | | |
|---|---|---|---|---|
| **2908-2909** | A804 | Set of 2 | 17.50 | 17.50 |

**Size: 100x100mm**

***Imperf***

| | | | | |
|---|---|---|---|---|
| **2910-2911** | A804 | Set of 2 | 16.50 | 16.50 |

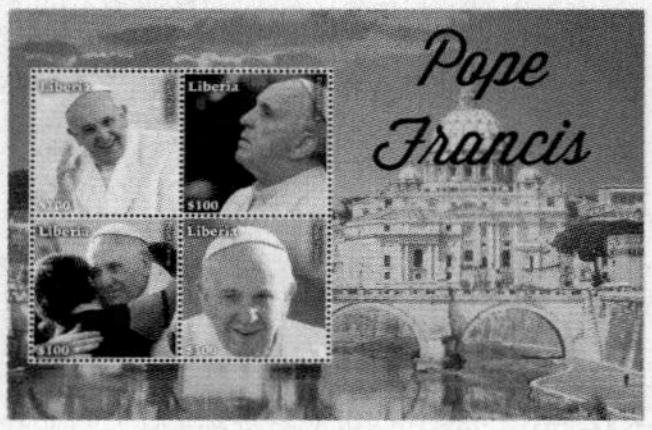


A805

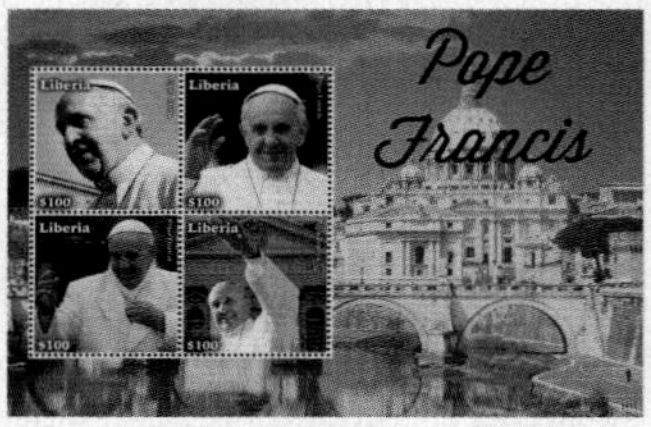


A806

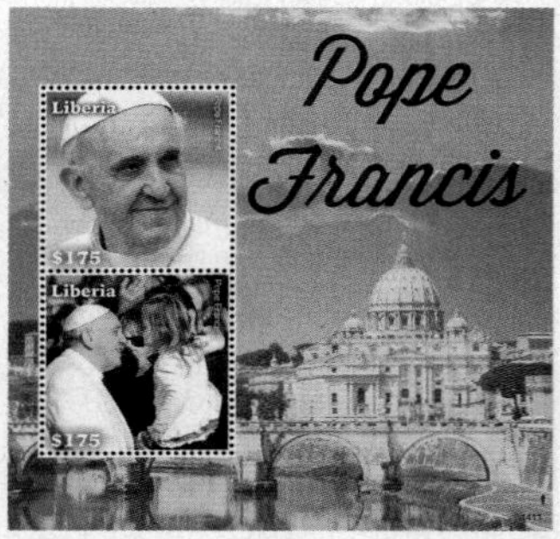


A807

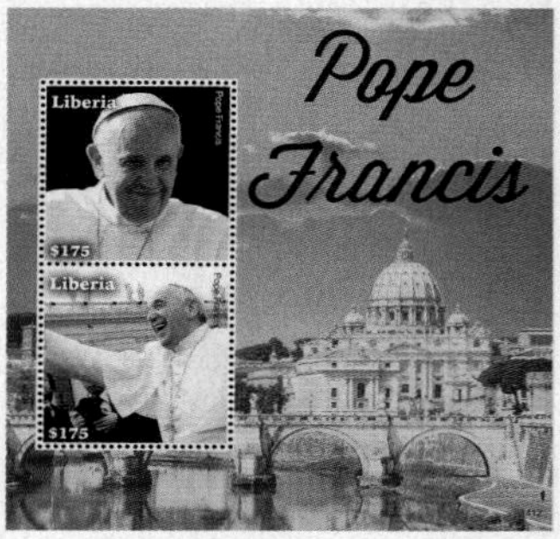


Pope Francis — A808

No. 2912 — Pope Francis: a, Waving. b, Looking up. c, Hugging boy. d, Smiling.
No. 2913 — Pope Francis: a, Looking left. b, Waving, diff. c, Waving, with other hand over heart. d, Waving in front of building.
No. 2914 — Pope Francis, denominations with large numerals: a, Looking right. b, Talking to young girl.
No. 2915 — Pope Francis, denominations with small numerals: a, Smiling, diff. b, With arm extended.

**2014, Mar. 24 Litho. *Perf. 13¾***

| | | | | |
|---|---|---|---|---|
| **2912** | A805 | $100 Sheet of 4, #a-d | 9.50 | 9.50 |
| **2913** | A806 | $100 Sheet of 4, #a-d | 9.50 | 9.50 |

**Souvenir Sheets**

| | | | | |
|---|---|---|---|---|
| **2914** | A807 | $175 Sheet of 2, #a-b | 8.25 | 8.25 |
| **2915** | A808 | $175 Sheet of 2, #a-b | 8.25 | 8.25 |

Mythical Creatures — A809

No. 2916, $100: a, Dragon. b, Minotaur. c, Centaur. d, Phoenix.
No. 2917, $100, vert.: a, Vampire. b, Leprechaun. c, Mermaid. d, Angel.
No. 2918, $175, vert.: a, Werewolf. b, Unicorn.
No. 2919, $175, vert.: a, Mermaid, with arms above head. b, Mermaid, swimming.

***Perf. 14 (#2916), 12¾***

**2014, Apr. 2 Litho.**

**Sheets of 4, #a-d**

| | | | | |
|---|---|---|---|---|
| **2916-2917** | A809 | Set of 2 | 19.00 | 19.00 |

**Souvenir Sheets of 2, #a-b**

| | | | | |
|---|---|---|---|---|
| **2918-2919** | A809 | Set of 2 | 16.50 | 16.50 |

No. 2917 contains four 38x51mm stamps. Nos. 2918-2919 each contain two 38x51mm stamps.

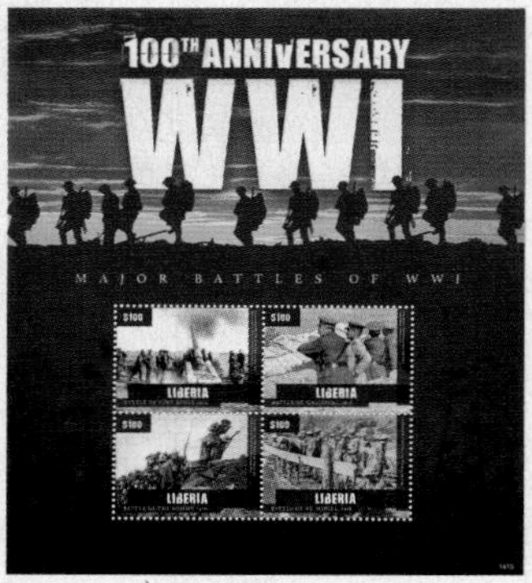


A810

World War I, Cent. — A811

No. 2920: a, Battle of Vimy Ridge, 1915. b, Battle of Gallipoli, 1915. c, Battle of the Somme, 1916. d, Battle of St. Mihiel, 1918.
No. 2921 — Battleships: a, Voltaire. b, Slava. c, Kaiser Barbarossa. d, Asahi.
No. 2922: a, Battle of Verdun, 1916. b, Third Battle of Ypres, 1917.
No. 2923 — Battleships: a, USS Alabama. b, SMS Helgoland.

**2014, May 19 Litho. *Perf. 12***

| | | | | |
|---|---|---|---|---|
| **2920** | A810 | $100 Sheet of 4, #a-d | 9.50 | 9.50 |
| **2921** | A811 | $100 Sheet of 4, #a-d | 9.50 | 9.50 |

**Souvenir Sheets**

| | | | | |
|---|---|---|---|---|
| **2922** | A810 | $175 Sheet of 2, #a-b | 8.25 | 8.25 |

***Perf. 14***

| | | | | |
|---|---|---|---|---|
| **2923** | A811 | $175 Sheet of 2, #a-b | 8.25 | 8.25 |

Korean Food — A812

No. 2924: a, Boneless ribs and Kimchi. b, Cucumber kimchi and Gyeongdan. c, Seafood pancake and Japchae.
$350, Soft tofu stew.

**2014, June 17 Litho. *Perf. 13***

**2924** A812 $125 Sheet of 3, #a-c, + central label 8.25 8.25

**Souvenir Sheet**

***Perf.***

**2925** A812 $350 multi 7.75 7.75

Philakorea 2014 World Stamp Exhibition, Seoul

2014 World Cup Soccer Championships, Brazil — A813

Team photographs: No. 2926, $30, Algeria. No. 2927, $30, Argentina. No. 2928, $30, Australia. No. 2929, $30, Belgium. No. 2930, $30, Bosnia & Herzegovina. No. 2931, $30, Brazil. No. 2932, $30, Cameroun. No. 2933, $30, Chile. No. 2934, $30, Colombia. No. 2935, $30, Costa Rica. No. 2936, $30, Cote d'Ivoire (Ivory Coast). No. 2937, $30, Croatia. No. 2938, $30, Ecuador. No. 2939, $30, England. No. 2940, $30, France. No. 2941, $30, Germany. No. 2942, $30, Ghana. No. 2943, $30, Greece. No. 2944, $30, Honduras. No. 2945, $30, Iran. No. 2946, $30, Italy. No. 2947, $30, Japan. No. 2948, $30, South Korea. No. 2949, $30, Mexico. No. 2950, $30, Netherlands. No. 2951, $30, Nigeria. No. 2952, $30, Portugal. No. 2953, $30, Russia. No. 2954, $30, Spain. No. 2955, $30, Switzerland. No. 2956, $30, United States. No. 2957, $30, Uruguay.

**2014, June 17 Litho. *Perf. 14***

**2926-2957** A813 Set of 32 21.50 21.50

Nos. 2926-2957 each were printed in sheets of 6. See No. 2980.

Orchids — A814

No. 2958, $100: a, Disa racemosa. b, Eulophia nutans. c, Eulophia hians. d, Eulophia ensata.
No. 2959, $100: a, Satyrium erectum. b, Satyrium coriifolium. c, Eulophia buchanani. d, Disa gladioflora.
No. 2960, $175: a, Habenaria bonatea. b, Polystachya pubescens.
No. 2961, $175: a, Eulophia reichenbachiana. b, Disa uniflora.

**2014, June 23 Litho. *Perf. 14***

**Sheets of 4, #a-d**

**2958-2959** A814 Set of 2 18.00 18.00

**Souvenir Sheets of 2, #a-b**

**2960-2961** A814 Set of 2 15.50 15.50

Bats — A815

No. 2962, $100: a, Lissonycteris angolensis. b, Epomophorus gambianus. c, Nanonycteris veldkampii. d, Epomops buettikoferi.
No. 2963, $100: a, Coleura afrea. b, Epomophorus wahlbergi. c, Miniopterus africanus. d, Rhinolophus ferrumequinum.
No. 2964, $175: a, Miniopterus inflatus. b, Taphozous mauritianus.
No. 2965, $175: a, Micropteropus pusillus. b, Rousettus aegyptiacus.

**2014, Aug. 14 Litho. *Perf. 12x12½***

**Sheets of 4, #a-d**

**2962-2963** A815 Set of 2 17.50 17.50

**Souvenir Sheets of 2, #a-b**

**2964-2965** A815 Set of 2 15.50 15.50

Mongooses — A816

No. 2966, $100: a, Dwarf mongoose. b, Selous's mongoose. c, Kusimanse. d, Long-nosed mongoose.
No. 2967, $100: a, Angolan slender mongoose. b, Yellow mongoose. c, Ethiopian dwarf mongoose. d, Banded mongoose.
No. 2968, $175: a, Meerkat. b, Alexander's kusimanse.
No. 2969, $175: a, Slender mongoose. b, Somalian slender mongoose.

**2014, Aug. 27 Litho. *Perf. 14***

**Sheets of 4, #a-d**

**2966-2967** A816 Set of 2 17.50 17.50

**Souvenir Sheets of 2, #a-b**

**2968-2969** A816 Set of 2 15.50 15.50

Paintings by Henri de Toulouse-Lautrec (1864-1901) — A817

No. 2970, $100: a, Party in the Moulin Rouge. b, Count Alphonse de Toulouse-Lautrec Driving a Four-Horse Hitch. c, Equestrienne. d, Two Girls in Bed.
No. 2971, $100, vert.: a, Moulin Rouge La Goulue. b, Babylone d'Allemagne. c, Portrait of Madame la Comtesse de Toulouse-Lautrec. d, Portait of Vincent van Gogh.
No. 2972, $200, vert.: a, La Clownesse Assise. b, La Clownesse.
No. 2973, $200, vert.: a, The Stage Mangaer Behind the Scenes. b, Portrait of Louis Pascal.

**2014, Aug. 27 Litho. *Perf. 14***

**Sheets of 4, #a-d**

**2970-2971** A817 Set of 2 17.50 17.50

**Souvenir Sheets of 2, #a-b**

**2972-2973** A817 Set of 2 17.50 17.50

National Parks of Africa — A818

No. 2974: a, Serengeti National Park, Tanzania (single tree). b, Victoria Falls, Zambia. c, Mt. Kilimanjaro, Kenya (view from mountain). d, Drakensberg Mountains, South Africa. e, Matopos National Park, Zimbabwe. f, Serengeti National Park (trees and vehicle path). g, Mt. Kilimanjaro (view of mountain). h, Sapo National Park, Liberia. i, Golden Gate Highlands National Park, South Africa.
$350, Namib-Naukluft National Park, Namibia.

**2014, Sept. 3 Litho. *Perf. 13¾***

**2974** A818 $85 Sheet of 9, #a-i 16.50 16.50

**Souvenir Sheet**

**2975** A818 $350 multi 7.50 7.50

Race Horses — A819

No. 2976, $100: a, Flying Childers. b, Highflyer. c, Regulus. d, Sceptre.
No. 2977, $100: a, Cherimoya. b, American Eclipse. c, Bay Middleton. d, Crucifix.
No. 2978, $175: a, Kincsem. b, Eclipse.
$350, Goldfinder.

**2014, Sept. 3 Litho. *Perf. 14***

**Sheets of 4, #a-d**

**2976-2977** A819 Set of 2 17.50 17.50

***Perf. 12½***

**2978** A819 $175 Sheet of 2, #a-b 7.50 7.50

**Souvenir Sheet**

**2979** A819 $350 multi 7.50 7.50

No. 2978 contains two 51x38mm stamps; No. 2979 contains one 51x38 stamp.

**No. 2941 With Inscription Added in Yellow**

and

German Soccer Team, 2014 World Cup Champions — A820

**2014, Sept. 4 Litho. *Perf. 14***

**2980** A813 $30 multi .65 .65

**Souvenir Sheet**

***Perf. 12½***

**2981** A820 $350 multi 7.50 7.50

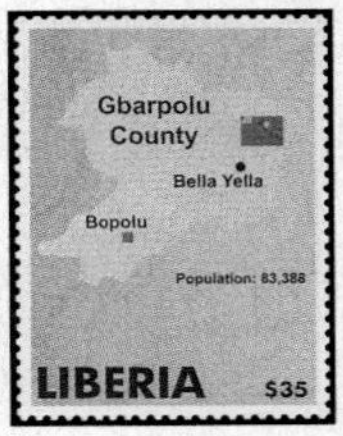


Maps and Flags of Liberian Counties — A821

County: $35, Gbarpolu. $45, Lofa. $55, Grand Cape Mount. $70, Bomi. $90, Montserrado. No. 2987, Bong. No. 2988, Margibi. $150, Grand Bassa. $175, Rivercess. $250, Nimba. $350, Sinoe. No. 2993, Grand Gedeh. No. 2994, Grand Kru. No. 2995, Maryland. No. 2996, Rivergee.

**2014, July 1 Litho. *Perf. 14***

| | | | | | |
|---|---|---|---|---|---|
| **2982** | A821 | $35 | multi | .80 | .80 |
| **2983** | A821 | $45 | multi | 1.00 | 1.00 |
| **2984** | A821 | $55 | multi | 1.25 | 1.25 |
| **2985** | A821 | $70 | multi | 1.60 | 1.60 |
| **2986** | A821 | $90 | multi | 2.00 | 2.00 |
| **2987** | A821 | $100 | multi | 2.25 | 2.25 |
| **2988** | A821 | $100 | multi | 2.25 | 2.25 |
| **2989** | A821 | $150 | multi | 3.50 | 3.50 |
| **2990** | A821 | $175 | multi | 4.00 | 4.00 |
| **2991** | A821 | $250 | multi | 5.50 | 5.50 |
| **2992** | A821 | $350 | multi | 7.75 | 7.75 |
| **2993** | A821 | $500 | multi | 11.00 | 11.00 |
| **2994** | A821 | $500 | multi | 11.00 | 11.00 |
| **2995** | A821 | $500 | multi | 11.00 | 11.00 |
| **2996** | A821 | $500 | multi | 11.00 | 11.00 |
| | *Nos. 2982-2996 (15)* | | | 75.90 | 75.90 |

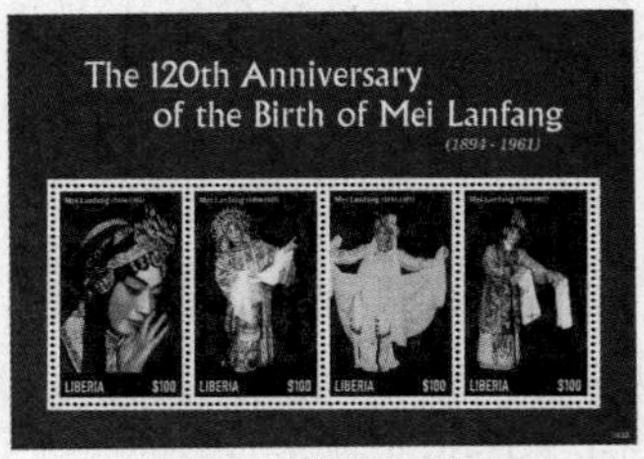


Mei Lanfang (1894-1961), Peking Opera Performer — A822

No. 2997 — Mei Lanfang in various costumes, as shown.
$350, Mei Lanfang, diff.

**2014, Sept. 4 Litho. *Perf. 12***

**2997** A822 $100 Sheet of 4, #a-d 8.75 8.75

**Souvenir Sheet**

**2998** A822 $350 multi 7.75 7.75

Gold Medalists at 2014 Winter Olympics, Sochi, Russia — A823

No. 2999: a, Vic Wild, snowboarding, Russia (40x30mm). b, Canadian ice hockey player (40x30mm). c, Jorgen Graabak, Nordic combined skiing, Norway (40x60mm).
No. 3000: a, Kamil Stoch, ski jumping, Poland (30x40mm). b, Anton Kushnir, freestyle skiing, Belarus (30x40mm).

**2014, Sept. 15 Litho. *Perf. 14***

**2999** A823 $125 Sheet of 3, #a-c 8.25 8.25

**Souvenir Sheet**

**3000** A823 $175 Sheet of 2, #a-b 7.75 7.75

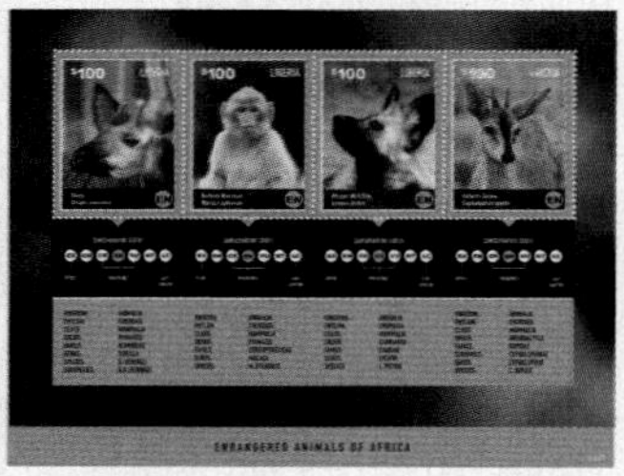

Endangered African Animals — A824

No. 3001, $100: a, Okapi. b, Barbary macaque. c, African wild dog. d, Abbott's duiker.
No. 3002, $100: a, Aldabra flying fox. b, Black and rufous elephant shrew. c, Mandrill. d, Sun-tailed monkey.
No. 3003, $350, Alaotran gentle lemur. No. 3004, $350, Mountain gorilla.

**2014, Oct. 20 Litho. *Perf. 14***

**Sheets of 4, #a-d**

**3001-3002** A824 Set of 2 17.50 17.50

**Souvenir Sheets**

***Perf. 12½***

**3003-3004** A824 Set of 2 15.00 15.00

Nos. 3003-3004 each contain one 38x51mm stamp.

Garden Flowers — A825

No. 3005, $125: a, Coneflowers. b, Calendulas. c, Purple asters.
No. 3006, $125: a, French marigolds. b, Tickseeds. c, Cosmos.
No. 3007, $350, Black-eyed Susans. No. 3008, $350, Forget-me-nots.

**2014, Oct. 20 Litho. *Perf. 12***

**Sheets of 3, #a-c**

**3005-3006** A825 Set of 2 16.50 16.50

**Souvenir Sheets**

**3007-3008** A825 Set of 2 15.00 15.00

A826

New Year 2015 (Year of the Ram) — A827

No. 3010 — Ram facing: a, Forward. b, Left.

**2014, Nov. 3 Litho. *Perf. 14***

**3009** A826 $100 multi 2.25 2.25

***Perf. 12½***

**3010** A827 $100 Horiz. pair, #a-b 4.50 4.50

No. 3009 was printed in sheets of 6. No. 3010 was printed in sheets containing two pairs.

Campaign Against Ebola Virus — A828

No. 3011: a, Medical worker wearing protective gear. b, Child. b, Mother holding child. c, Woman and medical device.

**2014, Nov. 11 Litho. *Perf. 14***

**3011** A828 $50 Block or horiz. strip of 4, #a-d 4.50 4.50

Printed in sheets of 16, containing 3 #3011c, 4 each #3011a, 3011b, 3011d, + label.

Christmas A829

Paintings by Peter Paul Rubens (1577-1640): $100, The Education of the Virgin. $125, Saint Francis Receiving the Infant Jesus from the Hands of the Virgin. No. 3014, $175, Teresa of Avila's Vision of the Dove. No. 3015, $175, The Assumption of the Virgin Mary.

**2014, Nov. 24 Litho. *Perf. 12½***

**3012-3015** A829 Set of 4 12.50 12.50

A830

Domestic Cats — A831

No. 3016 — British shorthair cat with background color of: a, Gray. b, Pink. c, Blue. d, Green blue.
No. 3017 — Various photographs of Maine Coon cats, as shown.
No. 3018, $350, Siberian cat. No. 3019, $350, Ragdoll cat.

**2014, Dec. 16 Litho. *Perf. 14***

**3016** A830 $100 Sheet of 4, #a-d 8.75 8.75

**3017** A831 $100 Sheet of 6, #a-f 13.00 13.00

**Souvenir Sheets**

**3018** A831 $350 multi 7.50 7.50

***Perf. 13¼***

**3019** A831 $350 multi 7.50 7.50

No. 3019 contains one 35x35mm stamp.

A832

Wild Cats — A833

No. 3020 — Various photographs of lions, as shown.
No. 3021 — Various photographs of cheetahs, as shown.
No. 3022, $350, Serval. No. 3023, $350, Caracal.

***Perf. 13 Syncopated***

**2014, Dec. 16 Litho.**

**3020** A832 $100 Sheet of 4, #a-d 8.75 8.75
**3021** A833 $100 Sheet of 4, #a-d 8.75 8.75

**Souvenir Sheets**

**3022** A833 $350 multi 7.50 7.50
**3023** A833 $350 multi 7.50 7.50

Economic Community of West African States, 40th Anniv. A834

**2015 Litho. *Perf. 13x13¼***

**3024** A834 $50 multi — —

Birds of Prey — A835

No. 3025, $125: a, Jackal buzzard (64x32mm). b, Spotted eagle owl (32x32mm). c, Cape vulture (32x32mm).
No. 3026, $125: a, African goshawk (32x64mm). b, Bateleur (32x32mm). c, Eurasian eagle owl (32x32mm).
No. 3027, $350, Golden eagle, vert. No. 3028, $350, Martial eagle, vert.

**2015, Jan. 5 Litho. *Perf. 12½***

**Sheets of 3, #a-c**

**3025-3026** A835 Set of 2 16.50 16.50

**Souvenir Sheets**

***Perf. 13¼***

**3027-3028** A835 Set of 2 15.00 15.00

Nos. 3027-3028 each contain one 38x51mm stamp.

Photographs of Earth Taken from Space — A836

No. 3029: a, Kizimen Volcano, Russia. b, Issaouane Erg, Algeria. c, Fringing Coral Reef, Red Sea. d, Ice on Lake Michigan, United States. e, Paris, France. f, Zambezi River Delta, Mozambique.
$350, Mr. Everest and nearby Himalayan peaks.

**2017, Jan. 21 Litho. *Perf. 11½x12***

**3029** A836 $100 Sheet of 6, #a-f 13.00 13.00

**Souvenir Sheet**

**3030** A836 $350 multi 7.75 7.75

A837

Spheniscus Demersus — A838

No. 3031: a, One penguin in water. b, Three penguins under water. c, Penguin out of water. d, Three penguins with heads above water.
No. 3032: a, One penguin facing right on beach, yellow sky. b, One penguin facing left on beach, light blue sky. c, One penguin facing right on beach, pale green water in background. d, One penguin, foliage in foreground. e, Two penguins. f, Three penguins.
No. 3033, $350, One penguin, diff. No. 3034, $350, Two penguins, diff.

**2015, Feb. 2 Litho. *Perf. 14***

**3031** A837 $100 Sheet of 4, #a-d 8.75 8.75
**3032** A838 $100 Sheet of 6, #a-f 13.00 13.00

**Souvenir Sheets**

**3033-3034** A838 Set of 2 15.00 15.00

Fennec Fox — A839

No. 3035: a, Fox facing left. b, Fox facing forward. c, Fox asleep.
$350, Fox facing forward, diff.

**2015, Feb. 2 Litho. *Perf. 12½***

**3035** A839 $125 Sheet of 3, #a-c 8.25 8.25

**Souvenir Sheet**

**3036** A839 $350 multi 7.75 7.75

World War I Alpine Troops of Italy — A840

No. 3037: a, Regiment members carrying bicycle. b, Regiment members on mountaintop. c, Regiment members climbing mountain. d, Soldier with camera on tripod.
$350, Regiment members near mountain barracks.

**2015, Feb. 2 Litho. *Perf. 14***

**3037** A840 $100 Sheet of 4, #a-d 8.75 8.75

**Souvenir Sheet**

***Perf. 12***

**3038** A840 $350 multi 7.75 7.75

World War I, cent.

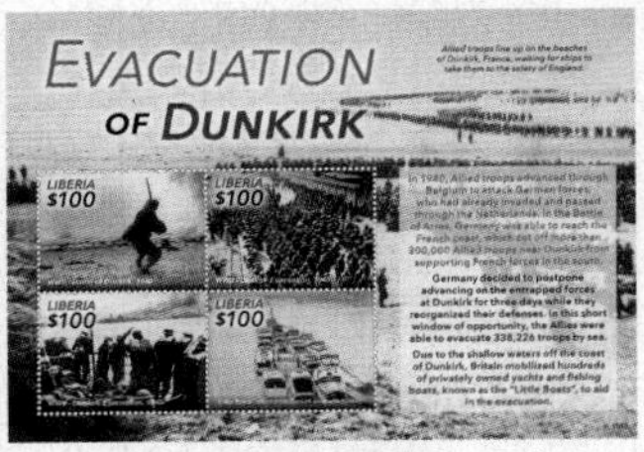


Evacuation of Dunkirk, 75th Anniv. — A841

No. 3039: a, Soldier on beach. b, Troops gathered for evacuation. c, Troops on ship. d, Little boats returning from evacuation.
$350, Troops on little boats.

**2015, Mar. 2 Litho. *Perf. 14***

**3039** A841 $100 Sheet of 4, #a-d 8.75 8.75

**Souvenir Sheet**

***Perf. 12½***

**3040** A841 $350 multi 7.75 7.75

No. 3040 contains one 51x38mm stamp.

Mammals — A842

No. 3041, $100: a, African bush elephant. b, Common warthog. c, Four-toed hedgehog. d, Common chimpanzee.
No. 3042, $100: a, Gambian epauletted fruit bat. b, Bushbuck. c, Leopard. d, Hippopotamus.
No. 3043, $350, Campbell's mona monkey, vert. No. 3044, $350, Giant pangolin, vert.

**2015, Mar. 2 Litho. *Perf. 14¾x14***

**Sheets of 4, #a-d**

**3041-3042** A842 Set of 2 17.50 17.50

**Souvenir Sheets**

***Perf. 14x14¾***

**3043-3044** A842 Set of 2 15.00 15.00

Stonehenge — A843

No. 3045: Various photographs of stone pillars at Stonehenge, as shown.
$350, Stonehenge, diff.

**2015, Mar. 3 Litho. *Perf. 11½x12***

**3045** A843 $100 Sheet of 4, #a-d 8.75 8.75

**Souvenir Sheet**

***Perf. 13½x13¼***

**3046** A843 $350 multi 7.75 7.75

2015 Europhilex Stamp Exhibition, London. No. 3046 contains one 50x30mm stamp.

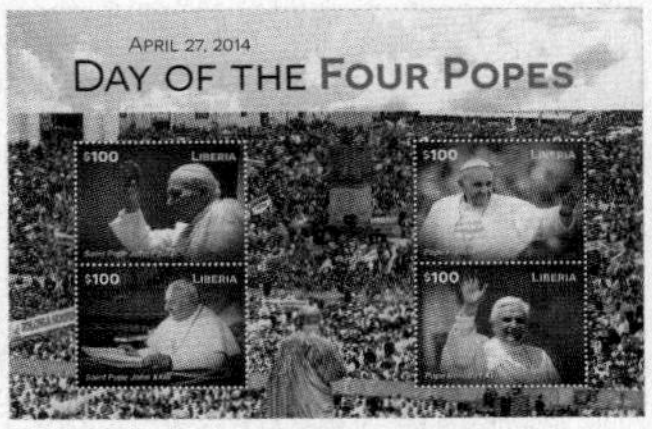


Popes — A844

No. 3047: a, St. John Paul II. b, Pope Francis. c, St. John XXIII. d, Pope Benedict XVI.
$350, Pope Benedict XVI, diff.

**2015, Mar. 24 Litho. *Perf. 14***

**3047** A844 $100 Sheet of 4, #a-d 8.75 8.75

**Souvenir Sheet**

***Perf. 12***

**3048** A844 $350 multi 7.75 7.75

Canonization of St. John Paul II and St. John XXIII.

Western Bongo — A845

No. 3049 — Western bongo: a, Blue green background, four legs visible. b, Red background, adult and juvenile. c, Red background, bongo facing right. d, Blue green background, no legs visible. e, Blue green background, head of bongo. f, Red background, bongo facing left.
$350, Head of bongo, vert.

**2015, Mar. 24 Litho. *Perf. 14***

**3049** A845 $100 Sheet of 6, #a-f 13.00 13.00

**Souvenir Sheet**

***Perf. 12***

**3050** A845 $350 multi 7.75 7.75

Visit of Prince William to Japan — A846

No. 3051 — Prince William and: a, Tokyo Governor Yoichi Masuzoe holding umbrellas. b, Crown Prince Naruhito shaking hands. c, Japanese Prime Minister Shinzo Abe with children at Koriyama park. d, Masuzoe at tea ceremony. e, Abe, Prince William waving. f, Dinner guests at Ryokan, Koriyama.
$350, Prince William visiting British Commonwealth war graves, Yokohama.

**2015, May 4 Litho. *Perf. 13x13¼***

**3051** A846 $100 Sheet of 6, #a-f 13.00 13.00

**Souvenir Sheet**

***Perf. 12x12½***

**3052** A846 $350 multi 7.75 7.75

Queen Elizabeth II, Longest-Reigning British Monarch — A847

No. 3051 — Photographs of Queen Elizabeth II with dogs taken in: a, 1974. b, 1972. c, 1936. d, 1976. e, 1971.
$350, Queen Elizabeth II and dog, 1971, diff.

**2015, May 25 Litho. *Perf. 14***

**3053** A847 $100 Sheet of 5, #a-e 11.00 11.00

**Souvenir Sheet**

***Perf. 12***

**3054** A847 $350 multi 7.75 7.75

Lee Kuan Yew (1923-2015), Prime Minister of Singapore — A848

No. 3055 — Lee with: a, Queen Elizabeth II, 1989. b, Pres. Barack Obama, 2009. c, Pres. George H. W. Bush, 1989. d, Chinese General Secretary Xi Jinping, 2010.
No. 3056: a, Lee Kuan Yew, 2009. b, Pres. Obama, 2009.

**2015, May 25 Litho. *Perf. 14***

**3055** A848 $100 Sheet of 4, #a-d 8.75 8.75

**Souvenir Sheet**

**3056** A848 $175 Sheet of 2, #a-b 7.75 7.75

Birth of Princess Charlotte of Cambridge — A849

No. 3057: a, Duke and Duchess of Cambridge holding Princess Charlotte, window behind Duke. b, As "a," window behind Duchess. c, Duchess of Cambridge holding Princess Charlotte. d, As "a," steps in background.
$350, Princess Charlotte.

**2015, July 13 Litho. *Perf. 14***

**3057** A849 $100 Sheet of 4, #a-d 8.75 8.75

**Souvenir Sheet**

**3058** A849 $350 multi 7.75 7.75

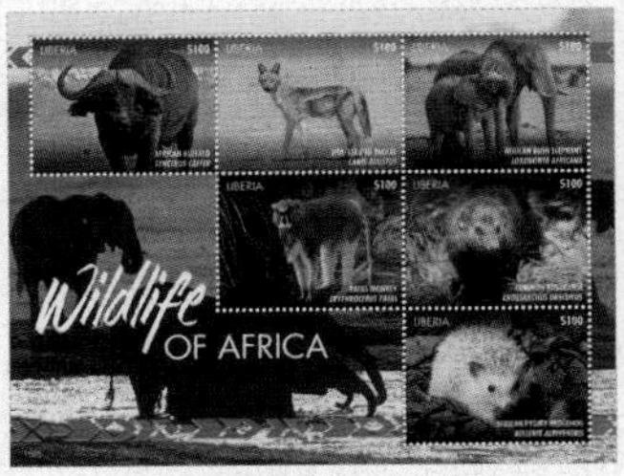


African Wildlife — A850

No. 3059: a, African buffalo. b, Side-striped jackal. c, African bush elephant. d, Patas monkey. e, Common kusimanse. f, African pygmy hedgehog.
$350, African leopard.

**2015, July 13 Litho. *Perf. 14***

**3059** A850 $100 Sheet of 6, #a-f 13.00 13.00

**Souvenir Sheet**

*Perf. 12*

**3060** A850 $350 multi 7.75 7.75

Sir Rowland Hill (1795-1879), Postal Reformer — A851

No. 3061: a, Hill as older man. b, Hill as younger man, hand on neck.
$3.50, Hill and Great Britain #1.

**2015, July 13 Litho.** ***Perf. 12***

**3061** A851 $100 Pair, #a-b 4.50 4.50

**Souvenir Sheet**

*Perf. 13¾*

**3062** A851 $350 multi 7.75 7.75

No. 3061 is printed in sheets containing two pairs. No. 3062 contains one 35x70mm stamp.

Miniature Sheets

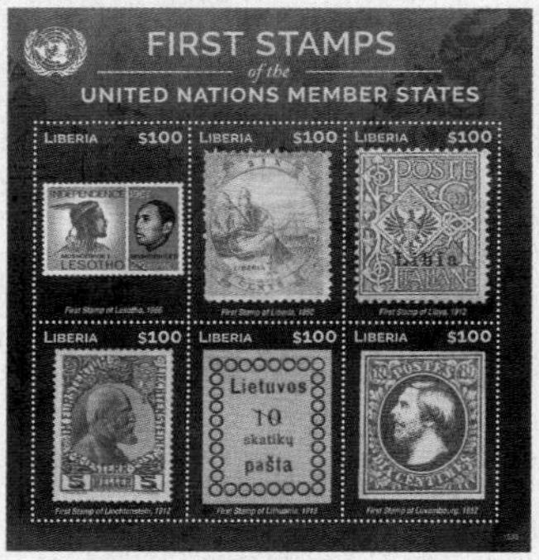


Stamps of United Nations Member Countries — A852

No. 3063, $100: a, Lesotho #1. b, Liberia #1. c, Libya #1. d, Liechtenstein #1. e, Lithuania #1. f, Luxembourg #1.
No. 3064, $100: a, Macedonia #1. b, Malagasy Republic (Madagascar) #8. c, Malawi #1. d, Malaysia #1. e, Maldive Islands #1. f, Mali #1.
No. 3065, $100: a, Malta #1. b, Marshall Islands #1. c, Mauritania #1. d, Mauritius #1. e, Mexico #1. f, Micronesia #1.
No. 3066, $100: a, Moldova #1. b, Monaco #1. c, Mongolia #1. d, Montenegro #123. e, Morocco #A1. f, Mozambique #1.
No. 3067, $100: a, Switzerland #41. b, Syria #11. c, Tajikistan #1. d, Tanzania #5. e, Thailand #1. f, Timor #1.
No. 3068, $100: a, Togo #1. b, Tonga #1. c, Trinidad & Tobago #1. d, Tunisia #1. e, Turkey #1. f, Turkmenistan #1.
No. 3069, $100: a, Tuvalu #1. b, Uganda #1. c, Ukraine #100. d, United Arab Emirates #1. e, Uruguay #1. f, Uzbekistan #1.
No. 3070, $100: a, Vanuatu #280a. b, Venezuela #4. c, Viet Nam #1. d, Yemen #2. e, Zambia #1. f, Zimbabwe #414.

**2015, July 13 Litho.** ***Perf. 12¾x12½***

**Sheets of 6, #a-f**

**3063-3070** A852 Set of 8 105.00 105.00

Magna Carta, 800th Anniv. — A853

No. 3071: a, King John. b, Dark brown image of riginal Magna Carta manuscript, 1215. c, King John on throne. d, As "b," beige image.
$350, Signing of the Magna Carta.

**2015, Aug. 3 Litho.** ***Perf. 14***

**3071** A853 $100 Sheet of 4, #a-d 8.75 8.75

**Souvenir Sheet**

**3072** A853 $350 multi 7.75 7.75

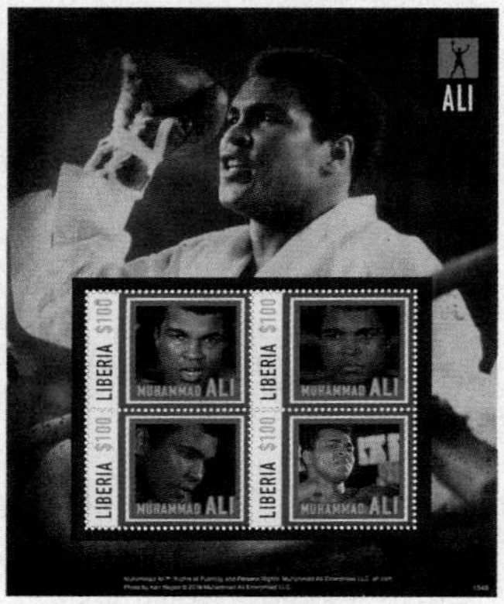


Muhammad Ali (1942-2016), Boxer — A854

No. 3073: Various photographs of Ali, as shown.
$350, Ali, diff.

**2015, Aug. 10 Litho.** ***Perf. 12½x12***

**3073** A854 $100 Sheet of 4, #a-d 8.75 8.75

**Souvenir Sheet**

**3074** A854 $350 multi 7.75 7.75

Pres. Abraham Lincoln (1809-65) — A855

No. 3073: Various photographs of Lincoln, as shown.
$350, Lincoln, diff.

**2015, Sept. 2 Litho.** ***Perf. 12***

**3075** A855 $100 Sheet of 4, #a-d 8.75 8.75

**Souvenir Sheet**

*Perf. 12¾*

**3076** A855 $350 multi 7.75 7.75

No. 3076 contains one 38x51mm stamp.

## SEMI-POSTAL STAMPS

**No. 127 Surcharged in Red**

**1915 Unwmk.** ***Perf. 14***

**B1** A49 2c + 3c on 10c 2.00 *3.50*
- *a.* Double red surcharge
- *b.* Double blue surcharge
- *c.* Both surcharges double
- *d.* Pair, one without "2c"

**Same Surcharge On Official Stamp of 1912**

**B2** A49 2c + 3c on 10c blk & ultra 2.00 *3.50*
- *a.* Double surcharge

**Regular Issue of 1918 Surcharged in Black and Red**

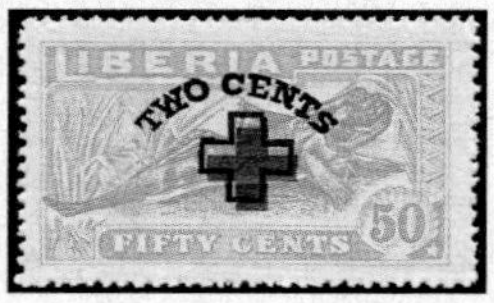


**1918** ***Perf. 12½, 14***

**B3** A59 1c + 2c dp grn & blk 1.40 *10.50*
**B4** A60 2c + 2c rose & blk 1.40 *10.50*
- *a.* Double surch., one inverted
- *b.* Invtd. surch., cross double
- *c.* Invtd. surch., cross omitted 17.00

**B5** A61 5c + 2c gray bl & blk .65 *3.00*
- *a.* Imperf., pair 19.00

**B6** A62 10c + 2c dk green 1.25 *3.00*
- *a.* Inverted surcharge 5.75 27.50

**B7** A63 15c + 2c blk & dk grn 5.25 10.50
**B8** A64 20c + 2c claret & blk 2.10 *8.50*
**B9** A65 25c + 2c dk grn & grn 4.25 *15.00*
**B10** A66 30c + 2c red vio & blk 10.00 *10.50*
**B11** A67 50c + 2c ultra & blk 8.50 *16.00*
**B12** A68 75c + 2c ol bis & blk 3.75 *30.00*
**B13** A69 $1 + 2c yel brn & bl 6.25 *57.50*
**B14** A70 $2 + 2c lt vio & blk 8.50 *80.00*
**B15** A71 $5 + 2c dk brown 20.00 *200.00*
*Nos. B3-B15 (13)* 73.30 *455.00*

Used values are for postally canceled stamps.

**Nos. 277-279 Surcharged in Red or Blue**

**1941 Unwmk.** ***Perf. 12***

**B16** A107 3c + 2c dk blue (R) 2.25 2.25
**B17** A108 5c + 2c dull red brn 2.25 2.25
**B18** A109 10c + 2c dk grn (R) 2.25 2.25
*Nos. B16-B18 (3)* 6.75 6.75

**Catalogue values for unused stamps in this section, from this point to the end of the section, are for Never Hinged items.**

Research — SP1

**Lithographed and Engraved**

**1954 Unwmk.** ***Perf. 12½***

**B19** SP1 5c + 5c rose lilac & blk .25 .25
*Nos. B19,CB4-CB6 (4)* 1.40 1.00

The surtax was for the Liberian Government Hospital. No. B19 exists imperforate.

Remember the African Child SP2

Designs: 25c + 10c, Village life. 70c + 20c, Mr. Sean feeding children. 75c + 15c, Fleeing conflict. 80c + 20c, Nuns teaching children. No. B24, Nuns killed in Oct. 1992, vert. No. B25, Sean Devereux (1964-93), vert.

*Perf. 13½x14*

**1994, Jan. 6 Unwmk. Litho.**

**B20** SP2 25c +10c multi 1.00 1.00
**B21** SP2 70c +20c multi 2.75 2.75
**B22** SP2 75c +15c multi 2.75 2.75
**B23** SP2 80c +20c multi 3.00 3.00
*Nos. B20-B23 (4)* 9.50 9.50

**Souvenir Sheets**

**B24** SP2 $1.50 +50c multi 6.00 6.00
**B25** SP2 $1.50 +50c multi 6.00 6.00

Surtax for Sean Devereux Liberian Children's Fund.

Charities — SP3

Designs: 25c+10c, No. B30, Natl. map in flag colors, blind man with cane. No. B27, Logo depicting children. No. B28, Blind man crossing street. No. B29, Dr. Herman Gmeiner, children.

**1995 Litho.** ***Perf. 14***

**B26** SP3 25c +10c multi .80 .80
**B27** SP3 80c +20c multi 2.40 2.40
**B28** SP3 80c +20c multi 2.40 2.40
**B29** SP3 $1.50 +50c multi 5.50 5.50
**B30** SP3 $1.50 +50c multi 5.50 5.50
*Nos. B26-B30 (5)* 16.60 16.60

Christian Assoc. of the Blind, 10th anniv. (Nos. B26, B28, B30). SOS Children's Village (Nos. B27, B29).
Issued: Nos. B27, B29, 4/26; others, 4/28.

George Weah, Soccer Player — SP4

Designs: 50c+20c, In AC Milan strip. 75c+25c, In Liberia Natl. strip. 80c+20c, With 1989 Golden Ball Award. $1.50+50c, Two-time Golden Ball Winner.

**1995, Oct. 6 Litho.** ***Perf. 13x13½***

**B31** SP4 50c +20c multi 2.00 2.00
**B32** SP4 75c +25c multi 2.75 2.75
**B33** SP4 80c +20c multi 2.75 2.75

| | | | | |
|---|---|---|---|---|
| **B34** | SP4 | $1.50 +50c multi | 5.25 | 5.25 |
| *a.* | | Souvenir sheet of 1, perf. 13 | 5.25 | 5.25 |
| | | *Nos. B31-B34 (4)* | 12.75 | 12.75 |

Issued: No. B34a, 6/24/96. Surcharge for Liberian charities supported by George Weah.

## AIR POST STAMPS

Regular Issue of 1928 Srchd. in Black

**1936, Feb. 28 Unwmk. *Perf. 12***

| | | | | |
|---|---|---|---|---|
| **C1** | A102 | 6c on 2c violet | 250.00 | *275.00* |
| **C2** | A102 | 6c on 3c bis brn | 250.00 | *275.00* |

Same Srch. on Official Stamp of 1928

| | | | | |
|---|---|---|---|---|
| **C3** | A102 | 6c on 1c green | 250.00 | *275.00* |
| *m.* | | On No. 230 (error) | *750.00* | |
| | | *Nos. C1-C3 (3)* | 750.00 | 825.00 |

Values are for stamps with disturbed gum. Many counterfeits exist.

Waco Plane — AP1

**1936, Sept. 30 Engr. *Perf. 14***

| | | | | |
|---|---|---|---|---|
| **C3A** | AP1 | 1c yellow grn & blk | .30 | .30 |
| **C3B** | AP1 | 2c carmine & blk | .30 | .30 |
| **C3C** | AP1 | 3c purple & blk | .30 | .30 |
| **C3D** | AP1 | 4c orange & blk | .30 | .30 |
| **C3E** | AP1 | 5c blue & blk | .30 | .30 |
| **C3F** | AP1 | 6c green & blk | .30 | .30 |
| | | *Nos. C3A-C3F (6)* | 1.80 | 1.80 |

Liberia's 1st air mail service of Feb. 28, 1936.

Nos. C3A-C3F exist in pairs imperf. between (value, $50 each) and in pairs imperf. (value $15 each).

Eagle in Flight — AP2

Trimotor Plane AP3

Egrets — AP4

Sikorsky Amphibian — AP5

Designs: 3c, 30c, Albatross.

**1938, Sept. 12 Photo. *Perf. 12½***

| | | | | |
|---|---|---|---|---|
| **C4** | AP2 | 1c green | .25 | .25 |
| **C5** | AP3 | 2c red orange | .40 | .25 |
| **C6** | AP3 | 3c olive green | .50 | .25 |
| **C7** | AP4 | 4c orange | .60 | .25 |
| **C8** | AP4 | 5c brt blue grn | 1.00 | .25 |
| **C9** | AP3 | 10c violet | 1.00 | .25 |
| **C10** | AP5 | 20c magenta | 1.25 | .25 |
| **C11** | AP3 | 30c gray black | 2.25 | .25 |
| **C12** | AP2 | 50c brown | 3.00 | .25 |
| **C13** | AP5 | $1 blue | 5.25 | .25 |
| | | *Nos. C4-C13 (10)* | 15.50 | 2.50 |

For surcharges see Nos. C17-C36, C45-C46, C47-C48, C49-C50.

### Nos. 280-282 Overprinted in Red or Dark Blue

**1941, Feb. 25 *Perf. 12***

| | | | | |
|---|---|---|---|---|
| **C14** | A107 | 3c dark blue (R) | 2.75 | 2.75 |
| **C15** | A108 | 5c dull red brn (DB) | 2.75 | 2.75 |
| **C16** | A109 | 10c dark green (R) | 2.75 | 2.75 |
| | | *Nos. C14-C16 (3)* | 8.25 | 8.25 |

Nos. C4-C13 Surcharged in Black

**1941 *Perf. 12½***

| | | | | |
|---|---|---|---|---|
| **C17** | AP2 | 50c on 1c green | *3,250.* | 325.00 |
| **C18** | AP3 | 50c on 2c red org | 200.00 | 105.00 |
| **C19** | AP3 | 50c on 3c ol grn | 200.00 | 105.00 |
| **C20** | AP4 | 50c on 4c org | 90.00 | 60.00 |
| **C21** | AP4 | 50c on 5c brt bl grn | 90.00 | 60.00 |
| **C22** | AP3 | 50c on 10c vio | 90.00 | 50.00 |
| **C23** | AP5 | 50c on 20c mag | *2,750.* | 70.00 |
| **C24** | AP3 | 50c on 30c gray blk | 75.00 | 40.00 |
| **C25** | AP2 | 50c brown | 75.00 | 40.00 |
| **C26** | AP5 | $1 blue | 90.00 | 40.00 |

Nos. C18, C19, C22, C24, and C26 exist with inverted overprints. Values C18 and C19, $225 each; others, $100 each.

Nos. C17 to C26 with Additional Overprint

**1942**

| | | | | |
|---|---|---|---|---|
| **C27** | AP2 | 50c on 1c green | 6.75 | 6.75 |
| **C28** | AP3 | 50c on 2c red org | 6.75 | 5.75 |
| **C29** | AP3 | 50c on 3c ol grn | 6.00 | 5.75 |
| **C30** | AP4 | 50c on 4c orange | 4.75 | 6.00 |
| **C31** | AP4 | 50c on 5c brt bl grn | 3.00 | 3.00 |
| **C32** | AP3 | 50c on 10c violet | 4.25 | 4.25 |
| **C33** | AP5 | 50c on 20c mag | 4.25 | 4.25 |
| **C34** | AP3 | 50c on 30c gray blk | 4.75 | 4.75 |
| **C35** | AP2 | 50c brown | 4.75 | 4.75 |
| **C36** | AP5 | $1 blue | 4.25 | 4.25 |
| | | *Nos. C27-C36 (10)* | 49.50 | 49.50 |

Plane and Air Route from United States to South America and Africa AP6

Plane over House AP7

**1942-44 Engr. *Perf. 12***

| | | | | |
|---|---|---|---|---|
| **C37** | AP6 | 10c rose | .25 | .25 |
| **C38** | AP7 | 12c brt ultra ('44) | .25 | .25 |
| **C39** | AP7 | 24c turq grn ('44) | .25 | .25 |
| **C40** | AP6 | 30c brt green | .25 | .25 |
| **C41** | AP6 | 35c red lilac ('44) | .25 | .25 |
| **C42** | AP6 | 50c violet | .25 | .25 |
| **C43** | AP6 | 70c olive gray ('44) | .35 | .25 |
| **C44** | AP6 | $1.40 scarlet ('44) | 1.00 | .45 |
| | | *Nos. C37-C44 (8)* | 2.85 | 2.20 |

### No. C3A-C3C, C5-C8, C12 Srchd. with New Values and Large Dot, Bar or Diagonal Line in Violet, Blue, Black or Violet and Black

No. C45

No. C46

No. C46A

No. C48

No. C48B

No. C49

No. C50

**1944-45 *Perf. 12½***

| | | | | |
|---|---|---|---|---|
| **C45** | AP3 | 10c on 2c (V+Bk) | 40.00 | 25.00 |
| **C46** | AP4 | 10c on 5c (V+Bk) ('45) | 14.00 | 12.00 |
| **C46A** | AP1 | 30c on 1c (Bk) | 150.00 | 70.00 |
| **C47** | AP3 | 30c on 3c (V) | 165.00 | 65.00 |
| **C48** | AP4 | 30c on 4c (V+Bk) | 14.00 | 12.00 |
| **C48A** | AP1 | 50c on 3c (Bk) | 37.50 | 32.50 |
| **C48B** | AP1 | 70c on 2c (Bk) | 70.00 | 60.00 |
| **C49** | AP3 | $1 on 3c (Bl) | 27.50 | 22.50 |
| **C50** | AP2 | $1 on 50c (V) | 42.50 | 26.50 |
| | | *Nos. C45-C50 (9)* | 560.50 | 325.50 |

These surcharges were handstamped with the possible exception of the large "10 CTS." of No. C46 and the "30 CTS." of No. C48. On No. C47, the new value was created by handstamping a small, violet, broken "O" beside the large "3" of the basic stamp.

Surcharges on Nos. C46A, C48A, C48B are found inverted. Values same as normal.

### Roosevelt Type of Regular Issue

**1945, Nov. 26 Engr.**

| | | | | |
|---|---|---|---|---|
| **C51** | A116 | 70c brn & blk, *grysh* | 2.25 | 1.40 |

Examples on thick white paper appeared later on the stamp market. Value, $1 unused or used.

### Monrovia Harbor Type

**1947, Jan. 2**

| | | | | |
|---|---|---|---|---|
| **C52** | A117 | 24c brt bluish grn | 1.50 | 1.25 |

### Without Inscription at Top

**1947, May 16**

| | | | | |
|---|---|---|---|---|
| **C53** | A117 | 25c dark carmine | .90 | .45 |

### 1st US Postage Stamps Type

**1947, June 6**

| | | | | |
|---|---|---|---|---|
| **C54** | A118 | 12c green | .25 | .25 |
| **C55** | A118 | 25c brt red violet | .30 | .25 |
| **C56** | A118 | 50c brt blue | .40 | .25 |
| *a.* | | Souv. sheet of 4, #300, C54-C56 | 50.00 | |
| | | Never hinged | 100.00 | |
| | | *Nos. C54-C56 (3)* | .60 | .60 |
| | | Set, never hinged | 2.10 | |

No. C56a exists imperf. Values: hinged $65; never hinged $160.

Matilda Newport Firing Cannon — AP11

**1947, Dec. 1 Engr. & Photo.**

| | | | | |
|---|---|---|---|---|
| **C57** | AP11 | 25c scar & gray blk | 1.25 | .30 |

See note after No. 304.

Monument to Joseph J. Roberts — AP12

Centenary Monument AP14

Design: 25c, Flag of Liberia.

**1947, Dec. 22** **Engr.**

**C58** AP12 12c brick red .30 .25
**C59** AP12 25c carmine .50 .25
**C60** AP14 50c red brown .80 .45
*Nos. C58-C60 (3)* 1.60 .85
Set, never hinged 6.00

Centenary of independence.

L. I. A. Plane in Flight AP15

**1948, Aug. 17** ***Perf. 11½***

**C61** AP15 25c red 1.50 1.50
**C62** AP15 50c deep blue 1.00 1.00
Set, never hinged 5.00

1st flight of Liberian Intl. Airways, Aug. 17, 1948. Exist imperf.

Map and Citizens — AP16

Farm Couple, Arms and Agricultural Products — AP17

**1949, Apr. 12** **Litho.** ***Perf. 11½***

**C63** AP16 25c multicolored .35 .65
**C64** AP17 50c multicolored .35 .65
Set, never hinged 2.00

Nos. C63-C64 exist perf. 12½. Definite information concerning the status of the perf. 12½ set has not reached the editors. The set also exists imperf.

**Type of Regular Issue of 1948-50**

Design: William V. S. Tubman.

**1949, July 21** **Engr.** ***Perf. 12½***

**C65** A128 25c blue & black .60 .65
Never hinged 1.60

See No. C118.

Sun and Open Book — AP18

**1950, Feb. 14** **Engr.** ***Perf. 12½***

**C66** AP18 25c rose carmine 1.00 .50
Never hinged 2.75
*a.* Souv. sheet of 2, #329, C66, imperf. 1.75 1.75
Never hinged 4.75

Campaign for National Literacy.

**Catalogue values for unused stamps in this section, from this point to the end of the section, are for Never Hinged items.**

UPU Monument AP19

**1950, Apr. 21**

**C67** AP19 25c orange & vio 2.75 2.75
*a.* Souv. sheet of 3, #330-331, C67, imperf. 24.00 24.00

UPU, 75th anniv. (in 1949).
No. C67 exists imperf.

Map of Monrovia, James Monroe and Ashmun — AP20

50c, Jehudi Ashmun, President Tubman & map.

**1952, Apr. 1** ***Perf. 10½***

**C68** AP20 25c lilac rose & blk .25 .25
**C69** AP20 50c dk blue & car .70 .70
*a.* Souvenir sheet of 8 24.00

Nos. C68-C69 exist imperf. Value about two and one half times that of the perf. set.

Nos. C68-C69 exist with center inverted. Value $50 each.

No. C69a contains one each of Nos. 332 and C68, and types of Nos. 333-337 and C69 with centers in black; imperf.

The 25c exists in colors of the 50c and vice versa. Value, each $8.

Flags of Five Nations — AP21

**1952, Dec. 10** ***Perf. 12½***

**C70** AP21 25c ultra & carmine .90 .65
*a.* Souvenir sheet 2.25 2.25

Nos. C70 and C70a exist imperforate. Value, No. C70a, imperf., $4.50.

Road Building — AP22

Designs: 25c, Ships in Monrovia harbor. 35c, Diesel locomotive. 50c, Free port, Monrovia. 70c, Roberts Field. $1, Wm. V. S. Tubman bridge.

**1953, Aug. 3** **Litho.**

**C71** AP22 12c orange brown .25 .25
**C72** AP22 25c lilac rose .25 .25
**C73** AP22 35c purple 1.00 .25
**C74** AP22 50c orange 1.00 .25
**C75** AP22 70c dull green 1.75 .25
**C76** AP22 $1 blue 2.25 1.00
*Nos. C71-C76 (6)* 6.50 2.25

Exist imperf. See Nos. C82-C87.

Flags, Emblem and Children — AP23

**1954, Sept. 27** **Size: 51x39mm**

**C77** AP23 $5 bl, red, vio bl & blk 40.00 40.00

A reproduction of No. C77, size 63x49mm, was prepared for presentation purposes. Value $35.

Half the proceeds from the sale of No. C77 was given to the UNICEF.

UN Technical Assistance Agencies — AP24

Designs: 15c, Printing instruction. 20c, Sawmill maintenance. 25c, Geography class.

**1954, Oct. 25**

**C78** AP24 12c black & blue .25 .25
**C79** AP24 15c dk brown & yel .25 .25
**C80** AP24 20c black & yel grn .25 .25
**C81** AP24 25c vio blue & red .80 .25
*Nos. C78-C81 (4)* 1.55 1.00

UN Technical Assistance program.

Nos. C78-C81 exist imperf.

**Type of 1953 Inscribed: "Commemorating Presidential Visit U. S. A.-1954"**

Designs as before.

**1954, Nov. 19**

**C82** AP22 12c vermilion .25 .25
**C83** AP22 25c blue .80 .25
**C84** AP22 35c carmine rose 3.50 2.00
**C85** AP22 50c rose violet .95 .30
**C86** AP22 70c orange brown 1.25 .55
**C87** AP22 $1 dull green 1.90 .80
*Nos. C82-C87 (6)* 8.65 4.15

Visit of Pres. William V.S. Tubman to the US. Exist imperforate.

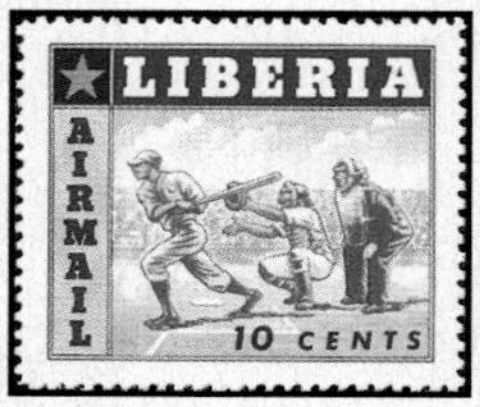

Baseball AP25

**1955, Jan. 26** **Litho.** ***Perf. 12½***

**C88** AP25 10c shown .30 .30
**C89** AP25 12c Swimming .30 .30
**C90** AP25 25c Running .30 .30
*a.* Souvenir sheet 18.00 18.00
*Nos. C88-C90 (3)* .90 .90

No. C90a contains 1 each of Nos. 349, C90 with colors transposed. Exists imperf.; same value.

Costus AP26

Design: 25c, Barteria nigritiana.

**1955, Sept. 28** **Unwmk.** ***Perf. 12½***

**C91** AP26 20c violet, grn & yel .40 .25
**C92** AP26 25c green, red & yel .40 .25

UN Emblem — AP27

UN Charter AP28

15c, General Assembly. 25c, Gabriel L. Dennis signing UN Charter for Liberia.

**1955, Oct. 24** **Unwmk.** ***Perf. 12***

**C93** AP27 10c ultra & red .25 .25
**C94** AP27 15c violet & blk .25 .25
**C95** AP27 25c green & red brn .60 .25
**C96** AP28 50c brick red & grn 1.50 .25
*Nos. C93-C96 (4)* 2.60 1.00

10th anniv. of the UN, Oct. 24, 1955.

Rotary International Headquarters, Evanston, Ill. — AP29

Design: 15c, View of Monrovia.

**1955, Dec. 5** **Litho.** ***Perf. 12½***

**C97** AP29 10c deep ultra & red .25 .25
**C98** AP29 15c redsh brn, red & bis .70 .25

**Souvenir Sheet**

**C99** AP29 50c deep ultra & red 1.75 1.75
*Nos. C97-C99 (3)* 2.70 2.25

No. C99 design as No. C97, but redrawn and with leaves omitted.

50th anniversary of Rotary International.

Nos. C97-C99 exist without Rotary emblem; No. C97 printed entirely in deep ultramarine; No. C98 with bister impression omitted.

**FIPEX Type of Regular Issue**

10c, New York Coliseum. 12c, Globe inscribed FIPEX. 15c, 50c, Statue of Liberty.

**1956, Apr. 28** **Unwmk.** ***Perf. 12***

**C100** A143 10c rose red & ultra .25 .25
**C101** A143 12c orange & purple .25 .25
**C102** A142 15c aqua & red lilac .90 .25
*Nos. C100-C102 (3)* 1.40 .75

**Souvenir Sheet**

**C103** A142 50c lt green & brn 1.75 1.75

Olympic Park, Melbourne — AP32

20c, 40c, Map of Australia & Olympic torch.

**1956, Nov. 15 Unwmk. *Perf. 12***

**C104** AP32 12c emerald & vio .50 .50

**C105** AP32 20c multicolored .50 .50

**Souvenir Sheet**

**C106** AP32 40c multicolored 7.50 7.50

*Nos. C104-C106 (3)* 8.50 8.50

16th Olympic Games, Melbourne, 11/22-12/8.

Nos. C104-C105 exist imperf.

**Type of Regular Issue, 1957.**

12c, 25c, Idlewild airport, NYC. 15c, 50c, Roberts Field, Liberia, plane & Pres. Tubman.

**Lithographed and Engraved**

**1957, May 4 *Perf. 12***

**C107** A146 12c brt grn & dk bl .25 .25

**C108** A146 15c red brn & blk .25 .25

**C109** A146 25c carmine & dk bl .75 .25

**C110** A146 50c lt ultra & blk 1.40 .25

*Nos. C107-C110 (4)* 2.65 1.00

**Type of Regular Issue, 1957**

Orphanage and: 15c, Nurse inoculating boy. 35c, The Kamara triplets. 70c, Children and flag.

**1957, Nov. 25 Litho. *Perf. 12***

**C111** A147 15c lt blue & brn .25 .25

**C112** A147 35c maroon & lt gray 1.00 .25

**Souvenir Sheet**

**C113** A147 70c ultra & rose car 1.50 1.25

*Nos. C111-C113 (3)* 2.75 1.75

**Type of Regular Issue, 1958**

10c, Italian flag & Colosseum. #C115, French flag & Arc de Triomphe. #C116, Swiss flag & chalet. #C117, Vatican flag & St. Peter's.

**Engr. and Litho.**

**1958, Jan. 10 *Perf. 10½***

**Flags in Original Colors**

**C114** A148 10c dark gray .45 .45

**C115** A148 15c dp yellow grn .45 .45

**C116** A148 15c ultra .45 .45

**C117** A148 15c purple .45 .45

*Nos. C114-C117 (4)* 1.80 1.80

**Type of Regular Issue, 1948-50**

Design: William V. S. Tubman.

**1958 Engr. *Perf. 12***

**C118** A128 25c lt green & blk 1.25 .90

Souvenir Sheet

Preamble to Declaration of Human Rights — AP33

**1958, Dec. 17 Litho. *Perf. 12***

**C119** AP33 20c blue & red 2.75 2.75

10th anniv. of the signing of the Universal Declaration of Human Rights. Exists imperf.

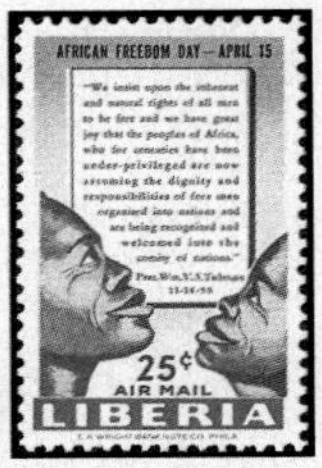


Liberians Reading Proclamation AP34

**1959, Apr. 15 Unwmk.**

**C120** AP34 25c blue & brown .60 .60

African Freedom Day, Apr. 15.

UNESCO Building, Paris AP35

**1959, May 1**

**C121** AP35 25c ultra & red .60 .50

*a.* Souvenir sheet 1.75 1.75

Opening of UNESCO Headquarters in Paris, Nov. 3, 1958.

**Lincoln Type of Regular Issue**

**1959, Nov. 20 Engr. *Perf. 12***

**C122** A152 25c emerald & black .90 .90

For souvenir sheet see No. 386a.

Touré, Tubman and Nkrumah AP36

**1960, Jan. 27 Litho. Unwmk.**

**C123** AP36 25c beige, vio bl & blk .60 .80

See note after No. 387.

**WRY Type of Regular Issue, 1960**

**1960, Apr. 7 *Perf. 11½***

**C124** A154 25c ultra & black .80 .70

*a.* Souv. sheet of 2, #388, C124, imperf. 3.50 2.75

Map of Africa — AP37

**1960, May 11 *Perf. 11½***

**C125** AP37 25c ultra & brown .80 .80

See note after No. 389.

**Olympic Games Type of 1960**

Designs: 25c, Javelin thrower and hunter, horiz. 50c, Runner and stadium, horiz.

**1960, Sept. 6 *Perf. 11½***

**C126** A156 25c brown & brt ultra .90 .70

**Souvenir Sheet**

***Imperf***

**C127** A156 50c lilac & brown 3.50 3.50

**Stamp Centenary Type of 1960**

**1960, Dec. 1 Litho. *Perf. 11½***

**C128** A157 25c multicolored 1.00 1.00

**Souvenir Sheet**

**C129** A157 50c multicolored 1.75 1.75

No. C129 exists imperf.

Globe, Dove and UN Emblem AP38

Design: 50c, Globe and dove.

**1961, May 19 Unwmk. *Perf. 11½***

**C130** AP38 25c indigo & red .50 .50

**Souvenir Sheet**

**C131** AP38 50c red brn & emerald 2.25 2.25

Liberia's membership in the UN Security Council.

A second souvenir sheet contains one each of Nos. 395, C130 and the 50c from No. C131, imperf. Size: 133x83mm. Value $8.

No. C130 exists imperf.

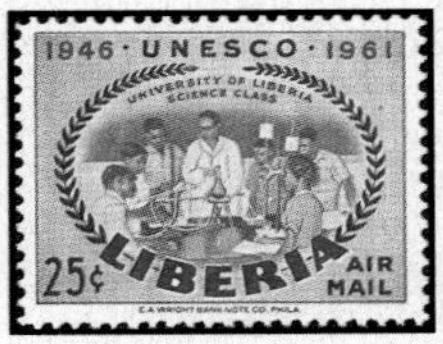


Science Class AP39

Design: 50c, Science class, different design.

**1961, Sept. 8 Litho.**

**C132** AP39 25c purple & brown .50 .25

**Souvenir Sheet**

**C133** AP39 50c blue & brown 1.75 1.75

15th anniv. of UNESCO.

Joseph J. Roberts and Providence Island — AP40

**1961, Oct. 25 Litho. *Perf. 11½***

**C134** AP40 25c emerald & sepia .70 .70

*a.* Souvenir sheet of 3 1.75 1.75

150th anniv. of the birth of Joseph J. Roberts, 1st pres. of Liberia.

No. C134a contains three imperf. stamps similar to Nos. 397-398 and C134, but printed in different colors; 5c, emerald & sepia. 10c, orange & sepia. 25c, ultramarine & sepia.

**Scout Type of Regular Issue and**

Boy Scout — AP41

**1961, Dec. 4 Unwmk. *Perf. 11½***

**C135** AP41 25c emerald & sepia 1.40 1.40

**Souvenir Sheet**

Design: Like No. 399.

**C136** A161 35c dull blue & sepia 3.50 3.50

No. C136 exists imperf. Value, $10.

**Dag Hammarskjold Type of 1962**

**1962, Feb. 1 Unwmk. *Perf. 12***

**C137** A162 25c black & red lilac .60 .60

**Souvenir Sheet**

***Imperf***

**C138** A162 50c black & ultra 1.75 1.75

Malaria Eradication Emblem AP42

**1962, Apr. 7 *Perf. 12½***

**C139** AP42 25c purple & orange .60 .50

**Souvenir Sheet**

***Imperf***

**C140** AP42 50c dark red & ultra 2.00 1.50

Pres. Tubman, Statue of Liberty, New York Skyline and Flags of US and Liberia AP43

**1962, Sept. 17 Litho. *Perf. 11½x12***

**C141** AP43 12c multicolored .25 .25

**C142** AP43 25c multicolored .60 .50

**C143** AP43 50c multicolored 1.25 .85

*Nos. C141-C143 (3)* 2.10 1.60

Pres. Tubman's visit to the US in 1961.

United Nations Emblem and Flags AP44

Design: 50c, UN emblem.

**1962, Oct. 22 *Perf. 12x12½***

**C144** AP44 25c lt ultra & dk bl .50 .50

**Souvenir Sheet**

***Imperf***

**C145** AP44 50c brt grnsh bl & blk 2.00 1.25

Observance of UN Day, Oct. 24, as a national holiday.

**Building Type of Regular Issue**

12c, 70c, Capitol. 50c, Information Service. $1, Treasury Department Building, Monrovia.

**1962-63 *Perf. 12x12½, 12 (70c)***

**C146** A165 12c brt yel grn & mar .25 .25

**C147** A165 50c orange & ultra 1.20 1.20

**C147A** A165 70c brt pink & dk bl ('63) 1.60 1.20

**C148** A165 $1 sal & blk ('63) 2.40 1.40

*Nos. C146-C148 (4)* 5.45 4.05

"FAO" Emblem and Globe — AP45

Design: 50c, "FAO" and UN Emblems.

**1963, Mar. 21 Unwmk. *Perf. 12½***

**C149** AP45 25c dk green & yel .65 .50

**Souvenir Sheet**

***Perf. 12***

**C150** AP45 50c emerald & ultra 2.00 1.75

FAO "Freedom from Hunger" campaign.

**Type of Regular Issue, 1963**

Designs: 25c, Telstar satellite, vert. 50c, Telstar and rocket, vert.

**1963, May 27 Litho. *Perf. 12½***

**C151** A167 25c Prus blue & org .55 .40

**Souvenir Sheet**

***Perf. 12***

**C152** A167 50c dp violet & yel 2.50 1.50

No. C152 exists imperf. Value $12.50.

**Red Cross Type of Regular Issue**

Design: 25c, Red Cross and globe. 50c, Centenary emblem and globe.

**1963, Aug. 26 Unwmk. *Perf. 12***

**C153** A168 25c purple & red .40 .40

**C154** A168 50c deep ultra & red .70 .70

Map of Africa — AP46

**1963, Oct. 28 *Perf. 12½***

**C156** AP46 25c red orange & grn .30 .30

See note after No. 412.

**Olympic Type of Regular Issue**

10c, Torch and mountains. 25c, Mountains, horiz. 50c, Torch, background like No. 413.

**1963, Dec. 11 Litho. *Perf. 12½***

**C157** A170 10c vio blue & red .25 .25

**C158** A170 25c green & orange .80 .80

**Souvenir Sheet**

***Perf. 12***

**C159** A170 50c gray & red 1.75 1.75

No. C159 exists imperf. Value $12.

**Kennedy Type of Regular Issue, 1964**

Designs: 25c, John F. Kennedy, vert. 50c, John F. Kennedy (like No. 414).

**1964, Apr. 6 Unwmk. *Perf. 12½***

**C160** A171 25c blk & red lil .60 .50

**Souvenir Sheet**

***Perf. 12***

**C161** A171 50c blk & red lil 1.75 1.40

An imperf. miniature sheet containing one of No. C160 exists. No marginal inscription. Value $10.

**Satellite Type of Regular Issue**

Souvenir Sheet

Design: Launching rocket separating from booster in space, vert.

**1964, June 22 Litho.**

**C162** A172 50c vio bl & red 3.00 3.00

Exists imperf. Value $9.

**Olympic Type of Regular Issue**

Souvenir Sheet

Design: 50c, Runner and Olympic rings.

**1964, Sept. 15 Unwmk. *Perf. 12***

**C163** A173 50c grnsh bl & red 3.00 1.25

Exists imperf. Value $6.

**Scout Type of Regular Issue, 1965**

Designs: 25c, Liberian flag and fleur-delis. 50c, Globe and Scout emblem.

**1965, Mar. 8 Litho. *Perf. 12½***

**C164** A174 25c crimson & ultra .80 .80

**Souvenir Sheet**

***Perf. 12***

**C165** A174 50c yellow & lilac 3.00 3.00

No. C165 exists imperf. Value $7.

**Lincoln Type of Regular Issue**

Souvenir Sheet

50c, Lincoln and John F. Kennedy, horiz.

**1965, May 3 Unwmk. *Perf. 12***

**C166** A175 50c dp plum & lt gray 1.75 1.75

Exists imperf. Value $5.50.

**ICY Type of Regular Issue, 1965**

Souvenir Sheet

**1965, June 21 Litho.**

**C167** A176 50c car rose & brn 1.75 1.75

**ITU Type of Regular Issue, 1965**

**1965, Sept. 21 Unwmk. *Perf. 12½***

**C168** A177 50c red org & vio bl .80 .70

**Tubman Type of Regular Issue**

25c, Pres. Tubman and coat of arms.

**1965, Nov. 29 Litho. *Perf. 12½***

**C169** A178 25c ultra, red & brn .70 .70

*a.* Souv. sheet of 2, #431, C169, imperf. 1.75 1.75

**Churchill Type of Regular Issue**

25c, "Angry Lion" portrait by Karsh & Parliament, London. 50c, "Williamsburg Award Dinner" portrait by Karsh & map of Europe.

**1966, Jan. 18 Litho. *Perf. 12½***

**C170** A179 25c blk & vio bl .70 .55

**Souvenir Sheet**

***Perf. 12***

**C171** A179 50c blk & red lil 1.75 1.75

No. C171 exists imperf.

**Soccer Type of Regular Issue**

Souvenir Sheet

Design: 50c, Soccer match in stadium.

**1966, May 3 Litho. *Perf. 11½***

**C172** A181 50c ultra & red brn 2.50 2.50

Exists imperf. Value $15.

**Kennedy Type of Regular Issue**

25c, UN General Assembly & Pres. Kennedy. 35c, Pres. Kennedy & rocket on launching pad, Cape Kennedy. 40c, Flame on grave at Arlington.

**1966, Aug. 16 Litho. *Perf. 12½***

**C173** A182 25c ultra, blk & ocher .40 .25

**C174** A182 35c dk vio bl & pink .50 .25

**Souvenir Sheet**

***Perf. 11½***

**C175** A182 40c dk vio bl & multi 2.00 2.00

No. C175 exists imperf. Value $20.

**Boy Scout Type of Regular Issue**

Souvenir Sheet

50c, Scout at campfire & vision of moon landing.

**1967, Mar. 23 Litho. *Perf. 12½***

**C176** A185 50c brt red lil & scar 4.00 4.00

Exists imperf. Value $8.

**Olympic Type of Regular Issue**

Souvenir Sheet

Design: 50c, Pre-Hispanic sculpture, serape and Olympic rings, horiz.

**1967, June 20 Litho. *Perf. 12½***

**C177** A186 50c vio & car 3.75 1.60

Exists imperf. Value $15.

**Winter Olympic Games Type of Regular Issue**

Souvenir Sheet

Design: 50c, Woman skater.

**1967, Nov. 20 Litho. *Perf. 11½***

**C178** A189 50c ver & blk 2.25 .70

Exists imperf. Value $15.

**Human Rights Type of Regular Issue**

Souvenir Sheet

**1968, Apr. 26 Litho. *Perf. 11½***

**C179** A191 80c bl & red 2.50 1.10

No. C179 exists imperf.

**M. L. King Type of Regular Issue**

Souvenir Sheet

55c, Pres. Kennedy congratulating Dr. King.

**1968, July 11 Litho. *Perf. 11½***

**C180** A192 55c brn & blk 3.00 1.00

Exist imperf. Value, $9.

**Olympic Type of Regular Issue**

Souvenir Sheet

Design: 50c, Steeplechase and ancient sculpture.

**1968, Aug. 22 Litho. *Perf. 11½***

**C181** A193 50c brt bl & org brn 2.25 1.10

Exists imperf. Value $15.

**President Type of Regular Issue 1966-69**

Design: 25c, Pres. William V. S. Tubman.

**1969, Feb. 18 Litho. *Perf. 11½x11***

**C182** A180 25c blk & emer .60 .30

**ILO Type of Regular Issue**

Design: 80c, "ILO" surrounded by cogwheel and wreath, vert.

**1969, Apr. 16 Litho. *Perf. 12½***

**C183** A196 80c emer & gold 2.00 1.10

No. C183 exists imperf.

**Apollo 11 Type of Regular Issue**

Souvenir Sheet

65c, Astronauts Neil A. Armstrong, Col. Edwin E. Aldrin, Jr., & Lieut. Col. Michael Collins, horiz.

**1969, Oct. 15 Litho. *Perf. 11½***

**C184** A199 65c dk vio bl & brt red 2.00 1.10

Exists imperf. Value $20.

**UN Type of 1970**

Design: $1, UN emblem, olive branch and plane as symbols of peace and progress, vert.

**1970, Apr. 16 Litho. *Perf. 12½***

**C185** A200 $1 ultra & sil 2.00 1.00

Exists imperf.

**Apollo 14 Type of Regular Issue**

Souvenir Sheet

Design: 50c, Moon, earth and star.

**1971, May 20 Litho. *Imperf.***

**C186** A208 50c multi 2.75 2.75

Souvenir Sheet

Olympic Yachting Village, Kiel, and Yachting — AP47

**1971, June 28 Litho. *Perf. 14½x14***

**C187** AP47 Sheet of 2 2.75 2.75

*a.* 25c multi .65 .65

*b.* 30c multi .80 .80

Publicity for the 20th Summer Olympic Games, and the yachting races in Kiel, Germany, 1972. Exists imperf.

**Boy Scout Type of Regular Issue**

Souvenir Sheet

Boy Scouts of various nations cooking, horiz.

**1971, Aug. 6 Litho. *Perf. 15***

**C188** A211 50c multi 3.50 3.50

Exists imperf.

**UNICEF Type of Regular Issue**

Souvenir Sheet

UNICEF emblem & Bengal tigress with cubs.

**1971, Oct. 1 *Imperf.***

**C189** A213 50c multi 3.00 3.00

Souvenir Sheet

Japanese Royal Family — AP48

**1971, Nov. 4 *Perf. 15***

**C190** AP48 50c multi 3.25 3.25

11th Winter Olympic Games, Sapporo, Japan, Feb. 3-13, 1972. Exists imperf. Value $15.

**Sesquicentennial Type of Regular Issue**

Souvenir Sheet

Design: 50c, Sailing ship "Elizabeth" between maps of America and Africa, horiz.

**1972, Jan. 1 Litho. *Imperf.***

**C191** A216 50c car & vio bl 2.40 2.40

**Olympic Type of Regular Issue**

Souvenir Sheet

Design: 55c, View of Olympic Stadium and symbol of "Motion."

**1972, May 19 Litho. *Perf. 15***

**C192** A218 55c multi 4.25 4.25

Exists imperf. Value, $8.

**Apollo 16 Type of Regular Issue**

Souvenir Sheet

Lt. Comdr. Thomas K. Mattingly, 2nd, Capt. John W. Young & Lt. Col. Charles M. Duke, Jr.

**1972, June 26 Litho. *Perf. 15***

**C193** A220 55c pink & multi 2.00 2.00

Exists imperf. Value $10.

**Ship Type of 1972**

Souvenir Sheet

Design: Lord Nelson's flagship Victory, and her figurehead (1765).

**1972, Sept. 6 Litho. *Perf. 15***

**C194** A222 50c multi 2.50 2.50

**Pres. Tolbert Type of 1972.**

Souvenir Sheet

**1972, Oct. 23 Litho. *Perf. 15***

**C195** A223 55c multi 1.60 1.60

**Apollo 17 Type of Regular Issue**

Souvenir Sheet

55c, Apollo 17 badge, moon and earth.

**1973, Mar. 28 Litho. *Perf. 11***

**C196** A225 55c bl & multi 1.90 1.90

Exists imperf. Value $10.

**Locomotive Type of Regular Issue**

Souvenir Sheet

Design: 55c, Swiss locomotive.

**1973, May 4 Litho. *Perf. 11***

**C197** A226 55c multi 2.75 2.75

**WHO Type of Regular Issue 1973**

Souvenir Sheet

Design: 55c, WHO emblem, Paul Ehrlich and poppy anemones.

**1973, June 26 Litho. *Perf. 11***

**C198** A228 55c lt vio & multi 2.00 2.00

**Automobile Type of Regular Issue**

Souvenir Sheet

Franklin 10 HP cross-engined 1904-05 models.

**1973, Sept. 11 Litho. *Perf. 11***

**C199** A229 55c multi 2.00 2.00

**Copernicus Type of Regular Issue**
Souvenir Sheet

Design: 55c, Copernicus and concept of orbiting station around Mars.

**1973, Dec. 14 Litho.** ***Perf. 13½***
**C200** A230 55c gray & multi 2.00 2.00
Exists imperf. Value $15.

**UPU Type of Regular Issue**
Souvenir Sheet

55c, UPU emblem and English coach, 1784.

**1974, Mar. 4 Litho.** ***Perf. 13½***
**C201** A232 55c multi 2.25 2.25
Exists imperf. Value $15.

**Dog Type of Regular Issue**
Souvenir Sheet

Design: Hungarian sheepdog (kuvasz).

**1974, Apr. 16 Litho.** ***Perf. 13½***
**C202** A233 75c multi 3.25 2.25
Exists imperf.

**Soccer Type of Regular Issue**
Souvenir Sheet

Design: 60c, World Soccer Championship Cup and Munich Stadium.

**1974, June 4 Litho.** ***Perf. 11***
**C203** A234 60c multi 2.00 2.00
Exists imperf. Value $12.

**Butterfly Type of Regular Issue**
Souvenir Sheet

Tropical butterfly: 60c, Pierella nereis.

**1974, Sept. 11 Litho.** ***Perf. 13½***
**C204** A235 60c gray & multi *3.50 2.50*

**Churchill Type of 1974**
Souvenir Sheet

60c, Churchill at easel painting landscape.

**1975, Jan. 17 Litho.** ***Perf. 13½***
**C205** A237 60c multi 1.50 1.50
Exists imperf. Value $10.

**Women's Year Type of 1975**
Souvenir Sheet

Design: 75c, Vijaya Lakshmi Pandit, Women's Year emblem and dais of UN General Assembly.

**1975, Mar. 14 Litho.** ***Perf. 13***
**C206** A238 75c gray & multi 1.25 1.25
Exists imperf. Value $10.

**American Bicentennial Type**
Souvenir Sheet

Design: 75c, Mayflower and US No. 548.

**1975, Apr. 25 Litho.** ***Perf. 13½***
**C207** A239 75c multi 2.50 2.50
Exists imperf. Value $11.

**Dr. Schweitzer Type, 1975**
Souvenir Sheet

Schweitzer as surgeon in Lambarene Hospital.

**1975, June 26 Litho.** ***Perf. 13½***
**C208** A240 60c multi 2.25 2.25
Exists imperf. Value $11.

**Apollo-Soyuz Type, 1975**
Souvenir Sheet

75c, Apollo-Soyuz link-up and emblem.

**1975, Sept. 18 Litho.** ***Perf. 13½***
**C209** A241 75c multi 1.90 1.90

**Winter Olympic Games Type, 1976**
Souvenir Sheet

Downhill skiing & Olympic Games emblem.

**1976, Jan. 23 Litho.** ***Perf. 13½***
**C210** A243 75c multi 1.50 1.50
Exists imperf. Value $9.

**Olympic Games Type, 1976**
Souvenir Sheet

Design: 75c, Dressage and jumping.

**1976, May 4 Litho.** ***Perf. 13½***
**C211** A245 75c multi 1.90 1.90
Exists imperf. Value $9.

**Bell Type**
Souvenir Sheet

Design: 75c, A. G. Bell making telephone call, UPU and ITU emblems.

**1976, June 4 Litho.** ***Perf. 13½***
**C212** A246 75c ocher & multi 2.25 2.25
Exists imperf. Value $11.

**Animal Type of 1976**
Souvenir Sheet

Design: 50c, Elephant, vert.

**1976, Sept. 1 Litho.** ***Perf. 13½***
**C213** A249 50c org & multi 3.00 2.00

**Bicentennial Type of 1976**
Souvenir Sheet

Design: 75c, Like No. 770.

**1976, Sept. 21 Litho.** ***Perf. 13½***
**C214** A250 75c multi 2.40 2.40
Exist imperf. Value, $12.

**Mask Type of 1977**
Souvenir Sheet

75c, Ibo mask and Festival emblem.

**1977, Jan. 20 Litho.** ***Perf. 13½***
**C215** A251 75c lil & multi 1.75 1.75

**Equestrian Type of 1977**

Designs: 55c, Military dressage (team), US. 80c, Winners receiving medals, vert.

**1977, Apr. 22 Litho.** ***Perf. 13½***
**C216** A253 55c ocher & multi 2.40 .60

**Souvenir Sheet**

**C217** A253 80c ocher & multi 2.10 2.10
No. C217 exists imperf. Value $9.

**Elizabeth II Type of 1977**
Souvenir Sheet

75c, Elizabeth II, laurel and crowns.

**1977, May 23 Litho.** ***Perf. 13½***
**C218** A254 75c sil & multi 1.25 1.25
Exists imperf. Value $9.

**Zeppelin Type of 1978**
Souvenir Sheet

75c, Futuristic Goodyear aerospace airship.

**1978, Mar. 9 Litho.** ***Perf. 13½***
**C219** A257 75c multi 1.75 1.40
Exists imperf. Value $10.

**Soccer Type of 1978**
Souvenir Sheet

Soccer game Netherlands & Uruguay, vert.

**1978, May 16 Litho.** ***Perf. 13½***
**C220** A258 75c multi 2.00 1.25
Exists imperf. Value $20.

**Coronation Type of 1978**
Souvenir Sheet

Design: 75c, Coronation coach, horiz.

**1978, June 12**
**C221** A259 75c multi 2.25 1.75
Exists imperf. Value $14.

**Soccer Winners' Type of 1978**
Souvenir Sheet

Design: 75c, Argentine team, horiz.

**1978, Dec. 8 Litho.** ***Perf. 13½***
**C222** A262 75c multi 2.50 1.20
Exists imperf. Value $12.50.

## AIR POST SEMI-POSTAL STAMPS

**Nos. C14-C16 Overprinted in Red or Blue Like Nos. B16-B18**

**1941 Unwmk.** ***Perf. 12***
**CB1** A107 3c +2c dk bl (R) 4.00 4.00
**CB2** A108 5c +2c dl red brn (Bl) 4.00 4.00
**CB3** A109 10c +2c dk grn (R) 4.00 4.00
*Nos. CB1-CB3 (3)* 12.00 12.00

**Catalogue values for unused stamps in this section, from this point to the end of the section, are for Never Hinged items.**

Nurses Taking Oath — SPAP1

Designs: 20c+5c, Liberian Government Hospital. 25c+5c, Medical examination.

**1954, June 21 Litho. & Engr.**
**Size: 39½x28½mm**
**CB4** SPAP1 10c +5c car & blk .30 .25
**CB5** SPAP1 20c +5c emer & blk .40 .25
**Size: 45x34mm**
**CB6** SPAP1 25c +5c ultra, car & blk .45 .25
*Nos. CB4-CB6 (3)* 1.15 .75

Surtax for the Liberian Government Hospital. Nos. CB4-CB6 exist imperf. No. CB6 exists with carmine omitted.

## AIR POST SPECIAL DELIVERY STAMP

**No. C15 Overprinted in Dark Blue Like No. E1**

**1941 Unwmk.** ***Perf. 12***
**CE1** A108 10c on 5c dl red brn 2.00 2.00

## AIR POST REGISTRATION STAMP

**No. 278 Overprinted in Dark Blue**

**1941 Unwmk.** ***Perf. 12***
**CF1** A108 10c on 5c dl red brn 2.00 2.00

## SPECIAL DELIVERY STAMP

**No. 278 Surcharged in Dark Blue**

**1941 Unwmk.** ***Perf. 12***
**E1** A108 10c on 5c dl red brn 2.00 2.00

## REGISTRATION STAMPS

R1

**1893 Unwmk. Litho.** ***Perf. 14, 15***
**Without Value Surcharged**
**F1** R1 (10c) blk (Buchanan) 250. 250.
**F2** R1 (10c) blk (Greenville) *2,500.* —
**F3** R1 (10c) blk (Harper) *2,500.* —
**F4** R1 (10c) blk (Monrovia) 30. 30.
**F5** R1 (10c) blk (Robertsport) 1,000. 1,000.

**Types of 1893 Surcharged in Black**

**1894** ***Perf. 14***
**F6** R1 10c bl, *pink* (Buchanan) 5.50 5.50
**F7** R1 10c grn, *buff* (Harper) 5.50 5.50
**F8** R1 10c red, *yel* (Monrovia) 5.50 5.50
**F9** R1 10c rose, *blue* (Robertsport) 5.50 5.50
*Nos. F6-F9 (4)* 22.00 22.00

Exist imperf or missing one 10. Value, each $10.

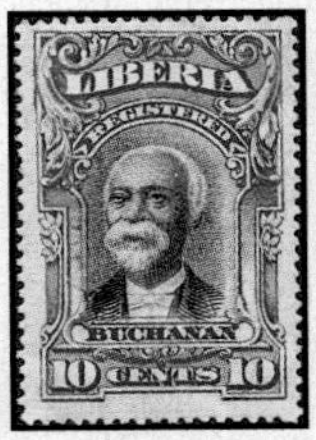

President Garretson W. Gibson — R6

**1903 Engr.** ***Perf. 14***
**F10** R6 10c bl & blk (Buchanan) 1.75 .25
*a.* Center inverted 100.00
**F11** R6 10c org red & blk ("Grenville") 1.75
*a.* Center inverted 100.00
*b.* 10c orange & black 1.90 .25
**F12** R6 10c grn & blk (Harper) 1.75 .25
*a.* Center inverted 100.00
**F13** R6 10c vio & blk (Monrovia) 1.75 .25
*a.* Center inverted 100.00
*b.* 10c lilac & black 1.90
**F14** R6 10c magenta & blk (Robertsport) 1.75 .25
*a.* Center inverted 100.00
*Nos. F10-F14 (5)* 8.75
*Nos. F10, F11b, F12-F14* .75

For surcharges see Nos. 178-182.

S.S. Quail on Patrol — R7

**1919 Litho.** ***Serrate Roulette 12***
**F15** R7 10c blk & bl (Buchanan) 1.40 2.75

***Serrate Roulette 12, Perf. 14***
**F16** R7 10c ocher & blk ("Grenville") 1.40 2.75
**F17** R7 10c grn & blk (Harper) 1.40 2.75
**F18** R7 10c vio & bl (Monrovia) 1.40 2.75
**F19** R7 10c rose & blk (Robertsport) 1.40 2.75
*Nos. F15-F19 (5)* 7.00 13.75

Gabon Viper — R8

**Wmk. Crosses and Circles (116)**

**1921 Engr. *Perf. 13x14***

F20 R8 10c cl & blk (Buchanan) 80.00 3.50
F21 R8 10c red & blk (Greenville) 30.00 3.50
F22 R8 10c ultra & blk (Harper) 40.00 3.50
F23 R8 10c org & blk (Monrovia) 30.00 3.50
*a.* Imperf., pair 225.00
F24 R8 10c grn & blk (Robertsport) 30.00 3.50
*a.* Imperf., pair 225.00
*Nos. F20-F24 (5)* 210.00 17.50

**Nos. F-20-F24 Overprinted in Black**

F25 R8 10c (Buchanan) 37.50 6.25
F26 R8 10c (Greenville) 37.50 6.25
F27 R8 10c (Harper) 37.50 6.25
F28 R8 10c (Monrovia) 37.50 6.25
F29 R8 10c (Robertsport) 37.50 6.25
*Nos. F25-F29 (5)* 187.50 31.25

Nos. F20-F24 are printed tete-beche. Thus, the "1921" overprint appears upright on half the stamps in a sheet and inverted on the other half. Values are the same for either variety.

Passengers Going Ashore from Ship — R9

Designs: No. F31, Transporting merchandise, shore to ship (Greenville). No. F32, Sailing ship (Harper). No. F33, Ocean liner (Monrovia). No. F34, Canoe in surf (Robertsport).

**1924 Litho. *Perf. 14***

F30 R9 10c gray & carmine 7.00 .60
F31 R9 10c gray & blue grn 7.00 .60
F32 R9 10c gray & orange 7.00 .60
F33 R9 10c gray & blue 7.00 .60
F34 R9 10c gray & violet 7.00 .60
*Nos. F30-F34 (5)* 35.00 3.00

**No. 278 Surcharged in Dark Blue**

**1941 Unwmk. *Perf. 12***

F35 A108 10c on 5c dull red brn 2.00 2.00

## POSTAGE DUE STAMPS

Nos. 26, 28 Surcharged

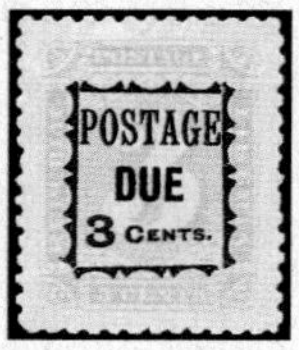


**1892 Unwmk. *Perf. 11***

J1 A5 3c on 3c violet 6.50 4.25
*a.* Imperf., pair 30.00
*b.* Inverted surcharge 45.00 45.00
*c.* As "a," inverted surcharge 110.00

***Perf. 12***

J2 A5 6c on 6c olive gray 15.00 13.50
*a.* Imperf., pair 40.00
*b.* Inverted surcharge 52.50 35.00

D2

**Engr.; Figures of Value Typographed in Black**

**1893 Wmk. 143 *Perf. 14, 15***

J3 D2 2c org, *yel* 2.00 1.00
J4 D2 4c rose, *rose* 2.00 1.00
J5 D2 6c brown, *buff* 2.00 1.25
J6 D2 8c blue, *blue* 2.00 1.25
J7 D2 10c grn, *lil rose* 2.25 1.50
J8 D2 20c vio, *gray* 2.25 1.50
*a.* Center inverted 110.00 110.00
J9 D2 40c ol brn, *grnsh* 4.50 3.00
*Nos. J3-J9 (7)* 17.00 10.50

All values of the above set exist imperforate. Each value also exists with center inverted.

## MILITARY STAMPS

"LFF" are the initials of "Liberian Frontier Force." Nos. M1-M7 were issued for the use of troops sent to guard the frontier.

Issues of 1905, 1906 and 1909 Surcharged

**1916 Wmk. 143**

M1 A23 1c on 1c lt grn 190.00 190.00
*a.* 2nd "F" inverted 250.00 250.00
*b.* "FLF" 250.00 250.00
*c.* Inverted surcharge 250.00 250.00

**Unwmk.**

M2 A33 1c on 1c grn & blk 600.00 550.00
*a.* 2nd "F" inverted 700.00 600.00
*b.* "FLF" 700.00 600.00
M3 A46 1c on 1c yel grn & blk 4.00 4.75
*a.* 2nd "F" inverted 7.50 7.50
*b.* "FLF" 7.50 7.50
M4 A47 1c on 2c lake & blk 4.00 4.75
*a.* 2nd "F" inverted 7.50 7.50
*b.* "FLF" 7.50 7.50

Surcharge exists sideways on Nos. M2, M5; double on Nos. M1-M4; inverted on Nos. M2-M4.

Nos. O46, O59-O60 Surcharged

M5 A33 1c on 1c 500.00 475.00
*a.* 2nd "F" inverted 700.00 650.00
*b.* "FLF" 700.00 650.00
M6 A46 1c on 1c 4.75 5.50
*a.* 2nd "F" inverted 9.00 9.00
*b.* "FLF" 9.00 9.00
*c.* "LFF 1c" inverted 12.50 12.50
*d.* As "a" and "1c" inverted 15.00
*e.* "FLF 1c" inverted 15.00
M7 A47 1c on 2c 3.25 4.00
*a.* 2nd "F" inverted 6.50 6.50
*b.* "FLF" 6.50 6.50
*c.* Pair, one without "LFF 1c"

## OFFICIAL STAMPS

Types of Regular Issues Overprinted in Various Colors

***Perf. 12½ to 15 and Compound***

**1892 Wmk. 143**

O1 A9 1c vermilion .80 .80
O2 A9 2c blue .80 .80
O3 A10 4c grn & blk .80 .80
O4 A11 6c bl grn .80 .80
O5 A12 8c brn & blk .80 .80
O6 A13 12c rose red 2.00 2.00
O7 A14 16c red lilac 2.00 2.00
O8 A15 24c ol grn, *yel* 2.00 2.00
O9 A16 32c grnsh bl 2.00 2.00
O10 A17 $1 bl & blk 40.00 16.00
O11 A18 $2 brn, *yel* 16.00 11.50
O12 A19 $5 car & blk 24.00 9.00
*Nos. O1-O12 (12)* 92.00 48.50

a

"5" With Short Flag

**1893**

O13 A11 5c on 6c bl grn (a) (No. 50) 1.20 1.20
*a.* "5" with short flag 6.00 6.00
*b.* Both 5's with short flags 6.00 6.00
*c.* "i" dot omitted 20.00 20.00
*d.* Overprinted on #50d 45.00 45.00

Overprinted in Various Colors

**1894**

O15 A9 1c vermilion .70 .35
O16 A9 2c blue .85 .40
*a.* Imperf.
O17 A10 4c grn & blk 1.00 .55
O18 A12 8c brn & blk 1.00 .55
O19 A13 12c rose red 1.40 .60
O20 A14 16c red lilac 1.40 .60
O21 A15 24c ol grn, *yel* 1.40 .70
O22 A16 32c grnsh bl 2.75 .80
O23 A17 $1 bl & blk 27.50 21.00
*a.* $1 ultra & black 27.50 21.00
O24 A18 $2 brn, *yel* 27.50 21.00
O25 A19 $5 car & blk 125.00 87.50
*Nos. O15-O25 (11)* 190.50 134.05

**Unwmk.**

***Imperf***

O26 A22 5c vio & grn 3.50 2.25

***Rouletted***

O27 A22 5c vio & grn 3.50 2.25

Regular Issue of 1896-1905 Overprinted in Black or Red

**1898-1905 Wmk. 143 *Perf. 14, 15***

O28 A23 1c lil rose 1.10 .90
O29 A23 1c dp grn ('00) 1.10 .90
O30 A23 1c lt grn (R) ('05) 1.10 .90
O31 A24 2c bis & blk 2.25 .60
*a.* Pair, one without overprint *900.00*
O32 A24 2c org red & blk ('00) 3.25 1.50
O33 A24 2c rose & blk ('05) 5.50 2.75
O34 A25 5c lake & blk 3.75 1.50
O35 A25 5c gray bl & blk ('00) 4.25 1.50
O36 A25 5c ultra & blk (R) ('05) 7.25 3.75
O37 A12 10c chr yel & ind 2.25 1.75
O38 A13 15c slate 2.25 1.75
O39 A14 20c vermilion 3.75 2.10
O40 A15 25c yel grn 2.25 1.75
O41 A16 30c steel blue 5.50 2.75
O42 A26 50c red brn & blk 5.50 2.75
*Nos. O28-O42 (15)* 51.05 27.15

For surcharge see No. O92.

Official stamps overprinted "ORDINARY" or with a bar with an additional surcharge are listed as Nos. 64B-90, 92-93, 99.

Red Overprint

**1903 Unwmk. *Perf. 14***

O43 A29 3c green .25 .25
*a.* Overprint omitted 5.00
*b.* Inverted overprint

Two overprint types: I — Thin, sharp, dark red. II — Thick, heavier, orange red. Same value.

No. 50 Surcharged in Black

No. 45 Surcharged in Red

**1904 Wmk. 143**

O44 A11 1c on 5c on 6c bl grn 1.60 2.00
*a.* "5" with short flag 4.25
*b.* Both "5s" with straight flag 8.00 8.00
O45 A16 2c on 30c steel blue 9.50 9.50
*a.* Double surcharge, red and black
*b.* Surcharge also on back

Types of Regular Issue Overprinted in Various Colors

a

**1906 Unwmk.**

O46 A33 1c grn & blk (R) .65 .40
O47 A34 2c car & blk (Bl) .25 .25
*a.* Center and overprint inverted 30.00 3.00
*b.* Inverted overprint 6.00
O48 A35 5c ultra & blk (Bk) .65 .40
*a.* Inverted overprint 15.00 15.00
*b.* Center and overprint invtd. 50.00
O49 A36 10c dl vio & blk (R) .75 .55
*a.* Inverted overprint 10.00 10.00
*b.* Center and overprint invtd. 50.00
O50 A37 15c brn & blk (Bk) 3.00 .55
*a.* Inverted overprint 4.50
*b.* Overprint omitted 12.00 6.00
*c.* Center and overprint invtd. 60.00
O51 A38 20c dp grn & blk (R) .75 .55
*a.* Overprint omitted 15.00
O52 A39 25c plum & gray (Bl) .50 .25
*a.* With 2nd ovpt. in blue, invtd. 15.00
O53 A40 30c dk brn (Bk) .55 .25
O54 A41 50c org brn & dp grn (G) .75 .25
*a.* Inverted overprint 5.00 4.00
O55 A42 75c ultra & blk (Bk) 1.40 .95
*a.* Inverted overprint 9.50 5.75
*b.* Overprint omitted 22.50
O56 A43 $1 dp grn & gray (R) .90 .25
*a.* Inverted overprint
O57 A44 $2 plum & blk (Bl) 2.75 .25
*a.* Overprint omitted 22.50 15.00

| | | | | |
|---|---|---|---|---|
| **O58** | A45 | $5 org & blk (Bk) | 5.50 | .25 |
| *a.* | | Overprint omitted | 11.00 | |
| *b.* | | Inverted overprint | 12.00 | 8.00 |
| | | *Nos. O46-O58 (13)* | 18.40 | 5.15 |

Nos. O52, O54, O55, O56 and O58 are known with center inverted.

For surcharges see Nos. O72, O82-O85, O96.

b

**1909-12**

| | | | | |
|---|---|---|---|---|
| **O59** | A46 | 1c emer & blk (R) | .40 | .25 |
| **O60** | A47 | 2c car rose & brn (Bl) | .40 | .25 |
| *a.* | | Overprint omitted | | |
| **O61** | A48 | 5c turq & blk (Bk) | .45 | .25 |
| *a.* | | Double overprint, one inverted | 7.50 | |
| **O62** | A49 | 10c blk & ultra (R) ('12) | .60 | .25 |
| **O63** | A50 | 15c cl & blk (Bl) | .60 | .45 |
| **O64** | A51 | 20c bis & grn (Bk) | 1.10 | .55 |
| **O65** | A52 | 25c ultra & grn (Bk) | 1.10 | .55 |
| *a.* | | Double overprint | 4.75 | 4.75 |
| **O66** | A53 | 30c dk bl (R) | .85 | .25 |
| **O67** | A54 | 50c brn & grn (Bk) | 1.40 | .40 |
| *a.* | | Center inverted | 27.50 | |
| *b.* | | Inverted overprint | 4.00 | 2.75 |
| **O68** | A55 | 75c pur & blk (R) | 1.50 | .25 |
| | | *Nos. O59-O68 (10)* | 8.40 | 3.45 |

Nos. O63, O64, O67 and O68 are known without overprint and with center inverted.

For surcharges see Nos. O74-O81, O86-O90, O97.

***Rouletted***

| | | | | |
|---|---|---|---|---|
| **O69** | A49 | 10c blk & ultra (R) | 1.00 | .95 |

### Nos. 126B and 127E Overprinted type "a" ("OS") in Red

**1910-12** ***Rouletted***

| | | | | |
|---|---|---|---|---|
| **O70** | A49 | 3c on 10c blk & ultra | .70 | 1.25 |

***Perf. 12½, 14, 12½x14***

| | | | | |
|---|---|---|---|---|
| **O71** | A49 | 3c on 10c blk & ultra ('12) | .70 | .40 |
| *a.* | | Pair, one without srch., the other with dbl. srch., one invtd. | | |
| *b.* | | Double surcharge, one inverted | 4.00 | |

Stamps of Preceding Issues Srchd. with New Values like Regular Issue and — c

**1914** **On Nos. O52 and 110**

| | | | | |
|---|---|---|---|---|
| **O72** | A39 (a) | 2c on 25c plum & gray | 30.00 | 10.50 |
| **O73** | A42 (c) | 20c on 75c brn & blk | 8.75 | 5.25 |

**On Nos. O66 and O68**

| | | | | |
|---|---|---|---|---|
| **O74** | A53 (b) | 5c on 30c dk bl | 8.75 | 5.25 |
| **O75** | A55 (c) | 20c on 75c pur & blk (R) | 13.00 | 5.25 |
| | | *Nos. O72-O75 (4)* | 60.50 | 26.25 |

### Official Stamps of 1906-09 Surcharged Like Regular Issues of Same Date

**1915-16**

| | | | | |
|---|---|---|---|---|
| **O76** | A50 (c) | 2c on 15c (Bk) | .95 | .50 |
| **O77** | A52 (d) | 2c on 25c (Bk) | 5.25 | 5.25 |
| **O78** | A51 (e) | 5c on 20c (Bk) | .95 | .65 |
| **O79** | A53 (g) | 5c on 30c (R) | 10.00 | 8.50 |
| **O80** | A54 (i) | 10c on 50c (Bk) | 5.50 | 3.25 |
| **O81** | A55 (j) | 20c on 75c (R) | 2.75 | 2.75 |
| **O82** | A43 (k) | 25c on $1 (R) | 20.00 | 20.00 |
| *a.* | | "25" double | 25.00 | |
| *b.* | | "OS" inverted | 25.00 | |
| **O83** | A44 (l) | 50c on $2 (Bk) | 50.00 | 50.00 |
| *a.* | | "Ceuts" | 70.00 | 70.00 |
| **O84** | A44 (m) | 50c on $2 (Br) | 22.50 | 22.50 |
| **O85** | A45 (n) | $1 on $5 (Bk) | 21.00 | 21.00 |

**Handstamped Surcharge**

| | | | | |
|---|---|---|---|---|
| **O86** | A54 (i) | 10c on 50c (Bk) | 11.00 | 11.00 |

### Nos. O60-O61 Surcharged like Nos. 153-154 in Black or Red

a1, b1

c1, d1

e1, f1

g1, h1

i1, j1

| | | | | |
|---|---|---|---|---|
| **O87** | A47 | 1c on 2c | 2.75 | 2.75 |
| | | Strip of 10 types | 30.00 | |
| **O88** | A48 | 2c on 5c (R) | 2.75 | 2.75 |
| | | Strip of 10 types (R) | 30.00 | |
| *a.* | | Black surcharge | 10.00 | 10.00 |
| | | Strip of 10 types (Bk) | 140.00 | |

See note following Nos. 153-154.

Nos. O60-O61 Surcharged

| | | | | |
|---|---|---|---|---|
| **O90** | A47 | 1c on 2c | 125.00 | 125.00 |
| **O91** | A48 | 2c on 5c | 100.00 | 100.00 |

No. O42 Surcharged

| | | | | |
|---|---|---|---|---|
| **O92** | A26 | 10c on 50c (Bk) | 11.00 | 11.00 |

No. O53 Surcharged

**1917**

| | | | | |
|---|---|---|---|---|
| **O96** | A40 | 5c on 30c dk brn | 21.00 | 21.00 |
| *a.* | | "FIV" | 35.00 | 35.00 |

The editors consider the 1915-17 issues unnecessary and speculative.

### No. O62 Surcharged in Red like No. 162

**1918**

| | | | | |
|---|---|---|---|---|
| **O97** | A49 | 3c on 10c blk & ultra | 2.40 | 2.40 |

Types of Regular Issue of 1918 Ovptd. Type "a" in Black, Blue or Red

**1918** **Unwmk.** ***Perf. 12½, 14***

| | | | | |
|---|---|---|---|---|
| **O98** | A59 | 1c dp grn & red brn (Bk) | .60 | .25 |
| **O99** | A60 | 2c red & blk (Bl) | .60 | .25 |
| **O100** | A61 | 5c ultra & blk (R) | 1.10 | .25 |
| **O101** | A62 | 10c ultra (R) | .60 | .25 |
| **O102** | A63 | 15c choc & dk grn (Bl) | 2.75 | .60 |
| **O103** | A64 | 20c gray lil & blk (R) | .85 | .25 |
| **O104** | A65 | 25c choc & grn (Bk) | 5.25 | .65 |
| **O105** | A66 | 30c brt vio & blk (R) | 6.50 | .65 |
| **O106** | A67 | 50c mar & blk (Bl) | 7.75 | .65 |
| *a.* | | Overprint omitted | 11.00 | |
| **O107** | A68 | 75c car brn & blk (Bl) | 3.00 | .25 |
| **O108** | A69 | $1 ol bis & turq bl (Bk) | 6.00 | .25 |
| **O109** | A70 | $2 ol bis & blk (R) | 9.25 | .25 |
| **O110** | A71 | $5 yel grn (Bk) | 12.00 | .40 |
| | | *Nos. O98-O110 (13)* | 56.25 | 4.95 |

For surcharges see Nos. 259-269, O111-O112, O155-O157. For overprint see No. 270.

### Official Stamps of 1918 Surcharged like Regular Issue

**1920**

| | | | | |
|---|---|---|---|---|
| **O111** | A59 | 3c on 1c grn & red brn | 1.10 | .70 |
| *a.* | | "CEETS" | 15.00 | 15.00 |
| *b.* | | Double surcharge | 8.00 | 8.00 |
| *c.* | | Double srch., one invtd. | 15.00 | 15.00 |
| *d.* | | Triple surcharge | 20.00 | 20.00 |
| **O112** | A60 | 4c on 2c red & blk | .70 | .70 |
| *a.* | | Inverted surcharge | 12.00 | 12.00 |
| *b.* | | Double surcharge | 12.00 | 12.00 |
| *c.* | | Double srch., one invtd. | 10.00 | 10.00 |
| *d.* | | Triple surcharge | 15.00 | 15.00 |

Types of Regular Issues of 1915-21 Overprinted

**1921** **Wmk. 116** ***Perf. 14***

| | | | | |
|---|---|---|---|---|
| **O113** | A57 | 2c rose red | 8.25 | .25 |
| **O114** | A58 | 3c brown | 1.75 | .25 |
| **O115** | A79 | 20c brn & ultra | 2.25 | .40 |

Regular Issues of 1921 Overprinted

| | | | | |
|---|---|---|---|---|
| **O116** | A75 | 1c dp grn | 1.75 | .25 |
| **O117** | A76 | 5c dp bl & brn | 1.75 | .25 |
| **O118** | A77 | 10c red vio & blk | .85 | .25 |
| **O119** | A78 | 15c blk & grn | 4.75 | .60 |
| *a.* | | Double overprint | | |
| **O120** | A80 | 25c org & grn | 6.50 | .60 |
| **O121** | A81 | 30c brn & red | 1.75 | .25 |
| **O122** | A82 | 50c grn & blk | 1.75 | .25 |
| *a.* | | Overprinted "S" only | | |
| **O123** | A83 | 75c bl & vio | 3.25 | .25 |
| **O124** | A84 | $1 bl & blk | 22.50 | .65 |
| **O125** | A85 | $2 grn & org | 12.00 | .95 |
| **O126** | A86 | $5 grn & bl | 13.50 | 2.10 |
| | | *Nos. O113-O126 (14)* | 82.60 | 7.30 |

Preceding Issues Overprinted

**1921**

| | | | | |
|---|---|---|---|---|
| **O127** | A75 | 1c dp grn | 7.50 | .25 |
| **O128** | A57 | 2c rose red | 7.50 | .25 |
| **O129** | A58 | 3c brown | 7.50 | .25 |
| **O130** | A76 | 5c dp bl & brn | 4.50 | .25 |
| **O131** | A77 | 10c red vio & blk | 7.50 | .25 |
| **O132** | A78 | 15c blk & grn | 8.50 | .25 |
| **O133** | A79 | 20c brn & ultra | 8.50 | .40 |
| **O134** | A80 | 25c org & grn | 8.25 | .80 |
| **O135** | A81 | 30c brn & red | 7.50 | .25 |
| **O136** | A82 | 50c grn & blk | 8.75 | .25 |
| **O137** | A83 | 75c bl & vio | 5.50 | .25 |
| **O138** | A84 | $1 bl & blk | 15.00 | 2.00 |
| **O139** | A85 | $2 org & grn | 19.00 | 2.25 |
| **O140** | A86 | $5 grn & bl | 15.00 | 3.25 |
| | | *Nos. O127-O140 (14)* | 130.50 | 10.95 |

Types of Regular Issue of 1923 Ovptd.

**1923** ***Perf. 13½x14½, 14½x13½***

**White Paper**

| | | | | |
|---|---|---|---|---|
| **O141** | A88 | 1c bl grn & blk | 8.75 | .25 |
| **O142** | A89 | 2c dl red & yel brn | 8.75 | .25 |
| **O143** | A90 | 3c gray bl & blk | 8.75 | .25 |
| **O144** | A91 | 5c org & dk grn | 8.75 | .25 |
| **O145** | A92 | 10c ol bis & dk vio | 8.75 | .25 |
| **O146** | A93 | 15c yel grn & bl | 1.10 | .40 |
| **O147** | A94 | 20c vio & ind | 1.10 | .40 |
| **O148** | A95 | 25c brn & red brn | 32.50 | .40 |

**White, Buff or Brownish Paper**

| | | | | |
|---|---|---|---|---|
| **O149a** | A96 | 30c dp ultra & brn | 1.10 | .30 |
| *b.* | | Overprint omitted | 2.00 | |
| **O150a** | A97 | 50c dl bis & red brn | 2.25 | .45 |
| **O151** | A98 | 75c gray & grn | 2.25 | .25 |
| **O152a** | A99 | $1 red org & grn | 2.25 | .65 |
| *b.* | | Overprint omitted | 11.00 | |
| **O153** | A100 | $2 red lil & ver | 6.00 | .25 |
| **O154a** | A101 | $5 bl & brn vio | 4.50 | 2.25 |
| | | *Nos. O141-O154a (14)* | 96.80 | 6.25 |

No. O98 Surcharged in Red Brown

**1926** **Unwmk.** ***Perf. 14***

| | | | | |
|---|---|---|---|---|
| **O155** | A59 | 2c on 1c | 2.25 | 2.25 |
| *a.* | | "Gents" | 15.00 | |
| *b.* | | Surcharged in black | 5.75 | |
| *c.* | | As "b," "Gents" | 15.00 | |

No. O98 Surcharged in Black

**1926**

| | | | | |
|---|---|---|---|---|
| **O156** | A59 | 2c on 1c | 1.00 | 1.00 |
| *a.* | | Inverted surcharge | 20.00 | |
| *b.* | | "Gents" | 10.00 | |

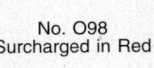

No. O98 Surcharged in Red

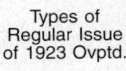

**1927**

| | | | | |
|---|---|---|---|---|
| **O157** | A59 | 2c on 1c | 35.00 | 35.00 |
| *a.* | | "Ceuts" | 55.00 | |
| *b.* | | "Vwo" | 55.00 | |
| *c.* | | "Twc" | 55.00 | |

Regular Issue of 1928 Overprinted in Red or Black

**1928** *Perf. 12*

| | | | | |
|---|---|---|---|---|
| **O158** | A102 | 1c grn (R) | 1.10 | .55 |
| **O159** | A102 | 2c gray vio (R) | 3.50 | 2.10 |
| **O160** | A102 | 3c bis brn (Bk) | 3.75 | 4.25 |
| **O161** | A103 | 5c ultra (R) | 1.10 | .55 |
| **O162** | A104 | 10c ol gray (R) | 3.50 | 1.75 |
| **O163** | A103 | 15c dl vio (R) | 3.50 | 1.00 |
| **O164** | A103 | $1 red brn (Bk) | 77.50 | 22.50 |
| | | *Nos. O158-O164 (7)* | 93.95 | 32.70 |

For surcharges see Nos. C3, O165.

**No. O162 Surcharged with New Value and Bar in Black**

**1945** **Unwmk.** *Perf. 12*

| | | | | |
|---|---|---|---|---|
| **O165** | A104 | 4c on 10c (Bk) | 12.00 | 12.00 |

## LIBYA

'li-bē-ə

(Libia)

LOCATION — North Africa, bordering on the Mediterranean Sea
GOVT. — Republic
AREA — 679,358 sq. mi.
POP. — 4,992,838 (1999 est.)
CAPITAL — Tripoli

In 1939, the four northern provinces of Libya, a former Italian colony, were incorporated in the Italian national territory. Included in the territory is the former Turkish Vilayet of Tripoli, annexed in 1912. Libya became a kingdom on Dec. 24, 1951. The Libyan Arab Republic was established Sept. 1, 1969. "People's Socialist . . ." was added to its name in 1977. See Cyrenaica and Tripolitania.

100 Centesimi = 1 Lira
Military Authority Lira (1951)
Franc (1951)
1,000 Milliemes = 1 Pound (1952)
1,000 Dirhams = 1 Dinar (1972)

**Watermarks**

Wmk. 140 — Crown

Wmk. 195 — Multiple Crown and Arabic F

Wmk. 310 — Multiple Crescent and Star

**Catalogue values for unused stamps in this country are for Never Hinged items, beginning with Scott 102 in the regular postage section, Scott C51 in the airpost section, Scott E13 in the special delivery section, Scott J25 in the postage due section, Scott O1 in the official section, Scott N1 in the Fezzan-Ghadames section, Scott 2N1 in the Fezzan section, Scott 2NB1 in the Fezzan semi-postal section, Scott 2NC1 in the Fezzan airpost section, Scott 2NJ1 in the Fezzan postage due section, Scott 3N1 in the Ghadames section, and Scott 3NC1 in the Ghadames airpost section.**

**Used values in italics are for postally used stamps. CTO's sell for about the same as unused, hinged stamps.**

Stamps of Italy Overprinted in Black

**1912-22** **Wmk. 140** *Perf. 14*

| | | | | |
|---|---|---|---|---|
| **1** | A42 | 1c brown ('15) | 1.40 | .85 |
| *a.* | | Double overprint | 250.00 | 250.00 |
| **2** | A43 | 2c orange brn | 1.40 | .50 |
| **3** | A48 | 5c green | 1.50 | .35 |
| *a.* | | Double overprint | 90.00 | 90.00 |
| *b.* | | Imperf., pair | 300.00 | |
| *c.* | | Inverted overprint | | — |
| *d.* | | Pair, one without overprint | 450.00 | 450.00 |
| **4** | A48 | 10c claret | 14.00 | .35 |
| *a.* | | Pair, one without overprint | 475.00 | 475.00 |
| *b.* | | Double overprint | 160.00 | 160.00 |
| **5** | A48 | 15c slate ('22) | 5.50 | *8.50* |
| **6** | A45 | 20c orange ('15) | 5.50 | .35 |
| *a.* | | Double overprint | 175.00 | *175.00* |
| *b.* | | Pair, one without overprint | 800.00 | 800.00 |
| **7** | A50 | 20c brn org ('18) | 4.25 | *5.50* |
| *a.* | | Double overprint | 175.00 | — |
| **8** | A49 | 25c blue | 5.50 | .35 |
| *b.* | | Double overprint | 175.00 | — |
| **9** | A49 | 40c brown | 14.00 | 1.00 |
| **10** | A45 | 45c ol grn ('17) | 37.50 | 30.00 |
| *a.* | | Inverted overprint | 675.00 | |
| **11** | A49 | 50c violet | 35.00 | 1.40 |
| **12** | A49 | 60c brn car ('18) | 19.00 | *25.00* |
| **13** | A46 | 1 l brn & grn ('15) | 62.50 | 1.75 |
| **14** | A46 | 5 l bl & rose ('15) | 425.00 | 500.00 |
| **15** | A51 | 10 l gray grn & red ('15) | 35.00 | *190.00* |
| | | *Nos. 1-15 (15)* | 667.05 | *765.90* |

Two types of overprint were applied to this issue. Type I has bold letters, with dots close within "i"; type II has thinner letters, with dots further away within "i." All values, along with Nos. E1 and E2, received the type I overprint, and values shown are for this type. Nos. 1, 3-4, 6, 8, 11, 13-15 and E1-E2 also received the type II overprint. For detailed listings, see the *Scott Classic Specialized Catalogue of Stamps and Covers.*

For surcharges see Nos. 37-38.

Overprinted in Violet

**1912** **Unwmk.**

| | | | | |
|---|---|---|---|---|
| **16** | A58 | 15c slate | 275.00 | 3.00 |
| *a.* | | Blue black overprint | *21,000.* | 42.50 |

No. 16 Surcharged

**1916, Mar.** **Unwmk.**

| | | | | |
|---|---|---|---|---|
| **19** | A58 | 20c on 15c slate | 60.00 | 12.50 |

Roman Legionary — A1

Diana of Ephesus — A2

Ancient Galley Leaving Tripoli — A3

"Victory" — A4

**1921** **Engr.** **Wmk. 140** *Perf. 14*

| | | | | |
|---|---|---|---|---|
| **20** | A1 | 1c blk & gray brn | 2.75 | *7.00* |
| **21** | A1 | 2c blk & red brn | 2.75 | *7.00* |
| **22** | A1 | 5c blk & grn | 3.50 | .70 |
| *a.* | | 5c black & red brown (error) | 1,900. | |
| *b.* | | Center inverted | 60.00 | 90.00 |
| *c.* | | Imperf., pair | 550.00 | 550.00 |
| **23** | A2 | 10c blk & rose | 3.50 | .70 |
| *a.* | | Center inverted | 60.00 | 90.00 |
| **24** | A2 | 15c blk brn & brn org | 85.00 | 2.75 |
| *a.* | | Center inverted | 150.00 | *275.00* |
| **25** | A2 | 25c dk bl & bl | 3.50 | .25 |
| *a.* | | Center inverted | 20.00 | 30.00 |
| *b.* | | Imperf., pair | 775.00 | 775.00 |
| **26** | A3 | 30c blk & blk brn | 35.00 | .70 |
| *a.* | | Center inverted | 2,750. | 3,000. |
| **27** | A3 | 50c blk & ol grn | 16.00 | .25 |
| *a.* | | 50c black & brown (error) | 625.00 | |
| *b.* | | Center inverted | | *4,750.* |
| **28** | A3 | 55c black & vio | 16.00 | *24.00* |
| **29** | A4 | 1 l dk brn & brn | 47.50 | .25 |
| **30** | A4 | 5 l blk & dk blue | 27.50 | 21.00 |
| **31** | A4 | 10 l dk bl & ol grn | 300.00 | 160.00 |
| | | *Nos. 20-31 (12)* | 543.00 | 224.60 |

See No. 47-61. For surcharges see No. 102-121.

***Perf. 14x13¼***

| | | | | |
|---|---|---|---|---|
| *20d* | A1 | 1c blk & gray brn | 5.50 | 11.00 |
| *21d* | A1 | 2c blk & red brn | 5.50 | 11.00 |
| *22d* | A1 | 5c blk & red green | 7.00 | 1.40 |
| *23d* | A2 | 10c blk & rose | 7.00 | 1.40 |
| *24d* | A2 | 15c blk & brn org | 160.00 | 5.50 |
| *25d* | A2 | 25c dk bl & bl | 7.00 | .35 |
| *26d* | A3 | 30c blk & blk brn | 70.00 | 1.40 |
| *27d* | A3 | 50c blk & ol grn | 32.50 | .35 |
| *28d* | A3 | 55c blk & vio | 32.50 | 55.00 |
| *29d* | A4 | 1 l dk brn & brn | 95.00 | .35 |
| *30d* | A4 | 5 l blk & dk blue | 55.00 | 30.00 |
| *31d* | A4 | 10 l blk & ol grn | 625.00 | 190.00 |

Italy Nos. 136-139 Overprinted

**1922, Apr.**

| | | | | |
|---|---|---|---|---|
| **33** | A64 | 5c olive green | 1.75 | *6.25* |
| *a.* | | Double overprint | 475.00 | 475.00 |
| **34** | A64 | 10c red | 1.75 | *6.25* |
| *a.* | | Double overprint | 475.00 | 475.00 |
| *b.* | | Inverted overprint | 950.00 | 950.00 |
| **35** | A64 | 15c slate green | 2.00 | *11.00* |
| **36** | A64 | 25c ultramarine | 2.00 | *11.00* |
| | | *Nos. 33-36 (4)* | 7.50 | *34.50* |

3rd anniv. of the victory of the Piave.

Nos. 11, 8 Surcharged

**1922, June 1**

| | | | | |
|---|---|---|---|---|
| **37** | A49 | 40c on 50c violet | 3.50 | 2.10 |
| **38** | A49 | 80c on 25c blue | 3.50 | *8.50* |

Libyan Sibyl — A6

**1924-31** **Unwmk.** *Perf. 14½x14*

| | | | | |
|---|---|---|---|---|
| **39** | A6 | 20c deep green | .70 | .25 |
| *c.* | | Vert. pair, imperf between and top | 1,400. | |
| *d.* | | Horiz. pair, imperf between and at right | 1,400. | |
| *e.* | | Horiz. pair, imperf between and at left | 1,400. | |
| **40** | A6 | 40c brown | 2.10 | .70 |
| *b.* | | Imperf single | 275.00 | *425.00* |
| **41** | A6 | 60c deep blue | .70 | .25 |
| *b.* | | Imperf single | 275.00 | |
| **42** | A6 | 1.75 l orange ('31) | 1.40 | .25 |
| **43** | A6 | 2 l carmine | 4.25 | 1.00 |
| *b.* | | Imperf single | 275.00 | *425.00* |
| **44** | A6 | 2.55 l violet ('31) | 8.50 | 17.50 |
| | | *Nos. 39-44 (6)* | 17.65 | 19.95 |

**1926-29** *Perf. 11*

| | | | | |
|---|---|---|---|---|
| *39a* | A6 | 20c | 45.00 | .30 |
| *40a* | A6 | 40c | 32.50 | 2.40 |
| *41a* | A6 | 60c | 32.50 | .45 |
| *43a* | A6 | 2 l ('29) | 15.00 | 5.00 |
| | | *Nos. 39a-43a (4)* | 125.00 | 8.15 |

**Type of 1921**

**1924-40** **Unwmk.** *Perf. 13½ to 14*

| | | | | |
|---|---|---|---|---|
| **47** | A1 | 1c blk & gray brown | 2.75 | 5.50 |
| **48** | A1 | 2c blk & red brn | 2.75 | 5.50 |
| **49** | A1 | 5c blk & green | 3.50 | .70 |
| **50** | A1 | 7½c blk & brn ('31) | 1.40 | 14.00 |
| **51** | A2 | 10c blk & dl red | 2.75 | .30 |
| *b.* | | 10c blk & carmine | 2.75 | .30 |
| *c.* | | As "b," center inverted | 175.00 | |
| **52** | A2 | 15c blk brn & org | 8.50 | 1.00 |
| *b.* | | Center inverted, perf. 11 | *4,500.* | *6,500.* |
| **53** | A2 | 25c dk bl & bl | 42.50 | .50 |
| *a.* | | Center inverted | 240.00 | 350.00 |
| **54** | A3 | 30c blk & blk brn | 2.75 | .50 |
| **55** | A3 | 50c blk & ol grn | 2.75 | .30 |
| *b.* | | Center inverted | 4,500. | |
| **56** | A3 | 55c black & vio | 625.00 | 825.00 |
| **57** | A4 | 75c vio & red ('31) | 6.50 | .25 |
| **58** | A4 | 1 l dk brn & brn | 10.00 | .35 |
| **59** | A3 | 1.25 l indigo & ultra ('31) | 1.40 | .25 |
| **60** | A4 | 5 l blk & dk bl ('40) | 150.00 | *175.00* |
| | | *Nos. 47-60 (14)* | 862.55 | 1,029. |

***Perf. 11***

| | | | | |
|---|---|---|---|---|
| *47a* | A1 | 1c | 375.00 | |
| *48a* | A1 | 2c | 375.00 | |
| *49a* | A1 | 5c | 70.00 | 17.50 |
| *51a* | A2 | 10c | 35.00 | 7.00 |
| *52a* | A2 | 15c | 475.00 | 45.00 |
| *54a* | A3 | 30c | 140.00 | 2.10 |
| *55a* | A3 | 50c | 775.00 | .25 |
| *58a* | A4 | 1 l | 350.00 | .35 |
| *60a* | A4 | 5 l ('37) | *2,400.* | 450.00 |
| **61** | A4 | 10 l dk bl & ol grn ('37) | 625.00 | 500.00 |

Nos. 47a and 48a were not sent to the colony. A few philatelically inspired covers exist.

**Italy Nos. 197 and 88 Overprinted Like Nos. 1-15**

**1929** **Wmk. 140** *Perf. 14*

| | | | | |
|---|---|---|---|---|
| **62** | A86 | 7½c light brown | 10.00 | *55.00* |
| *a.* | | Double overprint | — | — |
| **63** | A46 | 1.25 l blue & ultra | 60.00 | 21.00 |
| *a.* | | Inverted overprint | 3,750. | |

**Italy No. 193 Overprinted Like Nos. 33-36**

**1929** **Unwmk.** *Perf. 11*

| | | | | |
|---|---|---|---|---|
| **64** | A85 | 1.75 l deep brown | 75.00 | 2.10 |
| *h.* | | Perf 13¾ | | *12,000.* |

Water Carriers A7

Man of Tripoli — A8

Designs: 25c, Minaret. 30c, 1.25 l, Tomb of Holy Man near Tagiura. 50c, Statue of Emperor Claudius at Leptis. 75c, Ruins of gardens.

**1934, Feb. 17 Photo. *Perf. 14***

| | | | | |
|---|---|---|---|---|
| **64A** | A7 | 10c brown | 4.25 | *17.50* |
| **64B** | A8 | 20c car rose | 4.25 | *15.00* |
| **64C** | A8 | 25c green | 4.25 | *15.00* |
| **64D** | A7 | 30c dark brown | 4.25 | *15.00* |
| **64E** | A8 | 50c purple | 4.25 | *15.00* |
| **64F** | A7 | 75c rose | 4.25 | *27.50* |
| **64G** | A7 | 1.25 l blue | 55.00 | *95.00* |
| | | *Nos. 64A-64G (7)* | 80.50 | *200.00* |
| | | *Nos. 64A-64G,C14-C18 (12)* | 508.50 | *980.00* |

8th Sample Fair, Tripoli.

Bedouin Woman — A15

**1936, May 11 Wmk. 140 *Perf. 14***

| | | | | |
|---|---|---|---|---|
| **65** | A15 | 50c purple | 1.75 | *2.75* |
| **66** | A15 | 1.25 l deep blue | 1.75 | *7.75* |

10th Sample Fair, Tripoli.

Highway Memorial Arch — A16

**1937, Mar. 15**

| | | | | |
|---|---|---|---|---|
| **67** | A16 | 50c copper red | 2.75 | *5.50* |
| **68** | A16 | 1.25 l sapphire | 2.75 | *12.50* |
| | | *Nos. 67-68,C28-C29 (4)* | 11.00 | *36.00* |

Coastal road to the Egyptian frontier, opening.

Nos. 67-68 Overprinted in Black

**1937, Apr. 24**

| | | | | |
|---|---|---|---|---|
| **69** | A16 | 50c copper red | 14.00 | *35.00* |
| **70** | A16 | 1.25 l sapphire | 14.00 | *35.00* |
| | | *Nos. 69-70,C30-C31 (4)* | 56.00 | *140.00* |

11th Sample Fair, Tripoli.

Roman Wolf and Lion of St. Mark A17

View of Fair Buildings A18

**1938, Feb. 20**

| | | | | |
|---|---|---|---|---|
| **71** | A17 | 5c brown | .30 | 1.00 |
| **72** | A18 | 10c olive brown | .30 | .70 |
| **73** | A17 | 25c green | .55 | 1.25 |
| **74** | A18 | 50c purple | .55 | .55 |
| **75** | A17 | 75c rose red | 1.40 | *2.75* |
| **76** | A18 | 1.25 l dark blue | 1.40 | *7.00* |
| | | *Nos. 71-76,C32-C33 (8)* | 7.30 | *21.50* |

12th Sample Fair, Tripoli.

Augustus Caesar (Octavianus) A19

Goddess Abundantia A20

**1938, Apr. 25**

| | | | | |
|---|---|---|---|---|
| **77** | A19 | 5c olive brown | .25 | 1.40 |
| **78** | A20 | 10c brown red | .25 | 1.40 |
| **79** | A19 | 25c dk yel green | .50 | .70 |
| **80** | A20 | 50c dk violet | .50 | .45 |
| **81** | A19 | 75c orange red | 1.40 | *1.75* |
| **82** | A20 | 1.25 l dull blue | 1.40 | *2.75* |
| | | *Nos. 77-82,C34-C35 (8)* | 5.65 | *13.95* |

Birth bimillenary of Augustus Caesar (Octavianus), first Roman emperor.

Desert City — A21

View of Ghadames A22

**1939, Apr. 12 Photo.**

| | | | | |
|---|---|---|---|---|
| **83** | A21 | 5c olive brown | .70 | 1.00 |
| **84** | A22 | 20c red brown | .70 | 1.00 |
| **85** | A21 | 50c rose violet | .70 | 1.00 |
| **86** | A22 | 75c scarlet | .70 | *3.50* |
| **87** | A21 | 1.25 l gray blue | 1.40 | *4.25* |
| | | *Nos. 83-87,C36-C38 (8)* | 6.60 | *17.70* |

13th Sample Fair, Tripoli.

Modern City — A23

Oxen and Plow A24

Mosque — A25

**1940, June 3 Wmk. 140 *Perf. 14***

| | | | | |
|---|---|---|---|---|
| **88** | A23 | 5c brown | .70 | 1.00 |
| **89** | A24 | 10c red orange | .70 | .70 |
| **90** | A25 | 25c dull green | .70 | *1.00* |
| **91** | A23 | 50c dark violet | .70 | *.70* |
| **92** | A24 | 75c crimson | .70 | *3.50* |
| **93** | A25 | 1.25 l ultramarine | 1.40 | *5.50* |
| **94** | A24 | 2 l + 75c rose lake | 1.40 | *16.00* |
| | | *Nos. 88-94,C39-C42 (11)* | 9.70 | *50.50* |

Triennial Overseas Exposition, Naples.

"Two Peoples, One War," Hitler and Mussolini A26

**1941, May 16**

| | | | | |
|---|---|---|---|---|
| **95** | A26 | 5c orange | 2.10 | *7.00* |
| **96** | A26 | 10c brown | 2.10 | *7.00* |
| **97** | A26 | 20c dull violet | 3.50 | *7.00* |
| **98** | A26 | 25c green | 3.50 | *7.00* |
| **99** | A26 | 50c purple | 3.50 | *7.00* |
| **100** | A26 | 75c scarlet | 3.50 | *19.00* |
| **101** | A26 | 1.25 l sapphire | 3.50 | *19.00* |
| | | *Nos. 95-101,C43 (8)* | 24.45 | *115.50* |
| | | *Set, never hinged* | 42.50 | |

The Rome-Berlin Axis.

**Catalogue values for unused stamps in this section, from this point to the end of the section, are for Never Hinged items.**

## United Kingdom of Libya

Stamps of Cyrenaica 1950 Surcharged in Black

### For Use in Tripolitania

**1951, Dec. 24 Unwmk. *Perf. 12½***

| | | | | |
|---|---|---|---|---|
| **102** | A2 | 1mal on 2m rose car | .25 | .25 |
| **103** | A2 | 2mal on 4m dk grn | .25 | .25 |
| **104** | A2 | 4mal on 8m red org | .25 | .25 |
| **105** | A2 | 5mal on 10m pur | .45 | .45 |
| **106** | A2 | 6mal on 12m red | .45 | .45 |
| *a.* | | Inverted surcharge | 30.00 | 30.00 |
| **107** | A2 | 10mal on 20m dp bl | .85 | .85 |
| *a.* | | Arabic "20" for "10" | 25.00 | 25.00 |
| **108** | A3 | 24mal on 50m choc & ultra | 3.25 | 3.25 |
| **109** | A3 | 48mal on 100m bl blk & car rose | 13.50 | 13.50 |
| **110** | A3 | 96mal on 200m vio & pur | 30.00 | 30.00 |
| **111** | A3 | 240mal on 500m dk grn & org | 75.00 | 75.00 |
| | | *Nos. 102-111 (10)* | 124.25 | *124.25* |

The surcharge is larger on Nos. 108 to 111.

### For Use in Fezzan

Same Surcharge in Francs

| | | | | |
|---|---|---|---|---|
| **112** | A2 | 2fr on 2m rose car | .25 | .50 |
| **113** | A2 | 4fr on 4m dk grn | .25 | .50 |
| **114** | A2 | 8fr on 8m red org | .35 | .70 |
| **115** | A2 | 10fr on 10m pur | .50 | 1.00 |
| **116** | A2 | 12fr on 12m red | .90 | 1.75 |
| **117** | A2 | 20fr on 20m dp bl | 2.00 | *4.50* |
| **118** | A3 | 48fr on 50m choc & ultra | 42.50 | *45.00* |
| **119** | A3 | 96fr on 100m bl blk & car rose | 42.50 | *240.00* |
| **120** | A3 | 192fr on 200m vio & pur | 120.00 | *240.00* |
| **121** | A3 | 480fr on 500m dk grn & org | 225.00 | *260.00* |
| | | *Nos. 112-121 (10)* | 434.25 | *793.95* |

The surcharge is larger on Nos. 118-121.

A second printing of Nos. 118-121 has an elongated first character in second line of Arabic surcharge.

Cyrenaica Nos. 65-77 Overprinted in Black

### For Use in Cyrenaica

| | | | | |
|---|---|---|---|---|
| **122** | A2 | 1m dark brown | .25 | .40 |
| **123** | A2 | 2m rose carmine | .30 | .40 |
| **124** | A2 | 3m orange | .30 | .50 |
| **125** | A2 | 4m dark green | 35.00 | 55.00 |
| **126** | A2 | 5m gray | .30 | *.50* |
| **127** | A2 | 8m red orange | .75 | *1.25* |
| **128** | A2 | 10m purple | 1.25 | *1.90* |
| **129** | A2 | 12m red | 1.40 | *2.25* |
| **130** | A2 | 20m deep blue | 2.00 | *3.75* |
| **131** | A3 | 50m choc & ultra | 9.50 | *19.00* |
| **132** | A3 | 100m bl blk & car rose | 17.50 | *24.00* |
| **133** | A3 | 200m violet & pur | 55.00 | *70.00* |
| **134** | A3 | 500m dk grn & org | 180.00 | *190.00* |
| | | *Nos. 122-134 (13)* | 303.55 | *368.95* |

Wider spacing between the two lines on Nos. 131-134.

King Idris

A27 A28

**1952, Apr. 15 Engr. *Perf. 11½***

| | | | | |
|---|---|---|---|---|
| **135** | A27 | 2m yellow brown | .25 | .25 |
| **136** | A27 | 4m gray | .25 | .25 |
| **137** | A27 | 5m blue green | 20.00 | .65 |
| **138** | A27 | 8m vermilion | .85 | .55 |
| **139** | A27 | 10m purple | 20.00 | .40 |
| **140** | A27 | 12m lilac rose | 1.75 | .40 |
| **141** | A27 | 20m deep blue | 22.50 | .90 |
| **142** | A27 | 25m chocolate | 22.50 | .90 |
| **143** | A28 | 50m brown & blue | 3.00 | 1.40 |
| **144** | A28 | 100m gray blk & car rose | 5.25 | 3.00 |
| **145** | A28 | 200m dk blue & pur | 11.00 | 6.00 |
| **146** | A28 | 500m dk grn & brn orange | 37.50 | 21.00 |
| | | *Nos. 135-146 (12)* | 144.85 | 35.70 |

For surcharge and overprints see Nos. 168, O1-O8.

Globe — A29

***Perf. 13½x13***

**1955, Jan. 1 Photo. Wmk. 195**

| | | | | |
|---|---|---|---|---|
| **147** | A29 | 5m yellow brown | 2.00 | 1.30 |
| **148** | A29 | 10m green | 3.00 | 2.00 |
| **149** | A29 | 30m violet | 5.50 | 3.50 |
| | | *Nos. 147-149 (3)* | 10.50 | 6.80 |

Arab Postal Union founding, July 1, 1954.

Nos. 147-149 Overprinted

**1955, Aug. 1**

| | | | | |
|---|---|---|---|---|
| **150** | A29 | 5m yellow brn | 1.00 | .65 |
| **151** | A29 | 10m green | 2.00 | 1.10 |
| **152** | A29 | 30m violet | 3.75 | 2.00 |
| | | *Nos. 150-152 (3)* | 6.75 | 3.75 |

Arab Postal Congress, Cairo, Mar. 15.

Emblems of Tripolitania, Cyrenaica and Fezzan with Royal Crown — A30

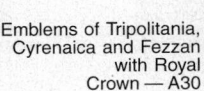

**1955 Engr. Wmk. 310 *Perf. 11½***

| | | | | |
|---|---|---|---|---|
| 153 | A30 | 2m lemon | 2.00 | .70 |
| 154 | A30 | 3m slate blue | .25 | .25 |
| 155 | A30 | 4m gray green | 2.75 | 1.25 |
| 156 | A30 | 5m light blue grn | .85 | .25 |
| 157 | A30 | 10m violet | 1.50 | .25 |
| 158 | A30 | 18m crimson | .25 | .25 |
| 159 | A30 | 20m orange | .50 | .25 |
| 160 | A30 | 30m blue | .85 | .25 |
| 161 | A30 | 35m brown | 1.25 | .25 |
| 162 | A30 | 40m rose carmine | 2.00 | .60 |
| 163 | A30 | 50m olive | 1.25 | .60 |

**Size: 27½x32½mm**

| | | | | |
|---|---|---|---|---|
| 164 | A30 | 100m dk green & pur | 2.75 | 1.20 |
| 165 | A30 | 200m ultra & rose car | 13.00 | 2.50 |
| 166 | A30 | 500m grn & orange | 20.00 | 12.00 |

**Size: 26½x32mm**

| | | | | |
|---|---|---|---|---|
| 167 | A30 | £1 ocher, brn & grn, *yel* | 30.00 | 18.00 |
| | | *Nos. 153-167 (15)* | 79.20 | 38.60 |

See Nos. 177-179, 192-206A.

No. 136 Surcharged

**1955, Aug. 25 Unwmk.**

168 A27 5m on 4m gray 2.00 .90

Tomb of El Senussi, Jagbub A31

***Perf. 13x13½***

**1956, Sept. 14 Photo. Wmk. 195**

| | | | | |
|---|---|---|---|---|
| 169 | A31 | 5m green | .50 | .50 |
| 170 | A31 | 10m bright violet | .60 | .50 |
| 171 | A31 | 15m rose carmine | 1.40 | 1.25 |
| 172 | A31 | 30m sapphire | 2.25 | 1.40 |
| | | *Nos. 169-172 (4)* | 4.75 | 3.65 |

Death centenary of the Imam Seyyid Mohammed Aly El Senussi (in 1859).

Map, Flags and UN Headquarters — A32

**1956, Dec. 14 Litho. *Perf. 13½x13***

| | | | | |
|---|---|---|---|---|
| 173 | A32 | 15m bl, ocher & ol bis | .75 | .35 |
| 174 | A32 | 35m bl, ocher & vio brn | 1.60 | .75 |

Libya's admission to the UN, 1st anniv.

Globe and Postal Emblems — A33

**1957 Wmk. 195 *Perf. 13½x13***

| | | | | |
|---|---|---|---|---|
| 175 | A33 | 15m blue | 1.50 | 1.50 |
| 176 | A33 | 500m yellow brown | 22.00 | 12.00 |

Arab Postal Congress, Tripoli, Feb. 9.

**Emblems Type of 1955**

**1957 Wmk. 310 Engr. *Perf. 11½***

| | | | | |
|---|---|---|---|---|
| 177 | A30 | 1m black, *yellow* | .25 | .25 |
| 178 | A30 | 2m bister brown | .25 | .25 |
| 179 | A30 | 4m brown carmine | .35 | .35 |
| | | *Nos. 177-179 (3)* | .85 | .85 |

UN Emblem and Broken Chain — A34

**Unwmk.**

**1958, Dec. 10 Photo. *Perf. 14***

| | | | | |
|---|---|---|---|---|
| 180 | A34 | 10m bluish violet | .35 | .25 |
| 181 | A34 | 15m green | .60 | .35 |
| 182 | A34 | 30m ultramarine | 1.50 | .85 |
| | | *Nos. 180-182 (3)* | 2.45 | 1.45 |

Universal Declaration of Human Rights, 10th anniv.

Date Palms and FAO Emblem A35

**1959, Dec. 5 Unwmk. *Perf. 14***

| | | | | |
|---|---|---|---|---|
| 183 | A35 | 10m pale vio & black | .40 | .25 |
| 184 | A35 | 15m bluish grn & blk | .60 | .45 |
| 185 | A35 | 45m light blue & blk | 1.50 | 1.20 |
| | | *Nos. 183-185 (3)* | 2.50 | 1.90 |

1st Intl. Dates Conf., Tripoli, Dec. 5-11.

Arab League Center, Cairo, and Arms of Libya A36

***Perf. 13x13½***

**1960, Mar. 22 Wmk. 328**

186 A36 10m dull grn & blk .60 .35

Opening of the Arab League Center and the Arab Postal Museum in Cairo.

Emblems of WRY and UN, Arms of Libya — A37

**1960, Apr. 7 Unwmk. *Perf. 14***

| | | | | |
|---|---|---|---|---|
| 187 | A37 | 10m violet & black | .60 | .35 |
| 188 | A37 | 45m blue & black | 1.75 | 1.25 |

World Refugee Year, 7/1/59-6/30/60.

Palm Tree and Radio Mast — A38

**1960, Aug. 4 Engr. *Perf. 13x13½***

| | | | | |
|---|---|---|---|---|
| 189 | A38 | 10m violet | .35 | .25 |
| 190 | A38 | 15m blue green | .50 | .25 |
| 191 | A38 | 45m dk carmine rose | 1.80 | 1.25 |
| | | *Nos. 189-191 (3)* | 2.65 | 1.75 |

3rd Arab Telecommunications Conf., Tripoli, Aug. 4.

**Emblems Type of 1955**

**1960 Wmk. 310 Engr. *Perf. 11½***

**Size: 18x21½mm**

| | | | | |
|---|---|---|---|---|
| 192 | A30 | 1m black, *gray* | .25 | .25 |
| 193 | A30 | 2m bis brn, *buff* | .25 | .25 |
| 194 | A30 | 3m blue, *bluish* | .25 | .25 |
| 195 | A30 | 4m brn car, *rose* | .25 | .25 |
| 196 | A30 | 5m grn, *greenish* | .25 | .25 |
| 197 | A30 | 10m vio, *pale vio* | .25 | .25 |
| 198 | A30 | 15m brown, *buff* | .25 | .25 |
| 199 | A30 | 20m orange, *buff* | .50 | .25 |
| 200 | A30 | 30m red, *pink* | .50 | .25 |
| 201 | A30 | 40m rose car, *rose* | .75 | .25 |
| 202 | A30 | 45m blue, *bluish* | .85 | .25 |
| 203 | A30 | 50m olive, *buff* | .85 | .25 |

**Size: 27½x32½mm**

| | | | | |
|---|---|---|---|---|
| 204 | A30 | 100m dk grn & pur, *gray* | 1.50 | .70 |
| 205 | A30 | 200m bl & rose car, *bluish* | 4.25 | 1.40 |
| 206 | A30 | 500m green & org, *greenish* | 30.00 | 9.00 |

**Size: 26½x32mm**

| | | | | |
|---|---|---|---|---|
| 206A | A30 | £1 ocher, brn & grn, *brn* | 35.00 | 18.00 |
| | | *Nos. 192-206A (16)* | 75.95 | 32.10 |

Watchtower and Broken Chain — A39

**1961, Aug. 9 Photo. Unwmk.**

| | | | | |
|---|---|---|---|---|
| 207 | A39 | 5m lt yel grn & brn | .50 | .25 |
| 208 | A39 | 15m light blue & brn | .85 | .35 |

Issued for Army Day, Aug. 9, 1961.

Map of Zelten Oil Field and Tanker at Marsa Brega — A40

**1961, Oct. 25 *Perf. 11½***

| | | | | |
|---|---|---|---|---|
| 209 | A40 | 15m ol grn & buff | .50 | .25 |
| 210 | A40 | 50m red brn & pale vio | 1.50 | 1.00 |
| 211 | A40 | 100m ultra & blue | 3.50 | 1.25 |
| | | *Nos. 209-211 (3)* | 5.50 | 2.50 |

Opening of first oil pipe line in Libya.

Hands Breaking Chain, Tractor and Cows — A41

Designs: 50m, Modern highways and buildings. 100m, Machinery.

**1961, Dec. 24 *Perf. 11½***

**Granite Paper**

| | | | | |
|---|---|---|---|---|
| 212 | A41 | 15m pale grn, grn & brown | .25 | .25 |
| 213 | A41 | 50m buff & brown | .90 | .60 |
| 214 | A41 | 100m sal, vio & brn | 3.25 | 1.25 |
| | | *Nos. 212-214 (3)* | 4.40 | 2.10 |

10th anniversary of independence.

Camel Riders — A42

15m, Well. 50m, Oil installations in desert.

**1962, Feb. 20 Photo. *Perf. 12***

| | | | | |
|---|---|---|---|---|
| 215 | A42 | 10m choc & org brn | .85 | .25 |
| 216 | A42 | 15m plum & yel grn | 1.00 | .60 |
| 217 | A42 | 50m emer & ultra | 2.75 | 2.10 |
| a. | | Souv. sheet of 3, #215-217, imperf. | 65.00 | 30.00 |
| | | *Nos. 215-217 (3)* | 4.60 | 2.95 |

Intl. Fair, Tripoli, Feb. 20-Mar. 20.

Nos. 215-217 exist imperf. Value about twice that of perf.

Malaria Eradication Emblem and Palm — A43

**1962, Apr. 7 Unwmk. *Perf. 11½***

| | | | | |
|---|---|---|---|---|
| 218 | A43 | 15m multicolored | .60 | .50 |
| 219 | A43 | 50m grn, yel & brn | 1.50 | 1.20 |

WHO drive to eradicate malaria.

Exist imperf. Value $10.

Two imperf. souvenir sheets exist, one containing the 15m, the other the 50m. Sold for 20m and 70m respectively. Value for both, $34.

Ahmed Rafik El Mehdawi (1898-1961), Poet — A44

**1962, July 6 Engr. *Perf. 13x14***

| | | | | |
|---|---|---|---|---|
| 220 | A44 | 15m green | .40 | .25 |
| 221 | A44 | 20m brown | .85 | .50 |

El Mehdawi, 1st death anniv.

Clasped Hands and Scout Emblem — A45

Designs: 10m, 30m, Boy Scouts. 15m, 50m, Scout emblem and tents.

**1962, July 13 Photo. *Perf. 12***

| | | | | |
|---|---|---|---|---|
| 222 | A45 | 5m yel, blk & red | .25 | .25 |
| 223 | A45 | 10m bl, blk & yel | .50 | .25 |
| 224 | A45 | 15m multicolored | .60 | .50 |
| | | *Nos. 222-224 (3)* | 1.35 | 1.00 |

**Souvenir Sheet**

***Imperf***

| | | | | |
|---|---|---|---|---|
| 225 | | Sheet of 3 | 20.00 | 20.00 |
| a. | | A45 20m yellow, black & red | 5.00 | 5.00 |
| b. | | A45 30m blue, black & yellow | 5.00 | 5.00 |
| c. | | A45 50m blue gray, yel, blk & grn | 5.00 | 5.00 |

Third Libyan Scout meeting (Philia).

Nos. 222-224 exist imperf. Value for set, $3.

Drop of Oil with New City, Desert, Oil Wells and Map of Coast Line — A46

**1962, Nov. 25 *Perf. 11x11½***

| | | | | |
|---|---|---|---|---|
| 226 | A46 | 15m grn & vio blk | .50 | .25 |
| 227 | A46 | 50m brn org & ol | 1.40 | .75 |

Opening of the Essider Terminal Sidrah pipeline system.

Centenary Emblem — A47

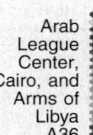

**Litho. & Photo.**

**1963, Jan. 1** ***Perf. 11½***

**228** A47 10m rose, blk, red & bl .75 .40
**229** A47 15m citron, blk, red & bl .85 .60
**230** A47 20m gray, blk, red & bl 1.60 .85
*Nos. 228-230 (3)* 3.20 1.85

Centenary of the International Red Cross.

Rainbow and Arches over Map of Africa and Libya — A48

**1963, Feb. 28** **Litho.** ***Perf. 13½***

**231** A48 15m multicolored .50 .35
**232** A48 30m multicolored .85 .35
**233** A48 50m multicolored 1.80 1.00
*Nos. 231-233 (3)* 3.15 1.70

Tripoli Intl. Fair "Gateway of Africa," Feb. 28-Mar. 28. Every other horizontal row inverted in sheet of 50 (25 tête bêche pairs). Value, set of tête bêche pairs, $6.50.

Date Palm and Well — A49

Designs: 15m, Camel and flock of sheep. 45m, Sower and tractor.

**1963, Mar. 21** **Photo.** ***Perf. 11½***

**234** A49 10m green, lt bl & bis .50 .25
**235** A49 15m pur, lt grn & bis .60 .50
**236** A49 45m dk bl, sal & sep 1.60 1.00
*Nos. 234-236 (3)* 2.70 1.75

FAO "Freedom from Hunger" campaign.

Man with Whip and Slave Reaching for UN Emblem A50

**1963, Dec. 10** **Unwmk.** ***Perf. 11½***

**237** A50 5m red brown & bl .25 .25
**238** A50 15m deep claret & bl .50 .25
**239** A50 50m green & blue 1.25 .75
*Nos. 237-239 (3)* 2.00 1.25

Universal Declaration of Human Rights, 15th anniv.

Exhibition Hall and Finger Pointing to Libya — A51

**1964, Feb. 28** **Photo.** ***Perf. 11½***

**240** A51 10m red brn, gray grn & brn 1.00 .25
**241** A51 15m pur, gray grn & brn 1.40 .60
**242** A51 30m dk bl, gray grn & brn 2.00 1.40
*Nos. 240-242 (3)* 4.40 2.25

3rd Intl. Fair, Tripoli, Feb. 28-Mar. 20.

Child Playing with Blocks — A52

Design: 15m, Child in bird's nest.

**1964, Mar. 22** ***Perf. 11½***

**243** A52 5m multicolored .25 .25
**244** A52 15m multicolored .60 .25
**245** A52 45m multicolored 1.75 .85
*a.* Souvenir sheet of 3, #243-245, imperf. 5.00 5.00
*Nos. 243-245 (3)* 2.60 1.35

Children's Day. Exist imperf. Value about 1½ times that of perf.
No. 245a sold for 100m.

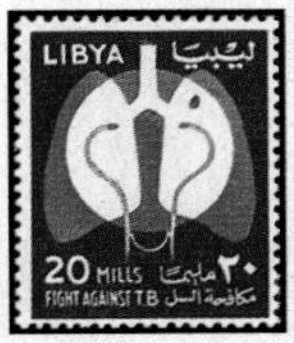


Lungs and Stethoscope — A53

**1964, Apr. 7** **Photo.** ***Perf. 13½x14***

**246** A53 20m deep purple 1.25 .60

Campaign against tuberculosis.

Map of Libya A54

**1964, Apr. 27** **Unwmk.** ***Perf. 11½***

**247** A54 5m emerald & org .25 .25
**248** A54 50m blue & yellow 1.50 .60

First anniversary of Libyan union.

Moth Emerging from Cocoon, Veiled and Modern Women — A55

**1964, June 15** **Litho. & Engraved**

**249** A55 10m vio bl & lt grn .35 .25
**250** A55 20m vio blue & yel .75 .60
**251** A55 35m vio bl & pink 1.25 1.10
*a.* Souv. sheet of 3, #249-251 5.50 5.50
*Nos. 249-251 (3)* 2.35 1.95

To honor Libyan women in a new epoch. No. 251a sold for 100m.

Hand Giving Scout Sign, Scout and Libyan Flags — A56

Design: 20m, Libyan Scout emblem and hands.

**1964, July 24** **Photo.** ***Perf. 12x11½***

**252** A56 10m lt bl & multi .85 .35
**253** A56 20m multicolored 1.75 .85
*a.* Souvenir sheet of 2, #252-253, imperf. 11.50 11.50

Opening of new Boy Scout headquarters; installation of Crown Prince Hassan al-Rida el Senussi as Chief Scout. No. 253a sold for 50m.

Nos. 252-253 exist imperf. Value about 1½ times that of perf.

Bayonet, Wreath and Map — A57

**1964, Aug. 9** **Litho.** ***Perf. 14x13½***

**254** A57 10m yel grn & brn .25 .25
**255** A57 20m org & blk .75 .35

Founding of the Senussi Army.

Ahmed Bahloul el-Sharef — A58

**1964, Aug. 11** **Engr.** ***Perf. 11½***

**256** A58 15m lilac .50 .25
**257** A58 20m greenish blue .85 .50

Poet Ahmed Bahloul el-Sharef, died 1953.

Soccer A59

**1964, Oct. 1** **Litho.** ***Perf. 14***

**Black Inscriptions and Gold Olympic Rings**

**258** A59 5m shown .75 .50
**259** A59 10m Bicycling .75 .50
**260** A59 20m Boxing .75 .50
**261** A59 30m Sprinter .75 .60
**262** A59 35m Woman diver .75 .60
**263** A59 50m Hurdling .75 .60
*a.* Block of 6, #258-263 5.00 5.00

18th Olympic Games, Tokyo, Oct. 10-25. No. 263a printed in sheet of 48. The two blocks in each double row are inverted in relation to the two blocks in the next row, providing various tete beche and se-tenant arrangements.

Nos. 258-263 exist imperf. Value for set, $27.50.

Perf. and imperf. souvenir sheets exist containing six 15m stamps in the designs and colors of Nos. 258-263. Sheets sold for 100m. Value for both, $32.50.

Arab Postal Union Emblem — A59a

**1964, Dec. 1** **Photo.** ***Perf. 11x11½***

**264** A59a 10m yellow & blue .25 .25
**265** A59a 15m pale vio & org brn .50 .25
**266** A59a 30m lt yel grn & brn 1.40 .85
*Nos. 264-266 (3)* 2.15 1.35

Permanent Office of the APU, 10th anniv.

International Cooperation Year Emblem — A60

**1965, Jan. 1** **Litho.** ***Perf. 14½x14***

**267** A60 5m vio bl & gold .50 .25
**268** A60 15m rose car & gold 1.50 .70

Imperfs. exist. Value about twice that of perfs.

See Nos. C51-C51a.

European Bee Eater — A61

Birds: 5m, Long-legged buzzard, vert. 15m, Chestnut-bellied sandgrouse. 20m, Houbara bustard. 30m, Spotted sandgrouse. 40m, Libyan Barbary partridge, vert..

**1965, Feb. 10** **Photo.** ***Perf. 11½***

**Granite Paper**

**Birds in Natural Colors**

**269** A61 5m gray & black 1.25 .50
**270** A61 10m lt bl & org brn 2.00 .55
**271** A61 15m lt green & blk 2.25 .60
**272** A61 20m pale lil & blk 3.75 .85
**273** A61 30m tan & dark brn 4.75 1.50
**274** A61 40m dull yel & blk 5.50 1.90
*Nos. 269-274 (6)* 19.50 5.90

Map of Africa with Libya A62

**1965, Feb. 28** **Photo.** ***Perf. 11½***

**Granite Paper**

**275** A62 50m multicolored 1.00 .55

4th Intl. Tripoli Fair, Feb. 28-Mar. 20.

Compass Rose, Rockets, Balloons and Stars — A63

**1965, Mar. 23** **Litho.**

**276** A63 10m multicolored .25 .25
**277** A63 15m multicolored .50 .35
**278** A63 50m multicolored 1.50 1.00
*Nos. 276-278 (3)* 2.25 1.60

Fifth World Meteorological Day.

ITU Emblem, Old and New Communication Equipment — A64

**1965, May 17** **Unwmk.**

**279** A64 10m sepia .25 .25
**280** A64 20m red lilac .35 .25
**281** A64 50m lilac rose 1.25 .90
*Nos. 279-281 (3)* 1.85 1.40

ITU, centenary.

Library Aflame and Lamp — A65

**1965, June** **Litho.** ***Perf. 11½***

**282** A65 15m multicolored .50 .25
**283** A65 50m multicolored 1.25 .55

Burning of the Library of Algiers, June 7, 1962.

Rose — A66

**1965, Aug. Litho. *Perf. 14***

**284** A66 1m shown .25 .25
**285** A66 2m Iris .25 .25
**286** A66 3m Opuntia .35 .25
**287** A66 4m Sunflower .75 .25
*Nos. 284-287 (4)* 1.60 1.00

Jet Plane and Globe — A67

**1965, Oct. Photo. *Perf. 11½***

**288** A67 5m multicolored .25 .25
**289** A67 10m multicolored .50 .25
**290** A67 15m multicolored 1.00 .25
*Nos. 288-290 (3)* 1.75 .75

Issued to publicize Libyan Airlines.

Forum, Cyrene — A68

Designs: 100m, Arch of Trajan. 200m, Temple of Apollo, Cyrene. 500m, Antonine Temple of Jupiter, Sabratha, horiz. £1, Theater, Sabratha.

***Perf. 12x11½, 11½x12***

**1965, Dec. 24 Engr. Wmk. 310**

**291** A68 50m vio blue & olive 2.00 .60
**292** A68 100m Prus bl & dp org 2.75 .85
**293** A68 200m pur & Prus bl 6.50 1.50
**294** A68 500m car rose & grn 15.00 4.00
**295** A68 £1 grn & dp org 32.50 10.00
*Nos. 291-295 (5)* 58.75 16.95

Nos. 293-295 with "Kingdom of Libia" in both Arabic and English blocked out with a blue felt-tipped pen were issued June 21, 1970, by the Republic.

Mausoleum at Germa — A69

***Perf. 11½***

**1966, Feb. 10 Unwmk. Litho.**

**296** A69 70m purple & salmon 3.00 1.00

"POLIGRAFICA & CARTEVALORI-NAPLES" and Libyan Coat of Arms printed on back in yellow green. See No. E13.

Booklet pane containing 4 No. 296 and 4 No. E13 exists. Value $30.

Globe in Space, Satellites — A70

**1966, Feb. 28 *Perf. 12***

**297** A70 15m multi & gold .50 .25
**298** A70 45m multi & gold 1.00 .45
**299** A70 55m multi & gold 1.25 .65
*Nos. 297-299 (3)* 2.75 1.35

5th Intl. Fair at Tripoli, Feb. 28-Mar. 20.

Arab League Center, Cairo, and Emblem — A71

**Litho. & Photo.**

**1966, Mar. 22 *Perf. 11***

**300** A71 20m car, emer & blk .35 .35
**301** A71 55m brt bl, ver & blk 1.50 .65

Issued to publicize the Arab League.

Souvenir Sheet

WHO Headquarters, Geneva, and Emblem — A72

**1966, May 3 Litho. *Imperf.***

**302** A72 50m multicolored 9.50 *15.00*

Inauguration of the WHO headquarters. See Nos. C55-C57.

Tuareg and Camel — A73

A74

Three Tuareg Riders — A75

Design: 20m, like 10m, facing left.

**1966, June 20 Unwmk. *Perf. 10***

**303** A73 10m bright red 1.25 .80
**304** A73 20m ultramarine 2.75 1.50
**305** A74 50m multicolored 6.00 4.00
*a.* Strip of 3, Nos. 303-305 11.00 8.50

***Imperf***

**306** A75 100m multicolored 16.00 16.00

Gazelle — A76

Emblem — A77

***Perf. 13x11, 11x13***

**1966, Aug. 12 Litho.**

**307** A76 5m lt grn, blk & red .50 .25
**308** A77 25m multicolored .90 .35
**309** A77 65m multicolored 2.50 .65
*Nos. 307-309 (3)* 3.90 1.25

1st Arab Girl Scout Camp (5m); 7th Arab Boy Scout Camp, Good Daim, Libya, Aug. 12 (25m, 60m).

UNESCO Emblem A78

**1967, Jan. Litho. *Perf. 10x10½***

**310** A78 15m multicolored .50 .25
**311** A78 25m multicolored 1.10 .45

UNESCO, 20th anniv. (in 1966).

Castle of Columns, Tolemaide — A79

Design: 55m, Sebha Fort, horiz.

***Perf. 13x13½, 13½x13***

**1966, Dec. 24 Engr.**

**312** A79 25m lil, red brn & blk .65 .35
**313** A79 55m blk, lil & red brn 1.25 .65

Fair Emblem — A80

**1967, Feb. 28 Photo. *Perf. 11½***

**314** A80 15m multicolored .65 .25
**315** A80 55m multicolored 1.00 .55

6th Intl. Fair, Tripoli, Feb. 28-Mar. 20.

Oil Tanker, Marsa Al Hariga Terminal — A81

**1967, Feb. 14 Litho. *Perf. 10***

**316** A81 60m multicolored 2.25 .75

Opening of Marsa Al Hariga oil terminal.

Tourist Year Emblem — A82

**1967, May 1 Litho. *Perf. 10½x10***

**317** A82 5m gray, blk & brt bl .25 .25
**318** A82 10m lt bl, blk & brt bl .25 .25
**319** A82 45m pink, blk & brt bl .75 .35
*Nos. 317-319 (3)* 1.25 .85

International Tourist Year.

Map of Mediterranean and Runners — A83

**1967, Sept. 8 Litho. *Perf. 10½***

**320** A83 5m shown .25 .25
**321** A83 10m Javelin .25 .25
**322** A83 15m Bicyling .25 .25
**323** A83 45m Soccer .75 .55
**324** A83 75m Boxing 1.10 .75
*Nos. 320-324 (5)* 2.60 2.05

5th Mediterranean Games, Tunis, Sept. 8-17.

A84

Arab League emblem and hands reaching for knowledge.

**1967, Oct. 1 Litho. *Perf. 12½x13***

**325** A84 5m orange & dk pur .25 .25
**326** A84 10m brt grn & dk pur .25 .25
**327** A84 15m lilac & dk pur .25 .25
**328** A84 25m blue & dk pur .50 .25
*Nos. 325-328 (4)* 1.25 1.00

Literacy campaign.

Human Rights Flame — A85

**1968, Jan. 15 Litho. *Perf. 13½x14***

**329** A85 15m grn & vermilion .35 .25
**330** A85 60m org & vio bl .90 .55

International Human Rights Year.

Map, Derrick, Plane and Camel Riders — A86

**1968, Feb. 28 Photo. *Perf. 11½***

| | | | | |
|---|---|---|---|---|
| **331** | A86 | 55m car rose, brn & yel | 1.25 | .75 |

7th Intl. Fair, Tripoli, Feb. 28-Mar. 20.

Arab League Emblem A87

**1968, Mar. 22 Engr. *Perf. 13½***

| | | | | |
|---|---|---|---|---|
| **332** | A87 | 10m blue gray & car | .25 | .25 |
| **333** | A87 | 45m fawn & green | .90 | .65 |

Issued for Arab League Week.

Children, Statuary Group A88

Children's Day: 55m, Mother and children.

**1968, Mar. 21 Litho. *Perf. 11***

| | | | | |
|---|---|---|---|---|
| **334** | A88 | 25m gray, blk & mag | .65 | .35 |
| **335** | A88 | 55m gray & multi | 1.25 | .65 |

Hands Reaching for WHO Emblem — A89

**1968, Apr. 7 Photo. *Perf. 13½x14½***

| | | | | |
|---|---|---|---|---|
| **336** | A89 | 25m rose cl, dk bl & gray bl | .60 | .25 |
| **337** | A89 | 55m bl, blk & gray | .90 | .55 |

WHO, 20th anniversary.

From Oil Field to Tanker A90

**1968, Apr. 23 Litho. *Perf. 11***

| | | | | |
|---|---|---|---|---|
| **338** | A90 | 10m multicolored | .50 | .25 |
| **339** | A90 | 60m multicolored | 1.50 | .80 |

Opening of the Zueitina oil terminal.

Teacher and Crowd A91

**1968, Sept. 8 Litho. *Perf. 13½***

| | | | | |
|---|---|---|---|---|
| **340** | A91 | 5m bright pink | .25 | .25 |
| **341** | A91 | 10m orange | .25 | .25 |
| **342** | A91 | 15m blue | .25 | .25 |
| **343** | A91 | 20m emerald | .50 | .50 |
| | | *Nos. 340-343 (4)* | 1.25 | 1.25 |

Literacy campaign.

Arab Labor Emblem A92

**1968, Nov. 3 Photo. *Perf. 14x13½***

| | | | | |
|---|---|---|---|---|
| **344** | A92 | 10m multicolored | .25 | .25 |
| **345** | A92 | 15m multicolored | .50 | .25 |

4th session of the Arab Labor Ministers' Conf., Tripoli, Nov. 3-10.

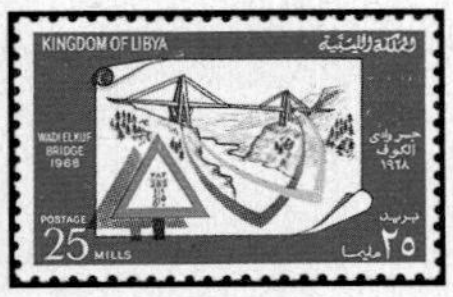

Wadi el Kuf Bridge and Road Sign — A93

**1968, Dec. 25 Litho. *Perf. 11x11½***

| | | | | |
|---|---|---|---|---|
| **346** | A93 | 25m ultra & multi | .40 | .35 |
| **347** | A93 | 60m emer & multi | 1.00 | .90 |

Opening of the Wadi el Kuf Bridge.

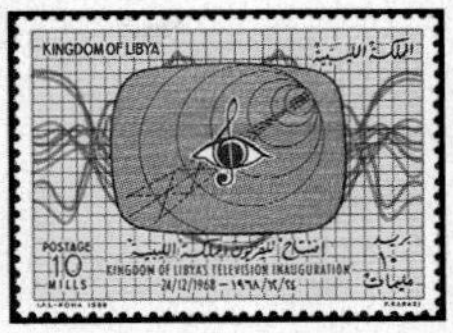

Television Screen and Chart A94

**1968, Dec. 25 Photo. *Perf. 14x13½***

| | | | | |
|---|---|---|---|---|
| **348** | A94 | 10m yellow & multi | .25 | .25 |
| **349** | A94 | 30m lilac & multi | .90 | .45 |

Inauguration of television service, Dec. 24.

Melons — A95

**1969, Jan. Photo. *Perf. 11½***

**Granite Paper**

| | | | | |
|---|---|---|---|---|
| **350** | A95 | 5m shown | .25 | .25 |
| **351** | A95 | 10m Peanuts | .25 | .25 |
| **352** | A95 | 15m Lemons | .25 | .25 |
| **353** | A95 | 20m Oranges | .40 | .25 |
| **354** | A95 | 25m Peaches | .65 | .35 |
| **355** | A95 | 35m Pears | 1.25 | .55 |
| | | *Nos. 350-355 (6)* | 3.05 | 1.90 |

Nos. 350-355 with "Kingdom of Libya" in both English and Arabic blocked out with a blue felt-tipped pen were issued in December, 1971, by the Republic.

Tripoli Fair Emblem A96

**1969, Apr. 8 Granite Paper**

| | | | | |
|---|---|---|---|---|
| **356** | A96 | 25m silver & multi | .40 | .25 |
| **357** | A96 | 35m bronze & multi | .65 | .35 |
| **358** | A96 | 40m gold & multi | .75 | .45 |
| | | *Nos. 356-358 (3)* | 1.80 | 1.05 |

8th Intl. Fair, Tripoli, Mar. 6-26.

Weather Balloon and Observer A97

**1969, Mar. 23 Photo. *Perf. 14x13***

| | | | | |
|---|---|---|---|---|
| **359** | A97 | 60m gray & multi | 1.50 | .80 |

World Meteorological Day, Mar. 23.

Cogwheel and Workers A98

**1969, Mar. 29 Litho. *Perf. 13½***

| | | | | |
|---|---|---|---|---|
| **360** | A98 | 15m blue & multi | .25 | .25 |
| **361** | A98 | 55m salmon & multi | .75 | .55 |

10th anniversary of Social Insurance.

ILO Emblem — A99

**1969, June 1 Photo. *Perf. 14***

| | | | | |
|---|---|---|---|---|
| **362** | A99 | 10m bl grn, blk & lt ol | .25 | .25 |
| **363** | A99 | 60m car rose, blk & lt ol | .90 | .65 |

ILO, 50th anniversary.

African Tourist Year Emblem — A100

**1969, July *Perf. 11½***

**Emblem in Emerald, Light Blue & Red**

| | | | | |
|---|---|---|---|---|
| **364** | A100 | 15m emer & silver | .45 | .25 |
| **365** | A100 | 30m blk & gold | .90 | .65 |

Issued to publicize African Tourist Year.

## Libyan Arab Republic

Soldiers, Tanks and Planes — A101

**1969, Dec. 7 Photo. *Perf. 12x12½***

| | | | | |
|---|---|---|---|---|
| **366** | A101 | 5m org & multi | .45 | .25 |
| **367** | A101 | 10m ultra & multi | .70 | .40 |
| **368** | A101 | 15m multicolored | 1.00 | .50 |
| **369** | A101 | 25m multicolored | 1.50 | .70 |
| **370** | A101 | 45m brt bl & multi | 1.75 | 1.10 |
| **371** | A101 | 60m multicolored | 3.00 | 1.50 |
| | | *Nos. 366-371 (6)* | 8.40 | 4.45 |

Establishment of the Libyan Arab Republic, Sept. 1, 1969. See Nos. 379-384.

Dish Antenna, Flags and Carrier Pigeon — A102

**1970, Mar. 1 Photo. *Perf. 11½***

**Granite Paper**

| | | | | |
|---|---|---|---|---|
| **372** | A102 | 15m multicolored | .70 | .25 |
| **373** | A102 | 20m multicolored | 1.10 | .40 |
| **374** | A102 | 25m multicolored | 1.50 | .50 |
| **375** | A102 | 40m multicolored | 2.10 | 1.10 |
| | | *Nos. 372-375 (4)* | 5.40 | 2.25 |

Map of Arab League Countries, Flag and Emblem A102a

**1970, Mar. 22**

| | | | | |
|---|---|---|---|---|
| **376** | A102a | 10m lt bl, brn & grn | .35 | .25 |
| **377** | A102a | 15m org, brn & grn | .60 | .25 |
| **378** | A102a | 20m ol, brn & grn | 1.00 | .45 |
| | | *Nos. 376-378 (3)* | 1.95 | .95 |

25th anniversary of the Arab League.

Type A101 Redrawn — A103

**1970, May 2 Photo. *Perf. 12x12½***

| | | | | |
|---|---|---|---|---|
| **379** | A103 | 5m org & multi | .40 | .25 |
| **380** | A103 | 10m ultra & multi | .70 | .60 |
| **381** | A103 | 15m multicolored | 1.00 | .50 |
| **382** | A103 | 25m multicolored | 1.50 | 1.40 |
| **383** | A103 | 45m brt bl & multi | 1.75 | 1.10 |
| **384** | A103 | 60m multicolored | 3.00 | 1.50 |
| | | *Nos. 379-384 (6)* | 8.35 | 5.35 |

On Nos. 379-384 the numerals are in black, the bottom inscription is in 2 lines and several other changes.

Inauguration of UPU Headquarters, Bern — A104

**1970, May 20 Photo. *Perf. 11½x11***

| | | | | |
|---|---|---|---|---|
| **385** | A104 | 10m multicolored | .25 | .25 |
| **386** | A104 | 25m multicolored | .60 | .25 |
| **387** | A104 | 60m multicolored | 1.25 | .65 |
| | | *Nos. 385-387 (3)* | 2.10 | 1.15 |

Arms of Libyan Arab Republic — A105

**1970, June 20 Photo. *Perf. 11***

| | | | | |
|---|---|---|---|---|
| **388** | A105 | 15m black & brt rose | .25 | .25 |
| **389** | A105 | 25m vio bl, yel & brt rose | .50 | .25 |
| **390** | A105 | 45m emer, yel & brt rose | 1.75 | .45 |
| | | *Nos. 388-390 (3)* | 2.50 | .95 |

Evacuation of US military base in Libya.

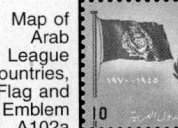

Flags, Soldiers and Tank — A106

**1970, Sept. 1 Photo.** ***Perf. 11x11½***

**391** A106 20m multicolored .75 .25
**392** A106 25m multicolored 1.00 .55
**393** A106 30m blue & multi 1.60 .75
*Nos. 391-393 (3)* 3.35 1.55

Libyan Arab Republic, 1st anniv.

UN Emblem, Dove and Scales — A107

**1970, Oct. 24 Photo.** ***Perf. 11x11½***

**394** A107 5m org & multi .60 .35
**395** A107 10m olive & multi .90 .45
**396** A107 60m multicolored 2.50 .90
*Nos. 394-396 (3)* 4.00 1.70

25th anniversary of the United Nations.

Map and Flags of UAR, Libya, Sudan A107a

**1970, Dec. 27 Photo.** ***Perf. 11½***

**397** A107a 15m lt grn, car & blk 7.00 2.25

Signing of the Charter of Tripoli affirming the unity of UAR, Libya and the Sudan, Dec. 27, 1970.

UN Emblem, Dove and Globe — A108

**1971, Jan. 10 Litho.** ***Perf. 12x11½***

**398** A108 15m multicolored .60 .25
**399** A108 20m multicolored .90 .45
**400** A108 60m lt vio & multi 2.50 .90
*Nos. 398-400 (3)* 4.00 1.60

UN declaration on granting of independence to colonial countries and peoples, 10th anniv.

Education Year Emblem — A109

**1971, Jan. 16**

**401** A109 5m red, blk & ocher .25 .25
**402** A109 10m red, blk & emer .60 .55
**403** A109 20m red, blk & vio bl 1.60 .80
*Nos. 401-403 (3)* 2.45 1.60

International Education Year.

Al Fatah Fighter — A110

**1971, Mar. 14 Photo.** ***Perf. 11***

**404** A110 5m ol & multi .50 .25
**405** A110 10m yel & multi .80 .25
**406** A110 100m multicolored 1.90 .25
*Nos. 404-406 (3)* 3.20 .75

Fight for the liberation of Palestine.

Tripoli Fair Emblem — A111

**1971, Mar. 18 Litho.** ***Perf. 14***

**407** A111 15m multicolored .35 .25
**408** A111 30m org & multi .90 .45

9th International Fair at Tripoli.

10th Anniv. of OPEC — A112

**1971, May 29 Litho.** ***Perf. 12***

**409** A112 10m yellow & brown .25 .25
**410** A112 70m pink & vio bl 1.60 .65

Globe and Waves A113

**1971, June 10** ***Perf. 14½x13½***

**411** A113 25m brt grn, blk & vio bl .50 .25
**412** A113 35m gray & multi 1.25 1.00

3rd World Telecommunications Day, May 17, 1971.

Map of Africa and Telecommunications Network — A114

**1971, June 10**

**413** A114 5m yel, blk & grn .25 .25
**414** A114 15m dl bl, blk & grn .40 .25

Pan-African telecommunications system.

Torchbearer and Banner — A115

**1971, June 15 Photo.** ***Perf. 11½x12***

**415** A115 5m yel & multi .25 .25
**416** A115 10m org & multi .35 .35
**417** A115 15m multicolored .50 .45
*Nos. 415-417 (3)* 1.10 1.05

Evacuation of US military base, 1st anniv.

Ramadan Suehli — A116

**1971, Aug. 24** ***Perf. 14x14½***

**418** A116 15m multicolored .25 .25
**419** A116 55m bl & multi 1.00 .55

Ramadan Suehli (1879-1920), freedom fighter.

See Nos. 422-423, 426-427, 439-440, 479-480.

Date Palm — A117

**1971, Sept. 1**

**420** A117 5m multicolored .25 .25
**421** A117 15m multicolored 1.25 1.25

Sept. 1, 1969 Revolution, 2nd anniv.

### Portrait Type of 1971

Portrait: Omar el Mukhtar (1858-1931), leader of the Martyrs.

**1971, Sept. 16** ***Perf. 14x14½***

**422** A116 5m lt grn & multi .25 .25
**423** A116 100m multicolored 2.50 1.50

Gamal Abdel Nasser (1918-1970), President of Egypt — A118

**1971, Sept. 28 Photo.** ***Perf. 11x11½***

**424** A118 5m lil, grn & blk .35 .25
**425** A118 15m grn, lil & blk 1.25 .25

### Portrait Type of 1971

Ibrahim Usta Omar (1908-50), patriotic poet.

**1971, Oct. 8 Litho.** ***Perf. 14x14½***

**426** A116 25m vio bl & multi .60 .60
**427** A116 30m multicolored 1.10 .45

Racial Equality Emblem A119

**1971, Oct. 24** ***Perf. 13½x14½***

**428** A119 25m multicolored .60 .25
**429** A119 35m multicolored 1.10 .45

Intl. Year Against Racial Discrimination.

Arab Postal Union Emblem — A120

**1971, Nov. 6 Litho.** ***Perf. 14½***

**Emblem in Black, Yellow and Blue**

**430** A120 5m red .25 .25
**431** A120 10m violet .40 .25
**432** A120 15m bright rose lilac .40 .25
*Nos. 430-432 (3)* 1.05 .75

Conference of Sofar, Lebanon, establishing Arab Postal Union, 25th anniv.

Postal Union Emblem and Letter A121

25m, 55m, APU emblem, letter and dove.

**1971, Dec. Photo.** ***Perf. 11½x11***

**433** A121 10m org brn, bl & blk .35 .25
**434** A121 15m org, lt bl & blk .50 .35
**435** A121 25m lt grn, org & blk .75 .55
**436** A121 55m lt brn, yel & blk 1.60 .70
*Nos. 433-436 (4)* 3.20 1.85

10th anniversary of African Postal Union.

Issued: 25m, 55m, 12/2; 10m, 15m, 12/12.

**Despite the change from milliemes to dirhams in 1972, both currencies appear on stamps until August.**

Book Year Emblem — A122

**1972, Jan. 1 Litho.** ***Perf. 12½x13***

**437** A122 15m ultra, brn, gold & blk .35 .35
**438** A122 20m gold, brn, ultra & blk .60 .60

International Book Year.

### Portrait Type of 1971

Ahmed Gnaba (1898-1968), poet of unity.

**1972, Jan. 12** ***Perf. 14x14½***

**439** A116 20m red & multi .60 .25
**440** A116 35m olive & multi .85 .45

Coat of Arms — A123

**1972, Feb. 10 Photo.** ***Perf. 14½***

**Size: 19x23mm**

**441** A123 5m gray & multi .25 .25
**442** A123 10m lt ol & multi .25 .25
**443** A123 15d lilac & multi .25 .25
**445** A123 25m lt bl & multi .25 .25
**446** A123 30m rose & multi .35 .25
**447** A123 35m lt ol & multi .45 .25
**448** A123 40m dl yel & multi .60 .25
**449** A123 45m lt grn & multi .75 .35
**451** A123 55m multicolored 1.00 .50
**452** A123 60m bister & multi 1.90 .65
**453** A123 65d multicolored .75 .55
**454** A123 70d lt vio & multi 1.00 .65
**455** A123 80d ocher & multi 1.50 .80
**456** A123 90m bl & multi 1.90 .90

**Size: 27x32mm**

***Perf. 14x14½***

| | | | | |
|---|---|---|---|---|
| **457** | A123 | 100d multicolored | 2.25 | 1.20 |
| **458** | A123 | 200d multicolored | 3.75 | 2.25 |
| **459** | A123 | 500d multicolored | 9.50 | 6.50 |
| **460** | A123 | £1 multicolored | 17.50 | 11.00 |
| | | *Nos. 441-460 (18)* | 44.20 | 27.10 |

During the transition from millimemes and pounds to dirhams and dinars, stamps were issued in both currencies.

A124

A124a

A124b

**Coil Stamps**

**1972, July 27 Photo.** ***Perf. 14½x14***

| | | | | |
|---|---|---|---|---|
| **461** | A124 | 5m sl bl, ocher & black | 2.75 | 2.25 |
| **462** | A124a | 20m bl, lil & blk | 12.00 | 2.25 |
| **463** | A124b | 50m bl, ol & blk | 27.50 | 5.50 |
| | | *Nos. 461-463 (3)* | 42.25 | 10.00 |

See Nos. 496-498, 575-577.

Tombs at Ghirza — A125

Designs: 10m, Kufic inscription, Agedabia, horiz. 15m, Marcus Aurelius Arch, Tripoli. 25m, Exchange of weapons, mural from Wan Amil Cave. 55m, Garamanthian (Berber) chariot, petroglyph, Wadi Zigza. 70m, Nymph Cyrene strangling a lion, bas-relief, Cyrene.

**1972, Feb. 15 Litho.** ***Perf. 14***

| | | | | |
|---|---|---|---|---|
| **464** | A125 | 5m lilac & multi | .50 | .50 |
| **465** | A125 | 10m multicolored | .50 | .50 |
| **466** | A125 | 15m dp org & multi | 1.00 | .35 |
| **467** | A125 | 25m emer & multi | 1.50 | .90 |
| **468** | A125 | 55m scar & multi | 3.50 | .90 |
| **469** | A125 | 70m ultra & multi | 7.00 | 1.25 |
| | | *Nos. 464-469 (6)* | 14.00 | 4.40 |

Fair Emblem A126

**1972, Mar. 1**

| | | | | |
|---|---|---|---|---|
| **470** | A126 | 25d gray & multi | .60 | .25 |
| **471** | A126 | 35d multicolored | .65 | .25 |
| **472** | A126 | 50d multicolored | 1.40 | .35 |
| **473** | A126 | 70d multicolored | 1.60 | .60 |
| | | *Nos. 470-473 (4)* | 4.25 | 1.45 |

10th International Fair at Tripoli.

Dissected Arm, and Heart — A127

**1972, Apr. 7** ***Perf. 14½***

| | | | | |
|---|---|---|---|---|
| **474** | A127 | 15d multicolored | 1.50 | .45 |
| **475** | A127 | 25d multicolored | 3.25 | 1.00 |

"Your heart is your health," World Health Day.

"Arab Unity" — A128

**Litho. & Engr.**

**1972, Apr. 17** ***Perf. 13½x13***

| | | | | |
|---|---|---|---|---|
| **476** | A128 | 15d bl, yel & blk | .25 | .25 |
| **477** | A128 | 20d lt grn, yel & blk | .60 | .25 |
| **478** | A128 | 25d lt ver, yel & blk | 1.25 | .80 |
| | | *Nos. 476-478 (3)* | 2.10 | 1.30 |

Fed. of Arab Republics Foundation, 1st anniv.

**Portrait Type of 1971**

Suleiman el Baruni (1870-1940), patriotic writer.

**1972, May 1 Litho.** ***Perf. 14x14½***

| | | | | |
|---|---|---|---|---|
| **479** | A116 | 10m yellow & multi | 1.25 | .80 |
| **480** | A116 | 70m dp org & multi | 2.00 | 1.00 |

Environment Emblem — A129

**1972, Aug. 15 Litho.** ***Perf. 14½***

| | | | | |
|---|---|---|---|---|
| **481** | A129 | 15m red & multi | .60 | .25 |
| **482** | A129 | 55m green & multi | 1.40 | .40 |

UN Conference on Human Environment, Stockholm, June 5-16.

Olympic Emblems — A130

**1972, Aug. 26**

| | | | | |
|---|---|---|---|---|
| **483** | A130 | 25d brt bl & multi | 2.00 | .60 |
| **484** | A130 | 35d red & multi | 3.00 | 1.25 |

20th Olympic Games, Munich, 8/26-9/11.

Emblem and Broken Chain — A131

**1972, Oct. 1 Litho.** ***Perf. 14x13½***

| | | | | |
|---|---|---|---|---|
| **485** | A131 | 15d blue & multi | .40 | .25 |
| **486** | A131 | 25d yellow & multi | .90 | .35 |

Libyan Arab Republic, 3rd anniv.

Dome of the Rock, Jerusalem — A132

**1972** ***Perf. 12½x13***

| | | | | |
|---|---|---|---|---|
| **487** | A132 | 10d multicolored | .40 | .25 |
| **488** | A132 | 25d multicolored | .60 | .25 |

Nicolaus Copernicus (1473-1543), Polish Astronomer — A133

Design: 25d, Copernicus in Observatory, by Jan Matejko, horiz.

***Perf. 14½x13½, 13½x14½***

**1973, Feb. 26**

| | | | | |
|---|---|---|---|---|
| **489** | A133 | 15d yellow & multi | .40 | .25 |
| **490** | A133 | 25d blue & multi | .60 | .35 |

Eagle and Fair Buildings A134

**1973, Mar. 1** ***Perf. 13½x14½***

| | | | | |
|---|---|---|---|---|
| **491** | A134 | 5d dull red & multi | .40 | .25 |
| **492** | A134 | 10d blue grn & multi | .60 | .25 |
| **493** | A134 | 15d vio blue & multi | 1.25 | .25 |
| | | *Nos. 491-493 (3)* | 2.25 | .75 |

11th International Fair at Tripoli.

Blind Person, Books, Loom and Basket — A135

**1973, Apr. 18 Photo.** ***Perf. 12x11½***

| | | | | |
|---|---|---|---|---|
| **494** | A135 | 20d gray & multi | 8.25 | 1.60 |
| **495** | A135 | 25d dull yel & multi | 12.00 | 5.25 |

Role of the blind in society.

**Numeral Type of 1972 Denominations in Dirhams**

A135a

A135b

A135c

**Coil Stamps**

**1973, Apr. 26 Photo.** ***Perf. 14½x14***

| | | | | |
|---|---|---|---|---|
| **496** | A135a | 5d sl bl, ocher & blk | 1.00 | 1.00 |
| **497** | A135b | 20d blue, lilac & blk | 1.50 | 1.50 |
| **498** | A135c | 50d blue, olive & blk | 5.50 | 5.50 |
| | | *Nos. 496-498 (3)* | 8.00 | 8.00 |

Map of Africa — A136

**1973, May 25 Photo.** ***Perf. 11x11½***

| | | | | |
|---|---|---|---|---|
| **499** | A136 | 15d yel, green & brown | .50 | .25 |
| **500** | A136 | 25d lt yel grn, grn & blk | 1.00 | .50 |

"Freedom in Unity" (Org. for African Unity).

INTERPOL Emblem and General Secretariat, Paris — A138

***Perf. 13½x14½***

**1973, June 30** **Litho.**

| | | | | |
|---|---|---|---|---|
| **501** | A138 | 10d lilac & multi | .25 | .25 |
| **502** | A138 | 15d ocher & multi | .50 | .25 |
| **503** | A138 | 25d lt grn & multi | .75 | .25 |
| | | *Nos. 501-503 (3)* | 1.50 | .75 |

50th anniv. of Intl. Criminal Police Org.

Map of Libya, Houses, People, Factories, Tractor A139

**1973, July 15 Photo.** ***Perf. 11½***

| | | | | |
|---|---|---|---|---|
| **504** | A139 | 10d rose red, black & ultra | 4.25 | .85 |
| **505** | A139 | 25d ultra, blk & grn | 6.00 | 1.90 |
| **506** | A139 | 35d grn, blk & org | 11.50 | 3.75 |
| | | *Nos. 504-506 (3)* | 21.75 | 6.50 |

General census.

World Meteorological Organization Emblem — A140

**1973, Aug. 1** ***Perf. 12½x11***

| | | | | |
|---|---|---|---|---|
| **507** | A140 | 5d ver, blk & bl | .25 | .25 |
| **508** | A140 | 10d yel grn, blk & bl | .50 | .50 |

Intl. meteorological cooperation, cent.

Soccer — A141

**1973, Aug. 10 Photo.** ***Perf. 11½***

| | | | | |
|---|---|---|---|---|
| **509** | A141 | 5d yel grn & dk brn | .50 | .25 |
| **510** | A141 | 25d orange & dk brn | 1.10 | .70 |

2nd Palestinian Cup Soccer Tournament.

Torch and Grain — A142

**1973, Sept. 1 Litho.** ***Perf. 14***

| | | | | |
|---|---|---|---|---|
| **511** | A142 | 15d brown & multi | .50 | .25 |
| **512** | A142 | 25d emer & multi | 1.40 | .25 |

4th anniv. of Sept. 1 Revolution.

Writing Hand, Lamp and Globe — A143

**1973, Sept. 8**

**513** A143 25d multicolored .60 .60

Literacy campaign.

Gate of First City Hall — A144

**1973, Sept. 18** ***Perf. 13***

**514** A144 10d shown .50 .50
**515** A144 25d Khondok fountain .60 .60
**516** A144 35d Clock tower .90 .35
*Nos. 514-516 (3)* 2.00 1.45

Centenary of Tripoli as a municipality.

Militia, Flag and Factories — A145

**1973, Oct. 7 Photo.** ***Perf. 11½x11***

**517** A145 15d yel, blk & red .50 .25
**518** A145 25d green & multi .75 .35

Libyan Militia.

Revolutionary Proclamation by Khadafy — A146

70d, as 25d, with English inscription.

**1973, Oct. 15 Litho.** ***Perf. 12½***

**519** A146 25d orange & multi .50 .50
**520** A146 70d green & multi 1.50 .75

Proclamation of People's Revolution by Pres. Muammar Khadafy.

FAO Emblem, Camel Pulling Plow A147

**1973, Nov. 1 Photo.** ***Perf. 11***

**521** A147 10d ocher & multi .25 .25
**522** A147 25d dk brn & multi .50 .50
**523** A147 35d black & multi .75 .35
*Nos. 521-523 (3)* 1.50 1.10

World Food Org., 10th anniv.

Human Rights Flame — A148

**1973, Dec. 20 Photo.** ***Perf. 11x11½***

**524** A148 25d pur, car & dk bl .35 .35
**525** A148 70d lt grn, car & dk bl 1.50 .65

Universal Declaration of Human Rights, 25th anniv.

Fish A149

Designs: Various fish from Libyan waters.

**1973, Dec. 31 Photo.** ***Perf. 14x13½***

**526** A149 5d light blue & multi .65 .50
**527** A149 10d light blue & multi 1.25 .45
**528** A149 15d light blue & multi 1.90 .55
**529** A149 20d light blue & multi 2.75 .60
**530** A149 25d light blue & multi 5.25 1.50
*Nos. 526-530 (5)* 11.80 3.60

**1975, Jan. 5**

*526a* A149 5d greenish blue & multi 2.25 1.50
*527a* A149 10d greenish blue & multi 4.50 1.50
*528a* A149 15d greenish blue & multi 4.50 1.50
*529a* A149 20d greenish blue & multi 6.50 .75
*530a* A149 25d greenish blue & multi 8.50 2.75
*Nos. 526a-530a (5)* 26.25 8.00

Scout, Sun and Scout Signs — A150

**1974, Feb. 1 Litho.** ***Perf. 11½***

**531** A150 5d lt. blue & multi 1.25 .40
**532** A150 20d light lilac & multi 3.50 .65
**533** A150 25d lt grn & multi 5.75 2.60
*Nos. 531-533 (3)* 10.50 3.65

Libyan Boy Scouts.

Fair Emblem, Flags of Participants — A151

**1974, Mar. 1 Litho.** ***Perf. 12x11½***

**534** A151 10d lt ultra & multi .65 .40
**535** A151 25d tan & multi 1.00 .55
**536** A151 35d lt green & multi 1.90 .25
*Nos. 534-536 (3)* 3.55 1.20

12th Tripoli International Fair.

Protected Family, WHO Emblem — A152

**1974, Apr. 7 Litho.** ***Perf. 12½***

**537** A152 5d lt green & multi .35 .25
**538** A152 25d red & multi .60 .60

World Health Day.

Minaret and Star — A153

**1974, Apr. 16** ***Perf. 11½x11***

**539** A153 10d pink & multi .50 .50
**540** A153 25d yellow & multi 1.00 .60
**541** A153 35d orange & multi 1.40 .50
*Nos. 539-541 (3)* 2.90 1.60

City University of Bengazi, inauguration.

UPU Emblem and Star — A154

**1974, May 22 Litho.** ***Perf. 13½x14½***

**542** A154 25d multicolored 7.50 1.10
**543** A154 70d multicolored 14.00 2.25

Centenary of Universal Postal Union.

Traffic Signs — A156

**1974, June 8 Photo.** ***Perf. 11***

**547** A156 5d gold & multi .25 .25
**548** A156 10d gold & multi .40 .25
**549** A156 25d gold & multi .50 .25
*Nos. 547-549 (3)* 1.15 .75

Automobile and Touring Club of Libya.

Tank, Oil Refinery, Book — A157

Symbolic "5" — A158

**1974, Sept. 1 Litho.** ***Perf. 14***

**550** A157 5d red & multi .25 .25
**551** A157 20d violet & multi .40 .40
**552** A157 25d vio bl & multi .40 .40
**553** A157 35d green & multi .50 .50
*Nos. 550-553 (4)* 1.55 1.55

**Souvenir Sheet**

***Perf. 13***

**554** A158 55d yel & maroon 9.50 9.50

Revolution of Sept. 1, 5th anniv. English inscription on No. 554.

WPY Emblem and Crowd — A159

**1974, Oct. 19** ***Perf. 14***

**555** A159 25d multicolored .35 .25
**556** A159 35d lt brn & multi .75 .60

World Population Year.

Libyan Woman — A160

Libyan Costumes: 10d, 15d, Women. 20d, Old man. 25d, Man riding camel. 50d, Man on horseback.

**1975, Mar. 1 Litho.** ***Perf. 13x12½***

**557** A160 5d org yel & multi .25 .25
**558** A160 10d org yel & multi .25 .25
**559** A160 15d org yel & multi .50 .25
**560** A160 20d org yel & multi .75 .25
**561** A160 25d org yel & multi 1.50 .75
**562** A160 50d org yel & multi 2.75 .75
*Nos. 557-562 (6)* 6.00 2.50

Congress Emblem — A161

**1975, Mar. 4 Litho.** ***Perf. 12x12½***

**563** A161 10d brown & multi .25 .25
**564** A161 25d vio & multi .40 .40
**565** A161 35d gray & multi .75 .25
*Nos. 563-565 (3)* 1.40 .90

Arab Labor Congress.

Teacher Pointing to Blackboard A162

**1975, Mar. 10** ***Perf. 11½***

**566** A162 10d gold & multi .25 .25
**567** A162 25d gold & multi .50 .25

Teacher's Day.

Bodies, Globe, Proclamation A163

**1975, Apr. 7 Litho.** ***Perf. 12½***

**568** A163 20d lilac & multi .40 .40
**569** A163 25d emer & multi .50 .25

World Health Day.

Woman and Man in Library — A164

**1975, May 25 Litho. *Perf. 12½***

| | | | | |
|---|---|---|---|---|
| **570** | A164 10d bl grn & multi | .25 | .25 |
| **571** | A164 25d olive & multi | .50 | .50 |
| **572** | A164 35d lt vio & multi | .60 | .60 |
| | *Nos. 570-572 (3)* | 1.35 | 1.35 |

Libyan Arab Book Exhibition.

Festival Emblem — A165

**1975, July 5 Litho. *Perf. 13x12½***

| | | | |
|---|---|---|---|
| **573** | A165 20d lt bl & multi | .40 | .40 |
| **574** | A165 25d orange & multi | .50 | .50 |

2nd Arab Youth Festival.

**Redrawn Type of 1973 Without "LAR"**

**Coil Stamps**

**1975, Aug. 15 Photo. *Perf. 14½x14***

| | | | |
|---|---|---|---|
| **575** | A124 5d blue, org & blk | .50 | .50 |
| **576** | A124 20d blue, yel & blk | 1.00 | 1.00 |
| **577** | A124 50d blue, grn & blk | 2.00 | 2.00 |
| | *Nos. 575-577 (3)* | 3.50 | 3.50 |

Games Emblem and Arms — A166

**1975, Aug. 23 *Perf. 13x12½***

| | | | |
|---|---|---|---|
| **578** | A166 10d salmon & multi | .25 | .25 |
| **579** | A166 25d lilac & multi | .50 | .50 |
| **580** | A166 50d yellow & multi | 1.40 | .40 |
| | *Nos. 578-580 (3)* | 2.15 | 1.15 |

7th Mediterranean Games, Algiers, 8/23-9/6.

Peace Dove, Symbols of Agriculture and Industry — A167

Khadafy's Head Over Desert — A168

Design: 70d, Peace dove, diff.

**1975, Sept. Litho. *Perf. 13x12½***

| | | | |
|---|---|---|---|
| **581** | A167 25d multicolored | .40 | .25 |
| **582** | A167 70d multicolored | 1.40 | .50 |

**Souvenir Sheet**

***Imperf***

**Litho. & Embossed**

| | | | |
|---|---|---|---|
| **583** | A168 100d multicolored | 6.00 | 6.00 |

6th anniversary of Sept. 1 revolution. No. 583 contains one stamp with simulated perforations.

Khalil Basha Mosque — A169

Al Kharruba Mosque — A170

Mosques: 10d, Sidi Abdulla El Shaab. 15d, Sidi Ali El Fergani. 25d, Katikhtha. 30d, Murad Agha. 35d, Maulai Mohammed.

**1975, Dec. 13 Litho. *Perf. 12½***

| | | | |
|---|---|---|---|
| **584** | A169 5d gray & multi | .25 | .25 |
| **585** | A169 10d purple & multi | .25 | .25 |
| **586** | A169 15d green & multi | .25 | .25 |
| **587** | A170 20d ocher & multi | .40 | .25 |
| **588** | A170 25d multicolored | .40 | .25 |
| **589** | A170 30d multicolored | .50 | .25 |
| **590** | A170 35d lilac & multi | .75 | .60 |
| | *Nos. 584-590 (7)* | 2.80 | 2.10 |

Mohammed's 1405th birthday.

Arms of Libya and People — A171

**1976, Jan. 15 Photo. *Perf. 13***

| | | | |
|---|---|---|---|
| **591** | A171 35d blue & multi | .50 | .25 |
| **592** | A171 40d multicolored | .60 | .25 |

General National (People's) Congress.

Islamic - Christian Dialogue Emblem — A172

**1976, Feb. 5 Litho. *Perf. 13x12½***

| | | | |
|---|---|---|---|
| **593** | A172 40d gold & multi | .60 | .25 |
| **594** | A172 115d gold & multi | 1.90 | .90 |

Seminar of Islamic-Christian Dialogue, Tripoli, Feb. 1-5.

Woman Blowing Horn — A173

National Costumes: 20d, Lancer. 30d, Drummer. 40d, Bagpiper. 100d, Woman carrying jug on head.

**1976, Mar. 1 Litho. *Perf. 13x12½***

| | | | |
|---|---|---|---|
| **595** | A173 10d multicolored | .25 | .25 |
| **596** | A173 20d multicolored | .50 | .40 |
| **597** | A173 30d pink & multi | 1.00 | .25 |
| **598** | A173 40d multicolored | 1.25 | .25 |
| **599** | A173 100d yel & multi | 3.00 | .50 |
| | *Nos. 595-599 (5)* | 6.00 | 1.65 |

14th Tripoli International Fair.

Telephones, 1876 and 1976, ITU and UPU Emblems — A174

70d, Alexander Graham Bell, telephone, satellites, radar, ITU & UPU emblems.

**1976, Mar. 10 Photo. *Perf. 13***

| | | | |
|---|---|---|---|
| **600** | A174 40d multicolored | 2.50 | .80 |
| *a.* | Souvenir sheet of 4 | 10.00 | 10.00 |
| **601** | A174 70d multicolored | 4.00 | .80 |
| *a.* | Souvenir sheet of 4 | 16.50 | 16.50 |

Centenary of first telephone call by Alexander Graham Bell, Mar. 10, 1876.

Nos. 600a and 601a exist imperf. Value, both sheets $100.

Mother and Child — A175

**1976, Mar. 21 *Perf. 12***

| | | | |
|---|---|---|---|
| **602** | A175 85d gray & multi | 1.50 | 1.25 |
| **603** | A175 110d pink & multi | 1.60 | 1.50 |

International Children's Day.

Hands, Eye and Head — A176

**1976, Apr. 7 Photo. *Perf. 13½x13***

| | | | |
|---|---|---|---|
| **604** | A176 30d multicolored | .35 | .35 |
| **605** | A176 35d multicolored | .50 | .50 |
| **606** | A176 40d multicolored | .60 | .60 |
| | *Nos. 604-606 (3)* | 1.45 | 1.45 |

"Foresight prevents blindness;" World Health Day.

Little Bittern A177

Birds of Libya: 10d, Great gray shrike. 15d, Songbird. 20d, European bee-eater, vert. 25d, Hoopoe.

***Perf. 13x13½, 13½x13***

**1976, May 1 Litho.**

| | | | |
|---|---|---|---|
| **607** | A177 5d orange & multi | .65 | .50 |
| **608** | A177 10d ultra & multi | 1.40 | 1.10 |
| **609** | A177 15d rose & multi | 2.75 | 1.40 |
| **610** | A177 20d yellow & multi | 4.75 | 1.50 |
| **611** | A177 25d blue & multi | 9.50 | 2.75 |
| | *Nos. 607-611 (5)* | 19.05 | 7.25 |

Al Barambekh A178

Designs: 15d, Whale, horiz. 30d, Lizard (alwaral), horiz. 40d, Mastodon skull, horiz. 70d, Hawk. 115d, Wild mountain sheep.

**1976, June 20 Litho. *Perf. 12½***

| | | | |
|---|---|---|---|
| **612** | A178 10d multicolored | 1.40 | 1.10 |
| **613** | A178 15d multicolored | 2.50 | 1.90 |
| **614** | A178 30d multicolored | 3.00 | 2.40 |
| **615** | A178 40d multicolored | 5.00 | 4.25 |
| **616** | A178 70d multicolored | 8.75 | 7.25 |
| **617** | A178 115d multicolored | 14.50 | 12.25 |
| | *Nos. 612-617 (6)* | 35.15 | 29.15 |

Museum of Natural History.

Bicycling — A179

**1976, July 17 Litho. *Perf. 12x11½***

**Granite Paper**

| | | | |
|---|---|---|---|
| **618** | A179 15d shown | .25 | .25 |
| **619** | A179 25d Boxing | .50 | .50 |
| **620** | A179 70d Soccer | 1.50 | 1.50 |
| | *Nos. 618-620 (3)* | 2.25 | 2.25 |

**Souvenir Sheet**

| | | | |
|---|---|---|---|
| **621** | A179 150d Symbolic of various sports | 16.00 | 16.00 |

21st Olympic Games, Montreal, Canada, July 17-Aug. 1.

Tree Growing from Globe — A180

**1976, Aug. 9 *Perf. 13***

| | | | |
|---|---|---|---|
| **622** | A180 115d multicolored | 1.25 | .90 |

5th Conference of Non-Aligned Countries, Colombo, Sri Lanka, Aug. 9-19.

Beginning with No. 622 numerous issues are printed with multiple coats of arms in pale green on back of stamps.

Symbols of Agriculture and Industry — A181

Drummer and Pipeline — A182

**1976, Sept. 1 *Perf. 14½x14***

| | | | |
|---|---|---|---|
| **623** | A181 30d yel & multi | .40 | .25 |
| **624** | A181 40d multicolored | .50 | .25 |
| **625** | A181 100d multicolored | 1.25 | .90 |
| | *Nos. 623-625 (3)* | 2.15 | 1.40 |

**Souvenir Sheet**

***Perf. 13***

| | | | |
|---|---|---|---|
| **626** | A182 200d multicolored | 6.00 | 6.00 |

Sept. 1 Revolution, 7th anniv.

Sports, Torch and Emblems A183

145d, Symbolic wrestlers and various emblems.

**1976, Oct. 6 Litho. *Perf. 13***

| | | | | |
|---|---|---|---|---|
| **627** | A183 | 15d multicolored | .25 | .25 |
| **628** | A183 | 30d multicolored | .35 | .35 |
| **629** | A183 | 100d multicolored | 1.60 | .90 |
| | | *Nos. 627-629 (3)* | 2.20 | 1.50 |

**Souvenir Sheet**

| | | | | |
|---|---|---|---|---|
| **630** | A183 | 145d multi, horiz. | 4.50 | 4.50 |

5th Arab Games, Damascus, Syria.

Chess Board, Rook, Knight, Emblem — A184

**1976, Oct. 24 Photo. *Perf. 11½***

| | | | | |
|---|---|---|---|---|
| **631** | A184 | 15d pink & multi | 2.10 | .45 |
| **632** | A184 | 30d buff & multi | 3.50 | 1.00 |
| **633** | A184 | 100d multicolored | 10.50 | 2.00 |
| | | *Nos. 631-633 (3)* | 16.10 | 3.45 |

The "Against" (protest) Chess Olympiad, Tripoli, Oct. 24-Nov. 15.

A185

Designs: Various local flowers.

**1976, Nov. 1 Photo. *Perf. 11½***
**Granite Paper**

| | | | | |
|---|---|---|---|---|
| **634** | A185 | 15d lilac & multi | .35 | .35 |
| **635** | A185 | 20d multicolored | .35 | .35 |
| **636** | A185 | 35d yellow & multi | .80 | .25 |
| **637** | A185 | 40d salmon & multi | 1.25 | .35 |
| **638** | A185 | 70d multicolored | 3.00 | .50 |
| | | *Nos. 634-638 (5)* | 5.75 | 1.80 |

International Archives Council Emblem and Document — A186

**1976, Nov. 10 Litho. *Perf. 13x13½***

| | | | | |
|---|---|---|---|---|
| **639** | A186 | 15d brown, org & buff | .25 | .25 |
| **640** | A186 | 35d brn, brt grn & buff | .35 | .35 |
| **641** | A186 | 70d brown, blue & buff | .75 | .75 |
| | | *Nos. 639-641 (3)* | 1.35 | 1.35 |

Arab Regional Branch of International Council on Archives, Baghdad.

Holy Ka'aba and Pilgrims — A187

**1976, Dec. 12 Litho. *Perf. 14***

| | | | | |
|---|---|---|---|---|
| **642** | A187 | 15d multicolored | .25 | .25 |
| **643** | A187 | 30d multicolored | .25 | .25 |
| **644** | A187 | 70d multicolored | .80 | .80 |
| **645** | A187 | 100d multicolored | 1.00 | 1.00 |
| | | *Nos. 642-645 (4)* | 2.30 | 2.30 |

Pilgrimage to Mecca.

Numeral — A188

**Coil Stamps**

**1977, Jan. 15 Photo. *Perf. 14½x14***

| | | | | |
|---|---|---|---|---|
| **646** | A188 | 5d multicolored | .25 | .25 |
| **647** | A188 | 20d multicolored | .35 | .35 |
| **648** | A188 | 50d multicolored | .90 | .90 |
| | | *Nos. 646-648 (3)* | 1.50 | 1.50 |

Covered Basket — A189

Designs: 20d, Leather bag. 30d, Vase. 40d, Embroidered slippers. 50d, Ornate saddle. 100d, Horse with saddle and harness.

**1977, Mar. 1 Litho. *Perf. 12½x12***

| | | | | |
|---|---|---|---|---|
| **649** | A189 | 10d multicolored | .25 | .25 |
| **650** | A189 | 20d multicolored | .25 | .25 |
| **651** | A189 | 30d multicolored | .35 | .25 |
| **652** | A189 | 40d multicolored | .60 | .35 |
| **653** | A189 | 50d multicolored | 1.00 | .35 |
| | | *Nos. 649-653 (5)* | 2.45 | 1.45 |

**Souvenir Sheet**
***Imperf***

| | | | | |
|---|---|---|---|---|
| **654** | A189 | 100d multicolored | 4.50 | 4.50 |

15th Tripoli International Fair. No. 654 contains one stamp 49x53mm with simulated perforations.

Girl and Flowers, UNICEF Emblem A190

Children's drawings, UNICEF Emblem and: 30d, Clothing store. 40d, Farm yard.

**1977, Mar. 28 Litho. *Perf. 13x13½***

| | | | | |
|---|---|---|---|---|
| **655** | A190 | 10d multicolored | .35 | .25 |
| **656** | A190 | 30d multicolored | .60 | .35 |
| **657** | A190 | 40d multicolored | .75 | .50 |
| | | *Nos. 655-657 (3)* | 1.70 | 1.10 |

Children's Day.

Gun, Fighters, UN Headquarters A191

**1977, Mar. 13 *Perf. 13½***

| | | | | |
|---|---|---|---|---|
| **658** | A191 | 15d multicolored | *.25* | .25 |
| **659** | A191 | 25d multicolored | *.25* | .25 |
| **660** | A191 | 70d multicolored | *1.25* | 1.25 |
| | | *Nos. 658-660 (3)* | *1.75* | 1.75 |

Battle of Al-Karamah, 9th anniversary.

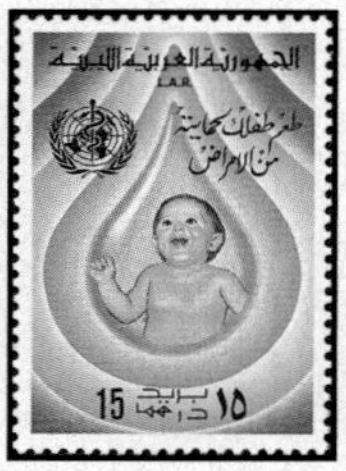

Child, Raindrop, WHO Emblem — A192

**1977, Apr. 7 Litho. *Perf. 13x12½***

| | | | | |
|---|---|---|---|---|
| **661** | A192 | 15d multicolored | .25 | .25 |
| **662** | A192 | 30d multicolored | .50 | .50 |

World Health Day.

Arab Postal Union, 25th Anniv. — A193

**1977, Apr. 12 *Perf. 13½***

| | | | | |
|---|---|---|---|---|
| **663** | A193 | 15d multicolored | .25 | .25 |
| **664** | A193 | 30d multicolored | .35 | .35 |
| **665** | A193 | 40d multicolored | .50 | .50 |
| | | *Nos. 663-665 (3)* | 1.10 | 1.10 |

Maps of Africa and Libya A194

**1977, May 8 Litho. *Perf. 14x13½***

| | | | | |
|---|---|---|---|---|
| **666** | A194 | 40d multicolored | 1.50 | 1.25 |
| **667** | A194 | 70d multicolored | 2.25 | 1.90 |

African Labor Day.

Map of Libya and Heart — A195

**1977, May 10 *Perf. 14½x14***

| | | | | |
|---|---|---|---|---|
| **668** | A195 | 5d multicolored | .35 | .25 |
| **669** | A195 | 10d multicolored | .50 | .35 |
| **670** | A195 | 30d multicolored | 1.40 | .60 |
| | | *Nos. 668-670 (3)* | 2.25 | 1.20 |

Libyan Red Crescent Society.

Electronic Tree, ITU Emblem, Satellite and Radar A196

Electronic Tree, ITU Emblem and: 115d, Communications satellite, Montreal Olympics emblem, boxer on TV screen. 200d, Spacecraft over earth. 300d, Solar system.

**1977, May 17 Litho. *Perf. 13½x13***

| | | | | |
|---|---|---|---|---|
| **671** | A196 | 60d multicolored | .80 | .80 |
| **672** | A196 | 115d multicolored | 2.00 | 2.00 |
| **673** | A196 | 200d multicolored | 3.75 | 3.75 |
| | | *Nos. 671-673 (3)* | 6.55 | 6.55 |

**Souvenir Sheet**

| | | | | |
|---|---|---|---|---|
| **674** | A196 | 300d multicolored | *8.50* | *6.50* |

9th World Telecommunications Day. No. 674 contains one stamp 52x35mm.

Nos. 671-673 exist imperf. Value, set $45. They also exist in miniature sheets of 4, perf and imperf. Values: set perf, $100; set imperf, $135.

Plane over Tripoli, Messenger A197

UPU Emblem and: 25d, Concorde, messenger on horseback. 150d, Loading transport plane and messenger riding camel. 300d, Graf Zeppelin LZ127 over Tripoli.

**1977, May 17 Litho. *Perf. 13½***

| | | | | |
|---|---|---|---|---|
| **675** | A197 | 20d multicolored | .80 | .80 |
| **676** | A197 | 25d multicolored | 1.75 | 1.75 |
| **677** | A197 | 150d multicolored | 3.50 | 3.50 |
| | | *Nos. 675-677 (3)* | 6.05 | 6.05 |

**Souvenir Sheet**

| | | | | |
|---|---|---|---|---|
| **678** | A197 | 300d multicolored | *8.50* | *6.50* |

UPU centenary (in 1974). No. 678 contains one stamp 52x35mm.

Nos. 675-678 exist imperf. Values: set $45; souvenir sheet, $50. Nos. 675-677 also exist in miniature sheets of 4, perf and imperf. Values: set perf, $60; set imperf, $125.

Mosque A198

Various Mosques. 50d, 100d, vertical.

**1977, June 1 Photo. *Perf. 14***

| | | | | |
|---|---|---|---|---|
| **679** | A198 | 40d multicolored | .55 | .55 |
| **680** | A198 | 50d multicolored | .80 | .80 |
| **681** | A198 | 70d multicolored | 1.10 | 1.10 |
| **682** | A198 | 90d multicolored | 1.40 | 1.40 |
| **683** | A198 | 100d multicolored | 1.60 | 1.60 |
| **684** | A198 | 115d multicolored | 2.10 | 2.10 |
| | | *Nos. 679-684 (6)* | 7.55 | 7.55 |

Palestinian Archbishop Hilarion Capucci, Jailed by Israel in 1974, Map of Palestine — A199

**1977, Aug. 18 Litho. *Perf. 13½***

| | | | | |
|---|---|---|---|---|
| **687** | A199 | 30d multicolored | .40 | .40 |
| **688** | A199 | 40d multicolored | .55 | .55 |
| **689** | A199 | 115d multicolored | 2.10 | 1.00 |
| | | *Nos. 687-689 (3)* | 3.05 | 1.95 |

Raised Hands, Pylons, Wheel, Buildings — A200

Star and Ornament — A201

**1977, Sept. 1 Litho. *Perf. 13½x12½***
**690** A200 15d multicolored .25 .25
**691** A200 30d multicolored .35 .35
**692** A200 85d multicolored 1.25 .60
*Nos. 690-692 (3)* 1.85 1.20

**Souvenir Sheet**
***Perf. 12½***
**693** A201 100d gold & multi 5.00 3.50

8th anniversary of Sept. 1 Revolution.

Team Handball — A202

**1977, Oct. 8 *Perf. 13½***
**694** A202 5d Swimmers, vert. .25 .25
**695** A202 10d shown .25 .25
**696** A202 15d Soccer, vert. .25 .25
**697** A202 25d Table tennis .75 .75
**698** A202 40d Basketball, vert. 1.60 .90
*Nos. 694-698 (5)* 3.10 2.40

7th Arab School Games.

Steeplechase — A203

Show Emblem and: 10d, Bedouin on horseback. 15d, Show emblem (Horse and "7"), vert. 45d, Steeplechase. 100d, Hurdles. 115d, Bedouins on horseback.

**1977, Oct. 10 *Perf. 14½***
**699** A203 5d multicolored .25 .25
**700** A203 10d multicolored .25 .25
**701** A203 15d multicolored .35 .35
**702** A203 45d multicolored .90 .90
**703** A203 115d multicolored 2.00 2.00
*Nos. 699-703 (5)* 3.75 3.75

**Souvenir Sheet**
**704** A203 100d multicolored 4.50 4.50

7th Intl. Turf Championships, Tripoli, Oct. 1977.

Dome of the Rock, Jerusalem — A204

**1977, Oct. 14 *Perf. 14½x14***
**705** A204 5d multicolored .30 .25
**706** A204 10d multicolored .45 .25

Palestinian fighters and their families.

"The Green Book" — A205

35d, Hands with broken chain holding hook over citadel. 40d, Hands above chaos. 115d, Dove and Green Book rising from Africa, world map.

**1977 Litho. *Perf. 14***
**707** A205 Strip of 3 2.75 2.75
*a.* 35d multicolored .35 .35
*b.* 40d multicolored .50 .50
*c.* 115d multicolored 1.75 1.75

The Greek Book, by Khadafy outlines Libyan democracy. Green descriptive inscription on back beneath gum, in English on 35d, French on 40d, Arabic on 115d.

Emblems A206

**1977 *Perf. 12½x13***
**708** A206 5d multicolored .60 .25
**709** A206 15d multicolored .80 .25
**710** A206 30d multicolored 1.10 .35
*Nos. 708-710 (3)* 2.50 .85

Standardization Day.

Elephant hunt. A207

Rock Carvings, Wadi Mathendous, c. 8000 B.C.: 10d, Crocodile and Young. 20d, Giraffe, vert. 30d, Antelope. 40d, Trumpeting elephant.

**1978, Jan. 1 *Perf. 12½x13, 13x12½***
**711** A207 10d multicolored .25 .25
**712** A207 15d multicolored .25 .25
**713** A207 20d multicolored .35 .35
**714** A207 30d multicolored .60 .60
**715** A207 40d multicolored 1.00 1.00
*Nos. 711-715 (5)* 2.45 2.45

Silver Pendant — A208

Silver Jewelry: 10d, Ornamental plate. 20d, Necklace with pendants. 25d, Crescent-shaped brooch. 115d, Armband.

**1978, Mar. 1 Litho. *Perf. 13x12½***
**716** A208 5d multicolored .25 .25
**717** A208 10d multicolored .25 .25
**718** A208 20d multicolored .25 .25
**719** A208 25d multicolored .25 .25
**720** A208 115d multicolored 1.50 1.50
*Nos. 716-720 (5)* 2.50 2.50

Tripoli International Fair.

Emblem, Compass and Lightning — A209

**1978, Mar. 10 *Perf. 13½***
**721** A209 30d multicolored .50 .50
**722** A209 115d multicolored 2.00 2.00

Arab Cultural Education Organization.

Children's Drawings and UNICEF Emblem — A210

a, Dancing. b, Children with posters. c, Shopping street. d, Playground. e, Bride and attendants.

**1978, Mar. 21**
**723** A210 40d Strip of 5, #a.-e. 7.25 7.25

Children's Day.

Clenched Fist, Made of Bricks A211

**1978, Mar. 22**
**728** A211 30d multicolored .65 .40
**729** A211 115d multicolored 1.50 .70

Determination of Arab people.

Blood Pressure Gauge, WHO Emblem — A212

**1978, Apr. 7 *Perf. 13x12½***
**730** A212 30d multicolored .35 .35
**731** A212 115d multicolored 1.75 .90

World Health Day, drive against hypertension.

Antenna and ITU Emblem A213

**1978, May 17 Photo. *Perf. 13½***
**732** A213 30d silver & multi .35 .25
**733** A213 115d gold & multi 1.50 .65

10th World Telecommunications Day.

Games Emblem — A214

**1978, July 13 Litho. *Perf. 12½***
**734** A214 15d multicolored .25 .25
**735** A214 30d multicolored .35 .35
**736** A214 115d multicolored 1.50 1.50
*Nos. 734-736 (3)* 2.10 2.10

3rd African Games, Algiers, 1978.

Inauguration of Tripoli International Airport — A215

**1978, Aug. 10 Litho. *Perf. 13½***
**737** A215 40d shown .50 .50
**738** A215 115d Terminal 2.00 .90

View of Ankara — A216

**1978, Aug. 17**
**739** A216 30d multicolored .50 .25
**740** A216 35d multicolored .60 .35
**741** A216 115d multicolored 1.60 1.60
*Nos. 739-741 (3)* 2.70 2.20

Turkish-Libyan friendship.

Soldiers, Jet, Ship — A217

35d, Tower, Green Book, oil derrick. 100d, View of Tripoli with mosque and modern buildings. 115d, View of Tripoli within cogwheel.

**1978, Sept. 1 *Perf. 14½***
**742** A217 30d multicolored .50 .50
**743** A217 35d org & multi .35 .35
**744** A217 115d blue & multi 1.50 1.25
*Nos. 742-744 (3)* 2.35 2.10

**Souvenir Sheet**
**745** A217 100d multicolored 2.75 2.75

9th anniversary of Sept. 1 Revolution. No. 745 contains one 50x41mm stamp.

Quarry and Symposium Emblem — A218

Designs: 40d, Oasis lake. 115d, Crater.

**1978, Sept. 16 *Perf. 13½***
**746** A218 30d multicolored .50 .50
**747** A218 40d multicolored .60 .60
**748** A218 115d multicolored 2.00 2.00
*Nos. 746-748 (3)* 3.10 3.10

2nd Symposium on Libyan Geology.

Green Book and Three Races A219

**1978, Oct. 18** *Perf. 12½*

| | | | | |
|---|---|---|---|---|
| 749 | A219 | 30d multicolored | .25 | .25 |
| 750 | A219 | 40d multicolored | .50 | .50 |
| 751 | A219 | 115d multicolored | 1.25 | 1.25 |
| | | *Nos. 749-751 (3)* | 2.00 | 2.00 |

International Anti-Apartheid Year.

Pilgrims, Minarets, Holy Kaaba A220

**1978, Nov. 9** **Photo.** *Perf. 12*

| | | | | |
|---|---|---|---|---|
| 752 | A220 | 5d multicolored | .25 | .25 |
| 753 | A220 | 10d multicolored | .25 | .25 |
| 754 | A220 | 15d multicolored | .25 | .25 |
| 755 | A220 | 20d multicolored | .25 | .25 |
| | | *Nos. 752-755 (4)* | 1.00 | 1.00 |

Pilgrimage to Mecca.

Handclasp over Globe — A221

**1978, Nov. 10** **Litho.** *Perf. 13½*

| | | | | |
|---|---|---|---|---|
| 756 | A221 | 30d multicolored | .40 | .30 |
| 757 | A221 | 40d multicolored | .50 | .40 |
| 758 | A221 | 115d multicolored | 1.50 | 1.25 |
| | | *Nos. 756-758 (3)* | 2.40 | 1.95 |

Technical Cooperation Among Developing Countries Conf., Buenos Aires, Argentina, Sept. 1978.

Fists, Guns, Map of Israel — A222

40d, 115d, Map of Arab countries and Israel, eagle and crowd. 145d, like 30d.

**1978, Dec. 5** **Litho.** *Perf. 13½*

| | | | | |
|---|---|---|---|---|
| 759 | A222 | 30d multi | .35 | .35 |
| 760 | A222 | 40d multi, horiz. | .50 | .50 |
| 761 | A222 | 115d multi, horiz. | 1.25 | 1.25 |
| 762 | A222 | 145d multi | 1.50 | .90 |
| | | *Nos. 759-762 (4)* | 3.60 | 3.00 |

Anti-Israel Summit Conf., Baghdad, Dec. 2-8.

Scales, Globe and Human Rights Flame — A223

**1978, Dec. 10**

| | | | | |
|---|---|---|---|---|
| 763 | A223 | 15d multicolored | .25 | .25 |
| 764 | A223 | 30d multicolored | .50 | .50 |
| 765 | A223 | 115d multicolored | 1.25 | 1.25 |
| | | *Nos. 763-765 (3)* | 2.00 | 2.00 |

Universal Declaration of Human Rights, 30th anniv.

Libyan Fort and Horse Racing — A224

**1978, Dec. 11**

| | | | | |
|---|---|---|---|---|
| 766 | A224 | 20d multicolored | .40 | .25 |
| 767 | A224 | 40d multicolored | .50 | .50 |
| 768 | A224 | 115d multicolored | 1.50 | 1.50 |
| | | *Nos. 766-768 (3)* | 2.40 | 2.25 |

Libyan Study Center.

Lilienthal's Glider, 1896 A225

25d, Spirit of St. Louis, 1927. 30d, Adm. Byrd's Polar flight, 1929. 50d, Graf Zeppelin, 1934, hydroplane and storks. 115d, Wilbur and Orville Wright and Flyer A. No. 774, Icarus falling. No. 775, Eagle and Boeing 727.

**1978, Dec. 26** **Litho.** *Perf. 14*

| | | | | |
|---|---|---|---|---|
| 769 | A225 | 20d multicolored | .25 | .25 |
| 770 | A225 | 25d multicolored | .45 | .45 |
| 771 | A225 | 30d multicolored | 1.40 | 1.40 |
| 772 | A225 | 50d multicolored | 1.60 | 1.60 |
| 773 | A225 | 115d multicolored | 1.40 | 1.40 |
| | | *Nos. 769-773 (5)* | 5.10 | 5.10 |

**Souvenir Sheets**

| | | | | |
|---|---|---|---|---|
| 774 | A225 | 100d multicolored | 3.00 | 3.00 |
| 775 | A225 | 100d multicolored | 3.00 | 3.00 |

75th anniversary of 1st powered flight.

Nos. 769-773 issued also in sheets of 4. Value, set perf. $45. Also exists imperf.

Nos. 774-775 exist imperf. Value, pair $50.

Mounted Stag's Head — A226

**Coil Stamps**

**1979, Jan. 15** **Photo.** *Perf. 14½x14*

| | | | | |
|---|---|---|---|---|
| 776 | A226 | 5d multicolored | .35 | .35 |
| 777 | A226 | 20d multicolored | .75 | .75 |
| 778 | A226 | 50d multicolored | 1.50 | 1.50 |
| | | *Nos. 776-778 (3)* | 2.60 | 2.60 |

Carpobrotus Acinaciformis A227

Flora of Libya: 15d, Caralluma europaea. 20d, Arum cirenaicum. 35d, Lavatera arborea. 40d, Capparis spinosa. 50d, Ranunculus asiaticus.

**1979, May 15** **Litho.** *Perf. 14*

| | | | | |
|---|---|---|---|---|
| 779 | A227 | 10d multicolored | .25 | .25 |
| 780 | A227 | 15d multicolored | .25 | .25 |
| 781 | A227 | 20d multicolored | .25 | .25 |
| 782 | A227 | 35d multicolored | .60 | .60 |
| 783 | A227 | 40d multicolored | .60 | .60 |
| 784 | A227 | 50d multicolored | .75 | .75 |
| | | *Nos. 779-784 (6)* | 2.70 | 2.70 |

People, Torch, Olive Branches — A228

**1979** **Litho.** *Perf. 13x12½*

**Size: 18x23mm**

| | | | | |
|---|---|---|---|---|
| 785 | A228 | 5d multi | .25 | .25 |
| 786 | A228 | 10d multi | .25 | .25 |
| 787 | A228 | 15d multi | .25 | .25 |
| 788 | A228 | 30d multi | .35 | .25 |
| 789 | A228 | 50d multi | .50 | .25 |
| 790 | A228 | 60d multi | .60 | .35 |
| 791 | A228 | 70d multi | .75 | .35 |
| 792 | A228 | 100d multi | 1.25 | .60 |
| 793 | A228 | 115d multi | 1.25 | .60 |

*Perf. 13½*

**Size: 26½x32mm**

| | | | | |
|---|---|---|---|---|
| 794 | A228 | 200d multi | 1.90 | 1.25 |
| 795 | A228 | 500d multi | 4.75 | 2.50 |
| 796 | A228 | 1000d multi | 10.00 | 6.25 |
| | | *Nos. 785-796 (12)* | 22.10 | 13.15 |

See Nos. 1053-1055.

Tortoise A229

Animals: 10d, Antelope. 15d, Hedgehog. 20d, Porcupine. 30d, Arabian camel. 35d, African wildcat. 45d, Gazelle. 115d, Cheetah. 10d, 30d, 35d, 45d, vert.

**1979, Feb. 1** **Litho.** *Perf. 14½*

| | | | | |
|---|---|---|---|---|
| 797 | A229 | 5d multicolored | .25 | .25 |
| 798 | A229 | 10d multicolored | .25 | .25 |
| 799 | A229 | 15d multicolored | .65 | .65 |
| 800 | A229 | 20d multicolored | .65 | .65 |
| 801 | A229 | 30d multicolored | 1.10 | .65 |
| 802 | A229 | 35d multicolored | 1.50 | .65 |
| 803 | A229 | 45d multicolored | 1.75 | .80 |
| 804 | A229 | 115d multicolored | 3.50 | 1.25 |
| | | *Nos. 797-804 (8)* | 9.65 | 5.15 |

Rug and Tripoli Fair Emblem — A230

Tripoli Fair emblem and various rugs.

**1979, Mar. 1** **Litho.** *Perf. 11*

| | | | | |
|---|---|---|---|---|
| 805 | A230 | 10d multicolored | .25 | .25 |
| 806 | A230 | 15d multicolored | .25 | .25 |
| 807 | A230 | 30d multicolored | .35 | .35 |
| 808 | A230 | 45d multicolored | .50 | .50 |
| 809 | A230 | 115d multicolored | 1.25 | 1.25 |
| | | *Nos. 805-809 (5)* | 2.60 | 2.60 |

17th Tripoli Fair.

Exist imperf. Value, set $30.

Children's Drawings and IYC Emblem A231

a, Families and planes. b, Shepherd, sheep and dog. c, Beach umbrellas. d, Boat in storm. e, Traffic policeman.

**1979, Mar. 20** *Perf. 13½*

| | | | | |
|---|---|---|---|---|
| 810 | A231 | 20d Strip of 5, #a.-e. | 5.00 | 3.50 |

Intl. Year of the Child.

Exists imperf. Value $30.

Book, World Map, Arab Achievements A232

**1979, Mar. 22** *Perf. 13*

| | | | | |
|---|---|---|---|---|
| 815 | A232 | 45d multicolored | .50 | .50 |
| 816 | A232 | 70d multicolored | .75 | .75 |

WMO Emblem, Weather Map and Tower — A233

**1979, Mar. 23**

| | | | | |
|---|---|---|---|---|
| 817 | A233 | 15d multicolored | .25 | .25 |
| 818 | A233 | 30d multicolored | .35 | .35 |
| 819 | A233 | 50d multicolored | .60 | .60 |
| | | *Nos. 817-819 (3)* | 1.20 | 1.20 |

World Meteorological Day.

Medical Services, WHO Emblem — A234

**1979, Apr. 7**

| | | | | |
|---|---|---|---|---|
| 820 | A234 | 40d multicolored | .60 | .60 |

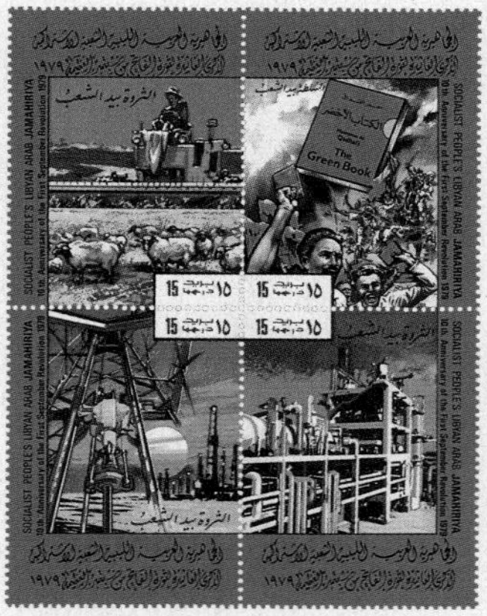


Farmer Plowing and Sheep — A235

**1979, Sept. 1** **Litho.** *Perf. 14½*

| | | | | |
|---|---|---|---|---|
| 821 | A235 | Block of 4 | 1.00 | 1.00 |
| a. | | 15d Harvester, sheep | .25 | .25 |
| b. | | 15d Men holding Green Book | .25 | .25 |
| c. | | 15d Oil field | .25 | .25 |
| d. | | 15d Oil refinery | .25 | .25 |
| 822 | A235 | Block of 4 | 2.00 | 2.00 |
| a. | | 30d Dish antenna | .40 | .40 |
| b. | | 30d Hospital | .40 | .40 |
| c. | | 30d Doctor examining patient | .40 | .40 |
| d. | | 30d Surgery | .40 | .40 |
| 823 | A235 | Block of 4 | 3.00 | 3.00 |
| a. | | 40d Street, Tripoli | .50 | .50 |
| b. | | 40d Steel mill | .50 | .50 |
| c. | | 40d Tanks | .50 | .50 |
| d. | | 40d Tuareg horsemen | .50 | .50 |
| 824 | A235 | Block of 4 | 4.00 | 4.00 |
| a. | | 70d Revolutionaries, Green Book | .90 | .90 |
| b. | | 70d Crowd, map of Libya | .90 | .90 |
| c. | | 70d Mullah | .90 | .90 |
| d. | | 70d Student | .90 | .90 |
| | | *Nos. 821-824 (4)* | 10.00 | 10.00 |

### Souvenir Sheets

*Imperf*

**825** A235 50d Revolution symbols, Green Book 2.50 2.50
**826** A235 50d Monument 2.50 2.50

Sept. 1st revolution, 10th anniversary.

Volleyball A236

**1979, Sept. 10**

**827** A236 45d shown .50 .50
**828** A236 115d Soccer 1.25 1.25

Universiade '79 World University Games, Mexico City, Sept.
Exists imperf. Value, set $17.50.

Mediterranean Games, Split, Yugoslavia — A237

**1979, Sept. 15 Litho.** ***Perf. 12x11½***

**829** A237 15d multicolored .50 .50
**830** A237 30d multicolored 1.40 .50
**831** A237 70d multicolored 3.50 1.00
*Nos. 829-831 (3)* 5.40 2.00

Exhibition Emblem — A238

**1979, Sept. 25 Photo.** ***Perf. 11½x11***

**832** A238 45d multicolored .50 .50
**833** A238 115d multicolored 1.50 1.50

TELECOM '79, 3rd World Telecommunications Exhibition, Geneva, Sept. 20-26.

A239

No. 834: a, 10d, Seminar emblem, Green Book, crowd. b, 35d, Meeting hall (Size: 67x43½mm). c, 100d, Col. Khadafy.
No. 835, Central portion of #834c.

**1979, Oct. 1**

**834** A239 Strip of 3, #a.-c. 2.50 2.50

### Size: 87x114mm

*Imperf*

**835** A239 100d multicolored 3.50 3.50

Intl. Seminar of the Green Book, Benghazi, Oct. 1-3. No. 834 has continuous design.

Evacuation of Foreign Forces — A240

**1979, Oct. 7**

**837** A240 30d shown .60 .40
**838** A240 40d Tuareg horsemen .90 .50

### Souvenir Sheet

*Imperf*

**839** A240 100d Vignettes 3.00 3.00

Cyclist, Championship Emblem — A241

15d, Cyclist, emblem on left side. 30d, Two cyclists, emblem on right side.

**1979, Nov. 21**

**840** A241 15d shown .25 .25
**841** A241 30d multicolored .50 .50

Junior Cycling Championships, Tripoli, Nov. 21-23. Issued in sheetlets of 4.

Hurdles, Olympic Rings, Moscow '80 Emblem — A242

**1979, Nov. 21**

**842** A242 45d Equestrian .50 .50
**843** A242 60d Javelin .75 .75
**844** A242 115d Hurdles 1.50 1.50
**845** A242 160d Soccer 1.75 1.75
*Nos. 842-845 (4)* 4.50 4.50

### Souvenir Sheets

**846** A242 150d shown 3.75 3.75
**847** A242 150d like #845 3.75 3.75

Pre-Olympics (Moscow '80 Olympic Games). Nos. 842-845 issued in sheetlets of 4 and sheets of 20 (4x5) with silver Moscow '80 Emblem covering background of every 20 stamps. Value, set of sheetlets of 4, $45.
Nos. 842-847 exist imperf. Values: set $55; souvenir sheets, $90.

Intl. Day of Cooperation with Palestinian People — A242a

**1979, Nov. 29 Photo.** ***Perf. 12***

**847A** A242a 30d multicolored .25 .25
**847B** A242a 115d multicolored 1.75 1.75

Tug of War, Jumping — A243

National Games: No. 848, Polo, leap frog. No. 849, Racing, ball game, No. 850, Wrestling, log rolling. No. 852, Horsemen.

**1980, Feb. 15**

**848** A243 Block of 4, #a.-d. 1.00 1.00
**849** A243 Block of 4, #a.-d. 1.00 1.00
**850** A243 Block of 4, #a.-d. 1.00 1.00
**851** A243 Block of 4, #a.-d. 2.00 2.00
**852** A243 Block of 4, #a.-d. 3.50 3.50
*Nos. 848-852 (5)* 8.50 8.50

Battles — A244

No. 853: a, 20d, Gardabia, 1915. b, 35d, same. No. 854: a, 20d, Shoghab, 1913. b, 35d, same. No. 855: a, 20d, Fundugh Al-Shibani, 1922. b, 35d, same. No. 856: a, 20d, Ghira. b, 35d, same.
Pairs have continuous design.

**1980 Litho.** ***Perf. 14½***

**853** A244 Pair, #a.-b. *1.25 1.25*
**854** A244 Pair, #a.-b. *1.25 1.25*
**855** A244 Pair, #a.-b. *1.25 1.25*
**856** A244 Pair, #a.-b. *1.25 1.25*
*Nos. 853-856 (4)* *5.00 5.00*

Issued: No. 853, 4/28; No. 854, 5/25; No. 855, 6/1; No. 856, 8/15.
See Nos. 893-896, 921-932, 980-991, 1059-1070.

Girl Guides Examining Plant — A245

30d, Guides cooking. 50d, Scouts at campfire. 115d, Scouts reading map.

**1980, Aug. 22** ***Perf. 13½***

**861** A245 15d shown .25 .25
**862** A245 30d multicolored .35 .35
**863** A245 50d multicolored .60 .60
**864** A245 115d multicolored 1.50 1.50
*Nos. 861-864 (4)* 2.70 2.70

### Souvenir Sheets

**865** A245 100d like #861 2.25 2.25
**866** A245 100d like #863 2.25 2.25

8th Pan Arab Girl Guide and 14th Pan Arab Scout Jamborees, Aug.

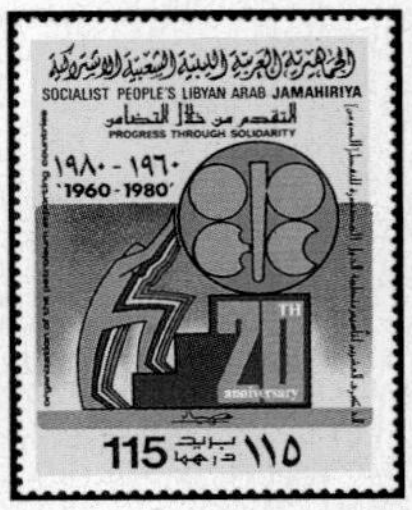

Men Holding OPEC Emblem A246

**1980, Sept. 15** ***Perf. 14½***

**867** A246 45d Emblem, globe .50 .50
**868** A246 115d shown 1.50 1.50

20th anniversary of OPEC.

Martyrdom of Omar Muktar, 1931 — A247

**1980, Sept. 16**

**869** A247 20d multicolored .25 .25
**870** A247 35d multicolored .50 .50

### Souvenir Sheet

**870A** A247 100d multicolored 2.50 2.50

UNESCO Emblem and Avicenna A248

**1980, Sept. 20**

**871** A248 45d Scientific symbols .50 .50
**872** A248 115d shown 1.50 1.50

School Scientific Exhibition, Sept. 20-24 and birth millenium of Arab physician Avicenna (115d).

18th Tripoli Fair A249

Various musical instruments. 15d vert.

**1980 Litho.** ***Perf. 13½***

**873** A249 5d multicolored .25 .25
**874** A249 10d multicolored .25 .25
**875** A249 15d multicolored .25 .25
**876** A249 20d multicolored .25 .25
**877** A249 25d multicolored .40 .40
*Nos. 873-877 (5)* 1.40 1.40

### Souvenir Sheet

**878** A249 100d Musicians 2.50 2.50

World Olive Oil Year A250

**1980, Jan. 15 Litho.** ***Perf. 13½***

**879** A250 15d multicolored .25 .25
**880** A250 30d multicolored .35 .35
**881** A250 45d multicolored .50 .50
*Nos. 879-881 (3)* 1.10 1.10

Intl. Year of the Child (1979) — A251

Children's drawings: a, Riding horses. b, water sports. c, Fish. d, Gift sale. e, Preparing feast.

**1980, Mar. 21**

| | | | | |
|---|---|---|---|---|
| **882** | | Strip of 5 | 5.00 | 5.00 |
| ***a.-e.*** | A251 | 20d any single | .50 | .40 |

The Hegira, 1500th Anniv. A252

**1980, Apr. 1**

| | | | | |
|---|---|---|---|---|
| **883** | A252 | 50d multicolored | .60 | .60 |
| **884** | A252 | 115d multicolored | 1.50 | 1.50 |

Operating Room, Hospital — A253

**1980, Apr. 7 Litho. *Perf. 13½***

| | | | | |
|---|---|---|---|---|
| **885** | A253 | 20d multicolored | .40 | .40 |
| **886** | A253 | 50d multicolored | .75 | .75 |

World Health Day.

Sheik Zarruq Festival, Misurata, June 16-20 — A254

**1980, June 16**

| | | | | |
|---|---|---|---|---|
| **887** | A254 | 40d multicolored | .50 | .50 |
| **888** | A254 | 115d multicolored | 1.50 | 1.50 |

**Souvenir Sheet**

| | | | | |
|---|---|---|---|---|
| **889** | A254 | 100d multicolored | 2.75 | 2.75 |

Arabian Towns Organization A255

**1980, July 1 *Perf. 11½x12***

| | | | | |
|---|---|---|---|---|
| **890** | A255 | 15d Ghadames | .25 | .25 |
| **891** | A255 | 30d Derna | .35 | .35 |
| **892** | A255 | 50d Tripoli | .60 | .60 |
| | | *Nos. 890-892 (3)* | 1.20 | 1.20 |

**Battles Type of 1980**

No. 893: a, 20d, Yefren, 1915, b, 35d, same. No. 894: a, 20d, El Hani, 1911, b, 35d, same. No. 895: a, 20d, Sebha, 1914, b, 35d, same. No. 896: a, 20d, Sirt, 1912, b, 35d, same.
Pairs have continuous design.

**1980 *Perf. 13½***

| | | | | |
|---|---|---|---|---|
| **893** | A244 | Pair, #a.-b. | 1.25 | 1.25 |
| **894** | A244 | Pair, #a.-b. | 1.25 | 1.25 |
| **895** | A244 | Pair, #a.-b. | 1.25 | 1.25 |
| **896** | A244 | Pair, #a.-b. | 1.25 | 1.25 |
| | | *Nos. 893-896 (4)* | 5.00 | 5.00 |

Issued: No. 893, 7/16; No. 894, 10/23; No. 895, 11/27; No. 896, 12/31.

Sept. 1 Revolution, 11th Anniv. — A256

Achievements of the Revolution: 5d, Oil industry. 10d, Youth festival. 15d, Agriculture. 25d, Transportation. 40d, Education. 115d, Housing.
100d, Montage of achievements.

**1980, Sept. 1**

| | | | | |
|---|---|---|---|---|
| **901** | A256 | 5d multicolored | .25 | .25 |
| **902** | A256 | 10d multicolored | .25 | .25 |
| **903** | A256 | 15d multicolored | .50 | .50 |
| **904** | A256 | 25d multicolored | 1.25 | .50 |
| **905** | A256 | 40d multicolored | 1.25 | .50 |
| **906** | A256 | 115d multicolored | 3.00 | 1.25 |
| | | *Nos. 901-906 (6)* | 6.50 | 3.25 |

**Souvenir Sheet**

| | | | | |
|---|---|---|---|---|
| **907** | A256 | 100d multicolored | 2.75 | 2.75 |

No. 907 contains one stamp 30x50mm.

World Tourism Conference A257

**1980, Sept. 10**

| | | | | |
|---|---|---|---|---|
| **908** | A257 | 45d multicolored | .50 | .50 |
| **909** | A257 | 115d multicolored | 1.50 | 1.50 |

Intl. Year of the Disabled — A258

Intl. Year of the Disabled emblem and: 20d, Eye, man on crutches. 45d, Stylized globe. 115d, Eye, man on crutch, hands.

**1981, Jan. 1 *Perf. 15***

| | | | | |
|---|---|---|---|---|
| **910** | A258 | 20d lt. green, blue & blk | .25 | .25 |
| **911** | A258 | 45d blue, blk & grn | .35 | .25 |
| **912** | A258 | 115d lt. grn, blue & grn | 1.50 | .50 |
| | | *Nos. 910-912 (3)* | 2.10 | 1.00 |

**Nos. 911-912 Redrawn with Arabic Writing and "Arab League" Above Emblem**

**1981, Nov. 21 Litho. *Perf. 15***

| | | | | |
|---|---|---|---|---|
| **913** | A258 | 45d blue & multi | .35 | .25 |
| **914** | A258 | 115d rose & multi | 1.10 | 1.10 |

UPA Disabled Persons Campaign. Design redrawn to include Arab League Emblem.

Mosaics — A259

**1981, Jan. 15 *Perf. 13½***

| | | | | |
|---|---|---|---|---|
| **915** | A259 | 10d Horse | 1.00 | .25 |
| **916** | A259 | 20d Sailing ship | 1.00 | .50 |
| **917** | A259 | 30d Peacocks | 2.00 | .50 |
| **918** | A259 | 40d Panther | 2.00 | .50 |
| **919** | A259 | 50d Musician | 2.50 | .50 |
| **920** | A259 | 115d Fish | 6.50 | 1.00 |
| | | *Nos. 915-920 (6)* | 15.00 | 3.25 |

**Battles Type of 1980**

No. 921: a, 20d, Dernah, 1912, b, 35d, same. No. 922: a, 20d, Bir Tagreft, 1928. b, 35d, same. No. 923: a, 20d, Tawargha, 1923. b, 35d, same. No. 924: a, 20d, .Funduk El-Jamel Misurata, 1915 b, 35d, same. No. 925: a, 20d, Zuara, 1912. b, 35d, same. No. 926: a, 20d, Sidi El-Khemri, 1915. b, 35d, same. No. 927: a, 20d, El-Khoms, 1913. b, 35d, same. No. 928: a, 20d, Roghdalin, 1912. b, 35d, same. No. 929: a, 20d, Rughbat El-Naga, 1925. b, 35d, same. No. 930: a, 20d, Tobruk. 1911. 1922, b, 35d, same. No. 931: a, 20d, Bir Ikshadia, 1924. b, 35d, same. No. 932: a, 20d, Ain Zara, 1924. b, 35d, same.
Pairs have continuous design.

**1981 *Perf. 13½, 14½ (#926, 932)***

| | | | | |
|---|---|---|---|---|
| **921** | A244 | Pair, #a.-b. | 1.25 | 1.25 |
| **922** | A244 | Pair, #a.-b. | 1.25 | 1.25 |
| **923** | A244 | Pair, #a.-b. | 1.25 | 1.25 |
| **924** | A244 | Pair, #a.-b. | 1.25 | 1.25 |
| **925** | A244 | Pair, #a.-b. | 1.25 | 1.25 |
| **926** | A244 | Pair, #a.-b. | 1.25 | 1.25 |
| **927** | A244 | Pair, #a.-b. | 1.25 | 1.25 |
| **928** | A244 | Pair, #a.-b. | 1.25 | 1.25 |
| **929** | A244 | Pair, #a.-b. | 1.25 | 1.25 |
| **930** | A244 | Pair, #a.-b. | 1.25 | 1.25 |
| **931** | A244 | Pair, #a.-b. | 1.25 | 1.25 |
| **932** | A244 | Pair, #a.-b. | 1.25 | 1.25 |
| | | *Nos. 921-932 (12)* | 15.00 | 15.00 |

Issued: No. 921, 1/17; No. 922, 2/25; No. 923, 3/20; No. 924, 4/13; No. 925, 5/26; No. 926, 6/4; No. 927, 7/27; No. 928, 8/15; No. 929, 9/16; No. 930, 10/27; No. 931, 11/19; No. 932, 12/4.

Tripoli Intl. Fair — A260

Ceramicware.

**1981, Mar. 1 *Perf. 13½***

| | | | | |
|---|---|---|---|---|
| **945** | A260 | 5d Bowls, horiz. | .25 | .25 |
| **946** | A260 | 10d Lamp | .25 | .25 |
| **947** | A260 | 15d Vase | .25 | .25 |
| **948** | A260 | 45d Water jar, horiz. | .60 | .25 |
| **949** | A260 | 115d Spouted water jar, horiz. | 1.75 | .60 |
| | | *Nos. 945-949 (5)* | 3.10 | 1.60 |

No. 707b, Crowd — A261

**1981, Mar. 2 *Perf. 15***

| | | | | |
|---|---|---|---|---|
| **950** | A261 | 50d multicolored | .35 | .35 |
| **951** | A261 | 115d multicolored | 1.50 | .50 |

People's Authority Declaration, The Green Book.

Children's Day, IYC — A262

Children's illustrations: a, Desert camp. b, Women doing chores. c, Village scene. d, Airplane over playground. e, Minaret, camel, man.

**1981, Mar. 21 Litho. *Perf. 13½***

| | | | | |
|---|---|---|---|---|
| **952** | | Strip of 5 | 5.00 | 5.00 |
| ***a.-e.*** | A262 | 20d any single | .50 | .40 |

Bank of Libya, 25th Anniv. — A263

**1981, Apr. 1 Litho. *Perf. 13½***

| | | | | |
|---|---|---|---|---|
| **953** | A263 | 45d multicolored | .50 | .35 |
| **954** | A263 | 115d multicolored | 1.75 | 1.10 |

**Souvenir Sheet**

| | | | | |
|---|---|---|---|---|
| **955** | A263 | 50d multicolored | 1.50 | 1.50 |

World Health Day A264

**1981, Apr. 7 *Perf. 14***

| | | | | |
|---|---|---|---|---|
| **956** | A264 | 45d multicolored | .50 | .50 |
| **957** | A264 | 115d multicolored | 1.50 | .75 |

Intl. Year for Combating Racial Discrimination A265

**1981, July 1 *Perf. 15***

| | | | | |
|---|---|---|---|---|
| **958** | A265 | 45d multicolored | 1.10 | .65 |
| **959** | A265 | 50d multicolored | 1.50 | .75 |

September 1 Revolution, 12th Anniv. — A266

No. 960: a-b, Helicopter and jets; c-d, Paratroopers. No. 961: a-b, Tanks; c-d, Frogman parade. No. 962: a-b, Twelve-barrel rocket launchers; c-d, Trucks with rockets. No. 963: a-b, Sailor parade; c-d, Jeep and trucks with twelve-barrel rocket launchers. No. 964: a-b, Wheeled tanks and jeeps; c-d, Tank parade. Nos. 960-962 vert. Pairs have continuous designs.

**1981, Sept. 1 *Perf. 14½***

| | | | | |
|---|---|---|---|---|
| **960** | A266 | 5d Block of 4, #a.-d. | 1.40 | 1.40 |
| **961** | A266 | 10d Block of 4, #a.-d. | 1.40 | 1.40 |

| | | | | |
|---|---|---|---|---|
| 962 | A266 | 15d Block of 4, #a.-d. | 1.40 | 1.40 |
| 963 | A266 | 20d Block of 4, #a.-d. | 1.40 | 1.40 |
| 964 | A266 | 25d Block of 4, #a.-d. | 2.75 | 2.75 |
| | | *Nos. 960-964 (5)* | 8.35 | 8.35 |

**Souvenir Sheet**

***Perf. 11***

| | | | | |
|---|---|---|---|---|
| 965 | A266 | 50d Naval troop marching | 7.00 | 7.00 |

No. 965 contains one 63x38mm stamp.

Miniature Sheet

Butterflies — A267

**1981, Oct. 1** ***Perf. 14½***

| | | | | |
|---|---|---|---|---|
| 966 | A267 | Sheet of 16 | 11.00 | |
| *a.-d.* | | 5d, any single | .25 | .25 |
| *e.-h.* | | 10d, any single | .45 | .25 |
| *i.-l.* | | 15d, any single | .50 | .40 |
| *m.-p.* | | 25d, any single | 1.00 | .60 |

No. 966 printed in a continuous design, stamps of same denomination in blocks of 4. Sheetlets exist containing blocks of 4 for each denomination. Value, set of 4 sheets, $20.

World Food Day — A268

**1981, Oct. 16** ***Perf. 15***

| | | | | |
|---|---|---|---|---|
| 967 | A268 | 45d multicolored | .50 | .50 |
| 968 | A268 | 200d multicolored | 2.50 | 2.50 |

Fruit — A269

**1981, Nov. 17** ***Perf. 13½***

| | | | | |
|---|---|---|---|---|
| 969 | A269 | 5d Grapes | .25 | .25 |
| 970 | A269 | 10d Dates | .25 | .25 |
| 971 | A269 | 15d Lemons | .25 | .25 |
| 972 | A269 | 20d Oranges | .40 | .25 |
| 973 | A269 | 35d Cactus fruit | .80 | .35 |
| 974 | A269 | 55d Pomegranates | 1.50 | .60 |
| | | *Nos. 969-974 (6)* | 3.45 | 1.95 |

Miniature Sheet

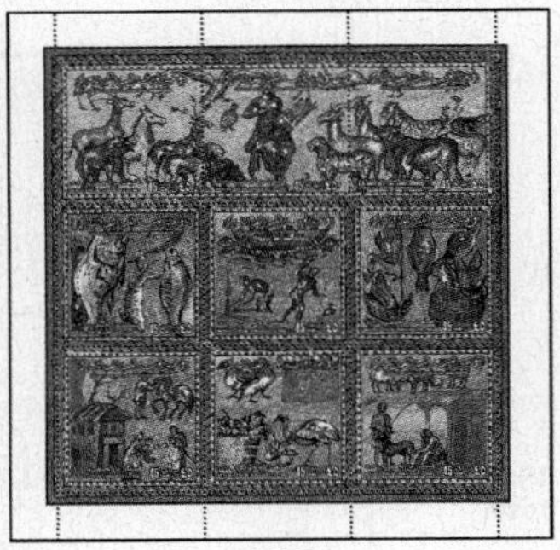

A270

Mosaics: a, Animals facing right. b, Orpheus playing music. c, Animals facing left. d, Fish. e, Fishermen. f, Fish in basket. g, Farm yard. h, Birds eating fruit. i, Milking a goat.

**1982, Jan. 1** ***Perf. 13½***

| | | | | |
|---|---|---|---|---|
| 975 | A270 | Sheet of 9 | 9.00 | 9.00 |
| *a.-i.* | | 45d any single | .75 | .75 |

Nos. 975a-975c, shown in illustration, printed in continuous design.

3rd Intl. Koran Reading Contest — A271

Designs: 10d, Stone tablets, Holy Ka'aba, Mecca. 35d, Open Koran, creation of the world. 115d, Scholar, students.

**1982, Jan. 7**

| | | | | |
|---|---|---|---|---|
| 976 | A271 | 10d multicolored | .25 | .25 |
| 977 | A271 | 35d multicolored | .50 | .25 |
| 978 | A271 | 115d multicolored | 1.50 | .75 |
| | | *Nos. 976-978 (3)* | 2.25 | 1.25 |

**Souvenir Sheet**

| | | | | |
|---|---|---|---|---|
| 979 | A271 | 100d like 115d | 3.50 | 3.50 |

**Battles Type of 1980**

No. 980: a, 20d, Hun Gioffra, 1915; b, 35d, same. No. 981: a, 20d, Gedabia, 1914; b, 35d, same. No. 982: a, 20d, El-Asaba, 1913; b, 35d, same. No. 983: a, 20d, El-Habela, 1917; b, 35d, same. No. 984: a, 20d, Suk El-Ahad, 1915; b, 35d, same. No. 985: a, 20d, El-Tangi, 1913; b, 35d, same. No. 986: a, 20d, Sokna, 1913; b, 35d, same. No. 987: a, 20d, Wadi Smalus, 1925; b, 35d, same. No. 988: a, 20d, Sidi Abuagela, 1917; b, 35d, same. No. 989: a, 20d, Sidi Surur, 1914; b, 35d, same. No. 990: a, 20d, Kuefia, 1911; b, 35d, same. No. 991: a, 20d, Abunjeim, 1940; b, 35d, same.

Pairs have continuous design.

**1982** ***Perf. 13½, 14½ (#985-988)***

| | | | | |
|---|---|---|---|---|
| 980 | A244 | Pair, #a.-b. | 1.25 | 1.25 |
| 981 | A244 | Pair, #a.-b. | 1.25 | 1.25 |
| 982 | A244 | Pair, #a.-b. | 1.25 | 1.25 |
| 983 | A244 | Pair, #a.-b. | 1.25 | 1.25 |
| 984 | A244 | Pair, #a.-b. | 1.25 | 1.25 |
| 985 | A244 | Pair, #a.-b. | 1.25 | 1.25 |
| 986 | A244 | Pair, #a.-b. | 1.25 | 1.25 |
| 987 | A244 | Pair, #a.-b. | 1.25 | 1.25 |
| 988 | A244 | Pair, #a.-b. | 1.25 | 1.25 |
| 989 | A244 | Pair, #a.-b. | 1.25 | 1.25 |
| 990 | A244 | Pair, #a.-b. | 1.25 | 1.25 |
| 991 | A244 | Pair, #a.-b. | 1.25 | 1.25 |
| | | *Nos. 980-991 (12)* | 15.00 | 15.00 |

Issued: No. 980, 1/26; No. 981, 3/8; No. 982, 3/23; No. 983, 4/24; No. 984, 5/15; No. 985, 6/19; No. 986, 7/23; No. 987, 8/11; No. 988, 9/4; No. 989, 10/14; No. 990, 11/28; No. 991, 12/13.

Tripoli Intl. Fair — A272

5d, Grinding stone. 10d, Ox-drawn plow. 25d, Pitching hay. 35d, Tapestry weaving. 45d, Traditional cooking. 100d, Grain harvest.

**1982, Mar. 1** ***Perf. 13x12½***

| | | | | |
|---|---|---|---|---|
| 1004 | A272 | 5d multicolored | .25 | .25 |
| 1005 | A272 | 10d multicolored | .25 | .25 |
| 1006 | A272 | 25d multicolored | .25 | .25 |
| 1007 | A272 | 35d multicolored | .50 | .25 |
| 1008 | A272 | 45d multicolored | .75 | .35 |
| 1009 | A272 | 100d multicolored | 1.50 | .75 |
| | | *Nos. 1004-1009 (6)* | 3.50 | 2.10 |

People's Authority Declaration, The Green Book — A273

**1982, Mar. 2** ***Perf. 13½***

| | | | | |
|---|---|---|---|---|
| 1010 | | Strip of 3 | 8.00 | 8.00 |
| *a.* | A273 | 100d Harvester combine | 1.25 | .60 |
| *b.* | A273 | 200d Khadafy, scholar, rifles | 2.50 | 2.25 |
| *c.* | A273 | 300d Govt. building, citizens | 3.25 | 2.25 |

Scouting Movement, 75th Anniv. — A274

**1982, Mar. 2**

| | | | | |
|---|---|---|---|---|
| 1011 | | Strip of 4 | 22.50 | 22.50 |
| *a.* | A274 | 100d Cub scout, blimp | 1.75 | .80 |
| *b.* | A274 | 200d Scouts, dog | 3.25 | 1.60 |
| *c.* | A274 | 300d Scholar, scout | 4.75 | 2.00 |
| *d.* | A274 | 400d Boy scout, rocket | 7.25 | 3.75 |

**Souvenir Sheets**

| | | | | |
|---|---|---|---|---|
| 1012 | A274 | 500d Green Book | 8.00 | 8.00 |
| 1013 | A274 | 500d Khadafy, scouts | 8.00 | 8.00 |

Nos. 1012-1013 each contain one stamp 39x42mm.

Nos. 1011-1013 exist imperf.

13th African Soccer Cup Championships A275

**1982, Mar. 5**

| | | | | |
|---|---|---|---|---|
| 1014 | A275 | 100d multi | 1.50 | .75 |
| 1015 | A275 | 200d multi | 3.00 | 1.50 |

1982 World Cup Soccer Championships, Spain — A276

World Cup trophy and various soccer plays.

**1982, Mar. 15** ***Perf. 14½***

| | | | | |
|---|---|---|---|---|
| 1016 | A276 | 45d multi | .60 | .60 |
| 1017 | A276 | 100d multi | 1.50 | 1.50 |
| 1018 | A276 | 200d multi | 2.75 | 2.75 |
| 1019 | A276 | 300d multi | 3.25 | 3.25 |
| | | *Nos. 1016-1019 (4)* | 8.10 | 8.10 |

**Souvenir Sheets**

| | | | | |
|---|---|---|---|---|
| 1020 | A276 | 500d like 45d | 7.50 | 7.50 |
| 1021 | A276 | 500d like 100d | 7.50 | 7.50 |

Nos. 1016-1019 issued in sheets of 8 overprinted in silver with soccer ball in motion. Value $75. Sheetlets of 4 in each denomination exist without overprint.

Nos. 1020-1021 have Arabic text in green on reverse. Value $35.

Nos. 1016-1019 exist imperf. Value $15. Nos. 1020-1021 also exist imperf.

Palestinian Children's Day — A277

Designs: a, Two children. b, Girl with bowl. c, Girl with kaffiyeh. d, Girl hiding. e, Boy.

**1982, Mar. 7** ***Perf. 13½***

| | | | | |
|---|---|---|---|---|
| 1022 | | Strip of 5 | 2.75 | 2.75 |
| *a.-e.* | A277 | 20d, any single | .40 | .40 |

Miniature Sheet

Birds — A278

**1982, Apr. 1** ***Perf. 14½***

| | | | | |
|---|---|---|---|---|
| 1023 | A278 | Sheet of 16 | 20.00 | 20.00 |
| *a.-d.* | | 15d, any single | .50 | .45 |
| *e.-h.* | | 25d, any single | .75 | .60 |
| *i.-l.* | | 45d, any single | 1.10 | 1.00 |
| *m.-p.* | | 95d, any single | 2.40 | 1.80 |

No. 1023a-1023p printed se-tenant in a continuous design; stamps of same denomination in blocks of 4.

Each denomination was also printed in a sheet of 16, each sheet containing four se-tenant blocks of the same denomination. Value, set of four sheets, $75.

Teaching Hospitals Anniv. A279

**1982, Apr. 7** ***Perf. 13x12½***

| | | | | |
|---|---|---|---|---|
| 1024 | A279 | 95d multi | 1.25 | 1.25 |
| 1025 | A279 | 100d multi | 1.25 | 1.25 |
| 1026 | A279 | 205d multi | 2.75 | 2.75 |
| | | *Nos. 1024-1026 (3)* | 5.25 | 5.25 |

Arab Postal Union, 30th — A280

**1982, Apr. 12** ***Perf. 13½***

| | | | | |
|---|---|---|---|---|
| 1027 | A280 | 100d multi | 1.50 | .75 |
| 1028 | A280 | 200d multi | 2.75 | 1.50 |

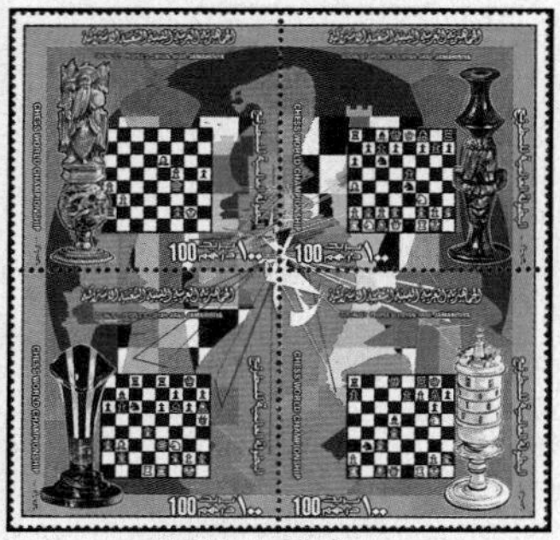

1982 World Chess Championships — A281

Board positions and chessmen: a, Chinese piece. b, African piece. c, Modern piece. d, European piece.
500d, Overhead view of chessboard.

**1982, May 1**

| | | | | |
|---|---|---|---|---|
| **1029** | A281 | Block of 4 | 10.00 | 10.00 |
| *a.-d.* | | 100d, any single | 2.25 | 1.10 |

**Souvenir Sheet**

| | | | | |
|---|---|---|---|---|
| **1030** | A281 | 500d multicolored | 10.00 | 10.00 |

No. 1030 contains one stamp 39x42mm.
Nos. 1029 and 1030 exist imperf.

World Telecommunications Day — A282

**1982, May 17**

| | | | | |
|---|---|---|---|---|
| **1031** | A282 | 100d multi | 1.25 | 1.25 |
| **1032** | A282 | 200d multi | 2.50 | 2.50 |

Map of Libya, Green Book A283

**1982, June 11**

| | | | | |
|---|---|---|---|---|
| **1033** | A283 | 200d multi | 2.50 | 1.50 |

**Souvenir Sheet**

| | | | | |
|---|---|---|---|---|
| **1034** | A283 | 300d multi | 5.00 | 5.00 |

Post Day, FIP 51st anniv.

Organization of African Unity, 19th Summit A284

50d, OAU flag, Arab family. 100d, Map of Africa, emblem. 200d, Khadafy, Green Book. 300d, Fist, map.

**1982, Aug. 5** *Perf. 14*

| | | | | |
|---|---|---|---|---|
| **1035** | A284 | 50d multicolored | .75 | .75 |
| **1036** | A284 | 100d multicolored | 1.25 | 1.25 |

**Size: 69x40mm**

| | | | | |
|---|---|---|---|---|
| **1037** | A284 | 200d multicolored | 2.50 | 2.50 |
| | | *Nos. 1035-1037 (3)* | 4.50 | 4.50 |

**Souvenir Sheet**

***Perf. 13x13½***

| | | | | |
|---|---|---|---|---|
| **1038** | A284 | 300d multicolored | 5.00 | 5.00 |

No. 1038 contains one stamp 29x42mm.

September 1 Revolution, 13th Anniv. — A285

Khadafy in uniforms and various armed forces' exercises.

**1982, Sept. 1** *Perf. 11½*

| | | | | |
|---|---|---|---|---|
| **1039** | A285 | 15d multi | .25 | .25 |
| **1040** | A285 | 20d multi | .25 | .25 |
| **1041** | A285 | 30d multi | 1.00 | 1.00 |
| **1042** | A285 | 45d multi | .60 | .60 |
| **1043** | A285 | 70d multi | 1.00 | 1.00 |
| **1044** | A285 | 100d multi | 1.50 | 1.50 |
| | | *Nos. 1039-1044 (6)* | 4.60 | 4.60 |

**Souvenir Sheet**

***Imperf***

| | | | | |
|---|---|---|---|---|
| **1045** | A285 | 200d multi | 4.00 | 4.00 |

Libyan Red Crescent, 25th Anniv. — A286

**1982, Oct. 5** *Perf. 13½*

| | | | | |
|---|---|---|---|---|
| **1046** | A286 | 100d Palm tree | 1.75 | 1.25 |
| **1047** | A286 | 200d "25," crescents | 3.50 | 2.50 |

Intl. Day of Cooperation with Palestinian People — A287

**1982, Nov. 29**

| | | | | |
|---|---|---|---|---|
| **1048** | A287 | 100d gray grn & blk | 1.50 | .75 |
| **1049** | A287 | 200d brt bl, gray grn & blk | 2.75 | 1.50 |

Al-Fateh University Symposium on Khadafy's Green Book — A288

100d, Khadafy in uniform. 200d, Khadafy, map, Green Book.

**1982, Dec. 1** *Perf. 12*

| | | | | |
|---|---|---|---|---|
| **1050** | A288 | 100d multicolored | 1.25 | 1.10 |
| **1051** | A288 | 200d multicolored | 2.50 | 2.50 |

Miniature Sheet

Flowers — A289

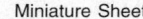

Designs: a, Philadelphus. b, Hypericum. c, Antinhinum. d, Lily. e, Capparis. f, Tropaeolum. g, Rose. h, Chrysanthemum. i, Nigella damascena. j, Gaillardia lanceolata. k, Dahlia. l, Dianthus carophyllus. m, Notobasis syriaca. n, Nerium oleander. o, Iris histriodes. p, Scolymus hispanicus.

**1983, Jan. 1** *Perf. 14½*

| | | | | |
|---|---|---|---|---|
| **1052** | A289 | Sheet of 16 | 10.00 | 10.00 |
| *a.-p.* | | 25d, any single | .50 | .40 |

**Torch Type of 1979**

**1983, Jan. 2** *Perf. 13½*

**Size: 26½x32mm**

| | | | | |
|---|---|---|---|---|
| **1053** | A228 | 250d multi | 3.25 | 2.00 |
| **1054** | A228 | 1500d multi | 20.00 | 12.50 |
| **1055** | A228 | 2500d multi | 37.50 | 25.00 |
| | | *Nos. 1053-1055 (3)* | 60.75 | 39.50 |

Customs Cooperation Council, 30th Anniv. — A290

**1983, Jan. 15** *Perf. 14½x14*

| | | | | |
|---|---|---|---|---|
| **1056** | A290 | 25d Arab riding horse | .25 | .25 |
| **1057** | A290 | 50d Riding camel | .60 | .60 |
| **1058** | A290 | 100d Drawing sword | 1.50 | 1.50 |
| | | *Nos. 1056-1058 (3)* | 2.35 | 2.35 |

**Battles Type of 1980**

No. 1059, Ghaser Ahmed, 1922. No. 1060, Sidi Abuarghub, 1923. No. 1061, Ghar Yunes, 1913. No. 1062, Bir Otman, 1926. No. 1063, Sidi Sajeh, 1922. No. 1064, Ras El-Hamam, 1915. No. 1065, Zawiet Ishghefa, 1913. No. 1066, Wadi Essania, 1930. No. 1067, El-Meshiashta, 1917. No. 1068, Gharara, 1925. No. 1069, Abughelan, 1922. No. 1070, Mahruka, 1913.
Pairs have continuous design.

**1983** *Perf. 13½*

| | | | | |
|---|---|---|---|---|
| **1059** | A244 | 50d Pair, #a.-b. | 2.00 | 2.00 |
| **1060** | A244 | 50d Pair, #a.-b. | 2.00 | 2.00 |
| **1061** | A244 | 50d Pair, #a.-b. | 2.00 | 2.00 |
| **1062** | A244 | 50d Pair, #a.-b. | 2.00 | 2.00 |
| **1063** | A244 | 50d Pair, #a.-b. | 2.00 | 2.00 |
| **1064** | A244 | 50d Pair, #a.-b. | 2.00 | 2.00 |
| **1065** | A244 | 50d Pair, #a.-b. | 2.00 | 2.00 |
| **1066** | A244 | 50d Pair, #a.-b. | 2.00 | 2.00 |
| **1067** | A244 | 50d Pair, #a.-b. | 2.00 | 2.00 |
| **1068** | A244 | 50d Pair, #a.-b. | 2.00 | 2.00 |
| **1069** | A244 | 50d Pair, #a.-b. | 2.00 | 2.00 |
| **1070** | A244 | 50d Pair, #a.-b. | 2.00 | 2.00 |
| | | *Nos. 1059-1070 (12)* | 24.00 | 24.00 |

Issued: No. 1059, 1/26; No. 1060, 2/2; No. 1061, 3/26; No. 1062, 4/9; No. 1063, 5/2; No. 1064, 6/24; No. 1065, 7/13; No. 1066, 8/8; No. 1067, 9/9; No. 1068, 10/22; No. 1069, 11/17; No. 1070, 12/24.

Miniature Sheet

Farm Animals — A291

Designs: a, Camel. b, Cow. c, Horse. d, Bull. e, Goat. f, Dog. g, Sheep. h, Ram. i, Goose. j, Turkey hen. k, Rabbit. l, Pigeon. m, Turkey. n, Rooster. o, Hen. p, Duck.

**1983, Feb. 15** *Perf. 14½*

| | | | | |
|---|---|---|---|---|
| **1083** | A291 | Sheet of 16 | 10.00 | 10.00 |
| *a.-p.* | | 25d any single | .50 | .40 |

Tripoli Intl. Fair A292

Libyans playing traditional instruments.

**1983, Mar. 5** *Perf. 14½x14, 14x14½*

| | | | | |
|---|---|---|---|---|
| **1084** | A292 | 40d multi, vert. | .60 | .40 |
| **1085** | A292 | 45d multicolored | .75 | .50 |
| **1086** | A292 | 50d multi, vert. | .75 | .50 |
| **1087** | A292 | 55d multicolored | 1.00 | .60 |
| **1088** | A292 | 75d multi, vert. | 1.25 | .90 |
| **1089** | A292 | 100d multi, vert. | 1.60 | 1.10 |
| | | *Nos. 1084-1089 (6)* | 5.95 | 4.00 |

Intl. Maritime Organization, 25th Anniv. — A293

Early sailing ships.

**1983, Mar. 17** *Perf. 14½*

| | | | | |
|---|---|---|---|---|
| **1090** | A293 | 100d Phoenician | 2.00 | .75 |
| **1091** | A293 | 100d Viking | 2.00 | .75 |
| **1092** | A293 | 100d Greek | 2.00 | .75 |
| **1093** | A293 | 100d Roman | 2.00 | .75 |
| **1094** | A293 | 100d Libyan | 2.00 | .75 |
| **1095** | A293 | 100d Pharoah's ship | 2.00 | .75 |
| | | *Nos. 1090-1095 (6)* | 12.00 | 4.50 |

Children's Day (1983) A294

Children's illustrations: a, Car. b, Tractor towing trailer. c, Children, dove. d, Boy Scouts. e, Dinosaur.

**1983, Mar. 21** *Perf. 14x14½*

| | | | | |
|---|---|---|---|---|
| **1096** | | Strip of 5 | 2.75 | 2.75 |
| *a.-e.* | A294 | 20d, any single | .40 | .30 |

1st Intl. Symposium on Khadafy's Green Book — A295

50d, Khadafy, Green Book, map. 70d, Lecture hall, emblem. 80d, Khadafy, Green Book, emblem.
100d, Khadafy, Green Books.

**1983, Apr. 1** ***Perf. 13½***

**1097** A295 50d multicolored .60 .40
**1098** A295 70d multicolored 1.00 .50
**1099** A295 80d multicolored 1.10 .75
*Nos. 1097-1099 (3)* 2.70 1.65

**Souvenir Sheet**

***Perf. 12½***

**1100** A295 100d multicolored 3.00 3.00

No. 1100 contains one stamp 57x48mm.

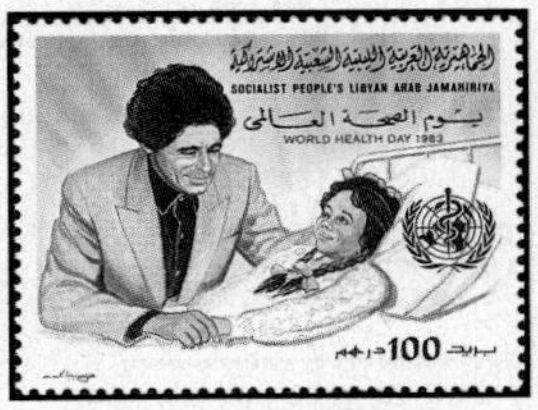

World Health Day A296

25d, Healthy children, vert. 50d, Man in wheelchair, vert. 100d, Girl in hospital bed.

**1983, Apr. 7** ***Perf. 12½***

**1101** A296 25d multicolored .25 .25
**1102** A296 50d multicolored .60 .40
**1103** A296 100d multicolored 1.25 .75
*Nos. 1101-1103 (3)* 2.10 1.40

Pan-African Economic Committee, 25th Anniv. — A297

**1983, Apr. 20** ***Perf. 13½***

**1104** A297 50d multi .60 .40
**1105** A297 100d multi 1.25 .75
**1106** A297 250d multi 3.00 2.00
*Nos. 1104-1106 (3)* 4.85 3.15

Miniature Sheet

Fish — A298

Designs: a, Labrus bimaculatus. b, Trigloporus lastoviza. c, Thalassoma pavo. d, Apogon imberbis. e, Scomber scombrus. f, Spondyliosoma cantharus. g, Trachinus draco. h, Blennius pavo. i, Scorpaena notata. j, Serranus scriba. k, Lophius piscatorius. l, Uranoscopus scaber. m, Auxis thazard. n, Zeus faber. o, Dactylopterus volitans. p, Umbrina cirrosa.

**1983, May 15** ***Perf. 14½***

**1107** A298 Sheet of 16 10.00 10.00
***a.-p.*** 25d any single .40 .30

Still-life by Gauguin (1848-1903) — A299

Paintings: No. 1108b, Abstract, unattributed. c, The Conquest of Tunis by Charles V, by Rubens. d, Arab Musicians in a Carriage, unattributed.
No. 1109a, Khadafy Glorified on Horseback, unattributed, vert. b, Triumph of David over the Syrians, by Raphael, vert. c, Laborers, unattributed, vert. d, Flower Vase, by van Gogh, vert.

**1983, June 1** ***Perf. 11***

**1108** Strip of 4 3.00 3.00
***a.-d.*** A299 50d, any single .50 .35
**1109** Strip of 4 3.00 3.00
***a.-d.*** A299 50d, any single .50 .35

Souvenir Sheet

Ali Siala — A300

Scientists: No. 1110b, Ali El-Najar.

**1983, June 1**

**1110** A300 Sheet of 2 3.50 3.50
***a.-b.*** 100d, any single 1.50 1.50

1984 Summer Olympic Games, Los Angeles — A301

**1983, June 15** ***Perf. 13½***

**1111** A301 10d Basketball .25 .25
**1112** A301 15d High jump .25 .25
**1113** A301 25d Running .25 .25
**1114** A301 50d Gymnastics .50 .40
**1115** A301 100d Wind surfing 1.25 .75
**1116** A301 200d Shot put 2.50 1.60
*Nos. 1111-1116 (6)* 5.00 3.50

**Souvenir Sheets**

**1117** A301 100d Equestrian *3.00 3.00*
**1118** A301 100d Soccer *3.00 3.00*

Nos. 1111-1116 exist imperf. Value, set $22.50. Nos. 1117-1118 also exist imperf.
Nos. 1111-1116 exist printed together in a miniature sheet of 6. Values: perf $35; imperf $50. Each value was also printed in a miniature sheet of 4. Value, set of 6 sheets, $45.

World Communications Year — A302

**1983, July 1** ***Perf. 13***

**1119** A302 10d multicolored .40 .30
**1120** A302 50d multicolored .90 .60
**1121** A302 100d multicolored 2.00 1.25
*Nos. 1119-1121 (3)* 3.30 2.15

The Green Book, by Khadafy A303

Ideologies: 10d, The House is to be served by its residents. 15d, Power, wealth and arms are in the hands of the people. 20d, Masters in their own castles, vert. 35d, No democracy without popular congress. 100d, The authority of the people, vert. 140d, The Green Book is the guide of humanity for final release.
200d, Khadafy in uniform.

**1983, Aug. 1** ***Perf. 13½***

**1122** A303 10d multi .25 .25
**1123** A303 15d multi .25 .25
**1124** A303 20d multi .25 .25
**1125** A303 35d multi .40 .25
**1126** A303 100d multi 1.25 .75
**1127** A303 140d multi 1.75 1.25
*Nos. 1122-1127 (6)* 4.15 3.00

**Souvenir Sheet**

**Litho. & Embossed**

**1128** A303 200d multi 4.50 4.50

No. 1128 contains one gold embossed stamp 36x51mm.

2nd African Youth Sports Festival — A304

Designs: a, Team Handball. b, Basketball. c, Javelin. d, Running. e, Soccer.

**1983, Aug. 22** **Litho.**

**1129** Strip of 5 7.50 4.00
***a.-e.*** A304 100d, any single 1.25 .75

September 1 Revolution, 14th Anniv. — A305

Women in the Armed Forces.

**1983, Sept. 1** ***Perf. 11½***

**1130** A305 65d multi .75 .75
**1131** A305 75d multi .90 .90
**1132** A305 90d multi 1.00 1.00
**1133** A305 100d multi 1.25 1.25
**1134** A305 150d multi 1.75 1.75
**1135** A305 250d multi 3.25 3.25
*Nos. 1130-1135 (6)* 8.90 8.90

**Souvenir Sheet**

***Perf. 11***

**1136** A305 200d multi 4.50 4.50

No. 1136 contains one stamp 63x38mm.

2nd Islamic Scout Jamboree — A306

**1983, Sept. 2** ***Perf. 12½***

**1137** A306 50d Saluting .75 .75
**1138** A306 100d Camping 2.00 2.00

**Souvenir Sheet**

**1139** Sheet of 2 4.50 4.50
***a.*** A306 100d like 50d 2.00 2.00

No. 1139 contains Nos. 1138 and 1139a.

Traffic Day — A307

30d, Youth traffic monitors. 70d, Traffic officer. 200d, Motorcycle police.

**1983, Oct. 1** ***Perf. 14½x14***

**1140** A307 30d multicolored 1.25 .75
**1141** A307 70d multicolored 2.50 1.00
**1142** A307 200d multicolored 8.00 3.50
*Nos. 1140-1142 (3)* 11.75 5.25

Saadun (1893-1923) A308

**1983, Oct. 11** ***Perf. 13½***

**1143** A308 100d multicolored 1.50 .75

1st Manned Flight, Bicent. — A309

Early aircraft and historic flights: a, Americana, 1910. b, Nulli Secundus, 1907. c, J. B. Meusnier, 1785. d, Blanchard and Jeffries, 1785, vert. e, Pilatre de Rozier, 1784, vert. f, Montgolfiere, Oct. 19, 1783, vert.

**1983, Nov. 1**

**1144** Strip of 6 11.00 11.00
***a.-f.*** A309 100d, any single 1.60 .85

Intl. Day of Cooperation with Palestinian People — A310

**1983, Nov. 29** ***Perf. 14½x14***

**1145** A310 30d pale vio & lt bl grn .50 .30
**1146** A310 70d lil & lt yel grn 1.40 .55
**1147** A310 200d lt ultra & grn 3.75 2.00
*Nos. 1145-1147 (3)* 5.65 2.85

Miniature Sheet

Roman Mosaic — A311

Designs: Nos. 1148a-1148c, Gladiators. Nos. 1148d-1148f, Musicians, Nos. 1148g-1148i, Hunters.

**1983, Dec. 1** *Perf. 12*

| | | | |
|---|---|---|---|
| **1148** A311 | Sheet of 9 | 7.00 | 7.00 |
| *a.-i.* | 50d, any single | .75 | .35 |

Nos. 1148a-1148c, 1148d-1148f and 1148g-1148i se-tenant in a continuous design.

Achievements of the Sept. 1 Revolution — A312

**1983, Dec. 15** *Perf. 13½*

| | | | |
|---|---|---|---|
| **1149** A312 | 10d Mosque | .25 | .25 |
| **1150** A312 | 15d Agriculture | .25 | .25 |
| **1151** A312 | 20d Industry | .40 | .25 |
| **1152** A312 | 35d Office building | .50 | .25 |
| **1153** A312 | 100d Health care | 1.50 | .60 |
| **1154** A312 | 140d Airport | 2.25 | 1.10 |
| | *Nos. 1149-1154 (6)* | 5.15 | 2.70 |

**Souvenir Sheet**

**Litho. & Embossed**

| | | | |
|---|---|---|---|
| **1155** A312 | 200d Khadafy | 4.50 | 4.50 |

No. 1155 contains one gold embossed stamp 36x51mm.

Khadafy, Irrigation Project Survey Map A313

**1983, Dec. 15**

| | | | |
|---|---|---|---|
| **1156** A313 | 150d multicolored | 2.25 | 1.25 |

A314

A315

Famous men: No. 1157a, Mahmud Burkis. No. 1157b, Ahmed El-Bakbak. No. 1157c, Mohamed El-Misurati. No. 1157d, Mahmud Ben Musa. No. 1157e, Abdulhamid Ben Ashiur. No. 1158a, Hosni Fauzi El-Amir. No. 1158b, Ali Haidar El-Saati. No. 1159, Mahmud Mustafa Dreza. No. 1160, Mehdi El-Sherif. No. 1161a, Ali El-Gariani. No. 1161b, Muktar Shakshuki. No. 1161c, Abdurrahman El-Busayri. No. 1161d, Ibbrahim Bakir. No. 1161e, Mahmud El-Janzuri. No. 1162a, Ahmed El-Feghi Hasan. No. 1162b, Bashir El Jawab.

**1984** **Litho.** *Perf. 13½*

| | | | |
|---|---|---|---|
| **1157** | Strip of 5 | 6.00 | 6.00 |
| *a.-e.* | A314 100d any single | 1.10 | 1.10 |
| **1158** | Pair | 3.50 | 1.50 |
| *a.-b.* | A314 100d any single | 1.50 | .60 |
| **1159** A314 | 100d multi | 1.75 | .60 |
| **1160** A315 | 100d multi | 1.75 | .60 |
| **1161** | Strip of 5 | 15.00 | 15.00 |
| *a.-e.* | A314 200d any single | 2.50 | 2.50 |
| **1162** | Pair | 6.00 | 6.00 |
| *a.-b.* | A315 200d any single | 2.50 | 2.50 |
| | *Nos. 1157-1162 (6)* | 34.00 | 29.70 |

Issued: Nos. 1157, 1161-1162, 1/1; No. 1158-1160, 2/20.

Miniature Sheet

Water Sports — A316

Designs: a, Two windsurfers. b, Two-man craft. c, Two-man craft, birds. d, Wind sailing, skis. e, Water skier facing front. f, Fisherman in boat. g, Power boating. h, Water skier facing right. i, Fisherman in surf. j, Kayaking. k, Surfing. l, Water skier wearing life jacket. m, Scuba diver sketching underwater. n, Diver. o, Snorkel diver removing fish from harpoon. p, Scuba diver surfacing.

**1984, Jan. 10** *Perf. 14½*

| | | | |
|---|---|---|---|
| **1164** A316 | Sheet of 16 | 8.50 | 8.50 |
| *a.-p.* | 25d any single | .50 | .50 |

African Children's Day — A317

Designs: a, Khadafy, girl scouts. b, Khadafy, children. c, Map, Khadafy, children (size: 63x44mm).

**1984, Jan. 15** **Litho.** *Perf. 14½*

| | | | |
|---|---|---|---|
| **1165** A317 | Strip of 3 | 3.50 | 3.50 |
| *a.-b.* | 50d, any single | .80 | .80 |
| *c.* | 100d multi | 2.00 | 2.00 |

Women's Emancipation — A318

70d, Women, diff., vert. 100d, Soldiers, Khadafy.

**1984, Jan. 20** *Perf. 12*

| | | | |
|---|---|---|---|
| **1166** A318 | 55d multicolored | .75 | .40 |
| **1167** A318 | 70d multicolored | 1.25 | .45 |
| **1168** A318 | 100d multicolored | 1.50 | .75 |
| | *Nos. 1166-1168 (3)* | 3.50 | 1.60 |

Irrigation — A319

No. 1169: a, Desert, water. b, Produce, sheep grazing. c, Khadafy, irrigation of desert (size: 63x44mm). Nos. 1170-1171, Khadafy, map.

**1984, Feb. 1** *Perf. 14½*

| | | | |
|---|---|---|---|
| **1169** A319 | Strip of 3 | 2.50 | 2.50 |
| *a.-b.* | 50d any single | .50 | .25 |
| *c.* | 100d multicolored | 1.50 | .60 |

**Size: 72x36mm**

*Perf. 13½*

| | | | |
|---|---|---|---|
| **1170** A319 | 100d multicolored | 1.50 | .60 |

**Souvenir Sheet**

| | | | |
|---|---|---|---|
| **1171** A319 | 300d multicolored | *7.00* | *7.00* |

World Heritage — A320

Architectural ruins: 50d, Theater, Sabratha. 60d, Temple, Cyrene. 70d, Monument, Sabratha, vert. 100d, Arena, Leptis Magna. 150d, Temple, Cyrene, diff. 200d, Basilica, Leptis Magna.

**1984, Feb. 10** *Perf. 12*

| | | | |
|---|---|---|---|
| **1172** A320 | 50d multicolored | .60 | .25 |
| **1173** A320 | 60d multicolored | .75 | .30 |
| **1174** A320 | 70d multicolored | .90 | .35 |
| **1175** A320 | 100d multicolored | 1.50 | .60 |
| **1176** A320 | 150d multicolored | 2.00 | .90 |
| **1177** A320 | 200d multicolored | 2.75 | 1.40 |
| | *Nos. 1172-1177 (6)* | 8.50 | 3.80 |

Silver Dirhams Minted A.D. 671-757 — A321

Designs: a, Hegira 115. b, Hegira 93. c, Hegira 121. d, Hegira 49. e, Hegira 135.

**Litho. & Embossed**

**1984, Feb. 15** *Perf. 13½*

| | | | |
|---|---|---|---|
| **1178** | Strip of 5 | 15.00 | 15.00 |
| *a.-e.* | A321 200d, any single | 2.75 | 1.25 |

Tripoli Intl. Fair A322

Tea served in various settings.

**1984, Mar. 5** **Litho.** *Perf. 12½*

| | | | |
|---|---|---|---|
| **1179** A322 | 25d multicolored | .25 | .25 |
| **1180** A322 | 35d multicolored | .40 | .25 |
| **1181** A322 | 45d multicolored | .75 | .25 |
| **1182** A322 | 55d multicolored | .90 | .40 |
| **1183** A322 | 75d multicolored | 1.10 | .40 |
| **1184** A322 | 100d multicolored | 1.75 | .95 |
| | *Nos. 1179-1184 (6)* | 5.15 | 2.50 |

Musicians — A323

Designs: a, Muktar Shiaker Murabet. b, El-Aref El-Jamal. c, Ali Shiaalia. d, Bashir Fehmi.

**1984, Mar. 15** *Perf. 14½*

| | | | |
|---|---|---|---|
| **1185** | Strip of 4 + label | 9.00 | 9.00 |
| *a.-d.* | A323 100d, any single | 1.90 | 1.00 |

Children's Day, IYC A324

Children's drawings: a, Recreation. b, Rainy day. c, Military strength. d, Playground. e, Porch swing, children, motorcycle.

**1984, Mar. 21** *Perf. 14*

| | | | |
|---|---|---|---|
| **1186** | Strip of 5 | 2.75 | 2.75 |
| *a.-e.* | A324 20d, any single | .45 | .25 |

Arab League Constitution, 39th Anniv. A325

**1984, Mar. 22** *Perf. 13½*

| | | | |
|---|---|---|---|
| **1187** A325 | 30d multicolored | .60 | .60 |
| **1188** A325 | 40d multicolored | .70 | .70 |
| **1189** A325 | 50d multicolored | 1.00 | 1.00 |
| | *Nos. 1187-1189 (3)* | 2.30 | 2.30 |

Miniature Sheet

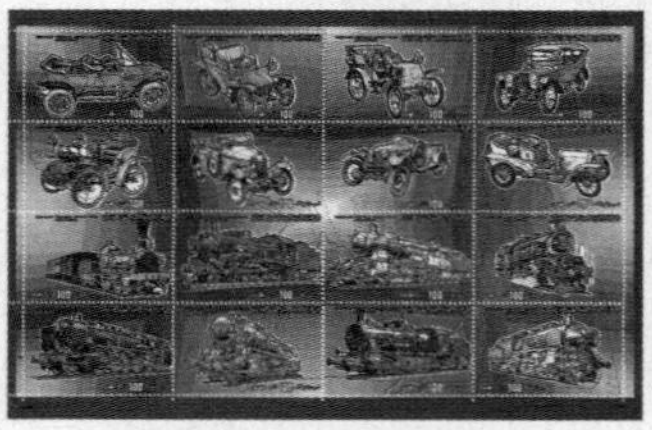

Automobiles, Locomotives — A326

**1984, Apr. 1**

| | | | |
|---|---|---|---|
| **1190** A326 | Sheet of 16 | 30.00 | 30.00 |
| *a.-h.* | 100d, Car, any single | 1.75 | .90 |
| *i.-p.* | 100d, Locomotive, any single | 1.75 | .90 |

No. 1190 pictures outline of two camels in gold. Size: 214x135mm.

World Health Day A327

**1984, Apr. 7** *Perf. 14½*

| | | | |
|---|---|---|---|
| **1191** A327 | 20d Stop Polio | .25 | .25 |
| **1192** A327 | 30d No. 910 | .40 | .25 |
| **1193** A327 | 40d Arabic text | .90 | .40 |
| | *Nos. 1191-1193 (3)* | 1.55 | .90 |

Crafts
A328

Designs: a, Shoemaker. b, Saddler. c, Women, wool. d, Spinner. e, Weaver. f, Tapestry weavers.

**1984, May 1** ***Perf. 12½***

**1194** Strip of 6 15.00 15.00
*a.-f.* A328 150d, any single 2.25 1.25

Postal and Telecommunications Union Congress — A329

Designs: a, Telephones, mail. b, Computer operators. c, Emblem.

**1984, May 15** ***Perf. 14½***

**1195** A329 Strip of 3 3.50 3.50
*a.-b.* 50d, any single .75 .40
*c.* 100d multicolored 1.50 .75

Armed Crowd — A330

A331

No. 1197a, Map, Fire, Military. No. 1197b, Soldiers. No. 1197c, Khadafy. No. 1198, Khadafy giving speech.

**1984, May 17** ***Perf. 12, 14½ (#1197)***

**1196** A330 50d multi .90 .40
**1197** A331 Strip of 3 3.00 3.00
*a.-b.* 50d, any single .75 .25
*c.* 100d multi 1.75 .90
**1198** A330 100d multi 1.50 .75
*Nos. 1196-1198 (3)* 5.40 4.15

Abrogation of the May 17 Treaty. Size of No. 1197c: 63x45mm.

Youth War Casualties
A332

70d, Damaged flag. 100d, Children imprisoned.

**1984, June 4** ***Perf. 10***

**1199** A332 70d multi 1.00 .40
**1200** A332 100d multi 1.50 .75

Miniature Sheet

Green Book Quotations — A333

Designs: a, The Party System Aborts Democracy. b, Khadafy. c, Partners Not Wage-Workers. d, No Representation in Lieu of the People . . . e, Green Book. f, Committees Everywhere. g, Forming Parties Splits Societies. h, Party building, text on track. i, No Democracy without Popular Congresses.

**1984, June 20** ***Perf. 14***

**1201** A333 Sheet of 9 14.00 14.00
*a.-i.* 100d, any single 1.50 .75

See No. 1270.

Folk Costumes — A334

Background colors: a, Green. b, Beige. c, Violet. d, Pale greenish blue. e, Salmon rose. f, Blue.

**1984, July 1** ***Perf. 14½x14***

**1202** Strip of 6 12.50 12.50
*a.-f.* A334 100d, any single 1.75 1.00

Miniature Sheet

Natl. Soccer Championships — A335

Stadium, star, world cup and various action scenes.

**1984, July 15** ***Perf. 13½***

**1203** A335 Sheet of 16 20.00 20.00
*a.-p.* 70d, any single 1.10 .60

1984 Los Angeles Olympics — A336

**1984, July 28**

**1204** A336 100d Soccer 2.00 1.10
**1205** A336 100d Basketball 2.00 1.10
**1206** A336 100d Swimming 2.00 1.10
**1207** A336 100d Sprinting 2.00 1.10
**1208** A336 100d Windsurfing 2.00 1.10
**1209** A336 100d Discus 2.00 1.10
*Nos. 1204-1209 (6)* 12.00 6.60

**Souvenir Sheets**

**1210** A336 250d Equestrian 6.25 6.25
**1211** A336 250d Arab equestrian 6.25 6.25

World Food Day — A337

1212, Forest scenes. 1213, Men riding camels, oasis.

**1984, Aug. 1** ***Perf. 12***

**1212** A337 100d multicolored 1.75 .75
**1213** A337 200d multicolored 3.50 1.25

Miniature Sheet

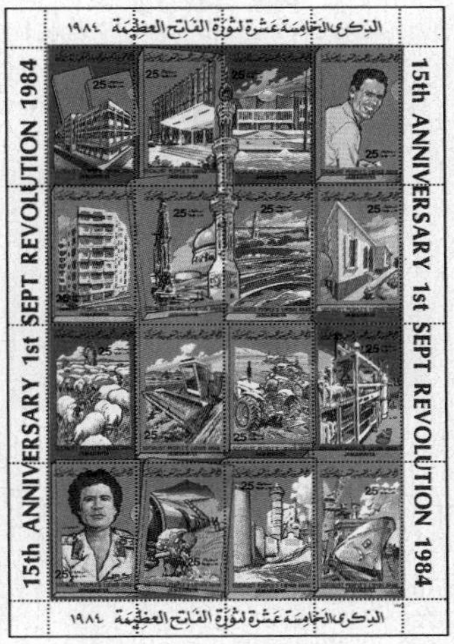


Sept. 1 Revolution, 15th Anniv. — A338

Designs: a, Green books, building at right angle. b, Green book, building, minaret. c, Minaret, party building and grounds. d, Revolution leader. e, Eight-story building. f, Construction, dome. g, Highway, bridge. h, Green book, building at left angle. i, Shepherd, sheep. j, Harvester. k, Tractors. l, Industry. m, Khadafy. n, Irrigation pipe, man drinking. o, Silos, factory. p, Shipping.

**1984, Sept. 15** ***Perf. 14½***

**1214** A338 Sheet of 16 9.00 9.00
*a.-p.* 25d any single .50 .25

A339

Evacuation Day — A340

No. 1215: b, Warrior facing left; c, Khadafy leading battle (size: 63x45mm). No. 1216, Female rider. No. 1217, Battle scene. No. 1218, Italian whipping Libyan.

**1984, Oct. 7**

**1215** A339 Strip of 3 3.50 3.50
*a.-b.* 50d, any single .75 .40
*c.* 100d multi 1.50 .60

***Perf. 11½***

**1216** A340 100d multicolored 1.50 .60
**1217** A340 100d multicolored 1.50 .60
**1218** A340 100d multicolored 1.50 .60
*Nos. 1215-1218 (4)* 8.00 5.30

Miniature Sheet

Equestrians — A341

Various jumping, racing and dressage exercises printed in a continuous design.

**1984, Oct. 15** ***Perf. 13½***

**1219** A341 Sheet of 16 9.00 9.00
*a.-p.* 25d any single .50 .50

PHILAKOREA '84.

Agricultural Traditions — A342

Designs: a, Farmer. b, Well, man, ox. c, Basket weaver. d, Shepherd, ram. e, Tanning hide. f, Coconut picker.

**1984, Nov. 1** ***Perf. 13½***

**1220** Strip of 6 12.50 12.50
*a.-f.* A342 100d, any single 1.75 1.00

Union of Arab Pharmacists, 9th Congress — A343

**1984, Nov. 6** ***Perf. 12***

**1221** A343 100d multicolored 1.75 1.75
**1222** A343 200d multicolored 3.50 3.50

Arab-African Union — A344

No. 1223, Map, banner, crowd. No. 1224, Men, flags.

**1984, Nov. 15** ***Perf. 12***

**1223** A344 100d multicolored 1.75 1.75
**1224** A344 100d multicolored 1.75 1.75

Nos. 1046, 1147
A345

**1984, Nov. 29** *Perf. 12½*

**1225** A345 100d pink & multi 3.75 3.75
**1226** A345 150d brt yel grn & multi 4.75 4.75

Intl. Day of Cooperation with the Palestinian People.

Miniature Sheet

Intl. Civil Aviation Organization, 40th Anniv. — A346

Aircraft: a, Boeing 747 SP, 1975. b, Concorde, 1969. c, Lockheed L1011-500 Tristar, 1978. d, Airbus A310, 1982. e, Tupolev TU-134A, 1962. f, Shorts 360, 1981. g, Boeing 727, 1963. h, Caravelle 10, 1965. i, Fokker F27, 1955. j, Lockheed 749A Constellation, 1946. k, Martin 130, 1955. l, Douglas DC-3, 1936. m, Junkers JU-52, 1932. n, Lindbergh's Spirit of St. Louis, 1927 Ryan. o, De Havilland Moth, 1925. p, Wright Flyer, 1903.

**1984, Dec. 7** *Perf. 13½*

**1227** A346 Sheet of 16 27.50 27.50
*a.-p.* 70d any single 1.50 .75

African Development Bank, 20th Anniv. — A347

"20" in different configurations and: 70d, Map, symbols of industry, education and agriculture. 100d, Symbols of research and development.

**1984, Dec. 15**

**1228** A347 50d multicolored .90 .90
**1229** A347 70d multicolored 1.25 1.25
**1230** A347 100d multicolored 1.75 1.75
*Nos. 1228-1230 (3)* 3.90 3.90

UN Child Survival Campaign A348

No. 1231, Mother, child. No. 1232, Children. No. 1233, Boys at military school. No. 1234, Khadafy, children.

**1985, Jan. 1** *Perf. 12*

**1231** A348 70d multicolored 1.50 .75
**1232** A348 70d multicolored 1.50 .75
**1233** A348 70d multicolored 1.50 .75
**1234** A348 70d multicolored 1.50 .75
*Nos. 1231-1234 (4)* 6.00 3.00

Irrigation — A349

Drop of Water, Map — A350

**1985, Jan. 15** *Perf. 14½x14*

**1235** A349 100d shown 2.00 1.00
**1236** A349 100d Flowers 2.00 1.00
**1237** A349 100d Map, water 2.00 1.00
*Nos. 1235-1237 (3)* 6.00 3.00

**Souvenir Sheet**

*Perf. 14x14½*

**1238** A350 200d shown 4.00 4.00

Musicians — A351

No 1239: a, Kamel El-Ghadi; b, Lute. No. 1240: a, Ahmed El-Khogia; b, Violin. No. 1241: a, Mustafa El-Fallah; b, Zither. No. 1242: a, Mohamed Hamdi; b, Mask.

**1985, Feb. 1** *Perf. 14½*

**1239** A351 Pair 5.00 3.75
*a.-b.* 100d, any single 2.25 1.75
**1240** A351 Pair 5.00 3.75
*a.-b.* 100d, any single 2.25 1.75
**1241** A351 Pair 5.00 3.75
*a.-b.* 100d, any single 2.25 1.75
**1242** A351 Pair 5.00 3.75
*a.-b.* 100d, any single 2.25 1.75
*Nos. 1239-1242 (4)* 20.00 15.00

Nos. 1239-1242 printed in sheets of 20, four strips of 5 consisting of two pairs each musician flanking center stamps picturing instruments.

Gold Dinars Minted A.D. 699-727 — A352

No. 1243: a, Hegira 105. b, Hegira 91. c, Hegira 77. No. 1244, Dinar from Zuela.

**Litho. and Embossed**

**1985, Feb. 15** *Perf. 13½*

**1243** Strip of 3 12.50 12.50
*a.-c.* A352 200d, any single 4.00 2.50

**Souvenir Sheet**

**1244** A352 300d multi 7.50 7.50

Fossils A353

**1985, Mar. 1** **Litho.** *Perf. 13½*

**1245** A353 150d Frog 6.00 3.00
**1246** A353 150d Fish 6.00 3.00
**1247** A353 150d Mammal 6.00 3.00
*Nos. 1245-1247 (3)* 18.00 9.00

People's Authority Declaration A354

Khadafy wearing: a, Folk costume. b, Academic robe. c, Khaki uniform. d, Black uniform. e, White uniform.

**1985, Mar. 2** **Litho.** *Perf. 14½*

**1248** Strip of 5 10.00 10.00
*a.-e.* A354 100d, any single 2.00 1.50

Tripoli Intl. Fair — A355

Musicians playing: a, Cymbals. b, Double flute, bongo. c, Wind instrument, drum. d, Drum. e, Tambourine.

**1985, Mar. 5** *Perf. 14*

**1249** Strip of 5 10.00 10.00
*a.-e.* A355 100d, any single 1.90 1.75

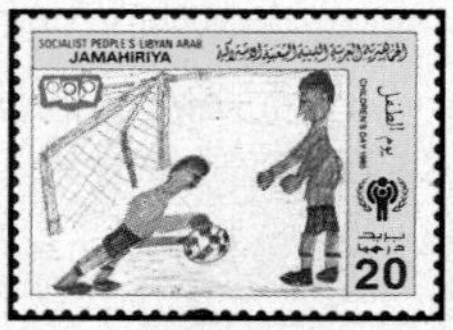

Children's Day, IYC A356

Children's drawings, various soccer plays: a, Goalie and player. b, Four players. c, Players as letters of the alphabet. d, Goalie save. e, Player heading the ball.

**1985, Mar. 21** *Perf. 12*

**1250** Strip of 5 7.50 7.50
*a.-e.* A356 20d, any single .40 .25

Intl. Program for Development of Telecommunications A357

**1985, Apr. 1**

**1251** A357 30d multicolored .40 .40
**1252** A357 70d multicolored 1.00 1.00
**1253** A357 100d multicolored 2.00 2.00
*Nos. 1251-1253 (3)* 3.40 3.40

World Health Day — A358

**1985, Apr. 7**

**1254** A358 40d Invalid, nurses 1.00 .60
**1255** A358 60d Nurse, surgery 1.50 1.00
**1256** A358 100d Nurse, child 2.50 1.60
*Nos. 1254-1256 (3)* 5.00 3.20

Miniature Sheet

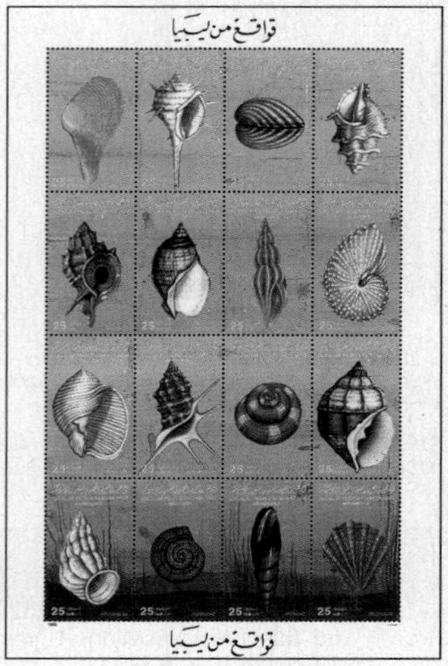

Sea Shells — A359

Designs: a, Mytilidae. b, Muricidae (white). c, Cardiidae. d, Corallophilidae. e, Muricidae. f, Muricacea. g, Turridae. h, Argonautidae. i, Tonnidae. j, Aporrhaidae. k, Trochidae. l, Cancellariidae. m, Epitoniidae. n, Turbinidae. o, Mitridae. p, Pectinidae.

**1985, Apr. 20**

**1257** A359 Sheet of 16 13.00 13.00
*a.-p.* 25d, any single .60 .25

Tripoli Intl. Book Fair — A360

**1985, Apr. 28** *Perf. 13½*

**1258** A360 100d multi 2.00 1.50
**1259** A360 200d multi 4.00 3.00

Intl. Youth Year — A361

Games: No. 1260a, Jump rope. No. 1260b, Board game. No. 1260c, Hopscotch. No. 1260d, Stickgame. No. 1260e, Tops. No. 1261a, Soccer. No. 1261b, Basketball.

**1985, May 1**

**1260** Strip of 5 6.00 6.00
*a.-e.* A361 20d, any single .40 .25

**Souvenir Sheet**

**1261** Sheet of 2 9.00 9.00
*a.-b.* A361 100d, any single 3.00 1.00

No. 1261 contains 2 stamps 30x42mm.

Miniature Sheet

Mosque Minarets and Towers — A362

Mosques: a, Abdussalam Lasmar. b, Zaoviat Kadria. c, Zaoviat Amura. d, Gurgi. e, Mizran. f, Salem. g, Ghat. h, Ahmed Karamanli. i, Atya. j, El Kettani. k, Benghazi. l, Derna. m, El Derug. n, Ben Moussa. o, Ghadames. p, Abdulwahab.

**1985, May 15** *Perf. 12*
**1262** A362 Sheet of 16 15.00 15.00
*a.-p.* 50d, any single .75 .60

Hamida El-Anezi — A363

**1985, June 1** **Litho.** *Perf. 13½*
**1263** A363 100d multicolored 2.00 1.50
**1264** A363 100d Jamila Zemerli 2.00 1.50

Teachers' Day.

A364

Battle of the Philadelphia: a, Ship sinking. b, Militia. c, Hand-to-hand combat.

**1985 June 12**
**1265** A364 Strip of 3 4.00 4.00
*a.-b.* 50d, any single 1.00 1.00
*c.* 100d multicolored 1.75 1.75

Size of No. 1265c: 60x48mm. Continuous design with No. 1265c in middle.

A365

Khadafy's Islamic Pilgrimage — A366

"The Holy Koran is the Law of Society" and Khadafy: a, Writing. b, Kneeling. c, With Holy Kaaba. d, Looking in window. e, Praying at pilgrimage ceremony.

**1985, June 16**
**1266** Strip of 5 22.50 22.50
*a.-e.* A365 200d, any single 4.00 2.50

**Souvenir Sheet**

**1267** A366 300d multicolored 6.50 6.50

Miniature Sheet

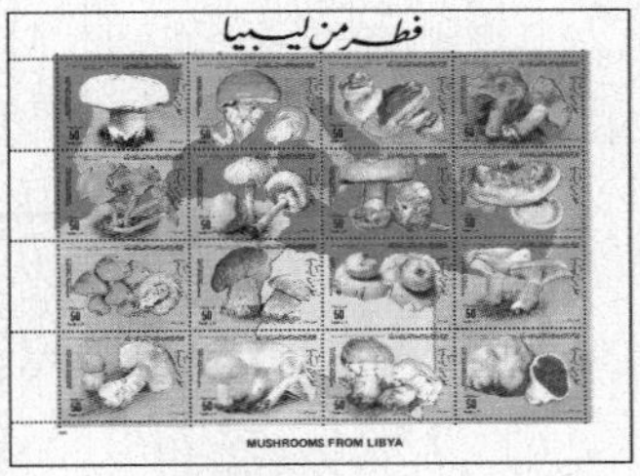

Mushrooms — A367

Designs: a, Leucopaxillus lepistoides. b, Amanita caesarea. c, Coriolus hirsutus. d, Cortinarius subfulgens. e, Dermocybe pratensis. f, Macrolepiota excoriata. g, Amanita curtipes. h, Trametes ljubarskyi. i, Pholiota aurivella. j, Boletus edulis. k, Geastrum sessile. l, Russula sanguinea. m, Cortinarius herculeus. n, Pholiota lenta. o, Amanita rubenscens. p, Scleroderma polyrhizum.

**1985, July 15**
**1268** A367 Sheet of 16 17.50 17.50
*a.-p.* 50d, any single 1.00 .40

No. 1268 exists imperf. Value $50.

Women's Folk Costumes — A368

Designs: a, Woman in violet. b, In white. c, In brown and blue. d, In blue. e, In red.

**1985, Aug. 1** *Perf. 14½x14*
**1269** Strip of 5 10.00 10.00
*a.-e.* A368 100d, any single 1.75 1.50

**Green Book Quotations Type of 1984**

Miniature Sheet

Designs: a, In Need Freedom Is Latent. b, Khadafy reading. c, To Make A Party You Split Society. d, Public Sport Is for All the Masses. e, Green Books, doves. f, Wage-Workers Are a Type of Slave . . . g, People Are Only Harmonious with Their Own Arts and Heritages. h, Khadafy orating. i, Democracy Means Popular Rule Not Popular Expression.

**1985, Aug. 15** *Perf. 14*
**1270** Sheet of 9 17.50 17.50
*a.-i.* A333 100d, any single 1.75 1.50

A369

September 1 Revolution, 16th Anniv. — A370

Designs: a, Food. b, Oil pipeline, refinery. c, Capital, olive branch. d, Mosque, modern buildings. e, Flag, mountains. f, Telecommunications apparatus.

**1985, Sept. 1** *Perf. 12½*
**1271** Strip of 6 12.50 12.50
*a.-f.* A369 100d, any single 2.00 1.50

**Souvenir Sheet**

**1272** A370 200d multi 4.50 4.50

Mosque Entrances A371

Designs: a, Zauiet Amoura, Janzour. b, Shiaieb El-ain, Tripoli. c, Zauiet Abdussalam El-asmar, Zliten. d, Karamanli, Tripoli. e, Gurgi, Tripoli.

**1985, Sept. 15** *Perf. 14*
**1273** Strip of 5 10.00 10.00
*a.-e.* A371 100d, any single 2.00 1.50

Miniature Sheet

Basketball A372

Various players in action.

**1985, Oct. 1** **Litho.** *Perf. 13x12½*
**1274** Sheet of 16 9.00 9.00
*a.-p.* A372 25d any single .50 .40

Evacuation — A373

Designs: a, Man on crutches, web, tree. b, Man caught in web held by disembodied hands. c, Three men basking in light.

**1985, Oct. 7** *Perf. 15*
**1275** A373 Strip of 3 7.00 7.00
*a.-c.* 100d any single 1.75 1.50

Stamp Day — A374

Italia 85: a, Man sitting at desk, Type A228, Earth. b, Magnifying glass, open stock book, Type A228. c, Stamps escaping envelope.

**1985, Oct. 25** *Perf. 12*
**1276** A374 Strip of 3 4.00 4.00
*a.-c.* 50d, any single 1.00 .60

1986 World Cup Soccer Championships — A375

No. 1277, Block, heading the ball. No. 1278, Kick, goalie catching ball. No. 1279, Goalie, block, dribble. No. 1280, Goalie, dribble, sliding block. No. 1281, Goalie catching the ball. No. 1282, Block.

No. 1283, Four players.

**1985, Nov. 1** *Perf. 13½*
**1277** A375 100d multicolored 2.00 1.50
**1278** A375 100d multicolored 2.00 1.50
**1279** A375 100d multicolored 2.00 1.50
**1280** A375 100d multicolored 2.00 1.50
**1281** A375 100d multicolored 2.00 1.50
**1282** A375 100d multicolored 2.00 1.50
*Nos. 1277-1282 (6)* 12.00 9.00

**Souvenir Sheet**

**1283** A375 200d multicolored 8.50 8.50

Intl. Day of Cooperation with the Palestinian People A376

**1985, Nov. 29** **Litho.** *Perf. 12½*
**1284** A376 100d multi 1.75 1.50
**1285** A376 150d multi 3.25 2.25

**Khadafy**

A377

A377a

*Perf. 12½x13, 13¼x13*

**1986, Jan. 1** **Engr.**
**1286** A377 50d vermilion *40.00 70.00*
**1287** A377 60d blue *40.00 70.00*
**1288** A377 70d carmine *40.00 70.00*
**1289** A377 80d violet *40.00 70.00*
**1290** A377 90d brown *40.00 70.00*
**1291** A377 100d dk grn *50.00 80.00*
**1292** A377 200d dk rose *50.00 80.00*
**1293** A377 250d brt grn *50.00 80.00*
**1294** A377a 300d grysh blue *50.00 80.00*
**1295** A377a 500d redsh brn *50.00 80.00*
**1296** A377a 1500d grysh grn *55.00 85.00*
**1297** A377a 2500d purple *65.00 95.00*
*Nos. 1286-1297 (12)* *570.00 930.00*

Supposedly Nos. 1286-1297 were on sale for two hours. Value on first day cover, $400.

Importation Prohibited
Importation of the stamps of Libya was prohibited as of Jan. 7, 1986.

General Post and Telecommunications Co. — A378

**1986, Jan. 15** *Perf. 12*

| | | | | |
|---|---|---|---|---|
| **1298** | A378 | 100d yel & multi | 2.25 | 1.50 |
| **1299** | A378 | 150d yel grn & multi | 2.75 | 2.00 |

Peoples Authority Declaration — A379

Designs: b, Hand holding globe and paper. c, Dove, Khadafy's Green Book (size: 53x37mm).

**1986, Mar. 2** *Perf. 12½x13*

| | | | | |
|---|---|---|---|---|
| **1300** | A379 | Strip of 3 | 4.50 | 4.50 |
| *a.-b.* | | 50d, any single | 1.00 | .60 |
| *c.* | | 100d multicolored | 2.00 | 1.25 |

Musical Instruments — A380

Designs: a, Flute. b, Drums. c, Horn. d, Cymbals. e, Hand drum.

**1986, Mar. 5**

| | | | |
|---|---|---|---|
| **1301** | Strip of 5 | 10.00 | 10.00 |
| *a.-e.* | A380 100d any single | 2.00 | 1.50 |

Tripoli International Fair.

Intl. Children's Day — A381

Designs: a, Boy Scout fishing. b, Riding camel. c, Chasing butterflies. d, Beating drum. e, Soccer game.

**1986, Mar. 21** *Perf. 13½*

| | | | |
|---|---|---|---|
| **1302** | Strip of 5 | 8.50 | 8.50 |
| *a.-e.* | A381 50d any single | 1.25 | .75 |

World Health Day — A382

**1986, Apr. 7**

| | | | | |
|---|---|---|---|---|
| **1303** | A382 | 250d sil & multi | 5.00 | 3.00 |
| **1304** | A382 | 250d gold & multi | 5.00 | 3.00 |

Government Programs — A383

Designs: a, Medical examinations. b, Education. c, Farming (size: 63x42mm).

**1986, May 1** *Perf. 14½*

| | | | | |
|---|---|---|---|---|
| **1305** | A383 | Strip of 3 | 3.75 | 3.75 |
| *a.-b.* | | 50d any single | .85 | .60 |
| *c.* | | 100d multicolored | 1.75 | 1.25 |

Miniature Sheet

World Cup Soccer Championships, Mexico — A384

Designs: No. 1306a, 2 players. No. 1306b, 3 players in red and white shirts, one in green. No. 1306c, 2 players, referee. No. 1306d, Shot at goal. No. 1306e, 2 players with striped shirts. No. 1306f, 2 players with blue shirts, one with red.

No. 1307, 7 players. No. 1308, 1st Libyan team, 1931.

**1986, May 31** *Perf. 13½*

| | | | | |
|---|---|---|---|---|
| **1306** | A384 | Sheet of 6 | 7.50 | 7.50 |
| *a.-f.* | | 50d any single | 1.10 | .75 |

**Souvenir Sheets**

| | | | | |
|---|---|---|---|---|
| **1307** | A384 | 200d multicolored | 6.50 | 6.50 |
| **1308** | A384 | 200d multicolored | 6.50 | 6.50 |

Nos. 1307-1308 each contain one 52x37mm stamp.

Miniature Sheet

Vegetables A385

Designs: a, Peas. b, Zucchini. c, Beans. d, Eggplant. e, Corn. f, Tomato. g, Red pepper. h, Cucumbers. i, Garlic. j, Cabbage. k, Cauliflower. l, Celery. m, Onions. n, Carrots. o, Potato. p, Radishes.

**1986, June 1** *Perf. 13x12½*

| | | | |
|---|---|---|---|
| **1309** | Sheet of 16 | 15.00 | 15.00 |
| *a.-p.* | A385 50d any single | .85 | .75 |

No. 1309 has a continuous design.

Miniature Sheet

Khadafy and Irrigation Project A386

Khadafy and: a, Engineer reviewing plans, drill rig. b, Map. c, Well. d, Drought conditions. e, Water pipe. f, Pipes, pulleys, equipment. g, Lowering water pipe. h, Construction workers, trailer. i, Hands holding water. j, Opening water valve. k, Laying pipeline. l, Trucks hauling pipes. m, Khadafy holding green book, city. n, Giving vegetables to people. o, Boy drinking, man cultivating field. p, Men in prayer, irrigation. (Khadafy not shown on Nos. 1310h, 1310i, 1310k, 1310 l, 1310o.)

**1986, July 1** *Perf. 13½*

| | | | |
|---|---|---|---|
| **1310** | Sheet of 16 | 35.00 | 35.00 |
| *a.-p.* | A386 100d any single | 2.00 | 1.40 |

A387

A388

American Attack on Libya, Apr. 15 — A389

Designs: Nos. 1311a-1311p, Various scenes in Tripoli during and after air raid. No. 1312a. F14 aircraft. No. 1312b, Aircraft carrier, people. No. 1312c, Sinking of USS *Philadelphia*, 1801.

**1986, July 13**

| | | | | |
|---|---|---|---|---|
| **1311** | A387 | Sheet of 16, #a.-p. | 26.00 | 26.00 |
| **1312** | A388 | Strip of 3 | 3.50 | 3.50 |
| *a.-b.* | | 50d multicolored | .85 | .65 |
| *c.* | | 100d multicolored | 1.75 | 1.25 |
| **1313** | A389 | 100d multicolored | 2.10 | 1.50 |

No. 1312 has a continuous design. Size of No. 1312b: 60x38mm.

Khadafy's Peace Methods A390

Khadafy: b, Reading Green Book. c, With old woman. d, Praying with children. e, Visiting sick. f, Driving tractor.

**1986, July 13**

| | | | |
|---|---|---|---|
| **1314** | Sheet of 6 | 12.50 | 12.50 |
| *a.-f.* | A390 100d any single | 2.00 | 1.40 |

Miniature Sheet

Green Book Quotations A391

Designs: a, The House Must be Served by its Own Tenant. b, Khadafy. c, The Child is Raised by His Mother. d, Democracy is the Supervision of the People by the People. e, Green Books. f, Representation is a Falsification of Democracy. g, The Recognition of Profit is an Acknowledgement of Exploitation. h, Flowers. i, Knowledge is a Natural Right of Every Human Being...

**1986, Aug. 1** *Perf. 14*

| | | | |
|---|---|---|---|
| **1315** | Sheet of 9 | 19.00 | 19.00 |
| *a.-i.* | A391 100d any single | 2.00 | 1.40 |

Sept. 1st Revolution, 17th Anniv. A392

a, Public health. b, Agriculture. c, Sunflowers by Vincent Van Gogh. d, Defense. e. Oil industry.

**1986, Sept. 1**

| | | | |
|---|---|---|---|
| **1316** | Strip of 5 | 22.50 | 22.50 |
| *a.-e.* | A392 200d any single | 4.00 | 2.75 |

A393

Arab-African Union, 1st Anniv. — A394

No. 1317, Libyan, Arab horsemen. No. 1318, Women in native dress.

**1986, Sept. 15** *Perf. 12*

| | | | | |
|---|---|---|---|---|
| **1317** | A393 | 250d multicolored | 5.00 | 4.00 |
| **1318** | A394 | 250d multicolored | 5.00 | 4.00 |

Evacuation Day — A395

Designs: a, Mounted warrior. b, Two horsemen, infantry. c, Cavalry charge.

**1986, Oct. 7** *Perf. 13½*

| | | | | |
|---|---|---|---|---|
| **1319** | A395 | Strip of 3 | 6.00 | 6.00 |
| *a.* | | 50d multicolored | 1.00 | .60 |
| *b.* | | 100d multicolored | 2.00 | 1.10 |
| *c.* | | 150d multicolored | 2.75 | 2.40 |

Intl. Peace Year A396

**1986, Oct. 24** *Perf. 14½*

| | | | | |
|---|---|---|---|---|
| **1320** | A396 | 200d bl & multi | 4.00 | 3.00 |
| **1321** | A396 | 200d grn & multi | 4.00 | 3.00 |

Solidarity with the Palestinians — A397

**1986, Nov. 29** *Perf. 12½*

| | | | | |
|---|---|---|---|---|
| **1322** | A397 | 250d pink & multi | 5.00 | 4.00 |
| **1323** | A397 | 250d blue & multi | 5.00 | 4.00 |

Music and Dance — A398

Designs: a, Man beating drum. b, Masked dancer. c, Woman dancing with jugs on her head. d, Man playing bagpipe. e, Man beating hand drum.

**1986, Dec. 1** *Perf. 12*

| | | | |
|---|---|---|---|
| **1324** | Strip of 5 | 8.00 | 8.00 |
| *a.-e.* | A398 70d any single | 1.50 | 1.25 |

Gazella Leptoceros — A399

**1987, Mar. 2** *Perf. 13½*

**1325** A399 100d Two adults 3.00 2.00
**1326** A399 100d Fawn nursing 3.00 2.00
**1327** A399 100d Adult sleeping 3.00 2.00
**1328** A399 100d Adult drinking 3.00 2.00
*Nos. 1325-1328 (4)* 12.00 8.00

World Wildlife Fund.

Nos. 1325-1328 exist imperf. Value, set $27.50.

A400

Crowd of People and: a, Oilfields. b, Buildings. c, Khadafy, buildings, globe.

**1987, Mar. 2** *Perf. 13½*

**1329** A400 Strip of 3 40.00 40.00
*a.-b.* 500d multicolored 10.00 8.00
*c.* 1000d multicolored 20.00 15.00

People's Authority declaration.

No. 1329 has a continuous design. Size of No. 1329c: 42x37mm.

Miniature Sheet

A401

Sept. 1st Revolution, 18th Anniv.: a, Shepherd, sheep. b, Khadafy. c, Mosque. d, Irrigation pipeline. e, Combine in field. f, Khadafy at microphones. g, Harvesting grain. h, Irrigation. i, Soldier. j, Militiaman. k, Fountain. l, Skyscrapers. m, House, women. n, Children. o, Assembly hall. p, Two girls.

**1987, Sept. 1** *Perf. 13½*

**1330** A401 Sheet of 16 70.00 70.00
*a.-p.* 150d any single 3.00 2.25

No. 1330 has a continuous design.

Libyan Freedom Fighters — A402

No. 1331: a, Omer Abed Anabi Al Mansuri. b, Ahmed Ali Al Emrayd. c, Khalifa Said Ben Asker. d, Mohamed Ben Farhat Azawi. e, Mohamed Souf Al Lafi Al Marmori.

**1988, Feb. 15**

**1331** Strip of 5 29.00 29.00
*a.* A402 100d multicolored 2.00 1.25
*b.* A402 200d multicolored 5.75 4.25
*c.* A402 300d multicolored 8.00 4.50
*d.* A402 400d multicolored
*e.* A402 500d multicolored 9.00 6.50

Freedom Festival Day — A403

**1988, June 1**

**1332** A403 100d yel & multi 1.75 1.25
**1333** A403 150d grn & multi 3.00 2.00
**1334** A403 250d brn org & multi 5.00 3.50
*Nos. 1332-1334 (3)* 9.75 6.75

Miniature Sheet

American Attack on Libya, 2nd Anniv. — A404

Khadafy: a, With woman and children. b, Playing chess. c, Fleeing from bombing with children. d, Praying in desert. e, Praying with children. f, Visiting wounded child. g, With infants and children, horiz. h, Delivering speech, horiz. i, With family, horiz.

No. 1336, In desert, vert. No. 1337, Making speech.

**1988, July 13**

**1335** A404 Sheet of 9 25.00 25.00
*a.-i.* 150d any single 2.75 2.00

**Souvenir Sheets**

**Litho. & Embossed**

**1336** A404 500d gold & multi 10.00 10.00
**1337** A404 500d gold & multi 10.00 10.00

No. 1335 exists imperf.

September 1st Revolution, 19th Anniv. — A405

**1988, Sept. 19** **Litho.**

**1338** A405 100d brt bl & multi 1.75 1.25
**1339** A405 250d gray & multi 4.50 3.00
**1340** A405 300d cit & multi 5.00 4.25
**1341** A405 500d bl grn & multi 10.00 7.00
*Nos. 1338-1341 (4)* 21.25 15.50

1988 Summer Olympics, Seoul — A406

**1988, Sept. 17**

**1342** A406 150d Tennis 2.75 2.00
**1343** A406 150d Equestrian 2.75 2.00
**1344** A406 150d Relay race 2.75 2.00
**1345** A406 150d Soccer 2.75 2.00
**1346** A406 150d Distance race 2.75 2.00
**1347** A406 150d Cycling 2.75 2.00
*Nos. 1342-1347 (6)* 16.50 12.00

**Souvenir Sheet**

**1348** A406 750d Soccer, diff. 13.00 13.00

No. 1348 contains one 30x42mm stamp. Exists imperf. Nos. 1342-1347 exist in miniature sheets of 1. Value, set $37.50.

Miniature Sheet

1988 Summer Olympics, Seoul — A407

**1988, Sept 17**

**1350** Sheet of 3 8.50 8.50
*a.* A407 100d Bedouin rider 2.00 2.00
*b.* A407 200d shown 3.00 3.00
*c.* A407 200d Show jumping, diff. 3.00 3.00

Olymphilex '88, Seoul.

A408

Design: Libyan Palm Tree.

**1988, Nov. 1**

**1351** A408 500d Fruit 10.00 6.50
**1352** A408 1000d Palm tree 18.00 12.00

A409

**1988**

**1353** A409 Strip of 3 11.50 11.50
*a.* 100d shown 2.00 1.40
*b.* 200d Boy with rocks 3.50 2.75
*c.* 300d Flag, map 5.75 4.25

Palestinian uprising. No. 1353b, size: 45x39mm.

People's Authority Declaration — A410

**1989**

**1354** A410 260d dk grn & multi 5.00 3.00
**1355** A410 500d gold & multi 10.00 6.00

Miniature Sheet

September 1 Revolution, 20th Anniv. — A411

Designs: a, Crowd, Green Books, emblem. b, Soldiers, Khadafy, irrigation pipeline. c, Military equipment, Khadafy, communication and transportation. d, Mounted warriors. e, Battle scenes.

**1989** *Perf. 13½*

**1356** A411 Sheet of 5 14.00 14.00
*a.-e.* 150d any single 2.75 2.00
*f.* Bklt. pane of 5, perf. 13½ horiz. 14.00 14.00

**Souvenir Sheet**

**1357** A411 250d Khadafy 4.00 4.00

No. 1357 contains one 36x51mm stamp. Stamps from No. 1356f have gold border at right.

Libyans Deported to Italy — A412

No. 1359, Libyans in boats. No. 1360, Khadafy, crescent moon. No. 1361, Khadafy at left, in desert. No.1362, Khadafy at right, soldiers. No. 1363, Khadafy in center, Libyans.

**1989**

**1358** A412 100d shown 1.75 1.25
**1359** A412 100d multicolored 1.75 1.25
**1360** A412 100d multicolored 1.75 1.25
**1361** A412 100d multicolored 1.75 1.25
**1362** A412 100d multicolored 1.75 1.25
*Nos. 1358-1362 (5)* 8.75 6.25

**Souvenir Sheet**

**1363** A412 150d multicolored 3.00 3.00

No. 1363 contains one 72x38mm stamp.

A413

**1989** *Perf. 12*

**1364** A413 150d multicolored 2.75 2.75
**1365** A413 200d multicolored 4.25 4.25

Demolition of Libyan-Tunisian border fortifications.

Solidarity with the Palestinians
A414

300d, Man, flag, crowd. 500d, Emblem.

**1989** *Perf. 12x11½*

**1366** A414 100d shown 2.25 2.25
**1367** A414 300d multicolored 6.50 6.50
**1368** A414 500d multicolored 10.00 10.00
*Nos. 1366-1368 (3)* 18.75 18.75

Ibn Annafis, Physician
A415

**1989** *Perf. 12*

**1369** A415 100d multicolored 2.75 2.75
**1370** A415 150d multicolored 4.00 4.00

Intl. Literacy Year — A416

**1990, Oct. 18** **Litho.** *Perf. 14*
**Granite Paper**

**1371** A416 100d multicolored 1.75 1.75
**1372** A416 300d multicolored 8.00 8.00

A417

**1990, Oct. 18** **Granite Paper**

**1373** A417 100d multicolored 1.75 1.75
**1374** A417 400d multicolored 5.25 5.25

Organization of Petroleum Exporting Countries (OPEC), 30th anniv.

A418

**1990, June 28** *Perf. 11½x12*

**1375** A418 100d brt org & multi 1.75 1.75
**1376** A418 400d grn & multi 8.00 8.00

Evacuation of US military base, 20th anniv.

People's Authority Declaration
A419

**1990, Apr. 24**

**1377** A419 300d bl & multi 5.00 5.00
**1378** A419 500d vio & multi 10.00 10.00

A420

Plowing Season in Libya: 2000d, Man on tractor plowing field.

**1990, Dec. 4** *Perf. 14*
**Granite Paper**

**1379** A420 500d multicolored 11.00 11.00
**1380** A420 2000d multicolored 37.50 37.50

A421

**1990, Nov. 5** *Perf. 14*
**Granite Paper**

**1381** A421 100d grn & multi 1.75 1.75
**1382** A421 400d vio & multi 8.00 8.00
**1383** A421 500d bl & multi 9.25 9.25
*Nos. 1381-1383 (3)* 19.00 19.00

**Souvenir Sheet**
***Perf. 11½***

**1384** A421 500d Trophy, map, horiz. 11.00 11.00

World Cup Soccer Championships, Italy. No. 1384 contains one 38x33mm stamp.

Sept. 1st Revolution, 21st Anniv.
A422

**1990, Sept. 3** *Perf. 14*
**Granite Paper**

**1385** A422 100d multicolored 2.00 2.00
**1386** A422 400d multicolored 8.50 8.50
**1387** A422 1000d multicolored 21.00 21.00
*Nos. 1385-1387 (3)* 31.50 31.50

***Imperf***
**Size: 120x90mm**

**1388** A422 200d multi, diff. 8.50 8.50

Maghreb Arab Union, 2nd Anniv. — A423

**1991, Mar. 10** **Litho.** *Perf. 13½*

**1389** A423 100d multicolored 2.00 2.00
**1390** A423 300d gold & multi 5.75 5.75

People's Authority Declaration — A424

**1991, Mar. 10**

**1391** A424 300d multicolored 5.00 5.00
**1392** A424 400d silver & multi 10.00 10.00

Children's Day — A425

100d, Butterflies, girl. 400d, Bird, boy.

**1991, Mar. 22**

**1393** A425 100d multicolored 2.75 2.75
**1394** A425 400d multicolored 10.00 10.00

World Health Day — A426

**1991, Apr. 7**

**1395** A426 100d blue & multi 1.75 1.75
**1396** A426 200d green & multi 3.50 3.50

Scenes from Libya
A427

100d, Wadi el Hayat, vert. 250d, Mourzuk. 500d, Ghadames.

**1991, June 20**

**1397** A427 100d multicolored 1.75 1.75
**1398** A427 250d multicolored 5.00 5.00
**1399** A427 500d multicolored 10.00 10.00
*Nos. 1397-1399 (3)* 16.75 16.75

Irrigation Project — A428

a, Laborers, heavy equipment. b, Khadafy, heavy equipment. c, Livestock, fruit & vegetables.

**1991, Aug. 28** *Perf. 12*

**1400** A428 50d Strip of 3, #a.-c. 3.50 3.50

No. 1400 has a continuous design. Size of No. 1400b: 60x36mm.

Sept. 1st Revolution, 22nd Anniv. — A429

300d, Chains, roses & "22". 400d, Chains, "22".

**1991, Sept. 1** *Perf. 13½*

**1401** A429 300d multicolored 5.75 5.75
**1402** A429 400d multicolored 7.25 7.25
*a.* Souv. sheet of 2, #1401-1402 16.00 16.00

Telecom '91
A430

100d, Emblems, vert. 500d, Buildings, satilite dish.

**1991, Oct. 7** **Litho.** *Perf. 13½*

**1403** A430 100d multicolored 1.75 1.75
**1404** A430 500d multicolored 9.25 9.25

Libyans Deported to Italy
A431

100d, Monument, soldier. 400d, Ship, refugees, soldiers.

**1991, Oct. 26** **Litho.** *Perf. 13½*

**1405** A431 100d multicolored 1.75 1.75
**1406** A431 400d multicolored 7.25 7.25
*a.* Souv. sheet of 2, #1405-1406 10.00 10.00

Arab Unity
A432

**1991, Nov. 15** *Perf. 12*

**1407** A432 50d tan & multi 1.00 1.00
**1408** A432 100d blue & multi 2.00 2.00

**Miniature Sheet**

Trucks, Automobiles and Motorcycles
A433

Designs: a-d, Various trucks. e-h, Various off-road race cars. i-p, Various motorcycles.

**1991, Dec. 28** *Perf. 14*

**1409** A433 50d Sheet of 16, #a.-p. 17.50 17.50

Eagle — A434

Col. Khadafy — A434a

**1992** *Perf. 11½*

**Granite Paper (#1412-1419)**

**Background Colors**

| | | | | |
|---|---|---|---|---|
| **1412** | A434 | 100d yellow | 1.40 | .85 |
| **1413** | A434 | 150d blue gray | 2.25 | 1.25 |
| **1414** | A434 | 200d brt blue | 2.75 | 1.75 |
| **1415** | A434 | 250d orange | 3.75 | 2.00 |
| **1416** | A434 | 300d purple | 4.25 | 2.50 |
| **1418** | A434 | 400d brt pink | 5.75 | 3.50 |
| **1419** | A434 | 450d brt grn | 7.25 | 3.75 |

***Perf. 13½***

| | | | | |
|---|---|---|---|---|
| **1420** | A434a | 500d yel grn | 6.50 | 3.50 |
| **1421** | A434a | 1000d rose | 13.00 | 7.00 |
| **1422** | A434a | 2000d blue | 26.00 | 14.00 |
| **1423** | A434a | 5000d violet | 65.00 | 37.50 |
| **1424** | A434a | 6000d yel brn | 80.00 | 45.00 |
| | | *Nos. 1412-1424 (12)* | 217.90 | 122.60 |

Issued: No 1412-1416, 1418-1419, 1/1; Nos. 1420-1424, 9/1.

People's Authority Declaration A435

**1992, Mar.** **Litho.** *Perf. 12*

| | | | | |
|---|---|---|---|---|
| **1425** | A435 | 100d yellow & multi | 1.50 | 1.50 |
| **1426** | A435 | 150d blue & multi | 2.25 | 2.25 |

African Tourism Year (in 1991) A436

**1992, Apr. 5** *Perf. 14½*

**Granite Paper**

| | | | | |
|---|---|---|---|---|
| **1427** | A436 | 50d purple & multi | .75 | .75 |
| **1428** | A436 | 100d pink & multi | 1.40 | 1.40 |

1992 Summer Olympics, Barcelona A437

**1992, June 15** *Perf. 12*

| | | | | |
|---|---|---|---|---|
| **1429** | A437 | 50d Tennis | .75 | .75 |
| **1430** | A437 | 50d Long jump | .75 | .75 |
| **1431** | A437 | 50d Discus | .75 | .75 |
| | | *Nos. 1429-1431 (3)* | 2.25 | 2.25 |

**Size: 106x82mm**

***Imperf***

| | | | | |
|---|---|---|---|---|
| **1432** | A437 | 100d Olympic torch, rings | 1.50 | 1.50 |

Revolutionary Achievements — A438

Designs: 100d, Palm trees. 150d, Steel mill. 250d, Cargo ship. 300d, Libyan Airlines. 400d, Natl. Assembly, Green Books. 500d, Irrigation pipeline, Khadafy.

**1992, June 30** *Perf. 14*

**Granite Paper**

| | | | | |
|---|---|---|---|---|
| **1433** | A438 | 100d multicolored | 1.40 | 1.40 |
| **1434** | A438 | 150d multicolored | 2.25 | 2.25 |
| **1435** | A438 | 250d multicolored | 3.75 | 3.75 |
| **1436** | A438 | 300d multicolored | 4.25 | 4.25 |
| **1437** | A438 | 400d multicolored | 5.75 | 5.75 |
| **1438** | A438 | 500d multicolored | 7.25 | 7.25 |
| | | *Nos. 1433-1438 (6)* | 24.65 | 24.65 |

Tripoli Intl. Fair — A439

50d, Horse & buggy. 100d, Horse & sulky.

**1992, Mar.** *Perf. 12*

| | | |
|---|---|---|
| **1439** | A439 | 50d multicolored |
| **1440** | A439 | 100d multicolored |

Maghreb Arab Union Philatelic Exhibition — A440

**1992, Feb. 17** *Perf. 14½*

| | | | | |
|---|---|---|---|---|
| **1441** | A440 | 75d blue green & multi | 2.50 | 1.75 |
| **1442** | A440 | 80d blue & multi | 2.50 | 1.75 |

**Miniature Sheet**

Fish A441

Designs: a, Fish with spots near eye. b, Thin fish. d, Brown fish, currents. e, Fish, plants at LR. f, Fish, plants at LL.

**1992, Apr. 15** *Perf. 14*

| | | | | |
|---|---|---|---|---|
| **1443** | A441 | 100d Sheet of 6, #a.-f. | 14.00 | 14.00 |

**Miniature Sheet**

Horsemanship — A442

Designs: a, Woman rider with gun. b, Man on white horse. c, Mongol rider. d, Roman officer. e, Cossack rider. f, Arab rider. 250d, Two Arab riders.

**1992, Apr. 25** *Perf. 13½x14*

| | | | | |
|---|---|---|---|---|
| **1444** | A442 | 100d Sheet of 6, #a.-f. | 9.50 | 9.50 |

**Souvenir Sheet**

| | | | | |
|---|---|---|---|---|
| **1445** | A442 | 250d multicolored | 5.00 | 5.00 |

Khadafy — A443

Designs: No. 1450a, like No. 1446. b, like No. 1447. c, like No. 1448. d, like No. 1449.

**1992, Jan. 1** *Perf. 14x13½*

| | | | | |
|---|---|---|---|---|
| **1446** | A443 | 100d blue grn & multi | 2.00 | 2.00 |
| **1447** | A443 | 100d gray & multi | 2.00 | 2.00 |
| **1448** | A443 | 100d rose lake & multi | 2.00 | 2.00 |
| **1449** | A443 | 100d yellow & multi | 2.00 | 2.00 |
| | | *Nos. 1446-1449 (4)* | 8.00 | 8.00 |

**Souvenir Sheet**

| | | | | |
|---|---|---|---|---|
| **1450** | A443 | 150d Sheet of 4, #a.-d. | 11.00 | 11.00 |

Evacuation of Foreign Forces — A444

75d, Horse, broken chain. 80d, Flag, broken chain.

**1992, Oct. 7** **Litho.** *Perf. 14*

| | | | | |
|---|---|---|---|---|
| **1451** | A444 | 75d multicolored | 1.00 | 1.00 |
| **1452** | A444 | 80d multicolored | 1.00 | 1.00 |

Costumes — A445

Women wearing various traditional costumes.

Denomination color: a, green. b, black. c, violet blue. d, sky blue. e, yellow brown.

**1992, Dec. 15** **Litho.** *Perf. 12*

| | | | | |
|---|---|---|---|---|
| **1453** | A445 | 50d Strip of 5, #a.-e. | 4.00 | 4.00 |

Sept. 1st Revolution, 23rd Anniv. — A446

50d, Torch, "23". 100d, Flag, "23". 250d, Eagle, "23".

**1992, Sept. 1**

| | | | | |
|---|---|---|---|---|
| **1454** | A446 | 50d multicolored | .75 | .75 |
| **1455** | A446 | 100d multicolored | 1.40 | 1.40 |

**Souvenir Sheet**

| | | | | |
|---|---|---|---|---|
| **1456** | A446 | 250d multicolored | 3.50 | 3.50 |

No. 1456 contains one 50x40mm stamp.

Libyans Deported to Italy — A447

**1992, Oct. 26**

| | | | | |
|---|---|---|---|---|
| **1457** | A447 | 100d tan & multi | 1.40 | 1.40 |
| **1458** | A447 | 250d blue & multi | 3.00 | 3.00 |

Oasis A448

Designs: 100d, Gazelle drinking. 200d, Camels, palm trees, vert. 300d, Palm trees, camel and rider.

**1992, Oct. 1** *Perf. 14*

| | | | | |
|---|---|---|---|---|
| **1459** | A448 | 100d multicolored | 1.50 | 1.50 |
| **1460** | A448 | 200d multicolored | 3.00 | 3.00 |
| **1461** | A448 | 300d multicolored | 5.00 | 5.00 |
| | | *Nos. 1459-1461 (3)* | 9.50 | 9.50 |

Palestinian Intifada — A449

Designs: 100d, Palestinian holding rock and flag. 300d, Map of Israel and Palestine, Dome of the Rock, Palestinian flag, olives, hand holding rock, vert.

**1992, Nov. 26** **Litho.** *Perf. 12*

| | | | | |
|---|---|---|---|---|
| **1462-1463** | A449 | Set of 2 | 4.50 | 4.50 |

Doctors — A450

Designs: 40d, Dr. Mohamed Ali Imsek (1883-1945). 60d, Dr. Aref Adhani Arif (1884-1935).

**1993, Feb. 1**

| | | | | |
|---|---|---|---|---|
| **1464-1465** | A450 | Set of 2 | 1.25 | 1.25 |

Intl. Conference on Nutrition, Rome — A451

Background colors: 70d, Blue. 80d, Green.

**1993, Feb. 15**

| | | | | |
|---|---|---|---|---|
| **1466-1467** | A451 | Set of 2 | 1.75 | 1.75 |

People's Authority Declaration — A452

Col. Khadafy, map of Libya, crowd, eagle, oil rig, pipeline and tanker: 60d, 65d, 75d.

**1993, Mar. 2** *Perf. 14¾*
**1468-1470** A452 Set of 3 2.25 2.25

Tripoli Intl. Fair A453

Various Fair participants, Fair emblem and panel color of: No. 1471, 60d, Pink. No. 1472, 60d, Yellow green. No. 1473, 60d, Blue, vert. No. 1474, 60d, Orange, vert.
100d, People on horses.

**1993, Mar. 15** *Perf. 14*
**1471-1474** A453 Set of 4 2.50 2.50

**Souvenir Sheet**

*Perf. 11¾*

**1475** A453 100d multi 1.50 1.50

No. 1475 contains one 38x32mm stamp.

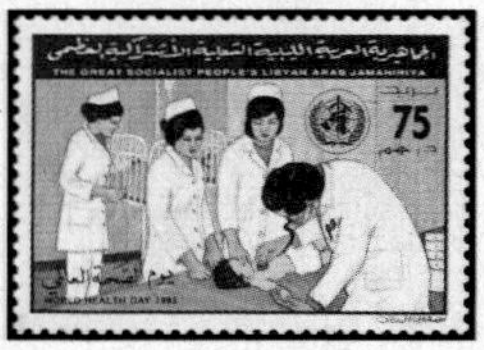

World Health Day A454

Designs: 75d, Doctor and three nurses examining child. 85d, Doctor and two nurses examining woman.

**1993, Apr. 7** *Perf. 13¼*
**1476-1477** A454 Set of 2 1.60 1.60

Children's Day — A455

No. 1478 — Various girls with background of: a, Gray green (red headdress). b, Red curtains. c, Gray. d, Home furnishings. e, Beige.

**1993, May 1** *Perf. 13¾*
**1478** Horiz. strip of 5 4.25 4.25
*a.-e.* A455 75d Any single .80 .80

Miniature Sheet

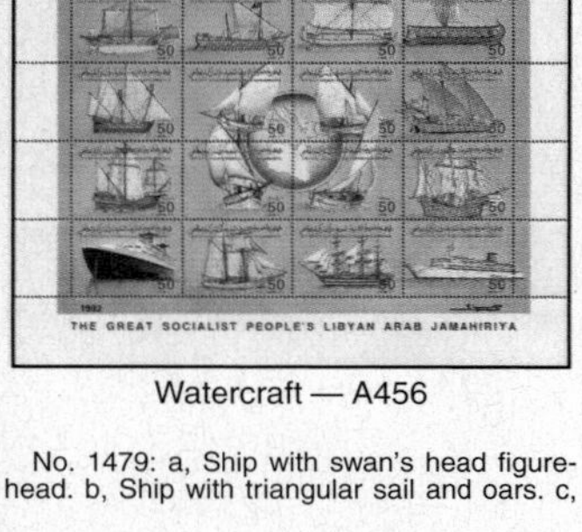

Watercraft — A456

No. 1479: a, Ship with swan's head figurehead. b, Ship with triangular sail and oars. c, Ship with one large white sail. d, Ship with rectangular sail and oars. e, Ship with three triangular sails. f, Sailboat, map of Western Mediterranean area. g, Sailboat, map of Eastern Mediterranean area. h, Ship with two red triangular sails. i, Ship with four sails, red flag. j, Sailboat, map of Western Libya. k, Sailboat, map of Eastern Libya. l, Ship with three sails on main mast. m, Ocean liner with black hull. n, Ship with six tan sails. o, Ship with furled sails. p, Ocean liner with white hull.

**1993, July 15** *Perf. 13¼*
**1479** A456 50d Sheet of 16, #a-p 10.00 10.00

Miniature Sheet

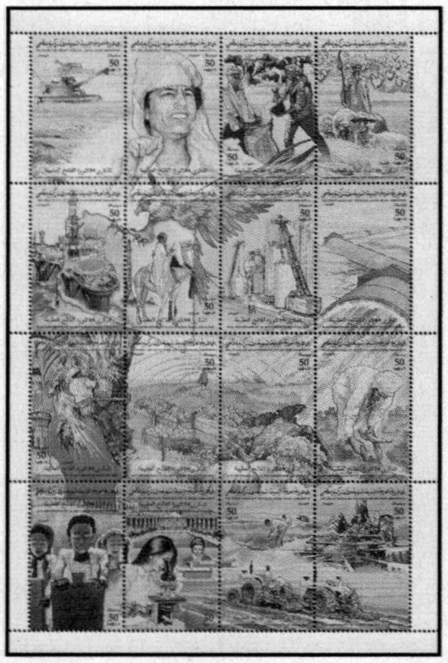

Sept. 1 Revolution, 24th Anniv. — A457

No. 1480: a, Grain combine. b, Col. Khadafy. c, Cows, man with feed bucket. d, Shepherd and sheep. e, Oil platform, map of Western Libya. f, Eagle, man on camel, map of Eastern Libya. g, Cranes lifting large tanks. h, Water pipeline. i, Man picking dates. j, Man in field, crates of vegetables. k, Crates of vegetables. l, Man picking vegetables. m, Three children. n, Building, women at typewriter and microscope. o, Man in field, tractor. p, Tractors in field.

**1993, Dec. 10** *Perf. 14*
**1480** A457 50d Sheet of 16, #a-p 12.00 12.00

Miniature Sheet

Libyans Deported to Italy — A458

No. 1481: a, Guard tower, soldier with gun, woman tending to sick man. b, Soldier with gun and bayonet guarding Libyans. c, Col. Khadafy with headdress. d, Man holding box and walking stick. e, Soldiers whipping man. f, Man on horse. g, Four men. h, Soldier guarding people looking at hanged man. i, Soldier standing near wooden post, soldier guarding Libyans. j, Woman on camel, soldiers. k, Soldiers on horses among Libyans. l, Boat with deportees. m, Col. Khadafy without headdress. n, Libyan with arm raised, hand of Col. Khadafy. o, Soldier pointing gun at horseman with sword. p, Horseman carrying gun.

**1993, Dec. 15** *Perf. 14½*
**1481** A458 50d Sheet of 16, #a-p 12.00 12.00

Miniature Sheet

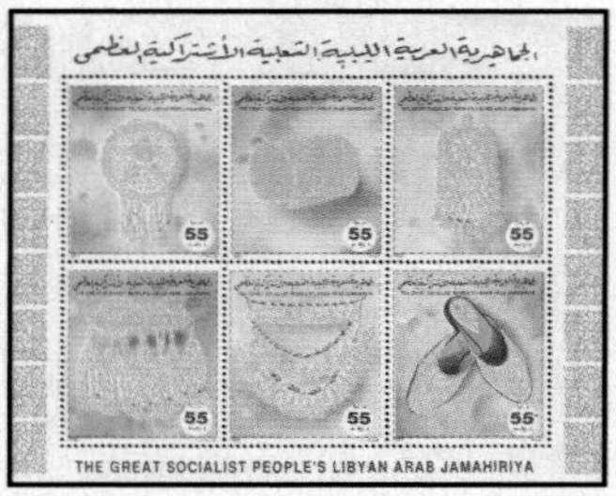

Items Made of Silver — A459

No. 1482: a, Medallion with five-pointed star and tassels. b, Wristband. c, Medallion with star with ten rays and tassels. d, Rod with tassels. e, Necklace. f, Slippers.

**Litho. & Embossed With Foil Application**

**1994, Aug. 10** *Perf. 13¼*
**1482** A459 55d Sheet of 6, #a-f 4.25 4.25

A460

Sept. 1 Revolution, 25th Anniv. — A461

No. 1483: a, Jet, Col. Khadafy in robe (40x40mm). b, Warriors on horseback, mother and child, Col. Khadafy in military uniform (60x40mm). c, Ship, shepherd, man and woman, man on camel (40x40mm).

**1994, Sept. 1** **Litho.** *Perf. 12*
**1483** A460 100d Horiz. strip of 3, #a-c 4.25 4.25

**Souvenir Sheet**

**1484** A461 1000d multi 13.50 13.50

1994 World Cup Soccer Championships, United States — A462

World Cup, and various soccer players with horizontal stripes in: No. 1485, 100d, Red and brown. No. 1486, 100d, Red violet, purple, and green. No. 1487, 100d, Green and purple. No. 1488, 100d, Green, black and yellow. No. 1489, 100d, Orange, brown and red. No. 1490, 100d, Yellow orange, brown and orange.
No. 1491, 500d, Soccer players, World Cup, red violet background. No. 1492, 500d, Soccer player, ball, "1990," horiz.

**1994, Oct. 15** *Perf. 13¼*
**1485-1490** A462 Set of 6 8.50 8.50

**Souvenir Sheets**

**1491-1492** A462 Set of 2 14.00 14.00

No. 1491 contains one 42x51mm stamp; No. 1492 contains one 51x42mm stamp.

Miniature Sheet

Libyans Deported to Italy — A463

No. 1493: a, Col. Khadafy. b, Airplane, man with rifle. c, Two men, one with rifle, nose of airplane. d, Tail of airplane, man with rifle. e, Soldier with bayoneted rifle, Libyans looking at dead animal. f, Libyans with rifles, camel. g, Nose of camel, horsemen and soldiers. h, Man carrrying child, drawn swords, horsemen. i, Soldier with whip. j, Man with open mouth. k, Tank and soldiers. l, Soldiers on horseback, women. m, Woman tending to injured man, man with bound hands, rifles. n, Soldier bayoneting man. o, Building, women, soldiers on horseback. p, Deportees in boats.

**1994, Oct. 26** *Perf. 12*
**1493** A463 95d Sheet of 16, #a-p 22.50 22.50

Mosques — A464

No. 1494 — Mosques in: a, Darghut. b, Benghazi. c, Kabao. d, Gouzgu. e, Siala. f, El Kettani.

**1994, Nov. 15** **Litho.**
**1494** Horiz. strip of 6 11.50 11.50
*a.-f.* A464 70d Any single 1.50 1.50

Miniature Sheet

People's Authority Declaration — A465

No. 1495: a, Navy ship, jet, women soldiers. b, Wheat, hand holding Green Book, tractor trailer cab. c, Family, water pipeline, tractor trailers. d, Fruit, vegetables, people holding Green Book. e, Col. Khadafy, butterfly, flowers. f, Young men, fruit and vegetables.

**1994, Dec. 1** *Perf. 14¾*
**1495** A465 80d Sheet of 6, #a-f 12.00 12.00

Evacuation of Foreign Forces — A466

Denomination in: 65d, Blue. 95f, Green.

**1994, Dec. 15** *Perf. 14*
**1496-1497** A466 Set of 2 2.75 2.75

Miniature Sheet

Khadafy Prize for Human Rights — A467

No. 1498: a, Helmeted soldiers, men with sticks, South African flag. b, Men with sticks, South African flag. c, South African Pres. Nelson Mandela. d, Col. Khadafy. e, Indian at fire, crescent moon. f, Armed Indians on horses. g, Indian chief. h, Indian dancer. i, Men with rifles, jets. j, Women, jet, open book. k, Open book. l, Surgeons. m, Palestinians with flag, denomination at left. n, Palestinians with flag, denomination at right. o, Palestinians throwing rocks. p, Palestinians, soldiers.

**1994, Dec. 31** *Perf. 13¼*
**1498** A467 95d Sheet of 16, #a-p *20.00 40.00*

No. 1498 was first issued with marginal inscription with incorrect spelling of "Prize" as "Price." Value is for sheet with corrected spelling. Value, sheet with incorrect spelling $300.

People's Authority Declaration A468

Background color: No. 1499, 100d, Green. No. 1500, 100d, Blue. No. 1501, 100d, Yellow.

**1995, July 1** *Perf. 12*
**1499-1501** A468 Set of 3 2.25 2.25

Arab League, 50th Anniv. A469

Background color: No. 1502, 200d, Green. No. 1503, 200d, Blue.

No. 1504: a, Emblem in silver. b, Emblem in gold.

**1995, July 20** **Litho.** *Perf. 13¼*
**1502-1503** A469 Set of 2 7.50 7.50

**Litho. & Embossed With Foil Application**

**1504** A469 1000d Sheet of 2, #a-b 13.00 13.00

Miniature Sheet

Libyan Soccer Players — A470

No. 1505: a, Messaud Zentuti. b, Salem Shermit. c, Ottoman Marfua. d, Ghaleb Siala. e, 1935 Libyan Team. f, Senussi Mresila.

**1995, Aug. 1** **Litho.**
**1505** A470 100d Sheet of 6, #a-f 9.50 9.50

Miniature Sheet

Zoo Animals — A471

No. 1506: a, Camel. b, Secretary bird. c, African wild dog. d, Oryx. e, Baboon. f, Golden jackal. g, Crowned eagle. h, Eagle owl. i, Desert hedgehog. j, Sand gerbil. k, Addax. l, Fennec. m, Lanner falcon. n, Desert wheatear. o, Pintailed sandgrouse. p, Jerboa.

**1995, Aug. 15** *Perf. 13¾x14*
**1506** A471 100d Sheet of 16, #a-p 25.00 25.00

Miniature Sheet

Fruit — A472

No. 1507: a, Grapefruit. b, Wild cherries. c, Mulberries. d, Strawberry tree fruit (arbutus). e, Plums. f, Pears. g, Apricots. h, Almonds. i, Prickly pears. j, Lemons. k, Peaches. l, Dates. m, Olives. n, Oranges. o, Figs. p, Grapes.

**1995, Aug. 20**
**1507** A472 100d Sheet of 16, #a-p 24.00 24.00

Miniature Sheet

Sept. 1 Revolution, 26th Anniv. — A473

No. 1508: a, Students and chemist. b, Minaret, fist of Col. Khadafy, men. c, Col. Khadafy. d, Scientists and buildings. e, Nurses, doctor and patients. f, Surgeons. g, Woman at keyboard, shoemakers. h, Audio technicians, musician. i, Crane, bulldozer and buildings. j, Grain elevator. k, Offshore oil rig, nose of airplane. l, Tail of airplane, ship. m, Goats and sheep. n, Water pipeline. o, Camels, vegetables, water. p, Fruit, grain combine.

**1995, Sept. 1**
**1508** A473 100d Sheet of 16, #a-p 22.50 22.50

Scouts — A474

No. 1509 — Scouting emblem and: a, Antelope, Scout and butterflies (40x40mm). b, Scouts, butterflies, antelope and cat (60x40mm). c, Scouts, wheat, butterfly, flower.

**1995, Sept. 10** *Perf. 12*
**1509** A474 250d Horiz. strip of 3, #a-c 17.00 17.00

American Attack on Libya, 9th Anniv. — A475

No. 1510: a, Ships and people (40x50mm). b, Airplanes, helicopters and people, hand holding Green Book (60x50mm). c, Airplane, mother and child (40x50mm).

**1995, Sept. 15**
**1510** A475 100d Horiz. strip of 3, #a-c 4.50 4.50

Tripoli Intl. Fair — A476

Horsemen with background colors of: No. 1511, 100d, Light blue. No. 1512, 100d, Blue. No. 1513, 100d, Violet. No. 1514, 100d, Blue green, vert. No. 1515, 100d, Blue green with black stripes, vert. No. 1516, 100d, Orange, vert.

1000d, Col. Khadafy on horse.

**1995, Sept. 20**
**1511-1516** A476 Set of 6 9.00 9.00

**Souvenir Sheet**

**1517** A476 1000d multi 14.00 14.00

No. 1517 contains one 80x50mm stamp.

Miniature Sheet

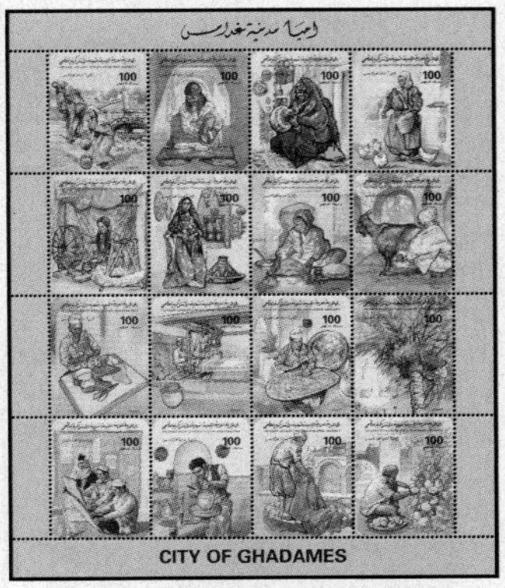


City of Ghadames — A477

No. 1518: a, Camel, woman with water jugs. b, Woman with bread on wooden board. c, Seated woman with vase. d, Woman feeding chickens. e, Woman at spinning wheel. f, Woman standing. g, Woman cooking. h, Woman milking goat. i, Shoemaker. j, Man at loom. k, Metalworker with hammer. l, Date picker. m, Men at religious school. n, Potter. o, Tanner. p, Man picking tomatoes.

*Perf. 14½x14¼*

**1995, Sept. 30** **Litho.**
**1518** A477 100d Sheet of 16, #a-p 21.00 21.00

Evacuation of Foreign Forces — A478

Panel color: 50d, Pink. 100d, Green. 200d, Lilac.

**1995, Oct. 7** **Litho.** *Perf. 14¾x14¼*
**1519-1521** A478 Set of 3 5.00 5.00

Bees and Flowers A479

Panel color: No. 1522, 100d, Green. No. 1523, 100d, Pink. No. 1524, 100d, Purple.

**1995, Oct. 10** *Perf. 14¼x14¾*
**1522-1524** A479 Set of 3 4.50 4.50

Dr. Mohamed Feituri — A480

**1995, Oct. 20** *Perf. 14¾x14¼*
**1525** A480 200d multi 2.75 2.75

Campaign Against Smoking — A481

Color of central stripe: No. 1526, 100d, Orange. No. 1527, 100d, Yellow.

**1995, Oct. 20**
**1526-1527** A481 Set of 2 3.25 3.25

Miniature Sheet

Libyans Deported to Italy — A482

No. 1528: a, Col. Khadafy. b, Horsemen. c, Battle scene with blue sky, denomination at LR. d, Battle scene with blue sky, airplane, denomination at LL. e, Battle scene, arch. f, Battle scene, red building at UR. g, Battle scene with red sky, soldier holding pistol. h, Battle scene with red sky, building at UR. i, Three Libyans in foreground. j, Battle scene with running soldiers. k, Battle scene of horsemen and riflemen facing right. l, Soldiers, Libyan man in foreground at LR. m, Two horesemen with arms raised. n, Man in foreground shooting at horsemen. o, Children. p, Child, deportees in boats.

**1995, Oct. 26** ***Perf. 12***
**1528** A482 100d Sheet of 16, #a-p 22.00 22.00

Miniature Sheet

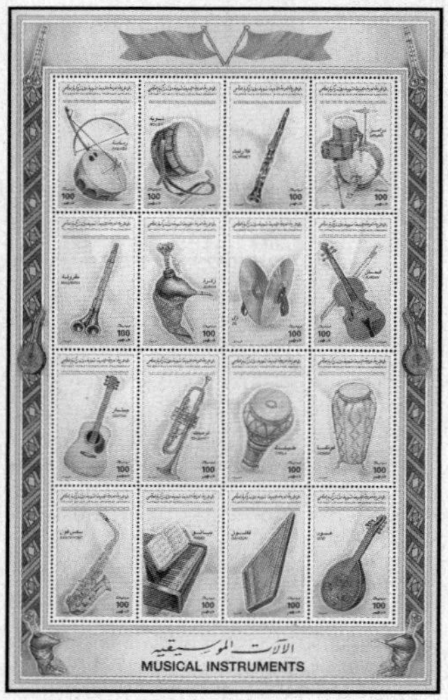


Musical Instruments — A483

No. 1529: a, Rababa. b, Nouba (drum). c, Clarinet. d, Drums. e, Magruna. f, Zukra. g, Zil (cymbals). h, Kaman (violin). i, Guitar. j, Trumpet. k, Tapla (drum). l, Gonga (drum). m, Saxophone. n, Piano. o, Gandon (zither). p, Ood.

**1995, Nov. 1** ***Perf. 13¾x14***
**1529** A483 100d Sheet of 16, #a-p 21.00 21.00

Doors of Mizda — A484

No. 1530: a, Blue door. b, Door with arched design in rectangular doorway. c, Log door. d, Door with rounded top in archway. e, Door of planks in rectangular doorway.

**1995, Nov. 10** ***Perf. 13¼***
**1530** Horiz. strip of 5 3.50 3.50
*a.-e.* A484 100d Any single .65 .65

Intl. Olympic Committee, Cent. — A485

Denomination color: No. 1531, 100d, Red. No. 1532, 100d, Black.

**1995, Nov. 15** ***Perf. 13½***
**1531-1532** A485 Set of 2 1.40 1.40

Prehistoric Animals — A486

No. 1533: a, Baryonyx. b, Oviraptor. c, Stenonychosaurus. d, Tenontosaurus. e, Yangchuanosaurus. f, Stegotetrabelodon, denomination at LR. g, Stegotetrabelodon, denomination at LL. h, Psittacosaurus. i, Heterodontosaurus. j, Loxodonta atlantica. k, Mammuthus. l, Erlikosaurus. m, Cynognathus. n, Plateosaurus. o, Staurikosaurus. p, Lystrosaurus.
500d, Stegotetrabelodon, horiz.

**1995, Nov. 20** ***Perf. 13½***
**1533** A486 Miniature sheet of 16 12.50 12.50
*a.-p.* 100d Any single .75 .70

**Souvenir Sheet**
***Perf. 13¼***

**1534** A486 500d multi 4.25 4.25

No. 1534 contains one 53x49mm stamp.

Children's Day A487

No. 1535: a, Boy, dinosaur with cane. b, Boy on elephant. c, Boy, Scout emblem, turtle and mushroom. d, Dinosaur and soccer ball. e, Boy with gun, pteranodon.

**1995, Nov. 25** ***Perf. 13½***
**1535** Horiz. strip of 5 15.00 15.00
*a.-e.* A487 100d Any single 2.75 2.75

Palestinian Intifada — A488

No. 1536: a, Boy throwing object at helicopter. b, Dome of the Rock, Palestinian with flag. c, People, Palestinian flag.

**1995, Nov. 29** ***Perf. 14***
**1536** A488 100d Horiz. strip of 3, #a-c 4.50 4.50

Intl. Civil Aviation Organization, 50th Anniv. — A489

Denomination color: No. 1537, 100d, Black. No. 1538, 100d, Blue.

**1995, Dec. 7** ***Perf. 13½x13¼***
**1537-1538** A489 Set of 2 1.40 1.40

United Nations, 50th Anniv. — A490

Background color: No. 1539, 100d, Dark red lilac. No. 1540, 100d, Light red lilac.

**1995, Dec. 20** ***Perf. 13½***
**1539-1540** A490 Set of 2 1.40 1.40

Miniature Sheet

Flowers — A491

No. 1541: a, Iris germanica. b, Canna edulis. c, Nerium oleander. d, Papaver rhoeas. e, Strelitzia reginae. f, Amygdalus communis.

**1995, Dec. 31** ***Perf. 14¾***
**1541** A491 200d Sheet of 6, #a-f 11.00 11.00

People's Authority Declaration A492

Panel color: 100d, Pink. 150d, Light blue. 200d, Light green.

**1996, Mar. 2** ***Perf. 13¼***
**1542-1544** A492 Set of 3 5.00 5.00

1996 Summer Olympics, Atlanta — A493

No. 1545: a, Soccer. b, Long jump. c, Tennis. d, Cycling. e, Boxing. f, Equestrian.
No. 1546, 500d, Runner. No. 1547, 500d, Equestrian, diff.

**1996, Aug. 15** ***Perf. 14½***
**1545** A493 100d Sheet of 6, #a-f 6.75 6.75

**Souvenir Sheets**

**1546-1547** A493 Set of 2 11.00 11.00

Miniature Sheet

Sept. 1 Revolution, 27th Anniv. — A494

No. 1548: a, Camel, man, fruits, water. b, Water pipeline, fruit. c, Tractor, water, women. d, Oil worker. e, Tailor. f, Seamstress, Col. Khadafy's fist. g, Col. Khadafy. h, Building, women with microscope. i, Nurses at anatomy lesson, man with microscope. j, School child. k, Woman with open book. l, Man playing zither. m, Airplanes. n, Dish antenna, ship, man on camel. o, Ship, television camera. p, Television actress, woman at microphone.

**1996, Sept. 1** ***Perf. 13¾x14***
**1548** A494 100d Sheet of 16, #a-p 20.00 20.00

Miniature Sheet

American Attack on Libya, 10th Anniv. — A495

No. 1549: a, Left side of missile, explosion. b, Right side of missile, man with raised arms. c, Casualties, airplanes. d, Airplane at left, man on ground. e, Firefighter spraying burning car. f, Damaged vehicles. g, Col. Khadafy. h, Casualties, airplane at top. i, Rescuers assisting casualties. j, Man with extended hand. k, Woman with hands to face. l, Stretcher bearers. m, Three men and casualty. n, Man with bloody hand. o, Woman and child casualties. p, Burning car, rescuers attending to bleeding casualty.

**1996, Sept. 15** ***Perf. 13¾***
**1549** A495 100d Sheet of 16, #a-p 20.00 20.00

Miniature Sheet

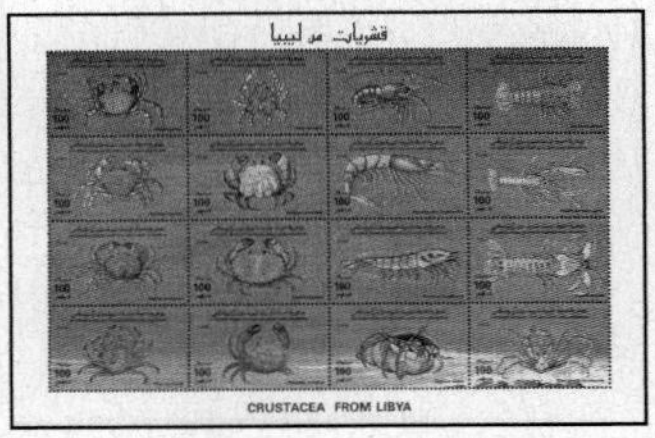


Crustaceans — A496

No. 1550: a, Necora puber. b, Lissa chiragra. c, Palinurus elephas. d, Scyllarus arctus. e, Carcinus maenas. f, Calappa granulata. g, Parapenaeus longirostris. h, Nephrops norvegicus. i, Eriphia verrucosa. j, Cancer pagurus. k, Penaeus kerathurus. l, Squilla mantis. m, Maja squinado. n, Pilumnus hirtellus. o, Pagurus alatus. p, Macropodia tenuirostris.

**1996, Oct. 1** ***Perf. 14x13¾***
**1550** A496 100d Sheet of 16, #a-p 20.00 20.00

Miniature Sheet

Intl. Day of Maghreb Handicrafts — A497

Various handicrafts.

**1996, Oct. 15** ***Perf. 13¾x14***
**1551** A497 100d Sheet of 16, #a-p 20.00 20.00

Miniature Sheet

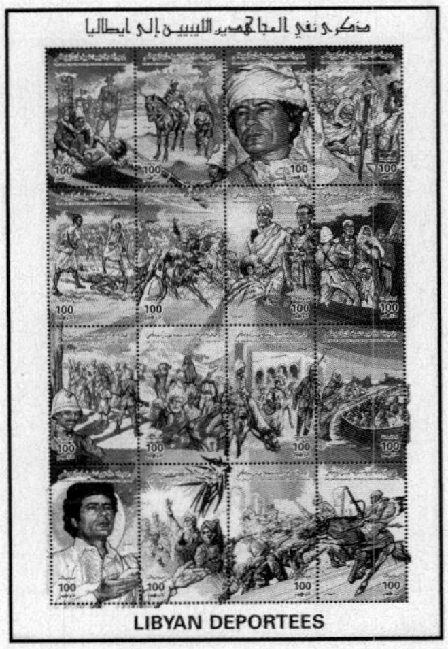


Libyans Deported to Italy — A498

No. 1552: a, Guard tower, soldier with gun, woman tending to sick man. b, Soldier with gun and bayonet, soldier on horseback. c, Col. Khadafy with headdress. d, Man holding box and walking stick. e, Soldiers whipping man. f, Man on horse. g, Four men. h, Soldier guarding people looking at hanged man. i, Soldier standing near wooden post, soldier guarding Libyans. j, Woman on camel, soldiers. k, Soldiers on horses among Libyans. l, Boat with deportees. m, Col. Khadafy without headdress. n, Libyan with arm raised, hand of Col. Khadafy. o, Soldier pointing gun at horseman with sword. p, Horseman carrying gun.

**1996, Oct. 26** ***Litho.***
**1552** A498 100d Sheet of 16, #a-p 20.00 20.00

Miniature Sheet

Horses — A499

No. 1553: a, Brown horse, lake at right. b, Brown horse in front of lake, tree at right. c, Brown horse in front of lake, tree at right. d, Dark brown horse, trees in background. e, Dark brown horse with raised leg. f, Horse at base of tree. g, Gray horse galloping. h, Piebald horse. i, Gray horse, palm tree at left. j, Head of black horse and tail of brown horse. k, Brown horse, palm fronds at upper right. l, Brown horse with gray mane, palm tree at right. m, Head of black horse, body of gray horse, tail of brown horse. n, Head of brown horse, body of black horse, hindquarters of two brown horses. o, Head of brown horse, parts of three other brown horses. p, Head of brown horse, chest of another brown horse, palm tree at right.

**1996, Oct. 30** ***Perf. 14x13¾***
**1553** A499 100d Sheet of 16, #a-p 20.00 20.00

Miniature Sheet

Camels — A500

No. 1554: a, Camelus dromedarius with head at right. b, Head of Camelus dromedarius. c, Camelus dromedarius with head at left. d, Camelus ferus bactrianus with head at right. e, Camelus ferus ferus. f, Camelus ferus bactrianus with head at left.

**1996, Nov. 15** ***Perf. 12***
**1554** A500 200d Sheet of 6, #a-f 13.50 13.50

Press and Information A501

Designs: 100d, Photographer, newspapers, computer. 200d, Musicians, video technician, computer, dish antenna.

**1996, Nov. 20**
**1555-1556** A501 Set of 2 3.25 3.25

Miniature Sheet

Fossils and Prehistoric Animals — A502

No. 1557: a, Mene rhombea fossil. b, Mesodon macrocephalus fossil. c, Eyron arctiformis fossil. d, Stegosaurus. e, Pteranodon. f, Allosaurus.

**1996, Nov. 25**
**1557** A502 200d Sheet of 6, #a-f 16.00 16.00

Palestinian Intifada — A503

Frame color: 100d, Yellow. 150d, Green. 200d, Blue.

**1996, Nov. 29**
**1558-1560** A503 Set of 3 5.00 5.00

African Children's Day — A504

Designs: 50d, Child, beige frame. 150d, Child, blue frame. 200d, Mother, child, dove.

**1996, Dec. 5** ***Perf. 13¼***
**1561-1563** A504 Set of 3 2.50 2.50

Children's Day — A505

No. 1564 — Various cats with background colors of: a, Rose. b, Blue green. c, Blue. d, Yellow green. e, Gray green.

**1996, Dec. 5**
**1564** Horiz. strip of 5 5.50 5.50
*a.-e.* A505 100d Any single 1.00 1.00

Intl. Family Day — A506

No. 1565 — Family and: a, 150d, Building (21x27mm). b, 150d, Automobile (21x27mm). c, 200d, Stylized globe (46x27mm).

**1996, Dec. 10** ***Perf. 13x13¼***
**1565** A506 Horiz. strip of 3, #a-c 3.00 3.00

Miniature Sheet

Teachers — A507

No. 1566: a, Mohamed Kamel El-Hammali. b, Mustafa Abdulla Ben-Amer. c, Mohamed Messaud Fesheka. d, Kairi Mustafa Serraj. e, Muftah El-Majri. f, Mohamed Hadi Arafa.

**1996, Dec. 15** ***Perf. 13¼***
**1566** A507 100d Sheet of 6, #a-f 3.75 3.75

Miniature Sheet

Singers — A508

No. 1567: a, Mohamed Salim and zither. b, Mohamed M. Sayed Bumedyen and flute. c, Otman Najim and ood. d, Mahmud Sherif and tapla. e, Mohamed Ferjani Marghani and piano. f, Mohamed Kabazi and violin.

**1996, Dec. 15**
**1567** A508 100d Sheet of 6, #a-f 3.75 3.75

Miniature Sheet

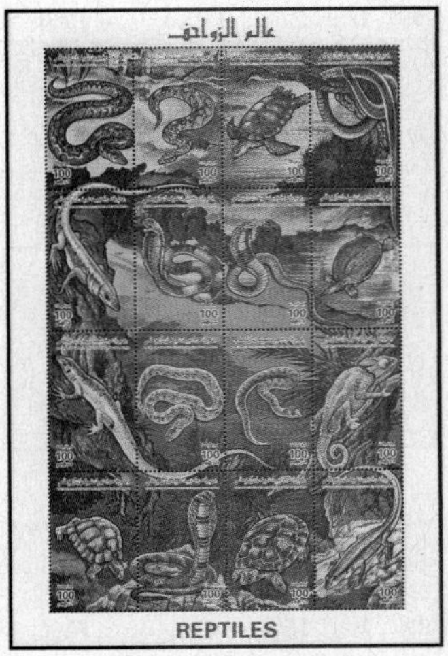


Reptiles — A509

No. 1568: a, Snake, leaves and building at top. b, Snake, building at top. c, Turtle, water and part of snake. d, Snake on tree branch. e, Brown lizard on rock. f, Cobra with head at left. g, Cobra and water. h, Turtle, water, tail of cobra. i, Green lizard on rock. j, Snake, foliage at bottom. k, Snake, foliage at bottom and right. l, Lizard with curled tail. m, Turtle on rock. n, Cobra with head at right. o, Turtle on grass. p, Gray lizard on rock.

**1996, Dec. 20** *Perf. 13¾x14*
**1568** A509 100d Sheet of 16, #a-p 18.50 18.50

Miniature Sheet

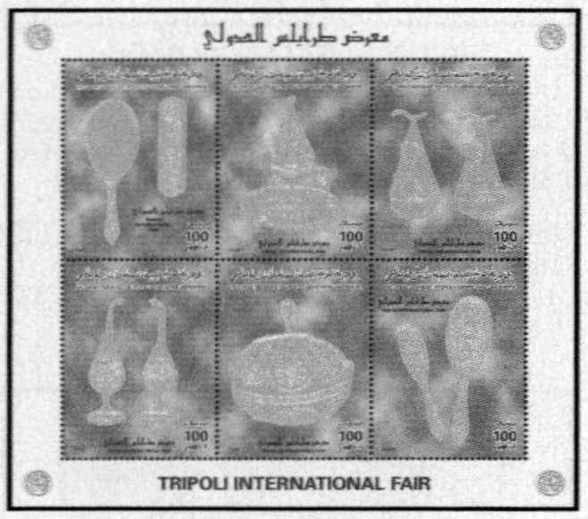


Tripoli Intl. Fair — A510

No. 1569: a, Mirror and brush. b, Container and plate. c, Two containers with rounded bases. d, Two containers on pedestals. e, Oval ornament. f, Brushes.

**Litho. & Embossed with Foil Application**

**1996, Dec. 30** *Perf. 13¾*
**1569** A510 100d Sheet of 6, #a-f 6.75 6.75

A511

People's Authority Declaration, 20th Anniv. — A512

Frame color: 100d, Yellow. 200d, Blue. 300d, Green.

**1997, Mar. 2** **Litho.** *Perf. 12*
**1570-1572** A511 Set of 3 7.75 7.75

**Souvenir Sheet**

*Imperf*

**1573** A512 10,000d multi 90.00 90.00

No. 1573 has a perforated label that bears the denomination but lacks the country name.

Scouts and Philately — A513

No. 1574: a, 50d, Group of scouts, open album, wheat, flag. b, 50d, Two scouts, two albums, wheat. c, 100d, Butterflies, books, scouts and flags.

**1997, Mar. 15** *Perf. 14*
**1574** A513 Horiz. strip of 3, #a-c 2.75 2.75

Health Care — A514

No. 1575: a, 50d, Doctor looking at test tube. b, 50d, Doctor, microscope. c, 100d, Doctor and nurse examining baby.

**1997, Apr. 7**
**1575** A514 Horiz. strip of 3, #a-c 2.25 2.25

Buildings A515

Designs: 50d, Shown. 100d, Building with attached tower, vert. 200d, Tower, vert.

*Perf. 14¼x14¾, 14¾x14¼*

**1997, Apr. 15**
**1576-1578** A515 Set of 3 5.00 5.00

Campaign Against Smoking — A516

Frame color: 100d, Blue. 150d, Green. 200d, Pink.

**1997, Apr. 30** *Perf. 14¾x14¼*
**1579-1581** A516 Set of 3 2.75 2.75

Arab National Central Library — A517

Building, map, open book, and olive branches with background in: 100d, Blue. 200d, Green.
1000d, Building, map, books, computer and Col. Khadafy, horiz.

**1997, Aug. 10** *Perf. 13¼*
**1582-1583** A517 Set of 2 1.75 1.75

**Souvenir Sheet**

**1584** A517 1000d multi 6.00 6.00

No. 1584 contains one 116x49mm stamp.

Arab Tourism Year — A518

*Perf. 13¼x13½*

**1997, Aug. 20** **Litho.**
**1585** A518 Horiz. strip of 3 10.50 10.50
*a.* 100d Black denomination 2.00 2.00
*b.* 200d Red denomination 3.75 3.75
*c.* 250d Blue denomination 4.75 4.75

Miniature Sheet

A519

Sept. 1 Revolution, 28th Anniv. — A520

No. 1586: a, 100d, Mother and child. b, 100d, Col. Khadafy as student. c, 100d, Khadafy at microphone. d, 100d, People on tank. e, 100d, Khadafy and man in suit. f, 100d, Khadafy with fist raised. g, 100d, Woman, child, corner of Green Book. h, 100d, Three people, corner of Green Book. i, 100d, Khadafy with pen. j, 100d, Man and child. k, 100d, Government buildings, helicopters. l, 100d, Khadafy in military uniform. m, 500d, Khadafy on horse. Size of Nos. 1586a-1586l: 28x43mm. Size of No. 1586m: 56x86mm.

**Litho., Litho with Foil Application (#1586m)**

**1997, Sept. 1** *Perf. 14*
**1586** A519 Sheet of 13, #a-m 17.50 17.50

**Souvenir Sheet**

*Perf. 13¾*

**1587** A520 500d multi 6.00 6.00

Miniature Sheet

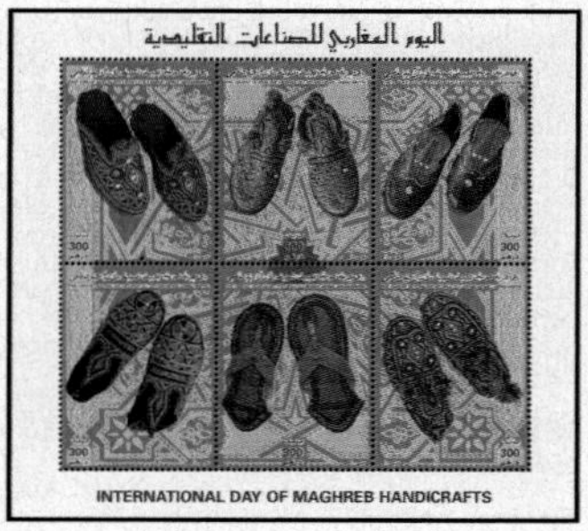


Intl. Day of Maghreb Handicrafts — A521

No. 1588 — Various shoes with toes pointing to: a, LR corner. b, Bottom. c, LL corner. d, UR corner. e, Top. f, UL corner.

**Litho. With Foil Application**

**1997, Sept. 20** *Perf. 13¾*
**1588** A521 300d Sheet of 6, #a-f 18.00 18.00

Miniature Sheet

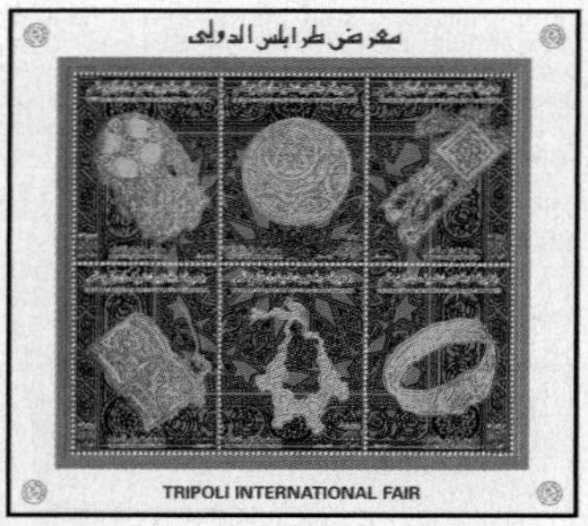


Tripoli Intl. Fair — A522

No. 1589 — Items made of silver: a, Medallion with tassels. b, Round medallion. c, Diamond-shaped medallion with tassels. d, Curved medallion. e, Necklace. f, Ring.

**Litho. & Embossed With Foil Application**

**1997, Sept. 20**
**1589** A522 500d Sheet of 6, #a-f 19.00 19.00

Evacuation of Foreign Forces — A523

Denominations: 100d, 150d, 250d.

**1997, Oct. 7** **Litho.** *Perf. 14¾x14¼*
**1590-1592** A523 Set of 3 2.75 2.75

Miniature Sheet

Libyans Deported to Italy — A524

No. 1593: a, Person carrying water jug. b, Col. Khadafy with headdress. c, Man, soldier on horse. d, Soldier and Libyans. e, Soldier whipping man. f, Soldier, man on horse. g, Libyan man and man in uniform. h, People at hanging. i, Man with purple fez, woman with red headdress. j, People, horse and camel. k, Col. Khadafy without headdress. l, Deportees on boats. m, Hand of Khadafy above pillars. n, Horsemen and pillars. o, Horsemen. p, Horsemen and hand of Khadafy.

**1997, Oct. 26** *Perf. 14*
**1593** A524 200d Sheet of 16, #a-p 32.50 32.50

Worldwide Fund for Nature (WWF) A525

No. 1594 — Felis lybica: a, With prey at water. b, Adult and kittens. c, Under tree. d, Two adults.

**1997, Nov. 1** ***Perf. 13¼***

**1594** Horiz. strip of 4 7.50 7.50
***a.-d.*** A525 200d Any single 1.75 1.75

Printed in sheets containing two strips.

Souvenir Sheet

Natl. Society for Wildlife Conservation — A526

No. 1595: a, Antelope facing forward. b, Ram. c, Antelope facing left.

**1997, Nov. 1** ***Perf. 13¼***

**1595** A526 100d Sheet of 3, #a-c 14.00 14.00

Miniature Sheet

American Attack on Libya, 11th Anniv. — A527

No. 1596: a, Explosion. b, Green Book, Libyan airplanes. c, Minarets, hand of Col. Khadafy. d, Col. Khadafy without headdress. e, Wing of American airplane. f, Nose of American airplane. g, Libyan airplanes. h, People looking at tail of American airplane. i, Rockets hitting American airplane. j, Arm of Col. Khadafy. k, Col. Khadafy with headdress. l, Man, fist of Col. Khadafy. m, Rockets and people. n, Col. Khadafy visiting injured person. o, Col. Khadafy kissing girl's hand. p, People with fists raised.

**1997, Nov. 15** ***Perf. 14***

**1596** A527 200d Sheet of 16, #a-p 34.00 34.00

Miniature Sheet

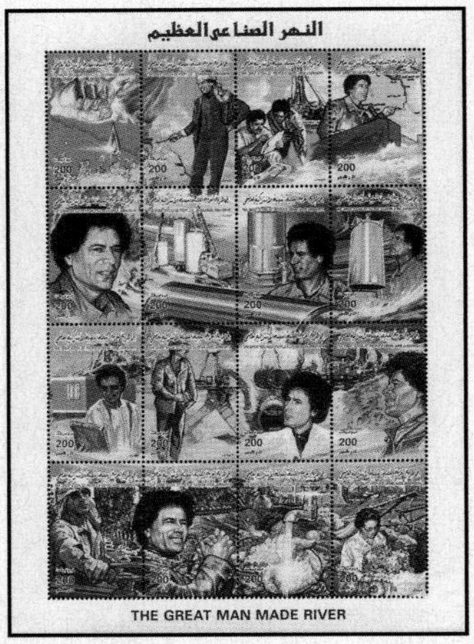


Great Man-Made River — A528

No. 1597: a, Fist, outline map of Libya. b, Col. Khadafy pointing to pipeline. c, Technicians reading paper, equipment. d, Col. Khadafy pointing to map. e, Col. Khadafy. f, Pipe, crane lifting cylinders. g, Col. Khadafy, pipe, vertical cylinder. h, Col. Khadafy, vertical cylinder. i, Col. Khadafy, construction trailer. j, Technician and equipment. k, Col. Khadafy, pipes lifted by crane. l, Col. Khadafy, line of trucks carrying pipe. m, Man with hand on spigot. n, Col. Khadafy with clasped hands. o, Hands under faucet, crops. p, Woman, child, flowers and fruit.

**1997, Dec. 1** ***Perf. 14***

**1597** A528 200d Sheet of 16, #a-p 34.00 34.00

People's Authority Declaration — A529

Panel color: 150d, Blue green. 250d, Purple. 300d, Blue.

**1998, Mar. 2** ***Perf. 13¼***

**1598-1600** A529 Set of 3 10.50 10.50

Miniature Sheet

Tripoli Intl. Fair — A530

No. 1601 — Items made of silver: a, Container with two spouts. b, Bowl on pedestal. c, Amphora. d, Container on tray. e, Lidded bowl. f, Three-legged container.

**Litho. & Embossed With Foil Application**

**1998, Mar. 5** ***Perf. 13¾***

**1601** A530 400d Sheet of 6, #a-f 24.00 24.00

Children's Day — A531

No. 1602 — Various girls in native dress with background colors of: a, Light blue. b, Yellow green. c, Red orange. d, Lilac. e, Yellow brown.

**1998, Mar. 21** **Litho.** ***Perf. 13¼***

**1602** Horiz. strip of 5 5.50 5.50
***a.-e.*** A531 100d Any single 1.00 1.00

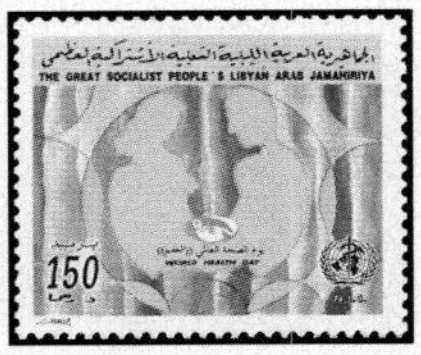

World Health Day — A532

Panel color: 150d, Buff. 250d, Light blue. 300d, Lilac.

**1998, Apr. 7**

**1603-1605** A532 Set of 3 7.75 7.75

American Attack on Libya, 12th Anniv. — A533

No. 1606 — Airplanes, ships and: a, Helicopters, people with raised fists (28x48mm). b, Mother and child, Col. Khadafy (60x48mm). c, Man, boy and birds (28x48mm).

**1998, Apr. 15**

**1606** A533 100d Horiz. strip of 3, #a-c 3.50 3.50

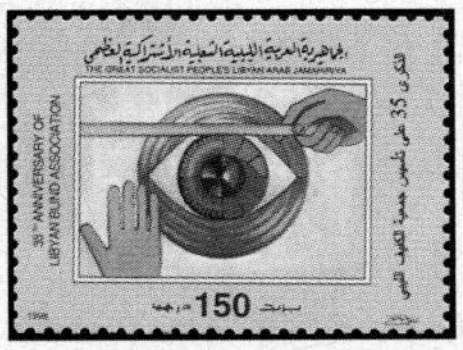

Libyan Blind Association, 35th Anniv. — A534

Designs: 150d, Eye, hand with cane, raised hand. 250d, Blind people, stringed instrument, books.

**1998, May 1** ***Perf. 12***

**1607-1608** A534 Set of 2 4.75 4.75

Arab Bee Union — A535

Frame color: 250d, Blue. 300d, Yellow. 400d, Light green.

**1998, June 1**

**1609-1611** A535 Set of 3 13.50 13.50

1998 World Cup Soccer Championships, France — A536

No. 1612 — Soccer player with: a, Ball at LR, orange and white lines at bottom. b, Top of World Cup. c, Ball at left, orange and white lines at bottom. d, No visible uniform number, left part of stadium at bottom. e, Bottom of World Cup, stadium. f, Uniform No. 5, right part of stadium at bottom.

No. 1613, 1000d, Player, World Cup, denomination at LL. No. 1614, 1000d, Player, World Cup, denomination at LR.

**1998, June 10** ***Perf. 13¼***

**1612** A536 200d Sheet of 6, #a-f *15.00 15.00*

**Souvenir Sheets**

**1613-1614** A536 Set of 2 *24.00 24.00*

Nos. 1613-1614 each contain one 42x51mm stamp.

Miniature Sheet

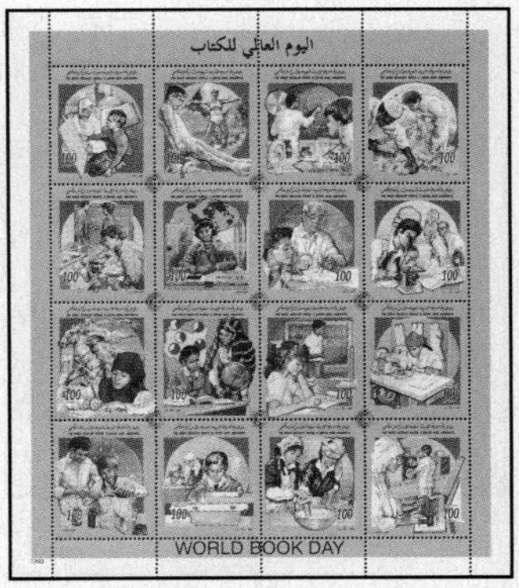


World Book Day — A537

No. 1615: a, Man, boy, mosque. b, Gymnasts. c, Science teacher at blackboard, student, ear. d, Men picking vegetables. e, Men at blackboard, man with machinery. f, Man with headset microphone, world map. g, Teacher with compass, student. h, Scientists with microscope. i, Girl writing, horseman. j, Teacher, student, map of Libya, globe. k, Music teacher at blackboard, student. l, Woman at sewing machine. m, Chemistry teacher and student. n, Teacher and women at typewriters. o, Cooks. p, Woman at computer keyboard, computer technician.

**1998, June 23**

**1615** A537 100d Sheet of 16, #a-p 17.50 17.50

Map of the Great Man-Made River A538

Denomination color: 300d, Green. 400d, Blue.
2000d, Bister.

**Litho. & Embossed With Foil Application**

**1998, July 1**

**1616-1617** A538 Set of 2 8.50 8.50

**Souvenir Sheet**

**1618** A538 2000d gold & multi 22.00 22.00

Miniature Sheet

Great Man-Made River and Vegetables — A539

No. 1619: a, Garlic. b, Peas. c, Potatoes. d, Corn. e, Leeks. f, Tomatoes. g, Carrots. h, Radishes. i, Beans. j, Peppers. k, Eggplant. l, Lettuce. m, Squash. n, Cucumbers. o, Onions, p, Cauliflower.

**1998, Sept. 1** **Litho.** ***Perf. 14***

**1619** A539 100d Sheet of 16, #a-p 21.00 21.00

Miniature Sheet

Children's Day — A540

No. 1620 — Scouting trefoil and: a, Scouts, dog. b, Scouts saluting, birds. c, Scouts saluting, flags, tents. d, Scouts, sheep. e, Scouts playing musical instruments, tying down tent. f, Scouts at campfire, bird, boat.

**1998, Aug. 1** ***Perf. 14¼***

**1620** A540 400d Sheet of 6, #a-f *55.00 55.00*

A541

Sept. 1 Revolution, 29th Anniv. — A542

No. 1621: a, Col. Khadafy. b, Horseman, pipeline, vegetables. c, Fruit, pipeline, head of eagle. d, Tail of eagle, minaret. e, Surgeons, students. f, Book, map of Northwestern Africa. g, Book, men, map of Northeastern Africa and Arabian Peninsula. h, Mosque. i, People with flags, grain combine. j, Ship. k, Apartment buildings, l, Boy. m, People, irrigation rig, building. n, Building with flagpole at right. o, Building with flagpole at right, irrigation rig. p, Building, irrigation rig.

**1998, Sept. 1** **Litho.** ***Perf. 14¼***

**1621** A541 200d Sheet of 16, #a-p *37.50 37.50*

**Souvenir Sheet**

**Litho. & Embossed**

***Perf. 13½x13¾***

**1622** A542 200d shown 2.50 2.50

Evacuation of Foreign Forces — A543

Panel color: 100d, Pink. 150d, Light green. 200d, Light blue.

**1998, Oct. 7** **Litho.** ***Perf. 13¼***

**1623-1625** A543 Set of 3 5.00 5.00

Stamp Day — A544

Panel color: 300d, Buff. 400d, Blue.

**1998, Oct. 9** ***Perf. 12***

**1626-1627** A544 Set of 2 10.00 10.00

Miniature Sheet

Libyans Deported to Italy — A545

No. 1628: a, Ship, trucks. b, Bound woman, barbed wire. c, Man, barbed wire. d, Soldiers marching Libyans at gunpoint. e, Airplane, battle scene. f, Barbed wire, line of Libyans. g, Barbed wire, soldier and Libyan. h, Soldiers aiming rifles at Libyans, man with camel. i, Horseman, man ladling water. j, Soldier in boat. k, Boats with deportees. l, Boats with deportees, ships. m, Horsemen, man carrying woman. n, Horsemen raising rifles. o, Horseman and flag. p, Mother and child.

**1998, Oct. 26** ***Perf. 13¼***

**1628** A545 150d Sheet of 16, #a-p 26.00 26.00

Miniature Sheet

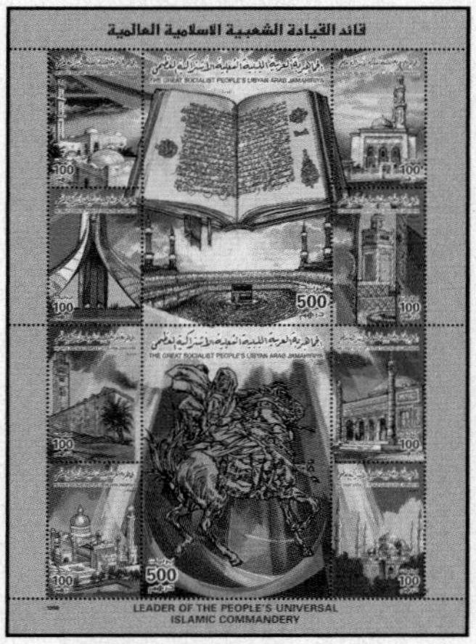


Leadership of Islam — A546

No. 1629: a, 100d, White mosque, minaret at left. b, 100d, White mosque, minaret at right. c, 100d, Modern mosque. d, 100d, Mosque seen through arch. e, 100d, Mosque and palm tree, minaret at left. f, 100d, Mosque with blue dome. g, 100d, Mosque with brown dome, six minarets. h, 100d, Mosque, five minarets. i, 500d, Koran, Holy Kaaba. j, 500d, Col. Khadafy on horse. Sizes: 100d stamps, 28x42mm; 500d stamps, 56x84mm.

**Litho., Litho. With Foil Application (#1629j)**

**1998, Nov. 1** ***Perf. 14***

**1629** A546 Sheet of 10, #a-j 22.00 22.00

Miniature Sheet

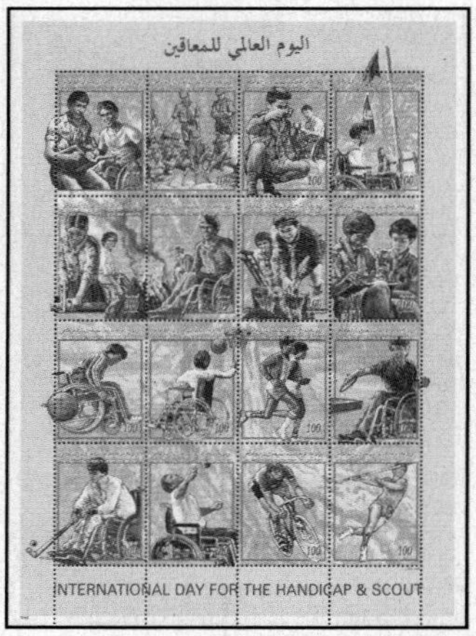


Scouts and the Handicapped — A547

No. 1630: a, Scout reading to boy in wheelchair, butterfly. b, Scout leader instructing group of Scouts. c, Scout photographing bird, boy in wheelchair. d, Scout raising flag, boy in wheelchair. e, Scout sawing log, boy in wheelchair. f, Scout near campfire, boy in wheelchair. g, Scouts with pots in fire, crutches. h, Scouts with pad of paper and pencil. i, Wheelchair basketball player in purple uniform. j, Wheelchair basketball player making shot. k, Handicapped runners. l, Man in wheelchair playing table tennis. m, Man in wheelchair playing hockey. n, Man in wheelchair throwing shot put. o, Handicapped cyclist. p, Handicapped javelin thrower.

**1998, Nov. 15** **Litho.** ***Perf. 13¼***

**1630** A547 100d Sheet of 16, #a-p 27.50 27.50

Miniature Sheet

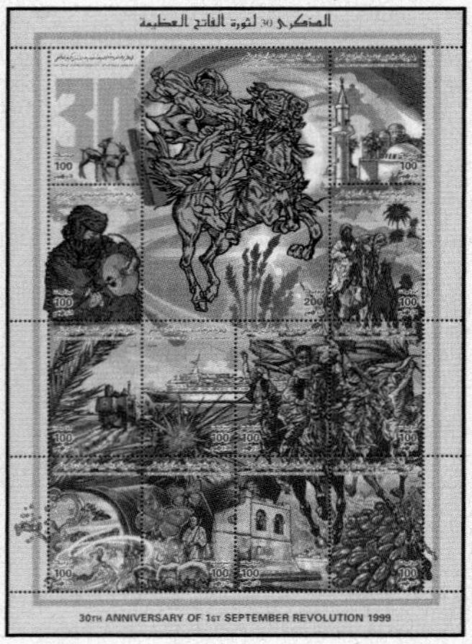


A548

Sept. 1 Revolution, 30th Anniv. — A549

No. 1631: a, 100d, Antelopes and "30." b, 100d, Mosque. c, 100d, Woman playing stringed instrument. d, 100d, Horsemen in desert. e, 100d, Grain combine. f, 100d, Ship. g, 100d, Ship, horsemen, flag. h, 100d, Horsemen, flag. i, 100d, Water pipeline, fruit. j, 100d, Butterflies, shepherd and sheep. k, 100d, Building, ship, horse's legs. l, 100d, Dates. m, 200d, Col. Khadafy on horse. Sizes: 100d stamps; 28x42mm, 200d, 56x84mm.

**Litho., Litho. With Foil Application (#1631m, 1632)**

**1999, Sept. 1** ***Perf. 14***

**1631** A548 Sheet of 13, #a-m 12.00 12.00

**Souvenir Sheet**

***Perf. 13¾***

**1632** A549 200d shown 2.00 2.00

A550

Organization of African Unity Assembly of Heads of State and Government, Tripoli — A551

No. 1633: a, Pipeline worker, musicians, minarets. b, Surgeons, woman carrying jug. c, Artisan, camel rider, satellite. d, Col. Khadafy, butterflies. e, Pipeline worker, fruit picker. f, Fruit picker, grain combine.

**1999, Sept. 8 Litho.** ***Perf. 14¼x14½***
**1633** A550 300d Sheet of 6, #a-f 13.50 13.50

### Souvenir Sheet
***Perf. 13¾x14***

**1634** A551 500d shown 4.00 4.00

Evacuation of Foreign Forces — A552

Frame color: 150d, Pink. 250d, Beige. 300d, Light blue.

**1999, Oct. 7** ***Perf. 12***
**1635-1637** A552 Set of 3 8.25 8.25

A553

People's Authority Declaration — A554

No. 1638: a, Col. Khadafy with fist raised, man on camel. b, People looking at book. c, Airplane, building, dish antenna. d, Antelope, weaver, tractor. e, Open faucet, pipeline. f, Pipleine, fruit pickers.

No. 1639, 300d, Map of Libya, Col. Khadafy with raised fist, building. No. 1640, 300d, Dove, people, Col. Khadafy.

**2000, Mar. 2 Litho.** ***Perf. 14½x14¼***
**1638** A553 100d Sheet of 6, #a-f 4.75 4.75

### Souvenir Sheets
***Perf. 13¾***
**Litho. & Embossed with Foil Application**

**1639-1640** A554 Set of 2 5.00 5.00

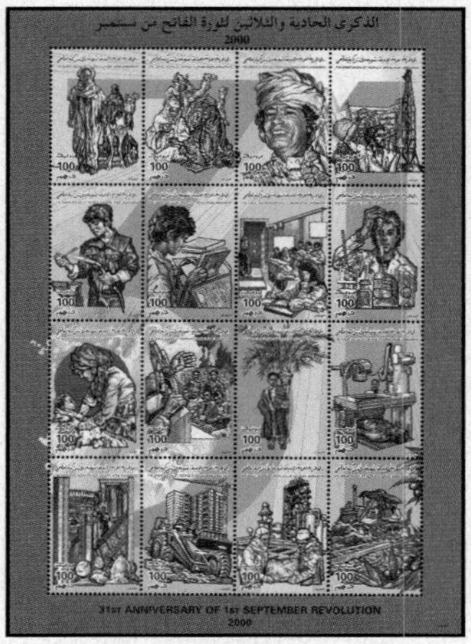


A555

Sept. 1 Revolution, 31st Anniv. — A556

No. 1641: a, Man walking, camel rider. b, Tea drinkers, camels. c, Col. Khadafy. d, Men with raised fists. e, Machinist with torch. f, Boy reading. g, Classroom. h, Scientist. i, Mother and child. j, People attending speech. k, Man and palm tree. l, Patient in X-ray machine. m, Mosque, n, Bulldozer, crane and building. o, Oil workers. p, Bulldozer.

No. 1642, 300d, Col. Khadafy, minaret. No. 1643, 300d, Col. Khadafy, boy and palm tree.

**2000, Sept. 1 Litho.** ***Perf. 14***
**1641** A555 100d Sheet of 16, #a-p 12.50 12.50

### Souvenir Sheets
**Litho. With Foil Application**
***Perf. 13¾***

**1642-1643** A556 Set of 2 5.00 5.00

El-Mujahed Mohamed Abdussalam Ahmeda Abouminiar El-Gaddafi — A557

No. 1644: a, Man holding box. b, Palm tree and horsemen. c, Horsemen and soldiers on horseback. d, Soldiers and armed horsemen. e, Horseman raising rifle above head. f, Men raising rifles, Col. Khadafy.

300d, Man reading book.

**2000, Sept. 9 Litho.** ***Perf. 13¼***
**1644** A557 200d Sheet of 6, #a-f 9.50 9.50

### Souvenir Sheet
**Litho. & Embossed With Foil Application**

**1645** A557 300d multi 2.50 2.50

### Souvenir Sheet

España 2000 Intl. Philatelic Exhibition — A558

No. 1646: a, A. Castellano (1926-97). b, M. B. Karamanli (1922-95).

**2000, Oct. 6 Litho.** ***Imperf.***
**1646** A558 250d Sheet of 2, #a-b 4.00 4.00

People's Authority Declaration A559

Denomination color: 150d, Pink. 200d, Blue.

**2001, Mar. 2** ***Perf. 14***
**1647-1648** A559 Set of 2 2.75 2.75

### Miniature Sheet

Organization of African Unity Assemby of Heads of State and Government — A560

No. 1649: a, Heads of various states. b, Heads of state, horsemen. c, Men on camels. d, People with hands raised. e, Man holding picture of Col. Khadafy. f, Col. Khadafy at microphone.

**2001, Mar. 2 Litho.** ***Perf. 13½x13¼***
**1649** A560 200d Sheet of 6, #a-f 9.50 9.50

### Souvenir Sheets

Organization of African Unity Assembly of Heads of State and Government — A561

Background colors: No. 1650, 500d, Gold. No. 1651, 500d, Silver.

**Litho. & Embossed With Foil Application**

**2001, Mar. 2** ***Perf. 13¼***
**1650-1651** A561 Set of 2 8.50 8.50

### Miniature Sheet

Tripoli Intl. Fair — A562

No. 1652: a, Rear view of saddle. b, Side view of saddle. c, Front view of saddle. d, Stirrup. e, Four pieces of tack. f, Two pieces of tack.

**Litho. & Embossed with Foil Application**

**2001, Apr. 2** ***Perf. 13¾***
**1652** A562 300d Sheet of 6, #a-f 22.00 22.00

### Miniature Sheet

Fight Against American Aggression — A563

No. 1653: a, Exploding jet. b, American jet. c, Pilot. d, American plane shooting missile. e, Parachute. f, Airplanes. g, Child crying. h, Palm tree, explosion. i, Missiles. j, Broken egg. k, Teddy bear. l, Clock. m, Explosion in city. n, Man rescuing casualty. o, Man holding child casualty. p, Family fleeing.

**2001, Apr. 15 Litho.** ***Perf. 13¼***
**1653** A563 100d Sheet of 16, #a-p *13.00 13.00*

Desertification Project — A564

No. 1654: a, Man with hoe (30x39mm). b, Men near stream (60x39mm). c, Camels (30x39mm).

**2001, June 26 Litho.** ***Perf. 13¼***
**1654** A564 250d Horiz. strip of 3, #a-c 12.00 12.00

Miniature Sheet

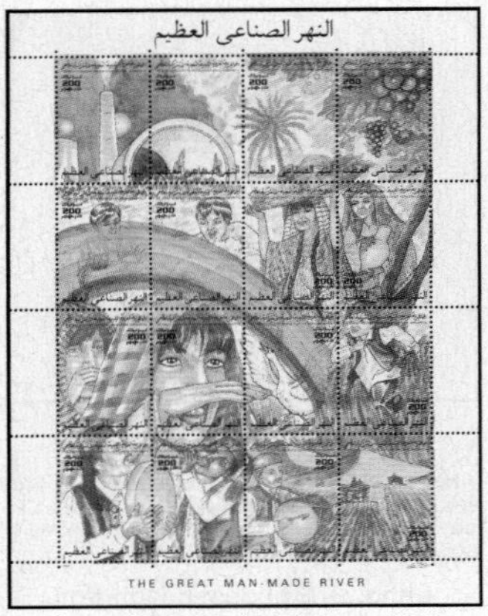


Great Man-Made River — A565

No. 1655: a, Smokestack. b, Pipeline and flags. c, Palm tree, fruit. d, Grapes. e, Clothed boy, rainbow. f, Bathing boy, rainbow. g, Woman carrying fruit. h, Woman holding jug. i, Woman with red and black headdress. j, Woman with green striped headdress. k, Duck, rainbow. l, Boy running. m, Drummer hitting drum with hand. n, Horn player. o, Drummer hitting drum with stick. p, Tractors in field.

**2001, Sept. 15 Litho. *Perf. 11¾***

**1655** A565 200d Sheet of 16, #a-p *29.00 29.00*

A566

Sept. 1 Revolution, 32nd Anniv. — A567

No. 1656: a, Col. Khadafy in headdress. b, Buildings, water pipeline, helicopters, tank, horsemen. c, Ship, airplane, camel rider. d, Tea drinkers. e, Children. f, Pillars, antelopes, woman. g, Man walking, camel rider. h, Camels, birds. i, Woman with container. j, Sword fight. k, Man and camel rider. l, Camels, pipeline worker, fruit. m, Potter. n, Musicians and weaver. o, Artisan. p, Col. Khadafy with clasped hands.

No. 1657, 300d, Col. Khadafy, pipeline and fruit (gold background). No. 1658, 300d, Col. Khadafy, pipeline and fruit (silver background).

**Litho. and Hologram**

**2001, Sept. 1 *Perf. 13¼***

**1656** A566 100d Sheet of 16, #a-p *27.50 27.50*

*q.* Booklet pane, #a-p, litho. *27.50* —

Complete booklet, #1656q *27.50*

**Souvenir Sheets**

**Litho. & Embossed With Foil Application**

**1657-1658** A567 Set of 2 *5.50 5.50*

Intl. Day of the Orphan — A568

Panel color: 100d, Blue. 200d, Red violet. 300d, Olive green.

**2001, Oct. 1 Litho. *Perf. 14¾x14½***

**1659-1661** A568 Set of 3 9.00 9.00

Health Care — A569

Arabic inscription color: 200d, Green. 300d, Yellow orange.

**2001, Dec. 1 Litho. *Perf. 14***

**1662-1663** A569 Set of 2 6.50 6.50

Miniature Sheet

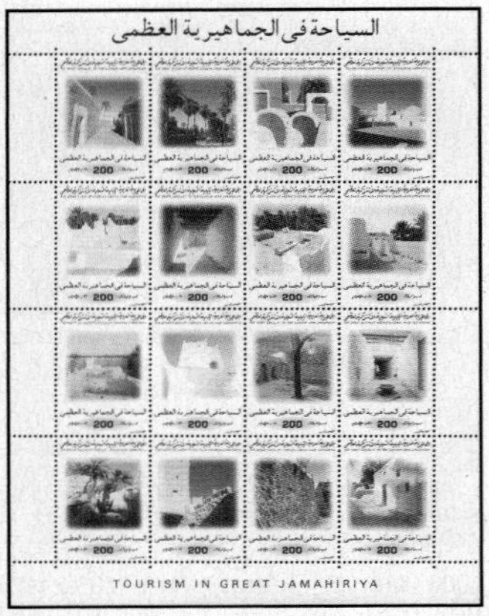


Tourism — A570

Various tourist attractions.

**2002, May 1 *Perf. 11¾***

**1664** A570 200d Sheet of 16, #a-p *52.50 52.50*

Intl. Customs Day — A571

Designs: 200d, 400d.

**2002, July 1 *Perf. 14***

**1665-1666** A571 Set of 2 8.25 8.25

A572

Sept. 1 Revolution, 33rd Anniv. — A573

No. 1667: a, Col. Khadafy. b, Airplanes. c, Camel rider, woman pouring tea. d, Artisans. e, Bulldozer, building. f, Chemist, oil rig. g, Ships. h, Doctors and patients. i, Technician at industrial plant. j, Man at computer, k, Man, spigot, water pipeline, crane. l, Chemist, man at microscope. m, Television camera and technician. n, Fruit, vegetables, grain combine. o, Spear carriers, musician. p, Map of Africa, musicians.

No. 1668, 300d, Col. Khadafy, map of Africa (gold background). No. 1669, 300d, Col. Khadafy, map of Africa (silver background).

**Litho. & Hologram**

**2002, Sept. 1 *Perf. 13¼***

**1667** A572 100d Sheet of 16, #a-p *22.50 22.50*

*q.* Booklet pane, #a-p, litho. *40.00* —

Complete booklet, #1667q *50.00*

**Souvenir Sheets**

**Litho. & Embossed With Foil Application**

**1668-1669** A573 Set of 2 *8.00 8.00*

Universal Declaration of Human Rights, 50th Anniv. — A576

Panel color: 250d, Red orange. 500d, Blue green.

**2002, Nov. 1 Litho. *Perf. 14***

**1672-1673** A576 Set of 2 9.50 9.50

Universal Postal Union, 125th Anniv. — A577

Panel color: 200d, Blue. 250d, Red violet.

**2002, Dec. 1**

**1674-1675** A577 Set of 2 5.50 5.50

A580

September 1 Revolution, 34th Anniv. — A581

No. 1679: a, 300d, Doctors and microscope (30x40mm). b, 300d, Nurses studying anatomy (30x40mm). c, 300d, Mother and child (30x40mm). d, 300d, Soldiers, white flag (30x40mm). e, 500d, Teachers, students, building (60x40mm). f, 500d, Helicopter, pilot, women, nurse and patients (60x40mm). g, 500d, Marching band, soldiers in vehicle (60x40mm). h, 1000d, Col. Khadafy, airplane, satellite dish.

**2003, May 20 Litho. *Perf. 12***

**1679** A580 Sheet of 8, #a-h *22.50 22.50*

**Souvenir Sheet**

**Litho. & Embossed With Foil Application**

**1680** A581 2000d multi *17.00 17.00*

September 1 Revolution, 35th Anniv. A582

Background color: 750d, Gray green. 1000d, Yellow green.

**2004 Litho. *Perf. 13***

**1681-1682** A582 Set of 2 4.50 4.50

Khairi Khaled Nuri (1943-2004), Philatelist — A583

**2004 Litho. & Hologram *Perf. 13¼***

**1683** A583 500d multi 2.00 2.00

People's Authority Declaration, 27th Anniv. A584

Color of rays: 400d, Yellow brown. 1000d, Blue green.

**2004** **Litho.** ***Perf. 13***
**1684-1685** A584 Set of 2 *12.00 12.00*

1st Communication and Information Technology Exhibition — A585

**2005, July 29** ***Perf. 13***
**1686** A585 750d multi *5.00 5.00*

**Souvenir Sheet**

***Imperf***

**1687** A585 1000d multi *6.00 6.00*

People's Authority Declaration, 28th Anniv. — A586

Delegates: 300d, Seated. 1000d, Voting.

**2005** ***Perf. 13***
**1688-1689** A586 Set of 2 *12.00 12.00*

September 1 Revolution, 36th Anniv. A587

Background color: 750d, Yellow orange. 1000d, Blue.

**2005**
**1690-1691** A587 Set of 2 *15.00 15.00*

Miniature Sheet

Total Solar Eclipse of March 29, 2006 — A588

No. 1692 — Eclipse and: a, Band of totality over map of Libya. b, Buildings, map of Libya. c, Altitude and duration figures. d, Stylized fish, camel, cactus, palm tree and Libyan. e, Saddled camel. f, Camels and riders.

**2006, Mar. 29**
**1692** A588 250d Sheet of 6, #a-f *12.50 12.50*

People's Authority Declaration, 29th Anniv. A589

Wheat ear, flag, fist and torch with background color of: 400d, Yellow. 1000d, Blue.

**2006, Nov. 1**
**1693-1694** A589 Set of 2 *11.00 11.00*

September 1 Revolution, 37th Anniv. — A590

**2006**
**1695** A590 1000d multi *8.00 8.00*

Famous African Leaders — A591

Map of Africa and: No. 1696, 500d, Gamal Abdel Nasser (1918-70), Egyptian President. No. 1697, 500d, Kwame Nkrumah (1909-72), President of Ghana. No. 1698, 500d, Ahmed Ben Bella, President of Algeria. No. 1699, 500d, Patrice Lumumba (1925-61), Congolese Prime Minister. No. 1700, 500d, Kenneth Kaunda, President of Zambia. No. 1701, 500d, Julius Nyerere (1922-99), President of Tanzania. No. 1702, 500d, Modibo Keita (1915-77), President of Mali.

1000d, Map of Africa, Nasser, Nkrumah, Ben Bella, Lumumba, Kaunda, Nyerere and Keita, horiz.

**2007, Mar. 6** ***Perf. 12¾***
**1696-1702** A591 Set of 7 *32.50 32.50*
*1702a* Miniature sheet of 7, #1696-1702 *32.50 32.50*

**Size: 98x75mm**

***Imperf***

**1703** A591 1000d multi *8.00 8.00*

Third Communication and Information Technology Exhibition — A592

**2007, May 27** ***Perf. 13***
**1704** A592 750d multi *6.50 6.50*

Tripoli, Capital of Islamic Culture A593

**2007, June 16** **Litho.**
**1705** A593 500d multi *4.50 4.50*

Intl. Day Against Drug Abuse and Illicit Trafficking A594

**2007, June 26**
**1706** A594 750d multi *6.50 6.50*

People's Authority Declaration, 30th Anniv. A595

**2007, July 4**
**1707** A595 750d multi *6.50 6.50*

36th Tripoli Intl. Fair — A596

No. 1708: a, Ring (orange background). b, Pendant (green background). c, Ring (purple background).
Illustration reduced.

**2007, July 4** ***Perf. 13x13x13¼***
**1708** Strip of 3 *16.00 16.00*
*a.-c.* A596 500d Any single *3.50 3.00*

Printed in sheets containing 2 strips + 2 labels. Value, $32.50.

Mosque A597

**2007, Aug. 24** **Litho.** ***Perf. 13***
**1709** A597 500d multi *5.00 5.00*
*a.* Souvenir sheet of 1 *5.00 5.00*

African Soccer Federation, 50th Anniv. A598

**2007, Aug. 25**
**1710** A598 750d multi *6.50 6.50*

Values are for stamps with surrounding selvage.

September 1 Revolution, 38th Anniv. — A599

**2007, Sept. 1** **Litho.** ***Perf. 13***
**1711** A599 1000d multi *8.00 8.00*
*a.* Souvenir sheet of 1 *8.00 8.00*

Khadafy Project for African Women, Children and Youth A600

**2007, Sept. 9**
**1712** A600 500d multi *4.25 4.25*

Libyan Red Crescent Society, 50th Anniv. A601

Red Crescent emblem and: 500d, Red Crescent volunteers. 1000d, 50th anniversary emblem.

**2007** *Perf. 13*
**1713-1714** A601 Set of 2 *12.50 12.50*

People's Authority Declaration, 31st Anniv. — A602

Type I — Two dots and vertical line in Arabic inscription directly above second "A" in "Jamahiriya."
Type II — No dots or vertical line in Arabic inscription directly above second "A" in "Jamahiriya."

**2008, Mar. 2** **Litho.** *Perf. 13*
**1715** A602 500d multi, type I *50.00 50.00*
*a.* Type II *4.50 4.50*

37th Tripoli International Fair — A603

No. 1716: a, Emblems, colored rectangles. b, Emblems. c, Emblems, buildings, displays.
Illustration reduced.

**2008, Apr. 2** *Perf. 13x12¾*
**1716** A603 500d Horiz. strip of 3, #a-c *13.00 13.00*

Printed in sheets of 6 containing two of each stamp.

Worldwide Fund for Nature (WWF) A604

Rueppell's fox: No. 1717, Head. No. 1718, Walking. No. 1719, Curled up. No. 1720, Sitting.

**2008, May 1** *Perf. 12*
**1717** A604 750f multi 1.50 1.50
*a.* Imperf. 6.00 6.00
**1718** A604 750f multi 1.50 1.50
*a.* Imperf. 6.00 6.00
**1719** A604 750f multi 1.50 1.50
*a.* Imperf. 6.00 6.00
**1720** A604 750f multi 1.50 1.50
*a.* Imperf. 6.00 6.00
*b.* Horiz. strip of 4, #1717-1720 8.00 8.00
*c.* Horiz. strip of 4, #1717a-1720a 35.00 35.00

Fourth Telecommunications and Information Technology Exhibition — A605

**2008, May 25** *Perf. 13*
**1721** A605 1000d multi 6.75 6.75

Gamal Abdel Nasser (1918-70), Egyptian President A606

**2008, July 23**
**1722** A606 500d multi 5.00 5.00

Egyptian Revolution, 56th anniv.

Khadafy 6+6 Mediterranean Project — A607

**2008, July 27**
**1723** A607 750d multi *5.00 5.00*

Tenth Meeting of Leaders and Heads of State of Community of Sahel-Sahara Countries — A608

**2008, Aug. 3**
**1724** A608 1000d multi *6.00 6.00*

Libyan Participation in 2008 Summer Olympics, Beijing A609

**2008, Aug. 18**
**1725** A609 1000d multi 8.00 8.00

September 1 Revolution, 39th Anniv. — A610

Col. Khadafy with denomination in: No. 1726, White. No. 1727, Green.

**2008, Sept. 1** *Perf. 13x12¾*
**1726** A610 1000d multi *8.00 8.00*

**Souvenir Sheet**

**1727** A610 1000d multi *8.00 8.00*

Total Mobile Phone Penetration in Libya A611

**2008, Sept. 11** *Perf. 13*
**1728** A611 750d multi 6.00 6.00

Fourth Intl. Waatasemu Women's Competition for Koran Memorization — A612

**2008, Sept. 23**
**1729** A612 750d multi 5.00 5.00

Koran Exhibition A613

**2008, Sept. 26**
**1730** A613 500d multi 3.50 3.50

People's Authority Declaration, 32nd Anniv. — A614

**2009, Mar. 9**
**1731** A614 500d multi 3.00 3.00

Support for Gaza Palestinians A615

**2009, May 7**
**1732** A615 1000d multi *5.00 5.00*

American Aggression Against Libya — A616

**2009, May 14** **Litho.** *Perf. 13*
**1733** A616 500d multi *4.00 4.00*

Fifth Telecommunications and Information Technology Exhibition — A617

**2009, May 30**
**1734** A617 500d multi 3.00 3.00

Omar Bongo (1935-2009), President of Gabon A618

**2009, June 20** **Litho.** *Perf. 13*
**1735** A618 750d multi 3.00 3.00

16th Mediterranean Games, Pescara, Italy — A619

**2009, June 26**
**1736** A619 500d multi 3.00 3.00

Jerusalem, Capital of Arab Culture — A620

**2009, Aug. 3**
**1737** A620 1000d multi 4.50 4.50

25th African Men's Basketball Championships, Libya — A621

**2009**

**1738** A621 500d multi 3.00 3.00

Souvenir Sheet

September 1 Revolution, 40th Anniv. — A622

No. 1739 — Col. Khadafy and background color of: a, 400d, Yellow. b, 600d, White. c, 750d, Green.

**2009**

**1739** A622 Sheet of 3, #a-c 7.50 7.50

Col. Khadafy, Map of Africa and African Union Emblem — A623

**Litho. & Embossed With Foil Application**

**2009** ***Serpentine Die Cut 11***

**Self-Adhesive**

**1740** A623 1000d multi 4.50 4.50

**Souvenir Sheet**

**1741** A623 2000d multi 9.00 9.00

First Al Fateh Futsal (Indoor Soccer) Contintental Cup Tournament A624

**2009, Oct. 12** **Litho.** ***Perf. 13***

**1742** A624 500d multi 1.50 1.50

Pan-African Postal Union, 30th Anniv. — A625

**2010, Jan. 18**

**1743** A625 500d multi 1.50 1.50

People's Authority Declaration, 33rd Anniv. — A626

**Litho. With Foil Application**

**2010, Mar. 2** ***Serpentine Die Cut 10***

**Self-Adhesive**

**1744** A626 500d multi 1.50 1.50

22nd Session of the Council of the League of Arab States, Sirt — A627

***Serpentine Die Cut 10***

**2010, Mar. 27** **Self-Adhesive**

**1745** A627 500d multi 1.50 1.50

Organization of Petroleum Exporting Countries, 50th Anniv. — A628

**2010, June 1** **Litho.** ***Perf. 13***

**1746** A628 1000d multi 2.75 2.75

Evacuation of US Forces From Bases in Libya, 40th Anniv. A629

**2010, June 9**

**1747** A629 1000d multi 3.00 3.00

Libyan Revolution After 40 Years — A630

No. 1748: a, Nationalization of banks and insurance companies. b, Nationalization of the oil sector. c, Declaration of the People's Revolution, 1973 d, Arab Republics Union. e, Italian evacuation from Libyan soil. f, Evacuation of American troops from Libyan soil. g, Evacuation of British troops from Libyan soil. h, Dawn of Great A-Fatah, 1969. i, Al-Fatah, an industrial revolution. j, Huge residential projects. k, Al-Fatah, an agricultural revolution. l, Establishment of the largest electricity networks. m, Establishment of roads network in Great Jamahiriya. n, Al-Fatah scientific revolution. o, Comprehensive health welfare. p, Al-Fatah, an Islamic revolution. q, Defining death line. r, The great Man-made River builder. s, Wajda City Agreement, 1984. t, Producer's revolution, 1978. u, The Green Book. v, The birth of first Jamahiriya in history, 1977. w, Student's revolution, 1976. x, Tunisia-Libya Jerba Unity Agreement. y, The African Arab Union, Sept. 9, 1999. z, By the Community of Sahel and Saharan States. aa, Break of the injustice embargo against Great Jamahiriya. ab, Demolition of borders. ac, The Arab Magreb Union, 1989. ad, Great Green Charter for Human Rights. ae, Demolition of jails. af, Courageous response to the failed NATO aggression. ag, The 40th anniversary of the 1st September Revolution. ah, Moammar Khadafy, heart of the world. ai, The return of the political hostage A. B. Almagrahi. aj, Italian apology to Libya about the Colonial period. ak, Moammar Khadafy, the king of Africa kings. al, Revolution of telecommunication and technology. am, The establishment of huge fleet maritime transports. an, Emancipation of women lost by the Great Al-Fatah Revolution.

**Litho. With Foil Application**

***Serpentine Die Cut 10***

**2010, Aug. 23** **Self-Adhesive**

**1748** Sheet of 40 57.50

*a.-an.* A630 400d Any single 1.40 1.40

Great Green Document of Human Rights, 22nd Anniv. — A631

Dr. Martin Luther King, Jr., civil rights marchers, and scroll with: 1500d, Arabic text. 2000d, English text.

**2010, Aug, 28** **Litho.** ***Perf. 13***

**1749-1750** A631 Set of 2 15.00 15.00

Miniature Sheets

Sept. 23, 2009 Speech of Col. Khadafy to United Nations Security Council, 1st Anniv. — A633

No. 1753, 1000d — Map of world, Col. Khadafy, U.N. emblem, text of speech in Arabic with: a, First line of text 53mm, second line of text 47mm. b, First line of text 68mm. c, First line of text 53mm, second line of text 52mm. d, First line of text 44mm, second line of text 42mm. e, First line of text 61mm. f, First line of text 45mm, second line of text 58mm.

No. 1754, 1000d — Map of world, Col. Khadafy, U.N. emblem, text of speech in English starting with: a, "Brothers, you can in our political life . . ." b, "In order that colonization is not repeated . . ." c, "The solution to achieve democracy . . ." d, "The International Court of Justice . . ." e, "Africa as of now . . ." f, "The International Atomic Energy Agency . . ."

No. 1755, 1000d — Map of world, Col. Khadafy, U.N. emblem, text of speech in French starting with: a, "Vous voyez, mes frères . . ." b, "Pour eviter une nouvelle colonisation . . ." c, "Donc la solution . . ." d, "La Cour Internationale de Justice . . ." e, "L'Afrique a besoin . . ." f, "L'Agence Internationale de l'Energie . . ."

**2010, Sept. 23** **Litho.** ***Perf. 13***

**Sheets of 6, #a-f**

**1753-1755** A633 Set of 3 60.00 60.00

February 17, 2011 Revolution A635

Denominations: 250d, 500d, 750d, 1000d, 5000d.

**2011** **Litho.** ***Perf. 13¼***

**1757-1761** A635 Set of 5 22.50 22.50

February 17 Revolution, 1st Anniv. A636

No. 1762: a, Woman in burqa, man waving flag. b, Crowd with flag. c, Flowers and emblem. No. 1763, Map of Libya, flag in circle.

**2012, Feb. 17** ***Perf. 13***

**1762** Horiz. strip of 3 6.00 6.00

*a.-b.* A636 500d Either single 1.50 1.50

*c.* A636 1000d multi 3.00 3.00

**Souvenir Sheet**

**1763** A636 1000d multi 3.00 3.00

Children's Drawings A637

No. 1764: a, Tree with colors of Libyan flag, flowers. b, Flowers and trees. c, People and various animals. d, Child with flag, house. e, Boat with flag, palm tree.

**2012, Sept. 12** *Perf. 12¾*

**1764** Horiz. strip of 5 8.25 8.25
- *a.* A637 100d multi .40 .40
- *b.* A637 200d multi .80 .80
- *c.* A637 250d multi 1.00 1.00
- *d.* A637 500d multi 2.00 2.00
- *e.* A637 1000d multi 4.00 4.00

Independence, 61st Anniv. — A638

National colors, "61," and: 500d, Crescent and star. 1000d, Olive branch, crescent and star.

**2012, Dec. 24** *Perf. 13¼*

**1765-1766** A638 Set of 2 16.50 16.50

Monument to the Foundation of the Libyan Army — A639

**2013, Feb. 17**

**1767** A639 500d multi 6.50 6.50

A640

A641

February 17 Revolution, 2nd Anniv. A642

**2013, Feb. 17** *Perf. 13*

**1768** Horiz. strip of 3 19.50 19.50
- *a.* A640 250d multi 2.75 2.75
- *b.* A641 500d multi 5.50 5.50
- *c.* A642 1000d multi 11.00 11.00

Miniature Sheet

Tripoli International Fair — A643

No. 1769: a, Necklace and pendants. b, Fair emblem. c, Triangular pendant. d, Semi-circular pendant. e, Pin. f, Earrings.

**2013, Apr. 2**

**1769** A643 500d Sheet of 6, #a-f 19.50 19.50

Intl. Letter Writing Competition for Young People A644

**2013, May 4** **Litho.** *Perf. 13*

**1770** A644 1000d multi 6.75 6.75

February 17 Revolution, 2nd Anniv. — A645

Libyan flag with background color of: 5000d, Light blue. 10,000d, Light orange.

**Litho. & Embossed With Foil Application**

**2013, May 27** *Serpentine Die Cut 10*

**Self-Adhesive**

**1771** A645 5000d multi 24.00 24.00
**1772** A645 10,000d multi 47.50 47.50

Campaign Against Desertification A646

**2013, June 17** **Litho.** *Perf. 13¼*

**1773** A646 500d multi 10.00 10.00

Libyan Parliament Building, Al Bayda, 50th Anniv. (in 2014) — A647

**2013, Aug. 20** **Litho.** *Perf. 13¼*

**1774** A647 500d multi 4.25 4.25

Benghazi Lighthouse A648

**2013, Aug. 20** **Litho.** *Perf. 13*

**1775** A648 1000d multi 11.00 11.00

Miniature Sheet

Dinosaurs — A651

No. 1779: a, Triceratops. b, Head of dinosaur, building ruins. c, Tyrannosaurus, sky in background. d, Tyrannosaurus, head upright, building ruins in background, no sky. e, Dinosaurs and flowers. f, Tyrannosaurus, head lowered, building ruins in background, no sky.

**2013, Dec. 11** **Litho.** *Perf. 12¾*

**1779** A651 250d Sheet of 6, #a-f 19.00 19.00

Independence, 62nd Anniv. — A652

No. 1780: a, King Idris, Libyan flag. b, Emblem. c, Horseman carrying flag, King Idris, Omar Mukhtar, map of Libya.

**2013, Dec. 24** **Litho.** *Perf. 13*

**1780** Horiz. strip of 3 13.00 13.00
- *a.* A652 250d multi 1.75 1.75
- *b.* A652 750d multi 5.00 5.00
- *c.* A652 1000d multi 6.50 6.50

National Post Day — A653

**2013, Dec. 24** **Litho.** *Perf. 13¼*

**1781** A653 100d multi 7.75 7.75

2013 National Stamp Exhibition A654

**2013, Dec. 25** **Litho.** *Perf. 13*

**1782** A654 100d multi 4.25 4.25

February 17th Revolution, 3rd Anniv. A655

No. 1783: a, Stylized people and emblem. b, Libyan people and flags. c, Torch and map of Libya.

**2014, Feb. 17** **Litho.** *Perf. 13*

**1783** Horiz. strip of 3 16.50 16.50
- *a.* A655 500d multi 3.75 3.75
- *b.* A655 750d multi 5.50 5.50
- *c.* A655 1000d multi 7.25 7.25

Libya, Champions of 2014 African Nations Soccer Championships — A656

No. 1784: a, 500d, Libyan team, trophy. b, 750d, Trophy, Libyan Soccer Federation emblem, map of Libya.

**2014, Feb. 17** **Litho.** *Perf. 13*

**1784** A656 Horiz. pair, #a-b 7.75 7.75

Miniature Sheet

Vegetables — A657

No. 1786: a, Garlic. b, Onions. c, Tomatoes. d, Peppers. e, Eggplants. f, Potatoes.

**2014, Feb. 24** **Litho.** *Perf. 12¾*

**1786** A657 500d Sheet of 6, #a-f 19.00 19.00

Scouting in Libya, 60th Anniv. — A658

No. 1787: a, 500d, Scouts. b, 1000d, Ali Khalefa Zaidi (1909-66), scouting leader.

**2014, Feb. 27** **Litho.** *Perf. 13*

**1787** A658 Horiz. pair, #a-b 19.00 19.00

Miniature Sheet

2014 Tripoli International Fair — A659

No. 1788: a, Bazin with meat. b, Fair emblem, map of Libya. c, Couscous with meat. d, Bazin with fish. e, Fair emblems. f, Couscous with fish.

**2014, Apr. 2** **Litho.** *Perf. 13*

**1788** A659 500d Sheet of 6, #a-f 19.00 19.00

Castles — A660

Designs: 100d, Sebha Castle. 1000d, Murzuq Castle.

**2014, June 26** **Litho.** *Perf. 13*

**1789-1790** A660 Set of 2 9.00 9.00

A661

A662

Mosques
A663

**2014, July 20 Litho. *Perf. 13***
**1791** Horiz. strip of 3 11.50 11.50
*a.* A661 500d multi 3.75 3.75
*b.* A662 500d multi 3.75 3.75
*c.* A663 500d multi 3.75 3.75

Euromed Postal Emblem and Mediterranean Sea — A664

**2014, July 28 Litho. *Perf. 13***
**1792** A664 500d multi 9.00 9.00

Libyan Army, 63rd Anniv.
A665

**2014, Aug. 9 Litho. *Perf. 13***
**1793** A665 500d multi 7.75 7.75

Liberation of Tripoli, 3rd Anniv. — A666

**2014, Aug. 20 Litho. *Perf. 13***
**1794** A666 500d multi 10.00 10.00

Martyr's Day — A667

**2014, Sept. 16 Litho. *Perf. 13***
**1795** A667 500d multi 7.75 7.75

Libya Insurance Company, 50th Anniv.
A668

**2014, Dec. 24 Litho. *Perf. 13***
**1796** A668 1000d multi 10.00 10.00

Independence, 63rd Anniv. — A669

**2014, Dec. 24 Litho. *Perf. 13***
**1797** A669 1000d multi 7.75 7.75

Intl. Children's Day
A670

No. 1798 — UNICEF emblem and: a, Scout, tent, butterflies, Libyan flag. b, Hands. c, Scout, butterflies, mushrooms.

**2014 Litho. *Perf. 13***
**1798** Horiz. strip of 3 14.00 14.00
*a.* A670 250d multi 1.75 1.75
*b.* A670 750d multi 5.25 5.25
*c.* A670 1000d multi 7.00 7.00

A671

A672

February 17 Revolution, 4th Anniv.
A673

**2015, Feb. 17 Litho. *Perf. 13***
**1799** Horiz. strip of 3 15.00 15.00
*a.* A671 1000d multi 5.00 5.00
*b.* A672 1000d multi 5.00 5.00
*c.* A673 1000d multi 5.00 5.00

Boats in Harbor
A674

**2015, July 9 Litho. *Perf. 13***
**1800** A674 750d multi 7.75 7.75

Miniature Sheet

2015 Tripoli International Fair — A675

No. 1801: a, Pot with handles, rope and wide bottom. b, Map of Libya. c, Pot with narrow bottom and two handles connected by rope. d, Mortar and pestle. e, Pot with three handles. f, Pot suspended from rope.

**2015, Apr. 2 Litho. *Perf. 13***
**1801** A675 500d Sheet of 6, #a-f 15.50 15.50

Martyr's Day — A676

Omar Mukhtar (1858-1931), resistance leader, and: 500d, Horsemen, eagle, flowers. 1000d, Libyan flag.

**2015, Sept. 16 Litho. *Perf. 13***
**1802** A676 500d multi 6.50 6.50

**Size: 120x80mm**

***Imperf***

**1803** A676 1000d multi 9.00 9.00

Miniature Sheet

Flowers — A677

No. 1804: a, Narcissi. b, Ophrys fuciflora. c, Calla lily. d, Cestrum nocturnum. e, Bird of paradise. f, Jasmine.

**2015, Nov. 1 Litho. *Perf. 13***
**1804** A677 500d Sheet of 6, #a-f 17.00 17.00

UNESCO, 70th Anniv. — A678

**2015, Nov. 16 Litho. *Perf. 13***
**1805** A678 500d multi 6.50 6.50

International Children's Day — A679

**2015, Nov. 20 Litho. *Perf. 13***
**1806** A679 500d multi 6.50 6.50

Architecture — A680

Designs: No. 1807, 750d, Nalut Archaeological Site. No. 1808, 750d, Building in Ghadames.

**2015, Dec. 10 Litho. *Perf. 13***
**1807-1808** A680 Set of 2 12.00 12.00

Independence Day — A681

**2015, Dec. 24 Litho. *Perf. 13***
**1809** A681 500d multi 6.50 6.50

Stamp Day — A682

**2015, Dec. 24 Litho. *Perf. 13***
**1810** A682 500d multi 6.50 6.50

Dates — A683

**2015, Dec. 31 Litho. *Perf. 13½***

**Background Color**

**1811** A683 500d yel grn 2.00 2.00
**1812** A683 1000d lilac 4.00 4.00
**1813** A683 2000d bistre yellow 8.00 8.00
**1814** A683 5000d turq blue 20.00 20.00
**1815** A683 10,000d brt green 40.00 40.00
*Nos. 1811-1815 (5)* 74.00 74.00

Second National Stamp Exhibition A684

**2016, Jan. 30 Litho. *Perf. 13***
**1816** A684 1000d multi 9.00 9.00

February 17 Revolution, 5th Anniv. A685

No. 1817 — Laurel branches and: a, Flag and map of Libya. b, Handshake. c, Map of Libya.

**2016, Feb. 17 Litho. *Perf. 13***
**1817** Horiz. strip of 3 12.00 12.00
***a.-c.*** A685 500d Any single 4.00 4.00

Martyr's Day A686

Omar Mukhtar (1858-1931), resistance leader, and: 500d, Building. 1000d, Map of Libya, building, Mukhtar on horse.

**2016, Sept. 16 Litho. *Perf. 13***
**1818** A686 500d multi 7.75 7.75

**Size: 110x76mm**

***Imperf***

**1819** A686 1000d multi 13.00 13.00

International Children's Day — A687

No. 1820 — UNICEF emblem and: a, Two children with sign. b, Three children holding pictures. c, Child reading book.

**2016, Nov. 20 Litho. *Perf. 13***
**1820** Horiz. strip of 3 10.50 10.50
***a.-c.*** A687 500d Any single 3.50 3.50

Independence Day — A688

**2016, Dec. 24 Litho. *Perf. 13***
**1821** A688 1000d multi 7.75 7.75

February 17 Revolution, 6th Anniv. — A689

No. 1822: a, 500d, Map and flag of Libya. b, 1000d, Map of Libya in circle.

**2017, Feb. 17 Litho. *Perf. 13***
**1822** A689 Horiz. pair, #a-b 10.00 10.00

Children's Day — A690

No. 1823: a, Map of Libya, children, flag, butterflies, flowers. b, Map of Libya, flowers, children with balloons. c, Boy with kites and camel.

**2017, Mar. 21 Litho. *Perf. 13¼x13***
**1823** A690 500d Horiz. strip of 3, #a-c 11.50 11.50

**Miniature Sheet**

2017 Tripoli International Fair — A691

No. 1824: a, Bowl with lid. b, Emblem. c, Lidded bowl with handles. d, Stirrups. e, Coffee pot. f, Candleholder.

**2017, Apr. 2 Litho. *Perf. 13***
**1824** A691 500d Sheet of 6, #a-f 14.50 14.50

Olives and Olive Tree A693

**2017, Aug. 6 Litho. *Perf. 13***
**1826** A693 5000d yel & multi 14.50 14.50
**1827** A693 10,000d rose lil & multi 29.00 29.00

---

## SEMI-POSTAL STAMPS

Many issues of Italy and Italian Colonies include one or more semipostal denominations. To avoid splitting sets, these issues are generally listed as regular postage, semipostals or airmails, etc.

Semi-Postal Stamps of Italy Overprinted

**1915-16 Wmk. 140 *Perf. 14***
**B1** SP1 10c + 5c rose 3.50 *14.00*
***a.*** Double overprint 825.00
**B2** SP2 15c + 5c slate 30.00 *24.00*
**B3** SP2 20c + 5c org ('16) 4.25 *30.00*
*Nos. B1-B3 (3)* 37.75 *68.00*

No. B2 with Additional Surcharge

**1916, Mar.**
**B4** SP2 20c on 15c + 5c slate 30.00 *30.00*
***a.*** Double surcharge 850.00

View of Port, Tripoli SP1

Designs: B5, B6, View of port, Tripoli. B7, B8, Arch of Marcus Aurelius. B9, B10, View of Tripoli.

**1927, Feb. 15 Litho.**
**B5** SP1 20c + 5c brn vio & black 3.50 *15.00*
**B6** SP1 25c + 5c bl grn & black 3.50 *15.00*
**B7** SP1 40c + 10c blk brn & black 3.50 *15.00*
**B8** SP1 60c + 10c org brn & black 3.50 *15.00*
**B9** SP1 75c + 20c red & black 3.50 *15.00*
**B10** SP1 1.25 l + 20c bl & blk 24.00 *42.50*
*Nos. B5-B10 (6)* 41.50 117.50

First Sample Fair, Tripoli. Surtax aided fair. See Nos. EB1-EB2.

View of Tripoli — SP2

Knights of Malta Castle SP3

Designs: 50c+20c, Date palm. 1.25 l+20c, Camel riders. 2.55 l+50c, View of Tripoli. 5 l+1 l, Traction well.

**1928, Feb. 20 Wmk. 140 *Perf. 14***
**B11** SP2 30c + 20c mar & blk 3.50 *15.00*
**B12** SP2 50c + 20c bl grn & blk 3.50 *15.00*
**B13** SP2 1.25 l + 20c red & blk 3.50 *15.00*
**B14** SP3 1.75 l + 20c bl & blk 3.50 *15.00*
**B15** SP3 2.55 l + 50c brn & blk 7.00 *22.50*
**B16** SP3 5 l + 1 l pur & blk 9.50 *35.00*
*Nos. B11-B16 (6)* 30.50 *117.50*

2nd Sample Fair, Tripoli, 1928. The surtax was for the aid of the Fair.

Olive Tree — SP4

Herding SP5

Designs: 50c+20c, Dorcas gazelle. 1.25 l+20c, Peach blossoms. 2.55 l+50c, Camel caravan. 5 l+1 l, Oasis with date palms.

**1929, Apr. 7**
**B17** SP4 30c + 20c mar & blk 14.00 *27.50*
**B18** SP4 50c + 20c bl grn & blk 14.00 *27.50*
**B19** SP4 1.25 l + 20c scar & blk 14.00 *27.50*
**B20** SP5 1.75 l + 20c bl & blk 14.00 *27.50*
**B21** SP5 2.55 l + 50c yel brn & blk 14.00 *27.50*
**B22** SP5 5 l + 1 l pur & blk 125.00 *300.00*
*Nos. B17-B22 (6)* 195.00 *437.50*

3rd Sample Fair, Tripoli, 1929. The surtax was for the aid of the Fair.

Harvesting Bananas — SP6

Water Carriers SP7

Designs: 50c, Tobacco plant. 1.25 l, Venus of Cyrene. 2.55 l+45c, Black bucks. 5 l+1 l, Motor and camel transportation. 10 l+2 l, Rome pavilion.

**1930, Feb. 20 Photo.**
**B23** SP6 30c dark brown 4.25 *17.50*
**B24** SP6 50c violet 4.25 *17.50*
**B25** SP6 1.25 l deep blue 4.25 *17.50*
**B26** SP7 1.75 l + 20c scar 7.00 *26.00*
**B27** SP7 2.55 l + 45c dp grn 16.00 *37.50*
**B28** SP7 5 l + 1 l dp org 16.00 *50.00*
**B29** SP7 10 l + 2 l dk vio 16.00 *62.50*
*Nos. B23-B29 (7)* 67.75 *228.50*

4th Sample Fair at Tripoli, 1930. The surtax was for the aid of the Fair.

Statue of Ephebus — SP8

Exhibition Pavilion SP9

Designs: 25c, Arab musician. 50c, View of Zeughet. 1.25 l, Snake charmer. 1.75 l+25c, Windmill. 2.75 l+45c, "Zaptie." 5 l+1 l, Mounted Arab.

**1931, Mar. 8**
**B30** SP8 10c black brown 5.50 *9.75*
**B31** SP8 25c green 5.50 *9.75*
**B32** SP8 50c purple 5.50 *9.75*
**B33** SP8 1.25 l blue 5.50 *14.00*
**B34** SP8 1.75 l + 25c car rose 5.50 *16.00*
**B35** SP8 2.75 l + 45c org 5.50 *24.00*

**B36** SP8 5 l + 1 l dl vio 15.00 *35.00*
**B37** SP9 10 l + 2 l brn 50.00 *70.00*
*Nos. B30-B37 (8)* 98.00 *188.25*
*Nos. B30-B37,C3,EB3 (10)* 104.90 229.75

Fifth Sample Fair, Tripoli. Surtax aided fair.

Papaya Tree
SP10

Dorcas Gazelle
SP12

Ar Tower, Mogadiscio
SP11

Designs: 10c, 50c, Papaya tree. 20c, 30c, Euphorbia abyssinica. 25c, Fig cactus. 75c, Mausoleum, Ghirza. 1.75 l+25c, Lioness. 5 l+1 l, Bedouin with camel.

**1932, Mar. 8**

**B38** SP10 10c olive brn 7.00 *16.00*
**B39** SP10 20c brown red 7.00 *16.00*
**B40** SP10 25c green 7.00 *16.00*
**B41** SP10 30c olive blk 7.00 *16.00*
**B42** SP10 50c dk violet 7.00 *16.00*
**B43** SP10 75c carmine 8.50 *16.00*
**B44** SP11 1.25 l dk blue 8.50 *24.00*
**B45** SP11 1.75 l + 25c ol brn 27.50 *77.50*
**B46** SP11 5 l + 1 l dp bl 27.50 *190.00*
**B47** SP12 10 l + 2 l brn violet 125.00 *350.00*
*Nos. B38-B47 (10)* 232.00 *737.50*
*Nos. B38-B47,C4-C7 (14)* 416.00 *1,168.*

Sixth Sample Fair, Tripoli. Surtax aided fair.

Ostrich — SP13

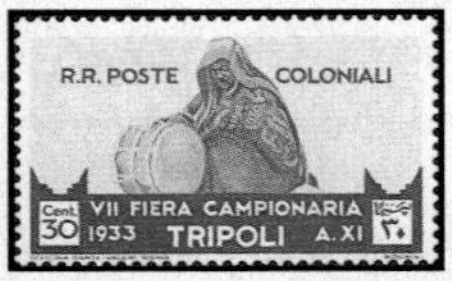


Arab Musician
SP14

Designs: 25c, Incense plant. 30c, Arab musician. 50c, Arch of Marcus Aurelius. 1.25 l, African eagle. 5 l+1 l, Leopard. 10 l+2.50 l, Tripoli skyline and fasces.

**1933, Mar. 2 Photo. Wmk. 140**

**B48** SP13 10c dp violet 37.50 42.50
**B49** SP13 25c dp green 21.00 *42.50*
**B50** SP14 30c org brn 21.00 *42.50*
**B51** SP13 50c purple 21.00 *42.50*
**B52** SP13 1.25 l dk blue 50.00 *77.50*
**B53** SP14 5 l + 1 l ol brn 110.00 *175.00*
**B54** SP13 10 l + 2.50 l car 110.00 *300.00*
*Nos. B48-B54 (7)* 370.50 *722.50*
*Nos. B48-B54,C8-C13 (13)* 481.50 *1,103.*

Seventh Sample Fair, Tripoli. Surtax aided fair.

Pomegranate Tree — SP15

Designs: 50c+10c, 2 l+50c, Musician. 75c+15c, 1.25 l+25c, Tribesman.

**1935, Feb. 16**

**B55** SP15 10c + 10c brn 1.75 *5.00*
**B56** SP15 20c + 10c rose red 1.75 *5.00*
**B57** SP15 50c + 10c pur 1.75 *5.00*
**B58** SP15 75c + 15c car 1.75 *5.00*
**B59** SP15 1.25 l + 25c dl blue 1.75 *5.00*
**B60** SP15 2 l + 50c ol grn 1.75 *12.50*
*Nos. B55-B60 (6)* 10.50 *37.50*
*Nos. B55-B60,C19-C24 (12)* 27.00 *108.00*

Ninth Sample Fair, Tripoli. Surtax aided fair.

## AIR POST STAMPS

Italy Nos. C3 and C5 Overprinted

**1928-29 Wmk. 140 *Perf. 14***

**C1** AP2 50c rose red 14.00 *27.50*
**C2** AP2 80c brn vio & brn ('29) 55.00 *77.50*

Airplane
AP1

**1931, Mar. 8 Photo. Wmk. 140**

**C3** AP1 50c blue 1.40 *14.00*

See note after No. B37.

Seaplane over Bedouin Camp
AP2

Designs: 50c, 1 l, Seaplane over Bedouin camp. 2 l+1 l, 5 l+2 l, Seaplane over Tripoli.

**1932, Mar. 1 *Perf. 14***

**C4** AP2 50c dark blue 15.00 *42.50*
**C5** AP2 1 l org brown 15.00 *42.50*
**C6** AP2 2 l + 1 l dk gray 29.00 *120.00*
**C7** AP2 5 l + 2 l car 125.00 *225.00*
*Nos. C4-C7 (4)* 207.50 *495.00*

See note after No. B47.

Seaplane Arriving at Tripoli
AP3

Designs: 50c, 2 l+50c, Seaplane arriving at Tripoli. 75c, 10 l+2.50 l, Plane over Tagiura. 1 l, 5 l+1 l, Seaplane leaving Tripoli.

**1933, Mar. 1**

**C8** AP3 50c dp green 11.00 *22.50*
**C9** AP3 75c carmine 11.00 *22.50*
**C10** AP3 1 l dk blue 11.00 *22.50*
**C11** AP3 2 l + 50c pur 18.00 *52.50*
**C12** AP3 5 l + 1 l org brn 30.00 *85.00*
**C13** AP3 10 l + 2.50 l gray blk 30.00 *175.00*
*Nos. C8-C13 (6)* 125.00 *390.00*

See note after No. B54.

Seaplane over Tripoli Harbor
AP4

Airplane and Camel — AP5

Designs: 50c, 5 l+1 l, Seaplane over Tripoli harbor. 75c, 10 l+2 l, Plane and minaret.

**1934, Feb. 17 Photo. Wmk. 140**

**C14** AP4 50c slate bl 14.00 *30.00*
**C15** AP4 75c red org 14.00 *30.00*
**C16** AP4 5 l + 1 l dp grn 125.00 *210.00*
**C17** AP4 10 l + 2 l dl vio 125.00 *210.00*
**C18** AP5 25 l + 3 l org brn 150.00 *300.00*
*Nos. C14-C18 (5)* 487.00 *900.00*

Eighth Sample Fair, Tripoli. Surtax aided fair. See Nos. CE1-CE2.

Plane and Ancient Tower — AP6

Camel Train
AP7

Designs: 25c+10c, 3 l+1.50 l, Plane and ancient tower. 50c+10c, 2 l+30c, Camel train. 1 l+25c, 10 l+5 l, Arab watching plane.

**1935, Apr. 12**

**C19** AP6 25c + 10c green 1.40 *5.50*
**C20** AP7 50c + 10c slate bl 1.40 *5.50*
**C21** AP7 1 l + 25c blue 1.40 *5.50*
**C22** AP7 2 l + 30c rose red 1.40 *9.50*
**C23** AP6 3 l + 1.50 l brn 1.40 *9.50*
**C24** AP7 10 l + 5 l dl vio 9.50 *35.00*
*Nos. C19-C24 (6)* 19.00 *81.50*

See note after No. B60.

Cyrenaica No. C6 Overprinted in Black

**1936, Oct.**

**C25** AP2 50c purple 24.00 .35

**Same on Tripolitania Nos. C8 and C12**

**1937**

**C26** AP1 50c rose carmine .70 .25
**C27** AP2 1 l deep blue 2.10 .85
Set, never hinged 7.00

See Nos. C45-C50.

Ruins of Odeon Theater, Sabrata
AP8

**1937, Mar. 15 Photo.**

**C28** AP8 50c dark violet 2.75 *7.00*
**C29** AP8 1 l vio black 2.75 *11.00*
Set, never hinged 13.50

Opening of a coastal road to the Egyptian frontier.

**Nos. C28-C29 Overprinted "XI FIERA DI TRIPOLI"**

**1937, Mar. 15**

**C30** AP8 50c dark violet 14.00 *35.00*
**C31** AP8 1 l violet blk 14.00 *35.00*
Set, never hinged 70.00

11th Sample Fair, Tripoli.

View of Tripoli — AP9

**1938, Mar. 12 *Perf. 14***

**C32** AP9 50c dk olive grn 1.40 *2.75*
**C33** AP9 1 l slate blue 1.40 *5.50*
Set, never hinged 7.00

12th Sample Fair, Tripoli.

Eagle Attacking Serpent — AP10

**1938, Apr. 25 Wmk. 140**

**C34** AP10 50c olive brown .35 *1.75*
**C35** AP10 1 l brn violet 1.00 *3.75*
Set, never hinged 3.25

Birth bimillenary Augustus Caesar (Octavianus), first Roman emperor.

Arab and Camel
AP11

Design: 50c, Fair entrance.

**1939, Apr. 12 Photo.**

**C36** AP11 25c green .70 *2.10*
**C37** AP11 50c olive brown .70 *2.10*
**C38** AP11 1 l rose violet 1.00 *2.75*
*Nos. C36-C38 (3)* 1.90 *6.70*
Set, never hinged 6.00

13th Sample Fair, Tripoli.

Plane Over Modern City
AP12

Design: 1 l, 5 l+2.50 l, Plane over oasis.

**1940, June 3**

**C39** AP12 50c brn blk .70 *.85*
**C40** AP12 1 l brn vio .70 *1.75*
**C41** AP12 2 l + 75c indigo 1.00 *7.00*
**C42** AP12 5 l + 2.50 l cop-per brn 1.00 *12.50*
*Nos. C39-C42 (4)* 4.10 *25.50*
Set, never hinged 8.50

Triennial Overseas Exposition, Naples.

Hitler, Mussolini and Inscription "Two Peoples, One War"
AP13

**1941, Apr. 24**
**C43** AP13 50c slate green 2.75 *42.50*
Never hinged 7.00

Rome-Berlin Axis.

### Cyrenaica No. C9 Overprinted in Black Like No. C25

**1941**
**C44** AP3 1 l black 12.50 *70.00*
Never hinged 30.00

### Same Overprint on Tripolitania Nos. C9-C11, C13-C15

**C45** AP1 60c red orange .70
**C46** AP1 75c deep blue .70 47.50
**C47** AP1 80c dull violet .70 100.00
**C48** AP2 1.20 l dark brown .70 140.00
**C49** AP2 1.50 l orange red .70 175.00
**C50** AP2 5 l green .70
*Nos. C45-C50 (6)* 4.20
*Set, never hinged* 10.00

**Catalogue values for unused stamps in this section, from this point to the end of the section, are for Never Hinged items.**

### United Kingdom of Libya

ICY Type of Regular Issue

***Perf. 14½x14***

**1965, Jan. 1 Litho. Unwmk.**
**C51** A60 50m blue, reddish lil & gold 1.90 .90
*a.* Souvenir sheet 5.00 5.00

No. C51a exists with simulated perfs.; same value.

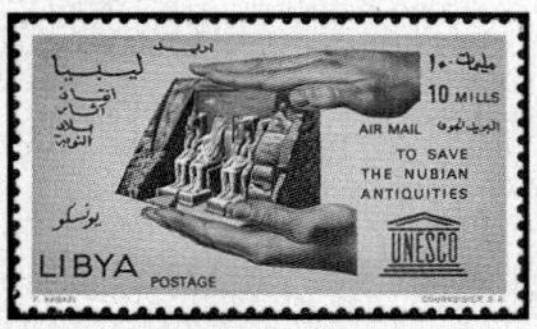


Hands Holding Facade of Abu Simbel — AP14

**1966, Jan. 1 Photo. *Perf. 11½***
**Granite Paper**
**C52** AP14 10m bis & dk brn .40 .25
*a.* Souvenir sheet of 4 2.00 3.75
**C53** AP14 15m gray grn & dk grn .50 .25
*a.* Souvenir sheet of 4 2.50 5.00
**C54** AP14 40m dl sal & dk brn 1.60 .65
*a.* Souvenir sheet of 4 6.50 13.00
*Nos. C52-C54 (3)* 2.50 1.15

UNESCO world campaign to save historic monuments in Nubia.

Inauguration of WHO Headquarters, Geneva — AP15

***Perf. 10x10½***

**1966, May 3 Litho. Unwmk.**
**C55** AP15 20m blk, yel & bl .25 .25
**C56** AP15 50m blk, yel grn & red .90 .65
**C57** AP15 65m blk, sal & brn red 1.40 1.40
*Nos. C55-C57 (3)* 2.55 2.30

Flag and Globe — AP16

**1966, Oct. 1 Photo. *Perf. 11½***
**Granite Paper**
**C58** AP16 25m multicolored .50 .40
**C59** AP16 60m multicolored 1.40 1.00
**C60** AP16 85m gray & multi 1.90 1.40
*Nos. C58-C60 (3)* 3.80 2.80

Inauguration of Kingdom of Libya Airlines, 1st anniv.

## AIR POST SPECIAL DELIVERY STAMPS

APSD1

**Wmk. 140**

**1934, Feb. 17 Photo. *Perf. 14***
**CE1** APSD1 2.25 l olive blk 55.00 *70.00*
**CE2** APSD1 4.50 l + 1 l gray blk 55.00 *70.00*
Set, never hinged 280.00

8th Sample Fair at Tripoli. The surtax was for the aid of the Fair.

## SPECIAL DELIVERY STAMPS

Special Delivery Stamps of Italy Overprinted

Two types of overprint. See note preceding No. 1 for descriptions.

**1915-16. Wmk. 140 *Perf. 14***
**E1** SD1 25c rose red, ovpt. type I 77.50 30.00
**E2** SD2 30c blue & rose, ovpt. type I 7.00 *30.00*
Set, never hinged 217.50

Issued: Nos. E1, E2, Nov. 1915.
For surcharges see Nos. E7-E8.

"Italia" SD3

No. E3

No. E4

No. E5

No. E6

Nos. E5-E6 bottom-corner denominations and words are reversed from Nos. E3-E4.

**1921-23 Engr. *Perf. 13½***
**E3** SD3 30c blue & rose 2.10 *7.00*
**E4** SD3 50c rose red & brn 4.25 *10.00*
**E5** SD3 60c dk red & brn ('23) 7.00 *15.00*
**E6** SD3 2 l dk bl & red ('23) 14.00 *27.50*
*Nos. E3-E6 (4)* 27.35 *59.50*
Set, never hinged 65.00

30c, 2 l inscribed "EXPRES."
For surcharges see Nos. E9-E12.

### Nos. E1-E2 Surcharged

**1922, June 1**
**E7** SD1 60c on 25c rose red 12.50 *17.50*
**E8** SD2 1.60 l on 30c bl & rose 15.00 *35.00*
Set, never hinged 67.50

### Nos. E5-E6 Surcharged in Blue or Red

No. E9

Nos. E10, E12

No. E11

**1926-36**
**E9** SD3 70c on 60c 7.50 *15.00*
**E10** SD3 2.50 l on 2 l (R) 14.00 *27.50*

***Perf. 11***
**E11** SD3 1.25 l on 60c 5.50 1.75
*a.* Perf. 14 ('36) 21.00 3.50
Never hinged 52.50
*b.* Black surcharge *105,000.* *18,000.*
**E12** SD3 2.50 l on 2 l (R) 240.00 *850.00*
*Nos. E9-E12 (4)* 267.00 *894.25*
Set, never hinged 625.00

Issued: Nos. E9-E10, July 1926; Nos. E11-E12, 1927.

**Catalogue values for unused stamps in this section, from this point to the end of the section, are for Never Hinged items.**

### United Kingdom of Libya

Zuela Saracen Castle SD4

***Perf. 11½***

**1966, Feb. 10 Unwmk. Litho.**
**E13** SD4 90m car rose & lt grn 3.00 1.60

Coat of Arms of Libya and "POLIGRAFICA & CARTEVALORI — NAPLES" printed on back in yellow green.

## SEMI-POSTAL SPECIAL DELIVERY STAMPS

Camel Caravan SPSD1

**Wmk. 140**

**1927, Feb. 15 Litho. *Perf. 14***
**EB1** SPSD1 1.25 l + 30c pur & blk 8.50 42.50
**EB2** SPSD1 2.50 l + 1 l yel & blk 8.50 42.50
Set, never hinged 42.00

See note after No. B10.
No. EB2 is inscribed "EXPRES."

War Memorial SPSD2

**1931, Mar. 8 Photo.**
**EB3** SPSD2 1.25 l + 20c car rose 5.50 *27.50*
Never hinged 14.00

See note after No. B37.

## AUTHORIZED DELIVERY STAMPS

Italy No. EY1 Overprinted in Black

**1929, May 11 Wmk. 140 *Perf. 14***
**EY1** AD1 10c dull blue 30.00 *70.00*
Never hinged 77.50
*a.* Perf. 11 125.00 275.00
Never hinged 300.00

Italy No. EY2 Overprinted in Black

**1941, May *Perf. 14***
**EY2** AD2 10c dark brown 11.00 47.50
Never hinged 27.50

A variety of No. EY2, with larger "LIBIA" and yellow gum, was prepared in 1942, but not issued. Value 85 cents, never hinged $2.10.

AD1

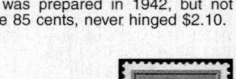

**1942 Litho. Wmk. 140**
**EY3** AD1 10c sepia .85
Never hinged 2.10

No. EY3 was not issued.

## POSTAGE DUE STAMPS

Italian Postage Due Stamps, 1870-1903 Overprinted in Black

**1915, Nov. Wmk. 140 *Perf. 14***

| | | | | |
|---|---|---|---|---|
| **J1** | D3 | 5c buff & mag | 2.10 | *10.00* |
| **J2** | D3 | 10c buff & mag | 2.10 | *5.50* |
| **J3** | D3 | 20c buff & mag | 2.75 | *8.50* |
| *a.* | | Double overprint | 500.00 | 500.00 |
| *b.* | | Inverted overprint | 500.00 | |
| **J4** | D3 | 30c buff & mag | 7.00 | *10.00* |
| **J5** | D3 | 40c buff & mag | 10.00 | *12.50* |
| *a.* | | "40" in black | *4,500.* | |
| **J6** | D3 | 50c buff & mag | 7.00 | *8.50* |
| **J7** | D3 | 60c buff & mag | 10.00 | *19.00* |
| **J8** | D3 | 1 l blue & mag | 7.00 | *19.00* |
| *a.* | | Double overprint | *10,500.* | *16,000.* |
| **J9** | D3 | 2 l blue & mag | 55.00 | *110.00* |
| **J10** | D3 | 5 l blue & mag | 77.50 | *190.00* |
| | | *Nos. J1-J10 (10)* | 180.45 | *393.00* |

**1926**

| | | | | |
|---|---|---|---|---|
| **J11** | D3 | 60c buff & brown | 175.00 | *325.00* |

Postage Due Stamps of Italy, 1934, Overprinted in Black

**1934**

| | | | | |
|---|---|---|---|---|
| **J12** | D6 | 5c brown | .35 | *2.75* |
| **J13** | D6 | 10c blue | .35 | *2.75* |
| **J14** | D6 | 20c rose red | 1.40 | 1.40 |
| **J15** | D6 | 25c green | 1.40 | 1.40 |
| **J16** | D6 | 30c red orange | 1.40 | *5.50* |
| **J17** | D6 | 40c black brn | 1.40 | *3.50* |
| **J18** | D6 | 50c violet | 1.75 | .35 |
| **J19** | D6 | 60c black | 1.75 | *17.50* |
| **J20** | D7 | 1 l red orange | 1.40 | .35 |
| **J21** | D7 | 2 l green | 42.50 | 17.50 |
| **J22** | D7 | 5 l violet | 95.00 | 37.50 |
| **J23** | D7 | 10 l blue | 12.50 | *52.50* |
| **J24** | D7 | 20 l carmine | 12.50 | *70.00* |
| | | *Nos. J12-J24 (13)* | 173.70 | *213.00* |

In 1942 a set of 11 "Segnatasse" stamps, picturing a camel and rider and inscribed "LIBIA," was prepared but not issued. Values for set: hinged $12; never hinged $30.

**Catalogue values for unused stamps in this section, from this point to the end of the section, are for Never Hinged items.**

### United Kingdom of Libya

Postage Due Stamps of Cyrenaica, 1950 Surcharged in Black

### For Use in Tripolitania

**1951 Unwmk. *Perf. 12½***

| | | | | |
|---|---|---|---|---|
| **J25** | D1 | 1mal on 2m dk brown | 9.00 | 18.00 |
| **J26** | D1 | 2mal on 4m dp grn | 15.00 | *30.00* |
| **J27** | D1 | 4mal on 8m scar | 25.00 | *50.00* |
| **J28** | D1 | 10mal on 20m org yel | 50.00 | *100.00* |
| *a.* | | Arabic "20" for "10" | — | |
| **J29** | D1 | 20mal on 40m dp bl | 80.00 | *160.00* |
| | | *Nos. J25-J29 (5)* | 179.00 | *358.00* |

Cyrenaica Nos. J1-J7 Overprinted in Black

### For Use in Cyrenaica

Overprint 13mm High

**1952 Unwmk. *Perf. 12½***

| | | | | |
|---|---|---|---|---|
| **J30** | D1 | 2m dark brown | 10.00 | *20.00* |
| **J31** | D1 | 4m deep green | 10.00 | *20.00* |
| **J32** | D1 | 8m scarlet | 15.00 | *30.00* |
| **J33** | D1 | 10m vermilion | 20.00 | *4.00* |
| **J34** | D1 | 20m orange yel | 30.00 | *60.00* |
| **J35** | D1 | 40m deep blue | 42.50 | *85.00* |
| **J36** | D1 | 100m dk gray | 92.50 | *180.00* |
| | | *Nos. J30-J36 (7)* | 220.00 | *399.00* |

D1

**1952 Litho. *Perf. 11½***

| | | | | |
|---|---|---|---|---|
| **J37** | D1 | 2m chocolate | 1.00 | .35 |
| **J38** | D1 | 5m blue green | 1.60 | .90 |
| **J39** | D1 | 10m carmine | 3.00 | 1.50 |
| **J40** | D1 | 50m violet blue | 11.00 | 4.00 |
| | | *Nos. J37-J40 (4)* | 16.60 | 6.75 |

Castle at Tripoli — D2

**1964, Feb. 1 Photo. *Perf. 14***

| | | | | |
|---|---|---|---|---|
| **J41** | D2 | 2m red brown | .25 | .25 |
| **J42** | D2 | 6m Prus green | .50 | .50 |
| **J43** | D2 | 10m rose red | 1.00 | 1.00 |
| **J44** | D2 | 50m brt blue | 2.00 | 2.00 |
| | | *Nos. J41-J44 (4)* | 3.75 | 3.75 |

Men in Boat, Birds, Mosaic — D3

Ancient Mosaics: 10d, Head of Medusa. 20d, Peacock. 50d, Fish.

**1976, Nov. 15 Litho. *Perf. 14***

| | | | | |
|---|---|---|---|---|
| **J45** | D3 | 5d bister & multi | .25 | .25 |
| **J46** | D3 | 10d orange & multi | .25 | .25 |
| **J47** | D3 | 20d blue & multi | .35 | .35 |
| **J48** | D3 | 50d emerald & multi | .80 | .80 |
| | | *Nos. J45-J48 (4)* | 1.65 | 1.65 |

Nos. J45-J48 have multiple coat of arms printed on back in pale green beneath gum.

## OFFICIAL STAMPS

**Catalogue values for unused stamps in this section are for Never Hinged items.**

### United Kingdom of Libya

Nos. 135-142 Overprinted in Black

**1952 Unwmk. *Perf. 11½***

| | | | | |
|---|---|---|---|---|
| **O1** | A27 | 2m yel brn | .90 | .60 |
| **O2** | A27 | 4m gray | 1.50 | .90 |
| **O3** | A27 | 5m bl grn | 7.50 | 3.00 |
| **O4** | A27 | 8m vermilion | 5.50 | 2.50 |
| **O5** | A27 | 10m purple | 7.00 | 3.00 |
| **O6** | A27 | 12m lil rose | 11.00 | 6.25 |
| **O7** | A27 | 20m dp bl | 19.00 | 9.50 |
| **O8** | A27 | 25m chocolate | 25.00 | 12.50 |
| | | *Nos. O1-O8 (8)* | 77.40 | 38.25 |

## PARCEL POST STAMPS

These stamps were used by affixing them to the way bill so that one half remained on it following the parcel, the other half staying on the receipt given the sender. Most used halves are right halves. Complete stamps were obtainable canceled, probably to order. Both unused and used values are for complete stamps.

Italian Parcel Post Stamps, 1914-22, Overprinted

**1915-24 Wmk. 140 *Perf. 13½***

| | | | | |
|---|---|---|---|---|
| **Q1** | PP2 | 5c brown | 7.00 | *14.00* |
| *a.* | | Double overprint | 375.00 | |
| **Q2** | PP2 | 10c deep blue | 7.00 | *14.00* |
| **Q3** | PP2 | 20c blk ('18) | 8.50 | *14.00* |
| **Q4** | PP2 | 25c red | 8.50 | *14.00* |
| **Q5** | PP2 | 50c orange | 10.00 | *14.00* |
| **Q6** | PP2 | 1 l violet | 10.00 | *21.00* |
| **Q7** | PP2 | 2 l green | 14.00 | *21.00* |
| **Q8** | PP2 | 3 l bister | 21.00 | *21.00* |
| **Q9** | PP2 | 4 l slate | 21.00 | *21.00* |
| **Q10** | PP2 | 10 l rose lil ('24) | 70.00 | *125.00* |
| **Q11** | PP2 | 12 l red brn ('24) | 140.00 | *260.00* |
| **Q12** | PP2 | 15 l ol grn ('24) | 140.00 | *425.00* |
| **Q13** | PP2 | 20 l brn vio ('24) | 210.00 | *510.00* |
| | | *Nos. Q1-Q13 (13)* | 667.00 | *1,474.* |

### Halves Used

| | |
|---|---|
| Q1 | 1.00 |
| Q2 | 1.50 |
| Q3 | 1.50 |
| Q4 | 1.50 |
| Q5 | 1.50 |
| Q6 | 1.50 |
| Q7 | 1.50 |
| Q8 | 1.50 |
| Q9 | 1.50 |
| Q10 | 10.00 |
| Q11 | 11.00 |
| Q12 | 25.00 |
| Q13 | 65.00 |

### Same Overprint on Parcel Post Stamps of Italy, 1927-36

**1927-38**

| | | | | |
|---|---|---|---|---|
| **Q14** | PP3 | 10c dp bl ('36) | 7.00 | *10.00* |
| **Q15** | PP3 | 25c red ('36) | 7.00 | *10.00* |
| **Q16** | PP3 | 30c ultra ('29) | 3.50 | *7.00* |
| **Q17** | PP3 | 50c orange | 50.00 | *350.00* |
| *a.* | | Overprint 8¾x2mm ('31) | 87.50 | *450.00* |
| **Q18** | PP3 | 60c red ('29) | 3.50 | *7.00* |
| **Q19** | PP3 | 1 l lilac ('36) | 37.50 | *140.00* |
| **Q20** | PP3 | 2 l grn ('38) | 45.00 | *140.00* |
| **Q21** | PP3 | 3 l bister | 4.25 | *14.00* |
| **Q22** | PP3 | 4 l gray | 4.25 | *21.00* |
| **Q23** | PP3 | 10 l rose lil ('36) | 275.00 | 625.00 |
| **Q24** | PP3 | 20 l brn vio ('36) | 300.00 | *850.00* |
| | | *Nos. Q14-Q24 (11)* | 737.00 | *2,174.* |

### Halves Used

| | |
|---|---|
| Q14 | .50 |
| Q15 | .50 |
| Q16 | .50 |
| Q17 | 12.50 |
| Q17a | 22.50 |
| Q18 | .50 |
| Q19 | 7.50 |
| Q20 | 7.50 |
| Q21 | 1.50 |
| Q22 | 2.50 |
| Q23 | 30.00 |
| Q24 | 35.00 |

The overprint measures 10x1½mm on No. Q17.

### Same Overprint on Italy No. Q24

**1939**

| | | | |
|---|---|---|---|
| **Q25** | PP3 | 5c brown | *15,000.* |
| | | Never hinged | *22,500.* |

The overprint was applied to the 5c in error. Few examples exist.

## OCCUPATION STAMPS

**Catalogue values for unused stamps in this section are for Never Hinged items.**

### Issued under French Occupation

Stamps of Italy and Libya were overprinted in 1943: "FEZZAN Occupation Française" and "R. F. FEZZAN" for use in this region when General Leclerc's forces 1st occupied it.

### Fezzan-Ghadames

Sebha Fort — OS1

Mosque and Fort Turc Murzuch OS2

Map of Fezzan-Ghadames, Soldier and Camel — OS3

**1946 Unwmk. Engr. *Perf. 13***

| | | | | |
|---|---|---|---|---|
| **1N1** | OS1 | 10c black | .35 | .35 |
| **1N2** | OS1 | 50c rose | .35 | .35 |
| **1N3** | OS1 | 1fr brown | .45 | .45 |
| **1N4** | OS1 | 1.50fr green | .55 | .55 |
| **1N5** | OS1 | 2fr ultramarine | .70 | .70 |
| **1N6** | OS2 | 2.50fr violet | .90 | .90 |
| **1N7** | OS2 | 3fr rose carmine | 1.20 | 1.20 |
| **1N8** | OS2 | 5fr chocolate | 1.20 | 1.20 |
| **1N9** | OS2 | 6fr dark green | 1.10 | 1.10 |
| **1N10** | OS2 | 10fr blue | 1.20 | 1.20 |
| **1N11** | OS3 | 15fr violet | 1.50 | 1.50 |
| **1N12** | OS3 | 20fr red | 1.75 | 1.75 |
| **1N13** | OS3 | 25fr sepia | 1.75 | 1.75 |
| **1N14** | OS3 | 40fr dark green | 2.25 | 2.25 |
| **1N15** | OS3 | 50fr deep blue | 2.50 | 2.50 |
| | | *Nos. 1N1-1N15 (15)* | 17.75 | 17.75 |

## FEZZAN

**Catalogue values for unused stamps in this section are for Never Hinged items.**

Monument, Djerma Oasis — OS1

Tombs of the Beni-Khettab — OS2

Well at Gorda OS3

Col. Colonna d'Ornano and Fort at Murzuch OS4

Philippe F. M. de Hautecloque (Gen. Jacques Leclerc) — OS5

**1949 Unwmk. Engr. *Perf. 13***

| | | | | |
|---|---|---|---|---|
| **2N1** | OS1 | 1fr black | 1.20 | 1.20 |
| **2N2** | OS1 | 2fr lil pink | 1.25 | 1.25 |
| **2N3** | OS2 | 4fr red brn | 2.10 | 2.10 |
| **2N4** | OS2 | 5fr emerald | 2.10 | 2.10 |
| **2N5** | OS3 | 8fr blue | 2.75 | 2.75 |

| | | | | |
|---|---|---|---|---|
| **2N6** | OS3 10fr brown | | 4.50 | 4.50 |
| **2N7** | OS3 12fr dk grn | | 7.00 | 7.00 |
| **2N8** | OS4 15fr sal red | | 10.00 | 10.00 |
| **2N9** | OS4 20fr brn blk | | 5.00 | 5.00 |
| **2N10** | OS5 25fr dk bl | | 5.50 | 5.50 |
| **2N11** | OS5 50fr cop red | | 10.00 | 10.00 |
| | *Nos. 2N1-2N11 (11)* | | 51.40 | 51.40 |

Camel Raising OS6

Agriculture OS7

Well Drilling — OS8 Ahmed Bey — OS9

**1951**

| | | | | |
|---|---|---|---|---|
| **2N12** | OS6 | 30c brown | 1.40 | 1.40 |
| **2N13** | OS6 | 1fr dp bl | 1.40 | 1.40 |
| **2N14** | OS6 | 2fr rose car | 1.40 | 1.40 |
| **2N15** | OS7 | 4fr red | 2.10 | 2.10 |
| **2N16** | OS7 | 5fr green | 2.10 | 2.10 |
| **2N17** | OS7 | 8fr dp bl | 2.10 | 2.10 |
| **2N18** | OS8 | 10fr sepia | 5.50 | 5.50 |
| **2N19** | OS8 | 12fr dp grn | 6.25 | 6.25 |
| **2N20** | OS8 | 15fr brt red | 7.00 | 7.00 |
| **2N21** | OS9 | 20fr blk brn & vio brn | 7.00 | 7.00 |
| **2N22** | OS9 | 25fr dk bl & bl | 7.75 | 7.75 |
| **2N23** | OS9 | 50fr ind & brn org | 8.50 | 8.50 |
| | | *Nos. 2N12-2N23 (12)* | 52.50 | 52.50 |

### OCCUPATION SEMI-POSTAL STAMPS

**Catalogue values for unused stamps in this section are for Never Hinged items.**

"The Unhappy Ones"
OSP1 OSP2

**1950 Unwmk. Engr. *Perf. 13***

| | | | |
|---|---|---|---|
| **2NB1** | OSP1 15fr + 5fr red brn | 3.25 | 3.25 |
| **2NB2** | OSP2 25fr + 5fr blue | 3.25 | 3.25 |

The surtax was for charitable works.

### OCCUPATION AIR POST STAMPS

**Catalogue values for unused stamps in this section are for Never Hinged items.**

Airport in Fezzan OAP1

Plane over Fezzan — OAP2

**1948 Unwmk. Engr. *Perf. 13***

| | | | |
|---|---|---|---|
| **2NC1** | OAP1 100fr red | 7.00 | 7.00 |
| **2NC2** | OAP2 200fr indigo | 10.00 | 10.00 |

Oasis OAP3

Murzuch OAP4

**1951**

| | | | |
|---|---|---|---|
| **2NC3** | OAP3 100fr dark blue | 9.75 | 9.75 |
| **2NC4** | OAP4 200fr vermilion | 14.00 | 14.00 |

### OCCUPATION POSTAGE DUE STAMPS

**Catalogue values for unused stamps in this section are for Never Hinged items.**

Oasis of Brak — D1

**1950 Unwmk. Engr. *Perf. 13***

| | | | | |
|---|---|---|---|---|
| **2NJ1** | D1 | 1fr brown black | 1.40 | 1.40 |
| **2NJ2** | D1 | 2fr deep green | 1.40 | 1.40 |
| **2NJ3** | D1 | 3fr red brown | 2.10 | 2.10 |
| **2NJ4** | D1 | 5fr purple | 2.10 | 2.10 |
| **2NJ5** | D1 | 10fr red | 4.25 | 4.25 |
| **2NJ6** | D1 | 20fr deep blue | 6.25 | 6.25 |
| | | *Nos. 2NJ1-2NJ6 (6)* | 17.50 | 17.50 |

## GHADAMES

**Catalogue values for unused stamps in this section are for Never Hinged items.**

Cross of Agadem — OS1

**1949 Unwmk. Engr. *Perf. 13***

| | | | | |
|---|---|---|---|---|
| **3N1** | OS1 | 4fr sep & red brn | 1.75 | 1.75 |
| **3N2** | OS1 | 5fr pck bl & dk grn | 1.75 | 1.75 |
| **3N3** | OS1 | 8fr sep & org brn | 4.50 | 4.50 |
| **3N4** | OS1 | 10fr blk & dk ultra | 4.50 | 4.50 |
| **3N5** | OS1 | 12fr vio & red vio | 12.00 | 12.00 |
| **3N6** | OS1 | 15fr brn & red brn | 8.50 | 8.50 |
| **3N7** | OS1 | 20fr sep & emer | 10.00 | 10.00 |
| **3N8** | OS1 | 25fr sepia & blue | 12.50 | 12.50 |
| | | *Nos, 3N1-3N8 (8)* | 55.50 | 55.50 |

### OCCUPATION AIR POST STAMPS

**Catalogue values for unused stamps in this section are for Never Hinged items.**

Cross of Agadem — OAP1

**1949 Unwmk. Engr. *Perf. 13***

| | | | | |
|---|---|---|---|---|
| **3NC1** | OAP1 | 50fr pur & rose | 16.00 | 16.00 |
| **3NC2** | OAP1 | 100fr sep & pur brn | 19.00 | 19.00 |

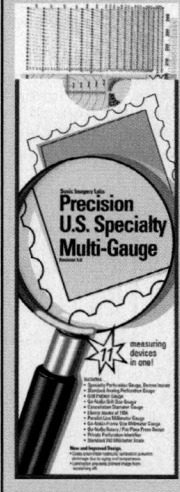

# LIECHTENSTEIN

ˈlik-tən-ˌshtin

LOCATION — Central Europe southeast of Lake Constance, between Austria and Switzerland
GOVT. — Principality
AREA — 61.8 sq. mi.
POP. — 31,320 (1997)
CAPITAL — Vaduz

The Principality of Liechtenstein is a sovereign state consisting of the two counties of Schellenberg and Vaduz. Since 1921 the post office has been administered by Switzerland.

100 Heller = 1 Krone
100 Rappen = 1 Franc (1921)

**Catalogue values for unused stamps in this country are for Never Hinged items, beginning with Scott 368 in the regular postage section, Scott B22 in the semi-postal section, Scott C24 in the air post section, and Scott O30 in the offical section.**

### Watermarks

Greek Cross — Wmk. 183

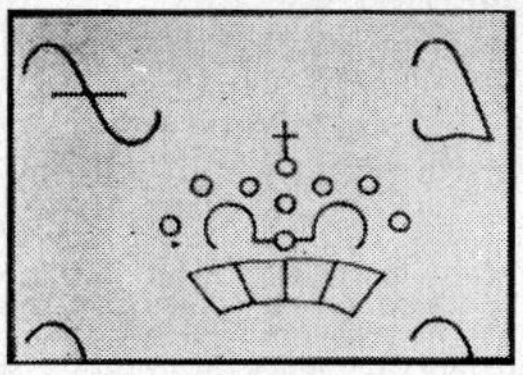

Crown and Initials — Wmk. 296

### Austrian Administration of the Post Office

Prince Johann II — A1

*Perf. 12½x13*

**1912, Feb. 1 Unwmk. Typo.**

**Thick Chalky Paper**

| | | | | |
|---|---|---|---|---|
| 1 | A1 | 5h yellow green | 42.50 | 17.50 |
| 2 | A1 | 10h rose | 85.00 | 17.50 |
| 3 | A1 | 25h dark blue | 85.00 | 55.00 |
| | | *Nos. 1-3 (3)* | 212.50 | 90.00 |
| | | Set, never hinged | 900.00 | |

**1915 Thin Unsurfaced Paper**

| | | | | |
|---|---|---|---|---|
| *1a* | A1 | 5h yellow green | 14.00 | *21.00* |
| *2a* | A1 | 10h rose | 85.00 | 32.50 |
| *3a* | A1 | 25h dark blue | 600.00 | 200.00 |
| *b.* | | 25h ultramarine | 350.00 | 425.00 |
| | | Never hinged | 1,550. | |
| | | #1a-3a, never hinged | 2,500. | |

Coat of Arms — A2

Prince Johann II — A3

**1917-18**

| | | | | |
|---|---|---|---|---|
| 4 | A2 | 3h violet | 2.00 | 2.00 |
| 5 | A2 | 5h yellow green | 2.00 | 2.00 |
| 6 | A3 | 10h claret | 2.00 | 2.00 |
| 7 | A3 | 15h dull red | 2.00 | 2.00 |
| 8 | A3 | 20h dark green | 2.00 | 2.00 |
| 9 | A3 | 25h deep blue | 2.00 | 2.00 |
| | | *Nos. 4-9 (6)* | 12.00 | 12.00 |
| | | Set, never hinged | 51.00 | |

Exist imperf. Value set unused original gum, $525; never hinged, $1,150.

For surcharges see Nos. 11-16.

Prince Johann II — A4

**Dates in Upper Corners**

**1918, Nov. 12**

| | | | | |
|---|---|---|---|---|
| 10 | A4 | 20h dark green | .70 | *2.75* |
| | | Never hinged | 5.50 | |

Accession of Prince Johann II, 60th anniv.

Exists imperf. Value, unused original gum, $225; never hinged, $560.

### National Administration of the Post Office

Stamps of 1917-18 Overprinted or Surcharged

a

b

c

**1920**

| | | | | |
|---|---|---|---|---|
| 11 | A2(a) | 5h yellow green | 2.75 | *8.75* |
| *a.* | | Inverted overprint | 70.00 | *175.00* |
| | | Never hinged | 140.00 | |
| *b.* | | Double overprint | 14.00 | *85.00* |
| | | Never hinged | 35.00 | |
| 12 | A3(a) | 10h claret | 2.75 | *9.50* |
| *a.* | | Inverted overprint | 70.00 | 175.00 |
| | | Never hinged | 140.00 | |
| *b.* | | Double overprint | 14.00 | *105.00* |
| | | Never hinged | 35.00 | |
| *c.* | | Overprint type "c" | 14.00 | *105.00* |
| | | Never hinged | 27.50 | |
| 13 | A3(a) | 25h deep blue | 2.75 | *9.50* |
| *a.* | | Inverted overprint | 70.00 | *175.00* |
| | | Never hinged | 140.00 | |
| *b.* | | Double overprint | 14.00 | *105.00* |
| | | Never hinged | 27.50 | |
| 14 | A2(b) | 40h on 3h violet | 2.75 | *9.50* |
| *a.* | | Inverted surcharge | 70.00 | *175.00* |
| | | Never hinged | 140.00 | |
| 15 | A3(c) | 1k on 15h dull red | 2.75 | *9.50* |
| *a.* | | Inverted surcharge | 70.00 | *175.00* |
| | | Never hinged | 140.00 | |
| *b.* | | Overprint type "a" | 87.50 | *350.00* |
| | | Never hinged | 315.00 | |
| 16 | A3(c) | 2½k on 20h dk grn | 2.75 | *9.50* |
| *a.* | | Inverted surcharge | 70.00 | *175.00* |
| | | Never hinged | 140.00 | |
| | | *Nos. 11-16 (6)* | 16.50 | *56.25* |
| | | Set, never hinged | 71.00 | |

Coat of Arms A5

Chapel of St. Mamertus A6

Coat of Arms with Supporters A15

Designs: 40h, Gutenberg Castle. 50h, Courtyard, Vaduz Castle. 60h, Red Tower, Vaduz. 80h, Old Roman Tower, Schaan. 1k, Castle at Vaduz. 2k, View of Bendern. 5k, Prince Johann I. 7½k, Prince Johann II.

**1920 Engr. *Imperf.***

| | | | | |
|---|---|---|---|---|
| 18 | A5 | 5h olive bister | .35 | *5.75* |
| 19 | A5 | 10h deep orange | .35 | *5.75* |
| 20 | A5 | 15h dark blue | .35 | *5.75* |
| 21 | A5 | 20h deep brown | .35 | *5.75* |
| 22 | A5 | 25h dark green | .35 | *5.75* |
| 23 | A5 | 30h gray black | .35 | *5.75* |
| 24 | A5 | 40h dark red | .35 | *5.75* |
| 25 | A6 | 1k blue | .35 | *5.75* |

***Perf. 12½***

| | | | | |
|---|---|---|---|---|
| 32 | A5 | 5h olive bister | .35 | *.70* |
| 33 | A5 | 10h deep orange | .35 | *.70* |
| 34 | A5 | 15h deep blue | .35 | *.70* |
| 35 | A5 | 20h red brown | .35 | *.70* |
| 36 | A6 | 25h olive green | .35 | *.70* |
| 37 | A5 | 30h dark gray | .35 | *.70* |
| 38 | A6 | 40h claret | .35 | *.70* |
| 39 | A6 | 50h yellow green | .35 | *.70* |
| 40 | A6 | 60h red brown | .35 | *.70* |
| 41 | A6 | 80h rose | .35 | *.70* |
| 42 | A6 | 1k dull violet | .70 | *1.00* |
| 43 | A6 | 2k light blue | .70 | *1.25* |
| 44 | A6 | 5k black | .70 | *1.50* |
| 45 | A6 | 7½k slate | .70 | *1.75* |
| 46 | A15 | 10k ocher | .70 | *3.00* |
| | | *Nos. 18-46 (23)* | 9.80 | *61.50* |
| | | Set, never hinged | 41.00 | |

No. 25 perf. 12½ was not officially issued. It is known mint, used and on cover.

Used values for Nos. 18-46 are for canceled to order stamps. Value with postal cancels approximately $95.

Many denominations of Nos. 32-46 are found imperforate, imperforate vertically and imperforate horizontally.

For surcharges see Nos. 51-52.

Madonna and Child — A16

**1920, Oct. 5**

| | | | | |
|---|---|---|---|---|
| 47 | A16 | 50h olive green | 1.00 | *2.10* |
| 48 | A16 | 80h brown red | 1.00 | *2.10* |
| 49 | A16 | 2k dark blue | 1.00 | *2.75* |
| | | *Nos. 47-49 (3)* | 3.00 | *6.95* |
| | | Set, never hinged | 10.50 | |

80th birthday of Prince Johann II.

**Imperf., Singles**

| | | | | |
|---|---|---|---|---|
| *47a* | A16 | 50h | 7.00 | *1,400.* |
| *48a* | A16 | 80h | 7.00 | *1,400.* |
| *49a* | A16 | 2k | 7.00 | *1,400.* |
| | | Set, never hinged | 63.00 | |

On 1/31/21 the Swiss took over the Post Office administration. Previous issues were demonetized and remainders of Nos. 4-49 were sold.

### Swiss Administration of the Post Office

No. 19 Surcharged

No. 51

No. 52

**1921 Unwmk. Engr. *Imperf.***

| | | | | |
|---|---|---|---|---|
| 51 | A5 | 2rp on 10h dp org | 1.40 | *50.00* |
| | | Never hinged | 7.00 | |
| *a.* | | Double surcharge | 105.00 | *140.00* |
| | | Never hinged | 140.00 | |
| *b.* | | Inverted surcharge | 105.00 | *160.00* |
| | | Never hinged | 140.00 | |
| *c.* | | Double surch., one inverted | 105.00 | *175.00* |
| | | Never hinged | 140.00 | |
| 52 | A5 | 2rp on 10h dp org | .70 | *50.00* |
| | | Never hinged | 5.50 | |
| | | First day cover (2/27/21) | | *875.00* |
| *a.* | | Double surcharge | 72.50 | *160.00* |
| | | Never hinged | 105.00 | |
| *b.* | | Inverted surcharge | 72.50 | *160.00* |
| | | Never hinged | 105.00 | |
| *c.* | | Double surch., one inverted | 87.50 | *190.00* |
| | | Never hinged | 140.00 | |

Arms with Supporters A19

Chapel of St. Mamertus A20

View of Vaduz A21

Designs: 25rp, Castle at Vaduz. 30rp, View of Bendern. 35rp, Prince Johann II. 40rp, Old Roman Tower at Schaan. 50rp, Gutenberg Castle. 80rp, Red Tower at Vaduz.

**1921 *Perf. 12½, 9½ (2rp, 10rp, 15rp)***

**Surface Tinted Paper (#54-61)**

| | | | | |
|---|---|---|---|---|
| 54 | A19 | 2rp lemon | 1.40 | *14.00* |
| 55 | A19 | 2½rp black | 2.10 | *17.50* |
| *a.* | | Perf. 9½ | 1.40 | *70.00* |
| | | Never hinged | 3.50 | |
| 56 | A19 | 3rp orange | 2.10 | *17.50* |
| *a.* | | Perf. 9½ | 140.00 | *5,000.* |
| | | Never hinged | 425.00 | |
| 57 | A19 | 5rp olive green | 14.00 | 2.10 |
| *a.* | | Perf. 9½ | 70.00 | *27.50* |
| | | Never hinged | 225.00 | |
| 58 | A19 | 7½rp dark blue | 7.00 | *42.50* |
| *a.* | | Perf. 9½ | 275.00 | *1,050.* |
| | | Never hinged | 675.00 | |

59 A19 10rp yellow green 27.50 17.50
a. Perf. 12½ 27.50 14.00
Never hinged 140.00
60 A19 13rp brown 10.50 *90.00*
a. Perf. 9½ 100.00 *2,450.*
Never hinged 250.00
b. Perf. 12½x9½ 210.00 —
Never hinged 425.00
61 A19 15rp dark violet 25.00 70.00
a. Perf. 12½ 27.50 *27.50*
Never hinged 50.00
62 A20 20rp dull vio & blk 70.00 2.10
63 A20 25rp rose red & blk 3.50 5.00
64 A20 30rp dp grn & blk 85.00 21.00
65 A20 35rp brn & blk, *straw* 7.00 *17.50*
66 A20 40rp dk blue & blk 10.50 7.00
67 A20 50rp dk grn & blk 17.50 10.50
68 A20 80rp gray & blk 32.00 *85.00*
69 A21 1fr dp claret & blk 55.00 55.00
*Nos. 54-69 (16)* 370.10 *474.20*
Set, never hinged 1,039.

Nos. 54-69 exist imperforate; Nos. 54-61, partly perforated. See Nos. 73, 81. For surcharges see Nos. 70-71.

Nos. 58, 60a Surcharged in Red

**1924** ***Perf. 12½, 9½***
70 A19 5rp on 7½rp 1.40 *3.50*
Never hinged 4.25
a. Perf. 9½ 19.00 17.50
Never hinged 50.00
71 A19 10rp on 13rp 1.75 *3.50*
Never hinged 5.25
a. Perf. 12½ 20.00 *52.50*
Never hinged 60.00

**Type of 1921**
**Granite Paper**

**1924** **Wmk. 183** ***Perf. 11½***
73 A19 10rp green 21.00 3.50
Never hinged 85.00

Peasant A28

Government Palace and Church at Vaduz A30

10rp, 20rp, Courtyard, Vaduz Castle.

**1924-28** **Typo.** ***Perf. 11½***
74 A28 2½rp ol grn & red vio ('28) 1.40 *5.50*
75 A28 5rp brown & blue 2.75 .75
76 A28 7½rp bl grn & brn ('28) 2.10 *5.50*
77 A28 15rp red brn & bl grn ('28) 10.50 *35.00*

**Engr.**
78 A28 10rp yellow grn 11.25 .70
79 A28 20rp deep red 42.50 .70
80 A30 1½fr blue 85.00 *110.00*
*Nos. 74-80 (7)* 155.50 *158.15*
Set, never hinged 503.00

**Bendern Type of 1921**

**1925**
81 A20 30rp blue & blk 17.50 3.50
Never hinged 55.00

Prince Johann II — A31

Prince Johann II as Boy and Man A32

**1928, Nov. 12** **Typo.** **Wmk. 183**
82 A31 10rp lt brn & ol grn 7.00 7.00
83 A31 20rp org red & ol grn 10.50 14.00
84 A31 30rp sl bl & ol grn 35.00 25.00
85 A31 60rp red vio & ol grn 70.00 *70.00*

**Engr.**
**Unwmk.**
86 A32 1.20fr ultra 50.00 *87.50*
87 A32 1.50fr blk brn 87.50 *210.00*
88 A32 2fr deep car 87.50 *210.00*
89 A32 5fr dark green 87.50 *245.00*
*Nos. 82-89 (8)* 435.00 *868.50*
Set, never hinged 1,040.

70th year of the reign of Prince Johann II.

Prince Francis I, as a Child — A33

Prince Francis I as a Man — A34

Princess Elsa — A35

Prince Francis and Princess Elsa — A36

**1929, Dec. 2** **Photo.**
90 A33 10rp olive green .55 *4.25*
91 A34 20rp carmine .85 *7.00*
92 A35 30rp ultra 1.40 *17.50*
93 A36 70rp brown 25.00 *110.00*
*Nos. 90-93 (4)* 27.80 *138.75*
Set, never hinged 77.00

Accession of Prince Francis I, Feb. 11, 1929.

Grape Girl — A37

Chamois Hunter — A38

Mountain Cattle — A39

Courtyard, Vaduz Castle — A40

Mt. Naafkopf — A41

Chapel at Steg — A42

Rofenberg Chapel — A43

Chapel of St. Mamertus — A44

Alpine Hotel, Malbun — A45

Gutenberg Castle — A46

Schellenberg Monastery — A47

Castle at Vaduz — A48

Mountain Cottage — A49

Prince Francis and Princess Elsa — A50

**1930** ***Perf. 10½, 11½, 11½x10½***
94 A37 3rp brown lake 1.10 2.80
95 A38 5rp deep green 2.80 7.00
96 A39 10rp dark violet 2.50 7.00
a. Perf. 11½x10½ 11.00 *120.00*
Never hinged 28.00
97 A40 20rp dp rose red 42.50 7.00
98 A41 25rp black 8.50 *45.00*
a. Perf. 11½ 105.00 *350.00*
Never hinged 350.00
99 A42 30rp dp ultra 8.50 10.50
a. Perf. 11½x10½ 1,050. *2,500.*
Never hinged 2,175.
100 A43 35rp dark green 11.00 *21.00*
a. Perf. 11½ *8,750.* *14,000.*
Never hinged *13,500.*
101 A44 40rp lt brown 11.00 11.00
102 A45 50rp blk brn 105.00 21.00
a. Perf. 11½ 165.00 *245.00*
Never hinged 600.00
103 A46 60rp olive blk 105.00 42.50
104 A47 90rp violet brn 105.00 *350.00*
105 A48 1.20fr olive brn 125.00 *375.00*
a. Perf. 11½x10½ *8,750.* *14,000.*
Never hinged *13,500.*
106 A49 1.50fr black violet 70.00 77.50
107 A50 2fr gray grn & red brn 85.00 *140.00*
a. Perf. 11½x10½ *3,850.* *7,750.*
Never hinged *6,750.*
*Nos. 94-107 (14)* 681.90 *1,117.*
Set, never hinged 1,600.

For overprints see Nos. O1-O8.

Mt. Naafkopf A51

Gutenberg Castle A52

Vaduz Castle — A53

**1933, Jan. 23** ***Perf. 14½***
108 A51 25rp red orange 200.00 87.50
109 A52 90rp dark green 10.50 *105.00*
110 A53 1.20fr red brown 85.00 *300.00*
*Nos. 108-110 (3)* 295.50 *492.50*
Set, never hinged 840.00

For overprints see Nos. O9-O10.

80th Birthday of Prince Francis I — A54

**1933, Aug. 28** ***Perf. 11***
111 A54 10rp purple 21.00 *42.50*
112 A54 20rp brn car 21.00 *42.50*
113 A54 30rp dark blue 21.00 *42.50*
*Nos. 111-113 (3)* 63.00 *127.50*
Set, never hinged 180.00

Prince Francis I — A55

**1933, Dec. 15** **Engr.** ***Perf. 12½***
114 A55 3fr violet blue 125.00 *250.00*
Never hinged 250.00

See No. 152.

**Agricultural Exhibition Issue**
Souvenir Sheet

Arms of Liechtenstein — A56

**1934, Sept. 29** *Perf. 12*

**Granite Paper**

| | | | |
|---|---|---|---|
| **115** A56 5fr brown | 1,400. | 2,500. |
| Never hinged | 2,250. | |
| Single stamp | 1,000. | 1,750. |
| Never hinged | 1,400. | |

See No. 131.

Coat of Arms A57

"Three Sisters" (Landmark) A58

Church of Schaan A59

Bendern A60

Rathaus, Vaduz — A61

Samina Valley — A62

Samina Valley in Winter A63

Ruin at Schellenberg — A64

Government Palace — A65

Vaduz Castle A66

Gutenberg Castle A68

Alpine Hut — A69

Princess Elsa — A70

Coat of Arms — A71

60rp, Vaduz castle, diff. 1.50fr, Valuna.

**1934-35** **Photo.** ***Perf. 11½***

| | | | |
|---|---|---|---|
| **116** A57 | 3rp copper red | .35 | *.70* |
| **117** A58 | 5rp emerald | 5.50 | 2.10 |
| **118** A59 | 10rp deep violet | 2.75 | 1.40 |
| **119** A60 | 15rp red org | .35 | 1.40 |
| **120** A61 | 20rp red | .70 | 1.40 |
| **121** A62 | 25rp brown | 28.00 | *65.00* |
| **122** A63 | 30rp dk blue | 5.50 | 2.10 |
| **123** A64 | 35rp gray grn | 2.75 | *8.50* |
| **124** A65 | 40rp brown | 1.75 | *7.00* |
| **125** A66 | 50rp lt brown | 25.00 | 21.00 |
| **126** A66 | 60rp claret | 2.10 | *9.00* |
| **127** A68 | 90rp deep green | 8.50 | *32.00* |
| **128** A69 | 1.20fr deep blue | 3.50 | *32.00* |
| **129** A69 | 1.50fr brn car | 4.25 | *35.00* |
| | *Nos. 116-129 (14)* | 91.00 | *218.60* |
| | Set, never hinged | 275.00 | |

**Engr.**

***Perf. 12½***

| | | | |
|---|---|---|---|
| **130** A70 | 2fr hen brn ('35) | 85.00 | *250.00* |
| | Never hinged | 140.00 | |
| **131** A71 | 5fr dk vio ('35) | 425.00 | *1,050.* |
| | Never hinged | 700.00 | |

No. 131 has the same design as the 5fr in the souvenir sheet, No. 115. See No. 226, B14. For overprints see Nos. O11-O20.

Bridge at Malbun A72

Labor: 20rp, Constructing Road to Triesenberg. 30rp, Binnen Canal. 50rp, Bridge near Planken.

**1937, June 30** **Photo.**

| | | | |
|---|---|---|---|
| **132** A72 | 10rp brt violet | 1.75 | 2.10 |
| **133** A72 | 20rp red | 1.75 | *2.75* |
| **134** A72 | 30rp brt blue | 1.75 | *3.50* |
| **135** A72 | 50rp yellow brown | 1.75 | *4.25* |
| | *Nos. 132-135 (4)* | 7.00 | 12.60 |
| | Set, never hinged | 21.00 | |

Ruin at Schalun — A76

Peasant in Rhine Valley A77

Ruin at Schellenberg — A78

Knight and Gutenberg Castle A79

Baron von Brandis and Vaduz Castle A80

Designs: 5rp, Chapel at Masescha. 10rp, Knight and Vaduz Castle. 15rp, Upper Valüna Valley. 20rp, Wooden Bridge over Rhine, Bendern. 25rp, Chapel at Steg. 90rp, "The Three Sisters". 1fr, Frontier stone. 1.20fr, Gutenberg Castle and Harpist. 1.50fr, Alpine View of Lawena and Schwartzhorn.

**1937-38**

| | | | |
|---|---|---|---|
| **136** A76 | 3rp yellow brown | .35 | *.70* |

**Pale Buff Shading**

| | | | |
|---|---|---|---|
| **137** A76 | 5rp emerald | .35 | .35 |
| **138** A76 | 10rp violet | .35 | .35 |
| **139** A76 | 15rp dk slate grn | .35 | *.70* |
| **140** A76 | 20rp brn org | .35 | *.70* |
| **141** A76 | 25rp chestnut | .70 | *3.50* |
| **142** A77 | 30rp blue & gray | 3.50 | 1.40 |
| **144** A78 | 40rp dark green | 2.10 | 2.75 |
| **145** A79 | 50rp dark brown | 1.40 | *7.00* |
| **146** A80 | 60rp dp claret ('38) | 2.75 | *3.50* |
| **147** A80 | 90rp gray vio ('38) | 7.00 | *42.50* |
| **148** A80 | 1fr red brown | 2.10 | *17.50* |
| **149** A80 | 1.20fr dp brn ('38) | 7.00 | *32.00* |
| **150** A80 | 1.50fr slate bl ('38) | 4.25 | *32.50* |
| | *Nos. 136-150 (14)* | 32.55 | *145.45* |
| | Set, never hinged | 97.00 | |

For overprints see Nos. O21-O29.

Souvenir Sheet

Josef Rheinberger — A91

**1938, July 30** **Engr.** ***Perf. 12***

| | | | |
|---|---|---|---|
| **151** A91 | Sheet of 4 | 27.50 | 27.50 |
| | Never hinged | 70.00 | |
| *a.* | 50rp slate gray | 3.50 | 5.25 |
| | Never hinged | 7.00 | |

Third Philatelic Exhibition of Liechtenstein. Sheet size: 99¾x135mm.

See No. 153.

**Francis Type of 1933**

Thick Wove Paper

**1938, Aug. 15** ***Perf. 12½***

| | | | |
|---|---|---|---|
| **152** A55 | 3fr black, *buff* | 10.50 | *100.00* |
| | Never hinged | 21.00 | |

Issued in memory of Prince Francis I, who died July 25, 1938. Sheets of 20.

Josef Gabriel Rheinberger (1839-1901), German Composer and Organist — A92

**1939, Mar. 31**

| | | | |
|---|---|---|---|
| **153** A92 | 50rp slate green | 1.10 | *6.25* |
| | Never hinged | 2.40 | |

Issued in sheets of 20. See No. 151.

Scene of Homage, 1718 — A93

**1939, May 29**

| | | | |
|---|---|---|---|
| **154** A93 | 20rp brown lake | 1.40 | 2.75 |
| **155** A93 | 30rp slate blue | 1.40 | 2.75 |
| **156** A93 | 50rp gray green | 1.40 | 2.75 |
| | *Nos. 154-156 (3)* | 4.20 | 8.25 |
| | Set, never hinged | 14.00 | |

Honoring Prince Franz Joseph II. Sheets of 20.

Cantonal Coats of Arms — A94

Prince Franz Joseph II — A96

Design: 3fr, Arms of Principality.

**1939**

| | | | |
|---|---|---|---|
| **157** A94 | 2fr dk green, *buff* | 7.00 | *42.50* |
| **158** A94 | 3fr indigo, *buff* | 4.50 | *42.50* |
| **159** A96 | 5fr brown, *buff* | 14.00 | *27.50* |
| *a.* | Sheet of 4 | 90.00 | *140.00* |
| | Never hinged | 175.00 | |
| | *Nos. 157-159 (3)* | 25.50 | *112.50* |
| | Set, never hinged | 63.00 | |

2fr, 3fr issued in sheets of 12; 5fr in sheets of 4.

Prince Johann as a Child A100

Memorial Tablet A101

Prince Johann II — A102

30rp, Prince Johann and Tower at Vaduz. 50rp, Prince Johann and Gutenberg Castle. 1fr, Prince Johann in 1920 and Vaduz Castle.

**1940** **Photo.** ***Perf. 11½.***

| | | | |
|---|---|---|---|
| **160** A100 | 20rp henna brown | .60 | *2.25* |
| **161** A100 | 30rp indigo | .60 | *3.25* |
| **162** A100 | 50rp dk slate grn | 1.10 | *10.50* |
| **163** A100 | 1fr brown vio | 8.25 | *70.00* |

| | | | | |
|---|---|---|---|---|
| **164** | A101 | 1.50fr violet blk | 10.50 | *67.50* |
| **165** | A102 | 3fr brown | 4.25 | *22.50* |
| | | *Nos. 160-165 (6)* | 25.30 | *176.00* |
| | | Set, never hinged | 52.50 | |

Birth centenary of Prince Johann II.
Nos. 160-164 issued in sheets of 25; No. 165 in sheets of 12.
Issue dates: 3fr, Oct. 5; others Aug. 10.

Gathering Corn A103

Wine Press A104

Sharpening Scythe — A105

Milkmaid and Cow A106

Native Costume A107

**1941, Apr. 7**

| | | | | |
|---|---|---|---|---|
| **166** | A103 | 10rp dull red brown | .75 | .45 |
| **167** | A104 | 20rp lake | .75 | 1.10 |
| **168** | A105 | 30rp royal blue | .75 | *2.50* |
| **169** | A106 | 50rp myrtle green | 2.40 | *14.00* |
| **170** | A107 | 90rp deep claret | 2.40 | *14.00* |
| | | *Nos. 166-170 (5)* | 7.05 | *32.05* |
| | | Set, never hinged | 16.00 | |

Madonna and Child — A108

**1941, July 7** **Engr.**

| | | | | |
|---|---|---|---|---|
| **171** | A108 | 10fr brown car | 37.50 | *97.50* |
| | | Never hinged | 75.00 | |

Issued in sheets of 4.

Johann Adam Andreas — A109

Designs: 30rp, Wenzel. 100rp, Anton Florian. 150rp, Joseph Adam.

**1941, Dec. 18** **Photo.**

| | | | | |
|---|---|---|---|---|
| **172** | A109 | 20rp brown car | .50 | *1.25* |
| **173** | A109 | 30rp royal blue | .70 | *2.50* |
| **174** | A109 | 100rp violet blk | 1.90 | *13.00* |
| **175** | A109 | 150rp slate green | 1.90 | *13.00* |
| | | *Nos. 172-175 (4)* | 5.00 | *29.75* |
| | | Set, never hinged | 11.00 | |

Saint Lucius A113

Designs: 30rp, Reconstruction of Vaduz Castle. 50rp, Signing the Treaty of May 3, 1342. 1fr, Battle of Gutenberg. 2fr, Scene of Homage, 1718.

**1942, Apr. 22** **Engr.** ***Perf. 11½***

| | | | | |
|---|---|---|---|---|
| **176** | A113 | 20rp brn org, *buff* | 1.40 | .95 |
| **177** | A113 | 30rp steel bl, *buff* | 1.40 | 1.40 |
| **178** | A113 | 50rp dk ol grn, *buff* | 1.90 | *5.50* |
| **179** | A113 | 1fr dull brn, *buff* | 2.50 | *13.50* |
| **180** | A113 | 2fr vio blk, *buff* | 2.75 | *14.00* |
| | | *Nos. 176-180 (5)* | 9.95 | *35.35* |
| | | Set, never hinged | 20.00 | |

600th anniversary of the separation of Liechtenstein from the House of Monfort.

Johann Karl — A118

30rp, Franz Joseph I. 1fr, Alois I. 1.50fr, Johann I.

**1942, Oct. 5** **Photo.**

| | | | | |
|---|---|---|---|---|
| **181** | A118 | 20rp rose | .50 | 1.25 |
| **182** | A118 | 30rp brt blue | .50 | *3.00* |
| **183** | A118 | 1fr rose lilac | 1.75 | *16.00* |
| **184** | A118 | 1.50fr deep brown | 2.00 | *16.00* |
| | | *Nos. 181-184 (4)* | 4.75 | *36.25* |
| | | Set, never hinged | 11.00 | |

Prince Franz Joseph II — A122

Countess Georgina von Wilczek — A123

Prince and Princess — A124

**1943, Mar. 5**

| | | | | |
|---|---|---|---|---|
| **185** | A122 | 10rp dp rose violet | .55 | *1.10* |
| **186** | A123 | 20rp henna brown | .55 | *1.10* |
| **187** | A124 | 30rp slate blue | .55 | *1.10* |
| | | *Nos. 185-187 (3)* | 1.65 | 3.30 |
| | | Set, never hinged | 3.50 | |

Marriage of Prince Franz Joseph II and Countess Georgina von Wilczek.

Prince Johann II — A126

Princes: 20rp, Alois II. 100rp, Franz Joseph I. 150rp, Franz Joseph II.

***Perf. 11½***

**1943, July 5** **Unwmk.** **Photo.**

| | | | | |
|---|---|---|---|---|
| **188** | A126 | 20rp copper brown | .35 | *.60* |
| **189** | A126 | 30rp deep ultra | .60 | *1.10* |
| **190** | A126 | 100rp olive gray | 1.10 | *7.00* |
| **191** | A126 | 150rp slate green | 1.25 | *7.00* |
| | | *Nos. 188-191 (4)* | 3.30 | *15.70* |
| | | Set, never hinged | 8.00 | |

Sheets of 20.

Terrain before Reclaiming A129

30rp, Draining the Canal. 50rp, Plowing Reclaimed Land. 2fr, Harvesting Crops.

**1943, Sept. 6**

| | | | | |
|---|---|---|---|---|
| **192** | A129 | 10rp violet black | .30 | *.55* |
| **193** | A129 | 30rp deep blue | .85 | *2.00* |
| **194** | A129 | 50rp slate green | 1.10 | *8.50* |
| **195** | A129 | 2fr olive brown | 2.00 | *12.50* |
| | | *Nos. 192-195 (4)* | 4.25 | *23.55* |
| | | Set, never hinged | 8.75 | |

Vaduz A133

Gutenberg A134

**1943, Dec. 27**

| | | | | |
|---|---|---|---|---|
| **196** | A133 | 10rp dark gray | .45 | .45 |
| **197** | A134 | 20rp chestnut brown | .50 | *1.00* |
| | | Set, never hinged | 2.40 | |

Planken — A135

Bendern — A136

Designs: 10rp, Triesen. 15rp, Ruggell. 20rp, Vaduz. 25rp, Triesenberg. 30rp, Schaan. 40rp, Balzers. 50rp, Mauren. 60rp, Schellenberg. 90rp, Eschen. 1fr, Vaduz Castle. 120rp, Valuna Valley. 150rp, Lawena.

**1944-45**

| | | | | |
|---|---|---|---|---|
| **198** | A135 | 3rp dk brn & buff | .25 | .25 |
| **199** | A136 | 5rp sl grn & buff | .25 | .25 |
| **200** | A136 | 10rp gray & buff | .25 | .25 |
| **201** | A136 | 15rp bl gray & buff | .30 | *.60* |
| **202** | A136 | 20rp org red & buff | .30 | .40 |
| **203** | A136 | 25rp dk rose vio & buff | .30 | *.80* |
| **204** | A136 | 30rp blue & buff | .35 | .40 |
| **205** | A136 | 40rp brown & buff | .55 | 1.00 |
| **206** | A136 | 50rp bluish blk & pale gray | .70 | 1.60 |
| **207** | A136 | 60rp green & buff | 3.75 | 5.00 |
| **208** | A136 | 90rp ol grn & buff | 3.75 | 5.00 |
| **209** | A136 | 1fr dp cl & buff | 2.25 | *5.00* |
| **210** | A136 | 120rp red brown | 2.25 | *5.75* |
| **211** | A136 | 150rp royal blue | 2.25 | *5.75* |
| | | *Nos. 198-211 (14)* | 17.50 | *32.05* |
| | | Set, never hinged | 40.00 | |

Issue years: 10rp, 15rp, 40rp-1fr, 1945; others, 1944. See No. 239. For surcharge and overprints see No. 236, O30-O36.

Crown and Rose — A149

**1945, Apr. 9**

| | | | | |
|---|---|---|---|---|
| **212** | A149 | 20rp multicolored | .85 | *.55* |
| **213** | A149 | 30rp multicolored | .85 | *1.40* |
| **214** | A149 | 1fr multicolored | 1.00 | *4.50* |
| | | *Nos. 212-214 (3)* | 2.70 | *6.45* |
| | | Set, never hinged | 4.50 | |

Birth of Prince Johann Adam Pius, Feb. 14, 1945. Sheets of 20.

Prince Franz Joseph II — A150

Arms of Liechtenstein and Vaduz Castle — A152

Design: 3fr, Princess Georgina.

**1944-45** **Photo.**

| | | | | |
|---|---|---|---|---|
| **215** | A150 | 2fr brown, *buff* | 6.00 | *16.00* |
| **216** | A150 | 3fr dark green | 3.50 | *11.50* |

**Engr.**

| | | | | |
|---|---|---|---|---|
| **217** | A152 | 5fr bl gray, *cr* ('45) | 10.50 | *32.50* |
| | | *Nos. 215-217 (3)* | 20.00 | *60.00* |
| | | Set, never hinged | 40.00 | |

Nos. 215-217 were issued in sheets of 8. See Nos. 222, 259-260.

Saint Lucius — A153

**1946, Mar. 14** **Unwmk.** ***Perf. 11½***

| | | | | |
|---|---|---|---|---|
| **218** | A153 | 10fr gray blk, *cr* | 16.00 | *30.00* |
| | | Never hinged | 45.00 | |
| | | Sheet of 4 | 150.00 | *200.00* |
| | | Never hinged | 190.00 | |

Issued in sheets measuring 105x130mm.

Red Deer — A154

Varying Hare — A155

Capercaillie A156

**1946, Dec. 10** **Photo.**

| | | | | |
|---|---|---|---|---|
| **219** | A154 | 20rp henna brown | 1.50 | *2.50* |
| **220** | A155 | 30rp grnsh blue | 1.50 | *3.25* |
| **221** | A156 | 150rp olive brown | 3.00 | *11.50* |
| | | *Nos. 219-221 (3)* | 6.00 | *17.25* |
| | | Set, never hinged | 12.00 | |

**Arms Type of 1945**

**1947, Mar. 20** **Engr.**

| | | | | |
|---|---|---|---|---|
| **222** | A152 | 5fr henna brn, *cream* | 11.00 | *37.50* |
| | | Never hinged | 25.00 | |

Issued in sheets of 8.

Chamois — A157

Alpine Marmot — A158

Golden Eagle — A159

**1947, Oct. 15 Photo. Unwmk.**

**223** A157 20rp henna brown 1.60 *1.90*
**224** A158 30rp grnsh blue 2.25 *3.25*
**225** A159 150rp dark brown 4.25 *19.00*
*Nos. 223-225 (3)* 8.10 *24.15*
Set, never hinged 17.00

### Elsa Type of 1935

**1947, Dec. 10 Engr. *Perf. 14½***

**226** A70 2fr black, *yelsh* 2.25 *12.50*
Never hinged 5.00

Issued in memory of Princess Elsa, who died Sept. 28, 1947. Sheets of 20.

Portrait of Ginevra dei Benci by Leonardo da Vinci — A160

Designs: 20rp, Girl, Rubens. 30rp, Self-portrait, Rembrandt. 40rp, Canon, Massys. 50rp, Madonna, Memling. 60rp, French Painter, 1456, Fouquet. 80rp, Lute Player, Gentileschi. 90rp, Man, Strigel. 120rp, Man, Raphael.

**1949, Mar. 15 Photo. *Perf. 11½***

**227** A160 10rp dark green .25 *.35*
**228** A160 20rp henna brown .60 *.80*
**229** A160 30rp sepia 1.25 .90
**230** A160 40rp blue 3.00 .90
**231** A160 50rp violet 2.50 *6.75*
**232** A160 60rp grnsh gray 5.50 6.25
**233** A160 80rp brown orange 1.25 *4.25*
**234** A160 90rp olive bister 5.50 5.75
**235** A160 120rp claret 1.25 *5.25*
*Nos. 227-235 (9)* 21.10 31.20
Set, never hinged 47.50

Issued in sheets of 12.
See No. 238.

### No. 198 Surcharged with New Value and Bars in Dark Brown

**1949, Apr. 14**

**236** A135 5rp on 3rp dk brn & buff .35 *.55*
Never hinged .85

Map, Post Horn and Crown A161

**1949, May 23**

**237** A161 40rp blue & indigo 2.00 4.00
Never hinged 3.75

75th anniversary of the UPU.
For surcharge see No. 246.

### Portrait Type of 1949
Souvenir Sheet
**Unwmk.**

**1949, Aug. 6 Photo. *Imperf.***

**238** Sheet of 3 55.00 *95.00*
Never hinged 110.00
*a.* A160 10rp dull green 4.75 *10.00*
*b.* A160 20rp lilac rose 30.00 *60.00*
*c.* A160 40rp blue 4.75 *10.00*

5th Philatelic Exhibition.
Sheet size: 121½x69½mm. Sold for 3fr.

### Scenic Type of 1944

**1949, Dec. 1 *Perf. 11½***

**239** A136 5rp dk brown & buff 12.00 1.20
Never hinged 26.00

Rossauer Castle, Vienna A163

Church at Bendern A164

Prince Johann Adam Andreas — A165

**1949, Nov. 15 Engr. *Perf. 14½***

**240** A163 20rp dark violet .90 2.00
**241** A164 40rp blue 2.25 6.25
**242** A165 150rp brown red 5.00 9.25
*Nos. 240-242 (3)* 8.15 17.50
Set, never hinged 20.00

250th anniv. of the purchase of the former dukedom of Schellenberg. Sheets of 20.
For surcharge see No. 265.

Roe Deer — A166

Black Grouse — A167

Badger — A168

**1950, Mar. 7 Photo. *Perf. 11½***

**243** A166 20rp red brown 6.00 6.00
**244** A167 30rp Prus green 6.25 9.00
**245** A168 80rp dark brown 13.50 45.00
*Nos. 243-245 (3)* 25.75 60.00
Set, never hinged 50.00

Issued in sheets of 20.

### No. 237 Surcharged with New Value and Bars Obliterating Commemorative Inscriptions

**1950, Nov. 7**

**246** A161 1fr on 40rp bl & ind 10.00 *45.00*

Boy Cutting Bread — A169

Designs: 10rp, Laborer. 15rp, Cutting hay. 20rp, Harvesting corn. 25rp, Load of hay. 30rp, Wine grower. 40rp, Farmer and scythe. 50rp, Cattle raising. 60rp, Plowing. 80rp, Woman with potatoes. 90rp, Potato cultivation. 1fr, Tractor with potatoes.

***Perf. 11½***

**1951, May 3 Unwmk. Photo.**

**247** A169 5rp claret .25 .25
**248** A169 10rp green .25 .45
**249** A169 15rp yellow brown 1.75 5.00
**250** A169 20rp olive brown .50 .65
**251** A169 25rp rose brown 2.25 5.00
**252** A169 30rp grnsh gray 1.25 .55
**253** A169 40rp deep blue 3.75 6.50
**254** A169 50rp violet brown 3.00 4.00
**255** A169 60rp brown 3.00 4.00
**256** A169 80rp henna brown 3.75 6.75
**257** A169 90rp olive green 7.00 7.50
**258** A169 1fr indigo 18.00 9.00
*Nos. 247-258 (12)* 44.75 49.65
Set, never hinged 110.00

### Types of 1944, Redrawn
***Perf. 12½x12***

**1951, Nov. 20 Engr. Wmk. 296**

**259** A150 2fr dark blue 9.00 *37.50*
*a.* Perf. 14½ 450.00 160.00
**260** A150 3fr dk red brown 80.00 110.00
*a.* Perf. 14½ 50.00 *210.00*
Set, never hinged 175.00
Set, perf. 14½, never hinged 900.00

Issued in sheets of 20.

Portrait, Savolodo — A170

Madonna, Botticelli — A171

Design: 40rp St. John, Del Sarto.

***Perf. 11½***

**1952, Mar. 27 Unwmk. Photo.**

**261** A170 20rp violet brown 15.00 2.75
**262** A171 30rp brown olive 10.50 7.00
**263** A170 40rp violet blue 5.25 5.75
*Nos. 261-263 (3)* 30.75 15.50
Set, never hinged 80.00

Issued in sheets of 12.

Vaduz Castle — A172

**Wmk. 296**

**1952, Sept. 25 Engr. *Perf. 14½***

**264** A172 5fr deep green 85.00 150.00
Never hinged 140.00

Issued in sheets of 9.

### No. 241 Surcharged with New Value and Wavy Lines in Red

**1952, Sept. 25 Unwmk.**

**265** A164 1.20fr on 40rp blue 12.00 *50.00*
Never hinged 24.00

Portrait of a Young Man — A173

St. Nicholas by Zeitblom — A174

Designs: 30rp, St. Christopher by Cranach. 40rp, Leonhard, Duke of Hag, by Kulmbach.

***Perf. 11½***

**1953, Feb. 5 Unwmk. Photo.**

**266** A173 10rp dk olive green 1.25 1.25
**267** A174 20rp olive brown 5.25 3.00
**268** A174 30rp violet brown 13.00 10.00
**269** A173 40rp slate blue 18.00 *40.00*
*Nos. 266-269 (4)* 37.50 *54.25*
Set, never hinged 75.00

Issued in sheets of 12.

Lord Baden-Powell A175

**1953, Aug. 4 Engr. *Perf. 13x13½***

**270** A175 10rp deep green .70 .90
**271** A175 20rp dark brown 6.75 2.25
**272** A175 25rp red 5.75 18.00
**273** A175 40rp deep blue 5.50 6.00
*Nos. 270-273 (4)* 18.70 27.15
Set, never hinged 37.50

Intl. Scout Conf. Sheets of 20.

Alemannic Disc, 600 A. D. — A176

Prehistoric Settlement of Borscht A177

Design: 1.20fr, Rössen jug.

**1953, Nov. 26 *Perf. 11½***

**274** A176 10rp orange brown 4.00 *11.50*
**275** A177 20rp deep gray green 4.75 *11.50*
**276** A176 1.20fr dark blue gray 17.50 *32.50*
*Nos. 274-276 (3)* 26.25 *55.50*
Set, never hinged 65.00

Opening of National Museum, Vaduz.

Soccer Players — A178

Designs: 20rp, Player kicking ball. 25rp, Goalkeeper. 40rp, Two opposing players.

**1954, May 18 Photo.**

**277** A178 10rp dull rose & brn 1.25 .90
**278** A178 20rp olive green 3.75 1.40
**279** A178 25rp orange brown 7.50 *30.00*
**280** A178 40rp lilac gray 7.50 9.00
*Nos. 277-280 (4)* 20.00 *41.30*
Set, never hinged 42.50

See Nos. 289-292, 297-300, 308-311, 320-323.

### Nos. B19-B21 Surcharged with New Value and Bars in Color of Stamp

**1954, Sept. 28 Unwmk. *Perf. 11½***

**281** SP15 35rp on 10rp+10rp 2.50 2.25
**282** SP16 60rp on 20rp+10rp 11.00 10.50
**283** SP15 65rp on 40rp+10rp 3.50 7.25
*Nos. 281-283 (3)* 17.00 20.00
Set, never hinged 30.00

Madonna in Wood, 14th Century — A179

**1954, Dec. 16** **Engr.**

**284** A179 20rp henna brown 1.50 1.90
**285** A179 40rp gray 8.50 17.50
**286** A179 1fr dark brown 8.50 17.00
*Nos. 284-286 (3)* 18.50 36.40
Set, never hinged 37.50

Prince Franz Joseph II — A180    Princess Georgina — A181

**1955, Apr. 5** ***Perf. 14½***

**Cream Paper**

**287** A180 2fr dark brown 32.50 37.50
**288** A181 3fr dark green 32.50 37.50
Set, never hinged 140.00

Issued in sheets of 9.

**Sports Type of 1954**

Designs: 10rp, Slalom. 20rp, Mountain climbing. 25rp, Skiing. 40rp, Resting on summit.

**1955, June 14** **Photo.** ***Perf. 11½***

**289** A178 10rp aqua & brn vio .45 .80
**290** A178 20rp green & ol bis 2.50 .80
**291** A178 25rp lt ultra & sep 7.50 16.00
**292** A178 40rp olive & pink 7.50 6.00
*Nos. 289-292 (4)* 17.95 23.60
Set, never hinged 37.50

Prince Johann Adam — A183

Portraits: 20rp, Prince Philipp. 40rp, Prince Nikolaus. 60rp, Princess Nora.

**Granite Paper**

**1955, Dec. 14** **Cross in Red**

**293** A183 10rp dull violet .75 .70
**294** A183 20rp slate green 3.00 1.60
**295** A183 40rp olive brown 3.00 7.25
**296** A183 60rp rose brown 3.25 4.00
*Nos. 293-296 (4)* 10.00 13.55
Set, never hinged 20.00

Liechtenstein Red Cross, 10th anniversary.

**Sports Type of 1954**

Designs: 10rp, Javelin thrower. 20rp, Hurdling. 40rp, Pole vaulting. 1fr, Sprinters.

***Perf. 11½***

**1956, June 21** **Unwmk.** **Photo.**

**Granite Paper**

**297** A178 10rp lt red brn & ol grn .45 .60
**298** A178 20rp lt ol grn & pur 1.90 .60
**299** A178 40rp blue & vio brn 2.75 3.25
**300** A178 1fr org ver & ol brn 6.50 12.00
*Nos. 297-300 (4)* 11.60 16.45
Set, never hinged 22.50

Eagle, Crown and Oak Leaves — A184

**1956, Aug. 21** **Granite Paper**

**301** A184 10rp dk brown & gold 1.10 1.00
**302** A184 120rp slate blk & gold 4.25 4.25
Set, never hinged 12.50

150th anniversary of independence.

Prince Franz Joseph II — A185

**1956, Aug. 21**

**303** A185 10rp dark green .95 .45
**304** A185 15rp bright ultra 1.40 2.75
**305** A185 25rp purple 1.40 2.75
**306** A185 60rp dark brown 4.75 2.25
*Nos. 303-306 (4)* 8.50 8.20
Set, never hinged 17.50

50th birthday of Prince Franz Joseph II.

Prince Johann Adam — A186

**1956, Aug. 21** **Granite Paper**

**307** A186 20rp olive green 1.75 .70
Never hinged 3.50

Issued to publicize the 6th Philatelic Exhibition, Vaduz, Aug. 25-Sept. 2. Sheets of 9.

**Sports Type of 1954**

Designs: 10rp, Somersault on bar. 15rp, Exercise on pommel horse. 25rp, Exercise on rings. 1.50fr, Somersault on parallel bars.

**1957, May 14** **Photo.** ***Perf. 11½***

**308** A178 10rp pale rose & ol grn .95 .95
**309** A178 15rp pale grn & dl pur 2.75 *7.00*
**310** A178 25rp ol bis & Prus grn 3.75 *8.25*
**311** A178 1.50fr lemon & sepia 11.00 *19.00*
*Nos. 308-311 (4)* 18.45 35.20
Set, never hinged 32.50

Pine — A187

Designs: 20rp, Wild roses. 1fr, Birches.

**1957, Sept. 10** ***Perf. 11½***

**Granite Paper**

**312** A187 10rp dark violet 1.90 2.25
**313** A187 20rp brown carmine 1.90 .95
**314** A187 1fr green 3.25 8.00
*Nos. 312-314 (3)* 7.05 11.20
Set, never hinged 16.00

See Nos. 326-328, 332-334, 353-355.

Lord Baden-Powell A188

Design: 10rp, Symbolical torchlight parade.

**1957, Sept. 10** **Unwmk.**

**315** A188 10rp blue black .75 1.50
**316** A188 20rp dark brown .75 1.50
*a.* Sheet, 6 each #315-316 12.00 21.00
Never hinged 21.00
Set, never hinged 3.00

Cent. of the birth of Lord Baden-Powell and the 60th anniv. of the Boy Scout movement.

Chapel of St. Mamertus — A189

40rp, Madonna and saints. 1.50fr, Pieta.

**1957, Dec. 16** ***Perf. 11½***

**317** A189 10rp dark brown .35 .35
**318** A189 40rp dark blue 1.10 *5.50*
**319** A189 1.50fr brown lake 6.50 9.50
*Nos. 317-319 (3)* 7.95 15.35
Set, never hinged 15.00

Issued in sheets of 20. Sheet inscribed: "Furstentum Liechtenstein" and "Weihnacht 1957" (Christmas 1957).

**Sports Type of 1954**

Designs: 15rp, Girl swimmer. 30rp, Fencers. 40rp, Tennis. 90rp, Bicyclists.

**1958, Mar. 18** **Photo.**

**Granite Paper**

**320** A178 15rp lt blue & pur .65 1.00
**321** A178 30rp pale rose lil & ol gray 1.50 6.00
**322** A178 40rp sal pink & sl bl 2.50 6.00
**323** A178 90rp lt ol grn & vio brn .80 4.00
*Nos. 320-323 (4)* 5.45 17.00
Set, never hinged 21.00

Relief Map of Liechtenstein A190

**1958, Mar. 18**

**324** A190 25rp bister, vio & red .35 .75
**325** A190 40rp blue, vio & red .75 .75
Set, never hinged 2.25

World's Fair, Brussels, Apr. 17-Oct. 19.

Sheets of 25. For surcharges see Nos. B22-B23.

**Tree-Bush Type of 1957**

Designs: 20rp, Maples at Lawena. 50rp, Holly at Schellenberg. 90rp, Yew at Maurerberg.

**1958, Aug. 12** ***Perf. 11½***

**Granite Paper**

**326** A187 20rp chocolate 1.75 .75
**327** A187 50rp olive green 7.00 4.50
**328** A187 90rp violet blue 1.75 2.75
*Nos. 326-328 (3)* 10.50 8.00
Set, never hinged 19.00

Sts. Moritz and Agatha — A191

Christmas: 35rp, St. Peter. 80rp, Chapel of St. Peter, Mals-Balzers.

**1958, Dec. 4** **Photo.** **Unwmk.**

**Granite Paper**

**329** A191 20rp dk slate green 1.90 2.50
**330** A191 35rp dk blue violet 1.90 2.50
**331** A191 80rp dark brown 1.90 2.50
*Nos. 329-331 (3)* 5.70 7.50
Set, never hinged 9.50

Issued in sheets of 20.

**Tree-Bush Type of 1957**

Designs: 20rp, Larch in Lawena. 50rp, Holly on Alpila. 90rp, Linden in Schaan.

**1959, Apr. 15** ***Perf. 11½***

**332** A187 20rp dark violet 2.50 2.40
**333** A187 50rp henna brown 2.50 2.40
**334** A187 90rp dark green 2.50 2.40
*Nos. 332-334 (3)* 7.50 7.20
Set, never hinged 14.00

"The Good Shepherd" — A192

**1959, Apr. 15** **Unwmk.**

**335** A192 30rp rose violet & gold .50 .85
Never hinged .90

Issued in memory of Pope Pius XII.

Flags and Rhine Valley — A193

Man Carrying Hay — A194

Apple Harvest A195

Designs: 5rp, Church at Bendern and sheaves. 20rp, Rhine embankment. 30rp, Gutenberg Castle. 40rp, View from Schellenberg. 50rp, Vaduz Castle. 60rp, Naafkopf, Falknis Range. 75rp, Woman gathering sheaves. 90rp, Woman in vineyard. 1fr, Woman in kitchen. 1.30fr, Return from the field. 1.50fr, Family saying grace.

**1959-64** **Granite Paper**

**336** A193 5rp gray olive ('61) .25 .25
**337** A193 10rp dull violet .25 .25
**338** A193 20rp lilac rose .25 .25
**339** A193 30rp dark red .25 .25
**340** A193 40rp olive grn ('61) 1.10 .55
**341** A193 50rp deep blue .30 .35
**342** A193 60rp brt grnsh bl .45 .55
**343** A194 75rp deep ocher ('60) 1.10 1.00
**344** A194 80rp olive grn ('61) .90 .90
**345** A194 90rp red lilac ('61) .90 .90
**346** A194 1fr chestnut ('61) .90 .90
**347** A195 1.20fr orange ver ('60) 1.40 1.10
**348** A195 1.30fr brt green ('64) 1.10 .90
**349** A195 1.50fr brt blue ('60) 1.40 1.40
*Nos. 336-349 (14)* 10.55 9.55
Set, never hinged 12.50

Belfry, Bendern Church — A196

Christmas: 60rp, Sculpture, bell, St. Theodul's church. 1fr, Sculpture, tower of St. Lucius' church.

**1959, Dec. 2** **Unwmk.** ***Perf. 11½***

| | | | |
|---|---|---|---|
| **350** A196 5rp dk slate green | .55 | .25 |
| **351** A196 60rp olive | 3.50 | 4.25 |
| **352** A196 1fr deep claret | 2.75 | 2.50 |
| *Nos. 350-352 (3)* | 6.80 | 7.00 |
| Set, never hinged | 11.00 | |

Issued in sheets of 20.

### Tree-Bush Type of 1957

Designs: 20rp, Beech tree on Gafadura. 30rp, Juniper on Alpila. 50rp, Pine on Sass.

**1960, Sept. 19**

| | | |
|---|---|---|
| **353** A187 20rp brown | 3.75 | 5.25 |
| **354** A187 30rp deep plum | 3.75 | 5.25 |
| **355** A187 50rp Prus green | 12.00 | 15.00 |
| *Nos. 353-355 (3)* | 19.50 | 25.50 |
| Set, never hinged | 32.50 | |

### Europa Issue

Honeycomb A197

**1960, Sept. 19** ***Perf. 14***

| | | |
|---|---|---|
| **356** A197 50rp multicolored | *30.00* | *30.00* |
| Never hinged | *55.00* | |

Issued to promote the idea of a united Europe. Sheets of 20.

Princess Gina — A198

Portraits: 1.70fr, Prince Johann Adam Pius. 3fr, Prince Franz Joseph II.

**1960-64** **Engr.** ***Perf. 14***

| | | |
|---|---|---|
| **356A** A198 1.70fr violet ('64) | 1.00 | 1.50 |
| *b.* Imperf., pair | *1,750.* | *1,750.* |
| **357** A198 2fr dark blue | 2.25 | 2.00 |
| *a.* Imperf., pair | *1,750.* | *1,750.* |
| **358** A198 3fr deep brown | 2.25 | 2.00 |
| *Nos. 356A-358 (3)* | 5.50 | 5.50 |
| Set, never hinged | 7.00 | |

Issued in sheets of 16.

Heinrich von Frauenberg — A199

Minnesingers: 20rp, King Konradin. 25rp, Ulrich von Liechtenstein. 30rp, Kraft von Toggenburg. 35rp, Ulrich von Gutenberg. 40rp, Heinrich von Veldig. 1fr, Konrad von Alstetten. 1.50fr, Walther von der Vogelweide. 2fr, Tannhäuser. (Designs from 14th century Manesse manuscript.)

**1961-62** **Photo.** ***Perf. 11½***

| | | |
|---|---|---|
| **359** A199 15rp multi | .60 | .75 |
| **360** A199 20rp multi ('62) | .30 | .30 |
| **361** A199 25rp multi | 1.25 | 1.65 |
| **362** A199 30rp multi ('62) | .40 | .40 |
| **363** A199 35rp multi | 1.50 | 2.00 |
| **364** A199 40rp multi ('62) | .65 | .65 |
| **365** A199 1fr multi | 2.50 | 2.00 |
| **366** A199 1.50fr multi | 9.25 | 15.00 |
| **367** A199 2fr multi ('62) | 1.65 | 1.65 |
| *Nos. 359-367 (9)* | 18.10 | 24.40 |
| Set, never hinged | 22.50 | |

Issued in sheets of 20. See Nos. 381-384, 471.

**Catalogue values for unused stamps in this section, from this point to the end of the section, are for Never Hinged items.**

### Europa Issue, 1961

Cogwheels A200

**1961, Oct. 3** **Unwmk.** ***Perf. 13½***

| | | |
|---|---|---|
| **368** A200 50rp multicolored | *.35* | .25 |

Printed in sheets of 20.

Souvenir Sheet

Prince Johann II — A201

Portraits: 10rp, Francis I. 25rp, Franz Joseph II.

**1962, Aug. 2** **Photo.** ***Perf. 11½***

| | | |
|---|---|---|
| **369** A201 Sheet of 3 | 7.00 | 5.00 |
| *a.* 5rp gray green | 2.00 | 1.25 |
| *b.* 10rp deep rose | 2.00 | 1.25 |
| *c.* 25rp blue | 2.00 | 1.25 |

50th anniv. of Liechtenstein's postage stamps and in connection with the Anniv. Stamp Exhib., Vaduz, Aug. 4-12. No. 369 sold for 3fr.

Hands A202

**1962, Aug. 2**

| | | |
|---|---|---|
| **370** A202 50rp indigo & red | *.45* | .45 |

Europa. Issued in sheets of 20.

Malaria Eradication Emblem — A203

**1962, Aug. 2** **Engr.**

| | | |
|---|---|---|
| **371** A203 50rp turquoise blue | .60 | .45 |

WHO drive to eradicate malaria. Sheets of 20.

Pietà — A204

Designs: 50rp, Angel with harp, fresco. 1.20fr, View of Mauren.

**1962, Dec. 6** **Photo.**

| | | |
|---|---|---|
| **372** A204 30rp magenta | .60 | .60 |
| **373** A204 50rp deep orange | .85 | .85 |
| **374** A204 1.20fr deep blue | 1.10 | 1.10 |
| *Nos. 372-374 (3)* | 2.55 | 2.55 |

Issued in sheets of 20.

Prince Franz Joseph II A205

**1963, Apr. 3** **Engr.** ***Perf. 13½x14***

| | | |
|---|---|---|
| **375** A205 5fr dull green | 4.00 | 3.00 |

Accession of Prince Franz Joseph II, 25th anniv.
Sheets of 8. Exists imperf. Value $1,500.

Angel of the Annunciation A206

***Perf. 11½***

**1963, Aug. 26** **Unwmk.** **Photo.**

| | | |
|---|---|---|
| **376** A206 20rp shown | .60 | .40 |
| **377** A206 80rp Three Kings | .60 | .40 |
| **378** A206 1fr Family | 1.00 | .80 |
| *Nos. 376-378 (3)* | 2.20 | 1.60 |

Centenary of the International Red Cross.

### Europa Issue

Greek Architectural Elements A207

**1963, Aug. 26**

| | | |
|---|---|---|
| **379** A207 50rp multicolored | *1.00* | *1.00* |

Bread and Milk — A208

**1963, Aug. 26**

| | | |
|---|---|---|
| **380** A208 50rp dk red pur & brn | .70 | .50 |

FAO "Freedom from Hunger" campaign.

### Minnesinger Type of 1961-62

Minnesingers: 25rp, Heinrich von Sax. 30rp, Kristan von Hamle. 75rp, Werner von Teufen. 1.70fr, Hartmann von Aue.

***Perf. 11½***

**1963, Dec. 5** **Unwmk.** **Photo.**

| | | |
|---|---|---|
| **381** A199 25rp multicolored | .45 | .45 |
| **382** A199 30rp multicolored | .45 | .45 |
| **383** A199 75rp multicolored | .75 | .75 |
| **384** A199 1.70fr multicolored | 1.50 | 1.50 |
| *Nos. 381-384 (4)* | 3.15 | 3.15 |

Issued in sheets of 20.

Olympic Rings, Flags of Austria and Japan A209

**1964, Apr. 15** ***Perf. 11½***

| | | |
|---|---|---|
| **385** A209 50rp Prus bl, red & blk | .60 | .60 |

Olympic Games 1964. Sheets of 20.

Arms of Counts of Werdenberg-Vaduz A210

Coats of Arms: 30rp, Barons of Brandis. 80rp, Counts of Sulz. 1.50fr, Counts of Hohenems.

**1964, Sept. 1** **Photo.**

| | | |
|---|---|---|
| **386** A210 20rp multicolored | .40 | .40 |
| **387** A210 30rp multicolored | .40 | .40 |
| **388** A210 80rp multicolored | .40 | .40 |
| **389** A210 1.50fr multicolored | .80 | .80 |
| *Nos. 386-389 (4)* | 2.00 | 2.00 |

See Nos. 396-399.

### Europa Issue

Roman Castle, Schaan A211

**1964, Sept. 1** ***Perf. 13x14***

| | | |
|---|---|---|
| **390** A211 50rp multicolored | *.75* | *.75* |

Masescha Chapel — A212

40rp, Mary Magdalene, altarpiece. 1.30fr, Madonna with Sts. Sebastian & Roch, altarpiece.

**1964, Dec. 9** **Photo.** ***Perf. 11½***

| | | |
|---|---|---|
| **391** A212 10rp violet black | .40 | .40 |
| **392** A212 40rp dark blue | .40 | .40 |
| **393** A212 1.30fr deep claret | 1.00 | 1.00 |
| *Nos. 391-393 (3)* | 1.80 | 1.80 |

Issued in sheets of 20.

Peter Kaiser — A213

**1964, Dec. 9** **Engr.**

| | | |
|---|---|---|
| **394** A213 1fr dk grn, *buff* | .95 | .95 |

Kaiser (1793-1864), historian. Sheets of 20.

Madonna, Wood Sculpture, 18th Century — A214

***Perf. 11½***

**1965, Apr. 22** **Unwmk.** **Engr.**

| | | |
|---|---|---|
| **395** A214 10fr orange red | 7.00 | 4.00 |

Issued in sheets of 4.

### Arms Type of 1965

Lords of: 20rp, Schellenberg. 30rp, Gutenberg. 80rp, Frauenberg. 1fr, Ramschwag.

*Perf. 11½*

**1965, Aug. 31 Unwmk. Photo.**

**396** A210 20rp multicolored .45 .45
**397** A210 30rp multicolored .45 .45
**398** A210 80rp multicolored .65 .65
**399** A210 1fr multicolored .65 .65
*Nos. 396-399 (4)* 2.20 2.20

Alemannic Ornament A215

Europa: The design is from a belt buckle, about 600 A.D., found in a man's tomb near Eschen.

**1965, Aug. 31**

**400** A215 50rp vio bl, gray & brn *.45 .35*

The Annunciation by Ferdinand Nigg — A216

Paintings by Nigg: 30rp, The Three Kings. 1.20fr, Jesus in the Temple, horiz.

**1965, Dec. 7 Photo. *Perf. 11½***

**401** A216 10rp yel grn & dk grn .40 .40
**402** A216 30rp orange & red brn .40 .40
**403** A216 1.20fr ultra & grnsh bl .60 .60
*Nos. 401-403 (3)* 1.40 1.40

Ferdinand Nigg (1865-1949), painter.

Princess Gina and Prince Franz Josef Wenzel — A217

**1965, Dec. 7**

**404** A217 75rp gray, buff & gold .60 .50

Communication Symbols — A218

**1965, Dec. 7**

**405** A218 25rp multicolored .60 .45

Centenary of the ITU.

Soil Conservation, Tree — A219

20rp, Clean air, bird. 30rp, Unpolluted water, fish. 1.50fr, Nature preservation, sun.

**1966, Apr. 26 Photo. *Perf. 11½***

**406** A219 10rp brt yellow & grn .40 .40
**407** A219 20rp blue & dk blue .40 .40
**408** A219 30rp brt green & ultra .40 .40
**409** A219 1.50fr yellow & red .70 .70
*Nos. 406-409 (4)* 1.90 1.90

Issued to publicize nature conservation.

Prince Franz Joseph II — A220

**1966, Apr. 26**

**410** A220 1fr gray, gold, buff & dk brn .75 .75

60th birthday of Prince Franz Joseph II.

Arms of Barons of Richenstein A221

Coats of Arms: 30rp, Vaistli knights. 60rp, Lords of Trisun. 1.20fr, von Schiel.

**Light Gray Background**

**1966, Sept. 6 Photo. *Perf. 11½***

**411** A221 20rp multicolored .30 .30
**412** A221 30rp multicolored .30 .30
**413** A221 60rp multicolored .30 .30
**414** A221 1.20fr multicolored .60 .60
*Nos. 411-414 (4)* 1.50 1.50

Common Design Types pictured following the introduction.

**Europa Issue, 1966**

Common Design Type

**1966, Sept. 6 Photo. *Perf. 14x13***

**Size: 25x32mm**

**415** CD9 50rp ultra, dp org & lt grn *.40 .35*

Vaduz Parish Church — A222

St. Florin — A223

30rp, Madonna. 1.70fr, God the Father.

**1966, Dec. 6 Photo. *Perf. 11½***

**416** A222 5rp orange red & cit .30 .25
**417** A223 20rp lemon & magenta .30 .25
**418** A223 30rp dull rose & dp bl .30 .25
**419** A223 1.70fr gray & red brown .85 .65
*Nos. 416-419 (4)* 1.75 1.40

Restoration of the Vaduz Parish Church.

**Europa Issue, 1967**

Common Design Type

**1967, Apr. 20 Photo. *Perf. 11½***

**420** CD10 50rp multicolored .45 *.40*

The Man from Malans and his White Horse — A225

Fairy Tales of Liechtenstein: 30rp, The Treasure of Gutenberg. 1.20fr, The Giant of Guflina slaying the Dragon.

**1967, Apr. 20**

**421** A225 20rp multicolored .30 .25
**422** A225 30rp multicolored .30 .25
**423** A225 1.20fr green & multi .85 .65
*Nos. 421-423 (3)* 1.45 1.15

See Nos. 443-445, 458-460.

Souvenir Sheet

Prince Hans Adam and Countess Kinsky — A226

**1967, June 26 Engr. *Perf. 14x13½***

**424** A226 Sheet of 2 2.40 2.00
*a.* 1.50fr slate blue (Prince) 1.00 1.00
*b.* 1.50fr red brown (Countess) 1.00 1.00

Wedding of Prince Hans Adam of Liechtenstein and Marie Aglae Countess Kinsky of Wichnitz and Tettau, July 30, 1967.

EFTA Emblem A227

**1967, Sept. 28 Photo. *Perf. 11½***

**425** A227 50rp multicolored .55 .45

European Free Trade Association. See note after Norway No. 501.

A228

Christian Symbols: 20rp, Alpha and Omega. 30rp, Trophaeum (The Victorious Cross). 70rp, Chrismon.

**1967, Sept. 28**

**426** A228 20rp rose cl, blk, & gold .25 .25
**427** A228 30rp multicolored .25 .25
**428** A228 70rp dp ultra, blk & gold .60 .45
*Nos. 426-428 (3)* 1.10 .95

A229

**1967, Sept. 28 Engr. & Litho.**

**429** A229 1fr rose claret & pale grn .75 .55

Johann Baptist Büchel (1853-1927), priest, educator, historian and poet. Printed on fluorescent paper.

Peter and Paul, Patron Saints of Mauren — A230

Patron Saints: 5rp, St. Joseph, Planken. 10rp, St. Laurentius, Schaan. 30rp, St. Nicholas, Balzers. 40rp, St. Sebastian, Nendeln. 50rp, St. George, Schellenberg Chapel. 60rp, St. Martin, Eschen. 70rp, St. Fridolin, Ruggell. 80rp, St. Gallus, Triesen. 1fr, St. Theodul, Triesenberg. 1.20fr, St. Ann, Vaduz Castle. 1.50fr, St. Mary, Bendern-Gamprin. 2fr, St. Lucius, patron saint of the Principality.

**1967-71 Photo. *Perf. 11½***

**430** A230 5rp multi ('68) .25 .25
**431** A230 10rp multi ('68) .25 .25
**432** A230 20rp blue & multi .25 .25
**433** A230 30rp dark red & multi .25 .25
**433A** A230 40rp multi ('71) .45 .35
**434** A230 50rp multi ('68) .40 .30
**435** A230 60rp multi ('68) .45 .35
**436** A230 70rp multi .50 .40
**437** A230 80rp multi ('68) .55 .50
**438** A230 1fr multi ('68) .75 .55
**439** A230 1.20fr violet bl & multi .80 .90
**440** A230 1.50fr multi ('68) 1.10 .95
**441** A230 2fr multi ('68) 1.25 1.25
*Nos. 430-441 (13)* 7.25 6.55

Issued: 20rp, 30rp, 70rp, 1.20fr, 12/7/67; 5rp, 1.50fr, 8/29/68; 40rp, 6/11/71; 2fr, 12/5/68; others 4/25/68.

**Europa Issue, 1968**

Common Design Type

**1968, Apr. 25**

**Size: 32½x23mm**

**442** CD11 50rp crimson, gold & ultra *.45 .40*

**Fairy Tale Type of 1967**

30rp, The Treasure of St. Mamerten. 50rp, The Goblin from the Bergerwald. 80rp, The Three Sisters. (Denominations at right.)

**1968, Aug. 29**

**443** A225 30rp Prus blue, yel & red .25 .25
**444** A225 50rp green, yel & bl .40 .30
**445** A225 80rp brt bl, yel & lt bl .65 .55
*Nos. 443-445 (3)* 1.30 1.10

Arms of Liechtenstein and Wilczek A231

**1968, Aug. 29**

**446** A231 75rp multicolored .65 .65

Silver wedding anniversary of Prince Franz Joseph II and Princess Gina.

Sir Rowland Hill — A232

Portraits: 30rp, Count Philippe de Ferrari. 80rp, Carl Lindenberg. 1fr, Maurice Burrus. 1.20fr, Théodore Champion.

**1968-69 Engr. *Perf. 14x13½***

**447** A232 20rp green .25 .25
**448** A232 30rp red brown .25 .25
**449** A232 80rp dark brown .55 .45
**450** A232 1fr black .70 .65
**451** A232 1.20fr dark blue .90 .70
*Nos. 447-451 (5)* 2.65 2.30

Issued to honor "Pioneers of Philately."

Issued: 80rp, 1.20fr, 8/28/69; others, 12/5/68.

See Nos. 509-511.

Coat of Arms — A233

**1969, Apr. 24 Engr. *Perf. 14x13½***
**452** A233 3.50fr dark brown 2.50 1.60

Sheets of 16.

**Europa Issue, 1969**
Common Design Type

**1969, Apr. 24 Photo. *Perf. 14***
**Size: 33x23mm**
**453** CD12 50rp brn red, yel & grn *.45 .45*

"Biology" (Man and DNA Molecule) A234

30rp, "Physics" (man and magnetic field). 50rp, "Astronomy" (man and planets). 80rp, "Art" (artist and Prince Franz Joseph II and Princess Gina).

**1969, Aug. 28 Photo. *Perf. 11½***
**454** A234 10rp grn, dk bl & dp cl .25 .25
**455** A234 30rp brown & multi .25 .25
**456** A234 50rp ultra & green .50 .30
**457** A234 80rp brn, dk brn & yel .75 .50
*Nos. 454-457 (4)* 1.75 1.30

250th anniv. of the Duchy of Liechtenstein.

**Fairy Tale Type of 1967**

20rp, The Cheated Devil. 50rp, The Fiery Red Goat. 60rp, The Grafenberg Treasure (toad). (Denominations at right.)

**1969, Dec. 4 Photo. *Perf. 11½***
**458** A225 20rp multicolored .25 .25
**459** A225 50rp yellow & multi .40 .35
**460** A225 60rp red & multi .55 .45
*Nos. 458-460 (3)* 1.20 1.05

"T" and Arms of Austria-Hungary, Liechtenstein and Switzerland — A235

**1969, Dec. 4 *Perf. 13½***
**461** A235 30rp gold & multi .45 .30

Cent. of the Liechtenstein telegraph system.

Arms of St. Lucius Monastery, Chur — A236

Arms of Ecclesiastic Patrons: 50rp, Pfäfers Abbey (dove). 1.50fr, Chur Bishopric (stag).

**1969, Dec. 4 *Perf. 11½***
**462** A236 30rp multicolored .45 .25
**463** A236 50rp multicolored .45 .35
**464** A236 1.50fr multicolored 1.25 1.00
*Nos. 462-464 (3)* 2.15 1.60

See Nos. 475-477, 486-488.

Prince Wenzel — A237

**1970, Apr. 30 Photo. *Perf. 11½***
**465** A237 1fr sepia & multi .80 .80

25th anniv. of the Liechtenstein Red Cross.

Orange Lily — A238

Native Flowers: 30rp, Bumblebee orchid. 50rp, Glacier crowfoot. 1.20fr, Buck bean.

**1970, Apr. 30**
**466** A238 20rp multicolored .25 .25
**467** A238 30rp green & multi .25 .25
**468** A238 50rp olive & multi .55 .55
**469** A238 1.20fr multicolored 1.10 .75
*Nos. 466-469 (4)* 2.15 1.80

Issued to publicize the European Conservation Year 1970. See Nos. 481-484, 500-503.

**Europa Issue, 1970**
Common Design Type

**1970, Apr. 30 Litho. *Perf. 14***
**Size: 31½x20½mm**
**470** CD13 50rp emerald, dk bl & yel *.45 .45*

**Minnesinger Type of 1961-62**
Souvenir Sheet

Minnesingers: 30rp, Wolfram von Eschenbach. 50rp, Reinmar der Fiedler. 80rp, Hartmann von Starkenberg. 1.20fr, Friedrich von Hausen.

**1970, Aug. 27 Photo. *Perf. 11½***
**471** Sheet of 4 2.50 2.25
*a.* A199 30rp multicolored .25 .25
*b.* A199 50rp multicolored .30 .30
*c.* A199 80rp multicolored .50 .50
*d.* A199 1.20fr multicolored .65 .65

Wolfram von Eschenbach (1170-1220), German minnesinger (poet). Sold for 3fr.

Prince Franz Joseph II — A239

Portrait: 2.50fr, Princess Gina.

**1970-71 Engr. *Perf. 14x13½***
**472** A239 2.50fr violet blue ('71) 1.90 1.40
**473** A239 3fr black 2.25 1.25

Issued: 2.50fr, 6/11; 3fr, 12/3. Sheets of 16.

Mother & Child, Sculpture by Rudolf Schädler — A240

**1970, Dec. 3 Photo. *Perf. 11½***
**474** A240 30rp dark red & multi .45 .35

Christmas.

**Ecclesiastic Arms Type of 1969**

Arms of Ecclesiastic Patrons: 20rp, Abbey of St. John in Thur Valley (Lamb of God). 30rp, Ladies' Abbey, Schänis (crown). 75rp, Abbey of St. Gallen (bear rampant).

**1970, Dec. 3**
**475** A236 20rp lt blue & multi .25 .25
**476** A236 30rp gray, red & gold .25 .25
**477** A236 75rp multicolored .60 .50
*Nos. 475-477 (3)* 1.10 1.00

Bronze Boar, La Tène Period A241

30rp, Peacock, Roman, 2nd cent. 75rp, Decorated copper bowl, 13th cent.

**1971, Mar. 11 Photo. *Perf. 11½***
**478** A241 25rp dp ultra & bluish blk .25 .25
**479** A241 30rp dk brown & green .25 .25
**480** A241 75rp green, yel & brn .60 .45
*Nos. 478-480 (3)* 1.10 .95

Opening of the National Museum, Vaduz.

**Flower Type of 1970**

Flowers: 10rp, Cyclamen. 20rp, Moonwort. 50rp, Superb pink. 1.50fr, Alpine columbine.

**1971, Mar. 11**
**481** A238 10rp multicolored .25 .25
**482** A238 20rp multicolored .25 .25
**483** A238 50rp multicolored .45 .35
**484** A238 1.50fr multicolored 1.25 .85
*Nos. 481-484 (4)* 2.20 1.70

**Europa Issue, 1971**
Common Design Type

**1971, June 11 Photo. *Perf. 13½***
**Size: 31x21mm**
**485** CD14 50rp grnsh bl, yel & blk *.45 .45*

**Ecclesiastic Arms Type of 1969**

Arms of Ecclesiastic Patrons: 30rp, Knights of St. John, Feldkirch (Latin and moline crosses). 50rp, Weingarten Abbey (grapes). 1.20fr, Ottobeuren Abbey (eagle and cross).

**1971, Sept. 2 Photo. *Perf. 11½***
**486** A236 30rp bister & multi .25 .25
**487** A236 50rp multicolored .40 .30
**488** A236 1.20fr gray & multi 1.00 .75
*Nos. 486-488 (3)* 1.65 1.30

Princely Crown A242

Design: 70rp, Page from constitution.

**1971, Sept. 2**
**489** A242 70rp grn, gold, blk & cop .55 .55
**490** A242 80rp dk bl, gold, red & plum .65 .65

50th anniversary of the constitution.

Madonna, by Andrea della Robbia — A243

**1971, Dec. 9**
**491** A243 30rp multicolored .45 .35

Christmas 1971.

Long-distance Skiing — A244

Olympic Rings and: 40rp, Ice hockey. 65rp, Downhill skiing, women's. 1.50fr, Figure skating, women's.

**1971, Dec. 9**
**492** A244 15rp lemon & dk brn .25 .25
**493** A244 40rp multicolored .35 .30
**494** A244 65rp multicolored .55 .45
**495** A244 1.50fr multicolored 1.25 .90
*Nos. 492-495 (4)* 2.40 1.90

11th Winter Olympic Games, Sapporo, Japan, Feb. 3-13, 1972.

**1972, Mar. 16 Photo. *Perf. 11***

10rp, Gymnast. 20rp, High jump. 40rp, Running, women's. 60rp, Discus. All horiz.

**496** A244 10rp claret, brn & gray .25 .25
**497** A244 20rp olive, brn & yel .25 .25
**498** A244 40rp red, brn & gray .30 .30
**499** A244 60rp brn, dk brn & bl .65 .50
*Nos. 496-499 (4)* 1.45 1.30

20th Olympic Games, Munich, Aug. 26-Sept. 10.

**Flower Type of 1970**

Flowers: 20rp, Anemone. 30rp, Turk's cap. 60rp, Alpine centaury. 1.20fr, Reed mace.

**1972, Mar. 16**
**500** A238 20rp dk blue & multi .25 .25
**501** A238 30rp olive & multi .25 .25
**502** A238 60rp multicolored .45 .40
**503** A238 1.20fr multicolored .85 .75
*Nos. 500-503 (4)* 1.80 1.65

**Europa Issue, 1972**
Common Design Type

**1972, Mar. 16**
**504** CD15 40rp dk ol, bl grn & rose red *.45 .45*

Souvenir Sheet

Bendern and Vaduz Castle — A246

**1972, June 8 Engr. *Perf. 13½***
**505** A246 Sheet of 2 2.40 1.75
*a.* 1fr violet blue .75 .65
*b.* 2fr carmine 1.50 1.10

8th Liechtenstein Philatelic Exhibition, LIBA 1972, Vaduz, Aug. 18-27.

Faun, by Rudolf Schädler — A247

**1972, Sept. 7 Photo. *Perf. 11½***
**506** A247 20rp shown .25 .25
**507** A247 30rp Dancer .25 .25
**508** A247 1.10fr Owl .85 .60
*Nos. 506-508 (3)* 1.35 1.10

Sculptures made of roots and branches by Rudolf Schädler.

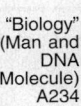

### Portrait Type of 1968-69

Portraits: 30rp, Emilio Diena. 40rp, André de Cock. 1.30fr, Theodore E. Steinway.

**1972, Sept. 7 Engr.** ***Perf. 14x13½***

| | | | | |
|---|---|---|---|---|
| **509** A232 | 30rp Prus green | .25 | .25 |
| **510** A232 | 40rp dk violet brn | .30 | .25 |
| **511** A232 | 1.30fr violet blue | 1.00 | .80 |
| | *Nos. 509-511 (3)* | 1.55 | 1.30 |

Pioneers of Philately.

Madonna with Angels, by Ferdinand Nigg — A248

**1972, Dec. 7 Photo.** ***Perf. 11½***

**512** A248 30rp black & multi .50 .40

Christmas 1972.

Silum — A249

Landscapes: 10rp, Lawena Springs. 15rp, Ruggell Marsh. 25rp, Steg, Kirchlispitz. 30rp, Fields, Schellenberg. 40rp, Rennhof, Mauren. 50rp, Tidrüfe Vaduz. 60rp, Eschner Riet. 70rp, Mittagspitz. 80rp, Three Sisters, Schaan Forest. 1fr, St. Peter's and Tower House, Mäls. 1.30fr, Road, Frommenhaus. 1.50fr, Ox Head Mountain. 1.80fr, Hehlawangspitz. 2fr, Saminaschlucht.

**1972-73 Engr. & Litho.** ***Perf. 11½***

| | | | |
|---|---|---|---|
| **513** A249 | 5rp brn, yel & mag | .25 | .25 |
| **514** A249 | 10rp slate grn & cit | .25 | .25 |
| **515** A249 | 15rp red brn & cit | .25 | .25 |
| **516** A249 | 25rp dk vio & pale grn | .25 | .25 |
| **517** A249 | 30rp purple & buff | .25 | .25 |
| **518** A249 | 40rp vio & pale salmon | .30 | .25 |
| **519** A249 | 50rp vio bl & rose | .40 | .35 |
| **520** A249 | 60rp grn & yel | .50 | .45 |
| **521** A249 | 70rp dk & lt blue | .60 | .50 |
| **522** A249 | 80rp Prus grn & cit | .65 | .55 |
| **523** A249 | 1fr red brn & lt grn | .85 | .65 |
| **524** A249 | 1.30fr ultra & lt grn | 1.10 | 1.00 |
| **525** A249 | 1.50fr brn & lt blue | 1.25 | 1.00 |
| **526** A249 | 1.80fr brown & buff | 1.50 | 1.25 |
| **527** A249 | 2fr sepia & pale grn | 1.65 | 1.40 |
| | *Nos. 513-527 (15)* | 10.05 | 8.65 |

Issued: 10rp, 15rp, 80rp, 1fr, 1.50fr, 12/7; 30rp, 1.30fr, 1.80fr, 3/8/73; 50rp, 60rp, 70rp, 6/7/73; 5rp, 25rp, 40rp, 2fr, 12/6/73.

### Europa Issue, 1973

Common Design Type

**1973, Mar. 8 Photo.** ***Perf. 11½***

**Size: 33x23mm**

| | | | |
|---|---|---|---|
| **528** CD16 | 30rp purple & multi | *.25* | *.25* |
| **529** CD16 | 40rp blue & multi | *.35* | *.35* |

Nautilus Cup — A250

70rp, Ivory tankard. 1.10fr, Silver goblet.

**1973, June 7 Photo.** ***Perf. 11½***

| | | | |
|---|---|---|---|
| **530** A250 | 30rp gray & multi | .25 | .25 |
| **531** A250 | 70rp multicolored | .50 | .40 |
| **532** A250 | 1.10fr dk blue & multi | .90 | .60 |
| | *Nos. 530-532 (3)* | 1.65 | 1.25 |

Drinking vessels from the Princely Treasury.

Arms of Liechtenstein and Municipalities — A251

**Engraved & Photogravure**

**1973, Sept. 6** ***Perf. 14x13½***

**533** A251 5fr black & multi 4.00 2.50

Coenonympha Oedippus — A252

Designs: 15rp, Alpine newt. 25rp, European viper (adder). 40rp, Common curlew. 60rp, Edible frog. 70rp, Dappled butterfly. 80rp, Grass snake. 1.10fr, Three-toed woodpecker.

**1973-74 Photo.** ***Perf. 11½***

| | | | |
|---|---|---|---|
| **534** A252 | 15rp multicolored | .25 | .25 |
| **535** A252 | 25rp multicolored | .30 | .25 |
| **536** A252 | 30rp orange & multi | .25 | .25 |
| **537** A252 | 40rp brown & multi | .35 | .35 |
| **538** A252 | 60rp multicolored | .60 | .60 |
| **539** A252 | 70rp multicolored | .65 | .60 |
| **540** A252 | 80rp multicolored | .70 | .70 |
| **541** A252 | 1.10fr multicolored | 1.00 | 1.00 |
| | *Nos. 534-541 (8)* | 4.10 | 4.00 |

Issue dates: 30rp, 40rp, 60rp, 80rp, Dec. 6. Others, June 6, 1974.

Virgin and Child, by Bartolomeo di Tommaso — A253

**Engraved & Lithographed**

**1973, Dec. 6** ***Perf. 13½***

**542** A253 30rp gold & multi .50 .30

Christmas 1973.

The Vociferant Horseman, by Andrea Riccio — A254

Europa: 40rp, Kneeling Venus, by Antonio Susini.

**1974, Mar. 21 Photo.** ***Perf. 11½***

| | | | |
|---|---|---|---|
| **543** A254 | 30rp tan & multi | *.35* | *.30* |
| **544** A254 | 40rp ultra & multi | *.50* | *.45* |

Chinese Vase, 19th Century — A255

Chinese vases from Princely Treasury.

**1974, Mar. 21**

| | | | |
|---|---|---|---|
| **545** A255 | 30rp shown | .30 | .25 |
| **546** A255 | 50rp from 1740 | .45 | .35 |
| **547** A255 | 60rp from 1830 | .55 | .40 |
| **548** A255 | 1fr circa 1700 | .95 | .60 |
| | *Nos. 545-548 (4)* | 2.25 | 1.60 |

Soccer A256

**1974, Mar. 21**

**549** A256 80rp lemon & multi .80 .75

World Soccer Championships, Munich June 13-July 7.

Post Horn and UPU Emblem A257

**1974, June 6** ***Perf. 13½***

| | | | |
|---|---|---|---|
| **550** A257 | 40rp gold, green & blk | .35 | .30 |
| **551** A257 | 60rp gold, red & blk | .55 | .40 |

Centenary of Universal Postal Union.

Bishop F. A. Marxer — A258

**Photogravure and Engraved**

**1974, June 6** ***Perf. 14x13½***

**552** A258 1fr multicolored .95 .75

Bicentenary of the death of Bishop Franz Anton Marxer (1703-1775).

Prince Constantin A259

Prince Hans Adam — A260

Princess Gina and Prince Franz Joseph II — A261

80rp, Prince Maximilian. 1.20fr, Prince Alois.

**1974-75 Photo.** ***Perf. 11½***

| | | | |
|---|---|---|---|
| **553** A259 | 70rp dk green & gold | .70 | .55 |
| **554** A259 | 80rp dp claret & gold | .75 | .65 |
| **555** A259 | 1.20fr bluish blk & gold | 1.10 | 1.00 |

**Engr.**

***Perf. 14x13½***

**556** A260 1.70fr slate green 1.40 1.00

**Photogravure and Engraved**

***Perf. 13½x14***

| | | | |
|---|---|---|---|
| **557** A261 | 10fr gold & choc | 6.50 | 4.50 |
| | *Nos. 553-557 (5)* | 10.45 | 7.70 |

No. 557 printed in sheets of 4.

Issued: 1.70fr, 12/5; 10fr, 9/5/74; others, 3/13/75.

St. Florian — A262

50rp, St. Wendelin. 60rp, Virgin Mary with Sts. Anna and Joachim. 70rp, Nativity.

**1974, Dec. 5 Photo.** ***Perf. 12***

| | | | |
|---|---|---|---|
| **560** A262 | 30rp multicolored | .30 | .25 |
| **561** A262 | 50rp multicolored | .40 | .35 |
| **562** A262 | 60rp multicolored | .50 | .40 |
| **563** A262 | 70rp multicolored | .65 | .50 |
| | *Nos. 560-563 (4)* | 1.85 | 1.50 |

Designs are from 19th century devotional glass paintings. Christmas 1974.

"Cold Sun," by Martin Frommelt A263

Europa: 60rp, "Village," by Louis Jaeger.

**1975, Mar. 13** ***Perf. 11½***

| | | | |
|---|---|---|---|
| **564** A263 | 30rp multicolored | *.25* | *.25* |
| **565** A263 | 60rp multicolored | *.50* | *.45* |

Red Cross Activities — A264

**1975, June 5 Photo.** ***Perf. 11½***

**566** A264 60rp dk blue & multi .55 .55

30th anniv. of the Liechtenstein Red Cross.

Coronation Robe — A265

Imperial Crown — A266

**1975 Engr. & Photo.** ***Perf. 14***

| | | | |
|---|---|---|---|
| **567** A266 | 30rp Imperial cross | .30 | .25 |
| **568** A266 | 60rp Imperial sword | .45 | .40 |
| **569** A266 | 1fr Orb | .90 | .75 |
| **570** A265 | 1.30fr shown | 1.75 | 1.60 |
| **571** A266 | 2fr shown | 3.50 | 2.75 |
| | *Nos. 567-571 (5)* | 6.90 | 5.75 |

Treasures of the Holy Roman Empire from the Treasury of the Hofburg in Vienna, Austria.

Issue dates: 1.30fr, Sept. 4; others, June 5.

See Nos. 617-620.

St. Mamerten, Triesen A267

Designs: 50rp, Red House, Vaduz, 14th century. 70rp, Prebendary House, Eschen, 14th century. 1fr, Gutenberg Castle.

**1975, Sept. 4 Photo. *Perf. 11½***

| | | | | |
|---|---|---|---|---|
| **572** A267 | 40rp multicolored | .40 | .30 |
| **573** A267 | 50rp multicolored | .45 | .30 |
| **574** A267 | 70rp plum & multi | .85 | .60 |
| **575** A267 | 1fr dk blue & multi | 1.10 | .75 |
| | *Nos. 572-575 (4)* | 2.80 | 1.95 |

European Architectural Heritage Year 1975.

Speed Skating A268

Designs (Olympic Rings and): 25rp, Ice hockey. 70rp, Downhill skiing. 1.20fr, Slalom.

**1975, Dec. 4 Photo. *Perf. 11½***

| | | | |
|---|---|---|---|
| **576** A268 | 20rp multicolored | .25 | .25 |
| **577** A268 | 25rp multicolored | .25 | .25 |
| **578** A268 | 70rp multicolored | .65 | .50 |
| **579** A268 | 1.20fr yellow & multi | 1.25 | .95 |
| | *Nos. 576-579 (4)* | 2.40 | 1.95 |

12th Winter Olympic Games, Innsbruck, Austria, Feb. 4-15, 1976.

Daniel in the Lions' Den — A269

Designs: 60rp, Virgin and Child. 90rp, St. Peter. All designs are after Romanesque sculptured capitals in Chur Cathedral, c. 1208.

**Photogravure and Engraved**

**1975, Dec. 4 *Perf. 14***

| | | | |
|---|---|---|---|
| **580** A269 | 30rp gold & purple | .25 | .25 |
| **581** A269 | 60rp gold & green | .45 | .40 |
| **582** A269 | 90rp gold & claret | .80 | .75 |
| | *Nos. 580-582 (3)* | 1.50 | 1.40 |

Christmas and Holy Year 1975.

River Crayfish — A270

World Wildlife Fund: 40rp, European pond turtle. 70rp, Old-world otter. 80rp, Lapwing.

**1976, Mar. 11 Photo. *Perf. 11½***

| | | | |
|---|---|---|---|
| **583** A270 | 25rp multicolored | .50 | .25 |
| **584** A270 | 40rp multicolored | .75 | .35 |
| **585** A270 | 70rp multicolored | 1.10 | .55 |
| **586** A270 | 80rp multicolored | 1.75 | 1.00 |
| | *Nos. 583-586 (4)* | 4.10 | 2.15 |

Mouflon — A271

Europa: 80rp, Pheasant family. Ceramics by Prince Hans von Liechtenstein.

**1976, Mar. 11**

| | | | |
|---|---|---|---|
| **587** A271 | 40rp multicolored | *.40* | *.35* |
| **588** A271 | 80rp violet & multi | *.80* | *.75* |

Roman Fibula, 3rd Century A272

**1976, Mar. 11**

**589** A272 90rp vio bl, grn & gold 1.00 .80

Historical Association of Liechtenstein, 75th anniversary.

Souvenir Sheet

Franz Josef II 50fr-Memorial Coin — A273

**1976, June 10 Photo. *Imperf.***

| | | | |
|---|---|---|---|
| **590** A273 | Sheet of 2 | 1.75 | 1.75 |
| *a.* | 1fr blue & multi | .85 | .85 |
| *b.* | 1fr red & multi | .85 | .85 |

70th birthday of Prince Franz Joseph II of Liechtenstein.

Judo and Olympic Rings — A274

Designs (Olympic Rings and): 50rp, volleyball. 80rp, Relay race. 1.10fr, Long jump, women's.

**1976, June 10 *Perf. 11½***

| | | | |
|---|---|---|---|
| **591** A274 | 35rp multicolored | .25 | .25 |
| **592** A274 | 50rp multicolored | .45 | .40 |
| **593** A274 | 80rp multicolored | .65 | .60 |
| **594** A274 | 1.10fr multicolored | 1.00 | .75 |
| | *Nos. 591-594 (4)* | 2.35 | 2.00 |

21st Olympic Games, Montreal, Canada, July 17-Aug. 1.

Rubens' Sons, Albrecht and Nikolas — A275

Rubens Paintings: 50rp, Singing Angels. 1fr, The Daughters of Cecrops, horiz. (from Collection of Prince of Liechtenstein).

**Size: 24x38mm**

**1976, Sept. 9 Engr. *Perf. 13½x14***

| | | | |
|---|---|---|---|
| **595** A275 | 50rp gold & multi | .70 | .70 |
| **596** A275 | 70rp gold & multi | 1.00 | 1.00 |

**Size: 48x38mm**

| | | | |
|---|---|---|---|
| **597** A275 | 1fr gold & multi | 2.75 | 2.75 |
| | *Nos. 595-597 (3)* | 4.45 | 4.45 |

400th anniversary of the birth of Peter Paul Rubens (1577-1640), Flemish painter. Sheets of 8 (2x4).

Zodiac Signs — A276

**1976-78 Photo. *Perf. 11½***

| | | | |
|---|---|---|---|
| **598** A276 | 20rp Pisces | .25 | .25 |
| **599** A276 | 40rp Aries | .35 | .35 |
| **600** A276 | 40rp Cancer ('77) | .40 | .35 |
| **601** A276 | 40rp Scorpio ('78) | .45 | .45 |
| **602** A276 | 50rp Sagittarius ('78) | .50 | .45 |
| **603** A276 | 70rp Leo ('77) | .65 | .65 |
| **604** A276 | 80rp Taurus | .75 | .70 |
| **605** A276 | 80rp Virgo ('77) | .75 | .75 |
| **606** A276 | 80rp Capricorn ('78) | .75 | .70 |
| **607** A276 | 90rp Gemini | 1.00 | .75 |
| **608** A276 | 1.10fr Libra ('77) | 1.10 | 1.10 |
| **609** A276 | 1.50fr Aquarius ('78) | 1.25 | 1.25 |
| | *Nos. 598-609 (12)* | 8.20 | 7.75 |

Flight into Egypt — A277

Monastic Wax Works: 20rp, Holy Infant of Prague, horiz. 80rp, Holy Family and Trinity. 1.50fr, Holy Family, horiz.

**1976, Dec. 9 Photo. *Perf. 11½***

| | | | |
|---|---|---|---|
| **610** A277 | 20rp multicolored | .25 | .25 |
| **611** A277 | 50rp multicolored | .45 | .35 |
| **612** A277 | 80rp multicolored | .60 | .50 |
| **613** A277 | 1.50fr multicolored | 1.40 | 1.10 |
| | *Nos. 610-613 (4)* | 2.70 | 2.20 |

Christmas 1976.

Ortlieb von Brandis, Sarcophagus A278

**Photogravure and Engraved**

**1976, Dec. 9 *Perf. 13½x14***

**614** A278 1.10fr gold & dk brown 1.00 .70

Ortlieb von Brandis, Bishop of Chur (1458-1491).

Map of Liechtenstein, by J. J. Heber, 1721 — A279

Europa: 80rp, View of Vaduz, by Ferdinand Bachmann, 1815.

**1977, Mar. 10 Photo. *Perf. 12½***

| | | | |
|---|---|---|---|
| **615** A279 | 40rp multicolored | *.40* | *.40* |
| **616** A279 | 80rp multicolored | *.80* | *.80* |

**Treasure Type of 1975**

40rp, Holy Lance and Particle of the Cross. 50rp, Imperial Evangel of St. Matthew. 80rp, St. Stephen's Purse. 90rp, Tabard of Imperial Herald.

**Engraved and Photogravure**

**1977, June 8 *Perf. 14***

| | | | |
|---|---|---|---|
| **617** A266 | 40rp gold & multi | .40 | .25 |
| **618** A266 | 50rp gold & multi | .50 | .40 |
| **619** A266 | 80rp gold & multi | .70 | .55 |
| **620** A266 | 90rp gold & multi | 1.00 | .80 |
| | *Nos. 617-620 (4)* | 2.60 | 2.00 |

Treasures of the Holy Roman Empire from the Treasury of the Hofburg in Vienna.

Emperor Constantius II Coin — A280

Coins: 70rp, Lindau bracteate, c. 1300. 80rp, Ortlieb von Brandis, 1458-1491.

**1977, June 8 Photo. *Perf. 11½***

**Granite Paper**

| | | | |
|---|---|---|---|
| **621** A280 | 35rp gold & multi | .35 | .25 |
| **622** A280 | 70rp silver & multi | .60 | .50 |
| **623** A280 | 80rp silver & multi | .80 | .55 |
| | *Nos. 621-623 (3)* | 1.75 | 1.30 |

Frauenthal Castle A281

Castles: 50rp, Gross Ullersdorf. 80rp, Liechtenstein Castle near Mödling, Austria. 90rp, Liechtenstein Palace, Vienna.

**Engraved and Photogravure**

**1977, Sept. 8 *Perf. 13½x14***

| | | | |
|---|---|---|---|
| **624** A281 | 20rp slate grn & gold | .25 | .25 |
| **625** A281 | 50rp magenta & gold | .50 | .40 |
| **626** A281 | 80rp dk violet & gold | .80 | .65 |
| **627** A281 | 90rp dk blue & gold | .90 | .75 |
| | *Nos. 624-627 (4)* | 2.45 | 2.05 |

Children — A282

Traditional Costumes: 70rp, Two girls. 1fr, Woman in festival dress.

**1977, Sept. 8 Photo. *Perf. 11½***

**Granite Paper**

| | | | |
|---|---|---|---|
| **628** A282 | 40rp multicolored | .50 | .35 |
| **629** A282 | 70rp multicolored | .75 | .60 |
| **630** A282 | 1fr multicolored | 1.25 | .75 |
| | *Nos. 628-630 (3)* | 2.50 | 1.70 |

Princess Tatjana A283

**1977, Dec. 7 Photo. *Perf. 11½***

**631** A283 1.10fr brown & gold 1.20 .75

Angel — A284

Sculptures by Erasmus Kern: 50rp, St. Rochus. 80rp, Virgin and Child. 1.50fr, God the Father.

**1977, Dec. 7**

| | | | |
|---|---|---|---|
| **632** A284 | 20rp multicolored | .25 | .25 |
| **633** A284 | 50rp multicolored | .45 | .35 |
| **634** A284 | 80rp multicolored | .75 | .50 |
| **635** A284 | 1.50fr multicolored | 1.50 | 1.00 |
| | *Nos. 632-635 (4)* | 2.95 | 2.10 |

Christmas 1977.

Liechtenstein Palace, Vienna
A285

Europa: 80rp, Feldsberg Castle.

**Photogravure and Engraved**

**1978, Mar. 2** ***Perf. 14***

| | | | | |
|---|---|---|---|---|
| **636** | A285 40rp gold & slate blue | *.35* | *.30* |
| **637** | A285 80rp gold & claret | *.75* | *.70* |

Farmhouse, Triesen — A286

Designs: 20rp, Houses, Upper Village, Triesen. 35rp, Barns, Balzers. 40rp, Monastery, Bendern. 50rp, Residential Tower, Balzers-Mäls. 70rp, Parish house. 80rp, Farmhouse, Schellenberg. 90rp, Parish house, Balzers. 1fr, Rheinberger House, Music School, Vaduz. 1.10fr, Street, Mitteldorf, Vaduz. 1.50fr, Town Hall, Triesenberg. 2fr, National Museum and Administrator's Residence, Vaduz.

**1978** **Photo.** ***Perf. 11½***

| | | | |
|---|---|---|---|
| **638** A286 | 10rp multicolored | .25 | .25 |
| **639** A286 | 20rp multicolored | .25 | .25 |
| **640** A286 | 35rp multicolored | .30 | .25 |
| **641** A286 | 40rp multicolored | .30 | .25 |
| **642** A286 | 50rp multicolored | .45 | .30 |
| **643** A286 | 70rp multicolored | .60 | .40 |
| **644** A286 | 80rp multicolored | .65 | .45 |
| **645** A286 | 90rp multicolored | .80 | .50 |
| **646** A286 | 1fr multicolored | .85 | .55 |
| **647** A286 | 1.10fr multicolored | 1.00 | .65 |
| **648** A286 | 1.50fr multicolored | 1.20 | .80 |
| **649** A286 | 2fr multicolored | 1.75 | 1.10 |
| | *Nos. 638-649 (12)* | 8.40 | 5.75 |

Vaduz Castle
A287

Vaduz Castle: 50rp, Courtyard. 70rp, Staircase. 80rp, Triptych from High Altar, Castle Chapel.

**Engraved and Photogravure**

**1978, June 1** ***Perf. 13½x14***

| | | | |
|---|---|---|---|
| **650** A287 | 40rp gold & multi | .40 | .30 |
| **651** A287 | 50rp gold & multi | .50 | .40 |
| **652** A287 | 70rp gold & multi | .70 | .60 |
| **653** A287 | 80rp gold & multi | .95 | .70 |
| | *Nos. 650-653 (4)* | 2.55 | 2.00 |

40th anniversary of reign of Prince Franz Joseph II. Sheet of 8.

Prince Karl I, Coin, 1614 — A288

Designs: 50rp, Prince Johann Adam, medal, 1694. 80rp, Prince Josef Wenzel, medal, 1773.

**1978, Sept. 7** **Photo.** ***Perf. 11½***

| | | | |
|---|---|---|---|
| **654** A288 | 40rp multicolored | .35 | .30 |
| **655** A288 | 50rp multicolored | .50 | .40 |
| **656** A288 | 80rp multicolored | .95 | .70 |
| | *Nos. 654-656 (3)* | 1.80 | 1.40 |

Adoration of the Shepherds — A289

Stained-glass Windows, Triesenberg: 50rp, Holy Family. 80rp, Adoration of the Kings.

**1978, Dec. 7** **Photo.** ***Perf. 11½***

| | | | |
|---|---|---|---|
| **657** A289 | 20rp multicolored | .25 | .25 |
| **658** A289 | 50rp multicolored | .50 | .40 |
| **659** A289 | 80rp multicolored | .80 | .70 |
| | *Nos. 657-659 (3)* | 1.55 | 1.35 |

Christmas 1978.

Piebald, by Hamilton and Faistenberger
A290

Golden Carriage of Prince Joseph Wenzel, by Martin von Meytens — A291

Design: 80rp, Black stallion, by Johann Georg von Hamilton.

**Photo. & Engr.**

**1978, Dec. 7** ***Perf. 13½x14***

| | | | |
|---|---|---|---|
| **660** A290 | 70rp multicolored | .60 | .50 |
| **661** A290 | 80rp multicolored | .70 | .60 |

***Perf. 12***

| | | | |
|---|---|---|---|
| **662** A291 | 1.10fr multicolored | .95 | .70 |
| | *Nos. 660-662 (3)* | 2.25 | 1.80 |

Sheets of 8.

Mail Plane over Schaan
A292

Europa: 80rp, Zeppelin over Vaduz Castle.

**1979, Mar. 8** **Photo.** ***Perf. 11½***

| | | | |
|---|---|---|---|
| **663** A292 | 40rp multicolored | *.50* | *.45* |
| **664** A292 | 80rp multicolored | *.65* | *.60* |

First airmail service, St. Gallen to Schaan, Aug. 31, 1930, and first Zeppelin flight to Liechtenstein, June 10, 1931.

Child Drinking — A293

90rp, Child eating. 1.10fr, Child reading.

**1979, Mar. 8**

| | | | |
|---|---|---|---|
| **665** A293 | 80rp silver & multi | .75 | .70 |
| **666** A293 | 90rp silver & multi | .85 | .85 |
| **667** A293 | 1.10fr silver & multi | .95 | .95 |
| | *Nos. 665-667 (3)* | 2.55 | 2.50 |

International Year of the Child.

Ordered Wave Fields
A294

Sun over Continents
A296

Council of Europe
A295

**1979, June 7** **Litho.** ***Perf. 11½***

| | | | |
|---|---|---|---|
| **668** A294 | 50rp multicolored | .50 | .40 |

**Photo.**

| | | | |
|---|---|---|---|
| **669** A295 | 80rp multicolored | .65 | .55 |
| **670** A296 | 100rp multicolored | .80 | .65 |
| | *Nos. 668-670 (3)* | 1.95 | 1.60 |

Intl. Radio Consultative Committee (CCIR) of the Intl. Telecommunications Union, 50th anniv. (50rp); Entry into Council of Europe (80rp); aid to developing countries (100rp).

Heraldic Panel of Carl Ludwig von Sulz — A297

Heraldic Panels of: 70rp, Barbara von Sulz, née zu Staufen. 1.10fr, Ulrich von Ramschwag and Barbara von Hallwil.

**Photogravure and Engraved**

**1979, June 1** ***Perf. 13½***

| | | | |
|---|---|---|---|
| **671** A297 | 40rp multicolored | .55 | .30 |
| **672** A297 | 70rp multicolored | .65 | .50 |
| **673** A297 | 1.10fr multicolored | 1.10 | .95 |
| | *Nos. 671-673 (3)* | 2.30 | 1.75 |

Sts. Lucius and Florin, Fresco in Waltensburg-Vuorz Church — A298

**Photogravure and Engraved**

**1979, Sept. 6** ***Perf. 13½***

| | | | |
|---|---|---|---|
| **674** A298 | 20fr multicolored | 14.00 | 7.50 |

Patron saints of Liechtenstein. Printed in sheets of 4.

Annunciation, Embroidery — A299

Christmas (Ferdnand Nigg Embroideries): 50rp, Christmas. 80rp, Blessed Are the Peacemakers.

**1979, Dec. 6** **Engr.** ***Perf. 13½***

| | | | |
|---|---|---|---|
| **675** A299 | 20rp multicolored | .50 | .25 |
| **676** A299 | 50rp multicolored | .50 | .35 |
| **677** A299 | 80rp multicolored | .80 | .50 |
| | *Nos. 675-677 (3)* | 1.80 | 1.10 |

Cross-Country Skiing
A300

Olympic Rings and: 70rp, Oxhead Mountain. 1.50fr, Ski lift.

**1979, Dec. 6** **Photo.** ***Perf. 12***

| | | | |
|---|---|---|---|
| **678** A300 | 40rp multicolored | .45 | .25 |
| **679** A300 | 70rp multicolored | .65 | .45 |
| **680** A300 | 1.50fr multicolored | 1.25 | 1.00 |
| | *Nos. 678-680 (3)* | 2.35 | 1.70 |

13th Winter Olympic Games, Lake Placid, NY, Feb. 12-24, 1980.

Arms of Bailiff Andreas Buchel, 1690 — A301

Various arms: 70rp, Georg Marxer, 1745. 80rp, Luzius Frick, 1503. 1.10rp, Adam Oehri, 1634.

**1980, Mar. 10** **Photo.** ***Perf. 11½***

**Granite Paper**

| | | | |
|---|---|---|---|
| **681** A301 | 40rp shown | .30 | .30 |
| **682** A301 | 70rp multicolored | .50 | .45 |
| **683** A301 | 80rp multicolored | .85 | .70 |
| **684** A301 | 1.10fr multicolored | .75 | .70 |
| | *Nos. 681-684 (4)* | 2.40 | 2.15 |

See Nos. 704-707, 729-732.

Princess Maria Leopoldine Esterhazy, by Antonio Canova — A302

Europa: 80rp, Maria Theresa, Duchess of Savoy, by Martin van Meytens.

**1980, Mar. 10**

| | | | |
|---|---|---|---|
| **685** A302 | 40rp multicolored | *.40* | *.35* |
| **686** A302 | 80rp multicolored | *.60* | *.50* |

Milking Pail — A303

Old Alpine Farm Tools: 50rp, Wooden heart, ceremonial cattle decoration. 80rp, Butter churn.

**1980, Sept. 8**

| | | | | |
|---|---|---|---|---|
| **687** | A303 | 20rp multicolored | .25 | .25 |
| **688** | A303 | 50rp multicolored | .45 | .35 |
| **689** | A303 | 80rp multicolored | .75 | .55 |
| | | *Nos. 687-689 (3)* | 1.45 | 1.15 |

Liechtenstein No. 94 — A304

**1980, Sept 8**

| | | | | |
|---|---|---|---|---|
| **690** | A304 | 80rp multicolored | .80 | .60 |

Postal Museum, 50th anniversary.

Crossbow with Spanning Device A305

90rp, Spear, knife. 1.10fr, Rifle, powderhorn.

**1980, Sept. 8 Engr. *Perf. 13½x14***

| | | | | |
|---|---|---|---|---|
| **691** | A305 | 80rp shown | .60 | .55 |
| **692** | A305 | 90rp multicolored | .75 | .60 |
| **693** | A305 | 1.10fr multicolored | .90 | .65 |
| | | *Nos. 691-693 (3)* | 2.25 | 1.80 |

Triesenberg Family In Traditional Costumes A306

70rp, Folk dancers, Schellenberg. 80rp, Brass band, Mauren.

**1980, Sept. 8 Photo. *Perf. 12***
**Granite Paper**

| | | | | |
|---|---|---|---|---|
| **694** | A306 | 40rp shown | .45 | .25 |
| **695** | A306 | 70rp multicolored | .70 | .50 |
| **696** | A306 | 80rp multicolored | .75 | .60 |
| | | *Nos. 694-696 (3)* | 1.90 | 1.35 |

Green Beeches, Matrula Forest — A307

50rp, White firs, Valorsch Valley. 80rp, Beech forest, Schaan. 1.50fr, Forest, Oberplanken.

**Photogravure and Engraved**
**1980, Dec. 9 *Perf. 14***

| | | | | |
|---|---|---|---|---|
| **697** | A307 | 40rp shown | .35 | .25 |
| **698** | A307 | 50rp multicolored | .45 | .40 |
| **699** | A307 | 80rp multicolored | .75 | .55 |
| **700** | A307 | 1.50fr multicolored | 1.40 | 1.00 |
| | | *Nos. 697-700 (4)* | 2.95 | 2.20 |

Glad Tidings — A308

**1980, Dec. 9 Photo. *Perf. 11½***
**Granite Paper**

| | | | | |
|---|---|---|---|---|
| **701** | A308 | 20rp shown | .25 | .25 |
| **702** | A308 | 50rp Creche | .45 | .35 |
| **703** | A308 | 80rp Epiphany | .70 | .60 |
| | | *Nos. 701-703 (3)* | 1.40 | 1.20 |

Christmas 1980.

**Bailiff Arms Type of 1980**

40rp, Anton Meier, 1748. 70rp, Kaspar Kindle, 1534. 80rp, Hans Adam Negele, 1600. 1.10fr, Peter Matt, 1693.

**1981, Mar. 9 Photo. *Perf. 11½***
**Granite Paper**

| | | | | |
|---|---|---|---|---|
| **704** | A301 | 40rp multicolored | .45 | .30 |
| **705** | A301 | 70rp multicolored | .75 | .50 |
| **706** | A301 | 80rp multicolored | .80 | .60 |
| **707** | A301 | 1.10fr multicolored | 1.10 | .90 |
| | | *Nos. 704-707 (4)* | 3.10 | 2.30 |

Fireworks at Vaduz Castle — A309

Europa: 80rp, National Day procession.

**1981, Mar. 9 *Perf. 12½***
**Granite Paper**

| | | | | |
|---|---|---|---|---|
| **708** | A309 | 40rp multicolored | *.35* | *.30* |
| **709** | A309 | 80rp multicolored | *.65* | *.60* |

Souvenir Sheet

Prince Alois, Princess Elisabeth and Prince Franz Joseph II — A310

**1981, June 9 Photo. *Perf. 13***
**Granite Paper**

| | | | | |
|---|---|---|---|---|
| **710** | A310 | Sheet of 3 | 2.75 | 2.50 |
| *a.* | | 70rp shown | .50 | .50 |
| *b.* | | 80rp Princes Alois and Franz Joseph II | .55 | .55 |
| *c.* | | 150rp Prince Franz Joseph II | 1.00 | 1.00 |

75th birthday of Prince Franz Joseph II.

Scout Emblems — A311

**1981, June 9**

| | | | | |
|---|---|---|---|---|
| **711** | A311 | 20rp multicolored | .50 | .40 |

50th anniversary of Boy Scouts and Girl Guides.

Man in Wheelchair — A312

**1981, June 9**

| | | | | |
|---|---|---|---|---|
| **712** | A312 | 40rp multicolored | .50 | .40 |

International Year of the Disabled.

St. Theodul, 1600th Birth Anniv. — A313

**1981, June 9**

| | | | | |
|---|---|---|---|---|
| **713** | A313 | 80rp multicolored | .80 | .55 |

Mosses and Lichens A314

40rp, Xanthoria parietina. 50rp, Parmelia physodes. 70rp, Sphagnum palustre. 80rp, Amblystegium.

**Photogravure and Engraved**
**1981, Sept. 7 *Perf. 13½***

| | | | | |
|---|---|---|---|---|
| **714** | A314 | 40rp multicolored | .45 | .30 |
| **715** | A314 | 50rp multicolored | .45 | .35 |
| **716** | A314 | 70rp multicolored | .60 | .50 |
| **717** | A314 | 80rp multicolored | .70 | .60 |
| | | *Nos. 714-717 (4)* | 2.20 | 1.75 |

Gutenberg Castle A315

**1981, Sept. 7**

| | | | | |
|---|---|---|---|---|
| **718** | A315 | 20rp shown | .45 | .25 |
| **719** | A315 | 40rp Castle yard | .45 | .30 |
| **720** | A315 | 50rp Parlor | .45 | .35 |
| **721** | A315 | 1.10fr Great Hall | .95 | .85 |
| | | *Nos. 718-721 (4)* | 2.30 | 1.75 |

St. Charles Borromeo (1538-1584) A316

Famous Visitors to Liechtenstein (Paintings): 70rp, Goethe (1749-1832), by Angelica Kauffmann. 80rp, Alexander Dumas (1824-1895). 1fr, Hermann Hesse (1877-1962), by Cuno Amiet.

**Lithographed and Engraved**
**1981, Dec. 7 *Perf. 14***

| | | | | |
|---|---|---|---|---|
| **722** | A316 | 40rp multicolored | .35 | .30 |
| **723** | A316 | 70rp multicolored | .60 | .50 |
| **724** | A316 | 80rp multicolored | .70 | .60 |
| **725** | A316 | 1fr multicolored | .80 | .70 |
| | | *Nos. 722-725 (4)* | 2.45 | 2.10 |

See Nos. 747-750.

St. Nicholas — A317

50rp, Adoration of the Kings. 80rp, Holy Family.

**1981, Dec. 7 Photo. *Perf. 11½***
**Granite Paper**

| | | | | |
|---|---|---|---|---|
| **726** | A317 | 20rp shown | .25 | .25 |
| **727** | A317 | 50rp multicolored | .45 | .40 |
| **728** | A317 | 80rp multicolored | .70 | .60 |
| | | *Nos. 726-728 (3)* | 1.40 | 1.25 |

Christmas 1981.

**Bailiff Arms Type of 1980**

40rp, Johann Kaiser, 1664. 70rp, Joseph Anton Kaufmann, 1748. 80rp, Christoph Walser, 1690. 1.10fr, Stephan Banzer, 1658.

**1982, Mar. 8 Photo.**
**Granite Paper**

| | | | | |
|---|---|---|---|---|
| **729** | A301 | 40rp multicolored | .35 | .35 |
| **730** | A301 | 70rp multicolored | .55 | .50 |
| **731** | A301 | 80rp multicolored | .70 | .60 |
| **732** | A301 | 1.10fr multicolored | 1.00 | .80 |
| | | *Nos. 729-732 (4)* | 2.60 | 2.25 |

Europa 1982 — A318

40rp, Peasants' Uprising, 1525. 80rp, Imperial Direct Rule, 1396.

**1982, Mar. 8 Granite Paper**

| | | | | |
|---|---|---|---|---|
| **733** | A318 | 40rp multicolored | *.35* | *.30* |
| **734** | A318 | 80rp multicolored | *.65* | *.60* |

Hereditary Prince Hans Adam — A319

No. 736, Princess Marie Aglae.

**1982, June 7 Granite Paper**

| | | | | |
|---|---|---|---|---|
| **735** | A319 | 1fr shown | .75 | .75 |
| **736** | A319 | 1fr multicolored | .75 | .75 |

LIBA '82, 10th Liechtenstein Philatelic Exhibition, Vaduz, July 31-Aug. 8.

1982 World Cup — A320

Designs: Sports arenas.

**1982, June 7 Granite Paper**

| | | | | |
|---|---|---|---|---|
| **737** | A320 | 15rp Triesenberg | .40 | .25 |
| **738** | A320 | 25rp Mauren | .40 | .25 |
| **739** | A320 | 1.80fr Balzers | 1.40 | 1.25 |
| | | *Nos. 737-739 (3)* | 2.20 | 1.75 |

Farming A321

**1982, Sept. 20 Photo. *Perf. 11½***
**Granite Paper**

| | | | | |
|---|---|---|---|---|
| **740** | A321 | 30rp shown | .40 | .25 |
| **741** | A321 | 50rp Horticulture | .40 | .40 |
| **742** | A321 | 70rp Forestry | .60 | .50 |
| **743** | A321 | 150rp Dairy farming | 1.25 | 1.10 |
| | | *Nos. 740-743 (4)* | 2.65 | 2.25 |

View of Neu-Schellenberg, 1861, by Moriz Menzinger (1832-1914) — A322

**Photogravure and Engraved**
**1982, Sept. 20 *Perf. 13½x14***

| | | | | |
|---|---|---|---|---|
| **744** | A322 | 40rp shown | .50 | .30 |
| **745** | A322 | 50rp Vaduz, 1860 | .60 | .35 |
| **746** | A322 | 100rp Bendern, 1868 | 1.00 | .85 |
| | | *Nos. 744-746 (3)* | 2.10 | 1.50 |

### Visitor Type of 1981

Paintings: 40rp, Emperor Maximilian I (1459-1519), by Bernhard Strigel. 70rp, Georg Jenatsch (1596-1639). 80rp, Angelika Kaufmann (1741-1807), self portrait. 1fr, Fidelis von Sigmaringen (1577-1622).

**1982, Dec. 6** ***Perf. 14***

| | | | | | |
|---|---|---|---|---|---|
| **747** | A316 | 40rp multicolored | .45 | .30 |
| **748** | A316 | 70rp multicolored | .70 | .45 |
| **749** | A316 | 80rp multicolored | .80 | .45 |
| **750** | A316 | 1fr multicolored | 1.00 | .65 |
| | | *Nos. 747-750 (4)* | 2.95 | 1.85 |

Christmas 1982 — A323

Chur Cathedral sculptures: 20rp, Angel playing lute. 50rp, Virgin and Child. 80rp, Angel playing organ.

**1982, Dec. 6** **Photo.** ***Perf. 11½***
**Granite Paper**

| | | | | |
|---|---|---|---|---|
| **751** | A323 | 20rp multicolored | .25 | .25 |
| **752** | A323 | 50rp multicolored | .50 | .35 |
| **753** | A323 | 80rp multicolored | .75 | .55 |
| | | *Nos. 751-753 (3)* | 1.50 | 1.15 |

Europa 1983 — A324

Designs: 40rp, Notker Balbulus of St. Gall (840-912), Benedictine monk, poet and liturgical composer. 80rp, St. Hildegard of Bingen (1098-1179).

**1983, Mar. 7** **Photo.**

| | | | | |
|---|---|---|---|---|
| **754** | A324 | 40rp multicolored | *.40* | *.30* |
| **755** | A324 | 80rp multicolored | *.65* | *.55* |

A325

Shrovetide and Lenten customs: 40rp, Last Thursday before Lent. 70rp, Begging for eggs on Shrove Tuesday. 180fr, Bonfire, first Sunday in Lent.

**Photogravure and Engraved**

**1983, Mar. 7** ***Perf. 14***

| | | | | |
|---|---|---|---|---|
| **756** | A325 | 40rp multicolored | .35 | .30 |
| **757** | A325 | 70rp multicolored | .60 | .45 |
| **758** | A325 | 1.80fr multicolored | 1.50 | 1.25 |
| | | *Nos. 756-758 (3)* | 2.45 | 2.00 |

See Nos. 844-846, 915-917, 952-954.

A326

Landscapes by Anton Ender (b. 1898): 40rp, Schaan, on the Zollstrasse. 50rp, Balzers with Gutenberg Castle. 2fr, Stag by the Reservoir.

**1983, June 6** **Photo.** ***Perf. 12***

| | | | | |
|---|---|---|---|---|
| **759** | A326 | 40rp multicolored | .35 | .30 |
| **760** | A326 | 50rp multicolored | .50 | .35 |
| **761** | A326 | 2fr multicolored | 2.00 | 1.50 |
| | | *Nos. 759-761 (3)* | 2.85 | 2.15 |

Protection of Shores and Coasts — A327

40rp, Manned flight bicentenary. 50rp, World communications year. 80rp, Humanitarian aid.

**1983, June 6**

| | | | | |
|---|---|---|---|---|
| **762** | A327 | 20rp shown | .25 | .25 |
| **763** | A327 | 40rp multicolored | .35 | .35 |
| **764** | A327 | 50rp multicolored | .45 | .45 |
| **765** | A327 | 80rp multicolored | .70 | .70 |
| | | *Nos. 762-765 (4)* | 1.75 | 1.75 |

Pope John Paul II A328

**1983, Sept. 5** **Photo.**

| | | | | |
|---|---|---|---|---|
| **766** | A328 | 80rp multicolored | .90 | .75 |

Princess Gina — A329

3fr, Prince Franz Joseph II.

**1983, Sept. 5** ***Perf. 12x11½***

| | | | | |
|---|---|---|---|---|
| **767** | A329 | 2.50fr shown | 2.25 | 1.25 |
| **768** | A329 | 3fr multicolored | 2.75 | 1.75 |

Christmas 1983 — A330

**1983, Dec. 5** **Photo.** ***Perf. 12***
**Granite Paper**

| | | | | |
|---|---|---|---|---|
| **769** | A330 | 20rp Seeking shelter | .25 | .25 |
| **770** | A330 | 50rp Child Jesus | .40 | .30 |
| **771** | A330 | 80rp The Three Magi | .70 | .55 |
| | | *Nos. 769-771 (3)* | 1.35 | 1.10 |

1984 Winter Olympics, Sarajevo — A331

Snowflakes.

**1983, Dec. 5** **Photo.** ***Perf. 11½x12***
**Granite Paper**

| | | | | |
|---|---|---|---|---|
| **772** | A331 | 40rp multicolored | .40 | .30 |
| **773** | A331 | 80rp multicolored | .80 | .60 |
| **774** | A331 | 1.80fr multicolored | 1.65 | 1.10 |
| | | *Nos. 772-774 (3)* | 2.85 | 2.00 |

Famous Visitors to Liechtenstein A332

Paintings: 40rp, Count Alexander Wassiljewitsch Suworow-Rimnikski (1730-1800), Austro-Russian Army general. 70rp, Karl Rudolf Count von Buol-Schauenstein (1760-1833). 80rp, Carl Zuckmayer (1896-1977), playwright. 1fr, Curt Goetz (1888-1960), actor and playwright.

**Photogravure and Engraved**

**1984, Mar. 12** ***Perf. 14***

| | | | | |
|---|---|---|---|---|
| **775** | A332 | 40rp multicolored | .40 | .30 |
| **776** | A332 | 70rp multicolored | .70 | .55 |
| **777** | A332 | 80rp multicolored | .80 | .60 |
| **778** | A332 | 1fr multicolored | 1.00 | .75 |
| | | *Nos. 775-778 (4)* | 2.90 | 2.20 |

Europa (1959-1984) A333

**1984, Mar. 12** **Photo.** ***Perf. 12***
**Granite Paper**

| | | | | |
|---|---|---|---|---|
| **779** | A333 | 50rp multicolored | *.45* | *.40* |
| **780** | A333 | 80rp multicolored | *.65* | *.60* |

A334

The Destruction of Trisona Fairy Tale Illustrations: Root Carvings by Beni Gassner — 35rp, Warning messenger. 50rp, Buried town. 80rp, Spared family.

**Photogravure and Engraved**

**1984, June 12** ***Perf. 14***

| | | | | |
|---|---|---|---|---|
| **781** | A334 | 35rp multicolored | .35 | .30 |
| **782** | A334 | 50rp multicolored | .50 | .40 |
| **783** | A334 | 80rp multicolored | .80 | .70 |
| | | *Nos. 781-783 (3)* | 1.65 | 1.40 |

1984 Summer Olympics A335

**1984, June 12** **Photo.** ***Perf. 11½***
**Granite Paper**

| | | | | |
|---|---|---|---|---|
| **784** | A335 | 70rp Pole vault | .65 | .50 |
| **785** | A335 | 80rp Discus | .75 | .55 |
| **786** | A335 | 1fr Shot put | 1.00 | .75 |
| | | *Nos. 784-786 (3)* | 2.40 | 1.80 |

Industries and Occupations — A336

5rp, Banking & trading. 10rp, Construction, plumbing. 20rp, Production, factory worker. 35rp, Contracting, draftswoman. 45rp, Manufacturing, sales rep. 50rp, Catering. 60rp, Carpentry. 70rp, Public health. 80rp, Industrial research. 1fr, Masonry. 1.20fr, Industrial management. 1.50fr, Post & communications.

**1984, Sept. 10** **Photo.** ***Perf. 11½***

| | | | | |
|---|---|---|---|---|
| **787** | A336 | 5rp multicolored | .25 | .25 |
| **788** | A336 | 10rp multicolored | .25 | .25 |
| **789** | A336 | 20rp multicolored | .25 | .25 |
| **790** | A336 | 35rp multicolored | .35 | .30 |
| **791** | A336 | 45rp multicolored | .45 | .35 |
| **792** | A336 | 50rp multicolored | .50 | .40 |
| **793** | A336 | 60rp multicolored | .60 | .50 |
| **794** | A336 | 70rp multicolored | .70 | .55 |
| **795** | A336 | 80rp multicolored | .80 | .65 |
| **796** | A336 | 1fr multicolored | 1.00 | .80 |
| **797** | A336 | 1.20fr multicolored | 1.25 | 1.00 |
| **798** | A336 | 1.50fr multicolored | 1.50 | 1.20 |
| | | *Nos. 787-798 (12)* | 7.90 | 6.50 |

Princess Marie Aglae — A337

2fr, Prince Hans Adam.

**Photogravure and Engraved**

**1984, Dec. 10** ***Perf. 14x13½***

| | | | | |
|---|---|---|---|---|
| **799** | A337 | 1.70fr shown | 1.50 | 1.25 |
| **800** | A337 | 2fr multicolored | 1.90 | 1.40 |

Christmas 1984 — A338

**1984, Dec. 10** **Photo.** ***Perf. 11***

| | | | | |
|---|---|---|---|---|
| **801** | A338 | 35rp Annunciation | .35 | .30 |
| **802** | A338 | 50rp Holy Family | .55 | .40 |
| **803** | A338 | 80rp Three Kings | .80 | .70 |
| | | *Nos. 801-803 (3)* | 1.70 | 1.40 |

Europa 1985 A339

**1985, Mar. 11** **Photo.** ***Perf. 11½***

| | | | | |
|---|---|---|---|---|
| **804** | A339 | 50rp Three Muses | *.45* | *.40* |
| **805** | A339 | 80rp Pan and Muses | *.70* | *.65* |

Orders and Monastaries A340

50rp, St. Elisabeth. 1fr, Schellenberg Convent. 1.70fr, Gutenberg Mission.

**Photogravure and Engraved**

**1985, Mar. 11** ***Perf. 13½x14***

| | | | | |
|---|---|---|---|---|
| **806** | A340 | 50rp multicolored | .55 | .45 |
| **807** | A340 | 1fr multicolored | 1.10 | .90 |
| **808** | A340 | 1.70fr multicolored | 1.90 | 1.60 |
| | | *Nos. 806-808 (3)* | 3.55 | 2.95 |

Cardinal Virtues — A341

**1985, June 10** **Photo.** ***Perf. 11½x12***

| | | | | |
|---|---|---|---|---|
| **809** | A341 | 35rp Justice | .35 | .30 |
| **810** | A341 | 50rp Temperance | .50 | .40 |
| **811** | A341 | 70rp Prudence | .70 | .55 |
| **812** | A341 | 1fr Fortitude | 1.00 | .80 |
| | | *Nos. 809-812 (4)* | 2.55 | 2.05 |

Princess Gina, President of Natl. Red Cross, 40th Anniv. A342

Portrait and: 20rp, Helping refugees, 1945. 50rp, Rescue service. 1.20fr, Child refugees, 1979.

**1985, June 10** *Perf. 12x11½*

| | | | | |
|---|---|---|---|---|
| 813 | A342 | 20rp multicolored | .25 | .25 |
| 814 | A342 | 50rp multicolored | .65 | .40 |
| 815 | A342 | 1.20fr multicolored | 1.50 | 1.10 |
| | | *Nos. 813-815 (3)* | 2.40 | 1.75 |

Souvenir Sheet

State Visit of Pope John Paul II — A343

Designs: 50rp, Papal coat of arms. 80rp, Chapel of St. Maria zum Trost, Dux, Schaan. 1.70fr, Our Lady of Liechtenstein, St. Mary the Comforter.

**1985, Feb. 2** *Perf. 11½*

| | | | | |
|---|---|---|---|---|
| 816 | A343 | Sheet of 3 | 3.25 | 2.75 |
| *a.* | | 50rp multi | 1.00 | .90 |
| *b.* | | 80rp multi | 1.00 | .90 |
| *c.* | | 1.70fr multi | 1.00 | .90 |

Paintings from the Princely Collections A344

50rp, Portrait of a Canon, by Quintin Massys (1466-1530). 1fr, Portrait of Clara Serena Rubens, by Peter Paul Rubens (1577-1640). 1.20fr, Portrait of the Duke of Urbino, by Raphael (1483-1520).

**Photogravure and Engraved**

**1985, Sept. 2** *Perf. 14*

| | | | | |
|---|---|---|---|---|
| 817 | A344 | 50rp multicolored | .55 | .50 |
| 818 | A344 | 1fr multicolored | 1.25 | 1.10 |
| 819 | A344 | 1.20fr multicolored | 1.50 | 1.40 |
| | | *Nos. 817-819 (3)* | 3.30 | 3.00 |

Christmas 1985 — A345

**1985, Dec. 9** **Photo.** *Perf. 11½x12*

| | | | | |
|---|---|---|---|---|
| 820 | A345 | 35rp Frankincense | .45 | .35 |
| 821 | A345 | 50rp Gold | .65 | .50 |
| 822 | A345 | 80rp Myrrh | 1.10 | .85 |
| | | *Nos. 820-822 (3)* | 2.20 | 1.70 |

Kirchplatz Theater, 15th Anniv. — A346

50rp, Tragedy. 80rp, Commedia dell'arte. 1.50rp, Opera buffa.

**Photogravure and Engraved**

**1985, Dec. 9** *Perf. 14*

| | | | | |
|---|---|---|---|---|
| 823 | A346 | 50rp multicolored | .40 | .35 |
| 824 | A346 | 80rp multicolored | .55 | .45 |
| 825 | A346 | 1.50rp multicolored | 1.75 | 1.40 |
| | | *Nos. 823-825 (3)* | 2.70 | 2.20 |

Weapons from the Prince's Armory A347

Designs: 35rp, Halberd, bodyguard of Prince Charles I. 50rp, German morion, 16th cent. 80rp, Halberd, bodyguard of Prince Carl Eusebius.

**1985, Dec. 9** *Perf. 13½x14½*

| | | | | |
|---|---|---|---|---|
| 826 | A347 | 35rp multicolored | .35 | .35 |
| 827 | A347 | 50rp multicolored | .45 | .40 |
| 828 | A347 | 80rp multicolored | .75 | .65 |
| | | *Nos. 826-828 (3)* | 1.55 | 1.40 |

Europa 1986 — A348

**1986, Mar. 10** **Photo.** *Perf. 12*

| | | | | |
|---|---|---|---|---|
| 829 | A348 | 50rp Swallows | *.45* | *.40* |
| 830 | A348 | 90rp Robin | *.95* | *.90* |

A349

Views of Vaduz Castle: 20rp, Outer courtyard. 25rp, View from the south ('89). 50rp, Castle, mountains. 90rp, Inner gate ('87). 1.10fr, Back view. 1.40fr, Inner courtyard ('87).

**Granite Paper**

**1986-89** **Photo.** *Perf. 11½x12*

| | | | | |
|---|---|---|---|---|
| 832 | A349 | 20rp multicolored | .25 | .25 |
| 833 | A349 | 25rp multicolored | .35 | .35 |
| 835 | A349 | 50rp multicolored | .40 | .35 |
| 838 | A349 | 90rp multicolored | 1.10 | .70 |
| 840 | A349 | 1.10fr multicolored | .90 | .75 |
| 841 | A349 | 1.40fr multicolored | 1.75 | 1.20 |
| | | *Nos. 832-841 (6)* | 4.75 | 3.60 |

Fasting Sacrifice — A350

**1986, Mar. 10** **Photo.** *Perf. 12*

| | | | | |
|---|---|---|---|---|
| 843 | A350 | 1.40fr multicolored | 1.50 | 1.25 |

**Customs Type of 1983**

35rp, Palm Sunday procession. 50rp, Wedding. 70rp, Rogation Day procession.

**Photogravure and Engraved**

**1986, June 9** *Perf. 13½*

| | | | | |
|---|---|---|---|---|
| 844 | A325 | 35rp multicolored | .40 | .35 |
| 845 | A325 | 50rp multicolored | .60 | .40 |
| 846 | A325 | 70rp multicolored | .80 | .60 |
| | | *Nos. 844-846 (3)* | 1.80 | 1.35 |

A352

Karl Freiherr Haus von Hausen (1823-89), founder.

**1986, June 9** **Photo.** *Perf. 11½*

| | | | | |
|---|---|---|---|---|
| 847 | A352 | 50rp multicolored | .65 | .50 |

Natl. Savings Bank, Vaduz, 125th anniv.

A353

**Photogravure and Engraved**

**1986, June 9** *Perf. 13½*

| | | | | |
|---|---|---|---|---|
| 848 | A353 | 3.50fr multicolored | 3.50 | 2.50 |

Prince Franz Joseph II, 80th birthday.

Hunting — A354

35rp, Roebuck, Ruggeller Riet. 50rp, Chamois in winter, Rappenstein. 1.70fr, Rutting stag, Lawena.

**1986, Sept. 9** *Perf. 13x13½*

| | | | | |
|---|---|---|---|---|
| 849 | A354 | 35rp multicolored | .35 | .25 |
| 850 | A354 | 50rp multicolored | .50 | .40 |
| 851 | A354 | 1.70fr multicolored | 1.90 | 1.50 |
| | | *Nos. 849-851 (3)* | 2.75 | 2.15 |

Crops A355

50rp, White cabbage, beets. 80rp, Red cabbage. 90rp, Potatoes, onions, garlic.

**1986, Sept. 9** **Photo.** *Perf. 12x11½*

| | | | | |
|---|---|---|---|---|
| 852 | A355 | 50rp multicolored | .55 | .45 |
| 853 | A355 | 80rp multicolored | .90 | .70 |
| 854 | A355 | 90rp multicolored | 1.00 | .80 |
| | | *Nos. 852-854 (3)* | 2.45 | 1.95 |

Christmas — A356

Archangels.

**1986, Dec. 9** *Perf. 11½*

| | | | | |
|---|---|---|---|---|
| 855 | A356 | 35rp Michael | .45 | .30 |
| 856 | A356 | 50rp Gabriel | .65 | .50 |
| 857 | A356 | 90rp Raphael | 1.25 | 1.00 |
| | | *Nos. 855-857 (3)* | 2.35 | 1.80 |

Trees — A357

**1986, Dec. 9**

| | | | | |
|---|---|---|---|---|
| 858 | A357 | 25rp Silver fir | .30 | .25 |
| 859 | A357 | 90rp Spruce | 1.10 | .85 |
| 860 | A357 | 1.40fr Oak | 1.65 | 1.25 |
| | | *Nos. 858-860 (3)* | 3.05 | 2.35 |

Europa 1987 — A358

Modern architecture: 50rp, Primary school, 1980, Gamprin. 90rp, Parish church, c. 1960, Schellenburg.

**1987, Mar. 9** **Photo.** *Perf. 11½x12*

**Granite Paper**

| | | | | |
|---|---|---|---|---|
| 861 | A358 | 50rp multicolored | *.60* | *.55* |
| 862 | A358 | 90rp multicolored | *1.25* | *1.00* |

Nicholas Among the Thorns — A359

**1987, Mar. 9** *Perf. 11½*

**Granite Paper**

| | | | | |
|---|---|---|---|---|
| 863 | A359 | 1.10fr multicolored | 1.40 | 1.00 |

Nicholas von der Flue (1417-1487), canonized in 1947.

Hereditary Prince Alois — A360

**Photo. & Engr.**

**1987, June 9** *Perf. 14*

| | | | | |
|---|---|---|---|---|
| 864 | A360 | 2fr multicolored | 2.50 | 2.00 |

No. 864 printed in sheets of 8.

Fish — A361

50rp, Cottus gobio. 90rp, Salmo trutta fario. 1.10fr, Thymallus thymallus.

**1987, June 9** **Photo.** *Perf. 11½*

| | | | | |
|---|---|---|---|---|
| 865 | A361 | 50rp multicolored | .60 | .50 |
| 866 | A361 | 90rp multicolored | 1.10 | .85 |
| 867 | A361 | 1.10fr multicolored | 1.40 | 1.10 |
| | | *Nos. 865-867 (3)* | 3.10 | 2.45 |

A362

Liechtenstein City Palace, Vienna.

**1987, Sept. 7 Photo. *Perf. 11½***
**Granite Paper**

| | | | | |
|---|---|---|---|---|
| **868** | A362 | 35rp Arch | .45 | .35 |
| **869** | A362 | 50rp Entrance | .60 | .50 |
| **870** | A362 | 90rp Staircase | 1.10 | .90 |
| | | *Nos. 868-870 (3)* | 2.15 | 1.75 |

House of Liechtenstein Coat of Arms — A363

**1987, Sept. 7 *Perf. 11½***

| | | | | |
|---|---|---|---|---|
| **871** | A363 | 1.40fr multicolored | 1.60 | 1.25 |

Purchase of County of Vaduz, 275th anniv.

Diet, 125th Anniv. A364

**1987, Sept. 7 *Perf. 11½***

| | | | | |
|---|---|---|---|---|
| **872** | A364 | 1.70fr Constitution of 1862 | 2.00 | 1.50 |

Christmas — A365

The Evangelists, illuminated codices from the Golden Book, c. 1100, Abbey of Pfafers, purportedly made under the direction of monks from Reichenau Is.

**Photo. & Engr.**
**1987, Dec. 7 *Perf. 14***

| | | | | |
|---|---|---|---|---|
| **873** | A365 | 35rp St. Matthew | .50 | .30 |
| **874** | A365 | 50rp St. Mark | .65 | .40 |
| **875** | A365 | 60rp St. Luke | .80 | .50 |
| **876** | A365 | 90rp St. John | 1.25 | .75 |
| | | *Nos. 873-876 (4)* | 3.20 | 1.95 |

1988 Winter Olympics, Calgary A366

Humorous drawings by illustrator Paul Flora of Austria: 25rp, The Toil of the Cross-country Skier. 90rp, Courageous Pioneer of Skiing. 1.10fr, As Grandfather Used to Ride on a Bobsled.

**1987, Dec. 7 *Perf. 14x13½***

| | | | | |
|---|---|---|---|---|
| **877** | A366 | 25rp multicolored | .30 | .30 |
| **878** | A366 | 90rp multicolored | 1.10 | 1.00 |
| **879** | A366 | 1.10fr multicolored | 1.40 | 1.25 |
| | | *Nos. 877-879 (3)* | 2.80 | 2.55 |

See Nos. 888-891.

Europa 1988 — A367

Modern communication & transportation: 50rp, Satellite dish. 90rp, High-speed monorail.

**1988, Mar. 7 Photo. *Perf. 11½x12***
**Granite Paper**

| | | | | |
|---|---|---|---|---|
| **880** | A367 | 50rp multicolored | *.60* | *.55* |
| **881** | A367 | 90rp multicolored | *1.00* | *.90* |

European Campaign to Protect Undeveloped and Developing Lands — A368

80rp, Forest preservation. 90rp, Layout for village development. 1.70rp, Traffic planning.

**1988, Mar. 7 *Perf. 12***
**Granite Paper**

| | | | | |
|---|---|---|---|---|
| **882** | A368 | 80rp multicolored | .85 | .75 |
| **883** | A368 | 90rp multicolored | .90 | .85 |
| **884** | A368 | 1.70rp multicolored | 1.75 | 1.50 |
| | | *Nos. 882-884 (3)* | 3.50 | 3.10 |

Balancing nature conservation with natl. development.

Souvenir Sheet

Succession to the Throne — A369

Portraits: a, Crown Prince Hans Adam. b, Prince Alois, successor to the crown prince. c, Prince Franz Josef II, ruler.

**Photo. & Engr.**
**1988, June 6 *Perf. 14½x13½***

| | | | | |
|---|---|---|---|---|
| **885** | A369 | Sheet of 3 | 4.50 | 3.50 |
| | *a.* | 50rp black, gold & bright blue | .70 | .55 |
| | *b.* | 50rp black, gold & sage green | .70 | .55 |
| | *c.* | 2fr black, gold & deep rose | 3.00 | 2.25 |

North and South Campaign A370

**1988, June 6 Photo. *Perf. 12x11½***
**Granite Paper**

| | | | | |
|---|---|---|---|---|
| **886** | A370 | 50rp Public radio | .85 | .55 |
| **887** | A370 | 1.40fr Adult education | 2.40 | 1.50 |

Cultural cooperation with Costa Rica. See Costa Rica Nos. 401-402.

**Olympics Type of 1988**

Humorous drawings by illustrator Paul Flora of Austria: 50rp, Cycling. 80rp, Gymnastics. 90rp, Running. 1.40fr, Equestrian.

**Photo. & Engr.**
**1988, Sept. 5 *Perf. 14x13½***

| | | | | |
|---|---|---|---|---|
| **888** | A366 | 50rp multicolored | .70 | .50 |
| **889** | A366 | 80rp multicolored | 1.10 | .75 |
| **890** | A366 | 90rp multicolored | 1.20 | .80 |
| **891** | A366 | 1.40fr multicolored | 1.90 | 1.40 |
| | | *Nos. 888-891 (4)* | 4.90 | 3.45 |

Roadside Shrines — A371

25rp, Kaltweh Chapel, Balzers. 35rp, Oberdorf, Vaduz, c. 1870. 50rp, Bangstrasse, Ruggell.

**1988, Sept. 5 Photo. *Perf. 11½x12***
**Granite Paper**

| | | | | |
|---|---|---|---|---|
| **892** | A371 | 25rp multicolored | .35 | .30 |
| **893** | A371 | 35rp multicolored | .45 | .40 |
| **894** | A371 | 50rp multicolored | .65 | .55 |
| | | *Nos. 892-894 (3)* | 1.45 | 1.25 |

Christmas — A372

35rp, Joseph, Mary. 50rp, Christ child. 90rp, Adoration of the Magi.

**1988, Dec. 5 Photo. *Perf. 11½x12***
**Granite Paper**

| | | | | |
|---|---|---|---|---|
| **895** | A372 | 35rp multicolored | .40 | .30 |
| **896** | A372 | 50rp multicolored | .55 | .40 |
| **897** | A372 | 90rp multicolored | 1.00 | .70 |
| | | *Nos. 895-897 (3)* | 1.95 | 1.40 |

The Letter — A373

Details of Portrait of Marie-Therese de Lamballe (The Letter), by Anton Hickel (1745-1798): 90rp, Handkerchief and writing materials in open desk. 2fr, Entire painting.

**Photo. & Engr.**
**1988, Dec. 5 *Perf. 13x13½***

| | | | | |
|---|---|---|---|---|
| **898** | A373 | 50rp shown | .65 | .50 |
| **899** | A373 | 90rp multicolored | 1.10 | .80 |
| **900** | A373 | 2fr multicolored | 2.50 | 1.90 |
| | | *Nos. 898-900 (3)* | 4.25 | 3.20 |

Europa 1989 — A374

Traditional children's games: 50rp, Cat and Mouse. 90rp,

**Granite Paper**
**1989, Mar. 6 Photo. *Perf. 11½x12***

| | | | | |
|---|---|---|---|---|
| **901** | A374 | 50rp multicolored | *.70* | *.65* |
| **902** | A374 | 90rp multicolored | *1.40* | *1.25* |

Josef Gabriel Rheinberger (1839-1901), Composer, and Score — A375

**Photo. & Engr.**
**1989, Mar. 6 *Perf. 14x13½***

| | | | | |
|---|---|---|---|---|
| **903** | A375 | 2.90fr multicolored | 3.25 | 2.50 |

Fish — A376

50rp, Esox lucius. 1.10fr, Salmo trutta lacustris. 1.40fr, Noemacheilus barbatulus.

**1989, June 5 Photo. *Perf. 12x11½***
**Granite Paper**

| | | | | |
|---|---|---|---|---|
| **904** | A376 | 50rp multicolored | .65 | .50 |
| **905** | A376 | 1.10fr multicolored | 1.40 | 1.00 |
| **906** | A376 | 1.40fr multicolored | 1.75 | 1.25 |
| | | *Nos. 904-906 (3)* | 3.80 | 2.75 |

World Wildlife Fund — A377

25rp, Charadrius dubuis. 35rp, Hyla arborea. 50rp, Libelloides coccajus. 90rp, Putorius putorius.

**1989, June 5 *Perf. 12***
**Granite Paper**

| | | | | |
|---|---|---|---|---|
| **907** | A377 | 25rp multicolored | .55 | .35 |
| **908** | A377 | 35rp multicolored | .90 | .55 |
| **909** | A377 | 50rp multicolored | 1.20 | .75 |
| **910** | A377 | 90rp multicolored | 2.25 | 1.40 |
| | | *Nos. 907-910 (4)* | 4.90 | 3.05 |

Mountains A378

**1989, Sept. 4 Photo. *Perf. 11½***
**Granite Paper**

| | | | | |
|---|---|---|---|---|
| **911** | A378 | 50rp Falknis | .50 | .45 |
| **912** | A378 | 75rp Plassteikopf | .75 | .65 |
| **913** | A378 | 80rp Naafkopf | .80 | .70 |
| **914** | A378 | 1.50fr Garselliturm | 1.50 | 1.25 |
| | | *Nos. 911-914 (4)* | 3.55 | 3.05 |

See Nos. 930-939.

**Customs Type of 1983**

Autumn activities: 35rp, Alpine herdsman and flock return from pasture. 50rp, Shucking corn. 80rp, Cattle market.

**Photo. & Engr.**
**1989, Sept. 4 *Perf. 14***

| | | | | |
|---|---|---|---|---|
| **915** | A325 | 35rp multicolored | .40 | .30 |
| **916** | A325 | 50rp multicolored | .60 | .45 |
| **917** | A325 | 80rp multicolored | .95 | .75 |
| | | *Nos. 915-917 (3)* | 1.95 | 1.50 |

Christmas A379

Details of the triptych *Adoration of the Magi*, by Hugo van der Goes (50rp) and student (35rp, 90rp), late 15th cent.: 35rp, Melchior and Balthazar. 50rp, Caspar and holy family. 90rp, Donor with St. Stephen.

**1989, Dec. 4 *Perf. 13½***
**Size of 35rp and 90rp: 23x41mm**

| | | | | |
|---|---|---|---|---|
| **918** | A379 | 35rp multicolored | .45 | .35 |
| **919** | A379 | 50rp shown | .60 | .45 |
| **920** | A379 | 90rp multicolored | 1.10 | .80 |
| | | *Nos. 918-920 (3)* | 2.15 | 1.60 |

Minerals A380

**1989, Dec. 4 *Perf. 13½x13***

| | | | | |
|---|---|---|---|---|
| **921** | A380 | 50rp Scepter quartz | .60 | .50 |
| **922** | A380 | 1.10fr Pyrite ball | 1.40 | 1.00 |
| **923** | A380 | 1.50fr Calcite | 1.75 | 1.25 |
| | | *Nos. 921-923 (3)* | 3.75 | 2.75 |

Europa 1990 — A381

Post offices.

**1990, Mar. 5 Photo.** *Perf. 11½x12*
**Granite Paper**

**924** A381 50rp shown *.70 .60*
**925** A381 90rp Modern p.o. *1.25 1.10*

Postage Stamps, 150th Anniv. — A382

**1990, Mar. 5** *Perf. 11½*
**Granite Paper**

**926** A382 1.50fr Penny Black 2.25 1.65

1990 World Cup Soccer Championships, Italy — A383

**1990, Mar. 5 Granite Paper** *Perf. 12*

**927** A383 2fr multicolored 2.75 1.75

1st Anniv. of Death A384

2fr, Princess Gina, (1921-1989). 3fr, Prince Franz Joseph II, (1906-1989).

**1990, June 5 Litho.** *Perf. 11½*
**Granite Paper**

**928** A384 2fr shown 2.25 1.40
**929** A384 3fr multi 3.25 2.25

**Mountains Type of 1989**

5rp, Augstenberg. 10rp, Hahnenspiel. 35rp, Nospitz. 40rp, Ochsenkopf. 45rp, Drei Schwestern. 60rp, Kuhgrat. 70rp, Galinakopf. 1fr, Schonberg. 1.20fr, Bleikaturm. 1.60fr, Schwarzhorn. 2fr, Scheienkopf.

**1990-93** **Granite Paper**

**930** A378 5rp multicolored .25 .25
**931** A378 10rp multicolored .25 .25
**933** A378 35rp multicolored .45 .30
**933A** A378 40rp multicolored .50 .45
**934** A378 45rp multicolored .45 .35
**935** A378 60rp multicolored .70 .55
**936** A378 70rp multicolored .75 .60
**938** A378 1fr multicolored .95 .75
**939** A378 1.20fr multicolored 1.40 1.10
**940** A378 1.60fr multicolored 2.00 1.40
**941** A378 2fr multicolored 2.50 1.75
*Nos. 930-941 (11)* 10.20 7.75

Issued: 5, 45, 70rp, 1fr, 6/5; 10, 35, 60rp, 1.20fr, 9/3; 40rp, 6/3/91; 1.60fr, 3/2/92; 2fr, 3/1/93.

A385

Paintings by Benjamin Steck (1902-1981): 80rp, Fruit, dish. 1.50fr, Basket, fruit, stein.

**Photo. & Engr.**
**1990, June 5** *Perf. 14*

**942** A385 50rp shown .70 .55
**943** A385 80rp multicolored 1.10 .80
**944** A385 1.50fr multicolored 2.25 1.60
*Nos. 942-944 (3)* 4.05 2.95

A386

Game birds.

**Photo. & Engr.**
**1990, Sept. 3** *Perf. 13x13½*

**945** A386 25rp Pheasant .35 .25
**946** A386 50rp Blackcock .70 .45
**947** A386 2fr Mallard duck 2.75 1.90
*Nos. 945-947 (3)* 3.80 2.60

European Postal Communications, 500th Anniv. — A387

**1990, Dec. 3** *Perf. 13½x14*

**948** A387 90rp multicolored 1.50 1.00

A388

Christmas (Lenten Cloth of Bendern): 35rp, The Annunciation. 50rp, Birth of Christ. 90rp, Adoration of the Magi.

**1990, Dec. 3 Photo.** *Perf. 12*
**Granite Paper**

**949** A388 35rp multicolored .50 .35
**950** A388 50rp multicolored .70 .50
**951** A388 90rp multicolored 1.25 .90
*Nos. 949-951 (3)* 2.45 1.75

A389

Holiday Customs: 35rp, St. Nicholas Visiting Children on Feast of St. Nicholas. 50rp, Waking "sleepyheads" on New Year's Day. 1.50fr, Good wishes on New Year's Day.

**Photo. & Engr.**
**1990, Dec. 3** *Perf. 14*

**952** A389 35rp multicolored .45 .30
**953** A389 50rp multicolored .65 .45
**954** A389 1.50fr multicolored 2.00 1.40
*Nos. 952-954 (3)* 3.10 2.15

Europa — A390

Designs: 50rp, Telecommunications satellite, Olympus I. 90rp, Weather satellite, Meteosat.

**1991, Mar. 4 Photo.** *Perf. 11½*
**Granite Paper**

**955** A390 50rp multicolored *.80 .60*
**956** A390 90rp multicolored *1.25 1.10*

St. Ignatius of Loyola (1491-1556), Founder of Jesuit Order — A391

90rp, Wolfgang Amadeus Mozart.

**1991, Mar. 4** *Perf. 11½*
**Granite Paper**

**957** A391 80rp multicolored 1.10 .80
**958** A391 90rp multicolored 1.25 .90

UN Membership, 1990 — A392

**1991, Mar. 4** *Perf. 11½*
**Granite Paper**

**959** A392 2.50fr multicolored 3.00 2.00

A393

Paintings: 50rp, Maloja, by Giovanni Giacometti. 80rp, Rheintal, by Ferdinand Gehr. 90rp, Bergell, by Augusto Giacometti. 1.10fr, Hoher Kasten, by Hedwig Scherrer.

**Granite Paper**

**1991, June 3 Photo.** *Perf. 11½*

**960** A393 50rp multicolored .60 .40
**961** A393 80rp multicolored .95 .65
**962** A393 90rp multicolored 1.00 .65
**963** A393 1.10fr multicolored 1.40 .95
*Nos. 960-963 (4)* 3.95 2.65

Swiss Confederation, 700th anniv.

Military Uniforms A394

Designs: 50rp, Non-commissioned officer, private. 70rp, Uniform tunic, trunk. 1fr, Sharpshooters, officer and private.

**Photo. & Engr.**
**1991, June 3** *Perf. 13½x14*

**964** A394 50rp multicolored .75 .55
**965** A394 70rp multicolored 1.10 .75
**966** A394 1fr multicolored 1.20 .85
*Nos. 964-966 (3)* 3.05 2.15

Last action of Liechtenstein's military, 1866 (70rp).

Princess Marie — A395

3.40fr, Prince Hans Adam II.

**Photo. & Engr.**
**1991, Sept. 2** *Perf. 13x13½*

**967** A395 3fr shown 2.90 2.25
**968** A395 3.40fr multicolored 3.25 2.60

LIBA 92, Natl. Philatelic Exhibition A396

**1991, Sept. 2 Photo.** *Perf. 11½*
**Granite Paper**

**969** A396 90rp multicolored 1.10 .95

A397

Christmas (Altar of St. Mamertus Chapel, Triesen): 50rp, Mary. 80rp, Madonna and Child. 90rp, Angel Gabriel.

**Photo. & Engr.**
**1991, Dec. 2** *Perf. 13½x14*

**970** A397 50rp multicolored .70 .50
**971** A397 80rp multicolored 1.10 .80
**972** A397 90rp multicolored 1.25 .90
*Nos. 970-972 (3)* 3.05 2.20

A398

1992 Winter Olympics, Albertville: 70rp, Cross-country skiers, doping check. 80rp, Hockey players, good sportsmanship. 1.60rp, Downhill skier, safety precautions.

**Granite Paper**

**1991, Dec. 2 Photo.** *Perf. 11½x12*

**973** A398 70rp multicolored .95 .70
**974** A398 80rp multicolored 1.10 .85
**975** A398 1.60fr multicolored 2.25 1.75
*Nos. 973-975 (3)* 4.30 3.30

**1992, Mar. 2 Photo.** *Perf. 11½*

1992 Summer Olympics, Barcelona: 50rp, Women's relay, drugs, broken medal. 70rp, Cycling, safety precautions. 2.50fr, Judo, good sportsmanship.

**Granite Paper**

**976** A398 50rp multicolored .65 .50
**977** A398 70rp multicolored .90 .70
**978** A398 2.50fr multicolored 3.25 2.50
*Nos. 976-978 (3)* 4.80 3.70

Discovery of America, 500th Anniv. A400

**1992, Mar. 2** **Granite Paper**

**979** A400 80rp shown *1.10 1.00*
**980** A400 90rp New York skyline *1.40 1.25*

Europa.

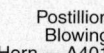

Postillion Blowing Horn — A401

Clown in Envelope A402

Designs: No. 982, Postillion delivering valentine. No. 984, Wedding violinist.

**Photo. & Engr.**

**1992, June 1** *Perf. 14x13½*

| | | | | |
|---|---|---|---|---|
| **981** | A401 | 50rp multicolored | .65 | .55 |
| **982** | A401 | 50rp multicolored | .65 | .55 |

**Photo.**

*Perf. 12½*

**Granite Paper**

| | | | | |
|---|---|---|---|---|
| **983** | A402 | 50rp multicolored | .65 | .55 |
| **984** | A402 | 50rp multicolored | .65 | .55 |
| | | *Nos. 981-984 (4)* | 2.60 | 2.20 |

Souvenir Sheet

Prince Hans-Adam and Princess Marie, 25th Wedding Anniv. — A403

Designs: a, 2fr, Coat of Arms of Liechtenstein-Kinsky Alliance. b, 2.50fr, Prince Hans-Adam and Princess Marie.

**1992, June 1** *Perf. 11½*

**Granite Paper**

| | | | | |
|---|---|---|---|---|
| **985** | A403 | Sheet of 2, #a.-b. | 5.75 | 4.00 |

Ferns — A404

40rp, Blechnum spicant. 50rp, Asplenium trichomanes. 70rp, Phyllitis scolopendrium. 2.50fr, Asplenium ruta-muraria.

**Photo. & Engr.**

**1992, Sept. 7** *Perf. 14*

| | | | | |
|---|---|---|---|---|
| **986** | A404 | 40rp multicolored | .50 | .35 |
| **987** | A404 | 50rp multicolored | .55 | .40 |
| **988** | A404 | 70rp multicolored | .85 | .60 |
| **989** | A404 | 2.50fr multicolored | 3.00 | 2.25 |
| | | *Nos. 986-989 (4)* | 4.90 | 3.60 |

Creation of Vaduz County, 650th Anniv. A405

**1992, Sept. 7** *Perf. 13½x14*

| | | | | |
|---|---|---|---|---|
| **990** | A405 | 1.60fr multicolored | 2.50 | 1.60 |

Christmas — A406

Scenes in Triesen: 50rp, Chapel, St. Mamertus. 90rp, Nativity scene, St. Gallus Church. 1.60rp, St. Mary's Chapel.

**1992, Dec. 7** **Photo.** *Perf. 11½*

**Granite Paper**

| | | | | |
|---|---|---|---|---|
| **991** | A406 | 50rp multicolored | .60 | .45 |
| **992** | A406 | 90rp multicolored | 1.10 | .80 |
| **993** | A406 | 1.60fr multicolored | 2.00 | 1.40 |
| | | *Nos. 991-993 (3)* | 3.70 | 2.65 |

Hereditary Prince Alois — A407

**Photo. & Engr.**

**1992, Dec. 7** *Perf. 13x13½*

| | | | | |
|---|---|---|---|---|
| **994** | A407 | 2.50fr multicolored | 3.50 | 3.50 |

A408

Europa (Contemporary paintings): 80rp, 910805, by Bruno Kaufmann. 1fr, The Little Blue, by Evi Kliemand.

**1993, Mar. 1** **Photo.** *Perf. 11½x12*

**Granite Paper**

| | | | | |
|---|---|---|---|---|
| **995** | A408 | 80rp multicolored | *.90* | *.75* |
| **996** | A408 | 1fr multicolored | *1.10* | *.90* |

A409

Paintings by Hans Gantner (1853-1914): 50rp, Chalets in Steg and Naafkopf. 60rp, Sass Mountain with Hunting Lodge. 1.80fr, Red House in Vaduz.

**1993, Mar. 1** *Perf. 11½*

**Granite Paper**

| | | | | |
|---|---|---|---|---|
| **997** | A409 | 50rp multicolored | .65 | .45 |
| **998** | A409 | 60rp multicolored | .75 | .50 |
| **999** | A409 | 1.80fr multicolored | 2.25 | 1.50 |
| | | *Nos. 997-999 (3)* | 3.65 | 2.45 |

Tibetan Art — A410

60rp, Detail from Thangka painting, Tale of the Ferryman. 80rp, Religious dance mask. 1fr, Detail from Thangka painting, The Tale of the Fish.

**1993, June 7** **Photo.** *Perf. 11½*

**Granite Paper**

| | | | | |
|---|---|---|---|---|
| **1000** | A410 | 60rp multicolored | .75 | .55 |
| **1001** | A410 | 80rp multicolored | 1.00 | .75 |
| **1002** | A410 | 1fr multicolored | 1.25 | .95 |
| | | *Nos. 1000-1002 (3)* | 3.00 | 2.25 |

Church Missionary Work — A411

**1993, June 7** *Perf. 11½x12*

**Granite Paper**

| | | | | |
|---|---|---|---|---|
| **1003** | A411 | 1.80fr Tree of life | 2.10 | 1.60 |

A412

Contemporary painting: Black Hatter, by Friedensreich Hundertwasser.

**Photo. & Engr.**

**1993, June 7** *Perf. 14x13½*

| | | | | |
|---|---|---|---|---|
| **1004** | A412 | 2.80fr multicolored | 4.00 | 2.40 |

Souvenir Sheet

Marriage of Hereditary Prince Alois and Duchess Sophie of Bavaria, July 3 — A413

**1993, June 7** **Photo.** *Perf. 11½*

**Granite Paper**

| | | | | |
|---|---|---|---|---|
| **1005** | A413 | 4fr multicolored | 5.25 | 3.50 |

Wild Animals — A414

**Photo. & Engr.**

**1993, Sept. 6** *Perf. 13x13½*

| | | | | |
|---|---|---|---|---|
| **1006** | A414 | 60rp Badger | .85 | .60 |
| **1007** | A414 | 80rp Marten | 1.10 | .75 |
| **1008** | A414 | 1fr Fox | 1.40 | .95 |
| | | *Nos. 1006-1008 (3)* | 3.35 | 2.30 |

Meadow Plants — A415

50rp, Origanum vulgare. 60rp, Salvia pratensis. 1fr, Seseli annuum. 2.50fr, Prunella grandiflora.

**1993, Sept. 6**

| | | | | |
|---|---|---|---|---|
| **1009** | A415 | 50rp multicolored | .65 | .45 |
| **1010** | A415 | 60rp multicolored | .80 | .55 |
| **1011** | A415 | 1fr multicolored | 1.25 | .85 |
| **1012** | A415 | 2.50fr multicolored | 3.25 | 2.25 |
| | | *Nos. 1009-1012 (4)* | 5.95 | 4.10 |

See Nos. 1056-1059.

Christmas — A416

Calligraphic Christmas texts by: 60rp, Rainer Maria Rilke. 80rp, Th. Friedrich. 1fr, Rudolph Alexander Schroder.

**1993, Dec. 6** **Photo.** *Perf. 11½x12*

**Granite Paper**

| | | | | |
|---|---|---|---|---|
| **1013** | A416 | 60rp multicolored | .80 | .55 |
| **1014** | A416 | 80rp multicolored | 1.00 | .70 |
| **1015** | A416 | 1fr multicolored | 1.25 | .90 |
| | | *Nos. 1013-1015 (3)* | 3.05 | 2.15 |

A417

**1993, Dec. 6** **Granite Paper**

| | | | | |
|---|---|---|---|---|
| **1016** | A417 | 60rp Ski jump | .80 | .65 |
| **1017** | A417 | 80rp Slalom skiing | 1.00 | .80 |
| **1018** | A417 | 2.40fr Bobsled | 3.00 | 2.40 |
| | | *Nos. 1016-1018 (3)* | 4.80 | 3.85 |

1994 Winter Olympics, Lillehammer.

Anniversaries and Events A418

A419

A420

**1994, Mar. 7** **Photo.** *Perf. 11½*

**Granite Paper**

| | | | | |
|---|---|---|---|---|
| **1019** | A418 | 60rp multicolored | .70 | .70 |
| **1020** | A419 | 1.80fr multicolored | 2.00 | 2.00 |
| **1021** | A420 | 2.80fr multicolored | 3.00 | 3.00 |
| | | *Nos. 1019-1021 (3)* | 5.70 | 5.70 |

Principality of Liechtenstein, 275th anniv. (No. 1019). Intl. Olympic Committee, cent. (No. 1020). 1994 World Cup Soccer Championships, US (No. 1021).

Alexander von Humboldt (1769-1859) A421

Europa: 80rp, Vultur gryphus. 1fr, Rhexia cardinalis.

**Photo. & Engr.**

**1994, Mar. 7** *Perf. 13x13½*

| | | | | |
|---|---|---|---|---|
| **1022** A421 | 80rp multicolored | | *1.10* | *.90* |
| **1023** A421 | 1fr multicolored | | *1.40* | *1.00* |

Mobile, by Jean Tinguely (1925-91) A422

**Photo. & Engr.**

**1994, June 6** *Perf. 13½x14*

| | | | |
|---|---|---|---|
| **1024** A422 4fr multicolored | | 4.50 | 4.50 |

Letter Writing — A423

**1994, June 6** **Photo.** *Perf. 12½*

**Granite Paper**

| | | | |
|---|---|---|---|
| **1025** A423 | 60rp Elephant | .90 | .80 |
| **1026** A423 | 60rp Cherub | .90 | .80 |
| **1027** A423 | 60rp Pig | .90 | .80 |
| **1028** A423 | 60rp Dog | .90 | .80 |
| | *Nos. 1025-1028 (4)* | 3.60 | 3.20 |

Life Cycle of Grape Vine A424

Designs: No. 1029, Spring, vine beginning to flower. No. 1030, Summer, green grapes on vine. No. 1031, Autumn, ripe grapes ready for harvest. No. 1032, Winter, bare vine in snow.

**1994, Sept 5** **Photo.** *Perf. 11½*

**Granite Paper**

| | | | |
|---|---|---|---|
| **1029** A424 | 60rp multicolored | .90 | .80 |
| **1030** A424 | 60rp multicolored | .90 | .80 |
| **1031** A424 | 60rp multicolored | .90 | .80 |
| **1032** A424 | 60rp multicolored | .90 | .80 |
| *a* | Block of 4, #1029-1032 | 4.00 | 4.00 |

No. 1032a is continuous design.

Minerals A425

60rp, Strontianite. 80rp, Faden quartz. 3.50fr, Ferrous dolomite.

**Photo. & Engr.**

**1994, Sept. 5** *Perf. 13½x12½*

| | | | |
|---|---|---|---|
| **1033** A425 | 60rp multicolored | .80 | .80 |
| **1034** A425 | 80rp multicolored | 1.10 | 1.10 |
| **1035** A425 | 3.50fr multicolored | 4.75 | 4.75 |
| | *Nos. 1033-1035 (3)* | 6.65 | 6.65 |

A426

Christmas contemporary art, by Anne Frommelt: 60rp, The True Light. 80rp, Peace on Earth. 1fr, See the House of God.

**1994, Dec. 5** **Photo.** *Perf. 11½*

**Granite Paper**

| | | | |
|---|---|---|---|
| **1036** A426 | 60rp multicolored | .80 | .60 |
| **1037** A426 | 80rp multicolored | 1.10 | .80 |
| **1038** A426 | 1fr multicolored | 1.40 | .90 |
| | *Nos. 1036-1038 (3)* | 3.30 | 2.30 |

A427

The Four Elements, by Ernst Steiner.

**Photo. & Engr.**

**1994, Dec. 5** *Perf. 14*

| | | | |
|---|---|---|---|
| **1039** A427 | 60rp Earth | .75 | .60 |
| **1040** A427 | 80rp Water | 1.10 | .80 |
| **1041** A427 | 1fr Fire | 1.25 | .90 |
| **1042** A427 | 2.50fr Air | 3.50 | 2.60 |
| | *Nos. 1039-1042 (4)* | 6.60 | 4.90 |

Peace and Freedom A428

Europa: 80rp, 1fr, Excerpts from speeches of Prince Franz Josef II.

**1995, Mar. 6** **Photo.** *Perf. 11½*

**Granite Paper**

| | | | |
|---|---|---|---|
| **1043** A428 | 80rp multicolored | *1.10* | *.90* |
| **1044** A428 | 1fr multicolored | *1.40* | *1.10* |

A429

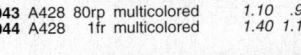

Anniversaries and Events
A430 A431

60rp, Princess Marie, Bosnian children.

**1995, Mar. 6** **Granite Paper**

| | | | |
|---|---|---|---|
| **1045** A429 | 60rp multicolored | .80 | .60 |
| **1046** A430 | 1.80fr multicolored | 2.50 | 2.00 |
| **1047** A431 | 3.50fr multicolored | 4.75 | 3.50 |
| | *Nos. 1045-1047 (3)* | 8.05 | 6.10 |

Liechtenstein Red Cross, 50th anniv. (No. 1045). UN, 50th anniv. (No. 1046). The Alps, European Landscape of the Year 1995-96 (No. 1047).

Falknis Group, by Anton Frommelt (1895-1975) A432

Paintings: 80rp, Three Oaks. 4.10fr, Rhine below Triesen.

**1995, June 6** **Photo.** *Perf. 12*

**Granite Paper**

| | | | |
|---|---|---|---|
| **1048** A432 | 60rp multicolored | .85 | .65 |
| **1049** A432 | 80rp multicolored | 1.20 | .90 |
| **1050** A432 | 4.10fr multicolored | 6.00 | 4.75 |
| | *Nos. 1048-1050 (3)* | 8.05 | 6.30 |

Letter Writing — A433

No. 1051, Girl, boy building heart with bricks. No. 1052, Boy, girl bandaging sunflower. No. 1053, Girl, boy & rainbow. No. 1054, Boy in hot air balloon delivering letter to girl.

**1995, June 6** *Perf. 12½*

**Granite Paper**

| | | | |
|---|---|---|---|
| **1051** A433 | 60rp multicolored | .85 | .65 |
| **1052** A433 | 60rp multicolored | .85 | .65 |
| **1053** A433 | 60rp multicolored | .85 | .65 |
| **1054** A433 | 60rp multicolored | .85 | .65 |
| *a.* | Vert. strip of 4, #1051-1054 + label | 3.50 | 3.50 |

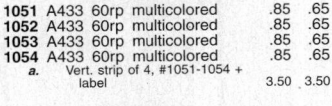

Liechtenstein-Switzerland Postal Relationship — A434

**Litho. & Engr.**

**1995, Sept. 5** *Perf. 13½*

| | | | |
|---|---|---|---|
| **1055** A434 60rp multicolored | | 1.00 | .65 |

See Switzerland No. 960.

No. 1055 and Switzerland No. 960 are identical. This issue was valid for postage in both countries.

**Plant Type of 1993**

60rp, Arnica montana. 80rp, Urtica dioica. 1.80fr, Valeriana officinalis. 3.50rp, Ranunculus ficaria.

**Photo. & Engr.**

**1995, Sept. 5** *Perf. 13x13½*

| | | | |
|---|---|---|---|
| **1056** A415 | 60rp multicolored | .75 | .65 |
| **1057** A415 | 80rp multicolored | 1.00 | .90 |
| **1058** A415 | 1.80fr multicolored | 2.25 | 2.00 |
| **1059** A415 | 3.50fr multicolored | 4.50 | 4.00 |
| | *Nos. 1056-1059 (4)* | 8.50 | 7.55 |

Christmas A435

Paintings by Lorenzo Monaco: 60rp, Angel kneeling, facing right. 80rp, Madonna and Child, two angels at her feet. 1fr, Angel kneeling, facing left.

**Photo. & Engr.**

**1995, Dec. 4** *Perf. 14½x13½*

| | | | |
|---|---|---|---|
| **1060** A435 | 60rp multicolored | .80 | .65 |
| **1061** A435 | 80rp multicolored | 1.10 | .90 |
| **1062** A435 | 1fr multicolored | 1.40 | 1.10 |
| | *Nos. 1060-1062 (3)* | 3.30 | 2.65 |

A436

Painting: 4fr, Lady with Lap Dog, by Paul Wunderlich.

**1995, Dec. 4**

| | | | |
|---|---|---|---|
| **1063** A436 4fr multicolored | | 5.50 | 4.50 |

Bronze Age in Europe — A437

**1996, Mar. 4** **Photo.** *Perf. 11½*

**Granite Paper**

| | | | |
|---|---|---|---|
| **1064** A437 90rp Crucible, pin | | 1.50 | 1.25 |

Countess Nora Kinsky (1888-1923), Nurse, Mother of Princess Gina — A438

Profile and: 90rp, Mar. 7, 1917 diary entry. 1.10fr, Feb. 28, 1917 diary entry.

**1996, Mar. 4** **Granite Paper**

| | | | |
|---|---|---|---|
| **1065** A438 | 90rp multicolored | *1.75* | *1.00* |
| **1066** A438 | 1.10fr multicolored | *2.25* | *1.25* |

Paintings of Village Views, by Marianne Siegl, Based on Sketches by Otto Zeiller A439

10rp, Eschen. 20rp, Farmhouse, St. Joseph's Chapel, Planken. 80rp, Farmhouse, Ruggell. 1fr, Postal auxiliary office, Nendeln. 1.20fr, Buildings, Triesen. 1.30fr, Upper Village, Triesen. 1.70fr, St. Theresa's Church, Schaanwald. 2fr, Rural houses, barns, Gamprin. 4fr, Parish Church, center of village, Triesenberg. 5fr, Vaduz Castle.

**1996-99** **Photo.** *Perf. 12*

**Granite Paper**

| | | | |
|---|---|---|---|
| **1068** A439 | 10rp multicolored | .25 | .25 |
| **1069** A439 | 20rp multicolored | .35 | .25 |
| **1070** A439 | 80rp multicolored | 1.25 | .90 |
| **1071** A439 | 1fr multicolored | 1.75 | .90 |
| **1072** A439 | 1.20fr multicolored | 2.00 | 1.10 |
| **1073** A439 | 1.30fr multicolored | 2.25 | 1.10 |
| **1074** A439 | 1.70fr multicolored | 2.75 | 1.50 |
| **1075** A439 | 2fr multicolored | 2.75 | 1.75 |
| **1076** A439 | 4fr multicolored | 6.75 | 3.50 |
| **1077** A439 | 5fr multicolored | 8.50 | 5.50 |
| | *Nos. 1068-1077 (10)* | 28.60 | 16.75 |

Issued: 10rp, 5fr, 3/4/96; 20rp, 1.30fr, 1.70fr, 3/3/97; 2fr, 4fr, 6/2/98; 80rp, 1fr, 1.20fr, 3/1/99.

See Nos. 1167-1175A

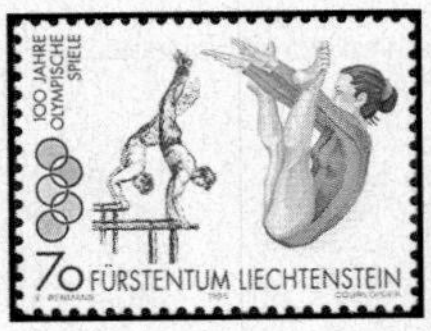


Modern Olympic Games, Cent. A440

**1996, June 3** **Photo.** ***Perf. 11½***
**Granite Paper**

**1079** A440 70rp Gymnastics 1.10 .90
**1080** A440 90rp Hurdles 1.40 1.00
**1081** A440 1.10fr Cycling 2.00 1.10
*Nos. 1079-1081 (3)* 4.50 3.00

Ferdinand Gehr, 100th Birthday A441

Various paintings of flowers.

**1996, June 3** **Granite Paper**

**1083** A441 70rp multicolored 1.10 .90
**1084** A441 90rp multicolored 1.40 1.00
**1085** A441 1.10fr multicolored 2.00 1.10

**Size: 33x23mm**

**1086** A441 1.80fr multicolored 2.75 2.00
*Nos. 1083-1086 (4)* 7.25 5.00

Austria, Millennium A442

**Photo. & Engr.**

**1996, Sept. 2** ***Perf. 13½***

**1087** A442 90rp multicolored 1.50 1.10

New Constitution, 75th Anniv. — A443

**Litho., Engr. & Embossed**

**1996, Sept. 2** ***Perf. 14***

**1088** A443 10fr Natl. arms 14.00 13.00

A444

Paintings by Russian Artist, Eugen Zotow (1881-1953): 70rp, "Country Estate in Poltava." 1.10fr, "Three Bathers in a Park in Berlin." 1.40fr, "View of Vaduz."

**Photo. & Engr.**

**1996, Dec. 2** ***Perf. 14***

**1089** A444 70rp multicolored 1.10 .75
**1090** A444 1.10fr multicolored 2.00 1.10
**1091** A444 1.40fr multicolored 2.25 1.50
*Nos. 1089-1091 (3)* 5.35 3.35

A445

Christmas: Illuminated manuscripts, symbols of the Evangelists.

**1996, Dec. 2**

**1092** A445 70rp Matthew 1.10 .75
**1093** A445 90rp Mark 1.40 .90
**1094** A445 1.10fr Luke 1.75 1.10
**1095** A445 1.80fr John 2.75 2.00
*Nos. 1092-1095 (4)* 7.00 4.75

A446

**Photo. & Engr.**

**1997, Mar. 3** ***Perf. 13½***

**1096** A446 70rp multicolored 1.10 .65

Franz Schubert (1797-1828), composer.

A447

Europa, Liechtenstein Myths: 90rp, Wild Gnomes. 1.10fr, Foal of Planken.

**1997, Mar. 3** **Photo.** ***Perf. 12***
**Granite Paper**

**1097** A447 90rp multicolored *1.75 1.00*
**1098** A447 1.10fr multicolored *2.25 1.10*

St. Lucius, Virgin Mary Holding Infant Jesus, St. Florin, by Gabriel Dreher A448

**Photo. & Engr.**

**1997, June 2** ***Perf. 13½x13***

**1099** A448 20fr multicolored 24.00 17.00

A449

Painting, "Jeune Fille en Fleur," by Enrico Baj.

**1997, Aug. 22** **Photo.** ***Perf. 11½***
**Granite Paper**

**1100** A449 70rp multicolored 1.40 1.00

Mushrooms A450

70rp, Phaeolepiota aurea. 90rp, Helvella silvicola. 1.10fr, Aleuria aurantia.

**Photo. & Engr.**

**1997, Aug. 22** ***Perf. 14***

**1101** A450 70rp multicolored 1.20 .60
**1102** A450 90rp multicolored 1.50 .80
**1103** A450 1.10fr multicolored 1.90 1.00
*Nos. 1101-1103 (3)* 4.60 2.40

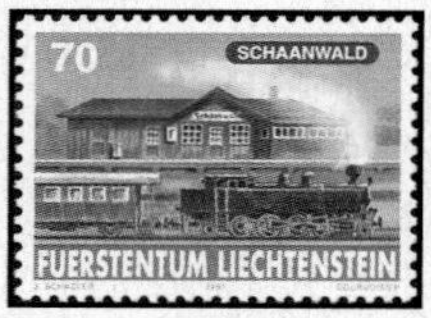


Railway in Liechtenstein, 125th Anniv. — A451

Train stations: 70rp, Schaanwald. 90rp, Nendeln. 1.80fr, Schaan-Vaduz.

**1997, Aug. 22** **Photo.** ***Perf. 11½***
**Granite Paper**

**1104** A451 70rp multicolored 1.20 .60
**1105** A451 90rp multicolored 1.50 .80
**1106** A451 1.80fr multicolored 2.90 1.60
*Nos. 1104-1106 (3)* 5.60 3.00

Christmas Tree Decorations A452

90rp, Bell. 1.10fr, Oval with pointed ends.

**Photo. & Engr.**

**1997, Dec. 1** ***Perf. 14***

**1107** A452 70rp shown 1.20 .60
**1108** A452 90rp multicolored 1.50 .80
**1109** A452 1.10fr multicolored 1.90 1.60
*Nos. 1107-1109 (3)* 4.60 3.00

A453

Skiing, 1998 Winter Olympic Games, Nagano.

**1997, Dec. 1** **Photo.** ***Perf. 12½***
**Granite Paper**

**1110** A453 70rp Cross-country 1.40 1.00
**1111** A453 90rp Slalom 1.75 1.25
**1112** A453 1.80fr Downhill 3.50 2.50
*Nos. 1110-1112 (3)* 6.65 4.75

A454

Contemporary Art, Paintings by Heinz Mack: No. 1113, Verano (Der Sommer). No. 1114, Hommage An Liechtenstein. No. 1115, Zwischen Tag Und Traum. No. 1116, Salute Chirico!.

**1998, Mar. 2** ***Perf. 12***
**Granite Paper**

**1113** A454 70rp multicolored 1.20 .85
**1114** A454 70rp multicolored 1.20 .85
**1115** A454 70rp multicolored 1.20 .85
**1116** A454 70rp multicolored 1.20 .85
*a.* Block or strip of 4, #1113-1116 5.00 3.50

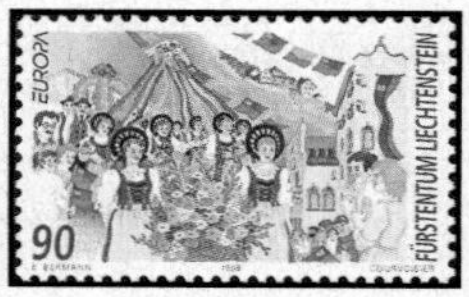


Festivals A455

Europa: 90rp, National holiday. 1.10fr, Festival of the Musical Societies.

**1998, Mar. 2** **Granite Paper**

**1117** A455 90rp multicolored *1.75 1.00*
**1118** A455 1.10fr multicolored *2.25 1.10*

Customs Treaty with Switzerland, 75th Anniv. — A456

**1998, Mar. 2** **Granite Paper**

**1119** A456 1.70fr multicolored 2.75 2.00

1998 World Cup Soccer Championships, France — A457

**1998, Mar. 2** **Granite Paper**

**1120** A457 1.80fr multicolored 2.75 2.00

Letter Writing — A458

Clown: No. 1121, With woman. No. 1122, Holding four leaf clovers. No. 1123, Tipping hat. No. 1124, Holding paper with heart.

**Photo. & Engr.**

**1998, June 2** ***Perf. 14***

**1121** A458 70rp multicolored 1.20 .60
**1122** A458 70rp multicolored 1.20 .60
**1123** A458 70rp multicolored 1.20 .60
**1124** A458 70rp multicolored 1.20 .60
*a.* Strip of 4, #1121-1124 5.00 3.50

1848 Protest March A459

**1998, Sept. 7** **Photo.** ***Perf. 12***
**Granite Paper**

**1125** A459 1.80fr multicolored 3.00 1.75

A460

Traditional Crafts: 90rp, Cooper's tools, tub. 2.20fr, Wooden shoemaker's tools, clog. 3.50fr, Cartwright's tools, wheel.

**1998, Sept. 7** **Granite Paper**

**1126** A460 90rp multicolored 1.40 1.00
**1127** A460 2.20fr multicolored 3.50 2.40
**1128** A460 3.50fr multicolored 5.50 3.75
*Nos. 1126-1128 (3)* 10.40 7.15

See Nos. 1215-1217.

A461

Christmas (Nativity Scene in high relief): 70rp, Soldier, Virgin Mary. 90rp, Entire nativity scene. 1.10fr, Joseph, donkey.

**Photo. & Engr.**

**1998, Dec. 7** *Perf. 14*

| | | | | |
|---|---|---|---|---|
| **1129** | A461 | 70rp multicolored | 1.20 | .75 |
| **1130** | A461 | 90rp multicolored | 1.40 | 1.00 |
| **1131** | A461 | 1.10fr multicolored | 1.75 | 1.25 |
| | | *Nos. 1129-1131 (3)* | 4.35 | 3.00 |

No. 1130 is 34x26mm.

Preservation of Historic Sites — A462

Older buildings, Hinterschellengerg: 90rp, Guest house. 1.70fr, St. George's Chapel, vert. 1.80fr, Farmhouse.

**1998, Dec. 7** **Photo.** *Perf. 11½*

**Granite Paper**

| | | | | |
|---|---|---|---|---|
| **1132** | A462 | 90rp multicolored | 1.40 | 1.00 |
| **1133** | A462 | 1.70fr multicolored | 2.75 | 2.00 |
| **1134** | A462 | 1.80fr multicolored | 2.75 | 2.00 |
| | | *Nos. 1132-1134 (3)* | 6.90 | 5.00 |

Telephone in Liechtenstein, Cent. — A463

**1998, Dec. 7** **Granite Paper**

| | | | | |
|---|---|---|---|---|
| **1135** | A463 | 2.80fr multicolored | 5.00 | 3.25 |

A464

Europa (Conservation Areas): 90rp, Snake, Schwabbrünnen-Aescher marshland. 1.10fr, Bird, Ruggell marsh.

**Granite Paper**

**1999, Mar. 1** **Photo.** *Perf. 11½x12*

| | | | | |
|---|---|---|---|---|
| **1136** | A464 | 90rp multicolored | *1.75* | *1.00* |
| **1137** | A464 | 1.10fr multicolored | *2.25* | *1.25* |

Unterland, 300th Anniv. — A465

Continuous scene of villages: a, Schellenberg, buildings, fortress. b, Mauren, domed steeple on church. c, Eschen,, church, houses. d, Ruggell, road leading into village. e, Gamprin, gray-roofed buildings, church.

**1999, Mar. 1** *Perf. 12*

**Granite Paper**

| | | | | |
|---|---|---|---|---|
| **1138** | A465 | Sheet of 5 + label | 9.00 | 6.25 |
| *a.-e.* | | 90rp any single | 1.75 | 1.25 |

Anniversaries A466

Stylized designs: No. 1139, Council of Europe 50th anniv. emblem. No. 1140, Bird holding letter. No. 1141, Hand holding heart.

**1999, May 25** **Photo.** *Perf. 11½x12*

**Granite Paper**

| | | | | |
|---|---|---|---|---|
| **1139** | A466 | 70rp multicolored | .90 | .60 |
| **1140** | A466 | 70rp multicolored | .90 | .60 |
| **1141** | A466 | 70rp multicolored | .90 | .60 |
| | | *Nos. 1139-1141 (3)* | 2.70 | 1.80 |

No. 1140, UPU, 125th anniv. No. 1141, Caritas Liechtenstein, 75th anniv.

8th Games of the Small European States A467

**1999, May 25** **Granite Paper**

| | | | | |
|---|---|---|---|---|
| **1142** | A467 | 70rp Judo | .90 | .60 |
| **1143** | A467 | 70rp Swimming | .90 | .60 |
| **1144** | A467 | 70rp Javelin | .90 | .60 |
| **1145** | A467 | 90rp Volleyball | 1.25 | .75 |
| **1146** | A467 | 90rp Squash | 1.25 | .75 |
| **1147** | A467 | 90rp Tennis | 1.25 | .75 |
| **1148** | A467 | 90rp Table tennis | 1.25 | .75 |
| **1149** | A467 | 90rp Cycling | 1.25 | .75 |
| **1150** | A467 | 90rp Shooting | 1.25 | .75 |
| | | *Nos. 1142-1150 (9)* | 10.20 | 6.30 |

Johann Wolfgang von Goethe (1749-1832), Poet — A468

Quotations and scenes from Faust: 1.40fr, "Grey, dear friend, is all theory and green the golden tree of life." 1.70fr, "I'll take the wager!...Done! And again, and again!"

**Photo. & Engr.**

**1999, Sept. 9** *Perf. 14*

| | | | | |
|---|---|---|---|---|
| **1151** | A468 | 1.40fr multicolored | 1.50 | 1.10 |
| **1152** | A468 | 1.70fr multicolored | 2.50 | 1.50 |

Paintings by Eugen Verling (1891-1968) A469

Designs: 70rp, Herrengasse. 2fr, Old Vaduz with Castle. 4fr, House in Fürst-Franz-Josef-Strasse, Vaduz.

**1999, Sept. 9**

| | | | | |
|---|---|---|---|---|
| **1153** | A469 | 70rp multicolored | .90 | .60 |
| **1154** | A469 | 2fr multicolored | 2.60 | 1.50 |
| **1155** | A469 | 4fr multicolored | 5.25 | 3.25 |
| | | *Nos. 1153-1155 (3)* | 8.75 | 5.35 |

A470

Walser house identification marks.

**1999, Dec. 6** **Photo.** *Perf. 11¾*

**Granite Paper**

| | | | | |
|---|---|---|---|---|
| **1156** | A470 | 70rp Door mark | .90 | .60 |
| **1157** | A470 | 90rp Picture mark | 1.10 | .75 |
| **1158** | A470 | 1.80fr Axe mark | 2.10 | 1.75 |
| | | *Nos. 1156-1158 (3)* | 4.10 | 3.10 |

A471

3.60fr, Johann Gutenberg, inventer of letterpress printing.

**Photo. & Engr.**

**1999, Dec. 6** *Perf. 13½*

| | | | | |
|---|---|---|---|---|
| **1159** | A471 | 3.60fr multicolored | 4.50 | 3.25 |

Christmas Paintings by Joseph Walser A472

70rp, The Annunciation. 90rp, Nativity. 1.10fr, Presentation of Jesus.

**1999, Dec. 6** *Perf. 13½x14¼*

| | | | | |
|---|---|---|---|---|
| **1160** | A472 | 70rp multicolored | .90 | .60 |
| **1161** | A472 | 90rp multicolored | 1.10 | .75 |
| **1162** | A472 | 1.10fr multicolored | 1.40 | .95 |
| | | *Nos. 1160-1162 (3)* | 3.40 | 2.30 |

Souvenir Sheet

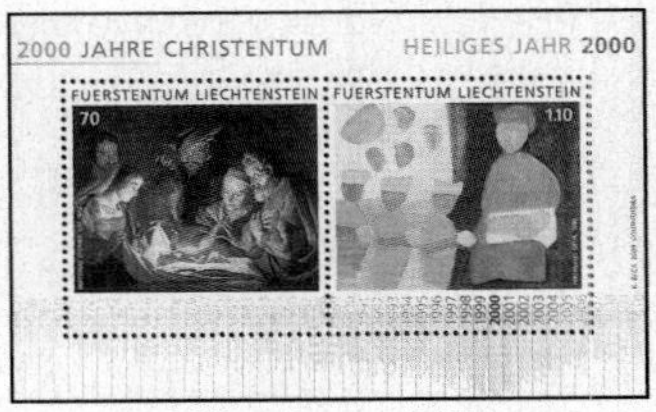


Millennium — A473

Designs: 70rp, The Adoration of the Shepherds, by Matthias Stomer. 1.10fr, The Magi, by Ferdinand Gehr.

**2000, Jan. 1** **Photo.** *Perf. 12*

**Granite Paper**

| | | | | |
|---|---|---|---|---|
| **1163** | A473 | Sheet of 2 | 4.00 | 2.25 |
| *a.* | | 70rp multi | 1.40 | .85 |
| *b.* | | 1.10fr multi | 2.25 | 1.40 |

Christianity, 2000th anniv.

Creation of Liechtenstein Post, Ltd. — A474

**2000, Jan. 1** *Perf. 11¾*

**Granite Paper**

| | | | | |
|---|---|---|---|---|
| **1164** | A474 | 90rp multi | 2.00 | 1.10 |

**Village Views Type of 1996**

Designs: 50rp, Church and vicarage, Ruggell. 60rp, Chapel of St. Peter, Balzers. 70rp, Parish church, Schellenberg. 1.10fr, Holy Cross Chapel, Eschen. 1.40fr, Farmhouse, parish church, Mauren. 1.80fr, Chapel of Peace, Malbun. 1.90fr, Tower of Church of St. Lawrence, Schaan. 2.20fr, Höfle District, Balzers. 4.50fr, Church mound, Bendern.

**2000-01** **Photo.** *Perf. 11¾*

**Granite Paper**

| | | | | |
|---|---|---|---|---|
| **1167** | A439 | 50rp multi | .75 | .45 |
| **1168** | A439 | 60rp multi | .95 | .50 |
| **1169** | A439 | 70rp multi | 1.10 | .65 |
| **1171** | A439 | 1.10fr multi | 1.75 | 1.10 |
| **1172** | A439 | 1.40fr multi | 2.10 | 1.40 |
| **1173** | A439 | 1.80fr multi | 2.75 | 1.75 |
| **1174** | A439 | 1.90fr multi | 2.75 | 1.75 |
| **1175** | A439 | 2.20fr multi | 3.50 | 2.00 |
| **1175A** | A439 | 4.50fr multi | 7.00 | 4.25 |
| | | *Nos. 1167-1175A (9)* | 22.65 | 13.85 |

Issued: 70rp, 1.80fr, 2.20fr, 4.50fr, 6/5/01.

"Gods Once Walked" Exhibition at Vaduz Museum of Art — A475

Designs: 70rp, Mars and Rhea Silvia, by Peter Paul Rubens. 1.80fr, Cupid With Soap Bubble, by Rembrandt.

**Photo. & Engr.**

**2000, Mar. 6** *Perf. 13½x12¾*

| | | | | |
|---|---|---|---|---|
| **1176** | A475 | 70rp multi | 1.10 | .65 |
| **1177** | A475 | 1.80fr multi | 2.60 | 1.75 |

**Europa, 2000**

Common Design Type

**2000, May 9** **Photo.** *Perf. 11½x11¾*

**Granite Paper**

| | | | | |
|---|---|---|---|---|
| **1178** | CD17 | 1.10fr multi | *2.25* | *1.75* |

Expo 2000, Hanover — A476

Art by Friedensreich Hundertwasser: 70rp, Fragrance of Humus. 90rp, Do Not Wait Houses — Move. 1.10fr, The Car: A Drive Towards Nature and Creation.

**Photo. & Engr.**

**2000, May 9** *Perf. 14¼x13½*

| | | | | |
|---|---|---|---|---|
| **1179** | A476 | 70rp multi | 1.40 | .80 |
| **1180** | A476 | 90rp multi | 1.75 | 1.00 |
| **1181** | A476 | 1.10fr multi | 2.25 | 1.25 |
| | | *Nos. 1179-1181 (3)* | 5.40 | 3.05 |

Images of Peace A477

Art by mouth and foot painters: 1.40fr, Dove of Peace, by Antonio Martini. 1.70fr, Universal Peace, by Alberto Alvarez. 2.20fr, Rainbow, by Eiichi Minami.

**2000, May 9** **Photo.** *Perf. 11¾x11½*

| | | | | |
|---|---|---|---|---|
| **1182** | A477 | 1.40fr multi | 2.25 | 1.25 |
| **1183** | A477 | 1.70fr multi | 2.60 | 1.50 |
| **1184** | A477 | 2.20fr multi | 3.50 | 2.00 |
| | | *Nos. 1182-1184 (3)* | 8.35 | 4.75 |

2000 Summer Olympics, Sydney A478

Designs: 80rp, Koalas on rings. 1fr, High jump by kangaroo joey. 1.30fr, Emus racing. 1.80fr, Platypuses swimming.

**2000, Sept. 4** **Photo.** *Perf. 11¾*

**Granite Paper**

| | | | | |
|---|---|---|---|---|
| **1185** | A478 | 80rp multi | 1.10 | .65 |
| **1186** | A478 | 1fr multi | 1.25 | .75 |
| **1187** | A478 | 1.30fr multi | 1.60 | 1.00 |
| **1188** | A478 | 1.80fr multi | 2.25 | 1.40 |
| | | *Nos. 1185-1188 (4)* | 6.20 | 3.80 |

Organization for Security and Co-operation In Europe, 25th Anniv. A479

**2000, Sept. 4** **Granite Paper**

| | | | | |
|---|---|---|---|---|
| **1189** | A479 | 1.30fr multi | 2.50 | 1.50 |

Issued in sheets of 20 stamps and 5 labels.

Opening Of Liechtenstein Art Museum — A480

Designs: 80rp, The Dreaming Bee, by Joan Miró. 1.20fr, Cube by Sol LeWitt. 2fr, A Bouquet of Flowers, by Roelant Savery.

**2000, Sept. 4 Photo. *Perf. 11¾***
**Granite Paper (#1190-1191)**

**1190** A480 80rp multi 1.60 .95
**1191** A480 1.20fr multi 2.40 1.40

**Size: 31x46mm**
**Photo. & Engr.**
***Perf. 13¾***

**1192** A480 2fr multi 4.00 2.40
*Nos. 1190-1192 (3)* 8.00 4.75

Mushrooms A481

90rp, Mycena adonis. 1.10fr, Chalciporus amarellus. 2fr, Hygrocybe caylptriformis.

**Photo. & Engr.**
**2000, Dec. 4 *Perf. 14¼***

**1193-1195** A481 Set of 3 8.00 4.50

Christmas A482

Various creches: 80rp, 1.30fr, 1.80fr.

**2000, Dec. 4 *Perf. 13¾x14***

**1196-1198** A482 Set of 3 6.50 4.00

Europa — A483

**2001, Mar. 5 Photo. *Perf. 11½x11¾***
**Granite Paper**

**1199** A483 1.30fr multi *2.25 1.50*

Liechtenstein's Presidency of Council of Europe — A484

**2001, Mar. 5 *Perf. 11¾***
**Granite Paper**

**1200** A484 1.80fr multi 2.90 1.75

Scratch-off Greetings A485

Postman in: No. 1201, 70rp, Red uniform (hidden flower bouquet). No. 1202, 70rp, Blue uniform (hidden envelope).

**2001, Mar. 5 Granite Paper**

**1201-1202** A485 Set of 2 unscratched 2.50 1.25
Set, scratched 1.50

Easter Eggs of the Russian Czars — A486

Designs: 1.20fr, Silver egg. 1.80fr, Cloisonné egg. 2fr, Porcelain egg.

**Photo. & Engr.**
**2001, Mar. 5 *Perf. 13¾***

**1203-1205** A486 Set of 3 10.00 6.00

Liechtenstein Historical Association, Cent. — A487

Designs: No. 1206, 70rp, Mars of Gutenberg. No. 1207, Carolignian cruciform fibula.

**2001, June 5 Photo. *Perf. 11¾***
**Granite Paper**

**1206-1207** A487 Set of 2 2.75 1.75

Josef Gabriel Rheinberger (1839-1901), Musician A488

**Photo. & Engr.**
**2001, Sept. 3 *Perf. 14***

**1208** A488 3.50fr multi 5.75 3.50

Votive Pictures — A489

Designs: 70rp, 1733 picture, Chapel of Our Lady, Dux. 1.20fr, 1802 picture, St. George's Chapel, Schellenberg. 1.30fr, 1718 picture, Chapel of Our Lady, Dux.

**2001, Sept. 3 *Perf. 13½***

**1209-1211** A489 Set of 3 6.50 4.00

Building Preservation A490

Designs: 70rp, St. Theresa's Chapel, Schaanwald. 90rp, St. Johann's winery, Mauren. 1.10fr, Pirsch transformer station, Schaanwald.

**2001, Sept. 3 Photo. *Perf. 11¾***
**Granite Paper**

**1212-1214** A490 Set of 3 5.25 3.25

See Nos. 1232-1233, 1251-1252, 1295-1296, 1323-1324, 1361-1362, 1394-1395, 1424.

**Traditional Crafts Type of 1998**

Designs: 70rp, Blacksmith's tools, horseshoe, yoke bars. 90rp, Rakemaker's tools, rake. 1.20fr, Saddler's tools, horse collar.

**2001, Dec. 3 Photo. *Perf. 11¾***
**Granite Paper**

**1215-1217** A460 Set of 3 4.50 3.00

Abstract Art by Gottfried Honegger A491

Untitled works: 1.80fr, 2.20fr.

**2001, Dec. 3 *Perf. 11½***
**Granite Paper**

**1218-1219** A491 Set of 2 6.50 4.00

Christmas — A492

Medallions: 70rp, Annunciation. 90rp, Nativity. 1.30fr, The Presentation of the Lord.

**2001, Dec. 3 *Perf. 12x11¾***
**Granite Paper**

**1220-1222** A492 Set of 3 4.00 3.50

Liechtenstein Students' Spice Bees Experiment on Space Shuttle A493

**2002, Mar. 4 Photo. *Perf. 13½x14¼***

**1223** A493 90rp multi 1.75 1.10

LIBA.02 Stamp Exhibition, Vaduz — A494

**2002, Mar. 4 *Perf. 13¾***

**1224** A494 1.20fr multi 2.10 1.10

Europa — A495

Designs: 90rp, Tightrope walker. 1.30fr, Juggler.

**Photo. & Engr.**
**2002, Mar. 4 *Perf. 14¼x14***

**1225-1226** A495 Set of 2 *4.25 3.75*

Intl. Year of Mountains A496

Intl. Commision for Protection of the Alps A497

**2002, Mar. 4 Photo. *Perf. 13¾x13½***

**1227** A496 70rp multi 1.40 .85
**1228** A497 1.20fr multi 2.40 1.40

Paintings by Friedrich Kaufmann (1892-1972) A498

Views of: 70rp, Schellenberg. 1.30fr, Schaan. 1.80fr, Steg.

**2002, Mar. 4 *Perf. 13½x13¾***

**1229-1231** A498 Set of 3 6.50 4.00

**Building Preservation Type of 2001**

Designs: 70rp, House, Popers, horiz. 1.20fr, House, Weiherring, horiz.

***Perf. 13¾x13½***
**2002, June 3 Photo.**

**1232-1233** A490 Set of 2 3.25 2.00

2002 World Cup Soccer Championships, Japan and Korea — A499

**2002, June 3 *Perf. 13½x14¼***

**1234** A499 1.80fr multi 3.25 2.00

Royalty A500

Designs: 3fr, Princess Marie. 3.50fr, Prince Hans Adam II.

**2002, June 3 *Perf. 13¾x13½***

**1235-1236** A500 Set of 2 10.00 7.00

Liba.02 Stamp Exhibition, Vaduz — A501

Liechtenstein stamps depicting: 90rp, Various topics. 1.30fr, Royalty.

**2002, Aug. 8** **Photo.** *Perf. 13½*
**1237-1238** A501 Set of 2 3.50 2.50

### Royalty Type of 2002

Designs: 2fr, Hereditary Princess Sophie. 2.50fr, Hereditary Prince Alois.

**2002, Aug. 8** *Perf. 13¾x13½*
**1239-1240** A500 Set of 2 7.00 4.00

Orchids — A502

Designs: 70rp, Epipogium aphyllum. 1.20fr, Ophrys insectifera. 1.30fr, Nigritella nigra.

**2002, Aug. 8** *Perf. 13½x13¾*
**1241-1243** A502 Set of 3 5.25 3.75

See Nos. 1288-1290.

Inn Sign Art — A503

Designs: 1.20fr, Eagle, Vaduz. 1.80fr, Angel, Balzers. 3fr, Eagle, Bendern.

**Photo. & Engr.**

**2002, Nov. 25** *Perf. 13½x14¼*
**1244-1246** A503 Set of 3 10.00 5.25

Christmas — A504

Batik art by Sister Regina Hassler: 70rp, Search for Shelter. 1.20fr, Nativity. 1.80fr, Flight to Egypt.

*Perf. 14¼x13½*

**2002, Nov. 25** **Photo.**
**1247-1249** A504 Set of 3 6.25 4.50

Europa A505

**2003, Mar. 3** **Photo.** *Perf. 13½x12¾*
**1250** A505 1.20fr multi *2.25 2.00*

### Building Preservation Type of 2001

Designs: 70rp, St. Fridolin Church, Ruggell. 2.50fr, House, Spidach, horiz..

*Perf. 13½x13¾, 13¾x3½*

**2003, Mar. 3**
**1251-1252** A490 Set of 2 5.50 4.25

Viticulture Throughout the Year — A506

Designs: 1.30fr, Pruning (February). 1.80fr, Tying vines to arbor (March). 2.20fr, Hoeing soil (April).

**2003** *Perf. 14¼*
**1253-1255** A506 Set of 3 9.00 6.50

Designs: 1.20fr, Looping vines (May). 1.80fr, Leaf work (June). 3.50fr, Removing high growth (July).

**1256-1258** A506 Set of 3 11.00 8.25

Designs: 70rp, Thinning out of vines (August). 90rp, Harvesting grapes (September). 1.10fr, Pressing grapes (October).

**1259-1261** A506 Set of 3 5.00 3.75

Designs: 70rp, First tasting of wine (November). 90rp, Harvest of frozen grapes (December). 1.20fr, Bottling wine (January).

**1262-1264** A506 Set of 3 5.00 3.75

Issued: Nos. 1253-1255, 3/3; Nos. 1256-1258, 6/2; Nos. 1259-1261, 9/1; Nos. 1262-1264, 11/24.

Liechtenstein Association for the Disabled, 50th Anniv. — A507

**2003, June 2** **Photo.** *Perf. 14¼*
**1265** A507 70rp multi 1.40 1.10

Reopening of National Museum — A508

Museum building and: 1.20fr, Ammonite fossil. 1.30fr, Shield of bailiff of Vaduz.

**2003, June 2** *Perf. 14*
**1266-1267** A508 Set of 2 5.00 3.75

White Storks and Nest — A509

**Photo. & Engr.**

**2003, Sept. 1** *Perf. 12¾x13½*
**1268** A509 2.20fr multi 3.75 2.75

Saints — A510

Designs: No. 1269, 1.20fr, St. Blasius. No. 1270, 1.20fr, St. George. No. 1271, 1.30fr, St. Erasmus. No. 1272, 1.30fr, St. Vitus.

**2003, Sept. 1** *Perf. 13½*
**1269-1272** A510 Set of 4 8.00 6.00

Stamps of the same denomination were printed in sheets of 20 arranged in blocks of 10 of each stamp separated by a horizontal gutter.

See Nos. 1280-1285, 1308-1311.

Children's Drawings A511

Designs: 70rp, Cow, by Laura Beck. No. 1274, 1.80fr, Apple Tree, by Patrick Marxer, vert. No. 1275, 1.80fr, Bee, by Laura Lingg.

*Perf. 13½x14¼, 14¼x13½*

**2003, Nov. 24** **Photo.**
**1273-1275** A511 Set of 3 7.00 5.00

Christmas — A512

Reverse glass paintings: 70rp, Archangel Gabriel. 90rp, Nativity. 1.30fr, Three Magi.

**2003, Nov. 24** *Perf. 14¼x13½*
**1276-1278** A512 Set of 3 5.75 4.25

AHV Old Age and Survivor's Insurance, 50th Anniv. — A513

**2004, Jan. 3** **Photo.** *Perf. 14*
**1279** A513 85rp multi 1.40 1.00

### Saints Type of 2003

Designs: No. 1280, 1fr, St. Achatius. No. 1281, 1fr, St. Margareta. No. 1282, 1.20fr, St. Christophorus. No. 1283, 1.20fr, St. Pantaleon. No. 1284, 2.50fr, St. Aegidius. No. 1285, 2.50fr, St. Cyriakus.

**Photo. & Engr.**

**2004, Mar. 1** *Perf. 13½*
**1280-1285** A510 Set of 6 15.00 13.00

Stamps of the same denomination were printed in sheets of 20 arranged in blocks of 10 of each stamp separated by a horizontal gutter.

Europa — A514

**2004, Mar. 1** **Photo.** *Perf. 13¾x13½*
**1286** A514 1.30fr multi *2.50 2.25*

2004 Summer Olympics, Athens — A515

**2004, June 1** **Photo.** *Perf. 14¼*
**1287** A515 85rp multi 1.50 1.25

### Orchid Type of 2002

Designs: 85rp, Ophrys apifera. 1fr, Orchis ustulata. 1.20fr, Epipactis purpurata.

**2004, June 1** *Perf. 13½x13¾*
**1288-1290** A502 Set of 3 6.00 4.75

Aerial Views A516

**2004, June 1** *Perf. 13½*

| | | | | | |
|---|---|---|---|---|---|
| **1291** | A516 | 15rp | Bendern | .30 | .25 |
| **1292** | A516 | 85rp | Gross-Steg | 1.50 | 1.20 |
| **1293** | A516 | 1fr | Tuass | 1.75 | 1.40 |
| **1294** | A516 | 6fr | Gutenberg | 10.00 | 7.75 |
| | | *Nos. 1291-1294 (4)* | | 13.55 | 10.60 |

See No. 1312, 1331-1333, 1340-1341, 1375-1377.

### Building Preservation Type of 2001

Designs: 2.20fr, House on Unterdorfstrasse, horiz. 2.50fr, Row of houses, Dorfstrasse, horiz.

*Perf. 13¾x13½*

**2004, Sept. 6** **Photo.**
**1295-1296** A490 Set of 2 7.50 6.00

Sciences — A517

Designs: 85rp, Mathematics. 1fr, Physics. 1.30fr, Chemistry. 1.80fr, Astronomy.

**2004, Sept. 6** *Perf. 13¾x14*
**1297-1300** A517 Set of 4 7.50 6.00

Digital Palimpsest Research A518

**Photo. & Engr.**

**2004, Nov. 22** *Perf. 14¼*
**1301** A518 2.50fr multi 4.25 3.50

Fossils — A519

Designs: 1.20fr, Ammonite. 1.30fr, Sea urchin. 2.20fr, Shark tooth.

**2004, Nov. 22**
**1302-1304** A519 Set of 3 7.50 6.50

Christmas
A520

Designs: 85rp, Annunciation. 1fr, Holy Family. 1.80fr, Adoration of the Magi.

**2004, Nov. 22 Photo. *Rouletted 6¾***

| | | | | |
|---|---|---|---|---|
| **1305-1307** | A520 | Set of 3 | 6.00 | 5.00 |

Punched holes are in stamp frames to give stamps a lace-like appearance.

**Saints Type of 2003**

Designs: No. 1308, 85rp, St. Eustachius. No. 1309, 85rp, St. Dionysius. No. 1310, 1.80fr, St. Catharine. No. 1311, 1.80fr, St. Barbara.

**Photo. & Engr.**

**2005, Mar. 7 *Perf. 13½***

| | | | | |
|---|---|---|---|---|
| **1308-1311** | A510 | Set of 4 | 9.00 | 7.50 |

**Aerial Views Type of 2004**

**2005, Mar. 7 Photo.**

| | | | | |
|---|---|---|---|---|
| **1312** | A516 | 3.60fr Triesenberg | 5.50 | 4.50 |

Europa
A521

**2005, Mar. 7**

| | | | | |
|---|---|---|---|---|
| **1313** | A521 | 1.30fr multi | *2.10* | *1.90* |

Venus at a Mirror, by Peter Paul Rubens
A522

**2005, Mar. 7 Photo. & Engr.**

| | | | | |
|---|---|---|---|---|
| **1314** | A522 | 2.20fr multi | 4.50 | 4.00 |

See Austria No. 1980.

Paintings of Flower Arrangements
A523

Designs: No. 1315, 85rp, Magnolia Flowers, by Chen Hongshou (shown). No. 1316, 85rp, Flower Vase in a Windoe Niche, by Ambrosius Bosschaert the Elder.

**2005, May 18 Photo. *Perf. 14***

| | | | | |
|---|---|---|---|---|
| **1315-1316** | A523 | Set of 2 | 3.50 | 3.00 |

See People's Republic of China Nos. 3433-3434.

Inn Signs — A524

Designs: 1fr, Stallion, Rössle Inn, Schaan. 1.40fr, Edelweiss Inn, Triesenberg. 2.50fr, Lion, Löwen Inn, Bendern.

**Photo. & Engr.**

**2005, June 6 *Perf. 14¼x13½***

| | | | | |
|---|---|---|---|---|
| **1317-1319** | A524 | Set of 3 | 7.50 | 6.25 |

Postal Museum, 75th Anniv.
A525

Designs: 1.10fr, Hermann E. Sieger, museum founder. 1.30fr, Liechtenstein stamps on stock page. 1.80fr, 1930 Zeppelin cover.

***Perf. 13½x14¼***

**2005, June 6 Photo.**

| | | | | |
|---|---|---|---|---|
| **1320-1322** | A525 | Set of 3 | 6.50 | 5.25 |

**Building Preservation Type of 2001**

Designs: 85rp, Oberbendern. 2.20fr, Church Hill, Bendern.

***Perf. 13¾x13½***

**2005, Sept. 5 Photo.**

| | | | | |
|---|---|---|---|---|
| **1323-1324** | A490 | Set of 2 | 5.00 | 4.00 |

Bats — A526

Designs: 1.80fr, Plecotus auritus. 2fr, Myotis myotis.

**2005, Sept. 5 *Perf. 14¼***

| | | | | |
|---|---|---|---|---|
| **1325-1326** | A526 | Set of 2 | 6.00 | 5.00 |

Pastures
A527

Designs: 85rp, Bargälla. 1fr, Pradamee. 1.30fr, Gritsch. 1.80fr, Valüna.

**2005, Sept. 5 *Perf. 13½x14¼***

| | | | | |
|---|---|---|---|---|
| **1327-1330** | A527 | Set of 4 | 7.50 | 6.00 |

See nos. 1356-1358, 1384-1386, 1403-1404.

**Aerial Views Type of 2004**

**2005, Nov. 21 Photo. *Perf. 13½***

| | | | | |
|---|---|---|---|---|
| **1331** | A516 | 1.50fr Oberland | 2.25 | 1.75 |
| **1332** | A516 | 1.60fr Ruggeller Riet | 2.50 | 1.90 |
| **1333** | A516 | 3fr Naafkopf | 4.50 | 3.50 |
| | | *Nos. 1331-1333 (3)* | 9.25 | 7.15 |

2006 Winter Olympics, Turin, Italy — A528

Designs: 1.20fr, Ski jumping. 1.30fr, Biathlon. 1.40fr, Slalom skiing.

**2005, Nov. 21 *Perf. 14¼x14***

| | | | | |
|---|---|---|---|---|
| **1334-1336** | A528 | Set of 3 | 7.00 | 5.50 |

Christmas
A529

Wood sculptures by Toni Gstöhl: 85rp, The Annunciation. 1fr, Holy Family. 1.30fr, Adoration of the Shepherds.

**Photo. & Engr.**

**2005, Nov. 21 *Perf. 14¼x13½***

| | | | | |
|---|---|---|---|---|
| **1337-1339** | A529 | Set of 3 | 5.00 | 4.00 |

**Aerial Views Type of 2004**

**2006, Mar. 6 Photo. *Perf. 13½***

| | | | | |
|---|---|---|---|---|
| **1340** | A516 | 2.50fr Rhine Canal | 3.75 | 3.00 |
| **1341** | A516 | 3.50fr Rhine Valley | 5.25 | 4.75 |

Lost in Her Dreams, by Friedrich von Amerling
A530

**2006, Mar. 6 Photo. & Engr.**

| | | | | |
|---|---|---|---|---|
| **1342** | A530 | 2.20fr multi | 3.50 | 2.75 |

See Austria No. 2041.

Paintings by Eugen Wilhelm Schüepp (1915-74)
A531

Designs: 1fr, Peat Cutters, Ruggell Marsh. 1.80fr, Neugut, Schaan.

**2006, Mar. 6 Photo. *Perf. 13½x14¼***

| | | | | |
|---|---|---|---|---|
| **1343-1344** | A531 | Set of 2 | 4.50 | 3.75 |

Europa
A532

Winning designs from stamp design contest: 1.20fr, Bridge, by Nadja Beck. 1.30fr, Face of Integration, by Elisabeth Müssner.

**2006, Mar. 6**

| | | | | |
|---|---|---|---|---|
| **1345-1346** | A532 | Set of 2 | *5.00* | *4.00* |

2006 World Cup Soccer Championships, Germany — A533

***Perf. 13½x14¼***

**2006, June 6 Photo.**

| | | | | |
|---|---|---|---|---|
| **1347** | A533 | 3.30fr multi | 5.00 | 5.00 |

Tourism Promotion — A534

Designs: 85rp, Woman holding G clef. 1fr, Backpacker. 1.20fr, Restaurant patron. 1.80fr, Skier.

**2006, June 6 *Perf. 13¾***

| | | | | |
|---|---|---|---|---|
| **1348-1351** | A534 | Set of 4 | 8.50 | 7.00 |

Full Sovereignty, Bicent. — A535

Designs: 85rp, Prince Johann I. 1fr, National flag. 1.30fr, Flag of the Princely House of Liechtenstein. 1.80fr, National arms.

**2006, June 6 Litho. & Engr.**

| | | | | |
|---|---|---|---|---|
| **1352-1355** | A535 | Set of 4 | 8.50 | 7.00 |

**Pastures Type of 2005**

Designs: 85rp, Lawena. 1.30fr, Gapfahl. 2.40fr, Gafadura.

***Perf. 13½x14¼***

**2006, Sept. 4 Photo.**

| | | | | |
|---|---|---|---|---|
| **1356-1358** | A527 | Set of 3 | 7.50 | 6.00 |

Wolfgang Amadeus Mozart (1756-91), Composer — A536

**2006, Sept. 4 *Perf. 13¾x14¼***

| | | | | |
|---|---|---|---|---|
| **1359** | A536 | 1.20fr multi | 2.50 | 2.00 |

Miniature Sheet

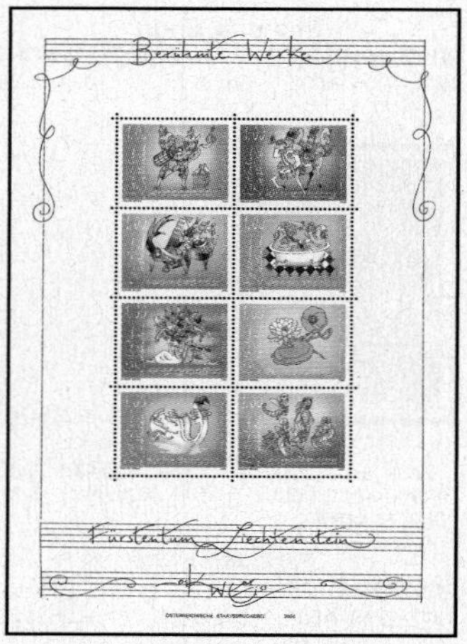

Classical Music — A537

No. 1360: a, The Magic Flute, by Wolfgang Amadeus Mozart. b, Radetzky March, by Johann Strauss. c, Rhapsody in Blue, by George Gershwin. d, Water Music, by George Frideric Handel. e, Pastoral Symphony, by Ludwig van Beethoven. f, Waltz of the Flowers, by Peter Ilich Tchaikovsky. g, The Swan, by Camille Saint-Saens. h, A Midsummer Night's Dream, by Felix Mendelssohn.

**2006, Sept. 4 *Perf. 13½x14¼***

| | | | | |
|---|---|---|---|---|
| **1360** | A537 | Sheet of 8 | 14.00 | 14.00 |
| *a.-h.* | | 1fr Any single | 1.75 | 1.50 |

### Building Preservation Type of 2001

Designs: 1.80fr, Governor's residence and Liechtenstein Institute, Bendern. 3.50fr, Bühl House, Gamprin, horiz.

*Perf. 13½x13¾, 13¾x13½*

**2006, Nov. 20** **Photo.**

**1361-1362** A490 Set of 2 8.00 6.50

Inventions A538

Designs: 1.30fr, Curta calculator. 1.40fr, Carena film camera. 2.40fr, PAV sliding caliper.

**2006, Nov. 20** ***Perf. 14¼x14***

**1363-1365** A538 Set of 3 8.00 6.50

Christmas A539

Frescos from Chapel of St. Mary, Dux: 85rp, The Annunciation. 1fr, Nativity. 1.30fr, Presentation at the Temple.

**Photo. & Engr.**

**2006, Nov. 20** ***Perf. 13½***

**1366-1368** A539 Set of 3 6.25 5.00

Scouting, Cent. — A540

**2007, Mar. 5** **Photo.** ***Perf. 14¼***

**1369** A540 1.30fr multi 2.00 1.75

Portrait of a Lady, by Bernardino Zaganelli da Cotignola A541

**Litho. & Engr.**

**2007, Mar. 5** ***Perf. 13¾***

**1370** A541 2.40fr multi 4.00 3.50

See Austria No. 2086.

Musical Terms A542

Designs: 85rp, Allegro. 1.80fr, Capriccio. 2fr, Crescendo. 3.50fr, Con fuoco.

**2007, Mar. 5** **Photo.** ***Perf. 13½***

**1371-1374** A542 Set of 4 14.00 12.00

### Aerial Views Type of 2004

**2007, June 4** **Photo.** ***Perf. 13½***

| | | | | |
|---|---|---|---|---|
| **1375** | A516 1.10fr | Nendeln | 1.75 | 1.40 |
| **1376** | A516 1.80fr | Malbun | 2.75 | 2.10 |
| **1377** | A516 2.60fr | Ackerland | 4.00 | 3.00 |
| | *Nos. 1375-1377 (3)* | | 8.50 | 6.50 |

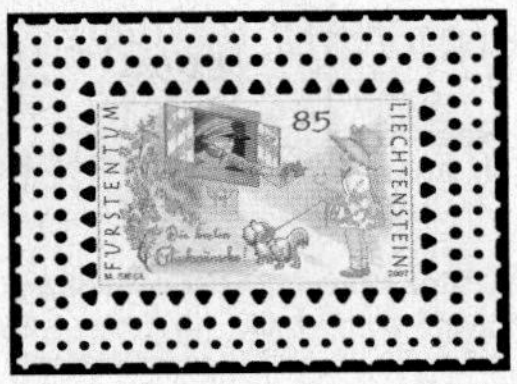


Greeting Card Art — A543

Designs: 85rp, Boy delivering flower and letter to girl. 1fr, Two children carrying litter with cake, flowers and letter. 1.30fr, Bird carrying letter.

**2007, June 4** ***Rouletted 6¾***

**1378-1380** A543 Set of 3 6.00 6.00

Punched holes are in stamp frames to give stamps a lacelike appearance.

Paintings of Rhine Landscapes by Johann Ludwig Bleuler (1792-1850) A544

Designs: 1fr, Castle and Village of Vaduz. 1.30fr, Rätikon Mountain. 2.40fr, Confluence of the Ill and Rhine.

*Perf. 13½x14¼*

**2007, June 4** **Photo. & Engr**

**1381-1383** A544 Set of 3 7.00 7.00

### Pastures Type of 2005

Designs: 1fr, Hintervalorsch. 1.40fr, Sücka. 2.20fr, Guschgfiel.

*Perf. 13½x14¼*

**2007, Sept. 3** **Photo.**

**1384-1386** A527 Set of 3 7.00 7.00

Technical Innovations From Liechtenstein A545

Designs: 1.30fr, Hilti hammer and drill. 1.80fr, Kaiser mobile walking excavator. 2.40fr, Hoval AluFer composite heating tube.

**2007, Sept. 3** ***Perf. 14¼***

**1387-1389** A545 Set of 3 8.00 6.00

See Nos. 1425-1427.

Beetles A546

Designs: 85rp, Trichodes apiarius. 100rp, Cetania aurata. 130rp, Dytiscus marginalis.

**2007, Sept. 3** **Litho.** ***Perf. 13¾x14***

**1390-1392** A546 Set of 3 5.75 4.00

Panoramic View of Liechtenstein — A547

**2007, Oct. 1** **Litho.** ***Perf. 14***

**1393** A547 130rp multi 2.50 2.00

### Building Preservation Type of 2001

Designs: 2fr, St. Martin's Church, Eschen. 2.70fr, Mill, Eschen, horiz.

*Perf. 13½x13¾, 13¾x13½*

**2007, Nov. 19** **Photo.**

**1394-1395** A490 Set of 2 7.00 5.00

New Parliament Building A548

**2007, Nov. 19** ***Perf. 13¾***

**1396** A548 130rp multi 2.00 1.50

Natural Phenomena A549

Designs: 85rp, Rainbow above Three Sisters Massif. 100rp, Lightning over Bendern. 180rp, Ice crystal halo around Moon over Malbun.

**2007, Nov. 19** **Litho.** ***Perf. 14¼***

**1397-1399** A549 Set of 3 5.00 4.00

Christmas A550

Designs: 85rp, Chapel of St. Mary, Gamprin-Oberbühl. 1fr, Büel Chapel, Eschen. 1.30fr, Chapel of St. Wolfgang, Triesen.

*Perf. 13½x14¼*

**2007, Nov. 19** **Photo.**

**1400-1402** A550 Set of 3 5.25 4.00

### Pastures Type of 2005

Designs: 2.60fr, Guschg. 3fr, Güschgle.

**2008, Mar. 3** **Photo.** ***Perf. 13½x14¼***

**1403-1404** A527 Set of 2 9.50 7.50

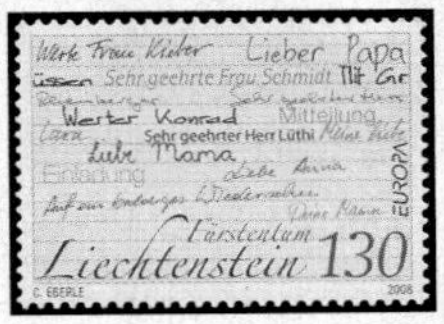


Europa A551

**2008, Mar. 3** **Litho.** ***Perf. 13½x13¾***

**1405** A551 130rp multi 2.00 1.50

Volunteer Fire Fighters A552

**2008, Mar. 3** ***Perf. 13½***

**1406** A552 1fr multi 2.00 1.50

Sleeping Princess Marie Franziska, by Friedrich von Amerling A553

**2008, Mar. 3** **Photo. & Engr.**

**1407** A553 2.40fr multi 4.00 3.50

See Austria No. 2144.

Spoerry-Areal, Vaduz — A554

Chapel of St. Mamertus, Triesen — A555

Vaduz Castle — A556

**2008, Mar. 3** **Litho.** ***Perf. 14***

| | | | | |
|---|---|---|---|---|
| **1408** | A554 85rp | multi | 1.50 | 1.10 |
| **1409** | A555 1fr | multi | 1.75 | 1.25 |
| **1410** | A556 1.30fr | multi | 2.25 | 1.60 |
| | *Nos. 1408-1410 (3)* | | 5.50 | 3.95 |

Mother and Queen of the Precious Blood with Child, by Unknown Artist — A557

**2008, June 2** **Litho.** ***Perf. 12¾x13½***

**1411** A557 220rp multi 4.25 3.50

Schellenberg Convent, 150th anniv.

2008 Summer Olympics, Beijing — A558

Mascots involved in: 85rp, Martial arts. 100rp, Soccer.

**2008, June 2** ***Perf. 14¼x13½***
**1412-1413** A558 Set of 2 3.50 2.75

2008 Paralympics, Beijing — A559

Designs: 130rp, Marathon. 180rp, Table tennis.

**2008, June 2** ***Perf. 13½x14¼***
**1414-1415** A559 Set of 2 5.00 4.00

2008 European Soccer Championships, Austria and Switzerland — A560

Designs: No. 1416, 130rp, St. Stephen's Cathedral, Vienna, soccer player waltzing, violinist. No. 1417, 130rp, Soccer fans holding Liechtenstein flag, wearing Swiss hat, and Austrian scarf. No. 1418, 130rp, Alphorn player, Matterhorn, soccer player.

**2008, June 2** ***Perf. 14***
**1416-1418** A560 Set of 3 7.50 6.50

Nos. 1416-1418 printed in sheets containing 4 No. 1417 and 6 each Nos. 1416 and 1418.

Hymenopterans A561

Designs: 85rp, Osmia brevicornis. 1fr, Epeoloides coecutiens. 1.30fr, Odynerus spinipes.

**2008, June 2** ***Perf. 14¼***
**1419-1421** A561 Set of 3 6.00 5.00

Souvenir Sheet

Prince Karl I (1569-1627) — A562

**Photo. & Engr.**

**2008, Sept. 1** ***Perf. 13¾x13½***
**1422** A562 5fr multi 9.00 9.00

Princely house of Liechtenstein, 400th anniv.

Miniature Sheet

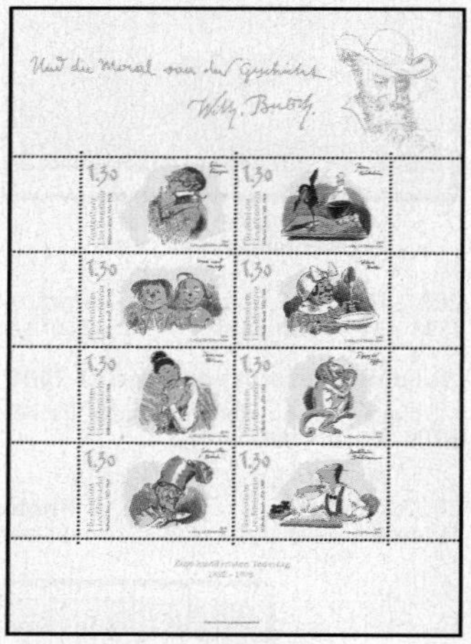

Drawings by Wilhelm Busch (1832-1908) — A563

No. 1423: a, Schoolmaster Lampel. b, Hans Huckebein. c, Max and Moritz. d, Widow Bolte. e, Pious Helene. f, Fipps the Monkey. g, Tailor Böck. h, Balduin Bählamm.

**2008, Sept. 1** **Photo.** ***Perf. 14x13¾***
**1423** A563 Sheet of 8 20.00 20.00
*a.-h.* 1.30fr Any single 2.50 2.00

**Building Preservation Type of 2001**

Design: Schädler Ceramics Building, Nendeln, horiz.

***Perf. 13¾x13½***

**2008, Nov. 17** **Photo.**
**1424** A490 3.80fr multi 7.50 6.50

**Technical Innovations Type of 2007**

Designs: 1.20fr, Neutrik NC3MX audio cable connectors. 1.40fr, Ivoclar Vivadent bluephase polymerization unit. 2.20fr, Presta DeltaValveControl variable valve-lift system.

**2008, Nov. 17** ***Perf. 14¼***
**1425-1427** A545 Set of 3 7.50 6.50

Christmas A564

Designs: 85rp, Candles, flowers and evergreen branches. 100rp, Children carrying holly, horiz. 130rp, Christmas tree and gifts.

***Perf. 14¼x14½, 14½x14¼***

**2008, Nov. 17** **Litho.**
**1428-1430** A564 Set of 3 6.00 5.00

Civil Protection Volunteers — A565

**2009, Mar. 2** **Litho.** ***Perf. 13¾x13½***
**1431** A565 1fr multi 1.75 1.40

See Nos. 1471-1472, 1566-1567.

Europa — A566

**Litho. With Hologram Affixed**

**2009, Mar. 2** ***Perf. 14¼***
**1432** A566 1.30fr multi 2.50 2.00

Land Registry, 200th Anniv. A567

**2009, Mar. 2** **Litho.** ***Perf. 13¾***
**1433** A567 330rp multi 6.25 5.00

Liechtenstein Post AG, 10th Anniv. — A568

Designs: 85rp, Counter clerk handling package. 100rp, Mail deliverer. 130rp, Mail sorter.

**2009, Mar. 2** ***Perf. 13¾x13½***
**1434-1436** A568 Set of 3 6.00 5.00

Linoleum Prints by Stephan Sude — A569

Designs: 1fr, Unfolding. 1.30fr, Awareness. 2.70fr, Fulfillment.

**2009, Mar. 2** ***Perf. 14x13¼***
**1437-1439** A569 Set of 3 9.50 7.50

Alpine Association, Cent. A570

Crosses on summits of: 100rp, Kuegrat. 130rp, Langspitz, vert. 220rp, Rappastein, vert. 240rp, Jahn-Turm and Wolan.

***Perf. 13¾x13½, 13½x13¾***

**2009, June 8** **Litho.**
**1440-1443** A570 Set of 4 12.00 8.00

Forests — A571

Designs: 85rp, Ants in forest. 1fr, Path in forest. 1.40fr, Boulder against tree on hillside. 1.60fr, Cut timber.

**2009, June 8** ***Perf. 13½***
**1444-1447** A571 Set of 4 9.00 7.00

Vaduz Castle A572

Castle in: 130rp, Spring. 180rp, Summer.

**2009, June 8** **Photo.** ***Perf. 13¾***
**1448-1449** A572 Set of 2 5.50 4.50

See Nos. 1488-1489.

Liechtenstein Philatelic Society, 75th Anniv. — A573

**2009, Sept. 7** **Litho.** ***Perf. 13x13¼***
**1450** A573 130rp multi 2.25 1.50

Holes are drilled along the map border.

Badminton Cabinet Ornamentation — A574

Panels with bird and flower designs: 1.30fr, Bird with blue head. 2fr, Three birds, vert. (35x50mm). 4fr, Bird with red head.

***Perf. 14, 13¾ (2fr)***

**2009, Sept. 7** **Photo. & Engr.**
**1451-1453** A574 Set of 3 12.50 9.00

Butterflies A575

Designs: 85rp, Pieris rapae. 100rp, Parnassius apollo. 130rp, Melanargia galathea. 200rp, Vanessa atalanta.

**2009, Sept. 7** **Litho.** ***Perf. 12x12½***

**Self-Adhesive**

**1454-1457** A575 Set of 4 9.00 7.00

See Nos. 1480-1482, 1515-1516.

Chapel of St. Mamerta, Triesen — A576

**2009, Sept. 16** ***Perf. 14***
**1458** A576 130rp multi 2.25 1.50

Contemporary Architecture — A577

Designs: 85rp, University of Applied Sciences, Vaduz. 260rp, Art Museum, Vaduz. 350rp, Border crossing, Rugell.

***Perf. 13½x13¾***

**2009, Nov. 16** **Litho.**
**1459-1461** A577 Set of 3 12.50 9.00

See Nos. 1473-1474.

Lifestyle Museum, Schellenberg
A578

Former Customs House, Vaduz — A579

Parish House, Bendern
A580

**2009, Nov. 16** ***Perf. 12¼***

**Self-Adhesive**

| | | | | |
|---|---|---|---|---|
| **1462** | A578 | 20rp multi | .35 | .25 |
| **1463** | A579 | 50rp multi | .85 | .65 |
| **1464** | A580 | 60rp multi | 1.10 | .75 |
| | | *Nos. 1462-1464 (3)* | 2.30 | 1.65 |

Christmas — A581

Advent windows by children: 85rp, Annunciation. 100rp, Journey to Bethlehem. 130rp, Nativity. 180rp, Magi and Star of Bethlehem.

**2009, Nov. 16** ***Perf. 13½x13¾***

**1465-1468** A581 Set of 4 8.00 6.00

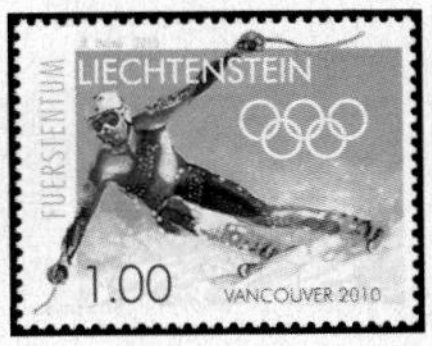

2010 Winter Olympics, Vancouver
A582

Designs: 1fr, Downhill skier. 1.80fr, Cross-country skier, horiz.

**2010, Feb. 12** **Litho.** ***Perf. 13¾***

**1469-1470** A582 Set of 2 4.50 3.50

**Civil Protection Volunteers Type of 2009**

Designs: 85rp, Mountain rescuers. 1.30rp, Water rescuers.

**2010, Mar. 1** ***Perf. 13¾x13½***

**1471-1472** A565 Set of 2 3.50 2.75

**Contemporary Architecture Type of 2009**

Designs: 260rp, Natural gas filling station, Vaduz. 360rp, Liechtenstein Electric Power Authority transformer station, Schaan.

**2010, Mar. 1** ***Perf. 13½x13¾***

**1473-1474** A577 Set of 2 9.50 7.00

Agriculture — A583

Designs: 85rp, Fields. 1fr, Flowers, hillside farmers. 1.10fr, Combine in field. 1.30fr, Cattle.

**2010, Mar. 1** **Photo.** ***Perf. 13½x13¼***

**1475-1478** A583 Set of 4 7.00 5.00

Souvenir Sheet

Expo 2010, Shanghai — A584

No. 1479: a, Atmospheric View of Vaduz, by Johann Jakob Schmidt (40x36mm). b, Tidal Bore on the Qiantang River, by Xu Gu (32x60mm).

**Photo. & Engr.**

**2010, May 1** ***Perf. 14***

| | | | | |
|---|---|---|---|---|
| **1479** | A584 | Sheet of 2 | 6.50 | 6.50 |
| *a.* | | 1.60fr multi | 3.00 | 3.00 |
| *b.* | | 1.90fr multi | 3.50 | 3.50 |
| *c.* | | As #1479, imperf. | 6.50 | 6.50 |
| *d.* | | As "a," imperf. | 3.00 | 3.00 |
| *e.* | | As "b," imperf. | 3.50 | 3.50 |

**Butterflies Type of 2009**

Designs: 140rp, Coenonympha oedippus. 160rp, Gonepteryx rhamni. 260rp, Papilio machaon.

**2010, June 7** **Litho.** ***Perf. 12x12½***

**Self-Adhesive**

**1480-1482** A575 Set of 3 9.75 8.00

Liechtenstein Disability Insurance, 50th Anniv. — A585

**2010, June 7** ***Perf. 14x13¼***

**1483** A585 1fr multi 1.75 1.40

European Free Trade Association, 50th Anniv.
A586

**2010, June 7** ***Perf. 12x12½***

**1484** A586 140rp multi 2.50 2.00

Interpol Vaduz, 50th Anniv. — A587

**2010, June 7** ***Perf. 12¼***

**1485** A587 1.90fr multi 3.50 2.75

Ceiling Frescoes in Liechtenstein Museum, Vienna — A588

Frescoes by Johann Michael Rottmayr: 1fr, Ariadne Giving Theseus the Thread. 1.40fr, Surrender of the Golden Fleece to Jason.

**Photo. & Engr.**

**2010, June 7** ***Perf. 14***

**1486-1487** A588 Set of 2 4.25 3.50

Values are for stamps with surrounding selvage.

**Vaduz Castle Type of 2009**

Castle in: 140rp, Autumn, vert. 190rp, Winter, vert.

**2010, Sept. 6** **Photo.** ***Perf. 13¾***

**1488-1489** A572 Set of 2 6.50 5.00

Europa — A589

**2010, Sept. 6** **Litho.** ***Perf. 14***

**1490** A589 140rp multi 2.75 2.25

Renewable Energy
A590

Designs: 100rp, Water. 140rp, Wood. 280rp, Geothermal.

**Litho. & Photo.**

**2010, Sept. 6** ***Perf. 14x13¾***

**1491-1493** A590 Set of 3 10.50 8.00

Parts of the designs of Nos. 1491-1493 were printed with thermochromic ink that changes color when warmed. See Nos. 1509-1511.

Rhine Valley Landscape — A591

No. 1494: a, Eschnerberg and Dreischwestern Mountains, cart path, denomination at LL. b, Alvier Mountains, denomination at LR.

**2010, Sept. 6** **Litho.** ***Perf. 14x13¼***

| | | | | |
|---|---|---|---|---|
| **1494** | | Horiz. pair | 4.00 | 4.00 |
| *a.-b.* | A591 | 1fr Either single | 2.00 | 1.75 |

Schaan-Vaduz Railroad Station — A592

Red House, Vaduz — A593

St. Joseph Church, Triesenberg
A594

**2010, Nov. 15** **Litho.** ***Perf. 12¼***

**Self-Adhesive**

| | | | | |
|---|---|---|---|---|
| **1495** | A592 | 1.10fr multi | 1.90 | 1.50 |
| **1496** | A593 | 1.80fr multi | 3.25 | 2.50 |
| **1497** | A594 | 1.90fr multi | 3.50 | 2.75 |
| | | *Nos. 1495-1497 (3)* | 8.65 | 6.75 |

Works From Liechtenstein Museum of Art — A595

Designs: 100rp, Normale e Anormale, embroidery by Alighiero Boetti. 220rp, Testa, sculpture by Marisa Merz. 360rp, Untitled sculpture by Jannis Kounellis.

**2010, Nov. 15** ***Perf. 13¾x13½***

**1498-1500** A595 Set of 3 12.00 9.00

Christmas
A596

Ceiling frescoes from Maria-Hilf Chapel, Mäls: 85rp, Annunciation. 1fr, Visitation of Mary. 1.40fr, Presentation of Jesus in the Temple.

**2010, Nov. 15** **Photo.** ***Perf. 14***

**1501-1503** A596 Set of 3 6.25 5.00

National Library, 50th Anniv — A597

**Litho. With Foil Application**

**2011, Mar. 14** ***Perf. 12½x12***

**Self-Adhesive**

**1504** A597 1fr black & gold 2.25 2.25

Liechtensteinische Landesbank, 150th Anniv. — A598

**2011, Mar. 14 Litho. *Perf. 12¼***
**Self-Adhesive**

**1505** A598 1fr multi 2.25 2.25

2011 Games of the Small States, Liechtenstein — A599

Designs: 85rp, Track, volleyball, cycling. 1fr, Judo, shooting, squash. 1.40fr, Table tennis, tennis, swimming.

**2011, Mar. 14 Litho. *Perf. 13½***

**1506-1508** A599 Set of 3 6.25 4.50

**Renewable Energy Type of 2010**

Designs: 100rp, Photovoltaics. 110rp, Solar energy. 290rp, Wind energy.

**Litho. & Photo.**

**2011, Mar. 14 *Perf. 14x13¾***

**1509-1511** A590 Set of 3 9.50 7.50

Parts of the designs of Nos. 1509-1511 were printed with thermochromic ink that changes color when warmed.

Decorative Eggs Collected by Adulf Peter Goop — A600

Designs: 1fr, Moscow Workshop Easter egg. 1.40fr, Apple Blossom Egg, by Karl Fabergé, horiz. (47x33mm). 2.60fr, Easter egg, by Pavel Akimovich Ovchinnikov.

**Litho. & Engr.**

**2011, Mar. 14 *Perf. 13¾***

**1512-1514** A600 Set of 3 9.50 7.50

**Butterflies Type of 2009**

Designs: 220rp, Inachis io. 500rp, Anthocharis cardamines.

**2011, June 6 Litho. *Perf. 12x12½***
**Self-Adhesive**

**1515-1516** A575 Set of 2 15.00 15.00

For surcharge, see No. 1556.

Europa — A601

**2011, June 6 *Perf. 12½x12***

**1517** A601 1.40fr multi 3.00 2.50

Intl. Year of Forests.

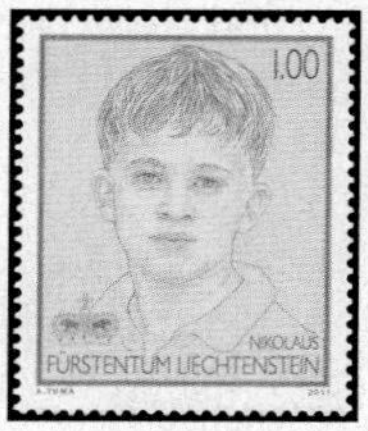


Children of Hereditary Prince Alois and Duchess Sophie — A602

Designs: 1fr, Prince Nikolaus. 1.80fr, Prince Georg. 2fr, Princess Marie Caroline. 2.60fr, Prince Joseph Wenzel.

**Photo. & Engr.**

**2011, June 6 *Perf. 13½***

**1518-1521** A602 Set of 4 15.00 12.00
*1521a* Souvenir sheet of 4, #1518-1521 15.00 15.00

Fruit, by Shirana Shahbazi A603

**2011, Sept. 9 Litho. *Perf. 13¼x13½***

**1522** A603 100rp multi 2.00 1.50

See Switzerland No. 1423.

Photographs of Liechtenstein by Xiao Hui Wang — A604

Designs: 1.30fr, Alpine Rhine. 3.70fr, Water Reflections.

**2011, Sept. 9 *Perf. 13¼x14***

**1523-1524** A604 Set of 2 9.50 7.50

Miniature Sheet

Worldwide Fund for Nature (WWF), 50th Anniv. — A605

No. 1525 — Endangered birds in Liechtenstein: a, Falco subbuteo. b, Glaucidium passerinum. c, Oriolus oriolus. d, Jynx torquilla. e, Luscinia megarhynchos. f, Phoenicurus phoenicurus. g, Lanius collurio. h, Saxicola rubetra.

**2011, Sept. 9 *Perf. 12½***
**Self-Adhesive**

**1525** A605 Sheet of 8 16.00 16.00
*a.-h.* 100rp Any single 2.00 2.00

Ruggell Marsh — A606

**2011, Sept. 28 *Perf. 14***

**1526** A606 140rp multi 2.75 2.25

Castles A607

Designs: 100rp, Gutenberg Castle. 140rp, Schellenberg Castle. 200rp, Schalun Castle. 260rp, Vaduz Castle.

**Photo. & Engr.**

**2011, Nov. 14 *Perf. 13½x14¼***

**1527-1530** A607 Set of 4 13.00 10.00

Christmas A608

Creche figures from: 85rp, St. Gallus Church, Triesen. 100rp, St. Florin Church, Vaduz (38x32mm). 140rp, Church of the Assumption, Bendern (32x38mm).

***Perf. 12¼, 12x12½ (100rp), 12½x12 (140rp)***

**2011, Nov. 14 Litho.**
**Self-Adhesive**

**1531-1533** A608 Set of 3 6.00 4.50

New Year 2012 (Year of the Dragon) A609

**Litho. With Foil Application**

**2011, Nov. 14 *Perf. 12½***
**Self-Adhesive**

**1534** A609 190rp red & gold 4.25 4.25

The dragon vignette was laser cut. Printed in sheets of 4.

Liechtenstein Postage Stamps, Cent. — A610

Princes of Liechtenstein: 1fr, Johann II. 1.40fr, Franz I. 2.20fr, Franz Josef II. 2.80fr, Hans Adam II.

**2012, Feb. 1 Litho. *Perf. 13½x13¾***

**1535-1538** A610 Set of 4 14.00 11.00
*1538a* Souvenir sheet of 4, #1535-1538, imperf. 14.00 14.00

A booklet containing four panes each containing eight examples of each stamp, No. 1538a, a designer-signed and numbered example of No. 1538a in changed colors, examples of Nos. 1535-1538 and their imperforates with first day cancels, and reproductions of Nos. 1-3 was printed in limited quantities and sold for 100fr.

Cattle Moving Past Parliament Building A611

**2012, Mar. 5 *Perf. 13¾***

**1539** A611 140rp multi 2.75 2.25

Europa.

Liechtenstein Parilament and Constitution, 150th Anniv. — A612

Designs: 1fr, Reverse of 1862 Vereinsthaler, excerpt from first page of Constitutional Charter. 1.40fr, Obverse of 1862 Vereinsthaler, letter authorizing the opening of Parliament.

**Litho. & Embossed**

**2012, Mar. 5 *Perf. 13½x13¾***

**1540-1541** A612 Set of 2 4.50 3.50

Pfälzer Hutte Mountain Lodge — A613

**2012, June 14 Litho. *Perf. 13¾***

**1542** A613 140rp multi 3.00 3.00

See Germany No. 2677.

2012 Summer Olympics, London — A614

Designs: 100rp, Swimming. 140rp, Tennis.

**2012, June 14 *Perf. 13¼***

**1543-1544** A614 Set of 2 4.50 3.50

Flowers — A615

Designs: 85rp, Dahlie (dahlia). 140pr, Pfingstrose (peony). 500rp, Zinnie (zinnia).

**2012, June 14 *Perf. 12½x12***
**Self-Adhesive**

**1545-1547** A615 Set of 3 15.00 15.00

See Nos. 1573-1575, 1643-1645.

Mountain Valleys — A616

No. 1548: a, Lawenatal Valley (denomination at LL). b, Valünatal Valley (denomination at LR).

**2012, June 14** ***Perf. 14x13¼***

| | | | | |
|---|---|---|---|---|
| **1548** | | Horiz. pair | 4.25 | 4.25 |
| *a.-b.* | A616 | 1fr Either single | 2.10 | 2.10 |

Souvenir Sheet

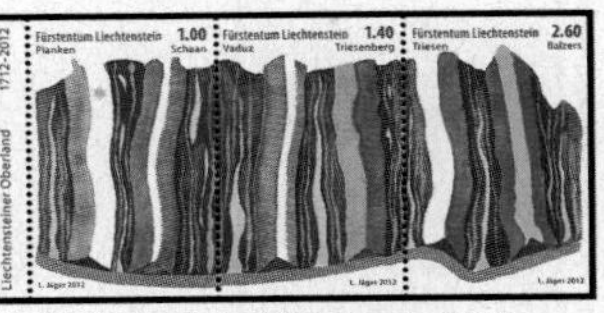

Liechtenstein Oberland, 300th Anniv. — A617

No. 1549 — Stylized flags of: a, Planken and Schaan. b, Vaduz and Tresenberg. c, Triesen and Balzers.

***Perf. 14 Vert. on 1 or 2 Sides***

**2012, June 14**

| | | | | |
|---|---|---|---|---|
| **1549** | A617 | Sheet of 3 | 9.50 | 9.50 |
| *a.* | | 1fr multi | 1.75 | 1.75 |
| *b.* | | 1.40fr multi | 2.50 | 2.50 |
| *c.* | | 2.60fr multi | 4.50 | 4.50 |

Souvenir Sheet

Winning Art in Stamp Design Contest — A618

No. 1550 — Art by: a, N. Schwarz. b, R. Graf. c, G. Rodrigues-Margreiter.

**2012, Aug. 16** ***Perf. 13¾x13½***

| | | | | |
|---|---|---|---|---|
| **1550** | A618 | Sheet of 3 | 13.00 | 13.00 |
| *a.* | | 100rp multi | 2.25 | 2.25 |
| *b.* | | 140rp multi | 3.00 | 3.00 |
| *c.* | | 360rp multi | 7.75 | 7.75 |

LIBA 2012 Stamp Exhibition, Schaan.

Antique Automobiles A619

Designs: 85rp, 1908 Brasier. 100rp, 1911 Stanley Steamer. 140rp, 1915 Ford Model T Speedster. 190rp, 1920 Hinstin.

**Litho. with Foil Application**

**2012, Sept. 3**

**1551-1554** A619 Set of 4 11.00 11.00

Miniature Sheet

Characters From Literature — A620

No. 1555: a, Till Eulenspiegel. b, Sherlock Holmes. c, Don Quixote. d, Hamlet. e, Robin Hood. f, Robinson Crusoe. g, Baron Münchhausen. h, Quasimodo.

**2012, Sept. 3** **Litho.** ***Perf. 13¾***

| | | | | |
|---|---|---|---|---|
| **1555** | A620 | Sheet of 8 | 18.00 | 18.00 |
| *a.-h.* | | 1fr Any single | 2.25 | 2.25 |

No. 1516 Surcharged in Purple

**Self-Adhesive**

**2012, Oct. 4** ***Perf. 12x12½***

**1556** A575 600rp on 500rp #1516 13.00 13.00

Reliefs by Massimiliano Soldani-Benzi (1656-1740) A621

Designs: 1fr, Christ's Descent from the Cross. 1.40fr, Christ on the Mount of Olives.

**Litho. & Engr.**

**2012, Nov. 12** ***Perf. 13¾x14***

**1557-1558** A621 Set of 2 5.25 5.25

Art by Hanna Roeckle A622

Designs: 100rp, Crystal B. 140rp, Crystal G.

**2012, Nov. 12** **Litho.** ***Perf. 13¾***

**1559-1560** A622 Set of 2 5.25 5.25

Christmas A623

Archangels: 85rp, Raphael. 100rp, Michael. 140rp, Gabriel. 190rp, Uriel.

**Self-Adhesive**

**Litho. With Foil Application**

**2012, Nov. 12** ***Perf. 12¼x12½***

**1561-1564** A623 Set of 4 11.00 11.00

New Year 2013 (Year of the Snake) A624

**Self-Adhesive**

**Litho. With Foil Application**

**2012, Nov. 12** ***Perf. 12½***

**1565** A624 190rp red & gold 4.25 4.25

The snake vignette was laser cut. Printed in sheets of 4.

**Civil Protection Volunteers Type of 2009**

Designs: 1fr, Avalanche rescue squad. 1.40fr, Civil protection and emergency management workers.

**2013, Mar. 4** **Litho.** ***Perf. 13¾x13½***

**1566-1567** A565 Set of 2 5.25 5.25

Europa — A625

**2013, Mar. 4** ***Perf. 14¼x14½***

**1568** A625 1.40fr multi 3.00 3.00

Mathematics and Nature — A626

Various leaves and: 100rp, Fibonacci sequence. 260rp, Sum of adjacent Fibonacci numbers. 400rp, Golden ratio.

**Litho. With Foil Application**

**2013, Mar. 4** ***Perf. 13¼x13½***

**1569-1571** A626 Set of 3 16.50 16.50

Switzerland-Liechtenstein Customs Treaty, 90th Anniv. — A627

No. 1572: a, Rhine Valley, Gonzen, Swiss flag, denomination at UL. b, Liechtenstein Valley, Ellhorn and Liechtenstein flag, denomination at UR.

**2013, Mar. 4** **Litho.** ***Perf. 13¼***

| | | | | |
|---|---|---|---|---|
| **1572** | | Horiz. pair | 8.75 | 8.75 |
| *a.-b.* | A627 | 2fr Either single | 4.25 | 4.25 |

**Flowers Type of 2012**

Designs: 100rp, Gentiana rhaetica. 190rp, Myosotis alpestris. 400rp, Rhododendrum hirsutum.

**2013, June 3** ***Perf. 12½x12***

**Self-Adhesive**

**1573-1575** A615 Set of 3 15.00 15.00

Landscapes by Hans Kliemand (1922-76) — A628

Designs: 100rp, View of Vaduz. 190rp, View Into the Rhine Valley.

**Litho. & Engr.**

**2013, June 3** ***Perf. 12¾x13***

**1576-1577** A628 Set of 2 6.50 6.50

Baby Animals A629

Designs: 85rp, Ibex. 100rp, Chamois.140rp, Marmot. 190rp, Alpine hare.

**2013, June 3** **Litho.** ***Perf. 12x12½***

**Self-Adhesive**

**1578-1581** A629 Set of 4 11.50 11.50

Bridges — A630

No. 1582: a, End of Vaduz-Sevelen Bridge over Rhine River (27x27mm). b, Entire Vaduz-Sevelen Bridge (57x27mm).

No. 1583: a, End of Schaan-Buchs Railway Bridge (27x27mm). b, Entire Schaan-Buchs Bridge (57x27mm).

**2013, June 3** ***Perf. 14x13¼***

| | | | | |
|---|---|---|---|---|
| **1582** | A630 | Horiz. pair | 4.25 | 4.25 |
| *a.* | | 85rp multi | 1.90 | 1.90 |
| *b.* | | 100rp multi | 2.25 | 2.25 |
| **1583** | A630 | Horiz. pair | 7.25 | 7.25 |
| *a.* | | 140rp multi | 3.00 | 3.00 |
| *b.* | | 190rp multi | 4.25 | 4.25 |

See Nos. 1600-1601.

Performing Arts — A631

Designs: 100rp, Ballet dancer. 140rp, Actors in theater production. 200rp, Actors in musical theater production. 400rp, Magician.

**2013, Sept. 2** ***Perf. 12x12½***

**Self-Adhesive**

**1584-1587** A631 Set of 4 18.00 18.00

Automobiles A632

Designs: 85rp, 1954 Aston Martin DB 2/4. 100rp, 1958 Ferrari 250 GT PF. 140rp, 1955 Jaguar XK 140. 190rp, 1956 Mercedes-Benz 300 SL.

**Litho. & Embossed With Foil Application**

**2013, Sept. 2** ***Perf. 13¼x13***

**1588-1591** A632 Set of 4 11.00 11.00

Paintings by Ivan Myasoyedov (Eugen Zotow) (1881-1953) — A633

No. 1592: a, Voyage of the Argonauts, 1909. b, Silum, 1945.

**2013, Sept. 2 Litho. *Perf. 14***

| | | | |
|---|---|---|---|
| **1592** | Pair | 8.75 | 8.75 |
| *a.* | A633 140rp multi | 3.00 | 3.00 |
| *b.* | A633 260rp multi | 5.75 | 5.75 |

Printed in sheets of 10 containing 5 each #1592a-1592b, + 2 labels. See Russia No. 7473.

2014 Winter Olympics, Sochi, Russia A634

**Litho. & Thermographed With Foil Application**

**2013, Nov. 11 *Perf. 13¼x13½***

**1593** A634 2.60fr multi 5.75 5.75

Portions of the design contain grit from a stone from Sochi.

Souvenir Sheet

Floral-Patterned Silk Wall Covering in Small Courbaril Room of Liechtenstein Palace, Vienna — A635

**Litho. & Embossed With Foil Application**

**2013, Nov. 11 *Perf. 14¼x14½***

**Silk-Faced Paper**

| | | | | |
|---|---|---|---|---|
| **1594** | A635 | Sheet of 3 | 13.00 | 13.00 |
| *a.* | | 1fr multi | 2.25 | 2.25 |
| *b.* | | 1.40fr multi | 3.00 | 3.00 |
| *c.* | | 3.60fr multi | 7.75 | 7.75 |

Christmas A636

Designs: 85rp, Annunciation. 1fr, Nativity. 1.40fr, Angel announcing birth of Christ to shepherds and sheep. 1.90fr, Three Kings.

**Litho. With Foil Application**

**2013, Nov. 11 *Perf. 12½x12***

**Self-Adhesive**

**1595-1598** A636 Set of 4 11.50 11.50

New Year 2013 (Year of the Horse) A637

**Litho. With Foil Application**

**2013, Nov. 11 *Perf. 12½***

**Self-Adhesive**

**1599** A637 190rp red & gold 4.25 4.25

The horse vignette was laser cut. Printed in sheets of 4.

---

In 2014, Liechtenstein began issuing personalizable stamps bearing the inscription "Liechtensteinsche Post AG." Stamps in three different orientations (square, landscape and portrait) could be created for two different frame types, each of which were made available initially in denominations of 55c, 85c, €1, €1.40, €1.90, and €2. These were sold in sheets of 20 stamps. Sheets containing 10 stamps with various non-personalizable images were to be produced and sold for special events.

---

**Bridges Type of 2013**

No. 1582: a, End of Buchs-Schaan Footbridge (27x27mm). b, Entire Buchs-Schaan Bridge (57x27mm).

No. 1583: a, End of Bendern-Haag Bridge over the Rhine River (27x27mm). b, Entire Bendern-Haag Bridge (57x27mm).

**2014, Mar. 10 Litho. *Perf. 14x13¼***

| | | | | |
|---|---|---|---|---|
| **1600** | A630 | Horiz. pair | 4.25 | 4.25 |
| *a.* | | 85rp multi | 1.90 | 1.90 |
| *b.* | | 100rp multi | 2.25 | 2.25 |
| **1601** | A630 | Horiz. pair | 7.50 | 7.50 |
| *a.* | | 140rp multi | 3.25 | 3.25 |
| *b.* | | 190rp multi | 4.25 | 4.25 |

Josef Gabriel Rheinberger (1839-1901), Composer — A638

***Perf. 13¾x13¼***

**2014, Mar. 10 Litho.**

**1602** A638 1.40fr multi 3.25 3.25

Europa — A639

**2014, Mar. 10 Litho. *Perf. 12½x12***

**1603** A639 140rp multi 3.25 3.25

Souvenir Sheet

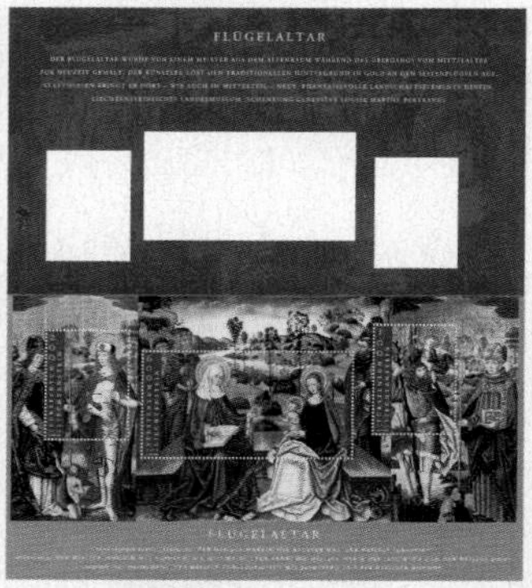


Winged Altarpiece Bequeathed to National Museum — A640

No. 1604 — Details of altarpiece: a, St. Christopher Carrying the Christ Child (33x45mm). b, St. Sebastian (33x45mm). c, St. Anne and St. Mary with the Christ Child (84x44mm).

***Perf. 14x13¾, 13½ (600rp)***

**2014, Mar. 10 Litho.**

| | | | | |
|---|---|---|---|---|
| **1604** | A640 | Sheet of 3 | 20.50 | 20.50 |
| *a.* | | 100rp multi | 2.25 | 2.25 |
| *b.* | | 200rp multi | 4.50 | 4.50 |
| *c.* | | 600rp multi | 13.50 | 13.50 |

No. 1640 is sold folded in half, with stamps appearing through the die cut holes in the sheet margin. The top part of the sheet margin, with the holes, is printed on both sides.

Souvenir Sheet

Canonization of Pope John Paul II — A641

**Litho. With Foil Application**

**2014, Apr. 28 *Perf. 14¼x14***

**1605** A641 1.40fr multi 3.25 3.25

Ancient Coins Found in Liechtenstein — A642

Map of Liechtenstein and: 85rp, Roman silver denarius of Julius Caesar, c. 49-48 B.C. 100rp, Florentine golden florin, c. 1360. 130rp, Silver penny, c. 1360.

**Litho. & Embossed With Foil Application**

**2014, June 2 *Perf. 13½x13¾***

**1606-1608** A642 Set of 3 7.00 7.00

Amphibians A643

Designs: 85rp, Yellow-bellied toad. 2.90fr, Great crested newt. 3.70fr, Alpine salamander.

**2014, June 2 Litho. *Perf. 12¼***

**Self-Adhesive**

**1609-1611** A643 Set of 3 17.00 17.00

Flowers — A644

Designs: 100rp, Iris sibirica. 280rp, Parnassia palustris. 360rp, Menyanthes trifoliata.

**2014, June 2 Litho. *Perf. 12½x12***

**Self-Adhesive**

**1612-1614** A644 Set of 3 16.50 16.50

Lindau Messenger Courier Service — A645

**2014, Sept. 1 Litho. *Perf. 14x13¼***

**1615** A645 140rp multi 3.00 3.00

No. 1615 was printed in sheets of 8 + 4 labels.

Etchings by Brigitte Hasler — A646

Designs: 100rp, Dust Image A. 140rp, Dust Image B.

**Litho. With Foil Application**

**2014, Sept. 1 *Perf. 13¼***

**1616-1617** A646 Set of 2 5.25 5.25

Intl. Year of Crystallography — A647

Designs: 100rp, Initial crystal metamorphosis sequence. 200rp, Final crystal metamorphosis sequence.

**Litho. & Embossed**

**2014, Sept. 1 *Perf. 13½x13¼***

**1618-1619** A647 Set of 2 6.50 6.50

Sedans A648

Designs: 85rp, 1933 Rolls-Royce Phantom II. 100rp, 1929 Pierce-Arrow Type 133. 140rp, 1935 Studebaker Big Six. 190rp, 1948 Jaguar Mark IV.

**Litho. With Foil Application**

**2014, Sept. 1** ***Perf. 13¼x13***

**1620-1623** A648 Set of 4 11.50 11.50
*1620a* Inscribed "Rolls-Royce" (with hyphen) 1.75 1.75

Issued: No. 1620a, 11/10. No. 1620 is inscribed "Rolls Royce" (without hyphen).

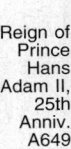

Reign of Prince Hans Adam II, 25th Anniv. A649

***Perf. 13¼x13¾***

**2014, Nov. 10** **Litho. & Engr.**

**1624** A649 2fr multi 4.25 4.25

Painting by Jens W. Beyrich A650

Painting by Hong Sek-Chern A651

**2014, Nov. 10** **Litho.** ***Perf. 13x13¼***

**1625** A650 190rp multi 4.00 4.00
**1626** A651 190rp multi 4.00 4.00

See Singapore Nos. 1706-1707.

Chinese Porcelain in Princely Collection A652

Designs: 1fr, Famille Rose plate, c. 1722-35. 1.90fr, Kraak kendi, c. 1572-1620 (27x43mm). 2.80fr, Imari baluster vase with lid, c. 1736-95 (27x43mm). 3.60fr, Imari plate with lotus blossoms, c. 1736-95.

***Perf. 13¾x13¼, 12x11¼ (#1628-1629)***

**Litho. & Engr. With Foil Application**

**2014, Nov. 10**

**1627-1630** A652 Set of 4 19.00 19.00

Christmas A653

Chapels: 85rp, Freedom Chapel, Malbun. 100rp, St. Wendelin's Chapel, Steg. 140rp, St. Theodul's Chapel, Masescha.

**Litho. With Foil Application**

**2014, Nov. 10** ***Perf. 12¼x12½***

**Self-Adhesive**

**1631-1633** A653 Set of 3 6.75 6.75

New Year 2015 (Year of the Ram) A654

**Litho. With Foil Application**

**2014, Nov. 10** ***Perf. 12½***

**Self-Adhesive**

**1634** A654 190rp red & gold 4.00 4.00

The ram vignette was laser cut. Printed in sheets of 4.

Prince Hans Adam II, 70th Birthday A655

***Perf. 13¼x13¾***

**2015, Feb. 14** **Litho. & Engr.**

**1635** Pair 6.50 6.50
*a.* A655 1fr green & multi 2.10 2.10
*b.* A655 2fr red & multi 4.25 4.25

No. 1635 was printed in sheets containing two pairs.

Liechtenstein Traditional Costume Association, 50th Anniv. A656

**2015, Mar. 2** **Litho.** ***Perf. 12x12½***

**Self-Adhesive**

**1636** A656 85rp multi 1.75 1.75

Liechtenstein Development Service, 50th Anniv. A657

**2015, Mar. 2** **Litho.** ***Perf. 12x12½***

**Self-Adhesive**

**1637** A657 100rp multi 2.10 2.10

Postage Stamps, 175th Anniv. — A658

**2015, Mar. 2** **Litho.** ***Perf. 12½x12***

**Self-Adhesive**

**1638** A658 1.40fr multi 3.00 3.00

Liechtenstein's Admission to United Nations, 25th Anniv. — A659

**2015, Mar. 2** **Litho.** ***Perf. 13½x13***

**1639** A659 190rp multi 4.00 4.00

International Year of Light — A660

**2015, Mar. 2** **Litho.** ***Perf. 13¾x13¼***

**1640** A660 1.90fr multi 4.00 4.00

Microperforations are incorporated in the vignette.

Europa — A661

Toys: No. 1641, 1.40fr, Polar bear in freezer. No. 1642, 1.40fr, Goat on lemon.

**2015, Mar. 2** **Litho.** ***Perf. 13½x13¼***

**1641-1642** A661 Set of 2 6.00 6.00

**Flowers Type of 2012**

Designs: 85rp, Succisa pratensis. 100rp, Astrantia major. 130rp, Leucanthemum vulgare.

**2015, June 1** **Litho.** ***Perf. 12½x12***

**Self-Adhesive**

**1643-1645** A615 Set of 3 6.75 6.75

Reptiles A662

Designs: 1.80fr, Zauneidechse (sand lizard). 2fr, Schlingnatter (smooth snake). 5fr, Bergeidechse (common lizard).

**2015, June 1** **Litho.** ***Perf. 12¼***

**Self-Adhesive**

**1646-1648** A662 Set of 3 19.00 19.00

Keystone Decorations From Cathedral of St. Florin, Vaduz — A663

Designs: 100rp, Pelican. 140rp, Lamb of God. 190rp, Eagle. 200rp, Lion.

**2015, June 1** **Litho.** ***Perf. 13***

**1649-1652** A663 Set of 4 13.50 13.50

Schwabbrünnen Nature Reserve — A664

No. 1653: a, Pond, denomination at UL. b, Pond, denomination at UR. c, Meadow, denomination at UL. d, Meadow, denomination at UR.

**2015, June 1** **Litho.** ***Perf. 13¼***

**1653** A664 Block of 4 8.50 8.50
*a.-d.* 100rp Any single 2.10 2.10

Alpine Landscapes — A665

No. 1654: a, Malbuntal, Liechtenstein. b, Herder's dwellings, Velika Planina, Slovenia.

**2015, Sept. 7** **Litho.** ***Perf. 14x13½***

**1654** A665 Pair 6.00 6.00
*a.-b.* 140rp Either single 3.00 3.00

See Slovenia No. 1141.

Commercial Vehicles A666

Designs: 85rp, 1945 Kaiser Auto tractor. 100rp, 1967 Raimündle tractor. 140rp, Unimog. 190rp, 1921 Fordson tractor.

**Litho. With Foil Application**

**2015, Sept. 7** ***Perf. 13¼x13***

**1655-1658** A666 Set of 4 10.50 10.50

Miniature Sheet

Apple Varieties — A667

No. 1659: a, Treisenberger Weinapfel. b, Damason Reinette. c, Leuser. d, Grosser Rheinischer Bohnapfel. e, Freiherr von Berlepsch. f, Rollapfel. g, Goldparmäne. h, Rösli Marie.

**2015, Sept. 7** **Litho.** ***Perf. 12½***

**Self-Adhesive**

**1659** A667 Sheet of 8 24.00 24.00
*a.-h.* 140rp Any single 3.00 3.00

Jewelry Found at Archaeological Sites — A668

Map of Liechtenstein and: 85rp, Red jasper brooch, 1st-2nd cent. 100rp, Gold ring with chalcedony cameo, 3rd cent. 130rp, Glass cameo, 1st cent.

**Litho. & Embossed With Foil Application**

**2015, Nov. 16** ***Perf. 13¼x13½***

**1660-1662** A668 Set of 3 6.25 6.25

Paintings by Jacques Jordaens (1593-1678) — A669

Designs: 100rp, Adoration of the Shepherds. 140rp, As the Old Sing, So the Young Ones Pipe (47x38mm). 190rp, Meleager and Atalante (44x38mm).

**2015, Nov. 16** **Litho.** ***Perf. 13¼***

**1663-1665** A669 Set of 3 8.50 8.50

Christmas A670

Designs (from Christmas carols): 85p, Rose (Lo, How a Rose E'er Blooming). 100rp, Nativity (Silent Night). 140rp, Angels (Oh, How Joyfully). 190rp, Shepherds and Star of Bethlehem (Come, All Ye Shepherds).

***Perf. 12¼x12½***

**2015, Nov. 16** **Litho.**

**Self-Adhesive**

**1666-1669** A670 Set of 4 10.00 10.00

New Year 2016 (Year of the Monkey) A671

**Litho. With Foil Application**

**2015, Nov. 16** ***Perf. 12½***

**Self-Adhesive**

**1670** A671 190rp red & gold 3.75 3.75

The monkey vignette was laser cut. Printed in sheets of 4.

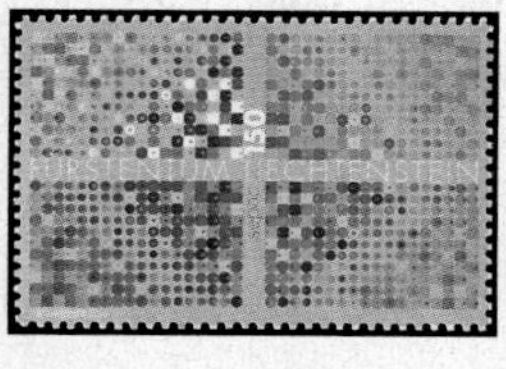

Four Seasons A672

**2016, Mar. 7** **Litho.** ***Perf. 13¼x14***

**1671** A672 150rp multi 3.00 3.00

A673

Europa A674

**2016, Mar. 7** **Litho.** ***Perf. 14x13½***

**1672** A673 150rp multi 3.00 3.00

**Self-Adhesive**

***Perf. 12x12½***

**1673** A674 150rp multi 3.00 3.00

Paintings by Alois Ritter (1910-86) — A675

Designs: 100rp, Ruggeller Riet, 1951. 200rp, Im Bofel, 1986.

**2016, Mar. 7** **Litho.** ***Perf. 13½x13¾***

**1674-1675** A675 Set of 2 6.00 6.00

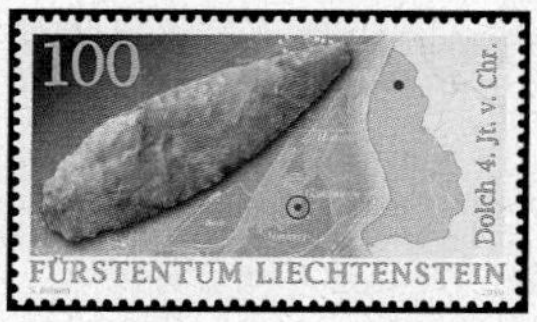


Tools Found at Archaeological Sites — A676

Map of Liechtenstein and: 100rp, Flint dagger, 4th cent. B.C. 150rp, Razor, 12th cent. B.C. 200rp, Winged axe, 5th cent. B.C.

**Litho. & Embossed With Foil Application**

**2016, Mar. 7** ***Perf. 13¼x13½***

**1676-1678** A676 Set of 3 9.00 9.00

Trees — A677

**2016, Mar. 7** **Litho.** ***Perf. 13x13¼***

**Self-Adhesive**

| | | | | | |
|---|---|---|---|---|---|
| **1679** | A677 | 85rp | Oak | 1.75 | 1.75 |
| **1680** | A677 | 100rp | Weeping willow | 2.00 | 2.00 |
| **1681** | A677 | 150rp | Walnut | 3.00 | 3.00 |
| **1682** | A677 | 170rp | Aspen | 3.50 | 3.50 |
| **1683** | A677 | 200rp | Birch | 4.00 | 4.00 |
| | | | *Nos. 1679-1683 (5)* | 14.25 | 14.25 |

2016 Summer Olympics, Rio de Janeiro — A678

Designs: 100rp, Archery. 200rp, Judo.

**Litho. With Foil Application**

**2016, June 6** ***Perf. 12½x12***

**Self-Adhesive**

**1684-1685** A678 Set of 2 6.25 6.25

17th Century Gold and Silver Items — A679

Designs: 1fr, Sailing boat drinking vessel. 1.50fr, Diana on a stag drinking vessel. 2fr, Turbo shell cup.

**Litho. With Foil Application**

**2016, June 6** ***Perf. 13¾x13½***

**1686-1688** A679 Set of 3 9.25 9.25

Ruggeller Riet Nature Reserve — A680

No. 1689: a, Pond, denomination at UL. b, Pond, denomination at UR. c, Meadow in fog, denomination at UL. d, Meadow in fog, denomination at UR.

**2016, June 6** **Litho.** ***Perf. 13¼***

**1689** A680 Block of 4 8.50 8.50
*a.-d.* 100rp Any single 2.10 2.10

Miniature Sheet

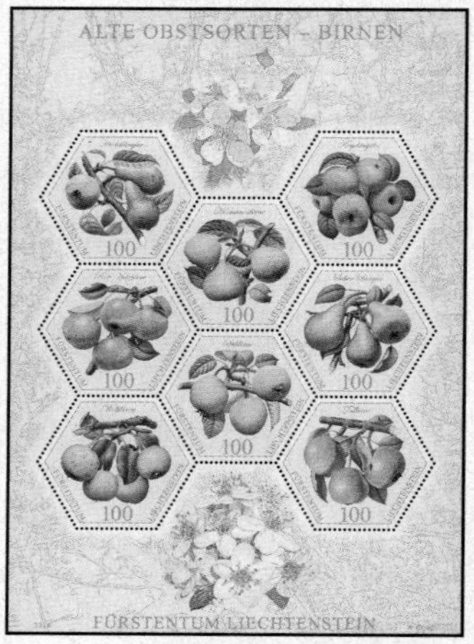


Pear Varieties — A681

No. 1690: a, Herbstlängler. b, Kugeläugstler. c, Hermannsbirne. d, Rote Holzbirne. e, Sulse Längler. f, Sülibirne. g, Wolfsbirne. h, Tollbirne.

**2016, June 6** **Litho.** ***Perf. 12½***

**Self-Adhesive**

**1690** A681 Sheet of 8 17.00 17.00
*a.-h.* 100rp Any single 2.10 2.10

Young Woman on a Balcony, by Gerrit Dou A682

**2016, Sept. 5** **Engr.** ***Perf. 11¾***

**1691** A682 150rp multi 3.25 3.25

See Czech Republic No. 3680.

Religious Fraternities — A683

Map of Liechtenstein and religious art: 100rp, Maria Hilf Fraternity (Madonna and Child altarpeice, Maria Hilf Chapel, Balzers). 150rp, St. Anne Fraternity (statue of St. Anne, Vaduz Castle) (42x35mm). 200rp, St. Sebastian Fraternity (St. Sebastian and angels, St. Sebastain Chapel, Nendeln).

**2016, Sept. 5** **Litho.** ***Perf. 14½***

**1692-1694** A683 Set of 3 9.25 9.25

Photographs of Tree Bark, by Erich Allgäuer — A684

Designs: 100rp, Woman. 150rp, Man. 200rp, Woman with Hat.

**2016, Sept. 5** **Litho.** ***Perf. 13½***

**1695-1697** A684 Set of 3 9.25 9.25

Motorcycles A685

Designs: 85rp, 1928 M. Thun. 100rp, 1920 Harley-Davidson. 150rp, 1948 Norton with Type Stolz sidecar. 200rp, 1933 Rudge.

**Litho. With Foil Application**

**2016, Sept. 5** ***Perf. 13¼***

**1698-1701** A685 Set of 4 11.00 11.00

Souvenir Sheet

Liechtenstein Without People — A686

No. 1702: a, Border marker, rusted sign, badger (20 years after people). b, Eagle (100 years after people). c, Parrots and rainbow (500 years after people).

**Litho. With Foil Application**

| | | | |
|---|---|---|---|
| **2016, Nov. 14** | | ***Perf. 14x13½*** | |
| **1702** A686 | Sheet of 3 | 12.00 | 12.00 |
| *a.-c.* | 200rp Any single | 4.00 | 4.00 |

No. 1702 was sold folded into thirds.

Christmas A687

Christmas card illustrations: 85rp, Child with lantern. 100rp, Family exchanges Christmas presents, vert. 150rp, City scene with snow, vert. 200rp, Children walking in forest.

**Litho. With Foil Application**

***Perf. 12x12½, 12½x12***

**2016, Nov. 14**

**Self-Adhesive**

| | | | |
|---|---|---|---|
| **1703-1706** A687 | Set of 4 | 11.00 | 11.00 |

New Year 2017 (Year of the Rooster) A688

**Litho. With Foil Application**

**2016, Nov. 14** ***Perf. 12½***

**Self-Adhesive**

| | | | |
|---|---|---|---|
| **1707** A688 | 200rp red & gold | 4.00 | 4.00 |

The rooster vignette was laser cut. Printed in sheets of 4.

Europa — A689

Designs: No. 1708, 150rp, Vaduz Castle. No. 1709, 150rp, Gutenberg Castle, Balzers.

| | | | | |
|---|---|---|---|---|
| **2017, Mar. 6** | **Litho.** | ***Perf. 14¼*** | | |
| **1708-1709** A689 | Set of 2 | | 6.00 | 6.00 |

Outdoor Sports A690

Winning photographs in youth photography contest: 85rp, Smooth Powder Turn, by Julius Tiefenthaler. 100rp, Winter Storm Windsurfing, by Yannick Oberhofer. 200rp, Sunset Backflip, by Tiefenthaler.

| | | | | |
|---|---|---|---|---|
| **2017, Mar. 6** | **Litho.** | ***Perf. 13½*** | | |
| **1710-1712** A690 | Set of 3 | | 7.75 | 7.75 |

Tools of Tradesmen A691

Hand and tools of: 130rp, Mason. 180rp, Tailor. 200rp, Goldsmith.

**2017, Mar. 6** **Litho.** ***Perf. 12½x12¼***

**Dated "2017"**

| | | | |
|---|---|---|---|
| **1713-1715** A691 | Set of 3 | 10.00 | 10.00 |

See Nos. 1741-1743.

Grain Crops — A692

Designs: 85rp, Oats. 100rp, Barley. 150rp, Corn. 200rp, Millet.

**2017, Mar. 6** **Litho.** ***Perf. 12¼***

**Self-Adhesive**

| | | | |
|---|---|---|---|
| **1716-1719** A692 | Set of 4 | 10.50 | 10.50 |

HPZ Remedial Education Center, Schaan, 50th Anniv. A693

**2017, June 6** **Litho.** ***Perf. 12x12½***

**Self-Adhesive**

| | | | |
|---|---|---|---|
| **1720** A693 | 1fr multi | 2.10 | 2.10 |

Paintings by Peter Fendi (1796-1842) A694

Designs: 85rp, Request for Admission. 1fr, Sneaking a Peek. 1.50fr, A Child's Prayer.

**Litho. With Foil Application**

| | | | |
|---|---|---|---|
| **2017, June 6** | | ***Perf. 13½x13¼*** | |
| **1721-1723** A694 | Set of 3 | 7.00 | 7.00 |

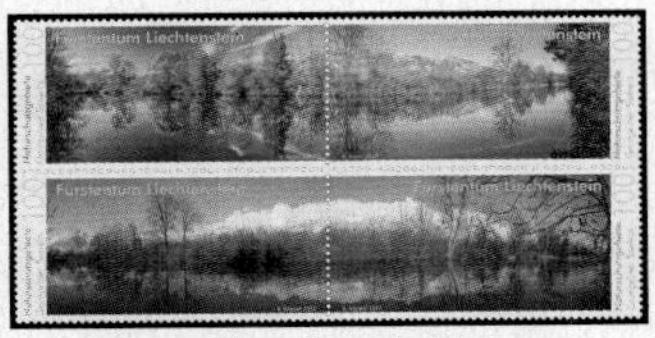

Gampriner Seelein Nature Reserve — A695

No. 1724 — Lake Gampriner Seelein in: a, Autumn, denomination at UL. b, Autumn, denomination at UR. c, Winter, denomination at UL. d, Winter, denomination at UR.

| | | | | |
|---|---|---|---|---|
| **2017, June 6** | **Litho.** | ***Perf. 13¼*** | | |
| **1724** A695 | Block of 4 | | 8.50 | 8.50 |
| *a.-d.* | 100rp Any single | | 2.10 | 2.10 |

Souvenir Sheet

50th Wedding Anniversary of Prince Hans-Adam II and Princess Marie — A696

No. 1725: a, Vaduz Castle and flower (18x60mm). b, Prince and Princess (46x60mm). c, Crown and joined wedding rings (41x60mm).

**Litho. With Foil Application, Litho. & Embossed With Foil Application (2.80fr)**

| | | | |
|---|---|---|---|
| **2017, June 6** | | ***Perf. 14¼x14½*** | |
| **1725** A696 | Sheet of 3 | 13.00 | 13.00 |
| *a.* | 1.30fr multi | 2.75 | 2.75 |
| *b.* | 2.20fr multi | 4.50 | 4.50 |
| *c.* | 2.80fr multi | 5.75 | 5.75 |

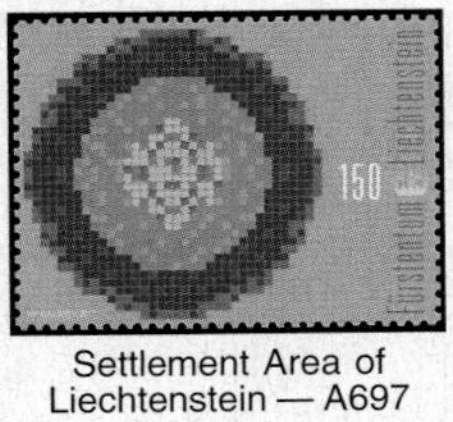

Settlement Area of Liechtenstein — A697

| | | | | |
|---|---|---|---|---|
| **2017, Sept. 4** | **Litho.** | ***Perf. 14x13¼*** | | |
| **1726** A697 | 150rp multi | | 3.25 | 3.25 |

Rappastein, Painting by Helmut Ditsch — A698

| | | | | |
|---|---|---|---|---|
| **2017, Sept. 4** | **Litho.** | ***Perf. 14x13½*** | | |
| **1727** A698 | 380rp multi | | 8.00 | 8.00 |

Souvenir Sheet

Balzers Mail Collection Station, 200th Anniv. — A699

No. 1728: a, Postman and girl. b, Posthorn. c, Horse-drawn mail coach.

**Litho. & Engr. With Foil Application**

| | | | |
|---|---|---|---|
| **2017, Sept. 4** | | ***Perf. 13¾x14¼*** | |
| **1728** A699 | Sheet of 3 | 13.50 | 13.50 |
| *a.* | 1.30fr multi | 2.75 | 2.75 |
| *b.* | 2.20fr multi | 4.75 | 4.75 |
| *c.* | 2.80fr multi | 6.00 | 6.00 |

Miniature Sheet

Stone Fruit Varieties — A700

No. 1729: a, Mombacher Frühaprikose apricots. b, Kirkespflaume plums. c, Grüne Reineclaude plums. d, Hauszwetschge plums. e, Ungarische Beste apricots. f, Schauenburger cherries. g, Mirabelle von Nancy plums. h, Gelbe Denise cherries.

**2017, Sept. 4** **Litho.** ***Perf. 12½***

**Self-Adhesive**

| | | | |
|---|---|---|---|
| **1729** A700 | Sheet of 8 | 17.00 | 17.00 |
| *a.-h.* | 100rp Any single | 2.10 | 2.10 |

2018 Winter Olympics, Pyeongchang, South Korea — A701

Designs: 170rp, Nordic skiing. 200rp, Alpine skiing.

| | | | | |
|---|---|---|---|---|
| **2017, Nov. 13** | **Litho.** | ***Perf. 12x12½*** | | |
| **1730-1731** A701 | Set of 2 | | 7.75 | 7.75 |

Worldwide Fund for Nature (WWF) A702

Designs: 85rp, Castor fiber. 100rp, Lynx lynx. 130rp, Canis lupus. 150rp, Ciconia ciconia.

**2017, Nov. 13** **Litho.** ***Perf. 12x12½***

**Self-Adhesive**

| | | | |
|---|---|---|---|
| **1732-1735** A702 | Set of 4 | 9.50 | 9.50 |

Christmas
A703

Designs: 85rp, Star of Bethlehem, trees and house. 100rp, Star, forest and house. 150rp, Moon, forest and house. 200rp, Moon over church.

**2017, Nov. 13 Litho. *Perf. 12½x12***
**Self-Adhesive**

| | | | |
|---|---|---|---|
| **1736-1739** | A703 | Set of 4 | 11.00 11.00 |

New Year 2018 (Year of the Dog)
A704

**Litho. With Foil Application**
**2017, Nov. 13 *Perf. 12½***
**Self-Adhesive**

| | | | |
|---|---|---|---|
| **1740** | A704 | 200rp red & gold | 4.25 4.25 |

The dog vignette was laser cut. Printed in sheets of 4.

**Tools of Tradesmen Type of 2017**

Hand and tools of: 100rp, Bookbinder. 130rp, Instrument maker. 180rp, Shoemaker.

**2018, Mar. 5 Litho. *Perf. 12½x12¼***
**Dated "2018"**

| | | | |
|---|---|---|---|
| **1741-1743** | A691 | Set of 3 | 8.75 8.75 |

Balzers Footbridge — A705

Old Rhine Bridge, Vaduz — A706

**Litho. With Foil Application**
**2018, Mar. 5 *Perf. 14x13¼***

| | | | |
|---|---|---|---|
| **1744** | A705 | 150rp sil & multi | 3.25 3.25 |
| **1745** | A706 | 150rp sil & multi | 3.25 3.25 |

Europa.

Paintings by Gustav Klimt (1862-1918)
A707

Designs: 2.60fr, The Kiss. 3.70fr, Death and Life.

**Litho. With Foil Application**
**2018, Mar. 5 *Perf. 14½***

| | | | |
|---|---|---|---|
| **1746-1747** | A707 | Set of 2 | 13.50 13.50 |

Vegetables
A708

Designs: 85rp, Eggplant. 100rp, Radishes. 150rp, Zucchinis. 200rp, Peperoni peppers.

**2018, Mar. 5 Litho. *Perf. 12¼***
**Self-Adhesive**

| | | | |
|---|---|---|---|
| **1748-1751** | A708 | Set of 4 | 11.50 11.50 |

---

## SEMI-POSTAL STAMPS

Prince Johann II — SP1

**Wmk. 183**
**1925, Oct. 5 Engr. *Perf. 11½***

| | | | | |
|---|---|---|---|---|
| **B1** | SP1 | 10rp yellow green | 42.50 | 22.50 |
| **B2** | SP1 | 20rp deep red | 21.00 | 22.50 |
| **B3** | SP1 | 30rp deep blue | 7.00 | 7.00 |
| | | *Nos. B1-B3 (3)* | 70.50 | 52.00 |
| | | Set, never hinged | 210.00 | |

85th birthday of the Prince Regent. Sold at a premium of 5rp each, the excess being devoted to charities.

Coat of Arms — SP2

**1927, Oct. 5 Typo.**

| | | | | |
|---|---|---|---|---|
| **B4** | SP2 | 10rp multicolored | 10.50 | *25.00* |
| **B5** | SP2 | 20rp multicolored | 10.50 | *25.00* |
| **B6** | SP2 | 30rp multicolored | 5.00 | *21.00* |
| | | *Nos. B4-B6 (3)* | 26.00 | *71.00* |
| | | Set, never hinged | 62.00 | |

87th birthday of Prince Johann II.

These stamps were sold at premiums of 5, 10 and 20rp respectively. The money thus obtained was devoted to charity.

Railroad Bridge Demolished by Flood
SP3

Designs: 10rp+10rp, Inundated Village of Ruggel. 20rp+10rp, Austrian soldiers rescuing refugees. 30rp+10rp, Swiss soldiers salvaging personal effects.

**1928, Feb. 6 Litho. Unwmk.**

| | | | | |
|---|---|---|---|---|
| **B7** | SP3 | 5rp + 5rp brn vio & brn | 17.50 | 26.00 |
| **B8** | SP3 | 10rp + 10rp bl grn & brn | 25.00 | 26.00 |
| **B9** | SP3 | 20rp + 10rp dl red & brn | 25.00 | 26.00 |
| **B10** | SP3 | 30rp + 10rp dp bl & brn | 21.00 | 26.00 |
| | | *Nos. B7-B10 (4)* | 88.50 | 104.00 |
| | | Set, never hinged | 220.00 | |

The surtax on these stamps was used to aid the sufferers from the Rhine floods.

Coat of Arms — SP7

Princess Elsa — SP8

Design: 30rp, Prince Francis I.

**1932, Dec. 21 Photo.**

| | | | | |
|---|---|---|---|---|
| **B11** | SP7 | 10rp (+ 5rp) olive grn | 17.50 | *25.00* |
| **B12** | SP8 | 20rp (+ 5rp) rose red | 17.50 | *22.50* |
| **B13** | SP8 | 30rp (+ 10rp) ultra | 22.50 | *32.50* |
| | | *Nos. B11-B13 (3)* | 57.50 | *80.00* |
| | | Set, never hinged | 160.00 | |

The surtax was for the Child Welfare Fund.

**Postal Museum Issue**
Souvenir Sheet

SP10

**1936, Oct. 24 Litho. *Imperf.***

| | | | | |
|---|---|---|---|---|
| **B14** | SP10 | Sheet of 4 | 15.00 | *35.00* |
| | | Never hinged | 60.00 | |

Sheet contains 2 each, Nos. 120, 122. Sold for 2fr.

"Protect the Child" — SP11

Designs: No. B16, "Take Care of the Sick." No. B17, "Help the Aged."

***Perf. 11½***
**1945, Nov. 27 Photo. Unwmk.**

| | | | | |
|---|---|---|---|---|
| **B15** | SP11 | 10rp + 10rp multi | .65 | *1.75* |
| **B16** | SP11 | 20rp + 20rp multi | .65 | *2.25* |
| **B17** | SP11 | 1fr + 1.40fr multi | 4.75 | *20.00* |
| | | *Nos. B15-B17 (3)* | 6.05 | *24.00* |
| | | Set, never hinged | 11.00 | |

Souvenir Sheet

Post Coach — SP14

**1946, Aug. 10**

| | | | | |
|---|---|---|---|---|
| **B18** | SP14 | Sheet of 2 | 21.00 | *32.50* |
| | | Never hinged | 35.00 | |
| *a.* | | 10rp dark violet brown & buff | 5.00 | *15.00* |
| | | Never hinged | 12.50 | |

25th anniv. of the Swiss-Liechtenstein Postal Agreement. Sheet, size: 82x60½mm, sold for 3fr.

Canal by Albert Cuyp — SP15

Willem van Huythuysen by Frans Hals — SP16

40rp+10rp, Landscape by Jacob van Ruysdael.

**1951, July 24 *Perf. 11½***

| | | | | |
|---|---|---|---|---|
| **B19** | SP15 | 10rp + 10rp ol grn | 5.00 | 7.00 |
| **B20** | SP16 | 20rp + 10rp dk vio brn | 5.00 | *7.00* |
| **B21** | SP15 | 40rp + 10rp blue | 5.00 | 7.00 |
| | | *Nos. B19-B21 (3)* | 15.00 | *21.00* |
| | | Set, never hinged | 30.00 | |

Issued in sheets of 12. For surcharges see Nos. 281-283.

**Catalogue values for unused stamps in this section, from this point to the end of the section, are for Never Hinged items.**

**Nos. 324-325 Surcharged with New Value and Uprooted Oak Emblem**

**1960, Apr. 7**

| | | | | |
|---|---|---|---|---|
| **B22** | A190 | 30rp + 10rp on 40rp | .55 | *1.00* |
| **B23** | A190 | 50rp + 10rp on 25rp | .90 | *2.00* |

World Refugee Year, July 1, 1959-June 30, 1960. The surtax was for aid to refugees.

Growth Symbol
SP17

**1967, Dec. 7 Photo. *Perf. 11½***

| | | | |
|---|---|---|---|
| **B24** | SP17 | 50rp + 20rp multi | .50 .60 |

Surtax was for development assistance.

---

## AIR POST STAMPS

Airplane over Snow-capped Mountain Peaks — AP1

Airplane above Vaduz Castle — AP2

Airplane over Rhine Valley — AP3

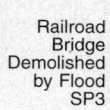

*Perf. 10½, 10½x11½*

**1930, Aug. 12 Photo. Unwmk.**

**Gray Wavy Lines in Background**

| | | | | |
|---|---|---|---|---|
| C1 | AP1 | 15rp dark brown | 10.50 | *17.50* |
| C2 | AP1 | 20rp slate | 25.00 | *25.00* |
| C3 | AP2 | 25rp olive brown | 14.00 | *45.00* |
| C4 | AP2 | 35rp slate blue | 21.00 | *42.50* |
| C5 | AP3 | 45rp olive green | 50.00 | *87.50* |
| C6 | AP3 | 1fr lake | 55.00 | *62.50* |
| | | *Nos. C1-C6 (6)* | 175.50 | *280.00* |
| | | Set, never hinged | 518.00 | |

For surcharge see No. C14.

Zeppelin over Naafkopf, Falknis Range AP4

Design: 2fr, Zeppelin over Valüna Valley.

**1931, June 1** *Perf. 11½*

| | | | | |
|---|---|---|---|---|
| C7 | AP4 | 1fr olive black | 70.00 | *125.00* |
| C8 | AP4 | 2fr blue black | 140.00 | *400.00* |
| | | Set, never hinged | 565.00 | |

Golden Eagle — AP6

15rp, Golden Eagle in flight, diff. 20rp, Golden Eagle in flight, diff. 30rp, Osprey. 50rp, Eagle.

**1934-35**

| | | | | |
|---|---|---|---|---|
| C9 | AP6 | 10rp brt vio ('35) | 9.00 | *32.50* |
| C10 | AP6 | 15rp red org ('35) | 22.50 | *30.00* |
| C11 | AP6 | 20rp red ('35) | 82.50 | *30.00* |
| C12 | AP6 | 30rp brt bl ('35) | 22.50 | *30.00* |
| C13 | AP6 | 50rp emerald | 15.00 | *35.00* |
| | | *Nos. C9-C13 (5)* | 151.50 | 157.50 |
| | | Set, never hinged | 300.00 | |

No. C6 Surcharged

**1935, June 24** *Perf. 10½x11½*

| | | | | |
|---|---|---|---|---|
| C14 | AP3 | 60rp on 1fr lake | 40.00 | 42.50 |
| | | Never hinged | 130.00 | |

Airship "Hindenburg" — AP11

Design: 2fr, Airship "Graf Zeppelin."

**1936, May 1** *Perf. 11½*

| | | | | |
|---|---|---|---|---|
| C15 | AP11 | 1fr rose carmine | 40.00 | 75.00 |
| C16 | AP11 | 2fr violet | 30.00 | 75.00 |
| | | Set, never hinged | 160.00 | |

AP13

10rp, Barn swallows. 15rp, Black-headed Gulls. 20rp, Gulls. 30rp, Eagle. 50rp, Northern Goshawk. 1fr, Lammergeier. 2fr, Lammergeier.

**1939, Apr. 3** **Photo.**

| | | | | |
|---|---|---|---|---|
| C17 | AP13 | 10rp violet | .60 | .70 |
| C18 | AP13 | 15rp red orange | .60 | 2.00 |
| C19 | AP13 | 20rp dark red | 2.75 | .80 |
| C20 | AP13 | 30rp dull blue | 1.20 | 1.50 |
| C21 | AP13 | 50rp brt green | 3.00 | 3.25 |
| C22 | AP13 | 1fr rose car | 2.25 | *12.00* |
| C23 | AP13 | 2fr violet | 2.25 | *12.00* |
| | | *Nos. C17-C23 (7)* | 12.65 | *32.25* |
| | | Set, never hinged | 40.00 | |

**Catalogue values for unused stamps in this section, from this point to the end of the section, are for Never Hinged items.**

AP20

Designs: 10rp, Leonardo da Vinci. 15rp, Joseph Montgolfier. 20rp, Jacob Degen. 25rp, Wilhelm Kress. 40rp, E. G. Robertson. 50rp, W. S. Henson. 1fr, Otto Lilienthal. 2fr, S. A. Andrée. 5fr, Wilbur Wright. 10fr, Icarus.

**1948**

| | | | | |
|---|---|---|---|---|
| C24 | AP20 | 10rp dark green | .75 | .25 |
| C25 | AP20 | 15rp dark violet | .75 | .80 |
| C26 | AP20 | 20rp brown | 1.00 | .25 |
| *a.* | | 20rp reddish brown | 95.00 | 3.25 |
| C27 | AP20 | 25rp dark red | 1.50 | 1.25 |
| C28 | AP20 | 40rp violet blue | 1.75 | 1.25 |
| C29 | AP20 | 50rp Prus blue | 2.00 | 1.25 |
| C30 | AP20 | 1fr chocolate | 3.50 | 2.75 |
| C31 | AP20 | 2fr rose lake | 5.25 | 3.50 |
| C32 | AP20 | 5fr olive green | 6.50 | 4.75 |
| C33 | AP20 | 10fr slate black | 42.50 | 14.00 |
| | | *Nos. C24-C33 (10)* | 65.50 | 30.05 |

Issued in sheets of 9.
Exist imperf. Value, set $6,500.

Helicopter, Bell 47-J AP21

Planes: 40rp, Boeing 707 jet. 50rp, Convair 600 jet. 75rp, Douglas DC-8.

**1960, Apr. 7 Unwmk.** *Perf. 11½*

| | | | | |
|---|---|---|---|---|
| C34 | AP21 | 30rp red orange | 2.25 | 2.25 |
| C35 | AP21 | 40rp blue black | 3.75 | 2.25 |
| C36 | AP21 | 50rp deep claret | 9.50 | 4.00 |
| C37 | AP21 | 75rp olive green | 2.00 | 2.25 |
| | | *Nos. C34-C37 (4)* | 17.50 | 10.75 |

30th anniv. of Liechtenstein's air post stamps.

## POSTAGE DUE STAMPS

### National Administration of the Post Office

D1

**1920 Unwmk. Engr.** *Perf. 12½*

| | | | | |
|---|---|---|---|---|
| J1 | D1 | 5h rose red | .35 | .40 |
| J2 | D1 | 10h rose red | .35 | .40 |
| J3 | D1 | 15h rose red | .35 | .40 |
| J4 | D1 | 20h rose red | .35 | .55 |
| J5 | D1 | 25h rose red | .35 | .55 |
| J6 | D1 | 30h rose red | .35 | .55 |
| J7 | D1 | 40h rose red | .35 | .55 |
| J8 | D1 | 50h rose red | .35 | .55 |
| J9 | D1 | 80h rose red | .35 | .55 |
| J10 | D1 | 1k dull blue | .40 | 1.40 |
| J11 | D1 | 2k dull blue | .40 | 1.40 |
| J12 | D1 | 5k dull blue | .40 | 1.75 |
| | | *Nos. J1-J12 (12)* | 4.35 | 9.05 |
| | | Set, never hinged | 12.50 | |

Nos. J1-J12 exist imperf. (value, unused, set $260) and part perf. (value, each: unused $2; never hinged $7; used $7).

J3 lacks the outside frame lines.

### Swiss Administration of the Post Office

D2

**1928 Litho. Wmk. 183** *Perf. 11½*

**Granite Paper**

| | | | | |
|---|---|---|---|---|
| J13 | D2 | 5rp pur & org | 1.20 | *3.00* |
| J14 | D2 | 10rp pur & org | 1.20 | *3.00* |
| J15 | D2 | 15rp pur & org | 1.75 | *13.50* |
| J16 | D2 | 20rp pur & org | 1.75 | *3.00* |
| J17 | D2 | 25rp pur & org | 1.75 | *9.00* |
| J18 | D2 | 30rp pur & org | 6.00 | *13.50* |
| J19 | D2 | 40rp pur & org | 7.00 | *14.00* |
| J20 | D2 | 50rp pur & org | 9.00 | *17.50* |
| | | *Nos. J13-J20 (8)* | 29.65 | *76.50* |
| | | Set, never hinged | 65.00 | |

Post Horn — D3

**Engraved; Value Typographed in Dark Red**

**1940 Unwmk.** *Perf. 11½*

| | | | | |
|---|---|---|---|---|
| J21 | D3 | 5rp gray blue | 1.25 | *2.75* |
| J22 | D3 | 10rp gray blue | .60 | *1.40* |
| J23 | D3 | 15rp gray blue | 1.25 | *5.00* |
| J24 | D3 | 20rp gray blue | .60 | *2.00* |
| J25 | D3 | 25rp gray blue | 1.25 | *3.50* |
| J26 | D3 | 30rp gray blue | 2.00 | *5.50* |
| J27 | D3 | 40rp gray blue | 2.00 | *5.50* |
| J28 | D3 | 50rp gray blue | 3.00 | *5.50* |
| | | *Nos. J21-J28 (8)* | 11.95 | *31.15* |
| | | Set, never hinged | 35.00 | |

## OFFICIAL STAMPS

Regular Issue of 1930 Overprinted in Various Colors

*Perf. 10½, 11½, 11½x10½*

**1932 Unwmk.**

| | | | | |
|---|---|---|---|---|
| O1 | A38 | 5rp dk grn (Bk) | 10.50 | 15.50 |
| O2 | A39 | 10rp dark vio (R) | 75.00 | 15.50 |
| O3 | A40 | 20rp dp rose red (Bl) | 90.00 | 15.50 |
| O4 | A42 | 30rp ultra (R) | 17.50 | 21.00 |
| O5 | A43 | 35rp dp grn (Bk) | 14.00 | *35.00* |
| O6 | A45 | 50rp blk brn (Bl) | 77.50 | *21.00* |
| O7 | A46 | 60rp olive blk (R) | 14.00 | *50.00* |
| O8 | A48 | 1.20fr olive brn (G) | 150.00 | 425.00 |
| | | *Nos. O1-O8 (8)* | 448.50 | 598.50 |
| | | Set, never hinged | 1,763. | |

Values are for the most common perf. variety. See Scott Classic Specialized catalogue for detailed listings.

Nos. 108, 110 Overprinted in Black

**1933** *Perf. 14½*

| | | | | |
|---|---|---|---|---|
| O9 | A51 | 25rp red orange | 42.50 | 45.00 |
| O10 | A53 | 1.20fr red brown | 85.00 | *275.00* |
| | | Set, never hinged | 360.00 | |

Regular Issue of 1934-35 Ovptd. in Various Colors

**1934-36** *Perf. 11½*

| | | | | |
|---|---|---|---|---|
| O11 | A58 | 5rp emerald (R) | 2.10 | *3.50* |
| O12 | A59 | 10rp dp vio (Bk) | 4.25 | *3.50* |
| O13 | A60 | 15rp red org (V) | .90 | *3.50* |
| O14 | A61 | 20rp red (Bk) | .70 | *3.50* |
| O15 | A62 | 25rp brown (R) | 35.00 | *115.00* |
| O16 | A62 | 25rp brown (Bk) | 3.50 | *15.00* |
| O17 | A63 | 30rp dark bl (R) | 5.00 | *10.50* |
| O18 | A66 | 50rp lt brown (V) | 1.40 | *17.50* |
| O19 | A68 | 90rp dp grn (Bk) | 7.50 | *10.50* |
| O20 | A69 | 1.50fr brn car (Bl) | 42.50 | *280.00* |
| | | *Nos. O11-O20 (10)* | 102.85 | *462.50* |
| | | Set, never hinged | 358.00 | |

Regular Issue of 1937-38 Overprinted in Black, Red or Blue

**1937-41**

| | | | | |
|---|---|---|---|---|
| O21 | A76 | 5rp emerald (Bk) | .40 | .75 |
| O22 | A76 | 10rp vio & buff (R) | .80 | 2.00 |
| O23 | A76 | 20rp brn org (Bl) | 1.60 | 2.00 |
| O24 | A76 | 20rp brn org (Bk) ('41) | 1.60 | 2.75 |
| O25 | A76 | 25rp chestnut (Bk) | .80 | 2.75 |
| O26 | A77 | 30rp blue & gray (Bk) | 2.75 | 2.75 |
| O27 | A79 | 50rp dk brn & buff (R) | 1.25 | 2.10 |
| O28 | A80 | 1fr red brown (Bk) | 1.25 | *12.00* |
| O29 | A80 | 1.50fr slate bl (Bk) ('38) | 5.00 | *17.50* |
| | | *Nos. O21-O29 (9)* | 15.45 | *44.60* |
| | | Set, never hinged | 49.50 | |

**Catalogue values for unused stamps in this section, from this point to the end of the section, are for Never Hinged items.**

Stamps of 1944-45 Overprinted in Black

**1947**

| | | | | |
|---|---|---|---|---|
| O30 | A136 | 5rp slate grn & buff | 1.60 | 1.10 |
| O31 | A136 | 10rp gray & buff | 1.60 | 1.10 |
| O32 | A136 | 20rp org red & buff | 2.10 | 1.10 |
| O33 | A136 | 30rp blue & buff | 2.75 | 1.75 |
| O34 | A136 | 50rp bluish blk & pale gray | 2.75 | 3.50 |
| O35 | A136 | 1fr dp cl & buff | 11.00 | 11.00 |
| O36 | A136 | 150rp royal blue | 11.00 | 14.00 |
| | | *Nos. O30-O36 (7)* | 32.80 | 33.55 |

Crown — O1

**Engr.; Value Typo.**

**1950-68 Unwmk.** *Perf. 11½*

**Buff Granite Paper**

**Narrow Gothic Numerals**

| | | | | |
|---|---|---|---|---|
| O37 | O1 | 5rp red vio & gray | .25 | .25 |
| O38 | O1 | 10rp ol grn & mag | .25 | .25 |
| O39 | O1 | 20rp org brn & bl | .25 | .25 |
| O40 | O1 | 30rp dk red brn & org red | .25 | .25 |
| O41 | O1 | 40rp blue & hn brn | .35 | .35 |
| O42 | O1 | 55rp dk gray grn & red | .70 | 1.10 |
| *a.* | | White paper ('68) | 45.00 | *125.00* |
| O43 | O1 | 60rp slate & mag | .70 | 1.10 |
| *a.* | | White paper ('68) | 6.00 | *22.50* |
| O44 | O1 | 80rp red org & gray | .70 | .90 |
| O45 | O1 | 90rp choc & blue | .90 | 1.25 |
| O46 | O1 | 1.20fr grnsh bl & org | 1.10 | 1.25 |
| | | *Nos. O37-O46 (10)* | 5.45 | 6.95 |

**1968-69** *Perf. 11½*

**White Granite Paper**

**Broad Numerals, Varying Thickness**

| | | | | |
|---|---|---|---|---|
| O47 | O1 | 5rp olive brn & org | .25 | .25 |
| O48 | O1 | 10rp violet & car | .25 | .25 |
| O49 | O1 | 20rp ver & emer | .25 | .25 |
| O50 | O1 | 30rp green & red | .25 | .25 |
| O51 | O1 | 50rp ultra & red | .35 | .35 |
| O52 | O1 | 60rp orange & ultra | .40 | .40 |
| O53 | O1 | 70rp maroon & emer | .50 | .50 |
| O54 | O1 | 80rp bl grn & car | .55 | .55 |
| O55 | O1 | 95rp slate & red ('69) | .65 | .65 |
| O56 | O1 | 1fr rose cl & grn | .70 | .70 |

| | | | | | |
|---|---|---|---|---|---|
| O57 | O1 | 1.20fr | lt red brn & grn | .80 | .80 |
| O58 | O1 | 2fr | brn & org ('69) | 1.25 | 1.25 |
| | | | *Nos. O47-O58 (12)* | 6.20 | 6.20 |

Government Building, Vaduz — O2

**Engr., Value Typo.**

**1976-89** ***Perf. 14***

| | | | | | |
|---|---|---|---|---|---|
| O59 | O2 | 10rp | yel brn & vio | .25 | .25 |
| O60 | O2 | 20rp | car lake & bl | .25 | .25 |
| O61 | O2 | 35rp | blue & red | .25 | .25 |
| O62 | O2 | 40rp | dull pur & grn | .30 | .30 |
| O63 | O2 | 50rp | slate & mag | .40 | .40 |
| O64 | O2 | 70rp | vio brn & bl grn | .55 | .55 |
| O65 | O2 | 80rp | green & mag | .60 | .60 |
| O66 | O2 | 90rp | vio & bl grn | .70 | .70 |
| O67 | O2 | 1fr | olive & mag | .80 | .80 |
| O68 | O2 | 1.10fr | brown & ultra | .85 | .85 |
| O69 | O2 | 1.50fr | dull grn & red | 1.25 | 1.25 |
| O70 | O2 | 2fr | orange & blue | 1.60 | 1.60 |
| O75 | O2 | 5fr | rose vio & brn org | 5.75 | 5.75 |
| | | | *Nos. O59-O75 (13)* | 13.55 | 13.55 |

Issued: 5fr, 9/4/89; others, 12/9/76.

## LITHUANIA

ˌli-thə-ˈwā-nē-ə

(Lietuva)

LOCATION — Northern Europe bordering on the Baltic Sea
GOVT. — Independent republic
AREA — 25,170 sq. mi.
POP. — 3,584,966 (1999 est.)
CAPITAL — Vilnius

Lithuania was under Russian rule when it declared its independence in 1918. The League of Nations recognized it in 1922. In 1940 it became a republic in the Union of Soviet Socialist Republics.

Lithuania declared its independence on March 11, 1990. Lithuanian independence was recognized by the Soviet Union on Sept. 6, 1991.

100 Skatiku = 1 Auksinas
100 Centai = 1 Litas (1922, 1993)
100 Kopecks = 1 Ruble (1991)
100 Cents = 1 Euro (2015)

**Catalogue values for unused stamps in this country are for Never Hinged items, beginning with Scott 371 in the regular postage section.**

Nos. 1-26 were printed in sheets of 20 (5x4) which were imperf. at the outer sides, so that only 6 stamps in each sheet were fully perforated. Values are for the stamps partly imperf. The stamps fully perforated sell for at least double these values. There was also a printing of Nos. 19-26 in a sheet of 160, composed of blocks of 20 of each stamp. Pairs or blocks with different values se-tenant sell for considerably more than the values for the stamps singly.

Nos. 1-26 are without gum.

**Watermarks**

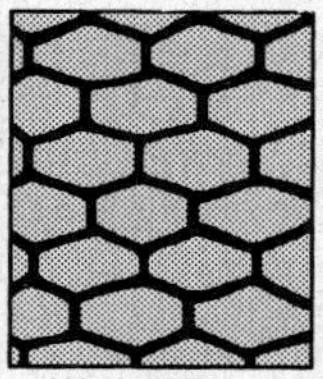

Wmk. 109 — Webbing

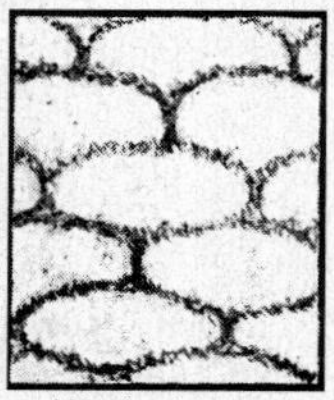

Wmk. 144 — Network

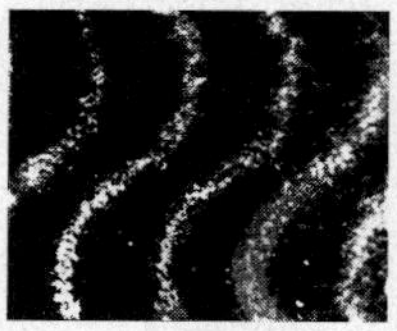

Wmk. 145 — Wavy Lines

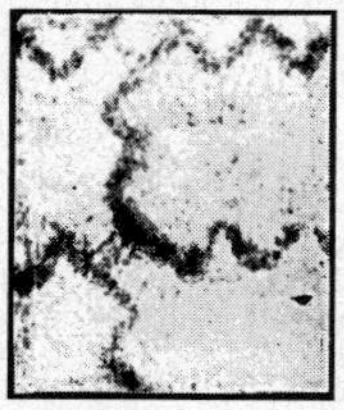

Wmk. 146 — Zigzag Lines Forming Rectangles

Wmk. 147 — Parquetry

Wmk. 198 — Intersecting Diamonds

Wmk. 209 — Multiple Ovals

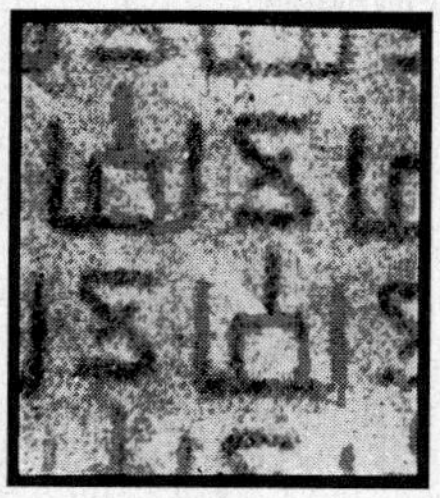

Wmk. 238 — Multiple Letters

**First Vilnius Printing**

A1

**Thin Figures**

***Perf. 11½***

**1918, Dec. 27** **Unwmk.** **Typeset**

| | | | | | |
|---|---|---|---|---|---|
| 1 | A1 | 10sk | black | 150.00 | 125.00 |
| 2 | A1 | 15sk | black | 150.00 | 100.00 |

**Second Vilnius Printing**

**1918, Dec. 31** **Thick Figures**

| | | | | | |
|---|---|---|---|---|---|
| 3 | A1 | 10sk | black | 70.00 | 55.00 |
| 4 | A1 | 15sk | black | 70.00 | 55.00 |
| 5 | A1 | 20sk | black | 30.00 | 16.00 |
| 6 | A1 | 30sk | black | 35.00 | 17.50 |
| 7 | A1 | 40sk | black | 50.00 | 25.00 |
| 8 | A1 | 50sk | black | 40.00 | 17.50 |
| | | | *Nos. 3-8 (6)* | 295.00 | 186.00 |

**First Kaunas Issue**

A2

**1919, Jan. 29**

| | | | | | |
|---|---|---|---|---|---|
| 9 | A2 | 10sk | black | 7.50 | 3.75 |
| 10 | A2 | 15sk | black | 7.50 | 3.75 |
| a. | | | "5" for "15" | 95.00 | 72.50 |
| 11 | A2 | 20sk | black | 7.50 | 3.75 |
| 12 | A2 | 30sk | black | 7.50 | 3.75 |
| | | | *Nos. 9-12 (4)* | 30.00 | 15.00 |

**Second Kaunas Issue**

A3

**1919, Feb. 18**

| | | | | | |
|---|---|---|---|---|---|
| 13 | A3 | 10sk | black | 4.25 | 2.50 |
| 14 | A3 | 15sk | black | 4.25 | 2.50 |
| 15 | A3 | 20sk | black | 4.25 | 2.50 |
| a. | | | "astas" for "pastas" | 80.00 | 75.00 |
| 16 | A3 | 30sk | black | 4.25 | 2.50 |
| 17 | A3 | 40sk | black | 4.25 | 2.50 |
| 18 | A3 | 50sk | black | 4.25 | 2.50 |
| 19 | A3 | 60sk | black | 4.25 | 2.50 |
| | | | *Nos. 13-19 (7)* | 29.75 | 17.50 |

**Third Kaunas Issue**

A4

**1919, Mar. 1**

| | | | | | |
|---|---|---|---|---|---|
| 20 | A4 | 10sk | black | 4.25 | 1.75 |
| 21 | A4 | 15sk | black | 4.25 | 1.75 |
| 22 | A4 | 20sk | black | 4.25 | 1.75 |
| 23 | A4 | 30sk | black | 4.25 | 1.75 |
| 24 | A4 | 40sk | black | 4.25 | 1.75 |
| 25 | A4 | 50sk | black | 4.25 | 1.75 |
| 26 | A4 | 60sk | black | 4.25 | 1.75 |
| | | | *Nos. 20-26 (7)* | 29.75 | 12.25 |

The White Knight "Vytis"
A5 A6

A7

***Perf. 10½ to 14 & Compound***

**1919** **Litho.** **Wmk. 144**

**Gray Granite Paper**

| | | | | | |
|---|---|---|---|---|---|
| 30 | A5 | 10sk | deep rose | 1.25 | .40 |
| a. | | | Wmk. vert. | 17.50 | 15.00 |
| 31 | A5 | 15sk | violet | 1.25 | .40 |
| a. | | | Wmk. vert. | 17.50 | 15.00 |
| 32 | A5 | 20sk | dark blue | 1.60 | .40 |
| 33 | A5 | 30sk | deep orange | 1.60 | .40 |
| a. | | | Wmk. vert. | 17.50 | 15.00 |
| 34 | A5 | 40sk | dark brown | 1.60 | .40 |
| 35 | A6 | 50sk | blue green | 1.60 | .50 |
| 36 | A6 | 75sk | org & dp rose | 1.60 | .50 |
| 37 | A7 | 1auk | gray & rose | 3.25 | .50 |
| 38 | A7 | 3auk | bis brn & rose | 3.25 | .50 |
| 39 | A7 | 5auk | blue grn & rose | 3.25 | .80 |
| | | | *Nos. 30-39 (10)* | 20.25 | 4.80 |

Nos. 30a, 31a and 33a are from the first printing with watermark vertical showing points to left; various perforations.

Nos. 30-39 exist imperf. Value in pairs, $100.

Issued: Nos. 30a, 31a, 33a, 2/17/19; Nos. 30-36, 3/20/19.

**Thick White Paper**

**1919** **Wmk. 145**

| | | | | | |
|---|---|---|---|---|---|
| 40 | A5 | 10sk | dull rose | .35 | .25 |
| 41 | A5 | 15sk | violet | .35 | .25 |
| 42 | A5 | 20sk | dark blue | .35 | .25 |
| 43 | A5 | 30sk | orange | .35 | .25 |
| 44 | A5 | 40sk | red brown | .35 | .25 |
| 45 | A6 | 50sk | pale grayish green | .35 | .25 |
| 46 | A6 | 75sk | yel & dp rose | .35 | .25 |
| 47 | A7 | 1auk | gray & rose | .95 | .35 |
| 48 | A7 | 3auk | yel brn & rose, perf. 12½ | .60 | .40 |
| 49 | A7 | 5auk | bl grn & rose | 1.00 | .40 |
| | | | *Nos. 40-49 (10)* | 5.00 | 2.90 |

Nos. 40-49 exist imperf. Value in pairs, $90.

A8

***Perf. 10½ to 14 & Compound***

**1919, May 8** **Thin White Paper**

| | | | | | |
|---|---|---|---|---|---|
| 50 | A5 | 10sk | red | .45 | .25 |
| 51 | A5 | 15sk | lilac | .45 | .25 |
| 52 | A5 | 20sk | dull blue | .45 | .25 |
| 53 | A5 | 30sk | buff | .45 | .25 |
| 54 | A5 | 40sk | gray brn | .45 | .25 |
| 55 | A6 | 50sk | lt green | .45 | .25 |
| 56 | A6 | 60sk | violet & red | .45 | .25 |
| 57 | A6 | 75sk | bister & red | .45 | .25 |
| 58 | A8 | 1auk | gray & red | .45 | .25 |
| 59 | A8 | 3auk | lt brown & red | .45 | .30 |
| 60 | A8 | 5auk | blue grn & red | .45 | .45 |
| | | | *Nos. 50-60 (11)* | 4.95 | 3.00 |

Nos. 50-60 exist imperf. Value, pairs $150.

See Nos. 93-96. For surcharges see Nos. 114-115, 120-139, 149-150.

"Lithuania" Receiving Benediction — A9

The Spirit of Lithuania Rises — A10

"Lithuania" with Chains Broken — A11

White Knight — A12

**1920, Feb. 16** **Wmk. 146** ***Perf. 11½***

| | | | | | |
|---|---|---|---|---|---|
| 70 | A9 | 10sk | dp rose | 3.75 | *5.25* |
| 71 | A9 | 15sk | lt violet | 3.75 | *5.25* |
| 72 | A9 | 20sk | gray blue | 3.75 | *5.25* |
| 73 | A10 | 30sk | yellow brn | 3.75 | *5.25* |
| 74 | A11 | 40sk | brown & grn | 3.75 | *5.25* |
| 75 | A10 | 50sk | deep rose | 3.75 | *5.25* |
| 76 | A10 | 60sk | lt violet | 3.75 | *5.25* |
| 77 | A11 | 80sk | purple & red | 3.75 | *5.25* |
| 78 | A11 | 1auk | green & red | 3.75 | *5.25* |
| 79 | A12 | 3auk | brown & red | 3.75 | *5.25* |
| 80 | A12 | 5auk | green & red | 3.75 | *5.25* |
| a. | | | Right "5" dbl., grn and red | 90.00 | 90.00 |
| | | | *Nos. 70-80 (11)* | 41.25 | *57.75* |

Anniv. of natl. independence. The stamps were on sale only 3 days in Kaunas. The stamps were available in other cities after that. Only a limited number of stamps was sold at post offices but 40,000 sets were delivered to the bank of Kaunas.

All values exist imperforate.

White Knight — A13

Grand Duke Vytautas — A14

Grand Duke Gediminas A15

Sacred Oak and Altar A16

**1920, Aug. 25**

| | | | | |
|---|---|---|---|---|
| 81 | A13 | 10sk rose | .80 | 1.60 |
| a. | | Imperf., pair | 40.00 | |
| 82 | A13 | 15sk dark violet | .80 | 1.60 |
| 83 | A14 | 20sk grn & lt grn | .80 | 1.60 |
| 84 | A13 | 30sk brown | .80 | 1.60 |
| a. | | Pair, #82, 84 | 40.00 | |
| 85 | A15 | 40sk gray grn & vio | .80 | 1.60 |
| 86 | A14 | 50sk brn & brn org | 2.00 | 2.00 |
| 87 | A14 | 60sk red & org | .80 | 1.60 |
| 88 | A15 | 80sk blk, db & red | .80 | 1.60 |
| 89 | A16 | 1auk orange & blk | 1.25 | 1.60 |
| 90 | A16 | 3auk green & blk | 1.25 | 1.60 |
| 91 | A16 | 5auk gray vio & blk | 3.25 | 2.40 |
| | | *Nos. 81-91 (11)* | 13.35 | 18.80 |

Opening of Lithuanian National Assembly. On sale for three days.

**1920**

| | | | |
|---|---|---|---|
| 92 | A14 | 20sk green & lilac | 125.00 |
| 92A | A15 | 40sk gray grn, buff & vio | 125.00 |
| 92B | A14 | 50sk brown & gray lil | 125.00 |
| 92C | A14 | 60sk red & green | 125.00 |
| 92D | A15 | 80sk black, grn & red | 125.00 |
| | | *Nos. 92-92D (5)* | 625.00 |

Nos. 92 to 92D were trial printings. By order of the Ministry of Posts, 2,000 examples of each were placed on sale at post offices.

**Type of 1919 Issue**

**1920 Unwmk. *Perf. 11½***

| | | | | |
|---|---|---|---|---|
| 93 | A5 | 15sk lilac | 6.00 | 4.50 |
| 94 | A5 | 20sk deep blue | 6.00 | 4.50 |

**Wmk. 109**

| | | | | |
|---|---|---|---|---|
| 95 | A5 | 20sk deep blue | 5.00 | 5.00 |
| 96 | A5 | 40sk gray brown | 9.75 | 8.50 |
| | | *Nos. 93-96 (4)* | 26.75 | 22.50 |
| | | Set, never hinged | 40.00 | |

Watermark vertical or horizontal on Nos. 95-96.

No. 96 exists perf. 10½x11½.

**Imperf., Pairs**

| | | | | |
|---|---|---|---|---|
| *93a* | A5 | 15sk | 32.00 | 32.00 |
| *94a* | A5 | 20sk | 32.00 | 32.00 |
| *95a* | A5 | 20sk | 17.00 | 17.00 |
| *96a* | A5 | 40sk | 48.00 | 48.00 |

Sower A17

Peasant Sharpening Scythe A18

Prince Kestutis A19

Black Horseman A20

***Perf. 11, 11½ and Compound***

**1921-22**

| | | | | |
|---|---|---|---|---|
| 97 | A17 | 10sk brt rose | .85 | .55 |
| 98 | A17 | 15sk violet | .35 | *.70* |
| 99 | A17 | 20sk ultra | .25 | .25 |
| 100 | A18 | 30sk brown | 2.50 | *1.10* |
| 101 | A19 | 40sk red | .25 | .25 |
| 102 | A18 | 50sk olive | .35 | .25 |
| 103 | A18 | 60sk grn & vio | 2.50 | *1.65* |
| 104 | A19 | 80sk brn org & car | .35 | .25 |
| 105 | A19 | 1auk brown & grn | .35 | .25 |
| 106 | A19 | 2auk gray bl & red | .35 | .25 |
| 107 | A20 | 3auk yel brn & dk bl | 1.00 | .40 |
| 108 | A17 | 4auk yel & dk bl ('22) | .45 | .25 |
| 109 | A20 | 5auk gray blk & rose | 1.00 | *1.50* |
| 110 | A17 | 8auk grn & blk ('22) | .45 | .25 |
| 111 | A20 | 10auk rose & vio | 1.00 | .55 |
| 112 | A20 | 25auk bis brn & grn | 1.25 | *2.75* |
| 113 | A20 | 100auk dl red & gray blk | 12.50 | 8.00 |
| | | *Nos. 97-113 (17)* | 25.75 | 19.20 |
| | | Set, never hinged | 85.00 | |

**Imperf., Pairs**

| | | | | |
|---|---|---|---|---|
| *97a* | A17 | 10sk | — | |
| *98a* | A17 | 15sk | — | |
| *99a* | A17 | 20sk | — | |
| *100a* | A18 | 30sk | — | |
| *101a* | A19 | 40sk | 25.00 | |
| *102a* | A18 | 50sk | 25.00 | |
| *103a* | A18 | 60sk | — | |
| *104a* | A19 | 80sk | — | |
| *105a* | A19 | 1auk | — | |
| *106a* | A19 | 2auk | 120.00 | |
| *107a* | A20 | 3auk | 120.00 | |
| *109a* | A20 | 5auk | 120.00 | |
| *110a* | A17 | 8auk | 10.00 | 10.00 |
| *111a* | A20 | 10auk | 50.00 | |
| *112a* | A20 | 25auk | 50.00 | |
| *113a* | A20 | 100auk | 50.00 | |

For surcharges see Nos. 140-148, 151-160.

No. 57 Surcharged

***Perf. 12½x11½***

**1922, May Wmk. 145**

| | | | | |
|---|---|---|---|---|
| 114 | A6 | 4auk on 75sk bis & red | .90 | .25 |
| a. | | Inverted surcharge | 35.00 | 35.00 |

**Same with Bars over Original Value**

| | | | | |
|---|---|---|---|---|
| 115 | A6 | 4auk on 75sk bis & red | 4.00 | *8.00* |
| a. | | Double surcharge | 30.00 | 30.00 |

Povilas Luksis — A20a

Justinas Staugaitis, Antanas Smetona, Stasys Silingas — A20b

Portraits: 40s, Lt. Juozapavicius. 50s, Dr. Basanavicius. 60s, Mrs. Petkeviciute. 1auk, Prof. Voldemaras. 2auk, Pranas Dovidaitis. 3auk, Dr. Slezevicius. 4auk, Dr. Galvanauskas. 5auk, Kazys Grinius. 6auk, Dr. Stulginskis. 8auk, Pres. Smetona.

**1922 Litho. Unwmk.**

| | | | | |
|---|---|---|---|---|
| 116 | A20a | 20s blk & car rose | 1.25 | *2.10* |
| 116A | A20a | 40s bl grn & vio | 1.25 | *2.10* |
| 116B | A20a | 50s plum & grnsh bl | 1.25 | *2.10* |
| 117 | A20a | 60s pur & org | 1.25 | *2.10* |
| 117A | A20a | 1auk car & lt bl | 1.25 | *2.10* |
| 117B | A20a | 2auk dp bl & yel brn | 1.25 | *2.10* |
| c. | | Center inverted | 100.00 | 100.00 |
| 118 | A20a | 3auk mar & ultra | 1.25 | *2.10* |
| 118A | A20a | 4auk dk grn & red vio | 1.25 | *2.10* |
| 118B | A20a | 5auk blk brn & dp rose | 1.25 | *2.10* |
| 119 | A20a | 6auk dk bl & grnsh bl | 1.25 | *2.10* |
| a. | | Cliché of 8auk in sheet of 6auk | 175.00 | *175.00* |
| 119B | A20a | 8auk ultra & bis | 1.25 | *2.10* |
| 119C | A20b | 10auk dk vio & bl grn | 1.25 | *2.10* |
| | | *Nos. 116-119C (12)* | 15.00 | 25.20 |
| | | Set, never hinged | 45.00 | |

League of Nations' recognition of Lithuania. Sold only on Oct. 1, 1922.

Forty sheets of the 6auk each included eight examples of the 8auk.

**Stamps of 1919-22 Surcharged in Black, Carmine or Green On Nos. 37-39**

**1922 Wmk. 144 *Perf. 11½x12***

**Gray Granite Paper**

| | | | | |
|---|---|---|---|---|
| 120 | A7 | 3c on 1auk | 100.00 | *100.00* |
| 121 | A7 | 3c on 3auk | 100.00 | *100.00* |
| 122 | A7 | 3c on 5auk | 150.00 | *150.00* |
| | | *Nos. 120-122 (3)* | 350.00 | 350.00 |
| | | Set, never hinged | 750.00 | |

**White Paper**

***Perf. 14, 11½, 12½x11½***

**Wmk. 145**

| | | | | |
|---|---|---|---|---|
| 123 | A5 | 1c on 10sk red | .55 | 1.50 |
| 124 | A5 | 1c on 15sk lilac | .80 | 1.50 |
| 125 | A5 | 1c on 20sk dull bl | .50 | 1.50 |
| 126 | A5 | 1c on 30sk org | *250.00* | *110.00* |
| 127 | A5 | 1c on 30sk buff | .25 | .40 |
| 128 | A5 | 1c on 40sk gray brn | 1.60 | 1.50 |
| 129 | A6 | 2c on 50sk green | .70 | 1.50 |
| 130 | A6 | 2c on 60sk vio & red | .25 | .25 |
| 131 | A6 | 2c on 75sk bis & red | .40 | 1.50 |
| 132 | A8 | 3c on 1auk gray & red | .25 | .25 |
| 133 | A8 | 3c on 3auk brn & red | .25 | .25 |
| 134 | A8 | 3c on 5auk bl grn & red | .25 | .25 |
| | | *Nos. 123-125,127-134 (11)* | 5.80 | 10.40 |
| | | Set, never hinged, *Nos. 123-125, 127-134)* | 24.00 | |

**On Stamps of 1920**

**1922 Unwmk. *Perf. 11***

| | | | | |
|---|---|---|---|---|
| 136 | A5 | 1c on 20sk dp bl (C) | 3.75 | 2.00 |

**Wmk. Webbing (109)**

***Perf. 11, 11½***

| | | | | |
|---|---|---|---|---|
| 138 | A5 | 1c on 20sk dp bl (C) | 3.50 | 2.00 |
| 139 | A5 | 1c on 40sk gray brn (C) | 7.50 | 1.25 |

Stamps of 1921-22 Surcharged

| | | | | |
|---|---|---|---|---|
| 140 | A18 | 1c on 50sk ol (C) | .25 | .25 |
| a. | | Imperf., pair | 45.00 | |
| b. | | Inverted surcharge | 40.00 | |
| c. | | Double surch., one invtd. | | |
| 141 | A17 | 3c on 10sk | 11.00 | 8.00 |
| 142 | A17 | 3c on 15sk | .25 | .25 |
| 143 | A17 | 3c on 20sk | .40 | 1.50 |
| 144 | A18 | 3c on 30sk | 18.50 | 12.00 |
| 145 | A19 | 3c on 40sk | .40 | .40 |
| a. | | Imperf., pair | | |
| 146 | A18 | 5c on 50sk | .25 | .25 |
| 147 | A18 | 5c on 60sk | 18.50 | 18.50 |
| 148 | A19 | 5c on 80sk | .55 | .55 |
| a. | | Imperf., pair | 35.00 | 15.00 |

**Wmk. Wavy Lines (145)**

***Perf. 12½x11½***

| | | | | |
|---|---|---|---|---|
| 149 | A6 | 5c on 4auk on 75sk (No. 114) (G) | 1.60 | 10.00 |
| 150 | A6 | 5c on 4auk on 75sk (No. 115) (G) | 16.00 | 17.50 |

**Wmk. Webbing (109)**

***Perf. 11, 11½***

| | | | | |
|---|---|---|---|---|
| 151 | A19 | 10c on 1auk | .80 | .25 |
| a. | | Inverted surcharge | 55.00 | |
| 152 | A19 | 10c on 2auk | .25 | .25 |
| a. | | Inverted surcharge | 50.00 | |
| b. | | Imperf., pair | 45.00 | |
| 153 | A17 | 15c on 4auk | .25 | .25 |
| a. | | Inverted surcharge | 45.00 | |
| 154 | A20 | 25c on 3auk | 18.50 | 18.50 |
| 155 | A20 | 25c on 5auk | 11.00 | 5.00 |
| 156 | A20 | 25c on 10auk | 2.25 | 1.50 |
| a. | | Imperf., pair | 45.00 | |
| 157 | A17 | 30c on 8auk (C) | 1.15 | .35 |
| a. | | Inverted surcharge | 45.00 | 25.00 |
| 158 | A20 | 50c on 25auk | 3.75 | 2.50 |
| 160 | A20 | 1 l on 100auk | 4.00 | 2.50 |
| | | *Nos. 136-160 (23)* | 124.40 | 105.55 |
| | | Set, never hinged | 140.00 | |

A21

Ruin — A22

Seminary Church, Kaunas — A23

**1923 Litho. Wmk. 109 *Perf. 11***

| | | | | |
|---|---|---|---|---|
| 165 | A21 | 10c violet | 7.00 | .25 |
| 166 | A21 | 15c scarlet | 2.50 | .25 |
| 167 | A21 | 20c olive brown | 2.50 | .25 |
| 168 | A21 | 25c deep blue | 2.50 | .25 |
| 169 | A22 | 50c yellow green | 2.50 | .25 |
| 170 | A22 | 60c red | 2.50 | .25 |
| 171 | A23 | 1 l orange & grn | 10.50 | .25 |
| 172 | A23 | 3 l red & gray | 15.00 | .45 |
| 173 | A23 | 5 l brown & blue | 21.00 | 1.00 |
| | | *Nos. 165-173 (9)* | 66.00 | 3.20 |
| | | Set, never hinged | 125.00 | |

See Nos. 189-209, 281-282. For surcharges see Nos. B1-B42.

Memel Coat of Arms — A24

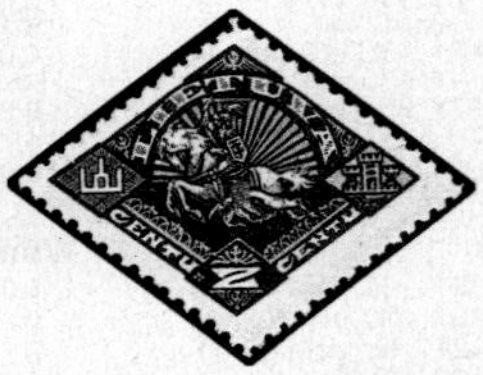
Lithuanian Coat of Arms — A25

Biruta Chapel — A26

Kaunas, War Memorial A27

Trakai Ruins A28

Memel Lighthouse — A29

Memel Harbor A30

*Perf. 11, 11½, 12*

**1923, Aug.** **Unwmk.**

| | | | | | |
|---|---|---|---|---|---|
| **176** | A24 | 1c | rose, grn & blk | 1.25 | 1.60 |
| **177** | A25 | 2c | dull vio & blk | 1.25 | 1.60 |
| **178** | A26 | 3c | yellow & blk | 1.25 | 1.60 |
| **179** | A24 | 5c | bl, buff & blk | 2.50 | 4.50 |
| **180** | A27 | 10c | orange & blk | 1.90 | 3.00 |
| **181** | A27 | 15c | green & blk | 1.90 | 3.00 |
| **182** | A28 | 25c | brt vio & blk | 1.90 | 3.00 |
| **183** | A25 | 30c | red vio & blk | 4.00 | *7.50* |
| **184** | A29 | 60c | ol grn & blk | 2.25 | *3.00* |
| **185** | A30 | 1 l | bl grn & blk | 2.25 | *3.00* |
| **186** | A26 | 2 l | red & black | 8.25 | 15.00 |
| **187** | A28 | 3 l | blue & black | 8.25 | 15.00 |
| **188** | A29 | 5 l | ultra & black | 8.25 | 15.00 |
| | | | *Nos. 176-188 (13)* | 45.20 | 76.80 |
| | | | Set, never hinged | 100.00 | |

This series was issued ostensibly to commemorate the incorporation of Memel with Lithuania.

**Type of 1923**

**1923** **Unwmk.** ***Perf. 11***

| | | | | | |
|---|---|---|---|---|---|
| **189** | A21 | 5c | pale green | 3.75 | .75 |
| **190** | A21 | 10c | violet | 5.00 | .75 |
| *a.* | | | Imperf., pair | 50.00 | |
| **191** | A21 | 15c | scarlet | 6.00 | .75 |
| *a.* | | | Imperf., pair | 50.00 | |
| **193** | A21 | 25c | blue | 10.00 | .75 |
| | | | *Nos. 189-193 (4)* | 24.75 | 3.00 |
| | | | Set, never hinged | 60.00 | |

**1923** **Wmk. 147**

| | | | | | |
|---|---|---|---|---|---|
| **196** | A21 | 2c | pale brown | 1.50 | .45 |
| **197** | A21 | 3c | olive bister | 2.25 | .45 |
| **198** | A21 | 5c | pale green | 2.25 | .45 |
| **199** | A21 | 10c | violet | 4.50 | .45 |
| **202** | A21 | 25c | deep blue | 11.00 | .45 |
| *a.* | | | Imperf., pair | 40.00 | |
| **204** | A21 | 36c | orange brown | 17.50 | 1.50 |
| | | | *Nos. 196-204 (6)* | 39.00 | 3.75 |
| | | | Set, never hinged | 70.00 | |

***Perf. 11½, 14½, 11½x14½***

**1923-25** **Wmk. 198**

| | | | | | |
|---|---|---|---|---|---|
| **207** | A21 | 25c | deep blue | 750.00 | 450.00 |
| **208** | A22 | 50c | deep green ('25) | *25.00* | 1.00 |
| **209** | A22 | 60c | carmine ('25) | *25.00* | .50 |

Double-barred Cross — A31

**1927, Jan.** ***Perf. 11½, 14½***

| | | | | | |
|---|---|---|---|---|---|
| **210** | A31 | 2c | orange | 1.50 | .35 |
| **211** | A31 | 3c | deep brown | 1.50 | .35 |
| **212** | A31 | 5c | green | 2.25 | .35 |
| *a.* | | | Imperf., pair | 25.00 | |
| **213** | A31 | 10c | violet | 3.25 | .35 |
| **214** | A31 | 15c | red | 3.25 | .35 |
| *a.* | | | Imperf., pair | 25.00 | |
| **215** | A31 | 25c | blue | 3.25 | .30 |
| | | | *Nos. 210-215 (6)* | 15.00 | 2.05 |
| | | | Set, never hinged | 45.00 | |

**1926-30** **Wmk. 147** ***Perf. 14½***

| | | | | | |
|---|---|---|---|---|---|
| **216** | A31 | 5c | green | 35.00 | *150.00* |
| **217** | A31 | 30c | blue ('30) | 30.00 | 10.00 |

See Nos. 233-240, 278-280.

Dr. Jonas Basanavicius — A32

**1927** **Unwmk.** ***Perf. 11½, 14½x11½***

| | | | | | |
|---|---|---|---|---|---|
| **219** | A32 | 15c | claret & blk | 3.00 | 1.50 |
| **220** | A32 | 25c | dull blue & blk | 3.00 | 1.50 |
| **221** | A32 | 50c | dk green & blk | 9.00 | 1.50 |
| **222** | A32 | 60c | dk violet & blk | 9.00 | 3.00 |
| | | | *Nos. 219-222 (4)* | 18.00 | 7.50 |
| | | | Set, never hinged | 35.00 | |

Dr. Jonas Basanavicius (1851-1927), patriot and folklorist.

National Arms — A33

**1927, Dec. 23** **Wmk. 109** ***Perf. 14½***

| | | | | | |
|---|---|---|---|---|---|
| **223** | A33 | 1 l | blue grn & gray | 6.50 | .80 |
| **224** | A33 | 3 l | vio & pale grn | 5.00 | .80 |
| **225** | A33 | 5 l | brown & gray | 6.00 | 1.40 |
| | | | *Nos. 223-225 (3)* | 17.50 | 3.00 |
| | | | Set, never hinged | 25.00 | |

Pres. Antanas Smetona — A34

Decade of Independence A35

Dawn of Peace — A36

**1928, Feb.** **Wmk. 109**

| | | | | | |
|---|---|---|---|---|---|
| **226** | A34 | 5c | org brn & grn | 1.00 | .75 |
| **227** | A34 | 10c | violet & blk | 1.25 | .75 |
| **228** | A34 | 15c | orange & brn | 1.25 | .75 |
| **229** | A34 | 25c | blue & indigo | 1.25 | .75 |
| **230** | A35 | 50c | ultra & dl vio | 1.50 | .75 |
| **231** | A35 | 60c | carmine & blk | 1.75 | .75 |
| **232** | A36 | 1 l | blk brn & drab | 2.00 | 2.25 |
| | | | *Nos. 226-232 (7)* | 10.00 | 6.75 |
| | | | Set, never hinged | 15.00 | |

10th anniv. of Lithuanian independence.

**Type of 1926**

**1929-31**

| | | | | | |
|---|---|---|---|---|---|
| **233** | A31 | 2c | orange ('31) | 12.00 | 1.60 |
| **234** | A31 | 5c | green | 4.00 | .35 |
| **235** | A31 | 10c | violet ('31) | 10.00 | 2.00 |
| **237** | A31 | 15c | red | 4.50 | .45 |
| *a.* | | | Tête bêche pair | 45.00 | 35.00 |
| **239** | A31 | 30c | dark blue | 6.00 | .45 |

**Unwmk.**

| | | | | | |
|---|---|---|---|---|---|
| **240** | A31 | 15c | red ('30) | 10.00 | .75 |
| | | | *Nos. 233-240 (6)* | 46.50 | 5.60 |
| | | | Set, never hinged | 85.00 | |

Grand Duke Vytautas A37

Grand Duke, Mounted A38

**1930, Feb. 16** ***Perf. 14***

| | | | | | |
|---|---|---|---|---|---|
| **242** | A37 | 2c | yel brn & dk brn | .30 | .25 |
| **243** | A37 | 3c | dk brn & vio | .30 | .25 |
| **244** | A37 | 5c | yel grn & dp org | .30 | .25 |
| **245** | A37 | 10c | vio & emer | .30 | .25 |
| **246** | A37 | 15c | dp rose & vio | .30 | .25 |
| **247** | A37 | 30c | dk bl & brn vio | .50 | .25 |
| **248** | A37 | 36c | brn vio & ol blk | .75 | .30 |
| **249** | A37 | 50c | dull grn & ultra | .50 | .35 |
| **250** | A37 | 60c | dk blue & rose | .50 | .40 |
| **251** | A38 | 1 l | bl grn, db & red brn | 2.10 | 1.00 |
| **252** | A38 | 3 l | dk brn, sal & dk vio | 3.25 | 1.75 |
| **253** | A38 | 5 l | ol brn, gray & red | 7.50 | 2.75 |
| **254** | A38 | 10 l | multicolored | 20.00 | 16.00 |
| **255** | A38 | 25 l | multicolored | 42.50 | 55.00 |
| | | | *Nos. 242-255 (14)* | 79.10 | 79.05 |
| | | | Set, never hinged | 200.00 | |

5th cent. of the death of the Grand Duke Vytautas.

Kaunas, Railroad Station A39

Cathedral at Vilnius — A39a

Designs: 15c, 25c, Landscape on the Neman River. 50c, Main Post Office, Kaunas.

**1932, July 21** **Wmk. 238** ***Perf. 14***

| | | | | | |
|---|---|---|---|---|---|
| **256** | A39 | 10c | dk red brn & ocher | .40 | *.40* |
| **257** | A39 | 15c | dk brown & ol | .40 | *.40* |
| **258** | A39 | 25c | dk blue & ol | 1.25 | *1.25* |
| **259** | A39 | 50c | gray blk & ol | 2.50 | 2.50 |
| **260** | A39a | 1 l | dk blue & ol | 6.50 | 6.50 |
| **261** | A39a | 3 l | red brn & gray grn | 6.50 | 6.50 |

**Wmk. 198**

| | | | | | |
|---|---|---|---|---|---|
| **262** | A39 | 5c | vio bl & ocher | .40 | *.40* |
| **263** | A39a | 60c | grnsh blk & lil | 6.50 | 6.50 |
| | | | *Nos. 256-263 (8)* | 24.45 | 24.45 |
| | | | Set, never hinged | 60.00 | |

**Imperf.**

| | | | | | |
|---|---|---|---|---|---|
| *256a* | A39 | 10c | dk red brn & ocher | .35 | .35 |
| *257a* | A39 | 15c | dk brown & ol | .65 | .65 |
| *258a* | A39 | 25c | dk blue & ol | 1.00 | 1.00 |
| *259a* | A39 | 50c | gray blk & ol | 2.00 | 2.00 |
| *260a* | A39a | 1 l | dk blue & ol | 5.25 | 5.25 |
| *261a* | A39a | 3 l | red brn & gray grn | 5.25 | 5.25 |
| *262a* | A39 | 5c | violet bl & ocher | .35 | .35 |
| *263a* | A39a | 60c | grnsh blk & lil | 5.25 | 5.25 |
| | | | Set, never hinged | 35.00 | |

Issued for the benefit of Lithuanian orphans.

In September, 1935, a red overprint was applied to No. 259: "ORO PASTAS / LITUANICA II / 1935 / NEW YORK-KAUNAS." Value, $400.

Vytautas Fleeing from Prison, 1382 A40

Designs: 15c, 25c, Conversion of Ladislas II Jagello and Vytautas (1386). 50c, 60c, Battle at Tannenberg (1410). 1 l, 3 l, Meeting of the Nobles (1429).

**1932** **Wmk. 209** ***Perf. 14***

| | | | | | |
|---|---|---|---|---|---|
| **264** | A40 | 5c | red & rose lake | .35 | *.35* |
| **265** | A40 | 10c | ol bis & org brn | .35 | *.35* |
| **266** | A40 | 15c | rose lil & ol grn | .35 | *.35* |
| **267** | A40 | 25c | dk vio brn & ocher | 1.00 | *1.00* |
| **268** | A40 | 50c | dp grn & bis brn | 1.00 | *1.00* |
| **269** | A40 | 60c | ol grn & brn car | 2.40 | *2.40* |
| **270** | A40 | 1 l | ultra & ol grn | 2.40 | *2.40* |
| **271** | A40 | 3 l | dk brn & dk grn | 2.40 | *2.40* |
| | | | *Nos. 264-271 (8)* | 10.25 | *10.25* |
| | | | Set, never hinged | 25.00 | |

**Imperf.**

| | | | | | |
|---|---|---|---|---|---|
| *264a* | A40 | 5c | red & rose lake | .65 | .65 |
| *265a* | A40 | 10c | ol bis & org brn | .65 | .65 |
| *266a* | A40 | 15c | rose lil & ol grn | .65 | .65 |
| *267a* | A40 | 25c | dk vio brn & ocher | 2.00 | 2.00 |
| *268a* | A40 | 50c | dp grn & bis brn | 4.50 | 4.50 |
| *269a* | A40 | 60c | ol grn & brn car | 4.50 | 4.50 |
| *270a* | A40 | 1 l | ultra & ol grn | 4.50 | 4.50 |
| *271a* | A40 | 3 l | dk brn & dk grn | 4.50 | 4.50 |
| | | | Set, never hinged | 35.00 | |

15th anniversary of independence.

A. Visteliauskas A41

Designs: 15c, 25c, Petras Vileisis. 50c, 60c, Dr. John Sliupas. 1 l, 3 l, Jonas Basanavicius.

**1933** ***Perf. 14***

| | | | | | |
|---|---|---|---|---|---|
| **272** | A41 | 5c | yel grn & car | .40 | .40 |
| **273** | A41 | 10c | ultra & car | .40 | .40 |
| **274** | A41 | 15c | orange & red | .40 | .40 |
| **275** | A41 | 25c | dk bl & blk brn | 1.25 | *1.25* |
| **276** | A41 | 50c | ol gray & dk bl | 1.25 | *1.25* |
| **277** | A41 | 60c | org brn & chnt | 5.50 | 5.50 |
| **277A** | A41 | 1 l | red & vio brn | 5.50 | 5.50 |
| **277B** | A41 | 3 l | turq grn & vio brn | 5.50 | 5.50 |
| | | | *Nos. 272-277B (8)* | 20.20 | 20.20 |
| | | | Set, never hinged | 35.00 | |

**Imperf.**

| | | | | | |
|---|---|---|---|---|---|
| *272a* | A41 | 5c | yel grn & car | .40 | .40 |
| *273a* | A41 | 10c | ultra & car | .40 | .40 |
| *274a* | A41 | 15c | orange & red | .40 | .40 |
| *275a* | A41 | 25c | dk bl & blk brn | 1.25 | 1.25 |
| *276a* | A41 | 50c | ol gray & dk bl | 1.25 | 1.25 |
| *277a* | A41 | 60c | org brn & chnt | 5.50 | 5.50 |
| *277Aa* | A41 | 1 l | red & vio brn | 5.50 | 5.50 |
| *277Ba* | A41 | 3 l | turq grn & vio brn | 5.50 | 5.50 |
| | | | Set, never hinged | 35.00 | |

50th anniv. of the 1st newspaper, "Ausra," in lithuanian language.

Mother and Child — A42

Designs: 15c, 25c, Boy reading. 50c, 60c, Boy playing with blocks. 1 l, 3 l, Woman and boy at the Spinning Wheel.

**1933, Sept.** ***Perf. 14***

| | | | | | |
|---|---|---|---|---|---|
| **277C** | A42 | 5c | dp yel grn & org brn | .35 | .35 |
| **277D** | A42 | 10c | rose brn & ultra | .35 | *.35* |
| **277E** | A42 | 15c | ol grn & plum | .35 | *.35* |
| **277F** | A42 | 25c | org & gray blk | 1.40 | *1.40* |
| **277G** | A42 | 50c | ol grn & car | 1.40 | *1.40* |
| **277H** | A42 | 60c | blk & yel org | 5.75 | 5.75 |
| **277I** | A42 | 1 l | dk brn & ultra | 5.75 | 5.75 |
| **277K** | A42 | 3 l | rose lil & ol grn | 5.75 | *5.75* |
| | | | *Nos. 277C-277K (8)* | 21.10 | *21.10* |
| | | | Set, never hinged | 35.00 | |

**Imperf.**

| | | | | | |
|---|---|---|---|---|---|
| *277Ca* | A42 | 5c | dp yel grn & org brn | .25 | .25 |
| *277Da* | A42 | 10c | rose brn & ultra | .25 | .25 |
| *277Ea* | A42 | 15c | ol grn & plum | .25 | .25 |
| *277Fa* | A42 | 25c | org & gray blk | 1.00 | 1.00 |
| *277Ga* | A42 | 50c | ol gray & dk bl | 1.00 | 1.00 |
| *277Ha* | A42 | 60c | org brn & chnt | 4.25 | 4.25 |
| *277Ia* | A42 | 1 l | dk brn & ultra | 4.25 | 4.25 |
| *277Ka* | A42 | 3 l | rose lil & ol grn | 4.25 | 4.25 |
| | | | Set, never hinged | 25.00 | |

Issued for the benefit of Lithuanian orphans.

### Types of 1923-26

**1933-34 Wmk. 238 *Perf. 14***

| | | | | |
|---|---|---|---|---|
| **278** | A31 2c orange | 42.50 | 6.50 |
| **279** | A31 10c dark violet | 60.00 | 9.50 |
| **280** | A31 15c red | 42.50 | 4.50 |
| **281** | A22 50c green | 42.50 | 9.50 |
| **282** | A22 60c red | 42.50 | 9.50 |
| | *Nos. 278-282 (5)* | 230.00 | 39.50 |
| | Set, never hinged | 400.00 | |

Pres. Antanas Smetona, 60th Birthday — A43

**1934 Engr. Unwmk. *Perf. 11½***

| | | | |
|---|---|---|---|
| **283** | A43 15c red | 6.50 | 1.50 |
| **284** | A43 30c green | 8.25 | 1.50 |
| **285** | A43 60c blue | 10.00 | 2.00 |
| | *Nos. 283-285 (3)* | 24.75 | 5.00 |
| | Set, never hinged | 42.50 | |

A44

Arms — A45

Girl with Wheat — A46

A47

Knight A48

**Wmk. 198; Wmk. 209 (35c, 10 l)**

**1934-35 Litho. *Perf. 14***

| | | | |
|---|---|---|---|
| **286** | A44 2c rose & dull org | 1.50 | .25 |
| **287** | A44 5c bl grn & grn | 1.50 | .25 |
| **288** | A45 10c chocolate | 3.50 | .25 |
| **289** | A46 25c dk brn & emer | 5.50 | .25 |
| **290** | A45 35c carmine | 5.50 | .25 |
| **291** | A46 50c dk blue & blue | 10.00 | .25 |
| **292** | A47 1 l salmon & mar | 92.50 | .25 |
| **293** | A47 3 l grn & gray grn | .45 | .25 |
| **294** | A48 5 l maroon & gray bl | .65 | .45 |
| **295** | A48 10 l choc & yel | 4.50 | 3.75 |
| | *Nos. 286-295 (10)* | 125.60 | 6.20 |
| | Set, never hinged | 275.00 | |

No. 290 exists imperf. Value, pair $65.
For overprint see No. 2N9.

**1936-37 Wmk. 238 *Perf. 14***
**Size: 17½x23mm**

| | | | |
|---|---|---|---|
| **296** | A44 2c orange ('37) | .40 | .30 |
| **297** | A44 5c green | .40 | .30 |

Pres. Smetona — A49

**1936-37 Unwmk.**

| | | | |
|---|---|---|---|
| **298** | A49 15c carmine | 5.50 | .35 |
| **299** | A49 30c green ('37) | 9.00 | .35 |
| **300** | A49 60c ultra ('37) | 10.00 | .35 |
| | *Nos. 298-300 (3)* | 24.50 | 1.05 |
| | Set, never hinged | 40.00 | |

Arms — A50

No. 304 exists in two types:
I — "50" is fat and broad, with "0" leaning to right.
II — "50" is thinner and narrower, with "0" straight.

### Paper with Gray Network

**1937-39 Wmk. 238 *Perf. 14***

| | | | |
|---|---|---|---|
| **301** | A50 10c green | .85 | .25 |
| **302** | A50 25c magenta | .25 | .25 |
| **303** | A50 35c red | .50 | .25 |
| **304** | A50 50c brown | .30 | .25 |
| **305** | A50 1 l dp vio bl ('39) | .35 | .45 |
| | *Nos. 301-305 (5)* | 2.25 | 1.45 |
| | Set, never hinged | 10.00 | |

For overprint see No. 2N10.

Jonas Basanavicius Reading Act of Independence A51

President Antanas Smetona A52

***Perf. 13x13½***

**1939, Jan. 15 Engr. Unwmk.**

| | | | |
|---|---|---|---|
| **306** | A51 15c dark red | .25 | *.30* |
| **307** | A52 30c deep green | .50 | .30 |
| **308** | A51 35c red lilac | .60 | .45 |
| **309** | A52 60c dark blue | .75 | .60 |
| *a.* | Souvenir sheet of 2, #308-309 | 5.00 | 10.00 |
| *b.* | As "a," imperf. | 35.00 | 45.00 |
| | *Nos. 306-309 (4)* | 2.10 | 1.65 |
| | Set, never hinged | 5.00 | |

20th anniv. of Independence.
Nos. 309a, 309b sold for 2 l.

Same Overprinted in Blue

**1939**

| | | | |
|---|---|---|---|
| **310** | A51 15c dark red | .50 | *.90* |
| **311** | A52 30c deep green | .50 | *.90* |
| **312** | A51 35c red lilac | 1.25 | 1.00 |
| **313** | A52 60c dark blue | 1.25 | 1.00 |
| | *Nos. 310-313 (4)* | 3.50 | 3.80 |
| | Set, never hinged | 7.00 | |

Recovery of Vilnius.

View of Vilnius A53

Gediminas — A54

Trakai Ruins A55

**Unwmk.**

**1940, May 6 Photo. *Perf. 14***

| | | | |
|---|---|---|---|
| **314** | A53 15c brn & pale brn | .40 | .25 |
| **315** | A54 30c dk grn & lt grn | .90 | .50 |
| **316** | A55 60c dk bl & lt bl | 2.00 | .70 |
| *a.* | Souv. sheet of 3, #314-316, imperf. | 8.00 | *16.00* |
| | *Nos. 314-316 (3)* | 3.30 | 1.45 |
| | Set, never hinged | 5.00 | |

Return of Vilnius to Lithuania, Oct. 10, 1939. Exist imperf.
No. 316a has simulated perforations in gold. Sold for 2 l.

White Knight — A56

Angel — A57

Woman Releasing Dove A58

Mother and Children A59

Liberty Bell — A60

Mythical Animal — A61

**1940**

| | | | |
|---|---|---|---|
| **317** | A56 5c brown carmine | .40 | *.30* |
| **318** | A57 10c green | .40 | *.45* |
| **319** | A58 15c dull orange | .40 | *.30* |
| **320** | A59 25c light brown | .40 | *.40* |
| **321** | A60 30c Prussian green | .40 | *.30* |
| **322** | A61 35c red orange | .40 | *.35* |
| | *Nos. 317-322 (6)* | 2.40 | *2.10* |
| | Set, never hinged | 4.50 | |

Nos. 317-322 exist imperf.
For overprints see Nos. 2N11-2N16.

**Catalogue values for unused stamps in this section, from this point to the end of the section, are for Never Hinged items.**

Nos. 371-399 were issued before the Soviet Union recognized the independence of Lithuania on Sept. 6, 1991, but were available and valid for use after that date.

Angel and Map — A66

Colors: 5k, Green. 10k, Brown violet. 20k, Blue. 50k, Red.

**1990, Oct. 7 Litho. *Imperf.***
**Without Gum**

| | | | |
|---|---|---|---|
| **371-374** | A66 Set of 4 | 1.75 | 1.75 |

### Simulated Perforations and Denomination in Brownish Gray

Colors as before.

**1990, Dec. 22 Without Gum**

| | | | |
|---|---|---|---|
| **375-378** | A66 Set of 4 | 1.60 | 1.60 |

White Knight "Vytis" — A67

Hill With Crosses, Siauliai — A68

Design: 200k, Liberty Bell.

**1991 Photo. *Perf. 14***

| | | | |
|---|---|---|---|
| **379** | A67 10k multi | .30 | .25 |
| **380** | A67 15k multi | .30 | .25 |
| **381** | A67 20k multi | .30 | .25 |
| **382** | A67 30k multi | .30 | .25 |
| **383** | A68 50k multi | .30 | .25 |
| **384** | A68 200k multi | .40 | .25 |

**Litho.**
***Imperf***
**Without Gum**

| | | | |
|---|---|---|---|
| **385** | A67 15k dl grn & blk | .30 | .25 |
| **386** | A67 25k brn & blk | .30 | .25 |
| **387** | A67 30k plum & blk | .30 | .25 |
| | *Nos. 379-387 (9)* | 2.80 | 2.25 |

Issued: 10k, 20k, No. 382, 50k, 200k, 1/10; No. 380, 3/15; No. 385, 3/13; 25k, No 387, 7/23.
No. 385 has a simulated outline of a perforated stamp.
See Nos. 411-418.

Liberty Statue — A69

**1991, Feb. 16 Photo. *Perf. 13¾x14***

| | | | |
|---|---|---|---|
| **388** | A69 20k multi | .50 | .25 |

Declaration of Independence from Soviet Union, 1st Anniv. — A70

**1991, Mar. 11 Litho. *Perf. 13¼x13***

| | | | |
|---|---|---|---|
| **389** | A70 20k multi | .50 | .25 |

Religious Symbols — A71

Designs: 40k, Crosses. 70k, Madonna. 100k, Spires, St. Anne's Church, Vilnius.

**1991, Mar. 15 Photo. *Perf. 13¾x14***

| | | | |
|---|---|---|---|
| **390-392** | A71 Set of 3 | 1.25 | .75 |

Resistance to Soviet and German Occupation, 50th Anniv. — A72

Designs: 20k, Candle, barbed wire. 50k, Heart, daggers. 70k, Sword, wreath.

**1991, June 14 Litho. *Perf. 13¼***
**393-395** A72 Set of 3 1.25 .75

Fourth World Lithuanian Games A73

Emblem and: 20k, Map. 50k+25k, Head.

**1991, July 27 Photo. *Perf. 13¼x13***
**396-397** A73 Set of 2 1.00 .50

Expedition to Mt. Everest — A74

Denominations: 20k, 70k.

**1991. Aug. 20 Litho. *Perf. 12½x13***
**398-399** A74 Set of 2 1.00 .75

A75

**1991, Sept. 28 Litho. *Perf. 13x13½***
**400** A75 30k Castle .50 .30
**401** A75 50k Grand Duke .50 .50
**402** A75 70k Early view of Vilnius 1.00 1.00
*Nos. 400-402 (3)* 2.00 1.80

Grand Duke Gediminas, 650th death anniv.

Ciconia Nigra — A76

Design: 50k, Grus grus.

**1991, Nov. 21 Litho. *Perf. 14***
**403** A76 30k +15k multi .90 .55
**404** A76 50k multicolored 1.00 .65

**White Knight Type of 1991**

**1991, Dec. 20 Photo. *Perf. 14***
**Background Colors**
**411** A67 40k black .25 .25
**412** A67 50k purple .25 .25
**415** A67 100k dark green .25 .25
**418** A67 500k blue 1.25 .55
*Nos. 411-418 (4)* 2.00 1.30

For surcharges see Nos. 450-452.

Lithuanian Admission to UN — A78

**1992, Mar. 15 Litho. *Perf. 13x13½***
**421** A78 100k multicolored .50 .30

Lithuanian Olympic Participation A79

Emblems: No. 422, Olympic Committee. No. 423, Albertville. No. 424, Barcelona.

**1992, Mar. 22**
**422** A79 50k +25k multi .30 .30
**423** A79 130k multi .45 .45
**424** A79 280k multi 1.25 1.25
*Nos. 422-424 (3)* 2.00 2.00

Surtax for Lithuanian Olympic Committee.

A80

200k, Cypripedium. 300k, Eringium maritimum.

**1992, July 11 *Perf. 12½x13***
**425** A80 200k multicolored .40 .30
**426** A80 300k multicolored .60 .50

A81

Birds of the Baltic Shores: No. 427, Pandion haliaetus. No. 428, Limosa limosa. No. 429, Mergus merganser. No. 430, Tadorna tadorna.

**Litho. & Engr.**

**1992, Oct. 3 *Perf. 12½x13***
**Booklet Stamps**
**427** A81 B grn & grnsh blk .70 .50
**428** A81 B grn & red brn .70 .50
**429** A81 B grn, red brn & brn .70 .50
**430** A81 B grn & red brn .70 .50
*a.* Booklet pane of 4, #427-430 3.50

Sold for 15r on day of issue.

See Estonia Nos. 231-234a, Latvia Nos. 332-335a and Sweden Nos. 1975-1978a.

Coats of Arms — A82

**1992, Oct. 11 Litho. *Perf. 14***
**431** A82 2r Kedainiai .25 .25
**432** A82 3r Vilnius .25 .25
**433** A82 10r National .55 .55
*Nos. 431-433 (3)* 1.05 1.05

See Nos. 454-456, 497-499, 521-522, 554-556, 586-588, 607-609, 642-644, 677-679, 704-706, 716-718, 736-740, 762-764, 788-789, 813-815, 833-835, 879-881, 887-889, 910-912, 945-947, 958-960.

19th Cent. Costumes — A83

Couples in different traditional costumes of the Suwalki region.

**1992, Oct. 18 *Perf. 13x13½***
**434** A83 2r multicolored .25 .25
**435** A83 5r multicolored .25 .25
**436** A83 7r multicolored .50 .35
*Nos. 434-436 (3)* 1.00 .85

See Nos. 465-467, 493-495, 511-513, 539-541.

Churches — A84

300k, Zapishkis Church, 16th cent. 1000k, Saints Peter & Paul Church, Vilnius, 17th cent. 1500k, Christ Church of the Resurrection, Kaunas, 1934.

**1993, Jan. 15 Litho. *Perf. 12***
**437** A84 300k bister & blk .30 .25
**438** A84 1000k blue green & blk .70 .25
**439** A84 1500k gray & blk 1.00 .30
*Nos. 437-439 (3)* 2.00 .80

See Nos. 502-504

Independence — A85

Designs: A, Jonas Basanavicius (1851-1927), journalist and politician. B, Jonas Vileisis (1872-1942), lawyer and politician.

**1993, Feb. 16**
**440** A85 (A) red & multi .25 .25
**441** A85 (B) green & multi .95 .65

No. 440 sold for 3r and No. 441 sold for 15r on day of issue.

See Nos. 479-480, 506-507, 536-537, 563-564, 592-593, 622-623, 660-661, 686-687, 711-712.

A86

Grand Duke Vytautas, 600th Birth Anniv. — A87

Designs: 500k, Royal Seal. 1000k, 5000k, Portrait. 1500k, Vytautas in Battle of Grunwald, by Jan Matejko.

**1993, Feb. 27**
**442** A86 500k bister, red & blk .30 .25
**443** A87 1000k citron, blk & red .70 .30
**444** A87 1500k lem, blk & red 1.00 .50
*Nos. 442-444 (3)* 2.00 1.05

**Souvenir Sheet**
**445** A87 5000k citron, black & red 2.00 2.00

Famous Lithuanians A88

Designs: 1000k, Simonas Daukantas (1793-1864), educator and historian. 2000k, Vydunas (1868-1953), preserver of Lithuanian traditional culture. 4500k, Vincas Mykolaitis Putinas (1893-1967), philosopher and psychologist.

**1993, Mar. 13**
**446** A88 1000k multicolored .25 .25
**447** A88 2000k multicolored .50 .50
**448** A88 4500k multicolored 1.25 .90
*Nos. 446-448 (3)* 2.00 1.65

See Nos. 475-477, 514-516, 533-535, 560-562, 599-601, 624-626.

No. 382, 387 and 411 Surcharged

**1993 Photo, Litho. (#451) *Perf. 14***
**450** A67 100k on 30k magenta .25 .25
**451** A67 100k on 30k magenta, imperf, without gum .50 .25
**452** A67 300k on 40k #411 .25 .25
*Nos. 450-452 (3)* 1.00 .75

Issued: 300k, 1/19; No. 450, 1/26; No. 451, 3/10.

**Coat of Arms Type of 1992**
Size: 24x31mm

**1993, July 3 Litho. *Perf. 11***
**454** A82 5c Skuodas .25 .25
*a.* Tete-beche pair .40 .40
**455** A82 30c Telsiai .35 .30
*a.* Tete-beche pair 1.20 .60
**456** A82 50c Klaipeda .55 .45
*a.* Tete-beche pair 1.70 .90
*Nos. 454-456 (3)* 1.15 1.00

World Lithuanian Unity Day — A89

5c, The Spring, by M. K. Ciurlionis. 80c, Capts. Steponas Darius and Stasys Girenas.

**1993, July 17 *Perf. 13***
**457** A89 5c multicolored .25 .25
*a.* Tete-beche pair .30
**458** A89 80c multicolored .75 .75
*a.* Tete-beche pair 2.40

Deaths of Darius and Girenas, 60th anniv. (No. 458).

Natl. Arms — A90

**1993, July 21 Litho. *Perf. 13x12½***
**459** A90 (A) bister & multi .30 .25
**460** A90 (B) green & multi .80 .25

No. 459 sold for 5c, No. 460 for 80c on day of issue.
Dated 1992.

Visit of Pope John Paul II — A91

**1993, Sept. 3 Litho.** *Perf. 13½x13*

| | | | | |
|---|---|---|---|---|
| **461** | A91 | 60c Kryziu Kalnas | .50 | .30 |
| **462** | A91 | 60c Siluva | .50 | .30 |
| **463** | A91 | 80c Vilnius | .70 | .35 |
| **464** | A91 | 80c Kaunas | .70 | .35 |
| | | *Nos. 461-464 (4)* | 2.40 | 1.30 |

### Natl. Costumes Type of 1992

Couples in different traditional costumes of the Dzukai.

**1993, Oct. 30 Litho.** *Perf. 12*

**Size: 23x36mm**

| | | | | |
|---|---|---|---|---|
| **465** | A83 | 60c multicolored | .40 | .25 |
| **466** | A83 | 80c multicolored | .60 | .35 |
| **467** | A83 | 1 l multicolored | 1.00 | .45 |
| | | *Nos. 465-467 (3)* | 2.00 | 1.05 |

Lithuanian Postal System, 75th Anniv. — A92

Post offices: No. 468, Klaipeda. No. 469, Kaunas. 80c, Vilnius. 1 l, No. 1.

**1993, Nov. 16**

| | | | | |
|---|---|---|---|---|
| **468** | A92 | 60c multicolored | .40 | .25 |
| **469** | A92 | 60c multicolored | .40 | .25 |
| **470** | A92 | 80c multicolored | .60 | .30 |
| **471** | A92 | 1 l multicolored | .90 | .40 |
| | | *Nos. 468-471 (4)* | 2.30 | 1.20 |

Europa — A93

80c, The Old Master, by A. Gudaitis, 1939.

**1993, Dec. 24 Litho.** *Perf. 12*

| | | | | |
|---|---|---|---|---|
| **472** | A93 | 80c multicolored | 2.00 | 1.40 |
| *a.* | | Tete-beche pair | 4.00 | 4.00 |

Endangered Species — A94

**1993, Dec. 30 Litho.** *Perf. 12*

| | | | | |
|---|---|---|---|---|
| **473** | A94 | 80c Emys orbicularis | .60 | .30 |
| **474** | A94 | 1 l Bufo calamita | 1.00 | .40 |

See Nos. 500-501, 519-520.

### Famous Lithuanians Type of 1993

Designs: 60c, Kristijonas Donelaitis (1714-80), poet. 80c, Vincas Kudirka (1858-99), physician, writer. 1 l, Maironis (1862-1932), poet.

**1994, Mar. 26 Litho.** *Perf. 12*

| | | | | |
|---|---|---|---|---|
| **475** | A88 | 60c multicolored | .40 | .25 |
| **476** | A88 | 80c multicolored | .65 | .30 |
| **477** | A88 | 1 l multicolored | 1.00 | .40 |
| | | *Nos. 475-477 (3)* | 2.05 | .95 |

1994 Winter Olympics, Lillehammer A95

**1994, Feb. 11**

| | | | | |
|---|---|---|---|---|
| **478** | A95 | 1.10 l multicolored | 1.00 | .40 |

### Independence Type of 1993

No. 479, Pres. Antanas Smetona (1874-1944). No. 480, Aleksandras Stulginskis.

**1994, Feb. 16**

| | | | | |
|---|---|---|---|---|
| **479** | A85 | 1 l red brown & multi | .80 | .35 |
| **480** | A85 | 1 l brown & multi | .80 | .35 |

A96

Natl. Arms — A96a

*Perf. 12, 13½ (40c), 13½x13 (50c)*

**1994-97 Litho.**

| | | | | |
|---|---|---|---|---|
| **481** | A96 | 5c dark brown | .25 | .25 |
| **482** | A96 | 10c deep violet | .25 | .25 |
| **483** | A96 | 20c dark green | .25 | .25 |
| **484** | A96 | 40c deep rose mag | .25 | .25 |
| **485** | A96 | 50c green blue | .30 | .25 |
| **486** | A96a | 1 l gray & multi | .50 | .25 |
| *a.* | | Souvenir sheet of 4 | 3.00 | 3.00 |
| **487** | A96a | 2 l buff & multi | 1.90 | .50 |
| **488** | A96a | 3 l green & multi | 2.50 | .75 |
| | | *Nos. 481-488 (8)* | 6.20 | 2.75 |

Independence, 5th anniv. (No. 486a).

Issued: 5c, 10c, 4/9/94; 20c, 11/19/94; 2 l, 3 l, 7/23/94; 1 l, 3/11/95; 40c, 5/4/96; 50c, 4/5/97.

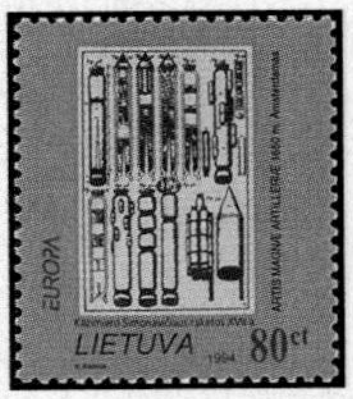


Europa — A97

80c, Artillery rockets, 17th cent.

**1994, May 7 Litho.** *Perf. 12*

| | | | | |
|---|---|---|---|---|
| **491** | A97 | 80c multicolored | .50 | .40 |

Souvenir Sheet

100th Postage Stamp — A98

**1994, May 21 Litho.** *Perf. 12*

| | | | | |
|---|---|---|---|---|
| **492** | A98 | 10 l multicolored | 10.00 | 10.00 |

No. 492 sold for 12 l.

### Natl. Costumes Type of 1992

Couples in different traditional costumes of Samogitia.

**1994, June 25 Litho.** *Perf. 12*

| | | | | |
|---|---|---|---|---|
| **493** | A83 | 5c multicolored | .30 | .25 |
| **494** | A83 | 80c multicolored | .60 | .25 |
| **495** | A83 | 1 l multicolored | .70 | .30 |
| | | *Nos. 493-495 (3)* | 1.60 | .80 |

Lithuanian World Song Festival — A99

**1994, July 6**

| | | | | |
|---|---|---|---|---|
| **496** | A99 | 10c multicolored | .50 | .25 |

### Coat of Arms Type of 1992

**1994, Sept. 10 Litho.** *Perf. 12*

**Size: 25x32mm**

| | | | | |
|---|---|---|---|---|
| **497** | A82 | 10c Punia | .25 | .25 |
| **498** | A82 | 60c Alytus | .45 | .25 |
| **499** | A82 | 80c Perloja | .60 | .30 |
| | | *Nos. 497-499 (3)* | 1.30 | .80 |

### Endangered Species Type of 1993

**1994, Oct. 22 Litho.** *Perf. 12*

| | | | | |
|---|---|---|---|---|
| **500** | A94 | 20c Nyctalus noctula | .35 | .25 |
| **501** | A94 | 20c Glis glis | .35 | .25 |

### Church Type of 1993

**1994, Nov. 12**

| | | | | |
|---|---|---|---|---|
| **502** | A84 | 10c Kaunus, 16th cent. | .25 | .25 |
| **503** | A84 | 60c Kedainiu, 17th cent. | .45 | .25 |
| **504** | A84 | 80c Vilnius, 18th cent. | .60 | .35 |
| | | *Nos. 502-504 (3)* | 1.30 | .85 |

Christmas A101

**1994, Dec. 3 Litho.** *Perf. 12*

| | | | | |
|---|---|---|---|---|
| **505** | A101 | 20c multicolored | .25 | .25 |

### Independence Type of 1993

No. 506, Pranas Dovydaitis. No. 507, Steponas Kairys.

**1995, Feb. 16 Litho.** *Perf. 12*

| | | | | |
|---|---|---|---|---|
| **506** | A85 | 20c multicolored | .25 | .25 |
| **507** | A85 | 20c multicolored | .25 | .25 |

A102

Via Baltica Highway Project: Nos. 508, 509c, Kaunas, Lithuania: No. 509a, Beach Hotel, Parnu, Estonia. No. 509b, Castle, Bauska, Latvia.

**1995, Apr. 20 Litho.** *Perf. 14*

| | | | | |
|---|---|---|---|---|
| **508** | A102 | 20c multicolored | .25 | .25 |

**Souvenir Sheet**

| | | | | |
|---|---|---|---|---|
| **509** | A102 | 1 l Sheet of 3, #a.-c. | 2.50 | 2.50 |

See Estonia Nos. 288-289, Latvia Nos. 394-395.

Sculpture, Mother's School — A103

**1995, Apr. 29 Litho.** *Perf. 12*

| | | | | |
|---|---|---|---|---|
| **510** | A103 | 1 l multicolored | 1.00 | 1.00 |

Europa.

### Natl. Costumes Type of 1992

Couples in traditional costumes of Aukstaiciai.

**1995, May 20 Litho.** *Perf. 12*

| | | | | |
|---|---|---|---|---|
| **511** | A83 | 20c multicolored | .25 | .25 |
| **512** | A83 | 70c multicolored | .60 | .25 |
| **513** | A83 | 1 l multicolored | .75 | .30 |
| | | *Nos. 511-513 (3)* | 1.60 | .80 |

### Famous People Type of 1993

Writers: 30c, Motiejus Valancius (1801-75). 40c, Zemaite (1845-1921). 70c, Kipras Petrauskas (1885-1968).

**1995, May 27 Litho.** *Perf. 12*

| | | | | |
|---|---|---|---|---|
| **514** | A88 | 30c multicolored | .25 | .25 |
| **515** | A88 | 40c multicolored | .40 | .25 |
| **516** | A88 | 70c multicolored | .60 | .25 |
| | | *Nos. 514-516 (3)* | 1.25 | .75 |

Day of Mourning & Hope — A104

**1995, June 14 Litho.** *Perf. 12*

| | | | | |
|---|---|---|---|---|
| **517** | A104 | 20c multicolored | .25 | .25 |

5th World Sports Games — A105

**1995, July 30 Litho.** *Perf. 12*

| | | | | |
|---|---|---|---|---|
| **518** | A105 | 30c multicolored | .25 | .25 |

### Endangered Species Type of 1993

**1995, Aug. 26 Litho.** *Perf. 12*

| | | | | |
|---|---|---|---|---|
| **519** | A94 | 30c Arctia villica | .40 | .25 |
| **520** | A94 | 30c Baptria tibiale | .40 | .25 |

### Coat of Arms Type of 1992

Size: 25x32mm

Arms of villages in Suvalkija: 40c, Virbalis. 1 l, Kudirkos Naumiestis, horiz.

**1995, Sept. 16 Litho.** *Perf. 12*

| | | | | |
|---|---|---|---|---|
| **521** | A82 | 40c multicolored | .30 | .25 |
| **522** | A82 | 1 l multicolored | .75 | .30 |

Valerie Mesalina, by Franciskus Smuglevicius — A106

**1995, Oct. 6 Litho.** *Perf. 12½*

| | | | | |
|---|---|---|---|---|
| **523** | A106 | 40c multicolored | .50 | .25 |

Castles — A107

**1995, Nov. 18** *Perf. 11½x12*

| | | | | |
|---|---|---|---|---|
| **524** | A107 | 40c Vilnius | .30 | .25 |
| **525** | A107 | 70c Trakai | .60 | .30 |
| **526** | A107 | 1 l Birzai | .90 | .45 |
| | | *Nos. 524-526 (3)* | 1.80 | 1.00 |

Christmas A108

Designs: 40c, People celebrating Christmas in outdoor snow scene. 1 l, People with lanterns walking toward church.

**1995, Dec. 2 Litho. *Perf. 13***

**527** A108 40c multicolored .30 .25
**528** A108 1 l multicolored .75 .45

Bison Bonasus A109

**1996, Jan. 20 *Perf. 13x13½***

**529** A109 30c shown .25 .25
**530** A109 40c Two adults .40 .25
**531** A109 70c Adult, calf .60 .40
**532** A109 1 l Two adults, calf .80 .80
*a.* Miniature sheet, 2 each #529-532 4.50 4.50
*Nos. 529-532 (4)* 2.05 1.70

World Wildlife Fund.

### Famous Lithuanians Type of 1993

Designs: 40c, Kazys Grinius (1866-1950). No. 534, Antanas Zmudzinavicius (1876-1966). No. 535, Balys Sruoga (1896-1947).

**1996, Feb. 2 Litho. *Perf. 13x13½***

**533** A88 40c multicolored .30 .25
**534** A88 1 l multicolored .60 .40
**535** A88 1 l multicolored .60 .40
*Nos. 533-535 (3)* 1.50 1.05

### Independence Type of 1993

No. 536, Vladas Mironas. No. 537, Jurgis Saulys.

**1996, Feb. 16 Litho. *Perf. 13½x13***

**536** A85 40c gray, blk & buff .30 .25
**537** A85 40c olive, blk & buff .30 .25

Barbora Radvilaite (1520-51) — A110

**1996, Apr. 27 Litho. *Perf. 13½x13***

**538** A110 1 l multicolored 1.00 1.00

Europa.

### 19th Cent. Costumes Type of 1992

Couples in different traditional costumes of the Klaipeda region: No. 540, Man in blue coat. No. 541, Man wearing wooden shoes.

**1996, May 25 Litho. *Perf. 13½***

**539** A83 40c multicolored .35 .25
**540** A83 1 l multicolored .75 .35
**541** A83 1 l multicolored .75 .35
*Nos. 539-541 (3)* 1.85 .95

Day of Mourning and Hope — A116

**1996, June 14 Litho. *Perf. 13½***

**547** A116 40c Christ .40 .25
**548** A116 40c Angel .40 .25

A117

Designs: No. 549, Greek discus thrower. No. 550, Basketball players.

**1996, July 19 *Perf. 13½x13***

**549** A117 1 l multicolored 1.00 .50
**550** A117 1 l multicolored 1.00 .50

1996 Summer Olympic Games, Atlanta.

Paintings, by M.K. Ciurlionis — A118

No. 551, Kapines, 1909. No. 552, Auka, 1909.

No. 553: a, Andante, 1908. b, Allegro, 1908.

**1996, Sept. 21 Litho. *Perf. 13½x13***

**551** A118 40c multicolored .35 .25
**552** A118 40c multicolored .35 .25

### Souvenir Sheet

***Perf. 12½x11½***

**553** A118 3 l Sheet of 2, #a.-b. 5.00 5.00

No. 553 contains 26x53mm stamps.

### Coat of Arms Type of 1992

Size: 25x33mm

**1996, Oct. 19 Litho. *Perf. 13½x13***

**554** A82 50c Seduva .45 .25
**555** A82 90c Panevezys .65 .35
**556** A82 1.20 l Zarasai .90 .50
*Nos. 554-556 (3)* 2.00 1.10

Souvenir Sheet

Lithuanian Basketball Team, Bronze Medalists, 1996 Summer Olympic Games, Atlanta — A119

**1996, Nov. 16 *Perf. 12½***

**557** A119 4.20 l multicolored 3.50 3.50

Christmas A120

**1996, Nov. 30 *Perf. 13½x13***

**558** A120 50c Angels .35 .25
**559** A120 1.20 l Santa on horse 1.00 .50

### Famous Lithuanians Type of 1993

Designs: 50c, Ieva Simonaityte (1897-1978). 90c, Jonas Sliupas (1861-1944). 1.20 l, Vladas Jurgutis (1885-1966).

**1997, Jan. 23 Litho. *Perf. 13x13½***

**560** A88 50c brown & greem .40 .25
**561** A88 90c gray & yellow .70 .35
**562** A88 1.20 l blue green & orange .90 .45
*Nos. 560-562 (3)* 2.00 1.05

### Independence Type of 1993

No. 563, Mykolas Birziska. No. 564, Kazimieras Saulys.

**1997, Feb. 16 Litho. *Perf. 13½x13***

**563** A85 50c multicolored .35 .25
**564** A85 50c multicolored .35 .25

First Lithuanian Book, 450th Anniv. — A121

**1997, Feb. 15 Litho. *Perf. 13½x13***

**565** A121 50c gray & red .45 .25

### Souvenir Sheet

**566** A121 4.80 l like #565 3.50 3.50

No. 566 contains one 29x38mm stamp.

Souvenir Sheet

Flag on Mountain Top — A122

**1997, Feb. 25 *Perf. 11½x12½***

**567** A122 4.80 l multicolored 4.00 4.00

Expeditions to highest peaks on each continent.

Stories and Legends A123

Children's drawings: No. 568, Girl, horse. No. 569, King, moon, stars, bird, vert.

**1997, Apr. 12 Litho. *Perf. 13***

**568** A123 1.20 l multicolored 1.00 1.00
**569** A123 1.20 l multicolored 1.00 1.00

Europa.

A124

**1997, May 9 Litho. *Perf. 13***

**570** A124 50c multicolored .45 .25

First Lithuanian School, 600th Anniv.

A125

Old Ships of the Baltic Sea: 50c, Kurenas, 16th cent.

No. 572: a, Kurenas, 16th cent., diff. b, Maasilinn ship, 16th cent. c, Linijkugis, 17th cent.

**1997, May 10 *Perf. 14x14½***

**571** A125 50c multicolored .45 .25
**572** A125 1.20 l Sheet of 3, #a.-c. 3.00 3.00

See Estonia Nos. 322-323, Latvia Nos. 443-444.

Palanga Botanical Park, Cent. — A126

**1997, June 1 Litho. *Perf. 13½x13***

**573** A126 50c multicolored .45 .25
*a.* Tete-beche pair .90 .90

Numbers 574-577 are unassigned.

2nd Baltic Sea Games — A127

**1997, June 25 Litho. *Perf. 13½***

**578** A127 90c multicolored .75 .35

Museum Art A128

Designs: 90c, Animal face carved on ritual staff. 1.20 l, Coins, 15th cent.

**1997, July 12 *Perf. 13½x13***

**579** A128 90c multicolored .75 .35
**580** A128 1.20 l multicolored 1.00 .50

Double Barred Crosses — A129

**1997, Aug. 2 Litho. *Perf. 13½***

**581** A129 20c olive .30 .25
**582** A129 50c brown .50 .25
*a.* Inscribed "1998" .50 .25

Nos. 581 and 582 are inscribed "1997." See Nos. 602, 604, 617-619.

Mushrooms
A130

Designs: No. 583, Morchella elata. No. 584, Boletus aereus.

**1997, Sept. 20 Litho. *Perf. 13½x13***

**583** A130 1.20 l multicolored 1.00 .50
*a.* Tete-beche pair 2.00 2.00
**584** A130 1.20 l multicolored 1.00 .50
*a.* Tete-beche pair 2.00 2.00

Letters of Grand Duke Gediminas
A131

**1997, Oct. 4 *Perf. 14***

**585** A131 50c multicolored .50 .25

**Coat of Arms Type of 1992**

Size: 25x33mm

**1997, Oct. 18 Litho. *Perf. 13½x13***

**586** A82 50c Neringa .45 .25
**587** A82 90c Vilkaviskis .80 .35
**588** A82 1.20 l Pasvalys 1.00 .45
*Nos. 586-588 (3)* 2.25 1.05

Christmas and New Year — A132

**1997, Nov. 22 Litho. *Perf. 13***

**589** A132 50c shown .40 .25
**590** A132 1.20 l Snow on trees 1.00 .50

1998 Winter Olympic Games, Nagano — A133

**1998, Jan. 17 Litho. *Perf. 14***

**591** A133 1.20 l multicolored 1.00 .45
*a.* Tete-beche pair 2.00 2.00

**Independence Type of 1993 and**

Declaration of Independence — A134

Designs: 50c, Alfonsas Petrulis. 90c, Jokubas Sernas.

***Perf. 13½x12½***

**1998, Feb. 16 Litho.**

**592** A85 50c olive and black .35 .25
**593** A85 90c brown and black .65 .40

**Souvenir Sheet**

***Perf. 12½x11½***

**594** A134 6.60 l multicolored 5.00 5.00

Independence, 80th anniv.

Souvenir Sheet

National Anthem, Cent. — A135

**1998, Feb. 16 *Perf. 12½***

**595** A135 5.20 l multicolored 4.00 4.00

Antanas Gustaitis, Aviator, Birth Cent.
A136

Designs: 2 l, Portrait of Gustaitis, ANBO 41. 3 l, Design drawings, ANBO-VIII.

**1998, Mar. 27 Litho. *Perf. 14***

**596** A136 2 l multicolored 1.50 .85
**597** A136 3 l multicolored 2.50 1.10

Natl. Song Festival — A137

**1998, Apr. 18 *Perf. 13½***

**598** A137 1.20 l multicolored 1.25 1.25
*a.* Tete-beche pair 3.25 3.25

Europa.

**Famous Lithuanians Type of 1993**

50c, Tadas Ivanauskas (1882-1971), scientist. No. 600, Jurgis Baltrusaitis (1873-1944), writer, Jurgis Baltrusaitis (1903-88), historian. No. 601, Stasys Lozoraitis (1898-1983), Stasys Lozoraitis (1924-94), politicians.

**1998, Apr. 25 *Perf. 13x13½***

**599** A88 50c multicolored .40 .25

**Size: 45x26mm**

**600** A88 90c multicolored .70 .35
**601** A88 90c multicolored .70 .35
*Nos. 599-601 (3)* 1.80 .95

**Double-Barred Crosses Type of 1997**

**1998, June 1 Litho. *Perf. 13½***

**602** A129 70c yellow bister .65 .30
*a.* Inscribed "1999" .90 .30

No. 602 is inscribed "1998."

2nd Lithuanian Olympic Games, 6th World Lithuanian Games
A138

**1998, June 23 *Perf. 14***

**603** A138 1.35 l multicolored 1.00 .55
*a.* Tete beche pair 2.00 2.00

**Double-Barred Crosses Type of 1997**

**1998, July 4 Litho. *Perf. 13½***

**604** A129 35c plum & pink .30 .25

Red Book of Lithuania
A139

Fish: No. 605, Coregonus lavaretus holsatus. No. 606, Salmo salar.

**1998, July 11 *Perf. 13x13½***

**605** A139 1.40 l multicolored 1.10 .55
**606** A139 1.40 l multicolored 1.10 .55

**Coat of Arms Type of 1992**

Size: 25x33mm

**1998, Sept. 12 Litho. *Perf. 13***

**607** A82 70c Kernave .50 .25
**608** A82 70c Trakai .50 .25
**609** A82 1.35 l Kaunas 1.00 .55
*Nos. 607-609 (3)* 2.00 1.05

Vilnius-Cracow Post Route Established, 1562 — A141

**1998, Oct. 9 Litho. *Perf. 14***

**611** A141 70c multicolored .60 .30

Souvenir Sheet

Lithuanian Post, 80th Anniv. — A142

**1998, Oct. 9 Litho. *Perf. 12***

**612** A142 13 l multicolored 10.00 10.00

No. 612 contains a holographic image. Soaking in water may affect the hologram.

Museum Paintings — A143

70c, "Through the Night," by Antanas Zmuidzinavicius (1876-1966). 1.35 l, "The Garden of Bernardines, Vilnius," by Juozapas Marsevskis (1825-83).

**1998, Oct. 17 Litho. *Perf. 13½x13***

**613** A143 70c multicolored .60 .30
**614** A143 1.35 l multicolored 1.00 .50

New Year — A144

Christmas: 1.35 l, Winter scene, people walking through giant tree, village.

**1998, Nov. 14 Litho. *Perf. 12½***

**615** A144 70c multicolored .50 .25
**616** A144 1.35 l multicolored 1.10 .55

**Double-Barred Crosses Type of 1997**

**1998, Nov. 14 Litho. *Perf. 13½***

**617** A129 5c lt & dk citron .25 .25
*a.* Inscribed "1999" .25 .25
**618** A129 10c tan & brown .25 .25
*a.* Inscribed "1999" .25 .25
**619** A129 20c lt & dk olive green .25 .25
*a.* Inscribed "1999" .25 .25
*Nos. 617-619 (3)* .75 .75

Nos. 617-619 inscribed "1998."

Adam Mickiewicz (1798-1855), Poet — A145

**1998, Dec. 24 *Perf. 14***

**620** A145 70c multicolored .60 .30
*a.* Tete beche pair 1.25 1.25

Souvenir Sheet

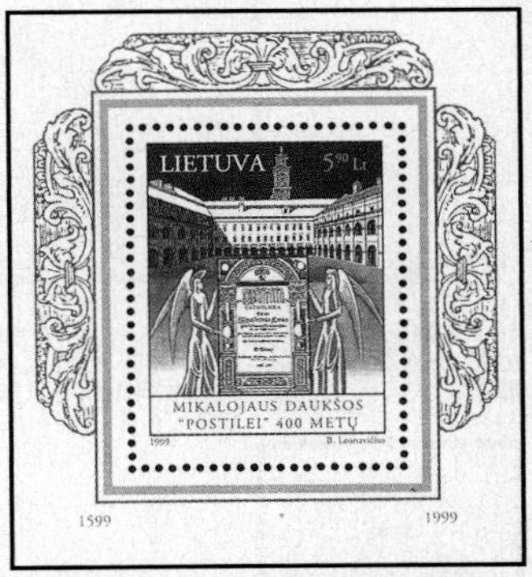


Publication of "Postile," by M. Dauksa (1527-1613), 400th Anniv. — A146

**1999, Jan. 23 Litho. *Perf. 12½***

**621** A146 5.90 l brown & gray 5.00 5.00

**Independence Type of 1993**

Designs: No. 622, Petras Klimas. No. 623, Donatas Malinauskas.

***Perf. 13½x12½***

**1999, Feb. 16 Litho.**

**622** A85 70c red & black .50 .30
**623** A85 70c blue & black .50 .30

**Famous Lithuanians Type of 1993**

Designs: No. 624, Juozas Matulis (1899-1993). No. 625, Augustinas Gricius (1899-1972). 1.35 l, Pranas Skardzius (1899-1975).

**1999, Mar. 19 Litho. *Perf. 13***

**624** A88 70c multicolored .50 .30
**625** A88 70c multicolored .50 .30
**626** A88 1.35 l multicolored 1.00 .55
*Nos. 624-626 (3)* 2.00 1.15

NATO, 50th Anniv. — A147

**1999, Mar. 27 Litho. *Perf. 13¾x14***

**627** A147 70c multicolored .60 .30

National Parks — A148

Europa: No. 628, Traditional homes, lake, islands, Aukotaitija Natl. Park. No. 629, Sand dunes, amber, Curonian Spit Natl. Park.

**1999, Apr. 10 Litho. *Perf. 13x13¼***

**628** A148 1.35 l multicolored 1.25 1.25
**629** A148 1.35 l multicolored 1.25 1.25

Council of Europe, 50th Anniv. — A149

**1999, May 1 Litho. *Perf. 14***

**630** A149 70c multicolored .60 .30

Melniai Windmill — A150

**1999, May 8 Litho. *Perf. 14***

**631** A150 70c shown 1.00 .35
**632** A150 70c Pumpenai Windmill 1.00 .35

Bees — A151

Designs: 70c, Dasypoda argentata. 2 l, Bombus pomorum.

**1999, June 12 *Perf. 13¼x13***

**633** A151 70c multicolored .70 .35
**634** A151 2 l multicolored 1.60 .80

UPU, 125th Anniv. A152

**1999, July 3 Litho. *Perf. 14***

**635** A152 70c multicolored .60 .30

Lithuanian Philatelic Society Emblems, No. 1, Pre-independence Stamp — A153

**1999, July 31 Litho. *Perf. 14***

**636** A153 1 l multicolored 1.00 .50
Complete booklet, 10 #636 11.00

Lithuanian Philatelic Society, 75th Anniv.

Souvenir Sheet

Centenary of First Performance of Play, "America in the Baths" — A154

Designs: a, Producers. b, Theater poster.

**1999, Aug. 20 Litho. *Perf. 12½***

**637** A154 4 l Sheet of 2, #a.-b. 5.00 5.00

A155

Baltic Chain, 10th Anniv. — Family and flags: 1 l, No. 640a, Lithuanian.
No. 640: b, Estonian. c, Latvian.

**1999, Aug. 23 Litho. *Perf. 12¾***

**639** A155 1 l multicolored .85 .40

**Souvenir Sheet**

**640** A155 2 l Sheet of 3, #a.-c. 5.00 5.00

See Estonia Nos. 366-367, Latvia Nos. 493-494.

A156

**1999, Aug. 28 Litho. *Perf. 14***

**641** A156 70c multicolored .60 .25

Freedom fight movement, 50th anniv.

**Coat of Arms Type of 1992**

Size: 25x33mm

**1999, Sept. 18 *Perf. 13½x13***

**642** A82 70c Marijampole .50 .25
**643** A82 1 l Siaulai 1.00 .35
**644** A82 1.40 l Rokiskis 1.25 .45
*Nos. 642-644 (3)* 2.75 1.05

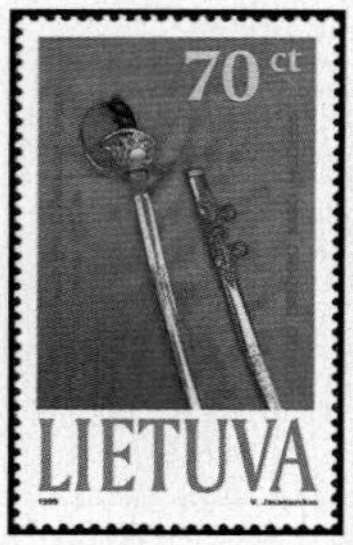


Museum Pieces — A157

Designs: 70c, Sword of Gen. S. Zukauskas. 3 l, Hussar armor.

**1999, Oct. 9 *Perf. 13¼x13½***

**645** A157 70c multicolored .40 .25
**646** A157 3 l multicolored 1.00 1.00

A158

**1999, Oct. 23 Litho. *Perf. 14***

**647** A158 70c multicolored .60 .25

Simonas Stanevicius (1799-1848), writer.

A159

Christmas and New Year's Day: 1.35 l, Buildings, candles.

***Perf. 12½x13½***

**1999, Nov. 13 Litho.**

**648** A159 70c shown .40 .25
**649** A159 1.35 l multicolored .75 .50

Forged Monument Tops — A160

Designs: 10c, Rietavas. 20c, Andriunal. 1 l, Veivirzenai. 1.30 l, Vaizgakiemis. 1.70 l, Baukai.

**2000-06 Litho. *Perf. 13½x13¼***

**Vignettes in Blue**

**Designs 22mm High**

**650** A160 10c tan .30 .25
*a.* Perf. 11¼, inscr. "2002" .30 .25
*b.* As "a," inscr. "2003" .30 .25
*c.* As "a," inscr. "2004" .30 .25
**651** A160 20c yellow .35 .25
*a.* Perf. 11¼, inscr. "2002" .35 .25
*b.* As "a," inscr. "2003" .35 .25
*c.* As "a," inscr. "2004" .35 .25
**652** A160 1 l pale rose .90 .45
*a.* Perf. 11¼, inscr. "2002" 1.00 .50
**653** A160 1.30 l lt green 1.10 .55
**654** A160 1.70 l lt blue 1.40 .70
*Nos. 651-654 (4)* 3.75 1.95

***Perf. 13x12½***

**Designs 20mm High**

**655** A160 10c tan .25 .25
*a.* Inscr. "2006" .25 .25
**656** A160 20c yellow .25 .25
*a.* Inscr. "2006" .25 .25

**Designs 21mm High**

**657** A160 1 l pale rose .75 .35
**658** A160 1.30 l lt green 1.00 .50
*Nos. 655-658 (4)* 2.25 1.35

Issued: Nos. 650-654, 1/3/00; Nos. 650a, 651a, 652a, 5/4/02; Nos. 655-656, 10/8/05; Nos. 657-658, 5/27/06.

**Independence Type of 1993**

Designs: 1.30 l, Jonas Vailokaitis (1886-1994), banker. 1.70 l, Jonas Smilgevicius (1870-1942), banker.

***Perf. 13¼x12¾***

**2000, Feb. 16 Litho.**

**660** A85 1.30 l multi .75 .50
**661** A85 1.70 l multi 1.25 .75

Souvenir Sheet

Declaration of Independence From Soviet Union, 10th Anniv. — A161

***Perf. 12¼x11½***

**2000, Mar. 11 Litho.**

**662** A161 7.40 l multi 5.00 5.00

Famous Lithuanians A162

Designs: 1 l, Vincas Pietaris (1850-1902), writer. 1.30 l, Kanutas Ruseckas (1800-60), artist. 1.70 l, Povilas Visinskis (1875-1906), writer.

**2000, Mar. 25 *Perf. 13x13¼***

**663** A162 1 l multi .80 .40
**664** A162 1.30 l multi .90 .50
**665** A162 1.70 l multi 1.25 .70
*Nos. 663-665 (3)* 2.95 1.60

See Nos. 688-690.

Items From Klaipeda Clock Museum — A163

1 l, Sundial. 2 l, Renaissance-style clock.

**2000, Apr. 15 *Perf. 12***

**666** A163 1 l multi 1.00 .50
**667** A163 2 l multi 1.25 .75

**Europa, 2000**

Common Design Type

**2000, May 9 *Perf. 13¼x13***

**668** CD17 1.70 l multi 1.50 1.50

Birds of Prey From Red Book of Lithuania — A164

1 l, Pandion haliaetus. 2 l, Milvus migrans.

**2000, June 2 *Perf. 13¼x13***

**669** A164 1 l multi .75 .45
**670** A164 2 l multi 1.60 .80

Sea Museum of Lithuania — A165

No. 671, Spheniscus magellanicus. No. 672, Halichoerus grypus.

**2000, Aug. 26** **Litho.** ***Perf. 12***
**671-672** A165 1 l Set of 2 1.50 1.00
*671a* Tete beche pair 2.25 2.25
*672a* Tete beche pair 2.25 2.25

2000 Summer Olympics, Sydney A166

Designs: 1 l, Cycling. 3 l, Swimming.

**2000, Sept. 2**
**673-674** A166 Set of 2 3.00 1.75

### Souvenir Sheet

Mikalojus Konstantinas Ciurlionis (1875-1911), Artist — A167

**2000, Sept. 22** **Litho.** ***Perf. 12***
**675** A167 4 l multi 3.00 3.00

Reappearance of Lithuanian Postage Stamps, 10th Anniv. — A168

**2000, Oct. 7** **Litho.** ***Perf. 12***
**676** A168 1 l multi .80 .40

### Arms Type of 1992

Designs: No. 677, 1 l, Raseiniai. No. 678, 1 l, Taurage. 1.30 l, Utena.

**2000, Oct. 21** **Litho.** ***Perf. 12***
**Size: 25x33mm**
**677-679** A82 Set of 3 2.50 1.40

Christmas and New Year's Day — A169

Roadside shrines: 1 l, 1.70 l.

**2000, Nov. 11**
**680-681** A169 Set of 2 2.00 1.00

### Souvenir Sheet

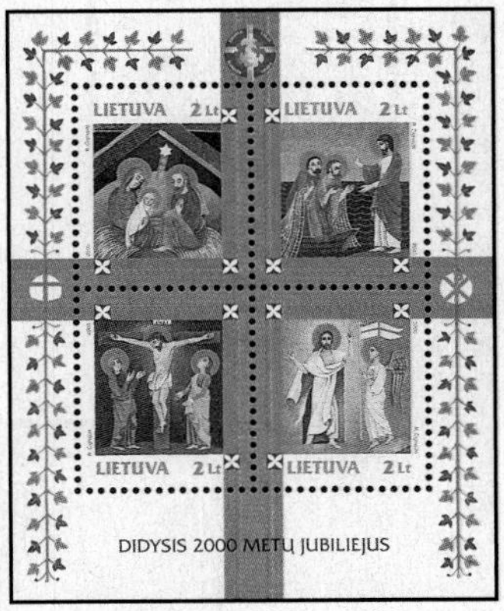


Holy Year 2000 — A170

No. 682: a, Nativity. b, Jesus and disciples. c, Crucifixion. d, Resurrection.

**2000, Nov. 25**
**682** A170 2 l Sheet of 4, #a-d 6.25 6.25

Advent of New Millennium A171

**2000, Dec. 2**
**683** A171 1 l multi .80 .40

### Souvenir Sheet

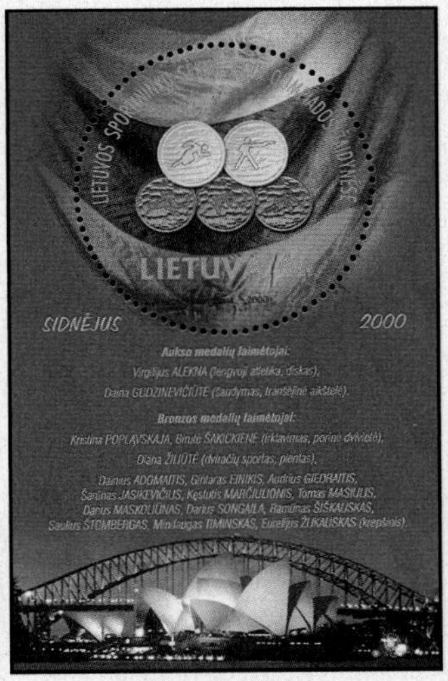


Medals Won at 2000 Summer Olympics, Sydney — A172

**2000, Dec. 9** **Litho.** ***Perf.***
**684** A172 4 l multi 3.25 3.25

Storming of TV Station by Soviet Troops, 10th Anniv. — A173

**2001, Jan. 13** ***Perf. 12***
**685** A173 1 l multi + label .85 .40

### Independence Type of 1993

Designs: 1 l, Saliamonas Banaitis (1866-1933), newspaper publisher and politician. 2 l, Justinas Staugaitis (1863-1943), bishop and politician.

**2001, Feb. 16** **Litho.** ***Perf. 12***
**686-687** A85 Set of 2 2.50 1.25

### Famous Lithuanians Type of 2000

Designs: No. 688, 1 l, Juozas Mikenas (1901-64), artist. No. 689, 1 l, Pranas Vaicaitis (1876-1901), poet. 1.70 l, Petras Vileisis (1851-1926), civil engineer.

**2001, Mar. 24** **Litho.** ***Perf. 12***
**688-690** A162 Set of 3 3.00 1.50

Europa A174

Designs: No. 691, 1.70 l, Neman River. No. 692, 1.70 l, Lake Galve.

**2001, Apr. 14** ***Perf. 13x13¼***
**691-692** A174 Set of 2 3.00 3.00

Flowers From Red Book of Lithuania — A175

Designs: 2 l, Nymphoide peltata. 3 l, Erica tetralix.

**2001, May 12** ***Perf. 13¼x13***
**693-694** A175 Set of 2 4.00 2.00

Bridges A176

Designs: 1 l, Papalauja Bridge. 1.30 l, Pakurojis Dam Bridge.

**2001, June 9** ***Perf. 12***
**695-696** A176 Set of 2 1.80 .95

### Souvenir Sheet

Lithuania, 1000th Anniv. (in 2009) — A177

Designs: a, Flag. b, Arms. c, Map of country. d, Map of Europe.

**2001, June 23** ***Perf. 11***
**697** A177 2 l Sheet of 4, #a-d + 2 labels 6.25 6.25

Baltic Coast Landscapes A178

Designs: 1 l, No. 699a, Palanga. No. 699b, Lahemaa. No. 699c, Vidzeme.

**2001, Sept. 15** **Litho.** ***Perf. 13½***
**698** A178 1 l multi .85 .40

### Souvenir Sheet

**699** Sheet of 3 4.75 4.75
***a.-c.*** A178 2 l Any single 1.40 1.10

See Estonia Nos. 423-424, Latvia Nos. 534-535.

Ethnographic Open Air Museum Exhibits — A179

19th cent. dwellings from: 1 l, Kirdeikiai. 2 l, Darbenai.

**2001, Sept. 22** ***Perf. 12***
**700-701** A179 Set of 2 2.40 1.25

Sculpture by Juozas Zikaras (1881-1944) A180

**2001, Oct. 4**
**702** A180 3 l multi 2.40 1.25

Postal Regulations Enacted by Stefan Bathory, 1583 — A181

**2001, Oct. 6**
**703** A181 1 l multi .85 .40

### Coat of Arms Type of 1992

**Size: 25x33mm**

Designs: 1 l, Lazdijai. 1.30 l, Birzai. 1.70 l, Veliuona.

**2001, Oct. 27** **Litho.** ***Perf. 12***
**704-706** A82 Set of 3 3.00 1.60

Christmas and New Year — A182

Birds on: 1 l, Covered tree. 1.70 l, Christ's cradle.

**2001, Nov. 10** **Litho.** ***Perf. 12***
**707-708** A182 Set of 2 2.00 1.00

### Souvenir Sheet

Dr. Jonas Basanavicius (1851-1927), Patriot, Folklorist — A183

**2001, Nov. 17** ***Perf. 12x11½***
**709** A183 5 l multi 4.00 4.00

2002 Winter Olympics, Salt Lake City — A184

**2002, Jan. 26 Litho. *Perf. 12***
**710** A184 1.70 l multi 1.40 .70

### Independence Type of 1993

Designs: No. 711, 1 l, Kazys Bizauskas (1892-1941), statesman. No. 712, 1 l, Stanislovas Narutavicius (1862-1932), politician.

**2002, Feb. 16**
**711-712** A85 Set of 2 1.50 .80

Famous Lithuanians A185

Designs: 1 l, Antanas Salys (1902-72), linguist. 1.30 l, Satrijos Ragana (1877-1930), writer. 1.70 l, Oskaras Milasius (1877-1939), poet.

**2002, Mar. 2 Litho. *Perf. 12***
**713-715** A185 Set of 3 3.00 1.50

See Nos. 734-735, 759-761, 782-784, 805-807, 830-832, 858-860, 884-886, 906-908, 934-936, 967-969.

### Coat of Arms Type of 1992
Size: 25x33mm

Designs: No. 716, 1 l, Anyksciai. No. 717, 1 l, Birstonas. 1.70 l, Prienai.

**2002, Mar. 23**
**716-718** A82 Set of 3 3.00 1.50

State Historical Archives, 150th Anniv. A186

**2002, Apr. 6**
**719** A186 1 l multi .85 .40

Mammals From Red Book of Lithuania A187

Designs: 1 l, Mustela erminea. 3 l, Lynx lynx.

**2002, Apr. 13 *Perf. 13x13¼***
**720-721** A187 Set of 2 3.00 1.60

Europa — A188

**2002, May 4 Litho. *Perf. 13¼x13***
**722** A188 1.70 l multi 1.50 1.50

Vilnius Fire ad Rescue Brigade, Bicent. A189

**2002, May 25 *Perf. 12***
**723** A189 1 l multi .85 .40

Narrow-gauge Railways — A190

Designs: 1.30 l, TU2 diesel locomotive. 2 l, PT4 steam engine.

**2002, June 8**
**724-725** A190 Set of 2 2.75 1.40

### Souvenir Sheet

Lithuania, 1000th Anniv. (in 2009) — A191

Designs: a, Artifact of first people in Lithuania, 10,000 B.C. b, Roman historian Tacitus mentions Aestii people, 98. c, Vikings attack Apuole Castle, 853. d, First mention of Lithuania in Quedlinburg Annals, 1009.

**2002, June 22 *Perf. 11***
**726** A191 2 l Sheet of 4, #a-d, + 2 labels 6.25 6.25

### Souvenir Sheet

Klaipeda, 750th Anniv. — A192

**2002, Aug. 1 *Perf. 11½x12¼***
**727** A192 5 l multi 4.00 4.00

Maironis Lithuanian Literature Museum, Kaunas A193

Designs: 1 l, Exhibits. 3 l, Museum exterior.

**2002, Sept. 7 *Perf. 12***
**728-729** A193 Set of 2 3.00 1.50

Establishment of Postal Service by King Sigismund III Vasa, 1620 — A194

**2002, Oct. 5**
**730** A194 1 l multi .85 .40

Christmas and New Year's Day — A195

Cross and: 1 l, Clock, candles and holly. 1.70 l, Christmas tree and angels.

**2002, Nov. 9**
**731-732** A195 Set of 2 2.10 1.00

European Children's Day — A196

**2002, Nov. 16**
**733** A196 1 l multi .85 .40

### Famous Lithuanians Type of 2002

Designs: 1 l, Laurynas Stuoka-Gucevicius (1753-98), architect. 1.30 l, Juozas Eretas (1896-1984), author and politician.

**2003, Jan. 25 *Perf. 12***
**734-735** A185 Set of 2 1.80 .85

### Coat of Arms Type of 1992

Designs: No. 736, 1 l, Gargzdai. No. 737, 1 l, Kretinga. No. 738, 1 l, Palanga. No. 739, 1 l, Papile. No. 740, 1 l, Rietavas.

**2003, Feb. 15 Litho. *Perf. 12***
**Size: 25x33mm**
**736-740** A82 Set of 5 4.00 2.00

Lighthouses A198

Designs: 1 l, Pervalka. 3 l, Uostodvaris.

**2003, Mar. 15**
**741-742** A198 Set of 2 3.25 1.50

Europa — A199

**2003, Apr. 19 Litho. *Perf. 13½x13***
**743** A199 1.70 l multi 1.50 1.50
*a.* Tete beche pair 3.25 3.25

Rebuilding of Palace of Lithuania's Rulers — A200

**2003, Apr. 26 *Perf. 12***
**744** A200 1 l multi .85 .40

Vilnius University Astronomical Observatory, 250th Anniv. — A201

**2003, May 10 *Perf. 12***
**745** A201 1 l multi .85 .40

Insects From Red Book of Lithuania A202

Designs: No. 746, 3 l, Lucanus cervus. No. 747, 3 l, Cerambyx cerdo.

**2003, May 24 *Perf. 13x13½***
**746-747** A202 Set of 2 5.00 2.50

### Souvenir Sheet

Lithuania, 1000th Anniv. (in 2009) — A203

No. 748: a, Rise of Lithuania, 1183. b, Battle of Siauliai, 1236. c, Coronation of Mindaugas, 1253. d, Selection of Vilnius as capital of Lithuania, 1323.

**2003, June 21 *Perf. 11***
**748** A203 2 l Sheet of 4, #a-d, + 2 labels 6.25 3.25

### Souvenir Sheet

Coronation of Mindaugas, 750th Anniv. — A204

**2003, July 5 *Perf. 11½x12¼***
**749** A204 5 l multi 4.00 2.00

13th European Hot Air Balloon Championships — A205

**2003, Aug. 8** *Perf. 12*
**750** A205 1.30 l multi 1.00 .55

Vincentas Cardinal Sladkevicius (1920-2000) A206

**2003, Aug. 20**
**751** A206 1 l multi .85 .40

Panevezys, 500th Anniv. — A207

**2003, Sept. 7**
**752** A207 1 l multi .85 .40

Map of Kaunas-Vilnius-Grodno Postal Route, 1664 — A208

**2003, Oct. 4**
**753** A208 1 l multi .85 .40

Christmas and New Year's Day — A209

Villages at: 1 l, Christmas. 1.70 l, New Year's Eve.

**2003, Nov. 8**
**754-755** A209 Set of 2 2.10 1.00

Souvenir Sheet

Lithuania, 2003 European Men's Basketball Champions — A210

**2003, Dec. 6 Litho.** *Perf. 12x11½*
**756** A210 5 l multi 4.00 2.00

Gliders in Lithuanian Aviation Museum A211

Designs: No. 757, 1 l, BK-7. No. 758, 1 l, BRO-12.

**2003, Dec. 17** *Perf. 12*
**757-758** A211 Set of 2 1.75 .80

**Famous Lithuanians Type of 2002**

Designs: No. 759, 1 l, Jonas Aistis (1904-73), poet. No. 760, 1 l, Kazimieras Buga (1879-1924), philologist. No. 761, Adolfas Jucys (1904-74), physicist.

**2004, Jan. 24 Litho.** *Perf. 12*
**759-761** A185 Set of 3 2.25 1.25

**Coat of Arms Type of 1992**

Designs: 1 l, Mazeikiai. 1.30 l, Radviliskis. 1.40 l, Ukmerge.

**2004, Feb. 14** **Size: 25x33mm**
**762-764** A82 Set of 3 2.75 1.50

Vilnius University, 425th Anniv. — A213

**2004, Mar. 20**
**765** A213 1 l multi .85 .40

Europa — A214

Designs: No. 766, 1.70 l, Sailboat. No. 767, 1.70 l, Beach umbrella.

**2004, Apr. 10 Litho.** *Perf. 12*
**766-767** A214 Set of 2 3.00 3.00

Return to Printing Lithuanian in Latin Letters, Cent. A215

**2004, May 1 Litho.** *Perf. 12*
**768** A215 1.30 l multi 1.00 .50

Admission to European Union — A216

No. 769: a, Stars, flags of newly-added countries, map of Europe. b, Stars and Lithuanian flag, map and arms.

**2004, May 1**
**769** A216 1.70 l Horiz. pair, #a-b 2.75 1.25

FIFA (Fédération Internationale de Football Association), Cent. — A217

**2004, May 15**
**770** A217 3 l multi 2.25 1.10

Chiune Sugihara (1900-86), Japanese Diplomat Who Issued Transit Visas to Jews in World War II — A218

**2004, June 19 Litho.** *Perf. 12*
**771** A218 1 l multi .85 .40

Souvenir Sheet

Lithuania, 1000th Anniv. — A219

No. 772: a, Defense of Pilenai Castle, 1336. b, Battle at the Blue Waters, 1362. c, Christening of Lithuania, 1387. d, Battle of Zalgiris, 1410.

**2004, July 3** *Perf. 11*
**772** A219 2 l Sheet of 4, #a-d, + 2 labels 6.00 4.00

Exhibits in Tadas Ivanauskas Zoology Museum, Kaunas — A220

No. 773: a, Aquila chrysaetos. b, Iguana iguana.

**2004, July 10** *Perf. 12*
**773** A220 1 l Horiz. pair, #a-b 1.50 .80

2004 Summer Olympics, Athens A221

2004 Olympic emblem and: 2 l, Pentathlon equestrian event. 3 l, Canoeing.

**2004, July 31**
**774-775** A221 Set of 2 4.00 2.00

Owls From Red Book of Lithuania — A222

Designs: 1.30 l, Bubo bubo. 3 l, Asio flammeus.

**2004, Oct. 2 Litho.** *Perf. 12*
**776-777** A222 Set of 2 3.25 1.75

Kaunas Funiculars A223

Designs: 1 l, Aleksotas Funicular. 1.30 l, Zaliakalnis Funicular.

**2004, Oct. 16**
**778-779** A223 Set of 2 1.75 .95

Christmas A224

Stars and: 1 l, Christmas tree. 1.70 l, Bird.

**2004, Nov. 6**
**780-781** A224 Set of 2 2.00 1.50

**Famous Lithuanians Type of 2002**

Designs: No. 782, 1 l, Kazys Boruta (1905-65), writer. No. 783, 1 l, Petras Kalpokas (1880-1945), painter. No. 784, 1 l, Jonas Puzinas (1905-78), archaeologist.

**2005, Jan. 8 Litho.** *Perf. 12*
**782-784** A185 Set of 3 2.00 1.50

Congratulations A225

Designs: No. 785, 1 l, Gerbera daisies, freesias and scroll. No. 786, 1 l, Lilies, freesias and box.

***Serpentine Die Cut 6¾***
**2005, Jan. 29 Litho.**
**Booklet Stamps**
**Self-Adhesive**

**785-786** A225 Set of 2 1.40 1.10
*786a* Booklet pane, 4 each #785-786 5.50

Sartai Horse Race, Cent.
A226

**2005, Feb. 5** ***Perf. 12***
**787** A226 1 l multi .65 .40

**Coat of Arms Type of 1992**

Designs: No. 788, 1 l, Druskininkai. No. 789, 1 l, Vabalninkas.

**2005, Mar. 5** **Size: 25x33mm**
**788-789** A82 Set of 2 1.40 1.10

Europa
A227

Designs: No. 790, 1.70 l, Cow, cheese. No. 791, 1.70 l, Loaf of black bread.

**2005, Apr. 9** **Litho.** ***Perf. 12***
**790-791** A227 Set of 2 3.00 3.00

National Museum, 150th Anniv. — A228

No. 792: a, Brass jewelry, 1st-2nd cent. b, Illustration of first exhibition in Aula Hall, Vilnius University.

**2005, May 7**
**792** A228 1 l Pair, #a-b 1.40 1.40

Train and Kaunas Railway Tunnel
A229

**2005, June 11**
**793** A229 3 l multi 2.00 1.50

Souvenir Sheet

Lithuania, 1000th Anniv. — A230

No. 794: a, Battle of Pabaiskas, 1435. b, Valakai Reform, 1557. c, First Lithuanian statute, 1529. d, Union of Lublin, 1569.

**2005, July 2** ***Perf. 11***
**794** A230 2 l Sheet of 4, #a-d, + 2 labels 5.50 5.50

90th World Esperanto Congress, Vilnius
A231

**2005, July 23** **Litho.** ***Perf. 12***
**795** A231 1 l multi .70 .50

Churches
A232

Designs: 1 l, Vilnius Evangelical Lutheran Church. 1.30 l, St. Casimir Church, Vilnius.

**2005, Sept. 3** ***Perf. 13½***
**796-797** A232 Set of 2 1.50 1.00

Flora and Fauna from Red Book of Lithuania — A233

No. 798: a, Gavia arctica. b, Trapa natans.

**2005, Sept. 10**
**798** A233 1 l Horiz. pair, #a-b 1.40 1.40

Souvenir Sheet

Mikolajus Konstantinas Ciurlionis (1875-1911), Painter and Composer — A234

No. 799 — Details from Sonata of the Sea triptych: a, Allegro. b, Andante. c, Finale.

**2005, Sept. 24** ***Perf. 14***
**799** A234 2 l Sheet of 3, #a-c, + label 4.00 4.00

Map of St. Petersburg-Warsaw Post Road, 1830-36 — A235

**2005, Oct. 8** **Litho.** ***Perf. 14¼x14***
**800** A235 1 l multi .65 .45

Christmas
A236

Designs: 1 l, Candle and snow-covered evergreen branch. 1.70 l, Santa Claus in sleigh.

**2005, Nov. 5** ***Perf. 12¾x13***
**801-802** A236 Set of 2 1.75 1.25

Dr. Jonas Basanavicius, Vilnius City Hall and Commemorative Medal — A237

**2005, Dec. 3** ***Perf. 14¼x14***
**803** A237 1 l multi .65 .45

Congress of Lithuanians, cent.

2006 Winter Olympics, Turin — A238

**2006, Jan. 28** **Litho.** ***Perf. 14x14¼***
**804** A238 1.70 l multi 1.25 .75

**Famous Lithuanians Type of 2002**

Designs: No. 805, 1 l, Adolfas Sapoka (1906-61), historian. No. 806, 1 l, Petras Rimsa (1881-1961), sculptor. No. 807, 1 l, Antanas Vaiciulaitis (1906-92), writer.

**2006, Feb. 11** ***Perf. 13½***
**805-807** A185 Set of 3 2.00 1.50

Vilnius Album, by Jonas K. Vilcinskis, 160th Anniv. of Publication
A239

**2006, Feb. 25** ***Perf. 13x12¾***
**808** A239 1 l multi .65 .45

Social Insurance System, 80th Anniv.
A240

**2006, Mar. 18** ***Perf. 14¼x14***
**809** A240 1 l multi .65 .45

Lithuanian Theater, Music and Cinema Museum, 80th Anniv. — A241

No. 810: a, Parvo camera, 1930s. b, Music box, 1900.

**2006, Mar. 18** ***Perf. 13½***
**810** A241 1 l Pair, #a-b 1.25 1.25

Printed in sheets containing 10 of each stamp + 5 labels. Each sheet contains se-tenant pairs of the same stamp.

Europa
A242

Designs: No. 811, 1.70 l, Woman dancing with man in wheelchair. No. 812, 1.70 l, People in wheelchairs being pushed around track.

**2006, Apr. 15**
**811-812** A242 Set of 2 3.00 3.00

**Coat of Arms Type of 1992**

Designs: No. 813, 1 l, Kupiskis. No. 814, 1 l, Sakiai. No. 815, 1 l, Silute.

**2006, May 13** ***Perf. 14x14¼***
**Size: 25x33mm**
**813-815** A82 Set of 3 2.00 1.50

Souvenir Sheet

Lithuania, 1000th Anniv. — A243

No. 816: a, Establishment of Vilnius University, 1579. b, Truce of Andrusov, 1667. c, Four-year Sejm, 1788. d, Uprising of 1794.

**2006, July 1** ***Perf. 11***
**816** A243 2 l Sheet of 4, #a-d, + 2 labels 5.25 5.25

Basilicas
A244

Designs: 1 l, Vilnius Basilica. 1.70 l, Kaunas Basilica.

**2006, Aug. 5** ***Perf. 12¾x13***
**817-818** A244 Set of 2 1.75 1.25

Birds and Fish From Red Book of Lithuania
A245

No. 819: a, Polysticta stelleri. b, Acipenser sturio.

**2006, Sept. 16** ***Perf. 13½***
**819** A245 1 l Vert. pair, #a-b 1.40 1.40

Establishment of Lithuania Post and First Postage Stamps, 1918 — A246

**2006, Oct. 7** *Perf. 14¼x14*
**820** A246 1 l multi .65 .45

Premiere of Opera "Birute," Cent. — A247

**2006, Nov. 4 Litho.** *Perf. 13¼x12¾*
**821** A247 2 l multi 1.25 .85

Christmas A248

Designs: 1 l, Birds, triangular window. 1.70 l, Trees, star, berries, straw.

**2006, Nov. 18** *Perf. 12¾x13¼*
**822-823** A248 Set of 2 1.75 1.40

18th Century Wooden Church Belfries — A249

Belfries from churches in: 10c, Pasvalys. 20c, Rozalimas. 50c, Tryskiai. 1 l, Saukenai. 1.30 l, Vaiguva. 1.70 l, Vajasiskis.

*Die Cut Perf. 12½*

**2007, Jan. 1 Litho.**

**Self-Adhesive**

**824** A249 10c blue & blk .25 .25
**825** A249 20c org & blk .25 .25
**826** A249 50c bl grn & blk .40 .40
*a.* Dated 2009 .40 .40
*b.* Dated 2011 .40 .40
**827** A249 1 l brn & blk .80 .80
*a.* Dated 2009 .80 .80
*b.* Dated 2011 .80 .80
**828** A249 1.30 l lil & blk 1.00 1.00
**829** A249 1.70 l ol brn & blk 1.40 1.40
*Nos. 824-829 (6)* 4.10 4.10

Issued: Nos. 826a, 827a, 2/21/09. Nos. 826b, 827b, 1/8/11.

See Nos. 842-846, 1034.

**Famous Lithuanians Type of 2002**

Designs: No. 830, 1 l, Bernardas Brazdzionis (1907-2002), writer. No. 831, 1 l, Vytautas Kazimieras Jonynas (1907-97), artist. 3 l, Leonas Sapiega (1557-1633), state chancellor of the Grand Duchy of Lithuania.

**2007, Jan. 27** *Perf. 13½*
**830-832** A185 Set of 3 3.75 3.00

**Coat of Arms Type of 1992**

Designs: 1 l, Svencionys. 1.30 l, Kelme. 2 l, Moletai.

**2007, Mar. 3** *Perf. 14x14¼*
**Size: 25x33mm**
**833-835** A82 Set of 3 3.25 2.50

Europa A250

Designs: No. 836, 1.70 l, Scouting flag, musical score. No. 837, 1.70 l, Symbols of Lithuanian Scouts.

**2007, Apr. 14 Litho.** *Perf. 13½*
**836-837** A250 Set of 2 2.25 1.60

Scouting, cent.

Churches A251

Designs: 1 l, St. Anne's and Bernardine Churches, Vilnius. 1.30 l, Church buildings, Pazaislis.

**2007, May 12** *Perf. 12¾x13*
**838-839** A251 Set of 2 2.00 1.50

Souvenir Sheet

Lithuania, 1000th Anniv. — A252

No. 840: a, Publication of first Lithuanian newspaper, "Ausra," 1883. b, Abolition of the prohibition on printing in Latin characters, 1904. c, Great Seimas of Vilnius, 1905. d, Lithuanian Declaration of Independence, 1918.

**2007, June 23 Litho.** *Perf. 11*
**840** A252 3 l Sheet of 4, #a-d, + 2 labels 9.00 9.00

Trakai History Museum — A253

No. 841: a, Map of New Trakai in 1600, by J. Kamarauskas. b, Chess pieces, 15th cent.

**2007, July 28 Litho.** *Perf. 13½*
**841** A253 2 l Pair, #a-b 3.00 3.00

Printed in sheets containing 10 of each stamp + 5 labels.

**Wooden Church Belfries Type of 2007**

Belfries from churches in: 5c, Vabalininkas, 19th cent. 35c, Varputenai, 18th cent. 1.35 l, Deguciai, 19th cent. 1.55 l, Geidziai, 19th cent. 2.15 l, Pavandenes, 17th cent.

*Die Cut Perf. 12½*

**2007, Sept. 1 Litho.**

**Self-Adhesive**

**842** A249 5c yel grn & blk .25 .25
**843** A249 35c gray & blk .30 .30
**844** A249 1.35 l yel & blk 1.00 .75
**845** A249 1.55 l brn org & blk 1.10 .80
**846** A249 2.15 l rose lake & blk 1.25 1.75
*Nos. 842-846 (5)* 3.90 3.85

Juozas Miltinis (1907-94), Actor and Theater Founder A254

**2007, Sept. 1 Litho.** *Perf. 12¾x13*
**847** A254 2.45 l multi 1.75 1.25

Birds — A255

No. 848 — Birds of the Cepkeliai Nature Reserve, Lithuania and Katra Sanctuary, Belarus: a, Gallinago media. b, Crex crex.

**2007, Oct. 3** *Perf. 14*
**848** Horiz. pair + central label 5.00 5.00
*a.-b.* A255 2.90 l Either single 2.25 2.25

See Belarus No. 625.

Stamps and Covers From Establishment of Lithuania Post in 1992 — A256

**2007, Oct. 6**
**849** A256 1.35 l multi 1.25 1.25

Christmas A257

Conifer sprigs and: 1.35 l, Snowflake, Christmas ornaments. 2.45 l, Stars, globe.

**2007, Nov. 10** *Perf. 13x12¾*
**850-851** A257 Set of 2 3.25 3.25

Wooden Churches — A258

Churches in: 5c, Antazave, 1794. 10c, Deguciai, 1757. 20c, Inturke, 1855. 35c, Prienai, 1750. 1.35 l, Siaudine, 1775. 1.55 l, Uzventis, 1703.

*Die Cut Perf. 12½*

**2008, Jan. 5 Litho.**

**Self-Adhesive**

**852** A258 5c multi .25 .25
*a.* Dated 2011 .25 .25
**853** A258 10c multi .25 .25
*a.* Dated 2009 .25 .25
*b.* Dated 2011 .25 .25
**854** A258 20c multi .25 .25
*a.* Dated 2009 .25 .25
*b.* Dated 2011 .25 .25
**855** A258 35c multi .30 .30
*a.* Dated 2011 .30 .30
**856** A258 1.35 l multi 1.00 1.00
*a.* Dated 2009 1.00 1.00
*b.* Dated 2011 1.10 1.10
**857** A258 1.55 l multi 1.10 1.10
*Nos. 852-857 (6)* 3.15 3.15

Issued: Nos. 853a, 854a, 856a, 2/21/09; Nos. 853b, 856b, 1/8/11. Nos. 852a, 854b, 855a, 10/8/11.

**Famous Lithuanians Type of 2002**

Designs: 2 l, Martynas Jankus (1858-1946), publisher. 2.15 l, Zenonas Ivinskis (1908-71), historian. 2.90 l, Antanas Maceina (1908-87), philosopher.

**2008, Jan. 19 Litho.** *Perf. 13½*
**858-860** A185 Set of 3 5.25 4.00

Restoration of Independence, 90th Anniv. — A259

**2008, Feb. 16**
**861** A259 1.35 l multi 1.10 .80

State Awards of the Baltic Countries — A260

Designs: Nos. 862, 863a, Order of Vytautas the Great, Lithuania. No. 863b, Order of the National Coat of Arms, Estonia. No. 863c, Order of Three Stars, Latvia.

*Perf. 13½x13¾*

**2008, Mar. 15 Litho.**
**862** A260 7 l multi 5.00 3.50

**Souvenir Sheet**

**863** A260 5 l Sheet of 3, #a-c, + label 13.00 13.00

See Estonia Nos. 592-593, Latvia Nos. 701-702.

Items From Rokiskis Regional Museum — A261

No. 864: a, Wood carving, by Lionginas Sepka. b, 19th cent. women's clothing.

**2008, Apr. 19 Litho.** *Perf. 14*
**864** A261 1.55 l Horiz. pair, #a-b 2.25 2.25

Europa A262

Designs: No. 865, 2.45 l, Grand Duke Gediminas and his letters of 1323. No. 866, 2.45 l, Vilnius, 2009 European Cultural Capital.

**2008, May 3**
**865-866** A262 Set of 2 3.50 2.75

Sajudis Party, 20th Anniv. A263

**2008, May 31**
**867** A263 1.35 l multi 1.00 .75

Expo Zaragoza 2008 — A264

**2008, June 7** ***Die Cut Perf. 12½***

**Self-Adhesive**

**868** A264 2.45 l multi 1.75 1.25

Miniature Sheet

Lithuania, 1000th Anniv. — A265

No. 869: a, First Lithuanian Cabinet of Ministers, 1918. b, Consitituent Assembly, 1920. c, Opening of Kaunas University, 1922. d, Occupation of Memel (Klaipeda) by Lithuania, 1923. e, Opening of Zemaiciai Road (man signing document, 1939). f, Return of Vilnius to Lithuania from Poland, 1939.

**2008, June 28** ***Perf. 14***

**869** A265 3 l Sheet of 6, #a-f 13.00 13.00

Crashed Transatlantic Flight of Captains Steponas Darius and Stasys Girenas, 75th Anniv. — A266

**2008, July 12**

**870** A266 2.90 l multi 2.25 1.60

2008 Summer Olympics, Beijing — A267

Designs: 2.15 l, Women's marathon. 2.45 l, Yachting.

**2008, July 26**

**871-872** A267 Set of 2 3.50 2.75

Apparitions of the Virgin Mary at Siluva, 400th Anniv. — A268

**2008, Aug. 30** **Litho.** ***Perf. 14***

**873** A268 1.55 l multi 1.25 1.00

Worldwide Fund for Nature (WWF) A269

Coracias garrulus: Nos. 874, 878a, 1.35 l, On branch with beak closed, denomination at LR. Nos. 875, 878b, 1.35 l, In flight. Nos. 876, 878c, 1.35 l, On branch with beak open, denomination at LL. Nos. 877, 878d, 1.35 l, On branch with beak closed, denomination at LL.

**2008, Sept. 6** ***Perf. 14***

**Stamps With White Frames**

**874-877** A269 Set of 4 4.00 3.00

**Souvenir Sheet**

**Stamps Without White Frames**

**878** A269 1.35 l Sheet of 4, #a-d 4.00 4.00

**Arms Type of 1992**

Designs: No. 879, 1.35 l, Jurbarkas. No. 880, 1.35 l, Joniskis. 3 l, Sirvintos.

**2008, Oct. 4** **Litho.**

**Size: 26x31mm**

**879-881** A82 Set of 3 4.25 3.50

Christmas and New Year's Day A270

Designs: 1.35 l, Holiday lights. 2.45 l, Snow-covered evergreen branch.

**2008, Nov. 8** ***Perf. 14***

**882-883** A270 Set of 2 2.75 2.10

**Famous Lithuanians Type of 2002**

Designs: 1.35 l, Jonas Zemaitas (1909-54), military officer. 2 l, Vaclovas Birziska (1884-1956), educator and library founder. 2.15 l, Mecislovas Reinys (1884-1953), archbishop.

**2009, Jan. 17** **Litho.** ***Perf. 14***

**884-886** A185 Set of 3 4.00 3.00

**Arms Type of 1992**

Designs: No. 887, 1.35 l, Krekenava. No. 888, 1.35 l, Pakruojis. 3 l, Salcininkai.

**2009, Feb. 21** **Litho.** ***Perf. 14***

**Size: 26x31mm**

**887-889** A82 Set of 3 4.50 3.25

Souvenir Sheet

Protection of Polar Regions and Glaciers — A271

No. 890 — Glacier with sky in: a, Dark blue. b, Light blue.

**2009, Mar. 27**

**890** A271 2.90 l Sheet of 2, #a-b 4.50 4.50

Vilnius, 2009 European Cultural Capital A272

**2009, Apr. 11**

**891** A272 2.15 l multi 1.75 1.25

Europa — A273

Telescope and: No. 892, Galileo Galilei, Moon. No. 893, Vilnius University Observatory, Sun.

**2009, Apr. 25** **Litho.** ***Perf. 14***

**892** A273 2.45 l multi 2.00 1.50

**893** A273 2.45 l multi 2.00 1.50

Intl. Year of Astronomy.

Great Synagogue of Vilnius — A274

**2009, May 23**

**894** A274 1.35 l multi 1.00 .75

Palanga Amber Museum — A275

No. 895: a, "Sun Stone" (large piece of amber). b, Museum building.

**2009, June 13**

**895** A275 1.55 l Pair, #a-b 2.50 2.50

Spindle A276

**2009, June 27** **Litho.** ***Perf. 14***

**896** A276 3.35 l multi 2.75 1.75

Millennium Song Festival, Vilnius.

Miniature Sheet

Lithuania, 1000th Anniv. — A277

No. 897: a, Acceptance of declaration of the Council of the Movement for the Freedom of Lithuania, 1949. b, Illegal production of "Chronicle of the Catholic Church in Lithuania," 1972. c, Lithuanian Reform Movement, 1988. d, Signing of declaration of Lithuanian independence, 1990. e, Entry into European Union, 2004. f, Acceptance into Schengen Area, 2007.

**2009, July 4** **Litho.** ***Perf. 14***

**897** A277 3 l Sheet of 6, #a-f 14.00 14.00

Tall Ships Regatta — A278

***Perf. 13½x13¾***

**2009, Sept. 25** **Litho.**

**898** A278 3 l multi + label 2.50 1.75

Railways in Lithuania, 150th Anniv. — A279

**2009, Aug. 8** **Litho.** ***Perf. 14***

**899** A279 2.90 l multi 2.40 1.75

Order of the Cross of Vytis — A280

**2009, Sept. 19** ***Perf. 13½x13¾***

**900** A280 7 l multi 6.00 4.50

Flora and Fauna From Red Book of Lithuania — A281

No. 901: a, Papilio machaon. b, Gentiana pneumonanthe.

**2009, Oct. 10** ***Perf. 14***

**901** A281 1.55 l Horiz. pair, #a-b 2.75 2.75

Struve Geodetic Arc UNESCO World Heritage Site — A282

Designs: No. 902, 2 l, Friedrich Georg Wilhelm von Struve and map of Europe. No. 903, 2 l, Arc post in Meskonys, map of triangulation points.

**2009, Oct. 24**

**902-903** A282 Set of 2 3.50 2.75

Christmas and New Year's Day — A283

Designs: 1.35 l, Village church. 2.45 l, Houses.

**2009, Nov. 7**

**904-905** A283 Set of 2 3.25 2.50

**Famous Lithuanians Type of 2002**

Designs: No. 906, 1.35 l, Jonas Karolis Chodkevicius (Jan Karol Chodkiewicz, 1560-1621), hetman and military leader. No. 907, 1.35 l, Jonas Jablonskis (1860-1930), linguist.

3 l, Mykolas Krupavicius (1885-1970), Minister of Agriculture.

**2010, Jan. 16** **Litho.** ***Perf. 14***
**906-908** A185 Set of 3 4.50 3.25

2010 Winter Olympics, Vancouver A284

**2010, Jan. 30**
**909** A284 2.45 l multi 2.00 1.50

**Arms Type of 1992**

Designs: 1.35 l, Silale. 2 l, Jonava. 2.15 l, Varena.

**2010, Feb. 20** ***Perf. 14***
**Size: 26x31mm**
**910-912** A82 Set of 3 4.25 3.25

Independence, 20th Anniv. — A285

**2010, Mar. 6** **Litho.**
**913** A285 1.35 l multi 1.00 .75

Easter — A286

**2010, Mar. 20** ***Perf. 14***
**914** A286 1.35 l multi 1.00 .75

Expo 2010, Shanghai A287

**2010, Apr. 10**
**915** A287 2.90 l multi 2.25 1.60

Vladas Mikenas (1910-92), Chess Grand Master A288

**2010, Apr. 17**
**916** A288 2 l multi 1.60 1.25

Europa A289

Half of book and: No. 917, 2.45 l, Rabbit, girl, numerals. No. 918, 2.45 l, Letters, bird, boy.

**2010, May 8**
**917-918** A289 Set of 2 3.50 3.50

Souvenir Sheet

Oak of Stelmuze — A290

**2010, June 5**
**919** A290 8 l multi 5.75 5.75

Battle of Grunwald, 600th Anniv. — A291

**2010, July 3**
**920** A291 2.45 l multi 1.90 1.50

Kretinga Museum, 75th Anniv. — A292

No. 921 — Items in Kretinga Museum: a, Fastener fron 2nd-3rd cent., monument b, St. George slaying the dragon, musuem.

**2010, July 10** **Litho.**
**921** A292 1.35 l Pair, #a-b 2.10 1.60

Printed in sheets containing 10 pairs and 5 labels.

2010 Youth Olympics, Singapore A293

**2010, July 31** ***Perf. 14***
**922** A293 2.90 l multi 2.25 1.60

Kernave Archaeological UNESCO World Heritage Site — A294

Designs: No. 923, 3 l, View of town and burial mounds. No. 924, 3 l, Road and burial mound.

**2010, Aug. 7**
**923-924** A294 Set of 2 4.50 3.50

Flora and Fauna from Red Book of Lithuania — A295

No. 925: a, Columba oenas. b, Anax parthenope and flowers.

**2010, Sept. 11**
**925** A295 1.35 l Horiz. pair, #a-b 2.00 1.50

Cathedrals A296

Designs: No. 926, 1.35 l, Transfiguration Cathedral, Kaisiadorys. No. 927, 1.35 l, St. Anthony of Padua Cathedral, Telsiai.

**2010, Oct. 16** ***Perf. 14***
**926-927** A296 Set of 2 2.00 1.50

See Nos. 949-950.

Christmas A297

New Year 2011 A298

**2010, Nov. 6** **Litho.**
**928** A297 1.35 l multi 1.00 .75
**929** A298 2.45 l multi 2.00 1.50

Grand Cross of the Order of the Lithuanian Grand Duke Gediminas — A299

**2010, Nov. 20** ***Perf. 13½x13¾***
**930** A299 7 l multi 5.25 3.75

Defenders of Freedom Day — A300

**2011, Jan. 8** **Litho.** ***Perf. 14***
**931** A300 1.35 l multi 1.10 .80

37th European Basketball Championships, Lithuania — A301

**2011, Jan. 22** ***Perf. 14¼x14***
**932** A301 2.45 l multi 1.90 1.50

2011 Census A302

**2011, Feb. 26** ***Perf. 14***
**933** A302 1.35 l multi 1.10 .80

**Famous Lithuanians Type of 2002**

Designs: 1.35 l, Gabriele Petkevicaite-Bite (1861-1943), writer. 2.15 l, Justinas Vienozinskis (1886-1960), artist. 2.90 l, Stasys Salkauskis (1886-1941), philosopher.

**2011, Mar. 5**
**934-936** A185 Set of 3 5.00 3.75

Souvenir Sheet

Kaunas, 650th Anniv. — A303

No. 937 — Buildings in Kaunas: a, Kauno Rotuse (City Hall). b, Kauno Centrinis Pastas (Main Post Office). c, Perkuno Namas Kaune (Perkunas House).

**2011, Mar. 19**
**937** A303 3 l Sheet of 3, #a-c 7.00 7.00

Europa A304

Tree in foreground, forest and: No. 938, 2.45 l, Field (denomination at LR). No. 939, 2.45 l, River (denomination at LL).

**2011, Apr. 23**
**938-939** A304 Set of 2 3.50 2.75

Intl. Year of Forests.

Pilgrim Route of Pope John Paul II — A305

**2011, May 7**
**940** A305 2.15 l multi 1.75 1.25

Miniature Sheet

Zoo Animals — A306

No. 941: a, Giraffa camelopardalis. b, Pelecanus. c, Cichlasoma octofasciatum. d, Ursus maritimus.

**2011, May 21** ***Perf. 14¼x13½***
**941** A306 4 l Sheet of 4, #a-d 12.50 12.50

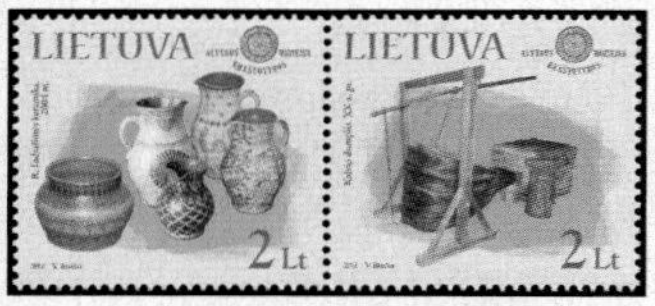


Items in Alytus Ethnographic Museum — A307

No. 942: a, Pot and pitchers. b, Blacksmith's bellows.

**2011, June 4** ***Perf. 14***
**942** A307 2 l Pair, #a-b 3.00 3.00

Czeslaw Milosz (1911-2004), 1980 Nobel Laureate in Literature A308

**2011, June 18** **Litho.**
**943** A308 3.35 l multi 2.75 1.75

Water Measuring Station, Smalininkai, 200th Anniv. — A309

**2011, July 16**
**944** A309 1.35 l multi 1.10 .80

Printed in sheets of 4.

**Arms Type of 1992**

Designs: 1.35 l, Plunge. 2.15 l, Kasiadorys. 2.90 l, Ignalina.

**2011, July 30** ***Perf. 14***
**945-947** A82 Set of 3 5.00 3.75

Souvenir Sheet

Stone of Puntukas — A310

**2011, Aug. 20**
**948** A310 8 l multi 6.25 6.25

Churches A311

Designs: No. 949, 1.55 l, Church, Trakai. No. 950, 1.55 l, Cathedral, Siauliai.

**2011, Sept. 3**
**949-950** A311 Set of 2 2.50 1.75

Battle of Saule, 775th Anniv. A312

**2011, Sept. 17**
**951** A312 2.45 l multi 2.00 1.50

Vilnius Historic Center UNESCO World Heritage Site — A313

Designs: No. 952, 3 l, Gate of Dawn (Ausros Vartai). No. 953, 3 l, St. John's Church.

**2011, Sept. 29** **Litho.**
**952-953** A313 Set of 2 4.50 3.75

Haliaeetus Albicilla A314

**2011, Oct. 8** ***Perf. 13½***
**954** A314 2.15 l multi 1.75 1.25

Endangered fauna from Red Book of Lithuania.

Christmas A315

Designs: 1.35 l, Snowman. 2.45 l, Snowflake.

**2011, Nov. 5** ***Perf. 14***
**955-956** A315 Set of 2 3.00 2.25

Grand Cross of the Order for Merits to Lithuania — A316

**2011, Nov. 26** ***Perf. 13½x13¾***
**957** A316 7 l multi 5.50 3.75

**Arms Type of 1992**

Designs: No. 958, 1.35 l, Kalvarija. No. 959, 1.35 l, Kavarskas. 2.45 l, Naujoji Akmene.

**2012, Jan. 7** ***Perf. 14***
**Size: 26x31mm**
**958-960** A82 Set of 3 4.00 2.75

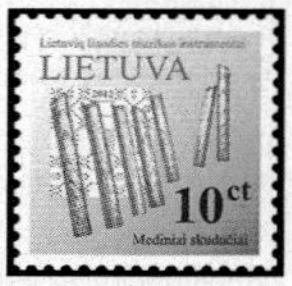


Traditional Musical Instruments — A317

Designs: 10c, Wooden panpipes. 20c, Clay pipes. 35c, Bladderbow bass. 1 l, Alder bark trumpet. 1.35 l, Zither. 2.15 l, Cowhorn reed pipes.

**2012, Jan. 7** ***Die Cut Perf. 12½***
**Self-Adhesive**

| | | | | | |
|---|---|---|---|---|---|
| **961** | A317 | 10c multi | | .25 | .25 |
| *a.* | | Dated "2013" | | .25 | .25 |
| **962** | A317 | 20c multi | | .25 | .25 |
| *a.* | | Dated "2013" | | .25 | .25 |
| **963** | A317 | 35c multi | | .25 | .25 |
| *a.* | | Dated "2013" | | .25 | .25 |
| **964** | A317 | 1 l multi | | .75 | .75 |
| *a.* | | Dated "2013" | | .80 | .80 |
| **965** | A317 | 1.35 l multi | | 1.00 | 1.00 |
| *a.* | | Dated "2013" | | 1.10 | 1.10 |
| **966** | A317 | 2.15 l multi | | 1.75 | 1.75 |
| | | *Nos. 961-966 (6)* | | 4.25 | 4.25 |

Issued: Nos. 964a, 965a, 5/11/13.

**Famous Lithuanians Type of 2002**

Designs: 1.55 l, Mikalojus Radvila Rudasis (Mikolaj Radziwill) (1512-84), Grand Chancellor of Lithuania. 2 l, Domicele Tarabildiene (1912-85), artist. 2.90 l, Stasys Simkus (1887-1943), composer.

**2012, Feb. 4** ***Perf. 14***
**967-969** A185 Set of 3 4.75 3.50

Maironis (1862-1932), Poet — A318

**2012, Feb. 25**
**970** A318 3.35 l multi 2.60 1.75

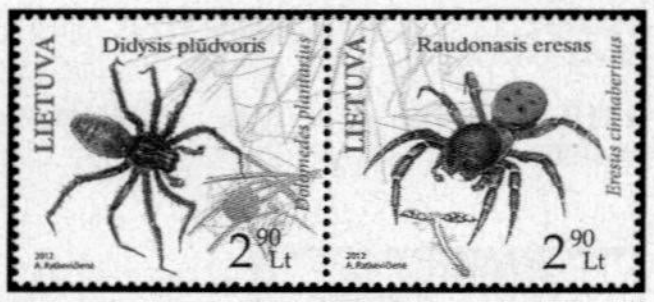


Spiders From Red Book of Lithuania — A319

No. 971: a, Dolomedes plantarius. b, Eresus cinnaberinus.

**2012, Mar. 17**
**971** A319 2.90 l Horiz. pair, #a-b 4.25 4.25

Christianization of Lithuania, 625th Anniv. — A320

**2012, Mar. 24** ***Perf. 14***
**972** A320 1.35 l multi 1.00 1.00

Europa — A321

Designs: No. 973, Hills, trees and river. No. 974, Buildings.

**2012, Apr. 28**
**973** A321 2.45 l multi 1.75 1.75
**974** A321 2.45 l multi 1.75 1.75

Souvenir Sheet

Year of Museums — A322

**2012, May 12**
**975** A322 7 l multi 5.25 5.25

Curonian Spit UNESCO World Heritage Site — A323

Designs: No. 976, 3 l, Fisherman's boat and house. No. 977, 3 l, Sand dunes.

**2012, May 26**
**976-977** A323 Set of 2 4.50 4.50

2012 Summer Olympics, London — A324

**2012, June 9**
**978** A324 3.35 l Boxing 2.40 2.40
**979** A324 3.55 l Rowing 2.60 2.60

Klaipeda, 760th Anniv. — A325

**2012, July 14**
**980** A325 2 l multi 1.50 1.50

Battle of Blue Waters, 650th Anniv. A326

**2012, Aug. 25**
**981** A326 2.45 l multi 1.90 1.90

Pres. Algirdas Brazauskas (1932-2010) A327

**2012, Sept. 22**
**982** A327 1.35 l multi 1.00 1.00

Establishment of Provisional Lithuanian Currency, 20th Anniv. A328

**2012, Sept. 29**
**983** A328 2 l multi 1.50 1.50

Oskar Minkowski (1858-1931), Diabetes Researcher A329

**2012, Oct. 20**
**984** A329 1.35 l multi 1.00 1.00

Railway Bridges A330

Train and: Nos. 985, 986a, Lyduvenai Bridge, Lithuania. No. 986b, Narva Bridge, Estonia. No. 986c, Carnikava Bridge, Latvia.

**2012, Oct. 25**
**985** A330 8 l multi 6.00 6.00

**Souvenir Sheet**
***Perf. 13½***
**986** A330 4 l Sheet of 3, #a-c 9.00 9.00

See Estonia Nos. 713-714, Latvia Nos. 815-816.

Christmas A331

Designs: 1.35 l, Body of water. 2.45 l, Snow-covered house.

**2012, Nov. 10** ***Perf. 14***
**987-988** A331 Set of 2 2.75 2.75

Christianization of Samogitia, 600th Anniv. — A332

**2013, Jan. 5** ***Perf. 13x13¼***
**989** A332 2.45 l multi 2.00 2.00

**Souvenir Sheet**

Flora and Fauna of Zuvintas Biosphere Reserve — A333

No. 990: a, Vulpes vulpes. b, Panurus biarmicus. c, Dactylorhiza maculata.

**2013, Jan. 19** ***Perf. 14¼x14½***
**990** A333 3 l Sheet of 3, #a-c 7.25 7.25

New Year 2013 (Year of the Snake) A334

**2013, Feb. 9** ***Perf. 13x13¼***
**991** A334 2.90 l multi 2.25 2.25

Lithuanian Laser Industry — A335

**2013, Feb. 23** ***Perf. 13¼x13***
**992** A335 1.35 l multi 1.00 1.00

Famous Lithuanians A336

Designs: 1.35 l, Antanas Strazdas (1763-1833), poet. 2 l, Pranas Masiotas (1863-1940), writer.

**2013, Mar. 9** ***Perf. 13¼x13***
**993-994** A336 Set of 2 2.50 2.50

Uprising of 1863, 150th Anniv. — A337

**2013, Mar. 23** ***Perf. 13x13¼***
**995** A337 1.35 l multi 1.00 1.00

Ciconia Ciconia A338

**2013, Apr. 6** ***Perf. 11***
**996** A338 7 l multi 5.50 5.50

No. 996 was printed in sheets of 2.

Europa A339

Postal vehicles: No. 997, 2.45 l, Tazzari Zero (yellow vehicle). No. 998, 2.45 l, Moskvitch 401 (blue vehicle).

**2013, Apr. 27** ***Perf. 13x13¼***
**997-998** A339 Set of 2 3.75 3.75

Mother's Day — A340

**2013, May 4** ***Perf. 13¼x13***
**999** A340 1.35 l multi 1.10 1.10

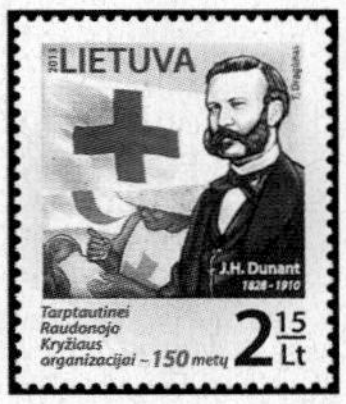

International Red Cross, 150th Anniv. — A341

**2013, May 11**
**1000** A341 2.15 l multi 1.75 1.75

Father's Day — A342

**2013, June 1**
**1001** A342 1.35 l multi 1.10 1.10

Kaunas Cathedral Basilica, 600th Anniv. A343

**2013, June 8** ***Perf. 13x13¼***
**1002** A343 1.35 l multi 1.10 1.10

Lithuanian Presidency of the European Union — A344

**2013, June 15** ***Perf. 14½x14***
**1003** A344 2.45 l multi 1.90 1.90

**Souvenir Sheet**

Transfer of Klaipeda (Memel) to Lithuanian Control, 90th Anniv. — A345

**2013, June 29** ***Perf. 14¼x14½***
**1004** A345 7 l multi 5.25 5.25

First Lithuanian National Olympics, 75th Anniv. A346

**2013, July 13** ***Perf. 13x13¼***
**1005** A346 1.35 l multi 1.10 1.10

A347

2.90 l, Death of Captains Steponas Darius and Stasys Girenas on New York-Kaunas Transatlantic Flight, 80th Anniv.

**2013, July 20**
**1006** A347 2.90 l multi 2.25 2.25

Lighthouses A348

Designs: No. 1007, 2.45 l, Cape Vente Lighthouse. No. 1008, 2.45 l, Kaunas Lighthouse.

**2013, July 27** ***Perf. 13¼x13***
**1007-1008** A348 Set of 2 3.75 3.75

Military Uniforms — A349

**2013, Aug. 24 Litho. *Perf. 13¼x13***
**1009** A349 1.35 l multi 1.10 1.10

Birds From Red Book of Lithuania — A350

Designs: 2.15 l, Acrocephalus paludicola. 2.90 l, Anthus campsetris.

**2013, Sept. 7 Litho. *Perf. 13¼x13***
**1010** A350 2.15 l multi 1.75 1.75
**1011** A350 2.90 l multi 2.25 2.25

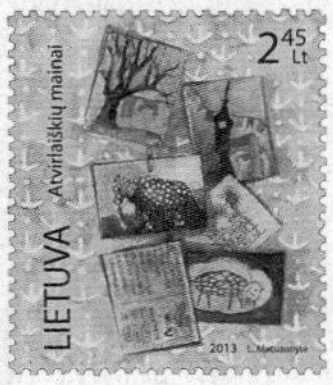


Postcrossing Post Cards — A351

**2013, Oct. 5 Litho. *Perf. 13¼x13***
**1012** A351 2.45 l multi 2.00 2.00

Christmas and New Year's Day A352

Bear and fox: 1.35 l, Exchanging gifts. 2.45 l, Watching fireworks display.

**2013, Nov. 9 Litho. *Perf. 13x13¼***
**1013-1014** A352 Set of 2 3.00 3.00

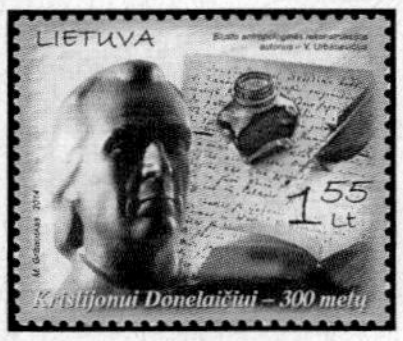


Kristijonas Donelaitis (1714-80), Poet — A353

**2014, Jan. 4 Litho. *Perf. 13x13¼***
**1015** A353 1.55 l multi 1.25 1.25

2014 Winter Olympics, Sochi, Russia A354

Designs: 2.15 l, Two-man bobsled. 2.90 l, Ice hockey.

**2014, Jan. 18**
**1016-1017** A354 Set of 2 4.00 4.00

Souvenir Sheet

New Year 2014 (Year of the Horse) — A355

**2014, Feb. 1 Litho. *Perf. 14¼x14½***
**1018** A355 7 l multi 5.50 5.50

Shrove Tuesday Masks A356

**2014. Feb. 15 Litho. *Perf. 13x13¼***
**1019** A356 2 l multi 1.60 1.60

Re-establishment of Vytautas Magnus University, 25th Anniv. — A357

**2014, Mar. 8 Litho. *Perf. 13¼x13***
**1020** A357 1.55 l multi 1.25 1.25

Admission to NATO, 10th Anniv. — A358

**2014, Mar. 29 Litho. *Perf. 13x13¼***
**1021** A358 2.15 l multi 1.75 1.75

Owls From Red Book of Lithuania — A359

Designs: 2 l, Tyto alba. 3 l, Glaucidium passerinum.

**2014, Apr. 5 Litho. *Perf. 13¼x13***
**1022-1023** A359 Set of 2 4.00 4.00
*1023a* Booklet pane of 6, 3 each #1022-1023 12.00 —
Complete booklet, #1023a 12.00

Admission to the European Union, 10th Anniv. A360

**2014, Apr. 26 Litho. *Perf. 13c13¼***
**1024** A360 2.15 l multi 1.75 1.75

Europa A361

Designs: No. 1025, 2.45 l, Goat horn (ozragis), wooden bells (skrabalai). No. 1026, 2.45 l, Reed pipe (birbyne), zither (kankles).

**2014, May 3 Litho. *Perf. 13x13¼***
**1025-1026** A361 Set of 2 4.00 4.00

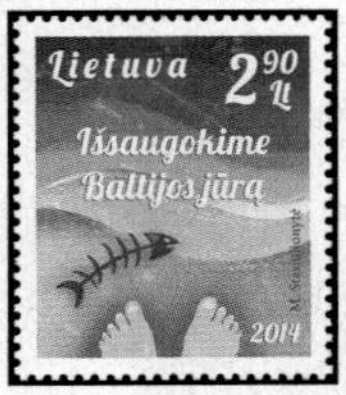


Protection of the Baltic Sea — A362

**2014, May 24 Litho. *Perf. 13¼x13***
**1027** A362 2.90 l multi 2.40 2.40
*a.* Tête-bêche pair 4.80 4.80
*b.* Souvenir sheet of 3 #1027a 14.50 —

No. 1027 was printed in sheets of 9, with the central stamp inverted in relation to the others. No. 1027b was sold with, but not attached to, a booklet cover.

Karaite Judaism — A363

No. 1028: a, Seraya Szapszal (1873-1961), leader of Lithuanian Karaite community. b, Kenesa (synagogue), Vilnius.

**2014, June 7 Litho. *Perf. 13x13¼***
**1028** A363 2.15 l Pair, #a-b 3.50 3.50

Lithuanian Song Festival, 90th Anniv. — A364

**2014, June 28 Litho. *Perf. 13¼x13***
**1029** A364 1.35 l multi 1.10 1.10

Lithuanian Term as Non-Permanent Member of United Nations Security Council — A365

**2014, July 12 Litho. *Perf. 13¼x13***
**1030** A365 1.35 l multi 1.10 1.10

In anticipation of Lithuania's official change to Euro currency in January 2015, No. 1030 and stamps issued through the end of 2014 are denominated in litas and the equivalent value in the not-yet-accepted euro currency.

Souvenir Sheet

Baltic Chain Demonstration, 25th Anniv. — A366

No. 1031: a, Five adults and one child. b, Three women. c, Man and child.

**2014, Aug. 23 Litho. *Perf. 13¼***
**1031** A366 7 l Sheet of 3, #a-c 16.00 16.00

See Estonia Nos. 764-765, Latvia Nos. 883-884.

Battle of Orsha, 500th Anniv. — A367

**2014, Sept. 6 Litho. *Perf. 13x13¼***
**1032** A367 2.60 l multi 1.90 1.90

Earth, LituanicaSAT-1 and Litsat-1 A368

**2014, Sept. 20 Litho. *Perf. 13x13¼***
**1033** A368 2.90 l multi 2.25 2.25
*a.* Tete-beche pair 4.50 4.50
*b.* Miniature sheet of 6 + 2 labels 13.50

No. 1033 was printed in sheets of 16 + 4 labels. No. 1033b was sold with, but unattached to, a booklet cover.

**Wooden Church Belfries Type of 2007 With Added Euro Denomination**

Design: 5c, Belfry from church in Vabalininkas, 19th cent.

***Die Cut Perf. 12½***

**2014, Oct. 11 Litho.**

**Self-Adhesive**

**1034** A249 5c multi .25 .25

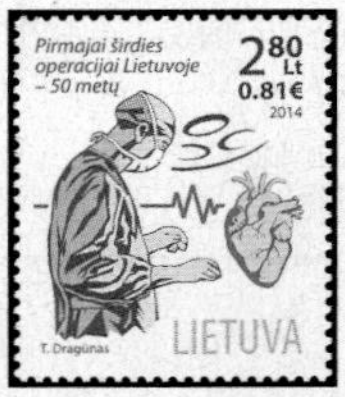


Open Heart Surgery, 50th Anniv. — A369

**2014, Oct. 11 Litho. *Perf. 13¼x13***
**1035** A369 2.80 l multi 2.10 2.10

Christmas A370

Designs: 1.35 l, Man holding letter and umbrella. 2.80 l, Santa Claus in balloon.

**2014, Nov. 8 Litho. *Perf. 13¼x13***
**1036-1037** A370 Set of 2 3.00 3.00

**100 Cents = 1 Euro**

Introduction of Euro Currency
A371

**2015, Jan. 2 Litho. *Perf. 13x13¼***

**1038** A371 75c multi 1.90 1.90

Coins Depicting White Knight "Vytis" — A372

Coin from: 1c, 1388-90. 3c, 1440-92. 10c, 1562. 29c, 1660. 39c, 1754. 62c, 1925.

***Die Cut Perf. 12½***

**2015, Jan. 2 Litho.**

**Self-Adhesive**

| | | | | | |
|---|---|---|---|---|---|
| **1039** | A372 | 1c ol bis & blk | | .25 | .25 |
| **1040** | A372 | 3c ol bis & blk | | .25 | .25 |
| **1041** | A372 | 10c ol bis & blk | | .25 | .25 |
| **1042** | A372 | 29c ol bis & blk | | .70 | .70 |
| **1043** | A372 | 39c ol bis & blk | | .95 | .95 |
| **1044** | A372 | 62c ol bis & blk | | 1.50 | 1.50 |
| | | *Nos. 1039-1044 (6)* | | 3.90 | 3.90 |

Endangered Animals — A373

Designs: 71c, Lutra lutra. 87c, Mustela lutreola.

**2015, Jan. 17 Litho. *Perf. 13¼x13***

**1045-1046** A373 Set of 2 3.75 3.75

Mikolaj Radziwill (the Black) (1515-65), Grand Hetman
A374

**2015, Feb. 7 Litho. *Perf. 13x13¼***

**1047** A374 45c multi 1.00 1.00

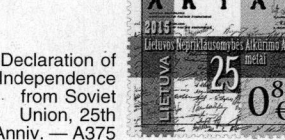

Declaration of Independence from Soviet Union, 25th Anniv. — A375

**2015, Mar. 7 Litho. *Perf. 13x13¼***

**1048** A375 84c multi 1.90 1.90

Kaunas Fortress
A376

**2015, Apr. 11 Litho. *Perf. 13x13¼***

**1049** A376 €2.03 multi 4.75 4.75

A377

Wooden Toys — A378

**2015, May 9 Litho. *Perf. 13¼x13***

**1050** A377 71c multi 1.60 1.60

**1051** A378 71c multi 1.60 1.60

Europa.

Jonas Juska (1815-86), Linguist
A379

**2015, June 6 Litho. *Perf. 13x13¼***

**1052** A379 58c multi 1.25 1.25

Pervalka Nature Preserve
A380

**2015, June 20 Litho. *Perf. 13x13¼***

**1053** A380 97c multi 2.25 2.25

Kretinga Railway Bridge
A381

**2015, July 4 Litho. *Perf. 13x13¼***

**1054** A381 87c multi 1.90 1.90

Miniature Sheet

Embroidery Designs — A382

No. 1055 — Embroidery designs of various ethnographic groups: a, Mazoji Lietuva. b, Zemaitija. c, Aukstaitija. d, Suvalkija. e, Dzukija.

**2015, July 18 Litho. *Perf. 13x13½***

**1055** A382 75c Sheet of 5, #a-e 8.25 8.25

Year of Ethnography.

Gown Designed by Juozas Statkevicius
A383

**2015, Aug. 8 Litho. *Perf. 13½x13¾***

**1056** A383 €2.03 multi 4.75 4.75

*a.* Sheet of 4 34.00 34.00

No. 1056 was printed in sheets of 2. No. 1056a was sold for €15 with a booklet cover, but unattached to it.

Education and Knowledge Day — A384

**2015, Aug. 29 Litho. *Perf. 13¼x13***

**1057** A384 45c multi 1.00 1.00

Michal Kleofas Oginski (1765-1833), Composer and Politician
A385

**2015, Sept. 26 Litho. *Perf. 13x13¼***

**1058** A385 81c multi 1.90 1.90

Information Technologies
A386

**2015, Oct. 24 Litho. *Perf. 13x13¼***

**1059** A386 84c multi 1.90 1.90

Traditional Handicrafts
A387

**2015, Nov. 7 Litho. *Perf. 13x13¼***

**1060** A387 75c multi 1.60 1.60

Christmas and New Year's Day
A388

Christmas tree, people and: 39c, House. 81c, Snowman.

**2015, Nov. 14 Litho. *Perf. 13x13¼***

**1061-1062** A388 Set of 2 2.60 2.60

White Knight "Vytis" and Flag — A389

Various depictions of Vytis on horseback and flags from: 1c, 1410. 3c, 1553. 10c, 1863. 29c, 1929. 39c, 1989. 62c, 1993.

***Die Cut Perf. 12½***

**2016, Jan. 2 Litho.**

**Self-Adhesive**

| | | | | | |
|---|---|---|---|---|---|
| **1063** | A389 | 1c red & black | | .25 | .25 |
| **1064** | A389 | 3c red & black | | .25 | .25 |
| **1065** | A389 | 10c red & black | | .25 | .25 |
| **1066** | A389 | 29c red & black | | .65 | .65 |
| **1067** | A389 | 39c red & black | | .85 | .85 |
| **1068** | A389 | 62c red & black | | 1.40 | 1.40 |
| | | *Nos. 1063-1068 (6)* | | 3.65 | 3.65 |

Soviet Military Actions Against Lithuania, 25th Anniv. — A390

**2016, Jan. 12 Litho. *Perf. 13¼x13***

**1069** A390 45c multi 1.00 1.00

Mushrooms
A391

Designs: No. 1070, 84c, Boletus radicans. No. 1071, 84c, Gomphus clavatus.

**2016, Feb. 13 Litho. *Perf. 13¼x13***

**1070-1071** A391 Set of 2 3.75 3.75

*1071a* Booklet pane of 6, 3 each #1070-1071 11.50 —

Complete booklet, #1071a 11.50

No. 1071a contains one example of No. 1070 that is tete-beche in relation to the three adjacent stamps.

Julius Juzeliunas (1916-2001), Composer
A392

**2016, Feb. 20 Litho. *Perf. 13x13¼***

**1072** A392 39c multi .85 .85

New Verkiai Paper Factory, Vilnius
A393

**2016, Mar. 5 Litho. *Perf. 13x13¼***

**1073** A393 58c multi 1.40 1.40

Oak Trees, Azuolynas Park, Kaunas
A395

**2016, Apr. 2 Litho. *Perf. 13x13¼***

**1075** A395 87c multi 2.00 2.00

*a.* Booklet pane of 4 8.00 —

Complete booklet, #1075a 8.00

No. 1075a contains two tete-beche pairs.

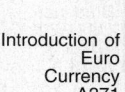

Diplomatic Relations Between Lithuania and Japan, 25th Anniv. A396

**2016, Apr. 16 Litho. *Perf. 13x13¼***

**1076** A396 €1 multi 2.40 2.40

George Maciunas (1931-78), Co-Founder of Fluxus Art Community A397

**2016, Apr. 16 Litho. *Perf. 13¼x13***

**1077** A397 75c multi 1.75 1.75

A398

Europa A399

**2016, May 7 Litho. *Perf. 13x13¼***

| | | | | |
|---|---|---|---|---|
| **1078** | A398 71c multi | 1.60 | 1.60 |
| **1079** | A399 71c multi | 1.60 | 1.60 |
| *a.* | Tete-beche pair | 3.20 | 3.20 |
| *b.* | Booklet pane of 6 #1079 | 9.75 | 9.75 |
| | Complete booklet, #1079b | 9.75 | |

Think Green Issue.

No. 1079a is found only in No. 1079b.

Cucumbers and Honey A400

**2016, July 9 Litho. *Perf. 13x13¼***

**1080** A400 39c multi .90 .90

Souvenir Sheet

Zemaitukas Horses — A401

**2016, July 9 Litho. *Perf. 13x13½***

**1081** A401 €1.56 multi 3.50 3.50

2016 Summer Olympics, Rio de Janeiro A402

Christ the Redeemer Statue, Rio de Janeiro, and: 81c, Swimming. 84c, Equestrian.

**2016, Aug. 6 Litho. *Perf. 13x13¼***

**1082-1083** A402 Set of 2 3.75 3.75

Lithuanian Admission to United Nations, 25th Anniv. — A403

**2016, Sept. 17 Litho. *Perf. 13¼x13***

**1084** A403 75c multi 1.75 1.75

Seated, by Petras Repsys A404

**2016, Oct. 9 Litho. *Perf. 13¾***

**1085** A404 48c multi 1.10 1.10

Pres. Kazys Grinius (1866-1950) A405

**2016, Oct. 29 Litho. *Perf. 13¼x13***

**1086** A405 45c multi 1.00 1.00

Souvenir Sheet

Revival of the Lithuanian State, Cent. — A406

No. 1087: a, Auszra Newspaper. b, Dr. Jonas Basanavicius (1851-1927), founder of Auszra. c, Varpas Newspaper.

**2016, Nov. 5 Litho. *Perf. 14***

**1087** A406 €1.16 Sheet of 3, #a-c 7.50 7.50

Baltic Assembly, 25th Anniv. — A407

**2016, Nov. 8 Litho. *Perf. 13½x13¼***

**Stamp With White Frame**

**1088** A407 45c multi .95 .95

**Souvenir Sheet**

**Stamp With Multicolored Frame**

**1089** A407 97c multi 2.10 2.10

See Estonia Nos. 827-828, Latvia Nos. 948-949.

Christmas and New Year's Day — A408

Designs: 39c, Adult and child with sled, snow-covered houses. 81c, People on city street in winter.

**2016, Nov. 12 Litho. *Perf. 13x12¾***

**1090-1091** A408 Set of 2 2.60 2.60

Protestant Reformation, 500th Anniv. A409

**2017, Jan. 7 Litho. *Perf. 14***

**1092** A409 39c multi .85 .85

Diplomatic Relations Between Lithuania and Israel, 25th Anniv. — A410

**2017, Jan. 7 Litho. *Perf. 14***

**1093** A410 97c multi 2.10 2.10

White Knight "Vytis" on Horseback — A411

Depiction of Vytis from: 3c, 14th-15th cent. 10c, 15th cent. 39c, 15th cent., diff. 42c, 16th cent. 94c, 17th-18th cent. €1, 20th cent.

***Die Cut Perf. 12½***

**2017, Jan. 14 Litho.**

**Self-Adhesive**

| | | | |
|---|---|---|---|
| **1094** | A411 3c black | .25 | .25 |
| **1095** | A411 10c black | .25 | .25 |
| **1096** | A411 39c black | .85 | .85 |
| **1097** | A411 42c black | .90 | .90 |
| **1098** | A411 94c black | 2.00 | 2.00 |
| **1099** | A411 €1 black | 2.25 | 2.25 |
| | *Nos. 1094-1099 (6)* | 6.50 | 6.50 |

Establishment of Samogitian Diocese, 600th Anniv. — A412

**2017, Feb. 10 Litho. *Perf. 14***

**1100** A412 €1 multi 2.10 2.10

See Vatican City No. 1641.

Kazys Bradunas (1917-2009), Writer A413

**2017, Feb. 11 Litho. *Perf. 14***

**1101** A413 39c multi .85 .85

Souvenir Sheet

Revival of the Lithuanian State, Cent. — A414

No. 1102: a, Return of Lithuanian press, 1904. b, Great Seimas of Vilnius, 1905. c, Vilnius Conference, 1917.

**2017, Feb. 11 Litho. *Perf. 14***

**1102** A414 €1.16 Sheet of 3, #a-c 7.50 7.50

Algirdas Julien Greimas (1917-92), Semiotician A415

**2017, Mar. 4 Litho. *Perf. 14***

**1103** A415 39c multi .85 .85

Mammals From Red Book of Lithuania A416

Designs: No. 1104, 42c, Sicista betulina. No. 1105, 42c, Eliomys quercinus.

**2017, Apr. 8 Litho. *Perf. 14***

**1104-1105** A416 Set of 2 1.90 1.90

Klaipeda Castle A417

Birzai Castle A418

**2017, Apr. 29 Litho. *Perf. 14***

**1106** A417 81c multi 1.75 1.75

**1107** A418 81c multi 1.75 1.75

Europa.

Caraway Seed Cheese A419

**2017, May 20 Litho. *Perf. 14***

**1108** A419 52c multi 1.25 1.25

King Wilhelm's Canal Lock — A420

**2017, June 10 Litho. *Perf. 14***
**1109** A420 94c multi 2.25 2.25

Seimyniskiai Hillfort A421

**2017, July 8 Litho. *Perf. 14***
**1110** A421 39c multi .95 .95

Lazarus Arise, by Stanislovas Kuzma A422

**2017, Aug. 26 Litho. *Perf. 14***
**1111** A422 94c multi 2.25 2.25

Souvenir Sheet

Animals — A423

No. 1112: a, Lepus europaeus (European hare). b, Meles meles (European Badger). c, Cervus elaphus (Red Deer).

**2017, Sept. 7 Litho. *Perf. 14***
**1112** A423 84c Sheet of 3, #a-c 6.00 6.00

Menorah — A424

**2017, Sept. 23 Litho. *Perf. 14***
**1113** A424 94c multi 2.25 2.25

Jewish minority in Lithuania.

Souvenir Sheet

Lithuanian Constitutions — A425

No. 1114 — Scroll and year: a, 1791. b, 1922. c, 1992.

**2017, Oct. 28 Litho. *Perf. 14***
**1114** A425 84c Sheet of 3, #a-c 6.00 6.00

Constitution of the Republic of Lithuania, 25th anniv.

Christmas — A426

New Year 2018 — A427

**2017, Nov. 25 Litho. *Perf. 12½x12***
**1115** A426 39c blue & red org .95 .95
**1116** A427 81c blue & red org 2.00 2.00

Columns of Gediminas — A428

Columns of Gediminas depictions from: 3c, 15th cent. 10c, 16th cent. 39c, 20th cent. 42c, 19th cent.

***Die Cut Perf. 12½***
**2018, Jan. 5 Litho.**
**Self-Adhesive**
**1117** A428 3c black .25 .25
**1118** A428 10c black .25 .25
**1119** A428 39c black 1.00 1.00
**1120** A428 42c black 1.10 1.10
*Nos. 1117-1120 (4)* 2.60 2.60

2018 Winter Olympics, PyeongChang, South Korea — A429

Designs: 84c, Curling. 94c, Speed skating.

**2018, Jan. 26 Litho. *Perf. 14***
**1121-1122** A429 Set of 2 4.50 4.50

## SEMI-POSTAL STAMPS

**Regular Issue of 1923-24 Surcharged in Blue, Violet or Black**

On A21

On A22

On A23

**1924, Feb. Wmk. 147 *Perf. 11***
**B1** A21 2c + 2c pale brn (Bl) .90 *2.25*
**B2** A21 3c + 3c ol bis (Bl) .90 *2.25*
**B3** A21 5c + 5c pale grn (V) .90 *2.25*
**B4** A21 10c + 10c vio (Bk) 2.25 *3.25*
**B5** A21 36c + 34c org brn (V) 4.75 *12.00*

**Wmk. Webbing (109)**
**B6** A21 10c + 10c vio (Bk) 7.50 *20.00*
**B7** A21 15c + 15c scar (V) 1.10 *2.50*
**B8** A21 20c + 20c ol brn (Bl) 2.25 *4.00*
**B9** A21 25c + 25c bl (Bk) 21.00 *55.00*
**B10** A22 50c + 50c yel grn (V) 5.25 *12.00*
**B11** A22 60c + 60c red (V) 5.25 *12.00*
**B12** A23 1 l + 1 l org & grn (V) 6.00 *16.00*
**B13** A23 3 l + 2 l red & gray (V) 9.00 *32.50*
**B14** A23 5 l + 3 l brn & bl (V) 15.00 *40.00*

**Unwmk.**
**B15** A21 25c + 25c dp bl (Bk) 4.75 *12.00*
*Nos. B1-B15 (15)* 86.80 228.00
Set, never hinged 225.00

**For War Invalids**

Semi-Postal Stamps of 1924 Surcharged in Gold or Copper

**1926, Dec. 3 Wmk. 147**
**B16** A21 1 + 1c on #B1 1.00 1.25
*a.* Inverted surcharge 40.00
**B17** A21 2 + 2c on #B2 (C) 1.00 1.25
**B19** A21 2 + 2c on #B3 1.00 1.25
*a.* Double surch., one inverted 40.00
**B20** A21 5 + 5c on #B4 2.00 2.00
**B21** A21 14 + 14c on #B5 6.00 7.00

**Wmk. Webbing (109)**
**B22** A21 5 + 5c on #B6 10.00 10.00
**B23** A21 5 + 5c on #B7 2.00 2.00
**B24** A21 10 + 10c on #B8 2.00 2.00
**B25** A21 10 + 10c on #B9 65.00 65.00

**Unwmk.**
**B26** A21 10 + 10c on #B15 4.00 5.00

**Surcharged in Copper or Silver**

On A22

On A23

**Wmk. Webbing (109)**
**B27** A22 20 + 20c on #B10 4.00 5.00
**B28** A22 25 + 25c on #B11 (S) 6.00 7.00
**B29** A23 30 + 30c on #B12 (S) 9.00 11.00
*Nos. B16-B29 (13)* 113.00 119.75
Set, never hinged 225.00

**For War Orphans**

Surcharged in Gold

**1926, Dec. 3 Wmk. 147**
**B30** A21 1 + 1c on #B1 .90 .90
**B31** A21 2 + 2c on #B2 .90 .90
*a.* Inverted surcharge 260.00
**B32** A21 2 + 2c on #B3 .90 .90
*a.* Inverted surcharge 30.00
**B33** A21 5 + 5c on #B4 2.00 2.25
**B34** A21 19 + 19c on #B5 4.00 5.00

**Wmk. Webbing (109)**
**B35** A21 5 + 5c on #B6 10.00 10.00
**B36** A21 10 + 10c on #B7 1.75 2.00
**B37** A21 15 + 15c on #B8 2.00 2.25
**B38** A21 15 + 15c on #B9 65.00 65.00

**Unwmk.**
**B39** A21 15 + 15c on #B15 3.00 3.00

**Surcharged in Gold**

On A22

On A23

**Wmk. 109**
**B40** A22 25c on #B10 5.00 6.00
**B41** A22 30c on #B11 8.00 7.00
**B42** A23 50c on #B12 10.00 11.00
*Nos. B30-B42 (13)* 113.45 116.20
Set, never hinged 225.00

Javelin throwing — SP1

Natl. Olympiad, July 15-20: 5c+5c, Archery. 30c+10c, Diving. 60c+15c, Running.

**Unwmk.**
**1938, July 13 Photo. *Perf. 14***
**B43** SP1 5c + 5c grn & dk grn 2.50 2.50
**B44** SP1 15c + 5c org & red org 2.50 2.50
**B45** SP1 30c + 10c bl & dk bl 4.50 4.50
**B46** SP1 60c + 15c tan & brn 5.75 5.75
*Nos. B43-B46 (4)* 15.25 15.25
Set, never hinged 45.00

**Same Overprinted in Red, Blue or Black**

Nos. B47, B50

Nos. B48-B49

**1938, July 13**
**B47** SP1 5c + 5c (R) 5.00 5.00
**B48** SP1 15c + 5c (Bl) 5.00 5.00
**B49** SP1 30c + 10c (R) 5.00 5.00
**B50** SP1 60c + 15c (Bk) 10.00 10.00
*Nos. B47-B50 (4)* 25.00 25.00
Set, never hinged 50.00

National Scout Jamboree, July 12-14.
Forged cancellations exist.

Basketball Players
SP6 SP7

Flags of Competing Nations and Basketball — SP8

**1939 Photo. *Perf. 14***

**B52** SP6 15c + 10c copper brn & brn 3.25 *6.50*
**B53** SP7 30c + 15c myrtle grn & grn 3.25 *6.50*
**B54** SP8 60c + 40c blue vio & gray vio 6.00 *12.00*
*Nos. B52-B54 (3)* 12.50 *25.00*
Set, never hinged 25.00

3rd European Basketball Championships held at Kaunas. The surtax was used for athletic equipment. Nos. B52-B54 exist imperf. Value, set pairs, $500.

## AIR POST STAMPS

Winged Posthorn AP1

Airplane over Neman River — AP2

Air Squadron AP3

Plane over Gediminas Castle — AP4

**1921 Litho. Wmk. 109 *Perf. 11½***

**C1** AP1 20sk ultra 1.25 .75
**C2** AP1 40sk red orange 1.00 .75
**C3** AP1 60sk green *1.10* .75
a. Imperf., pair *45.00*
**C4** AP1 80sk lt rose 1.50 .75
a. Horiz. pair, imperf. vert. *50.00 40.00*
**C5** AP2 1auk green & red *1.50* .75
a. Imperf., pair 90.00 *175.00*
**C6** AP3 2auk brown & blue 1.60 .75
**C7** AP4 5auk ol blk & yel 2.00 1.75
*Nos. C1-C7 (7)* 9.95 6.25
Set, never hinged 30.00

For surcharges see Nos. C21-C26, C29.

Allegory of Flight — AP5

**1921, Nov. 6**

**C8** AP5 20sk org & gray bl 1.40 *2.00*
**C9** AP5 40sk dl bl & lake 1.40 *2.00*
**C10** AP5 60sk vio bl & ol grn 1.40 *2.00*
**C11** AP5 80sk ocher & dp grn 1.40 *2.00*
a. Vert. pair, imperf. btwn. 35.00 35.00
**C12** AP5 1auk bl grn & bl 1.40 *2.00*
**C13** AP5 2auk gray & brn org 1.40 *2.00*
**C14** AP5 5auk dl lil & Prus bl 1.40 *2.00*
*Nos. C8-C14 (7)* 9.80 *14.00*
Set, never hinged 17.50

Opening of airmail service.

Plane over Kaunas — AP6

**Black Overprint**

**1922, July 16 *Perf. 11, 11½***

**C15** AP6 1auk ol brn & red 1.00 *2.75*
a. Imperf., pair 60.00
**C16** AP6 3auk violet & grn 1.00 *2.75*
**C17** AP6 5auk dp blue & yel 1.00 *4.00*
*Nos. C15-C17 (3)* 3.00 *9.50*
Set, never hinged 9.75

Nos. C15-C17, without overprint, were to be for the founding of the Air Post service but they were not put in use at that time. Subsequently the word "ZENKLAS" (stamp) was overprinted over "ISTEIGIMAS" (founding) and the date "1921, VI, 25" was obliterated by short vertical lines.

For surcharge see No. C31.

Plane over Gediminas Castle — AP7

**1922, July 22**

**C18** AP7 2auk blue & rose 1.10 .85
**C19** AP7 4auk brown & rose 1.10 .85
**C20** AP7 10auk black & gray bl 1.25 1.40
*Nos. C18-C20 (3)* 3.45 3.10
Set, never hinged 11.00

For surcharges see Nos. C27-C28, C30.

### Nos. C1-C7, C17-C20 Surcharged like Regular Issues in Black or Carmine

**1922**

**C21** AP1 10c on 20sk 3.25 2.50
**C22** AP1 10c on 40sk 1.75 1.50
**C23** AP1 10c on 60sk 1.75 1.50
a. Inverted surcharge 45.00
**C24** AP1 10c on 80sk 1.75 1.50
**C25** AP2 20c on 1auk 11.00 6.00
**C26** AP3 20c on 2auk 11.00 7.50
a. Without "CENT" 200.00 140.00
**C27** AP7 25c on 2auk 1.00 *1.00*
a. Inverted surcharge 45.00 40.00
**C28** AP7 30c on 4auk (C) 1.00 *1.00*
a. Double surcharge 50.00 45.00
**C29** AP4 50c on 5auk 2.00 1.50
**C30** AP7 50c on 10auk 1.00 *1.00*
a. Inverted surcharge 50.00 45.00
**C31** AP6 1 l on 5auk 16.00 15.00
a. Double surcharge 50.00
*Nos. C21-C31 (11)* 51.50 40.00
Set, never hinged 92.50

Airplane and Carrier Pigeons AP8

"Flight" AP9

**1924, Jan. 28 Wmk. 147 *Perf. 11***

**C32** AP8 20c yellow 1.15 .75
**C33** AP8 40c emerald 1.15 .75
a. Horiz. or vert. pair, imperf. between 60.00
**C34** AP8 60c rose 1.15 .75
a. Imperf., pair 75.00
**C35** AP9 1 l dk brown 2.50 .75
*Nos. C32-C35 (4)* 5.95 3.00
Set, never hinged 25.00

Most stamps, if not all, of the "unwatermarked" varieties show faint traces of watermark, according to experts.

For surcharges see Nos. CB1-CB4.

Swallow — AP10

**1926, June 17 Wmk. 198 *Perf. 14½***

**C37** AP10 20c carmine rose 1.10 .50
a. Horiz. or vert. pair, imperf. between 55.00
**C38** AP10 40c violet & red org 1.10 .50
a. Horiz. or vert. pair, imperf. between 55.00
**C39** AP10 60c blue & black 2.25 .50
a. Horiz. or vert. pair, imperf. between 55.00
c. Center inverted 250.00 160.00
*Nos. C37-C39 (3)* 4.45 1.50
Set, never hinged 6.00

Juozas Tubelis — AP11

Vytautas and Airplane over Kaunas AP12

Vytautas and Antanas Smetona AP13

**1930, Feb. 16 Wmk. 109 *Perf. 14***

**C40** AP11 5c blk, bis & brn 1.50 .35
**C41** AP11 10c dk bl, db & blk 1.50 .35
**C42** AP11 15c mar, gray & bl 1.50 .35
**C43** AP12 20c dk brn, org & dl red 1.50 .80
**C44** AP12 40c dk bl, lt bl & vio 4.00 .80
**C45** AP13 60c bl grn, lil & blk 5.00 .85
**C46** AP13 1 l dl red, lil & blk 9.00 1.60
*Nos. C40-C46 (7)* 24.00 5.10
Set, never hinged 100.00

5th cent. of the death of the Grand Duke Vytautas.

Map of Lithuania, Klaipeda and Vilnius — AP14

15c, 20c, Airplane over Neman. 40c, 60c, City Hall, Kaunas. 1 l, 2 l, Church of Vytautas, Kaunas.

**Wmk. Multiple Letters (238)**

**1932, July 21 *Perf. 14***

**C47** AP14 5c ver & ol grn .35 *.70*
**C48** AP14 10c dk red brn & ocher .35 *.70*
**C49** AP14 15c dk bl & org yel .35 *.70*
**C50** AP14 20c sl blk & org 1.75 *5.50*
**C51** AP14 60c ultra & ocher 2.50 *7.00*
**C52** AP14 2 l dk bl & yel 2.75 *7.00*

**Wmk. 198**

**C53** AP14 40c vio brn & yel 2.00 *5.50*
**C54** AP14 1 l vio brn & grn 3.00 *7.00*
*Nos. C47-C54 (8)* 13.05 *34.10*
Set, never hinged 50.00

**Imperf.**

*C47a* AP14 5c ver & ol grn .35 *.70*
*C48a* AP14 10c dk red brn & ocher .35 *.70*
*C49a* AP14 15c dk bl & org yel .35 *.70*
*C50a* AP14 20c sl blk & org 1.75 *5.50*
*C51a* AP14 60c ultra & ocher 2.50 *5.50*
*C52a* AP14 2 l dk bl & yel 2.75 *7.00*
*C53a* AP14 40c vio brn & yel 2.00 *7.00*
*C54a* AP14 1 l vio brn & grn 3.00 *7.00*
Set, never hinged 50.00

Issued for the benefit of Lithuanian orphans.

Mindaugas in the Battle of Shauyai, 1236 — AP15

15c, 20c, Coronation of Mindaugas (1253). 40c, Grand Duke Gediminas and his followers. 60c, Founding of Vilnius by Gediminas (1332). 1 l, Gediminas capturing the Russian Fortifications. 2 l, Grand Duke Algirdas before Moscow (1368).

**1932, Nov. 28 Wmk. 209 *Perf. 14***

**C55** AP15 5c grn & red lil .45 *.70*
**C56** AP15 10c emer & rose .45 *.70*
**C57** AP15 15c rose vio & bis brn .45 *.70*
**C58** AP15 20c rose red & blk brn 2.25 *3.50*
**C59** AP15 40c choc & dk gray 3.25 *4.75*
**C60** AP15 60c org & gray blk 4.50 *7.00*
**C61** AP15 1 l rose vio & grn 4.50 *7.00*
**C62** AP15 2 l dp bl & brn 4.50 *7.00*
*Nos. C55-C62 (8)* 20.35 *31.35*
Set, never hinged 45.00

**Imperf.**

*C55a* AP15 5c grn & red lil .45 .70
*C56a* AP15 10c emer & rose .45 .70
*C57a* AP15 15c rose vio & bis brn .45 .70
*C58a* AP15 20c rose red & blk brn 2.25 3.50
*C59a* AP15 40c choc & dk gray 3.25 4.75
*C60a* AP15 60c org & gray blk 4.50 7.00
*C61a* AP15 1 l rose vio & grn 4.50 7.00
*C62a* AP15 2 l dp bl & brn 4.50 7.00
Set, never hinged 45.00

Anniv. of independence.

Nos. C58-C62 exist with overprint "DARIUS-GIRENAS / NEW YORK-1933- KAUNAS" below small plane. The overprint was applied in New York with the approval of the Lithuanian consul general. Lithuanian postal authorities seem not to have been involved in the creation or release of these overprints.

Trakai Castle, Home of the Grand Duke Kestutis — AP16

Designs: 15c, 20c, Meeting of Kestutís and the Hermit Birute. 40c, 60c, Hermit Birute. 1 l, 2 l, Kestutis and his Brother Algirdas.

**1933, May 6 *Perf. 14***

**C63** AP16 5c ol gray & dp bl .40 *.70*
**C64** AP16 10c gray vio & org brn .40 *.70*
**C65** AP16 15c dp blue & lilac .40 *.70*
**C66** AP16 20c org brn & lilac 2.00 *4.00*
**C67** AP16 40c lt ultra & lilac 2.00 *4.00*
**C68** AP16 60c brown & lt ultra 5.25 *9.75*
**C69** AP16 1 l ol gray & dp bl 5.25 *9.75*
**C70** AP16 2 l vio gray & yel grn 5.25 *9.75*
*Nos. C63-C70 (8)* 20.95 *39.35*
Set, never hinged 35.00

**Imperf.**

*C63a* AP16 5c ol gray & dp bl .40 *.70*
*C64a* AP16 10c gray vio & org brn .40 *.70*
*C65a* AP16 15c dp blue & lilac .70 *.70*
*C66a* AP16 20c org brn & lilac 2.00 *4.00*
*C67a* AP16 40c lt ultra & lilac 2.00 *4.00*
*C68a* AP16 60c brown & lt ultra 5.25 *9.75*
*C69a* AP16 1 l ol gray & dp bl 5.25 *9.75*
*C70a* AP16 2 l vio gray & yel grn 5.25 *9.75*
Set, never hinged 35.00

Reopening of air service to Berlin-Kaunas-Moscow, and 550th anniv. of the death of Kestutis.

Joseph Maironis — AP17

Joseph Tumas-Vaizgantas — AP17a

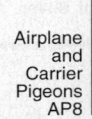

Designs: 40c, 60c, Vincas Kudirka. 1 l, 2 l, Julia A. Zemaite.

**1933, Sept. 15** *Perf. 14*

| | | | | |
|---|---|---|---|---|
| **C71** | AP17 | 5c crim & dp bl | .25 | *.30* |
| **C72** | AP17 | 10c bl vio & grn | .25 | *.30* |
| **C73** | AP17a | 15c dk grn & choc | .25 | *.30* |
| **C74** | AP17a | 20c brn car & ultra | .50 | *.60* |
| **C75** | AP17 | 40c red brn & ol grn | 1.50 | *2.50* |
| **C76** | AP17 | 60c dk bl & choc | 1.50 | *6.00* |
| **C77** | AP17 | 1 l citron & indigo | 2.50 | *6.25* |
| **C78** | AP17 | 2 l dp grn & red brn | 3.50 | *10.00* |
| | | *Nos. C71-C78 (8)* | 10.25 | *26.25* |
| | | Set, never hinged | 25.00 | |

**Imperf.**

| | | | | |
|---|---|---|---|---|
| *C71a* | AP17 | 5c crim & dp bl | .25 | .30 |
| *C72a* | AP16 | 10c bl vio & grn | .25 | .30 |
| *C73a* | AP17a | 15c dk grn & choc | .25 | .30 |
| *C74a* | AP17a | 20c brn car & ol grn | .50 | .60 |
| *C75a* | AP17 | 40c red brn & ol grn | 1.50 | 2.50 |
| *C76a* | AP17 | 60c dk bl & choc | 1.50 | 6.00 |
| *C77a* | AP17 | 1 l citron & indigo | 2.50 | 6.25 |
| *C78a* | AP17 | 2 l dp grn & red brn | 3.50 | 10.00 |
| | | Set, never hinged | 25.00 | |

Issued for the benefit of Lithuanian orphans.

Capts. Steponas Darius and Stasys Girenas AP18

Ill-Fated Plane "Lituanica" AP19

The Dark Angel of Death — AP20

"Lituanica" over Globe — AP21

"Lituanica" and White Knight — AP22

*Perf. 11½*

**1934, May 18 Unwmk. Engr.**

| | | | | |
|---|---|---|---|---|
| **C79** | AP18 | 20c scarlet & blk | .25 | .25 |
| **C80** | AP19 | 40c dp rose & bl | .25 | .25 |
| **C81** | AP18 | 60c dk vio & blk | .25 | .25 |
| **C82** | AP20 | 1 l black & rose | .35 | .25 |
| **C83** | AP21 | 3 l gray grn & org | .45 | *.50* |
| **C84** | AP22 | 5 l dk brn & bl | 1.75 | *3.25* |
| | | *Nos. C79-C84 (6)* | 3.30 | 4.75 |
| | | Set, never hinged | 5.50 | |

Death of Capts. Steponas Darius and Stasys Girenas on their New York-Kaunas flight of 1933.

No. C80 exists with diagonal overprint: "F. VAITKUS / nugalejo Atlanta / 21-22-IX-1935." Value $400.

Felix Waitkus and Map of Transatlantic Flight — AP23

**Wmk. 238**

**1936, Mar. 24 Litho.** *Perf. 14*

| | | | | |
|---|---|---|---|---|
| **C85** | AP23 | 15c brown lake | 2.25 | .85 |
| **C86** | AP23 | 30c dark green | 3.25 | .85 |
| **C87** | AP23 | 60c blue | 4.50 | 2.50 |
| | | *Nos. C85-C87 (3)* | 10.00 | 4.20 |
| | | Set, never hinged | 13.75 | |

Transatlantic Flight of the Lituanica II, Sept. 21-22, 1935.

## AIR POST SEMI-POSTAL STAMPS

**Nos. C32-C35 Surcharged like Nos. B1-B9 (No. CB1), Nos. B10-B11 (Nos. CB2-CB3), and Nos. B12-B14 (No. CB4) in Red, Violet or Black**

**1924 Wmk. 147** *Perf. 11*

| | | | | |
|---|---|---|---|---|
| **CB1** | AP8 | 20c + 20c yellow (R) | 12.00 | 12.00 |
| **CB2** | AP8 | 40c + 40c emerald (V) | 12.00 | 12.00 |
| **CB3** | AP8 | 60c + 60c rose (V) | 12.00 | 12.00 |
| **CB4** | AP9 | 1 l + 1 l dk brown | 12.00 | 12.00 |
| | | *Nos. CB1-CB4 (4)* | 48.00 | 48.00 |
| | | Set, never hinged | 80.00 | |

Surtax for the Red Cross. See note following No. C35.

## SOUTH LITHUANIA

### GRODNO DISTRICT

Russian Stamps of 1909-12 Surcharged in Black or Red

**1919 Unwmk.** *Perf. 14, 14½x15*

| | | | | |
|---|---|---|---|---|
| **L1** | A14 | 50sk on 3k red | 60.00 | 57.50 |
| *a.* | | Double surcharge | *250.00* | *250.00* |
| **L2** | A14 | 50sk on 5k claret | 60.00 | 57.50 |
| *a.* | | Imperf., pair | 550.00 | 475.00 |
| **L3** | A15 | 50sk on 10k dk bl (R) | 60.00 | 57.50 |
| **L4** | A11 | 50sk on 15k red brn & bl | 60.00 | 57.50 |
| *a.* | | Imperf., pair | 650.00 | 550.00 |
| **L5** | A11 | 50sk on 25k grn & gray vio (R) | 60.00 | 57.50 |
| **L6** | A11 | 50sk on 35k red brn & grn | 60.00 | 57.50 |
| **L7** | A8 | 50sk on 50k vio & grn | 60.00 | 57.50 |
| **L8** | A11 | 50sk on 70k brn & org | 60.00 | 57.50 |
| | | *Nos. L1-L8 (8)* | 480.00 | 460.00 |

Excellent counterfeits are plentiful.

This surcharge exists on Russia No. 119, the imperf. 1k orange of 1917. Value, unused $90, used $60.

## OCCUPATION STAMPS

The issue formerly listed as Lithuania 1N1-1N12 is now listed as Russia N1-N12.

### Issued under Russian Occupation

Lithuanian Stamps of 1937-40 Overprinted in Red or Blue

**1940 Wmk. 238** *Perf. 14*

| | | | | |
|---|---|---|---|---|
| **2N9** | A44 | 2c orange (Bl) | .25 | .25 |
| | | Never hinged | .30 | |
| **2N10** | A50 | 50c brown (Bl) | .25 | .25 |
| | | Never hinged | .75 | |

**Unwmk.**

| | | | | |
|---|---|---|---|---|
| **2N11** | A56 | 5c brown car (Bl) | .25 | .40 |
| | | Never hinged | .30 | |
| **2N12** | A57 | 10c green (R) | 3.75 | 8.00 |
| | | Never hinged | 10.00 | |
| **2N13** | A58 | 15c dull orange (Bl) | .25 | .35 |
| | | Never hinged | .30 | |
| **2N14** | A59 | 25c lt brown (R) | .25 | .35 |
| | | Never hinged | .65 | |
| **2N15** | A60 | 30c Prus green (R) | .25 | .50 |
| | | Never hinged | .65 | |
| **2N16** | A61 | 35c red orange (Bl) | .35 | .50 |
| | | Never hinged | .90 | |
| | | *Nos. 2N9-2N16 (8)* | 5.60 | 10.60 |
| | | Set, never hinged | 10.00 | |

Values for used stamps are for CTOs. Postally used examples are considerably more.

The Lithuanian Soviet Socialist Republic was proclaimed July 21, 1940.

# LOURENCO MARQUES

lə-ˈren‚t‚-‚sō-‚mär-ˈkes

LOCATION — In the southern part of Mozambique in Southeast Africa
GOVT. — Part of Portuguese East Africa Colony
AREA — 28,800 sq. mi. (approx.)
POP. — 474,000 (approx.)
CAPITAL — Lourenço Marques

Stamps of Mozambique replaced those of Lourenço Marques in 1920. See Mozambique No. 360.

1000 Reis = 1 Milreis
100 Centavos = 1 Escudo (1913)

King Carlos — A1

*Perf. 11½, 12½, 13½*

**1895 Typo. Unwmk.**

| | | | | |
|---|---|---|---|---|
| **1** | A1 | 5r yellow | 1.00 | .25 |
| **2** | A1 | 10r redsh violet | 1.00 | .35 |
| **3** | A1 | 15r chocolate | 1.50 | .50 |
| **4** | A1 | 20r lavender | 1.50 | .50 |
| **5** | A1 | 25r blue green | 1.50 | .30 |
| *a.* | | Perf. 11½ | 3.50 | 1.00 |
| **6** | A1 | 50r light blue | 2.00 | 1.00 |
| *a.* | | Perf. 13½ | 15.00 | 5.00 |
| *b.* | | Perf. 11½ | — | — |
| **7** | A1 | 75r rose | 4.00 | 1.25 |
| **8** | A1 | 80r yellow grn | 5.00 | 3.00 |
| **9** | A1 | 100r brn, *yel* | 3.50 | 1.00 |
| *a.* | | Perf. 12½ | 5.00 | 3.25 |
| **10** | A1 | 150r car, *rose* | 6.00 | 3.00 |
| **11** | A1 | 200r dk bl, *bl* | 7.00 | 3.00 |
| **12** | A1 | 300r dk bl, *sal* | 8.00 | 4.00 |
| | | *Nos. 1-12 (12)* | 42.00 | 18.15 |

For surcharges and overprints see Nos. 29, 58-69, 132-137, 140-143, 156-157, 160.

**Saint Anthony of Padua Issue**

Regular Issues of Mozambique, 1886 and 1894, Overprinted in Black

**On 1886 Issue**

**1895 Without Gum** *Perf. 12½*

| | | | | |
|---|---|---|---|---|
| **13** | A2 | 5r black | 22.50 | 12.00 |
| **14** | A2 | 10r green | 25.00 | 12.00 |
| **15** | A2 | 20r rose | 35.00 | 14.00 |
| **16** | A2 | 25r lilac | 40.00 | 14.00 |
| **17** | A2 | 40r chocolate | 35.00 | 15.00 |
| **18** | A2 | 50r bl, perf. 13½ | 30.00 | 14.00 |
| *a.* | | Perf. 12½ | 50.00 | 27.50 |
| **19** | A2 | 100r yellow brn | 110.00 | 90.00 |
| **20** | A2 | 200r gray vio | 50.00 | 32.50 |
| **21** | A2 | 300r orange | 70.00 | 40.00 |

**On 1894 Issue**

*Perf. 11½*

| | | | | |
|---|---|---|---|---|
| **22** | A3 | 5r yellow | 35.00 | 25.00 |
| **23** | A3 | 10r redsh vio | 40.00 | 15.00 |
| **24** | A3 | 50r light blue | 50.00 | 32.50 |
| *a.* | | Perf. 12½ | 275.00 | 275.00 |
| **25** | A3 | 75r rose, perf. 12½ | 65.00 | 50.00 |
| **26** | A3 | 80r yellow grn | 80.00 | 65.00 |
| **27** | A3 | 100r brown, *buff* | 350.00 | 160.00 |
| **28** | A3 | 150r car, *rose*, perf. 12½ | 50.00 | 40.00 |
| | | *Nos. 13-28 (16)* | 1,088. | 631.00 |

No. 12 Surcharged in Black

**1897, Jan. 2**

| | | | | |
|---|---|---|---|---|
| **29** | A1 | 50r on 300r | 200.00 | 150.00 |

Most examples of No. 29 were issued without gum.

King Carlos — A2

**Name, Value in Black except 500r**

**1898-1903** *Perf. 11½*

| | | | | |
|---|---|---|---|---|
| **30** | A2 | 2½r gray | .35 | .30 |
| **31** | A2 | 5r orange | .35 | .30 |
| **32** | A2 | 10r lt green | .35 | .30 |
| **33** | A2 | 15r brown | 1.25 | .85 |
| **34** | A2 | 15r gray green ('03) | .75 | .50 |
| *a.* | | Imperf. | | |
| **35** | A2 | 20r gray violet | .65 | .40 |
| *a.* | | Imperf. | | |
| **36** | A2 | 25r sea green | .70 | .40 |
| *a.* | | Perf. 13½ | 25.00 | 8.50 |
| *b.* | | 25r light green (error) | *30.00* | *30.00* |
| *c.* | | Perf. 12½ | *40.00* | 35.00 |
| **37** | A2 | 25r car ('03) | .35 | .30 |
| *a.* | | Imperf. | | |
| **38** | A2 | 50r blue | 2.00 | .50 |
| **39** | A2 | 50r brown ('03) | .90 | .75 |
| **40** | A2 | 65r dull bl ('03) | 30.00 | 8.50 |
| **41** | A2 | 75r rose | 2.00 | 1.50 |
| **42** | A2 | 75r lilac ('03) | 1.25 | .95 |
| *a.* | | Imperf. | | |
| **43** | A2 | 80r violet | 2.50 | 1.25 |
| **44** | A2 | 100r dk blue, *blue* | 1.75 | .65 |
| *a.* | | Perf. 13½ | 18.00 | 5.00 |
| **45** | A2 | 115r org brn, *pink* ('03) | 6.00 | 5.00 |
| **46** | A2 | 130r brn, *straw* ('03) | 6.00 | 5.00 |
| **47** | A2 | 150r brn, *straw* | 3.00 | 1.40 |
| **48** | A2 | 200r red lil, *pnksh* | 3.00 | 1.25 |
| **49** | A2 | 300r dk bl, *rose* | 3.25 | 1.50 |
| **50** | A2 | 400r dl bl, *straw* ('03) | 10.00 | 5.00 |
| **51** | A2 | 500r blk & red, *bl* ('01) | 12.00 | 3.00 |
| **52** | A2 | 700r vio, *yelsh* ('01) | 15.00 | 7.00 |
| | | *Nos. 30-52 (23)* | 103.40 | 46.60 |

For surcharges and overprints see Nos. 57, 71-74, 76-91, 138, 144-155.

Coat of Arms — A3

**Surcharged On Upper and Lower Halves of Stamp**

**1899** *Imperf.*

| | | | | |
|---|---|---|---|---|
| **53** | A3 | 5r on 10r grn & brn | 20.00 | 7.00 |
| **54** | A3 | 25r on 10r grn & brn | 20.00 | 7.00 |
| **55** | A3 | 50r on 30r grn & brn | 30.00 | 11.00 |
| *a.* | | Inverted surcharge | 100.00 | 50.00 |
| **56** | A3 | 50r on 800r grn & brn | 40.00 | 20.00 |
| | | *Nos. 53-56 (4)* | 110.00 | 45.00 |

The lower half of No. 55 can be distinguished from that of No. 56 by the background of the label containing the word "REIS." The former is plain, while the latter is formed of white intersecting curved horizontal lines over vertical shading of violet brown.

Values are for undivided stamps. Halves sell for ¼ as much.

Most examples of Nos. 53-56 were issued without gum. Values for stamps with gum are two times the values shown.

No. 41 Surcharged in Black

**1899** ***Perf. 11½***

| | | | | |
|---|---|---|---|---|
| 57 | A2 | 50r on 75r rose | 6.00 | 2.50 |

Most examples of No. 57 were issued without gum. Values are for stamp without gum.

Surcharged in Black

### On Issue of 1895

**1902** ***Perf. 11½, 12½***

| | | | | |
|---|---|---|---|---|
| 58 | A1 | 65r on 5r yellow | 6.00 | 2.50 |
| 59 | A1 | 65r on 15r choc | 6.00 | 2.50 |
| 60 | A1 | 65r on 20r lav | 7.00 | 2.50 |
| a. | | Perf. 12½ | 25.00 | 15.00 |
| 61 | A1 | 115r on 10r red vio | 7.00 | 3.00 |
| 62 | A1 | 115r on 200r bl, *bl* | 7.00 | 3.00 |
| 63 | A1 | 115r on 300r bl, *sal* | 7.00 | 3.00 |
| 64 | A1 | 130r on 25r grn, perf. 12½ | 4.00 | 2.00 |
| a. | | Perf. 11½ | 30.00 | 22.50 |
| 65 | A1 | 130r on 80r yel grn | 4.00 | 3.00 |
| 66 | A1 | 130r on 150r car, *rose* | 5.00 | 3.00 |
| 67 | A1 | 400r on 50r lt bl | 8.00 | 6.00 |
| 68 | A1 | 400r on 75r rose | 8.00 | 6.00 |
| 69 | A1 | 400r on 100r brn, *buff* | 7.00 | 6.00 |

### On Newspaper Stamp of 1893

| | | | | |
|---|---|---|---|---|
| 70 | N1 | 65r on 2½ brn | 5.00 | 2.00 |
| | | *Nos. 58-70 (13)* | 81.00 | 44.50 |

Surcharge exists inverted on Nos. 61, 70.

*Nos. 64, 67 and 68 have been reprinted on thin white paper with shiny white gum and clean-cut perforation 13½. Value $6 each.*

For overprints see Nos. 132-137, 140-143, 156-157, 160.

Issue of 1898-1903 Overprinted in Black

**1903** ***Perf. 11½***

| | | | | |
|---|---|---|---|---|
| 71 | A2 | 15r brown | 2.00 | .85 |
| 72 | A2 | 25r sea green | 1.50 | .85 |
| 73 | A2 | 50r blue | 2.50 | .85 |
| 74 | A2 | 75r rose | 3.00 | 1.40 |
| a. | | Inverted overprint | 50.00 | 50.00 |
| | | *Nos. 71-74 (4)* | 9.00 | 3.95 |

Surcharged in Black

**1905**

| | | | | |
|---|---|---|---|---|
| 76 | A2 | 50r on 65r dull blue | 5.00 | 2.00 |

Regular Issues Overprinted in Carmine or Green

**1911**

| | | | | |
|---|---|---|---|---|
| 77 | A2 | 2½r gray | .30 | .25 |
| 78 | A2 | 5r orange | .30 | .25 |
| a. | | Double overprint | 10.00 | 10.00 |
| b. | | Inverted overprint | 10.00 | 10.00 |
| 79 | A2 | 10r lt grn | .40 | .35 |
| 80 | A2 | 15r gray grn | .40 | .35 |
| a. | | Inverted overprint | 10.00 | 10.00 |
| 81 | A2 | 20r dl vio | .40 | .40 |
| 82 | A2 | 25r car (G) | .90 | .50 |
| 83 | A2 | 50r brown | .80 | .50 |
| 84 | A2 | 75r lilac | 1.00 | .50 |
| 85 | A2 | 100r dk bl, *bl* | .80 | .55 |
| 86 | A2 | 115r org brn, *pink* | 10.00 | 3.50 |
| 87 | A2 | 130r brn, *straw* | .80 | .60 |
| 88 | A2 | 200r red lil, *pnksh* | .85 | .60 |
| 89 | A2 | 400r dl bl, *straw* | 2.00 | 1.10 |
| 90 | A2 | 500r blk & red, *bl* | 3.00 | 1.10 |
| 91 | A2 | 700r vio, *yelsh* | 4.00 | 1.25 |
| | | *Nos. 77-91 (15)* | 25.95 | 11.80 |

Vasco da Gama Issue of Various Portuguese Colonies Common Design Types Surcharged

### On Stamps of Macao

**1913** ***Perf. 12½-16***

| | | | | |
|---|---|---|---|---|
| 92 | CD20 | ¼c on ½a bl grn | 2.50 | 2.25 |
| 93 | CD21 | ½c on la red | 2.50 | 2.25 |
| 94 | CD22 | 1c on 2a red vio | 2.50 | 2.25 |
| 95 | CD23 | 2½c on 4a yel grn | 2.50 | 2.25 |
| 96 | CD24 | 5c on 8a dk bl | 2.50 | 2.25 |
| 97 | CD25 | 7½c on 12a vio brn | 4.25 | 4.25 |
| 98 | CD26 | 10c on 16a bis brn | 3.50 | 3.50 |
| a. | | Inverted surcharge | 40.00 | 40.00 |
| 99 | CD27 | 15c on 24a bister | 3.75 | 3.75 |
| | | *Nos. 92-99 (8)* | 24.00 | 22.75 |

### On Stamps of Portuguese Africa

| | | | | |
|---|---|---|---|---|
| 100 | CD20 | ¼c on 2½r bl grn | 2.00 | 1.75 |
| 101 | CD21 | ½c on 5r red | 2.00 | 1.75 |
| 102 | CD22 | 1c on 10r red vio | 2.00 | 1.75 |
| 103 | CD23 | 2½c on 25r yel grn | 2.00 | 1.75 |
| 104 | CD24 | 5c on 50r dk bl | 2.00 | 1.75 |
| 105 | CD25 | 7½c on 75r vio brn | 4.00 | 4.00 |
| 106 | CD26 | 10c on 100r bis brn | 2.75 | 2.75 |
| 107 | CD27 | 15c on 150r bis | 2.75 | 2.75 |
| | | *Nos. 100-107 (8)* | 19.50 | 18.25 |

### On Stamps of Timor

| | | | | |
|---|---|---|---|---|
| 108 | CD20 | ¼c on ½a bl grn | 2.00 | 1.75 |
| 109 | CD21 | ½c on 1a red | 2.00 | 1.75 |
| 110 | CD22 | 1c on 2a red vio | 2.00 | 1.75 |
| 111 | CD23 | 2½c on 4a yel grn | 2.00 | 1.75 |
| 112 | CD24 | 5c on 8a dk bl | 2.50 | 1.75 |
| 113 | CD25 | 7½c on 12a vio brn | 4.00 | 4.00 |
| 114 | CD26 | 10c on 16a bis brn | 2.75 | 2.75 |
| 115 | CD27 | 15c on 24a bister | 2.75 | 2.75 |
| | | *Nos. 108-115 (8)* | 20.00 | 18.25 |
| | | *Nos. 92-115 (24)* | 63.50 | 59.25 |

Ceres — A4

### Chalky Paper
### Name and Value in Black

**1914** **Typo.** ***Perf. 15x14***

| | | | | |
|---|---|---|---|---|
| 116 | A4 | ¼c olive brn | .35 | .35 |
| 117 | A4 | ½c black | .35 | .35 |
| 118 | A4 | 1c blue grn | .35 | .35 |
| 119 | A4 | 1½c lilac brn | .75 | .75 |
| 120 | A4 | 2c carmine | .75 | .75 |
| 121 | A4 | 2½c lt vio | .75 | .75 |
| 122 | A4 | 5c dp blue | .75 | .75 |
| 123 | A4 | 7½c yellow brn | .95 | .75 |
| 124 | A4 | 8c slate | .95 | .75 |
| 125 | A4 | 10c orange brn | 1.50 | .85 |
| 126 | A4 | 15c plum | 2.00 | .70 |
| 127 | A4 | 20c yellow grn | 2.50 | .90 |
| 128 | A4 | 30c brown, *green* | 4.00 | 1.00 |
| 129 | A4 | 40c brown, *pink* | 12.00 | 4.00 |
| 130 | A4 | 50c orange, *sal* | 10.00 | 3.00 |
| 131 | A4 | 1e green, *blue* | 12.00 | 3.00 |
| | | *Nos. 116-131 (16)* | 39.25 | 16.00 |

### Glazed Paper

| | | | | |
|---|---|---|---|---|
| 131A | A4 | 1c blue grn | 1.75 | 1.45 |
| 131B | A4 | 2½c lt vio | 1.75 | 1.45 |

**1918** **Ordinary Paper**

| | | | | |
|---|---|---|---|---|
| 131C | A4 | ¼c olive brn | .25 | .25 |
| 131D | A4 | ½c black | .25 | .25 |
| a. | | Value omitted | 20.00 | |
| 131E | A4 | 1c blue grn | .25 | .25 |
| 131F | A4 | 1½c lilac brn | .25 | .25 |
| a. | | Imperf. | | |
| 131G | A4 | 2c carmine | .25 | .25 |
| 131H | A4 | 2½c lt vio | .25 | .25 |
| 131I | A4 | 5c dp blue | .25 | .25 |
| 131J | A4 | 7½c yellow brn | .50 | .40 |
| 131K | A4 | 8c slate | .50 | .40 |
| 131L | A4 | 10c orange brn | 25.00 | 18.50 |
| 131M | A4 | 15c plum | 2.00 | .70 |
| | | *Nos. 131C-131M (11)* | 29.75 | 21.75 |

For surcharges see Nos. 139, 159, 161-162, B1-B12.

In 1921 Nos. 131D and 131F were surcharged 10c and 30c respectively, for use in Mozambique as Nos. 230 and 231. These same values, surcharged 5c and 10c respectively, with the addition of the word "PORTEADO," were used in Mozambique as postage dues, Nos. J44 and J45.

Provisional Issue of 1902 Overprinted Locally in Carmine

**1914** ***Perf. 11½, 12½***

| | | | | |
|---|---|---|---|---|
| 132 | A1 | 115r on 10r red vio | 1.50 | .45 |
| a. | | "Republica" inverted | 20.00 | |
| 133 | A1 | 115r on 200r bl, *bl* | 1.50 | .45 |
| 134 | A1 | 115r on 300r bl, *sal* | 1.50 | .45 |
| a. | | Double overprint | 40.00 | 40.00 |
| 135 | A1 | 130r on 25r grn | 2.00 | .70 |
| a. | | Perf. 12½ | 3.25 | 1.60 |
| 136 | A1 | 130r on 80r yel grn | 1.50 | .35 |
| 137 | A1 | 130r on 150r car, *rose* | 1.50 | .35 |
| | | *Nos. 132-137 (6)* | 9.50 | 2.75 |

No. 135a was issued without gum.

Nos. 78 and 117 Perforated Diagonally and Surcharged in Carmine

**1915** ***Perf. 11½***

| | | | | |
|---|---|---|---|---|
| 138 | A2 | ¼c on half of 5r org, pair | 5.00 | 5.00 |
| a. | | Pair without dividing perfs. | 20.00 | 20.00 |

***Perf. 15x14***

| | | | | |
|---|---|---|---|---|
| 139 | A4 | ¼c on half of ½c blk, pair | 9.00 | 9.00 |

The added perforation on Nos. 138-139 runs from lower left to upper right corners, dividing the stamp in two. Values are for pairs, both halves of the stamp.

Provisional Issue of 1902 Overprinted in Carmine

**1915** ***Perf. 11½, 12½***

| | | | | |
|---|---|---|---|---|
| 140 | A1 | 115r on 10r red vio | .55 | .40 |
| 141 | A1 | 115r on 200r bl, *bl* | .70 | .40 |
| 142 | A1 | 115r on 300r bl, *sal* | .70 | .40 |
| 143 | A1 | 130r on 150r car, *rose* | .75 | .40 |
| | | *Nos. 140-143 (4)* | 2.70 | 1.60 |

Nos. 34 and 80 Surcharged

**1915** **On Issue of 1903**

| | | | | |
|---|---|---|---|---|
| 144 | A2 | 2c on 15r gray grn | 1.00 | .80 |

### On Issue of 1911

| | | | | |
|---|---|---|---|---|
| 145 | A2 | 2c on 15r gray grn | 1.00 | .80 |
| a. | | New value inverted | 22.50 | |

Regular Issues of 1898-1903 Overprinted Locally in Carmine

**1916**

| | | | | |
|---|---|---|---|---|
| 146 | A2 | 15r gray grn | 2.00 | 1.00 |
| 147 | A2 | 50r brown | 3.50 | 2.00 |
| a. | | Inverted overprint | | |
| 148 | A2 | 75r lilac | 3.50 | 2.00 |
| 149 | A2 | 100r blue, *bl* | 3.00 | 1.00 |
| 150 | A2 | 115r org brn, *pink* | 3.00 | 1.00 |
| 151 | A2 | 130r brown, *straw* | 10.00 | 5.00 |
| 152 | A2 | 200r red lil, *pnksh* | 8.00 | 2.00 |
| 153 | A2 | 400r dull bl, *straw* | 12.00 | 4.00 |
| 154 | A2 | 500r blk & red, *bl* | 8.00 | 3.00 |
| 155 | A2 | 700r vio, *yelsh* | 12.00 | 5.00 |
| | | *Nos. 146-155 (10)* | 65.00 | 26.00 |

### Same Overprint on Nos. 67-68

**1917**

| | | | | |
|---|---|---|---|---|
| 156 | A1 | 400r on 50r lt blue | 1.25 | .65 |
| a. | | Perf. 13½ | 11.50 | 9.00 |
| 157 | A1 | 400r on 75r rose | 2.50 | 1.00 |

No. 69 exists with this overprint. It was not officially issued.

Type of 1914 Surcharged in Red

**1920** ***Perf. 15x14***

| | | | | |
|---|---|---|---|---|
| 159 | A4 | 4c on 2½c violet | 1.00 | .30 |

### Stamps of 1914 Surcharged in Green or Black

a

b

**1921**

| | | | | |
|---|---|---|---|---|
| 160 | A1(a) | ¼c on 115r on 10r red vio (G) | .80 | .80 |
| 161 | A4(b) | 1c on 2½c vio (Bk) | .60 | .40 |
| a. | | Inverted surcharge | 40.00 | |
| 162 | A4(b) | 1½c on 2½c vio (Bk) | .80 | .60 |
| | | *Nos. 160-162 (3)* | 2.20 | 1.80 |

Nos. 159-162 were postally valid throughout Mozambique. No. 162 exists on glazed paper. Value the same as No. 162.

## SEMI-POSTAL STAMPS

### Regular Issue of 1914 Overprinted or Surcharged

a

b

c

**1918** ***Perf. 15x14½***

| | | | | |
|---|---|---|---|---|
| B1 | A4(a) | ¼c olive brn | 3.00 | *3.00* |
| B2 | A4(a) | ½c black | 3.00 | *4.00* |
| B3 | A4(a) | 1c bl grn | 3.00 | *4.00* |
| B4 | A4(a) | 2½c violet | 4.00 | *4.00* |
| B5 | A4(a) | 5c blue | 4.00 | *6.00* |

### Chalky Paper

| | | | | |
|---|---|---|---|---|
| B5A | A4(a) | 5c blue | 4.00 | *6.00* |
| B6 | A4(a) | 10c org brn | 5.00 | *7.00* |
| B7 | A4(b) | 20c on 1½c lil brn | 5.00 | *8.00* |
| B8 | A4(a) | 30c brn, *grn* | 8.00 | *9.00* |
| B9 | A4(b) | 40c on 2c car | 8.00 | *10.00* |
| B10 | A4(b) | 50c on 7½c bis | 12.00 | *12.00* |
| B11 | A4(b) | 70c on 8c slate | 15.00 | *15.00* |
| B12 | A4(c) | $1 on 15c mag | 20.00 | *15.00* |
| | | *Nos. B1-B12 (13)* | 94.00 | *103.00* |

Nos. B1-B12 were used in place of ordinary postage stamps on Mar. 9, 1918. Nos. B3 and B4 also exist on glazed paper. The unsurfaced paper on which Nos. B1-B5 were printed show a diamond pattern when held to the light. This pattern is used to determine genuine stamps.

### NEWSPAPER STAMPS

Numeral of Value — N1

*Perf. 11½*

**1893, July 28 Typo. Unwmk.**

| | | | | |
|---|---|---|---|---|
| **P1** | N1 | 2½r brown | .25 | .65 |
| *a.* | | Perf. 12½ | 20.00 | 17.50 |

For surcharge see No. 70.

**Saint Anthony of Padua Issue**

Mozambique No. P6 Overprinted

**1895, July 1** ***Perf. 11½, 13½***

| | | | | |
|---|---|---|---|---|
| **P2** | N3 | 2½r brown | 20.00 | 17.50 |
| *a.* | | Inverted overprint | 30.00 | 30.00 |

## LUXEMBOURG

'lək-səm-ˌbərg

LOCATION — Western Europe between southern Belgium, Germany and France
GOVT. — Grand Duchy
AREA — 999 sq. mi.
POP. — 476,200 (2007)
CAPITAL — Luxembourg

12½ Centimes = 1 Silbergroschen
100 Centimes = 1 Franc
100 Cents = 1 Euro (2002)

**Catalogue values for unused stamps in this country are for Never Hinged items, beginning with Scott 321 in the regular postage section, Scott B216 in the semi-postal section.**

### Watermarks

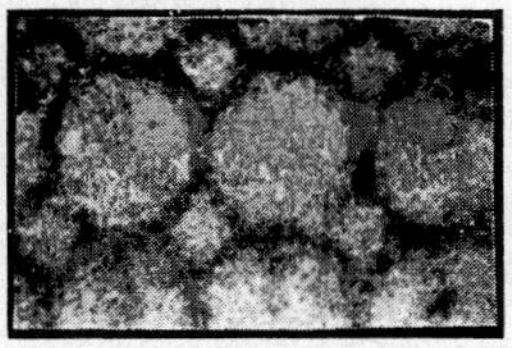
Wmk. 110 — Octagons

Wmk. 149 — W

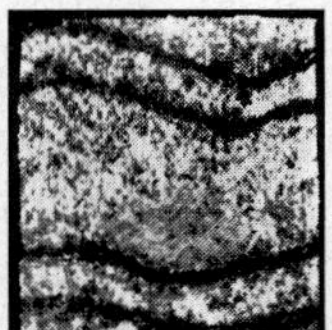
Wmk. 213 — Double Wavy Lines

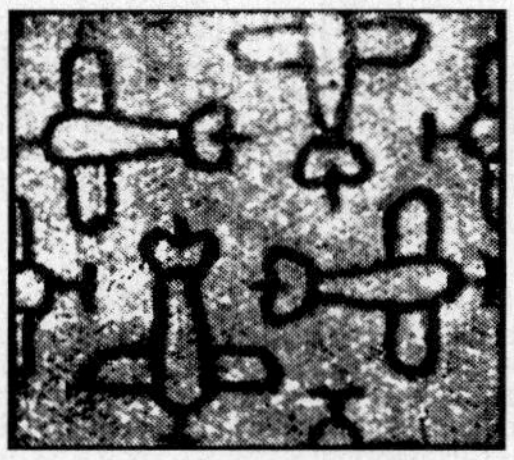
Wmk. 216 — Multiple Airplanes

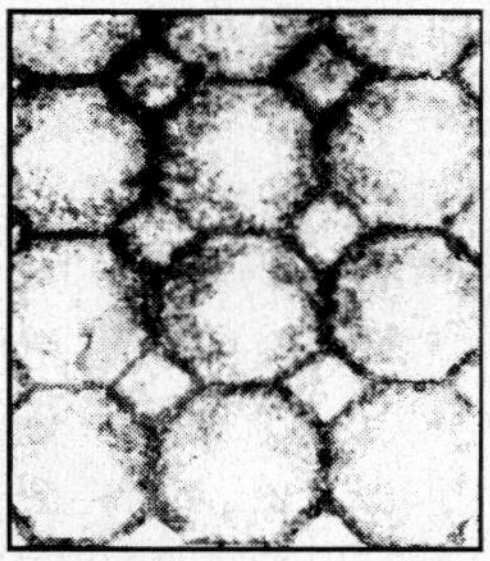
Wmk. 246 — Multiple Cross Enclosed in Octagons

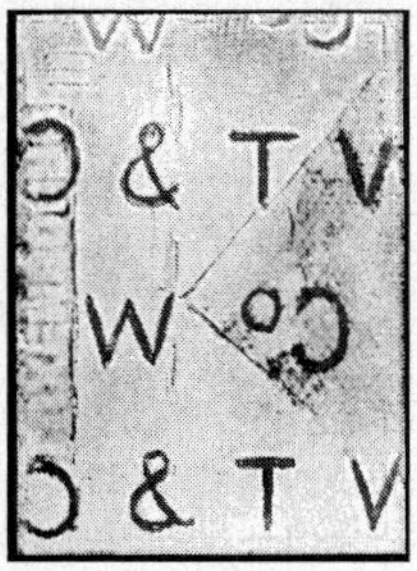
Wmk. 247 — Multiple Letters

Unused values of Nos. 1-47 are for stamps without gum. Though these stamps were issued with gum, most examples offered are without gum. Stamps with original gum sell for more.

Grand Duke William III — A1

**Luxembourg Print**

**Wmk. 149**

**1852, Sept. 15 Engr.** ***Imperf.***

| | | | | |
|---|---|---|---|---|
| **1** | A1 | 10c gray black | *2,100.* | 55.00 |
| *a.* | | 10c greenish black ('53) | *2,250.* | 55.00 |
| *b.* | | 10c intense black ('54) | *2,400.* | 120.00 |
| **2** | A1 | 1sg brown red ('53) | 1,500. | 75.00 |
| *a.* | | 1sg brick red | 1,500. | 80.00 |
| *b.* | | 1sg orange red ('54) | 1,300. | 87.50 |
| *c.* | | 1sg blood red | 2,750. | 475.00 |
| **3** | A1 | 1sg rose ('55) | 1,350. | 87.50 |
| *a.* | | 1sg carmine rose ('56) | 1,250. | 80.00 |
| *b.* | | 1sg dark carmine rose, thin paper ('59) | *1,400.* | *240.00* |
| | | *Nos. 1-3 (3)* | | 217.50 |

*Reprints of both values exist on watermarked paper. Some of the reprints show traces of lines cancelling the plates, but others can be distinguished only by an expert.*
See Nos. 278-279, 603.

Coat of Arms
A2 A3

**Frankfurt Print**

**1859-64 Typo. Unwmk.**

| | | | | |
|---|---|---|---|---|
| **4** | A2 | 1c buff ('63) | 130.00 | *450.00* |
| **5** | A2 | 2c black ('60) | 95.00 | *550.00* |
| **6** | A2 | 4c yellow ('64) | 175.00 | 175.00 |
| *a.* | | 4c orange ('64) | 190.00 | 190.00 |
| **7** | A3 | 10c blue | 175.00 | 20.00 |
| **8** | A3 | 12½c rose | 275.00 | 160.00 |
| **9** | A3 | 25c brown | 350.00 | 275.00 |
| **10** | A3 | 30c rose lilac | 290.00 | 225.00 |
| **11** | A3 | 37½c green | 325.00 | 200.00 |
| **12** | A3 | 40c red orange | 875.00 | 240.00 |

Counterfeits of Nos. 1-12 exist.
See Nos. 13-25, 27-38, 40-47. For surcharges and overprints see Nos. 26, 39, O1-O51.

**1865-71** ***Rouletted***

| | | | | |
|---|---|---|---|---|
| **13** | A2 | 1c red brown | 200.00 | 240.00 |
| **14** | A2 | 2c black ('67) | 20.00 | 13.50 |
| **15** | A2 | 4c yellow ('67) | 600.00 | 175.00 |
| **16** | A2 | 4c green ('71) | 40.00 | 24.00 |
| | | *Nos. 13-16 (4)* | 860.00 | 452.50 |

A4

**1865-74** ***Rouletted in Color***

| | | | | |
|---|---|---|---|---|
| **17** | A2 | 1c red brn ('72) | 35.00 | 8.00 |
| **18** | A2 | 1c orange ('69) | 40.00 | 8.00 |
| *a.* | | 1c brown orange ('67) | 120.00 | 35.00 |
| *b.* | | 1c red orange ('69) | 1,350. | 325.00 |
| **19** | A3 | 10c rose lilac | 120.00 | 4.00 |
| *a.* | | 10c lilac | 100.00 | 4.00 |
| *b.* | | 10c gray lilac | 100.00 | 4.00 |
| **20** | A3 | 12½c car ('71) | 175.00 | 8.00 |
| *a.* | | 12½c rose | 175.00 | 8.00 |
| **21** | A3 | 20c gray brn ('72) | 120.00 | 8.00 |
| *a.* | | 20c yellow brown ('69) | 125.00 | 8.00 |
| **22** | A3 | 25c blue ('72) | 1,100. | 11.00 |
| **22A** | A3 | 25c ultra ('65) | 1,100. | 11.00 |
| **23** | A3 | 30c lilac rose | 1,200. | 80.00 |
| **24** | A3 | 37½c bister ('66) | 750.00 | 240.00 |
| **25** | A3 | 40c pale org ('74) | 40.00 | 80.00 |
| *a.* | | 40c orange red ('66) | 1,050. | 60.00 |
| **26** | A4 | 1fr on 37½c bis ('73) | 875.00 | 80.00 |
| *a.* | | Surcharge inverted | | *3,600.* |

**Luxembourg Print**

**1874 Typo.** ***Imperf.***

| | | | | |
|---|---|---|---|---|
| **27** | A2 | 4c green | 110.00 | 110.00 |

A5

**1875-79 Narrow Margins** ***Perf. 13***

| | | | | |
|---|---|---|---|---|
| **29** | A2 | 1c red brn ('78) | 35.00 | 8.00 |
| **30** | A2 | 2c black | 125.00 | 27.50 |
| **31** | A2 | 4c green | 2.40 | *9.50* |
| **32** | A2 | 5c yellow ('76) | 175.00 | 24.00 |
| *a.* | | 5c orange yellow | 600.00 | 125.00 |
| *b.* | | Imperf. | 925.00 | 1,100. |
| **33** | A3 | 10c gray lilac | 475.00 | 2.40 |
| *b.* | | 10c lilac | 1,350. | 29.00 |
| *c.* | | Imperf. | 2,700. | *3,250.* |
| **34** | A3 | 12½c lil rose ('77) | 600.00 | 20.00 |
| **35** | A3 | 12½c car rose ('76) | 400.00 | 27.50 |
| **36** | A3 | 25c blue ('77) | 800.00 | 14.00 |
| **37** | A3 | 30c dull rose ('78) | 750.00 | 450.00 |
| **38** | A3 | 40c orange ('79) | 1.60 | *9.50* |
| **39** | A5 | 1fr on 37½c bis ('79) | 8.00 | *27.50* |
| *a.* | | "Pranc" | *5,250.* | *6,400.* |
| *b.* | | Without surcharge | 475.00 | |
| *c.* | | As "b," imperf. | 700.00 | |
| | | As "c," pair | *1,400.* | |

In the Luxembourg print the perforation is close to the border of the stamp. Excellent forgeries of No. 39a are plentiful, as well as faked cancellations on Nos. 31, 38 and 39.
Nos. 32b and 33c are said to be essays; Nos. 39b and 39c printer's waste.

**Haarlem Print**

***Perf. 11½x12, 12½x12, 13½***

**1880-81 Wide Margins**

| | | | | |
|---|---|---|---|---|
| **40** | A2 | 1c yel brn ('81) | 8.75 | 6.00 |
| **41** | A2 | 2c black | 7.25 | 1.60 |
| **42** | A2 | 5c yellow ('81) | 200.00 | 95.00 |
| **43** | A3 | 10c gray lilac | 160.00 | 1.60 |
| **44** | A3 | 12½c rose ('81) | 190.00 | 190.00 |
| **45** | A3 | 20c gray brn ('81) | 45.00 | 20.00 |
| **46** | A3 | 25c blue | 240.00 | 4.75 |
| **47** | A3 | 30c dull rose ('81) | 8.00 | *24.00* |

**Gray Yellowish Paper**

***Perf. 12½***

| | | | | |
|---|---|---|---|---|
| *42a* | A2 | 5c | 7.25 | |
| *43a* | A3 | 10c | 4.00 | |
| *44a* | A3 | 12½c | 9.50 | |
| *46a* | A3 | 25c | 5.50 | |
| | | *Nos. 42a-46a (4)* | 26.25 | |

Nos. 42a-46a were not regularly issued.

"Industry" and "Commerce" — A6

***Perf. 11½x12, 12½x12, 12½, 13½***

**1882, Dec. 1 Typo.**

| | | | | |
|---|---|---|---|---|
| **48** | A6 | 1c gray lilac | .25 | *.40* |
| **49** | A6 | 2c olive gray | .25 | *.40* |
| **50** | A6 | 4c olive bister | .25 | *2.00* |
| **51** | A6 | 5c lt green | .80 | .40 |
| **52** | A6 | 10c rose | 8.00 | .40 |
| **53** | A6 | 12½c slate | 1.25 | *24.00* |
| **54** | A6 | 20c orange | 3.25 | 1.60 |
| **55** | A6 | 25c ultra | 175.00 | 1.60 |
| **56** | A6 | 30c gray green | 24.00 | 12.00 |
| **57** | A6 | 50c bister brown | 1.20 | *12.00* |
| **58** | A6 | 1fr pale violet | 1.60 | *24.00* |
| **59** | A6 | 5fr brown orange | 37.50 | *160.00* |
| | | *Nos. 48-59 (12)* | 253.35 | *238.80* |

For overprints see Nos. O52-O64.

Grand Duke Adolphe — A7

***Perf. 11, 11½, 11½x11, 12½***

**1891-93 Engr.**

| | | | | |
|---|---|---|---|---|
| **60** | A7 | 10c carmine | .35 | *.30* |
| *a.* | | Sheet of 25, perf. 11½ | 125.00 | |
| **61** | A7 | 12½c slate grn ('93) | 1.00 | *.70* |
| **62** | A7 | 20c orange ('93) | 13.00 | 1.00 |
| *a.* | | 20c brown, perf. 11½ | *160.00* | 240.00 |
| **63** | A7 | 25c blue | 1.00 | 1.00 |
| *a.* | | Sheet of 25, perf. 11½ | *1,000.* | |
| **64** | A7 | 30c olive grn ('93) | 1.00 | 1.00 |
| **65** | A7 | 37½c green ('93) | 2.60 | 3.00 |
| **66** | A7 | 50c brown ('93) | 10.50 | 4.00 |
| **67** | A7 | 1fr dp violet ('93) | 16.00 | 9.00 |
| **68** | A7 | 2½fr black ('93) | 1.60 | *10.00* |
| **69** | A7 | 5fr lake ('93) | 35.00 | 70.00 |
| | | *Nos. 60-69 (10)* | 82.05 | 100.00 |

No. 62a was never on sale at any post office, but exists postally used.
Perf. 11½ stamps are from the sheets of 25.
For overprints see Nos. O65-O74.

Grand Duke Adolphe — A8

**1895, May 4 Typo.** ***Perf. 12½***

| | | | | |
|---|---|---|---|---|
| **70** | A8 | 1c pearl gray | 3.25 | .40 |
| **71** | A8 | 2c gray brown | .30 | *.25* |
| **72** | A8 | 4c olive bister | .30 | *.75* |
| **73** | A8 | 5c green | 4.25 | .25 |
| **74** | A8 | 10c carmine | 11.00 | .25 |
| | | *Nos. 70-74 (5)* | 19.10 | 1.90 |

For overprints see Nos. O75-O79.

Coat of Arms — A9

Grand Duke William IV — A10

**1906-26 Typo.** ***Perf. 12½***

| | | | | |
|---|---|---|---|---|
| **75** | A9 | 1c gray ('07) | .25 | .25 |
| **76** | A9 | 2c ol brn ('07) | .25 | .25 |
| **77** | A9 | 4c bister ('07) | .25 | .25 |
| **78** | A9 | 5c green ('07) | .25 | .25 |
| **79** | A9 | 5c lilac ('26) | .25 | .25 |
| **80** | A9 | 6c violet ('07) | .25 | .25 |
| **81** | A9 | 7½c orange ('19) | .25 | *1.50* |

**Engr.**

***Perf. 11, 11½x11***

| | | | | |
|---|---|---|---|---|
| **82** | A10 | 10c scarlet | 2.00 | .25 |
| *a.* | | Souvenir sheet of 10 | 450.00 | *1,200.* |
| **83** | A10 | 12½c sl grn ('07) | 2.00 | .45 |
| **84** | A10 | 15c org brn ('07) | 2.60 | .75 |
| **85** | A10 | 20c orange ('07) | 3.25 | .75 |
| **86** | A10 | 25c ultra ('07) | 65.00 | .45 |
| **87** | A10 | 30c ol grn ('08) | .65 | .75 |
| **88** | A10 | 37½c green ('07) | .65 | 1.00 |
| *a.* | | Perf. 12½ | 16.00 | 12.00 |
| **89** | A10 | 50c brown ('07) | 5.25 | 1.25 |
| **90** | A10 | 87½c dk blue ('08) | 2.00 | 12.50 |
| **91** | A10 | 1fr violet ('08) | 8.00 | 2.00 |
| **92** | A10 | 2½fr ver ('08) | 52.50 | *95.00* |
| **93** | A10 | 5fr claret ('08) | 6.50 | 45.00 |
| | | *Nos. 75-93 (19)* | 152.15 | *163.15* |

No. 82a for accession of Grand Duke William IV to the throne.
For surcharges and overprints see Nos. 94-96, 112-117, O80-O98.

Nos. 90, 92-93 Surcharged in Red or Black

**1912-15**

| No. | Type | Description | Unused | Used |
|---|---|---|---|---|
| 94 | A10 | 62½c on 87½c (R) | 2.75 | 2.50 |
| 95 | A10 | 62½c on 2½fr (Bk) ('15) | 2.75 | *4.50* |
| 96 | A10 | 62½c on 5fr (Bk) ('15) | 2.00 | *3.00* |
| | | *Nos. 94-96 (3)* | 7.50 | *10.00* |

Grand Duchess Marie Adelaide — A11

**1914-17 Engr. *Perf. 11½, 11½x11***

| No. | Type | Description | Unused | Used |
|---|---|---|---|---|
| 97 | A11 | 10c lake | .25 | .25 |
| 98 | A11 | 12½c dull green | .25 | .25 |
| 99 | A11 | 15c sepia | .25 | *.25* |
| 100 | A11 | 17½c dp brown ('17) | .25 | *.40* |
| 101 | A11 | 25c ultra | .25 | .25 |
| 102 | A11 | 30c bister | .25 | *.50* |
| 103 | A11 | 35c dark blue | .25 | *.30* |
| 104 | A11 | 37½c black brn | .25 | *.30* |
| 105 | A11 | 40c orange | .25 | *.30* |
| 106 | A11 | 50c dark gray | .25 | *.60* |
| 107 | A11 | 62½c blue green | .40 | *2.00* |
| 108 | A11 | 87½c orange ('17) | .40 | *2.00* |
| 109 | A11 | 1fr orange brown | 2.00 | 1.50 |
| 110 | A11 | 2½fr red | .40 | *1.50* |
| 111 | A11 | 5fr dark violet | 9.50 | *35.00* |
| | | *Nos. 97-111 (15)* | 15.20 | *45.40* |
| | | Set, never hinged | 65.00 | |

For surcharges and overprints see Nos. 118-124, B7-B10, O99-O113. Nos. 97, 98, 101, 107, 109 and 111 overprinted "Droits de statistique" are revenue stamps.

**Stamps of 1906-19 Surcharged with New Value and Bars in Black or Red**

**1916-24**

| No. | Type | Description | Unused | Used |
|---|---|---|---|---|
| 112 | A9 | 2½c on 5c ('18) | .25 | .25 |
| *a.* | | Double surcharge | 75.00 | |
| 113 | A9 | 3c on 2c ('21) | .25 | *.25* |
| 114 | A9 | 5c on 1c ('23) | .25 | *.25* |
| 115 | A9 | 5c on 4c ('23) | .25 | *.40* |
| 116 | A9 | 5c on 7½c ('24) | .25 | *.25* |
| 117 | A9 | 6c on 2c (R) ('22) | .25 | *.25* |
| 118 | A11 | 7½c on 10c ('18) | .25 | .25 |
| 119 | A11 | 17½c on 30c | .25 | *.40* |
| 120 | A11 | 20c on 17½c ('21) | .25 | *.25* |
| 121 | A11 | 25c on 37½c ('23) | .25 | *.25* |
| *a.* | | Double surcharge | 90.00 | |
| 122 | A11 | 75c on 62½c (R) ('22) | .25 | *.25* |
| 123 | A11 | 80c on 87½c ('22) | .25 | *.25* |
| 124 | A11 | 87½c on 1fr | .55 | *5.50* |
| | | *Nos. 112-124 (13)* | 3.55 | *8.80* |

Grand Duchess Charlotte — A12

**1921, Jan. 6 Engr. *Perf. 11½***

| No. | Type | Description | Unused | Used |
|---|---|---|---|---|
| 125 | A12 | 15c rose | .25 | *.25* |
| *a.* | | Sheet of 5, perf 11 | 400.00 | *250.00* |
| | | Never hinged | 350.00 | |
| *b.* | | Sheet of 25, perf. 11½, 11x11½, 12x11½ | 8.00 | *17.00* |

Birth of Prince Jean, first son of Grand Duchess Charlotte, Jan. 5 (No. 125a). No. 125 was printed in sheets of 100.

See Nos. 131-150. For surcharges and overprints see Nos. 154-158, O114-O131, O136.

Vianden Castle — A13

Foundries at Esch — A14

Adolphe Bridge — A15

**1921-34 *Perf. 11, 11½, 11x11½***

| No. | Type | Description | Unused | Used |
|---|---|---|---|---|
| 126 | A13 | 1fr carmine | .25 | *.40* |
| 127 | A13 | 1fr dk blue ('26) | .25 | *.45* |

***Perf. 11½x11; 11½ (#129, 130)***

| No. | Type | Description | Unused | Used |
|---|---|---|---|---|
| 128 | A14 | 2fr indigo | .30 | *.80* |
| 129 | A14 | 2fr dk brown ('26) | 7.00 | 2.00 |
| 130 | A15 | 5fr dk violet | 20.00 | 9.50 |
| | | *Nos. 126-130 (5)* | 27.80 | 13.15 |

For overprints see Nos. O132-O135, O137-138, O140.

See No. B85.

**Charlotte Type of 1921**

**1921-26 *Perf. 11½***

| No. | Type | Description | Unused | Used |
|---|---|---|---|---|
| 131 | A12 | 2c brown | .25 | .25 |
| 132 | A12 | 3c olive green | .25 | .25 |
| *a.* | | Sheet of 25 | 10.00 | 25.00 |
| 133 | A12 | 6c violet | .25 | .25 |
| *a.* | | Sheet of 25 | 10.00 | 25.00 |
| 134 | A12 | 10c yellow grn | .25 | .25 |
| 135 | A12 | 10c olive brn ('24) | .25 | .25 |
| 136 | A12 | 15c brown olive | .25 | .25 |
| 137 | A12 | 15c pale grn ('24) | .25 | .25 |
| 138 | A12 | 15c dp orange ('26) | .25 | .25 |
| 139 | A12 | 20c dp orange | .25 | .25 |
| *a.* | | Sheet of 25 | 60.00 | *110.00* |
| 140 | A12 | 20c yellow grn ('26) | .25 | .25 |
| 141 | A12 | 25c dk green | .25 | .25 |
| 142 | A12 | 30c carmine rose | .25 | .25 |
| 143 | A12 | 40c brown orange | .25 | .25 |
| 144 | A12 | 50c deep blue | .25 | .25 |
| 145 | A12 | 50c red ('24) | .25 | .25 |
| 146 | A12 | 75c red | .25 | 1.00 |
| *a.* | | Sheet of 25 | 325.00 | |
| 147 | A12 | 75c deep blue ('24) | .25 | .25 |
| 148 | A12 | 80c black | .25 | .70 |
| *a.* | | Sheet of 25 | 325.00 | |
| | | *Nos. 131-148 (18)* | 4.50 | 5.70 |

For surcharges and overprints see Nos. 154-158, O114-O131, O136.

**Philatelic Exhibition Issue**

**1922, Aug. 27 *Imperf.***

**Laid Paper**

| No. | Type | Description | Unused | Used |
|---|---|---|---|---|
| 149 | A12 | 25c dark green | 1.75 | *6.00* |
| 150 | A12 | 30c carmine rose | 1.75 | *6.00* |

Nos. 149 and 150 were sold exclusively at the Luxembourg Phil. Exhib., Aug. 1922.

Souvenir Sheet

View of Luxembourg — A16

**1923, Jan. 3 *Perf. 11***

| No. | Type | Description | Unused | Used |
|---|---|---|---|---|
| 151 | A16 | 10fr dp grn, sheet | 1,500. | *2,400.* |
| | | Never hinged | 2,250. | |

Birth of Princess Elisabeth.

**1923, Mar. *Perf. 11½***

| No. | Type | Description | Unused | Used |
|---|---|---|---|---|
| 152 | A16 | 10fr black | 4.50 | *12.00* |
| *a.* | | Perf. 12½ ('34) | 4.50 | *12.00* |

For overprint see No. O141.

The Wolfsschlucht near Echternach — A17

**1923-34 *Perf. 11½***

| No. | Type | Description | Unused | Used |
|---|---|---|---|---|
| 153 | A17 | 3fr dk blue & blue | 1.50 | .80 |
| *a.* | | Perf. 12½ ('34) | 1.50 | .80 |

For overprint see No. O139.

**Stamps of 1921-26 Surcharged with New Values and Bars**

**1925-28**

| No. | Type | Description | Unused | Used |
|---|---|---|---|---|
| 154 | A12 | 5c on 10c yel grn | .25 | .30 |
| 155 | A12 | 15c on 20c yel grn ('28) | .25 | .25 |
| *a.* | | Bars omitted | | |
| 156 | A12 | 35c on 40c brn org ('27) | .25 | .25 |
| 157 | A12 | 60c on 75c dp bl ('27) | .25 | .25 |
| 158 | A12 | 60c on 80c blk ('28) | .40 | .35 |
| | | *Nos. 154-158 (5)* | 1.40 | 1.40 |

Grand Duchess Charlotte — A18

**1926-35 Engr. *Perf. 12***

| No. | Type | Description | Unused | Used |
|---|---|---|---|---|
| 159 | A18 | 5c dk violet | .25 | .25 |
| 160 | A18 | 10c olive grn | .25 | .25 |
| 161 | A18 | 15c black ('30) | .25 | .25 |
| 162 | A18 | 20c orange | .25 | .30 |
| 163 | A18 | 25c yellow grn | .25 | .30 |
| 164 | A18 | 25c vio brn ('27) | .25 | .30 |
| 165 | A18 | 30c yel grn ('27) | .25 | .30 |
| 166 | A18 | 30c gray vio ('30) | .55 | .25 |
| 167 | A18 | 35c gray vio ('28) | 3.25 | .25 |
| 168 | A18 | 35c yel grn ('30) | .25 | .25 |
| 169 | A18 | 40c olive gray | .25 | .25 |
| 170 | A18 | 50c red brown | .25 | .25 |
| 171 | A18 | 60c blue grn ('28) | 3.25 | .25 |
| 172 | A18 | 65c black brn | .25 | .90 |
| 173 | A18 | 70c blue vio ('35) | .25 | .25 |
| 174 | A18 | 75c rose | .25 | .30 |
| 175 | A18 | 75c bis brn ('27) | .25 | .25 |
| 176 | A18 | 80c bister brn | .25 | 1.25 |
| 177 | A18 | 90c rose ('27) | 1.25 | 1.40 |
| 178 | A18 | 1fr black | 1.25 | .30 |
| 179 | A18 | 1fr rose ('30) | .55 | .25 |
| 180 | A18 | 1¼fr dk blue | .25 | .55 |
| 181 | A18 | 1¼fr yellow ('30) | 9.50 | 1.75 |
| 182 | A18 | 1¼fr blue grn ('31) | .45 | .45 |
| 183 | A18 | 1¼fr rose car ('34) | 15.00 | 2.00 |
| 184 | A18 | 1½fr dp blue ('27) | 1.75 | 1.50 |
| 185 | A18 | 1¾fr dk blue ('30) | .90 | .40 |
| | | *Nos. 159-185 (27)* | 41.70 | 15.00 |
| | | Set, never hinged | 140.00 | |

For surcharges and overprints see Nos. 186-193, N17-N29, O142-O178.

**Stamps of 1926-35, Surcharged with New Values and Bars**

**1928-39**

| No. | Type | Description | Unused | Used |
|---|---|---|---|---|
| 186 | A18 | 10(c) on 30c yel grn ('29) | .40 | .40 |
| 187 | A18 | 15c on 25c yel grn | .30 | .65 |
| 187A | A18 | 30c on 60c bl grn ('39) | .25 | 1.40 |
| 188 | A18 | 60c on 65c blk brn | .25 | .30 |
| 189 | A18 | 60c on 75c rose | .25 | .30 |
| 190 | A18 | 60c on 80c bis brn | .30 | .60 |
| 191 | A18 | 70(c) on 75c bis brn ('35) | 6.00 | .40 |
| 192 | A18 | 75(c) on 90c rose ('29) | 2.00 | .40 |
| 193 | A18 | 1¾(fr) on 1½fr dp bl ('29) | 4.50 | 1.60 |
| | | *Nos. 186-193 (9)* | 14.25 | 6.05 |
| | | Set, never hinged | 45.00 | |

The surcharge on No. 187A has no bars.

View of Clervaux A19

**1928-34 *Perf. 12½***

| No. | Type | Description | Unused | Used |
|---|---|---|---|---|
| 194 | A19 | 2fr black ('34) | 1.50 | .80 |
| | | Never hinged | 4.00 | |
| *a.* | | Perf. 11½ ('28) | 2.75 | .80 |
| | | Never hinged | 6.00 | — |

See No. B66. For overprint see No. O179.

Coat of Arms — A20

**1930, Dec. 20 Typo. *Perf. 12½***

| No. | Type | Description | Unused | Used |
|---|---|---|---|---|
| 195 | A20 | 5c claret | .85 | .40 |
| 196 | A20 | 10c olive green | 1.10 | .25 |
| | | Set, never hinged | 5.50 | |

View of the Lower City of Luxembourg A21

**1931, June 20 Engr.**

| No. | Type | Description | Unused | Used |
|---|---|---|---|---|
| 197 | A21 | 20fr deep green | 3.50 | *12.00* |
| | | Never hinged | 8.00 | |

For overprint see No. O180.

Gate of "Three Towers" — A22

**1934, Aug. 30 *Perf. 14x13½***

| No. | Type | Description | Unused | Used |
|---|---|---|---|---|
| 198 | A22 | 5fr blue green | 2.50 | *10.00* |
| | | Never hinged | 7.50 | |

For surcharge and overprint see Nos. N31, O181.

Castle From Our Valley A23

**1935, Nov. 15 *Perf. 12½x12***

| No. | Type | Description | Unused | Used |
|---|---|---|---|---|
| 199 | A23 | 10fr green | 3.00 | *12.00* |
| | | Never hinged | 6.50 | |

For surcharge and overprint see Nos. N32, O182.

Municipal Palace — A24

**1936, Aug. 26 Photo. *Perf. 11½***

**Granite Paper**

| No. | Type | Description | Unused | Used |
|---|---|---|---|---|
| 200 | A24 | 10c brown | .25 | .30 |
| 201 | A24 | 35c green | .30 | .30 |
| 202 | A24 | 70c red orange | .40 | *.75* |
| 203 | A24 | 1fr carmine rose | 1.10 | *1.50* |
| 204 | A24 | 1.25fr violet | 2.00 | *9.00* |
| 205 | A24 | 1.75fr brt ultra | 1.25 | *6.00* |
| | | *Nos. 200-205 (6)* | 5.30 | *17.85* |
| | | Set, never hinged | 16.00 | |

11th Cong. of Intl. Federation of Philately. See No. 859.

Arms of Luxembourg A25

William I A26

Designs: 70c, William II. 75c, William III. 1fr, Prince Henry. 1.25fr, Grand Duke Adolphe. 1.75fr, William IV. 3fr, Regent Marie Anne. 5fr, Grand Duchess Marie Adelaide. 10fr, Grand Duchess Charlotte.

**1939, May 27 Engr. *Perf. 12½x12***

| | | | | |
|---|---|---|---|---|
| **206** | A25 | 35c brt green | .25 | .25 |
| **207** | A26 | 50c orange | .25 | .25 |
| **208** | A26 | 70c slate green | .25 | .25 |
| **209** | A26 | 75c sepia | .65 | *1.25* |
| **210** | A26 | 1fr red | 1.75 | *2.50* |
| **211** | A26 | 1.25fr brown violet | .25 | .25 |
| **212** | A26 | 1.75fr dark blue | .25 | .25 |
| **213** | A26 | 3fr lt brown | .25 | .70 |
| **214** | A26 | 5fr gray black | .50 | *3.00* |
| **215** | A26 | 10fr copper red | 1.00 | *6.50* |
| | | *Nos. 206-215 (10)* | 5.40 | *15.20* |
| | | Set, never hinged | 11.00 | |

Centenary of Independence.

Allegory of Medicinal Baths — A35

**1939, Sept. 18 Photo. *Perf. 11½***

| | | | | |
|---|---|---|---|---|
| **216** | A35 | 2fr brown rose | .50 | 2.50 |
| | | Never hinged | 1.25 | |

Elevation of Mondorf-les-Bains to town status.

See No. B104. For surcharge see No. N30.

Souvenir Sheet

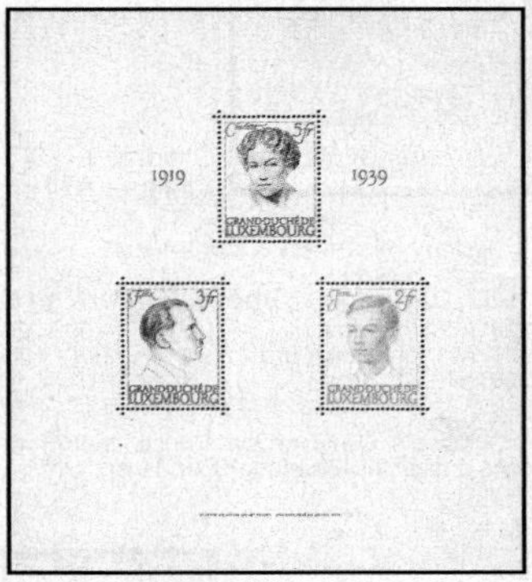


A36

**1939, Dec. 20 Engr. *Perf. 14x13***

| | | | | |
|---|---|---|---|---|
| **217** | A36 | Sheet of 3 | 45.00 | *100.00* |
| | | Sheet, never hinged | 100.00 | |
| *a.* | | 2fr vermilion, *buff* | 12.00 | *22.50* |
| *b.* | | 3fr dark green, *buff* | 12.00 | *22.50* |
| *c.* | | 5fr blue, *buff* | 12.00 | *22.50* |

20th anniv. of the reign of Grand Duchess Charlotte (Jan. 15, 1919) and her marriage to Prince Felix (Nov. 6, 1919).

See Nos. B98-B103.

Grand Duchess Charlotte — A37

**1944-46 Unwmk. *Perf. 12***

| | | | | |
|---|---|---|---|---|
| **218** | A37 | 5c brown red | .25 | .25 |
| **219** | A37 | 10c black | .25 | .25 |
| **219A** | A37 | 20c orange ('46) | .25 | .25 |
| **220** | A37 | 25c sepia | .25 | .25 |
| **220A** | A37 | 30c carmine ('46) | .25 | .40 |
| **221** | A37 | 35c green | .25 | .40 |
| **221A** | A37 | 40c dk blue ('46) | .25 | .40 |
| **222** | A37 | 50c dk violet | .25 | .25 |
| **222A** | A37 | 60c orange ('46) | .80 | .25 |
| **223** | A37 | 70c rose pink | .25 | .25 |
| **223A** | A37 | 70c dp green ('46) | .35 | *.65* |
| **223B** | A37 | 75c sepia ('46) | .25 | .25 |
| **224** | A37 | 1fr olive | .25 | .25 |
| **225** | A37 | 1¼fr red orange | .25 | *.25* |
| **226** | A37 | 1½fr red orange ('46) | .25 | .25 |
| **227** | A37 | 1¾fr blue | .25 | .25 |
| **228** | A37 | 2fr rose car ('46) | 1.40 | .25 |
| **229** | A37 | 2½fr dp violet ('46) | 2.50 | *4.50* |
| **230** | A37 | 3fr dp yel grn ('46) | .35 | .50 |
| **231** | A37 | 3½fr brt blue ('46) | .35 | *.75* |
| **232** | A37 | 5fr dk blue grn | .25 | .25 |
| **233** | A37 | 10fr carmine | .25 | 1.20 |
| **234** | A37 | 20fr deep blue | .45 | *8.00* |
| | | *Nos. 218-234 (23)* | 10.20 | *20.30* |
| | | Set, never hinged | 16.00 | |

Lion from Duchy Arms — A38

**1945 Engr. *Perf. 14x13***

| | | | | |
|---|---|---|---|---|
| **235** | A38 | 20c black | .25 | .25 |
| **236** | A38 | 30c brt green | .25 | .40 |
| **237** | A38 | 60c deep violet | .25 | .25 |
| **238** | A38 | 75c brown red | .25 | .25 |
| **239** | A38 | 1.20fr red | .25 | .25 |
| **240** | A38 | 1.50fr rose lilac | .25 | .25 |
| **241** | A38 | 2.50fr lt blue | .25 | .40 |
| | | Set, never hinged | 1.60 | |

Issued: 1.20fr, 5/15/45; 30c, 1.50fr, 2.50fr, 7/19; 20c, 75c, 10/1; 60c, 12/13.

Patton's Grave, US Military Cemetery, Hamm A39

Gen. Patton, Broken Chain and Advancing Tanks A40

**1947, Oct. 24 Photo. *Perf. 11½***

| | | | | |
|---|---|---|---|---|
| **242** | A39 | 1.50fr dk carmine | .25 | *.25* |
| **243** | A40 | 3.50fr dull blue | 1.00 | *2.00* |
| **244** | A39 | 5fr dk slate grn | 1.00 | *2.90* |
| **245** | A40 | 10fr chocolate | 5.25 | *40.00* |
| | | *Nos. 242-245 (4)* | 7.50 | *45.15* |
| | | Set, never hinged | 15.00 | |

George S. Patton, Jr. (1885-1945), American general.

Esch-sur-Sûre Fortifications A41

Luxembourg A44

Moselle River A42

Steel Mills — A43

***Perf. 11½x11, 11x11½***

**1948, Aug. 5 Engr. Unwmk.**

| | | | | |
|---|---|---|---|---|
| **246** | A41 | 7fr dark brown | 6.00 | .80 |
| **247** | A42 | 10fr dark green | 1.00 | .25 |
| **248** | A43 | 15fr carmine | 1.00 | .80 |
| **249** | A44 | 20fr dark blue | 1.00 | .80 |
| | | *Nos. 246-249 (4)* | 9.00 | 2.65 |
| | | Set, never hinged | 29.00 | |

Grand Duchess Charlotte — A45

**1948-49 *Perf. 11½***

| | | | | |
|---|---|---|---|---|
| **250** | A45 | 15c olive brn ('49) | .25 | .25 |
| **251** | A45 | 25c slate | .25 | .25 |
| **252** | A45 | 60c brown ('49) | .25 | .25 |
| **253** | A45 | 80c green ('49) | .25 | .25 |
| **254** | A45 | 1fr red lilac | .70 | .25 |
| **255** | A45 | 1.50fr grnsh bl | .70 | .25 |
| **256** | A45 | 1.60fr slate gray ('49) | .70 | *1.40* |
| **257** | A45 | 2fr dk vio brn | .70 | .25 |
| **258** | A45 | 4fr violet blue | 1.40 | .40 |
| **259** | A45 | 6fr brt red vio ('49) | 2.25 | .40 |
| **260** | A45 | 8fr dull green ('49) | 2.25 | 1.20 |
| | | *Nos. 250-260 (11)* | 9.70 | 5.15 |
| | | Set, never hinged | 26.00 | |

See Nos. 265-271, 292, 337-340, B151.

Self-Inking Canceller A46

**1949, Oct. 6 Photo.**

| | | | | |
|---|---|---|---|---|
| **261** | A46 | 80c blk, Prus grn & pale grn | .25 | .55 |
| **262** | A46 | 2.50fr dk brn, brn red & sal rose | 1.00 | *2.00* |
| **263** | A46 | 4fr blk, bl & pale bl | 2.75 | *6.00* |
| **264** | A46 | 8fr dk brn, brn & buff | 9.00 | *20.00* |
| | | *Nos. 261-264 (4)* | 13.00 | *28.55* |
| | | Set, never hinged | 25.00 | |

UPU, 75th anniv.

**Charlotte Type of 1948-49**

**1951, Mar. 15 Engr. Unwmk.**

| | | | | |
|---|---|---|---|---|
| **265** | A45 | 5c red orange | .25 | .25 |
| **266** | A45 | 10c ultra | .25 | .25 |
| **267** | A45 | 40c crimson | .25 | .25 |
| **268** | A45 | 1.25fr dk brown | .70 | .35 |
| **269** | A45 | 2.50fr red | .70 | .25 |
| **270** | A45 | 3fr blue | 4.50 | .35 |
| **271** | A45 | 3.50fr rose lake | 1.90 | .40 |
| | | *Nos. 265-271 (7)* | 8.55 | 2.10 |
| | | Set, never hinged | 22.50 | |

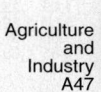

Agriculture and Industry A47

Globe and Scales A48

1fr, 3fr, People of Europe & Charter of Freedom.

**1951, Oct. 25 Photo. *Perf. 11½***

| | | | | |
|---|---|---|---|---|
| **272** | A47 | 80c deep green | *4.00* | *9.50* |
| **273** | A47 | 1fr purple | *1.75* | *.55* |
| **274** | A48 | 2fr black brown | *12.00* | *.55* |
| **275** | A47 | 2.50fr dk carmine | *12.00* | *20.00* |
| **276** | A47 | 3fr orange brn | *22.50* | *30.00* |
| **277** | A48 | 4fr blue | *32.50* | *40.00* |
| | | *Nos. 272-277 (6)* | *84.75* | *100.60* |
| | | Set, never hinged | *175.00* | |

Issued to promote a united Europe.

Grand Duke William III — A49

***Perf. 13½x13***

**1952, May 24 Engr. Unwmk.**

**Dates, Ornaments in Olive Green**

| | | | | |
|---|---|---|---|---|
| **278** | A49 | 2fr black | 21.00 | *30.00* |
| | | Never hinged | 30.00 | |
| **279** | A49 | 4fr red brown | 21.00 | *30.00* |
| | | Never hinged | 30.00 | |
| *a.* | | Se-tenant pair, #278-279 | 47.50 | *75.00* |
| | | Never hinged | 75.00 | |

Printed in sheets containing two panes of eight stamps each, alternating the two denominations. Centenary of Luxembourg's postage stamps. Price per set, 26fr, which included admission to the CENTILUX exhibition.

See Nos. C16-C20.

Hurdle Race — A50

Designs: 2fr, Football. 2.50fr, Boxing. 3fr, Water polo. 4fr, Bicycle racing. 8fr, Fencing.

**1952, Aug. 20 Photo. *Perf. 11½***

**Designs in Black**

| | | | | |
|---|---|---|---|---|
| **280** | A50 | 1fr pale green | .25 | .25 |
| **281** | A50 | 2fr brown buff | 1.00 | .25 |
| **282** | A50 | 2.50fr salmon pink | 1.50 | .35 |
| **283** | A50 | 3fr buff | 1.75 | .80 |
| **284** | A50 | 4fr lt blue | 10.50 | 6.00 |
| **285** | A50 | 8fr lilac | 6.00 | 3.50 |
| | | *Nos. 280-285 (6)* | 21.00 | 11.15 |
| | | Set, never hinged | 50.00 | |

15th Olympic Games, Helsinki; World Bicycling Championships of 1952.

Wedding of Princess Josephine-Charlotte of Belgium and Hereditary Grand Duke Jean — A51

**1953, Apr. 1**

| | | | | |
|---|---|---|---|---|
| **286** | A51 | 80c dull violet | .25 | .25 |
| **287** | A51 | 1.20fr lt brown | .25 | .25 |
| **288** | A51 | 2fr green | .25 | .25 |
| **289** | A51 | 3fr red lilac | .25 | .30 |
| **290** | A51 | 4fr brt blue | 2.50 | 1.00 |
| **291** | A51 | 9fr brown red | 3.50 | 1.00 |
| | | *Nos. 286-291 (6)* | 7.00 | 3.05 |
| | | Set, never hinged | 17.50 | |

**Charlotte Type of 1948-49**

**1953, May 18 Engr.**

| | | | | |
|---|---|---|---|---|
| **292** | A45 | 1.20fr gray | .40 | .25 |
| | | Never hinged | .90 | |

Radio Luxembourg — A52

Victor Hugo's Home, Vianden A53

**1953, May 18 *Perf. 11½x11***

| | | | | |
|---|---|---|---|---|
| **293** | A52 | 3fr purple | 2.75 | 1.50 |
| **294** | A53 | 4fr Prussian blue | 1.75 | 1.50 |
| | | Set, never hinged | 9.50 | |

150th birth anniv. of Victor Hugo (No. 294).

St. Willibrord Basilica Restored — A54

Design: 2.50fr, Interior view.

**1953, Sept. 18** ***Perf. 13x13½***

**295** A54 2fr red 1.60 .40
**296** A54 2.50fr dk gray grn 2.75 5.60
Set, never hinged 8.50

Consecration of St. Willibrord Basilica at Echternach.

Pierre d'Aspelt — A55

**1953, Sept. 25**

**297** A55 4fr black 4.00 4.00
Never hinged 7.00

Pierre d'Aspelt (1250-1320), chancellor of the Holy Roman Empire and Archbishop of Mainz.

Fencing Swords, Mask and Glove — A56

**1954, May 6** ***Perf. 13½x13***

**298** A56 2fr red brn & blk brn, *gray* 1.75 .75
Never hinged 3.75

World Fencing Championship Matches, Luxembourg, June 10-22.

Winged "L" Over Map — A57

**1954, May 6** **Photo.** ***Perf. 11½***

**299** A57 4fr dp bl, yel & red 6.00 3.50
Never hinged 9.00

6th Intl. Fair, Luxembourg, July 10-25.

Flowers — A58

**1955, Apr. 1**

**300** A58 80c Tulips .25 .25
**301** A58 2fr Daffodils .25 .25
**302** A58 3fr Hyacinths 1.75 3.25
**303** A58 4fr Parrot tulips 2.25 5.00
*Nos. 300-303 (4)* 4.50 8.75
Set, never hinged 8.50

Flower festival at Mondorf-les-Bains. See Nos. 351-353.

Artisan, Wheel and Tools — A59

**1955, Sept. 1** **Engr.** ***Perf. 13***

**304** A59 2fr dk gray & blk brn .70 .35
Never hinged 1.25

Natl. Handicraft Exposition at Luxembourg — Limpertsburg, Sept. 3-12.

Dudelange Television Station A60

**1955, Sept. 1** **Unwmk.**

**305** A60 2.50fr dk brn & redsh brn .65 .55
Never hinged 1.75

Installation of the Tele-Luxembourg station at Dudelange.

United Nations Emblem and Children Playing A61

UN, 10th anniv.: 80c, "Charter." 4fr, "Justice" (Sword and Scales). 9fr, "Assistance" (Workers).

**1955, Oct. 24** ***Perf. 11x11½***

**306** A61 80c black & dk bl .25 .30
**307** A61 2fr red & brown 1.75 .25
**308** A61 4fr dk blue & red 2.00 3.25
**309** A61 9fr dk brn & sl grn .65 .80
*Nos. 306-309 (4)* 4.65 4.60
Set, never hinged 11.00

A62

2fr, Anemones. 2.50fr, 4fr, Roses. 3fr, Crocuses.

**1956** **Photo.** ***Perf. 11½***

**Flowers in Natural Colors**

**310** A62 2fr gray violet .25 .25
**311** A62 2.50fr brt blue 2.50 3.75
**312** A62 3fr red brown 1.00 2.00
**313** A62 4fr purple 1.25 1.60
*Nos. 310-313 (4)* 5.00 7.60
Set, never hinged 10.00

Flower Festival at Mondorf-les-Bains (Nos. 310, 312). Nos. 311 and 313 are inscribed: "Luxembourg-Ville des Roses."

Issued: Nos. 310, 312, 4/27; Nos. 311, 313, 5/30.

A63

Steel beam and city emblem.

**1956, May 30**

**314** A63 2fr brt grnsh bl, red & blk .95 .50
Never hinged 2.25

50th anniversary of Esch-sur-Alzette.

Bessemer Converter and Blast Furnaces A64

Steel Beam and Model of City of Luxembourg — A65

Design: 4fr, 6-link chain, miner's lamp.

***Perf. 11x11½, 11½x11***

**1956, Aug. 10** **Engr.**

**315** A64 2fr dull red 11.00 .30
**316** A65 3fr dark blue 11.00 *17.00*
**317** A64 4fr green 2.00 *2.75*
*Nos. 315-317 (3)* *24.00 20.05*
Set, never hinged 45.00

4th anniv. of the establishment in Luxembourg of the headquarters of the European Coal and Steel Community.

"Rebuilding Europe" — A66

**1956, Sept. 15** ***Perf. 13***

**318** A66 2fr brown & black *37.50 .50*
**319** A66 3fr brick red & car *25.00 37.50*
**320** A66 4fr brt bl & dp bl *3.00 4.00*
*Nos. 318-320 (3)* 65.50 42.00
Set, never hinged *155.00*

Cooperation among the six countries comprising the Coal and Steel Community.

**Catalogue values for unused stamps in this section, from this point to the end of the section, are for Never Hinged items.**

Central Station from Train Window A67

**1956, Sept. 29** ***Perf. 13x12½***

**321** A67 2fr black & sepia 2.50 .55

Electrification of Luxembourg railways.

Ignace de la Fontaine A68

Design: 7fr, Grand Duchess Charlotte.

**1956, Nov. 7** ***Perf. 11½***

**322** A68 2fr gray brown 1.00 .25
**323** A68 7fr dull purple 2.75 .90

Centenary of the Council of State.

Lord Baden-Powell and Luxembourg Scout Emblems — A69

Designs: 2.50fr, Lord Baden-Powell and Luxembourg Girl Scout emblems.

**1957, June 17** ***Perf. 11½x11***

**324** A69 2fr ol grn & red brn 1.00 .50
**325** A69 2.50fr dk vio & claret 2.50 2.50

Birth centenary of Robert Baden-Powell and 50th anniv. of the founding of the Scout movement.

Prince Henry — A70

Children's Clinic — A71

Design: 4fr, Princess Marie-Astrid.

**1957, June 17** **Photo.** ***Perf. 11½***

**326** A70 2fr brown .60 .25
**327** A71 3fr bluish grn 3.00 *1.75*
**328** A70 4fr ultra 2.00 *2.10*
*Nos. 326-328 (3)* 5.60 *4.10*

Children's Clinic of the Prince Jean-Princess Josephine-Charlotte Foundation.

"United Europe" — A72

**1957, Sept. 16** **Engr.** ***Perf. 12½x12***

**329** A72 2fr reddish brn *3.00 .35*
**330** A72 3fr red *23.00 10.00*
**331** A72 4fr rose lilac *23.00 10.00*
*Nos. 329-331 (3)* 49.00 *20.35*
Set, hinged 19.00

A united Europe for peace and prosperity.

Fair Building and Flags — A73

**1958, Apr. 16** ***Perf. 12x11½***

**332** A73 2fr ultra & multi .40 .25

10th International Luxembourg Fair.

Luxembourg Pavilion, Brussels A74

**1958, Apr. 16** **Unwmk.**

**333** A74 2.50fr car & ultra .30 .25

International Exposition at Brussels.

St. Willibrord — A75

1fr, Sts. Willibrord & Irmina from "Liber Aureus." 5fr, St. Willibrord, young man & wine cask.

**1958, May 23 Engr. *Perf. 13x13½***

**334** A75 1fr red .25 .25
**335** A75 2.50fr olive brn .45 .25
**336** A75 5fr blue 1.00 *.90*
*Nos. 334-336 (3)* 1.70 *1.40*

1300th birth anniv. of St. Willibrord, apostle of the Low Countries and founder of Echternach Abbey.

**Charlotte Type of 1948-49**

**1958 Unwmk. *Perf. 11½***

**337** A45 20c dull claret .25 .25
**338** A45 30c olive .25 .25
**339** A45 50c dp org .35 .25
**340** A45 5fr violet 8.25 .40
*Nos. 337-340 (4)* 9.10 1.15

Issued: No. 337, 8/1; Nos. 338-340, 7/1.

---

Common Design Types pictured following the introduction.

---

**Europa Issue, 1958**
Common Design Type

**1958, Sept. 13 Litho. *Perf. 12½x13***
**Size: 21x34mm**

**341** CD1 2.50fr car & bl *.25* .25
**342** CD1 3.50fr green & org *.35* *.25*
**343** CD1 5fr blue & red *.75* *.40*
*Nos. 341-343 (3)* 1.35 .90

Wiltz Open-Air Theater A76

Vintage, Moselle A77

**1958, Sept. 13 Engr. *Perf. 11x11½***

**344** A76 2.50fr slate & sepia .60 .25
**345** A77 2.50fr lt grn & sepia .60 .25

No. 345 issued to publicize 2,000 years of grape growing in Luxembourg region.

Grand Duchess Charlotte — A78

**1959, Jan. 15 Photo. *Perf. 11½***

**346** A78 1.50fr pale grn & dk grn .65 .25
**347** A78 2.50fr pink & dk brn .65 .25
**348** A78 5fr lt bl & dk bl 1.25 *.90*
*Nos. 346-348 (3)* 2.55 *1.40*

40th anniv. of the accession to the throne of the Grand Duchess Charlotte.

NATO Emblem — A79

**1959, Apr. 3 *Perf. 12½x12***

**349** A79 2.50fr brt ol & bl .25 .25
**350** A79 8.50fr red brn & bl .40 .35

NATO, 10th anniversary.

**Flower Type of 1955, Inscribed "1959"**

1fr, Iris. 2.50fr, Peonies. 3fr, Hydrangea.

**1959, Apr. 3 *Perf. 11½***
**Flowers in Natural Colors**

**351** A58 1fr dk bl grn .25 .25
**352** A58 2.50fr deep blue .40 .25
**353** A58 3fr deep red lilac .65 .65
*Nos. 351-353 (3)* 1.30 1.15

Flower festival, Mondorf-les-Bains.

**Europa Issue, 1959**
Common Design Type
***Perf. 12½x13½***

**1959, Sept. 19 Litho.**
**Size: 22x33mm**

**354** CD2 2.50fr olive *.90* .35
**355** CD2 5fr dk blue *1.75* .65

Locomotive of 1859 and Hymn — A80

**1959, Sept. 19 Engr. *Perf. 13½***

**356** A80 2.50fr red & ultra 2.00 .40

Centenary of Luxembourg's railroads.

Man and Child Knocking at Door — A81

Holy Family, Flight into Egypt A82

***Perf. 11½x11, 11x11½***

**1960, Apr. 7 Unwmk.**

**357** A81 2.50fr org & slate .25 .25
**358** A82 5fr pur & slate .40 .40

World Refugee Year, July 1, 1959-June 30, 1960.

Steel Worker Drawing CECA Initials and Map of Member Countries A83

**1960, May 9 *Perf. 11x11½***

**359** A83 2.50fr dk car rose .50 .25

10th anniv. of the Schumann Plan for a European Steel and Coal Community.

European School and Children A84

**1960, May 9**

**360** A84 5fr bl & gray blk 1.00 .85

Establishment of the first European school in Luxembourg.

Heraldic Lion and Tools A85

**1960, June 14 Photo. *Perf. 11½***

**361** A85 2.50fr gray, red, bl & blk 1.40 .30

Natl. Exhibition of Craftsmanship, Luxembourg-Limpertsberg, July 9-18.

Grand Duchess Charlotte — A86

**1960-64 Engr. Unwmk.**

**362** A86 10c claret ('61) .25 .25
**363** A86 20c rose red ('61) .25 .25
**363A** A86 25c org ('64) .25 .25
**364** A86 30c gray olive .25 .25
**365** A86 50c dull grn .60 .25
**366** A86 1fr vio blue .75 .25
**367** A86 1.50fr rose lilac .75 .25
**368** A86 2fr blue ('61) .80 .25
**369** A86 2.50fr rose vio 1.40 .25
**370** A86 3fr vio brn ('61) 1.60 .25
**371** A86 3.50fr aqua ('64) 2.25 1.90
**372** A86 5fr lt red brn 2.25 .25
**373** A86 6fr slate ('64) 2.75 .25
*Nos. 362-373 (13)* 14.15 4.90

The 50c, 1fr and 3fr were issued in sheets and in coils. Every fifth coil stamp has control number on back.

**Europa Issue, 1960**
Common Design Type

**1960, Sept. 19 *Perf. 11x11½***
**Size: 37x27mm**

**374** CD3 2.50fr indigo & emer *.50* *.40*
**375** CD3 5fr maroon & blk *.50* *.40*

Great Spotted Woodpecker — A87

Designs: 1.50fr, Cat, horiz. 3fr, Filly, horiz. 8.50fr, Dachshund.

**1961, May 15 Photo. *Perf. 11½***

**376** A87 1fr multicolored .25 .25
**377** A87 1.50fr multicolored .30 .25
**378** A87 3fr gray, buff & red brn .55 .30
**379** A87 8.50fr lt grn, blk & ocher .90 .40
*Nos. 376-379 (4)* 2.00 1.20

Issued to publicize animal protection.

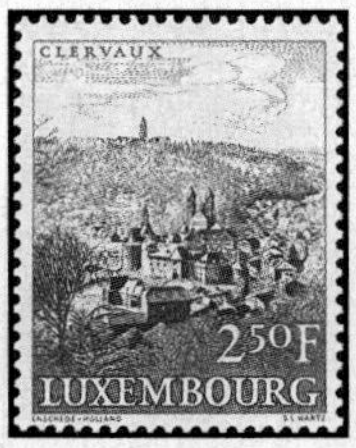


Clervaux and Abbey of St. Maurice and St. Maur — A88

**1961, June 8 Engr. *Perf. 11½x11***

**380** A88 2.50fr green .50 .25

General Patton Monument, Ettelbruck A89

**1961, June 8 *Perf. 11x11½***

**381** A89 2.50fr dark blue & gray .50 .25

The monument commemorates the American victory of the 3rd Army under Gen. George S. Patton, Jr., Battle of the Ardennes Bulge, 1944-45.

**Europa Issue, 1961**
Common Design Type

**1961, Sept. 18 *Perf. 13x12½***
**Size: 29½x27mm**

**382** CD4 2.50fr red *.25* *.25*
**383** CD4 5fr blue *.30* *.30*

Cyclist Carrying Bicycle — A90

Design: 5fr, Emblem of 1962 championship.

**1962, Jan. 22 Photo. *Perf. 11½***

**384** A90 2.50fr lt ultra, crim & blk .25 .25
**385** A90 5fr multicolored .30 .30

Intl. Cross-country Bicycle Race, Esch-sur-Alzette, Feb. 18.

**Europa Issue, 1962**
Common Design Type

**1962, Sept. 17 Unwmk. *Perf. 11½***
**Size: 32½x23mm**

**386** CD5 2.50fr ol bis, yel grn & brn blk *.30* *.25*
**387** CD5 5fr rose lil, lt grn & brn blk *.45* *.30*

St. Laurent's Church, Diekirch — A91

**1962, Sept. 17 Engr. *Perf. 11½x11***

**388** A91 2.50fr brown & blk .50 .25

Bock Rock Castle, 10th Century A92

Gate of Three Towers, 11th Century — A93

Designs (each stamp represents a different century): No. 391, Benedictine Abbey, Munster. No. 392, Great Seal of Luxembourg, 1237. No. 393, Rham Towers. No. 394, Black Virgin, Grund. No. 395, Grand Ducal Palace. No. 396, The Citadel of the Holy Ghost. No. 397, Castle Bridge. No. 398, Town Hall. No. 399, Municipal theater, bridge and European Community Center.

***Perf. 14x13 (A92), 11½ (A93)***
**Engr. (A92), Photo. (A93)**

**1963, Apr. 13**

| | | | | | |
|---|---|---|---|---|---|
| **389** | A92 | 1fr | slate blue | .25 | .25 |
| **390** | A93 | 1fr | multicolored | .25 | .25 |
| **391** | A92 | 1.50fr | dl red brn | .25 | .25 |
| **392** | A93 | 1.50fr | multicolored | .25 | .25 |
| **393** | A92 | 2.50fr | gray grn | .25 | .25 |
| **394** | A93 | 2.50fr | multicolored | .25 | .25 |
| **395** | A92 | 3fr | brown | .25 | .25 |
| **396** | A93 | 3fr | multicolored | .25 | .25 |
| **397** | A92 | 5fr | brt violet | .25 | .25 |
| **398** | A93 | 5fr | multicolored | .50 | .50 |
| **399** | A92 | 11fr | multicolored | 1.00 | .65 |
| | *Nos. 389-399 (11)* | | | 3.75 | 3.40 |

Millennium of the city of Luxembourg; MELUSINA Intl. Phil. Exhib., Luxembourg, Apr. 13-21. Set sold only at exhibition. Value of 62fr included entrance ticket. Nos. 390, 392, 394 and 396 however were sold without restriction.

Blackboard Showing European School Buildings — A94

**1963, Apr. 13 Photo. *Perf. 11½***

**400** A94 2.50fr gray, grn & mag .35 .25

10th anniv. of the European Schools in Luxembourg, Brussels, Varese, Mol and Karlsruhe.

Colpach Castle and Centenary Emblem A95

**1963, May 8 Engr. *Perf. 13***

**401** A95 2.50fr hn brn, gray & red .35 .25

Centenary of the Intl. Red Cross. Colpach Castle, home of Emile Mayrisch, was donated to the Luxembourg League of the Red Cross for a rest home.

Twelve Stars of Council of Europe — A96

**1963, June 25 *Perf. 13x14***

**402** A96 2.50fr dp ultra, *gold* .30 .25

10th anniv. of the European Convention of Human Rights.

**Europa Issue, 1963**
Common Design Type

**1963, Sept. 16 Photo. *Perf. 11½***
**Size: 32½x23mm**

| | | | | | |
|---|---|---|---|---|---|
| **403** | CD6 | 3fr | bl grn, lt grn & org | *.30* | *.25* |
| **404** | CD6 | 6fr | red brn, org red & org | *.45* | *.30* |

Brown Trout Taking Bait — A97

**1963, Sept. 16 Engr. *Perf. 13***

**405** A97 3fr indigo .30 .25

World Fly-Fishing Championship, Wormeldange, Sept. 22.

Map of Luxembourg, Telephone Dial and Stars — A98

**1963, Sept. 16 Photo. *Perf. 11½***

**406** A98 3fr ultra, brt grn & blk .30 .25

Completion of telephone automation.

Power House — A99

3fr, Upper reservoir, horiz. 6fr, Lohmuhle dam.

**1964, Apr. 17 Engr. *Perf. 13***

| | | | | | |
|---|---|---|---|---|---|
| **407** | A99 | 2fr | red brn & sl | .25 | .25 |
| **408** | A99 | 3fr | red, sl grn & lt bl | .25 | .25 |
| **409** | A99 | 6fr | choc, grn & bl | .25 | .25 |
| | *Nos. 407-409 (3)* | | | .75 | .75 |

Inauguration of the Vianden hydroelectric station.

Barge Entering Lock at Grevenmacher Dam — A100

**1964, May 26 Unwmk.**

**410** A100 3fr indigo & brt bl .30 .25

Opening of Moselle River canal system.

**Europa Issue, 1964**
Common Design Type

**1964, Sept. 14 Photo. *Perf. 11½***
**Size: 22x38mm**

| | | | | | |
|---|---|---|---|---|---|
| **411** | CD7 | 3fr | org brn, yel & dk bl | *.30* | *.25* |
| **412** | CD7 | 6fr | yel grn, yel & dk brn | *.45* | *.30* |

New Atheneum Educational Center and Students A101

**1964, Sept. 14 Unwmk.**

**413** A101 3fr dk bl grn & blk .30 .25

**Benelux Issue**

King Baudouin, Queen Juliana and Grand Duchess Charlotte — A101a

**1964, Oct. 12 Size: 45x26mm**

**414** A101a 3fr dull bl, yel & brn .30 .25

20th anniv. of the customs union of Belgium, Netherlands and Luxembourg.

Grand Duke Jean and Grand Duchess Josephine Charlotte A102

**1964, Nov. 11 Photo. *Perf. 11½***

| | | | | | |
|---|---|---|---|---|---|
| **415** | A102 | 3fr | indigo | .30 | .25 |
| **416** | A102 | 6fr | dk brown | .40 | .30 |

Grand Duke Jean's accession to throne.

Rotary Emblem and Cogwheels — A103

**1965, Apr. 5 Photo. *Perf. 11½***

**417** A103 3fr gold, car, gray & ultra .30 .25

Rotary International, 60th anniversary.

Grand Duke Jean — A104

**1965-71 Engr. Unwmk.**

| | | | | | |
|---|---|---|---|---|---|
| **418** | A104 | 25c | olive bister ('66) | .25 | .25 |
| **419** | A104 | 50c | rose red | .25 | .25 |
| **420** | A104 | 1fr | ultra | .25 | .25 |
| **421** | A104 | 1.50fr | dk vio brn ('66) | .25 | .25 |
| **422** | A104 | 2fr | magenta ('66) | .25 | .25 |
| **423** | A104 | 2.50fr | orange ('71) | .35 | .25 |
| **424** | A104 | 3fr | gray | .50 | .25 |
| **425** | A104 | 3.50fr | brn org ('66) | .35 | .40 |
| **426** | A104 | 4fr | vio brn ('71) | .30 | .25 |
| **427** | A104 | 5fr | green ('71) | .35 | .25 |
| **428** | A104 | 6fr | purple | .75 | .25 |
| **429** | A104 | 8fr | bl grn ('71) | .65 | .25 |
| | *Nos. 418-429 (12)* | | | 4.50 | 3.15 |

The 50c, 1fr, 2fr, 3fr, 4fr, 5fr and 6fr were issued in sheets and in coils. Every fifth coil stamp has control number on back.

See Nos. 570-576.

ITU Emblem, Old and New Communication Equipment — A105

**1965, May 17 Litho. *Perf. 13½***

**431** A105 3fr dk pur, claret & blk .35 .25

ITU, centenary.

**Europa Issue, 1965**
Common Design Type

***Perf. 13x12½***

**1965, Sept. 27 Photo. Unwmk.**
**Size: 30x23½mm**

| | | | | | |
|---|---|---|---|---|---|
| **432** | CD8 | 3fr | grn, maroon & blk | .35 | *.25* |
| **433** | CD8 | 6fr | tan, dk bl & grn | .40 | *.30* |

Inauguration of WHO Headquarters, Geneva — A106

**1966, Mar. 7 Engr. *Perf. 11x11½***

**434** A106 3fr green .30 .25

Torch and Banner — A107

**1966, Mar. 7 Photo. *Perf. 11½***

**435** A107 3fr gray & brt red .30 .25

50th anniversary of the Workers' Federation in Luxembourg.

Key and Arms of City of Luxembourg, and Arms of Prince of Chimay — A108

Designs: 2fr, Interior of Cathedral of Luxembourg, painting by Juan Martin. 3fr, Our Lady of Luxembourg, engraving by Richard Collin. 6fr, Column and spandrel with sculptured angels from Cathedral.

**1966, Apr. 28 Engr. *Perf. 13x14***

| | | | | | |
|---|---|---|---|---|---|
| **436** | A108 | 1.50fr | green | .25 | .25 |
| **437** | A108 | 2fr | dull red | .25 | .25 |
| **438** | A108 | 3fr | dk blue | .25 | .25 |
| **439** | A108 | 6fr | red brown | .25 | .25 |
| | *Nos. 436-439 (4)* | | | 1.00 | 1.00 |

300th anniv. of the Votum Solemne (Solemn Promise) which made the Virgin Mary Patron Saint of the City of Luxembourg.

**Europa Issue, 1966**
Common Design Type

***Perf. 13½x12½***

**1966, Sept. 26 Litho.**
**Size: 25x37mm**

| | | | | | |
|---|---|---|---|---|---|
| **440** | CD9 | 3fr | gray & vio bl | .30 | *.25* |
| **441** | CD9 | 6fr | olive & dk grn | .40 | *.30* |

Diesel Locomotive A109

Design: 3fr, Electric locomotive.

**1966, Sept. 26 Photo. *Perf. 11½***

| | | | | | |
|---|---|---|---|---|---|
| **442** | A109 | 1.50fr | multicolored | *.75* | .25 |
| **443** | A109 | 3fr | multicolored | *.75* | .30 |

5th Intl. Philatelic Exhibition of Luxembourg Railroad Men, Sept. 30-Oct. 3.

Grand Duchess Charlotte Bridge A110

**1966, Sept. 26 Engr. *Perf. 13***

**444** A110 3fr dk car rose .30 .25

Tower Building, Kirchberg, Seat of European Community — A111

Design: 13fr, Design for Robert Schuman monument, Luxembourg.

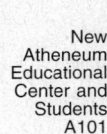

**1966, Sept. 26**

**445** A111 1.50fr dk green .25 .25
**446** A111 13fr deep blue .60 .25

"Luxembourg, Center of Europe."

View of Luxembourg, 1850, by Nicolas Liez — A112

Map of Luxembourg Fortress, 1850, by Theodore de Cederstolpe — A113

**1967, Mar. 6 Engr. *Perf. 13***

**447** A112 3fr bl, vio brn & grn .25 .25
**448** A113 6fr blue, brn & red .25 .25

Centenary of the Treaty of London, which guaranteed the country's neutrality after the dismantling of the Fortress of Luxembourg.

**Europa Issue, 1967**

Common Design Type

**1967, May 2 Photo. *Perf. 11½***

**Size: 33x22mm**

**449** CD10 3fr cl brn, gray & buff *.50 .35*
**450** CD10 6fr dk brn, vio gray & lt bl *.50 .35*

Lion, Globe and Lions Emblem — A115

**1967, May 2 Photo. *Perf. 11½***

**451** A115 3fr multicolored .30 .25

Lions International, 50th anniversary.

Canceled to Order

Luxembourg's Office des Timbres, Direction des Postes, was offering, at least as early as 1967, to sell commemorative issues canceled to order.

NATO Emblem and European Community Administration Building — A116

**1967, June 13 Litho. *Perf. 13x12½***

**452** A116 3fr lt grn & dk grn .25 .25
**453** A116 6fr dp rose & dk car .40 .40

NATO Council meeting, Luxembourg, June 13-14.

Youth Hostel, Ettelbruck — A117

**1967, Sept. 14 Photo. *Perf. 11½***

**454** A117 1.50fr multicolored .25 .25

Luxembourg youth hostels.

Home Gardener — A118

**1967, Sept. 14**

**455** A118 1.50fr brt grn & org .25 .25

16th Congress of the Intl. Assoc. of Home Gardeners.

Shaving Basin with Wedding Scene, 1819 — A119

Design: 3fr, Ornamental vase, 1820, vert.

**1967, Sept. 14**

**456** A119 1.50fr ol grn & multi .25 .25
**457** A119 3fr ultra & lt gray .25 .25

Faience industry in Luxembourg, 200th anniv.

Wormeldange - Moselle River — A120

Mertert, Moselle River Port A121

**1967, Sept. 14 Engr. *Perf. 13***

**458** A120 3fr dp bl, claret & ol .40 .25
**459** A121 3fr violet bl & slate .25 .25

Swimming — A122

Sport: 1.50fr, Soccer. 2fr, Bicycling. 3fr, Running. 6fr, Walking. 13fr, Fencing.

**1968, Feb. 22 Photo. *Perf. 11½***

**460** A122 50c bl & grnsh bl .25 .25
**461** A122 1.50fr brt grn & emer .25 .25
**462** A122 2fr yel grn & lt yel grn .25 .25
**463** A122 3fr dp org & dl org .25 .25
**464** A122 6fr grnsh bl & pale grn .55 .25
**465** A122 13fr rose cl & rose .60 .25
*Nos. 460-465 (6)* 2.15 1.50

Issued to publicize the 19th Olympic Games, Mexico City, Oct. 12-27.

**Europa Issue, 1968**

Common Design Type

**1968, Apr. 29 Photo. *Perf. 11½***

**Size: 32½x23mm**

**466** CD11 3fr ap grn, blk & org brn *.40 .35*
**467** CD11 6fr brn org, blk & ap grn *.40 .35*

Kind Spring Pavilion A123

**1968, Apr. 29 Photo. *Perf. 11½***

**468** A123 3fr multicolored .25 .25

Issued to publicize Mondorf-les-Bains.

Fair Emblem A124

**1968, Apr. 29**

**469** A124 3fr dp vio, dl bl gold & red .25 .25

20th Intl. Fair, Luxembourg City, May 23-June 2.

Children's Village of Mersch A125

Orphan and Foster Mother — A126

**1968, Sept. 18 Engr. *Perf. 13***

**470** A125 3fr slate grn & dk red brn .25 .25
**471** A126 6fr slate bl, blk & brn .40 .25

Mersch children's village. (Modeled after Austrian SOS villages for homeless children.)

Red Cross and Symbolic Blood Transfusion — A127

**1968, Sept. 18 Photo. *Perf. 11½***

**472** A127 3fr lt blue & car .40 .25

Voluntary Red Cross blood donors.

Luxair Plane over Luxembourg — A128

**1968, Sept. 18 Engr. *Perf. 13***

**473** A128 50fr olive, bl & dk bl 3.25 .25

Issued for tourist publicity.

Souvenir Sheet

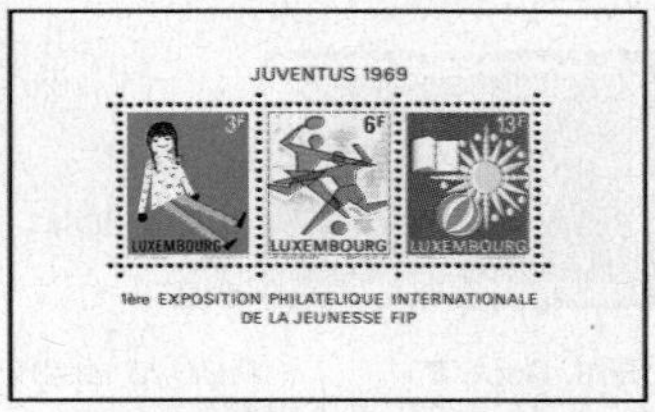


"Youth and Leisure" — A129

Designs, a, 3fr, Doll. b, 6fr, Ballplayers. c, 13fr, Book, compass rose and ball.

**1969, Apr. 3 Photo. *Perf. 11½***

**Granite Paper**

**474** A129 Sheet of 3 3.25 3.50
*a.-c.* any single 1.00 1.00

1st Intl. Youth Phil. Exhib., JUVENTUS 1969, Luxembourg, Apr. 3-8.

No. 474 was on sale only at the exhibition. Sold only with entrance ticket for 40fr.

**Europa Issue, 1969**

Common Design Type

**1969, May 19 Photo. *Perf. 11½***

**Size: 32½x23mm**

**475** CD12 3fr gray, brn & org *.45 .25*
**476** CD12 6fr vio gray, blk & yel *.50 .25*

Boy on Hobbyhorse, by Joseph Kutter (1894-1941) — A130

Design: 6fr, View of Luxembourg, by Kutter.

**1969, May 19 Engr. *Perf. 12x13***

**477** A130 3fr multicolored .45 .25
*a.* Green omitted *150.00 150.00*
**478** A130 6fr multicolored .45 .35

ILO, 50th Anniv. A131

**Photo.; Gold Impressed (Emblem)**

**1969, May 19 *Perf. 14x14½***

**479** A131 3fr brt grn, vio & gold .25 .25

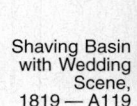

Mobius Strip in Benelux Colors — A131a

**1969, Sept. 8 Litho. *Perf. 12½x13½***
**480** A131a 3fr multicolored .30 .25

25th anniv. of the signing of the customs union of Belgium, Netherlands and Luxembourg.

NATO, 20th Anniv. A132

**1969, Sept. 8 *Perf. 13½x12½***
**481** A132 3fr org brn & dk brn .35 .25

Grain and Mersch Agricultural Center — A133

**1969, Sept. 8 Photo. *Perf. 11½***
**482** A133 3fr bl grn, gray & blk .25 .25

Issued to publicize agricultural progress.

St. Willibrord's Basilica and Abbey, Echternach A134

No. 484, Castle and open-air theater, Wiltz.

**1969, Sept. 8 Engr. *Perf. 13***
**483** A134 3fr dark blue & indigo .30 .25
**484** A134 3fr slate green & indigo .30 .25

Pasqueflower A135

Design: 6fr, Hedgehog and 3 young.

**1970, Mar. 9 Photo. *Perf. 11½***
**485** A135 3fr multicolored .25 .25
**486** A135 6fr green & multi .40 .30

European Conservation Year.

Goldcrest A136

**1970, Mar. 9 Engr. *Perf. 13***
**487** A136 1.50fr org, grn & blk brn .30 .25

Luxembourg Society for the protection and study of birds, 50th anniv.

Traffic Sign and Street Scene A137

**1970, May 4 Photo. *Perf. 11½***
**488** A137 3fr rose mag, red & blk .30 .25

The importance of traffic safety.

**Europa Issue, 1970**
Common Design Type

**1970, May 4 Size: 32½x23mm**
**489** CD13 3fr brown & multi *.40 .25*
**490** CD13 6fr green & multi *.40 .30*

Empress Kunigunde and Emperor Henry II, Window, Luxembourg Cathedral — A138

**1970, Sept. 14 Photo. *Perf. 12***
**491** A138 3fr multicolored .25 .25

Centenary of the Diocese of Luxembourg.

Census Symbol A139

**1970, Sept. 14 *Perf. 11½***
**492** A139 3fr dk grn, grnsh bl & red .25 .25

Census of Dec. 31, 1970.

Lion, Luxembourg City Hall — A140

**1970, Sept. 14**
**493** A140 3fr bister, lt bl & dk brn .25 .25

50th anniversary of the City of Luxembourg through the union of 5 municipalities.

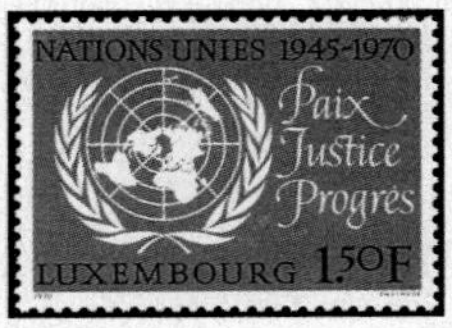

UN Emblem A141

***Perf. 12½x13½***
**1970, Sept. 14 Litho.**
**494** A141 1.50fr bl & vio bl .25 .25

25th anniversary of the United Nations.

Monks in Abbey Workshop — A142

Miniatures Painted at Echternach, about 1040: 3fr, Laborers going to the vineyard (Matthew 20:1-6). 6fr, Laborers toiling in vineyard. 13fr, Workers searching for graves of the saints.

**1971, Mar. 15 Photo. *Perf. 12***
**495** A142 1.50fr gold & multi .25 .25
**496** A142 3fr gold & multi .25 .25
**497** A142 6fr gold & multi .30 .25
**498** A142 13fr gold & multi 1.20 .45
*Nos. 495-498 (4)* 2.00 1.20

Olympic Rings, Arms of Luxembourg A143

**1971, May 3 Photo. *Perf. 12½***
**499** A143 3fr ultra & multi .35 .25

Intl. Olympic Committee, 71st session.

**Europa Issue, 1971**
Common Design Type

**1971, May 3 *Perf. 12½x13***
**Size: 34x25mm**
**500** CD14 3fr ver, brn & blk *.50 .25*
**501** CD14 6fr brt grn, brn & blk *.50 .40*

A145

**1971, May 3 Litho. *Perf. 13x13½***
**502** A145 3fr org, dk brn & yel .25 .25

Christian Workers Union, 50th anniv.

Artificial Lake, Upper Sure A146

Designs: No. 504, Water treatment plant, Esch-sur-Sure. 15fr, ARBED Steel Corporation Headquarters, Luxembourg.

**1971, Sept. 13 Engr. *Perf. 13***
**503** A146 3fr ol, grnsh bl & indigo .40 .25
**504** A146 3fr brn, sl grn & grnsh bl .45 .25
**505** A146 15fr indigo & blk brn 1.00 .25
*Nos. 503-505 (3)* 1.85 .75

School Girl with Coin — A147

**1971, Sept. 13 Photo. *Perf. 11½***
**506** A147 3fr violet & multi .30 .25

School children's savings campaign.

Coins of Luxembourg and Belgium — A148

**1972, Mar. 6**
**507** A148 1.50fr lt grn, sil & blk .25 .25

Economic Union of Luxembourg and Belgium, 50th anniversary.

Bronze Mask — A149

Archaeological Objects, 4th to 1st centuries, B.C.: 1fr, Earthenware bowl, horiz. 8fr, Limestone head. 15fr, Glass jug in shape of head.

**1972, Mar. 6**
**508** A149 1fr lemon & multi .25 .25
**509** A149 3fr multicolored .35 .25
**510** A149 8fr multicolored .75 .60
**511** A149 15fr multicolored .90 .45
*Nos. 508-511 (4)* 2.25 1.55

**Europa Issue 1972**
Common Design Type

**1972, May 2 Photo. *Perf. 11½***
**Size: 22x33mm**
**512** CD15 3fr rose vio & multi .45 *.25*
**513** CD15 8fr gray blue & multi .50 *.40*

Archer A150

**1972, May 2**
**514** A150 3fr crimson, blk & olive .45 .25

3rd European Archery Championships.

Robert Schuman Medal — A151

**1972, May 2 Engr. *Perf. 13***
**515** A151 3fr gray & slate green .60 .25

Establishment in Luxembourg of the European Coal and Steel Community, 20th anniv.

The Fox Wearing Tails — A152

**1972, Sept. 11 Photo. *Perf. 11½***
**516** A152 3fr scarlet & multi .30 .25

Centenary of the publication of "Renert," satirical poem by Michel Rodange.

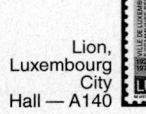

National Monument A153

Court of Justice of European Communities, Kirchberg — A154

**1972, Sept. 11 Engr. *Perf. 13***

| | | | | |
|---|---|---|---|---|
| **517** | A153 | 3fr sl grn, olive & vio | .45 | .25 |
| **518** | A154 | 3fr brn, bl & slate grn | .75 | .25 |

Epona on Horseback — A155

Archaeological Objects: 4fr, Panther killing swan, horiz. 8fr, Celtic gold stater inscribed Pottina. 15fr, Bronze boar, horiz.

**1973, Mar. 14 Photo. *Perf. 11½***

| | | | | |
|---|---|---|---|---|
| **519** | A155 | 1fr salmon & multi | .25 | .25 |
| **520** | A155 | 4fr beige & multi | .30 | .25 |
| **521** | A155 | 8fr multicolored | 1.75 | .60 |
| **522** | A155 | 15fr multicolored | .75 | .60 |
| | | *Nos. 519-522 (4)* | 3.05 | 1.70 |

**Europa Issue 1973**

Common Design Type

**1973, Apr. 30 Photo. *Perf. 11½***

**Size: 32x22mm**

| | | | | |
|---|---|---|---|---|
| **523** | CD16 | 4fr org, dk vio & lt bl | *.45* | *.25* |
| **524** | CD16 | 8fr ol, vio blk & yel | *.45* | *.50* |

Bee on Honeycomb — A156

**1973, Apr. 30 Photo. *Perf. 11½***

| | | | | |
|---|---|---|---|---|
| **525** | A156 | 4fr ocher & multi | .45 | .25 |

Publicizing importance of beekeeping.

Nurse Holding Child — A157

**1973, Apr. 30**

| | | | | |
|---|---|---|---|---|
| **526** | A157 | 4fr multicolored | .40 | .25 |

Publicizing importance of day nurseries.

Laurel Branch A158

**1973, Sept. 10 Photo. *Perf. 11½***

| | | | | |
|---|---|---|---|---|
| **527** | A158 | 3fr violet bl & multi | .25 | .25 |

50th anniv. of Luxembourg Board of Labor.

Jerome de Busleyden — A159

**1973, Sept. 10 Engr. *Perf. 13***

| | | | | |
|---|---|---|---|---|
| **528** | A159 | 4fr black, brn & pur | .30 | .25 |

Council of Mechelen, 500th anniv.

National Strike Memorial, Wiltz — A160

**1973, Sept. 10**

| | | | | |
|---|---|---|---|---|
| **529** | A160 | 4fr ol bis, sl & sl grn | .50 | .25 |

In memory of the Luxembourg resistance heroes who died during the great strike of 1942.

Capital, Byzantine Hall, Vianden — A161

St. Gregory the Great — A161a

Designs: No. 534, Sts. Cecilia and Valerian crowned by angel, Hollenfels Church. No. 535, Interior, Septfontaines Church. 8fr, Madonna and Child, St. Irmina's Chapel, Rosport. 12fr, St. Augustine Sculptures by Jean-Georges Scholtus from pulpit in Feulen parish church, c. 1734.

**1973-77 *Perf. 13x12½, 14 (6fr, 12fr)***

| | | | | |
|---|---|---|---|---|
| **533** | A161 | 4fr green & rose vio | .30 | .25 |
| **534** | A161 | 4fr red brn, grn & lil | .40 | .25 |
| **535** | A161 | 4fr gray, brn & dk vio | .40 | .25 |
| **536** | A161a | 6fr maroon | .50 | .25 |
| **537** | A161 | 8fr sepia & vio bl | 1.00 | .60 |
| **538** | A161a | 12fr slate blue | 1.00 | .65 |
| | | *Nos. 533-538 (6)* | 3.60 | 2.25 |

Architecture of Luxembourg: Romanesque, Gothic, Baroque.

Issued: No. 533, 8fr, 9/10/73; Nos. 534-535, 9/9/74; 6fr, 12fr, 9/16/77.

Princess Marie Astrid — A162

**1974, Mar. 14 Photo. *Perf. 11½***

| | | | | |
|---|---|---|---|---|
| **540** | A162 | 4fr blue & multi | 1.50 | .30 |

Princess Marie-Astrid, president of the Luxembourg Red Cross Youth Section.

Torch — A163

**1974, Mar. 14**

| | | | | |
|---|---|---|---|---|
| **541** | A163 | 4fr ultra & multi | .50 | .20 |

50th anniversary of Luxembourg Mutual Insurance Federation.

Royal Seal of Henri VII — A164

Seals from 13th-14th Centuries: 3fr, Equestrian, seal of Jean, King of Bohemia: 4fr, Seal of Town of Diekirch. 19fr, Virgin and Child, seal of Convent of Marienthal.

**1974, Mar. 14**

| | | | | |
|---|---|---|---|---|
| **542** | A164 | 1fr purple & multi | .25 | .25 |
| **543** | A164 | 3fr green & multi | .30 | .25 |
| **544** | A164 | 4fr multicolored | .35 | .25 |
| **545** | A164 | 19fr multicolored | 1.00 | .75 |
| | | *Nos. 542-545 (4)* | 1.90 | 1.50 |

Hind, by Auguste Trémont — A165

Europa: 8fr, "Growth," abstract sculpture, by Lucien Wercollier.

**1974, Apr. 29 Photo. *Perf. 11½***

| | | | | |
|---|---|---|---|---|
| **546** | A165 | 4fr ocher & multi | *.50* | .30 |
| **547** | A165 | 8fr brt blue & multi | *1.50* | *1.20* |

Winston Churchill, by Oscar Nemon — A166

**1974, Apr. 29**

| | | | | |
|---|---|---|---|---|
| **548** | A166 | 4fr lilac & multi | .40 | .25 |

Sir Winston Churchill (1874-1965), statesman.

Fairground, Aerial View — A167

**1974, Apr. 29**

| | | | | |
|---|---|---|---|---|
| **549** | A167 | 4fr silver & multi | .40 | .25 |

Publicity for New International Fairground, Luxembourg-Kirchberg.

Theis, the Blind — A168

**1974, Apr. 29**

| | | | | |
|---|---|---|---|---|
| **550** | A168 | 3fr multicolored | .40 | .25 |

Mathias Schou, Theis the Blind (1747-1824), wandering minstrel.

UPU Emblem and "100" — A169

**1974, Sept. 9 Photo. *Perf. 11½***

| | | | | |
|---|---|---|---|---|
| **551** | A169 | 4fr multicolored | .30 | .25 |
| **552** | A169 | 8fr multicolored | .90 | .55 |

Centenary of Universal Postal Union.

"BENELUX" A170

**1974, Sept. 9**

| | | | | |
|---|---|---|---|---|
| **553** | A170 | 4fr bl grn, dk grn & lt bl | .90 | .25 |

30th anniversary of the signing of the customs union of Belgium, Netherlands and Luxembourg.

View of Differdange A171

**1974, Sept. 9 Engr. *Perf. 13***

| | | | | |
|---|---|---|---|---|
| **554** | A171 | 4fr rose claret | 1.00 | .25 |

Bourglinster A172

Designs: 1fr, Fish Market, Old Luxembourg, vert. 4fr, Market Square, Echternach. 19fr, St. Michael's Square, Mersch, vert.

***Perf. 14x13½, 13½x14***

**1975, Mar. 10 Engr.**

| | | | | |
|---|---|---|---|---|
| **555** | A172 | 1fr olive green | .60 | .25 |
| **556** | A172 | 3fr deep brown | .90 | .30 |
| **557** | A172 | 4fr dark purple | .90 | .25 |
| **558** | A172 | 19fr copper red | 1.25 | .65 |
| | | *Nos. 555-558 (4)* | 3.65 | 1.45 |

European Architectural Heritage Year.

Joseph Kutter, Self-portrait A173

Moselle Bridge, Remich, by Nico Klopp — A174

Paintings: 8fr, Still Life, by Joseph Kutter. 20fr, The Dam, by Dominique Lang.

**1975, Apr. 28 Photo. *Perf. 11½***
**559** A173 1fr multicolored .30 .25
**560** A174 4fr multicolored *1.20 .25*
**561** A174 8fr multicolored 1.75 1.25
**562** A173 20fr multicolored 1.50 .50
*Nos. 559-562 (4)* 4.75 2.25

Cultural series. Nos. 560-561 are Europa Issue.

Robert Schuman, Gaetano Martino, Paul-Henri Spaak Medals A175

**1975, Apr. 28**
**563** A175 4fr yel grn, gold & brn .70 .25

Robert Schuman's declaration establishing European Coal and Steel Community, 25th anniv.

Albert Schweitzer (1875-1965), Medical Missionary — A176

**1975, Apr. 28 Engr. *Perf. 13***
**564** A176 4fr bright blue .70 .25

Civil Defense Emblem — A177

**1975, Sept. 8 Photo. *Perf. 11½***
**565** A177 4fr multicolored .60 .25

Civil Defense Org. for protection and rescue.

Figure Skating — A178

4fr, Water skiing, horiz. 15fr, Mountain climbing.

**1975, Sept. 8 Engr. *Perf. 13***
**566** A178 3fr green, bl & lilac .30 .25
**567** A178 4fr dk brn, grn & lt brn .45 .25
**568** A178 15fr brown, indigo & grn 1.40 .55
*Nos. 566-568 (3)* 2.15 1.05

### Grand Duke Type of 1965-71

**1975-91 Engr. *Perf. 11½***
**Granite Paper (14fr, 22fr)**
**570** A104 7fr orange .45 .25
**571** A104 9fr yellow green .90 .25
**572** A104 10fr black .50 .25
**573** A104 12fr brick red 1.20 .25
**573A** A104 14fr dark blue .65 .30
**574** A104 16fr green 1.00 .25
**574A** A104 18fr brown olive .80 .40
**575** A104 20fr blue 1.20 .25
**576** A104 22fr orange brown 1.10 .80
*Nos. 570-576 (9)* 7.80 3.00

Issued: 10fr, 1/9; 9fr, 12fr, 20fr, 12/23; 16fr, 2/25/82; 7fr, 7/1/83; 18fr, 3/3/86; 14fr, 1/2/90; 22fr, 9/23/91.

Grand Duchess Charlotte A179

Design: No. 580, Prince Henri.

**1976, Mar. 8 Litho. *Perf. 14x13½***
**579** A179 6fr green & multi 1.60 .30
**580** A179 6fr dull blue & multi 1.60 .30

80th birthday of Grand Duchess Charlotte and 21st birthday of Prince Henri, heir to the throne.

Gold Brooch — A180

5fr, Footless beaker, horiz. 6fr, Decorated vessel, horiz. 12fr, Gold coin. All designs show excavated items of Franco-Merovingian period.

***Perf. 13½x12½, 12½x13½***
**1976, Mar. 8**
**581** A180 2fr blue & multi .25 .25
**582** A180 5fr black & multi .25 .25
**583** A180 6fr lilac & multi .45 .25
**584** A180 12fr multicolored .75 .75
*Nos. 581-584 (4)* 1.70 1.50

Soup Tureen A181

Europa: 12fr, Deep bowl. Tureen and bowl after pottery from Nospelt, 19th century.

**1976, May 3 Photo. *Perf. 11½***
**585** A181 6fr lt violet & multi *.90 .25*
**586** A181 12fr yel grn & multi *1.00 1.00*

Independence Hall, Philadelphia — A182

**1976, May 3**
**587** A182 6fr lt blue & multi .50 .25

American Bicentennial.

Boomerang — A183

**1976, May 3**
**588** A183 6fr brt rose lil & gold .50 .25

21st Olympic Games, Montreal, Canada, July 17-Aug. 1.

"Vibrations of Sound" A184

**1976, May 3**
**589** A184 6fr red & multi .50 .25

Jeunesses Musicales (Young Music Friends), association to foster interest in music and art.

Alexander Graham Bell — A185

**1976, Sept. 9 Engr. *Perf. 13***
**590** A185 6fr slate green .50 .25

Centenary of first telephone call by Alexander Graham Bell, Mar. 10, 1876.

Virgin and Child with St. Anne — A186

Renaissance sculptures: 12fr, Grave of Bernard de Velbruck, Lord of Beaufort.

**1976, Sept. 9 Photo. *Perf. 11½***
**591** A186 6fr gold & multi .30 .25
**592** A186 12fr gold, gray & blk 1.20 .70

Johann Wolfgang von Goethe — A187

Portraits: 5fr, J. M. William Turner. 6fr, Victor Hugo. 12fr, Franz Liszt.

**1977, Mar. 14 Engr. *Perf. 13***
**593** A187 2fr lake .25 .25
**594** A187 5fr purple .30 .25
**595** A187 6fr slate green .75 .25
**596** A187 12fr violet blue .75 .45
*Nos. 593-596 (4)* 2.05 1.20

Famous visitors to Luxembourg.

Old Luxembourg A188

Europa: 12fr, Adolphe Bridge and European Investment Bank headquarters.

**1977, May 3 Photo. *Perf. 11½***
**597** A188 6fr multicolored *.90 .25*
**598** A188 12fr multicolored *1.00 .80*

Esch-sur-Sure A189

Design: 6fr, View of Ehnen.

**1977, May 3 Engr. *Perf. 13***
**599** A189 5fr Prus blue .50 .25
**600** A189 6fr deep brown .50 .25

Marguerite de Busbach — A190

No. 602, Louis Braille, by Lucienne Filippi.

**1977, May 3 Photo. *Perf. 11½***
**601** A190 6fr multicolored .50 .25
**602** A190 6fr multicolored .50 .25

Notre Dame Congregation, founded by Marguerite de Busbach, 350th anniversary; Louis Braille (1809-1852), inventor of the Braille system of writing for the blind.

Souvenir Sheet

Luxembourg Nos. 1-2 — A191

**Engr. & Photo.**
**1977, Sept. 15 *Perf. 13½***
**603** A191 40fr gray & red brown 4.50 5.25

125th anniv. of Luxembourg's stamps.

Head of Medusa, Roman Mosaic, Diekirch, 3rd Century A.D. — A192

**1977, Sept. 15 Photo. *Perf. 11½***
**604** A192 6fr multicolored 1.00 .25

Orpheus and Eurydice, by C. W. Gluck A193

**1977, Sept. 15** *Perf. 11½x12*

**605** A193 6fr multicolored .70 .25

Intl. Wiltz Festival, 25th anniv.

Europa Tamed, by R. Zilli, and Map of Europe A194

**1977, Dec. 5** **Photo.** *Perf. 11½*

**606** A194 6fr multicolored .70 .25

20th anniversary of the Treaties of Rome, setting up the European Economic Community and the European Atomic Energy Commission.

Souvenir Sheet

Grand Duke and Grand Duchess of Luxembourg — A195

**Photogravure and Engraved**

**1978, Apr. 3** *Perf. 13½x14*

**607** A195 Sheet of 2 1.75 1.75
- ***a.*** 6fr dark blue & multi .60 .75
- ***b.*** 12fr dark red & multi .60 .75

Silver wedding anniversary of Grand Duke Jean and Grand Duchess Josephine Charlotte.

Souvenir Sheet

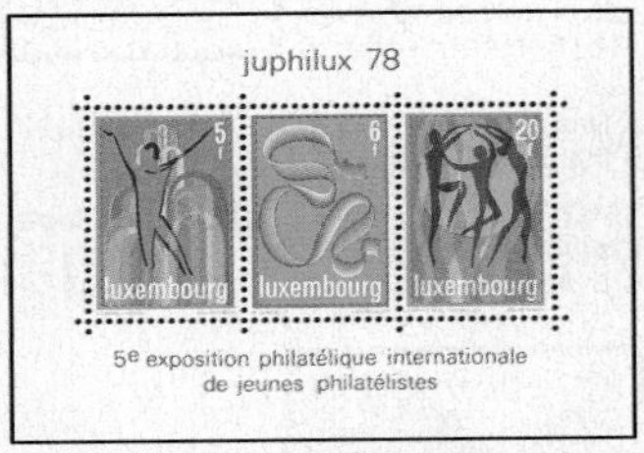


Youth Fountain, Streamer and Dancers — A196

**1978, Apr. 3** **Photo.** *Perf. 11½*

**608** A196 Sheet of 3 3.75 3.75
- ***a.*** 5fr ultra & multi 1.00 1.20
- ***b.*** 6fr orange & multi 1.00 1.20
- ***c.*** 20fr yellow green & multi 1.00 1.20

Juphilux 78, 5th International Young Philatelists' Exhibition, Luxembourg, Apr. 6-10.

Charles IV, Statue, Charles Bridge, Prague — A197

Europa: 12fr, Pierre d'Aspelt, tomb, Mainz Cathedral.

**1978, May 18** **Engr.** *Perf. 13½*

**609** A197 6fr dark violet blue *.60 .25*

**610** A197 12fr dull rose lilac *1.00 .80*

Charles IV (1316-78), Count of Luxembourg, Holy Roman Emperor. Pierre d'Aspelt (c. 1250-1320), Archbishop of Mainz and Prince-Elector.

Emile Mayrisch, by Theo Van Rysselberghe A198

**1978, May 18** *Perf. 11½*

**611** A198 6fr multicolored 1.00 .25

Emile Mayrisch (1862-1928), president of International Steel Cartel and promoter of United Europe.

Our Lady of Luxembourg A199

Trumpeters and Old Luxembourg A200

**1978, May 18** **Photo.** *Perf. 11½*

**612** A199 6fr multicolored .50 .25

**613** A200 6fr multicolored .50 .25

Our Lady of Luxembourg, patroness, 300th anniv.; 135th anniv. of Grand Ducal Military Band.

Starving Child, Helping Hand, Millet — A201

League Emblem, Lungs, Open Window — A202

Open Prison Door — A203

**1978, Sept. 11** **Photo.** *Perf. 11½*

**614** A201 2fr multicolored .25 .25

**615** A202 5fr multicolored .25 .25

**616** A203 6fr multicolored .50 .25

*Nos. 614-616 (3)* 1.00 .75

"Terre des Hommes," an association to help underprivileged children; Luxembourg Anti-Tuberculosis League, 70th anniv.; Amnesty Intl. and 30th anniv. of Universal Declaration of Human Rights.

Squared Stone Emerging from Rock, City of Luxembourg — A204

**1978, Sept. 11** **Engr.** *Perf. 13½x13*

**617** A204 6fr violet blue .60 .25

Masonic Grand Lodge of Luxembourg, 175th anniversary.

Julius Caesar on Denarius, c. 44 B.C. — A205

Roman Coins, Found in Luxembourg: 6fr, Empress Faustina I on Sestertius, 141 A.D. 9fr, Empress Helena on Follis, c. 324-330. 26fr, Emperor Valens on Solidus, c. 367-375.

**1979, Mar. 5** **Photo.** *Perf. 11½*

**618** A205 5fr multicolored .35 .25

**619** A205 6fr multicolored .40 .25

**620** A205 9fr multicolored .60 .40

**621** A205 26fr multicolored 1.40 .90

*Nos. 618-621 (4)* 2.75 1.80

St. Michael's Church, Mondorf-les-Bains A206

Design: 6fr, Luxembourg Central Station.

**1979, Mar. 5** **Engr.** *Perf. 13*

**622** A206 5fr multicolored .45 .25

**623** A206 6fr rose claret .90 .25

Troisvierges Stagecoach A207

Europa: 12fr, Early wall telephone, vert.

**1979, Apr. 30** **Photo.** *Perf. 11½*

**624** A207 6fr multicolored *1.90* .25

**625** A207 12fr multicolored *1.90 1.50*

Michel Pintz Facing Jury A208

**1979, Apr. 30** **Engr.** *Perf. 13*

**626** A208 2fr rose lilac .45 .25

180th anniversary of peasant uprising against French occupation.

Antoine Meyer — A209

Abundance Crowning Work and Thrift, by Auguste Vinet — A210

Design: 6fr, Sidney Gilchrist Thomas.

**1979, Apr. 30**

**627** A209 5fr carmine .40 .25

**628** A209 6fr light blue .40 .25

**629** A210 9fr black .40 .25

*Nos. 627-629 (3)* 1.20 .75

Antoine Meyer (1801-1857), mathematician and first national poet; centenary of acquisition of Thomas process for production of high-quality steel; 50th anniversary of Luxembourg Stock Exchange.

European Parliament A211

**1979, June 7** **Photo.** *Perf. 11½*

**630** A211 6fr multi 1.40 .45

European Parliament, first direct elections, June 7-10.

Angel with Chalice, by Barthelemy Namur — A212

Rococo Art: 12fr, Angel with anchor, by Namur, from High Altar, St. Michael's Church, Luxembourg.

**Engraved and Photogravure**

**1979, Sept. 10** *Perf. 13½*

**631** A212 6fr multi .30 .25

**632** A212 12fr multi .60 .50

Road Safety for Children A213

**1979, Sept. 10** **Photo.** *Perf. 11½*

**633** A213 2fr multi .25 .25

International Year of the Child.

Radio Tele-Luxembourg Emblem — A214

**1979, Sept. 10**

**634** A214 6fr ultra, blue & red .50 .25

50 years of broadcasting in Luxembourg.

John the Blind, Silver Coin, 1331 — A215

14th Century Coins: 2fr, Sts. Gervase and Protais, silver grosso. 6fr, Easter lamb, gold coin. 20fr, Crown and arms, silver grosso.

**1980, Mar. 5** **Photo.** *Perf. 11½*

**635** A215 2fr multi .25 .25

**636** A215 5fr multi .25 .25

**637** A215 6fr multi .75 .25

**638** A215 20fr multi 1.50 .60

*Nos. 635-638 (4)* 2.75 1.35

See Nos. 651-654.

Ettelbruck Town Hall — A216

No. 640, State Archives Building, horiz.

| **1980, Mar. 5** | **Engr.** | ***Perf. 13*** | | |
|---|---|---|---|---|
| **639** | A216 | 6fr brn & dk red | .75 | .25 |
| **640** | A216 | 6fr multi | .75 | .25 |

Jean Monnet — A217

Europa: 12fr, St. Benedict of Nursia.

| **1980, Apr. 28** | | ***Perf. 13½*** | | |
|---|---|---|---|---|
| **641** | A217 | 6fr dark blue | *.85* | *.30* |
| **642** | A217 | 12fr olive green | *.85* | *.45* |

Sports for All — A218

**1980, Apr. 28 Photo. *Perf. 11½***

**Granite Paper**

| | | | | |
|---|---|---|---|---|
| **643** | A218 | 6fr multi | 1.00 | .30 |

Worker Pouring Molten Iron — A219

Design: 6fr, Man, hand, gears, horiz.

| **1980, Apr. 28** | | | | |
|---|---|---|---|---|
| **644** | A219 | 2fr multi | .25 | .25 |
| **645** | A219 | 6fr multi | .40 | .25 |

9th World Congress on Prevention of Occupational Accidents & Diseases, Amsterdam, May 6-9.

Mercury by Jean Mich — A220

Art Nouveau Sculpture by Jean Mich.

| **1980, Sept. 10** | **Engr.** | ***Perf. 14*** | | |
|---|---|---|---|---|
| **646** | A220 | 8fr shown | .45 | .30 |
| **647** | A220 | 12fr Ceres | .75 | .45 |

Introduction of Postal Code — A221

| **1980, Sept. 10** | **Photo.** | ***Perf. 11½*** | | |
|---|---|---|---|---|
| **648** | A221 | 4fr multi | .70 | .25 |

Police Car and Officers A222

| **1980, Sept. 10** | | | | |
|---|---|---|---|---|
| **649** | A222 | 8fr multi | .70 | .25 |

State control of police force, 50th anniv.

Grand Duke Jean, Personal Arms — A223

**Photo. & Engr.**

| **1981, Jan. 5** | | ***Perf. 13½*** | | |
|---|---|---|---|---|
| **650** | A223 | Sheet of 3 | 2.10 | 2.10 |
| *a.* | | 8fr multi | .35 | .35 |
| *b.* | | 12fr multi | .55 | .55 |
| *c.* | | 30fr multi | 1.00 | 1.00 |

Grand Duke Jean, 60th birthday.

**Coin type of 1980**

Silver Coins: 4fr, Philip IV patagon, 1635. 6fr, Empress Maria Theresa 12 sol, 1775. 8fr, Emperor Joseph II 12 sol, 1789. 30fr, Emperor Francois II 72 sol, 1795.

| **1981, Mar. 5** | **Photo.** | ***Perf. 11½*** | | |
|---|---|---|---|---|
| **651** | A215 | 4fr multi | .25 | .25 |
| **652** | A215 | 6fr multi | .30 | .25 |
| **653** | A215 | 8fr multi | .45 | .25 |
| **654** | A215 | 30fr multi | 1.40 | .90 |
| | | *Nos. 651-654 (4)* | 2.40 | 1.65 |

National Library A225

No. 656, European Hemicycle, Kirchberg.

| **1981, Mar. 5** | **Engr.** | ***Perf. 13*** | | |
|---|---|---|---|---|
| **655** | A225 | 8fr shown | .50 | .25 |
| **656** | A225 | 8fr multicolored | .50 | .25 |

Hammelsmarsch (Sheep Procession) A226

Europa: 12fr, Bird-shaped whistle, Eimaischen market.

| **1981, May 4** | **Photo.** | ***Perf. 13½*** | | |
|---|---|---|---|---|
| **657** | A226 | 8fr multi | *.60* | *.25* |
| **658** | A226 | 12fr multi | *.85* | *.45* |

Knight on Chessboard A227

Savings Account Book, State Bank A228

First Bank Note, 1856 — A229

**1981, May 4 *Perf. 11½***

**Granite Paper**

| | | | | |
|---|---|---|---|---|
| **659** | A227 | 4fr multi | .50 | .30 |
| **660** | A228 | 8fr multi | .45 | .25 |
| **661** | A229 | 8fr multi | .45 | .30 |

Luxembourg Chess Federation, 50th anniv.; State Savings Bank, 125th anniv.; Intl. Bank of Luxembourg, 125th anniv. of issuing rights.

Wedding of Prince Henri and Maria Teresa Mestre, Feb. 14 A230

**Photo. & Engr.**

| **1981, June 22** | | ***Perf. 13½*** | | |
|---|---|---|---|---|
| **662** | A230 | 8fr multi | .55 | .35 |

Sheets of 12.

Single-seater Gliders — A231

16fr, Propeller planes, horiz. 35fr, Jet, Luxembourg Airport, horiz.

**1981, Sept. 28 Photo. *Perf. 11½***

**Granite Paper**

| | | | | |
|---|---|---|---|---|
| **663** | A231 | 8fr shown | .40 | .30 |
| **664** | A231 | 16fr multicolored | 1.00 | .60 |
| **665** | A231 | 35fr multicolored | 1.50 | .75 |
| | | *Nos. 663-665 (3)* | 2.90 | 1.65 |

Energy Conservation A232

| **1981, Sept. 28** | | **Granite Paper** | | |
|---|---|---|---|---|
| **666** | A232 | 8fr multi | .50 | .25 |

Apple Trees in Blossom, by Frantz Seimetz (1858-1914) A233

Landscape Paintings: 6fr, Summer Landscape, by Pierre Blanc (1872-1946). 8fr, The Larger Hallerbach, by Guido Oppenheim (1862-1942). 16fr, Winter Evening, by Eugene Mousset (1877-1941).

| **1982, Feb. 25** | **Engr.** | ***Perf. 11½*** | | |
|---|---|---|---|---|
| **667** | A233 | 4fr multi | .25 | .25 |
| **668** | A233 | 6fr multi | .35 | .25 |
| **669** | A233 | 8fr multi | .75 | .25 |
| **670** | A233 | 16fr multi | .75 | .55 |
| | | *Nos. 667-670 (4)* | 2.10 | 1.30 |

World War II Resistance — A234

Design: Cross of Hinzert (Natl. Monument of the Resistance and Deportation) and Political Prisoner, by Lucien Wercollier.

| **1982, Feb. 25** | | | | |
|---|---|---|---|---|
| **671** | A234 | 8fr multi | .50 | .25 |

Europa — A235

8fr, Treaty of London, 1867. 16fr, Treaty of Paris, 1951.

**1982, May 4 Photo.**

**Granite Paper**

| | | | | |
|---|---|---|---|---|
| **672** | A235 | 8fr multicolored | *.75* | .25 |
| **673** | A235 | 16fr multicolored | *.90* | .65 |

St. Theresa of Avila (1515-1582) — A236

Design: 8fr, Raoul Follereau (1903-1977), "Apostle of the Lepers."

| **1982, May 4** | | **Granite Paper** | | |
|---|---|---|---|---|
| **674** | A236 | 4fr multi | .25 | .25 |
| **675** | A236 | 8fr multi | .45 | .25 |

State Museum A237

No. 677, Synagogue of Luxembourg.

| **1982, May 4** | | **Photo. & Engr.** | | |
|---|---|---|---|---|
| **676** | A237 | 8fr shown | .35 | .25 |
| **677** | A237 | 8fr multicolored | .35 | .25 |

Bourscheid Castle — A238

Designs: Restored castles.

**1982, Sept. 9 Engr. *Perf. 11½***

**Granite Paper**

| | | | | |
|---|---|---|---|---|
| **678** | A238 | 6fr shown | .45 | .25 |
| **679** | A238 | 8fr Vianden, horiz. | .75 | .25 |

Intl. Youth Hostel Federation, 50th Anniv. — A239

**1982, Sept. 9** **Photo.**

**680** A239 4fr shown .45 .25
**681** A239 8fr Scouting year, vert. .45 .30

Civilian and Military Deportation Monument — A240

**1982, Sept. 9**

**682** A240 8fr multi .55 .25

Mercury, Sculpture by Auguste Tremont — A241

**1983, Mar. 7** **Photo.** ***Perf. 11½***
**Granite Paper**

**683** A241 4fr multi .25 .25

FOREX '83, 25th Intl. Assoc. of Foreign Exchange Dealers' Congress, June 2-5.

NATO Emblem, Flags — A242

**1983, Mar. 7** **Granite Paper**

**684** A242 6fr multi .30 .25

25th anniv. of NAMSA (NATO Maintenance and Supply Agency).

Echternach Cross of Justice, 1236 — A243

**1983, Mar. 7** **Granite Paper**

**685** A243 8fr multi .35 .25

30th Cong. of Intl. Union of Barristers, July 3-9.

Globe, CCC Emblem — A244

**1983, Mar. 7** **Granite Paper**

**686** A244 8fr multi .35 .25

30th anniv. of Council of Customs Cooperation.

Natl. Federation of Fire Brigades Centenary A245

**1983, Mar. 7** **Granite Paper**

**687** A245 8fr Fire engine, 1983 .60 .20
**688** A245 16fr Hand pump, 1740 1.20 .60

Europa 1983 — A246

The Good Samaritan, Codex Aureus Escorialensis Miniatures, 11th Cent., Echternach.

**1983, May 3** **Photo.**

**689** A246 8fr Highway robbers *1.00 .45*
**690** A246 16fr Good Samaritan *1.75 .45*

Giant Bible, 11th Cent. — A247

Illuminated Letters. 8fr, "h," Book of Baruch. 35fr, "B," letter of St. Jerome.

**Photo. & Engr.**

**1983, May 3** ***Perf. 14***

**691** A247 8fr multicolored .45 .25
**692** A247 35fr multicolored 1.40 1.00

World Communications Year — A248

No. 693, Post code. No. 694, Satellite relay, horiz.

**1983, May 3** **Photo.** ***Perf. 11½***

**693** A248 8fr multicolored .90 .30
**694** A248 8fr multicolored 1.75 .30

Town Hall, Dudelange A249

7fr, St. Lawrence Church, Diekirch, vert.

**1983, Sept. 7** **Photo. & Engr.**

**695** A249 7fr multi .35 .30
**696** A249 10fr multi .55 .30

Basketball Fed., 50th Anniv. A250

European Working Dog Championship A251

Tourism — A252

No. 698, Alsatian sheepdog. No. 699, View of Luxembourg.

**1983, Sept. 7** **Photo.**
**Granite Paper**

**697** A250 7fr multicolored .45 .25
**698** A251 10fr multicolored .75 .35
**699** A252 10fr multicolored 1.20 .30
*Nos. 697-699 (3)* 2.40 .90

Environment Protection A253

**1984, Mar. 6** **Photo.** ***Perf. 11½***
**Granite Paper**

**700** A253 7fr Pedestrian zoning .60 .25
**701** A253 10fr Water purification .75 .35

2nd European Parliament Election — A254

**1984, Mar. 6** **Granite Paper**

**702** A254 10fr Hands holding emblem .70 .30

A255

**1984, Mar. 6** **Engr.** ***Perf. 12½x13***

**703** A255 10fr No. 1 .75 .30
**704** A255 10fr Union meeting .75 .30
**705** A255 10fr Mail bag .75 .30
**706** A255 10fr Train .75 .30
*Nos. 703-706 (4)* 3.00 1.20

Philatelic Federation (1934); Civil Service Trade Union (1909); Postal Workers' Union (1909); Railroad (1859).

1984 Summer Olympics — A256

10fr, The Race, by Jean Jacoby (1891-1936).

**1984, May 7** **Photo.** ***Perf. 11½x12***

**707** A256 10fr multicolored .70 .25

Europa (1959-84) A257

**1984, May 7** ***Perf. 11½***
**Granite Paper**

**708** A257 10fr green *1.50 .30*
**709** A257 16fr orange *1.60 .80*

Young Turk Caressing His Horse, by Delacroix A258

Paintings: 4fr, The Smoker, by David Teniers the Younger (1610-90). 10fr, Epiphany, by Jan Steen (1626-79). 50fr, The Lacemaker, by Pieter van Slingelandt (1640-91). 4fr, 50fr vert.

**Photo. & Engr.**

**1984, May 7** ***Perf. 14***

**710** A258 4fr multi .35 .30
**711** A258 7fr multi .55 .30
**712** A258 10fr multi .90 .30
**713** A258 50fr multi 3.75 1.75
*Nos. 710-713 (4)* 5.55 2.65

Marine Life Fossils — A259

4fr, Pecten sp. 7fr, Gryphaea arcuata. 10fr, Coeloceras raqyinianum. 16fr, Daildius.

**1984, Sept. 10** **Photo.** ***Perf. 11½***

**714** A259 4fr multicolored .30 .25
**715** A259 7fr multicolored .50 .25
**716** A259 10fr multicolored .80 .25
**717** A259 16fr multicolored 1.40 .90
*Nos. 714-717 (4)* 3.00 1.65

Restored Castles — A260

**1984, Sept. 10** **Engr.**

**718** A260 7fr Hollenfels .35 .25
**719** A260 10fr Larochette .55 .35

A261

**1984, Sept. 10** ***Perf. 12x12½***

**720** A261 10fr Soldier, US flag 1.75 .30

40th Anniv. of D Day (June 6).

A262

Portrait medals in the state museum: 4fr, Jean Bertels (1544-1607), Historian, Abbott of Echternach. 7fr, Emperor Charles V (1500-1558). 10fr, King Philip II of Spain (1527-1598). 30fr, Prince Maurice of Orange-Nassau, Count of Vianden (1567-1625).

### Granite Paper

**1985, Mar. 4 Photo. *Perf. 11½***

| | | | | |
|---|---|---|---|---|
| **721** | A262 | 4fr multi | .25 | .25 |
| **722** | A262 | 7fr multi | .35 | .25 |
| **723** | A262 | 10fr multi | .60 | .25 |
| **724** | A262 | 30fr multi | 2.10 | .90 |
| | | *Nos. 721-724 (4)* | 3.30 | 1.65 |

See Nos. 739-742.

Anniversaries A263

No. 725, Benz Velo, First automobile in Luxembourg, 1895. No. 726, Push-button telephone, sound waves. No. 727, Fencers.

**1985, Mar. 4 *Perf. 12x11½***
**Granite Paper**

| | | | | |
|---|---|---|---|---|
| **725** | A263 | 10fr multi | .90 | .30 |
| **726** | A263 | 10fr multi | .60 | .25 |
| **727** | A263 | 10fr multi | .75 | .25 |
| | | *Nos. 725-727 (3)* | 2.25 | .80 |

Centenary of the first automobile; Luxembourg Telephone Service, cent.; Luxembourg Fencing Federation, 50th anniv.

Visit of Pope John Paul II — A264

**1985, Mar. 4 *Perf. 11½x12***
**Granite Paper**

| | | | | |
|---|---|---|---|---|
| **728** | A264 | 10fr Papal arms | .70 | .25 |

Europa 1985 — A265

Designs: 10fr, Grand-Duke Adolphe Music Federation. 16fr, Luxembourg Music School.

**1985, May 8 *Perf. 11½***

| | | | | |
|---|---|---|---|---|
| **729** | A265 | 10fr multi | *1.60* | *.45* |
| **730** | A265 | 16fr multi | *2.40* | *1.10* |

**Souvenir Sheet**

End of World War II, 40th Anniv. — A266

Designs: a, Luxembourg resistance fighters, Wounded Fighters medal. b, Luxembourg War Cross. c, Badge of the Union of Luxembourg Resistance Movements. d, Liberation of the concentration camps.

**1985, May 8 *Perf. 11½x12***
**Granite Paper**

| | | | | |
|---|---|---|---|---|
| **731** | A266 | Sheet of 4 | 4.00 | 4.00 |
| *a.-d.* | | 10fr, any single | .75 | .60 |

Endangered Wildlife — A267

4fr, Athene nocturna, vert. 7fr, Felis silvestris. 10fr, Vanessa atalantica. 50fr, Hyla arborea, vert.

**1985, Sept. 23 Photo. *Perf. 12x11½***

| | | | | |
|---|---|---|---|---|
| **732** | A267 | 4fr multicolored | .90 | .30 |
| **733** | A267 | 7fr multicolored | 1.50 | .30 |
| **734** | A267 | 10fr multicolored | 2.40 | .30 |
| **735** | A267 | 50fr multicolored | 5.25 | 1.75 |
| | | *Nos. 732-735 (4)* | 10.05 | 2.65 |

Historic Monuments A268

7fr, Echternach Orangery, 1750. 10fr, Mohr de Waldt House, 17th cent.

**1985, Sept. 23 Engr. *Perf. 11½***

| | | | | |
|---|---|---|---|---|
| **736** | A268 | 7fr multicolored | .45 | .25 |
| **737** | A268 | 10fr multicolored | .50 | .25 |

Natl. Art Collection A269

10fr, 18th cent. book cover, Natl. Library.

**Photo. & Engr.**
**1985, Sept. 23 *Perf. 14***

| | | | | |
|---|---|---|---|---|
| **738** | A269 | 10fr multicolored | .70 | .25 |

**Portrait Medals Type of 1985**

10fr, Count of Monterey, 1675. 12fr, Louis XIV, 1684. 18fr, Pierre de Weyms, c. 1700. 20fr, Duke of Marlborough, 1706.

**1986, Mar. 3 Photo. *Perf. 11½***
**Granite Paper**

| | | | | |
|---|---|---|---|---|
| **739** | A262 | 10fr multicolored | .45 | .30 |
| **740** | A262 | 12fr multicolored | .60 | .25 |
| **741** | A262 | 18fr multicolored | .75 | .45 |
| **742** | A262 | 20fr multicolored | 1.25 | .60 |
| | | *Nos. 739-742 (4)* | 3.05 | 1.60 |

Federation of Luxembourg Beekeepers' Associations, Cent. A270

Mondorf State Spa, Cent. — A271

Natl. Table Tennis Federation, 50th Anniv. — A272

No. 743, Bee collecting pollen. No. 744, Mosaic. No. 745, Boy playing table tennis.

**1986, Mar. 3 *Perf. 11½***

| | | | | |
|---|---|---|---|---|
| **743** | A270 | 12fr multicolored | .85 | .30 |
| **744** | A271 | 12fr multicolored | .85 | .30 |
| **745** | A272 | 12fr multicolored | .85 | .30 |
| | | *Nos. 743-745 (3)* | 2.55 | .90 |

Europa 1986 — A273

12fr, Polluted forest, city. 20fr, Man, pollution sources.

**1986, May 5 Photo. *Perf. 12***
**Granite Paper**

| | | | | |
|---|---|---|---|---|
| **751** | A273 | 12fr multicolored | *1.25* | *.25* |
| **752** | A273 | 20fr multicolored | *1.75* | *1.00* |

Fortifications A274

15fr, Ft. Thungen, horiz. 18fr, Invalid's Gate. 50fr, Malakoff Tower.

**1986, May 5 Granite Paper**

| | | | | |
|---|---|---|---|---|
| **753** | A274 | 15fr multicolored | 1.40 | .35 |
| **754** | A274 | 18fr multicolored | 1.40 | .45 |
| **755** | A274 | 50fr multicolored | 3.00 | .75 |
| | | *Nos. 753-755 (3)* | 5.80 | 1.55 |

Robert Schuman (1886-1963), European Cooperation Promulgator — A275

**1986, June 26 *Perf. 12 on 3 Sides***
**Granite Paper**

| | | | | |
|---|---|---|---|---|
| **756** | A275 | 2fr pink & blk | .25 | .25 |
| *a.* | | Bklt. pane of 4 | .30 | |
| **757** | A275 | 10fr lt bl & blk | .45 | .30 |
| *a.* | | Bklt. pane of 4 | 2.75 | |
| *b.* | | Bklt. pane of 2, #756-757 + 2 labels | 1.40 | |

Nos. 756-757 issued in booklets only.

European Road Safety Year — A276

**1986, Sept. 15 Photo. *Perf. 11½***

| | | | | |
|---|---|---|---|---|
| **758** | A276 | 10fr multi | .60 | .25 |

Bas-relief, Town Hall, Esch-Sur-Alzette — A277

Design: No. 760, Stairs to the Chapel of the Cross, Grevenmacher.

**Photogravure & Engraved**
**1986, Sept. 15 *Perf. 14x13½***

| | | | | |
|---|---|---|---|---|
| **759** | A277 | 12fr shown | 1.00 | .30 |
| **760** | A277 | 12fr multi | 1.00 | .30 |

Countess Ermesinde (1186-1247), Ruler of Luxembourg A278

Designs: No. 761, Presentation of the letter of freedom to Echternach inhabitants, 1236, engraving (detail) by P.H. Witkamp, c. 1873. 30fr, Charter seal, Marienthal Convent, 1238.

**1986, Sept. 15 *Perf. 13½x14***

| | | | | |
|---|---|---|---|---|
| **761** | A278 | 12fr multi | .60 | .25 |
| **762** | A278 | 30fr multi | 1.50 | .75 |

Wildlife Conservation A279

6fr, Eliomys quercinus, horiz. 10fr, Calopteryx splendens. 12fr, Cinclus cinclus. 25fr, Salamandra salamandra terrestris, horiz.

**1987, Mar. 9 Photo. *Perf. 11½***

| | | | | |
|---|---|---|---|---|
| **763** | A279 | 6fr multicolored | .45 | .30 |
| **764** | A279 | 10fr multicolored | .90 | .45 |
| **765** | A279 | 12fr multicolored | 1.40 | .30 |
| **766** | A279 | 25fr multicolored | 2.50 | 1.10 |
| | | *Nos. 763-766 (4)* | 5.25 | 2.15 |

A280

**1987, Mar. 9**

| | | | | |
|---|---|---|---|---|
| **767** | A280 | 12fr multi | .70 | .30 |

Natl. Home Amateur Radio Operators Network, 50th anniv.

A281

**1987, Mar. 9**

| | | | | |
|---|---|---|---|---|
| **768** | A281 | 12fr multi | .70 | .25 |

Luxembourg Intl. Fair, 50th anniv.

Europa 1987 — A282

12fr, Aquatic Sports Center. 20fr, European Communities Court of Justice and abstract sculpture by Henry Moore (1898-1986).

**1987, May 4 Photo. *Perf. 11½***

| | | | | |
|---|---|---|---|---|
| **769** | A282 | 12fr multi | *1.50* | *.30* |
| **770** | A282 | 20fr multi | *1.75* | *.90* |

St. Michael's Church Millenary A283

Designs: 12fr, Consecration of the church by Archbishop Egbert of Trier, 987, stained glass window by Gustav Zanter. 20fr, Baroque organ-chest, 17th century.

**Photogravure & Engraved**
**1987, May 4 *Perf. 14***

| | | | | |
|---|---|---|---|---|
| **771** | A283 | 12fr multi | 1.00 | .30 |
| **772** | A283 | 20fr multi | 1.40 | .60 |

15th Century Paintings by Giovanni Ambrogio Bevilacqua
A284

Polyptych panels in the State Museum: 10fr, St. Bernard of Sienna and St. John the Baptist. 18fr, St. Jerome and St. Francis of Assisi.

| **1987, May 4** | *Perf. 11½* | |
|---|---|---|
| **773** A284 10fr multi | .60 | .30 |
| **774** A284 18fr multi | 1.25 | .60 |

Rural Architecture
A285

10fr, Hennesbau Bark Mill, 1826, Niederfeulen. 12fr, Health Center, 18th cent., Mersch. 100fr, Post Office, 18th cent., Bertrange.

**Photo. & Engr.**

| **1987, Sept. 14** | *Perf. 13½* | |
|---|---|---|
| **775** A285 10fr multicolored | .60 | .30 |
| **776** A285 12fr multicolored | .60 | .25 |
| **777** A285 100fr multicolored | 5.00 | 1.10 |
| *Nos. 775-777 (3)* | 6.20 | 1.65 |

Chamber of Deputies (Parliament) 139th Anniv. — A286

Designs: 6fr, Charles Metz (1799-1853), first President. 12fr, Parliament, 1860, designed by Antoine Hartmann (1817-1891).

| **1987, Sept. 14** **Engr.** | *Perf. 14* | |
|---|---|---|
| **778** A286 6fr violet brn | .30 | .25 |
| **779** A286 12fr blue black | .75 | .35 |

Flowers by Botanical Illustrator Pierre-Joseph Redoute (1759-1840)
A287

6fr, Orange lily, water lily. 10fr, Primula, double narcissus. 12fr, Tulip. 50fr, Iris, gorteria.

| **1988, Feb. 8** **Photo.** | *Perf. 11½x12* | |
|---|---|---|
| **780** A287 6fr multicolored | .80 | .30 |
| **781** A287 10fr multicolored | .80 | .30 |
| **782** A287 12fr multicolored | 1.60 | .45 |
| **783** A287 50fr multicolored | 4.00 | 1.60 |
| *Nos. 780-783 (4)* | 7.20 | 2.65 |

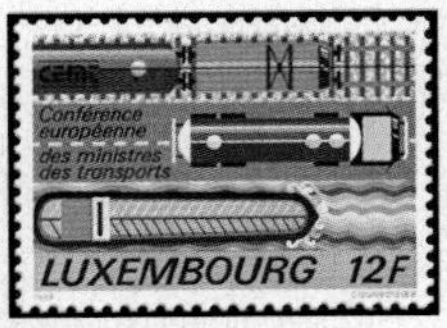


European Conf. of Ministers of Transport
A288

Eurocontrol, 25th Anniv.
A289

| **1988, Feb. 8** | *Perf. 12* | |
|---|---|---|
| **784** A288 12fr multi | .75 | .30 |
| **785** A289 20fr multi | 1.40 | .75 |

Souvenir Sheet

Family of Prince Henri — A290

| **1988, Mar. 29** **Photo.** | *Perf. 12* | |
|---|---|---|
| **786** A290 Sheet of 3 | 5.50 | 5.50 |
| *a.* 12fr Maria Theresa | .60 | .60 |
| *b.* 18fr Guillaume, Felix and Louis | .90 | .90 |
| *c.* 50fr Prince Henri | 2.75 | 2.75 |

JUVALUX '88, 9th intl. youth philatelic exhibition, Mar. 29-Apr. 4.

Europa 1988 — A291

Communication: 12fr, Automatic mail handling. 20fr, Electronic mail.

| **1988, June 6** **Photo.** | *Perf. 11½* | |
|---|---|---|
| **787** A291 12fr multicolored | *1.75* | *.40* |
| **788** A291 20fr multicolored | *1.75* | *1.75* |

Tourism — A292

Designs: 10fr, Wiltz town hall and Cross of Justice Monument, c. 1502. 12fr, Castle, Differdange, 16th cent., vert.

**Photo. & Engr.**

| **1988, June 6** | *Perf. 13½* | |
|---|---|---|
| **789** A292 10fr multi | .90 | .30 |
| **790** A292 12fr multi | .90 | .30 |

See Nos. 824-825, 841-842.

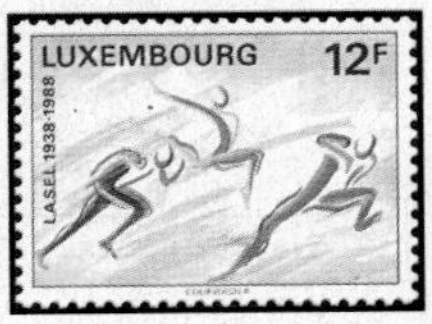


League of Luxembourg Student Sports Associations (LASEL), 50th Anniv.
A293

| **1988, June 6** **Photo.** | *Perf. 11½* | |
|---|---|---|
| **791** A293 12fr multi | .80 | .35 |

Doorways
A294

Architectural drawings by Joseph Wegener (1895-1980) and his students, 1949-1951: 12fr, Septfontaines Castle main entrance, 1785. 25fr, National Library regency north-wing entrance, c. 1720. 50fr, Holy Trinity Church baroque entrance, c. 1740.

**Litho. & Engr.**

| **1988, Sept. 12** | *Perf. 14* | |
|---|---|---|
| **792** A294 12fr black & buff | .65 | .30 |
| **793** A294 25fr blk & citron | 1.25 | .60 |
| **794** A294 50fr blk & yel bister | 2.60 | 1.25 |
| *Nos. 792-794 (3)* | 4.50 | 2.15 |

Jean Monnet (1888-1979), French Economist — A295

| **1988, Sept. 12** | **Engr.** | |
|---|---|---|
| **795** A295 12fr multi | 1.00 | .35 |

European Investment Bank, 30th Anniv.
A296

| **1988, Sept. 12** | **Litho. & Engr.** | |
|---|---|---|
| **796** A296 12fr yel grn & blk | .90 | .30 |

1988 Summer Olympics, Seoul — A297

| **1988, Sept. 12** **Photo.** | *Perf. 11½* | |
|---|---|---|
| **797** A297 12fr multi | .85 | .30 |

A298

Design: 12fr, Portrait and excerpt from his speech to the Chamber of Deputies, 1896.

| **1989, Mar. 6** **Photo.** | *Perf. 11½x12* | |
|---|---|---|
| **798** A298 12fr multi | .65 | .35 |

C.M. Spoo (1837-1914), advocate of Luxembourgish as the natl. language.

Book Workers' Fed., 125th Anniv. — A299

| **1989, Mar. 6** | | |
|---|---|---|
| **799** A299 18fr multi | .95 | .50 |

Natl. Red Cross, 75th Anniv. — A300

| **1989, Mar. 6** | | |
|---|---|---|
| **800** A300 20fr Henri Dunant | 1.60 | .90 |

Independence of the Grand Duchy, 150th Anniv. — A301

Design: 12fr, Lion, bronze sculpture by Auguste Tremont (1892-1980) guarding the grand ducal family vault, Cathedral of Luxembourg.

**Photo. & Engr.**

| **1989, Mar. 6** | *Perf. 14* | |
|---|---|---|
| **801** A301 12fr multi | 1.00 | .35 |

Astra Telecommunications Satellite — A302

| **1989, Mar. 6** **Photo.** | *Perf. 11½* | |
|---|---|---|
| **802** A302 12fr multi | 1.00 | .35 |

Europa 1989 — A303

Paintings (children at play): 12fr, *Three Children in a Park*, 19th cent., anonymous. 20fr, *Child with Drum*, 17th cent., anonymous.

| **1989, May 8** **Photo.** | *Perf. 11½x12* | |
|---|---|---|
| **803** A303 12fr multi | *.90* | *.90* |
| **804** A303 20fr multi | *.90* | *.90* |

Tour de France — A304

| **1989, May 8** | *Perf. 11½* | |
|---|---|---|
| **805** A304 9fr multi | .90 | .45 |

Start of the bicycle race in Luxembourg City.

Interparliamentary Union, Cent. — A305

| **1989, May 8** | *Perf. 11½x12* | |
|---|---|---|
| **806** A305 12fr multi | .75 | .40 |

A306

**1989, May 8**
**807** A306 12fr multi .85 .45

European Parliament 3rd elections.

Council of Europe, 40th Anniv. A307

**1989, May 8** ***Perf. 12x11½***
**808** A307 12fr multi .85 .45

Reign of Grand Duke Jean, 25th Anniv. — A308

**1989, Sept. 18 Photo.** ***Perf. 12x11½***
**Booklet Stamps**

| | | | |
|---|---|---|---|
| **810** | A308 3fr black & orange | 1.50 | 1.40 |
| *a.* | Bklt. pane of 4 | 6.00 | |
| **811** | A308 9fr black & blue green | 1.25 | 1.25 |
| *a.* | Bklt. pane of 4 | 5.00 | |
| *b.* | Bklt. pane, 1 each #810, 811 + 2 labels | 2.50 | |
| | Booklet, 1 each #810a, 811a, 811b | 16.00 | |

Charles IV (1316-1378) A309

Stained-glass windows by Joseph Oberberger in the Grand Ducal Loggia, Cathedral of Luxembourg: 20fr, John the Blind (1296-1346). 25fr, Wenceslas II (1361-1419).

**Photo. & Engr.**

**1989, Sept. 18** ***Perf. 13½x14***

| | | | |
|---|---|---|---|
| **821** | A309 12fr shown | .70 | .25 |
| **822** | A309 20fr multi | 1.10 | .85 |
| **823** | A309 25fr multi | 1.40 | 1.00 |
| | *Nos. 821-823 (3)* | 3.20 | 2.10 |

Independence of the Grand Duchy, 150th anniv.

**Tourism Type of 1988**

Designs: 12fr, Clervaux Castle interior courtyard, circa 12th cent. 18fr, Bronzed wild boar of Titelberg, 1st cent., vert.

**Litho. & Engr.**

**1989, Sept. 18** ***Perf. 13½***

| | | | |
|---|---|---|---|
| **824** | A292 12fr multi | .70 | .35 |
| **825** | A292 18fr multi | 1.40 | .55 |

Views of the Former Fortress of Luxembourg, 1814-1815, Engravings by Christoph Wilhelm Selig (1791-1837) — A310

**1990, Mar. 5 Photo.** ***Perf. 12x11½***

| | | | |
|---|---|---|---|
| **826** | A310 9fr shown | .55 | .35 |
| **827** | A310 12fr multi, diff. | .70 | .35 |
| **828** | A310 20fr multi, diff. | 1.50 | .90 |
| **829** | A310 25fr multi, diff. | 2.00 | 1.00 |
| | *Nos. 826-829 (4)* | 4.75 | 2.60 |

Congress of Vienna, 1815, during which the Duchy of Luxembourg was elevated to the Grand Duchy of Luxembourg.

Schueberfouer Carnival, 650th Anniv. — A311

**1990, Mar. 15** ***Perf. 11½x12***
**830** A311 9fr Carnival ride .75 .30

Batty Weber (1860-1940), Writer — A312

**1990, Mar. 15**
**831** A312 12fr multi .75 .30

ITU, 125th Anniv. — A313

**1990, Mar. 15**
**832** A313 18fr multicolored 1.10 .60

A314

Europa (Post Offices): 12fr, Luxembourg City. 20fr, Esch-Sur-Alzette, vert.

**Litho. & Engr.**

**1990, May 28** ***Perf. 13½***

| | | | |
|---|---|---|---|
| **833** | A314 12fr buff & blk | *1.75* | *.30* |
| **834** | A314 20fr lt bl & blk | *1.75* | *1.20* |

A315

Prime Ministers: 9fr, Paul Eyschen (1841-1915). 12fr, Emmanuel Servais (1811-1890).

**Photo. & Engr.**

**1990, May 28** ***Perf. 14x13½***

| | | | |
|---|---|---|---|
| **835** | A315 9fr multicolored | .55 | .35 |
| **836** | A315 12fr multicolored | .75 | .35 |

Psallus Pseudoplatani A316

**1990, May 28 Photo.** ***Perf. 11½***
**837** A316 12fr multicolored .75 .35

Luxembourg Naturalists' Society, cent.

A317

Fountains: 12fr, Sheep's march by Will Lofy. 25fr, Fountain of Doves. 50fr, "Maus Ketty" by Lofy.

**Litho. & Engr.**

**1990, Sept. 24** ***Perf. 14***

| | | | |
|---|---|---|---|
| **838** | A317 12fr multicolored | .75 | .25 |
| **839** | A317 25fr multicolored | 1.50 | .90 |
| **840** | A317 50fr multicolored | 3.25 | 1.60 |
| | *Nos. 838-840 (3)* | 5.50 | 2.75 |

**Tourism Type of 1988**

**1990, Sept. 24** ***Perf. 13½***

| | | | |
|---|---|---|---|
| **841** | A292 12fr Mondercange | 1.00 | .35 |
| **842** | A292 12fr Schifflange | 1.00 | .35 |

Souvenir Sheet

Nassau-Weilburg Dynasty, Cent. — A318

Designs: a, Grand Duke Adolphe. b, Grand Duchess Marie-Adelaide. c, Grand Ducal House arms. d, Grand Duchess Charlotte. e, Grand Duke Guillaume. f, Grand Duke Jean.

**Photo. & Engr.**

**1990, Nov. 26** ***Perf. 14x13½***

| | | | |
|---|---|---|---|
| **843** | A318 Sheet of 6 | 8.50 | 8.50 |
| *a.-b.* | 12fr multicolored | 1.25 | 1.25 |
| *c.-d.* | 18fr mulitcolored | 1.40 | 1.40 |
| *e.-f.* | 20fr multicolored | 1.60 | 1.60 |

View From the Trier Road by Sosthene Weis (1872-1941) — A319

Paintings: 18fr, Vauban Street and the Viaduct. 25fr, St. Ulric Street.

***Perf. 12x11½, 11½x12***

**1991, Mar. 4** **Photo.**

| | | | |
|---|---|---|---|
| **844** | A319 14fr multicolored | .90 | .50 |
| **845** | A319 18fr multicolored | 1.25 | .75 |
| **846** | A319 25fr multi, vert. | 1.50 | .90 |
| | *Nos. 844-846 (3)* | 3.65 | 2.15 |

Fungi — A320

No. 847, Geastrum varians. No. 848, Agaricus (Gymnopus) thiebautii. No. 849, Agaricus (lepiota) lepidocephalus. No. 850, Morchella favosa.

**1991, Mar. 4** ***Perf. 11½***

| | | | |
|---|---|---|---|
| **847** | A320 14fr multicolored | .90 | .45 |
| **848** | A320 14fr multicolored | .90 | .45 |
| **849** | A320 18fr multicolored | 1.25 | .90 |
| **850** | A320 25fr multicolored | 2.25 | 1.10 |
| | *Nos. 847-850 (4)* | 5.30 | 2.90 |

Europa A321

No. 851, Astra 1A, 1B satellites. No. 852, Betzdorf ground station.

**1991, May 13 Photo.** ***Perf. 12x11½***

| | | | |
|---|---|---|---|
| **851** | A321 14fr multicolored | *1.50* | *.35* |
| **852** | A321 18fr multicolored | *1.75* | *1.40* |

Natl. Miners' Monument, Kayl — A322

Designs: No. 854, Magistrates' Court, Redange-Sur-Attert, horiz.

**1991, May 23** ***Perf. 11½x12, 12x11½***

| | | | |
|---|---|---|---|
| **853** | A322 14fr multicolored | 1.00 | .40 |
| **854** | A322 14fr multicolored | 1.00 | .40 |

Art by Emile Kirscht — A323

No. 856, Edmund de la Fontaine (1823-91), poet.

**1991, May 23** ***Perf. 11½***

| | | | |
|---|---|---|---|
| **855** | A323 14fr multicolored | 1.00 | .40 |
| **856** | A323 14fr multicolored | 1.00 | .40 |

Labor Unions, 75th anniv. (No. 855).

Post and Telecommunications Museum — A324

***Perf. 11½ on 3 sides***

**1991, Sept. 23** **Photo.**

**Booklet Stamps**

| | | | |
|---|---|---|---|
| **857** | A324 4fr Old telephone | 2.50 | 1.40 |
| *a.* | Bklt. pane of 1 + 3 labels | 3.50 | |
| **858** | A324 14fr Old postbox | .75 | .35 |
| *a.* | Bklt. pane of 4 | 3.00 | |

Stamp Day, 50th Anniv. — A325

**1991, Sept. 23** ***Perf. 11½***

| | | | |
|---|---|---|---|
| **859** A325 14fr Stamp of Type A24 | 1.00 | .50 |

A326

Gargoyles: 14fr, Young girl's head. 25fr, Woman's head. 50fr, Man's head.

**Photo. & Engr.**

**1991, Sept. 23** ***Perf. 14***

| | | |
|---|---|---|
| **860** A326 14fr multicolored | .75 | .40 |
| **861** A326 25fr multicolored | 1.50 | .65 |
| **862** A326 50fr multicolored | 2.50 | 1.40 |
| *Nos. 860-862 (3)* | 4.75 | 2.45 |

See Nos. 874-876.

Jean-Pierre Pescatore Foundation, Cent. A327

Buildings: No. 864, High Technology Institute. No. 865, New Fair and Congress Centre.

**1992, Mar. 16** **Photo.** ***Perf. 11½***

| | | |
|---|---|---|
| **863** A327 14fr lil rose & multi | .85 | .45 |
| **864** A327 14fr grn & multi | .85 | .45 |
| **865** A327 14fr brt bl & multi | .85 | .45 |
| *Nos. 863-865 (3)* | 2.55 | 1.35 |

Bettembourg Castle A328

25fr, Walferdange station.

**1992, Mar. 16**

| | | |
|---|---|---|
| **866** A328 18fr shown | 1.00 | .35 |
| **867** A328 25fr multicolored | 1.50 | .75 |

Europa A329

Emigrants to US: 14fr, Nicholas Gonner (1835-1892), newspaper editor. 22fr, N. E. Becker (1842-1920), journalist.

**Photo. & Engr.**

**1992, May 18** ***Perf. 13½x14½***

| | | |
|---|---|---|
| **868** A329 14fr multicolored | *1.75* | *.50* |
| **869** A329 22fr multicolored | *1.75* | *1.25* |

Lions Clubs Intl., 75th Anniv. — A330

General Strike, 50th Anniv. — A331

**1992, May 18** **Photo.** ***Perf. 11½***

| | | |
|---|---|---|
| **870** A330 14fr multicolored | 1.00 | .35 |
| **871** A331 18fr sepia & lake | 1.10 | .55 |

1992 Summer Olympics, Barcelona A332

**1992, May 18** ***Perf. 12x11½***

| | | |
|---|---|---|
| **872** A332 14fr multicolored | 1.50 | .45 |

Expo '92, Seville A333

**1992, May 18** ***Perf. 11½***

| | | |
|---|---|---|
| **873** A333 14fr Luxembourg pavilion | .85 | .50 |

**Gargoyle Type of 1991**

**Photo. & Engr.**

**1992, Oct. 5** ***Perf. 14***

| | | |
|---|---|---|
| **874** A326 14fr Ram's head | .75 | .35 |
| **875** A326 22fr Lion's head | 1.25 | .90 |
| **876** A326 50fr Satyr's head | 2.50 | 1.50 |
| *Nos. 874-876 (3)* | 4.50 | 2.75 |

Stained Glass Windows, by Auguste Tremont — A334

**1992, Oct. 5** **Photo.** ***Perf. 11½x12***

| | | |
|---|---|---|
| **877** A334 14fr Post horn, letters | .75 | .50 |
| **878** A334 22fr Post rider | 1.25 | 1.00 |
| **879** A334 50fr Insulators | 2.60 | 1.40 |
| *Nos. 877-879 (3)* | 4.60 | 2.90 |

Luxembourg Post and Telecommunications, 150th anniv.

Single European Market A335

**1992, Oct. 5** ***Perf. 11½x12***

| | | |
|---|---|---|
| **880** A335 14fr multicolored | .85 | .40 |

Fountain of the Children with Grapes, Schwebsingen — A336

Design: No. 882, Old Ironworks Cultural Center, Steinfort.

**1993, Mar. 8** **Photo.** ***Perf. 12x11½***

| | | |
|---|---|---|
| **881** A336 14fr multicolored | .85 | .35 |
| **882** A336 14fr multicolored | .85 | .35 |

Grand Duke Jean — A337

**Litho. & Engr.**

**1993-95** ***Perf. 13½x13***

**Background Color**

| | | | | | |
|---|---|---|---|---|---|
| **883** | A337 | 1fr | yellow brown | .25 | .25 |
| **883A** | A337 | 2fr | olive gray | .25 | .25 |
| **884** | A337 | 5fr | yellow green | .25 | .25 |
| **885** | A337 | 7fr | brick red | .25 | .25 |
| **886** | A337 | 10fr | blue | .55 | .25 |
| **887** | A337 | 14fr | pink | 1.40 | .30 |
| **888** | A337 | 15fr | green | .85 | .25 |
| **889** | A337 | 16fr | orange | 1.00 | .50 |
| **890** | A337 | 18fr | orange | .70 | .35 |
| **891** | A337 | 20fr | red | 1.00 | .45 |
| **892** | A337 | 22fr | dark green | .90 | .75 |
| **893** | A337 | 25fr | gray blue | 1.00 | .65 |
| **894** | A337 | 100fr | brown | 5.00 | 2.75 |
| | | | *Nos. 883-894 (13)* | 13.40 | 7.25 |

Issued: 5, 7, 14, 18, 22, 25fr, 3/8/93; 1, 15, 20, 100fr, 3/7/94; 2, 10, 16fr, 1/30/95.

See Nos. 957, 1026.

New Technologies in Surgery A338

**1993, May 10** **Photo.** ***Perf. 11½***

| | | |
|---|---|---|
| **895** A338 14fr multicolored | .85 | .45 |

Contemporary Paintings — A339

Europa: 14fr, Rezlop, by Fernand Roda. 22fr, So Close, by Sonja Roef.

**1993, May 10**

| | | |
|---|---|---|
| **896** A339 14fr multicolored | *1.25* | *.40* |
| **897** A339 22fr multicolored | *1.75* | *.80* |

A340

Designs: 14fr, Burgundy Residence. 20fr, Simons House. 50fr, Cassal House.

**Photo. & Engr.**

**1993, May 10** ***Perf. 14***

| | | |
|---|---|---|
| **898** A340 14fr multicolored | .75 | .35 |
| **899** A340 20fr multicolored | 1.50 | .45 |
| **900** A340 50fr multicolored | 3.50 | 1.90 |
| *Nos. 898-900 (3)* | 5.75 | 2.70 |

A341

**1993, Sept. 20** **Photo.** ***Perf. 11½***

| | | |
|---|---|---|
| **901** A341 14fr multicolored | .90 | .45 |

Environmental protection.

A342

A343

**1993, Sept. 20**

| | | |
|---|---|---|
| **902** A342 14fr multicolored | .90 | .45 |
| **903** A343 14fr multicolored | .90 | .45 |

Jean Schortgen (1880-1918), 1st worker elected to Parliament (No. 902); Artistic Circle of Luxembourg, cent.

Museum Exhibits A344

14fr, Electric tram, Tram & Bus Museum, City of Luxembourg. 22fr, Iron ore tipper wagon, Natl. Mining Museum, Rumelange. 60fr, Horse-drawn carriage, Wiltz Museum of Ancient Crafts.

**Photo. & Engr.**

**1993, Sept. 20** ***Perf. 14***

| | | |
|---|---|---|
| **904** A344 14fr multicolored | .90 | .35 |
| **905** A344 22fr multicolored | 1.25 | .70 |
| **906** A344 60fr multicolored | 3.25 | 2.00 |
| *Nos. 904-906 (3)* | 5.40 | 3.05 |

See Nos. 933-935.

Snow-Covered Landscape, by Joseph Kutter (1894-1941) — A345

Design: No. 908, The Moselle, by Nico Klopp (1894-1930).

**1994, Mar. 7** **Photo.** ***Perf. 11½x12***

| | | |
|---|---|---|
| **907** A345 14fr multicolored | .90 | .45 |
| **908** A345 14fr multicolored | .90 | .45 |

4th General Elections to European Parliament A346

**1994, May 16** **Photo.** ***Perf. 11½***

| | | |
|---|---|---|
| **909** A346 14fr multicolored | .85 | .70 |

European Inventions, Discoveries
A347

**1994, May 16**

**910** A347 14fr Armillary sphere *1.00 .40*
**911** A347 22fr Sail boats, map *1.25 1.00*

Europa.

21st Intl. Congress of Genealogy & Heraldry — A348

14th World Congress of Intl. Police Assoc. — A349

Intl. Year of the Family
A350

**1994, May 16** ***Perf. 11½***

**912** A348 14fr multicolored 1.25 .35
**913** A349 18fr multicolored 1.25 .45
**914** A350 25fr multicolored 1.75 1.25
*Nos. 912-914 (3)* 4.25 2.05

Europe
A351

**1994, Sept. 19** ***Perf. 11½***

**915** A351 14fr Dove, stars 1.25 .45
**916** A351 14fr Circle of stars 1.25 .45
**917** A351 14fr Bronze Age bowl 2.50 2.75
*Nos. 915-917 (3)* 5.00 3.65

Western European Union, 40th anniv. (No. 915). Office for Official Publications of European Communities, 25th anniv. (No. 916). European Bronze Age Research Campaign (No. 917).

Liberation, 50th Anniv.
A352

**1994, Sept. 19 Photo.** ***Perf. 12x11½***

**918** A352 14fr multicolored .75 .50

Former Refuges in Luxembourg
A353

Designs: 15fr, Munster Abbey. 25fr, Holy Spirit Convent. 60fr, St. Maximine Abbey of Trier.

**Photo. & Engr.**

**1994, Sept. 19** ***Perf. 14***

**919** A353 15fr multicolored .85 .35
**920** A353 25fr multicolored 1.25 1.00
**921** A353 60fr multicolored 3.25 1.75
*Nos. 919-921 (3)* 5.35 3.10

A354

City of Luxembourg, 1995 European City of Culture — A355

A356

Paintings by Hundertwasser
A357

Panoramic view of city showing buildings and: No. 923a, Steeples, trees. b, Gateway through fortress wall. c, Angles in fortress wall. d, Roof of church.

Designs: No. 924, The King of the Antipodes. No. 925, The House with the Arcades and the Yellow Tower. No. 926, Small Path.

***Perf. 12x11½, 11½x12***

**1995, Mar. 6** **Photo.**

**922** A354 16fr multicolored 1.60 .90
**923** A355 Strip of 4 4.25 3.50
*a.-d.* 16fr any single .90 .45

**Photo. & Engr.**

***Perf. 14***

**924** A356 16fr gold, silver & multi 1.60 .90
**925** A357 16fr black & multi 1.60 .90
**926** A357 16fr yellow & multi 1.60 .90
*Nos. 922-926 (5)* 10.65 7.10

No. 923 is a continuous design.

Liberation of the Concentration Camps, 50th Anniv. — A358

Europa: 25fr, Barbed wire, cracked plaster.

**1995, May 15 Photo.** ***Perf. 11½x12***

**927** A358 16fr multicolored *1.25 .50*
**928** A358 25fr multicolored *2.00 .80*

European Nature Conservation Year — A359

**1995, May 15 Litho.** ***Perf. 13½***

**929** A359 16fr multicolored .85 .55

A360

**1995, May 15 Photo.** ***Perf. 11½x12***

**930** A360 16fr multicolored .90 .40

Small States of Europe Games, Luxembourg.

European Geodynamics and Seismology Center
A361

**1995, May 15** ***Perf. 11½***

**931** A361 32fr multicolored 2.00 1.00

UN, 50th Anniv. — A362

**1995, May 15** ***Perf. 11½x12***

**932** A362 80fr multicolored 4.00 2.50

**Museum Exhibits Type of 1993**

Designs, vert: 16fr, Churn, Country Art Museum, Vianden. 32fr, Wine press, Wine Museum, Ehnen. 80fr, Sculpture of a Potter, by Leon Nosbusch, Pottery Museum, Nospelt.

**Photo. & Engr.**

**1995, Sept. 18** ***Perf. 14***

**933** A344 16fr multicolored .85 .40
**934** A344 32fr multicolored 1.75 1.00
**935** A344 80fr multicolored 4.00 2.50
*Nos. 933-935 (3)* 6.60 3.90

Luxembourg-Reykjavik, Iceland Air Route, 40th Anniv. — A363

**1995, Sept. 18 Litho.** ***Perf. 13***

**936** A363 16fr multicolored 1.00 .55

See Iceland No. 807.

Tourism
A364

**1995, Sept. 18 Photo.** ***Perf. 11½***

**937** A364 16fr Erpeldange 1.00 .55
**938** A364 16fr Schengen 1.00 .55

Portrait of Emile Mayrisch (1862-1928), by Théo Van Rysselberghe (1862-1926) — A365

**1996, Mar. 2 Photo.** ***Perf. 11½***

**939** A365 (A) multicolored 1.00 .55

On day of issue No. 939 was valued at 16fr. See Belgium No. 1602.

National Railway, 50th Anniv. — A366

Passenger train: a, Cab facing left. b, Hooked together. c, Cab facing right.

**1996, Mar. 4 Photo.** ***Perf. 11½***

**940** Strip of 3 4.25 2.50
*a.-c.* A366 16fr Any single 1.25 .55

No. 940 is a continuous design.

Grand Duchess Charlotte (1896-1985) — A367

Design: Statue, Luxembourg City.

**1996, Mar. 4** **Booklet Stamp**

**941** A367 16fr multicolored 1.25 .55
*a.* Booklet pane of 8 10.00
Complete booklet, #941a 10.00

Mihály Munkácsy (1844-1900), Hungarian Painter — A368

Designs: No. 942, Portrait of Munkácsy, by Edouard Charlemont, 1884. No. 943, Portrait of Marie Munchen, by Munkácsy, 1885, vert.

**1996, May 20 Photo.** ***Perf. 11½***

**942** A368 16fr multicolored 1.00 .55
**943** A368 16fr multicolored 1.00 .55

Famous Women — A369

Europa: 16fr, Marie de Bourgogne (1457-82), duchess of Luxembourg. 25fr, Empress Maria-Theresa of Austria (1717-80), duchess of Luxembourg.

**Photo. & Engr.**

**1996, May 20** *Perf. 14x13½*

**944** A369 16fr multicolored 1.00 .70
**945** A369 25fr multicolored 1.50 .90

Luxembourg Confederation of Christian Trade Unions, 75th Anniv. A370

Radio, Cent. — A371

Modern Olympic Games, Cent. — A372

Motion Pictures, Cent. — A373

*Perf. 12x11½, 11½x12*

**1996, May 20** **Photo.**

**946** A370 16fr multicolored .90 .30
**947** A371 20fr multicolored 1.10 .45
**948** A372 25fr multicolored 1.25 1.10
**949** A373 32fr multicolored 2.10 1.40
*Nos. 946-949 (4)* 5.35 3.25

Registration and Property Administration, Bicent. — A374

**1996, Sept. 23** **Photo.** *Perf. 11½*

**950** A374 16fr multicolored 1.00 .55

Let Us Live Together A375

No. 951, Four children. No. 952, "L'Abbraccio," bronze statue by M.J. Kerschen, vert.

**1996, Sept. 23**

**951** A375 16fr multicolored .90 .50
**952** A375 16fr multicolored .90 .50

Mustelidae A376

**Litho. & Engr.**

**1996, Sept. 23** *Perf. 13½*

**953** A376 16fr Meles meles .85 .35
**954** A376 20fr Mustela putorius 1.10 .55
**955** A376 80fr Lutra lutra 4.00 2.75
*Nos. 953-955 (3)* 5.95 3.65

John the Blind (1296-1346), King of Bohemia, Count of Luxembourg A377

**Litho. & Engr.**

**1996, Dec. 9** *Perf. 13½*

**956** A377 32fr multicolored 1.75 1.00

**Grand Duke Jean Type of 1993**

**Litho. & Engr.**

**1997, Jan. 2** *Perf. 13½x13*

**957** A337 8fr green & black .70 .30

Treaties of Rome, 40th Anniv. A378

Belgian-Luxembourg Economic Union, 75th Anniv. — A379

**1997, Mar. 3** **Photo.** *Perf. 11½*

**958** A378 16fr multicolored 1.00 .60
**959** A379 20fr multicolored 1.25 .60

Tourism A380

Designs: No. 960, Servais House, Mersch. No. 961, Baroque Church, Koerich, vert.

**1997, Mar. 3**

**960** A380 16fr multicolored .85 .50
**961** A380 16fr multicolored .85 .50

11th World Congress of Rose Societies — A381

Roses: 16fr, Grand Duchess Charlotte. 20fr, Beautiful Sultana. 80fr, In Memory of Jean Soupert.

**1997, Mar. 3** *Perf. 11½*

**962** A381 16fr multicolored 1.10 .55

**Size: 33x25mm**

**963** A381 20fr multicolored 1.40 .75
**964** A381 80fr multicolored 4.50 2.50
*Nos. 962-964 (3)* 7.00 3.80

Stories and Legends — A382

Europa: 16fr, Melusina of Luxembourg. 25fr, Hunter of Hollenfels.

**1997, May 12**

**965** A382 16fr multicolored 1.25 .60
**966** A382 25fr multicolored 2.25 .80

A383 A384

Mondorf Spa, 150th Anniv. A385

**1997, May 12**

**967** A383 16fr multicolored 1.00 .55
**968** A384 16fr multicolored 1.00 .55
**969** A385 16fr multicolored 1.00 .55
*Nos. 967-969 (3)* 3.00 1.65

Grand-Ducal Gendarmerie, bicent. (No. 967). Union of Small Domestic Animals Farming Societies, 75th anniv. (No. 968).

JUVALUX 98 — A386

**1997, May 12**

**970** A386 16fr Emblem 1.10 .55
**971** A386 80fr Postal history 4.50 2.75

Saar-Lorraine-Luxembourg Summit — A387

**1997, Oct. 16** **Photo.** *Perf. 11½*

**972** A387 16fr multicolored 1.00 .50

See Germany No. 1982 & France No. 2613.

Mills — A388

**Litho. & Engr.**

**1997, Oct. 16** *Perf. 13½*

**973** A388 16fr Kalborn Mill, horiz. 1.25 .55
**974** A388 50fr Ramelli Mill 2.60 1.60

Clocks — A389

Designs: 16fr, Oak wall clock, 1816. 32fr, Astronomic clock with walnut case, mid 19th cent. 80fr, Pear tree wood wall clock, 1815.

**Photo. & Engr.**

**1997, Oct. 16** *Perf. 13x13½*

**975** A389 16fr multicolored 1.10 .50
**976** A389 32fr multicolored 1.75 .90
**977** A389 80fr multicolored 4.25 2.50
*Nos. 975-977 (3)* 7.10 3.90

Henry V, the Blonde (1247-81), Count of Luxembourg A390

**1997, Dec. 8** **Photo.** *Perf. 11½*

**978** A390 32fr multicolored 1.75 .90

Tourism A391

No. 979, Hesperange. No. 980, Rodange Church, vert.

**1998, Mar. 23** **Photo.** *Perf. 11½*

**979** A391 16fr multicolored 1.00 .55
**980** A391 16fr multicolored 1.00 .55

See Nos. 1023-1024, 1048-1049.

Freshwater Fish A392

Designs: 16fr, Salmo trutta. 25fr, Cottus gobio. 50fr, Alburnoides bipunctatus.

**Litho. & Engr.**

**1998, Mar. 23** *Perf. 13½x13*

**981** A392 16fr multicolored 1.40 .55
**982** A392 25fr multicolored 2.00 1.25
**983** A392 50fr multicolored 3.50 2.00
*Nos. 981-983 (3)* 6.90 3.80

NGL (Independent Luxembourg Trade Union), 50th Anniv. — A393

Broom Festival, Wiltz, 50th Anniv. — A394

Jean Antoine Zinnen (1827-98), Composer A395

Abolition of Censorship, 150th Anniv. A396

**1998, Mar. 23** **Photo.** *Perf. 11½*

**984** A393 16fr multicolored 1.00 .45
**985** A394 16fr multicolored 1.00 .45
**986** A395 20fr multicolored 1.40 .55
**987** A396 50fr multicolored 3.50 2.00
*Nos. 984-987 (4)* 6.90 3.45

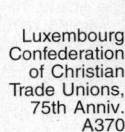

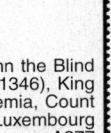

King Henri VII (1275?-1313) of Luxembourg, King of Germany, Holy Roman Emperor — A397

**1998, June 18 Photo. *Perf. 11½***

**988** A397 (A) multicolored 1.00 .50

Granting of the Right to hold a Luxembourg Fair, 700th anniv.

No. 988 was valued at 16fr on the day of issue.

Natl. Holidays and Festivals — A398

Europa: 16fr, Fireworks over bridge, National Day. 25fr, Flame, stained glass window, National Remembrance Day.

**1998, June 18**

**989** A398 16fr multicolored *1.40 .50*
**990** A398 25fr multicolored *1.60 .65*

Juvalux 98 — A399

A400

16fr, Town postman, 1880. 25fr, Letter, 1590, horiz. 50fr, Country postman, 1880.

No. 994, Engraving showing 1861 view of Luxembourg.

**1998, June 18 Photo. & Engr.**

**991** A399 16fr multicolored 1.25 .55
**992** A399 25fr multicolored 1.60 1.25
**993** A399 50fr multicolored 2.75 1.40
*Nos. 991-993 (3)* 5.60 3.20

**Souvenir Sheet**

**994** A400 Sheet of 2 6.00 6.00
***a.*** 16fr multicolored .90 .90
***b.*** 80fr multicolored 4.00 4.00

St. Jean de L'Esperance, Grand Lodge of Luxembourg, 150th Anniv. — A401

**1998, Sept. 21 Litho. *Perf. 13½***

**995** A401 16fr multicolored 1.00 .55

Abbey of Echternach, 1300th Anniv. A402

Various architectural drawings.

**1998, Sept 21 Photo. *Perf. 11½***

**996** A402 16fr multicolored 1.25 .55
**997** A402 48fr multicolored 2.50 1.75
**998** A402 60fr multicolored 3.25 1.75
*Nos. 996-998 (3)* 7.00 4.05

Museum Exhibits A403

City of Luxembourg History Museum: 16fr, Spanish army helmet, 16th cent. 80fr, Wayside Cross, Hollerich, 1718.

**Litho. & Engr.**

**1998, Sept. 21 *Perf. 13½***

**999** A403 16fr multicolored .90 .55
**1000** A403 80fr multicolored 4.50 2.75

NAMSA (NATO Maintenance and Supply Organization), 40th Anniv. — A404

**1998, Dec. 7 Photo. *Perf. 11½***

**1001** A404 36fr multicolored 2.25 1.25

Introduction of the Euro A405

**1999, Mar. 8 Photo. *Perf. 11½***

**1002** A405 (A) multicolored 1.25 .70

No. 1002 was valued at 16fr on the day of issue.

Council of Europe, 50th Anniv. — A406

**1999, Mar. 8**

**1003** A406 16fr multicolored 1.25 .85

Owls A407

**1999, Mar. 8 *Perf. 12***

**1004** A407 (A) Strix aluco, vert. .90 .65
**1005** A407 32fr Bubo bubo 1.60 1.10
**1006** A407 60fr Tyto alba 3.50 2.50
*Nos. 1004-1006 (3)* 6.00 4.25

No. 1004 was valued at 16fr on the day of issue.

NATO, 50th Anniv. A408

**1999, Mar. 8 *Perf. 11½***

**1007** A408 80fr multicolored 5.50 3.50

Europa — A409

National Parks: 16fr, Haute-Sûre. 25fr, Ardennes-Eifel.

**1999, May 17 Photo. *Perf. 11½x12***

**1008** A409 16fr multicolored *1.25 .45*
**1009** A409 25fr multicolored *1.75 .80*

Natl. Federation of Mutuality, 75th Anniv. — A410

Intl. Year of Older Persons — A411

UPU, 125th Anniv. A412

A413

A414

**1999, May 17 *Perf. 11½***

**1010** A410 16fr multicolored .85 .65
**1011** A411 16fr multicolored .90 .55
**1012** A412 16fr multicolored .90 .55
**1013** A413 32fr multicolored 1.60 1.40
**1014** A414 80fr multicolored 4.50 2.75
*Nos. 1010-1014 (5)* 8.75 5.90

Luxembourg Federation of Amateur Photographers, 50th anniv. (No. 1013). Luxembourg Gymnastics Federation, cent. (No. 1014).

18th Birthday of Prince Guillaume A415

**Photo. & Engr.**

**1999, Sept. 21 *Perf. 13½***

**1015** A415 16fr multicolored .85 .55

Aline Mayrisch-de Saint-Hubert (1874-1947), President of Luxembourg Red Cross — A416

**1999, Sept. 21 Litho. & Engr.**

**1016** A416 20fr multicolored 1.60 .55

Travelling Into the Future A417

16fr, Communication by road. 20fr, Information age. 80fr, Conquering space.

**1999, Sept. 21 Photo. *Perf. 11¾***

**1017** A417 16fr multicolored .85 .55
**1018** A417 20fr multicolored 1.00 .85
**1019** A417 80fr multicolored 4.25 1.75
*Nos. 1017-1019 (3)* 6.10 3.15

See Nos. 1063-1065.

Johann Wolfgang von Goethe (1749-1832), German Poet — A418

**1999, Nov. 30 Photo. *Perf. 11¾***

**1020** A418 20fr henna & dk brn 1.25 .70

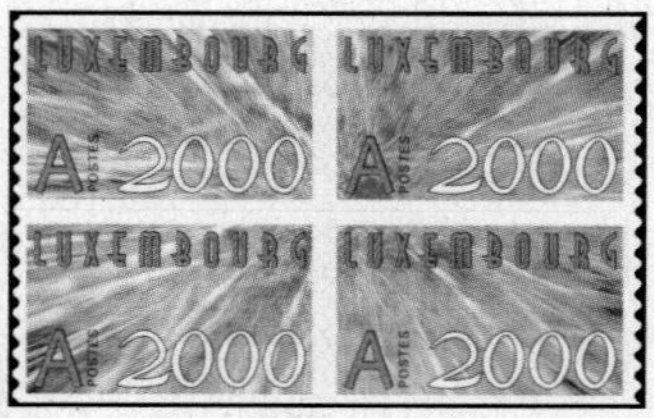

Year 2000 — A419

No. 1021: a, Large white area under A and 2000. b, Large blue area under A. c, Large blue area under A and URG. d, Large blue area under LUX.

***Serpentine Die Cut 8 Vert.***

**2000, Jan. 3 Photo.**

**Self-Adhesive**

**Booklet Stamps**

**1021** A419 Booklet pane of 4 4.25
***a.-d.*** (A) Any single 1.00 .70
Booklet, 2 #1021 8.50

Nos. 1021a-1021d sold for 16fr on day of issue.

Holy Roman Emperor Charles V (1500-58) A420

**Litho. & Engr.**

**2000, Mar. 7 *Perf. 13½***

**1022** A420 A multi .90 .50

Sold for 16fr on day of issue.

**Tourism Type of 1998**

Designs: No. 1023, Walferdange Castle. No. 1024, Wasserbillig railway station, vert.

*Perf. 11¾x11½, 11½x11¾*

**2000, Mar. 7** **Photo.**

**Granite Paper**

**1023** A391 A multi 1.00 .50
**1024** A391 A multi 1.00 .50

Sold for 16fr on day of issue.

World Mathematics Year A421

**2000, Mar. 7** *Perf. 11½x11¾*

**1025** A421 80fr multi 4.50 2.75

**Grand Duke Jean Type of 1993**

**Litho. & Engr.**

**2000, Mar. 31** *Perf. 13¼x13*

**Background Color**

**1026** A337 9fr pink .60 .30

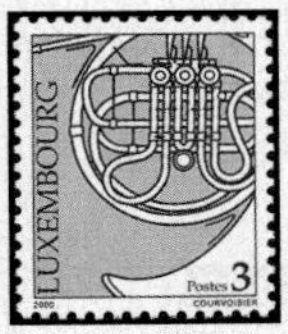


Musical Instruments — A422

*Perf. 11½x11¾*

**2000, Mar. 31** **Photo.**

**Granite Paper**

**1027** A422 3fr French horn .25 .25
**1028** A422 12fr Saxophone .60 .35
**1029** A422 21fr Violin 1.25 .55
**1030** A422 30fr Piano 1.50 1.10
*Nos. 1027-1030 (4)* 3.60 2.25

See Nos. 1045-1046.

Ducks A423

Designs: 18fr, Anas platyrhynchos. 24fr, Aythya ferina, vert. 30fr, Aythya fuligula.

**2000, May 9** *Perf. 11¾x11½*

**Granite Paper**

**1031** A423 18fr multi 1.25 .70

*Perf. 11½x11¾*

**1032** A423 24fr multi 1.60 .90
**1033** A423 30fr multi 1.75 1.25
*Nos. 1031-1033 (3)* 4.60 2.85

Esch-sur-Alzette Gas Works, Cent. (in 1999) — A424

**2000, May 9** *Perf. 11¾x11½*

**Granite Paper**

**1034** A424 18fr multi 1.25 .65

**Europa, 2000**

Common Design Type

**2000, May 9** *Perf. 11½x11¾*

**Granite Paper**

**1035** CD17 21fr multi *1.40* .85

Robert Schuman's European Unity Plan, 50th Anniv. A425

**2000, May 9** *Perf. 11½x11¾*

**1036** A425 21fr multi 1.40 .85

Art Collection of Luxembourg Posts & Telecommunications — A426

Art by: 21fr, Will Kesseler. 24fr, Joseph Probst, vert. 36fr, Mett Hoffmann.

*Perf. 11¾x11½, 11½x11¾*

**2000, Sept. 27** **Photo.**

**Granite Paper**

**1037** A426 21fr multi 1.10 .60
**1038** A426 24fr multi 1.50 1.00
**1039** A426 36fr multi 2.25 1.40
*Nos. 1037-1039 (3)* 4.85 3.00

Towers on Historic Walking Trails A427

Designs: 18fr, Tower of Jacob, Wenzel trail. 42fr, Bons Malades Gate, Vauban trail.

**Photo. & Engr.**

**2000, Sept. 27** *Perf. 13½x14¼*

**1040** A427 18fr multi 1.25 .55
**1041** A427 42fr multi 2.75 1.60

Blast Furnace "B," Esch-Belval A428

**2000, Sept. 27** *Perf. 11¾x11½*

**1042** A428 A multi 1.25 .55

No. 1042 sold for 18fr on day of issue.

Accession of Grand Duke Henri A429

Designs: 18fr, Prince Henri in uniform, Princess Maria Teresa in pink suit. 100fr, Prince in suit, Princess in red blouse.

**2000, Sept. 27** **Photo.** *Perf. 11¾*

**Granite Paper (18fr)**

**1043** A429 18fr multi 1.00 .55

**Souvenir Sheet**

**Photo. (margin Photo. & Engr.)**

*Perf. 11½*

**1044** A429 100fr multi 6.50 6.50

No. 1043 issued in sheets of 12, five of which (positions 6, 8, 9, 10 and 11) have a red and blue "ribbon" running diagonally through stamp margin. No. 1044 contains one 46x35mm stamp.

**Musical Instruments Type of 2000**

**2000, Dec. 5** **Photo.** *Perf. 11½x11¾*

**Granite Paper**

**1045** A422 9fr Electric guitar .90 .35
**1046** A422 24fr Accordion 1.60 1.00

Treaty Establishing European Coal and Steel Community, 50th Anniv. — A430

*Perf. 11¼x11½*

**2001, Mar. 20** **Photo.**

**1047** A430 21fr multi 1.25 .85

**Tourism Type of 1998**

Designs: No. 1048, 18fr, Bestgen Mill, Schifflange. No. 1049, 18fr, Chapel, Wormeldange, and millstone, Ahn, vert.

*Perf. 11¾x11½, 11½x11¾*

**2001, Mar. 20**

**Granite Paper**

**1048-1049** A391 Set of 2 2.00 1.10

Writers — A431

Designs: 18fr, Nik Welter (1871-1951). 24fr, André Gide (1869-1951). 30fr, Michel Rodange (1827-76).

*Perf. 13½x13¼*

**2001, Mar. 20** **Litho. & Engr.**

**1050-1052** A431 Set of 3 4.50 3.00

Europa A432

Designs: A (18fr), Stream, Mullerthal region. 21fr, Pond and Kaltreis water tower, Luxembourg-Bonnevoie.

*Perf. 11¾x11½, 11½x11¾*

**2001, May 22** **Photo.**

**Granite Paper**

**1053-1054** A432 Set of 2 2.25 1.60

Rescue Workers — A433

Designs: 18fr, Air rescue. 30fr, Rescue divers. 45fr, Fire fighters.

**2001, May 22** *Perf. 11½x11¾*

**Granite Paper**

**1055-1057** A433 Set of 3 6.00 4.00

Humanitarian Services — A434

Designs: 18fr, Humanitarian aid. 24fr, Intl. Organization for Migration, 50th anniv.

**2001, May 22** *Perf. 11½*

**1058-1059** A434 Set of 2 2.75 1.75

Old Postal Vehicles — A435

Designs: 3fr, Citroen 2CV Mini-van, 1960s. 18fr, Volkswagen Beetle, 1970s.

**Granite Paper**

***Serpentine Die Cut 8¼ Vert.***

**2001, May 22** **Booklet Stamps**

**1060** A435 3fr multi .25 .25
**1061** A435 18fr multi 1.10 .75
*a.* Booklet, 6 each #1060-1061 8.50

European Year of Languages A436

**2001, Oct. 1** **Photo.** *Perf. 11¾x11½*

**Granite Paper**

**1062** A436 A multi 1.25 .70

Luxembourg postal officials state that No. 1062 sold for 45 eurocents on the day of issue, though euro currency was not in circulation on the day of issue. On the day of issue, 45 eurocents was the equivalent of approximately 18fr.

---

Nos. 1063-1071, 1074, 1076, 1078, 1080, 1084, and B425-B429 are denominated solely in euro currency though euro currency would not circulate until Jan. 1, 2002. From their date of issue until Dec. 31, 2001, these stamps could be purchased for Luxembourg francs. The official pegged rate of 40.3399 francs to the euro made rounding the franc purchase price a necessity for such purchases. The approximate franc equivalent of the euro denominations is shown in parentheses in the listings.

---

**Traveling Into the Future Type of 1999**

Designs: 45c (18fr), Renewable energy. 59c (24fr), Waste recycling. 74c (30fr), Biological research.

**2001, Oct. 1** *Perf. 11¾*

**Granite Paper**

**1063-1065** A417 Set of 3 5.50 4.00

Euro Coinage A437

Designs: Coin obverses with values of stamp denominations.

**2001, Oct. 1** *Perf. 11½*

**1066** A437 5c (2fr) multi .25 .25
**1067** A437 10c (4fr) multi .25 .25
**1068** A437 20c (8fr) multi .60 .40
**1069** A437 50c (20fr) multi 1.40 1.00

| | | | | | |
|---|---|---|---|---|---|
| **1070** | A437 | €1 (40fr) multi | 3.00 | 1.75 |
| **1071** | A437 | €2 (80fr) multi | 6.00 | 4.50 |
| | | *Nos. 1066-1071 (6)* | 11.50 | 8.15 |

Grand Duke Henri — A438

**Photo. & Engr.**

**2001-03** ***Perf. 11¾x11½***

**Vignette Color**

| | | | | |
|---|---|---|---|---|
| **1072** | A438 | 1c blue | .25 | .25 |
| **1073** | A438 | 3c green | .25 | .25 |
| **1074** | A438 | 7c (3fr) blue | .25 | .25 |
| **1075** | A438 | 22c (9fr) brown | .50 | .40 |
| **1076** | A438 | 30c (12fr) green | .90 | .45 |
| **1077** | A438 | 45c (18fr) violet | 1.40 | .65 |
| **1078** | A438 | 52c brown | 1.25 | .75 |
| **1079** | A438 | 59c blue | 1.50 | 1.00 |
| **1080** | A438 | 74c brown | 2.00 | 1.00 |
| **1081** | A438 | 89c red violet | 2.50 | 1.25 |
| | | *Nos. 1072-1081 (10)* | 10.80 | 6.25 |

Issued: 7c, 22c, 30c, 45c, 10/1/01. 52c, 59c, 74c, 89c, 3/5/02. 1c, 3c, 10/1/03.

See Nos. 1126, 1129-1133A.

Kiwanis International A439

**2001, Dec. 6** **Photo.** ***Perf. 11½***
**1084** A439 52c (21fr) multi 1.75 1.25

**100 Cents = 1 Euro (€)**

Art Collection of Luxembourg Posts & Telecommunications — A440

Art by: 22c, Moritz Ney, vert. 45c, Dany Prüm. 59c, Christiane Schmit, vert.

***Perf. 14¼x14, 14x14¼***

**2002, Mar. 5** **Photo.**
**1085-1087** A440 Set of 3 4.00 3.00

European Court Anniversaries A441

Designs: 45c, European Court of Auditors, 25th anniv. 52c, Court of Justice of the European communities, 50th anniv.

**2002, Mar. 5** **Litho.** ***Perf. 13½***
**1088-1089** A441 Set of 2 3.00 2.00

Sports — A442

No. 1090: a, Snowboarding. b, Skateboarding. c, Rollerblading. d, Bicycling. e, Volleyball. f, Basketball.

**Booklet Stamps**

***Die Cut Perf. 10 on 3 Sides***

**2002, Mar. 5** **Self-Adhesive**

| | | | | |
|---|---|---|---|---|
| **1090** | | Booklet pane of 6 | 4.50 | |
| *a.-c.* | A442 | 7c Any single | .25 | .25 |
| *d.-f.* | A442 | 45c Any single | 1.25 | 1.00 |
| | | Booklet, 2 #1090 | 9.00 | |

Europa — A443

Designs: 45c, Tightrope walker. 52c, Clown.

**2002, May 14** **Litho.** ***Perf. 13½***
**1091-1092** A443 Set of 2 *3.00 1.75*

Cultural Anniversaries — A444

Designs: A, 50th Wiltz Festival. €1.12, Victor Hugo (1802-85), writer.

**2002, May 14** ***Perf. 13¼***
**1093-1094** A444 Set of 2 5.00 3.50

No. 1093 sold for 45c on day of issue.

Start of Tour de France in Luxembourg A445

Designs: 45c, Stylized bicycle. 52c, François Faber (1887-1915), 1909 champion. €2.45, The Champion, by Joseph Kutter.

**Litho. (45c), Litho. & Engr.**

***Perf. 13¼x13½, 13½x13¼***

**2002, May 14**
**1095-1097** A445 Set of 3 9.00 6.25

Grevenmacher Charter of Freedom, 750th Anniv. — A446

**2002, Sept. 14** **Litho.** ***Perf. 13¼x13***
**1098** A446 74c multi 1.90 1.50

Nature Museum, Museum of Natural History A447

No. 1099: a, Water drop on spruce needle. b, Butterfly. c, Leaf rosette of *Echeveria* plant. d, Berries.

***Serpentine Die Cut 8 Vert.***

**2002, Sept. 14** **Photo.**

**Self-Adhesive**

| | | | | |
|---|---|---|---|---|
| **1099** | | Booklet pane of 4 | 4.50 | |
| *a.-d.* | A447 | A Any single | 1.10 | .80 |
| | | Booklet, 2 #1099 | 9.00 | |

Nos. 1099a-1099d had franking value of 45c on day of issue, but booklet sold for discounted price of €3.35.

Souvenir Sheet

Luxembourg Stamps, 150th Anniv. — A448

No. 1100: a, Grand Duke William II, man and woman, 1852 (47x27mm). b, Grand Duke Adolphe, woman, 1902 (47x27mm). c, Grand Duchess Charlotte, street scene, 1952 (47x27mm). d, Grand Duke Henri, hot air balloons in street, 2002 (71x27mm).

**Photo. & Engr.**

**2002, Sept. 14** ***Perf. 11¾***
**1100** A448 45c Sheet of 4, #a-d 4.75 4.75

The Post in 50 Years A449

Designs: 22c, Postmen in spacecraft, buildings, vert. A, Spacecraft in flight, cell phone, letter and "@" in orbit around planet.

***Perf. 14x14½, 14½x14***

**2002, Oct. 19** **Litho.**
**1101-1102** A449 Set of 2 1.75 1.40

No. 1102 sold for 45c on day of issue.

Grand Duke Jean and Princess Joséphine-Charlotte, 50th Wedding Anniv. — A450

***Perf. 14¼x14½***

**2003, Mar. 18** **Litho.**
**1103** A450 45c multi 1.10 .95

Official Journal of the European Communities, 50th Anniv. — A451

**2003, Mar. 18** ***Perf. 14½x14***
**1104** A451 52c multi 1.40 1.10

Famous Women A452

Designs: No. 1105, 45c, Catherine Schleimer-Kill (1884-1973), feminist leader. No. 1106, 45c, Lou Koster (1889-1973), composer.

**2003, Mar. 18** **Photo.** ***Perf. 11½***
**1105-1106** A452 Set of 2 2.40 1.90

Tourism A453

Designs: 50c, Fontaine Marie Convent, Differdange. €1, Castle, Mamer. €2.50, St. Joseph Church, Esch-sur-Alzette, vert.

***Perf. 14½x14, 14x14½***

**2003, Mar. 18** **Litho.**
**1107-1109** A453 Set of 3 9.50 9.50

Luxembourg Athénée, 400th Anniv. A454

**2003, May 20** **Litho.** ***Perf. 14¼x14½***
**1110** A454 45c multi 1.10 1.00

Europa A455

Poster art: 45c, 1952 poster for National Lottery, by Roger Gerson. 52c, 1924 poster for Third Commercial Fair, by Auguste Trémont.

**2003, May 20** ***Perf. 13¼x13***
**1111-1112** A455 Set of 2 *2.25 1.75*

Bridges — A456

Designs: 45c, Adolphe Bridge, 1903. 59c, Stierchen Bridge, 14th cent. (36x26mm). 89c, Victor Bodson Bridge, 1994 (36x26mm).

**Photo. & Engr.**

**2003, May 20** ***Perf. 11½***
**1113-1115** A456 Set of 3 5.00 4.25

Electrification of Luxembourg, 75th Anniv. — A457

**Litho. & Embossed**

**2003, Sept. 23** ***Perf. 13¼x13***
**1116** A457 A multi 1.25 1.25

Sold for 50c on day of issue.

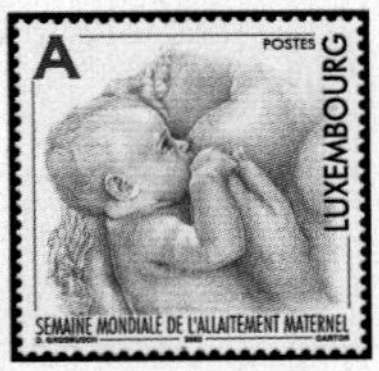


Breastfeeding
A458

**2003, Sept. 23 Litho. *Perf. 13½***
**1117** A458 A multi 1.25 1.25

Sold for 50c on day of issue.

Gaart an Heem Agricultural Cooperatives, 75th Anniv. — A459

Gardeners with: 25c, Spade. A, Basket and rake. €2, Watering can.

**2003, Sept. 23 *Perf. 14½x14***
**1118-1120** A459 Set of 3 7.00 6.50

No. 1119 sold for 50c on day of issue.

Industrial Products Made in Luxembourg
A460

Designs: 60c, Steel. 70c, Industrial valve. 80c, Polyester film.

**2003, Oct. 1 Photo. *Perf. 11½***
**1121-1123** A460 Set of 3 5.00 5.00

**Grand Duke Henri Type of 2001-03**
**Photo. & Engr.**
**2004-2010 *Perf. 11¾x11½***
**Vignette Color**

| | | | | | |
|---|---|---|---|---|---|
| **1124** | A438 | 5c violet brn | .25 | .25 |
| **1125** | A438 | 10c black | .30 | .30 |
| **1126** | A438 | 25c claret | .65 | .65 |
| **1129** | A438 | 50c black | 1.25 | 1.25 |
| **1130** | A438 | 60c blue | 1.50 | 1.50 |
| **1131** | A438 | 70c purple | 1.75 | 1.75 |
| **1132** | A438 | 80c olive black | 2.10 | 2.00 |
| **1133** | A438 | 90c brown | 2.25 | 2.25 |
| **1133A** | A438 | €1 blue | 2.60 | 2.60 |
| | *Nos. 1126-1133A (7)* | | 12.10 | 12.00 |

Issued: 25c, 50c, 60c, 80c, 3/16/04; 70c, 90c, €1, 9/26/06; 5c, 10c, 12/7/10.

Emigrants to the United States
A461

Designs: 50c, Edward Steichen (1879-1973), photographer. 70c, Hugo Gernsbach (1884-1967), science fiction writer.

**Photo. & Engr.**
**2004, Mar. 16 *Perf. 11½***
**1134-1135** A461 Set of 2 3.25 3.00

Anniversaries of Commercial Events
A462

Designs: No. 1136, 50c, Commercial Union of Esch-sur-Alzette, cent. No. 1137, 50c, Luxembourg City Annual Street Market, 75th anniv.

**2004, Mar. 16 Litho. *Perf. 14¼***
**1136-1137** A462 Set of 2 2.60 2.60

Mushrooms — A463

No. 1138: a, Cantharellus tubaeformis. b, Ramaria flava. c, Stropharia cyanea. d, Helvella lacunosa. e, Anthurus archeri. f, Clitopilus prunulus.

***Die Cut Perf. 10***
**2004, Mar. 16 Litho.**
**Self-Adhesive**

| | | | |
|---|---|---|---|
| **1138** | Booklet pane of 6 | 4.50 | |
| *a.-c.* | A463 10c Any single | .25 | .25 |
| *d.-f.* | A463 50c Any single | 1.25 | 1.25 |
| | Complete booklet, 2 #1138 | 9.00 | |

European Parliament Elections
A464

**2004, May 9 Litho. *Perf. 13¼x13***
**1139** A464 50c multi 1.25 1.25

2004 Summer Olympics, Athens
A465

European Sports Education Year
A466

**2004, May 9 Photo. *Perf. 11½x11¾***
**1140** A465 50c multi 1.25 1.25
**1141** A466 60c multi 1.40 1.40

European School, 50th Anniv.
A467

**2004, May 9 Litho. *Perf. 14¼x14½***
**1142** A467 70c multi 1.75 1.75

Europa
A468

Designs: 50c, Stone bridge over Schiessentuempel. 60c, Bourscheid Beach, Bourscheid Castle.

**2004, May 9 *Perf. 13¼x13***
**1143-1144** A468 Set of 2 *3.00 3.00*

Luxembourg Stock Exchange, 75th Anniv. — A469

***Perf. 11¼x11½***
**2004, Sept. 28 Litho. & Engr.**
**1145** A469 50c multi 1.25 1.25

Food Products Made in Luxembourg — A470

Designs: 35c, Baked goods, beer. 60c, Meats, wine. 70c, Dairy products.

***Perf. 13½x13¾***
**2004, Sept. 28 Litho.**
**1146-1148** A470 Set of 3 4.00 4.00

National Museum of History and Art — A471

Designs: 50c, Museum building. €1.10, Young Woman with a Fan, by Luigi Rubio. €3, Charity, by Lucas Cranach the Elder or Lucas Cranach the Younger.

**2004, Sept. 28 Photo. *Perf. 11¾***
**1149-1151** A471 Set of 3 11.50 11.50

World War II Liberation, 60th Anniv.
A472

**2004, Dec. 7 Litho. *Perf. 14x13½***
**1152** A472 70c multi 1.90 1.90

Luxembourg's Presidency of European Union — A473

No. 1153: a, Building with glass facade. b, Arch, Echternach Basilica. c, Vineyard along Moselle River. d, Rusted iron girder.

***Serpentine Die Cut 8¼ Vert.***
**2005, Jan. 25 Photo.**
**Self-Adhesive**

| | | | |
|---|---|---|---|
| **1153** | Booklet pane of 4 | 5.00 | |
| *a.-d.* | A473 A any single | 1.25 | 1.25 |
| | Complete booklet, 2 #1153 | 10.00 | |

On the day of issue, Nos. 1153a-1153d each had a franking value of 50c, but complete booklet sold for €3.80.

Rotary International, Cent. — A474

**2005, Mar. 15 Litho. *Perf. 13½x13***
**1154** A474 50c multi 1.40 1.40

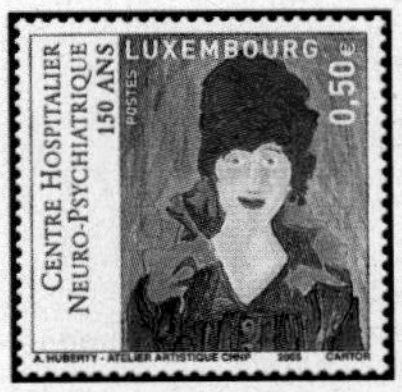


Ettelbrück Neuro-psychiatric Medical Center, 150th Anniv. — A475

**2005, Mar. 15 *Perf. 13½***
**1155** A475 50c multi 1.40 1.40

76th Intl. Congress of Applied Mathematics and Mechanics
A476

**2005, Mar. 15**
**1156** A476 60c multi 1.60 1.60

Benelux Parliament, 50th Anniv. — A477

**2005, Mar. 15 *Perf. 13¼x12¾***
**1157** A477 60c multi 1.60 1.60

Tourism
A478

Designs: 50c, Shoe factory, Kayl-Tétange. 60c, Village scene and website address of National Tourist Office (44x31mm). €1, Statue of St. Eloi, Rodange, and foundry worker.

***Perf. 14x13¼, 12¾ (60c)***
**2005, Mar. 15**
**1158-1160** A478 Set of 3 5.50 5.50

Opening of Grand Duchess Joséphine-Charlotte Concert Hall — A479

**2005, May 24 *Perf. 13¼x13¾***
**1161** A479 50c multi 1.25 1.25

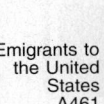

Europa
A480

Designs: 50c, Judd mat Gaardebounen (pork and beans). 60c, Feirstengszalot (beef, egg and pickle salad).

**2005, May 24** ***Perf. 13½***
**1162-1163** A480 Set of 2 *2.75 2.75*

Railways
A481

Designs: 50c, Niederpallen Station, CVE 357 car of De Jhangeli narrow-gauge railway. 60c, AL-T3 locomotive. €2.50, PH 408 passenger car.

**2005, May 24** **Photo.** ***Perf. 11½***
**1164-1166** A481 Set of 3 9.00 9.00

Hand Lifting Self-Adhesive Paper From Backing — A482

**Coil Stamps**

***Serpentine Die Cut 11x11¼***

**2005, May 24** **Self-Adhesive**

| | | | |
|---|---|---|---|
| **1167** | Vert. strip of 4 | 2.50 | |
| *a.* | A482 25c dark red & multi | .60 | .60 |
| *b.* | A482 25c red orange & multi | .60 | .60 |
| *c.* | A482 25c orange & multi | .60 | .60 |
| *d.* | A482 25c yellow & multi | .60 | .60 |
| **1168** | Vert. strip of 4 | 5.00 | |
| *a.* | A482 50c dark green & multi | 1.25 | 1.25 |
| *b.* | A482 50c green & multi | 1.25 | 1.25 |
| *c.* | A482 50c emerald & multi | 1.25 | 1.25 |
| *d.* | A482 50c yellow green & multi | 1.25 | 1.25 |

Rolls of 100 of the 25c stamps sold for €24, and rolls of 100 of the 50c stamps sold for €48.

Famous People
A483

Designs: 50c, Jean-Pierre Pescatore (1793-1855), philanthropist. 90c, Marcel Reuland (1905-56), writer. €1, Marie-Henriette Steil (1898-1930), writer, vert.

**Photo. & Engr.**

**2005, Sept. 27** ***Perf. 11½***
**1169-1171** A483 Set of 3 6.00 6.00

Butterflies
A484

Designs: 35c, Papilio machaon. 70c, Argynnis paphia, vert. €1.80, Lysandra coridon.

**2005, Sept. 27** **Litho.**
**1172-1174** A484 Set of 3 7.25 7.25

Rocks
A485

No. 1175: a, Schist. b, Rocks with iron (minerai de fer). c, Luxembourg sandstone. d, Conglomerate rocks.

***Serpentine Die Cut 12¾ Vert.***

**2005, Sept. 27** **Self-Adhesive**

| | | | |
|---|---|---|---|
| **1175** | Booklet pane of 4 | 4.75 | |
| *a.-d.* | A485 A Any single | 1.10 | 1.10 |
| | Complete booklet, 2 #1175 | 9.50 | |

The complete booklet sold for €3.80, but each stamp had a franking value of 50c on the day of issue.

Seeing Eye Dog
A486

**Litho. & Embossed**

**2005, Dec. 6** ***Perf. 13x13¼***
**1176** A486 70c dk blue & lemon 1.75 1.75

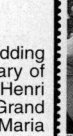

25th Wedding Anniversary of Grand Duke Henri and Grand Duchess Maria Teresa — A487

**2006, Feb. 7** **Litho.** ***Perf. 13¼x13¾***
**1177** A487 50c multi 1.25 1.25

**Souvenir Sheet**

***Perf. 13¼x13***

**1178** A487 €2.50 multi 6.25 6.25

No. 1178 contains one 26x37mm stamp.

Blood Donation
A488

**2006, Mar. 14** **Litho.** ***Perf. 13¼***
**1179** A488 50c multi 1.25 1.25

Tourism
A489

Designs: No. 1180, 50c, Parc Merveilleux, Bettembourg. No. 1181, 50c, Birelerhaff Pigeon Tower, Sandweiler, vert.

**2006, Mar. 14** ***Perf. 11½***
**1180-1181** A489 Set of 2 2.40 1.25

Electrification of Railway Network, 50th Anniv. — A490

Designs: 50c, Train passing station. 70c, Train on bridge. €1, Railway workers repairing electrical wires, vert.

**2006, Mar. 14** ***Perf. 13¼x13, 13x13¼***
**1182-1184** A490 Set of 3 5.25 5.25

Personalized Stamp Website "meng.post.lu" — A491

**2006, May 16** **Litho.** ***Perf. 11½***
**1185** A491 A multi + label 1.40 1.40

No. 1185 sold for 50c on day of issue. Labels could be personalized for a fee.

Esch-sur-Alzette, Cent. — A492

**2006, May 16** ***Perf. 13½***
**1186** A492 50c multi 1.40 1.40

Soccer Teams in Luxembourg, Cent. — A493

2006 World Cup Soccer Championships, Germany — A494

**2006, May 16** ***Perf. 13x13¼***
**1187** A493 50c multi 1.40 1.40
**1188** A494 90c multi 2.40 2.40

Europa
A495

Contest-winning cell phone photos: 50c, Hands making heart. 70c, People holding globe.

**2006, May 16** ***Perf. 12½***
**1189-1190** A495 Set of 2 3.25 3.25

State Council, 150th Anniv. — A496

**Litho. & Embossed**

**2006, Sept. 26** ***Perf. 13½***
**1191** A496 50c multi 1.25 1.25

Luxembourg Chess Federation, 75th Anniv. — A497

**2006, Sept. 26**
**1192** A497 90c multi 2.25 2.25

Bank Sesquicentenaries — A498

Designs: No. 1193, 50c, State Savings Bank (Spuerkeess). No. 1194, 50c, Dexia-BIL Bank.

**2006, Sept. 26** **Litho.** ***Perf. 13¼x13***
**1193-1194** A498 Set of 2 2.60 2.60

Fight Against Drug Addiction
A499

Designs: 50c, Children's drawing of man and "No Drugs" sign. €1, Ashtray with vegetables and cheese, vert.

**2006, Sept. 26** ***Perf. 11½***
**1195-1196** A499 Set of 2 3.75 3.75

Luxembourg Horticultural Federation, 75th Anniv. — A500

No. 1197: a, Flowers. b, Fruits and vegetables.

**2006, Dec. 5** **Litho.** ***Perf. 13¼x13¾***

| | | | |
|---|---|---|---|
| **1197** | A500 Horiz. pair | 3.75 | 3.75 |
| *a.-b.* | 70c Either single | 1.75 | 1.75 |

Luxembourg, 2007 European Cultural Capital — A501

No. 1198 — Silhouettes of deer and men with deer heads with background color of: a, Blue. b, Orange. c, Bright yellow green. d, Red violet.

***Serpentine Die Cut 8½ Vert.***

**2007, Jan. 30** **Litho.**

| | | | |
|---|---|---|---|
| **1198** | Booklet pane of 4 | 5.25 | |
| *a.-d.* | A501 A Any single | 1.25 | 1.25 |
| | Complete booklet, 2 #1198 | 10.50 | |

Nos. 1198a-1198d each sold for 50c on day of issue.

Luxembourg Caritas, 75th Anniv. A502

**2007, Mar. 20 Litho. *Perf. 11½***
**1199** A502 50c multi 1.40 1.40

Luxembourg Automobile Club, 75th Anniv. A503

**2007, Mar. 20**
**1200** A503 50c multi 1.40 1.40

Treaty of Rome, 50th Anniv. A504

Designs: 70c, Delegates. €1, Text and stars.

**2007, Mar. 20 *Perf. 13x13¼***
**1201-1202** A504 Set of 2 4.75 4.75

"Postes" A505 Denomination A506

***Serpentine Die Cut 11x11¼***
**2007, Mar. 20 Photo.**
**Self-Adhesive**
**Coil Stamps**

| | | | |
|---|---|---|---|
| **1203** | A505 25c pur & multi | .70 | .70 |
| **1204** | A506 25c brn & multi | .70 | .70 |
| **1205** | A505 25c dk bl & multi | .70 | .70 |
| **1206** | A506 25c dk grn & multi | .70 | .70 |
| *a.* | Vert. strip of 4, #1203-1206 | 2.80 | |
| **1207** | A505 50c red vio & multi | 1.40 | 1.40 |
| **1208** | A506 50c red & multi | 1.40 | 1.40 |
| **1209** | A505 50c bl & multi | 1.40 | 1.40 |
| **1210** | A506 50c grn & multi | 1.40 | 1.40 |
| *a.* | Vert. strip of 4, #1207-1210 | 5.60 | |
| | *Nos. 1203-1210 (8)* | 8.40 | 8.40 |

Europa A507

Designs: 50c, Scout campground. 70c, Scouts, globe, knot.

**2007, May 22 Litho. *Perf. 13x13¼***
**1211-1212** A507 Set of 2 3.25 3.25

Scouting, cent.

Town Centenaries — A508

Designs: No. 1213, 50c, Differdange. No. 1214, 50c, Dudelenge. No. 1215, 50c, Ettelbruck. No. 1216, 50c, Rumelange.

**2007, May 22 Photo. *Perf. 11½***
**1213-1216** A508 Set of 4 5.50 5.50

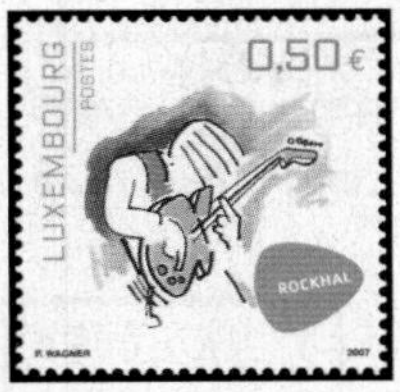


Places of Culture A509

Designs: 50c, Rockhal. 70c, Grand Duke Jean Museum of Modern Art. €1, Neumünster Abbey.

**2007, May 22 *Perf. 12½***
**1217-1219** A509 Set of 3 6.00 6.00

"Transborderism" A510

**2007, Sept. 3 Photo. *Perf. 11½***
**1220** A510 50c multi 1.40 1.40

Rotunda of Luxembourg Train Station — A511

**2007, Sept. 3 Photo. & Engr.**
**1221** A511 70c multi 1.90 1.90

See Belgium No. 2253.

Casa Luxemburg, Sibiu, Romania — A512

**2007, Sept. 3 Litho. *Perf. 13x13¼***
**1222** A512 70c multi 1.90 1.90

See Romania Nos. 4993-4994.

Luxembourg Army Peace-keeping Missions — A513

**2007, Sept. 3 Photo. *Perf. 11½***
**1223** A513 70c multi 1.90 1.90

Souvenir Sheet

Roman Mosaic, Vichten — A514

No. 1224: a, Thalia and Euterpe. b, Terpsichore and Melpomene. c, Clio and Urania. d, Polymnia and Erato. e, Calliope and Homer. Nos. 1224a-1224d are 58x29mm octagonal stamps, No. 1224e is a 55x55mm diamond-shaped stamp.

**2007, Sept. 3 Litho. *Perf. 14¼***

| | | | |
|---|---|---|---|
| **1224** | A514 Sheet of 5 | 8.25 | 8.25 |
| *a.-d.* | 50c Any single | 1.40 | 1.40 |
| *e.* | €1 multi | 2.60 | 2.60 |

Esch-sur-Sure Dam — A515

Uewersauer Stauséi — A516

***Serpentine Die Cut 12½x13½***
**2007, Dec. 4 Litho. Self-Adhesive**

| | | | |
|---|---|---|---|
| **1225** | Horiz. pair | 4.25 | |
| *a.* | A515 70c multi | 2.10 | 2.10 |
| *b.* | A516 70c multi | 2.10 | 2.10 |

St. Willibrord (658-739) A517

**2008, Mar. 18 Litho. *Perf. 13***
**1226** A517 50c multi 1.60 1.60

European Investment Bank, 50th Anniv. A518

**2008, Mar. 18 *Perf. 13x13¼***
**1227** A518 70c purple & silver 2.25 2.25

Eurosystem, 10th Anniv. — A519

**2008, Mar. 18 *Perf. 13½x13¾***
**1228** A519 €1 multi 3.25 3.25

Luxembourg Philharmonic Orchestra, 75th Anniv. — A520

Henri Pensis (1900-58), Conductor — A521

**2008, Mar. 18**
**1229** A520 50c multi 1.60 1.60
**1230** A521 70c multi 2.25 2.25

2008 Summer Olympics, Beijing A522

**2008, May 20 Litho. *Perf. 14x13½***
**1231** A522 70c multi 2.25 2.25

Luxembourg Basketball Federation, 75th Anniv. — A523

Luxembourg Soccer Federation, Cent. — A524

**2008, May 20 *Perf. 12½***
**1232** A523 A multi 1.60 1.60
**1233** A524 A multi 1.60 1.60

Nos. 1232 and 1233 each sold for 50c on day of issue.

Europa A525

Smiling letter with wings: 50c, Standing on hand. 70c, Flying.

**2008, May 20**
**1234-1235** A525 Set of 2 4.00 4.00

Tourism A526

Designs: No. 1236, A, Bridge, Diekirch, and city arms. No. 1237, A, Building, Leudelange, and city arms. No. 1238, A, Rindschleiden Church, Wahl, vert.

**2008, May 20** ***Perf. 11½***
**1236-1238** A526 Set of 3 4.75 4.75

Diekirch, 125th anniv., Leudelange, 150th anniv. Nos. 1236-1238 each sold for 50c on day of issue.

Medico-social League, Cent. — A527

**2008, Sept. 30 Litho.** ***Perf. 13¾***
**1239** A527 A multi 1.40 1.40

Sold for 50c on day of issue.

Agricultural Technical School, Ettelbruck, 125th Anniv. A528

**2008, Sept. 30**
**1240** A528 A multi 1.40 1.40

Sold for 50c on day of issue.

Federation of Popular Education Associations, Cent. — A529

**2008, Sept. 30** ***Perf. 13x13¼***
**1241** A529 A multi 1.40 1.40

Sold for 50c on day of issue.

Natl. League for the Protection of Animals, Cent. A530

**2008, Sept. 30**
**1242** A530 A multi 1.40 1.40

Sold for 50c on day of issue.

NATO Maintenance and Supply Agency, 50th Anniv. — A531

**2008, Sept. 30**
**1243** A531 70c multi 2.00 2.00

Greetings A532

Winning art from children's stamp design contest by: 70c, A. Wainer. €1, S. Rauschenberger.

**2008, Sept. 30** ***Perf. 11½***
**1244-1245** A532 Set of 2 4.75 4.75

A533

A534

Different shapes of colored background lines with "ATR" at: No. 1246, LR. No. 1247, UL. No. 1248, LL. No. 1249, UR.
Different shapes of colored background lines with "A" at: No. 1250, LL. No. 1251, UL. No. 1252, LR. No. 1253, UR.

### Coil Stamps

***Serpentine Die Cut 11***

**2008, Sept. 30 Self-Adhesive**

| | | | | |
|---|---|---|---|---|
| **1246** | A533 ATR blue | | .70 | .70 |
| **1247** | A533 ATR purple | | .70 | .70 |
| **1248** | A533 ATR green | | .70 | .70 |
| **1249** | A533 ATR red | | .70 | .70 |
| *a.* | Vert. strip of 4, #1246-1249 | | 2.80 | |
| **1250** | A534 A multi | | 1.40 | 1.40 |
| **1251** | A534 A multi | | 1.40 | 1.40 |
| **1252** | A534 A multi | | 1.40 | 1.40 |
| **1253** | A534 A multi | | 1.40 | 1.40 |
| *a.* | Vert. strip of 4, #1250-1253 | | 5.60 | |
| | *Nos. 1246-1253 (8)* | | 8.40 | 8.40 |

On day of issue, Nos. 1246-1249 each sold for 25c, Nos. 1250-1253, for 50c.

Happiness — A535

No. 1254: a, Bowling pins, denomination over red violet. b, Gift, denomination over yellow green. c, Wrapped candies, denomination over green. d, Wrapped candies, denomination over blue. e, Gift, denomination over green. f, Bowling pins, denomination over yellow green. g, Dice, "A" over red violet. h, Drum and sticks, "A" over yellow green. i, Four-leaf clovers, "A" over green. j, Four-leaf clovers, "A" over blue. k, Drum and sticks, "A" over green. l, Dice, "A" over yellow green.

***Die Cut Perf. 10 on 3 Sides***

**2008, Sept. 30 Self-Adhesive**

| | | | |
|---|---|---|---|
| **1254** | Booklet pane of 12 | 12.00 | |
| *a.-f.* | A535 20c Any single | .55 | .55 |
| *g.-l.* | A535 A Any single | 1.40 | 1.40 |

Nos. 1254g-1254l each sold for 50c on day of issue.

New Courthouse of Court of Justice of the European Communities — A536

**2008, Dec. 2 Litho.** ***Perf. 14x13¼***
**1255** A536 70c multi 1.90 1.90

Election of Holy Roman Emperor Henry VII (c. 1269-1313), 700th Anniv. — A537

**2008, Dec. 2** ***Perf. 13¼x13***
**1256** A537 €1 multi 2.60 2.60

Introduction of the Euro, 10th Anniv. — A538

**2009, Mar. 17 Litho.** ***Perf. 12½***
**1257** A538 A multi 1.25 1.25

No. 1257 sold for 50c on day of issue.

Luxembourg Aero Club, Cent. — A539

New Airport Terminal A540

No. 1258: a, Satellite, airplane, hang glider, left half of balloon. b, Right half of balloon, glider, parachutist, jet plane.

**2009, Mar. 17** ***Perf. 11½***
**1258** A539 50c Horiz. pair, #a-b 2.60 2.60
**1259** A540 90c multi 2.25 2.25

Natl. Federation of Fire Fighters, 125th Anniv. A541

Designs: 20c, Modern fire truck. A, Fire fighter rescuing child. €2, Antique fire truck.

**2008, Mar. 17** ***Perf. 13x13¼***
**1260-1262** A541 Set of 3 7.00 7.00

No. 1261 sold for 50c on day of issue.

Postmen's Federation, Cent. A542

General Confederation of the Civil Service, Cent. — A543

Natl. Federation of Railroad and Transportation Workers, Cent. — A544

**2009, Mar. 17** ***Perf. 14x13¼***

| | | | |
|---|---|---|---|
| **1263** | A542 50c multi | 1.25 | 1.25 |
| **1264** | A543 A multi | 1.25 | 1.25 |
| **1265** | A544 A multi | 1.25 | 1.25 |
| | *Nos. 1263-1265 (3)* | 3.75 | 3.75 |

On day of issue, Nos. 1264-1265 each sold for 50c.

June 7 European Elections — A545

**2009, May 12 Litho.** ***Perf. 13***
**1266** A545 50c multi 1.40 1.40

National Research Fund, 10th Anniv. — A546

**2009, May 12** ***Perf. 13½***
**1267** A546 A multi 1.40 1.40

No. 1267 sold for 50c on day of issue.

Children's Houses, 125th Anniv. — A547

**2009, May 12** ***Perf. 12½***
**1268** A547 A multi 1.40 1.40

No. 1268 sold for 50c on day of issue.

Europa A548

Designs: 50c, Father and child watching comet. 70c, Galileo, telescope, planets.

**2009, May 12** ***Perf. 13½***
**1269-1270** A548 Set of 2 3.25 3.25

Intl. Year of Astronomy.

Personalized Stamps — A549

Stripe color: A, Red. A Europe, Blue.

**2009, May 12** ***Perf. 11¾x11½***
**Stamp + Label**

**1271-1272** A549 Set of 2 3.25 3.25

On day of issue, No. 1271 sold for 50c; No. 1272, 70c. Labels bearing text "PostMusée" and pictures are generic and sold for these prices. Labels could be personalized for an additional fee.

Famous People A550

Designs: 70c, Foni Tissen (1909-75), painter. 90c, Charles Bernhoeft (1859-1933), photographer. €1, Henri Tudor (1859-1928), electrical engineer.

**Litho. & Engr.**

**2009, May 12** ***Perf. 13½***
**1273-1275** A550 Set of 3 7.00 7.00

Vianden Castle A551

***Perf. 13¼x12¾***

**2009, Sept. 16** **Litho.**
**1276** A551 70c multi 2.00 2.00

Louis Braille (1809-52), Educator of the Blind — A552

**Litho. & Embossed**

**2009, Sept. 16** ***Perf. 13¼x13***
**1277** A552 90c multi 2.60 2.60

Railroads in Luxembourg, 150th Anniv. — A553

Designs: 50c, Modern electric train. €1, Older electric train. €3, Steam locomotive.

**2009, Sept. 16** **Litho.** ***Perf. 12½***
**1278-1280** A553 Set of 3 13.00 13.00

Souvenir Sheet

Luxembourg Federation of Philatelic Societies, 75th Anniv. — A554

No. 1281: a, Luxembourg #198. b, Gate of Three Towers.

**Litho. & Embossed**

**2009, Sept. 16** ***Perf. 13¾x14***

| | | | | |
|---|---|---|---|---|
| **1281** | A554 | Sheet of 2 | 3.50 | 3.50 |
| *a.* | | 50c multi | 1.50 | 1.50 |
| *b.* | | 70c multi | 2.00 | 2.00 |

Johannes Gutenberg (c. 1390-1468), Inventor of Movable Type Presses A555

Website Addresses and Movable Type — A556

**2009, Dec. 1** **Litho.** ***Perf. 13¼x13½***
**1282** A555 50c multi 1.50 1.50
**1283** A556 70c multi 2.10 2.10

See Switzerland No. 1344.

Schengen Convention, 25th Anniv. — A557

**2010, Mar. 16** **Litho.** ***Perf. 13½x13***
**1284** A557 70c multi 1.90 1.90

Luxembourg Pavilion, Expo 2010, Shanghai — A558

**2010, Mar. 16** ***Perf. 14x13½***
**1285** A558 90c multi 2.50 2.50

Eisch Valley Castles — A559

No. 1286 — Various castles with country name at: a, UL. b, LR.

***Serpentine Die Cut 12¼x13¼***

**2010, Mar. 16** **Self-Adhesive**

| | | | | |
|---|---|---|---|---|
| **1286** | | Horiz. pair | 4.00 | |
| *a.-b.* | A559 | A Either single | 1.90 | 1.90 |

On day of issue, Nos. 1286a-1287a each sold for 70c.

Countdown 2010 — A560

Designs: 70c, Arnica montana. €1, Mussels.

**2010, Mar. 16** ***Perf. 11½***
**1287-1288** A560 Set of 2 4.75 4.75

A561

Royalty — A562

Designs: 50c, Grand Duke Henri. €1, Grand Duchess Charlotte (1896-1985).

€3, Grand Duke Henri and Grand Duchess Maria Teresa.

**2010, Mar. 16** ***Perf. 11½***
**1289-1290** A561 Set of 2 4.25 4.25

**Souvenir Sheet**

**1291** A562 €3 multi 8.25 8.25

Grand Duke Henri's accession to the throne, 10th anniv. (No. 1289).

Marriage of John of Luxembourg and Elizabeth of Bohemia, 700th Anniv. — A563

**Photo. & Engr.**

**2010, June 16** ***Perf. 11¾x11¼***
**1292** A563 70c multi 1.75 1.75

Accession to the throne of Bohemia by the House of Luxembourg. See Czech Republic No. 3457.

Europa — A564

Designs: 50c, Child and dragon reading book. 70c, Girl with lasso riding book.

**2010, June 16** **Litho.** ***Perf. 13½***
**1293-1294** A564 Set of 2 3.00 3.00

Outdoor Activities — A565

Designs: No. 1295, A, Motorcycling. No. 1296, A Europe, Camping.

**2010, June 16** ***Perf. 13½x13***
**1295-1296** A565 Set of 2 3.00 3.00

On day of issue, No. 1295 sold for 50c, and No. 1296 sold for 70c. See Nos. 1337-1338.

Souvenir Sheet

Philalux 2011 Intl. Philatelic Exhibition, Luxembourg — A566

No. 1297 — Various sites in Luxembourg: a, 50c (38x38mm). b, 70c, (38x38mm). c, €3, (60x38mm).

***Perf. 13¾, 13¼x13¾ (#1297c)***

**2010, June 16**

| | | | | |
|---|---|---|---|---|
| **1297** | A566 | Sheet of 3 | 10.50 | 10.50 |
| *a.* | | 50c multi | 1.25 | 1.25 |
| *b.* | | 70c multi | 1.75 | 1.75 |
| *c.* | | €3 multi | 7.50 | 7.50 |

Souvenir Sheet

Superjhemp, Comic Strip by Lucien Czuga — A567

No. 1298: a, Bernie the Dog. b, Man smoking pipe. c, Woman, vert. d, Superjhemp. e, Man with glasses, vert.

***Serpentine Die Cut 12¼***

**2010, June 16** **Self-Adhesive**

| | | | | |
|---|---|---|---|---|
| **1298** | A567 | Sheet of 5 | 6.25 | 6.25 |
| *a.-e.* | | A Any single | 1.25 | 1.25 |

On day of issue, Nos. 1298a-1298e each sold for 50c.

A568

Winning Art in Children's "Fight Against Poverty" Stamp Design Contest
A569

**2010, Sept. 27 Litho. *Perf. 11½***

**1299** A568 A multi 1.25 1.25
**1300** A569 A Europe multi 1.75 1.75

On day of issue No. 1299 sold for 50c and No. 1300 sold for 70c.

Famous People
A570

Designs: 70c, Anne Beffort (1880-1966), educator and writer. 90c, Jean Soupert (1834-1910), rose cultivator. €1, Nicolas Frantz (1899-1985), cyclist.

**Litho. & Engr.**

**2010, Sept. 27 *Perf. 13½***

**1301-1303** A570 Set of 3 6.75 6.75

Bagatelle Rose — A571

Bona Rose — A572

Bordeaux Rose — A573

Reine Marguerite d'Italie Rose — A574

Souvenir de Maria de Zayas Rose — A575

Clotilde Rose — A576

Prince Jean de Luxembourg Rose — A577

Pierre Watine Rose — A578

Ivan Misson Rose — A579

William Notting Rose — A580

***Serpentine Die Cut 9¾***

**2010, Sept. 27 Litho.**

**Self-Adhesive**

| | | | |
|---|---|---|---|
| **1304** | Booklet pane of 10 | 12.50 | |
| *a.* | A571 A multi | 1.25 | 1.25 |
| *b.* | A572 A multi | 1.25 | 1.25 |
| *c.* | A573 A multi | 1.25 | 1.25 |
| *d.* | A574 A multi | 1.25 | 1.25 |
| *e.* | A575 A multi | 1.25 | 1.25 |
| *f.* | A576 A multi | 1.25 | 1.25 |
| *g.* | A577 A multi | 1.25 | 1.25 |
| *h.* | A578 A multi | 1.25 | 1.25 |
| *i.* | A579 A multi | 1.25 | 1.25 |
| *j.* | A580 A multi | 1.25 | 1.25 |

Nos. 1304a-1304j each sold for 50c on day of issue.

Luxembourg Maritime Cluster — A581

No. 1305 — Ships with lion emblem at: a, Left. b, Right.

**2010, Dec. 7 Litho. *Perf. 11½***

**1305** A581 A Horiz. pair, #a-b 4.75 4.75

Nos. 1305a and 1305b each sold for 85c on day of issue.

European Year of Volunteering
A582

**2011, Mar. 15 *Perf. 13¼x13***

**1306** A582 A multi 1.75 1.75

No. 1306 sold for 60c on day of issue.

Royalty
A583

Designs: 85c, Prince Guillaume, 30th birthday. €1.10, Grand Duke Jean, 90th birthday.

**2011, Mar. 15 *Perf. 11½***

**1307-1308** A583 Set of 2 5.50 5.50

Anniversaries
A584

Designs: No. 1309, 60c, Luxembourg Federation of Quilleurs (nine-pin bowling), 50th anniv. No. 1310, 60c, Amnesty International, 50th anniv. No. 1311, 60c, Stamp Day, 75th anniv.

**2011, Mar. 15**

**1309-1311** A584 Set of 3 5.00 5.00

Europa
A585

Designs: 60c, Forest. 80c, Hills.

**2011, May 17 Litho. *Perf. 13½***

**1312-1313** A585 Set of 2 4.25 4.25

Intl. Year of Forests.

Viticulture — A586

Designs: 60c, Sun with grapes, wine glass and bottle. 85c, Cork of Crémant de Luxembourg sparkling wine bottle.

**2011, May 17 *Perf. 11½***

**1314-1315** A586 Set of 2 4.25 4.25

Federation of Viticulture Associations of Luxembourg, cent. (No. 1314), Crémant de Luxembourg, 20th anniv. (No. 1315).

Personalized Stamps — A587

Denominations: 60c, 85c, vert.

***Perf. 11¼x11½, 11½x11¼***

**2011, May 17 Self-Adhesive**

**1316-1317** A587 Set of 2 4.25 4.25

Vignettes showing picture and "Mäi Moment / Meng Photo / Meng Post" text are generic and sold at their face values. Vignettes could be personalized for an additional fee.

Miniature Sheet

The Last Knight, Comic Strip by Lucien Czuga and Andy Genen — A588

No. 1318: a, Dragon. b, Knight wearing sunglasses, horiz. c, Man, horiz. d, Cat.

***Serpentine Die Cut 12¼***

**2011, May 17 Self-Adhesive**

**1318** A588 Sheet of 4 7.00
*a.-d.* A Any single 1.75 1.75

On day of issue, Nos. 1318a-1318d each sold for 60c.

Luxembourg Consumers Union, 50th Anniv. — A589

**2011, Sept. 27 *Perf. 11½***

**1319** A589 60c multi 1.75 1.75

Campaign Against AIDS, 30th Anniv.
A590

**2011, Sept. 27**

**1320** A590 60c multi 1.75 1.75

Cercle Cité, Luxembourg
A591

**2011, Sept. 27**

**1321** A591 A multi 1.75 1.75

No. 1321 sold for 60c on day of issue.

Franz Liszt (1811-86), Composer
A592

**2011, Sept. 27 *Perf. 14¼x14¾***

**1322** A592 85c multi 2.40 2.40

Chemin de la Corniche, Luxembourg — A593

**2011, Sept. 27 *Perf. 11½***

**1323** A593 85c multi 2.40 2.40

Post Checks, Cent. — A594

**2011, Dec. 6 Litho. *Perf. 11½x11¾***

**1324** A594 60c multi 1.60 1.60

Souvenir Sheet

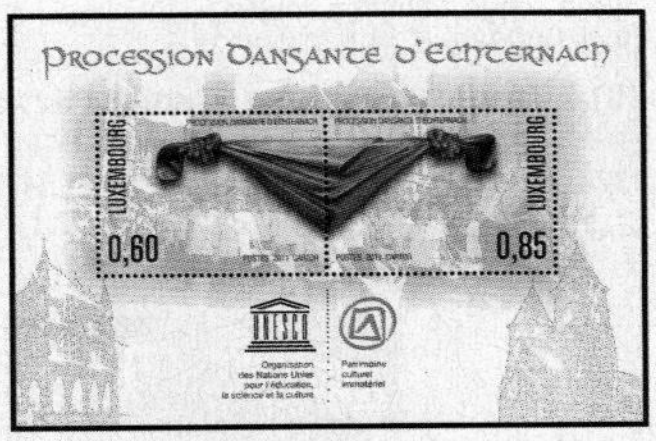


Echternacht Hopping Procession (UNESCO Intangible Heritage) — A595

No. 1325 — Procession participants and: a, Left side of scarf. b, Right side of scarf.

**2011, Dec. 6** ***Perf. 14***

| | | | | |
|---|---|---|---|---|
| **1325** | A595 | Sheet of 2 | 4.00 | 4.00 |
| *a.* | | 60c multi | 1.60 | 1.60 |
| *b.* | | 85c multi | 2.40 | 2.40 |

Architecture — A596

No. 1326 — Designs: a, Eislek. b, Réidener Streech. c, Iechternacher Streech. d, Minett.

***Serpentine Die Cut 12½***

**2011, Dec. 6** **Self-Adhesive**

| | | | | |
|---|---|---|---|---|
| **1326** | | Booklet pane of 4 | 6.50 | |
| *a.-d.* | A596 | A Any single | 1.60 | 1.60 |
| | | Complete booklet, 2 #1326 | 13.00 | |

Nos. 1326a-1326d each sold for 60c on day of issue.

Luxembourg Amateur Radio Society, 75th Anniv. — A597

**2012, Mar. 13** ***Perf. 11½***

**1327** A597 60c multi 1.60 1.60

Grand Ducal Institute Arts and Letters Section, 50th Anniv. A598

**2012, Mar. 13**

**1328** A598 60c multi 1.60 1.60

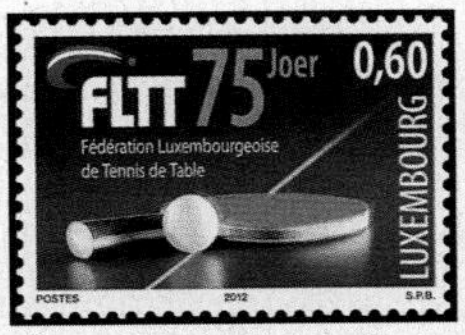


Luxembourg Table Tennis Federation, 75th Anniv. — A599

**2012, Mar. 13**

**1329** A599 60c multi 1.60 1.60

Introduction of Euro Currency, 10th Anniv. A600

**Litho. & Embossed**

**2012, Mar. 13** ***Perf. 13***

**1330** A600 85c multi 2.25 2.25

Natl. Institute of Statistics and Economic Studies, 50th Anniv. A601

**2012, May 15** **Litho.** ***Perf. 12½***

**1331** A601 60c multi 1.60 1.60

Luxembourg Olympic Committee, Cent. — A602

2012 Summer Olympics, London A603

**2012, May 15** ***Perf. 14¼x14¾***

| | | | | |
|---|---|---|---|---|
| **1332** | A602 | 60c multi | 1.60 | 1.60 |
| **1333** | A603 | €1.10 multi | 3.00 | 3.00 |

Europa A604

Luxembourg tourism website address and various Luxembourg buildings and monuments: 60c, 85c.

**2012, May 15** ***Perf. 13½***

**1334-1335** A604 Set of 2 4.00 4.00

Miniature Sheet

Characters from Mil's Adventures, Comic Strip by Gab Weis — A605

No. 1336 — Various unnamed characters with country name in: a, Red violet (Mil). b, Green. c, Orange. d, Lilac, vert. e, Red violet (2 characters), vert.

***Serpentine Die Cut 12¼***

**2012, May 15** **Self-Adhesive**

| | | | | |
|---|---|---|---|---|
| **1336** | A605 | Sheet of 5 | 8.00 | |
| *a.-e.* | | A Any single | 1.60 | 1.60 |

On day of issue, Nos. 1336a-1336e each sold for 60c.

**Outdoor Activities Type of 2010**

Designs: 60c, Paragliding. 85c, Diving.

**2012, Sept. 25** ***Perf. 13¼x13***

**1337-1338** A565 Set of 2 3.75 3.75

A606

Potable Water A607

**2012, Sept. 25** ***Perf. 11½***

| | | | | |
|---|---|---|---|---|
| **1339** | A606 | 60c multi | 1.50 | 1.50 |
| **1340** | A607 | 85c multi | 2.25 | 2.25 |

Architecture A608

Paintings by Christian Frantzen of: €1.20, Footbridge, Esch-sur-Alzette. €2.20, Belval-Université Station, Esch-sur-Alzette. €4, Pfaffenthal-Upper Town Link, Luxembourg.

**2012, Sept. 25**

**1341-1343** A608 Set of 3 19.00 19.00

Wedding of Prince Guillaume and Countess Stéphanie de Lannoy A609

Designs: 60c, Couple. 85c, Couple, diff.

**2012, Sept. 25** ***Perf. 13½***

**1344** A609 60c multi 1.50 1.50

**Souvenir Sheet**

| | | | | |
|---|---|---|---|---|
| **1345** | | Sheet of 2, #1344, 1345a | 3.75 | 3.75 |
| *a.* | A609 | 85c multi | 2.25 | 2.25 |

Souvenir Sheet

Wedding of Prince Guillaume and Countess Stéphanie de Lannoy — A610

**2012, Oct. 20** ***Perf. 13¼***

**1346** A610 €4 multi 10.50 10.50

European Court of Justice, 60th Anniv. A611

**2012, Dec. 4** ***Perf. 12½***

**1347** A611 85c maroon & lt blue 2.25 2.25

European Year of Citizens A612

**2013, Mar. 12** ***Perf. 13¼x13***

**1348** A612 60c multi 1.60 1.60

Grand Duke Adolphe Union, 150th Anniv. A613

**2013, Mar. 12** ***Perf. 11½***

**1349** A613 60c multi 1.60 1.60

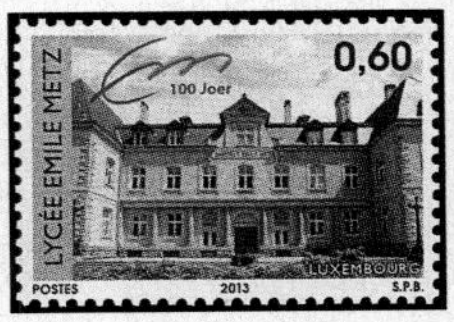


Emile Metz Private Technical High School, Cent. A614

**2013, Mar. 12**

**1350** A614 60c multi 1.60 1.60

Round Table Luxembourg, 50th Anniv. — A615

**2013, Mar. 12**

**1351** A615 60c multi 1.60 1.60

Holy Roman Emperor Henry VII (c.1275-1313) — A616

**2013, Mar. 12**
**1352** A616 €1.10 multi 3.00 3.00

Famous Men — A617

Designs: No. 1353, 60c, Nicolas Adames (1813-87), theologian. No. 1354, 60c, Putty Stein (1888-1955), composer.

**2013, May 2**
**1353-1354** A617 Set of 2 3.25 3.25

Europa A618

Postal vehicles: 60c, Citroen 2 CV AZU. 85c, Renault Kangoo.

**2013, May 2** ***Perf. 13x13¼***
**1355-1356** A618 Set of 2 3.75 3.75

15th Games of the Small States of Europe, Luxembourg — A619

**2013, May 2** ***Perf. 11½***
**1357** A619 Horiz. pair 3.25 3.25
*a.-b.* 60c Either single 1.60 1.60

Souvenir Sheet

100th Tour de France Bicycle Race — A620

**2013, May 2** ***Perf. 12***
**1358** A620 €4 multi 10.50 10.50

Completion of 11th Turbine for Société Electrique de l'Our — A621

**2013, Sept. 24** ***Perf. 11½***
**1359** A621 60c multi 1.60 1.60

Wild Cats A622

Designs: 20c, Panthera tigris sumatrae. 30c, Lynx lynx. 60c, Felis silvestris.

**2013, Sept. 24**
**1360-1362** A622 Set of 3 3.00 3.00

Souvenir Sheet

Selection of "The Family of Man" Photographic Exhibition to UNESCO Memory of the World Register — A623

No. 1363: a, Photograph of crowd. b, Self-portrait of Edward Steichen.

**2013, Sept. 24** ***Perf. 13¾x14***
**1363** A623 Sheet of 2 4.00 4.00
*a.* 60c blue & black 1.60 1.60
*b.* 85c blue & black 2.25 2.25

A624

A625

A626

A627

***Serpentine Die Cut 11***
**2013, Sept. 24** **Self-Adhesive**
**Coil Stamps**
**1364** Vert. strip of 4 6.50
*a.* A624 (60c) multi 1.60 1.60
*b.* A625 (60c) multi 1.60 1.60
*c.* A626 (60c) multi 1.60 1.60
*d.* A627 (60c) multi 1.60 1.60

Moselle Valley — A628

No. 1365 — Various buildings and: a, Bridge over river in foreground. b, Moselle River running through town.

***Serpentine Die Cut 12½x13½***
**2013, Sept. 24** **Self-Adhesive**
**1365** A628 Horiz. pair 4.50
*a.-b.* (85c) Either single 2.25 2.25

Pierre Werner (1913-2002), Prime Minister — A629

**2013, Dec. 3** **Litho.** ***Perf. 11½***
**1366** A629 60c multi 1.75 1.75

Mushrooms A630

Designs: No. 1367, Pezize orangée. No. 1368, Bolet bai. No. 1369, Polypore versicolore. No. 1370, Amanite "tue-mouche." No. 1371, Vesse de loup perlée.

***Serpentine Die Cut 12¼***
**2013, Dec. 3** **Litho.**
**Booklet Stamps**
**Self-Adhesive**
**1367** A630 (60c) multi 1.75 1.75
**1368** A630 (60c) multi 1.75 1.75
**1369** A630 (60c) multi 1.75 1.75
**1370** A630 (60c) multi 1.75 1.75
**1371** A630 (60c) multi 1.75 1.75
*a.* Booklet pane of 10, 2 each #1367-1371 17.50
*Nos. 1367-1371 (5)* 8.75 8.75

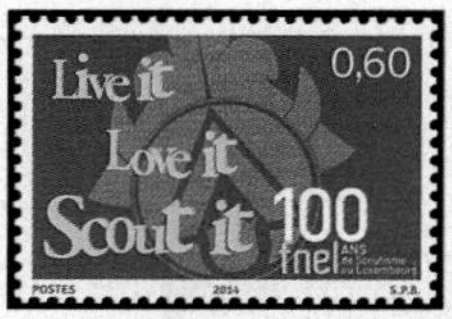


Scouting in Luxembourg, Cent. — A631

**2014, Mar. 11** **Litho.** ***Perf. 11½***
**1372** A631 60c multi 1.75 1.75

Primary Schools Sports League, 50th Anniv. A632

**2014, Mar. 11** **Litho.** ***Perf. 11½***
**1373** A632 60c multi 1.75 1.75

Ligue HMC, 50th Anniv. A633

**2014, Mar. 11** **Litho.** ***Perf. 11½***
**1374** A633 60c multi 1.75 1.75

Luxembourg Red Cross, Cent. — A634

**2014, Mar. 11** **Litho.** ***Perf. 11½***
**1375** A634 60c multi 1.75 1.75

Souvenir Sheet

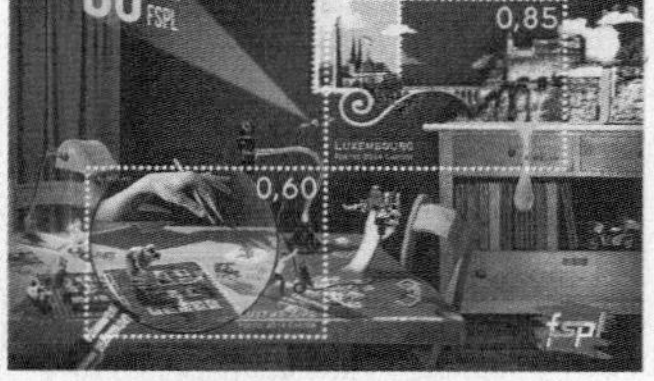


Luxembourg Federation of Philatelic Societies, 80th Anniv. — A635

No. 1376: a, Magnifying glass, hand holding stamp tongs, children looking at stamps on stock page. b, Bridge, buildings.

**2014, Mar. 11** **Litho.** ***Perf. 13¾x14***
**Silk-Faced Paper**
**1376** A635 Sheet of 2 4.00 4.00
*a.* 60c multi 1.75 1.75
*b.* 85c multi 2.25 2.25

May 25, 2014 European Elections A636

**2014, May 8** **Litho.** ***Perf. 13¼x13***
**1377** A636 60c multi 1.75 1.75

First Public Recital of Lyrics to National Anthem, 150th Anniv. A637

Independence, 175th Anniv. — A638

**2014, May 8** **Litho.** ***Perf. 11½***
**1378** A637 60c multi 1.75 1.75
**1379** A638 60c multi 1.75 1.75

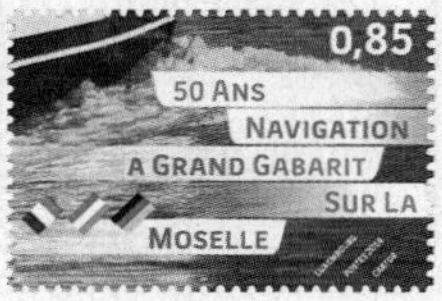


Moselle Commission, 50th Anniv. — A639

**2014, May 8** **Litho.** ***Perf. 13x13¼***
**1380** A639 85c multi 2.40 2.40

Europa A640

Various musicians: 60c, 85c.

**2014, May 8** **Litho.** ***Perf. 12½***
**1381-1382** A640 Set of 2 4.25 4.25

Souvenir Sheet

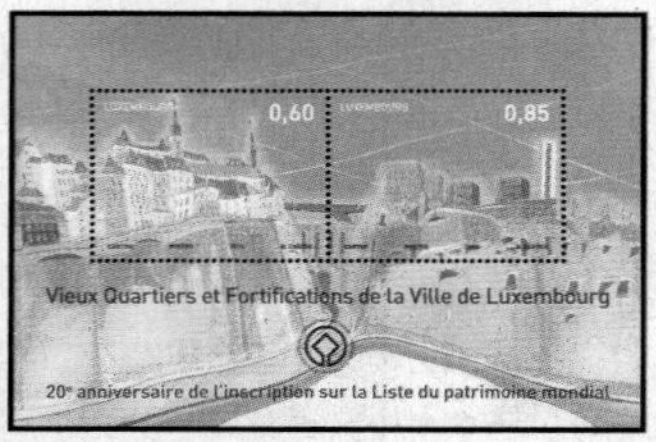


City of Luxembourg as UNESCO World Heritage Site, 20th Anniv. — A641

No. 1383 — Buildings and fortifications of Old City: a, 60c. b, 85c.

**2014, May 8** **Litho.** ***Perf. 13¾x14***
**1383** A641 Sheet of 2 4.25 4.25
*a.* 60c multi 1.75 1.75
*b.* 85c multi 2.40 2.40

German Invasion of Luxembourg, Cent. — A642

**2014, Sept. 23** **Litho.** ***Perf. 11½***
**1384** A642 60c multi 1.50 1.50

World War I, cent.

A643

Winning Designs in Children's Art Contest on Soil and the Environment A644

**2014, Sept. 23** **Litho.** ***Perf. 11½***
**1385** A643 60c multi 1.50 1.50
**1386** A644 85c multi 2.25 2.25

Famous People — A645

Designs: No. 1387, 60c, Samuel Hirsch (1809-89), rabbi. No. 1388, 60c, Nikolaus Hein (1889-1969), writer. No. 1389, 60c, Marie Speyer (1880-1914), educator.

**2014, Sept. 23** **Litho.** ***Perf. 11½***
**1387-1389** A645 Set of 3 4.50 4.50

Vegetables — A646

Designs: 85c, Tragopogon porrifolius. €1, Pisum sativum. €1.10, Cichorium intybus.

**2014, Sept. 23** **Litho.** ***Perf. 11½***
**1390-1392** A646 Set of 3 7.50 7.50

See Nos. 1410-1412, 1437-1439.

Accession to Throne of Grand Duke Jean, 50th Anniv. — A647

**2014, Dec. 2** **Litho.** ***Perf. 13¼x13***
**1393** A647 (60c) multi 1.50 1.50

Grand Duke Henri — A648

**Litho. & Engr.**

**2015, Mar. 3** ***Perf. 13½x13***

**Panel Color**

**1394** A648 L green 1.40 1.40
**1395** A648 E blue 1.90 1.90
**1396** A648 M rose carmine 2.50 2.50
*Nos. 1394-1396 (3)* 5.80 5.80

On day of issue, Nos. 1394-1396 each sold for 60c, 85c and €1.10 respectively.

Organized Philately in Luxembourg, 125th Anniv. — A649

**2015, Mar. 3** **Litho.** ***Perf. 11½***
**1397** A649 60c multi 1.40 1.40

Order of Architects and Consulting Engineers, 25th Anniv. A650

**2015, Mar. 3** **Litho.** ***Perf. 11½***
**1398** A650 60c multi 1.40 1.40

Omega 90, 25th Anniv. — A651

**2015, Mar. 3** **Litho.** ***Perf. 11½***
**1399** A651 60c multi 1.40 1.40

Creation of Grand Duchy of Luxembourg, 200th Anniv. — A652

**2015, Mar. 3** **Litho.** ***Perf. 11½***
**1400** A652 60c multi 1.40 1.40

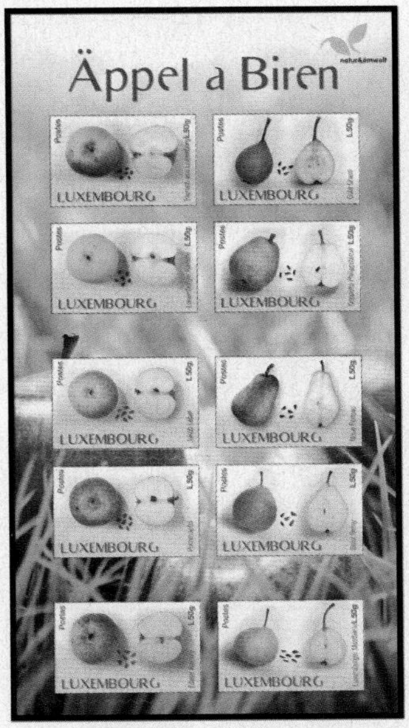


Fruit — A653

No. 1401 — Apple and pear varieties: a, Triumph aus Luxemburg apples. b, Gute Graue pears. c, Luxemburger Renette apples. d, Doppelte Philippsbirne pears. e, Jakob Lebel apples. f, Neue Poiteau pears. g, Porzenapfel apples. h, Saint Remy pears. i, Eifeler Rambur apples. j, Luxemburger Mostbirne pears.

***Serpentine Die Cut 9¾***

**2015, Mar. 3** **Litho.**

**Self-Adhesive**

**1401** A653 Booklet pane of 10 14.00
*a.-j.* L Any single 1.40 1.40

On day of issue, Nos. 1401a-1401j each sold for 60c.

Europa — A654

Designs: 60c, Building blocks. 85c, Doll and doll house furniture.

**2015, May 5** **Litho.** ***Perf. 13½***
**1402-1403** A654 Set of 2 3.25 3.25

Famous Men — A655

Designs: No. 1404, 60c, Claus Cito (1882-1965), sculptor. No. 1405, 60c, Robert Krieps (1922-90), politician. No. 1406, 60c, René Engelmann (1880-1915), writer.

**2015, May 5** **Litho.** ***Perf. 11½***
**1404-1406** A655 Set of 3 4.25 4.25

Miniature Sheet

End of World War II, 70th Anniv. — A656

No. 1407: a, Railroad car and concentration camp gate (40x30mm). b, Star of David, triangles and "70" (40x30mm). c, Luxembourger in German uniform holding Luxembourg flag (30x30mm). d, Civil courage (30x30mm). e, Blindfolded person behind barbed wire (40x30mm). f, Resistance (40x30mm).

**2015, May 5** **Litho.** ***Perf. 12***
**1407** A656 Sheet of 6 8.50 8.50
*a.-f.* 60c Any single 1.40 1.40

A657

Luxembourg Presidency of the Council of the European Union — A658

**2015, July 1** **Litho.** ***Perf. 12½x12***

**Self-Adhesive**

**1408** A657 (60c) multi 1.40 1.40
**1409** A658 (85c) multi 1.90 1.90

**Vegetables Type of 2014**

Root vegetables: 20c, Pastinaca sativa. 25c, Apium graveolens. 35c, Beta vulgaris.

**2015, Sept. 22** **Litho.** ***Perf. 11½***
**1410-1412** A646 Set of 3 1.90 1.90

Luxembourg No. 1 — A659

**2015, Sept. 22** **Litho.** ***Perf. 15x14½***
**1413** A659 70c blk & gold 1.60 1.60

Penny Black, 175th anniv.

Grand Duke Henri and Grand Duchess Maria Teresa — A660

**Litho. & Engr.**

**2015, Sept. 22** ***Perf. 13***
**1414** A660 70c multi 1.60 1.60

Opening of Wiltheim Wing of National Museum of History and Art — A661

Designs: 70c, Museum. 95c, Silver tea caddy made by Johann Michael Kutzer (1700-60). €1.30, Helios, ceramic sculpture by Villeroy & Boch.

**Litho., Litho. & Embossed (95c, €1.30)**

**2015, Sept. 22** *Perf. 13x13¼*
**1415-1417** A661 Set of 3 6.75 6.75

Nature Reserves — A662

Designs: No. 1418, (70c), Mellerdall Nature Reserve. No. 1419, (70c), Oewersauer Nature Reserve. No. 1420, (70c), Our Nature Reserve.

**2015, Sept. 22 Litho.** *Perf. 12¾*
**1418-1420** A662 Set of 3 4.75 4.75

Nos. 1418-1420 are each inscribed "L50g."

Flowers — A663

No. 1421: a, Maargréitchen (daisy). b, Karblumm (cornflower). c, Deschtel (thistle). d, Feierblumm (red poppy).

***Die Cut Perf. 13x12¾***

**2015, Dec. 1 Coil Stamps Litho.**

**Self-Adhesive**

**1421** Vert. strip of 4 3.00
*a.-d.* A663 (35c) Any single .75 .75

Nos. 1421a-1421d are each inscribed "ATR 50g."

Opening of Belval Campus Headquarters of University of Luxembourg A664

**2016, Mar. 3 Litho.** *Perf. 14*

**Foil-faced Paper**

**1422** A664 70c multi 1.50 1.50

Port of Mertert, 50th Anniv. A665

Luxembourg Maritime Register, 25th Anniv. — A666

Center for Equal Treatment, 10th Anniv. A667

**2016, Mar. 3 Litho.** *Perf. 11½*
**1423** A665 70c multi 1.50 1.50
**1424** A666 70c multi 1.50 1.50
**1425** A667 70c multi 1.50 1.50
*Nos. 1423-1425 (3)* 4.50 4.50

Royalty — A668

No. 1426: a, Grand Duchess Maria Teresa. b, Grand Duchess Maria Teresa, Prince Sébastien, Princess Alexandra.

**2016, Mar. 3 Litho.** *Perf. 13¼x13*
**1426** A668 Horiz. pair 3.00 3.00
*a.-b.* 70c Either single 1.50 1.50

2016 Summer Olympics, Rio de Janeiro — A669

**Litho. & Embossed**

**2016, May 10** *Perf. 13¾x13½*
**1427** A669 70c multi 1.60 1.60

A670

Europa A671

**2016, May 10 Litho.** *Perf. 11½*
**1428** A670 70c multi 1.60 1.60
**1429** A671 95c multi 2.10 2.10

Think Green Issue.

Famous Men — A672

Designs: No. 1430, 70c, Marcel Noppeney (1877-1966), President of Society of Francophone Luxembourgian Writers. No. 1431, 70c, Joseph Hackin (1886-1941), archaeologist. No. 1432, 70c, Jean Jacoby (1891-1936), artist.

**2016, May 10 Litho.** *Perf. 11½*
**1430-1432** A672 Set of 3 4.75 4.75

Meng.post.lu Website for Personalized Stamps, 10th Anniv. — A673

Pets: 70c, Cat named Margot. 95c, Dog named Goethe. €1.30, Cat named Mäischen.

**2016, May 10 Litho.** *Perf. 11¼*

**Self-Adhesive**

**1433-1435** A673 Set of 3 6.75 6.75

**Souvenir Sheet**

Passage Through Luxembourg of Thurn and Taxis Postal Route, 500th Anniv. — A674

**Litho. & Embossed**

**2016, May 10** *Perf. 11½*
**1436** A674 €4 multi + label 9.00 9.00

**Vegetables Type of 2014**

Designs: 95c, Cucumis sativus. €1.30, Phaseolus vulgaris. €2, Allium cepa var. proliferum.

**2016, Sept. 13 Litho.** *Perf. 11½*
**1437-1439** A646 Set of 3 9.50 9.50

Jesus Christ and Virgin Mary, by Albrecht Bouts (c. 1451-1549) — A675

**2016, Sept. 13 Litho.** *Perf. 11½*
**1440** A675 70c multi 1.60 1.60

Luxembourg National Museum of History and Art exhibition of paintings by Bouts.

Election of the Virgin Mary as Patroness of Luxembourg, 350th Anniv. — A676

**2016, Sept. 13 Engr.** *Perf. 13*
**1441** A676 70c multi 1.60 1.60

No. 1441 was printed in sheets of 4. See Vatican City No. 1631.

Grand Duchess Charlotte Bridge (Red Bridge), 50th Anniv. — A677

**2016, Sept. 13 Litho.** *Perf. 12*
**1442** A677 70c multi 1.60 1.60

Spring in the Ostling A678

**2016, Sept. 13 Litho.** *Perf. 11½*
**1443** A678 95c multi 2.25 2.25

Biodiversity A679

Winning designs in children's stamp design contest: 70c, Woodpecker, by Yann Klees. 95c, Wolf, by Christine Guirsch, horiz.

***Perf. 14x14¾, 14¾x14***

**2016, Sept. 13 Litho.**
**1444-1445** A679 Set of 2 3.75 3.75

A680

A681

New Emblem for Luxembourg A682

**2016, Oct. 10 Litho.** *Perf. 12½x12*

**Self-Adhesive**

**1446** A680 70c multi 1.60 1.60
**1447** A681 95c multi 2.10 2.10
**1448** A682 €1.30 multi 3.00 3.00
*Nos. 1446-1448 (3)* 6.70 6.70

Museums A683

Designs: No. 1449, Steam locomotive, Minett Park, Differdange. No. 1450, Playing cards, Kulturhuef Printing Museum, Grevenmacher. No. 1451, Carriage, Rural and Artisanal Museum, Peppange. No. 1452, Slate, hammer and pick, Slate Museum, Haut-Martelange. No. 1453, Airplane, Luxembourg Aviation Museum, Mondorf-les-Bains.

***Die Cut Perf. 11½***

**2016, Dec. 6** **Litho.**

**Booklet Stamps**
**Self-Adhesive**

**1449** A683 70c multi 1.50 1.50
**1450** A683 70c multi 1.50 1.50
**1451** A683 70c multi 1.50 1.50
**1452** A683 70c multi 1.50 1.50
**1453** A683 70c multi 1.50 1.50
*a.* Booklet pane of 10, 2 each #1449-1453 15.00
*Nos. 1449-1453 (5)* 7.50 7.50

Josy Barthel (1927-92), Olympic Gold Medalist Runner A684

**2017, Mar. 7** **Litho.** ***Perf. 11½***
**1454** A684 70c multi 1.50 1.50

Fieldgen Private School, 125th Anniv. A685

Fifty-One International, 51st Anniv. — A686

Luxembourg Alzheimer Association, 30th Anniv. — A687

**2017, Mar. 7** **Litho.** ***Perf. 11½***
**1455** A685 70c multi 1.50 1.50
**1456** A686 70c multi 1.50 1.50
**1457** A687 70c multi 1.50 1.50
*Nos. 1455-1457 (3)* 4.50 4.50

Famous Men — A688

Designs: No. 1458, 70c, Jean Jules Linden (1817-98), botanist. No. 1459, 70c, Pierre Frieden (1892-1959), politician. No. 1460, 70c, Tony Bourg (1912-91), literature professor.

**2017, Mar. 7** **Litho.** ***Perf. 11½***
**1458-1460** A688 Set of 3 4.50 4.50

Souvenir Sheet

Apparition of the Virgin Mary at Fatima, Portugal, Cent. — A689

**2017, Mar. 7** **Litho.** ***Perf. 11¾x12***
**1461** A689 95c multi 2.00 2.00

See Poland No. 4277, Portugal No. 3888, Slovakia No. 759.

Treaty of London, 150th Anniv. — A690

**Litho. With Foil Application**

**2017, May 9** ***Perf. 13***
**1462** A690 70c multi 1.60 1.60

Count Peter-Ernst von Mansfeld (1517-1604), Governor of Luxembourg A691

**2017, May 9** **Litho.** ***Perf. 11½***
**1463** A691 95c multi 2.10 2.10

Military Anniversaries — A692

Designs: 70c, Military musicians. 95c, Soldiers in fatigues.

**2017, May 9** **Litho.** ***Perf. 12x12½***

**Self-Adhesive**

**1464-1465** A692 Set of 2 3.75 3.75

Luxembourg Military Band, 175th anniv. (No. 1464); voluntary military service, 50th anniv. (No. 1465).

Europa A693

Designs: 70c, Beggen Castle. 95c, Dommeldange Castle.

**2017, May 9** **Litho.** ***Perf. 11½***
**1466-1467** A693 Set of 2 3.75 3.75

Luxembourgish Cycling Federation, Cent. — A694

**2017, July 4** **Litho.** ***Perf. 11½***
**1468** A694 70c multi 1.75 1.75

Start of Fourth Stage of 2017 Tour de France Bicycle Race in Mondorf-les-Bains — A695

**2017, July 4** **Litho.** ***Perf. 11½***
**1469** A695 70c multi 1.75 1.75

Souvenir Sheet

Multilateral Philatelic Exhibition, s'Hertogenbosch, Netherlands — A696

No. 1470: a, Zoete Lieve Gerritje Statue, St. John's Cathedral, s'Hertogenbosch. b, Grand Duke's Palace, Remembrance Monument, Luxembourg Philharmonic, Luxembourg, Church of the Assumption, Ljubljana, Slovenia.

**2017, Aug. 25** **Litho.** ***Perf. 14½***
**1470** A696 Sheet of 2 4.00 4.00
*a.* 70c multi 1.75 1.75
*b.* 95c multi 2.25 2.25

A souvenir sheet containing No. 1470a and Netherlands No. 1553b was given free to standing order subscribers of Luxembourg Post, but was available for sale from the Dutch Post in a package that sold for €15 that contained this sheet, Luxembourg No. 1470 and Netherlands No. 1553. See Netherlands No. 1553.

Parish Church of Simmer (Septfontaines), 700th Anniv. — A697

**2017, Sept. 19** **Litho.** ***Perf. 11½***
**1471** A697 70c multi 1.75 1.75

Green Fingers, Ceramic Sculpture by Ellen van der Woude A698

**2017, Sept. 19** **Litho.** ***Perf. 13½***
**1472** A698 95c multi 2.25 2.25

Souvenir Sheet

Luxembourg Postal Service, 175th Anniv. — A699

No. 1473: a, Letter, post card, building, postal van, credit cards. b, Telephone, telephone booth, computer, cell phone, satellite dish.

**2017, Sept. 19** **Litho.** ***Perf. 13¾x14***
**1473** A699 Sheet of 2 4.00 4.00
*a.* 70c multi 1.75 1.75
*b.* 95c multi 2.25 2.25

Rose Varieties — A700

No. 1474: a, Grand-Duc Adolphe de Luxembourg, 1891. b, Princesse Marie-Adélaide, 1893. c, Grande-Duchesse Charlotte, 1939. d, Grand-Duc Jean, 2010. e, Grand-Duc Henri, 2001. f, Indépendence du Luxembourg, 1990.

***Serpentine Die Cut 11¼***

**2017, Dec. 5** **Litho.**

**Coil Stamps**
**Self-Adhesive**

**1474** Vert. strip of 6 10.50
*a.-f.* A700 (70c) Any single 1.75 1.75

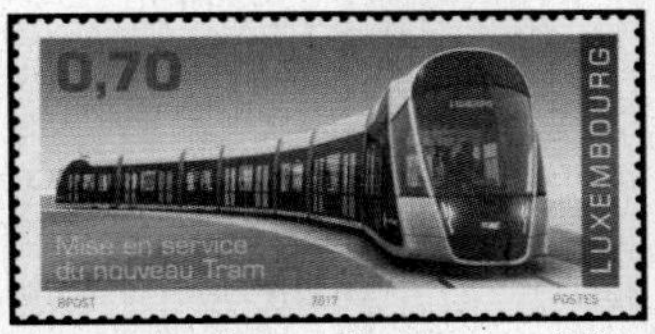


New Luxembourg City Tram — A701

Pfaffenthal-Kirchberg Funicular — A702

**2017, Dec. 5** **Litho.** ***Perf. 12***
**1475** A701 70c multi 1.75 1.75

***Perf. 11½***

**1476** A702 70c multi 1.75 1.75

National Orders of Merit — A703

Designs: No. 1477, 70c, Order of Merit of the Grand Duchy of Luxembourg (carmine red panel at right). No. 1478, 70c, Civil and Military Order of Merit of Adolphe of Nassau (royal blue panel at right). No. 1479, 70c, Order of the Oak Crown (green panel at right).

**Photo. & Embossed**

**2017, Dec. 5** ***Perf. 13¼x13***
**1477-1479** A703 Set of 3 5.25 5.25

SOS Children's Village in Luxembourg, 50th Anniv. — A704

**2018, Mar. 6 Litho.** ***Perf. 11½x11¾***
**1480** A704 70c multi 1.75 1.75

Association of Parents of Mentally Handicapped Children, 50th Anniv. — A705

**2018, Mar. 6 Litho.** ***Perf. 11½x11¾***
**1481** A705 70c multi 1.75 1.75

Lycée de Garçons (Boys High School), Luxembourg, 125th Anniv. — A706

**2018, Mar. 6 Litho.** ***Perf. 11¾x11½***
**1482** A706 70c multi 1.75 1.75

NATO Support and Procurement Agency, 50th Anniv. in Luxembourg A707

**2018, Mar. 6 Litho.** ***Perf. 12½***
**1483** A707 70c multi 1.75 1.75

European Year of Cultural Heritage A708

**2018, Mar. 6 Litho.** ***Perf. 12½***
**1484** A708 70c multi 1.75 1.75

## SEMI-POSTAL STAMPS

Clervaux Monastery SP1

Designs: 15c+10c, View of Pfaffenthal. 25c+10c, View of Luxembourg.

**Engr.; Surcharge Typo. in Red**

**1921, Aug. 2 Unwmk.** ***Perf. 11½***
**B1** SP1 10c + 5c green .25 2.00
**B2** SP1 15c + 10c org red .40 3.00
**B3** SP1 25c + 10c dp grn .25 2.00
*Nos. B1-B3 (3)* .90 7.00
Set, never hinged 2.00

The amount received from the surtax on these stamps was added to a fund for the erection of a monument to the soldiers from Luxembourg who died in World War I.

Nos. B1-B3 with Additional Surcharge in Red or Black

**1923, May 27**
**B4** SP1 25c on #B1 (R) 1.00 *11.00*
**B5** SP1 25c on #B2 1.00 *16.00*
**B6** SP1 25c on #B3 1.00 *11.00*
*Nos. B4-B6 (3)* 3.00 *38.00*
Set, never hinged 10.00

Unveiling of the monument to the soldiers who died in World War I.

Regular Issue of 1914-15 Surcharged in Black or Red

**1924, Apr. 17** ***Perf. 11½x11***
**B7** A11 12½c + 7½c grn .25 1.00
**B8** A11 35c + 10c dk bl (R) .25 1.00
**B9** A11 2½fr + 1fr red .65 *10.00*
**B10** A11 5fr + 2fr dk vio .45 *8.00*
*Nos. B7-B10 (4)* 1.60 *20.00*
Set, never hinged 4.00

Nurse and Patient — SP4

**1925, Dec. 21 Litho.** ***Perf. 13***
**B11** SP4 5c (+ 5c) dl vio .25 .30
**B12** SP4 30c (+ 5c) org .25 .50
**B13** SP4 50c (+ 5c) red brn .25 *1.25*
**B14** SP4 1fr (+ 10c) dp bl .40 *5.00*
*Nos. B11-B14 (4)* 1.15 *7.05*
Set, never hinged 1.75

Prince Jean — SP5

**1926, Dec. 15 Photo.** ***Perf. 12½x12***
**B15** SP5 5c (+ 5c) vio & blk .25 .25
**B16** SP5 40c (+ 10) grn & blk .25 .40
**B17** SP5 50c (+ 15c) lem & blk .25 .40
**B18** SP5 75c (+ 20c) lt red & blk .25 *3.50*
**B19** SP5 1.50fr (+ 30c) gray bl & blk .35 *3.50*
*Nos. B15-B19 (5)* 1.35 *8.05*
Set, never hinged 2.50

Grand Duchess Charlotte and Prince Felix — SP6

**1927, Sept. 4 Engr.** ***Perf. 11½***
**B20** SP6 25c dp vio 1.10 *6.00*
**B21** SP6 50c green 1.50 *8.00*
**B22** SP6 75c rose lake 1.10 *7.00*
**B23** SP6 1fr gray blk 1.10 *7.00*
**B24** SP6 1½fr dp bl 1.10 *7.00*
*Nos. B20-B24 (5)* 5.90 *35.00*
Set, never hinged 16.00

Introduction of postage stamps in Luxembourg, 75th anniv. These stamps were sold exclusively at the Luxembourg Philatelic Exhibition, September 4-8, 1927, at a premium of 3 francs per set, which was donated to the exhibition funds.

Princess Elisabeth — SP7

**1927, Dec. 1 Photo.** ***Perf. 12½***
**B25** SP7 10c (+ 5c) turq bl & blk .25 .25
**B26** SP7 50c (+ 10c) dk brn & blk .25 .30
**B27** SP7 75c (+ 20c) org & blk .25 .65
**B28** SP7 1fr (+ 30c) brn lake & blk .25 *3.50*
**B29** SP7 1½fr (+ 50c) ultra & blk .25 *3.50*
*Nos. B25-B29 (5)* 1.25 *8.20*
Set, never hinged 3.50

The surtax was for Child Welfare societies.

Princess Marie Adelaide — SP8

**1928, Dec. 12** ***Perf. 12½x12***
**B30** SP8 10c (+ 5c) ol grn & brn vio .30 .25
**B31** SP8 60c (+ 10c) brn & ol grn .50 .20
**B32** SP8 75c (+ 15c) vio rose & bl grn .75 *1.50*
**B33** SP8 1fr (+ 25c) dk grn & brn 1.25 *4.50*
**B34** SP8 1½fr (+ 50c) cit & bl 1.25 *5.00*
*Nos. B30-B34 (5)* 4.05 *11.45*
Set, never hinged 11.00

Princess Marie Gabrielle — SP9

**1929, Dec. 14** ***Perf. 13***
**B35** SP9 10c (+ 10c) mar & dp grn .25 *.75*
**B36** SP9 35c (+ 15c) dk grn & red brn 1.50 *2.25*
**B37** SP9 75c (+ 30c) ver & blk 1.75 *3.00*
**B38** SP9 1¼fr (+ 50c) mag & bl grn 2.25 *10.00*
**B39** SP9 1¾fr (+ 75c) Prus bl & sl 2.75 *14.00*
*Nos. B35-B39 (5)* 8.50 *30.00*
Set, never hinged 20.00

The surtax was for Child Welfare societies.

Prince Charles — SP10

**1930, Dec. 10** ***Perf. 12½***
**B40** SP10 10c (+ 5c) bl grn & ol brn .25 .50
**B41** SP10 75c (+ 10c) vio brn & bl grn 1.10 *2.00*
**B42** SP10 1fr (+ 25c) car rose & vio 2.50 *6.50*
**B43** SP10 1¼fr (+ 75c) ol bis & dk brn 4.00 *10.50*
**B44** SP10 1¾fr (+ 1.50fr) ultra & red brn 4.50 *13.00*
*Nos. B40-B44 (5)* 12.35 *32.50*
Set, never hinged 36.00

The surtax was for Child Welfare societies.

Princess Alix — SP11

**1931, Dec. 10**
**B45** SP11 10c (+ 5c) brn org & gray .30 .65
**B46** SP11 75c (+ 10c) clar & bl grn 3.00 *6.00*
**B47** SP11 1fr (+ 25c) dp grn & gray 8.00 *16.00*
**B48** SP11 1¼fr (+ 75c) dk vio & bl grn 6.50 *16.00*
**B49** SP11 1¾fr (+ 1.50fr) bl & gray 13.00 *40.00*
*Nos. B45-B49 (5)* 30.80 *78.65*
Set, never hinged 85.00

The surtax was for Child Welfare societies.

Countess Ermesinde — SP12

**1932, Dec. 8**
**B50** SP12 10c (+ 5c) ol bis .25 .35
**B51** SP12 75c (+ 10c) dp vio 1.40 *5.00*
**B52** SP12 1fr (+ 25c) scar 9.00 *21.00*
**B53** SP12 1¼fr (+ 75c) red brn 9.00 *25.00*
**B54** SP12 1¾fr (+ 1.50fr) dp bl 9.00 *26.00*
*Nos. B50-B54 (5)* 28.65 *77.35*
Set, never hinged 85.00

The surtax was for Child Welfare societies.

Count Henry VII — SP13

**1933, Dec. 12**
**B55** SP13 10c (+ 5c) yel brn .35 .75
**B56** SP13 75c (+ 10c) dp vio 5.00 *7.00*
**B57** SP13 1fr (+ 25c) car rose 10.00 *26.00*
**B58** SP13 1¼fr (+ 75c) org brn 12.00 *30.00*
**B59** SP13 1¾fr (+ 1.50fr) brt bl 12.00 *37.50*
*Nos. B55-B59 (5)* 39.35 *101.25*
Set, never hinged 115.00

John the Blind — SP14

**1934, Dec. 5**
**B60** SP14 10c (+ 5c) dk vio .25 1.00
**B61** SP14 35c (+ 10c) dp grn 2.50 *7.00*
**B62** SP14 75c (+ 15c) rose lake 2.50 *7.00*
**B63** SP14 1fr (+ 25c) dp rose 14.50 *45.00*
**B64** SP14 1¼fr (+ 75c) org 14.50 *45.00*
**B65** SP14 1¾fr (+ 1.50fr) brt bl 14.50 *45.00*
*Nos. B60-B65 (6)* 48.75 *150.00*
Set, never hinged 125.00

Teacher SP15

Sculptor and Painter — SP16

Journalist SP17

Engineer SP18

Scientist SP19

Lawyer — SP20

Savings Bank and Adolphe Bridge — SP21

Surgeon SP22

**1935, May 1 Unwmk. *Perf. 12½***

| | | | | |
|---|---|---|---|---|
| **B65A** | SP15 | 5c violet | .30 | *.25* |
| **B65B** | SP16 | 10c brn red | .30 | *.45* |
| **B65C** | SP17 | 15c olive | .60 | *.70* |
| **B65D** | SP18 | 20c orange | .60 | *.90* |
| **B65E** | SP19 | 35c yel grn | .60 | *1.10* |
| **B65F** | SP20 | 50c gray blk | 1.25 | *1.50* |
| **B65G** | SP21 | 70c dk green | 1.75 | *3.50* |
| **B65H** | SP22 | 1fr car red | 1.75 | *5.00* |
| **B65J** | SP19 | 1.25fr turq | 8.00 | *17.00* |
| **B65K** | SP18 | 1.75fr blue | 9.00 | *22.50* |
| **B65L** | SP16 | 2fr lt brown | 25.00 | *67.50* |
| **B65M** | SP17 | 3fr dk brown | 30.00 | *95.00* |
| **B65N** | SP20 | 5fr lt blue | 60.00 | *160.00* |
| **B65P** | SP15 | 10fr red vio | 150.00 | *350.00* |
| **B65Q** | SP22 | 20fr dk green | 160.00 | *400.0* |
| | | *Nos. B65A-B65Q (15)* | 449.15 | *1,125.* |
| | | Set, never hinged | 1,100. | |

Sold at double face, surtax going to intl. fund to aid professional people.

### Philatelic Exhibition Issue

Type of Regular Issue of 1928

**Wmk. 246**

**1935, Aug. 15 Engr. *Imperf.***

| | | | | |
|---|---|---|---|---|
| **B66** | A19 | 2fr (+ 50c) blk | 6.00 | *13.00* |
| | | Never hinged | 13.00 | |

Philatelic exhibition held at Esch-sur-Alzette.

Charles I — SP23

***Perf. 11½***

**1935, Dec. 2 Photo. Unwmk.**

| | | | | |
|---|---|---|---|---|
| **B67** | SP23 | 10c (+ 5c) vio | .25 | .30 |
| **B68** | SP23 | 35c (+ 10c) grn | .30 | *.55* |
| **B69** | SP23 | 70c (+ 20c) dk brn | .55 | *1.50* |
| **B70** | SP23 | 1fr (+ 25c) rose lake | 11.00 | *21.00* |
| **B71** | SP23 | 1.25fr (+ 75c) org brn | 12.00 | *22.00* |
| **B72** | SP23 | 1.75fr (+ 1.50fr) bl | 12.00 | *27.00* |
| | | *Nos. B67-B72 (6)* | 36.10 | *72.35* |
| | | Set, never hinged | 110.00 | |

Wenceslas I, Duke of Luxembourg — SP24

**1936, Dec. 1 *Perf. 11½x13***

| | | | | |
|---|---|---|---|---|
| **B73** | SP24 | 10c + 5(c) blk brn | .25 | .25 |
| **B74** | SP24 | 35c + 10(c) bl grn | .25 | *.50* |
| **B75** | SP24 | 70c + 20(c) blk | .35 | *.75* |
| **B76** | SP24 | 1fr + 25(c) rose car | 2.00 | *6.50* |
| **B77** | SP24 | 1.25fr + 75(c) vio | 4.50 | *10.00* |
| **B78** | SP24 | 1.75fr + 1.50(fr) saph | 4.50 | *12.00* |
| | | *Nos. B73-B78 (6)* | 11.85 | *30.00* |
| | | Set, never hinged | 32.50 | |

Wenceslas II — SP25

**1937, Dec. 1 *Perf. 11½x12½***

| | | | | |
|---|---|---|---|---|
| **B79** | SP25 | 10c + 5c car & blk | .25 | .25 |
| **B80** | SP25 | 35c + 10c red vio & grn | .25 | .35 |
| **B81** | SP25 | 70c + 20c ultra & red brn | .35 | .35 |
| **B82** | SP25 | 1fr + 25c dk grn & scar | 1.25 | *5.00* |
| **B83** | SP25 | 1.25fr + 75c dk brn & vio | 2.25 | *7.00* |
| **B84** | SP25 | 1.75fr + 1.50fr blk & ultra | 2.25 | *8.50* |
| | | *Nos. B79-B84 (6)* | 6.60 | *21.45* |
| | | Set, never hinged | 20.00 | |

Souvenir Sheet

SP26

**Wmk. 110**

**1937, July 25 Engr. *Perf. 13***

| | | | | |
|---|---|---|---|---|
| **B85** | SP26 | Sheet of 2 | 5.00 | *11.50* |
| | | Never hinged | 11.00 | |
| *a.* | | 2fr red brown, single stamp | 1.50 | *5.50* |

National Philatelic Exposition at Dudelange on July 25-26.

Sold for 5fr per sheet, of which 1fr was for the aid of the exposition.

Portrait of St. Willibrord — SP28

St. Willibrord, after a Miniature SP29

Abbey at Echternach — SP30

Designs: No, B87, The Rathaus at Echternach. No. B88, Pavilion in Abbey Park, Echternach. No. B91, Dancing Procession in Honor of St. Willibrord.

***Perf. 14x13, 13x14***

**1938, June 5 Engr. Unwmk.**

| | | | | |
|---|---|---|---|---|
| **B86** | SP28 | 35c + 10c dk bl grn | .40 | *.55* |
| **B87** | SP28 | 70c + 10c ol gray | .70 | *.55* |
| **B88** | SP28 | 1.25fr + 25c brn car | 1.50 | *2.50* |
| **B89** | SP29 | 1.75fr + 50c sl bl | 2.50 | *2.75* |
| **B90** | SP30 | 3fr + 2fr vio brn | 5.50 | *9.00* |
| **B91** | SP30 | 5fr + 5fr dk vio | 6.50 | *7.25* |
| | | *Nos. B86-B91 (6)* | 17.10 | 22.60 |
| | | Set, never hinged | 50.00 | |

12th centenary of the death of St. Willibrord. The surtax was used for the restoration of the ancient Abbey at Echternach.

Duke Sigismond — SP32

**1938, Dec. 1 Photo. *Perf. 11½***

| | | | | |
|---|---|---|---|---|
| **B92** | SP32 | 10c + 5c lil & blk | .25 | .25 |
| **B93** | SP32 | 35c + 10c grn & blk | .25 | .50 |
| **B94** | SP32 | 70c + 20c buff & blk | .25 | *.50* |
| **B95** | SP32 | 1fr + 25c red org & blk | 2.40 | *7.50* |
| **B96** | SP32 | 1.25fr + 75c gray bl & blk | 2.40 | *9.00* |
| **B97** | SP32 | 1.75fr + 1.50fr bl & blk | 3.50 | *12.00* |
| | | *Nos. B92-B97 (6)* | 9.05 | *29.75* |
| | | Set, never hinged | 22.00 | |

Prince Jean — SP33

Designs: Nos. B99, B102, Prince Felix. Nos. B100, B103, Grand Duchess Charlotte.

**1939, Dec. 1 Litho. *Perf. 14x13***

| | | | | |
|---|---|---|---|---|
| **B98** | SP33 | 10c + 5c red brn, *buff* | .25 | .25 |
| **B99** | SP33 | 35c + 10c sl grn, *buff* | .25 | .30 |
| **B100** | SP33 | 70c + 20c blk, *buff* | .95 | *1.50* |
| **B101** | SP33 | 1fr + 25c red org, *buff* | 4.00 | *13.00* |
| **B102** | SP33 | 1.25fr + 75c vio brn, *buff* | 4.75 | *13.00* |
| **B103** | SP33 | 1.75fr + 1.50fr lt bl, *buff* | 5.50 | *26.00* |
| | | *Nos. B98-B103 (6)* | 15.70 | *54.05* |
| | | Set, never hinged | 36.00 | |

See No. 217 (souvenir sheet).

Allegory of Medicinal Baths — SP36

**1940, Mar. 1 Photo. *Perf. 11½***

| | | | | |
|---|---|---|---|---|
| **B104** | SP36 | 2fr + 50c gray, blk & slate grn | 1.25 | *10.00* |
| | | Never hinged | 4.00 | |

For similar stamp see No. 216.

Stamps of 1944, type A37, surcharged "+50C," "+5F" or "+15F" in black, were sold only in canceled condition, affixed to numbered folders. The surtax was for the benefit of Luxembourg evacuees. Value for folder, $15.

Homage to France SP37

Thanks to: No. B118, USSR. No. B119, Britannia. No. B120, America.

**1945, Mar. 1 Engr. *Perf. 13***

| | | | | |
|---|---|---|---|---|
| **B117** | SP37 | 60c + 1.40fr dp grn | .25 | .25 |
| **B118** | SP37 | 1.20fr + 1.80fr red | .25 | .25 |
| **B119** | SP37 | 2.50fr + 3.50fr dp bl | .25 | .25 |
| **B120** | SP37 | 4.20fr + 4.80fr dp vio | .25 | .25 |
| | | *Nos. B117-B120 (4)* | 1.00 | 1.00 |
| | | Set, never hinged | 1.25 | |

Issued to honor the Allied Nations. Exist imperf. Value, set $175.

Statue Carried in Procession SP41

Statue of Our Lady "Patrona Civitatis" SP42

"Our Lady of Luxembourg" SP43

Cathedral Façade SP44

Altar with Statue of Madonna — SP45

**1945, June 4**

**B121** SP41 60c + 40c grn .25 .50
**B122** SP42 1.20fr + 80c red .25 .50
**B123** SP43 2.50fr + 2.50fr dp bl .25 *3.00*
**B124** SP44 5.50fr + 6.50fr dk vio .55 *11.00*
**B125** SP45 20fr + 20fr choc .55 *12.50*
*Nos. B121-B125 (5)* 1.85 *27.50*
Set, never hinged 3.50

Exist imperf. Value, set $250.

Souvenir Sheet

"Our Lady of Luxembourg" — SP46

**1945, Sept. 30 Engr. *Imperf.***

**B126** SP46 50fr + 50fr blk 1.00 *42.50*
Never hinged 2.25

Young Fighters — SP47

Refugee Mother and Children — SP48

Political Prisoner — SP49

Executed Civilian — SP50

**1945, Dec. 20 Photo. *Perf. 11½***

**B127** SP47 20c + 30c sl grn & buff .25 *1.00*
**B128** SP48 1.50fr + 1fr brn red & buff .25 *1.00*
**B129** SP49 3.50fr + 3.50fr bl, dp bl & buff .25 *8.50*
**B130** SP50 5fr + 10fr brn, dk brn & buff .25 *8.50*
*Nos. B127-B130 (4)* 1.00 *19.00*
Set, never hinged 1.25

**Souvenir Sheet**

**1946, Jan. 30 Unwmk. *Perf. 11½***

**B131** Sheet of 4 12.00 *350.00*
Never hinged 25.00
*a.* SP47 2.50fr + 2.50fr sl grn & buff 3.00 *50.00*
*b.* SP48 3.50fr + 6.50fr brown red & buff 3.00 *50.00*
*c.* SP49 5fr + 15fr bl, dp bl & buff 3.00 *50.00*
*d.* SP50 20fr + 20fr brown, dark brown & buff 3.00 *50.00*

Tribute to Luxembourg's heroes and martyrs.

The surtax was for the National Welfare Fund.

Souvenir Sheet

Old Rolling Mill, Dudelange — SP52

**1946, July 28 Engr. & Typo.**

**B132** SP52 50fr brn & dk bl, *buff* 7.00 *30.00*
Never hinged 14.00

National Postage Stamp Exhibition, Dudelange, July 28-29, 1946. The sheets sold for 55fr.

Jean l'Aveugle — SP53

**1946, Dec. 5 Photo.**

**B133** SP53 60c + 40c dk grn .25 *1.00*
**B134** SP53 1.50fr + 50c brn red .25 *2.00*
**B135** SP53 3.50fr + 3.50fr dp bl .60 *7.00*
**B136** SP53 5fr + 10fr sepia .30 *10.00*
*Nos. B133-B136 (4)* 1.40 *20.00*
Set, never hinged 3.50

600th anniv. of the death of Jean l'Aveugle (John the Blind), Count of Luxembourg.

Ruins of St. Willibrord Basilica — SP54

Twelfth Century Miniature of St. Willibrord SP59

Designs: No. B138, Statue of Abbot Jean Bertels. No. B139, Emblem of Echternach Abbey. No. B140, Ruins of the Basilica's Interior. No. B141, St. Irmine and Pepin of Hersta Holding Model of the Abbey.

***Perf. 13x14, 14x13***

**1947, May 25 Engr.**

**B137** SP54 20c + 10c blk .25 .25
**B138** SP54 60c + 10c dk grn .40 .55
**B139** SP54 75c + 25c dk car .55 .75
**B140** SP54 1.50fr + 50c dk brn .70 .75
**B141** SP54 3.50fr + 2.50fr dk bl 2.25 *4.75*
**B142** SP59 25fr + 25fr dk pur 15.00 *25.00*
*Nos. B137-B142 (6)* 19.15 *32.05*
Set, never hinged 40.00

The surtax was to aid in restoring the Basilica of Saint Willibrord at Echternach.

Michel Lentz — SP60

**1947, Dec. 4 Photo. *Perf. 11½***

**B143** SP60 60c + 40c sep & buff .25 1.10
**B144** SP60 1.50fr + 50c dp plum & buff .25 1.10
**B145** SP60 3.50fr + 3.50fr dp bl & gray 2.75 *16.00*
**B146** SP60 10fr + 5fr dk grn & gray 2.40 *16.00*
*Nos. B143-B146 (4)* 5.65 *34.20*
Set, never hinged 14.00

Edmond de La Fontaine (Dicks) — SP61

**1948, Nov. 18**

**B147** SP61 60c + 40c brn & pale bis .25 .65
**B148** SP61 1.50fr + 50c brn car & buff .35 .65
**B149** SP61 3.50fr + 3.50fr dp bl & gray 4.50 *9.00*
**B150** SP61 10fr + 5fr dk grn & gray 3.50 *9.00*
*Nos. B147-B150 (4)* 8.60 *19.30*
Set, never hinged 19.00

125th anniversary of the birth of Edmond de La Fontaine, poet and composer.

**Type of Regular Issue of 1948**

Souvenir Sheet

**1949, Jan. 8 Unwmk. *Perf. 11½***

**B151** Sheet of 3 45.00 45.00
Never hinged 90.00
*a.* A45 8fr + 3fr blue gray 13.00 15.00
*b.* A45 12fr + 5fr green 13.00 15.00
*c.* A45 15fr + 7fr brown 13.00 15.00

30th anniversary of Grand Duchess Charlotte's ascension to the throne. Border and dates "1919-1949" in gray.

Michel Rodange — SP62

**1949, Dec. 5**

**B152** SP62 60c + 40c ol grn & gray .40 .50
**B153** SP62 2fr + 1fr dk vio & rose 2.75 *5.00*
**B154** SP62 4fr + 2fr sl blk & gray 4.50 *7.50*
**B155** SP62 10fr + 5fr brn & buff 4.50 *12.00*
*Nos. B152-B155 (4)* 12.15 *25.00*
Set, never hinged 22.50

Wards of the Nation
SP63 SP64

**1950, June 24 Engr. *Perf. 12½x12***

**B156** SP63 60c + 15c dk sl bl .50 .65
**B157** SP64 1fr + 20c dk car rose .80 1.00
**B158** SP63 2fr + 30c red brn 1.00 1.00
**B159** SP64 4fr + 75c dk bl 6.50 *10.50*
**B160** SP63 8fr + 3fr blk 18.00 *32.50*
**B161** SP64 10fr + 5fr lil rose 19.00 *32.50*
*Nos. B156-B161 (6)* 45.80 *78.15*
Set, never hinged 90.00

The surtax was for child welfare.

Jean A. Zinnen — SP65

**1950, Dec. 5 Photo. *Perf. 11½***

**B162** SP65 60c + 10c ind & gray .35 .25
**B163** SP65 2fr + 15c cer & buff .35 .40
**B164** SP65 4fr + 15c vio bl & bl gray 3.25 *6.50*
**B165** SP65 8fr + 5fr dk brn & buff 9.25 *25.00*
*Nos. B162-B165 (4)* 13.20 *32.15*
Set, never hinged 27.50

Laurent Menager — SP66

**1951, Dec. 5 Gray Background**

**B166** SP66 60c + 10c sepia .25 .40
**B167** SP66 2fr + 15c dl ol grn .25 .40
**B168** SP66 4fr + 15c blue 2.50 *4.00*
**B169** SP66 8fr + 5fr vio brn 10.50 *30.00*
*Nos. B166-B169 (4)* 13.50 *34.80*
Set, never hinged 29.00

50th anniversary of the death of Laurent Menager, composer.

J. B. Fresez — SP67

**1952, Dec. 3**

**B170** SP67 60c + 15c dk bl grn & pale bl .25 .35
**B171** SP67 2fr + 25c chnt brn & buff .25 .35
**B172** SP67 4fr + 25c dk vio bl & gray 1.50 *2.75*
**B173** SP67 8fr + 4.75fr dp plum & lil gray 12.50 *29.00*
*Nos. B170-B173 (4)* 14.50 *32.45*
Set, never hinged 32.50

Traditions — SP68

Designs: Nos. B174, B177, Candlemas Singing. Nos. B175, B178, Procession with ratchets. Nos. B176, B179, Breaking Easter eggs.

**1953, Dec. 3**

**B174** SP68 25c + 15c red org & dp car .25 .25
**B175** SP68 80c + 20c vio brn & bl gray .25 .25
**B176** SP68 1.20fr + 30c bl grn & ol grn .50 1.00
**B177** SP68 2fr + 25c brn car & brn .25 .60
**B178** SP68 4fr + 50c grnsh bl & vio bl 4.00 *8.00*
**B179** SP68 7fr + 3.35fr vio & pur 6.00 *16.00*
*Nos. B174-B179 (6)* 11.25 *26.10*
Set, never hinged 24.00

The surtax was for the National Welfare Fund of Grand Duchess Charlotte.

Clay Censer and Whistle — SP69

Designs: 80c+20c, 4fr+50c, Sheep and bass drum. 1.20fr+30c, 7fr+3.45fr, Merry-go-round horses. 2fr+25c, As No. B180.

**1954, Dec. 3**

**B180** SP69 25c + 5c car lake & cop brn .25 .40
**B181** SP69 80c + 20c dk gray .25 .40
**B182** SP69 1.20fr + 30c dk bl grn & cr .65 1.25
**B183** SP69 2fr + 25c brn & ocher .35 .70
**B184** SP69 4fr + 50c brt bl 3.50 *5.00*
**B185** SP69 7fr + 3.45fr pur 9.00 *18.00*
*Nos. B180-B185 (6)* 14.00 *25.75*
Set, never hinged 29.00

Toys for St. Nicholas Day — SP70

Designs: 80c+20c, 4fr+50c, Christ child and lamb (Christmas). 1.20fr+30c, 7fr+3.45fr, Star, crown and cake (Epiphany).

**1955, Dec. 5 Unwmk. *Perf. 11½***

**B186** SP70 25c + 5c sal & dk car .25 .25
**B187** SP70 80c + 20c gray & gray blk .25 .25
**B188** SP70 1.20fr + 30c ol grn & sl grn .25 .50
**B189** SP70 2fr + 25c buff & dk brn .35 .25
**B190** SP70 4fr + 50c lt bl & brt bl 2.50 *7.00*
**B191** SP70 7fr + 3.45fr rose vio & claret 6.50 *13.00*
*Nos. B186-B191 (6)* 10.10 *21.25*
Set, never hinged 20.00

Coats of Arms — SP71

Arms: 25c+5c, 2fr+25c, Echternach. 80c+20c, 4fr+50c, Esch-sur-Alzette. 1.20fr+30c, 7fr+3.45fr, Grevenmacher.

**1956, Dec. 5 Photo.**

**Arms in Original Colors**

**B192** SP71 25c + 5c blk & sal pink .25 .25
**B193** SP71 80c + 20c ultra & yel .25 .25
**B194** SP71 1.20fr + 30c ultra & gray .25 .45
**B195** SP71 2fr + 25c blk & buff .25 .25
**B196** SP71 4fr + 50c ultra & lt bl 1.90 *3.25*
**B197** SP71 7fr + 3.45fr ultra & pale vio 4.00 *8.50*
*Nos. B192-B197 (6)* 6.90 *12.95*
Set, never hinged 12.50

**1957, Dec. 4 Unwmk. *Perf. 11½***

25c+5c, 2fr+25c, Luxembourg. 80c+20c, 4fr+50c, Mersch. 1.20fr+30c, 7fr+3.45fr, Vianden.

**Arms in Original Colors**

**B198** SP71 25c + 5c ultra & org .25 *.25*
**B199** SP71 80c + 20c blk & lem .25 *.25*
**B200** SP71 1.20fr + 30c ultra & lt bl grn .25 *.35*
**B201** SP71 2fr + 25c ultra & pale brn .25 *.30*
**B202** SP71 4fr + 50c blk & pale vio bl .50 *4.00*
**B203** SP71 7fr + 3.45fr ultra & rose lil 3.00 *7.00*
*Nos. B198-B203 (6)* 4.50 12.15
Set, never hinged 11.50

**1958, Dec. 3 *Perf. 11½***

30c+10c, 2.50fr+50c, Capellen. 1fr+25c, 5fr+50c, Diekirch. 1.50fr+25c, 8.50fr+4.60fr, Redange.

**Arms in Original Colors**

**B204** SP71 30c + 10c blk & pink .25 *.25*
**B205** SP71 1fr + 25c ultra & buff .25 *.25*
**B206** SP71 1.50fr + 25c ultra & pale grn .25 *.40*
**B207** SP71 2.50fr + 50c blk & gray .25 *.25*
**B208** SP71 5fr + 50c ultra 1.75 *3.00*
**B209** SP71 8.50fr + 4.60fr ultra & lil 2.00 *7.00*
*Nos. B204-B209 (6)* 4.75 *11.15*
Set, never hinged 9.00

**1959, Dec. 2**

30c+10c, 2.50fr+50c, Clervaux. 1fr+25c, 5fr+50c, Remich. 1.50fr+25c, 8.50fr+4.60fr, Wiltz.

**Arms in Original Colors**

**B210** SP71 30c + 10c ultra & pink .25 .25
**B211** SP71 1fr + 25c ultra & pale lem .25 .25
**B212** SP71 1.50fr + 25c blk & pale grn .25 .45
**B213** SP71 2.50fr + 50c ultra & pale fawn .25 .25
**B214** SP71 5fr + 50c ultra & lt bl .65 *1.60*
**B215** SP71 8.50fr + 4.60fr blk & pale vio 2.75 *8.00*
*Nos. B210-B215 (6)* 4.40 *10.80*
Set, never hinged 8.00

**Catalogue values for unused stamps in this section, from this point to the end of the section, are for Never Hinged items.**

Princess Marie-Astrid — SP72

1fr+25c, 5fr+50c, Princess in party dress. 1.50fr+25c, 8.50fr+4.60fr, Princess with book.

**1960, Dec. 5 Photo. *Perf. 11½***

**B216** SP72 30c + 10c brn & lt bl .25 .25
**B217** SP72 1fr + 25c brn & pink .25 .25
**B218** SP72 1.50fr + 25c brn & lt bl .55 .40
**B219** SP72 2.50fr + 50c brn & yel .40 .30
**B220** SP72 5fr + 50c brn & pale lil 1.25 *1.00*
**B221** SP72 8.50fr + 4.60fr brn & pale ol 8.00 *6.00*
*Nos. B216-B221 (6)* 10.70 8.20

**Type of 1960**

Prince Henri: 30c+10c, 2.50fr+50c, Infant in long dress. 1fr+25c, 5fr+50c, Informal portrait. 1.50fr+25c, 8.50fr+4.60fr, In dress suit.

**1961, Dec. 4 Unwmk. *Perf. 11½***

**B222** SP72 30c + 10c brn & brt pink .25 .25
**B223** SP72 1fr + 25c brn & lt vio .30 .25
**B224** SP72 1.50fr + 25c brn & sal .35 .30
**B225** SP72 2.50fr + 50c brn & pale grn .40 .40
**B226** SP72 5fr + 50c brn & cit 2.00 1.40
**B227** SP72 8.50fr + 4.60fr brn & gray 3.75 *4.50*
*Nos. B222-B227 (6)* 7.05 7.10

Prince Jean — SP73

Designs: Different portraits of the twins Prince Jean and Princess Margaretha. Nos. B228 and B233 are horizontal.

**Inscriptions and Portraits in Dark Brown**

**1962, Dec. 3 Photo. *Perf. 11½***

**B228** SP73 30c + 10c org yel .25 .25
**B229** SP73 1fr + 25c lt bl .25 .25
**B230** SP73 1.50fr + 25c pale ol .35 .35
**B231** SP73 2.50fr + 50c rose .35 .25
**B232** SP73 5fr + 50c lt yel grn 1.00 *1.25*
**B233** SP73 8.50fr + 4.60fr lil gray 3.25 *3.50*
*Nos. B228-B233 (6)* 5.45 5.85

St. Roch, Patron of Bakers — SP74

Patron Saints: 1fr+25c, St. Anne, tailors. 2fr+25c, St. Eloi, smiths. 3fr+50c, St. Michael, shopkeepers. 6fr+50c, St. Bartholomew, butchers. St. Theobald, seven crafts.

**1963, Dec. 2 Unwmk. *Perf. 11½***

**Background Color**

**B234** SP74 50c + 10c pale lil .25 .25
**B235** SP74 1fr + 25c tan .25 .25
**B236** SP74 2fr + 25c lt grnsh bl .25 .25
**B237** SP74 3fr + 50c lt bl .25 .25
**B238** SP74 6fr + 50c buff .90 *.90*
**B239** SP74 10fr + 5.90fr pale yel grn 1.50 *2.00*
*Nos. B234-B239 (6)* 3.40 3.90

Three Towers — SP75

Children's paintings: 1fr+25c, 6fr+50c, Grand Duke Adolphe Bridge, horiz. 2fr+25c, 10fr+5.90fr, The Lower City.

**1964, Dec. 7 Photo. *Perf. 11½***

**B240** SP75 50c + 10c multi .25 .25
**B241** SP75 1fr + 25c multi .25 .25
**B242** SP75 2fr + 25c multi .25 .25
*a.* Value omitted 300.00
**B243** SP75 3fr + 50c multi .25 .25
**B244** SP75 6fr + 50c multi .90 1.00
**B245** SP75 10fr + 5.90fr multi 1.10 *1.75*
*Nos. B240-B245 (6)* 3.00 3.75

The Roman Lady of Titelberg — SP76

Fairy Tales of Luxembourg: 1fr+25c, Schäppchen, the Huntsman. 2fr+25c, The Witch of Koerich. 3fr+50c, The Gnomes of Schoenfels. 6fr+50c, Tollchen, Watchman of Hesperange. 10fr+5.90fr, The Old Spinster of Heispelt.

**1965, Dec. 6 Photo. *Perf. 11½***

**B246** SP76 50c + 10c multi .25 .25
**B247** SP76 1fr + 25c multi .25 .25
**B248** SP76 2fr + 25c multi .25 .25
**B249** SP76 3fr + 50c multi .25 .25
**B250** SP76 6fr + 50c multi .40 *.40*
**B251** SP76 10fr + 5.90fr multi 1.00 *1.25*
*Nos. B246-B251 (6)* 2.40 2.65

**Fairy Tale Type of 1965**

Fairy Tales of Luxembourg: 50c+10c, The Veiled Matron of Wormeldange. 1.50fr+25c, Jekel, Warden of the Wark. 2fr+25c, The Black Man of Vianden. 3fr+50c, The Gracious Fairy of Rosport. 6fr+1fr, The Friendly Shepherd of Donkolz. 13fr+6.90fr, The Little Sisters of Trois-Vièrges.

**1966, Dec. 6 Photo. *Perf. 11½***

**B252** SP76 50c + 10c multi .25 .25
**B253** SP76 1.50fr + 25c multi .25 .25
**B254** SP76 2fr + 25c multi .25 .25
**B255** SP76 3fr + 50c multi .25 .25
**B256** SP76 6fr + 1fr multi .35 *.40*
**B257** SP76 13fr + 6.90fr multi .85 *1.00*
*Nos. B252-B257 (6)* 2.20 2.40

Prince Guillaume SP77

Castle of Berg SP78

Portraits: 1.50fr+25c, Princess Margaretha. 2fr+25c, Prince Jean. 3fr+50c, Prince Henri as Boy Scout. 6fr+1fr, Princess Marie-Astrid.

**1967, Dec. 6 Photo. *Perf. 11½***

**B258** SP77 50c + 10c yel & brn .25 .25
**B259** SP77 1.50fr + 25c gray bl & brn .25 .25
**B260** SP77 2fr + 25c pale rose & brn .25 .25
**B261** SP77 3fr + 50c lt ol & brn .50 .25
**B262** SP77 6fr + 1fr lt vio & brn .35 *.50*
**B263** SP78 13fr + 6.90fr multi .50 *1.00*
*Nos. B258-B263 (6)* 2.10 2.50

Medico-professional Institute at Cap — SP79

Deaf-mute Child Imitating Bird — SP80

Handicapped Children: 2fr+25c, Blind child holding candle. 3fr+50c, Nurse supporting physically handicapped child. 6fr+1fr, Cerebral palsy victim. 13fr+6.90fr, Mentally disturbed child.

**1968, Dec. 5 Photo. *Perf. 11½***

**Designs and Inscriptions in Dark Brown**

**B264** SP79 50c + 10c lt bl .25 .25
**B265** SP80 1.50fr + 25c lt grn .25 .25
**B266** SP80 2fr + 25c yel .25 .25
**B267** SP80 3fr + 50c bl .25 .25
**B268** SP80 6fr + 1fr buff .40 .55
**B269** SP80 13fr + 6.90fr pink 1.00 *1.50*
*Nos. B264-B269 (6)* 2.40 3.05

Vianden Castle — SP81

Luxembourg Castles: 1.50fr+25c, Lucilinburhuc. 2fr+25c, Bourglinster. 3fr+50c, Hollenfels. 6fr+1fr, Ansembourg. 13fr+6.90fr, Beaufort.

**1969, Dec. 8 Photo. *Perf. 11½***

**B270** SP81 50c + 10c multi .25 .25
**B271** SP81 1.50fr + 25c multi .25 .25
**B272** SP81 2fr + 25c multi .25 .25
**B273** SP81 3fr + 50c multi .25 .25
**B274** SP81 6fr + 1fr multi .45 *.75*
**B275** SP81 13fr + 6.90fr multi .60 *1.25*
*Nos. B270-B275 (6)* 2.05 3.00

**1970, Dec. 7 Photo. *Perf. 11½***

Luxembourg Castles: 50c+10c, Clervaux. 1.50fr+25c, Septfontaines. 2fr+25c, Bourscheid. 3fr+50c, Esch-sur-Sure. 6fr+1fr, Larochette. 13fr+6.90fr, Brandenbourg.

**B276** SP81 50c + 10c multi .25 .25
**B277** SP81 1.50fr + 25c multi .25 .25
**B278** SP81 2fr + 25c multi .25 .25
**B279** SP81 3fr + 50c multi .25 .25
**B280** SP81 6fr + 1fr multi .40 *.55*
**B281** SP81 13fr + 6.90fr multi .75 *1.25*
*Nos. B276-B281 (6)* 2.15 2.80

The surtax on Nos. B180-B281 was for charitable purposes.

Children of Bethlehem — SP82

Wooden Statues from Crèche of Beaufort Church: 1.50fr+25c, Shepherds. 3fr+50c, Nativity. 8fr+1fr, Herdsmen. 18fr+6.50fr, King offering gift.

**1971, Dec. 6 Photo. *Perf. 11½***

**Sculptures in Shades of Brown**

| | | | | |
|---|---|---|---|---|
| **B282** | SP82 | 1fr + 25c lilac | .25 | .25 |
| **B283** | SP82 | 1.50fr + 25c olive | .25 | .25 |
| **B284** | SP82 | 3fr + 50c gray | .25 | .25 |
| **B285** | SP82 | 8fr + 1fr lt ultra | .50 | *.75* |
| **B286** | SP82 | 18fr + 6.50fr grn | 1.75 | *2.50* |
| | | *Nos. B282-B286 (5)* | 3.00 | 4.00 |

The surtax was for various charitable organizations.

Angel — SP83

Stained Glass Windows, Luxembourg Cathedral: 1.50fr+25c, St. Joseph. 3fr+50c, Virgin and Child. 8fr+1fr, People of Bethlehem. 18fr+6.50fr, Angel facing left.

**1972, Dec. 4**

| | | | | |
|---|---|---|---|---|
| **B287** | SP83 | 1fr + 25c multi | .25 | .25 |
| **B288** | SP83 | 1.50fr + 25c multi | .25 | .25 |
| **B289** | SP83 | 3fr + 50c multi | .25 | .25 |
| **B290** | SP83 | 8fr + 1fr multi | .75 | *1.40* |
| **B291** | SP83 | 18fr + 6.50fr multi | 2.40 | *3.50* |
| | | *Nos. B287-B291 (5)* | 3.90 | 5.65 |

Surtax was for charitable purposes.

Sts. Anne and Joachim — SP84

Sculptures: 3fr+25c, Mary meeting Elizabeth. 4fr+50c, Virgin and Child and a King. 8fr+1fr, Shepherds. 15fr+7fr, St. Joseph holding candle. Designs from 16th century reredos, Hermitage of Hachiville.

**1973, Dec. 5 Photo. *Perf. 11½***

| | | | | |
|---|---|---|---|---|
| **B292** | SP84 | 1fr + 25c multi | .25 | .25 |
| **B293** | SP84 | 3fr + 25c multi | .25 | .25 |
| **B294** | SP84 | 4fr + 50c multi | .25 | .25 |
| **B295** | SP84 | 8fr + 1fr multi | .90 | *1.50* |
| **B296** | SP84 | 15fr + 7fr multi | 2.00 | *3.25* |
| | | *Nos. B292-B296 (5)* | 3.65 | 5.50 |

Annunciation — SP85

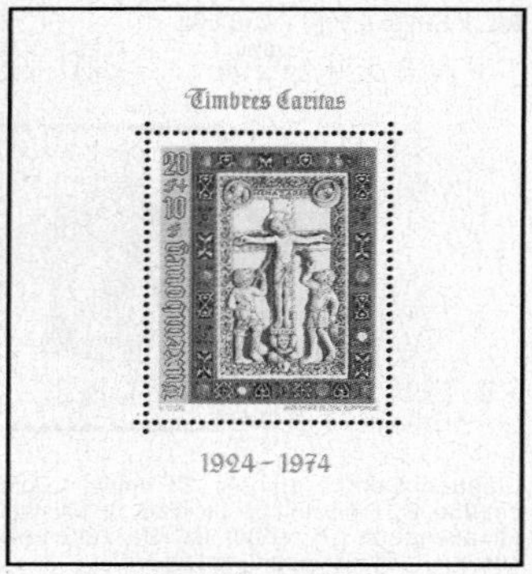

Crucifixion — SP86

Designs: 3fr+25c, Visitation. 4fr+50c, Nativity. 8fr+1fr, Adoration of the King. 15fr+7fr, Presentation at the Temple. Designs of Nos. B297-B301 are from miniatures in the "Codex Aureus Epternacensis" (Gospel from Echternach Abbey). The Crucifixion is from the carved ivory cover of the Codex, by the Master of Echternach, c. 983-991.

**1974, Dec. 5 Photo. *Perf. 11½***

| | | | | |
|---|---|---|---|---|
| **B297** | SP85 | 1fr + 25c multi | .25 | .25 |
| **B298** | SP85 | 3fr + 25c multi | .25 | .25 |
| **B299** | SP85 | 4fr + 50c multi | .25 | .25 |
| **B300** | SP85 | 8fr + 1fr multi | .85 | *1.25* |
| **B301** | SP85 | 15fr + 7fr multi | 2.00 | *3.00* |
| | | *Nos. B297-B301 (5)* | 3.60 | 5.00 |

**Souvenir Sheet**

**Photogravure & Engraved**

***Perf. 13½***

| | | | | |
|---|---|---|---|---|
| **B302** | SP86 | 20fr + 10fr multi | 3.50 | 6.00 |

50th anniversary of Caritas issues. No. B302 contains one 34x42mm stamp.

Fly Orchid — SP87

Flowers: 3fr+25c, Pyramidal orchid. 4fr+50c, Marsh hellebore. 8fr+1fr, Pasqueflower. 15fr+7fr, Bee orchid.

**1975, Dec. 4 Photo. *Perf. 11½***

| | | | | |
|---|---|---|---|---|
| **B303** | SP87 | 1fr + 25c multi | .25 | .25 |
| **B304** | SP87 | 3fr + 25c multi | .30 | .25 |
| **B305** | SP87 | 4fr + 50c multi | .40 | .40 |
| **B306** | SP87 | 8fr + 1fr multi | .90 | *1.50* |
| **B307** | SP87 | 15fr + 7fr multi | 2.75 | *3.00* |
| | | *Nos. B303-B307 (5)* | 4.60 | 5.40 |

The surtax on Nos. B303-B317 was for various charitable organizations.

**1976, Dec. 6**

Flowers: 2fr+25c, Gentian. 5fr+25c, Narcissus. 6fr+50c, Red hellebore. 12fr+1fr, Late spider orchid. 20fr+8fr, Two-leafed squill.

| | | | | |
|---|---|---|---|---|
| **B308** | SP87 | 2fr + 25c multi | .25 | .25 |
| **B309** | SP87 | 5fr + 25c multi | .25 | .25 |
| **B310** | SP87 | 6fr + 50c multi | .30 | .30 |
| **B311** | SP87 | 12fr + 1fr multi | .90 | *1.25* |
| **B312** | SP87 | 20fr + 8fr multi | 2.40 | *3.50* |
| | | *Nos. B308-B312 (5)* | 4.10 | 5.55 |

Lilies of the Valley — SP88

Flowers: 5fr+25c, Columbine. 6fr+50c, Mezereon. 12fr+1fr, Early spider orchid. 20fr+8fr, Spotted orchid.

**1977, Dec. 5 Photo. *Perf. 11½***

| | | | | |
|---|---|---|---|---|
| **B313** | SP88 | 2fr + 25c multi | .25 | .25 |
| **B314** | SP88 | 5fr + 25c multi | .30 | .30 |
| **B315** | SP88 | 6fr + 50c multi | .45 | .45 |
| **B316** | SP88 | 12fr + 1fr multi | 1.25 | *2.00* |
| **B317** | SP88 | 20fr + 8fr multi | 2.40 | *3.25* |
| | | *Nos. B313-B317 (5)* | 4.65 | 6.25 |

St. Matthew — SP89

Behind-glass Paintings, 19th Century: 5fr+25c, St. Mark. 6fr+50c, Nativity. 12fr+1fr, St. Luke. 20fr+8fr, St. John.

**1978, Dec. 5 Photo. *Perf. 11½***

| | | | | |
|---|---|---|---|---|
| **B318** | SP89 | 2fr + 25c multi | .25 | .25 |
| **B319** | SP89 | 5fr + 25c multi | .30 | .30 |
| **B320** | SP89 | 6fr + 50c multi | .45 | .45 |
| **B321** | SP89 | 12fr + 1fr multi | 1.10 | 1.40 |
| **B322** | SP89 | 20fr + 8fr multi | 1.60 | *2.00* |
| | | *Nos. B318-B322 (5)* | 3.70 | 4.40 |

Surtax was for charitable organizations.

Spring — SP90

Behind-glass Paintings, 19th Century: 5fr+25c, Summer. 6fr+50c, Charity. 12fr+1fr, Autumn. 20fr+8fr, Winter.

**1979, Dec. 5 Photo. *Perf. 12***

| | | | | |
|---|---|---|---|---|
| **B323** | SP90 | 2fr + 25c multi | .25 | .25 |
| **B324** | SP90 | 5fr + 25c multi | .25 | .25 |
| **B325** | SP90 | 6fr + 50c multi | .30 | .25 |
| **B326** | SP90 | 12fr + 1fr multi | .65 | *1.10* |
| **B327** | SP90 | 20fr + 8fr multi | 1.50 | *2.75* |
| | | *Nos. B323-B327 (5)* | 2.95 | 4.60 |

St. Martin — SP91

Behind-glass Paintings, 19th Century: 6fr+50c, St. Nicholas. 8fr+1fr, Madonna and Child. 30fr+1fr, St. George the Martyr.

**1980, Dec. 5 Photo. *Perf. 11½***

| | | | | |
|---|---|---|---|---|
| **B328** | SP91 | 4fr + 50c multi | .25 | .25 |
| **B329** | SP91 | 6fr + 50c multi | .30 | .30 |
| **B330** | SP91 | 8fr + 1fr multi | .60 | .60 |
| **B331** | SP91 | 30fr + 10fr multi | 1.60 | 2.25 |
| | | *Nos. B328-B331 (4)* | 2.75 | 3.40 |

Surtax was for charitable organizations.

Arms of Petange SP92

Nativity, by Otto van Veen (1556-1629) SP93

**1981, Dec. 4 Photo.**

**Granite Paper**

| | | | | |
|---|---|---|---|---|
| **B332** | SP92 | 4fr + 50c shown | .25 | .25 |
| **B333** | SP92 | 6fr + 50c Larochette | .25 | .25 |
| **B334** | SP93 | 8fr + 1fr shown | .35 | .35 |
| **B335** | SP92 | 16fr + 2fr Stadtbredimus | .75 | 1.00 |
| **B336** | SP92 | 35fr + 12fr Weiswampach | 2.00 | 2.50 |
| | | *Nos. B332-B336 (5)* | 3.60 | 4.35 |

Surtax was for charitable organizations.

**1982, Dec. 6 Photo. *Perf. 11½***

Design: 8fr+1fr, Adoration of the Shepherds, stained-glass window, by Gust Zanter, Hoscheid Parish Church.

**Granite Paper**

| | | | | |
|---|---|---|---|---|
| **B337** | SP92 | 4fr + 50c Bettembourg | .25 | .25 |
| **B338** | SP92 | 6fr + 50c Frisange | .30 | .30 |
| **B339** | SP93 | 8fr + 1fr multi | .35 | .30 |
| **B340** | SP92 | 16fr + 2fr Mamer | 1.00 | 1.40 |
| **B341** | SP92 | 35fr + 12fr Heinerscheid | 2.25 | 2.25 |
| | | *Nos. B337-B341 (5)* | 4.15 | 4.50 |

Surtax was for charitable organizations.

**1983, Dec. 5 Photo.**

| | | | | |
|---|---|---|---|---|
| **B342** | SP92 | 4fr + 1fr Winseler | .25 | .25 |
| **B343** | SP92 | 7fr + 1fr Beckerich | .35 | .35 |
| **B344** | SP93 | 10fr + 1fr Nativity | .60 | .55 |
| **B345** | SP92 | 16fr + 2fr Feulen | .75 | .85 |
| **B346** | SP92 | 40fr + 13fr Mertert | 2.25 | 2.75 |
| | | *Nos. B342-B346 (5)* | 4.20 | 4.75 |

Surtax was for charitable organizations.

Inquisitive Child — SP94

Children Exhibiting Various Moods.

**1984, Dec. 5 Photo.**

| | | | | |
|---|---|---|---|---|
| **B347** | SP94 | 4fr + 1fr shown | .45 | .45 |
| **B348** | SP94 | 7fr + 1fr Daydreaming | .75 | .75 |
| **B349** | SP94 | 10fr + 1fr Nativity | .80 | 1.00 |
| **B350** | SP94 | 16fr + 2fr Sulking | 2.00 | 2.25 |
| **B351** | SP94 | 40fr + 13fr Admiring | 5.00 | 5.00 |
| | | *Nos. B347-B351 (5)* | 9.00 | 9.45 |

Surtax was for charitable organizations.

**1985, Dec. 5 Photo.**

| | | | | |
|---|---|---|---|---|
| **B352** | SP94 | 4fr + 1fr Girl drawing | .50 | .50 |
| **B353** | SP94 | 7fr + 1fr Two boys | .60 | .60 |
| **B354** | SP94 | 10fr + 1fr Adoration of the Magi | .90 | .90 |
| **B355** | SP94 | 16fr + 2fr Fairy tale characters | 2.00 | 2.00 |
| **B356** | SP94 | 40fr + 13fr Embarrassed girl | 6.50 | 6.50 |
| | | *Nos. B352-B356 (5)* | 10.50 | 10.50 |

Surtax was for charitable organizations.

SP95

Christmas: Illuminated text — No. B357, Annunciation. No. B358, Angel appears to the Shepherds. No. B359, Nativity. No. B360, Adoration of the Magi. No. B361, Flight into Egypt.

**1986, Dec. 8 Photo. *Perf. 11½***

| | | | | |
|---|---|---|---|---|
| **B357** | SP95 | 6fr + 1fr multi | .90 | .90 |
| **B358** | SP95 | 10fr + 1fr multi | .60 | .60 |
| **B359** | SP95 | 12fr + 2fr multi | .90 | .90 |
| **B360** | SP95 | 18fr + 2fr multi | 1.75 | 1.75 |
| **B361** | SP95 | 20fr + 8fr multi | 4.25 | 4.25 |
| | | *Nos. B357-B361 (5)* | 8.40 | 8.40 |

SP96

No. B362, Annunciation. No. B363, Visitation. No. B364, Adoration of the Magi. No. B365, Presentation in the Temple. No. B366, Flight into Egypt.

**1987, Dec. 1** *Perf. 12*

**B362** SP96 6fr + 1fr multi .60 .60
**B363** SP96 10fr + 1fr multi .90 .90
**B364** SP96 12fr + 2fr multi 1.50 1.50
**B365** SP96 18fr + 2fr multi 2.40 2.40
**B366** SP96 20fr + 8fr multi 4.75 4.75
*Nos. B362-B366 (5)* 10.15 10.15

Book of Hours, France, c. 1550, Natl. Library — SP97

No. B367, Annunciation to the Shepherds. No. B368, Adoration of the Magi. No. B369, Virgin and Child. No. B370, Pentecost.

**1988, Dec. 5** *Perf. 11½*

**B367** SP97 9fr +1fr multi .60 .60
**B368** SP97 12fr +2fr multi .60 .60
**B369** SP97 18fr +2fr multi 2.00 2.00
**B370** SP97 20fr +8fr multi 2.75 2.75
*Nos. B367-B370 (4)* 5.95 5.95

Surtax for charitable organizations.

Christmas SP98

Chapels: No. B371, St. Lambert and St. Blase, Fennange, vert. No. B372, St. Quirinus, Luxembourg. No. B373, St. Anthony the Hermit, Reisdorf, vert. No. B374, The Hermitage, Hachiville.

**1989, Dec. 11** **Photo.** *Perf. 12x11½*

**B371** SP98 9fr +1fr multi .45 .45
**B372** SP98 12fr +2fr multi .60 .60
**B373** SP98 18fr +3fr multi 1.75 1.75
**B374** SP98 25fr +8fr multi 2.75 2.75
*Nos. B371-B374 (4)* 5.55 5.55

Surtax for social work.

**1990, Nov. 26** **Photo.** *Perf. 11½*

Chapels: No. B375, Congregation of the Blessed Virgin Mary, Vianden, vert. No. B376, Our Lady, Echternach. No. B377, Our Lady, Consoler of the Afflicted, Grentzingen. B378, St. Pirmin, Kaundorf, vert.

**B375** SP98 9fr +1fr multi .50 .50
**B376** SP98 12fr +2fr multi 1.00 1.00
**B377** SP98 18fr +3fr multi 2.00 1.50
**B378** SP98 25fr +8fr multi 3.50 3.50
*Nos. B375-B378 (4)* 7.00 6.50

Surtax for charitable organizations.

**1991, Dec. 9** **Photo.** *Perf. 11½*

Chapels: No. B379, St. Donatus, Arsdorf, vert. No. B380, Our Lady of Sorrows, Brandenbourg. No. B381, Our Lady, Luxembourg. No. B382, The Hermitage, Wolwelange, vert.

**B379** SP98 14fr +2fr multi .90 .90
**B380** SP98 14fr +2fr multi .90 .90
**B381** SP98 18fr +3fr multi 1.75 1.75
**B382** SP98 22fr +7fr multi 3.00 3.00
*Nos. B379-B382 (4)* 6.55 6.55

Surtax used for philanthropic work.

Endangered Birds — SP99

Designs: No. B383, Hazel grouse. No. B384, Golden oriole, vert. 18fr+3fr, Black stork. 22fr+7fr, Red kite, vert.

**1992, Dec. 7** **Photo.** *Perf. 11½*

**B383** SP99 14fr +2fr multi .90 .90
**B384** SP99 14fr +2fr multi .90 .90
**B385** SP99 18fr +3fr multi 2.75 2.25
**B386** SP99 22fr +7fr multi 3.75 3.25
*Nos. B383-B386 (4)* 8.30 7.30

Surtax for Luxembourg charitable organizations.

**1993, Dec. 6** **Photo.** *Perf. 11½*

Designs: No. B387, Snipe. No. B388, Kingfisher, vert. 18fr+3fr, Little ringed plover. 22fr+7fr, Sand martin, vert.

**B387** SP99 14fr +2fr multi .90 .90
**B388** SP99 14fr +2fr multi .90 .90
**B389** SP99 18fr +3fr multi 2.75 1.75
**B390** SP99 22fr +7fr multi 4.00 2.75
*Nos. B387-B390 (4)* 8.55 6.30

Surtax for Luxembourg charitable organizations.

**1994, Sept. 19** **Photo.** *Perf. 11½*

Designs: No. B391, Partridge. No. B392, Stonechat, vert. 18fr+3fr, Blue-headed wagtail. 22fr+7fr, Great grey shrike, vert.

**B391** SP99 14fr +2fr multi 1.00 .90
**B392** SP99 14fr +2fr multi 1.00 .90
**B393** SP99 18fr +3fr multi 2.75 2.25
**B394** SP99 22fr +7fr multi 3.50 2.50
*Nos. B391-B394 (4)* 8.25 6.55

Christmas — SP100

Design: 16fr + 2fr, Stained glass window, parish church of Alzingen.

**1995, Dec. 4** **Photo.** *Perf. 11½*

**B395** SP100 16fr +2fr multi 2.50 1.75

Surtax for Luxembourg charitable organizations.

Trees — SP101

Designs: No. B396, Tilia platyphyllos. No. B397, Aesculus hippocastanum, horiz. 20fr+3fr, Quercus pedunculata, horiz. 32fr+7fr, Betula pendula.

**1995, Dec. 4**

**B396** SP101 16fr +2fr multi .90 .90
**B397** SP101 16fr +2fr multi .90 .90
**B398** SP101 20fr +3fr multi 1.75 1.75
**B399** SP101 32fr +7fr multi 2.75 2.75
*Nos. B396-B399 (4)* 6.30 6.30

Surtax for Luxembourg charitable organizations.
See Nos. B400-B403, B405-B408.

**1996, Dec. 9**

Designs: No. B400, Fraxinus excelsior. No. B401, Salix SSP, horiz. 20fr+3fr, Sorbus domestica, horiz. 32fr+7fr, Fagus silvatica.

**B400** SP101 16fr +2fr multi .90 .90
**B401** SP101 16fr +2fr multi .90 .90
**B402** SP101 20fr +3fr multi 1.75 1.75
**B403** SP101 32fr +7fr multi 3.00 3.00
*Nos. B400-B403 (4)* 6.55 6.55

Surtax for Luxembourg charitable organizations.

Christmas SP102

**1996, Dec. 9**

**B404** SP102 16fr +2fr multi 1.50 1.50

Surtax for Luxembourg charitable organizations.

**Tree Type of 1995**

Designs: No. B405, Ulmus glabra. No. B406, Acer platanoides. 20fr+3fr, Prunus avium. 32fr+7fr, Juglans regia, horiz.

**1997, Dec. 8** **Photo.** *Perf. 11½*

**B405** SP101 16fr +2fr multi .90 .90
**B406** SP101 16fr +2fr multi .90 .90
**B407** SP101 20fr +3fr multi 2.00 2.00
**B408** SP101 32fr +7fr multi 2.75 2.50
*Nos. B405-B408 (4)* 6.55 6.30

Christmas SP103

**1997, Dec. 8**

**B409** SP103 16fr +2fr multi 1.50 1.50

Christmas SP104

**1998, Dec. 7** **Photo.** *Perf. 11½*

**B410** SP104 16fr +2fr multi 1.50 1.50

Charity Stamps SP105

Drawings of villages by Abbot Jean Bertels, 16th cent.: No. B411, Bech. No. B412, Ermesturf (Ermsdorf). 20fr+3fr, Itsich (Itzig). 32fr+7fr, Steinhem (Steinheim).

**1998, Dec. 7**

**B411** SP105 16fr +2fr grn & multi 1.00 1.00
**B412** SP105 16fr +2fr brn & multi 1.00 1.00
**B413** SP105 20fr +3fr red & multi 1.25 1.25
**B414** SP105 32fr +7fr blue & multi 2.25 2.25
*Nos. B411-B414 (4)* 5.50 5.50

See Nos. B415-B418, B420-B423.

*Perf. 11¾x11½*
**1999, Nov. 30** **Photo.**

Drawings of villages by Abbot Jean Bertels, 16th cent.: No. B415, Oswiler (Osweiler). No. B416, Bettemburch (Bettembourg). 20fr+3fr, Cruchte auf der Alset (Cruchten). 32fr+7fr, Berchem.

**B415** SP105 16fr +2fr red vio & multi 1.25 1.25
**B416** SP105 16fr +2fr blue & multi 1.25 1.25
**B417** SP105 20fr +3fr bl grn & multi 1.25 1.25
**B418** SP105 32fr +7fr brown & multi 2.25 2.25
*Nos. B415-B418 (4)* 6.00 6.00

Surtax for Luxembourg charitable organizations.

Christmas SP106

**1999, Nov. 30** *Perf. 11¾*

**B419** SP106 16fr +2fr multi 1.25 1.25

Surtax for Luxembourg charitable organizations.

**Village Drawings Type of 1998**

By Abbot Jean Bertels, 16th cent.: 18fr+2fr, Lorentzwiler (Lorentzweiler). 21fr+3fr, Costurf (Consdorf). 24fr+3fr, Elfingen (Elvange). 36fr+7fr, Sprenckigen (Sprinkange).

**2000, Dec. 5** **Photo.** *Perf. 11¾x11½*
**Granite Paper**

**B420** SP105 18fr +2fr grn & multi .90 .90
**B421** SP105 21fr +3fr brn & multi 1.25 1.25
**B422** SP105 24fr +3fr red & multi 1.25 1.25
**B423** SP105 36fr +7fr bl & multi 2.25 2.25
*Nos. B420-B423 (4)* 5.65 5.65

Surtax for Luxembourg charitable organizations.

Christmas SP107

**2000, Dec. 5** *Perf. 11¾*
**Granite Paper**

**B424** SP107 18fr +2fr multi 2.00 2.00

Surtax for Luxembourg charitable organizations.

Christmas SP108

**2001, Dec. 6** **Photo.** *Perf. 14*

**B425** SP108 45c +5c (18fr+2fr) multi 1.25 1.25

See note before No. 1063. A star-shaped hole is found at the UL portion of the design.

Fauna SP109

Designs: 45c+5c (18fr+2fr), Squirrel. 52c+8c (21fr+3fr), Wild boar. 59c+11c (24fr+4fr), Hare, vert. 89c+21c (36fr+8fr), Wood pigeon, vert.

*Perf. 11¾x11½, 11½x11¾*
**2001, Dec. 6** **Granite Paper**

**B426-B429** SP109 Set of 4 7.00 7.00

Christmas SP110

**2002, Dec. 10** **Photo.** *Perf. 13¾*

**B430** SP110 45c +5c multi 1.25 1.25

Surtax for Grand Duchess Charlotte charities.

Fauna SP111

Designs: 45c+5c, Red fox. 52c+8c, Hedgehog and snail, vert. 59c+11c, Pheasant. 89c+21c, Deer, vert.

**2002, Dec. 10** ***Perf. 11½***
**B431-B434** SP111 Set of 4 7.00 7.00

Christmas — SP112

No. B435: a, Round Church of Ehnen, Christmas tree. b, Wormer Koeppchen Chapel.

**2003, Dec. 9** **Litho.** ***Perf. 14¼***
**B435** SP112 50c +5c Pair, #a-b 2.75 2.75

Surtax for Luxembourg charitable organizations.

Fauna
SP113

Designs: 50c+5c, Roe deer, vert. 60c+10c, Raccoons. 70c+10c, Weasel, vert. €1+25c, Goshawk.

**2003, Dec. 9** **Photo.** ***Perf. 11½***
**B436-B439** SP113 Set of 4 8.00 8.00

Surtax for Luxembourg charitable organizations.

Christmas
SP114

**Litho. & Embossed**

**2004, Dec. 7** ***Perf. 13***
**B440** SP114 50c +5c multi 1.50 1.50

Sports
SP115

Designs: 50c+5c, Skiing. 60c+10c, Running, vert. 70c+10c, Swimming. €1+25c, Soccer, vert.

***Perf. 13x13½, 13½x13***

**2004, Dec. 7** **Litho.**
**B441-B444** SP115 Set of 4 8.75 8.75

See Nos. B446-B449.

Christmas
SP116

**2005, Dec. 6** **Litho.** ***Perf. 13¼***
**B445** SP116 50c +5c multi 1.40 1.40

**Sports Type of 2004**

Designs: 50c+5c, Figure skating, vert. 70c+10c, Basketball, vert. 90c+10c, Judo, vert. €1+25c, Tennis, vert.

**2005, Dec. 6** ***Perf. 13½x13***
**B446-B449** SP115 Set of 4 8.50 8.50

Christmas
SP117

**2006, Dec. 5** **Litho.** ***Perf. 12½***
**B450** SP117 50c +5c multi 1.40 1.40

Modern Pipe
Organs
SP118

Organ from: 50c+5c, Grand Auditorium of the Luxembourg Music Conservatory. 70c+10c, Bridel. 90c+10c, Mondercange Parish Church. €1+25c, Luxembourg-Grund.

**2006, Dec. 5** ***Perf. 13¼x13***
**B451-B454** SP118 Set of 4 9.25 9.25

See Nos. B456-B459, B461-B464, B466-B469.

Christmas
SP119

**2007, Dec. 4** **Litho.** ***Perf. 12½***
**B455** SP119 50c +5c multi 1.60 1.60

**Modern Pipe Organs Type of 2006**

Organ from: 50c+5c, Church of Niederwiltz. 70c+10c, Sandweiler, horiz. 90c+10c, Echternacht Basilica, horiz. €1+25c, St. Joseph's Church, Esch-sur-Alzette.

**2007, Dec. 4** ***Perf. 13½x13, 13x13½***
**B456-B459** SP118 Set of 4 10.50 10.50

Christmas
SP120

**2008, Dec. 2** **Litho.** ***Perf. 12½***
**B460** SP120 50c +5c multi 1.40 1.40

**Modern Pipe Organs Type of 2006**

Organ from: 50c+5c, Junglinster. 70c+10c, Church, Mondorf-les-Bains, horiz. 90c+10c, Church, Vianden. €1+25c, Notre Dame Cathedral, Luxembourg.

**2008, Dec. 2** ***Perf. 13½x13, 13x13½***
**B461-B464** SP118 Set of 4 9.25 9.25

Christmas
SP121

**2009, Dec. 1** **Litho.** ***Perf. 12½***
**B465** SP121 50c + 5c multi 1.75 1.75

**Modern Pipe Organs Type of 2006**

Organ from: 50c+5c, Luxembourg Philharmonic. 70c+10c, St. Martin's Church, Dudelange. 90c+10c, Church, Nommern. 1fr+25c, Saint-Pierre aux Liens Church, Heiderscheid.

**2009, Dec. 1** ***Perf. 13½x13***
**B466-B469** SP118 Set of 4 11.00 11.00

Christmas
SP122

**2010, Dec. 7** **Litho.** ***Perf. 12½***
**B470** SP122 60c + 5c multi 1.90 1.90

Occupations of the
Past — SP123

Designs: 60c+5c, Blacksmith. 85c+10c, Basketmaker. €1.10+10c, Grinder, horiz. €1.20+25c, Cooper, horiz.

**Litho. & Embossed With Foil Application**

**2010, Dec. 7** ***Perf. 13¼x13, 13x13¼***
**B471-B474** SP123 Set of 4 12.00 12.00

See Nos. B476-B479, B482-B485, B488-B491.

Christmas
SP124

**2011, Dec. 6** **Litho.** ***Perf. 12½***
**B475** SP124 60c+5c multi 1.75 1.75

No. B475 is impregnated with a pine scent.

**Occupations of the Past Type of 2010**

Designs: 60c+5c, Wood joiner (schräiner). 85c+10c, Potter (aulebacker). €1.10+10c, Stonemason (steemetzer), horiz. €1.20+25c, Printer (buchdréker), horiz.

**Litho. & Embossed With Foil Application**

**2011, Dec. 6** ***Perf. 13¼x13, 13x13¼***
**B476-B479** SP123 Set of 4 11.50 11.50

Christmas
SP125

Stars, Christmas tree and: 60c+5c, Open mailbox. 85c+10c, Open envelope.

**Litho. With Foil Application**

**2012, Dec. 4** ***Perf. 13¼***
**B480-B481** SP125 Set of 2 4.25 4.25

**Occupations of the Past Type of 2010**

Designs: 60c+5c, Washerwomen, horiz. 85c+10c, Hatter. €1.10+10c, Farmer. €1.20+25c, Vegetable sellers, horiz.

**Litho. & Embossed With Foil Application**

**2012, Dec. 4** ***Perf. 13x13¼, 13¼x13***
**B482-B485** SP123 Set of 4 11.00 11.00

Christmas
SP126

Designs: 60c+5c, One Christmas ornament. 85c+10c, Two Christmas ornaments.

**2013, Dec. 3** **Litho.** ***Perf. 13***
**B486-B487** SP126 Set of 2 4.50 4.50

Nos. B486 and B487 have laser-cut holes as part of the design.

**Occupations of the Past Type of 2010**

Designs: 60c+5c, Miller. 85c+10c, Distiller, horiz. €1.10+10c, Wheelwright. €1.20+25c, Cobbler, horiz.

**Litho. & Embossed With Foil Application**

**2013, Dec. 3** ***Perf. 13¼x13, 13x13¼***
**B488-B491** SP123 Set of 4 12.00 12.00

Christmas
SP127

Designs: 60c+5c, Fox and rabbit. 85c+10c, Owl and mouse.

**2014, Dec. 2** **Litho.** ***Perf. 14¼***

**Flocked Granite Paper**

**B492-B493** SP127 Set of 2 4.00 4.00

Automobiles — SP128

Designs: 60c+5c, 1899 De Dion-Bouton Vis-à-vis Type D. 85c+10c, 1904 Peugeot Bébé. €1.10+10c, 1909 Opel 10/20. €1.20+25c, 1910 Renault AX.

### Litho. & Embossed With Foil Application

**2014, Dec. 2** *Perf. 13x13¼*
**B494-B497** SP128 Set of 4 10.50 10.50

See Nos. B500-B503, B506-B509.

Christmas
SP129

Trees in winter with denomination in: 70c+5c, Blue. 95c+10c, Orange.

### Litho. & Thermography

**2015, Dec. 1** *Perf. 13¼*
**B498-B499** SP129 Set of 2 4.00 4.00

### Automobiles Type of 2014

Designs: 70c+5c, 1913 Philos A 4M. 95c+10c, 1914 Morris Oxford Bullnose. €1.30+10c, 1918 Delaunay Belleville. €1.40+25c, 1919 Berliet V8.

### Litho. & Embossed

**2015, Dec. 1** *Perf. 13x13¼*
**B500-B503** SP128 Set of 4 10.50 10.50

Christmas
SP130

St. Nicholas with: 70c+5c, Boy. 95c+10c, Girl and crowd.

**2016, Dec. 6** **Litho.** *Perf. 13*
**B504-B505** SP130 Set of 2 3.75 3.75

### Automobiles Type of 2014

Designs: 70c+5c, 1924 Ford Model T. 95c+10c, 1924 Donnet Zedel CI-6. €1.30+10c, 1927 Paige 6-45 sedan. €1.40+25c, 1928 Chenard Walcker Z5.

### Litho. & Embossed

**2016, Dec. 6** *Perf. 13x13¼*
**B506-B509** SP128 Set of 4 10.00 10.00

Christmas
SP131

Designs: 70c+5c, Boy kissing girl. 95c+10c, Children putting star on top of Christmas tree.

**2017, Dec. 5** **Litho.** *Perf. 13*
**B510-B511** SP131 Set of 2 4.50 4.50

### Automobiles Type of 2014

Designs: 70c+5c, 1931 Packard Standard Eight 833. 95c+10c, 1934 Rolls-Royce 20/25. €1.30+10c, 1936 Panhard & Levassor Panoramique 6DS X71. €1.40+25c, 1940 Buick 56C.

### Litho. & Embossed

**2017, Dec. 5** *Perf. 13x13¼*
**B512-B515** SP128 Set of 4 12.00 12.00

## AIR POST STAMPS

Airplane over Luxembourg — AP1

**1931-33** **Unwmk.** **Engr.** *Perf. 12½*
**C1** AP1 50c green ('33) .55 *1.10*
**C2** AP1 75c dark brown .55 *1.50*
**C3** AP1 1fr red .55 *1.50*
**C4** AP1 1¼fr dark violet .55 *1.50*
**C5** AP1 1¾fr dark blue .55 *1.50*
**C6** AP1 3fr gray black ('33) 1.10 *5.00*
*Nos. C1-C6 (6)* 3.85 *12.10*
Set, never hinged 9.50

Aerial View of Moselle River — AP2

Wing and View of Luxembourg AP3

Vianden Castle — AP4

**1946, June 7** **Photo.** *Perf. 11½*
**C7** AP2 1fr dk ol grn & gray .25 .25
**C8** AP3 2fr chnt brn & buff .25 *.25*
**C9** AP4 3fr sepia & brown .25 *.25*
**C10** AP2 4fr dp vio & gray vio .25 *.40*
**C11** AP3 5fr dp mag & buff .25 *.40*
**C12** AP4 6fr dk brown & gray .25 *.55*
**C13** AP2 10fr henna brn & buff .40 *.55*
**C14** AP3 20fr dk blue & cream .80 *2.00*
**C15** AP4 50fr dk green & gray 1.25 2.50
*Nos. C7-C15 (9)* 3.95 7.15
Set, never hinged 8.00

1852 and 1952 AP5

### Stamps in Gray and Dark Violet Brown

**1952, May 24**
**C16** AP5 80c olive grn .25 .45
**C17** AP5 2.50fr brt car .50 1.00
**C18** AP5 4fr brt blue 1.60 2.50
**C19** AP5 8fr brown red 17.50 *40.00*
**C20** AP5 10fr dull brown 15.00 *30.00*
*Nos. C16-C20 (5)* 34.85 *73.95*
Set, never hinged 75.00

Centenary of Luxembourg's postage stamps. Nos. C16-C18 were available at face, but complete sets sold for 45.30fr, which included admission to the CENTILUX exhibition.

## POSTAGE DUE STAMPS

Coat of Arms — D1

**1907** **Unwmk.** **Typo.** *Perf. 12½*
**J1** D1 5c green & black .25 *.25*
**J2** D1 10c green & black .95 .25
**J3** D1 12½c green & black .25 *.80*
**J4** D1 20c green & black .55 *.80*
**J5** D1 25c green & black 16.00 1.20
**J6** D1 50c green & black .45 *3.50*
**J7** D1 1fr green & black .25 *3.50*
*Nos. J1-J7 (7)* 18.70 10.30

See Nos. J10-J22.

Nos. J3, J5 Surcharged

**1920**
**J8** D1 15c on 12½c .50 *7.25*
**J9** D1 30c on 25c .60 *9.00*
Set, never hinged 3.50

### Arms Type of 1907

**1921-35**
**J10** D1 5c green & red .25 *.40*
**J11** D1 10c green & red .25 *.35*
**J12** D1 20c green & red .25 *.35*
**J13** D1 25c green & red .25 *.35*
**J14** D1 30c green & red .55 *.60*
**J15** D1 35c green & red ('35) .55 .35
**J16** D1 50c green & red .55 *.60*
**J17** D1 60c green & red ('28) .45 *.50*
**J18** D1 70c green & red ('35) .55 .35
**J19** D1 75c green & red ('30) .55 .25
**J20** D1 1fr green & red .55 *1.10*
**J21** D1 2fr green & red ('30) .55 *6.50*
**J22** D1 3fr green & red ('30) 1.60 *18.00*
*Nos. J10-J22 (13)* 6.90 29.70
Set, never hinged 27.50

D2

D3

**1946-48** **Photo.** *Perf. 11½*
**J23** D2 5c bright green .25 *.65*
**J24** D2 10c bright green .25 *.50*
**J25** D2 20c bright green .25 *.50*
**J26** D2 30c bright green .25 *.50*
**J27** D2 50c bright green .25 *.70*
**J28** D2 70c bright green .25 *.70*
**J29** D3 75c brt green ('48) .70 .25
**J30** D3 1fr carmine .25 *.25*
**J31** D3 1.50fr carmine .25 *.25*
**J32** D3 2fr carmine .25 *.25*
**J33** D3 3fr carmine .25 *.35*
**J34** D3 5fr carmine .55 .45
**J35** D3 10fr carmine .95 *4.00*
**J36** D3 20fr carmine 2.75 *22.50*
*Nos. J23-J36 (14)* 7.45 31.85
Set, never hinged 22.50

## OFFICIAL STAMPS

Forged overprints on Nos. O1-O64 abound.

Unused values of Nos. O1-O51 are for stamps without gum. Though these stamps were issued with gum, most examples offered are without gum. Stamps with original gum sell for somewhat more.

Regular Issues Overprinted Reading Diagonally Up or Down

### Frankfurt Print

***Rouletted in Color except 2c***

**1875** **Unwmk.**
**O1** A2 1c red brown 27.50 37.50
**O2** A2 2c black 27.50 37.50
**O3** A3 10c lilac 2,400. 2,400.
**O4** A3 12½c rose 475.00 600.00
**O5** A3 20c gray brn 37.50 57.50
**O6** A3 25c blue 250.00 140.00
**O7** A3 25c ultra 2,100. 1,400.
**O8** A3 30c lilac rose 32.50 *75.00*
**O9** A3 40c pale org 160.00 240.00
*a.* 40c org red, thick paper 250.00 325.00
*c.* As "a," thin paper 1,650. 1,400.
**O10** A3 1fr on 37½c bis 150.00 22.50

Double overprints exist on Nos. O1-O6, O8-O10.

Overprints reading diagonally down sell for more.

### Inverted Overprint

*O1a* A2 1c 190.00 225.00
*O2a* A2 2c 190.00 225.00
*O3a* A3 10c 2,500. 2,500.
*O4a* A3 12½c 650.00 925.00
*O5a* A3 20c 55.00 75.00
*O6a* A3 25c 1,100. 1,300.
*O7a* A3 25c 2,100. 1,500.
*O8a* A3 30c 650.00 925.00
*O9b* A3 40c pale orange 325.00 450.00
*O10a* A3 1fr on 37½c 175.00 75.00

### Luxembourg Print

**1875-76** *Perf. 13*
**O11** A2 1c red brown 9.50 27.50
**O12** A2 2c black 12.00 32.50
**O13** A2 4c green 90.00 160.00
**O14** A2 5c yellow 65.00 80.00
*a.* 5c orange yellow 75.00 110.00
**O15** A3 10c gray lilac 92.50 120.00
**O16** A3 12½c rose 85.00 120.00
**O17** A3 12½c lilac rose 225.00 275.00
**O18** A3 25c blue 11.00 *32.50*
**O19** A3 1fr on 37½c bis 35.00 60.00
*Nos. O11-O19 (9)* 625.00 907.50

Double overprints exist on Nos. O11-O15.

### Inverted Overprint

*O11a* A2 1c 92.50 *110.00*
*O12a* A2 2c 150.00 190.00
*O13a* A2 4c 160.00 190.00
*O14b* A2 5c 500.00 650.00
*O15a* A3 10c 500.00 190.00
*O16a* A3 12½c 400.00 550.00
*O17a* A3 12½c 450.00 525.00
*O18a* A3 25c 125.00 175.00
*O19a* A5 1fr on 37½c 190.00 250.00
*Nos. O11a-O19a (9)* 2,568. 2,830.

### Haarlem Print

**1880** ***Perf. 11½x12, 12½x12, 13½***
**O22** A3 25c blue 2.25 2.75

Overprinted

### Frankfurt Print

**1878** ***Rouletted in Color***
**O23** A2 1c red brown 140.00 160.00
**O25** A3 20c gray brn 190.00 225.00
**O26** A3 30c lilac rose 750.00 575.00
**O27** A3 40c orange 325.00 450.00
**O28** A3 1fr on 37½c bis 550.00 110.00
*Nos. O23-O28 (5)* 1,955. 1,520.

### Inverted Overprint

*O23a* A2 1c 225.00 300.00
*O25a* A3 20c 325.00 400.00
*O26a* A3 30c 925.00 700.00
*O27a* A3 40c 875.00 925.00
*O28a* A3 1fr on 37½c 650.00 200.00

### Luxembourg Print

**1878-80** *Perf. 13*
**O29** A2 1c red brown 750.00 925.00
**O30** A2 2c black 190.00 225.00
**O31** A2 4c green 190.00 225.00
**O32** A2 5c yellow 375.00 450.00
**O33** A3 10c gray lilac 375.00 400.00
**O34** A3 12½c rose 65.00 110.00
**O35** A3 25c blue 525.00 550.00
*Nos. O29-O35 (7)* 2,470. 2,885.

### Inverted Overprint

*O29a* A2 1c 140.00 160.00
*O30a* A2 2c 14.50 27.50
*O31a* A2 4c 150.00 190.00
*O32a* A2 5c 1,500. 1,500.
*O33a* A3 10c 92.50 110.00
*O34a* A3 12½c 525.00 600.00
*O35a* A3 25c 850.00 1,000.

Overprinted

### Frankfurt Print

**1881** ***Rouletted in Color***
**O39** A3 40c orange 37.50 75.00
*a.* Inverted overprint 210.00 275.00

"S.P." are initials of "Service Public."

### Luxembourg Print
*Perf. 13*

**O40** A2 1c red brown 125.00 160.00
**O41** A2 4c green 175.00 200.00
a. Inverted overprint 250.00
**O42** A2 5c yellow 600.00 750.00
**O43** A3 1fr on 37½c bis 32.50 47.50
*Nos. O40-O43 (4)* 932.50 1,158.

### Haarlem Print
*Perf. 11½x12, 12½x12, 13½*

**O44** A2 1c yellow brn 8.50 9.25
**O45** A2 2c black 9.25 9.25
**O46** A2 5c yellow 160.00 200.00
a. Inverted overprint 225.00
**O47** A3 10c gray lilac 160.00 200.00
**O48** A3 12½c rose 175.00 240.00
**O49** A3 20c gray brown 72.50 92.50
**O50** A3 25c blue 72.50 92.50
**O51** A3 30c dull rose 75.00 120.00
*Nos. O44-O51 (8)* 732.75 963.50

Stamps of the 1881 issue with the overprint of the 1882 issue shown below were never issued.

Overprinted

*Perf. 11½x12, 12½x12, 12½, 13½*

**1882**

**O52** A6 1c gray lilac .25 .40
**O53** A6 2c ol gray .25 .40
a. "S" omitted 110.00
**O54** A6 4c ol bister .25 .45
**O55** A6 5c lt green .25 .55
**O56** A6 10c rose 12.00 16.00
**O57** A6 12½c slate 1.60 4.75
**O58** A6 20c orange 1.60 4.00
**O59** A6 25c ultra 19.00 24.00
**O60** A6 30c gray grn 4.00 8.75
**O61** A6 50c bis brown .95 2.75
**O62** A6 1fr pale vio .95 4.00
**O63** A6 5fr brown org 16.00 40.00
*Nos. O52-O63 (12)* 57.10 106.05

Nos. O52-O63 exist without one or both periods, also with varying space between "S" and "P." Nine denominations exist with double overprint, six with inverted overprint.

Overprinted

**1883** *Perf. 13½*

**O64** A6 5fr brown org *2,200. 2,200.*

Overprinted

**1891-93** *Perf. 11, 11½, 11½x11, 12½*

**O65** A7 10c carmine .25 .50
a. Sheet of 25 55.00
**O66** A7 12½c slate grn 8.00 7.25
**O67** A7 20c orange 13.00 8.50
**O68** A7 25c blue .25 .45
a. Sheet of 25 65.00
**O69** A7 30c olive grn 8.00 8.00
**O70** A7 37½c green 8.00 8.00
**O71** A7 50c brown 6.00 8.75
**O72** A7 1fr dp vio 8.00 9.50
**O73** A7 2½fr black 45.00 72.50
**O74** A7 5fr lake 40.00 55.00
*Nos. O65-O74 (10)* 136.50 178.45

**1895** *Perf. 12½*

**O75** A8 1c pearl gray 1.90 2.50
**O76** A8 2c gray brn .75 2.00
**O77** A8 4c olive bis .75 2.00
**O78** A8 5c green 2.25 3.50
**O79** A8 10c carmine 40.00 40.00
*Nos. O75-O79 (5)* 45.65 50.00

Nos. O66-O79 exist without overprint and perforated "OFFICIEL" through the stamp. Values for set: unused, $12; used, $45.

Nos. O65a and O68a were issued to commemorate the coronation of Grand Duke Adolphe.

Regular Issue of 1906-26 Overprinted

**1908-26** *Perf. 11x11½, 12½*

**O80** A9 1c gray .25 .40
a. Inverted overprint 125.00
**O81** A9 2c olive brn .25 .40
**O82** A9 4c bister .25 .40
a. Double overprint 140.00
**O83** A9 5c green .25 .40
**O84** A9 5c lilac ('26) .25 .40
**O85** A9 6c violet .25 .40
**O86** A9 7½c org ('19) .25 .40
**O87** A10 10c scarlet .25 .40
**O88** A10 12½c slate grn .25 *.55*
**O89** A10 15c orange brn .25 *.55*
**O90** A10 20c orange .25 *.75*
**O91** A10 25c ultra .25 *.75*
**O92** A10 30c olive grn 2.75 *6.50*
**O93** A10 37½c green .45 .75
**O94** A10 50c brown .75 *1.50*
**O95** A10 87½c dk blue 2.00 *3.50*
**O96** A10 1fr violet 2.75 *4.00*
**O97** A10 2½fr vermilion 75.00 65.00
**O98** A10 5fr claret 55.00 40.00
*Nos. O80-O98 (19)* 141.70 132.05

### On Regular Issue of 1914-17

**1915-17**

**O99** A11 10c lake .25 *.75*
**O100** A11 12½c dull grn .25 *.75*
**O101** A11 15c olive blk .25 *.75*
**O102** A11 17½c dp brn ('17) .25 *.75*
**O103** A11 25c ultra .25 *.75*
**O104** A11 30c bister 1.40 *5.00*
**O105** A11 35c dk blue .25 *1.20*
**O106** A11 37½c blk brn .25 *1.60*
**O107** A11 40c orange .30 *1.20*
**O108** A11 50c dk gray .30 *.95*
**O109** A11 62½c blue grn .30 *1.60*
**O110** A11 87½c org ('17) .30 *1.60*
**O111** A11 1fr orange brn .30 *1.60*
**O112** A11 2½fr red .30 *2.50*
**O113** A11 5fr dk violet .30 *2.75*
*Nos. O99-O113 (15)* 5.25 23.75

### On Regular Issues of 1921-26 in Black

**1922-26** *Perf. 11½, 11½x11, 12½*

**O114** A12 2c brown .25 .25
**O115** A12 3c olive grn .25 .25
**O116** A12 6c violet .25 .40
**O117** A12 10c yellow grn .25 .40
**O118** A12 10c ol grn ('24) .25 .40
**O119** A12 15c brown ol .25 .40
**O120** A12 15c pale grn ('24) .25 .40
**O121** A12 15c dp org ('26) .25 .40
**O122** A12 20c dp orange .25 .40
**O123** A12 20c yel grn ('26) .25 .40
**O124** A12 25c dk green .25 .40
**O125** A12 30c car rose .25 .40
**O126** A12 40c brown org .25 .40
**O127** A12 50c dp blue .25 .45
**O128** A12 50c red ('24) .25 .55
**O129** A12 75c red .25 .55
**O130** A12 75c dp bl ('24) .25 .45
**O131** A12 80c black 4.75 8.00
**O132** A13 1fr carmine .40 2.00
**O133** A14 2fr indigo 3.00 6.00
**O134** A14 2fr dk brn ('26) 1.75 5.00
**O135** A15 5fr dk vio 17.50 40.00
*Nos. O114-O135 (22)* 31.65 67.90

### On Regular Issues of 1921-26 in Red

**1922-34** *Perf. 11, 11½, 11½x11, 12½*

**O136** A12 80c blk, perf. 11½ .25 .45
**O137** A13 1fr dk bl, perf. 11½ ('26) .25 1.20
**O138** A14 2fr ind, perf. 11½x11 .55 2.00
**O139** A17 3fr dk bl & bl, perf. 11 2.75 2.75
a. Perf. 11½ .60 1.40
b. Perf. 12½ .50 1.40
**O140** A15 5fr dk vio, perf. 11½x11 4.00 9.00
a. Perf. 12½ ('34) 12.00 20.00
**O141** A16 10fr blk, perf. 11½ 12.00 24.00
a. Perf. 12½ 12.00 27.50
*Nos. O136-O141 (6)* 19.80 39.40

### On Regular Issue of 1926-35

**1926-27** *Perf. 12*

**O142** A18 5c dk violet .25 .25
**O143** A18 10c olive grn .25 .25
**O144** A18 20c orange .25 .25
**O145** A18 25c yellow grn .25 .25
**O146** A18 25c blk brn ('27) .35 .55
**O147** A18 30c yel grn ('27) .65 1.20
**O148** A18 40c olive gray .25 .25
**O149** A18 50c red brown .25 .25
**O150** A18 65c black brn .25 .25
**O151** A18 75c rose .25 .25
**O152** A18 75c bis brn ('27) .35 .55
**O153** A18 80c bister brn .25 .40
**O154** A18 90c rose ('27) .35 .55
**O155** A18 1fr black .25 .45
**O156** A18 1¼fr dk blue .25 .45
**O157** A18 1¼fr dp blue ('27) .55 1.20
*Nos. O142-O157 (16)* 5.00 7.35

Type of Regular Issue, 1926-35, Overprinted

**1928-35** **Wmk. 213**

**O158** A18 5c dk violet .25 .40
**O159** A18 10c olive grn .25 .40
**O160** A18 15c black ('30) .25 1.20
**O161** A18 20c orange .45 .75
**O162** A18 25c violet brn .45 .75
**O163** A18 30c yellow grn .50 1.40
**O164** A18 30c gray vio ('30) .25 1.20
**O165** A18 35c yel grn ('30) .25 1.20
**O166** A18 35c gray vio .35 .90
**O167** A18 40c olive gray .35 .75
**O168** A18 50c red brown .35 .75
**O169** A18 60c blue grn .35 .75
**O170** A18 70c blue vio ('35) 3.50 7.25
**O171** A18 75c bister brn .35 .75
**O172** A18 90c rose .35 1.20
**O173** A18 1fr black .35 1.20
**O174** A18 1fr rose ('30) .45 2.40
**O175** A18 1¼fr yel ('30) 4.00 6.50
**O176** A18 1¼fr bl grn ('31) 1.50 4.00
**O177** A18 1½fr deep blue .35 1.40
**O178** A18 1¾fr dk blue ('30) .45 1.60
*Nos. O158-O178 (21)* 15.35 36.75

### Type of Regular Issues of 1928-31 Overprinted Like Nos. O80-O98

**1928-31** **Wmk. 216** *Perf. 11½*

**O179** A19 2fr black .50 1.60

**Wmk. 110** *Perf. 12½*

**O180** A21 20fr dp green ('31) 2.25 8.00

### No. 198 Overprinted Like Nos. O80-O98

**1934** **Unwmk.** *Perf. 14x13½*

**O181** A22 5fr blue green 2.10 6.00

### Type of Regular Issue of 1935 Overprinted Like Nos. O158-O178 in Red

**1935** **Wmk. 247** *Perf. 12½x12*

**O182** A23 10fr green 1.75 7.00

---

## OCCUPATION STAMPS

### Issued under German Occupation

Stamps of Germany, 1933-36, Overprinted in Black

**1940, Oct. 1** **Wmk. 237** *Perf. 14*

**N1** A64 3pf olive bis .25 *.25*
**N2** A64 4pf dull blue .25 *.25*
**N3** A64 5pf brt grn .25 *.25*
**N4** A64 6pf dark green .25 *.25*
**N5** A64 8pf vermilion .25 *.25*
**N6** A64 10pf chocolate .25 *.25*
**N7** A64 12pf deep car .25 *.25*
**N8** A64 15pf maroon .35 *.45*
a. Inverted overprint *450.00 1,300.*
**N9** A64 20pf bright blue .50 *.45*
**N10** A64 25pf ultra .50 *.60*
**N11** A64 30pf olive green .50 *.60*
**N12** A64 40pf red violet .50 *.75*
**N13** A64 50pf dk grn & blk .60 *.75*
**N14** A64 60pf claret & blk .90 *3.00*
**N15** A64 80pf dk blue & blk 2.25 *9.00*
**N16** A64 100pf org & blk 1.60 *4.50*
*Nos. N1-N16 (16)* 9.45 *21.85*
Set, never hinged 24.00

### Nos. 159-162, 164, 168-171, 173, 175, 179, 182, 216, 198-199 Surcharged in Black

a

b

c

d

*Perf. 12, 14x13½, 12½x12, 11½*

**1940, Dec. 5** **Unwmk.**

**N17** A18(a) 3rpf on 15c .25 *.35*
**N18** A18(a) 4rpf on 20c .25 *.35*
**N19** A18(a) 5rpf on 35c .25 *.35*
**N20** A18(a) 6rpf on 10c .25 *.35*
**N21** A18(a) 8rpf on 25c .25 *.35*
**N22** A18(a) 10rpf on 40c .25 *.35*
**N23** A18(a) 12rpf on 60c .25 *.35*
**N24** A18(a) 15rpf on 1fr rose .25 *.35*
**N25** A18(a) 20rpf on 50c .25 *.60*
**N26** A18(a) 25rpf on 5c .25 *1.20*
**N27** A18(a) 30rpf on 70c .25 *.60*
**N28** A18(a) 40rpf on 75c .30 *1.20*
**N29** A18(a) 50rpf on 1¼fr .25 *.60*
**N30** A35(b) 60rpf on 2fr 1.40 *9.50*
**N31** A22(c) 80rpf on 5fr .40 *2.00*
**N32** A23(d) 100rpf on 10fr .65 *2.75*
*Nos. N17-N32 (16)* 5.75 *21.25*
Set, never hinged 9.00

---

## OCCUPATION SEMI-POSTAL STAMPS

Semi-Postal Stamps of Germany, 1940 Overprinted in Black

**1941, Jan. 12** **Unwmk.** *Perf. 14*

**NB1** SP153 3pf + 2pf dk brn .25 *.45*
**NB2** SP153 4pf + 3pf bluish blk .25 *.45*
**NB3** SP153 5pf + 3pf yel grn .25 *.45*
**NB4** SP153 6pf + 4pf dk grn .25 *.45*
**NB5** SP153 8pf + 4pf dp org .25 *.45*
**NB6** SP153 12pf + 6pf carmine .25 *.45*
**NB7** SP153 15pf + 10pf dk vio brn 1.25 *1.60*
**NB8** SP153 25pf + 15pf dp ultra 1.25 *3.50*
**NB9** SP153 40pf + 35pf red lil 2.25 *6.00*
*Nos. NB1-NB9 (9)* 6.25 *13.80*
Set, never hinged 10.00

# ScottMounts

**Sign-up now to get weekly email exclusive online deals and the latest product updates. Visit AmosAdvantage.com/Newsletter and register today.**

| ITEM | W x H (mm) | DESCRIPTION | MOUNTS | RETAIL | AA* |
|---|---|---|---|---|---|
| **PRE-CUT SINGLE MOUNTS** | | | | | |
| 901 | 40 x 25 | U.S. Standard Comm. Hor. Water Activated | 40 | $3.50 | **$2.39** |
| 902 | 25 x 40 | U.S. Standard Comm. Vert. Water Activated | 40 | $3.50 | **$2.39** |
| 903 | 25 x 22 | U.S. Regular Issue – Hor. Water Activated | 40 | $3.50 | **$2.39** |
| 904 | 22 x 25 | U.S. Regular Issue – Vert. Water Activated | 40 | $3.50 | **$2.39** |
| 905 | 41 x 31 | U.S. Semi-Jumbo – Horizontal | 40 | $3.50 | **$2.39** |
| 906 | 31 x 41 | U.S. Semi-Jumbo – Vertical | 40 | $3.50 | **$2.39** |
| 907 | 50 x 31 | U.S. Jumbo – Horizontal | 40 | $3.50 | **$2.39** |
| 908 | 31 x 50 | U.S. Jumbo – Vertical | 40 | $3.50 | **$2.39** |
| 909 | 25 x 27 | U.S. Famous Americans/Champions Of Liberty | 40 | $3.50 | **$2.39** |
| 910 | 33 x 27 | United Nations | 40 | $3.50 | **$2.39** |
| 911 | 40 x 27 | United Nations | 40 | $3.50 | **$2.39** |
| 976 | 67 x 25 | Plate Number Coils, Strips of Three | 40 | $6.25 | **$3.99** |
| 984 | 67 x 34 | Pacific '97 Triangle | 10 | $3.50 | **$2.39** |
| 985 | 111 x 25 | Plate Number Coils, Strips of Five | 25 | $6.25 | **$3.99** |
| 986 | 51 x 36 | U.S. Hunting Permit/Express Mail | 40 | $6.25 | **$3.99** |
| 1045 | 40 x 26 | U.S. Standard Comm. Hor. Self-Adhesive | 40 | $3.50 | **$2.39** |
| 1046 | 25 x 41 | U.S. Standard Comm. Vert. Self-Adhesive | 40 | $3.50 | **$2.39** |
| 1047 | 22 x 26 | U.S. Definitives Vert. Self Adhesive | 40 | $3.50 | **$2.39** |
| 966 | Value Pack | (Assortment pre-cut sizes) | 320 | $23.25 | **$15.25** |
| 975 | Best Pack | (Assortment pre-cut sizes - Black Only) | 160 | $14.75 | **$9.99** |
| **PRE-CUT PLATE BLOCK, FDC, POSTAL CARD MOUNTS** | | | | | |
| 912 | 57 x 55 | Regular Issue Plate Block | 25 | $6.25 | **$3.99** |
| 913 | 73 x 63 | Champions of Liberty | 25 | $6.25 | **$3.99** |
| 914 | 106 x 55 | Rotary Press Standard Commemorative | 20 | $6.25 | **$3.99** |
| 915 | 105 x 57 | Giori Press Standard Commemorative | 20 | $6.25 | **$3.99** |
| 916 | 127 x 70 | Giori Press Jumbo Commemorative | 10 | $6.25 | **$3.99** |
| 917 | 165 x 94 | First Day Cover | 10 | $6.25 | **$3.99** |
| 918 | 140 x 90 | Postal Card Size/Submarine Booklet Pane | 10 | $6.25 | **$3.99** |
| 1048 | 152 x 107 | Large Postal Cards | 8 | $10.25 | **$6.99** |
| **STRIPS 215MM LONG** | | | | | |
| 919 | 20 | U.S. 19th Century, Horizontal Coil | 22 | $7.99 | **$5.25** |
| 920 | 22 | U.S. Early Air Mail | 22 | $7.99 | **$5.25** |
| 921 | 24 | U.S., Vertical Coils, Christmas (#2400, #2428 etc.) | 22 | $7.99 | **$5.25** |
| 922 | 25 | U.S. Commemorative and Regular | 22 | $7.99 | **$5.25** |
| 1049 | 26 | U.S. Commemorative and Regular | 22 | $7.99 | **$5.25** |
| 923 | 27 | U.S. Famous Americans | 22 | $7.99 | **$5.25** |
| 924 | 28 | U.S. 19th Century, Liechtenstein | 22 | $7.99 | **$5.25** |
| 1050 | 29 | Virginia Dare, British Empire, etc. | 22 | $7.99 | **$5.25** |
| 925 | 30 | U.S. 19th Century; Jamestown, etc; Foreign | 22 | $7.99 | **$5.25** |
| 926 | 31 | U.S. Horizontal Jumbo and Semi-Jumbo | 22 | $7.99 | **$5.25** |
| 927 | 33 | U.S. Stampin' Future, UN | 22 | $7.99 | **$5.25** |
| 1054 | 34 | U.S. American Landmarks, Eclipse | 22 | $7.99 | **$5.25** |
| 928 | 36 | U.S. Hunting Permit, Canada | 15 | $7.99 | **$5.25** |
| 1051 | 37 | U.S., British Colonies | 22 | $7.99 | **$5.25** |
| 929 | 39 | U.S. Early 20th Century | 15 | $7.99 | **$5.25** |
| 930 | 41 | U.S. Vert. Semi-Jumbo ('77 Lafayette, Pottery, etc.) | 15 | $7.99 | **$5.25** |
| 931 | | Multiple Assortment: One strip of each size 22-41 above (SMKB) (2 x 25mm strips) | 12 | $7.99 | **$5.25** |
| 1052 | 42 | U.S., British Colonies | 22 | $7.99 | **$5.25** |
| 1053 | 43 | U.S., British Colonies | 22 | $7.99 | **$5.25** |
| 932 | 44 | U.S. Vertical Coil Pair Garden Flowers Booklet Pane | 15 | $7.99 | **$5.25** |
| 933 | 48 | U.S. Farley, Gutter Pair | 15 | $7.99 | **$5.25** |
| 934 | 50 | U.S. Jumbo (Lyndon Johnson, '74 U.P.U., etc.) | 15 | $7.99 | **$5.25** |
| 935 | 52 | U.S. Standard Commemorative Block (Butterflies) | 15 | $7.99 | **$5.25** |
| 936 | 55 | U.S. Standard Plate Block - normal margins | 15 | $7.99 | **$5.25** |
| 937 | 57 | U.S. Standard Plate Block - wider margins | 15 | $7.99 | **$5.25** |
| 938 | 61 | U.S. Blocks, Israel Tabs, '99 Christmas Madonna Pane | 15 | $7.99 | **$5.25** |
| **STRIPS 240MM LONG** | | | | | |
| 939 | 63 | U.S. Jumbo Commemorative Horizontal Block | 10 | $9.25 | **$5.99** |
| 940 | 66 | U.S. CIPEX Souvenir Sheet, Self-Adhesive Booklet Pane (#2803a, 3012a) | 10 | $9.25 | **$5.99** |
| 941 | 68 | U.S. ATM Booklet Pane, Farley Gutter Pair & Souvenir Sheet | 10 | $9.25 | **$5.99** |
| 942 | 74 | U.S. TIPEX Souvenir Sheet | 10 | $9.25 | **$5.99** |
| 943 | 80 | U.S. Standard Commemorative Vertical Block | 10 | $9.25 | **$5.99** |
| 944 | 82 | U.S. Blocks of Four, U.N. Chagall | 10 | $9.25 | **$5.99** |
| 945 | 84 | Israel Tab Block, Mars Pathfinder Sheetlet | 10 | $9.25 | **$5.99** |
| 946 | 89 | Submarine Booklet, Souvenir Sheet World Cup, Rockwell | 10 | $9.25 | **$5.99** |
| 947 | 100 | U.S. '74 U.P.U. Block, U.N. Margin Inscribed Block | 7 | $9.25 | **$5.99** |
| 948 | 120 | Various Souvenir Sheets and Blocks | 7 | $9.25 | **$5.99** |
| **STRIPS 265MM LONG** | | | | | |
| 1035 | 25 | U.S. Coils Strips of 11 | 12 | $9.25 | **$5.99** |
| 949 | 40 | U.S. Postal People Standard Standard & Semi-Jumbo Commemorative Strip | 10 | $9.25 | **$5.99** |
| 981 | 44 | U.S. Long self-adhesive booklet panes | 10 | $9.25 | **$5.99** |
| 1030 | 45 | Various (Canada Scott #1725-1734) | 10 | $9.25 | **$5.99** |
| 1036 | 46 | U.S. Long self adhesive booklet panes of 15 | 10 | $9.25 | **$5.99** |
| 950 | 55 | U.S. Regular Plate Block or Strip of 20 | 10 | $9.25 | **$5.99** |
| 951 | 59 | U.S. Double Issue Strip | 10 | $9.25 | **$5.99** |
| 952 | 70 | U.S. Jumbo Commemorative Plate Block | 10 | $12.50 | **$8.50** |
| 1031 | 72 | Various (Canada Scott #1305a-1804a) | 10 | $12.50 | **$8.50** |
| 1032 | 75 | Plate Blocks: Lance Armstrong, Prehistoric Animals, etc. | 10 | $12.50 | **$8.50** |
| 1060 | 76 | U.S. 1994 Stamp Printing Centennial Souvenir Sheet, etc. | 10 | $12.50 | **$8.50** |
| 953 | 91 | U.S. Self-Adhesive Booklet Pane '98 Wreath, '95 Santa | 10 | $12.50 | **$8.50** |
| 1033 | 95 | Mini-Sheet Plate Blocks w/top header | 10 | $12.50 | **$8.50** |
| 1061 | 96 | U.S., Foreign | 10 | $12.50 | **$8.50** |
| 954 | 105 | U.S. Standard Semi-Jumbo Commemorative Plate Number Strip | 10 | $12.50 | **$8.50** |
| 955 | 107 | Same as above–wide margin | 10 | $12.50 | **$8.50** |
| 956 | 111 | U.S. Gravure-Intaglio Plate Number Strip | 10 | $14.75 | **$9.99** |
| 1062 | 115 | Foreign Small Sheets | 10 | $17.50 | **$11.99** |
| 957 | 127 | U.S. 2000 Space S/S, World War II S/S | 10 | $17.50 | **$11.99** |
| 1063 | 131 | Looney Tunes sheets; World War II Souvenir Sheet Plate Block | 10 | $17.50 | **$11.99** |
| 1064 | 135 | U.S., Japan Gifts of Friendship sheet | 10 | $17.50 | **$11.99** |
| 958 | 137 | Great Britain Coronation | 10 | $17.50 | **$11.99** |
| 1065 | 139 | Sheets: Soda Fountain, Lady Bird Johnson, Earthscapes, etc. | 10 | $17.50 | **$11.99** |
| 1066 | 143 | Sheets: Merchant Marine Ships, 2013 Hanukkah, etc. | 10 | $17.50 | **$11.99** |
| 1067 | 147 | Sheets: Pickup Trucks, Animal Rescue, Washington D.C., etc. | 10 | $17.50 | **$11.99** |
| 1068 | 151 | Sheets: Go Green, Bicycling, Happy New Year, Ben Franklin, etc. | 10 | $17.50 | **$11.99** |

| ITEM | W x H (mm) | DESCRIPTION | MOUNTS | RETAIL | AA* |
|---|---|---|---|---|---|
| **STRIPS 265MM LONG, continued** | | | | | |
| 959 | 158 | American Glass, U.S. Football Coaches Sheets | 10 | $17.99 | **$12.50** |
| 1077 | 160 | Sheets: Pacific '97 Triangle Mini, Trans-Mississippi | 5 | $12.50 | **$8.50** |
| 1069 | 163 | Sheets: Modern Architecture, UN Human Rights, etc. | 5 | $12.50 | **$8.50** |
| 1070 | 167 | Sheets: John F. Kennedy, Classics Forever, Made in America, etc. | 5 | $12.50 | **$8.50** |
| 1071 | 171 | Film Directors, Foreign Souvenir Sheets | 5 | $12.50 | **$8.50** |
| 960 | 175 | Large Block, Souvenir Sheet | 5 | $12.50 | **$8.50** |
| 1072 | 181 | Sheets: Jimi Hendrix, Johnny Cash, American Photography, etc. | 5 | $17.50 | **$11.99** |
| 1073 | 185 | Frank Sinatra, Ronald Reagan, Arthur Ashe, Creast Cancer, etc. | 5 | $17.50 | **$11.99** |
| 1074 | 188 | Sheets: Yoda, 9/11 Heroes, Andy Warhol, Frida Kahlo, etc | 5 | $17.50 | **$11.99** |
| 1078 | 192 | Olympic, etc. | 5 | $17.50 | **$11.99** |
| 1075 | 198 | Sheets: Modern American Art, Super Heroes, Baseball Sluggers, etc. | 5 | $17.50 | **$11.99** |
| 1076 | 215 | Celebrity Chefs sheets; Foreign sheets | 5 | $17.50 | **$11.99** |
| 961 | 231 | U.S. Full Post Office Pane Regular and Commemorative | 5 | $17.99 | **$12.50** |
| **SOUVENIR SHEETS/SMALL PANES** | | | | | |
| 962 | 204 x 153 | New Year 2000, U.S. Bicentennial S/S | 4 | $9.25 | **$5.99** |
| 963 | 187 x 144 | 55¢ Victorian Love Pane, U.N. Flag Sheet | 9 | $15.50 | **$10.25** |
| 964 | 160 x 200 | U.N., Israel Sheet | 10 | $15.50 | **$10.25** |
| 965 | 120 x 207 | U.S. AMERIPEX Presidential Sheet | 4 | $6.25 | **$3.99** |
| 968 | 229 x 131 | World War II S/S Plate Block Only | 5 | $9.25 | **$5.99** |
| 970 | 111 x 91 | Columbian Souvenir Sheet | 6 | $6.25 | **$4.75** |
| 972 | 148 x 196 | Apollo Moon Landing/Carnivorous Plants | 4 | $7.99 | **$5.25** |
| 989 | 129 x 122 | U.S. Definitive Sheet: Harte, Hopkins, etc. | 8 | $10.25 | **$6.99** |
| 990 | 189 x 151 | Chinese New Year | 5 | $10.25 | **$6.99** |
| 991 | 150 x 185 | Breast Cancer/Fermi/Soccer/'96 Folk Heroes | 5 | $10.25 | **$6.99** |
| 992 | 198 x 151 | Cherokee Strip Sheet | 5 | $10.25 | **$6.99** |
| 993 | 185 x 151 | Bernstein/NATO/Irish/Lunt/Gold Rush Sheets | 5 | $10.25 | **$6.99** |
| 994 | 198 x 187 | Postal Museum | 4 | $10.25 | **$6.99** |
| 995 | 156 x 187 | Sign Language/Statehood | 5 | $10.25 | **$6.99** |
| 996 | 188 x 197 | Illustrators, '98 Music: Folk, Gospel; Country/Western | 4 | $10.25 | **$6.99** |
| 997 | 151 x 192 | Olympic | 5 | $10.25 | **$6.99** |
| 998 | 174 x 185 | Buffalo Soldiers | 5 | $10.25 | **$6.99** |
| 999 | 130 x 198 | Silent Screen Stars | 5 | $10.25 | **$6.99** |
| 1000 | 190 x 199 | Stars Stripes/Baseball/Insects & Spiders/Legends West/ Aircraft, Comics, '96 Olympics, Civil War | 4 | $10.25 | **$6.99** |
| 1001 | 178 x 181 | Cranes | 4 | $10.25 | **$6.99** |
| 1002 | 183 x 212 | Wonders of the Sea, We the People | 3 | $10.25 | **$6.99** |
| 1003 | 156 x 264 | $14 Eagle | 4 | $10.25 | **$6.99** |
| 1004 | 159 x 270 | $9.95 Moon Landing | 4 | $10.25 | **$6.99** |
| 1005 | 159 x 259 | $2.90 Priority/$9.95 Express Mail | 4 | $10.25 | **$6.99** |
| 1006 | 223 x 187 | Hubble, Hollywood Legends, O'Keefe Sheets | 3 | $10.25 | **$6.99** |
| 1007 | 185 x 181 | Deep Sea Creatures, Olmsted Sheets | 4 | $10.25 | **$6.99** |
| 1008 | 152 x 228 | Indian Dances/Antique Autos | 5 | $10.25 | **$6.99** |
| 1009 | 165 x 150 | River Boat/Hanukkah | 6 | $10.25 | **$6.99** |
| 1010 | 275 x 200 | Dinosaurs/Large Gutter Blocks | 2 | $10.25 | **$6.99** |
| 1011 | 161 x 160 | Pacific '97 Triangle Mini Sheets | 6 | $10.25 | **$6.99** |
| 1012 | 174 x 130 | Road Runner, Daffy, Bugs, Sylvester & Tweety | 6 | $10.25 | **$6.99** |
| 1013 | 196 x 158 | Football Coaches | 4 | $10.25 | **$6.99** |
| 1014 | 184 x 184 | American Dolls, Flowering Trees Sheets | 4 | $10.25 | **$6.99** |
| 1015 | 186 x 230 | Classic Movie Monsters | 3 | $10.25 | **$6.99** |
| 1016 | 187 x 160 | Trans-Mississippi Sheet | 4 | $10.25 | **$6.99** |
| 1017 | 192 x 230 | Celebrate The Century | 3 | $10.25 | **$6.99** |
| 1018 | 156 x 204 | Space Discovery | 5 | $10.25 | **$6.99** |
| 1019 | 182 x 209 | American Ballet | 5 | $10.25 | **$6.99** |
| 1020 | 139 x 151 | Christmas Wreaths | 5 | $10.25 | **$6.99** |
| 1021 | 129 x 126 | Justin Morrill, Henry Luce | 8 | $10.25 | **$6.99** |
| 1022 | 184 x 165 | Baseball Fields, Bright Eyes | 4 | $10.25 | **$6.99** |
| 1023 | 185 x 172 | Shuttle Landing Pan Am Invert Sheets | 4 | $10.25 | **$6.99** |
| 1024 | 172 x 233 | Sonoran Desert | 3 | $10.25 | **$6.99** |
| 1025 | 150 x 166 | Prostate Cancer | 5 | $10.25 | **$6.99** |
| 1026 | 201 x 176 | Famous Trains | 4 | $10.25 | **$6.99** |
| 1027 | 176 x 124 | Canada - Historic Vehicles | 5 | $10.25 | **$6.99** |
| 1028 | 245 x 114 | Canada - Provincial Leaders | 5 | $10.25 | **$6.99** |
| 1029 | 177 x 133 | Canada - Year of the Family | 5 | $10.25 | **$6.99** |
| 1034 | 181 x 213 | Arctic Animals | 3 | $10.25 | **$6.99** |
| 1037 | 179 x 242 | Louise Nevelson | 3 | $10.25 | **$6.99** |
| 1038 | 179 x 217 | Library Of Congress | 3 | $10.25 | **$6.99** |
| 1039 | 182 x 232 | Youth Team Sports | 3 | $10.25 | **$6.99** |
| 1040 | 183 x 216 | Lucille Ball Scott #3523 | 3 | $10.25 | **$6.99** |
| 1041 | 182 x 244 | American Photographers | 3 | $10.25 | **$6.99** |
| 1042 | 185 x 255 | Andy Warhol | 3 | $10.25 | **$6.99** |
| 1043 | 165 x 190 | American Film Making | 4 | $10.25 | **$6.99** |
| 1044 | 28 x 290 | American Eagle PNC Strips of 11 | 12 | $9.25 | **$5.99** |

Available in clear or black backgrounds. Please specify color choice when ordering.

### 2017 NATIONAL, MINUTEMAN OR ALL-AMERICAN SUPPLEMENT MOUNT PACKS

| *ITEM* | *DESCRIPTION* | *RETAIL* | *AA** |
|---|---|---|---|
| 2017 B | 2017 National, Minuteman or All-American Supplement Mount Pack - BLACK | $49.99 | **$39.99** |
| 2017 C | 2017 National, Minuteman or All-American Supplement Mount Pack - CLEAR | $49.99 | **$39.99** |

## Visit AmosAdvantage.com

## Call 1-800-572-6885

Outside U.S. & Canada 937-498-0800

Mail to: P.O. Box 4129, Sidney OH 45365

**ORDERING INFORMATION:** *AA prices apply to paid subscribers of Amos Media titles, or orders placed online. Prices, terms and product availability subject to change. Taxes will apply in CA, OH, & IL. Shipping and handling rates will apply.

**SHIPPING & HANDLING: United States:** Order total $0-$10.00 charged $3.99 shipping; Order total $10.01-$79.99 charged $7.99 shipping; Order total $80.00 or more charged 10% of order total for shipping. Maximum Freight Charge $45.00. **Canada:** 20% of order total. Minimum charge $19.99; maximum charge $200.00. **Foreign:** Orders are shipped via FedEx Int'l. or USPS and billed actual freight.

# Vols. 4A-4B Number Additions, Deletions & Changes

| Number in 2018 Catalogue | Number in 2019 Catalogue |
|---|---|
| **Jamaica** | |
| new | 85a |
| **Japan** | |
| new | 95a |
| new | 96a |
| new | 98a |
| new | 99b |
| new | 101a |
| new | 103a |
| new | 118a |
| new | 120a |
| new | 122a |
| new | 2855A-2855J |
| **Korea (South)** | |
| new | 1895a-1896a |
| **Korea, Democratic People's Republic** | |
| 3870a | 3871a |
| new | 3871b |
| **Luxembourg** | |
| new | 279a |
| **Mexico** | |
| new | 2418a |
| **Mozambique** | |
| new | 225d |
| new | 229d |
| new | 229e |
| new | 965A |
| new | 965B |
| new | 31b |

# TOOLS OF THE EXPERTS!

### 6-IN-1 LED POCKET MAGNIFIER/MICROSCOPE (55X)

A powerful LED microscope (up to 55X magnification) teams up with two aspheric Perspex lenses (3X magnification large and 10X magnification small) to examine objects at various levels of detail. Built-in focus wheel ensures clarity. View objects even in low-light conditions with three lighting functions: three LED flashlight, simple UV light, one white LED. Black composite housing.

| Item | Retail | AA* |
|---|---|---|
| MG61LED | $21.95 | $19.95 |

### ZOOM 20X-40X MICROSCOPE WITH LED

This practical zoom microscope provides what collectors have been waiting for – outstanding clarity and resolution. Magnification is continuously adjustable between 20X and 40X. Powerful LED lighting illuminates the stage (3 #LR44 batteries included). Stand, examination slides, and slide covers also included.

| Item | Retail | AA* |
|---|---|---|
| LHPM3 | $29.95 | $21.95 |

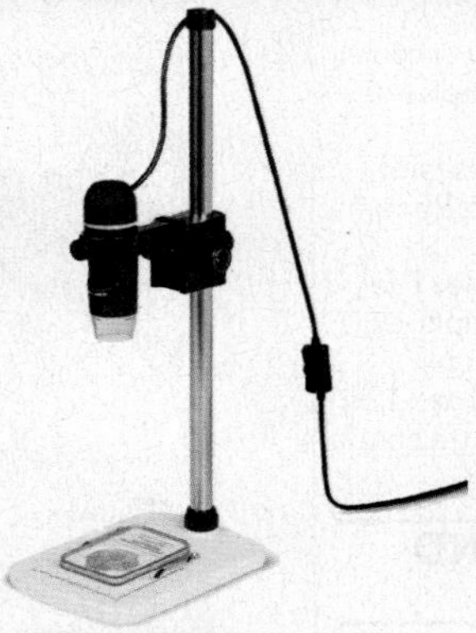

### UNIVERSAL MICROSCOPE STAND

(Add next to Digital Microscope) Upgrade your USB Digital Microscope with this high-quality stainless steel and plastic stand for superior results with photo and video imaging. Stand is fully adjustable with extra high rod (16"/405mm). Holder fits all 13/8" (35mm) diameter microscopes; adapter allows 1¼" (33mm) diameter as well. Easy and quick to assemble, no tools required, instructions included.

| Item | Retail | AA* |
|---|---|---|
| LHDMST2 | $69.95 | $64.95 |

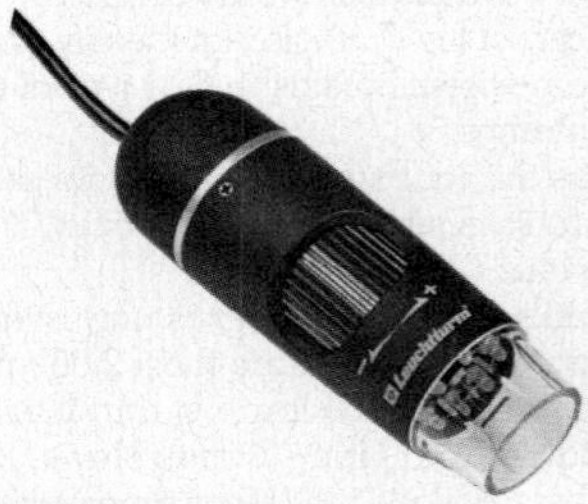

### ZOOM 10X-300X USB DIGITAL MICROSCOPE, 5.0 MEGAPIXEL

The industry-leading 5.0 megapixel resolution makes the smallest details on coins and stamps visible on your computer screen via the included USB cable. Up to 10x - 300x magnification available with this high-end digital microscope

| Item | Retail | AA* |
|---|---|---|
| LHDM4 | $179.95 | $169.95 |

### 3.2X LED ILLUMINATED MAGNIFIER

This 7" aluminum 3.2X magnifier is both beautiful and functional. Six LEDs surround the 1.375" lens to provide glare-free illumination. Zippered protective case and 2 AA batteries included.

| Item | Retail | AA* |
|---|---|---|
| MG32XL | $35.95 | $31.95 |

### 10X POCKET MAGNIFIER

This compact, portable and easy-to-use 10x pocket magnifier comes with its own illumination from a brilliant white LED. The glass lens is 18mm (3/4") in diameter.

| Item | Retail | AA* |
|---|---|---|
| MG10XLED | $12.95 | $11.95 |

### SHERLOCK WATERMARK DETECTOR

Reveal every detail of your stamps, whether it is watermarks or paper irregularities, quality defects, or repairs. Easy to use: Insert stamp, turn on the light, and you can already see the secrets of your stamps in every detail. The special feature of this watermark detector is the different light colors (white, red, green, and blue), which can be chosen to light up the stamp. The brightness can be infinitely adjusted. Overall size: 35/8" x 51/8" x 57/8"

| Item | Retail | AA* |
|---|---|---|
| LHWZ2 | $325.00 | $276.25 |

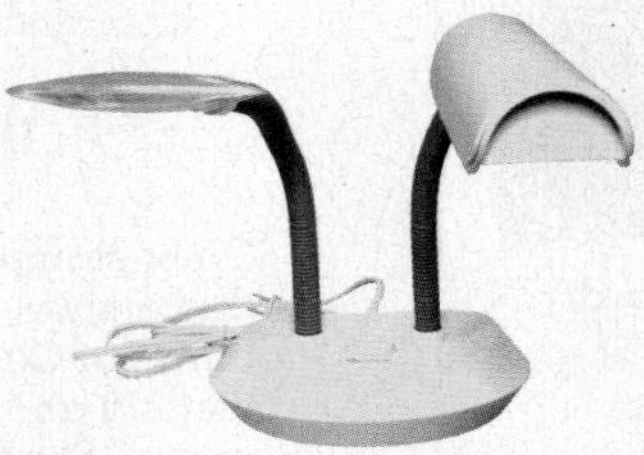

### 13W DUOFLEX MAGNIFIER DESK LAMP

The OttLite DuoFlex has a two-pronged approach to enhance your vision. First, the large 3X-5X magnifier enlarges your subject. Then the energy-efficient 13w "E" bulb spotlights the field. Flexible arms allow nearly infinite positioning. Long-term bulb is rated to last up to 10,000 hours.

| Item | Retail | AA* |
|---|---|---|
| ACC213W | $109.99 | $59.99 |

### BLACK TRUE COLOR LIGHT

A versatile, compact light that provides superior image and color rendering while reducing glare and eye strain. Technologically advanced light produces a precise blend of light for contrast and brightness that makes colors vibrant and details incredibly clear. The lamp comes with an "E"(electronic) tube for a quicker starting time. This does plug into an outlet for long uses.

| Item | Retail | AA* |
|---|---|---|
| ACC191BB | $79.99 | $49.99 |

### PHONESCOPE DIGITAL MICROSCOPE

Clip this compact Lighthouse Phonescope lens on your smartphone or tablet to transform it into a powerful digital microscope. See the smallest details and instantly capture high-quality images and videos. The precision macro glass lens offers up to 60X magnification and requires no batteries. Field of view: 1/2" (13mm). Phonescope works with all popular smartphones without scratching display. Image resolution and zoom function dependent upon your device.

| Item | Retail | AA* |
|---|---|---|
| LHSCOPE | $25.99 | $21.99 |

**Visit: AmosAdvantage.com**

**Call: 1-800-572-6885**

Outside U.S. & Canada Call: 1-937-498-0800

**ORDERING INFORMATION:** *AA prices apply to paid subscribers of Amos Media titles, or orders placed online. Prices, terms and product availability subject to change. Taxes will apply in CA, OH, & IL. Shipping and handling rates will apply. See below.

# Illustrated Identifier

This section pictures stamps or parts of stamp designs that will help identify postage stamps that do not have English words on them.

Many of the symbols that identify stamps of countries are shown here as well as typical examples of their stamps.

See the Index and Identifier for stamps with inscriptions such as "sen," "posta," "Baja Porto," "Helvetia," "K.S.A.", etc.

*Linn's Stamp Identifier* is now available. The 144 pages include more than 2,000 inscriptions and more than 500 large stamp illustrations. Available from Linn's Stamp News, P.O. Box 4129, Sidney, OH 45365-4129, or amosadvantage.com

## 1. HEADS, PICTURES AND NUMERALS

### GREAT BRITAIN

Great Britain stamps never show the country name, but, except for postage dues, show a picture of the reigning monarch.

Victoria

Edward VII George V Edward VIII

George VI

Elizabeth II

Some George VI and Elizabeth II stamps are surcharged in annas, new paisa or rupees. These are listed under Oman.

Silhouette (sometimes facing right, generally at the top of stamp)

The silhouette indicates this is a British stamp. It is not a U.S. stamp.

### VICTORIA

Queen Victoria

### INDIA

Other stamps of India show this portrait of Queen Victoria and the words "Service" (or "Postage") and "Annas."

### AUSTRIA

### YUGOSLAVIA

(Also BOSNIA & HERZEGOVINA if imperf.)

### BOSNIA & HERZEGOVINA

Denominations also appear in top corners instead of bottom corners.

### HUNGARY

Another stamp has posthorn facing left

### BRAZIL

### AUSTRALIA

Kangaroo and Emu

### GERMANY

#### Mecklenburg-Vorpommern

## SWITZERLAND

## PALAU

## 2. ORIENTAL INSCRIPTIONS

### CHINA

中 中

Any stamp with this one character is from China (Imperial, Republic or People's Republic). This character appears in a four-character overprint on stamps of Manchukuo. These stamps are local provisionals, which are unlisted. Other overprinted Manchukuo stamps show this character, but have more than four characters in the overprints. These are listed in People's Republic of China.

Some Chinese stamps show the Sun.

中華民國郵票

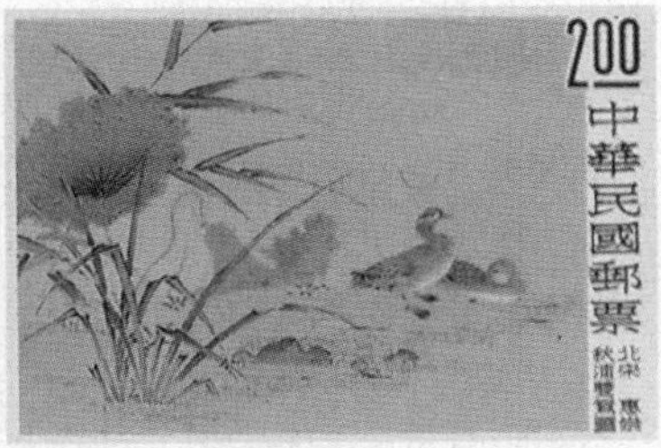

Most stamps of Republic of China show this series of characters.

Stamps with the China character and this character are from People's Republic of China. 人

中国人民邮政

T.34.(5-1)

Calligraphic form of People's Republic of China

| (一) | (二) | (三) | (四) | (五) | (六) |
|---|---|---|---|---|---|
| 1 | 2 | 3 | 4 | 5 | 6 |
| (七) | (八) | (九) | (十) | (一十) | (二十) |
| 7 | 8 | 9 | 10 | 11 | 12 |

**Chinese stamps without China character**

### REPUBLIC OF CHINA

### PEOPLE'S REPUBLIC OF CHINA

Mao Tse-tung

## MANCHUKUO

Temple

Emperor Pu-Yi

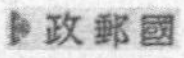

The first 3 characters are common to many Manchukuo stamps.

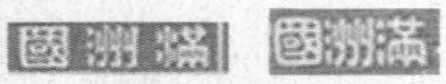

The last 3 characters are common to other Manchukuo stamps.

Orchid Crest

Manchukuo stamp without these elements

## JAPAN

Chrysanthemum Crest

Country Name

Japanese stamps without these elements

The number of characters in the center and the design of dragons on the sides will vary.

## RYUKYU ISLANDS

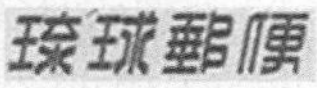

Country Name

## PHILIPPINES (Japanese Occupation)

Country Name

## NETHERLANDS INDIES (Japanese Occupation)

Indicates Japanese Occupation

### Java

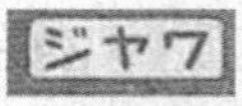

Country Name

### Sumatra

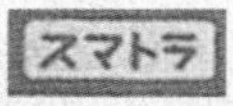

Country Name

## Moluccas, Celebes and South Borneo

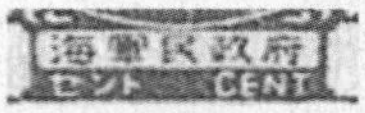

Country Name

## NORTH BORNEO (Japanese Occupation)

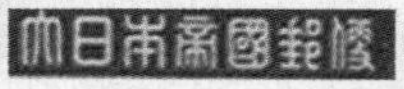

Indicates Japanese Occupation

Country Name

## MALAYA (Japanese Occupation)

Indicates Japanese Occupation

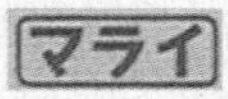

Country Name

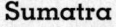

## BURMA

### Union of Myanmar

Union of Myanmar

### (Japanese Occupation)

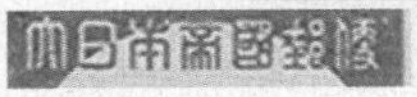

Indicates Japanese Occupation

Country Name

Other Burma Japanese Occupation stamps without these elements

Burmese Script

## KOREA

These two characters, in any order, are common to stamps from the Republic of Korea (South Korea) or of the People's Democratic Republic of Korea (North Korea).

This series of four characters can be found on the stamps of both Koreas. Most stamps of the Democratic People's Republic of Korea (North Korea) have just this inscription.

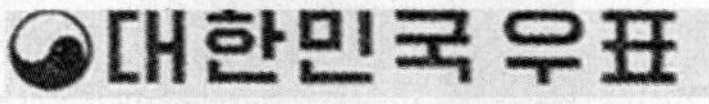

Indicates Republic of Korea (South Korea)

South Korean postage stamps issed after 1952 do not show currency expressed in Latin letters. Stamps wiith " HW," "HWAN," "WON," "WN," "W" or "W" with two lines through it, if not illustrated in listings of stamps before this date, are revenues. North Korean postage stamps do not have currency expressed in Latin letters.

Yin Yang appears on some stamps.

South Korean stamps show Yin Yang and starting in 1966, 'KOREA" in Latin letters

Example of South Korean stamps lacking Latin text, Yin Yang and standard Korean text of country name. North Korean stamps never show Yin Yang and starting in 1976 are inscribed "DPRK" or "DPR KOREA" in Latin letters.

## THAILAND

Country Name

King Chulalongkorn

King Prajadhipok and Chao P'ya Chakri

# 3. CENTRAL AND EASTERN ASIAN INSCRIPTIONS

## INDIA - FEUDATORY STATES

### Alwar

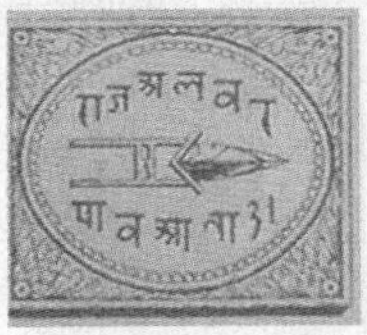

### Bhor

## Bundi

Similar stamps come with different designs in corners and differently drawn daggers (at center of circle).

## Dhar

## Duttia

## Faridkot

## Hyderabad

Similar stamps exist with different central design which is inscribed "Postage" or "Post & Receipt."

## Indore

## Jammu & Kashmir

Text varies.

## Jasdan

## Jhalawar

## Kotah

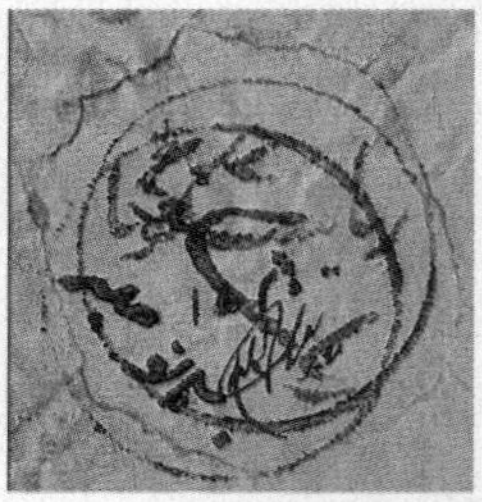

Size and text varies

### Nandgaon

### Nowanuggur

### Poonch

Similar stamps exist in various sizes with different text

### Rajasthan

### Rajpeepla

### Soruth

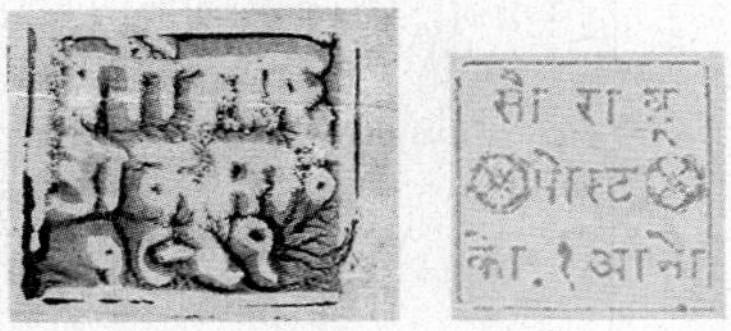

### Tonk

### BANGLADESH

Country Name

### NEPAL

Similar stamps are smaller, have squares in upper corners and have five or nine characters in central bottom panel.

### TANNU TUVA

### ISRAEL

### GEORGIA

This inscription is found on other pictorial stamps.

Country Name

### ARMENIA

The four characters are found somewhere on pictorial stamps. On some stamps only the middle two are found.

## 4. AFRICAN INSCRIPTIONS

### ETHIOPIA

## 5. ARABIC INSCRIPTIONS

١ ٢ ٣ ٤ ٥
1 2 3 4 5

٦ ٧ ٨ ٩ ٠
6 7 8 9 0

### AFGHANISTAN

Many early Afghanistan stamps show Tiger's head, many of these have ornaments protruding from outer ring, others show inscriptions in black.

Arabic Script

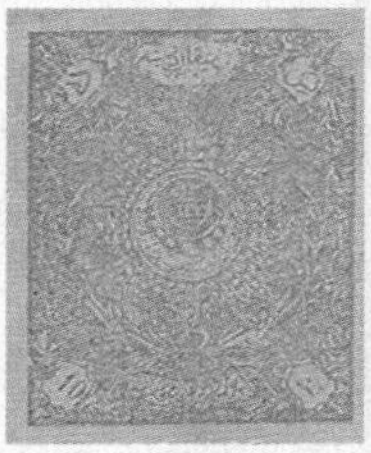

Crest of King Amanullah

Mosque Gate & Crossed Cannons

The four characters are found somewhere on pictorial stamps. On some stamps only the middle two are found.

### BAHRAIN

## EGYPT

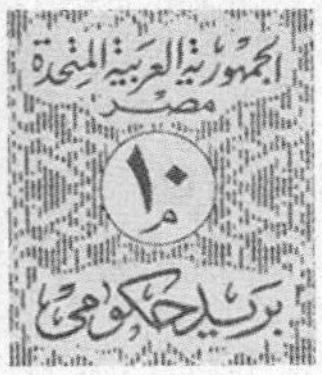

Postage

## IRAN

Country Name

Royal Crown

Lion with Sword

Symbol

Emblem

## IRAQ

## JORDAN

## LEBANON

Similar types have denominations at top and slightly different design.

## LIBYA

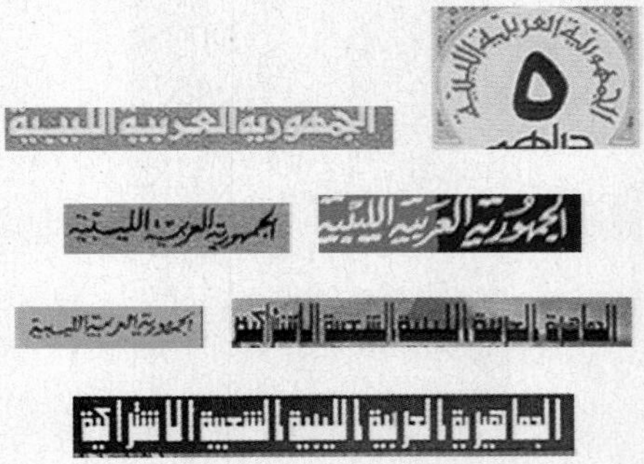

Country Name in various styles

Other Libya stamps show Eagle and Shield (head facing either direction) or Red, White and Black Shield (with or without eagle in center).

Without Country Name

## SAUDI ARABIA

Tughra (Central design)

Palm Tree and Swords

## SYRIA

## Arab Government Issues

THRACE YEMEN

## PAKISTAN

## PAKISTAN - BAHAWALPUR

Country Name in top panel, star and crescent

## TURKEY

Star & Crescent is a device found on many Turkish stamps, but is also found on stamps from other Arabic areas (see Pakistan-Bahawalpur)

Tughra (similar tughras can be found on stamps of Turkey in Asia, Afghanistan and Saudi Arabia)

Mohammed V

Mustafa Kemal

Plane, Star and Crescent

## TURKEY IN ASIA

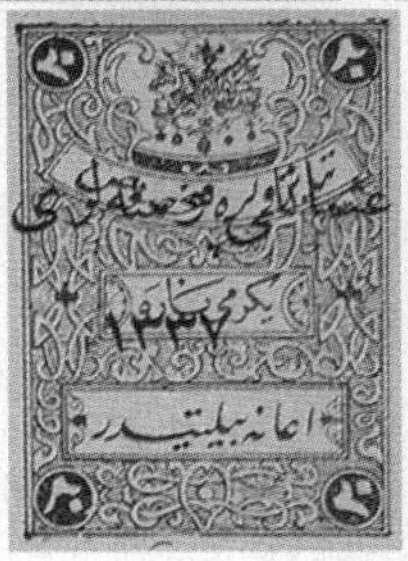

Other Turkey in Asia pictorials show star & crescent.
Other stamps show tughra shown under Turkey.

## 6. GREEK INSCRIPTIONS

### GREECE

Country Name in various styles
(Some Crete stamps overprinted with the Greece country name are listed in Crete.)

Lepta

Drachma Drachmas Lepton

Abbreviated Country Name 

Other forms of Country Name

No country name

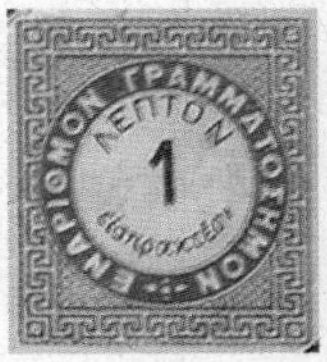

### CRETE

Country Name

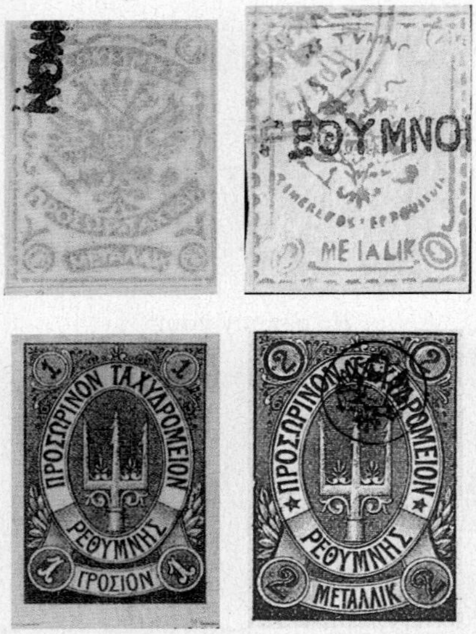

Crete stamps with a surcharge that have the year "1922" are listed under Greece.

**EPIRUS**

Similar stamps have text above the eagle.

**IONIAN IS.**

## 7. CYRILLIC INSCRIPTIONS

**RUSSIA**

Postage Stamp Imperial Eagle

Postage in various styles

Abbreviation for Kopeck Abbreviation for Ruble Russia

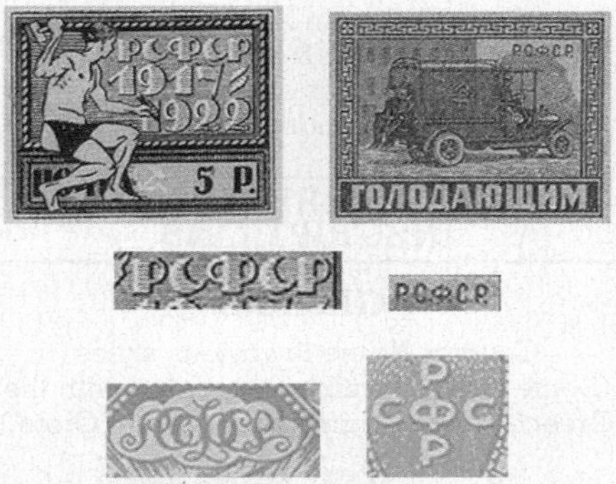

Abbreviation for Russian Soviet Federated Socialist Republic RSFSR stamps were overprinted (see below)

Abbreviation for Union of Soviet Socialist Republics

This item is footnoted in Latvia

**RUSSIA - Army of the North**

"OKCA"

**RUSSIA - Wenden**

**RUSSIAN OFFICES IN THE TURKISH EMPIRE**

These letters appear on other stamps of the Russian offices.

The unoverprinted version of this stamp and a similar stamp were overprinted by various countries (see below).

## ARMENIA

## BELARUS

## FAR EASTERN REPUBLIC

Country Name

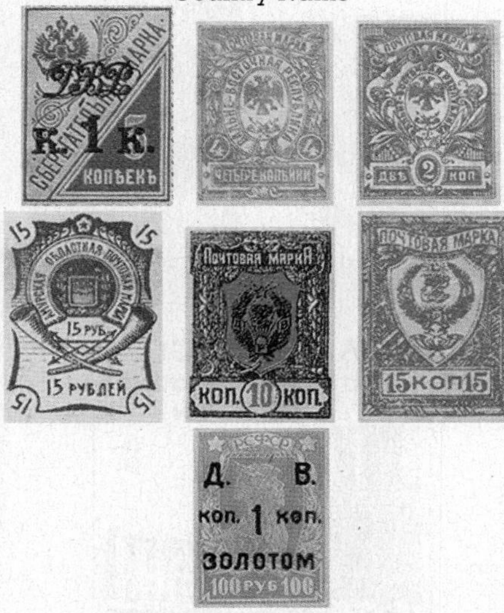

## FINLAND

Circles and Dots on stamps similar to Imperial Russia issues

## SOUTH RUSSIA

Country Name

## BATUM

Forms of Country Name

## TRANSCAUCASIAN FEDERATED REPUBLICS

Abbreviation for Country Name

## KAZAKHSTAN

## COUNTRY NAME KYRGYZSTAN

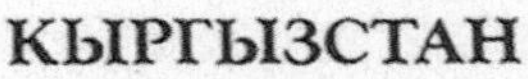

Country Name

## ROMANIA

## TAJIKISTAN

Country Name & Abbreviation

## UKRAINE

Country Name in various forms

The trident appears on many stamps, usually as an overprint.

Abbreviation for Ukrainian Soviet Socialist Republic

## WESTERN UKRAINE

Abbreviation for Country Name

## AZERBAIJAN

AZƏRBAYCAN

Country Name

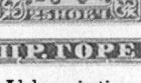

A.C.C.P. Abbreviation for Azerbaijan Soviet Socialist Republic

## MONTENEGRO

ЦРНЕГОРЕ

ЦРНА ГОРА

Country Name in various forms

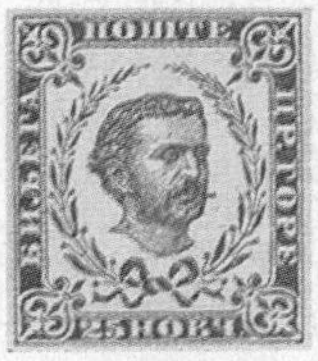

Ц.Р.ГОРЕ

Abbreviation for country name

No country name (A similar Montenegro stamp without country name has same vignette.)

## SERBIA

СРПСКА СРБИЈА

Country Name in various forms

СРП. К. С.

Abbreviation for country name

No country name

## MACEDONIA

МАКЕДОНИЈА

МАКЕДОНИЈА

Country Name

МАКЕДОНСКИ

Different form of Country Name

## SERBIA & MONTENEGRO

## YUGOSLAVIA

ЈУГОСЛАВИЈА

Showing country name

No Country Name

## BOSNIA & HERZEGOVINA (Serb Administration)

РЕПУБЛИКА СРПСКА

Country Name

РЕПУБЛИКЕ СРПСКЕ

Different form of Country Name

No Country Name

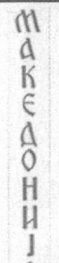

## BULGARIA

Country Name Postage

Stotinka

Stotinki (plural) Abbreviation for Stotinki

Country Name in various forms and styles

No country name

Abbreviation for Lev, leva

## MONGOLIA

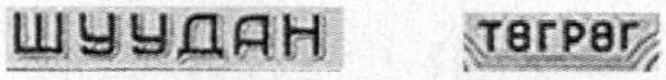


Country name in one word Tugrik in Cyrillic

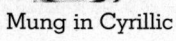

Country name in two words Mung in Cyrillic

Mung in Mongolian

Tugrik in Mongolian

Arms

No Country Name

# 2017 Scott Series Supplement Releases

Come check out our newest 2017 Scott supplement releases on our brand NEW website! Customers are able to see sample pages along with the suggested mounts page for the National and Minuteman series. We are dedicated to improve the shopping experience for all of our customers!

## United States National Series

| Item# | Description | Retail | AA | Release |
|---|---|---|---|---|
| 100S017 | U.S. National | $22.99 | **$19.99** | February |
| 130S017 | U.S. Commemorative Singles | $16.99 | **$13.99** | February |
| 114S017 | U.S. Plate Number Coils–Comprehensive | $19.99 | **$16.99** | January |
| 113S017 | U.S. Plate Number Coils–Simplified | $11.99 | **$9.99** | January |
| 101S017 | U.S. Booklet Panes | $16.99 | **$13.99** | April |
| 118S017 | U.S. Small Panes | $34.99 | **$29.99** | April |
| 110S017 | U.S. Postal Cards | $11.99 | **$9.99** | April |
| 120S017 | U.S. Commemorative & Air Plate Blocks | $19.99 | **$16.99** | April |
| 125S017 | U.S. Regular & Air Plate Blocks | $11.99 | **$9.99** | April |
| 105S017 | U.S. Postal Stationery | $11.99 | **$9.99** | March |

## United Nations National Series

| | | | | |
|---|---|---|---|---|
| 552S017 | U.N. Imprint Blocks | $19.99 | **$16.99** | March |
| 551S017 | U.N. Singles & Postal Stationery | $25.99 | **$21.99** | March |

## Territories National Series

| | | | | |
|---|---|---|---|---|
| 111MI17 | Federated States of Micronesia | $34.99 | **$29.99** | April |
| 111PA17 | Republic of Palau | $34.99 | **$29.99** | April |
| 111MA17 | Republic of the Marshall Islands | $22.99 | **$19.99** | April |

## Standard U.S. PNC Series

| | | | | |
|---|---|---|---|---|
| 117S017 | U.S. Plate Number Coil Singles | $19.99 | **$16.99** | January |

## Specialty Series

| | | | | |
|---|---|---|---|---|
| 170S017 | American (includes U.N.) | $34.99 | **$29.99** | March |

## Minuteman Series

| | | | | |
|---|---|---|---|---|
| 180S017 | U.S. Minuteman | $22.99 | **$19.99** | February |
| 181S017 | U.N. Minuteman | $25.99 | **$21.99** | March |

## Pony Express Series

| | | | | |
|---|---|---|---|---|
| 178S017 | U.S. Pony Express (double-sided) | $22.99 | **$19.99** | March |

## United States - Hingeless

| | | | | |
|---|---|---|---|---|
| 199S017 | U.S. Platinum - Hingeless | $78.99 | **$67.99** | April |
| HUSA2017 | U.S. Scott/Schaubek - Hingeless | $78.99 | **$67.99** | April |

## 2017 U.S. Mount Packs

| | | | | |
|---|---|---|---|---|
| 2017 B | 2017 U.S. Scott Mount Pack, Black | $49.99 | **$39.99** | February |
| 2017 C | 2017 U.S. Scott Mount Pack, Clear | $49.99 | **$39.99** | February |
| 100S017BB | U.S. National+U.S. Scott Mount Set, Black | $69.98 | **$47.98** | February |
| 100S017BC | U.S. National+U.S. Scott Mount Set, Clear | $69.98 | **$47.98** | February |
| 180S017BB | U.S. Minuteman+U.S. Scott Mount Set, Black | $69.98 | **$47.98** | February |
| 180S017BC | U.S. Minuteman+U.S. Scott Mount Set, Clear | $69.98 | **$47.98** | February |

## Call 800-572-6885 - Outside U.S. & Canada call: (937) 498-0800

# Visit AmosAdvantage.com

**Ordering Information:** *AA prices apply to paid subscribers of Amos Media titles, or for orders placed online. Prices, terms and product availability subject to change. **Shipping & Handling:** U.S.: Orders total $0-$10.00 charged $3.99 shipping. U.S. Order total $10.01-$79.99 charged $7.99 shipping. U.S. Order total $80.00 or more charged 10% of order total for shipping. Taxes will apply in CA, OH, & IL. Canada: 20% of order total. Minimum charge $19.99 Maximum charge $200.00. Foreign orders are shipped via FedEx Intl. or USPS and billed actual freight.

# INDEX AND IDENTIFIER

All page numbers shown are those in this Volume 4A.

Postage stamps that do not have English words on them are shown in the Illustrated Identifier.

# INDEX TO ADVERTISERS 2019 VOLUME 4A

# 2019
# VOLUME 4A
# DEALER DIRECTORY
# YELLOW PAGE LISTINGS

**This section of your Scott Catalogue contains advertisements to help you conveniently find what you need, when you need it...!**

## Appraisals

**DR. ROBERT FRIEDMAN & SONS STAMP & COIN BUYING CENTER**
2029 W. 75th St.
Woodridge, IL 60517
PH: 800-588-8100
FAX: 630-985-1588
stampcollections@drbobstamps.com
www.drbobfriedmanstamps.com

## Argentina

**GUILLERMO JALIL**
Maipu 466,local 4
1006 Buenos Aires
Argentina
guillermo@jalilstamps.com
philatino@philatino.com
www.philatino.com
www.jalilstamps.com

## Auctions

**DUTCH COUNTRY AUCTIONS**
The Stamp Center
4115 Concord Pike
Wilmington, DE 19803
PH: 302-478-8740
FAX: 302-478-8779
auctions@dutchcountryauctions.com
www.dutchcountryauctions.com

**KELLEHER & ROGERS LTD.**
4 Finance Drive, Ste. 200
Danbury, CT 06810
PH: 203-297-6056
FAX: 203-297-6059
info@kelleherauctions.com
www.kelleherauctions.com

## British Asia

**THE STAMP ACT**
PO Box 1136
Belmont, CA 94002
PH: 650-703-2342
thestampact@sbcglobal.net

## British Commonwealth

**COLLECTORS EXCHANGE ORLANDO STAMP SHOP**
1814A Edgewater Drive
Orlando, FL 32804
PH: 407-620-0908
PH: 407-947-8603
FAX: 407-730-2131
jlatter@cfl.rr.com
www.BritishStampsAmerica.com
www.OrlandoStampShop.com

**WORLDSTAMPS/ FRANK GEIGER PHILATELISTS**
PO Box 4743
Pinehurst, NC 28374
PH: 910-295-2048
info@WorldStamps.com
www.WorldStampsScott.com

**ARON R. HALBERSTAM PHILATELISTS, LTD.**
PO Box 150168
Van Brunt Station
Brooklyn, NY 11215-0168
PH: 718-788-3978
arh@arhstamps.com
www.arhstamps.com

## British Commonwealth

**ROY'S STAMPS**
PO Box 28001
600 Ontario Street
St. Catharines, ON
CANADA L2N 7P8
Phone: 905-934-8377
Email: roystamp@cogeco.ca

## Buying

**DR. ROBERT FRIEDMAN & SONS STAMP & COIN BUYING CENTER**
2029 W. 75th St.
Woodridge, IL 60517
PH: 800-588-8100
FAX: 630-985-1588
stampcollections@drbobstamps.com
www.drbobfriedmanstamps.com

## Canada

**CANADA STAMP FINDER**
PO Box 92591
Brampton, ON L6W 4R1
PH: 514-238-5751
Toll Free in North America:
877-412-3106
FAX: 323-315-2635
canadastampfinder@gmail.com
www.canadastampfinder.com

**ROY'S STAMPS**
PO Box 28001
600 Ontario Street
St. Catharines, ON
CANADA L2N 7P8
Phone: 905-934-8377
Email: roystamp@cogeco.ca

## China

**THE STAMP ACT**
PO Box 1136
Belmont, CA 94002
PH: 650-703-2342
thestampact@sbcglobal.net

## Collections

**DR. ROBERT FRIEDMAN & SONS STAMP & COIN BUYING CENTER**
2029 W. 75th St.
Woodridge, IL 60517
PH: 800-588-8100
FAX: 630-985-1588
stampcollections@drbobstamps.com
www.drbobfriedmanstamps.com

## Ducks

**MICHAEL JAFFE**
PO Box 61484
Vancouver, WA 98666
PH: 360-695-6161
PH: 800-782-6770
FAX: 360-695-1616
mjaffe@brookmanstamps.com
www.brookmanstamps.com

## German Colonies

**COLONIAL STAMP COMPANY**
5757 Wilshire Blvd. PH #8
Los Angeles, CA 90036
PH: 323-933-9435
FAX: 323-939-9930
Toll Free in North America
PH: 877-272-6693
FAX: 877-272-6694
info@colonialstampcompany.com
www.colonialstampcompany.com

## Great Britain

**COLONIAL STAMP COMPANY**
5757 Wilshire Blvd. PH #8
Los Angeles, CA 90036
PH: 323-933-9435
FAX: 323-939-9930
Toll Free in North America
PH: 877-272-6693
FAX: 877-272-6694
info@colonialstampcompany.com
www.colonialstampcompany.com

## Japan

**WORLDSTAMPS/ FRANK GEIGER PHILATELISTS**
PO Box 4743
Pinehurst, NC 28374
PH: 910-295-2048
info@WorldStamps.com
www.WorldStampsScott.com

**THE STAMP ACT**
PO Box 1136
Belmont, CA 94002
PH: 650-703-2342
thestampact@sbcglobal.net

## Kenya, Uganda, Tanzania

**COLONIAL STAMP COMPANY**
5757 Wilshire Blvd. PH #8
Los Angeles, CA 90036
PH: 323-933-9435
FAX: 323-939-9930
Toll Free in North America
PH: 877-272-6693
FAX: 877-272-6694
info@colonialstampcompany.com
www.colonialstampcompany.com

## British Commonwealth

*British Empire 1840 - 1935*

Aden to Zululand Mint & Used
Most complete stock in North America

For over 40 years, we have built some of the world's finest collections. Our expert ***Want List Services*** can do the same for you. Over 50 volumes filled with singles, sets and rare stamps, we are sure we have what you need. We welcome your Want Lists in Scott or Stanley Gibbons numbers.

**Put our expertise to work for you today! You'll be glad you did!**

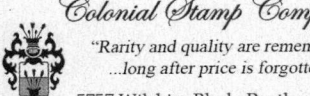

*Colonial Stamp Company*
*"Rarity and quality are remembered ...long after price is forgotten."*
5757 Wilshire Blvd., Penthouse 8
Los Angeles, CA 90036 USA
Tel: +1 (323) 933-9435 Fax: +1 (323) 939-9930
Email: *Info@ColonialStamps.com*
*www.ColonialStamps.com*

**Ask for your free Public Auction Catalogue today!**

Collectors Club New York

## British Commonwealth

THE BRITISH COMMONWEALTH
O • F N • A • T • I • O • N • S

**We are active buyers and sellers of stamps and postal history of all areas of pre-1960 British Commonwealth, including individual items, collections or estates. Want lists from all reigns are accepted with references.**

**"VISIT OUR BOOTH AT MOST MAJOR SHOWS"**

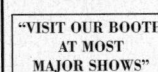

**L. W. Martin, Jr.**
CROWN COLONY STAMPS
**P.O. Box 1198**
**BELLAIRE, TEXAS 77402**
**PH. (713) 781-6563 • FAX (713) 789-9998**
**E-mail: lwm@crowncolony.com**

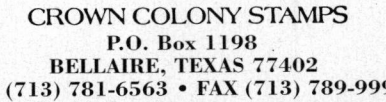

## Kiauchau (German)

**COLONIAL STAMP COMPANY**
5757 Wilshire Blvd. PH #8
Los Angeles, CA 90036
PH: 323-933-9435
FAX: 323-939-9930
Toll Free in North America
PH: 877-272-6693
FAX: 877-272-6694
info@colonialstampcompany.com
www.colonialstampcompany.com

## Korea

**WORLDSTAMPS/ FRANK GEIGER PHILATELISTS**
PO Box 4743
Pinehurst, NC 28374
PH: 910-295-2048
info@WorldStamps.com
www.WorldStampsScott.com

## Kosovo

**WORLDSTAMPS/ FRANK GEIGER PHILATELISTS**
PO Box 4743
Pinehurst, NC 28374
PH: 910-295-2048
info@WorldStamps.com
www.WorldStampsScott.com

## Latvia

**WORLDSTAMPS/ FRANK GEIGER PHILATELISTS**
PO Box 4743
Pinehurst, NC 28374
PH: 910-295-2048
info@WorldStamps.com
www.WorldStampsScott.com

## Leeward Islands

**COLONIAL STAMP COMPANY**
5757 Wilshire Blvd. PH #8
Los Angeles, CA 90036
PH: 323-933-9435
FAX: 323-939-9930
Toll Free in North America
PH: 877-272-6693
FAX: 877-272-6694
info@colonialstampcompany.com
www.colonialstampcompany.com

## Liechtenstein

**WORLDSTAMPS/ FRANK GEIGER PHILATELISTS**
PO Box 4743
Pinehurst, NC 28374
PH: 910-295-2048
info@WorldStamps.com
www.WorldStampsScott.com

**HENRY GITNER PHILATELISTS, INC.**
PO Box 3077-S
Middletown, NY 10940
PH: 845-343-5151
PH: 800-947-8267
FAX: 845-343-0068
hgitner@hgitner.com
www.hgitner.com

## Luxembourg

**WORLDSTAMPS/ FRANK GEIGER PHILATELISTS**
PO Box 4743
Pinehurst, NC 28374
PH: 910-295-2048
info@WorldStamps.com
www.WorldStampsScott.com

## Luxembourg

**HENRY GITNER PHILATELISTS, INC.**
PO Box 3077-S
Middletown, NY 10940
PH: 845-343-5151
PH: 800-947-8267
FAX: 845-343-0068
hgitner@hgitner.com
www.hgitner.com

## Madagascar (British Issues)

**COLONIAL STAMP COMPANY**
5757 Wilshire Blvd. PH #8
Los Angeles, CA 90036
PH: 323-933-9435
FAX: 323-939-9930
Toll Free in North America
PH: 877-272-6693
FAX: 877-272-6694
info@colonialstampcompany.com
www.colonialstampcompany.com

## Malaya

**COLONIAL STAMP COMPANY**
5757 Wilshire Blvd. PH #8
Los Angeles, CA 90036
PH: 323-933-9435
FAX: 323-939-9930
Toll Free in North America
PH: 877-272-6693
FAX: 877-272-6694
info@colonialstampcompany.com
www.colonialstampcompany.com

**THE STAMP ACT**
PO Box 1136
Belmont, CA 94002
PH: 650-703-2342
thestampact@sbcglobal.net

## Mariana Islands (Ger & Sp)

**COLONIAL STAMP COMPANY**
5757 Wilshire Blvd. PH #8
Los Angeles, CA 90036
PH: 323-933-9435
FAX: 323-939-9930
Toll Free in North America
PH: 877-272-6693
FAX: 877-272-6694
info@colonialstampcompany.com
www.colonialstampcompany.com

## Marshall Islands

**COLONIAL STAMP COMPANY**
5757 Wilshire Blvd. PH #8
Los Angeles, CA 90036
PH: 323-933-9435
FAX: 323-939-9930
Toll Free in North America
PH: 877-272-6693
FAX: 877-272-6694
info@colonialstampcompany.com
www.colonialstampcompany.com

**WORLDSTAMPS/ FRANK GEIGER PHILATELISTS**
PO Box 4743
Pinehurst, NC 28374
PH: 910-295-2048
info@WorldStamps.com
www.WorldStampsScott.com

## Mauritius

**COLONIAL STAMP COMPANY**
5757 Wilshire Blvd. PH #8
Los Angeles, CA 90036
PH: 323-933-9435
FAX: 323-939-9930
Toll Free in North America
PH: 877-272-6693
FAX: 877-272-6694
info@colonialstampcompany.com
www.colonialstampcompany.com

## Mesopotamia

**COLONIAL STAMP COMPANY**
5757 Wilshire Blvd. PH #8
Los Angeles, CA 90036
PH: 323-933-9435
FAX: 323-939-9930
Toll Free in North America
PH: 877-272-6693
FAX: 877-272-6694
info@colonialstampcompany.com
www.colonialstampcompany.com

## Mexico

**WORLDSTAMPS/ FRANK GEIGER PHILATELISTS**
PO Box 4743
Pinehurst, NC 28374
PH: 910-295-2048
info@WorldStamps.com
www.WorldStampsScott.com

## Micronesia

**WORLDSTAMPS/ FRANK GEIGER PHILATELISTS**
PO Box 4743
Pinehurst, NC 28374
PH: 910-295-2048
info@WorldStamps.com
www.WorldStampsScott.com

## Monaco

**WORLDSTAMPS/ FRANK GEIGER PHILATELISTS**
PO Box 4743
Pinehurst, NC 28374
PH: 910-295-2048
info@WorldStamps.com
www.WorldStampsScott.com

## Natal

**COLONIAL STAMP COMPANY**
5757 Wilshire Blvd. PH #8
Los Angeles, CA 90036
PH: 323-933-9435
FAX: 323-939-9930
Toll Free in North America
PH: 877-272-6693
FAX: 877-272-6694
info@colonialstampcompany.com
www.colonialstampcompany.com

## New Britain

**COLONIAL STAMP COMPANY**
5757 Wilshire Blvd. PH #8
Los Angeles, CA 90036
PH: 323-933-9435
FAX: 323-939-9930
Toll Free in North America
PH: 877-272-6693
FAX: 877-272-6694
info@colonialstampcompany.com
www.colonialstampcompany.com

## New Issues

**DAVIDSON'S STAMP SERVICE**
Personalized Service since 1970
PO Box 36355
Indianapolis, IN 46236-0355
PH: 317-826-2620
ed-davidson@earthlink.net
www.newstampissues.com

## New Zealand

**COLONIAL STAMP COMPANY**
5757 Wilshire Blvd. PH #8
Los Angeles, CA 90036
PH: 323-933-9435
FAX: 323-939-9930
Toll Free in North America
PH: 877-272-6693
FAX: 877-272-6694
info@colonialstampcompany.com
www.colonialstampcompany.com

## Niger Coast Protectorate

**COLONIAL STAMP COMPANY**
5757 Wilshire Blvd. PH #8
Los Angeles, CA 90036
PH: 323-933-9435
FAX: 323-939-9930
Toll Free in North America
PH: 877-272-6693
FAX: 877-272-6694
info@colonialstampcompany.com
www.colonialstampcompany.com

## Orange River Colony

**COLONIAL STAMP COMPANY**
5757 Wilshire Blvd. PH #8
Los Angeles, CA 90036
PH: 323-933-9435
FAX: 323-939-9930
Toll Free in North America
PH: 877-272-6693
FAX: 877-272-6694
info@colonialstampcompany.com
www.colonialstampcompany.com

## Proofs & Essays

**HENRY GITNER PHILATELISTS, INC.**
PO Box 3077-S
Middletown, NY 10940
PH: 845-343-5151
PH: 800-947-8267
FAX: 845-343-0068
hgitner@hgitner.com
www.hgitner.com

## Rhodesia

**COLONIAL STAMP COMPANY**
5757 Wilshire Blvd. PH #8
Los Angeles, CA 90036
PH: 323-933-9435
FAX: 323-939-9930
Toll Free in North America
PH: 877-272-6693
FAX: 877-272-6694
info@colonialstampcompany.com
www.colonialstampcompany.com

## Sovereign Military Order of Malta

**WORLDSTAMPS/ FRANK GEIGER PHILATELISTS**
PO Box 4743
Pinehurst, NC 28374
PH: 910-295-2048
info@WorldStamps.com
www.WorldStampsScott.com

## Stamp Stores

## California

**BROSIUS STAMP, COIN & SUPPLIES**
2105 Main St.
Santa Monica, CA 90405
PH: 310-396-7480
FAX: 310-396-7455
brosius.stamp.coin@hotmail.com

## Stamp Stores

### California

**COLONIAL STAMP COMPANY**
5757 Wilshire Blvd. PH #8
Los Angeles, CA 90036
PH: 323-933-9435
FAX: 323-939-9930
Toll Free in North America
PH: 877-272-6693
FAX: 877-272-6694
info@colonialstampcompany.com
www.colonialstampcompany.com

### Delaware

**DUTCH COUNTRY AUCTIONS**
The Stamp Center
4115 Concord Pike
Wilmington, DE 19803
PH: 302-478-8740
FAX: 302-478-8779
auctions@dutchcountryauctions.com
www.dutchcountryauctions.com

### Florida

**DR. ROBERT FRIEDMAN & SONS STAMP & COIN BUYING CENTER**
PH: 800-588-8100
FAX: 630-985-1588
stampcollections@drbobstamps.com
www.drbobfriedmanstamps.com

### Illinois

**DR. ROBERT FRIEDMAN & SONS STAMP & COIN BUYING CENTER**
2029 W. 75th St.
Woodridge, IL 60517
PH: 800-588-8100
FAX: 630-985-1588
stampcollections@drbobstamps.com
www.drbobfriedmanstamps.com

### Indiana

**KNIGHT STAMP & COIN CO.**
237 Main St.
Hobart, IN 46342
PH: 219-942-4341
PH: 800-634-2646
knight@knightcoin.com
www.knightcoin.com

### New Jersey

**BERGEN STAMPS & COLLECTIBLES**
306 Queen Anne Rd.
Teaneck, NJ 07666
PH: 201-836-8987
bergenstamps@gmail.com

**TRENTON STAMP & COIN CO**
Thomas DeLuca
Store: Forest Glen Plaza
1804 Highway 33
Hamilton Square, NJ 08690
Mail: PO Box 8574
Trenton, NJ 08650
PH: 609-584-8100
FAX: 609-587-8664
TOMD4TSC@aol.com

### New York

**CHAMPION STAMP CO., INC.**
432 West 54th St.
New York, NY 10019
PH: 212-489-8130
FAX: 212-581-8130
championstamp@aol.com
www.championstamp.com

## Stamp Stores

### New York

**CK STAMPS**
42-14 Union St. # 2A
Flushing, NY 11355
PH: 917-667-6641
ckstampsllc@yahoo.com

### Ohio

**HILLTOP STAMP SERVICE**
Richard A. Peterson
PO Box 626
Wooster, OH 44691
PH: 330-262-8907 (0)
PH: 330-262-5378 (H)
hilltop@bright.net
www.hilltopstamps.com

## Supplies

**BROOKLYN GALLERY COIN & STAMP, INC.**
8725 4th Ave.
Brooklyn, NY 11209
PH: 718-745-5701
FAX: 718-745-2775
info@brooklyngallery.com
www.brooklyngallery.com

## Topicals

**E. JOSEPH McCONNELL, INC.**
PO Box 683
Monroe, NY 10949
PH: 845-783-9791
FAX: 845-782-0347
ejstamps@gmail.com
www.EJMcConnell.com

## Topicals - Columbus

**MR. COLUMBUS**
PO Box 1492
Fennville, MI 49408
PH: 269-543-4755
David@MrColumbus1492.com
www.MrColumbus1492.com

## United Nations

**BRUCE M. MOYER**
Box 99
East Texas, PA 18046
PH: 610-395-8410
FAX: 610-421-8020
moyer@unstamps.com
www.unstamps.com

## United States

**KEITH WAGNER**
ACS Stamp Company
2914 W 135th Ave
Broomfield, Colorado 80020
303-841-8666
www.ACSStamp.com

**BROOKMAN STAMP CO.**
PO Box 90
Vancouver, WA 98666
PH: 360-695-1391
PH: 800-545-4871
FAX: 360-695-1616
info@brookmanstamps.com
www.brookmanstamps.com

## U.S. Classics/Moderns

**BARDO STAMPS**
PO Box 7437
Buffalo Grove, IL 60089
PH: 847-634-2676
jfb7437@aol.com
www.bardostamps.com

## U.S.-Collections Wanted

**DUTCH COUNTRY AUCTIONS**
The Stamp Center
4115 Concord Pike
Wilmington, DE 19803
PH: 302-478-8740
FAX: 302-478-8779
auctions@dutchcountryauctions.com
www.dutchcountryauctions.com

**DR. ROBERT FRIEDMAN & SONS STAMP & COIN BUYING CENTER**
2029 W. 75th St.
Woodridge, IL 60517
PH: 800-588-8100
FAX: 630-985-1588
stampcollections@drbobstamps.com
www.drbobfriedmanstamps.com

## Want Lists - British Empire 1840-1935 German Cols./Offices

**COLONIAL STAMP COMPANY**
5757 Wilshire Blvd. PH #8
Los Angeles, CA 90036
PH: 323-933-9435
FAX: 323-939-9930
Toll Free in North America
PH: 877-272-6693
FAX: 877-272-6694
info@colonialstampcompany.com
www.colonialstampcompany.com

## Wanted - Worldwide Collections

**DUTCH COUNTRY AUCTIONS**
The Stamp Center
4115 Concord Pike
Wilmington, DE 19803
PH: 302-478-8740
FAX: 302-478-8779
auctions@dutchcountryauctions.com
www.dutchcountryauctions.com

**KELLEHER & ROGERS LTD.**
4 Finance Drive, Ste. 200
Danbury, CT 06810
PH: 203-297-6056
FAX: 203-297-6059
info@kelleherauctions.com
www.kelleherauctions.com

## Websites

**KEITH WAGNER**
ACS Stamp Company
2914 W 135th Ave
Broomfield, Colorado 80020
303-841-8666
www.ACSStamp.com

## Worldwide-Collections

**DR. ROBERT FRIEDMAN & SONS STAMP & COIN BUYING CENTER**
2029 W. 75th St.
Woodridge, IL 60517
PH: 800-588-8100
FAX: 630-985-1588
stampcollections@drbobstamps.com
www.drbobfriedmanstamps.com

## Worldwide

**WANT LISTS WELCOME!**
*Any Catalogue # • Any Main Language*

**ALL COUNTRIES A-Z**
**ALL TOPICS**
**VERY LARGE WORLDWIDE STOCK**
*including varieties, cancels, covers, etc.*

Search online:
**www.ercolegloria.com**

**ERCOLE GLORIA srl - Zuskis Family**
Via Tommaso Agudio, 4, 20154 Milano, ITALY *Since 1926*
TEL. +39-2-804106 • FAX +39-2-864217 • E-MAIL: info@ercolegloria.it